Baseball Card
TEAM CHECKLIST

By

JEFF FRITSCH

NUMBER 7

EDGEWATER BOOK COMPANY • CLEVELAND

EDGEWATER BOOK COMPANY
P.O. BOX 40238
CLEVELAND, OHIO 44140

Manufactured in the United States of America

First Printing

ISBN 0-937424-78-1

TEAM CHECKLIST
TABLE OF CONTENTS

HOW TO USE THE TEAM CHECKLIST 5

BOWMAN
- 1948 7
- 1949 7
- 1950 8
- 1951 10
- 1952 11
- 1953 COLOR 13
- 1953 BLACK & WHITE 14
- 1954 15
- 1955 16
- 1989 17
- 1990 20
- 1991 22
- 1992 25
- 1993 28
- 1994 31
- 1994 BEST 34

DIAMOND STARS 36

DONRUSS
- 1981 37
- 1982 39
- 1983 42
- 1984 45
- 1985 48
- 1986 51
- 1986 ROOKIES 54
- 1987 54
- 1987 ROOKIES 57
- 1988 58
- 1988 ROOKIES 61
- 1989 61
- 1989 TRADED 64
- 1989 ROOKIES 65
- 1990 66
- 1990 ROOKIES 69
- 1991 69
- 1991 ROOKIES 72
- 1992 73
- 1992 ROOKIES 77
- 1993 78
- 1994 81
- 1995 84

DONRUSS-LEAF
- 1990 87
- 1991 89
- 1992 92
- 1993 94
- 1994 97
- 1994 LIMITED 99
- 1994 LIMITED ROOKIES 100
- 1995 101

LEAF-STUDIO
- 1991 103
- 1992 104
- 1993 106
- 1994 107

FLEER
- 1963 109
- 1981 109
- 1982 112
- 1983 115
- 1984 118
- 1984 TRADED 121
- 1985 122
- 1985 TRADED 125
- 1986 126
- 1986 TRADED 129
- 1987 130
- 1987 TRADED 133
- 1988 134
- 1988 TRADED 137
- 1989 138
- 1989 TRADED 141
- 1990 142
- 1990 TRADED 145
- 1991 146
- 1991 TRADED 150
- 1992 151
- 1992 TRADED 154
- 1993 155
- 1993 FINAL EDITION 158
- 1994 160
- 1994 TRADED 163
- 1995 164

FLEER-ULTRA
- 1991 168
- 1991 TRADED 170
- 1992 171
- 1993 173
- 1994 176
- 1995 179

FLEER-FLAIR
- 1993 181
- 1994 182
- 1995 185

GOUDEY
- 1933 187
- 1934 188
- 1935 188
- 1936 189
- 1938 190
- 1941 190

PLAY BALL
- 1939 191
- 1940 192
- 1941 193

SCORE
- 1988 194
- 1988 ROOKIE & TRADED 196
- 1989 197
- 1989 ROOKIE & TRADED 200
- 1990 201
- 1990 ROOKIE & TRADED 204
- 1991 205
- 1991 ROOKIE & TRADED 209
- 1992 210
- 1992 ROOKIE & TRADED 213
- 1993 214
- 1994 217
- 1994 ROOKIE & TRADED 220
- 1995 221

SCORE-PINNACLE
- 1992 223
- 1993 226
- 1994 229
- 1995 231

SCORE-SELECT
- 1993 233
- 1993 TRADED 235
- 1994 236

TOPPS
- 1951 TEAM (DATED) 239
- 1951 TEAM (UNDATED) 239
- 1951 RED BACKS 239
- 1951 BLUE BACKS 240
- 1952 240
- 1953 242
- 1954 243
- 1955 245
- 1956 246
- 1957 247
- 1958 249
- 1959 251
- 1960 253
- 1961 255
- 1962 257
- 1963 260
- 1964 262
- 1965 265
- 1966 268
- 1967 271
- 1968 274
- 1969 276
- 1970 279
- 1971 282
- 1972 286
- 1973 289
- 1974 292
- 1974 TRADED 295
- 1975 296
- 1975 MINI'S 296
- 1976 299
- 1976 TRADED 302
- 1977 302
- 1978 305
- 1979 309
- 1980 312
- 1981 315
- 1981 TRADED 319
- 1982 320
- 1982 TRADED 323
- 1983 324
- 1983 TRADED 327
- 1984 328
- 1984 TRADED 331
- 1985 332
- 1985 TRADED 336
- 1986 337
- 1986 TRADED 340
- 1987 341
- 1987 TRADED 344
- 1988 345
- 1988 TRADED 349
- 1989 350
- 1989 TRADED 353
- 1990 354
- 1990 TRADED 357
- 1991 358
- 1991 TRADED 362
- 1992 363
- 1992 TRADED 366
- 1993 367
- 1993 TRADED 371
- 1994 372
- 1994 TRADED 376
- 1995 377

TOPPS-STADIUM CLUB
- 1991 379
- 1992 382
- 1993 386
- 1994 389
- 1995 392

TOPPS-FINEST
- 1993 394
- 1994 395

T205 398

T206 399

T207 402

UPPER DECK
- 1989 403
- 1990 406
- 1991 410
- 1991 FINAL EDITION 413
- 1992 414
- 1993 417
- 1994 420
- 1995 423

UPPER DECK-COLLECTOR'S CHOICE
- 1994 424
- 1995 427
- 1995 SE 429

UPPER DECK SP
- 1993 430
- 1994 431

HOW TO USE THE TEAM CHECKLIST BOOK

While the text of this book is straight forward and easy to follow, several conventions and clarifying abbreviations are used in the text to attain consistency. These abbreviations and conventions are explained below.

ABBREVIATIONS

(B) BACK ONLY -appears when the team name of a player is different on the back from that on the front.

(CA) COMING ATTRACTIONS -more than one player per card listed as Coming Attractions.

(C) COACH -appears when the card is of a coach of that particular team.

(F) FRONT ONLY -appears when the team name of a player is different on the front from that on the back.

(FS) FUTURE STAR -more than one player per card listed as Future Stars.

(HC) HEAD COACH -appears only on the Topps cards of Bob Kennedy of 1964 and 1965 when he is listed as Head Coach of the Cubs, and on the Topps and Topps traded cards featuring the Head Coach of Olympic Teams and Team USA.

(M) MANAGER -appears when the card is a manager of that particular team.

(P) PROSPECT -more than one player per card; listed as Prospects or similar terms.

(R) ROOKIE -more than one player per card listed as Rookie Stars.

CONVENTIONS

For Bowman, Goudey and Play Ball issues, the team on the front of the card is determined by the uniform worn. The team on the back of the card is determined by the team name actually printed on the back. For all Topps, Fleer, Donruss, Score and Upper Deck issues (except the 1951 Topps Red and Blue Backs which have no writing on the back), the team name is determined by the team name printed on the front and back respectively. When a difference in the team name printed on the front and back exists; e.g. 1979 Topps Bump Wills exist with both the Rangers (correct) and Blue Jays (error) printed on the front, and the 1969 Topps Donn Clendenon exists with both Houston (correct) and Expos (error) printed on the front the correct version only is used in the text.

There are several cards in many of the sets that have been omitted from the checklists within because the players are not committed to any current team; e.g. old timers from the 1940 Play Ball set, 1976 Topps All-Time Greats, 1933 Goudey Lajoie, etc. Likewise, special cards have been omitted, e.g., All-Star Cards, multi-player cards, League Leader cards, Donruss Diamond Kings, boyhood picture cards, etc. All sets are in color unless noted as being in black and white.

ABOUT THE AUTHOR

A leading expert in the field of card collecting, Jeff Fritsch has been involved in cards for as long has he can remember. "I recall opening 1963 Topps with my father at age 4." Jeff explains. He has been active in Larry Fritsch Cards, the country's first full-time mail order sports cards business since 1966 on a part-time basis. Now Vice President, Jeff joined the company full-time in 1979 after attending college. Along with this edition of the *Team Baseball Card Checklist* he also has co-authored two volumes of the *Team Football and Basketball Card Checklist Book*. He currently resides in Stevens Point, Wisconsin with his wife, Sue and their children, Jeremy, Jaycie and Allison.

ACKNOWLEDGMENTS

The author would like to extend a thank you to the following people who helped make this book possible. Vinnie Freeman from the Upper Deck Company and Kurt Iverson from Pinnacle Brands for providing all the necessary checklists. My wife Sue for countless hours of proofing the text. Ginger Nelson for data entry of the never ending lists of new sets since Volume 6. Suzy Sevcik for formatting and outputting all the new updated pages since Volume 6. Russ Kalpinski for his help in finalizing this project. My dad, Larry Fritsch for his understanding in allowing me the use of the Larry Fritsch Cards staff, staff-time and equipment. My wife Sue and my children for their support while undertaking this endeavor.

From "A League Of Their Own" To Their Own Baseball Cards!

Stevens Point, WI, May 19, 1995 — Larry Fritsch Cards in cooperation with the AAGPBL-Player's Association is proud to announce the most comprehensive card set of the All-American Girls Professional Baseball League ever produced. In 1943 American sport history was enriched by a venture that became both successful and popular in the Midwest. The AAGPBL was conceived, financed and organized by Phillip K. Wrigley, the owner of the Chicago Cubs and a group of colleagues in Chicago.

The players of the AAGPBL were pioneers in establishing new social and athletic standards for women in sports. On November 5, 1988, the league was honored as part of the "Women in Baseball" display at the National Baseball Hall of Fame in Cooperstown, New York. In 1992 a feature film, "A League of Their Own," was released, bringing national attention to a league that had been forgotten by all but those who had been a part of it.

Larry Fritsch Cards, a mail-order sports card business, has just released The All-American Girls Professional Baseball League Card Set to honor a league whose memory has faded. The set includes 229 Player Cards, 3 History of the League Cards featuring photos of the historic and unique uniforms of the AAGPBL and 2 Checklist Cards. The card fronts have a black & white player photo trimmed with a red or blue border. Card backs contain vitals, league statistics and a brief bio of the player. They're printed on a standard size (2½ X 3½") high quality glossy stock and packaged in a multi-color Deluxe Collector's Box. The suggested retail price is $24.95 per set, plus shipping. The sets are available by writing to Larry Fritsch Cards, 735 Old Wausau Road, P.O. Box 863, Stevens Point, WI 54481-0863, or calling (715) 344-8687.

This unique set was a special project Larry Fritsch Cards undertook to bring attention to the women who played baseball and the legacy they left behind. The response to the set has been overwhelming. "I want to thank you very much for the baseball cards. I just jumped for joy when I received them...I've been waiting so long (to be on a baseball card)," says Eleanor Dapkus Wolf of the Racine Belles, 1943-1950. Jeff Fritsch, Vice President of Larry Fritsch Cards admits, "Putting this set together was a tremendous project, but well worth it. These talented baseball players deserve recognition for their part in baseball history."

Sample cards of the set are available by writing to Larry Fritsch Cards and enclosing a self-addressed, stamped envelope. "In addition to be a great collector's item, I feel this set is also a valuable learning tool. This set is the missing link in baseball card history and the three History of the League Cards are great sources of information about the league and how it was formed," adds Fritsch.

1948 BOWMAN (48)
2 1/16" X 2 1/2"
BLACK & WHITE

BOSTON BRAVES

- □ 1. BOB ELLIOTT
- □ 12. JOHNNY SAIN
- □ 18. WARREN SPAHN

BOSTON RED SOX

NO CARDS ISSUED

BROOKLYN DODGERS

- □ 7. PETE REISER
- □ 41. REX BARNEY
- □ 43. BRUCE EDWARDS

CHICAGO CUBS

NO CARDS ISSUED

CHICAGO WHITE SOX

NO CARDS ISSUED

CINCINATTI REDS

- □ 2. EWELL BLACKWELL
- □ 39. AUGIE GALAN
- □ 44. JOHNNY WYROSTEK
- □ 45. HANK SAUER
- □ 46. HERMAN WEHMEIER

CLEVELAND INDIANS

- □ 5. BOB FELLER

DETROIT TIGERS

NO CARDS ISSUED

NEW YORK GIANTS

- □ 4. JOHNNY MIZE
- □ 9. WALKER COOPER
- □ 13. WILLARD MARSHALL
- □ 16. JACK LOHRKE
- □ 20. BUDDY KERR
- □ 23. LARRY JANSEN
- □ 27. SID GORDON
- □ 30. WHITEY LOCKMAN
- □ 32. BILL RIGNEY
- □ 34. SHELDON JONES
- □ 37. CLINT HARTUNG
- □ 42. RAY POAT
- □ 47. BOBBY THOMSON
- □ 48. DAVE KOSLO

NEW YORK YANKEES

- □ 6. YOGI BERRA
- □ 8. PHIL RIZZUTO
- □ 11. JOHNNY LINDELL
- □ 14. ALLIE REYNOLDS
- □ 19. TOMMY HENRICH
- □ 22. BILL BEVENS
- □ 26. FRANK SHEA
- □ 29. JOE PAGE
- □ 33. BILLY JOHNSON
- □ 35. GEORGE STIRNWEISS

PHILADELPHIA ATHLETICS

- □ 10. BUDDY ROSAR
- □ 15. EDDIE JOOST
- □ 21. FERRIS FAIN
- □ 25. BARNEY MCCOSKEY
- □ 31. BILL MCCAHAN

PHILADELPHIA PHILLIES

- □ 24. DUTCH LEONARD
- □ 28. EMIL VERBAN

PITTSBURGH PIRATES

- □ 3. RALPH KINER

ST. LOUIS BROWNS

NO CARDS ISSUED

ST. LOUIS CARDINALS

- □ 17. ENOS SLAUGHTER
- □ 36. STAN MUSIAL
- □ 38. RED SCHOENDIENST
- □ 40. MARTY MARION

WASHINGTON SENATORS

NO CARDS ISSUED

1949 BOWMAN (240)
2 1/16" X 2 1/2"

BOSTON BRAVES

- □ 1. VERN BICKFORD
- □ 17. EARL TORGESON
- □ 33. WARREN SPAHN
- □ 47. JOHNNY SAIN
- □ 58. BOB ELLIOTT
- □ 67. ALVIN DARK
- □ 72. TOMMY HOLMES
- □ 88. BILL SALKELD
- □ 104. ED STANKY
- □ 153. PHIL MASI
- □ 169. JEFF HEATH
- □ 185. PETE REISER
- □ 201. SIBBY SISTI
- □ 213. CHARLES BARRETT
- □ 235. JIM RUSSELL
- □ 239. FRANK MCCORMICK

BOSTON RED SOX

- □ 7. JOE DOBSON
- □ 23. BOBBY DOERR
- □ 39. BILL GOODMAN
- □ 53. JACK KRAMER
- □ 64. DOM DIMAGGIO
- □ 71. VERN STEPHENS
- □ 86. JOHNNY PESKY
- □ 102. STAN SPENCE
- □ 118. SAM MELE
- □ 151. MICKEY HARRIS
- □ 167. BORIS MARTIN
- □ 183. LOU STRINGER
- □ 199. TEX HUGHSON
- □ 211. DAVE FERRISS
- □ 231. EARL JOHNSON

BROOKLYN DODGERS

- □ 20. GENE HERMANSKI
- □ 36. PEE WEE REESE
- □ 50. JACKIE ROBINSON
- □ 61. REX BARNEY
- □ 70. CARL FURILLO
- □ 73. BILLY COX
- □ 84. ROY CAMPANELLA
- □ 100. GIL HODGES
- □ 116. JOE HATTEN
- □ 146. MIKE MCCORMICK
- □ 162. PREACHER ROE
- □ 178. TOMMY BROWN
- □ 179. HUGH CASEY(F)
- □ 194. RALPH BRANCA
- □ 206. BRUCE EDWARDS
- □ 226. DUKE SNIDER

CHICAGO CUBS

- □ 6. PHIL CAVARRETTA
- □ 22. PEANUTS LOWREY
- □ 38. EMIL VERBAN
- □ 52. JOHNNY SCHMITZ
- □ 63. ANDY PAFKO
- □ 76. BILL NICHOLSON(F)
- □ 83. BOB SCHEFFING
- □ 99. FRANK GUSTINE(B)
- □ 115. DUTCH LEONARD(B)
- □ 130. HARRY WALKER(B)
- □ 134. HANK BOROWY(F)
- □ 142. EDDIE WAITKUS(F)
- □ 152. CLARENCE MADDERN
- □ 168. DOYLE LADE
- □ 184. BOB CHIPMAN
- □ 200. JESS DOBERNIC
- □ 212. RALPH HAMNER

CHICAGO WHITE SOX

- □ 12. CASS MICHAELS
- □ 28. DON KOLLOWAY
- □ 44. DAVE PHILLEY
- □ 87. RANDY GUMPERT(B)
- □ 96. TAFT WRIGHT(F)
- □ 103. JOE TIPTON(B)
- □ 119. FLOYD BAKER
- □ 133. AARON ROBINSON(F)
- □ 141. TONY LUPIEN(F)
- □ 159. GLEN MOULDER

1949 Bowman

- ☐ 175. LUKE APPLING
- ☐ 191. JOE HAYNES
- ☐ 217. MARINO PIERETTI

CINCINNATI REDS

- ☐ 5. HANK SAUER
- ☐ 21. FRANK BAUMHOLTZ
- ☐ 37. JOHN WYROSTEK
- ☐ 51. HERMAN WEHMEIER
- ☐ 62. GRADY HATTON
- ☐ 81. VIRGIL STALLCUP
- ☐ 97. DANNY LITWHILER
- ☐ 113. RAY LAMANNO
- ☐ 128. JOHNNY VANDER MEER
- ☐ 160. JIM BLACKBURN
- ☐ 176. KEN RAFFENSBERGER
- ☐ 192. HARRY GUMBERT

CLEVELAND INDIANS

- ☐ 11. LOU BOUDREAU(M)
- ☐ 27. BOB FELLER
- ☐ 43. DALE MITCHELL
- ☐ 57. GENE BEARDEN
- ☐ 78. SAM ZOLDAK
- ☐ 94. MICKEY VERNON(B)
- ☐ 103. JOE TIPTON(F)
- ☐ 110. EARLY WYNN(B)
- ☐ 125. KEN KELTNER
- ☐ 136. HANK EDWARDS
- ☐ 150. ALLIE CLARK
- ☐ 166. MIKE TRESH
- ☐ 182. HAL PECK
- ☐ 198. STEVE GROMEK
- ☐ 210. JOE GORDON
- ☐ 224. SATCHELL PAIGE
- ☐ 233. LARRY DOBY
- ☐ 238. BOB LEMON

DETROIT TIGERS

- ☐ 10. TED GRAY
- ☐ 26. GEORGE KELL
- ☐ 42. HOOT EVERS
- ☐ 56. PAT MULLIN
- ☐ 75. EDDIE MAYO
- ☐ 91. DICK WAKEFIELD
- ☐ 107. EDDIE LAKE
- ☐ 122. GEORGE VICO
- ☐ 133. AARON ROBINSON(B)
- ☐ 141. TONY LUPIEN(B)
- ☐ 148. BOB SWIFT
- ☐ 164. VIC WERTZ
- ☐ 180. CONNIE BERRY
- ☐ 196. FRED HUTCHINSON
- ☐ 208. DIZZY TROUT
- ☐ 219. VIRGIL TRUCKS

NEW YORK GIANTS

- ☐ 2. WHITEY LOCKMAN
- ☐ 18. BOBBY THOMSON
- ☐ 34. DAVE KOSLO
- ☐ 48. WILLARD MARSHALL
- ☐ 59. JACK LOHRKE
- ☐ 68. SHELDON JONES
- ☐ 85. JOHNNY MIZE
- ☐ 101. SID GORDON
- ☐ 117. WALKER COOPER
- ☐ 154. CLINT HARTUNG
- ☐ 170. BILL RIGNEY
- ☐ 186. BUDDY KERR
- ☐ 202. LARRY JANSEN
- ☐ 220. JOHNNY MCCARTHY
- ☐ 221. BOB MUNCRIEF(F)
- ☐ 223. BOB HOFMAN
- ☐ 230. AUGIE GALAN
- ☐ 237. MONTE KENNEDY

NEW YORK YANKEES

- ☐ 3. BOB PORTERFIELD
- ☐ 19. BOBBY BROWN
- ☐ 35. VIC RASCHI
- ☐ 49. FRANK SHEA
- ☐ 60. YOGI BERRA
- ☐ 69. TOMMY HENRICH
- ☐ 82. JOE PAGE
- ☐ 87. RANDY GUMPERT(F)
- ☐ 98. PHIL RIZZUTO
- ☐ 114. ALLIE REYNOLDS
- ☐ 129. BILL JOHNSON
- ☐ 149. ROY PARTEE
- ☐ 165. GEORGE STIRNWEISS
- ☐ 181. GUS NIARHOS
- ☐ 197. JOHNNY LINDELL
- ☐ 209. CHARLIE KELLER
- ☐ 218. DICK KRYHOSKI
- ☐ 225. GERRY COLEMAN
- ☐ 229. ED LOPAT
- ☐ 232. GEORGE MCQUINN
- ☐ 236. FRED SANFORD
- ☐ 240. NORMAN YOUNG

PHILDELPHIA ATHLETICS

- ☐ 9. FERRIS FAIN
- ☐ 25. CARL SHEIB
- ☐ 41. LOU BRISSIE
- ☐ 55. EDDIE JOOST
- ☐ 66. ELMER VALO
- ☐ 80. BILL MCCAHAN
- ☐ 96. TAFT WRIGHT(B)
- ☐ 112. SAM CHAPMAN
- ☐ 127. HENRY MAJESKI
- ☐ 138. BUDDY ROSAR
- ☐ 155. MIKE GUERRA
- ☐ 171. DICK FOWLER
- ☐ 187. PHIL MARCHILDON
- ☐ 203. BARNEY MCCOSKY
- ☐ 222. ALEX KELLNER

PHILADELPHIA PHILLIES

- ☐ 14. CURT SIMMONS
- ☐ 30. ANDY SEMINICK
- ☐ 46. ROBIN ROBERTS
- ☐ 76. BILL NICHOLSON(B)
- ☐ 92. WILLIE JONES
- ☐ 108. KEN HEINTZELMAN
- ☐ 115. DUTCH LEONARD(F)
- ☐ 123. JOHNNY BLATNIK
- ☐ 130. HARRY WALKER(F)
- ☐ 134. HANK BOROWY(B)
- ☐ 142. EDDIE WAITKUS(B)
- ☐ 145. BLIX DONNELLY
- ☐ 161. JOCKO THOMPSON
- ☐ 177. STAN LOPATA
- ☐ 193. KEN TRINKLE
- ☐ 205. DICK SISLER
- ☐ 214. RICHIE ASHBURN
- ☐ 216. SCHOOLBOY ROWE
- ☐ 228. JACKIE MAYO

PITTSBURGH PIRATES

- ☐ 8. MURRY DICKSON
- ☐ 13. BOB CHESNES
- ☐ 29. RALPH KINER
- ☐ 45. WALLY WESTLAKE
- ☐ 77. ERNIE BONHAM
- ☐ 93. ED STEVENS
- ☐ 99. FRANK GUSTINE(F)
- ☐ 109. ED FITZGERALD
- ☐ 124. DANNY MURTAUGH
- ☐ 135. STAN ROJEK
- ☐ 147. BERT SINGLETON
- ☐ 163. CLYDE MCCULLOUGH
- ☐ 179. HUGH CASEY(B)
- ☐ 195. EDDIE BOCKMAN
- ☐ 207. JOHNNY HOPP
- ☐ 215. KIRBY HIGBE
- ☐ 221. BOB MUNCRIEF(B)
- ☐ 227. FRITZ OSTERMUELLER
- ☐ 234. RIP SEWELL

ST. LOUIS BROWNS

- ☐ 4. JERRY PRIDDY
- ☐ 15. NED GARVER
- ☐ 31. DICK KOKOS
- ☐ 89. MIZELL PLATT
- ☐ 105. BILL KENNEDY
- ☐ 120. CLIFF FANNIN
- ☐ 131. PAUL LEHNER
- ☐ 139. HANK ARFT
- ☐ 143. BOB DILLINGER
- ☐ 156. AL ZARILLA
- ☐ 172. EDDIE PELLAGRINI
- ☐ 188. KARL DREWS
- ☐ 204. BOB SAVAGE

ST. LOUIS CARDINALS

- ☐ 24. STAN MUSIAL
- ☐ 40. RED MUNGER
- ☐ 54. MARTY MARION
- ☐ 65. ENOS SLAUGHTER
- ☐ 79. RON NORTHEY
- ☐ 95. HOWIE POLLET
- ☐ 111. RED SCHOENDIENST
- ☐ 126. AL BRAZLE
- ☐ 137. TED WILKS
- ☐ 158. HARRY BRECHEEN
- ☐ 174. TERRY MOORE(C)
- ☐ 190. JIM HEARN

WASHINGTON SENATORS

- ☐ 16. AL KOZAR
- ☐ 32. EDDIE YOST
- ☐ 74. TOM MCBRIDE
- ☐ 90. GIL COAN
- ☐ 94. MICKEY VERNON(F)
- ☐ 106. JAKE EARLY
- ☐ 110. EARLY WYNN(F)
- ☐ 121. MARK CHRISTMAN
- ☐ 132. AL EVANS
- ☐ 140. RAY SCARBOROUGH
- ☐ 144. MICKEY HAEFNER
- ☐ 157. WALT MASTERSON
- ☐ 173. EDDIE STEWART
- ☐ 189. EARL WOOTEN

1950 BOWMAN (252)
2 1/16" X 2 1/2"

BOSTON BRAVES

- ☐ 19. WARREN SPAHN
- ☐ 20. BOB ELLIOTT
- ☐ 55. BUDDY KERR
- ☐ 56. DEL CRANDALL
- ☐ 57. VERN BICKFORD
- ☐ 73. WILLARD MARSHALL
- ☐ 74. JOHNNY ANTONELLI
- ☐ 109. SID GORDON
- ☐ 110. TOMMY HOLMES
- ☐ 111 WALKER COOPER
- ☐ 163. EARL TORGESON
- ☐ 164. SIBBY SISTI
- ☐ 192. BOB CHIPMAN
- ☐ 193. PETE REISER
- ☐ 248. SAM JETHROE

BOSTON RED SOX

- □ 1. MEL PARNELL
- □ 2. VERN STEPHENS
- □ 3. DOM DIMAGGIO
- □ 43. BOBBY DOERR
- □ 44. JOE DOBSON
- □ 45. AL ZARILLA
- □ 97. MICKEY MCDERMOTT
- □ 98. TED WILLIAMS
- □ 99. BILLY GOODMAN
- □ 136. WARREN ROSAR
- □ 137. JOHNNY PESKY
- □ 152. ELLIS KINDER
- □ 153. WALT MASTERSON
- □ 186. KEN KELTNER
- □ 187. LOU STRINGER
- □ 188. EARL JOHNSON
- □ 245. AL PAPAI
- □ 246. WALT DROPO

BROOKLYN DODGERS

- □ 21. PEE WEE REESE
- □ 22. JACKIE ROBINSON
- □ 23. DON NEWCOMBE
- □ 58. CARL FURILLO
- □ 59. RALPH BRANCA
- □ 75. ROY CAMPANELLA
- □ 76. REX BARNEY
- □ 77. DUKE SNIDER
- □ 112. GIL HODGES
- □ 113. GENE HERMANSKI
- □ 165. BRUCE EDWARDS
- □ 166. JOE HATTEN
- □ 167. PREACHER ROE
- □ 194. BILLY COX
- □ 222. BOBBY MORGAN
- □ 223. JIMMY RUSSELL
- □ 224. JACK BANTA

CHICAGO CUBS

- □ 24. JOHNNY SCHMITZ
- □ 25. HANK SAUER
- □ 60. ANDY PAFKO
- □ 61. BOB RUSH
- □ 78. MICKEY OWEN
- □ 79. JOHNNY VANDER MEER
- □ 114. WAYNE TERWILLIGER
- □ 115. ROY SMALLEY
- □ 169. HANK EDWARDS
- □ 170. EMIL LEONARD
- □ 195. PHIL CAVARRETTA
- □ 196. DOYLE LADE
- □ 229. FRANK FRISCH(M)
- □ 230. BILL SERENA
- □ 231. PRESTON WARD

CHICAGO WHITE SOX

- □ 4. GUS ZERNIAL
- □ 5. BOB KUZAVA
- □ 37. LUKE APPLING
- □ 38. BILL WIGHT
- □ 91. CASS MICHAELS
- □ 92. HANK MAJESKI
- □ 127. DAVE PHILLEY
- □ 128. PHIL MASI
- □ 146. FLOYD BAKER
- □ 183. MICKEY HAEFNER
- □ 184. RANDY GUMPERT
- □ 185. HOWIE JUDSON
- □ 236. BOB CAIN
- □ 237. BILL SALKELD

CINCINNATI REDS

- □ 26. GRADY HATTON
- □ 27. HERMAN WEHMEIER
- □ 62. TED KLUSZEWSKI
- □ 63. EWELL BLACKWELL
- □ 80. HOWARD FOX
- □ 81. RON NORTHEY
- □ 116. VIRGIL STALLCUP
- □ 168. BOB SCHEFFING
- □ 172. PEANUTS LOWREY
- □ 173. LLOYD MERRIMAN
- □ 197. JOHNNY WYROSTEK
- □ 198. DANNY LITWHILER

CLEVELAND INDIANS

- □ 6. BOB FELLER
- □ 7. JIM HEGAN
- □ 39. LARRY DOBY
- □ 40. BOB LEMON
- □ 93. GENE BEARDEN
- □ 94. LOU BOUDREAU(M)
- □ 129. JOE GORDON
- □ 130. DALE MITCHELL
- □ 131. STEVE GROMEK
- □ 132. MICKEY VERNON
- □ 147. MIKE GARCIA
- □ 148. EARLY WYNN
- □ 181. MARINO PIERETTI
- □ 182. SAM ZOLDAK
- □ 232. AL ROSEN
- □ 233. ALLIE CLARK

DETROIT TIGERS

- □ 8. GEORGE KELL
- □ 9. VIC WERTZ
- □ 41. HOOT EVERS
- □ 42. ART HOUTTEMAN
- □ 95. AARON ROBINSON
- □ 96. VIRGIL TRUCKS
- □ 133. DON KOLLOWAY
- □ 134. DIZZY TROUT
- □ 135. PAT MULLIN
- □ 149. BOB SWIFT
- □ 150. GEORGE VICO
- □ 151. FRED HUTCHINSON
- □ 210. TED GRAY
- □ 211. CHARLIE KELLER
- □ 212. GERRY PRIDDY
- □ 240. EDDIE LAKE
- □ 241. NEIL BERRY
- □ 242. DICK KRYHOSKI
- □ 243. JOHNNY GROTH

NEW YORK GIANTS

- □ 28. BOBBY THOMSON
- □ 29. ED STANKY
- □ 64. AL DARK
- □ 65. DAVE KOSLO
- □ 66. LARRY JANSEN
- □ 82. WHITEY LOCKMAN
- □ 83. SHELDON JONES
- □ 117. BILL RIGNEY
- □ 118. CLINT HARTUNG
- □ 174. HANK THOMPSON
- □ 175. MONTE KENNEDY
- □ 199. JACK KRAMER
- □ 200. KIRBY HIGBE
- □ 220. LEO DUROCHER(M)
- □ 221. DON MUELLER
- □ 235. TOOKIE GILBERT

NEW YORK YANKEES

- □ 10. TOMMY HENRICH
- □ 11. PHIL RIZZUTO
- □ 12. JOE PAGE
- □ 46. YOGI BERRA
- □ 47. JERRY COLEMAN
- □ 100. VIC RASCHI
- □ 101. BOBBY BROWN
- □ 102. BILLY JOHNSON
- □ 138. ALLIE REYNOLDS
- □ 139. JOHNNY MIZE
- □ 154. GUS NIARHOS
- □ 155. FRANK SHEA
- □ 156. FRED SANFORD
- □ 215. ED LOPAT
- □ 216. BOB PORTERFIELD
- □ 217. CASEY STENGEL(M)
- □ 218. CLIFF MAPES
- □ 219. HANK BAUER

PHILADELPHIA ATHLETICS

- □ 13. FERRIS FAIN
- □ 14. ALEX KELLNER
- □ 48. LOU BRISSIE
- □ 49. ELMER VALO
- □ 103. EDDIE JOOST
- □ 104. SAM CHAPMAN
- □ 105. BOB DILLINGER
- □ 140. PETE SUDER
- □ 141. JOE COLEMAN
- □ 157. MIKE GUERRA
- □ 158. PAUL LEHNER
- □ 159. JOE TIPTON
- □ 213. CARL SCHEIB
- □ 214. DICK FOWLER
- □ 234. BOBBY SHANTZ

PHILADELPHIA PHILLIES

- □ 30. EDDIE WAITKUS
- □ 31. DEL ENNIS
- □ 32. ROBIN ROBERTS
- □ 67. WILLIE JONES
- □ 68. CURT SIMMONS
- □ 84. RICHIE ASHBURN
- □ 85. KEN HEINTZELMAN
- □ 119. DICK SISLER
- □ 120. JOHN THOMPSON
- □ 121. ANDY SEMINICK
- □ 176. BLIX DONNELLY
- □ 177. HANK BOROWY
- □ 204. GRANNY HAMNER
- □ 205. MIKE GOLIAT
- □ 206. STAN LOPATA
- □ 225. EDDIE SAWYER(M)
- □ 226. JIM KONSTANTY
- □ 227. BOB J. MILLER
- □ 228. BILL NICHOLSON

PITTSBURGH PIRATES

- □ 33. RALPH KINER
- □ 34. MURRY DICKSON
- □ 69. WALLY WESTLAKE
- □ 70. BOB CHESNES
- □ 86. STAN ROJEK
- □ 87. BILL WERLE
- □ 122. JOHNNY HOPP
- □ 123. DINO RESTELLI
- □ 124. CLYDE MCCULLOUGH
- □ 171. HARRY GUMBERT
- □ 178. ED FITZGERALD
- □ 201. PETE CASTIGLIONE
- □ 202. CLIFF CHAMBERS
- □ 203. DANNY MURTAUGH
- □ 244. DALE COOGAN

ST. LOUIS BROWNS

- □ 16. ROY SIEVERS
- □ 50. DICK KOKOS
- □ 51. NED GARVER
- □ 106. CLIFF FANNIN
- □ 142. SHERMAN LOLLAR
- □ 145. JACK GRAHAM
- □ 189. OWEN FRIEND
- □ 190. KEN WOOD
- □ 191. DICK STARR
- □ 249. GEORGE STIRNWEISS
- □ 250. RAY COLEMAN
- □ 251. LES MOSS
- □ 252. BILLY DEMARS

ST. LOUIS CARDINALS

- □ 35. ENOS SLAUGHTER
- □ 36. EDDIE KAZAK
- □ 71. RED SCHOENDIENST
- □ 72. HOWIE POLLET
- □ 88. MARTY MARION
- □ 89. RED MUNGER
- □ 90. HARRY BRECHEEN
- □ 125. DEL RICE

- ☐ 126. AL BRAZLE
- ☐ 179. CHUCK DIERING
- ☐ 180. HARRY WALKER
- ☐ 207. MAX LANIER
- ☐ 208. JIM HEARN
- ☐ 209. JOHNNY LINDELL
- ☐ 238. NIPPY JONES
- ☐ 239. BILL HOWERTON

WASHINGTON SENATORS

- ☐ 15. AL KOZAR
- ☐ 17. SID HUDSON
- ☐ 18. EDDIE ROBINSON
- ☐ 52. SAM MELE
- ☐ 53. CLYDE VOLLMER
- ☐ 54. GIL COAN
- ☐ 107. SAM DENTE
- ☐ 108. RAY SCARBOROUGH
- ☐ 143. EDDIE STEWART
- ☐ 144. AL EVANS
- ☐ 160. MICKEY HARRIS
- ☐ 161. SHERRY ROBERTSON
- ☐ 162. EDDIE YOST
- ☐ 247. IRV NOREN

1951 BOWMAN (324)
2 1/16" X 3 1/8"

BOSTON BRAVES

- ☐ 19. SID GORDON
- ☐ 20. DEL CRANDALL
- ☐ 42. VERN BICKFORD
- ☐ 66. BOB ELLIOTT
- ☐ 98. WILLARD MARSHALL
- ☐ 99. EARL TORGESON
- ☐ 134. WARREN SPAHN
- ☐ 135. WALKER COOPER
- ☐ 170. SIBBY SISTI
- ☐ 171. BUDDY KERR
- ☐ 207. BILLY SOUTHWORTH(M)
- ☐ 208. BLIX DONNELLY
- ☐ 242. SAM JETHROE
- ☐ 243. JOHNNY ANTONELLI
- ☐ 277. ROY HARTSFIELD
- ☐ 278. NORMAN ROY
- ☐ 312. GENE MAUCH
- ☐ 313. RAY MUELLER
- ☐ 314. JOHNNY SAIN

BOSTON RED SOX

- ☐ 15. JOHNNY PESKY
- ☐ 16. MICKEY MCDERMOTT
- ☐ 38. AL EVANS
- ☐ 39. RAY SCARBOROUGH
- ☐ 62. LOU BOUDREAU
- ☐ 91. CLYDE VOLLMER
- ☐ 92. VERN STEPHENS
- ☐ 128. ELLIS KINDER
- ☐ 129. MATT BATTS
- ☐ 164. BILL WIGHT
- ☐ 165. TED WILLIAMS
- ☐ 201. STEVE O'NEIL(M)
- ☐ 202. MIKE GUERRA(F)
- ☐ 210. LES MOSS(B)
- ☐ 236. WARREN ROSAR
- ☐ 237. BILLY GOODMAN
- ☐ 270. WILLARD NIXON
- ☐ 271. TOMMY WRIGHT
- ☐ 306. JIM PIERSALL
- ☐ 307. WALT MASTERSON

BROOKLYN DODGERS

- ☐ 6. DON NEWCOMBE
- ☐ 7. GIL HODGES
- ☐ 31. ROY CAMPANELLA
- ☐ 32. DUKE SNIDER
- ☐ 55. GENE HERMANSKI
- ☐ 56. RALPH BRANCA
- ☐ 80. PEE WEE REESE
- ☐ 81. CARL FURILLO
- ☐ 116. BRUCE EDWARDS
- ☐ 117. EDDIE MIKSIS
- ☐ 118. PREACHER ROE
- ☐ 152. CAL ABRAMS
- ☐ 153. REX BARNEY
- ☐ 189. ERV PALICA
- ☐ 190. JOE HATTEN
- ☐ 224. BILLY COX
- ☐ 225. DAN BANKHEAD
- ☐ 259. CHARLIE DRESSEN(M)
- ☐ 260. CARL ERSKINE
- ☐ 299. CLYDE KING

CHICAGO CUBS

- ☐ 22. HANK SAUER
- ☐ 44. ROY SMALLEY
- ☐ 69. JOHNNY SCHMITZ
- ☐ 70. RON NORTHEY
- ☐ 102. DUTCH LEONARD
- ☐ 103. ANDY PAFKO
- ☐ 138. PHIL CAVARRETTA
- ☐ 139. DOYLE LADE
- ☐ 174. MICKEY OWEN
- ☐ 175. WAYNE TERWILLIGER
- ☐ 211. HAL JEFFCOAT
- ☐ 212. BOB RUSH
- ☐ 246. BILL SERENA
- ☐ 247. BOB RAMAZZOTTI
- ☐ 248. JOHNNY KLIPPSTEIN
- ☐ 282. FRANK FRISCH(M)
- ☐ 283. WALT DUBIEL
- ☐ 317. SMOKY BURGESS
- ☐ 318. WARREN HACKER

CHICAGO WHITE SOX

- ☐ 12. HANK MAJESKI
- ☐ 35. AL ZARILLA
- ☐ 36. JOE DOBSON
- ☐ 59. RANDY GUMPERT
- ☐ 60. CHICO CARRASQUEL
- ☐ 87. FLOYD BAKER
- ☐ 88. EDDIE ROBINSON
- ☐ 123. HOWIE JUDSON
- ☐ 124. GUS NIARHOS
- ☐ 159. EDDIE STEWART
- ☐ 160. PHIL MASI
- ☐ 195. PAUL RICHARDS(M)
- ☐ 196. BILLY PIERCE
- ☐ 197. BOB CAIN(F)
- ☐ 231. LUIS ALOMA
- ☐ 232. NELSON FOX
- ☐ 266. HARRY DORISH
- ☐ 267. KEN HOLCOMBE
- ☐ 302. JIM BUSBY
- ☐ 303. MARV ROTBLATT

CINCINNATI REDS

- ☐ 24. EWELL BLACKWELL
- ☐ 47. GRADY HATTON
- ☐ 48. KEN RAFFENSBERGER
- ☐ 72. LLOYD MERRIMAN
- ☐ 107. JOHNNY WYROSTEK
- ☐ 108. VIRGIL STALLCUP
- ☐ 143. TED KLUSZEWSKI
- ☐ 144. HERMAN WEHMEIER
- ☐ 179. DANNY LITWHILER
- ☐ 180. HOWIE FOX
- ☐ 215. KEN PETERSON
- ☐ 216. CONNIE RYAN
- ☐ 251. WILLARD RAMSDELL
- ☐ 252. DIXIE HOWELL
- ☐ 286. BOB USHER
- ☐ 287. JIM BLACKBURN
- ☐ 288. BOBBY ADAMS
- ☐ 322. LUKE SEWELL(M)
- ☐ 323. JOE ADCOCK
- ☐ 324. JOHNNY PRAMESA

CLEVELAND INDIANS

- ☐ 5. DALE MITCHELL
- ☐ 21. GEORGE STIRNWEISS(B)
- ☐ 29. ALLIE CLARK
- ☐ 30. BOB FELLER
- ☐ 53. BOB LEMON
- ☐ 54. RAY BOONE
- ☐ 78. EARLY WYNN
- ☐ 79. JIM HEGAN
- ☐ 114. SAM ZOLDAK(F)
- ☐ 115. STEVE GROMEK
- ☐ 150. MIKE GARCIA
- ☐ 151. LARRY DOBY
- ☐ 155. LOU BRISSIE(B)
- ☐ 187. AL ROSEN
- ☐ 188. BOBBY AVILA
- ☐ 222. THURMAN TUCKER
- ☐ 223. JOHNNY VANDER MEER
- ☐ 257. BIRDIE TEBBETTS
- ☐ 258. LUKE EASTER
- ☐ 295. AL LOPEZ(M)
- ☐ 296. BOB KENNEDY

DETROIT TIGERS

- ☐ 23. HOOT EVERS
- ☐ 45. ART HOUTTEMAN
- ☐ 46. GEORGE KELL
- ☐ 71. JERRY PRIDDY
- ☐ 104. VIRGIL TRUCKS
- ☐ 105. DON KOLLOWAY
- ☐ 106. PAT MULLIN
- ☐ 140. EDDIE LAKE
- ☐ 141. FRED HUTCHINSON
- ☐ 142. AARON ROBINSON
- ☐ 176. VIC WERTZ
- ☐ 177. CHARLIE KELLER
- ☐ 178. TED GRAY
- ☐ 197. BOB CAIN(B)
- ☐ 213. NEIL BERRY
- ☐ 214. BOB SWIFT
- ☐ 249. JOHNNY GROTH
- ☐ 250. HANK BOROWY
- ☐ 284. GENE BEARDEN
- ☐ 285. JOHNNY LIPON
- ☐ 319. RED ROLFE(M)
- ☐ 320. HAL WHITE
- ☐ 321. EARL JOHNSON

NEW YORK GIANTS

- □ 13. ED STANKY
- □ 14. AL DARK
- □ 37. WHITEY LOCKMAN
- □ 61. JIM HEARN
- □ 89. HENRY THOMPSON
- □ 90. DAVE KOSLO
- □ 125. BILL RIGNEY
- □ 126. BOBBY THOMSON
- □ 127. SAL MAGLIE
- □ 161. WES WESTRUM
- □ 162. LARRY JANSEN
- □ 163. MONTE KENNEDY
- □ 198. MONTE IRVIN
- □ 199. SHELDON JONES
- □ 200. JACK KRAMER(F)
- □ 233. LEO DUROCHER(M)
- □ 234. CLINT HARTUNG
- □ 235. JACK LOHRKE
- □ 268. DON MUELLER
- □ 269. RAY NOBLE
- □ 304. ALLEN GETTEL
- □ 305. WILLIE MAYS

NEW YORK YANKEES

- □ 1. WHITEY FORD
- □ 2. YOGI BERRA
- □ 25. VIC RASCHI
- □ 26. PHIL RIZZUTO
- □ 49. JERRY COLEMAN
- □ 50. JOHNNY MIZE
- □ 73. TOMMY BYRNE
- □ 74. BILLY JOHNSON
- □ 109. ALLIE REYNOLDS
- □ 110. BOBBY BROWN
- □ 145. FRED SANFORD
- □ 146. JOHNNY HOPP
- □ 181. CASEY STENGEL(M)
- □ 182. TOM FERRICK
- □ 183. HANK BAUER
- □ 200. JACK KRAMER(B)
- □ 217. JOE PAGE
- □ 218. ED LOPAT
- □ 219. GENE WOODLING
- □ 253. MICKEY MANTLE
- □ 254. JACKIE JENSEN
- □ 280. FRANK OVERMIRE(B)
- □ 289. CLIFF MAPES
- □ 290. BILL DICKEY(C)
- □ 291. TOMMY HENRICH(C)

PHILADELPHIA ATHLETICS

- □ 8. PAUL LEHNER
- □ 9. SAM CHAPMAN
- □ 33. BOB HOOPER
- □ 57. ALEX KELLNER
- □ 82. JOE TIPTON
- □ 83. CARL SCHEIB
- □ 84. BARNEY MCCOSKY
- □ 114. SAM ZOLDAK(B)
- □ 119. EDDIE JOOST
- □ 120. JOE COLEMAN
- □ 154. PETE SUDER
- □ 155. LOU BRISSIE(F)
- □ 191. BILLY HITCHCOCK
- □ 192. HANK WYSE(F)
- □ 226. JIMMY DYKES(M)
- □ 227. BOBBY SHANTZ
- □ 261. WALLY MOSES
- □ 262. GUS ZERNIAL
- □ 297. DAVE PHILLEY
- □ 298. JOE ASTROTH

PHILADELPHIA PHILLIES

- □ 3. ROBIN ROBERTS
- □ 4. DEL ENNIS
- □ 27. JIM KONSTANTY
- □ 28. EDDIE WAITKUS
- □ 51. ANDY SEMINICK
- □ 52. DICK SISLER
- □ 75. RUSS MEYER
- □ 76. STAN LOPATA
- □ 77. MIKE GOLIAT
- □ 111. CURT SIMMONS
- □ 112. WILLIE JONES
- □ 113. BILL NICHOLSON
- □ 147. KEN HEINTZELMAN
- □ 148. GRANNY HAMNER
- □ 149. BUBBA CHURCH
- □ 184. EDDIE SAWYER(M)
- □ 185. JIMMY BLOODWORTH
- □ 186. RICHIE ASHBURN
- □ 220. BOB J. MILLER
- □ 221. DICK WHITMAN
- □ 255. MILO CANDINI
- □ 256. KEN SILVESTRI
- □ 292. EDDIE PELLAGRINI
- □ 293. KEN JOHNSON
- □ 294. JOCKO THOMPSON

PITTSBURGH PIRATES

- □ 17. PETE CASTIGLIONE
- □ 40. GUS BELL
- □ 63. BOB DILLINGER
- □ 64. BILL WERLE
- □ 93. DANNY O'CONNELL
- □ 94. CLYDE MCCULLOUGH
- □ 130. TOM SAFFELL
- □ 131. CLIFF CHAMBERS
- □ 166. STAN ROJEK(F)
- □ 167. MURRY DICKSON
- □ 203. VERNON LAW
- □ 204. VIC LOMBARDI
- □ 229. BILL HOWERTON(B)
- □ 238. PETE REISER
- □ 239. BILL MACDONALD
- □ 263. HOWIE POLLET(B)
- □ 272. BILLY MEYER(M)
- □ 273. DANNY MURTAUGH
- □ 274. GEORGE METKOVICH
- □ 308. TED BEARD
- □ 309. MEL QUEEN
- □ 310. ERV DUSAK

ST. LOUIS BROWNS

- □ 21. GEORGE STIRNWEISS(F)
- □ 43 BILLY DEMARS
- □ 67. ROY SIEVERS
- □ 68. DICK KOKOS
- □ 100. SHERM LOLLAR
- □ 101. OWEN FRIEND
- □ 136. RAY COLEMAN
- □ 137. DICK STARR
- □ 172. NED GARVER
- □ 173. HANK ARFT
- □ 209. KEN WOOD
- □ 210. LES MOSS(F)
- □ 244. CLIFF FANNIN
- □ 245. JOHN BERARDINO
- □ 279. JIM DELSING
- □ 280. FRANK OVERMIRE(F)
- □ 281. AL WIDMAR
- □ 315. ZACK TAYLOR(M)
- □ 316. DUANE PILLETTE

ST. LOUIS CARDINALS

- □ 10. RED SCHOENDIENST
- □ 11. RED MUNGER
- □ 34. MARTY MARION(M)
- □ 58. ENOS SLAUGHTER
- □ 85. EDDIE KAZAK
- □ 86. HARRY BRECHEEN
- □ 121. GERRY STALEY
- □ 122. JOE GARAGIOLA
- □ 156. DEL RICE
- □ 157. AL BRAZLE
- □ 158. CHUCK DIERING
- □ 166. STAN ROJEK(B)
- □ 193. TED WILKS
- □ 194. HARRY LOWREY
- □ 228. CLOYD BOYER
- □ 229. BILL HOWERTON(F)
- □ 230. MAX LANIER
- □ 263. HOWIE POLLET(F)
- □ 264. DON RICHMOND
- □ 265. STEVE BILKO
- □ 300. HAL RICE
- □ 301. TOMMY GLAVIANO

WASHINGTON SENATORS

- □ 18. GIL COAN
- □ 41. EDDIE YOST
- □ 65. MICKEY VERNON
- □ 95. SHERRY ROBERTSON
- □ 96. SANDY CONSUEGRA
- □ 97. BOB KUZAVA
- □ 132. CASS MICHAELS
- □ 133. SAM DENTE
- □ 168. SAM MELE
- □ 169. SID HUDSON
- □ 192. HANK WYSE(B)
- □ 202. MIKE GUERRA(B)
- □ 205. MICKEY GRASSO
- □ 206. CONRADO MARRERO
- □ 240. JOE HAYNES
- □ 241. IRV NOREN
- □ 275. BUCKY HARRIS(M)
- □ 276. FRANK QUINN
- □ 311. MICKEY HARRIS

1952 BOWMAN (252)
2 1/16" X 3 1/8"

BOSTON BRAVES

- □ 12. MAX SURKONT
- □ 28. ROY HARTSFIELD
- □ 48. VERN BICKFORD
- □ 60. SID GORDON
- □ 72. EARL TORGESON
- □ 84. SAM JETHROE
- □ 97. WILLARD MARSHALL
- □ 100. SIBBY SISTI
- □ 120. CHET NICHOLS
- □ 132. DAVE COLE
- □ 156. WARREN SPAHN
- □ 172. EBBA ST. CLAIRE
- □ 192. JOHN CUSICK
- □ 208. WALKER COOPER
- □ 215. SHELDON JONES
- □ 228. BOB CHIPMAN
- □ 244. LEW BURDETTE

BOSTON RED SOX

- □ 9. VERN STEPHENS
- □ 25. MICKEY MCDERMOTT
- □ 45. JOHNNY PESKY
- □ 57. CLYDE VOLLMER

□ 81. BILLY GOODMAN
□ 106. RANDY GUMPERT
□ 117. BILL WIGHT
□ 129. GUS NIARHOS
□ 140. RAY SCARBOROUGH
□ 153. FRED HATFIELD
□ 169. WALT DROPO
□ 189. JIM PIERSALL
□ 205. WALT MASTERSON
□ 225. DEL WILBER
□ 241. MEL PARNESS
□ 250. IVAN DELOCK

BROOKLYN DODGERS

□ 8. PEE WEE REESE
□ 24. CARL FURILLO
□ 44. ROY CAMPANELLA
□ 56. CLYDE KING
□ 70. CARL ERSKINE
□ 80. GIL HODGES
□ 86. CAL ABRAMS
□ 96. RALPH BRANCA
□ 116. DUKE SNIDER
□ 128. DON NEWCOMBE
□ 152. BILLY COX
□ 168. PREACHER ROE
□ 188. CHARLIE DRESSEN(M)
□ 204. ANDY PAFKO
□ 224. JOHNNY SCHMITZ
□ 240. BILLY LOES

CHICAGO CUBS

□ 16. TURK LOWN
□ 22. WILLARD RAMSDELL
□ 32. EDDIE MIKSIS
□ 64. ROY SMALLEY
□ 88. BRUCE EDWARDS
□ 104. HAL JEFFCOAT
□ 126. PHIL CAVARRETTA(M)
□ 136. GENE HERMANSKI
□ 144. JOE HATTEN
□ 159. DUTCH LEONARD
□ 175. RANSOM JACKSON
□ 195. FRANK BAUMHOLTZ
□ 211. PAUL MINNER
□ 231. DEE FONDY
□ 236. TOMMY BROWN(B)
□ 247. JOHN PRAMESA

CHICAGO WHITE SOX

□ 5. MINNIE MINOSO
□ 21. NELSON FOX
□ 41. CHICO CARRASQUEL
□ 54. BILLY PIERCE
□ 68. JIM BUSBY
□ 77. EDDIE ROBINSON
□ 93. PAUL RICHARDS(M)
□ 113. AL ZARILLA
□ 149. HOWIE JUDSON
□ 165. SAUL ROGOVIN
□ 185. EDDIE STEWART
□ 201. RAY COLEMAN
□ 221. LOU KRETLOW
□ 237. SHERMAN LOLLAR

CINCINNATI REDS

□ 6. VIRGIL STALLCUP
□ 42. JOHNNY WYROSTEK
□ 55. KEN RAFFENSBERGER
□ 69. JOE ADCOCK
□ 78. LLOYD MERRIMAN
□ 94. LUKE SEWELL(M)
□ 114. FRANK HILLER
□ 127. DICK SISLER
□ 141. HANK EDWARDS
□ 150. HERMAN WEHMEIER
□ 166. BOBBY ADAMS
□ 186. FRANK SMITH
□ 202. HARRY PERKOWSKI
□ 222. DIXIE HOWELL
□ 238. ROY MCMILLAN

CLEVELAND INDIANS

□ 7. MIKE GARCIA
□ 23. BOB LEMON
□ 43. BOB FELLER
□ 79. LOU BRISSIE
□ 95. LUKE EASTER
□ 115. LARRY DOBY
□ 124. BIRDIE TEBBETTS
□ 142. EARLY WYNN
□ 151. AL ROSEN
□ 167. BOB AVILA
□ 187. JIM HEGAN
□ 203. STEVE GROMEK
□ 214. RAY BOONE
□ 223. HARRY SIMPSON
□ 239. DALE MITCHELL

DETROIT TIGERS

□ 3. FRED HUTCHINSON
□ 13. CLIFF MAPES
□ 39. VIC WERTZ
□ 67. JOHNNY GROTH
□ 75. GEORGE KELL
□ 91. DON KOLLOWAY
□ 111. HOOT EVERS
□ 131. BOB SWIFT
□ 139. JERRY PRIDDY
□ 147. MARLIN STUART
□ 163. JOHNNY LIPON
□ 183. PAT MULLIN
□ 199. TED GRAY
□ 209. DICK LITTLEFIELD
□ 216. MATT BATTS
□ 219. NEIL BERRY
□ 235. STEVE SOUCHOCK

NEW YORK GIANTS

□ 2. BOBBY THOMSON
□ 18. DON MUELLER
□ 34. AL DARK
□ 38. WHITEY LOCKMAN
□ 49. JIM HEARN
□ 66. SAL MAGLIE
□ 74. WES WESTRUM
□ 90. LARRY JANSEN
□ 110. MAX LANIER
□ 121. AL CORWIN
□ 146. LEO DUROCHER(M)
□ 162. MONTE IRWIN
□ 178. DAVE WILLIAMS
□ 182. DAVE KOSLO
□ 198. CHUCK DIERING
□ 213. MONTE KENNEDY
□ 218. WILLIE MAYS
□ 234. FRED FITZSIMMONS(C)
□ 249. HANK THOMPSON

NEW YORK YANKEES

□ 1. YOGI BERRA
□ 17. ED LOPAT
□ 33. GIL MCDOUGALD
□ 37. VIC RASCHI
□ 52. PHIL RIZZUTO
□ 65. HANK BAUER
□ 73. JERRY COLEMAN
□ 101. MICKEY MANTLE
□ 105. BOBBY BROWN
□ 109. TOM MORGAN
□ 145. JOHNNY MIZE
□ 161. JACKIE JENSEN(F)
□ 177. GENE WOODLING
□ 181. JOE COLLINS
□ 197. CHARLIE SILVERA
□ 217. CASEY STENGEL(M)
□ 233. BOB KUZAVA
□ 252. FRANK CROSETTI(C)

PHILADELPHIA ATHLETICS

□ 10. BOB HOOPER
□ 26. EDDIE JOOST
□ 46. CARL SCHEIB
□ 58. HANK MAJESKI
□ 82. GUS ZERNIAL
□ 89. BILLY HITCHCOCK
□ 98. JIMMY DYKES(M)
□ 118. RAY MURRAY
□ 130. ALLIE CLARK
□ 154. FERRIS FAIN
□ 170. JOE ASTROTH
□ 179. PETE SUDER
□ 190. DICK FOWLER
□ 206. ELMER VALO
□ 226. ALEX KELLNER
□ 242. EVERETT KELL

PHILADELPHIA PHILLIES

□ 4. ROBIN ROBERTS
□ 20. WILLIE JONES
□ 35. GRANNY HAMNER
□ 40. BUBBA CHURCH
□ 53. RICHIE ASHBURN
□ 76. DEL ENNIS
□ 92. EDDIE WAITKUS
□ 112. SMOKEY BURGESS
□ 125. HOWIE FOX
□ 148. KEN HEINTZELMAN
□ 164. CONNIE RYAN
□ 184. CURT SIMMONS
□ 200. KEN SILVESTRI
□ 220. RUSS MEYER
□ 236. TOMMY BROWN(F)
□ 251. JACK LOHRKE

PITTSBURGH PIRATES

□ 11. RALPH KINER
□ 27. JOE GARAGIOLA
□ 47. PETE CASTIGLIONE
□ 59. MURRAY DICKSON
□ 71. VERNON LAW
□ 83. HOWIE POLLET
□ 99. CLYDE MCCULLOUGH
□ 108. GEORGE METKOVICH
□ 119. BILL HOWERTON
□ 138. TED WILKS
□ 155. BILL MEYER(M)
□ 171. MEL QUEEN
□ 180. ED FITZ GERALD
□ 191. BOB FRIEND
□ 207. GEORGE STRICKLAND
□ 227. CLYDE SUKEFORTH(C)
□ 243. RED MUNGER

ST. LOUIS BROWNS

- □ 19. BOB CAIN
- □ 29. NED GARVER
- □ 61. TOMMY BYRNE
- □ 85. MARTY MARION(C)
- □ 133. DICK KRYHOSKI
- □ 137. STAN ROJEK
- □ 157. JIM DELSING
- □ 173. GENE BEARDEN
- □ 193. BOBBY YOUNG
- □ 229. HANK ARFT
- □ 245. GEORGE SCHMEES

ST. LOUIS CARDINALS

- □ 14. CLIFF CHAMBERS
- □ 30. RED SCHOENDIENST
- □ 50. GERRY STALEY
- □ 62. JOE PRESKO
- □ 102. PEANUTS LOWREY
- □ 107. DEL RICE
- □ 122. BILLY JOHNSON
- □ 134. AL BRAZLE
- □ 160. EDDIE STANKY(M)
- □ 176. HARRY BRECHEEN
- □ 196. STAN MUSIAL
- □ 212. SOLLY HEMUS
- □ 232. ENOS SLAUGHTER
- □ 248. BILL WERLE

WASHINGTON SENATORS

- □ 15. SAM MELE
- □ 31. EDDIE YOST
- □ 36. CASS MICHAELS
- □ 51. GIL COAN
- □ 63. IRV NOREN
- □ 87. MICKEY VERNON
- □ 103. JOE HAYNES
- □ 123. SID HUDSON
- □ 135. MICKEY HARRIS
- □ 143. SANDY CONSUEGRA
- □ 158. BUCKY HARRIS(M)
- □ 161. JACKIE JENSEN(B)
- □ 174. MICKEY GRASSO
- □ 194. BOB PORTERFIELD
- □ 210. ARCHIE WILSON
- □ 230. FRANK SHEA
- □ 246. JERRY SNYDER

1953 BOWMAN (160)
2 1/2" X 3 3/4"
COLOR

BOSTON RED SOX

- □ 25. HOOT EVERS
- □ 35. MICKEY MCDERMOTT
- □ 41. SAMMY WHITE
- □ 57. LOU BOUDREAU(M)
- □ 61. GEORGE KELL
- □ 66. MEL PARNELL
- □ 123. JOHNNY LIPON
- □ 148. BILLY GOODMAN

BROOKLYN DODGERS

- □ 12. CARL ERSKINE
- □ 14. BILLY LOES
- □ 33. PEE WEE REESE
- □ 46. ROY CAMPANELLA
- □ 78. CARL FURILLO
- □ 92. GIL HODGES
- □ 117. DUKE SNIDER
- □ 124. CHARLIE DRESSEN(M)
- □ 129. RUSS MEYER
- □ 135. BOBBY MORGAN
- □ 145. GEORGE SHUBA

CHICAGO CUBS

- □ 7. HARRY CHITI
- □ 30. PHIL CAVARRETTA(M)
- □ 42. TOMMY BROWN
- □ 48. HANK SAUER
- □ 71. PAUL MINNER
- □ 94. BOB ADDIS
- □ 110. BOB RUSH
- □ 112. TOBY ATWELL
- □ 122. BILL SERENA
- □ 144. WARREN HACKER
- □ 154. TURK LOWN

CHICAGO WHITE SOX

- □ 18. NELSON FOX
- □ 36. MINNIE MINOSO
- □ 39. PAUL RICHARDS(M)
- □ 50. LOU KRETLOW
- □ 54. CHICO CARRASQUEL
- □ 73. BILLY PIERCE
- □ 75. SAUL ROGOVIN
- □ 88. JOE DOBSON
- □ 98. HECTOR RODRIQUEZ
- □ 137. SAM DENTE
- □ 157. SHERMAN LOLLAR

CINCINNATI REDS

- □ 23. HERMAN WEHMEIER
- □ 26. ROY MCMILLAN
- □ 58. WILLARD MARSHALL
- □ 62. TED KLUSZEWSKI
- □ 87. HARRY PERKOWSKI
- □ 90. JOE NUXHALL
- □ 106. KEN RAFFENSBERGER
- □ 108. BOBBY ADAMS
- □ 138. BUBBA CHURCH

CLEVELAND INDIANS

- □ 8. AL ROSEN
- □ 29. BOBBY AVILA
- □ 40. LARRY DOBY
- □ 43. MIKE GARCIA
- □ 79. RAY BOONE
- □ 86. HARRY SIMPSON
- □ 102. JIM HEGAN
- □ 104. LUKE EASTER
- □ 114. BOB FELLER
- □ 119. DALE MITCHELL
- □ 143. AL LOPEZ(M)
- □ 146. EARLY WYNN

DETROIT TIGERS

- □ 4. ART HOUTTEMAN
- □ 6. JOE GINSBERG
- □ 45. WALT DROPO
- □ 47. NED GARVER
- □ 72. TED GRAY
- □ 91. STEVE SOUCHOCK
- □ 100. BILL WIGHT
- □ 125. FRED HATFIELD
- □ 132. FRED HUTCHINSON(M)
- □ 134. JOHNNY PESKY

MIKWAUKEE BRAVES

- □ 3. SAM JETHROE*
- □ 5. SID GORDON*
- □ 37. JIM WILSON*
- □ 69. CHARLIE GRIMM(M)
- □ 83. JACK DANIELS
- □ 97. EDDIE MATHEWS
- □ 99. WARREN SPAHN
- □ 151. JOE ADCOCK
- □ 156. MAX SURKONT

NEW YORK GIANTS

- □ 1. DAVEY WILLIAMS
- □ 19. AL DARK
- □ 51. MONTE IRVIN
- □ 55. LEO DUROCHER(M)
- □ 74. DON MUELLER
- □ 76. JIM HEARN
- □ 96. SAL MAGLIE
- □ 126. AL CORWIN
- □ 128. WHITEY LOCKMAN
- □ 149. AL CORWIN

NEW YORK YANKEES

- □ 9. PHIL RIZZUTO
- □ 27. VIC RASCHI
- □ 59. MICKEY MANTLE
- □ 63. GIL MCDOUGALD
- □ 68. ALLIE REYNOLDS
- □ 84. HANK BAUER
- □ 118. BILLY MARTIN
- □ 121. YOGI BERRA
- □ 136. JIM BRIDEWESER
- □ 153. WHITEY FORD

PHILADELPHIA ATHLETICS

- □ 11. BOBBY SHANTZ
- □ 13. GUS ZERNIAL
- □ 31. JIMMY DYKES(M)
- □ 38. HARRY BYRD
- □ 82. JOE ASTROTH
- □ 95. WALLY MOSES(C)
- □ 105. EDDIE JOOST
- □ 107. ALEX KELLNER
- □ 130. CASS MICHAELS
- □ 150. CARL SCHEIB
- □ 155. ALLIE CLARK

PHILADELPHIA PHILLIES

- □ 10. RICHIE ASHBURN
- □ 28. SMOKY BURGESS
- □ 60. GRANNY HAMNER
- □ 64. CURT SIMMONS
- □ 65. ROBIN ROBERTS

* Nos. 3, 5, 37 appear with Boston Braves on the back of the card.

- ☐ 67. MEL CLARK
- ☐ 103. DEL ENNIS
- ☐ 113. KARL DREWS
- ☐ 131. CONNIE RYAN
- ☐ 133. WILLIE JONES
- ☐ 158. HOWARD FOX

PITTSBURGH PIRATES

- ☐ 16. BOB FRIEND
- ☐ 21. JOE GARAGIOLA
- ☐ 80. RALPH KINER
- ☐ 147. CLEM KOSHOREK
- ☐ 160. CAL ABRAMS

ST. LOUIS BROWNS

- ☐ 2. VIC WERTZ
- ☐ 20. DON LENHARDT
- ☐ 52. MARTY MARION(M)
- ☐ 56. BOB CAIN
- ☐ 70. CLINT COURTNEY
- ☐ 111. JIM DYCK
- ☐ 120. MARLIN STUART
- ☐ 127. DICK KRYHOSKI

ST. LOUIS CARDINALS

- ☐ 17. GERRY STALEY
- ☐ 32. STAN MUSIAL
- ☐ 49. EDDIE STANKY(M)
- ☐ 53. DEL RICE
- ☐ 81. ENOS SLAUGHTER
- ☐ 85. SOLLY HEMUS
- ☐ 101. RED SCHOENDIENST
- ☐ 115. CLOYD BOYER
- ☐ 140. AL BRAZLE
- ☐ 142. LARRY MIGGINS

WASHINGTON SENATORS

- ☐ 15. JIM BUSBY
- ☐ 22. BOB PORTERFIELD
- ☐ 24. JACKIE JENSEN
- ☐ 34. GIL COAN
- ☐ 77. MICKEY GRASSO
- ☐ 89. SANDY CONSUEGRA
- ☐ 109. KEN WOOD
- ☐ 116. EDDIE YOST
- ☐ 139. PETE RUNNELS
- ☐ 141. FRANK SHEA
- ☐ 152. CLYDE VOLLMER
- ☐ 159. MICKEY VERNON

1953 BOWMAN (64) 2 1/2" X 3 3/4" BLACK & WHITE

BOSTON RED SOX

- ☐ 2. WILLARD NIXON
- ☐ 11. DICK GERNERT
- ☐ 24. DEL WILBER
- ☐ 29. SID HUDSON
- ☐ 36. JIM PIERSALL
- ☐ 49. FLOYD BAKER

BROOKLYN DODGERS

- ☐ 26. PREACHER ROE
- ☐ 52. RALPH BRANCA
- ☐ 60. BILLY COX

CHICAGO CUBS

- ☐ 5. DEE FONDY
- ☐ 12. RANDY JACKSON
- ☐ 37. HAL JEFFCOAT
- ☐ 41. BOB RAMAZZOTTI
- ☐ 50. DUTCH LEONARD
- ☐ 56. ROY SMALLEY

CHICAGO WHITE SOX

NO CARDS ISSUED

CINCINATTI REDS

- ☐ 1. GUS BELL
- ☐ 7. ANDY SEMINICK
- ☐ 21. BUD PODBIELAN
- ☐ 32. ROCKY BRIDGES
- ☐ 42. HOWIE JUDSON

CLEVELAND INDIANS

- ☐ 13. JOE TIPTON
- ☐ 27. BOB LEMON
- ☐ 63. STEVE GROMEK

DETROIT TIGERS

- ☐ 4. PAT MULLIN
- ☐ 18. BILLY HOEFT
- ☐ 22. MATT BATTS
- ☐ 44. JIM DELSING

MILWAUKEE BRAVES

- ☐ 30. WALKER COOPER
- ☐ 34. EBBA ST. CLAIR
- ☐ 38. DAVE COLE
- ☐ 51. LOU BURDETTE
- ☐ 57. ANDY PAFKO

NEW YORK GIANTS

- ☐ 3. BILL RIGNEY
- ☐ 28. HOYT WILHELM
- ☐ 40. LARRY JANSEN

NEW YORK YANKEES

- ☐ 15. JOHNNY MIZE
- ☐ 25. JOHN SAIN
- ☐ 31. GENE WOODLING
- ☐ 33. BOB KUZAVA
- ☐ 39. CASEY STENGEL(M)
- ☐ 45. IRV NOREN
- ☐ 54. BILL MILLER
- ☐ 61. TOM GORMAN

PHILADELPHIA ATHLETICS

- ☐ 6. RAY MURRAY
- ☐ 8. PETE SUDER
- ☐ 20. EDDIE ROBINSON
- ☐ 43. HAL BEVAN
- ☐ 53. MORRIS MARTIN
- ☐ 62. KEITH THOMAS

PHILADELPHIA PHILLIES

- ☐ 14. BILL NICHOLSON
- ☐ 35. JOHNNY WYROSTEK
- ☐ 47. JACK LOHRKE
- ☐ 48. STEVE RIDZIK
- ☐ 58. JIM KONSTANTY
- ☐ 64. ANDY HANSEN

PITTSBURGH PIRATES

- ☐ 19. PAUL LA PALME

ST. LOUIS BROWNS

☐ 17. VIRGIL TRUCKS
☐ 59. DUANE PILLETTE

ST. LOUIS CARDINALS

☐ 10. DICK SISLER
☐ 16. STU MILLER
☐ 23. WILMER MIZELL

WASHINGTON SENATORS

☐ 9. WALT MASTERSON
☐ 46. BUCKY HARRIS(M)
☐ 55. DON JOHNSON

1954 BOWMAN (224)
2 1/2" X 3 3/4"

BALTIMORE ORIOLES

☐ 5. BILL HUNTER
☐ 21. VIC WERTZ
☐ 37. DICK KOKOS
☐ 53. DON LENHARDT
☐ 69. CLINT COURTNEY
☐ 85. JIM DYCK
☐ 101. DON LARSEN
☐ 117. DICK KRYHOSKI
☐ 133. DUANE PILLETTE
☐ 149. BOB YOUNG
☐ 165. JOHNNY GROTH
☐ 181. LES MOSS
☐ 197. LOU KRETLOW
☐ 213. DICK LITTLEFIELD

BOSTON RED SOX

☐ 2. JACKIE JENSEN
☐ 18. HOOT EVERS
☐ 34. SAMMY WHITE
☐ 50. GEORGE KELL
☐ 66. TED WILLIAMS
☐ 66. JIM PIERSALL
☐ 82. BILLY GOODMAN
☐ 98. ELLIS KINDER
☐ 114. WILLARD NIXON
☐ 130. MILT BOLLING
☐ 146. DICK GERNERT
☐ 162. TED LEPCIO
☐ 178. DEL WILBER
☐ 194. SID HUDSON
☐ 210. JIM PIERSALL

BROOKLYN DODGERS

☐ 10. CARL ERSKINE
☐ 26. BILLY COX
☐ 42. BILLY LOES
☐ 58. PEE WEE REESE
☐ 74. JIM GILLIAM
☐ 90. ROY CAMPANELLA
☐ 106. CLEM LABINE
☐ 122. CARL FURILLO
☐ 138. GIL HODGES
☐ 154. DON NEWCOMBE
☐ 170. DUKE SNIDER
☐ 186. RUSS MEYER
☐ 202. GEORGE SHUBA
☐ 218. PREACHER ROE

CHICAGO CUBS

☐ 13. PAUL MINNER
☐ 29. JOHNNY KLIPPSTEIN
☐ 45. RALPH KINER
☐ 61. EDDIE MIKSIS
☐ 77. BOB RUSH
☐ 93. BILL SERENA
☐ 109. ROY SMALLEY
☐ 125. WARREN HACKER
☐ 141. JOE GARAGIOLA
☐ 157. TURK LOWN
☐ 173. DEE FONDY
☐ 189. RANDY JACKSON
☐ 205. HAL JEFFCOAT
☐ 221. FRANK BAUMHOLTZ

CHICAGO WHITE SOX

☐ 6. NELSON FOX
☐ 22. SAM MELE
☐ 38. MINNIE MINOSO
☐ 54. CHICO CARRASQUEL
☐ 70. WILLARD MARSHALL(B)
☐ 86. HARRY DORISH
☐ 102. BILLY PIERCE
☐ 118. BOB BOYD
☐ 134. LUIS ALOMA
☐ 150. CASS MICHAELS
☐ 166. SANDY CONSUEGRA
☐ 182. SHERMAN LOLLAR
☐ 198. VIRGIL TRUCKS
☐ 214. FERRIS FAIN

CINCINNATI REDS

☐ 12. ROY MCMILLAN
☐ 28. JIM GREENGRASS
☐ 44. HARRY PERKOWSKI
☐ 60. FRED BACZEWSKI
☐ 70. WILLARD MARSHALL(F)
☐ 76. JOE NUXHALL
☐ 92. KEN RAFFENSBERGER
☐ 108. BOBBY ADAMS
☐ 124. GUS BELL
☐ 140. SAUL ROGOVIN
☐ 156. ROCKY BRIDGES
☐ 172. ANDY SEMINICK
☐ 188. FRANK SMITH
☐ 204. JACKIE COLLUM
☐ 220. HOBIE LANDRITH

CLEVELAND INDIANS

☐ 4. BOB HOOPER
☐ 20. ART HOUTTEMAN
☐ 36. GEORGE STRICKLAND
☐ 52. JOE GINSBERG
☐ 68. BOBBY AVILA
☐ 84. LARRY DOBY
☐ 100. MIKE GARCIA
☐ 116. LUKE EASTER
☐ 132. BOB FELLER
☐ 148. DALE MITCHELL
☐ 164. EARLY WYNN
☐ 184. MICKEY GRASSO
☐ 196. BOB LEMON
☐ 212. OWEN FRIEND

DETROIT TIGERS

☐ 7. WALT DROPO
☐ 23. HARVEY KUENN
☐ 39. NED GARVER
☐ 55. JIM DELSING
☐ 71. TED GRAY
☐ 87. DON LUND
☐ 103. STEVE SOUCHOCK
☐ 119. FRED HATFIELD
☐ 135. JOHNNY PESKY
☐ 151. PAT MULLIN
☐ 167. BILLY HOEFT
☐ 183. MATT BATTS
☐ 199. STEVE GROMEK
☐ 215. JOHNNY BUCHA

MILWAUKEE BRAVES

☐ 16. JIM WILSON
☐ 32. DEL CRANDALL
☐ 48. JACK DITTMER
☐ 64. EDDIE MATHEWS
☐ 80. JOHNNY LOGAN
☐ 96. JOE ADCOCK
☐ 112. ANDY PAFKO
☐ 144. ERNIE JOHNSON
☐ 160. DANNY O'CONNELL
☐ 176. VERN BICKFORD
☐ 192. LEW BURDETTE
☐ 201. BOBBY THOMSON
☐ 224. BILL BRUTON

NEW YORK GIANTS

☐ 9. DAVE WILLIAMS
☐ 25. WES WESTRUM
☐ 41. AL DARK
☐ 57. HOYT WILHELM
☐ 73. DON MUELLER
☐ 89. WILLIE MAYS
☐ 105. SAL MAGLIE
☐ 121. RAY KATT
☐ 128. EBBA ST. CLAIRE
☐ 137. AL CORWIN
☐ 153. WHITEY LOCKMAN
☐ 169. LARRY JANSEN
☐ 185. DARYL SPENCER
☐ 208. JOHNNY ANTONELLI
☐ 217. HANK THOMPSON

NEW YORK YANKEES

☐ 1. PHIL RIZZUTO
☐ 17. TOM GORMAN
☐ 33. VIC RASCHI
☐ 49. HARRY BYRD
☐ 65. MICKEY MANTLE
☐ 81. JERRY COLEMAN
☐ 97. GIL MCDOUGALD
☐ 113. ALLIE REYNOLDS
☐ 129. HANK BAUER
☐ 145. BILLY MARTIN
☐ 161. YOGI BERRA
☐ 177. WHITEY FORD
☐ 193. EDDIE ROBINSON
☐ 209. GENE WOODLING

PHILADELPHIA ATHLETICS

☐ 3. MARION FRICANO
☐ 19. BOBBY SHANTZ
☐ 35. EDDIE JOOST
☐ 51. ALEX KELLNER
☐ 67. CARL SCHEIB
☐ 83. RAY MURRAY
☐ 99. PETE SUDER
☐ 115. DON BOLLWEG
☐ 131. JOE ASTROTH
☐ 147. JOE DEMAESTRI
☐ 163. DAVE PHILLEY
☐ 179. MORRIS MARTIN
☐ 195. BOB CAIN
☐ 211. AL ROBERTSON

PHILADELPHIA PHILLIES

- ☐ 15. RICHIE ASHBURN
- ☐ 31. SMOKEY BURGESS
- ☐ 47. GRANNY HAMNER
- ☐ 63. EARL TORGESON
- ☐ 79. CURT SIMMONS
- ☐ 95. ROBIN ROBERTS
- ☐ 111. MURRY DICKSON
- ☐ 127. DEL ENNIS
- ☐ 143. WILLIE JONES
- ☐ 159. JOHNNY LINDELL
- ☐ 175. MEL CLARK
- ☐ 191. KARL DREWS
- ☐ 207. STAN LOPATA
- ☐ 223. STEVE RIDZIK

PITTSBURGH PIRATES

- ☐ 11. SID GORDON
- ☐ 27. DICK COLE
- ☐ 43. BOB FRIEND
- ☐ 59. BOB SCHULTZ
- ☐ 75. MAX SURKONT
- ☐ 91. CAL ABRAMS
- ☐ 107. PAUL LA PALME
- ☐ 123. TOBY ATWELL
- ☐ 139. PRESTON WARD
- ☐ 155. FRANK THOMAS
- ☐ 171. CARLOS BERNIER
- ☐ 187. VERN LAW
- ☐ 203. VIC JANOWICZ
- ☐ 219. HAL RICE

ST. LOUIS CARDINALS

- ☐ 14. GERRY STALEY
- ☐ 30. DEL RICE
- ☐ 46. RIP REPULSKI
- ☐ 62. ENOS SLAUGHTER
- ☐ 78. SAL YVARS
- ☐ 94. SOLLY HEMUS
- ☐ 110. RED SCHOENDIENST
- ☐ 126. CLIFF CHAMBERS
- ☐ 142. AL BRAZLE
- ☐ 158. STU MILLER
- ☐ 174. PETE CASTIGLIONE
- ☐ 190. JOE PRESKO
- ☐ 206. STEVE BILKO
- ☐ 222. MEMO LUNA

WASHINGTON SENATORS

- ☐ 8. JIM BUSBY
- ☐ 24. BOB PORTERFIELD
- ☐ 40. GIL COAN
- ☐ 56. MICKEY MCDERMOTT
- ☐ 72. EDDIE YOST
- ☐ 88. TOM UMPHLETT
- ☐ 104. FRANK SHEA
- ☐ 120. MEL HODERLEIN
- ☐ 136. CLYDE VOLLMER
- ☐ 152. MICKEY VERNON
- ☐ 168. ED FITZ GERALD
- ☐ 180. JOE TIPTON
- ☐ 200. CONNIE MARRERO
- ☐ 216. JERRY SNYDER

1955 BOWMAN (320)
2 1/2" X 3 3/4"

BALTIMORE ORIOLES

- ☐ 3. JOE COLEMAN
- ☐ 4. EDDIE WAITKUS
- ☐ 55. CAL ABRAMS
- ☐ 56. BILLY COX
- ☐ 77. JIM MCDONALD
- ☐ 78. GIL COAN
- ☐ 79. WILLIE MIRANDA
- ☐ 101. DON JOHNSON
- ☐ 108. LOU KRETLOW
- ☐ 109. VERN STEPHENS
- ☐ 159. HARRY BYRD
- ☐ 161. MATT BATTS
- ☐ 162. CHARLIE MAXWELL
- ☐ 215. BOB KUZAVA
- ☐ 216. PREACHER ROE
- ☐ 225. PAUL RICHARDS(M)
- ☐ 241. JOHN PESKY
- ☐ 244. DUANE PILLETTE
- ☐ 245. BILL MILLER

BOSTON RED SOX

- ☐ 15. FRANK SULLIVAN
- ☐ 16. JIM PIERSALL
- ☐ 47. SAMMY WHITE
- ☐ 48. MILT BOLLING
- ☐ 126. BILLY GOODMAN
- ☐ 147. SAM MELE
- ☐ 150. BILL KLAUS
- ☐ 177. WILLARD NIXON
- ☐ 178. TOM BREWER
- ☐ 221. HECTOR BROWN
- ☐ 222. RUSS KEMMERER
- ☐ 256. OWEN FRIEND
- ☐ 264. BILL R. HENRY
- ☐ 276. IVAN DELOCK
- ☐ 290. HERSHELL FREEMAN
- ☐ 302. FRANK MALZONE
- ☐ 318. SID HUDSON
- ☐ 319. AL SCHROLL
- ☐ 320. GEORGE SUSCE

BROOKLYN DODGERS

- ☐ 21. DON HOAK
- ☐ 22. ROY CAMPANELLA
- ☐ 37. PEE WEE REESE
- ☐ 39. BOB DARNELL
- ☐ 65. DON ZIMMER
- ☐ 66. GEORGE SHUBA
- ☐ 97. JOHNNY PODRES
- ☐ 98. JIM GILLIAM
- ☐ 143. DON NEWCOMBE
- ☐ 156. JIM HUGHES
- ☐ 158. GIL HODGES
- ☐ 169. CARL FURILLO
- ☐ 170. CARL ERSKINE
- ☐ 195. ERV PALICA
- ☐ 196. RUSS MEYER
- ☐ 240. BILLY LOES
- ☐ 261. WALT MORYN
- ☐ 270. CHICO FERNANDEZ
- ☐ 278. CHARLIE NEAL
- ☐ 310. KEN LEHMAN

CHICAGO CUBS

- ☐ 7. GENE BAKER
- ☐ 8. WARREN HACKER
- ☐ 52. HAL RICE
- ☐ 87. RANDY JACKSON
- ☐ 88. STEVE BILKO
- ☐ 137. BOB TALBOT
- ☐ 181. EDDIE MIKSIS
- ☐ 182. BOB RUSH
- ☐ 223. HAL JEFFCOAT
- ☐ 224. DEE FONDY
- ☐ 227. FRANK BAUMHOLTZ
- ☐ 229. JIM BROSNAN
- ☐ 242. ERNIE BANKS
- ☐ 247. DUTCH LEONARD(C)
- ☐ 273. BUBBA CHURCH
- ☐ 280. CLYDE MCCULLOUGH
- ☐ 304. HARRY CHITI

CHICAGO WHITE SOX

- ☐ 25. MINNIE MINOSO
- ☐ 26. VIRGIL TRUCKS
- ☐ 33. NELSON FOX
- ☐ 34. CLINT COURTNEY
- ☐ 85. CASS MICHAELS
- ☐ 86. TED GRAY
- ☐ 116. SANDY CONSUEGRA
- ☐ 117. JOHNNY GROTH
- ☐ 131. WILLARD MARSHALL
- ☐ 135. LLOYD MERRIMAN
- ☐ 145. BOB NIEMAN
- ☐ 148. BOB CHAKALES
- ☐ 151. JIM BRIDEWESER
- ☐ 173. CHICO CARRASQUEL
- ☐ 174. SHERMAN LOLLAR
- ☐ 213. GEORGE KELL
- ☐ 214. BILLY PIERCE
- ☐ 230. AL BRAZLE
- ☐ 233. BILL SERENA
- ☐ 248. HARRY DORISH
- ☐ 251. STAN JOK
- ☐ 266. MIKE FORNIELES
- ☐ 282. PHIL CAVARRETTA
- ☐ 285. WALT DROPO

CINCINNATI REDS

- ☐ 31. JOHNNY TEMPLE
- ☐ 32. WALLY POST
- ☐ 49. JIM GREENGRASS
- ☐ 50. HOBIE LANDRITH
- ☐ 51. ELVIN TAPPE
- ☐ 93. ANDY SEMINICK
- ☐ 118. BOBBY ADAMS
- ☐ 136. ROCKY BRIDGES
- ☐ 152. JOHNNY KLIPPSTEIN
- ☐ 155. GERRY STALEY
- ☐ 189. JACK COLLUM
- ☐ 190. FRED BACZEWSKI
- ☐ 193. HOWIE JUDSON
- ☐ 194. JOE NUXHALL
- ☐ 232. BIRDIE TEBBETTS(M)
- ☐ 234. DICK BARTELL(C)
- ☐ 243. GUS BELL

CLEVELAND INDIANS

- ☐ 19. BOBBY AVILA
- ☐ 20. AL SMITH
- ☐ 38. EARLY WYNN
- ☐ 40. VIC WERTZ
- ☐ 96. RAY NARLESKI
- ☐ 127. HANK MAJESKI

- □ 128. MIKE GARCIA
- □ 129. HAL NARAGON
- □ 134. BOB FELLER
- □ 142. RUDY REGALADO
- □ 144. ART HOUTTEMAN
- □ 191. BOB LEMON
- □ 192. GEORGE STRICKLAND
- □ 197. RALPH KINER
- □ 198. DAVE POPE
- □ 259. DON MOSSI
- □ 263. EDDIE JOOST
- □ 271. BOB HOOPER
- □ 308. AL LOPEZ(M)
- □ 312. BILL WIGHT
- □ 314. DALE MITCHELL

DETROIT TIGERS

- □ 23. AL KALINE
- □ 24. AL ABER
- □ 35. BILL TUTTLE
- □ 36. WAYNE BELARDI
- □ 91. DICK MARLOWE
- □ 92. GEORGE ZUVERINK
- □ 121. RUFUS CRAWFORD
- □ 132. HARVEY KUENN
- □ 133. CHARLES KING
- □ 154. FRANK LARY
- □ 187. FRED HATFIELD
- □ 188. NED GARVER
- □ 203. STEVE GROMEK
- □ 204. FRANK BOLLING
- □ 228. BUBBA PHILLIPS
- □ 254. BENNETT FLOWERS
- □ 274. JIM DELSING

KANSAS CITY ATHLETICS

- □ 5. JIM ROBERTSON
- □ 6. PETE SUDER
- □ 53. ALEX KELLNER
- □ 54. DON BOLLWEG
- □ 80. LOU LIMMER
- □ 89. LOU BOUDREAU(M)
- □ 90. ART DITMAR
- □ 119. JOE ASTROTH
- □ 120. ED BURTSCHY
- □ 140. BOBBY SHANTZ
- □ 149. CLOYD BOYER
- □ 175. BILLY SHANTZ
- □ 176. JOE DEMAESTRI
- □ 211. SONNY DIXON
- □ 316. MARION FRICANO

MILWAUKEE BRAVES

- □ 11. BILLY BRUTON
- □ 12. ANDY PAFKO
- □ 43. BOB BUHL
- □ 44. DANNY O'CONNELL
- □ 70. LOU BURDETTE
- □ 71. DAVE JOLLY
- □ 72. CHET NICHOLS
- □ 102. BOBBY THOMSON
- □ 103. EDDIE MATHEWS
- □ 157. ERNIE JOHNSON
- □ 179. HANK AARON
- □ 180. JOHNNY LOGAN
- □ 212. JACK DITTMER
- □ 217. DEL CRANDALL
- □ 218. JOE ADCOCK
- □ 252. ROY SMALLEY
- □ 253. JIM WILSON
- □ 298. CHARLIE GRIMM(M)

NEW YORK GIANTS

- □ 1. HOYT WILHELM
- □ 2. AL DARK
- □ 94. HANK THOMPSON
- □ 95. SAL MAGLIE
- □ 122. AL CORWIN
- □ 123. MARV GRISSOM
- □ 124. JOHNNY ANTONELLI
- □ 125. PAUL GIEL
- □ 138. DAVEY WILLIAMS
- □ 141. WES WESTRUM
- □ 146. DON LIDDLE
- □ 183. RAY KATT
- □ 184. WILLIE MAYS
- □ 219. WHITEY LOCKMAN
- □ 220. JIM HEARN
- □ 249. BILLY GARDNER
- □ 269. JOE AMALFITANO

NEW YORK YANKEES

- □ 9. GIL MCDOUGALD
- □ 10. PHIL RIZZUTO
- □ 59. WHITEY FORD
- □ 60. ENOS SLAUGHTER
- □ 63. IRV NOREN
- □ 67. DON LARSEN
- □ 68. ELSTON HOWARD
- □ 69. BILL HUNTER
- □ 99. JERRY COLEMAN
- □ 100. TOM MORGAN
- □ 153. EDDIE ROBINSON
- □ 160. BILL SKOWRON
- □ 167. BOB GRIM
- □ 168. YOGI BERRA
- □ 201. ALLIE REYNOLDS
- □ 202. MICKEY MANTLE
- □ 231. JIM KONSTANTY
- □ 246. HANK BAUER
- □ 300. TOMMY BYRNE
- □ 306. BOB CERV

PHILADELPHIA PHILLIES

- □ 17. DEL ENNIS
- □ 18. STAN LOPATA
- □ 41. MEL CLARK
- □ 42. BOB GREENWOOD
- □ 64. CURT SIMMONS
- □ 81. BOB MORGAN
- □ 110. BOB J. MILLER
- □ 111. STEVE RIDZIK
- □ 112. GRANNY HAMNER
- □ 130. RICHIE ASHBURN
- □ 171. ROBIN ROBERTS
- □ 172. WILLIE JONES
- □ 209. SMOKY BURGESS
- □ 210. EARL TORGESON
- □ 236. MURRAY DICKSON
- □ 237. JOHNNY WYROSTEK
- □ 287. RON MROZINSKI
- □ 292. MARV BLAYLOCK
- □ 294. WALLY MOSES(C)

PITTSBURGH PIRATES

- □ 27. PRESTON WARD
- □ 28. DICK COLE
- □ 57. BOB FRIEND
- □ 58. FRANK THOMAS
- □ 82. LEE WALLS
- □ 83. MAX SURKONT
- □ 84. GEORGE FREESE
- □ 113. BOB HALL
- □ 114. VIC JANOWICZ
- □ 115. ROGER BOWMAN
- □ 163. SID GORDON
- □ 164. TOBY ATWELL
- □ 199. VERNON LAW
- □ 200. DICK LITTLEFIELD
- □ 288. DICK SMITH

ST. LOUIS CARDINALS

- □ 29. RED SCHOENDIENST
- □ 30. BILL SARNI
- □ 61. PAUL LAPALME
- □ 62. ROYCE LINT
- □ 75. BROOKS LAWRENCE
- □ 76. TOM POHOLSKY
- □ 106. DEL RICE
- □ 107. SOLLY HEMUS
- □ 185. VIC RASCHI
- □ 186. ALEX GRAMMAS
- □ 205. RIP REPULSKI
- □ 206. RALPH BEARD
- □ 238. EDDIE STANKY(M)
- □ 257. TOM ALSTON
- □ 296. BILL VIRDON

WASHINGTON SENATORS

- □ 13. CLYDE VOLLMER
- □ 14. GUS KERIAZAKOS
- □ 45. TOM UMPHLETT
- □ 46. MICKEY VERNON
- □ 73. EDDIE YOST
- □ 74. JERRY SNYDER
- □ 104. BOB PORTERFIELD
- □ 105. JOHNNY SCHMITZ
- □ 165. MICKEY MCDERMOTT
- □ 166. JIM BUSBY
- □ 207. FRANK SHEA
- □ 208. ED FITZ GERALD
- □ 255. PETE RUNNELS
- □ 262. JIM LEMON
- □ 268. ROY HAWES

1989 BOWMAN (484)
2 1/2" X 3 3/4"

ATLANTA BRAVES

- □ 262. ZANE SMITH
- □ 263. CHARLIE PULEO
- □ 264. DEREK LILLIQUIST
- □ 265. PAUL ASSENMACHER
- □ 266. JOHN SMOLTZ
- □ 267. TOM GLAVINE
- □ 268. STEVE AVERY
- □ 269. PETE SMITH
- □ 270. JODY DAVIS
- □ 271. BRUCE BENEDICT
- □ 272. ANDRES THOMAS
- □ 273. GERALD PERRY
- □ 274. RON GANT
- □ 275. DARRELL EVANS
- □ 276. DALE MURPHY
- □ 277. DION JAMES
- □ 278. LONNIE SMITH
- □ 279. GERONIMO BERROA

BALTIMORE ORIOLES

- □ 1. OSWALD PERAZA
- □ 2. BRIAN HOLTON
- □ 3. JOSE BAUTISTA
- □ 4. PETE HARNISCH
- □ 5. DAVE SCHMIDT
- □ 6. GREGG OLSON
- □ 7. JEFF BALLARD
- □ 8. BOB MELVIN
- □ 9. CAL RIPKEN
- □ 10. RANDY MILLIGAN
- □ 11. JUAN BELL
- □ 12. BILLY RIPKEN
- □ 13. JIM TRABER

- ☐ 14. PETE STANICEK
- ☐ 15. STEVE FINLEY
- ☐ 16. LARRY SHEETS
- ☐ 17. PHIL BRADLEY
- ☐ 18. BRADY ANDERSON
- ☐ 260. CAL RIPKEN, SR. (C)

BOSTON RED SOX

- ☐ 19. LEE SMITH
- ☐ 20. TOM FISCHER
- ☐ 21. MIKE BODDICKER
- ☐ 22. ROB MURPHY
- ☐ 23. WES GARDNER
- ☐ 24. JOHN DOPSON
- ☐ 25. BOB STANLEY
- ☐ 26. ROGER CLEMENS
- ☐ 27. RICH GEDMAN
- ☐ 28. MARTY BARRETT
- ☐ 29. LUIS RIVERS
- ☐ 30. JODY REED
- ☐ 31. NICK ESASKY
- ☐ 32. WADE BOGGS
- ☐ 33. JIM RICE
- ☐ 34. MIKE GREENWELL
- ☐ 35. DWIGHT EVANS
- ☐ 36. ELLIS BURKS

CALIFORNIA ANGELS

- ☐ 37. CHUCK FINLEY
- ☐ 38. KIRK MCCASKILL
- ☐ 39. JIM ABBOTT
- ☐ 40. BRYAN HARVEY
- ☐ 41. BERT BLYLEVEN
- ☐ 42. MIKE WITT
- ☐ 43. BOB MCCLURE
- ☐ 44. BILL SCHROEDER
- ☐ 45. LANCE PARRISH
- ☐ 46. DICK SCHOFIELD
- ☐ 47. WALLY JOYNER
- ☐ 48. JACK HOWELL
- ☐ 49. JOHNNY RAY
- ☐ 50. CHILI DAVIS
- ☐ 51. TONY ARMAS
- ☐ 52. CLAUDELL WASHINGTON
- ☐ 53. BRIAN DOWNING
- ☐ 54. DEVON WHITE

CHICAGO CUBS

- ☐ 280. STEVE WILSON
- ☐ 281. RICK SUTCLIFFE
- ☐ 282. KEVIN COFFMAN
- ☐ 283. MITCH WILLIAMS
- ☐ 284. GREG MADDUX
- ☐ 285. PAUL KILGUS
- ☐ 286. MIKE HARKEY
- ☐ 287. LLOYD MCCLENDON
- ☐ 288. DAMON BERRYHILL
- ☐ 289. TY GRIFFIN
- ☐ 290. RYNE SANDBERG
- ☐ 291. MARK GRACE
- ☐ 292. CURT WILKERSON
- ☐ 293. VANCE LAW
- ☐ 294. SHAWON DUNSTON
- ☐ 295. JEROME WALTON
- ☐ 296. MITCH WEBSTER
- ☐ 297. DWIGHT SMITH
- ☐ 298. ANDRE DAWSON

CHICAGO WHITE SOX

- ☐ 55. BOBBY THIGPEN
- ☐ 56. BILL LONG
- ☐ 57. JERRY REUSS
- ☐ 58. SHAWN HILLEGAS
- ☐ 59. MELIDO PEREZ
- ☐ 60. JEFF BITTIGER
- ☐ 61. JACK MCDOWELL
- ☐ 62. CARLTON FISK
- ☐ 63. STEVE LYONS
- ☐ 64. OZZIE GUILLEN
- ☐ 65. ROBIN VENTURA
- ☐ 66. FRED MANRIQUE
- ☐ 67. DAN PASQUA
- ☐ 68. IVAN CALDERON
- ☐ 69. RON KITTLE
- ☐ 70. DARYL BOSTON
- ☐ 71. DAVE GALLAGHER
- ☐ 72. HAROLD BAINES

CINCINNATI REDS

- ☐ 259. KEN GRIFFEY
- ☐ 299. JEFF SELLERS
- ☐ 300. JOSE RIJO
- ☐ 301. JOHN FRANCO
- ☐ 302. RICK MAHLER
- ☐ 303. RON ROBINSON
- ☐ 304. DANNY JACKSON
- ☐ 305. ROB DIBBLE
- ☐ 306. TOM BROWNING
- ☐ 307. BO DIAZ
- ☐ 308. MANNY TRILLO
- ☐ 309. CHRIS SABO
- ☐ 310. RON OESTER
- ☐ 311. BARRY LARKIN
- ☐ 312. TODD BENZINGER
- ☐ 313. PAUL O'NEILL
- ☐ 314. KAL DANIELS
- ☐ 315. JOEL YOUNGBLOOD
- ☐ 316. ERIC DAVIS

CLEVELAND INDIANS

- ☐ 73. CHARLES NAGY
- ☐ 74. JOHN FARRELL
- ☐ 75. KEVIN WICKANDER
- ☐ 76. GREG SWINDELL
- ☐ 77. MIKE WALKER
- ☐ 78. DOUG JONES
- ☐ 79. RICH YETT
- ☐ 80. TOM CANDIOTTI
- ☐ 81. JESSE OROSCO
- ☐ 82. BUD BLACK
- ☐ 83. ANDY ALLANSON
- ☐ 84. PETE O'BRIEN
- ☐ 85. JERRY BROWNE
- ☐ 86. BROOK JACOBY
- ☐ 87. MARK LEWIS
- ☐ 88. LUIS AGUAYO
- ☐ 89. CORY SNYDER
- ☐ 90. ODDIBE MCDOWELL
- ☐ 91. JOE CARTER

DETROIT TIGERS

- ☐ 92. FRANK TANANA
- ☐ 93. JACK MORRIS
- ☐ 94. DOYLE ALEXANDER
- ☐ 95. STEVE SEARCY
- ☐ 96. RANDY BOCKUS
- ☐ 97. JEFF ROBINSON
- ☐ 98. MIKE HENNEMAN
- ☐ 99. PAUL GIBSON
- ☐ 100. FRANK WILLIAMS
- ☐ 101. MATT NOKES
- ☐ 102. RICCO BROGNA
- ☐ 103. LOU WHITAKER
- ☐ 104. AL PEDRIQUE
- ☐ 105. ALAN TRAMMELL
- ☐ 106. CHRIS BROWN
- ☐ 107. PAT SHERIDAN
- ☐ 108. CHET LEMON
- ☐ 109. KEITH MORELAND

HOUSTON ASTROS

- ☐ 317. DAVE SMITH
- ☐ 318. MARK PORTUGAL
- ☐ 319. BRIAN MEYER
- ☐ 320. JIM DESHAIES
- ☐ 321. JUAN AGOSTO
- ☐ 322. MIKE SCOTT
- ☐ 323. RICK RHODEN
- ☐ 324. JIM CLANCY
- ☐ 325. LARRY ANDERSEN
- ☐ 326. ALEX TREVINO
- ☐ 327. ALAN ASHBY
- ☐ 328. CRAIG REYNOLDS
- ☐ 329. BILL DORAN
- ☐ 330. RAFAEL RAMIREZ
- ☐ 331. GLENN DAVIS
- ☐ 332. WILLIE ANSLEY
- ☐ 333. GERALD YOUNG
- ☐ 334. CAMERON DREW

KANSAS CITY ROYALS

- ☐ 110. MEL STOTTLEMYRE, JR.
- ☐ 111. BRET SABERHAGEN
- ☐ 112. FLOYD BANNISTER
- ☐ 113. JEFF MONTGOMERY
- ☐ 114. STEVE FARR
- ☐ 115. TOM GORDON
- ☐ 116. CHARLIE LEIBRANDT
- ☐ 117. MARK GUBICZA
- ☐ 118. MIKE MACFARLANE
- ☐ 119. BOB BOONE
- ☐ 120. KURT STILLWELL
- ☐ 121. GEORGE BRETT
- ☐ 122. FRANK WHITE
- ☐ 123. KEVIN SEITZER
- ☐ 124. WILLIE WILSON
- ☐ 125. PAT TABLER
- ☐ 126. BO JACKSON
- ☐ 127. HUGH WALKER
- ☐ 128. DANNY TARTABULL

LOS ANGELES DODGERS

- ☐ 335. JAY HOWELL
- ☐ 336. TIM BELCHER
- ☐ 337. FERNANDO VALENZUELA
- ☐ 338. RICKY HORTON
- ☐ 339. TIM LEARY
- ☐ 340. BILL BENE
- ☐ 341. OREL HERSHISER
- ☐ 342. MIKE SCIOSCIA
- ☐ 343. RICK DEMPSEY
- ☐ 344. WILLIE RANDOLPH
- ☐ 345. ALFREDO GRIFFIN
- ☐ 346. EDDIE MURRAY
- ☐ 347. MICKEY HATCHER
- ☐ 348. MIKE SHARPERSON
- ☐ 349. JOHN SHELBY
- ☐ 350. MIKE MARSHALL
- ☐ 351. KIRK GIBSON
- ☐ 352. MIKE DAVIS

MILWAUKEE BREWERS

- ☐ 129. TEDDY HIGUERA
- ☐ 130. DON AUGUST
- ☐ 131. JUAN NIEVES
- ☐ 132. MIKE BIRKBECK
- ☐ 133. DAN PLESAC
- ☐ 134. CHRIS BOSIO
- ☐ 135. BILL WEGMAN
- ☐ 136. CHUCK CRIM
- ☐ 137. B. J. SURHOFF
- ☐ 138. JOEY MEYER
- ☐ 139. DALE SVEUM
- ☐ 140. PAUL MOLITOR
- ☐ 141. JIM GANTNER
- ☐ 142. GARY SHEFFIELD
- ☐ 143. GREG BROCK
- ☐ 144. ROBIN YOUNT
- ☐ 145. GLENN BRAGGS
- ☐ 146. ROB DEER

MINNESOTA TWINS

- ☐ 147. FRED TOLIVER
- ☐ 148. JEFF REARDON
- ☐ 149. ALLAN ANDERSON
- ☐ 150. FRANK VIOLA
- ☐ 151. SHANE RAWLEY
- ☐ 152. JUAN BERENGUER
- ☐ 153. JOHNNY ARD
- ☐ 154. TIM LAUDNER
- ☐ 155. BRIAN HARPER
- ☐ 156. AL NEWMAN

□ 157. KENT HRBEK
□ 158. GARY GAETTI
□ 159. WALLY BACKMAN
□ 160. GENE LARKIN
□ 161. GREG GAGNE
□ 162. KIRBY PUCKETT
□ 163. DANNY GLADDEN
□ 164. RANDY BUSH

MONTREAL EXPOS

□ 353. BRYN SMITH
□ 354. PASCUAL PEREZ
□ 355. KEVIN GROSS
□ 356. ANDY MCGAFFIGAN
□ 357. BRIAN HOLMAN
□ 358. DAVE WAINHOUSE
□ 359. DENNY MARTINEZ
□ 360. TIM BURKE
□ 361. NELSON SANTOVENIA
□ 362. TIM WALLACH
□ 363. SPIKE OWEN
□ 364. REX HUDLER
□ 365. ANDRES GALARRAGA
□ 366. OTIS NIXON
□ 367. HUBIE BROOKS
□ 368. MIKE ALDRETE
□ 369. TIM RAINES
□ 370. DAVE MARTINEZ

NEW YORK METS

□ 261. MEL STOTTLEMYRE (C)
□ 371. BOB OJEDA
□ 372. RON DARLING
□ 373. WALLY WHITEHURST
□ 374. RANDY MYERS
□ 375. DAVID CONE
□ 376. DWIGHT GOODEN
□ 377. SID FERNANDEZ
□ 378. DAVE PROCTOR
□ 379. GARY CARTER
□ 380. KEITH MILLER
□ 381. GREGG JEFFERIES
□ 382. TIM TEUFEL
□ 383. KEVIN ELSTER
□ 384. DAVE MAGADAN
□ 385. KEITH HERNANDEZ
□ 386. MOOKIE WILSON
□ 387. DARRYL STRAWBERRY
□ 388. KEVIN MCREYNOLDS
□ 389. MARK CARREON

NEW YORK YANKEES

□ 165. DAVE LAPOINT
□ 166. ANDY HAWKINS
□ 167. DAVE REGHETTI
□ 168. LANCE MCCULLERS
□ 169. JIMMY JONES
□ 170. AL LEITER
□ 171. JOHN CANDELARIA
□ 172. DON SLAUGHT
□ 173. JAMIE QUIRK
□ 174. RAFAEL SANTANA
□ 175. MIKE PAGLIARULO
□ 176. DON MATTINGLY
□ 177. KEN PHELPS
□ 178. STEVE SAX
□ 179. DAVE WINFIELD
□ 180. STAN JEFFERSON
□ 181. RICKEY HENDERSON
□ 182. BOB BROWER
□ 183. ROBERTO KELLY

OAKLAND A'S

□ 184. CURT YOUNG
□ 185. GENE NELSON
□ 186. BOB WELCH
□ 187. RICK HONEYCUTT
□ 188. DAVE STEWART
□ 189. MIKE MOORE
□ 190. DENNIS ECKERSLEY
□ 191. ERIC PLUNK
□ 192. STORM DAVIS
□ 193. TERRY STEINBACH
□ 194. RON HASSEY
□ 195. STAN ROYER
□ 196. WALT WEISS
□ 197. MARK MCGWIRE

□ 198. CARNEY LANSFORD
□ 199. GLENN HUBBARD
□ 200. DAVE HENDERSON
□ 201. JOSE CANSECO
□ 202. DAVE PARKER

PHILADELPHIA PHILLIES

□ 390. JEFF PARRETT
□ 391. MIKE MADDUX
□ 392. DON CARMAN
□ 393. BRUCE RUFFIN
□ 394. KEN HOWELL
□ 395. STEVE BEDROSIAN
□ 396. FLOYD YOUMANS
□ 397. LARRY MCWILLIAMS
□ 398. PAT COMBS
□ 399. STEVE LAKE
□ 400. DICKIE THON
□ 401. RICKY JORDAN
□ 402. MIKE SCHMIDT
□ 403. TOM HERR
□ 404. CHRIS JAMES
□ 405. JUAN SAMUEL
□ 406 VON HAYES
□ 407. RON JONES
□ 408. CURT FORD

PITTSBURGH PIRATES

□ 409. BOB WALK
□ 410. JEFF ROBINSON
□ 411. JIM GOTT
□ 412. SCOTT MEDVIN
□ 413. JOHN SMILEY
□ 414. BOB KIPPER
□ 415. BRIAN FISHER
□ 416. DOUG DRABEK
□ 417. MIKE LAVALLIERE
□ 418. KEN OBERKFELL
□ 419. SID BREAM
□ 420. AUSTIN MANAHAN
□ 421. JOSE LIND
□ 422. BOBBY BONILLA
□ 423. GLENN WILSON
□ 424. ANDY VAN SLYKE
□ 425. GARY REDUS
□ 426. BARRY BONDS

ST. LOUIS CARDINALS

□ 427. DON HEINKEL
□ 428. KEN DAYLEY
□ 429. TODD WORRELL
□ 430. BRAD DUVALL
□ 431. JOSE DELEON
□ 432. JOE MAGRANE
□ 433. JOHN ERICKS
□ 434. FRANK DIPINO
□ 435. TONY PENA
□ 436. OZZIE SMITH
□ 437. TERRY PENDLETON
□ 438. JOSE OQUENDO
□ 439. TIM JONES
□ 440. PEDRO GUERRERO
□ 441. MILT THOMPSON
□ 442. WILLIE MCGEE
□ 443. VINCE COLEMAN
□ 444. TOM BRUNANSKY

SAN DIEGO PADRES

□ 258. SANDY ALOMAR (C)
□ 445. WALT TERRELL
□ 446. ERIC SHOW
□ 447. MARK DAVIS
□ 448. ANDY BENES
□ 449. EDDIE WHITSON
□ 450. DENNIS RASMUSSEN
□ 451. BRUCE HURST
□ 452. PAT CLEMENTS
□ 453. BENNY SANTIAGO
□ 454. SANDY ALOMAR, JR.
□ 455. GARRY TEMPLETON
□ 456. JACK CLARK
□ 457. TIM FLANNERY
□ 458. ROBERTO ALOMAR
□ 459. CARMELO MARTINEZ
□ 460. JOHN KRUK
□ 461. TONY GWYNN
□ 462. JERALD CLARK

SAN FRANCISCO GIANTS

□ 463. DON ROBINSON
□ 464. CRAIG LEFFERTS
□ 465. KELLY DOWNS
□ 466. RICK REUSCHEL
□ 467. SCOTT GARRELTS
□ 468. WIL TEJADA
□ 469. KIRT MANWARING
□ 470. TERRY KENNEDY
□ 471. JOSE URIBE
□ 472. ROYCE CLAYTON
□ 473. ROBBY THOMPSON
□ 474. KEVIN MITCHELL
□ 475. ERNIE RILES
□ 476. WILL CLARK
□ 477. DONELL NIXON
□ 478. CANDY MALDONADO
□ 479. TRACY JONES
□ 480. BRETT BULTER

SEATTLE MARINERS

□ 203. SCOTT BANKHEAD
□ 204. TOM NIEDENFUER
□ 205. MARK LANGSTON
□ 206. ERIK HANSON
□ 207. MIKE JACKSON
□ 208. DAVE VALLE
□ 209. SCOTT BRADLEY
□ 210. HAROLD REYNOLDS
□ 211. TINO MARTINEZ
□ 212. RICH RENTERIA
□ 213. REY QUINONES
□ 214. JIM PRESLEY
□ 215. ALVIN DAVIS
□ 216. EDGAR MARTINEZ
□ 217. DARNELL COLES
□ 218. JEFFREY LEONARD
□ 219. JAY BUHNER
□ 220. KEN GRIFFEY, JR.

TEXAS RANGERS

□ 221. DREW HALL
□ 222. BOBBY WITT
□ 223. JAMIE MOYER
□ 224. CHARLIE HOUGH
□ 225. NOLAN RYAN
□ 226. JEFF RUSSELL
□ 227. JIM SUNDBERG
□ 228. JULIO FRANCO
□ 229. BUDDY BELL
□ 230. SCOTT FLETCHER
□ 231. JEFF KUNKEL
□ 232. STEVE BUECHELE
□ 233. MONTY FARISS
□ 234. RICK LEACH
□ 235. RUBEN SIERRA
□ 236. CECIL ESPY
□ 237. RAFAEL PALMEIRO
□ 238. PETE INCAVIGLIA

TORONTO BLUE JAYS

□ 239. DAVE STIEB
□ 240. JEFF MUSSELMAN
□ 241. MIKE FLANAGAN

- ☐ 242. TODD STOTTLEMYRE
- ☐ 243. JIMMY KEY
- ☐ 244. TONY CASTILLO
- ☐ 245. ALEX SANCHEZ
- ☐ 246. TOM HENKE
- ☐ 247. JOHN CERUTTI
- ☐ 248. ERINE WHITT
- ☐ 249. BOB BRENLY
- ☐ 250. RANCE MULLINIKS
- ☐ 251. KELLY GRUBER
- ☐ 252. ED SPRAGUE
- ☐ 253. FRED MCGRIFF
- ☐ 254. TONY FERNANDEZ
- ☐ 255. TOM LAWLESS
- ☐ 256. GEORGE BELL
- ☐ 257. JESSE BARFIELD

1990 BOWMAN (528)
2 1/2" X 3 1/2"

ATLANTA BRAVES

- ☐ 1. TOMMY GREENE
- ☐ 2. TOM GLAVINE
- ☐ 3. ANDY NEZELEK
- ☐ 4. MIKE STANTON
- ☐ 5. RICK LUECKEN
- ☐ 6. KENT MERCKER
- ☐ 7. DEREK LILLIQUIST
- ☐ 8. CHARLIE LEIBRANDT
- ☐ 9. STEVE AVERY
- ☐ 10. JOHN SMOLTZ
- ☐ 11. MARK LEMKE
- ☐ 12. LONNIE SMITH
- ☐ 13. ODDIBE MCDOWELL
- ☐ 14. TYLER HOUSTON
- ☐ 15. JEFF BLAUSER
- ☐ 16. ERNIE WHITT
- ☐ 17. ALEXIS INFANTE
- ☐ 18. JIM PRESLEY
- ☐ 19. DALE MURPHY
- ☐ 20. NICK ESASKY

BALTIMORE ORIOLES

- ☐ 243. BEN MCDONALD
- ☐ 244. JEFF BALLARD
- ☐ 245. JOE PRICE
- ☐ 246. CURT SCHILLING
- ☐ 247. PETE HARNISCH
- ☐ 248. MARK WILLIAMSON
- ☐ 249. GREGG OLSON
- ☐ 250. CHRIS MYERS
- ☐ 251. DAVID SEGUI
- ☐ 252. JOE ORSULAK
- ☐ 253. CRAIG WORTHINGTON
- ☐ 254. MICKEY TETTLETON
- ☐ 255. CAL RIPKEN
- ☐ 256. BILLY RIPKEN
- ☐ 257. RANDY MILLIGAN
- ☐ 258. BRADY ANDERSON
- ☐ 259. CHRIS HOILES
- ☐ 260. MIKE DEVEREAUX
- ☐ 261. PHIL BRADLEY
- ☐ 262. LEO GOMEZ

BOSTON RED SOX

- ☐ 263. LEE SMITH
- ☐ 264. MIKE ROCHFORD
- ☐ 265. JEFF REARDON
- ☐ 266. WES GARDNER
- ☐ 267. MIKE BODDICKER
- ☐ 268. ROGER CLEMENS
- ☐ 269. ROB MURPHY
- ☐ 270. MICKEY PINA
- ☐ 271. TONY PENA
- ☐ 272. JODY REED
- ☐ 273. KEVIN ROMINE
- ☐ 274. MIKE GREENWELL
- ☐ 275. MO VAUGHN
- ☐ 276. DANNY HEEP
- ☐ 277. SCOTT COOPER
- ☐ 278. GREG BLOSSER
- ☐ 279. DWIGHT EVANS
- ☐ 280. ELLIS BURKS
- ☐ 281. WADE BOGGS
- ☐ 282. MARTY BARRETT

CALIFORNIA ANGELS

- ☐ 283. KIRK MCCASKILL
- ☐ 284. MARK LANGSTON
- ☐ 285. BERT BLYLEVEN
- ☐ 286. MIKE FETTERS
- ☐ 287. KYLE ABBOTT
- ☐ 288. JIM ABBOTT
- ☐ 289. CHUCK FINLEY
- ☐ 290. GARY DISARCINA
- ☐ 291. DICK SCHOFIELD
- ☐ 292. DEVON WHITE
- ☐ 293. BOBBY ROSE
- ☐ 294. BRIAN DOWNING
- ☐ 295. LANCE PARRISH
- ☐ 296. JACK HOWELL
- ☐ 297. CLAUDELL WASHINGTON
- ☐ 298. JOHN ORTON
- ☐ 299. WALLY JOYNER
- ☐ 300. LEE STEVENS
- ☐ 301. CHILI DAVIS
- ☐ 302. JOHNNY RAY

CHICAGO CUBS

- ☐ 21. RICK SUTCLIFFE
- ☐ 22. MIKE BIELECKI
- ☐ 23. STEVE WILSON
- ☐ 24. KEVIN BLANKENSHIP
- ☐ 25. MITCH WILLIAMS
- ☐ 26. DEAN WILKINS
- ☐ 27. GREG MADDUX
- ☐ 28. MIKE HARKEY
- ☐ 29. MARK GRACE
- ☐ 30. RYNE SANDBERG
- ☐ 31. GREG SMITH
- ☐ 32. DWIGHT SMITH
- ☐ 33. DAMON BERRYHILL
- ☐ 34. EARL CUNNINGHAM
- ☐ 35. JEROME WALTON
- ☐ 36. LLOYD MCCLENDON
- ☐ 37. TY GRIFFIN
- ☐ 38. SHAWON DUNSTON
- ☐ 39. ANDRE DAWSON
- ☐ 40. LUIS SALAZAR

CHICAGO WHITE SOX

- ☐ 303. GREG HIBBARD
- ☐ 304. ERIC KING
- ☐ 305. JACK MCDOWELL
- ☐ 306. BOBBY THIGPEN
- ☐ 307. ADAM PETERSON
- ☐ 308. SCOTT RADINSKY
- ☐ 309. WAYNE EDWARDS
- ☐ 310. MELIDO PEREZ
- ☐ 311. ROBIN VENTURA
- ☐ 312. SAMMY SOSA
- ☐ 313. DAN PASQUA
- ☐ 314. CARLTON FISK
- ☐ 315. OZZIE GUILLEN
- ☐ 316. IVAN CALDERON
- ☐ 317. DARYL BOSTON
- ☐ 318. CRAIG GREBECK
- ☐ 319. SCOTT FLETCHER
- ☐ 320. FRANK THOMAS
- ☐ 321. STEVE LYONS
- ☐ 322. CARLOS MARTINEZ

CINCINNATI REDS

- ☐ 41. TIM LAYANA
- ☐ 42. ROB DIBBLE
- ☐ 43. TOM BROWNING
- ☐ 44. DANNY JACKSON
- ☐ 45. JOSE RIJO
- ☐ 46. SCOTT SCUDDER
- ☐ 47. RANDY MYERS
- ☐ 48. BRIAN LANE
- ☐ 49. PAUL O'NEILL
- ☐ 50. BARRY LARKIN
- ☐ 51. REGGIE JEFFERSON
- ☐ 52. JEFF BRANSON
- ☐ 53. CHRIS SABO
- ☐ 54. JOE OLIVER
- ☐ 55. TODD BENZINGER
- ☐ 56. ROLANDO ROOMES
- ☐ 57. HAL MORRIS
- ☐ 58. ERIC DAVIS
- ☐ 59. SCOTT BRYANT
- ☐ 60. KEN GRIFFEY

CLEVELAND INDIANS

- ☐ 323. JOE SKALSKI
- ☐ 324. TOM CANDIOTTI
- ☐ 325. GREG SWINDELL
- ☐ 326. STEVE OLIN
- ☐ 327. KEVIN WICKANDER
- ☐ 328. DOUG JONES
- ☐ 329. JEFF SHAW
- ☐ 330. KEVIN BEARSE
- ☐ 331. DION JAMES
- ☐ 332. JERRY BROWNE
- ☐ 333. JOEY BELLE
- ☐ 334. FELIX FERMIN
- ☐ 335. CANDY MALDONADO
- ☐ 336. CORY SNYDER
- ☐ 337. SANDY ALOMAR
- ☐ 338. MARK LEWIS
- ☐ 339. CARLOS BAERGA
- ☐ 340. CHRIS JAMES
- ☐ 341. BROOK JACOBY
- ☐ 342. KEITH HERNANDEZ

DETROIT TIGERS

- ☐ 343. FRANK TANANA
- ☐ 344. SCOTT ALDRED
- ☐ 345. MIKE HENNEMAN
- ☐ 346. STEVE WAPNICK
- ☐ 347. GREG GOHR
- ☐ 348. ERIC STONE
- ☐ 349. BRIAN DUBOIS
- ☐ 350. KEVIN RITZ
- ☐ 351. RICO BROGNA
- ☐ 352. MIKE HEATH
- ☐ 353. ALAN TRAMMELL
- ☐ 354. CHET LEMON
- ☐ 355. DAVE BERGMAN
- ☐ 356. LOU WHITAKER
- ☐ 357. CECIL FIELDER
- ☐ 358. MILT CUYLER
- ☐ 359. TONY PHILLIPS
- ☐ 360. TRAVIS FRYMAN
- ☐ 361. ED ROMERO
- ☐ 362. LLOYD MOSEBY

HOUSTON ASTROS

- ☐ 61. DARRYL KILE
- ☐ 62. DAVE SMITH
- ☐ 63. MARK PORTUGAL
- ☐ 64. JEFF JUDEN
- ☐ 65. BILL GULLICKSON
- ☐ 66. DANNY DARWIN
- ☐ 67. LARRY ANDERSEN
- ☐ 68. JOSE CANO
- ☐ 69. DAN SCHATZEDER
- ☐ 70. JIM DESHAIES
- ☐ 71. MIKE SCOTT
- ☐ 72. GERALD YOUNG
- ☐ 73. KEN CAMINITI
- ☐ 74. KEN OBERKFELL
- ☐ 75. DAVE ROHDE
- ☐ 76. BILL DORAN
- ☐ 77. ANDUJAR CEDENO
- ☐ 78. CRAIG BIGGIO
- ☐ 79. KARL RHODES
- ☐ 80. GLENN DAVIS
- ☐ 81. ERIC ANTHONY

KANSAS CITY ROYALS

- ☐ 363. MARK GUBICZA
- ☐ 364. BRET SABERHAGEN
- ☐ 365. TOM GORDON
- ☐ 366. STEVE FARR
- ☐ 367. KEVIN APPIER
- ☐ 368. STORM DAVIS
- ☐ 369. MARK DAVIS
- ☐ 370. JEFF MONTGOMERY
- ☐ 371. FRANK WHITE
- ☐ 372. BRENT MAYNE
- ☐ 373. BOB BOONE
- ☐ 374. JIM EISENREICH
- ☐ 375. DANNY TARTABULL
- ☐ 376. KURT STILLWELL
- ☐ 377. BILL PECOTA
- ☐ 378. BO JACKSON
- ☐ 379. BOB HAMELIN
- ☐ 380. KEVIN SEITZER
- ☐ 381. REY PALACIOS
- ☐ 382. GEORGE BRETT
- ☐ 383. GERALD PERRY

LOS ANGELES DODGERS

- ☐ 82. JOHN WETTELAND
- ☐ 83. JAY HOWELL
- ☐ 84. OREL HERSHISER
- ☐ 85. TIM BELCHER
- ☐ 86. KIKI JONES
- ☐ 87. MIKE HARTLEY
- ☐ 88. RAMON MARTINEZ
- ☐ 89. MIKE SCIOSCIA
- ☐ 90. WILLIE RANDOLPH
- ☐ 91. JUAN SAMUEL
- ☐ 92. JOSE OFFERMAN
- ☐ 93. DAVE HANSEN
- ☐ 94. JEFF HAMILTON
- ☐ 95. ALFREDO GRIFFIN
- ☐ 96. TOM GOODWIN
- ☐ 97. KIRK GIBSON
- ☐ 98. JOSE VIZCAINO
- ☐ 99. KAL DANIELS
- ☐ 100. HUBIE BROOKS
- ☐ 101. EDDIE MURRAY

MILWAUKEE BREWERS

- ☐ 384. TEDDY HIGUERA
- ☐ 385. TOM FILER
- ☐ 386. DAN PLESAC
- ☐ 387. CAL ELDRED
- ☐ 388. JAIME NAVARRO
- ☐ 389. CHRIS BOSIO
- ☐ 390. RANDY VERES
- ☐ 391. GARY SHEFFIELD
- ☐ 392. GEORGE CANALE
- ☐ 393. B.J. SURHOFF
- ☐ 394. TIM MCINTOSH
- ☐ 395. GREG BROCK
- ☐ 396. GREG VAUGHN
- ☐ 397. DARRYL HAMILTON
- ☐ 398. DAVE PARKER
- ☐ 399. PAUL MOLITOR
- ☐ 400. JIM GANTNER
- ☐ 401. ROB DEER
- ☐ 402. BILLY SPIERS
- ☐ 403. GLENN BRAGGS
- ☐ 404. ROBIN YOUNT

MINNESOTA TWINS

- ☐ 405. RICK AGUILERA
- ☐ 406. JOHNNY ARD
- ☐ 407. KEVIN TAPANI
- ☐ 408. PARK PITTMAN
- ☐ 409. ALLAN ANDERSON
- ☐ 410. JUAN BERENGUER
- ☐ 411. WILLIE BANKS
- ☐ 412. RICH YETT
- ☐ 413. DAVE WEST
- ☐ 414. GREG GAGNE
- ☐ 415. CHUCK KNOBLAUCH
- ☐ 416. RANDY BUSH
- ☐ 417. GARY GAETTI
- ☐ 418. KENT HRBEK
- ☐ 419. AL NEWMAN
- ☐ 420. DANNY GLADDEN
- ☐ 421. PAUL SORRENTO
- ☐ 422. DEREK PARKS
- ☐ 423. SCOTT LEIUS
- ☐ 424. KIRBY PUCKETT

MONTREAL EXPOS

- ☐ 102. DENNIS BOYD
- ☐ 103. TIM BURKE
- ☐ 104. BILL SAMPEN
- ☐ 105. BRETT GIDEON
- ☐ 106. MARK GARDNER
- ☐ 107. HOWARD FARMER
- ☐ 108. MEL ROJAS
- ☐ 109. KEVIN GROSS
- ☐ 110. DAVE SCHMIDT
- ☐ 111. DENNY MARTINEZ
- ☐ 112. JERRY GOFF
- ☐ 113. ANDRES GALARRAGA
- ☐ 114. TIM WALLACH
- ☐ 115. MARQUIS GRISSOM
- ☐ 116. SPIKE OWEN
- ☐ 117. LARRY WALKER
- ☐ 118. TIM RAINES
- ☐ 119. DELINO DESHIELDS
- ☐ 120. TOM FOLEY
- ☐ 121. DAVE MARTINEZ

NEW YORK METS

- ☐ 122. FRANK VIOLA
- ☐ 123. JULIO VALERA
- ☐ 124. ALEJANDRO PENA
- ☐ 125. DAVID CONE
- ☐ 126. DWIGHT GOODEN
- ☐ 127. KEVIN BROWN
- ☐ 128. JOHN FRANCO
- ☐ 129. TERRY BROSS
- ☐ 130. BLAINE BEATTY
- ☐ 131. SID FERNANDEZ
- ☐ 132. MIKE MARSHALL
- ☐ 133. HOWARD JOHNSON
- ☐ 134. JAIME ROSEBORO
- ☐ 135. ALAN ZINTER
- ☐ 136. KEITH MILLER
- ☐ 137. KEVIN ELSTER
- ☐ 138. KEVIN MCREYNOLDS
- ☐ 139. BARRY LYONS
- ☐ 140. GREGG JEFFERIES
- ☐ 141. DARRYL STRAWBERRY
- ☐ 142. TODD HUNDLEY

NEW YORK YANKEES

- ☐ 425. WILLIE SMITH
- ☐ 426. DAVE RIGHETTI
- ☐ 427. JEFF ROBINSON
- ☐ 428. ALAN MILLS
- ☐ 429. TIM LEARY
- ☐ 430. PASCUAL PEREZ
- ☐ 431. ALVARO ESPINOZA
- ☐ 432. DAVE WINFIELD
- ☐ 433. JESSE BARFIELD
- ☐ 434. RANDY VELARDE
- ☐ 435. RICK CERONE
- ☐ 436. STEVE BALBONI
- ☐ 437. MEL HALL
- ☐ 438. BOB GEREN
- ☐ 439. BERNIE WILLIAMS
- ☐ 440. KEVIN MAAS
- ☐ 441. MIKE BLOWERS
- ☐ 442. STEVE SAX
- ☐ 443. DON MATTINGLY
- ☐ 444. ROBERTO KELLY

OAKLAND A'S

- ☐ 445. MIKE MOORE
- ☐ 446. REGGIE HARRIS
- ☐ 447. SCOTT SANDERSON
- ☐ 448. DAVE OTTO
- ☐ 449. DAVE STEWART
- ☐ 450. RICK HONEYCUTT
- ☐ 451. DENNIS ECKERSLEY
- ☐ 452. CARNEY LANSFORD
- ☐ 453. SCOTT HEMOND
- ☐ 454. MARK MCGWIRE
- ☐ 455. FELIX JOSE
- ☐ 456. TERRY STEINBACH
- ☐ 457. RICKEY HENDERSON
- ☐ 458. DAVE HENDERSON
- ☐ 459. MIKE GALLEGO
- ☐ 460. JOSE CANSECO
- ☐ 461. WALT WEISS
- ☐ 462. KEN PHELPS
- ☐ 463. DARREN LEWIS
- ☐ 464. RON HASSEY

PHILADELPHIA PHILLIES

- ☐ 143. SCOTT SERVICE
- ☐ 144. CHUCK MALONE
- ☐ 145. STEVE ONTIVEROS
- ☐ 146. ROGER MCDOWELL
- ☐ 147. KEN HOWELL
- ☐ 148. PAT COMBS
- ☐ 149. JEFF PARRETT
- ☐ 150. CHUCK MCELROY
- ☐ 151. JASON GRIMSLEY
- ☐ 152. LEN DYKSTRA
- ☐ 153. MICKEY MORANDINI
- ☐ 154. JOHN KRUK
- ☐ 155. DICKIE THON
- ☐ 156. RICKY JORDAN
- ☐ 157. JEFF JACKSON
- ☐ 158. DARREN DAULTON
- ☐ 159. TOM HERR
- ☐ 160. VON HAYES
- ☐ 161. DAVE HOLLINS
- ☐ 162. CARMELO MARTINEZ

PITTSBURGH PIRATES

- ☐ 163. BOB WALK
- ☐ 164. DOUG DRABEK
- ☐ 165. WALT TERRELL
- ☐ 166. BILL LANDRUM
- ☐ 167. SCOTT RUSKIN
- ☐ 168. BOB PATTERSON
- ☐ 169. BOBBY BONILLA
- ☐ 170. JOSE LIND
- ☐ 171. ANDY VAN SLYKE
- ☐ 172. MIKE LAVALLIERE
- ☐ 173. WILLIE GREENE
- ☐ 174. JAY BELL
- ☐ 175. SID BREAM
- ☐ 176. TOM PRINCE

- ☐ 177. WALLY BACKMAN
- ☐ 178. MOISES ALOU
- ☐ 179. STEVE CARTER
- ☐ 180. GARY REDUS
- ☐ 181. BARRY BONDS
- ☐ 182. DON SLAUGHT

ST. LOUIS CARDINALS

- ☐ 183. JOE MAGRANE
- ☐ 184. BRYN SMITH
- ☐ 185. TODD WORRELL
- ☐ 186. JOSE DELEON
- ☐ 187. FRANK DIPINO
- ☐ 188. JOHN TUDOR
- ☐ 189. HOWARD HILTON
- ☐ 190. JOHN ERICKS
- ☐ 191. KEN DAYLEY
- ☐ 192. RAY LANKFORD
- ☐ 193. TODD ZEILE
- ☐ 194. WILLIE MCGEE
- ☐ 195. OZZIE SMITH
- ☐ 196. MILT THOMPSON
- ☐ 197. TERRY PENDLETON
- ☐ 198. VINCE COLEMAN
- ☐ 199. PAUL COLEMAN
- ☐ 200. JOSE OQUENDO
- ☐ 201. PEDRO GUERRERO
- ☐ 202. TOM BRUNANSKY

SAN DIEGO PADRES

- ☐ 203. ROGER SMITHBERG
- ☐ 204. EDDIE WHITSON
- ☐ 205. DENNIS RASMUSSEN
- ☐ 206. CRAIG LEFFERTS
- ☐ 207. ANDY BENES
- ☐ 208. BRUCE HURST
- ☐ 209. ERIC SHOW
- ☐ 210. RAFAEL VALDEZ
- ☐ 211. JOEY CORA
- ☐ 212. THOMAS HOWARD
- ☐ 213. ROB NELSON
- ☐ 214. JACK CLARK
- ☐ 215. GARRY TEMPLETON
- ☐ 216. FRED LYNN
- ☐ 217. TONY GWYNN
- ☐ 218. BENNY SANTIAGO
- ☐ 219. MIKE PAGLIARULO
- ☐ 220. JOE CARTER
- ☐ 221. ROBERTO ALOMAR
- ☐ 222. BIP ROBERTS

SAN FRANCISCO GIANTS

- ☐ 223. RICK REUSCHEL
- ☐ 224. RUSS SWAN
- ☐ 225. ERIC GUNDERSON
- ☐ 226. STEVE BEDROSIAN
- ☐ 227. MIKE REMLINGER
- ☐ 228. SCOTT GARRELTS
- ☐ 229. ERNIE CAMACHO
- ☐ 230. ANDRES SANTANA
- ☐ 231. WILL CLARK
- ☐ 232. KEVIN MITCHELL
- ☐ 233. ROBBY THOMPSON
- ☐ 234. BILL BATHE
- ☐ 235. TONY PEREZCHICA
- ☐ 236. GARY CARTER
- ☐ 237. BRETT BUTLER
- ☐ 238. MATT WILLIAMS
- ☐ 239. ERNIE RILES
- ☐ 240. KEVIN BASS
- ☐ 241. TERRY KENNEDY
- ☐ 242. STEVE HOSEY

SEATTLE MARINERS

- ☐ 465. ROGER SALKELD
- ☐ 466. SCOTT BANKHEAD
- ☐ 467. KEITH COMSTOCK
- ☐ 468. RANDY JOHNSON
- ☐ 469. ERIK HANSON
- ☐ 470. MIKE SCHOOLER
- ☐ 471. GARY EAVE
- ☐ 472. JEFFREY LEONARD
- ☐ 473. DAVE VALLE
- ☐ 474. OMAR VIZQUEL
- ☐ 475. PETE O'BRIEN
- ☐ 476. HENRY COTTO
- ☐ 477. JAY BUHNER
- ☐ 478. HAROLD REYNOLDS
- ☐ 479. ALVIN DAVIS
- ☐ 480. DARNELL COLES
- ☐ 481. KEN GRIFFEY, JR.
- ☐ 482. GREG BRILEY
- ☐ 483. SCOTT BRADLEY
- ☐ 484. TINO MARTINEZ

TEXAS RANGERS

- ☐ 485. JEFF RUSSELL
- ☐ 486. NOLAN RYAN
- ☐ 487. ROBB NEN
- ☐ 488. KEVIN BROWN
- ☐ 489. BRIAN BOHANON
- ☐ 490. RUBEN SIERRA
- ☐ 491. PETE INCAVIGLIA
- ☐ 492. JUAN GONZALEZ
- ☐ 493. STEVE BUECHELE
- ☐ 494. SCOTT COOLBAUGH
- ☐ 495. GENO PETRALLI
- ☐ 496. RAFAEL PALMEIRO
- ☐ 497. JULIO FRANCO
- ☐ 498. GARY PETTIS
- ☐ 499. DONALD HARRIS
- ☐ 500. MONTY FARISS
- ☐ 501. HAROLD BAINES
- ☐ 502. CECIL ESPY
- ☐ 503. JACK DAUGHERTY

TORONTO BLUE JAYS

- ☐ 504. WILLIE BLAIR
- ☐ 505. DAVE STIEB
- ☐ 506. TOM HENKE
- ☐ 507. JOHN CERUTTI
- ☐ 508. PAUL KILGUS
- ☐ 509. JIMMY KEY
- ☐ 510. JOHN OLERUD
- ☐ 511. ED SPRAGUE
- ☐ 512. MANNY LEE
- ☐ 513. FRED MCGRIFF
- ☐ 514. GLENALLEN HILL
- ☐ 515. GEORGE BELL
- ☐ 516. MOOKIE WILSON
- ☐ 517. LUIS SOJO
- ☐ 518. NELSON LIRIANO
- ☐ 519. KELLY GRUBER
- ☐ 520. GREG MYERS
- ☐ 521. PAT BORDERS
- ☐ 522. JUNIOR FELIX
- ☐ 523. EDDIE ZOSKY
- ☐ 524. TONY FERNANDEZ

1991 BOWMAN (704)
2 1/2" X 3 1/2"

ATLANTA BRAVES

- ☐ 566. STEVE AVERY
- ☐ 567. LONNIE SMITH
- ☐ 568. KENT MERCKER
- ☐ 569. CHIPPER JONES
- ☐ 570. TERRY PENDLETON
- ☐ 571. OTIS NIXON
- ☐ 572. JUAN BERENGUER
- ☐ 573. CHARLIE LEIBRANDT
- ☐ 574. DAVID JUSTICE
- ☐ 575. KEITH MITCHELL
- ☐ 576. TOM GLAVINE
- ☐ 577. GREG OLSON
- ☐ 578. RAFAEL BELLIARD
- ☐ 579. BEN RIVERA
- ☐ 580. JOHN SMOLTZ
- ☐ 581. TYLER HOUSTON
- ☐ 582. MARK WOHLERS
- ☐ 583. RON GANT
- ☐ 584. RAMON CARABALLO
- ☐ 585. SID BREAM
- ☐ 586. JEFF TREADWAY
- ☐ 587. JAVIER LOPEZ
- ☐ 588. DEION SANDERS
- ☐ 589. MIKE HEATH
- ☐ 590. RYAN KLESKO

BALTIMORE ORIOLES

- ☐ 83. GLENN DAVIS
- ☐ 84. JOE ORSULAK
- ☐ 85. MARK WILLIAMSON
- ☐ 86. BEN MCDONALD
- ☐ 87. BILLY RIPKEN
- ☐ 88. LEO GOMEZ
- ☐ 89. BOB MELVIN
- ☐ 90. JEFF ROBINSON
- ☐ 91. JOSE MESA
- ☐ 92. GREGG OLSON
- ☐ 93. MIKE DEVEREAUX
- ☐ 94. LUIS MERCEDES
- ☐ 95. ARTHUR RHODES
- ☐ 96. JUAN BELL
- ☐ 97. MIKE MUSSINA
- ☐ 98. JEFF BALLARD
- ☐ 99. CHRIS HOILES
- ☐ 100. BRADY ANDERSON
- ☐ 101. BOB MILACKI
- ☐ 102. DAVID SEGUI
- ☐ 103. DWIGHT EVANS
- ☐ 104. CAL RIPKEN
- ☐ 105. MIKE LINSKEY
- ☐ 106. JEFF TACKETT

BOSTON RED SOX

- ☐ 107. JEFF REARDON
- ☐ 108. DANA KIECKER
- ☐ 109. ELLIS BURKS
- ☐ 110. DAVE OWEN
- ☐ 111. DANNY DARWIN
- ☐ 112. MO VAUGHN
- ☐ 113. JEFF MCNEELY
- ☐ 114. TOM BOLTON
- ☐ 115. GREG BLOSSER
- ☐ 116. MIKE GREENWELL
- ☐ 117. PHIL PLANTIER
- ☐ 118. ROGER CLEMENS
- ☐ 119. JOHN MARZANO
- ☐ 120. JODY REED
- ☐ 121. SCOTT TAYLOR
- ☐ 122. JACK CLARK
- ☐ 123. DEREK LIVERNOIS
- ☐ 124. TONY PENA
- ☐ 125. TOM BRUNANSKY
- ☐ 126. CARLOS QUINTANA
- ☐ 127. TIM NAEHRING
- ☐ 128. MATT YOUNG
- ☐ 129. WADE BOGGS
- ☐ 130. KEVIN MORTON

CALIFORNIA ANGELS

- ☐ 186. JIMMIE REESE(C)
- ☐ 187. KYLE ABBOTT
- ☐ 188. LANCE PARRISH
- ☐ 189. RAFAEL MONTALVO
- ☐ 190. FLOYD BANNISTER
- ☐ 191. DICK SCHOFIELD
- ☐ 192. SCOTT LEWIS
- ☐ 193. JEFF ROBINSON
- ☐ 194. KENT ANDERSON
- ☐ 195. WALLY JOYNER
- ☐ 196. CHUCK FINLEY
- ☐ 197. LUIS SOJO
- ☐ 198. JEFF RICHARDSON
- ☐ 199. DAVE PARKER
- ☐ 200. JIM ABBOTT
- ☐ 201. JUNIOR FELIX
- ☐ 202. MARK LANGSTON

- ☐ 203. TIM SALMON
- ☐ 204. CLIFF YOUNG
- ☐ 205. SCOTT BAILES
- ☐ 206. BOBBY ROSE
- ☐ 207. GARY GAETTI
- ☐ 208. RUBEN AMARO
- ☐ 209. LUIS POLONIA
- ☐ 210. DAVE WINFIELD
- ☐ 211. BRYAN HARVEY

CHICAGO CUBS

- ☐ 411. LANCE DICKSON
- ☐ 412. DANNY JACKSON
- ☐ 413. JEROME WALTON
- ☐ 414. SEAN CHEETHAM
- ☐ 415. JOE GIRARDI
- ☐ 416. RYNE SANDBERG
- ☐ 417. MIKE HARKEY
- ☐ 418. GEORGE BELL
- ☐ 419. RICK WILKINS
- ☐ 420. EARL CUNNINGHAM
- ☐ 421. HEATHCLIFF SLOCUMB
- ☐ 422. MIKE BIELECKI
- ☐ 423. JESSIE HOLLINS
- ☐ 424. SHAWON DUNSTON
- ☐ 425. DAVE SMITH
- ☐ 426. GREG MADDUX
- ☐ 427. JOSE VIZCAINO
- ☐ 428. LUIS SALAZAR
- ☐ 429. ANDRE DAWSON
- ☐ 430. RICK SUTCLIFFE
- ☐ 431. PAUL ASSENMACHER
- ☐ 432. ERIK PAPPAS
- ☐ 433. MARK GRACE
- ☐ 535. GARY SCOTT

CHICAGO WHITE SOX

- ☐ 342. BOBBY THIGPEN
- ☐ 343. ROBERTO HERNANDEZ
- ☐ 344. MELIDO PEREZ
- ☐ 345. CARLTON FISK
- ☐ 346. NORBERTO MARTIN
- ☐ 347. JOHNNY RUFFIN
- ☐ 348. JEFF CARTER
- ☐ 349. LANCE JOHNSON
- ☐ 350. SAMMY SOSA
- ☐ 351. ALEX FERNANDEZ
- ☐ 352. JACK MCDOWELL
- ☐ 353. BOB WICKMAN
- ☐ 354. WILSON ALVAREZ
- ☐ 355. CHARLIE HOUGH
- ☐ 356. OZZIE GUILLEN
- ☐ 357. CORY SNYDER
- ☐ 358. ROBIN VENTURA
- ☐ 359. SCOTT FLETCHER
- ☐ 360. CESAR BERNHARDT
- ☐ 361. DAN PASQUA
- ☐ 362. TIM RAINES
- ☐ 363. BRIAN DRAHMAN
- ☐ 364. WAYNE EDWARDS
- ☐ 365. SCOTT RADINSKY
- ☐ 366. FRANK THOMAS

CINCINNATI REDS

- ☐ 537. REGGIE SANDERS
- ☐ 666. RANDY MYERS
- ☐ 667. ROB DIBBLE
- ☐ 668. GLENN SUTKO
- ☐ 669. GLENN BRAGGS
- ☐ 670. BILLY HATCHER
- ☐ 671. JOE OLIVER
- ☐ 672. FREDDIE BENAVIDES
- ☐ 673. BARRY LARKIN
- ☐ 674. CHRIS SABO
- ☐ 675. MARIANO DUNCAN
- ☐ 676. CHRIS JONES
- ☐ 677. GINO MINUTELLI
- ☐ 678. REGGIE JEFFERSON
- ☐ 679. JACK ARMSTRONG
- ☐ 680. CHRIS HAMMOND
- ☐ 681. JOSE RIJO
- ☐ 682. BILL DORAN
- ☐ 683. TERRY LEE
- ☐ 684. TOM BROWNING
- ☐ 685. PAUL O'NEILL
- ☐ 686. ERIC DAVIS
- ☐ 687. DAN WILSON
- ☐ 688. TED POWER
- ☐ 689. TIM LAYANA
- ☐ 690. NORM CHARLTON
- ☐ 691. HAL MORRIS

CLEVELAND INDIANS

- ☐ 57. SANDY ALOMAR
- ☐ 58. GREG SWINDELL
- ☐ 59. BROOK JACOBY
- ☐ 60. EFRAIN VALDEZ
- ☐ 61. EVER MAGALLANES
- ☐ 62. TOM CANDIOTTI
- ☐ 63. ERIC KING
- ☐ 64. ALEX COLE
- ☐ 65. CHARLES NAGY
- ☐ 66. MITCH WEBSTER
- ☐ 67. CHRIS JAMES
- ☐ 68. JIM THOME
- ☐ 69. CARLOS BAERGA
- ☐ 70. MARK LEWIS
- ☐ 71. JERRY BROWNE
- ☐ 72. JESSE OROSCO
- ☐ 73. MIKE HUFF
- ☐ 74. JOSE ESCOBAR
- ☐ 75. JEFF MANTO
- ☐ 76. TURNER WARD
- ☐ 77. DOUG JONES
- ☐ 78. BRUCE EGLOFF
- ☐ 79. TIM COSTO
- ☐ 80. BEAU ALLRED
- ☐ 81. ALBERT BELLE
- ☐ 82. JOHN FARRELL

DETROIT TIGERS

- ☐ 131. PETE INCAVIGLIA
- ☐ 132. ROB DEER
- ☐ 133. BILL GULLICKSON
- ☐ 134. RICO BROGNA
- ☐ 135. LLOYD MOSEBY
- ☐ 136. CECIL FIELDER
- ☐ 137. TONY PHILLIPS
- ☐ 138. MARK LEITER
- ☐ 139. JOHN CERUTTI
- ☐ 140. MICKEY TETTLETON
- ☐ 141. MILT CUYLER
- ☐ 142. GREG GOHR
- ☐ 143. TONY BERNAZARD
- ☐ 144. DAN GAKELER
- ☐ 145. TRAVIS FRYMAN
- ☐ 146. DAN PETRY
- ☐ 147. SCOTT ALDRED
- ☐ 148. JOHN DESILVA
- ☐ 149. RUSTY MEACHAM
- ☐ 150. LOU WHITAKER
- ☐ 151. DAVE HAAS
- ☐ 152. LUIS DE LOS SANTOS
- ☐ 153. IVAN CRUZ
- ☐ 154. ALAN TRAMMELL

HOUSTON ASTROS

- ☐ 183. JEFF BAGWELL
- ☐ 539. RYAN BOWEN
- ☐ 540. ERIC ANTHONY
- ☐ 541. JIM DESHAIES
- ☐ 542. TOM NEVERS
- ☐ 543. KEN CAMINITI
- ☐ 544. KARL RHODES
- ☐ 545. XAVIER HERNANDEZ
- ☐ 546. MIKE SCOTT
- ☐ 547. JEFF JUDEN
- ☐ 548. DARRYL KILE
- ☐ 549. WILLIE ANSLEY
- ☐ 550. LUIS GONZALEZ
- ☐ 551. MIKE SIMMS
- ☐ 552. MARK PORTUGAL
- ☐ 553. JIMMY JONES
- ☐ 554. JIM CLANCY
- ☐ 555. PETE HARNISCH
- ☐ 556. CRAIG BIGGIO
- ☐ 557. ERIC YELDING
- ☐ 558. DAVE ROHDE
- ☐ 559. CASEY CANDAELE
- ☐ 560. CURT SCHILLING
- ☐ 561. STEVE FINLEY
- ☐ 562. JAVIER ORTIZ
- ☐ 563. ANDUJAR CEDENO
- ☐ 564. RAFAEL RAMIREZ
- ☐ 565. KENNY LOFTON

KANSAS CITY ROYALS

- ☐ 184. JEFF CONINE
- ☐ 291. BRET SABERHAGEN
- ☐ 292. BRIAN MCRAE
- ☐ 293. STORM DAVIS
- ☐ 294. DANNY TARTABULL
- ☐ 295. DAVID HOWARD
- ☐ 296. MIKE BODDICKER
- ☐ 297. JOEL JOHNSTON
- ☐ 298. TIM SPEHR
- ☐ 299. HECTOR WAGNER
- ☐ 300. GEORGE BRETT
- ☐ 301. MIKE MACFARLANE
- ☐ 302. KIRK GIBSON
- ☐ 303. HARVEY PULLIAM
- ☐ 304. JIM EISENREICH
- ☐ 305. KEVIN SEITZER
- ☐ 306. MARK DAVIS
- ☐ 307. KURT STILLWELL
- ☐ 308. JEFF MONTGOMERY
- ☐ 309. KEVIN APPIER
- ☐ 310. BOB HAMELIN
- ☐ 311. TOM GORDON
- ☐ 312. KERWIN MOORE
- ☐ 313. HUGH WALKER
- ☐ 314. TERRY SHUMPERT
- ☐ 315. WARREN CROMARTIE
- ☐ 316. GARY THURMAN

LOS ANGELES DODGERS

- ☐ 182. JOSE OFFERMAN
- ☐ 185. HENRY RODRIGUEZ
- ☐ 591. BOB OJEDA
- ☐ 592. ALFREDO GRIFFIN
- ☐ 593. RAUL MONDESI
- ☐ 594. GREG SMITH
- ☐ 595. OREL HERSHISER
- ☐ 596. JUAN SAMUEL
- ☐ 597. BRETT BUTLER
- ☐ 598. GARY CARTER
- ☐ 599. STAN JAVIER
- ☐ 600. KAL DANIELS
- ☐ 601. JAMIE MCANDREW
- ☐ 602. MIKE SHARPERSON
- ☐ 603. JAY HOWELL

- ☐ 604. ERIC KARROS
- ☐ 605. TIM BELCHER
- ☐ 606. DAN OPPERMAN
- ☐ 607. LENNY HARRIS
- ☐ 608. TOM GOODWIN
- ☐ 609. DARRYL STRAWBERRY
- ☐ 610. RAMON MARTINEZ
- ☐ 611. KEVIN GROSS
- ☐ 612. ZAKARY SHINALL
- ☐ 613. MIKE SCIOSCIA
- ☐ 614. EDDIE MURRAY
- ☐ 615. RONNIE WALDEN
- ☐ 696. DOMINGO MOTA

MILWAUKEE BREWERS

- ☐ 31. DANTE BICHETTE
- ☐ 32. PAUL MOLITOR
- ☐ 33. GREG VAUGHN
- ☐ 34. DAN PLESAC
- ☐ 35. CHRIS GEORGE
- ☐ 36. TIM MCINTOSH
- ☐ 37. FRANKLIN STUBBS
- ☐ 38. BO DODSON
- ☐ 39. RON ROBINSON
- ☐ 40. ED NUNEZ
- ☐ 41. GREG BROCK
- ☐ 42. JAIME NAVARRO
- ☐ 43. CHRIS BOSIO
- ☐ 44. B.J. SURHOFF
- ☐ 45. CHRIS JOHNSON
- ☐ 46. WILLIE RANDOLPH
- ☐ 47. NARCISO ELVIRA
- ☐ 48. JIM GANTNER
- ☐ 49. KEVIN BROWN
- ☐ 50. JULIO MACHADO
- ☐ 51. CHUCK CRIM
- ☐ 52. GARY SHEFFIELD
- ☐ 53. ANGEL MIRANDA
- ☐ 54. TEDDY HIGUERA
- ☐ 55. ROBIN YOUNT
- ☐ 56. CAL ELDRED

MINNESOTA TWINS

- ☐ 317. STEVE BEDROSIAN
- ☐ 318. DANNY GLADDEN
- ☐ 319. JACK MORRIS
- ☐ 320. KIRBY PUCKETT
- ☐ 321. KENT HRBEK
- ☐ 322. KEVIN TAPANI
- ☐ 323. DENNY NEAGLE
- ☐ 324. RICH GARCES
- ☐ 325. LARRY CASIAN
- ☐ 326. SHANE MACK
- ☐ 327. ALLAN ANDERSON
- ☐ 328. JUNIOR ORTIZ
- ☐ 329. PAUL ABBOTT
- ☐ 330. CHUCK KNOBLAUCH
- ☐ 331. CHILI DAVIS
- ☐ 332. TODD RITCHIE
- ☐ 333. BRIAN HARPER
- ☐ 334. RICK AGUILERA
- ☐ 335. SCOTT ERICKSON
- ☐ 336. PEDRO MUNOZ
- ☐ 337. SCOTT LEIUS
- ☐ 338. GREG GAGNE
- ☐ 339. MIKE PAGLIARULO
- ☐ 340. TERRY LEACH
- ☐ 341. WILLIE BANKS
- ☐ 695. PAUL RUSSO

MONTREAL EXPOS

- ☐ 434. DENNY MARTINEZ
- ☐ 435. MARQUIS GRISSOM
- ☐ 436. WILFREDO CORDERO
- ☐ 437. TIM WALLACH
- ☐ 438. BRIAN BARNES
- ☐ 439. BARRY JONES
- ☐ 440. IVAN CALDERON
- ☐ 441. STAN SPENCER
- ☐ 442. LARRY WALKER
- ☐ 443. CHRIS HANEY
- ☐ 444. HECTOR RIVERA
- ☐ 445. DELINO DESHIELDS
- ☐ 446. ANDRES GALARRAGA
- ☐ 447. GILBERTO REYES
- ☐ 448. WILLIE GREENE
- ☐ 449. GREG COLBRUNN
- ☐ 450. RONDELL WHITE
- ☐ 451. STEVE FREY
- ☐ 452. SHANE ANDREWS
- ☐ 453. MIKE FITZGERALD
- ☐ 454. SPIKE OWEN
- ☐ 455. DAVE MARTINEZ
- ☐ 456. DENNIS BOYD
- ☐ 457. ERIC BULLOCK
- ☐ 458. REID CORNELIUS
- ☐ 459. CHRIS NABHOLZ

NEW YORK METS

- ☐ 460. DAVID CONE
- ☐ 461. HUBIE BROOKS
- ☐ 462. SID FERNANDEZ
- ☐ 463. DOUG SIMONS
- ☐ 464. HOWARD JOHNSON
- ☐ 465. CHRIS DONNELS
- ☐ 466. ANTHONY YOUNG
- ☐ 467. TODD HUNDLEY
- ☐ 468. RICK CERONE
- ☐ 469. KEVIN ELSTER
- ☐ 470. WALLY WHITEHURST
- ☐ 471. VINCE COLEMAN
- ☐ 472. DWIGHT GOODEN
- ☐ 473. CHARLIE O'BRIEN
- ☐ 474. JEROMY BURNITZ
- ☐ 475. JOHN FRANCO
- ☐ 476. DARYL BOSTON
- ☐ 477. FRANK VIOLA
- ☐ 478. D.J. DOZIER
- ☐ 479. KEVIN MCREYNOLDS
- ☐ 480. TOM HERR
- ☐ 481. GREGG JEFFERIES
- ☐ 482. PETE SCHOUREK
- ☐ 483. RON DARLING
- ☐ 484. DAVE MAGADAN
- ☐ 536. NIKCO RIESGO
- ☐ 538. TIM HOWARD

NEW YORK YANKEES

- ☐ 155. PAT KELLY
- ☐ 156. CARL EVERETT
- ☐ 157. GREG CADARET
- ☐ 158. KEVIN MAAS
- ☐ 159. JEFF JOHNSON
- ☐ 160. WILLIE SMITH
- ☐ 161. GERALD WILLIAMS
- ☐ 162. MIKE HUMPHREYS
- ☐ 163. ALVARO ESPINOZA
- ☐ 164. MATT NOKES
- ☐ 165. WADE TAYLOR
- ☐ 166. ROBERTO KELLY
- ☐ 167. JOHN HABYAN
- ☐ 168. STEVE FARR
- ☐ 169. JESSE BARFIELD
- ☐ 170. STEVE SAX
- ☐ 171. JIM LEYRITZ
- ☐ 172. ROBERT EENHOORN
- ☐ 173. BERNIE WILLIAMS
- ☐ 174. SCOTT LUSADER
- ☐ 175. TOREY LOVULLO
- ☐ 176. CHUCK CARY
- ☐ 177. SCOTT SANDERSON
- ☐ 178. DON MATTINGLY
- ☐ 179. MEL HALL
- ☐ 181. HENSLEY MEULENS
- ☐ 693. SAM MILITELLO

OAKLAND A'S

- ☐ 212. MIKE MOORE
- ☐ 213. RICKEY HENDERSON
- ☐ 214. STEVE CHITREN
- ☐ 215. BOB WELCH
- ☐ 216. TERRY STEINBACH
- ☐ 217. ERNIE RILES
- ☐ 218. TODD VAN POPPEL
- ☐ 219. MIKE GALLEGO
- ☐ 220. CURT YOUNG
- ☐ 221. TODD BURNS
- ☐ 222. VANCE LAW
- ☐ 223. ERIC SHOW
- ☐ 224. DON PETERS
- ☐ 225. DAVE STEWART
- ☐ 226. DAVE HENDERSON
- ☐ 227. JOSE CANSECO
- ☐ 228. WALT WEISS
- ☐ 229. DANN HOWITT
- ☐ 230. WILLIE WILSON
- ☐ 231. HAROLD BAINES
- ☐ 232. SCOTT HEMOND
- ☐ 233. JOE SLUSARSKI
- ☐ 234. MARK MCGWIRE
- ☐ 235. KIRK DRESSENDORFER
- ☐ 236. CRAIG PAQUETTE
- ☐ 237. DENNIS ECKERSLEY
- ☐ 238. DANA ALLISON

PHILADELPHIA PHILLIES

- ☐ 485. ANDY ASHBY
- ☐ 486. DALE MURPHY
- ☐ 487. VON HAYES
- ☐ 488. KIM BATISTE
- ☐ 489. TONY LONGMIRE
- ☐ 490. WALLY BACKMAN
- ☐ 491. JEFF JACKSON
- ☐ 492. MICKEY MORANDINI
- ☐ 493. DARREL AKERFELDS
- ☐ 494. RICKY JORDAN
- ☐ 495. RANDY READY
- ☐ 496. DARRIN FLETCHER
- ☐ 497. CHUCK MALONE
- ☐ 498. PAT COMBS
- ☐ 499. DICKIE THON
- ☐ 500. ROGER MCDOWELL
- ☐ 501. LEN DYKSTRA
- ☐ 502. JOE BOEVER
- ☐ 503. JOHN KRUK
- ☐ 504. TERRY MULHOLLAND
- ☐ 505. WES CHAMBERLAIN
- ☐ 506. MIKE LIEBERTHAL
- ☐ 507. DARREN DAULTON
- ☐ 508. CHARLIE HAYES

PITTSBURGH PIRATES

- ☐ 509. JOHN SMILEY
- ☐ 510. GARY VARSHO
- ☐ 511. CURT WILKERSON
- ☐ 512. ORLANDO MERCED
- ☐ 513. BARRY BONDS
- ☐ 514. MIKE LAVALLIERE
- ☐ 515. DOUG DRABEK
- ☐ 516. GARY REDUS
- ☐ 517. WILLIAM PENNYFEATHER
- ☐ 518. RANDY TOMLIN
- ☐ 519. MIKE ZIMMERMAN
- ☐ 520. JEFF KING
- ☐ 521. KURT MILLER
- ☐ 522. JAY BELL
- ☐ 523. BILL LANDRUM
- ☐ 524. ZANE SMITH
- ☐ 525. BOBBY BONILLA
- ☐ 526. BOB WALK
- ☐ 527. AUSTIN MANAHAN
- ☐ 528. JOE AUSANIO
- ☐ 529. ANDY VAN SLYKE
- ☐ 530. JOSE LIND
- ☐ 531. CARLOS GARCIA
- ☐ 532. DON SLAUGHT

ST. LOUIS CARDINALS

- ☐ 385. PAUL COLEMAN
- ☐ 386. MILT THOMPSON
- ☐ 387. LEE SMITH
- ☐ 388. RAY LANKFORD
- ☐ 389. TOM PAGNOZZI
- ☐ 390. KEN HILL
- ☐ 391. JAMIE MOYER
- ☐ 392. GREG CARMONA
- ☐ 393. JOHN ERICKS
- ☐ 394. BOB TEWKSBURY
- ☐ 395. JOSE OQUENDO
- ☐ 396. RHEAL CORMIER
- ☐ 397. MIKE MILCHIN
- ☐ 398. OZZIE SMITH
- ☐ 399. AARON HOLBERT
- ☐ 400. JOSE DELEON
- ☐ 401. FELIX JOSE
- ☐ 402. JUAN AGOSTO
- ☐ 403. PEDRO GUERRERO
- ☐ 404. TODD ZEILE
- ☐ 405. GERALD PERRY
- ☐ 407. BRYN SMITH
- ☐ 408. BERNARD GILKEY
- ☐ 409. REX HUDLER
- ☐ 410. DONOVAN OSBORNE

SAN DIEGO PADRES

☐ 642. TONY FERNANDEZ
☐ 643. RICKY BONES
☐ 644. THOMAS HOWARD
☐ 645. DAVE STATON
☐ 646. JIM PRESLEY
☐ 647. TONY GWYNN
☐ 648. MARTY BARRETT
☐ 649. SCOTT COOLBAUGH
☐ 650. CRAIG LEFFERTS
☐ 651. EDDIE WHITSON
☐ 652. OSCAR AZOCAR
☐ 653. WES GARDNER
☐ 654. BIP ROBERTS
☐ 655. ROBBIE BECKETT
☐ 656. BENNY SANTIAGO
☐ 657. GREG HARRIS
☐ 658. JERALD CLARK
☐ 659. FRED MCGRIFF
☐ 660. LARRY ANDERSEN
☐ 661. BRUCE HURST
☐ 662. STEVE MARTIN
☐ 663. RAFAEL VALDEZ
☐ 664. PAUL FARIES
☐ 665. ANDY BENES
☐ 694. MATT MIESKE

SAN FRANCISCO GIANTS

☐ 616. WILL CLARK
☐ 617. ADAM HYZDU
☐ 618. MATT WILLIAMS
☐ 619. DON ROBINSON
☐ 620. JEFF BRANTLEY
☐ 621. GREG LITTON
☐ 622. STEVE DECKER
☐ 623. ROBBY THOMPSON
☐ 624. MARK LEONARD
☐ 625. KEVIN BASS
☐ 626. SCOTT GARRELTS
☐ 627. JOSE URIBE
☐ 628. ERIC GUNDERSON
☐ 629. STEVE HOSEY
☐ 630. TREVOR WILSON
☐ 631. TERRY KENNEDY
☐ 632. DAVE RIGHETTI
☐ 633. KELLY DOWNS
☐ 634. JOHNNY ARD
☐ 635. ERIC CHRISTOPHERSON
☐ 636. KEVIN MITCHELL
☐ 637. JOHN BURKETT
☐ 638. KEVIN ROGERS
☐ 639. BUD BLACK
☐ 640. WILLIE MCGEE
☐ 641. ROYCE CLAYTON

SEATTLE MARINERS

☐ 239. SCOTT BRADLEY
☐ 240. BRIAN HOLMAN
☐ 241. MIKE SCHOOLER
☐ 242. RICH DELUCIA
☐ 243. EDGAR MARTINEZ
☐ 244. HENRY COTTO
☐ 245. OMAR VIZQUEL
☐ 246. KEN GRIFFEY
☐ 246. KEN GRIFFEY, JR.
☐ 247. JAY BUHNER
☐ 248. BILL KRUEGER
☐ 249. DAVE FLEMING
☐ 250. PATRICK LENNON
☐ 251. DAVE VALLE
☐ 252. HAROLD REYNOLDS
☐ 253. RANDY JOHNSON
☐ 254. SCOTT BANKHEAD
☐ 256. GREG BRILEY
☐ 257. TINO MARTINEZ
☐ 258. ALVIN DAVIS
☐ 259. PETE O'BRIEN
☐ 260. ERIK HANSON
☐ 261. BRET BOONE
☐ 262. ROGER SALKELD
☐ 263. DAVE BURBA
☐ 264. KERRY WOODSON
☐ 534. FRANK BOLICK
☐ 698. MARC NEWFIELD

TEXAS RANGERS

☐ 180. JUAN GONZALEZ
☐ 265. JULIO FRANCO
☐ 266. DAN PELTIER
☐ 267. JEFF RUSSELL
☐ 268. STEVE BUECHELE
☐ 269. DONALD HARRIS
☐ 270. ROBB NEN
☐ 271. RICH GOSSAGE
☐ 272. IVAN RODRIGUEZ
☐ 273. JEFF HUSON
☐ 274. KEVIN BROWN
☐ 275. DAN SMITH
☐ 276. GARY PETTIS
☐ 277. JACK DAUGHERTY
☐ 278. MIKE JEFFCOAT
☐ 279. BRAD ARNSBERG
☐ 280. NOLAN RYAN
☐ 281. ERIC MCCRAY
☐ 282. SCOTT CHIAMPARINO
☐ 283. RUBEN SIERRA
☐ 284. GENO PETRALLI
☐ 285. MONTY FARISS
☐ 286. RAFAEL PALMEIRO
☐ 287. BOBBY WITT
☐ 288. DEAN PALMER
☐ 289. TONY SCRUGGS
☐ 290. KENNY ROGERS
☐ 697. TODD GUGGIANA

TORONTO BLUE JAYS

☐ 6. WILLIE FRASER
☐ 7. JOHN OLERUD
☐ 8. WILLIAM SUERO
☐ 9. ROBERTO ALOMAR
☐ 10. TODD STOTTLEMYRE
☐ 11. JOE CARTER
☐ 12. STEVE KARSAY
☐ 13. MARK WHITEN
☐ 14. PAT BORDERS
☐ 15. MIKE TIMLIN
☐ 16. TOM HENKE
☐ 17. EDDIE ZOSKY
☐ 18. KELLY GRUBER
☐ 19. JIMMY KEY
☐ 20. JERRY SCHUNK
☐ 21. MANNY LEE
☐ 22. DAVE STIEB
☐ 23. PAT HENTGEN
☐ 24. GLENALLEN HILL
☐ 25. RENE GONZALES
☐ 26. ED SPRAGUE
☐ 27. KEN DAYLEY
☐ 28. PAT TABLER
☐ 29. DENIS BOUCHER
☐ 30. DEVON WHITE

1992 BOWMAN (705)
2 1/2" X 3 1/2"

ATLANTA BRAVES

☐ 28. CHIPPER JONES
☐ 34. NAPOLEON ROBINSON
☐ 62. KEITH MITCHELL
☐ 75. RAFAEL BELLIARD
☐ 143. MELVIN NIEVES
☐ 160. DEION SANDERS
☐ 180. STEVE AVERY
☐ 254. TERRY PENDLETON
☐ 312. DAVID JUSTICE
☐ 347. JOHN SMOLTZ
☐ 356. SID BREAM
☐ 396. MARK WOHLERS
☐ 443. VINCE MOORE
☐ 452. JAVIER LOPEZ
☐ 470. JERRY WILLARD
☐ 504. DAVID NIED
☐ 534. RON GANT
☐ 549. RYAN KLESKO
☐ 577. GREG OLSON
☐ 662. BRIAN HUNTER
☐ 663. MARK LEMKE
☐ 669. OTIS NIXON
☐ 699. TOM GLAVINE

BALTIMORE ORIOLES

☐ 19. CHITO MARTINEZ
☐ 41. MANNY ALEXANDER
☐ 61. BOB MILACKI
☐ 103. RICKY GUTIERREZ
☐ 106. RICK SUTCLIFFE
☐ 136. BRAD PENNINGTON
☐ 150. BRENT MILLER
☐ 163. LUIS MERCEDES
☐ 177. SAM HORN
☐ 224. DAMON BUFORD
☐ 250. ALEX OCHOA
☐ 284. JEFF WILLIAMS
☐ 318. VAUGHN ESHELMAN
☐ 342. ALAN MILLS
☐ 344. LEO GOMEZ
☐ 359. BEN MCDONALD
☐ 373. BILLY RIPKEN
☐ 400. CAL RIPKEN
☐ 428. GLENN DAVIS
☐ 432. JOE ORSULAK
☐ 446. MARK MCLEMORE
☐ 472. CHRIS HOILES
☐ 556. MARK SMITH
☐ 612. MIKE MUSSINA
☐ 631. ARTHUR RHODES
☐ 677. GREGG OLSON
☐ 688. MIKE DEVEREAUX

BOSTON RED SOX

☐ 23. PAUL QUANTRILL
☐ 45. FRANK RODRIGUEZ
☐ 70. WADE BOGGS
☐ 83. SCOTT HATTEBERG
☐ 129. SCOTT COOPER
☐ 193. JEFFREY MCNEELY
☐ 233. JACK CLARK
☐ 251. GREG BLOSSER
☐ 292. PETER HOY
☐ 306. LUIS ORTIZ
☐ 311. AARON SELE
☐ 355. LUIS RIVERA
☐ 364. TONY PENA
☐ 397. MO VAUGHN
☐ 416. TIM NAEHRING
☐ 459. PHIL PLANTIER
☐ 475. JEFF REARDON
☐ 491. FRANK VIOLA
☐ 570. ELLIS BURKS
☐ 615. MIKE GREENWELL
☐ 618. SCOTT TAYLOR
☐ 642. JODY REED
☐ 691. ROGER CLEMENS

CALIFORNIA ANGELS

☐ 8. JORGE FABREGAS
☐ 32. CHUCK FINLEY
☐ 51. CLIFTON GARRETT
☐ 59. J.R. PHILLIPS
☐ 97. HUBIE BROOKS
☐ 159. GARY DISARCINA
☐ 172. BRYAN HARVEY
☐ 185. JIM ABBOTT
☐ 186. MIKE FITZGERALD
☐ 197. VON HAYES
☐ 259. TIM SALMON
☐ 283. KEVIN FLORA
☐ 290. TROY PERCIVAL
☐ 298. GARRET ANDERSON

☐ 341. ALVIN DAVIS
☐ 404. JUNIOR FELIX
☐ 418. LUIS SOJO
☐ 422. JULIO VALERA
☐ 427. LEE STEVENS
☐ 474. JOHN MORRIS
☐ 520. MARK LANGSTON
☐ 564. GARY GAETTI
☐ 582. LUIS POLONIA
☐ 627. CHAD CURTIS
☐ 672. DAMION EASLEY

CHICAGO CUBS

☐ 27. JEROME WALTON
☐ 81. EARL CUNNINGHAM
☐ 85. ROBERT NUTTING
☐ 95. ELVIN PAULINO
☐ 116. SAMMY SOSA
☐ 128. GARY SCOTT
☐ 138. RYAN HAWBLITZEL
☐ 142. DANNY JACKSON
☐ 148. GREG MADDUX
☐ 156. RICK WILKINS
☐ 169. PHIL DAUPHIN
☐ 271. PETE CASTELLANO
☐ 287. DOUG DASCENZO
☐ 300. RYNE SANDBERG
☐ 316. LANCE DICKSON
☐ 322. DOUG STRANGE
☐ 333. DAVE SMITH
☐ 580. MARK GRACE
☐ 625. ANDRE DAWSON
☐ 636. JOE GIRARDI
☐ 647. MIKE MORGAN
☐ 693. TURK WENDELL

CHICAGO WHITE SOX

☐ 2. KIRK MCCASKILL
☐ 36. BOBBY THIGPEN
☐ 69. WILSON ALVAREZ
☐ 88. SCOTT RUFFCORN
☐ 114. FRANK THOMAS
☐ 133. ROBERTO HERNANDEZ
☐ 153. CHARLIE HOUGH
☐ 201. ALEX FERNANDEZ
☐ 204. ROCK RAINES
☐ 208. LANCE JOHNSON
☐ 210. DEREK LEE
☐ 240. ROD BOLTON
☐ 275. ROBIN VENTURA
☐ 282. GREG PERSCHKE
☐ 297. SCOTT CEPICKY
☐ 309. CHRIS HOWARD
☐ 325. GREG HIBBARD
☐ 358. JASON BERE
☐ 371. JACK MCDOWELL
☐ 380. DONN PALL
☐ 451. JOHNNY RUFFIN
☐ 458. ESTEBAN BELTRE
☐ 469. STEVE SAX
☐ 565. OZZIE GUILLEN
☐ 585. CARLTON FISK
☐ 632. BRANDON WILSON
☐ 687. MIKE ROBERTSON

CINCINNATI REDS

☐ 11. TREVOR HOFFMAN
☐ 46. GREG SWINDELL
☐ 65. BRIAN KOELLING
☐ 86. CALVIN REESE
☐ 118. REGGIE SANDERS
☐ 161. TOM BROWNING
☐ 220. DAVE MARTINEZ
☐ 234. BILL DORAN
☐ 242. ROB DIBBLE
☐ 267. PAUL O'NEILL
☐ 281. MO SANFORD
☐ 319. TIM BELCHER
☐ 328. CHRIS HAMMOND
☐ 353. BARRY LARKIN
☐ 382. DARNELL COLES
☐ 429. WILLIE GREENE
☐ 468. HAL MORRIS
☐ 471. DAN WILSON
☐ 489. TIM COSTO
☐ 509. TROY AFENIR
☐ 512. JEFF BRANSON
☐ 525. BIP ROBERTS
☐ 528. JOHN ROPER
☐ 594. JOE OLIVER
☐ 595. CHRIS SABO
☐ 621. KEVIN TATAR
☐ 680. JOSE RIJO

CLEVELAND INDIANS

☐ 25. REGGIE JEFFERSON
☐ 42. TRACY SANDERS
☐ 57. MARK WHITEN
☐ 92. JERRY DIPOTO
☐ 110. KENNY LOFTON
☐ 140. SANDY ALOMAR
☐ 173. ALEX COLE
☐ 203. CHARLES NAGY
☐ 236. STEVE OLIN
☐ 252. JACK ARMSTRONG
☐ 329. ALBERT BELLE
☐ 349. PAUL BYRD
☐ 374. MIKE CHRISTOPHER
☐ 387. ALAN EMBREE
☐ 410. JEFF SHAW
☐ 413. DAVE MLICKI
☐ 430. KEVIN WICKANDER
☐ 439. MARK LEWIS
☐ 460. JIM THOME
☐ 497. DENNIS COOK
☐ 531. CARLOS BAERGA
☐ 532. MANNY RAMIREZ
☐ 571. SCOTT SCUDDER
☐ 619. DAVE OTTO
☐ 659. GLENALLEN HILL
☐ 346. RYAN TURNER

DETROIT TIGERS

☐ 3. SCOTT LIVINGSTONE
☐ 37. TRAVIS FRYMAN
☐ 90. CECIL FIELDER
☐ 111. MARK CARREON
☐ 117. MICKEY TETTLETON
☐ 164. RICCARDO INGRAM
☐ 170. IVAN CRUZ
☐ 196. MILT CUYLER
☐ 229. JOHN DESILVA
☐ 246. JOE PERONA
☐ 256. RICO BROGNA
☐ 272. TONY PHILLIPS
☐ 317. ERIC KING
☐ 345. TARRIK BROCK
☐ 363. ROB DEER
☐ 419. KEVIN RITZ
☐ 441. MIKE HENNEMAN
☐ 453. GREG GOHR
☐ 476. MARK LEITER
☐ 515. CHAD KREUTER
☐ 518. JOHN DOHERTY
☐ 543. JUSTIN THOMPSON
☐ 558. BILL GULLICKSON
☐ 630. LOU WHITAKER
☐ 690. ALAN TRAMMELL

FLORIDA MARLINS

☐ 417. CLEMENTE NUNEZ

HOUSTON ASTROS

☐ 9. ANDUJAR CEDENO
☐ 31. ROBERTO PETAGINE
☐ 43. PETE INCAVIGLIA
☐ 125. BRIAN WILLIAMS
☐ 137. JERMAINE SWINTON
☐ 145. LUIS GONZALEZ
☐ 188. JEFF JUDEN
☐ 200. JEFF BAGWELL
☐ 202. TODD JONES
☐ 226. TOM NEVERS
☐ 327. SHANE REYNOLDS
☐ 401. RYAN BOWEN
☐ 414. BENNY DISTEFANO
☐ 457. CHRIS GARDNER
☐ 463. SCOTT SERVAIS
☐ 484. CRAIG BIGGIO
☐ 502. BUTCH HENRY
☐ 514. PETE HARNISCH
☐ 530. DENNY WALLING
☐ 538. KEN CAMINITI
☐ 555. ORLANDO MILLER
☐ 574. STEVE FINLEY
☐ 601. DARRYL KILE
☐ 639. AL OSUNA
☐ 656. MARK PORTUGAL
☐ 697. EDDIE TAUBENSEE

KANSAS CITY ROYALS

☐ 13. GREGG JEFFERIES
☐ 54. GARY CARABALLO
☐ 66. BRIAN MCRAE
☐ 79. RYAN LONG
☐ 122. JEFF MONTGOMERY
☐ 132. MIKE BODDICKER
☐ 157. TERRY SHUMPERT
☐ 199. JOEL JOHNSTON
☐ 215. MARK GUBICZA
☐ 285. KEITH MILLER
☐ 307. DAVID HOWARD
☐ 337. KEVIN MCREYNOLDS
☐ 383. TOM SMITH
☐ 390. RICO ROSSY
☐ 424. DARREN BURTON
☐ 435. WALLY JOYNER
☐ 477. TOM GORDON
☐ 486. RUSTY MEACHAM
☐ 500. GEORGE BRETT
☐ 529. PHIL HIATT
☐ 589. MIKE MACFARLANE
☐ 593. KERWIN MOORE
☐ 633. LANCE JENNINGS
☐ 640. KEVIN APPIER

LOS ANGELES DODGERS

☐ 5. CARLOS HERNANDEZ
☐ 40. DARRYL STRAWBERRY
☐ 64. RAUL MONDESI
☐ 82. PEDRO MARTINEZ
☐ 108. HENRY RODRIGUEZ
☐ 141. TODD BENZINGER
☐ 168. BILLY ASHLEY
☐ 253. JUAN SAMUEL
☐ 255. RAMON MARTINEZ
☐ 288. ERIC KARROS
☐ 304. JOSE OFFERMAN
☐ 314. GREG HANSELL
☐ 368. MIKE SCIOSCIA
☐ 379. BOB OJEDA
☐ 394. DAVE ANDERSON
☐ 408. JAY HOWELL
☐ 461. MIKE PIAZZA
☐ 487. KAL DANIELS
☐ 517. OREL HERSHISER
☐ 591. JAMIE MCANDREW
☐ 597. BRETT BUTLER
☐ 606. TOM CANDIOTTI
☐ 657. ROGER MCDOWELL
☐ 671. ERIC DAVIS
☐ 689. PEDRO ASTACIO

MILWAUKEE BREWERS

☐ 7. SCOTT FLETCHER
☐ 15. MIKE IGNASIAK
☐ 49. FRANKLIN STUBBS
☐ 63. ANGEL MIRANDA
☐ 74. DARRYL HAMILTON
☐ 126. KEVIN SEITZER
☐ 167. JAIME NAVARRO
☐ 181. WILLIAM SUERO
☐ 213. CHRIS GEORGE
☐ 223. TEDDY HIGUERA
☐ 243. MICHAEL CARTER
☐ 264. DANTE BICHETTE
☐ 299. CAL ELDRED
☐ 301. JIM GANTNER
☐ 354. BRUCE RUFFIN
☐ 375. PAUL MOLITOR
☐ 399. JOHN JAHA
☐ 402. TIM MCINTOSH
☐ 447. BILL WEGMAN
☐ 481. B.J. SURHOFF
☐ 496. GREG VAUGHN
☐ 526. PAT LISTACH
☐ 536. BILLY SPIERS
☐ 545. JOE KMAK
☐ 653. DAVE NILSSON
☐ 674. MARK KIEFER
☐ 679. DUANE SINGLETON
☐ 700. ROBIN YOUNT

1992 Bowman

MINNESOTA TWINS

- ☐ 24. CHUCK KNOBLAUCH
- ☐ 53. SCOTT ERICKSON
- ☐ 80. KIRBY PUCKETT
- ☐ 89. RICK AGUILERA
- ☐ 102. MIKE TROMBLEY
- ☐ 112. J.T. BRUETT
- ☐ 131. PAT MAHOMES
- ☐ 149. BRIAN HARPER
- ☐ 195. CHILI DAVIS
- ☐ 209. SCOTT LEIUS
- ☐ 221. ALAN NEWMAN
- ☐ 257. JOHN SMILEY
- ☐ 330. RICH BECKER
- ☐ 360. SCOTT STAHOVIAK
- ☐ 445. KENT HRBEK
- ☐ 466. CARL WILLIS
- ☐ 479. GENE LARKIN
- ☐ 524. TODD RITCHIE
- ☐ 552. KEVIN TAPANI
- ☐ 553. WILLIE BANKS
- ☐ 592. SHANE MACK
- ☐ 660. GREG GAGNE
- ☐ 685. MIKE PAGLIARULO

MONTREAL EXPOS

- ☐ 14. MARQUIS GRISSOM
- ☐ 47. DELINO DESHIELDS
- ☐ 68. JOHN WETTELAND
- ☐ 121. SPIKE OWEN
- ☐ 165. TAVO ALVAREZ
- ☐ 179. IVAN CALDERON
- ☐ 194. WIL CORDERO
- ☐ 232. JOHN VANDER WAL
- ☐ 261. UGUETH URBINA
- ☐ 279. GABE WHITE
- ☐ 289. GLENN MURRAY
- ☐ 305. DENNY MARTINEZ
- ☐ 348. BILL SAMPEN
- ☐ 372. TIM WALLACH
- ☐ 385. GARY CARTER
- ☐ 388. JONATHAN HURST
- ☐ 434. MATT STAIRS
- ☐ 436. RONDELL WHITE
- ☐ 450. ARCHI CIANFROCCO
- ☐ 467. BRET BARBERIE
- ☐ 478. KENT BOTTENFIELD
- ☐ 493. CHRIS MARTIN
- ☐ 501. BRIAN BARNES
- ☐ 507. KEN HILL
- ☐ 537. DARREN REED
- ☐ 562. MARK GARDNER
- ☐ 609. DARRIN FLETCHER
- ☐ 648. LARRY WALKER
- ☐ 678. CLIFF FLOYD

NEW YORK METS

- ☐ 10. HOWARD JOHNSON
- ☐ 56. BROOK FORDYCE
- ☐ 101. TODD HUNDLEY
- ☐ 139. TITO NAVARRO
- ☐ 189. JEROMY BURNITZ
- ☐ 219. D.J. DOZIER
- ☐ 235. BOBBY BONILLA
- ☐ 238. DAVID CONE
- ☐ 263. DAVE MAGADAN
- ☐ 268. ANTHONY YOUNG
- ☐ 296. SID FERNANDEZ
- ☐ 326. ERIC HILLMAN
- ☐ 357. JULIAN VASQUEZ
- ☐ 389. BOBBY JONES
- ☐ 433. EDDIE MURRAY
- ☐ 480. DOC GOODEN
- ☐ 516. JOE VITKO
- ☐ 539. BUTCH HUSKEY
- ☐ 546. JOHN FRANCO
- ☐ 586. BRET SABERHAGEN
- ☐ 613. VINCE COLEMAN
- ☐ 681. WILLIE RANDOLPH

NEW YORK YANKEES

- ☐ 12. ROBERTO KELLY
- ☐ 21. SAM MILITELLO
- ☐ 52. MIKE GARDELLA
- ☐ 87. DAVE SILVESTRI
- ☐ 113. GERALD WILLIAMS
- ☐ 124. BRIEN TAYLOR
- ☐ 130. DOMINGO JEAN
- ☐ 147. CHARLIE HAYES
- ☐ 205. KEVIN MAAS
- ☐ 207. RANDY VELARDE
- ☐ 231. GREG CADARET
- ☐ 258. CARL EVERETT
- ☐ 273. MIKE GALLEGO
- ☐ 278. ROBERT EENHOORN
- ☐ 295. JESSE BARFIELD
- ☐ 302. MARIANO RIVERA
- ☐ 308. RUSS SPRINGER
- ☐ 338. HENSLEY MEULENS
- ☐ 340. DON MATTINGLY
- ☐ 362. JEFF JOHNSON
- ☐ 365. MELIDO PEREZ
- ☐ 370. MIKE STANLEY
- ☐ 407. BERNIE WILLIAMS
- ☐ 425. MEL HALL
- ☐ 482. ANDY STANKIEWICZ
- ☐ 494. DION JAMES
- ☐ 523. ROBERTO MUNOZ
- ☐ 535. PAT KELLY
- ☐ 540. MATT NOKES
- ☐ 550. DANNY TARTABULL
- ☐ 598. MARK HUTTON
- ☐ 607. ED MARTEL
- ☐ 622. STEVE FARR

OAKLAND A'S

- ☐ 30. RON DARLING
- ☐ 58. JOE SLUSARSKI
- ☐ 78. CARNEY LANSFORD
- ☐ 91. KIRK DRESSENDORFER
- ☐ 94. CRAIG PAQUETTE
- ☐ 99. DAVID ZANCANARO
- ☐ 166. RICKEY HENDERSON
- ☐ 171. HAROLD BAINES
- ☐ 174. CURTIS SHAW
- ☐ 198. TODD REVENIG
- ☐ 216. MIKE MOORE
- ☐ 244. DON PETERS
- ☐ 262. JASON WOOD
- ☐ 266. MIKE NEILL
- ☐ 270. TODD VAN POPPEL
- ☐ 280. DAVE STEWART
- ☐ 350. MIKE BORDICK
- ☐ 384. MARK MCGWIRE
- ☐ 392. TERRY STEINBACH
- ☐ 431. DENNIS ECKERSLEY
- ☐ 488. DAVE HENDERSON
- ☐ 506. STEVE CHITREN
- ☐ 521. DANN HOWITT
- ☐ 527. SCOTT BROSIUS
- ☐ 600. JOSE CANSECO
- ☐ 651. WALT WEISS

PHILADELPHIA PHILLIES

- ☐ 6. DAVE HOLLINS
- ☐ 39. TERRY MULHOLLAND
- ☐ 44. KIM BATISTE
- ☐ 72. JEFF JACKSON
- ☐ 104. BRAULIO CASTILLO
- ☐ 120. CLIFF BRANTLEY
- ☐ 152. MIKE WILLIAMS
- ☐ 184. RUBEN AMARO
- ☐ 227. TOMMY GREENE
- ☐ 247. MITCH WILLIAMS
- ☐ 286. ANDY ASHBY
- ☐ 303. RON LOCKETT
- ☐ 310. KYLE ABBOTT
- ☐ 367. DALE SVEUM
- ☐ 412. WES CHAMBERLAIN
- ☐ 440. DARREN DAULTON
- ☐ 541. JOHN KRUK
- ☐ 628. MICKEY MORANDINI
- ☐ 635. LEN DYKSTRA
- ☐ 684. DALE MURPHY

PITTSBURGH PIRATES

- ☐ 17. WILLIAM PENNYFEATHER
- ☐ 35. ANDY VAN SLYKE
- ☐ 60. BARRY BONDS
- ☐ 71. DARRYL RATLIFF
- ☐ 146. DAVE DOORNEWEERD
- ☐ 155. KEVIN YOUNG
- ☐ 211. JOE SONDRINI
- ☐ 239. VICTOR COLE
- ☐ 245. MIKE LAVALLIERE
- ☐ 274. STEVE COOKE
- ☐ 291. ORLANDO MERCED
- ☐ 321. SCOTT BULLETT
- ☐ 335. STEVE BUECHELE
- ☐ 351. JOSE LIND
- ☐ 393. JON FARRELL
- ☐ 409. ZANE SMITH
- ☐ 438. JOE REDFIELD
- ☐ 444. JOHN WEHNER
- ☐ 455. STAN BELINDA
- ☐ 465. DOUG DRABEK
- ☐ 485. DENNY NEAGLE
- ☐ 495. RANDY TOMLIN
- ☐ 498. ROSARIO RODRIGUEZ
- ☐ 519. JAY BELL
- ☐ 568. BEN SHELTON
- ☐ 576. CARLOS GARCIA
- ☐ 666. BOB WALK
- ☐ 686. PAUL MILLER

ST. LOUIS CARDINALS

- ☐ 26. JEREMY MCGARITY
- ☐ 29. BRIAN BARBER
- ☐ 48. JOHN ERICKS
- ☐ 96. DONOVAN OSBORNE
- ☐ 109. MARK CLARK
- ☐ 176. FELIX JOSE
- ☐ 241. TOM PAGNOZZI
- ☐ 265. JOSE DELEON
- ☐ 320. ANDRES GALARRAGA
- ☐ 331. EDDIE WILLIAMS
- ☐ 377. PEDRO GUERRERO
- ☐ 403. BERNARD GILKEY
- ☐ 420. OMAR OLIVARES
- ☐ 464. BRIAN JORDAN
- ☐ 473. RHEAL CORMIER
- ☐ 505. LEE SMITH
- ☐ 567. MIKE MILCHIN
- ☐ 634. ALLEN WATSON
- ☐ 643. RAY LANKFORD
- ☐ 675. OZZIE SMITH
- ☐ 695. TODD ZEILE

SAN DIEGO PADRES

- ☐ 50. TONY GWYNN
- ☐ 73. JEREMY HERNANDEZ
- ☐ 105. CRAIG LEFFERTS
- ☐ 135. KURT STILLWELL
- ☐ 154. RANDY MYERS
- ☐ 187. BRUCE HURST
- ☐ 214. GARY SHEFFIELD
- ☐ 249. ANDY BENES
- ☐ 269. GREG HARRIS
- ☐ 293. TONY FERNANDEZ
- ☐ 323. JERALD CLARK
- ☐ 395. BENNY SANTIAGO
- ☐ 449. MARK ANTHONY
- ☐ 454. TIM SCOTT
- ☐ 456. DARRIN JACKSON
- ☐ 499. DAVE STATON
- ☐ 508. ROBBIE BECKETT
- ☐ 553. PAT CLEMENTS
- ☐ 561. FRANK SEMINARA
- ☐ 650. FRED MCGRIFF
- ☐ 698. GUILLERMO VELASQUEZ

1992 Bowman

SAN FRANCISCO GIANTS

- ☐ 4. SALOMON TORRES
- ☐ 38. ERIC CHRISTOPHERSON
- ☐ 67. JOHN PATTERSON
- ☐ 93. MIKE FELDER
- ☐ 119. TREVOR WILSON
- ☐ 175. MATT WILLIAMS
- ☐ 182. BILL SWIFT
- ☐ 190. DAVE BURBA
- ☐ 212. ROYCE CLAYTON
- ☐ 217. RICK HUISMAN
- ☐ 260. WILL CLARK
- ☐ 324. DAVE RIGHETTI
- ☐ 343. KELLY DOWNS
- ☐ 361. KIRT MANWARING
- ☐ 415. KEVIN ROGERS
- ☐ 448. ROBBY THOMPSON
- ☐ 492. CORY SNYDER
- ☐ 513. MIKE JACKSON
- ☐ 544. STEVE HOSEY
- ☐ 604. WILLIE MCGEE
- ☐ 616. KEVIN MCGEHEE
- ☐ 683. DARREN LEWIS
- ☐ 692. BUD BLACK

SEATTLE MARINERS

- ☐ 33. EDGAR MARTINEZ
- ☐ 98. DEREK LOWE
- ☐ 100. KEN GRIFFEY, JR
- ☐ 123. ALEX SUTHERLAND
- ☐ 134. DAVE VALLE
- ☐ 144. JIM CAMPANIS
- ☐ 151. SHAWN ESTES
- ☐ 178. RANDY JOHNSON
- ☐ 192. PATRICK LENNON
- ☐ 248. JAY BUHNER
- ☐ 276. KEVIN MITCHELL
- ☐ 313. PETE O'BRIEN
- ☐ 336. MIKE SCHOOLER
- ☐ 366. CLAY PARKER
- ☐ 369. ROGER SALKELD
- ☐ 378. RUSS SWAN
- ☐ 386. RICH AMARAL
- ☐ 398. RANDY KRAMER
- ☐ 406. MARC NEWFIELD
- ☐ 411. KERRY WOODSON
- ☐ 423. OMAR VIZQUEL
- ☐ 426. DENNIS POWELL
- ☐ 462. MATT SINATRO
- ☐ 483. TINO MARTINEZ
- ☐ 503. HAROLD REYNOLDS
- ☐ 511. BRET BOONE
- ☐ 583. ERIK HANSON
- ☐ 624. DAVE FLEMING
- ☐ 638. MIKE HAMPTON
- ☐ 654. GREG PIRKL
- ☐ 665. RICH DELUCIA

TEXAS RANGERS

- ☐ 1. IVAN RODRIGUEZ
- ☐ 22. HECTOR FAJARDO
- ☐ 55. JOSE OLIVA
- ☐ 84. JUAN GONZALEZ
- ☐ 107. DEAN PALMER
- ☐ 115. KEVIN REIMER
- ☐ 162. DICKIE THON
- ☐ 191. KEVIN BROWN
- ☐ 206. JULIO FRANCO
- ☐ 218. JEFF RUSSELL
- ☐ 222. NOLAN RYAN
- ☐ 225. RUBEN SIERRA
- ☐ 230. BOBBY WITT
- ☐ 332. DONALD HARRIS
- ☐ 334. STEVE FIREOVID
- ☐ 339. BENJI GIL
- ☐ 391. DAN SMITH
- ☐ 405. CRIS COLON
- ☐ 437. ROB MAURER
- ☐ 442. JOHN CANGELOSI
- ☐ 490. DOUG DAVIS
- ☐ 522. BOBBY REED
- ☐ 610. RAFAEL PALMEIRO
- ☐ 668. JOSE GUZMAN

TORONTO BLUE JAYS

- ☐ 16. JACK MORRIS
- ☐ 18. TODD STOTTLEMYRE
- ☐ 20. ROBERTO ALOMAR
- ☐ 76. RICKY TRLICEK
- ☐ 77. FELIPE CRESPO
- ☐ 127. CARLOS DELGADO
- ☐ 158. STEVE KARSAY
- ☐ 183. HOWARD BATTLE
- ☐ 228. NIGEL WILSON
- ☐ 237. DEREK BELL
- ☐ 277. DOUG LINTON
- ☐ 294. JUAN GUZMAN
- ☐ 315. DAVE WINFIELD
- ☐ 352. DAVID WELLS
- ☐ 376. DAVE STIEB
- ☐ 381. EDDIE ZOSKY
- ☐ 421. MANUEL LEE
- ☐ 510. KELLY GRUBER
- ☐ 547. DEVON WHITE
- ☐ 573. JOE CARTER
- ☐ 588. JIMMY KEY
- ☐ 596. ALEX GONZALEZ
- ☐ 644. JOHN OLERUD
- ☐ 646. PAT BORDERS
- ☐ 696. PAT HENTGEN

1993 BOWMAN (708)
2 1/2" X 3 1/2"

ATLANTA BRAVES

- ☐ 2. HECTOR ROA
- ☐ 30. MIKE HOSTETLER
- ☐ 58. DONNIE ELLIOTT
- ☐ 86. CHIPPER JONES
- ☐ 114. LEE HEATH
- ☐ 142. JEFF BLAUSER
- ☐ 170. DAMON HOLLINS
- ☐ 198. STEVE AVERY
- ☐ 226. PEDRO BORBON
- ☐ 254. TERRY PENDLETON
- ☐ 282. JOSE OLIVA
- ☐ 310. OTIS NIXON
- ☐ 317. GREG MCMICHAEL
- ☐ 382. RON GANT
- ☐ 410. TOM GLAVINE
- ☐ 438. DEION SANDERS
- ☐ 466. JAVY LOPEZ
- ☐ 494. JOHN SMOLTZ
- ☐ 522. TONY TARASCO
- ☐ 550. GREG MADDUX
- ☐ 578. DAVID JUSTICE
- ☐ 634. RYAN KLESKO
- ☐ 662. MELVIN NIEVES
- ☐ 689. SID BREAM

BALTIMORE ORIOLES

- ☐ 1. GLENN DAVIS
- ☐ 29. SHERMAN OBANDO
- ☐ 57. HAROLD REYNOLDS
- ☐ 74. MIKE OQUIST
- ☐ 85. T.R. LEWIS
- ☐ 113. RICK SUTCLIFFE
- ☐ 141. DAMON BUFORD
- ☐ 169. ARTHUR RHODES
- ☐ 197. JOHN O'DONOGHUE
- ☐ 225. CAL RIPKEN
- ☐ 253. MARK SMITH
- ☐ 281. HAROLD BAINES
- ☐ 309. JOSE MERCEDES
- ☐ 381. LEO GOMEZ
- ☐ 409. BRADY ANDERSON
- ☐ 437. BEN MCDONALD
- ☐ 465. GREGG OLSON
- ☐ 493. JIMMY HAYNES
- ☐ 521. ALEX OCHOA
- ☐ 549. CHRIS HOILES
- ☐ 577. MANNY ALEXANDER
- ☐ 605. MIKE DEVEREAUX
- ☐ 633. MIKE MUSSINA
- ☐ 661. BRAD PENNINGTON
- ☐ 678. JACK VOIGT

BOSTON RED SOX

- ☐ 3. KEN RYAN
- ☐ 31. NATE MINCHEY
- ☐ 87. SCOTT HATTEBERG
- ☐ 115. JEFF RUSSELL
- ☐ 143. FRANK RODRIGUEZ
- ☐ 171. FRANK VIOLA
- ☐ 199. GREG BLOSSER
- ☐ 227. CARLOS QUINTANA
- ☐ 255. AARON SELE
- ☐ 311. GETTYS GLAZE
- ☐ 383. SCOTT FLETCHER
- ☐ 411. DOUG HECKER
- ☐ 439. TONY PENA
- ☐ 467. SCOTT COOPER
- ☐ 495. ANDRE DAWSON
- ☐ 523. LUIS ORTIZ
- ☐ 536. MO VAUGHN
- ☐ 551. JOE CICCARELLA
- ☐ 579. BRIAN CONROY
- ☐ 607. MIKE GREENWELL
- ☐ 635. ROGER CLEMENS
- ☐ 663. IVAN CALDERON
- ☐ 690. JOHN VALENTIN

CALIFORNIA ANGELS

- ☐ 5. JORGE FABREGAS
- ☐ 33. BRIAN GREBECK

☐ 61. HILLY HATHAWAY
☐ 117. MARK HOLZEMER
☐ 145. GARY DISARCINA
☐ 173. J.T. SNOW
☐ 201. JOE GRAHE
☐ 229. TIM SALMON
☐ 257. DAMION EASLEY
☐ 285. RUSS SPRINGER
☐ 313. CHAD CURTIS
☐ 385. CHUCK FINLEY
☐ 413. LUIS POLONIA
☐ 441. EDUARDO PEREZ
☐ 469. MARK LANGSTON
☐ 497. TY VAN BURKLEO
☐ 525. CHRIS TURNER
☐ 553. CHILI DAVIS
☐ 581. RON WATSON
☐ 609. TROY PERCIVAL
☐ 637. ORLANDO PALMEIRO
☐ 641. PETE JANICKI
☐ 665. CHRIS PRITCHETT

CHICAGO CUBS

☐ 4. DEREK WALLACE
☐ 32. RANDY MYERS
☐ 60. KEVIN ROBINSON
☐ 88. GREG HIBBARD
☐ 116. DAVE STEVENS
☐ 144. MIKE MORGAN
☐ 172. STEVE TRACHSEL
☐ 200. RYNE SANDBERG
☐ 228. TOMMY SHIELDS
☐ 256. JOSE VIERA
☐ 284. BRANT BROWN
☐ 312. CANDY MALDONADO
☐ 384. MATT WALBECK
☐ 412. JOSE GUZMAN
☐ 440. MARK GRACE
☐ 468. WILLIE WILSON
☐ 496. REY SANCHEZ
☐ 524. RICK WILKINS
☐ 552. OZZIE TIMMONS
☐ 580. JESSIE HOLLINS
☐ 608. STEVE BUECHELE
☐ 636. SAMMY SOSA
☐ 648. JEFF HARTSOCK
☐ 664. TURK WENDELL

CHICAGO WHITE SOX

☐ 7. BRANDON WILSON
☐ 35. LARRY THOMAS
☐ 91. JASON BERE
☐ 119. BOBBY THIGPEN
☐ 147. JOHNNY RUFFIN
☐ 175. CARLTON FISK
☐ 188. CLEMENTE ALVAREZ
☐ 231. ELLIS BURKS
☐ 259. CHRIS SNOPEK
☐ 287. OZZIE GUILLEN
☐ 315. MIKE ROBERTSON
☐ 387. WILSON ALVAREZ
☐ 415. BO JACKSON
☐ 443. SCOTT RUFFCORN
☐ 471. ROD BOLTON
☐ 499. TIM RAINES
☐ 527. JACK MCDOWELL
☐ 555. FRANK THOMAS
☐ 611. JAMES BALDWIN
☐ 639. GEORGE BELL
☐ 667. ROBIN VENTURA
☐ 691. STEVE OLSEN

CINCINNATI REDS

☐ 6. JOE OLIVER
☐ 34. JOHN ROPER
☐ 62. JOSE RIJO
☐ 90. CHAD MOTTOLA
☐ 118. TIM BELCHER
☐ 146. CALVIN REESE
☐ 174. KEITH GORDON
☐ 202. DAN WILSON
☐ 230. JOHN SMILEY
☐ 258. ROD LOFTON
☐ 286. CHRIS SABO
☐ 314. TIM COSTO
☐ 386. KEVIN MITCHELL
☐ 442. TIM PUGH
☐ 470. BARRY LARKIN
☐ 498. BOBBY AYALA
☐ 526. ROB DIBBLE
☐ 554. BRIAN KOELLING
☐ 582. BIP ROBERTS
☐ 610. BOBBY KELLY
☐ 638. WILLIE GREENE
☐ 666. REGGIE SANDERS

CLEVELAND INDIANS

☐ 9. TRACY SANDERS
☐ 37. TOM KRAMER
☐ 65. GLENALLEN HILL
☐ 93. SANDY ALOMAR
☐ 121. TONY MITCHELL
☐ 149. CHARLES NAGY
☐ 177. MIKE CROSBY
☐ 205. JAMIE TAYLOR
☐ 233. PAUL BYRD
☐ 261. MIKE MATTHEWS
☐ 289. CHAD OGEA
☐ 389. ALAN EMBREE
☐ 417. KENNY LOFTON
☐ 445. ALBERT BELLE
☐ 451. DAVE MLICKI
☐ 473. KEN RAMOS
☐ 501. PAUL SORRENTO
☐ 529. BILL WERTZ
☐ 557. REGGIE JEFFERSON
☐ 585. CARLOS BAERGA
☐ 586. JEFF MUTIS
☐ 613. ALBIE LOPEZ
☐ 669. MANNY RAMIREZ

COLORADO ROCKIES

☐ 8. MARK THOMPSON
☐ 36. ALEX COLE
☐ 64. RYAN HAWBLITZEL
☐ 89. LANCE PAINTER
☐ 92. DANTE BICHETTE
☐ 120. ROGER BAILEY
☐ 148. DAVID NIED
☐ 176. JASON BATES
☐ 204. ANDRES GALARRAGA
☐ 232. PEDRO CASTELLANO
☐ 260. QUINTON MCCRACKEN
☐ 288. MARCUS MOORE
☐ 388. JOHN BURKE
☐ 416. ERIC YOUNG
☐ 444. JAY GAINER
☐ 472. FREDDIE BENAVIDES
☐ 500. CHARLIE HAYES
☐ 528. DARYL BOSTON
☐ 556. VINNY CASTILLA
☐ 584. JASON HUTCHINS
☐ 612. JERALD CLARK
☐ 640. GARVIN ALSTON
☐ 668. JOE GIRARDI
☐ 692. ROBERTO MEJIA

DETROIT TIGERS

☐ 11. LOU WHITAKER
☐ 39. CHRIS GOMEZ
☐ 67. TRAVIS FRYMAN
☐ 95. DANNY BAUTISTA
☐ 151. KENNY CARLYLE
☐ 179. MIKE MOORE
☐ 207. BEN BLOMDAHL
☐ 235. SCOTT LIVINGSTONE
☐ 263. RICK GREENE
☐ 291. BRIAN EDMONDSON
☐ 319. IVAN CRUZ
☐ 332. ROB DEER
☐ 391. ALAN TRAMMELL
☐ 419. TONY PHILLIPS
☐ 447. JUSTIN MASHORE
☐ 475. CECIL FIELDER
☐ 503. JASON PFAFF
☐ 531. SEAN BERGMAN
☐ 559. MIKE HENNEMAN
☐ 587. JUSTIN THOMPSON
☐ 615. MICKEY TETTLETON
☐ 643. FELIPE LIRA
☐ 671. GREG GOHR

FLORIDA MARLINS

☐ 10. RICH RENTERIA
☐ 38. MATT WHISENANT
☐ 66. RAMON MARTINEZ
☐ 79. BILL HASELMAN
☐ 94. CARL EVERETT
☐ 122. JUNIOR FELIX
☐ 135. JOHN CUMMINGS
☐ 150. MIKE MYERS
☐ 178. BENNY SANTIAGO
☐ 206. DARRELL WHITMORE
☐ 234. BRYAN HARVEY
☐ 262. HECTOR CARRASCO
☐ 290. WALT WEISS
☐ 316. NIGEL WILSON
☐ 318. SCOTT POSE
☐ 331. JOSE MARTINEZ
☐ 390. TREVOR HOFFMAN
☐ 418. ORESTES DESTRADE
☐ 446. BRET BARBERIE
☐ 474. CHUCK CARR
☐ 502. RICHIE LEWIS
☐ 530. CHARLIE HOUGH
☐ 558. ROB NATAL
☐ 614. DAVE MAGADAN
☐ 642. CHRIS SHEFF
☐ 670. JEFF CONINE

HOUSTON ASTROS

☐ 12. BRIAN HUNTER
☐ 40. LUIS GONZALEZ
☐ 68. TOM NEVERS
☐ 96. STEVE FINLEY
☐ 152. ERIC ANTHONY
☐ 180. JEFF JUDEN
☐ 208. DOUG DRABEK
☐ 236. JAMES MOUTON
☐ 264. CHRIS HOLT
☐ 292. JIMMY GONZALEZ
☐ 320. GREG SWINDELL
☐ 392. TODD JONES
☐ 414. BRIAN WILLIAMS
☐ 420. JEFF BAGWELL
☐ 448. PETE HARNISCH
☐ 476. EDDIE TAUBENSEE
☐ 504. KEN CAMINITI
☐ 532. DOUG JONES
☐ 560. CRAIG BIGGIO
☐ 588. ORLANDO MILLER
☐ 616. SEAN RUNYAN
☐ 644. ROBERTO PETAGINE
☐ 672. ANDUJAR CEDENO

KANSAS CITY ROYALS

☐ 13. JOE VITIELLO
☐ 41. KEVIN APPIER
☐ 69. PHIL HIATT
☐ 97. DAVID CONE
☐ 125. BRIAN BEVIL
☐ 153. JOSE LIND
☐ 181. DARREN BURTON
☐ 209. KEITH MILLER
☐ 237. JOE RANDA
☐ 265. GEORGE BRETT
☐ 293. DANNY MICELI
☐ 321. KEVIN MCREYNOLDS
☐ 393. FELIX JOSE
☐ 421. MARK GARDNER
☐ 449. GREG GAGNE
☐ 477. CHRIS EDDY
☐ 505. MIKE MACFARLANE
☐ 533. JEFF MONTGOMERY
☐ 561. BILLY BREWER
☐ 589. BRIAN MCRAE
☐ 617. BOB HAMELIN
☐ 645. WALLY JOYNER
☐ 673. LES NORMAN

LOS ANGELES DODGERS

☐ 14. ERIC KARROS
☐ 42. OMAR DAAL
☐ 70. TIM WALLACH
☐ 98. TODD HOLLANDSWORTH
☐ 126. DARRYL STRAWBERRY
☐ 154. PEDRO MARTINEZ
☐ 182. TODD WILLIAMS
☐ 210. BILLY ASHLEY
☐ 238. PEDRO ASTACIO
☐ 266. RICK GORECKI
☐ 294. JOSE OFFERMAN
☐ 322. TOM CANDIOTTI

- ☐ 394. OREL HERSHISER
- ☐ 422. BRETT BUTLER
- ☐ 450. ERIC DAVIS
- ☐ 478. GREG HANSELL
- ☐ 506. JODY REED
- ☐ 534. ROGER CEDENO
- ☐ 562. DAN MELENDEZ
- ☐ 590. RAMON MARTINEZ
- ☐ 618. RAUL MONDESI
- ☐ 646. MIKE PIAZZA
- ☐ 674. MIKE JAMES

MILWAUKEE BREWERS

- ☐ 15. JOE KMAK
- ☐ 43. DUANE SINGLETON
- ☐ 71. B.J. SURHOFF
- ☐ 99. MATT MIESKE
- ☐ 127. CAL ELDRED
- ☐ 155. MARK KIEFER
- ☐ 183. JOHN JAHA
- ☐ 211. MIKE FARRELL
- ☐ 239. DARRYL HAMILTON
- ☐ 267. FRANCISCO GAMEZ
- ☐ 295. GREG VAUGHN
- ☐ 323. ROB WISHNEVSKI
- ☐ 395. PAT LISTACH
- ☐ 423. GRAEME LLOYD
- ☐ 479. KEVIN REIMER
- ☐ 507. BOBBY HUGHES
- ☐ 535. ROBIN YOUNT
- ☐ 563. KENNY FELDER
- ☐ 591. DAVE NILSSON
- ☐ 619. TYRONE HILL
- ☐ 647. JAIME NAVARRO
- ☐ 675. MARSHALL BOZE

MINNESOTA TWINS

- ☐ 17. STEVE DUNN
- ☐ 45. PAT MEARES
- ☐ 73. DENNY HOCKING
- ☐ 76. WILLIE BANKS
- ☐ 101. SHANE MACK
- ☐ 129. ALAN NEWMAN
- ☐ 157. PAT MAHOMES
- ☐ 185. PEDRO GRIFOL
- ☐ 241. EDGAR HERRERA
- ☐ 269. KEVIN TAPANI
- ☐ 297. MIKE MAKSUDIAN
- ☐ 325. KIRBY PUCKETT
- ☐ 335. DEREK LEE
- ☐ 397. DAN SERAFINI
- ☐ 425. SCOTT ERICKSON
- ☐ 453. RICK AGUILERA
- ☐ 481. CHUCK KNOBLAUCH
- ☐ 509. GEORGE TSAMIS
- ☐ 537. BRIAN HARPER
- ☐ 565. DAVE WINFIELD
- ☐ 593. RICH BECKER
- ☐ 621. MIKE TROMBLEY
- ☐ 649. DAVID MCCARTY
- ☐ 677. KENT HRBEK

MONTREAL EXPOS

- ☐ 16. TAVO ALVAREZ
- ☐ 44. BILL RISLEY
- ☐ 72. RONDELL WHITE
- ☐ 100. LARRY WALKER
- ☐ 128. CLIFF FLOYD
- ☐ 156. TIM LAKER
- ☐ 184. MIKE LANSING
- ☐ 212. JOHN WETTELAND
- ☐ 240. JOEY EISCHEN
- ☐ 268. MARQUIS GRISSOM
- ☐ 296. FRANK BOLICK
- ☐ 324. KEN HILL
- ☐ 378. SHANE ANDREWS
- ☐ 396. GABE WHITE
- ☐ 424. DELINO DESHIELDS
- ☐ 452. MOISES ALOU
- ☐ 480. DENNY MARTINEZ
- ☐ 508. WIL CORDERO
- ☐ 564. MIGUEL BATISTA
- ☐ 592. JOSE VIDRO
- ☐ 620. DARRIN FLETCHER
- ☐ 676. B.J. WALLACE

NEW YORK METS

- ☐ 18. TONY FERNANDEZ
- ☐ 46. BUTCH HUSKEY
- ☐ 102. AARON LEDESMA
- ☐ 130. HOWARD JOHNSON
- ☐ 158. BOBBY BONILLA
- ☐ 186. VINCE COLEMAN
- ☐ 214. SID FERNANDEZ
- ☐ 215. QUILVIO VERAS
- ☐ 242. DOC GOODEN
- ☐ 270. RYAN THOMPSON
- ☐ 298. JOHN FRANCO
- ☐ 326. TIM BOGAR
- ☐ 333. BROOK FORDYCE
- ☐ 398. TODD HUNDLEY
- ☐ 426. JEFF KENT
- ☐ 454. EDDIE MURRAY
- ☐ 482. MIKE DRAPER
- ☐ 510. BRET SABERHAGEN
- ☐ 538. JUAN CASTILLO
- ☐ 566. AL SHIRLEY
- ☐ 594. PRESTON WILSON
- ☐ 622. JEROMY BURNITZ
- ☐ 650. BOBBY JONES

NEW YORK YANKEES

- ☐ 19. MELIDO PEREZ
- ☐ 47. BOBBY MUNOZ
- ☐ 75. PAUL O'NEILL
- ☐ 103. ANDY PETTITTE
- ☐ 124. ANDY COOK
- ☐ 131. JIM ABBOTT
- ☐ 159. DOMINGO JEAN
- ☐ 187. PAT KELLY
- ☐ 243. SAM MILITELLO
- ☐ 271. GERALD WILLIAMS
- ☐ 299. DANNY TARTABULL
- ☐ 327. MARIANO RIVERA
- ☐ 334. MATT NOKES
- ☐ 399. WADE BOGGS
- ☐ 427. JIMMY KEY
- ☐ 455. BOB WICKMAN
- ☐ 483. SPIKE OWEN
- ☐ 511. DEREK JETER
- ☐ 539. STEVE FARR
- ☐ 567. ROBERT EENHOORN
- ☐ 595. DON MATTINGLY
- ☐ 606. STERLING HITCHOCK
- ☐ 623. BERNIE WILLIAMS
- ☐ 651. MARK HUTTON
- ☐ 679. BRIEN TAYLOR

OAKLAND A'S

- ☐ 21. TERRY STEINBACH
- ☐ 49. SCOTT LYDY
- ☐ 77. BOB WELCH
- ☐ 105. MIKE MOHLER
- ☐ 133. MIGUEL JIMENEZ
- ☐ 161. MARK MCGWIRE
- ☐ 189. RON DARLING
- ☐ 217. MIKE NEILL
- ☐ 245. RUBEN SIERRA
- ☐ 273. LANCE BLANKENSHIP
- ☐ 301. BOBBY WITT
- ☐ 329. CRAIG PAQUETTE
- ☐ 401. MIKE BORDICK
- ☐ 429. MARCOS ARMAS
- ☐ 457. BRENT GATES
- ☐ 485. DENNIS ECKERSLEY
- ☐ 513. CURTIS SHAW
- ☐ 541. TROY NEEL
- ☐ 569. TANYON STURTZE
- ☐ 597. KEVIN SEITZER
- ☐ 625. RICKEY HENDERSON
- ☐ 653. STEVE COX
- ☐ 681. TODD VAN POPPEL

PHILADELPHIA PHILLIES

- ☐ 20. MIKE LIEBERTHAL
- ☐ 48. JUAN BELL
- ☐ 104. KEVIN STOCKER
- ☐ 132. CHAD MCCONNELL
- ☐ 160. DARREN DAULTON
- ☐ 216. DAVE HOLLINS
- ☐ 244. RON BLAZIER
- ☐ 272. PAUL FLETCHER
- ☐ 300. LEN DYKSTRA
- ☐ 328. MITCH WILLIAMS
- ☐ 400. TYLER GREEN
- ☐ 428. MICKEY MORANDINI
- ☐ 456. WES CHAMBERLAIN
- ☐ 484. TERRY MULHOLLAND
- ☐ 512. GENE SCHALL
- ☐ 540. JOHN KRUK
- ☐ 568. MIKE WILLIAMS
- ☐ 596. TONY LONGMIRE
- ☐ 624. MIKE FARMER
- ☐ 652. KYLE ABBOTT
- ☐ 680. CURT SCHILLING

PITTSBURGH PIRATES

- ☐ 22. STAN BELINDA
- ☐ 50. DENNIS MOELLER
- ☐ 78. JOSE SANDOVAL
- ☐ 106. TONY MENENDEZ
- ☐ 123. RICH ROBERTSON
- ☐ 134. BRETT BACKLUND
- ☐ 162. JASON KENDALL
- ☐ 190. ORLANDO MERCED
- ☐ 213. RANDY TOMLIN
- ☐ 218. ANDY VAN SLYKE
- ☐ 246. AL MARTIN
- ☐ 274. MARTY NEFF
- ☐ 302. TREY BEAMON
- ☐ 330. JAY BELL
- ☐ 402. SCOTT BULLETT
- ☐ 430. DON SLAUGHT
- ☐ 458. PAUL WAGNER
- ☐ 486. BLAS MINOR
- ☐ 514. STEVE COOKE
- ☐ 542. DANNY CLYBURN
- ☐ 570. TIM WAKEFIELD
- ☐ 598. MIDRE CUMMINGS
- ☐ 626. CARLOS GARCIA
- ☐ 654. JEFF KING
- ☐ 682. KEVIN YOUNG

ST. LOUIS CARDINALS

- ☐ 24. ALLEN WATSON
- ☐ 52. TRIPP CROMER
- ☐ 80. RHEAL CORMIER
- ☐ 108. BASIL SHABAZZ
- ☐ 136. BRIAN BARBER
- ☐ 164. OZZIE CANSECO
- ☐ 192. STEVE DIXON
- ☐ 220. TOM PAGNOZZI
- ☐ 248. BOB TEWKSBURY
- ☐ 276. RENE AROCHA
- ☐ 304. AARON HOLBERT
- ☐ 336. PAUL ELLIS
- ☐ 376. DONOVAN OSBORNE
- ☐ 404. RAY LANKFORD
- ☐ 432. OMAR OLIVARES
- ☐ 460. OZZIE SMITH
- ☐ 488. DAN CHOLOWSKY
- ☐ 516. MIKE MILCHIN
- ☐ 544. GREGG JEFFERIES
- ☐ 572. SEAN LOWE
- ☐ 583. TOM URBANI
- ☐ 600. LEE SMITH
- ☐ 604. GERONIMO PENA
- ☐ 628. TODD ZEILE
- ☐ 656. MIKE GULAN
- ☐ 684. BERNARD GILKEY

SAN DIEGO PADRES

- ☐ 26. RAY MCDAVID
- ☐ 54. JIM PENA
- ☐ 63. KERRY TAYLOR
- ☐ 82. PAT GOMEZ
- ☐ 110. SCOTT SANDERS
- ☐ 138. TIM WORRELL
- ☐ 166. STEVE PEGUES
- ☐ 194. RAY HOLBERT
- ☐ 222. FRANK SEMINARA
- ☐ 250. LUIS LOPEZ
- ☐ 278. PHIL PLANTIER
- ☐ 306. BILLY HALL
- ☐ 406. ROBBIE BECKETT
- ☐ 434. KURT STILLWELL
- ☐ 462. RICKY GUTIERREZ
- ☐ 490. GARY SHEFFIELD
- ☐ 518. ANDY BENES
- ☐ 546. JULIO BRUNO
- ☐ 574. KEVIN HIGGINS
- ☐ 602. DARRELL SHERMAN
- ☐ 630. TONY GWYNN
- ☐ 658. CAMERON CAIRNCROSS
- ☐ 686. FRED MCGRIFF

SAN FRANCISCO GIANTS

- ☐ 28. BUD BLACK
- ☐ 56. MATT WILLIAMS
- ☐ 84. CARL HANSELMAN
- ☐ 112. BENJI SIMONTON
- ☐ 140. BARRY BONDS
- ☐ 168. LARRY CARTER
- ☐ 196. WILLIE MCGEE
- ☐ 224. D.J. THIELEN
- ☐ 252. WILL CLARK
- ☐ 280. CHRIS GAMBS
- ☐ 308. ROD BECK
- ☐ 380. BILL SWIFT
- ☐ 408. ADELL DAVENPORT
- ☐ 436. ROBBY THOMPSON
- ☐ 464. JOEL CHIMELIS
- ☐ 492. STEVE HOSEY
- ☐ 520. JOHN BURKETT
- ☐ 548. ROYCE CLAYTON
- ☐ 576. KEVIN ROGERS
- ☐ 632. JOE ROSSELLI
- ☐ 660. SALOMON TORRES
- ☐ 688. KIRT MANWARING

SEATTLE MARINERS

- ☐ 23. JAY BUHNER
- ☐ 51. MARC NEWFIELD
- ☐ 107. DEREK LOWE
- ☐ 163. DESI RELAFORD
- ☐ 191. CHRIS BOSIO
- ☐ 219. BRET BOONE
- ☐ 223. RON VILLONE
- ☐ 247. MIKE FELDER
- ☐ 275. SHAWN ESTES
- ☐ 303. TINO MARTINEZ
- ☐ 375. KEN GRIFFEY, JR.
- ☐ 403. LAGRANDE RUSSELL
- ☐ 431. RANDY JOHNSON
- ☐ 459. MIKE HAMPTON
- ☐ 487. DAVE FLEMING
- ☐ 515. EDGAR MARTINEZ
- ☐ 543. JIM CONVERSE
- ☐ 571. GREG PIRKL
- ☐ 599. OMAR VIZQUEL
- ☐ 627. JEFF DARWIN
- ☐ 655. NORM CHARLTON
- ☐ 683. TOMMY ADAMS

TEXAS RANGERS

- ☐ 25. DARYL HENDERSON
- ☐ 53. KURT MILLER
- ☐ 59. JON SHAVE
- ☐ 81. DEAN PALMER
- ☐ 109. DAN SMITH
- ☐ 137. RAFAEL PALMEIRO
- ☐ 165. RICK HELLING
- ☐ 193. DOUG DASCENZO
- ☐ 221. MIKE WELCH
- ☐ 249. CRAIG LEFFERTS
- ☐ 277. SCOTT EYRE
- ☐ 283. MATT WHITESIDE
- ☐ 305. JUAN GONZALEZ
- ☐ 337. DESI WILSON
- ☐ 377. RITCHIE MOODY
- ☐ 405. NOLAN RYAN
- ☐ 433. CHARLIE LEIBRANDT
- ☐ 461. TOM HENKE
- ☐ 489. IVAN RODRIGUEZ
- ☐ 517. BILLY RIPKEN
- ☐ 545. JOSE CANSECO
- ☐ 573. TERRY BURROWS
- ☐ 601. DAVID HULSE
- ☐ 629. BENJI GIL
- ☐ 657. JULIO FRANCO
- ☐ 685. KEVIN BROWN

TORONTO BLUE JAYS

- ☐ 27. SHAWN GREEN
- ☐ 55. JUAN GUZMAN
- ☐ 83. STEVE KARSAY
- ☐ 111. TODD STOTTLEMYRE
- ☐ 139. JOSE PETT
- ☐ 167. PAUL MOLITOR
- ☐ 195. HOWARD BATTLE
- ☐ 203. DOMINGO MARTINEZ
- ☐ 251. DEVON WHITE
- ☐ 279. PAUL SPOLJARIC
- ☐ 307. DUANE WARD
- ☐ 338. ROBERTO ALOMAR
- ☐ 379. CARLOS DELGADO
- ☐ 407. BRENT BOWERS
- ☐ 435. SCOTT BROW
- ☐ 463. JACK MORRIS
- ☐ 491. ED SPRAGUE
- ☐ 519. JUAN DE LA ROSA
- ☐ 547. ROB BUTLER
- ☐ 575. JOE CARTER
- ☐ 603. ALEX GONZALEZ
- ☐ 631. AARON SMALL
- ☐ 659. JOHN OLERUD
- ☐ 687. PAT BORDERS

1994 BOWMAN (682)
2 1/2" X 3 1/2"

ATLANTA BRAVES

- ☐ 21. TOM GLAVINE
- ☐ 77. TONY TARASCO
- ☐ 105. RYAN KLESKO
- ☐ 133. DAVID JUSTICE
- ☐ 161. DAMON HOLLINS
- ☐ 189. STEVE AVERY
- ☐ 217. ANDRE KING
- ☐ 245. GREG MADDUX
- ☐ 261. MIKE KELLY
- ☐ 273. JAVY LOPEZ
- ☐ 301. DEION SANDERS
- ☐ 329. TERRELL WADE
- ☐ 401. KEVIN LOMON
- ☐ 405. FRED MCGRIFF
- ☐ 433. JERMAINE DYE
- ☐ 461. GREGG OLSON
- ☐ 489. CHIPPER JONES
- ☐ 517. JEFF BLAUSER
- ☐ 545. JASON GREEN
- ☐ 573. TERRY PENDLETON
- ☐ 601. TONY GRAFFANINO
- ☐ 629. JOHN SMOLTZ
- ☐ 641. BRAD CLONTZ
- ☐ 665. DAVID CATLETT

BALTIMORE ORIOLES

- ☐ 19. HAROLD BAINES
- ☐ 36. DAVID LAMB
- ☐ 47. MARK SMITH
- ☐ 75. CAL RIPKEN
- ☐ 86. SCOTT KLINGENBECK
- ☐ 103. ALEX OCHOA
- ☐ 131. CHRIS HOILES
- ☐ 159. RICK KRIVDA
- ☐ 187. CHRIS SABO
- ☐ 215. MANNY ALEXANDER
- ☐ 233. BRADY ANDERSON
- ☐ 243. BRAD PENNINGTON
- ☐ 271. GREG ZAUN
- ☐ 299. LEE SMITH
- ☐ 327. RICK FORNEY
- ☐ 349. BRYAN LINK
- ☐ 403. MIKE DEVEREAUX
- ☐ 431. VAUGHN ESHELMAN
- ☐ 459. BEN MCDONALD
- ☐ 487. CURTIS GOODWIN
- ☐ 515. RAFAEL PALMEIRO
- ☐ 543. JIMMY HAYNES
- ☐ 571. SID FERNANDEZ
- ☐ 599. MATT JARVIS
- ☐ 627. MIKE MUSSINA
- ☐ 655. JAY POWELL

BOSTON RED SOX

- ☐ 7. J.J. JOHNSON
- ☐ 35. FRANK VIOLA
- ☐ 63. TIM VANEGMOND
- ☐ 91. OTIS NIXON
- ☐ 119. LUIS ORTIZ
- ☐ 175. JEFFREY MCNEELY
- ☐ 203. SCOTT COOPER
- ☐ 231. GAR FINNVOLD
- ☐ 259. MIKE GREENWELL
- ☐ 287. JOEL BENNETT
- ☐ 315. MO VAUGHN
- ☐ 391. JEFF SUPPAN
- ☐ 447. CORY BAILEY
- ☐ 475. ROGER CLEMENS
- ☐ 503. SCOTT FLETCHER
- ☐ 531. ANDRE DAWSON
- ☐ 559. RYAN MCGUIRE
- ☐ 587. SHAYNE BENNETT
- ☐ 615. FRANK RODRIGUEZ
- ☐ 643. AARON SELE
- ☐ 671. JOSE MALAVE

CALIFORNIA ANGELS

- ☐ 11. J.T. SNOW
- ☐ 39. BRIAN ANDERSON
- ☐ 67. CHUCK FINLEY
- ☐ 95. CHRIS TURNER
- ☐ 154. CHRIS SMITH
- ☐ 171. JORGE FABREGAS
- ☐ 179. CHAD CURTIS
- ☐ 201. TIM HARKRIDER
- ☐ 207. DESHAWN WARREN
- ☐ 235. MARK LANGSTON
- ☐ 263. MARQUIS RILEY
- ☐ 291. EDUARDO PEREZ
- ☐ 395. TIM SALMON
- ☐ 419. MATT PERISHO
- ☐ 423. JIM EDMONDS
- ☐ 451. CHILI DAVIS
- ☐ 479. GARRET ANDERSON
- ☐ 507. GARY DISARCINA
- ☐ 535. BO JACKSON
- ☐ 563. DAMION EASLEY
- ☐ 591. JEFF KNOX
- ☐ 619. RYAN HANCOCK
- ☐ 647. MARK RATEKIN
- ☐ 675. ANDREW LORRAINE

CHICAGO CUBS

- ☐ 26. MIKE MORGAN
- ☐ 49. AMAURY TELEMACO
- ☐ 82. SAMMY SOSA
- ☐ 110. DEREK WALLACE
- ☐ 166. KEVIN ORIE
- ☐ 177. DOUG GLANVILLE

- ☐ 188. BLAISE ILSLEY
- ☐ 194. RANDY MYERS
- ☐ 222. KARL RHODES
- ☐ 250. RYNE SANDBERG
- ☐ 278. JESSIE HOLLINS
- ☐ 306. RICK WILKINS
- ☐ 334. JON RATLIFF
- ☐ 337. EDDIE ZAMBRANO
- ☐ 410. MARK GRACE
- ☐ 438. BROOKS KIESCHNICK
- ☐ 466. OZZIE TIMMONS
- ☐ 494. BRANT BROWN
- ☐ 522. STEVE BUECHELE
- ☐ 550. TURK WENDELL
- ☐ 578. JOSE GUZMAN
- ☐ 606. MIKE HUBBARD
- ☐ 634. STEVE TRACHSEL
- ☐ 662. HECTOR TRINIDAD

CHICAGO WHITE SOX

- ☐ 15. FRANK THOMAS
- ☐ 18. ROD BOLTON
- ☐ 43. MIKE ROBERTSON
- ☐ 54. WILSON ALVAREZ
- ☐ 71. RON KARKOVICE
- ☐ 99. GLENN DI SARCINA
- ☐ 127. TIM RAINES
- ☐ 138. ROBERTO HERNANDEZ
- ☐ 155. JAMES BALDWIN
- ☐ 183. ROBERT ELLIS
- ☐ 211. SCOTT CHRISTMAN
- ☐ 239. ALEX FERNANDEZ
- ☐ 267. BRANDON WILSON
- ☐ 295. ROBIN VENTURA
- ☐ 399. JULIO FRANCO
- ☐ 427. EDDIE PEARSON
- ☐ 455. JACK MCDOWELL
- ☐ 483. JIMMY HURST
- ☐ 511. OZZIE GUILLEN
- ☐ 539. CHRIS SNOPEK
- ☐ 567. JASON BERE
- ☐ 595. SCOTT RUFFCORN
- ☐ 623. LANCE JOHNSON
- ☐ 651. JOE HALL

CINCINNATI REDS

- ☐ 46. CLEVELAND LADELL
- ☐ 102. JOHNNY RUFFIN
- ☐ 130. HECTOR CARRASCO
- ☐ 158. PAUL BAKO
- ☐ 186. HAL MORRIS
- ☐ 214. CHAD MOTTOLA
- ☐ 242. REGGIE SANDERS
- ☐ 270. CALVIN REESE
- ☐ 298. JOE OLIVER
- ☐ 344. BUBBA SMITH
- ☐ 402. JOSE RIJO
- ☐ 416. TIM COSTO
- ☐ 430. WILLIE GREENE
- ☐ 458. BRET BOONE
- ☐ 471. BARRY LARKIN
- ☐ 486. MIKE FERRY
- ☐ 514. KEVIN MITCHELL
- ☐ 542. BRIAN KOELLING
- ☐ 570. JOHN COURTRIGHT
- ☐ 588. TIM BELK
- ☐ 598. SCOTT SULLIVAN
- ☐ 626. ROBERTO KELLY
- ☐ 654. ROD STEPH

CLEVELAND INDIANS

- ☐ 55. MANNY RAMIREZ
- ☐ 83. PAUL SORRENTO
- ☐ 139. SANDY ALOMAR
- ☐ 167. CASEY WHITTEN
- ☐ 195. KENNY LOFTON
- ☐ 251. CHARLES NAGY
- ☐ 279. JULIAN TAVAREZ
- ☐ 307. CARLOS BAERGA
- ☐ 335. ALEX RAMIREZ
- ☐ 338. JIM THOME
- ☐ 411. ALBERT BELLE
- ☐ 467. EDDIE MURRAY
- ☐ 495. DARON KIRKREIT
- ☐ 523. DENNY MARTINEZ
- ☐ 551. HERB PERRY
- ☐ 579. OMAR VIZQUEL
- ☐ 607. CHAD OGEA
- ☐ 635. ALBIE LOPEZ
- ☐ 663. JOHN CARTER

COLORADO ROCKIES

- ☐ 2. MARCUS MOORE
- ☐ 30. JOE GIRARDI
- ☐ 58. JAMEY WRIGHT
- ☐ 114. TOM SCHMIDT
- ☐ 142. HOWARD JOHNSON
- ☐ 151. JOEL MOORE
- ☐ 170. MARK THOMPSON
- ☐ 198. ARMANDO REYNOSO
- ☐ 226. JOHN BURKE
- ☐ 254. CHARLIE HAYES
- ☐ 282. NEIFI PEREZ
- ☐ 310. DARREN HOLMES
- ☐ 404. MIKE ZOLECKI
- ☐ 414. ELLIS BURKS
- ☐ 442. DOUG WALLS
- ☐ 470. DAVID NIED
- ☐ 498. JASON JOHNSON
- ☐ 526. ANDRES GALARRAGA
- ☐ 554. BRYAN REKAR
- ☐ 582. WALT WEISS
- ☐ 610. ANGEL ECHEVARRIA
- ☐ 638. ROBERTO MEJIA
- ☐ 666. DANTE BICHETTE

DETROIT TIGERS

- ☐ 13. CHAD KREUTER
- ☐ 28. MATT BRUNSON
- ☐ 41. SEAN BERGMAN
- ☐ 69. CECIL FIELDER
- ☐ 97. DANNY BAUTISTA
- ☐ 125. MICKEY TETTLETON
- ☐ 181. MIKE HENNEMAN
- ☐ 204. PHIL STIDHAM
- ☐ 209. TONY CLARK
- ☐ 237. LOU WHITAKER
- ☐ 265. BRIAN EDMONDSON
- ☐ 293. ERIC DAVIS
- ☐ 321. CHRIS GOMEZ
- ☐ 397. TONY PHILLIPS
- ☐ 425. RICK GREENE
- ☐ 453. JOE PERONA
- ☐ 481. JOSE LIMA
- ☐ 509. ALAN TRAMMELL
- ☐ 537. DAVID MYSEL
- ☐ 561. KEITH KIMSEY
- ☐ 565. MIKE MOORE
- ☐ 621. TRAVIS FRYMAN
- ☐ 649. JUSTIN THOMPSON
- ☐ 677. TIM BELCHER

FLORIDA MARLINS

- ☐ 10. BRYAN HARVEY
- ☐ 66. CHUCK CARR
- ☐ 94. EDGAR RENTERIA
- ☐ 122. BENNY SANTIAGO
- ☐ 123. DARRELL WHITMORE
- ☐ 150. CHRIS HAMMOND
- ☐ 178. JAVIER DE LA HOYA
- ☐ 206. MATT WHISENANT
- ☐ 234. VIC DARENSBOURG
- ☐ 262. ANDY LARKIN
- ☐ 290. GARY SHEFFIELD
- ☐ 318. CARL EVERETT
- ☐ 343. TIM CLARK
- ☐ 394. JEFF CONINE
- ☐ 439. YORKIS PEREZ
- ☐ 450. DAVE MAGADAN
- ☐ 478. KURT MILLER
- ☐ 488. MIKE MYERS
- ☐ 506. ORESTES DESTRADE
- ☐ 534. KURT ABBOTT
- ☐ 562. TIM CLARK
- ☐ 590. NIGEL WILSON
- ☐ 618. CHARLIE HOUGH
- ☐ 646. MARC VALDES
- ☐ 674. BRET BARBERIE

HOUSTON ASTROS

- ☐ 6. GREG SWINDELL
- ☐ 22. TODD JONES
- ☐ 34. JOHN HUDEK
- ☐ 62. LUIS GONZALEZ
- ☐ 90. DOMINGO JEAN
- ☐ 118. JEFF BAGWELL
- ☐ 146. ORLANDO MILLER
- ☐ 174. DOUG DRABEK
- ☐ 202. KEVIN GALLAHER
- ☐ 230. KEN CAMINITI
- ☐ 258. JAMES MOUTON
- ☐ 286. PETE HARNISCH
- ☐ 314. ALVIN MORMAN
- ☐ 339. JAMES MOUTON
- ☐ 342. ROBERTO PETAGINE
- ☐ 390. CRAIG BIGGIO
- ☐ 418. OSCAR HENRIQUEZ
- ☐ 446. MITCH WILLIAMS
- ☐ 502. STEVE FINLEY
- ☐ 530. ROBERTO PETAGINE
- ☐ 558. ANDUJAR CEDENO
- ☐ 586. RICHARD HIDALGO
- ☐ 614. DARRYL KILE
- ☐ 642. BILLY WAGNER
- ☐ 670. BRIAN HUNTER

KANSAS CITY ROYALS

- ☐ 31. SHANE HALTER
- ☐ 59. JEFF MONTGOMERY
- ☐ 87. DARIO PEREZ
- ☐ 115. BRIAN MCRAE
- ☐ 143. BOB HAMELIN
- ☐ 162. FELIX MARTINEZ
- ☐ 199. JOE RANDA
- ☐ 227. MIKE MACFARLANE
- ☐ 283. GREG GAGNE
- ☐ 311. ROBERT TOTH
- ☐ 415. JOE VITIELLO
- ☐ 443. WALLY JOYNER
- ☐ 499. VINCE COLEMAN
- ☐ 527. JEFF GRANGER
- ☐ 555. KEVIN APPIER
- ☐ 583. OSCAR JIMENEZ
- ☐ 593. DAVID CONE
- ☐ 611. JOSE LIND
- ☐ 639. DARREN BURTON
- ☐ 667. FELIX JOSE

LOS ANGELES DODGERS

- ☐ 14. ERIC KARROS
- ☐ 42. JOSE PARRA
- ☐ 98. CHAN HO PARK
- ☐ 126. TOM CANDIOTTI
- ☐ 157. KYM ASHWORTH
- ☐ 182. JOSE OFFERMAN
- ☐ 238. ROGER CEDENO
- ☐ 266. EDUARDO LANTIGUA
- ☐ 294. PEDRO ASTACIO
- ☐ 322. TODD WILLIAMS
- ☐ 398. RAMON MARTINEZ
- ☐ 426. TODD HOLLANDSWORTH
- ☐ 454. DELINO DESHIELDS
- ☐ 482. RICK GORECKI
- ☐ 510. MIKE PIAZZA
- ☐ 538. RAUL MONDESI
- ☐ 566. OREL HERSHISER
- ☐ 594. PAUL LO DUCA
- ☐ 622. BRETT BUTLER
- ☐ 650. MIKE BUSCH
- ☐ 678. ANTONIO OSUNA

MILWAUKEE BREWERS

- ☐ 37. MARSHALL BOZE
- ☐ 65. JOHN JAHA
- ☐ 93. JOSE VALENTIN
- ☐ 121. JAIME NAVARRO
- ☐ 149. MARK LORETTA
- ☐ 205. JEFF D'AMICO
- ☐ 289. DARRYL HAMILTON
- ☐ 317. GABBY MARTINEZ
- ☐ 393. CAL ELDRED
- ☐ 421. KENNY FELDER
- ☐ 449. GREG VAUGHN
- ☐ 477. SCOTT KARL
- ☐ 505. SCOTT TALANOA
- ☐ 533. DUANE SINGLETON
- ☐ 589. MATT MIESKE
- ☐ 617. PAT LISTACH
- ☐ 645. BRIAN HARPER
- ☐ 657. TODD DUNN
- ☐ 673. MIKE MATHENY

MINNESOTA TWINS

- ☐ 20. MATT WALBECK
- ☐ 104. TORII HUNTER
- ☐ 132. RICK AGUILERA
- ☐ 160. PAT MAHOMES
- ☐ 216. RICH BECKER
- ☐ 229. CHUCK KNOBLAUCH
- ☐ 272. TODD RITCHIE
- ☐ 300. DAVE WINFIELD
- ☐ 328. CARLOS PULIDO
- ☐ 432. PAT MEARES
- ☐ 460. KIRBY PUCKETT
- ☐ 516. DAVID MCCARTY
- ☐ 544. MARTY CORDOVA
- ☐ 572. CHAD ROPER
- ☐ 597. OSCAR MUNOZ
- ☐ 628. KEVIN TAPANI
- ☐ 656. KEITH GARAGOZZO

MONTREAL EXPOS

- ☐ 4. PEDRO MARTINEZ
- ☐ 32. JOSE PANIAGUA
- ☐ 60. KIRK RUETER
- ☐ 76. BRAD FULLMER
- ☐ 88. UGUETH URBINA
- ☐ 116. MOISES ALOU
- ☐ 144. J.J. THOBE
- ☐ 153. WIL CORDERO
- ☐ 172. JOHN WETTELAND
- ☐ 200. CLIFF FLOYD
- ☐ 228. MIKE LANSING
- ☐ 256. ROB FITZPATRICK
- ☐ 284. MARQUIS GRISSOM
- ☐ 312. GABE WHITE
- ☐ 340. CLIFF FLOYD
- ☐ 444. KEN HILL
- ☐ 472. BRIAN LOONEY
- ☐ 500. LARRY WALKER
- ☐ 528. JOEY EISCHEN
- ☐ 556. CHRIS SCHWAB
- ☐ 584. ROD HENDERSON
- ☐ 612. DARRIN FLETCHER
- ☐ 640. B.J. WALLACE
- ☐ 668. RONDELL WHITE

NEW YORK METS

- ☐ 16. BRET SABERHAGEN
- ☐ 23. ALBERTO CASTILLO
- ☐ 44. PETE WALKER
- ☐ 70. TOM ENGLE
- ☐ 72. JOE ORSULAK
- ☐ 100. BUTCH HUSKEY
- ☐ 128. BOBBY BONILLA
- ☐ 156. EDGARDO ALFONZO
- ☐ 184. JOHN FRANCO
- ☐ 210. JASON JACOME
- ☐ 212. BILL PULSIPHER
- ☐ 240. RYAN THOMPSON
- ☐ 268. MIKE WELCH
- ☐ 296. JEFF KENT
- ☐ 324. KIRK PRESLEY
- ☐ 326. JASON ISRINGHAUSEN
- ☐ 400. DOC GOODEN
- ☐ 428. QUILVIO VERAS
- ☐ 456. TODD HUNDLEY
- ☐ 484. PRESTON WILSON
- ☐ 512. JEROMY BURNITZ
- ☐ 540. BROOK FORDYCE
- ☐ 568. KEVIN MCREYNOLDS
- ☐ 596. CHRIS ROBERTS
- ☐ 624. PETE SMITH
- ☐ 652. BOBBY JONES
- ☐ 653. KELLY STINNETT

NEW YORK YANKEES

- ☐ 25. DON MATTINGLY
- ☐ 27. JIM MUSSELWHITE
- ☐ 38. JORGE POSADA
- ☐ 48. KEVIN JARVIS
- ☐ 53. MATT DREWS
- ☐ 81. TERRY MULHOLLAND
- ☐ 109. RUSS DAVIS
- ☐ 137. MIKE STANLEY
- ☐ 165. BRIEN TAYLOR
- ☐ 193. JIM ABBOTT
- ☐ 221. JOSE MUSSET
- ☐ 249. PAUL O'NEILL
- ☐ 277. ROBERT EENHOORN
- ☐ 305. WADE BOGGS
- ☐ 333. STERLING HITCHCOCK
- ☐ 348. RUBEN RIVERA
- ☐ 396. RAY SUPLEE
- ☐ 409. LUIS POLONIA
- ☐ 437. MARK HUTTON
- ☐ 465. JIMMY KEY
- ☐ 493. ANDY PETTITTE
- ☐ 521. BERNIE WILLIAMS
- ☐ 541. RON FRAZIER
- ☐ 549. PAT KELLY
- ☐ 577. DANNY TARTABULL
- ☐ 605. MELIDO PEREZ
- ☐ 633. DEREK JETER
- ☐ 661. TATE SEEFRIED

OAKLAND A'S

- ☐ 24. RUBEN SIERRA
- ☐ 52. CURTIS SHAW
- ☐ 80. RICKEY HENDERSON
- ☐ 108. MIGUEL JIMENEZ
- ☐ 136. BOB WELCH
- ☐ 164. IZZY MOLINA
- ☐ 192. MARK MCGWIRE
- ☐ 220. STEVE KARSAY
- ☐ 248. BOBBY WITT
- ☐ 276. BILL TAYLOR
- ☐ 304. BRENT GATES
- ☐ 319. KERWIN MOORE
- ☐ 332. MARK ACRE
- ☐ 408. TERRY STEINBACH
- ☐ 413. SCOTT SPIEZIO
- ☐ 436. FAUSTO CRUZ
- ☐ 464. TROY NEEL
- ☐ 492. CARLOS REYES
- ☐ 520. DENNIS ECKERSLEY
- ☐ 548. TODD VAN POPPEL
- ☐ 576. MIKE BORDICK
- ☐ 604. JOSE HERRERA
- ☐ 632. WILLIE ADAMS
- ☐ 660. JOHN WASDIN

PHILADELPHIA PHILLIES

- ☐ 56. BOBBY MUNOZ
- ☐ 84. PETE INCAVIGLIA
- ☐ 112. MIKE LIEBERTHAL
- ☐ 140. DARREN DAULTON
- ☐ 168. TONY LONGMIRE
- ☐ 196. MARIANO DUNCAN
- ☐ 224. KEVIN JORDAN
- ☐ 252. KEVIN STOCKER
- ☐ 280. GENE SCHALL
- ☐ 308. CURT SCHILLING
- ☐ 336. PHIL GEISLER
- ☐ 412. JOHN KRUK
- ☐ 422. TYLER GREEN
- ☐ 440. LEN DYKSTRA
- ☐ 468. MARK TRANBERG
- ☐ 496. RICKY BOTTALICO
- ☐ 524. DAVE HOLLINS
- ☐ 552. RYAN KARP
- ☐ 580. TOMMY GREENE
- ☐ 608. WAYNE GOMEZ
- ☐ 636. JASON MOLER
- ☐ 664. LARRY MITCHELL

PITTSBURGH PIRATES

- ☐ 50. ANDY VAN SLYKE
- ☐ 78. TERRY FARRAR
- ☐ 106. JAY BELL
- ☐ 134. ESTEBAN LOAIZA
- ☐ 190. RICK WHITE
- ☐ 218. CARLOS GARCIA
- ☐ 246. JASON KENDALL
- ☐ 274. KEVIN YOUNG
- ☐ 302. RAVELO MANZANILLO
- ☐ 330. AL MARTIN
- ☐ 406. DANNY CLYBURN
- ☐ 434. STEVE COOKE
- ☐ 462. RICH AUDE
- ☐ 490. JEFF KING
- ☐ 518. TREY BEAMON
- ☐ 546. ORLANDO MERCED
- ☐ 574. DANNY MICELI
- ☐ 602. DON SLAUGHT
- ☐ 630. MIDRE CUMMINGS
- ☐ 658. CHARLES PETERSON

ST. LOUIS CARDINALS

- ☐ 3. DOUG CREEK
- ☐ 12. ALAN BENES
- ☐ 40. MARK WHITEN
- ☐ 68. AARON HOLBERT
- ☐ 96. RAY LANKFORD
- ☐ 124. JOHN MABRY
- ☐ 147. DMITRI YOUNG
- ☐ 152. TODD ZEILE
- ☐ 180. BRIAN BARBER
- ☐ 208. RENE AROCHA
- ☐ 223. FRANK CIMORELLI
- ☐ 236. T.J. MATHEWS
- ☐ 244. BRYAN EVERSGERD
- ☐ 264. BOB TEWKSBURY
- ☐ 292. BASIL SHABAZZ
- ☐ 320. TOM PAGNOZZI
- ☐ 346. JOE BIASUCCI
- ☐ 424. OZZIE SMITH
- ☐ 452. GERALD SANTOS
- ☐ 480. ALLEN WATSON
- ☐ 508. WILLIE SMITH
- ☐ 536. GREGG JEFFERIES
- ☐ 564. CLINT DAVIS
- ☐ 592. BERNARD GILKEY
- ☐ 620. DARREL DEAK
- ☐ 648. TERRY BRADSHAW
- ☐ 676. BRIAN JORDAN

SAN DIEGO PADRES

- ☐ 8. HOMER BUSH
- ☐ 64. BIP ROBERTS
- ☐ 92. ANDRES BERUMEN
- ☐ 111. KEITH LOCKHART
- ☐ 120. TONY GWYNN
- ☐ 148. TIM HYERS
- ☐ 176. MELVIN NIEVES
- ☐ 232. DERREK LEE
- ☐ 255. DONNIE ELLIOTT
- ☐ 260. RAY MCDAVID
- ☐ 288. DEREK BELL
- ☐ 316. BRYCE FLORIE
- ☐ 345. RANDY CURTIS
- ☐ 392. ANDY BENES
- ☐ 420. JULIO BRUNO

- ☐ 448. DAVE STATON
- ☐ 474. A.J. SAGER
- ☐ 476. VINCE MOORE
- ☐ 504. BRAD AUSMUS
- ☐ 525. JOEY HAMILTON
- ☐ 532. RAY HOLBERT
- ☐ 560. RICKY GUTIERREZ
- ☐ 616. PHIL PLANTIER
- ☐ 644. CAMERON CAIRNCROSS
- ☐ 672. ARCHI CIANFROCCO

SAN FRANCISCO GIANTS

- ☐ 51. RIKKERT FANEYTE
- ☐ 79. MATT WILLIAMS
- ☐ 107. KURT PELTZER
- ☐ 135. BARRY BONDS
- ☐ 163. JASON MYERS
- ☐ 191. ROD BECK
- ☐ 219. RON PEZZONI
- ☐ 247. J.R. PHILLIPS
- ☐ 275. KIRT MANWARING
- ☐ 303. MARK PORTUGAL
- ☐ 331. DAN CARLSON
- ☐ 352. JASON MYERS
- ☐ 407. ROBBY THOMPSON
- ☐ 435. BILL SWIFT
- ☐ 463. JOHN BURKETT
- ☐ 491. BILL VAN LANDINGHAM
- ☐ 519. ROYCE CLAYTON
- ☐ 547. LOU POTE
- ☐ 575. JOE ROSSELLI
- ☐ 603. BRETT KING
- ☐ 631. SALOMON TORRES
- ☐ 659. DARREN LEWIS

SEATTLE MARINERS

- ☐ 5. KEN GRIFFEY, JR.
- ☐ 9. ARQUIMEDEZ POZO
- ☐ 33. PAUL PERKINS
- ☐ 61. EDGAR MARTINEZ
- ☐ 74. CRAIG CLAYTON
- ☐ 89. DAVE VANHOF
- ☐ 117. DAVE FLEMING
- ☐ 145. ROGER SALKELD
- ☐ 173. DAN WILSON
- ☐ 257. TIM DAVIS
- ☐ 285. RANDY JOHNSON
- ☐ 313. MAC SUZUKI
- ☐ 389. RICH AMARAL
- ☐ 417. MARC NEWFIELD
- ☐ 445. ERIC ANTHONY
- ☐ 473. SHAWN ESTES
- ☐ 501. BOBBY AYALA
- ☐ 529. DESI RELAFORD
- ☐ 557. JAY BUHNER
- ☐ 585. DEREK LOWE
- ☐ 613. CHRIS BOSIO
- ☐ 669. TINO MARTINEZ

TEXAS RANGERS

- ☐ 17. TERRELL LOWERY
- ☐ 45. JUAN GONZALEZ
- ☐ 73. DUFF BRUMLEY
- ☐ 101. IVAN RODRIGUEZ
- ☐ 129. JOHN DETTMER
- ☐ 185. BENJI GIL
- ☐ 213. DEAN PALMER
- ☐ 241. KERRY LACY
- ☐ 269. TOM HENKE
- ☐ 297. RICK HELLING
- ☐ 325. KEVIN BROWN
- ☐ 350. MIKE BELL
- ☐ 351. MARTY WATSON
- ☐ 429. KENNY ROGERS
- ☐ 457. RITCHIE MOODY
- ☐ 485. WILL CLARK
- ☐ 513. DARREN OLIVER
- ☐ 569. LELAND MACON
- ☐ 600. JOSE CANSECO
- ☐ 625. JAMES HURST

TORONTO BLUE JAYS

- ☐ 1. JOE CARTER
- ☐ 29. ADAM MEINERSHAGEN
- ☐ 57. ED SPRAGUE
- ☐ 85. DARREN HALL
- ☐ 113. DAVE STEWART
- ☐ 141. ANGEL MARTINEZ
- ☐ 169. JOHN OLERUD
- ☐ 197. LEE DANIELS
- ☐ 225. DUANE WARD
- ☐ 253. SHAWN GREEN
- ☐ 281. PAUL MOLITOR
- ☐ 309. SHANNON STEWART
- ☐ 323. PAT HENTGEN
- ☐ 341. CARLOS DELGADO
- ☐ 347. D.J. BOSTON
- ☐ 441. PAT BORDERS
- ☐ 469. ALEX GONZALEZ
- ☐ 497. DEVON WHITE
- ☐ 553. JUAN GUZMAN
- ☐ 581. PAUL SPOLJARIC
- ☐ 609. ROBERTO ALOMAR
- ☐ 637. CARLOS DELGADO

1994 BOWMAN'S BEST (200) 2 1/2" X 3 1/2"

ATLANTA BRAVES

- ☐ 1B. CHIPPER JONES
- ☐ 12R. TOM GLAVINE
- ☐ 15R. FRED MCGRIFF
- ☐ 20R. STEVE AVERY
- ☐ 23B. TERRELL WADE
- ☐ 36R. GREG MADDUX
- ☐ 54B. MIKE KELLY
- ☐ 63R. DAVID JUSTICE
- ☐ 84R. RYAN KLESKO
- ☐ 85R. JAVY LOPEZ

BALTIMORE ORIOLES

- ☐ 5R. LEE SMITH
- ☐ 15B. JIMMY HAYNES
- ☐ 22R. BEN MCDONALD
- ☐ 38B. CURTIS GOODWIN
- ☐ 51R. RAFAEL PALMEIRO
- ☐ 52B. ALEX OCHOA
- ☐ 54R. MIKE MUSSINA
- ☐ 71R. CAL RIPKEN

BOSTON RED SOX

- ☐ 22B. JOSE MALAVE
- ☐ 30B. FRANK RODRIGUEZ
- ☐ 37R. ROGER CLEMENS
- ☐ 44R. AARON SELE
- ☐ 80R. MO VAUGHN

CALIFORNIA ANGELS

- ☐ 12B. DESHAWN WARREN
- ☐ 25R. TIM SALMON

CHICAGO CUBS

- ☐ 5B. BROOKS KIESCHNICK
- ☐ 9R. MARK GRACE
- ☐ 58R. RANDY MYERS
- ☐ 70R. SAMMY SOSA
- ☐ 71B. KEVIN ORIE

CHICAGO WHITE SOX

- ☐ 4B. JAMES BALDWIN
- ☐ 10R. LANCE JOHNSON
- ☐ 14B. EDDIE PEARSON
- ☐ 23R. JACK MCDOWELL
- ☐ 26R. WILSON ALVAREZ
- ☐ 30R. ROBIN VENTURA
- ☐ 36B. SCOTT RUFFCORN
- ☐ 43B. CHRIS SNOPEK
- ☐ 55R. FRANK THOMAS
- ☐ 58B. JIMMY HURST
- ☐ 74R. JULIO FRANCO
- ☐ 84B. OLMEDO SAENZ

CINCINNATI REDS

- ☐ 9B. CALVIN REESE
- ☐ 21B. CHAD MOTTOLA
- ☐ 33R. KEVIN MITCHELL
- ☐ 34B. JOHN ROPER
- ☐ 38R. DEION SANDERS
- ☐ 56R. JOSE RIJO
- ☐ 57B. TIM BELK
- ☐ 69B. WILLIE GREENE
- ☐ 89R. HECTOR CARRASCO

CLEVELAND INDIANS

- ☐ 2R. EDDIE MURRAY
- ☐ 35R. CARLOS BAERGA
- ☐ 41R. ALBERT BELLE
- ☐ 47B. JOHN CARTER
- ☐ 68R. KENNY LOFTON
- ☐ 72B. CHAD OGEA
- ☐ 76B. HERB PERRY
- ☐ 88R. MANNY RAMIREZ

COLORADO ROCKIES

- ☐ 11B. JOHN BURKE
- ☐ 17R. DANTE BICHETTE
- ☐ 43R. ANDRES GALARRAGA
- ☐ 72R. ELLIS BURKS

DETROIT TIGERS

- ☐ 6B. JUSTIN THOMPSON
- ☐ 16B. DANNY BAUTISTA
- ☐ 32R. CECIL FIELDER
- ☐ 61R. TRAVIS FRYMAN
- ☐ 62B. TONY CLARK

FLORIDA MARLINS

- ☐ 13R. GARY SHEFFIELD
- ☐ 34R. JEFF CONINE
- ☐ 35B. MARC VALDES
- ☐ 51B. TIM CLARK
- ☐ 56B. CARL EVERETT
- ☐ 63B. EDGAR RENTERIA
- ☐ 66R. CHUCK CARR
- ☐ 85B. JESUS TAVAREZ

1994 Bowman's Best

HOUSTON ASTROS

- ☐ 19B. BILLY WAGNER
- ☐ 28B. ORLANDO MILLER
- ☐ 31B. BRIAN HUNTER
- ☐ 42B. ROBERTO PETAGINE
- ☐ 53R. JEFF BAGWELL
- ☐ 82R. JAMES MOUTON

KANSAS CITY ROYALS

- ☐ 41B. JOHNNY DAMON
- ☐ 46R. DAVID CONE
- ☐ 48B. JIM PITTSLEY
- ☐ 73R. JEFF MONTGOMERY
- ☐ 90R. JEFF GRANGER

LOS ANGELES DODGERS

- ☐ 17B. ROGER CEDENO
- ☐ 25B. CHANE HO PARK
- ☐ 32B. BILLY ASHLEY
- ☐ 39R. DELINO DESHIELDS
- ☐ 40B. RICK GORECKI
- ☐ 45B. TODD HOLLANDSWORTH
- ☐ 48R. BRETT BUTLER
- ☐ 60B. MICHAEL MOORE
- ☐ 73B. BEN VAN RYN
- ☐ 74B. KYM ASHWORTH
- ☐ 81R. MIKE PIAZZA
- ☐ 82B. GAREY INGRAM
- ☐ 86R. RAUL MONDESI

MILWAUKEE BREWERS

- ☐ 29R. GREG VAUGHN

MINNESOTA TWINS

- ☐ 6R. DAVE WINFIELD
- ☐ 53B. CHAD ROPER
- ☐ 65B. LATROY HAWKINS
- ☐ 70B. DAVE STEVENS
- ☐ 75R. KIRBY PUCKETT

MONTREAL EXPOS

- ☐ 21R. JOHN WETTELAND
- ☐ 24B. SHANE ANDREWS
- ☐ 33B. RONDELL WHITE
- ☐ 37B. ROD HENDERSON
- ☐ 52R. MOISES ALOU
- ☐ 55B. BRAD FULLMER
- ☐ 69R. MARQUIS GRISSOM
- ☐ 76R. LARRY WALKER
- ☐ 77B. JOEY EISCHEN
- ☐ 79B. UGUETH URBINA
- ☐ 87R. CLIFF FLOYD

NEW YORK METS

- ☐ 3B. BILL PULSIPHER
- ☐ 13B. EDGARDO ALFONZO
- ☐ 26B. KIRK PRESLEY
- ☐ 50R. BOBBY BONILLA

NEW YORK YANKEES

- ☐ 2B. DEREK JETER
- ☐ 18R. DANNY TARTABULL
- ☐ 20B. TATE SEEFRIED
- ☐ 29B. JORGE POSADA
- ☐ 31R. PAUL O'NEILL
- ☐ 39B. RUSS DAVIS
- ☐ 42R. WADE BOGGS
- ☐ 45R. DON MATTINGLY
- ☐ 60R. JIMMY KEY
- ☐ 89B. KEITH HEBERLING

OAKLAND A'S

- ☐ 4R. RICKEY HENDERSON
- ☐ 44B. MARK ACRE
- ☐ 49B. JOHN WASDIN
- ☐ 57R. RUBEN SIERRA

PHILADELPHIA PHILLIES

- ☐ 11R. DARREN DAULTON
- ☐ 47R. LEN DYKSTRA
- ☐ 66B. WAYNE GOMES

PITTSBURGH PIRATES

- ☐ 7B. MIDRE CUMMINGS
- ☐ 18B. JON LIEBER
- ☐ 64B. TREY BEAMON
- ☐ 77R. ANDY VAN SLYKE

ST. LOUIS CARDINALS

- ☐ 3R. OZZIE SMITH
- ☐ 10B. BRIAN BARBER
- ☐ 27R. GREGG JEFFERIES
- ☐ 61B. ALAN BENES
- ☐ 64R. RAY LANKFORD
- ☐ 65R. BOB TEWKSBURY
- ☐ 75B. DMITRI YOUNG
- ☐ 81B. JOHN FRASCATORE
- ☐ 87B. GERALD WITASICK, JR

SAN DIEGO PADRES

- ☐ 8B. JOEY HAMILTON
- ☐ 27B. ROBBIE BECKETT
- ☐ 67B. RAY MCDAVID
- ☐ 78R. TONY GWYNN

SAN FRANCISCO GIANTS

- ☐ 8R. MATT WILLIAMS
- ☐ 14R. ROD BECK
- ☐ 28R. JOHN BURKETT
- ☐ 49R. BILL SWIFT
- ☐ 59R. BARRY BONDS
- ☐ 80B. KEITH WILLIAMS

SEATTLE MARINERS

- ☐ 40R. KEN GRIFFEY, JR
- ☐ 59B. MAC SUZUKI
- ☐ 67R. JAY BUHNER
- ☐ 78B. ARQUIMEDEZ POZO

TEXAS RANGERS

- ☐ 19R. JUAN GONZALEZ
- ☐ 24R. JOSE CANSECO
- ☐ 68B. JOHN DETTMER
- ☐ 79R. WILL CLARK
- ☐ 90B. RUSTY GREER

TORONTO BLUE JAYS

- ☐ 1R. PAUL MOLITOR
- ☐ 7R. ROBERTO ALOMAR
- ☐ 16R. JOE CARTER
- ☐ 46B. SHAWN GREEN
- ☐ 50B. D.J. BOSTON
- ☐ 62R. JOHN OLERUD
- ☐ 83B. AARON SMALL
- ☐ 83R. CARLOS DELGADO
- ☐ 86B. JOSE SILVA
- ☐ 88B. JAY MALDONADO

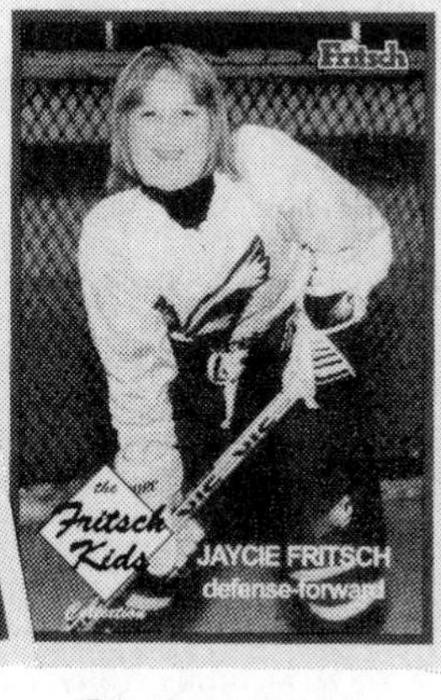

The Fritsch Kids

Jeremy, Jaycie, Allison

1934–36 DIAMOND STARS (108) 2 3/8" X 2 7/8"

The National Chicle Diamond Stars baseball cards were released over a period of three years. Some of the players changed teams during that period of time; consequently, some of the cards in the lists below appear with more than one team.

BOSTON BRAVES

□ 3. WALTER (RABBIT) MARANVILLE
□ 20. FRANCIS (FRANK) HOGAN
□ 25. WALTER (WALLY) BERGER
□ 37. BILL URBANSKI
□ 49. BAXTER (BUCK) JORDAN
□ 62. FRED FRANKHOUSE
□ 82. JOHNNY BABICH
□ 108. WALTER BERGER

BOSTON RED SOX

□ 1. LEFTY GROVE
□ 6. MAX BISHOP
□ 30. HENRY (HEINIE) MANUSH
□ 48. RICK FERRELL
□ 61. BILLY WERBER
□ 73. FRED (FRITZ) OSTERMUELLER
□ 94. WES FERRELL

BROOKLYN DODGERS

□ 19. VAN MUNGO
□ 28. AL LOPEZ
□ 55. TONY CUCCINELLO
□ 68. SAM LESLIE
□ 82. JOHNNY BABICH
□ 89. JOE STRIPP
□ 97. AL LOPEZ
□ 102. VAN MUNGO

CHICAGO CUBS

□ 31. HAZEN (KIKI) CUYLER
□ 34. STANLEY HACK
□ 52. GEORGE STAINBACK
□ 107. STANLEY HACK

CHICAGO WHITE SOX

□ 2. AL SIMMONS
□ 7. LEW FONSECA
□ 42. JIMMY DYKES
□ 43. TED LYONS
□ 51. JOHN WHITEHEAD
□ 65. HENRY (ZEKE) BONURA
□ 72. ANTHONY (TONY) PIET
□ 95. LUKE APPLING

CINCINNATI REDS

□ 18. CHARLES (CHICK) HAFEY
□ 24. EARL (SPARKY) ADAMS
□ 31. KIKI CUYLER
□ 36. ERNEST (ERNIE) LOMBARDI
□ 46. CHARLES (RED) LUCAS
□ 59. JIMMY BOTTOMLEY
□ 84. SAM BYRD
□ 96. LEW RIGGS
□ 105. ERNEST (ERNIE) LOMBARDI
□ 106. CHARLES (RED) LUCAS

CLEVELAND INDIANS

□ 2. JOE VOSMIK
□ 13. GEORGE BLAEHOLDER
□ 32. EDGAR (SAM) RICE
□ 35. EARL AVERILL
□ 58. GLENN MYATT
□ 70. HAROLD (HAL) TROSKY
□ 79. WILLIS HUDLIN
□ 87. STEVE O'NEIL
□ 100. EARL AVERILL

DETROIT TIGERS

□ 2. AL SIMMONS
□ 5. TOM BRIDGES
□ 9. GORDON (MICKEY) COCHRANE
□ 33. LYNWOOD (SCHOOLBOY) ROWE
□ 45. JOYNER (JO-JO) WHITE
□ 54. HANK GREENBERG
□ 67. MARVIN OWEN
□ 76. BILL ROGELL
□ 77. CHARLEY GEHRINGER
□ 90. RAY HAYWORTH
□ 93. ALVIN CROWDER
□ 98. LYNWOOD (SCHOOLBOY) ROWE

NEW YORK GIANTS

□ 14. BILL TERRY
□ 15. DICK BARTELL
□ 21. JOHNNY VERGES
□ 39. CARL HUBBELL
□ 50. MEL OTT
□ 63. TRAVIS JACKSON
□ 101. DICK BARTELL

NEW YORK YANKEES

□ 11. BILL DICKEY
□ 12. FRED (DIXIE) WALKER
□ 29. ROBERT (RED) ROLFE
□ 38. WILLIAM (BEN) CHAPMAN
□ 60. CHARLES (RED) RUFFING
□ 74. ANTHONY (TONY) LAZZERI
□ 86. FRANK CROSETTI
□ 88. GEORGE SELKIRK
□ 103. BILL DICKEY
□ 104. ROBERT (RED) ROLFE

PHILADELPHIA ATHLETICS

□ 10. ROY MAHAFFEY
□ 64. JIMMIE("Y") FOXX

PHILADELPHIA PHILLIES

□ 15. DICK BARTELL
□ 21. JOHNNY VERGES
□ 22. JIMMIE WILSON
□ 40. JOHN (BLONDY) RYAN
□ 41. HARVEY HENDRICK
□ 80. LOU CHIOZZA
□ 92. ETHAN ALLEN

PITTSBURGH PIRATES

□ 16. LLOYD WANER
□ 27. HAROLD (PIE) TRAYNOR
□ 56. AUGUST (GUS) SUHR
□ 57. DARRELL (CY) BLANTON
□ 69. EARL GRACE
□ 83. PAUL WANER
□ 99. HAROLD (PIE) TRAYNOR

ST. LOUIS BROWNS

□ 10. ROY MAHAFFEY
□ 13. GEORGE BLAEHOLDER
□ 44. ROGERS HORNSBY
□ 53. OSCAR MELILLO
□ 75. IRVING (JACK) BURNS
□ 85. JULIUS SOLTERS

ST. LOUIS CARDINALS

□ 17. FRANK FRISCH
□ 23. BILL HALLAHAN
□ 26. JOHN (PEPPER) MARTIN
□ 66. JOSEPH (DUCKY) MEDWIC
□ 81. BILL DELANCEY

WASHINGTON SENATORS

□ 4. CHARLES (BUDDY) MEYE
□ 30. HENRY (HEINIE) MANUSH
□ 47. CLIFF BOLTON
□ 71. OSWALD (OSSIE) BLUEGE
□ 78. JOE KUHEL
□ 91. BUCKY HARRIS

1981 DONRUSS (605)
2 1/2" X 3 1/2"

ATLANTA BRAVES

- □ 66. JEFF BURROUGHS
- □ 77. GENE GARBER
- □ 88. LUIS GOMEZ
- □ 99. BOB HORNER
- □ 186. BRIAN ASSELSTINE
- □ 197. RICK CAMP
- □ 208. BRUCE BENEDICT
- □ 219. CHRIS CHAMBLISS
- □ 306. GARY MATTHEWS
- □ 317. RICK MATULA
- □ 328. PHIL NIEKRO
- □ 339. JERRY ROYSTER
- □ 426. BOBBY COX(M)
- □ 437. DALE MURPHY
- □ 448. DOYLE ALEXANDER
- □ 459. GLENN HUBBARD
- □ 523. PRESTON HANNA
- □ 550. AL HRABOSKY
- □ 584. LARRY BRADFORD
- □ 597. TOMMY BOGGS

BALTIMORE ORIOLES

- □ 112. EDDIE MURRAY
- □ 113. RICK DEMPSEY
- □ 114. SCOTT MCGREGOR
- □ 115. KEN SINGLETON
- □ 116. GARY ROENICKE
- □ 232. RICH DAUER
- □ 233. DAN GRAHAM
- □ 234. MIKE FLANAGAN
- □ 235. JOHN LOWENSTEIN
- □ 236. BENNY AYALA
- □ 352. DOUG DECINCES
- □ 353. JIM PALMER
- □ 354. TIPPY MARTINEZ
- □ 355. AL BUMBRY
- □ 356. EARL WEAVER(M)
- □ 472. MARK BELANDER
- □ 473. JIM PALMER
- □ 474. SAMMY STEWART
- □ 475. TIM STODDARD
- □ 476. STEVE STONE
- □ 499. LENN SAKATA
- □ 507. TERRY CROWLEY
- □ 514. KIKO GARCIA
- □ 533. DENNIS MARTINEZ
- □ 552. DAVE FORD
- □ 600. H. PAT KELLY

BOSTON RED SOX

- □ 94. CARL YASTRZEMSKI
- □ 95. GLENN HOFFMAN
- □ 96. DENNIS ECKERSLEY
- □ 97. TOM BURGMEIER
- □ 98. WIN REMMERSWAAL
- □ 214. CARL YASTRZEMSKI
- □ 215. JERRY REMY
- □ 216. MIKE TORREZ
- □ 217. SKIP LOCKWOOD
- □ 218. FRED LYNN
- □ 334. TONY PEREZ
- □ 335. CARLTON FISK
- □ 336. DICK DRAGO
- □ 337. STEVE RENKO
- □ 338. JIM RICE
- □ 454. RICK BURLESON
- □ 455. GARY ALLENSON
- □ 456. BOB STANLEY
- □ 457. JOHN TUDOR
- □ 458. DWIGHT EVANS
- □ 512. DAVE RADER
- □ 544. DAVE STAPLETON
- □ 577. JIM DWYER

CALIFORNIA ANGELS

- □ 49. ROD CAREW
- □ 50. BERT CAMPANERIS
- □ 51. TOM DONOHUE
- □ 52. DAVE FROST
- □ 53. ED HALICKI
- □ 54. DAN FORD
- □ 169. ROD CAREW
- □ 170. FRED PATEK
- □ 171. FRANK TANANA
- □ 172. ALFREDO MARTINEZ
- □ 173. CHRIS KNAPP
- □ 174. JOE RUDI
- □ 289. BOBBY GRICH
- □ 290. DICKIE THON
- □ 291. MARK CLEAR
- □ 292. DAVE LEMANCZYK
- □ 293. JASON THOMPSON
- □ 294. RICK MILLER
- □ 409. CARNEY LANSFORD
- □ 410. BRIAN DOWNING
- □ 411. DON AASE
- □ 412. JIM BARR
- □ 413. DON BAYLOR
- □ 414. JIM FREGOSI(M)
- □ 532. GEOFF ZAHN
- □ 542. BUTCH HOBSON
- □ 572. BOBBY CLARK
- □ 581. ANDY HASSLER

CHICAGO CUBS

- □ 482. BILL BUCKNER
- □ 483. IVAN DEJESUS
- □ 485. LENNY RANDLE
- □ 501. STEVE DILLAR
- □ 513. MICK KELLEHER
- □ 515. LARRY BIITTNER
- □ 519. SCOT THOMPSON
- □ 520. JIM TRACY
- □ 521. CARLOS LEZCANO
- □ 522. JOE AMALFITANO(M)
- □ 535. STEVE MACKO
- □ 551. DICK TIDROW
- □ 553. DAVE KINGMAN
- □ 558. BARRY FOOTE
- □ 559. TIM BLACKWELL
- □ 561. RICK REUSCHEL
- □ 562. LYNN MCGLOTHEN
- □ 573. DENNIS LAMP
- □ 586. BILL CAUDILL
- □ 587. DOUG CAPILLA
- □ 588. GEORGE RILEY
- □ 589. WILLIE HERNANDEZ

CHICAGO WHITE SOX

- □ 38. LAMAR JOHNSON
- □ 39. KEVIN BELL
- □ 40. ED FARMER
- □ 41. ROSS BAUMGARTEN
- □ 42. LEO SUTHERLAND
- □ 158. JIM MORRISON
- □ 159. GLENN BORGMANN
- □ 160. LAMARR HOYT
- □ 161. RICH WORTHAM
- □ 162. THAD BOSLEY
- □ 278. GREG PRYOR
- □ 279. BRITT BURNS
- □ 280. RICH DOTSON
- □ 281. CHET LEMON
- □ 282. RUSTY KUNTZ
- □ 398. MIKE SQUIRES
- □ 399. MARVIS FOLEY
- □ 400. STEVE TROUT
- □ 401. WAYNE NORDHAGEN
- □ 402. TONY LARUSSA(M)
- □ 503. JIM ESSIAN
- □ 576. RON LEFLORE
- □ 596. MIKE PROLY

CINCINNATI REDS

- □ 61. RAY KNIGHT
- □ 62. JOHNNY BENCH
- □ 63. MARIO SOTO
- □ 64. DOUG BAIR
- □ 65. GEORGE FOSTER
- □ 181. DAVE CONCEPCION
- □ 182. JOHNNY BENCH
- □ 183. MIKE LACOSS
- □ 184. KEN GRIFFEY
- □ 185. DAVE COLLINS
- □ 301. DAN DRIESSEN
- □ 302. JOE NOLAN
- □ 303. PAUL HOUSEHOLDER
- □ 304. HARRY SPILMAN
- □ 305. CESAR GERONIMO
- □ 421. CHARLIE LEIBRANDT
- □ 422. TOM SEAVER
- □ 423. RON OESTER
- □ 424. JUNIOR KENNEDY
- □ 425. TOM SEAVER
- □ 554. MIKE VAIL

CLEVELAND INDIANS

- □ 78. MIKE HARGROVE
- □ 79. DAVE ROSELLO
- □ 80. RON HASSEY
- □ 81. SID MONGE
- □ 82. JOE CHARBONEAU
- □ 198. ANDRE THORNTON
- □ 199. TOM VERYZER
- □ 200. GARY ALEXANDER
- □ 201. RICK WAITS
- □ 202. RICK MANNING
- □ 318. TOBY HARRAH
- □ 319. DUANE KUIPER
- □ 320. LEN BARKER
- □ 321. VICTOR CRUZ
- □ 322. DELL ALSTON
- □ 438. JERRY DYBZINSKI
- □ 439. JORGE ORTA
- □ 440. WAYNE GARLAND
- □ 441. MIGUEL DILONE
- □ 442. DAVE GARCIA(M)
- □ 517. BO DIAZ

DETROIT TIGERS

- □ 5. ALAN TRAMMELL
- □ 6. TOM BROOKENS
- □ 7. DUFFY DYER
- □ 8. MARK FIDRYCH
- □ 9. DAVE ROZEMA
- □ 10. RICKY PETERS
- □ 125. RICHIE HEBNER
- □ 126. MARK WAGNER
- □ 127. JACK MORRIS
- □ 128. DAN PETRY
- □ 129. BRUCE ROBBINS
- □ 130. CHAMP SUMMERS
- □ 245. JOHN WOCKENFUSS
- □ 246. STAN PAPI
- □ 247. MILT WILCOX
- □ 248. DAN SCHATZEDER
- □ 249. STEVE KEMP
- □ 250. JIM LENTINE
- □ 365. LOU WHITAKER
- □ 366. LANCE PARRISH
- □ 367. TIM CORCORAN
- □ 368. PAT UNDERWOOD
- □ 369. AL COWENS
- □ 370. SPARKY ANDERSON(M)

HOUSTON ASTROS

- □ 18. JOE MORGAN
- □ 19. RAFAEL LANDESTOY
- □ 20. BRUCE BOCHY
- □ 21. JOE SAMBITO
- □ 23. DAVE SMITH
- □ 24. TERRY PUHL
- □ 138. ENOS CABELL

- ☐ 139. DAVE BERGMAN
- ☐ 140. J.R. RICHARD
- ☐ 141. KEN FORSCH
- ☐ 143. FRANK LACORTE
- ☐ 144. DENNIS WALLING
- ☐ 258. ART HOWE
- ☐ 259. ALAN ASHBY
- ☐ 260. NOLAN RYAN
- ☐ 261. VERN RUHLE
- ☐ 263. CESAR CEDENO
- ☐ 264. JEFF LEONARD
- ☐ 378. CRAIG REYNOLDS
- ☐ 379. LUIS PUJOLS
- ☐ 380. JOE NIEKRO
- ☐ 381. JOAQUIN ANDUJAR
- ☐ 383. JOSE CRUZ
- ☐ 384. BILL VIRDON(M)
- ☐ 490. DAVE W. ROBERTS

KANSAS CITY ROYALS

- ☐ 100. GEORGE BRETT
- ☐ 101. DAVE CHALK
- ☐ 102. DENNIS LEONARD
- ☐ 103. RENIE MARTIN
- ☐ 104. AMOS OTIS
- ☐ 220. WILLIE AIKENS
- ☐ 221. JOHN WATHAN
- ☐ 222. DAN QUISENBERRY
- ☐ 223. WILLIE WILSON
- ☐ 224. CLINT HURDLE
- ☐ 340. FRANK WHITE
- ☐ 341. JAMIE QUIRK
- ☐ 342. PAUL SPLITTORFF
- ☐ 343. MARTY PATTIN
- ☐ 344. PETE LACOCK
- ☐ 460. U.L. WASHINGTON
- ☐ 461. LARRY GURA
- ☐ 462. RICH GALE
- ☐ 463. HAL MCRAE
- ☐ 464. JIM FREY(M)
- ☐ 504. RANCE MULLINIKS

LOS ANGELES DODGERS

- ☐ 56. STEVE GARVEY
- ☐ 57. BILL RUSSELL
- ☐ 58. DON SUTTON
- ☐ 59. REGGIE SMITH
- ☐ 60. RICK MONDAY
- ☐ 176. STEVE GARVEY
- ☐ 177. JOE FERGUSON
- ☐ 178. BOB WELCH
- ☐ 179. DUSTY BAKER
- ☐ 180. RUDY LAW
- ☐ 296. RON CEY
- ☐ 297. STEVE YEAGER
- ☐ 298. BOBBY CASTILLO
- ☐ 299. MANNY MOTA
- ☐ 300. JAY JOHNSTONE
- ☐ 416. DAVE LOPES
- ☐ 417. JERRY REUSS
- ☐ 418. RICK SUTCLIFFE
- ☐ 419. DERREL THOMAS
- ☐ 420. TOM LASORDA(M)
- ☐ 511. STEVE HOWE
- ☐ 526. MICKEY HATCHER
- ☐ 534. GARY THOMASSON
- ☐ 541. BURT HOOTON
- ☐ 557. DON STANHOUSE

MILWAUKEE BREWERS

- ☐ 83. CECIL COOPER
- ☐ 84. SAL BANDO
- ☐ 85. MOOSE HAAS
- ☐ 86. MIKE CALDWELL
- ☐ 87. LARRY HISLE
- ☐ 203. PAUL MOLITOR
- ☐ 204. JIM GANTNER
- ☐ 205. PAUL MITCHELL
- ☐ 206. REGGIE CLEVELAND
- ☐ 207. SIXTO LEZCANO
- ☐ 323. ROBIN YOUNT
- ☐ 324. CHARLIE MOORE
- ☐ 325. LARY SORENSEN
- ☐ 326. GORMAN THOMAS
- ☐ 327. BOB RODGERS(M)
- ☐ 443. DON MONEY
- ☐ 444. BUCK MARTINEZ
- ☐ 445. JERRY AUGUSTINE
- ☐ 446. BEN OGLIVIE
- ☐ 447. JIM SLATON
- ☐ 508. BILL TRAVERS
- ☐ 510. BOB MCCLURE
- ☐ 528. DICK DAVIS
- ☐ 578. BILL CASTRO

MINNESOTA TWINS

- ☐ 487. ROY SMALLEY
- ☐ 488. JOHN CASTINO
- ☐ 489. RON JACKSON
- ☐ 492. MIKE CUBBAGE
- ☐ 493. ROB WILFONG
- ☐ 494. DANNY GOODWIN
- ☐ 495. JOSE MORALES
- ☐ 527. JOHN GORYL(M)
- ☐ 529. BUTCH WYNEGAR
- ☐ 530. SAL BUTERA
- ☐ 531. JERRY KOOSMAN
- ☐ 546. DOUG CORBETT
- ☐ 547. DARRELL JACKSON
- ☐ 548. PETE REDFERN
- ☐ 549. ROGER ERICKSON
- ☐ 564. JOHN VERHOEVEN
- ☐ 565. KEN LANDREAUX
- ☐ 566. GLENN ADAMS
- ☐ 567. HOSKEN POWELL
- ☐ 592. RICK SOFIELD
- ☐ 593. BOMBO RIVERA
- ☐ 594. GARY WARD

MONTREAL EXPOS

- ☐ 89. LARRY PARRISH
- ☐ 90. GARY CARTER
- ☐ 91. BILL GULLICKSON
- ☐ 92. FRED NORMAN
- ☐ 93. TOMMY HUTTON
- ☐ 209. RODNEY SCOTT
- ☐ 210. JOHN TAMARGO
- ☐ 211. BILL LEE
- ☐ 212. ANDRE DAWSON
- ☐ 213. ROWLAND OFFICE
- ☐ 329. CHRIS SPEIER
- ☐ 330. STEVE ROGERS
- ☐ 331. WOODIE FRYMAN
- ☐ 332. WARREN CROMARTIE
- ☐ 333. JERRY WHITE
- ☐ 449. TONY BERNAZARD
- ☐ 450. SCOTT SANDERSON
- ☐ 451. DAVE PALMER
- ☐ 452. STAN BAHNSEN
- ☐ 453. DICK WILLIAMS(M)
- ☐ 538. TIM RAINES
- ☐ 540. KEN MACHA
- ☐ 545. BOB PATE
- ☐ 599. ELIAS SOSA

NEW YORK METS

- ☐ 34. LEE MAZZILLI
- ☐ 35. JOHN STEARNS
- ☐ 36. ROY JACKSON
- ☐ 37. MIKE SCOTT
- ☐ 154. FRANK TAVERAS
- ☐ 155. CRAIG SWAN
- ☐ 156. JEFF REARDON
- ☐ 157. STEVE HENDERSON
- ☐ 274. MIKE JORGENSEN
- ☐ 275. PAT ZACHRY
- ☐ 276. NEIL ALLEN
- ☐ 277. JOEL YOUNGBLOOD
- ☐ 394. DOUG FLYNN
- ☐ 395. PETE FALCONE
- ☐ 396. TOM HAUSMAN
- ☐ 397. ELLIOTT MADDOX
- ☐ 506. JOE TORRE(M)
- ☐ 524. RAY BURRIS
- ☐ 575. MOOKIE WILSON

NEW YORK YANKEES

- ☐ 105. GRAIG NETTLES
- ☐ 106. ERIC SODERHOLM
- ☐ 107. TOMMY JOHN
- ☐ 108. TOM UNDERWOOD
- ☐ 109. LOU PINIELLA
- ☐ 111. BOBBY MURCER
- ☐ 225. BOB WATSON
- ☐ 226. JIM SPENCER
- ☐ 227. RON GUIDRY
- ☐ 228. REGGIE JACKSON
- ☐ 229. OSCAR GAMBLE
- ☐ 231. LUIS TIANT
- ☐ 345. WILLIE RANDOLPH
- ☐ 346. RICK CERONE
- ☐ 347. RICH GOSSAGE
- ☐ 348. REGGIE JACKSON
- ☐ 349. RUPPERT JONES
- ☐ 351. YOGI BERRA(C)
- ☐ 465. BUCKY DENT
- ☐ 466. DENNIS WERTH
- ☐ 467. RON DAVIS
- ☐ 468. REGGIE JACKSON
- ☐ 469. BOBBY BROWN
- ☐ 471. GAYLORD PERRY
- ☐ 486. LARRY MILBOURNE
- ☐ 500. GENE MICHAEL(M)
- ☐ 571. JOE LEFEBVRE

OAKLAND A'S

- ☐ 110. MICKEY KLUTTS
- ☐ 117. DAVE REVERING
- ☐ 118. MIKE NORRIS
- ☐ 119. RICKEY HENDERSON
- ☐ 120. MIKE HEATH
- ☐ 230. JEFF COX
- ☐ 237. WAYNE GROSS
- ☐ 238. RICK LANGFORD
- ☐ 239. TONY ARMAS
- ☐ 240. BOB LACEY
- ☐ 350. DAVE MCKAY
- ☐ 357. ROB PICCIOLO
- ☐ 358. MATT KEOUGH
- ☐ 359. DWAYNE MURPHY
- ☐ 360. BRIAN KINGMAN
- ☐ 470. MIKE DAVIS
- ☐ 477. JEFF NEWMAN
- ☐ 478. STEVE MCCATTY
- ☐ 479. BILLY MARTIN(M)
- ☐ 480. MITCHELL PAGE
- ☐ 484. CLIFF JOHNSON
- ☐ 497. MIKE EDWARDS
- ☐ 585. FRED STANLEY

PHILADELPHIA PHILLIES

- ☐ 11. MIKE SCHMIDT
- ☐ 22. MANNY TRILLO
- ☐ 33. STEVE CARLTON
- ☐ 44. RON REED
- ☐ 55. GARRY MADDOX
- ☐ 131. PETE ROSE
- ☐ 142. LARRY BOWA
- ☐ 153. DICK RUTHVEN
- ☐ 164. DEL UNSER
- ☐ 175. GREG LUZINSKI
- ☐ 251. PETE ROSE
- ☐ 262. BOB BOONE
- ☐ 273. TUG MCGRAW
- ☐ 284. SPARKY LYLE
- ☐ 295. LONNIE SMITH
- ☐ 371. PETE ROSE
- ☐ 382. KEITH MORELAND
- ☐ 393. BOB WALK
- ☐ 404. BAKE MCBRIDE
- ☐ 415. DALLAS GREEN(M)
- ☐ 568. DICK NOLES
- ☐ 574. RANDY LERCH
- ☐ 598. GREG GROSS

PITTSBURGH PIRATES

☐ 12. WILLIE STARGELL
☐ 13. TIM FOLI
☐ 14. MANNY SANGUILLEN
☐ 15. GRANT JACKSON
☐ 16. EDDIE SOLOMON
☐ 17. OMAR MORENO
☐ 132. WILLIE STARGELL
☐ 133. ED OTT
☐ 134. JIM BIBBY
☐ 135. BERT BLYLEVEN
☐ 136. DAVE PARKER
☐ 137. BILL ROBINSON
☐ 252. BILL MADLOCK
☐ 253. DALE BERRA
☐ 254. KENT TEKULVE
☐ 255. ENRIQUE ROMO
☐ 256. MIKE EASLER
☐ 257. CHUCK TANNER(M)
☐ 372. PHIL GARNER
☐ 373. STEVE NICOSIA
☐ 374. JOHN CANDELARIA
☐ 375. DON ROBINSON
☐ 376. LEE LACY
☐ 377. JOHN MILNER
☐ 563. BOB OWCHINKO

ST. LOUIS CARDINALS

☐ 67. KEITH HERNANDEZ
☐ 68. TOM HERR
☐ 69. BOB FORSCH
☐ 70. JOHN FULGHAM
☐ 71. BOBBY BONDS
☐ 187. GARRY TEMPLETON
☐ 188. MIKE PHILLIPS
☐ 189. PETE VUCKOVICH
☐ 190. JOHN URREA
☐ 191. TONY SCOTT
☐ 307. KEN REITZ
☐ 308. TED SIMMONS
☐ 309. JOHN LITTLEFIELD
☐ 310. GEORGE FRAZIER
☐ 311. DANE IORG
☐ 427. LEON DURHAM
☐ 428. TERRY KENNEDY
☐ 429. SILVIO MARTINEZ
☐ 430. GEORGE HENDRICK
☐ 431. RED SCHOENDIENST(C)
☐ 505. DARRELL PORTER
☐ 536. JIM KAAT
☐ 539. KEITH SMITH
☐ 560. BRUCE SUTTER
☐ 580. MARK LITTELL
☐ 583. KEN OBERKFELL

SAN DIEGO PADRES

☐ 1. OZZIE SMITH
☐ 2. ROLLIE FINGERS
☐ 3. RICK WISE
☐ 4. GENE RICHARDS
☐ 121. DAVE CASH
☐ 122. RANDY JONES
☐ 123. ERIC RASMUSSEN
☐ 124. JERRY MUMPHREY
☐ 241. GENE TENACE
☐ 242. BOB SHIRLEY
☐ 243. GARY LUCAS
☐ 244. JERRY TURNER
☐ 361. BILL FAHEY
☐ 362. STEVE MURA
☐ 363. DENNIS KINNEY
☐ 364. DAVE WINFIELD
☐ 525. BRODERICK PERKINS
☐ 595. DAVE EDWARDS

SAN FRANCISCO GIANTS

☐ 72. RENNIE STENNETT
☐ 73. JOE STRAIN
☐ 74. ED WHITSON
☐ 75. TOM GRIFFIN
☐ 76. BILL NORTH
☐ 192. DARRELL EVANS
☐ 193. MILT MAY
☐ 194. BOB KNEPPER
☐ 195. RANDY MOFFITT
☐ 196. LARRY HERNDON
☐ 312. MIKE IVIE
☐ 313. DENNIS LITTLEJOHN
☐ 314. GARY LAVELLE
☐ 315. JACK CLARK
☐ 316. JIM WOHLFORD
☐ 432. JOHN LEMASTER
☐ 433. VIDA BLUE
☐ 434. JOHN MONTEFUSCO
☐ 435. TERRY WHITFIELD
☐ 436. DAVE BRISTOL(M)
☐ 498. MIKE SADEK
☐ 555. JERRY MARTIN
☐ 556. JESUS FIGUEROA
☐ 579. GREG MINTON

SEATTLE MARINERS

☐ 43. DAN MEYER
☐ 45. MARIO MENDOZA
☐ 46. RICK HONEYCUTT
☐ 47. GLENN ABBOTT
☐ 48. LEON ROBERTS
☐ 163. JULIO CRUZ
☐ 165. JIM ANDERSON
☐ 166. JIM BEATTIE
☐ 167. SHANE RAWLEY
☐ 168. JOE SIMPSON
☐ 283. TED COX
☐ 285. LARRY COX
☐ 286. FLOYD BANNISTER
☐ 287. BYRON MCLAUGHLIN
☐ 288. RODNEY CRAIG
☐ 403. BRUCE BOCHTE
☐ 405. JERRY NARRON
☐ 406. ROB DRESSLER
☐ 407. DAVE HEAVERLO
☐ 408. TOM PACIOREK
☐ 501. DAVE A. ROBERTS
☐ 516. WILLIE NORWOOD
☐ 518. JUAN BENIQUEZ
☐ 543. BILL STEIN

TEXAS RANGERS

☐ 25. BUMP WILLS
☐ 26. JOHN ELLIS
☐ 27. JIM KERN
☐ 28. RICHIE ZISK
☐ 145. BUDDY BELL
☐ 146. FERGUSON JENKINS
☐ 147. DANNY DARWIN
☐ 148. JOHN GRUBB
☐ 265. PAT PUTNAM
☐ 266. JON MATLACK
☐ 267. DAVE RAJSICH
☐ 268. BILLY SAMPLE
☐ 385. JIM SUNDBERG
☐ 386. DOC MEDICH
☐ 387. AL OLIVER
☐ 388. JIM NORRIS
☐ 496. MICKEY RIVERS
☐ 509. NELSON NORMAN

TORONTO BLUE JAYS

☐ 29. JOHN MAYBERRY
☐ 30. BOB DAVIS
☐ 31. JACKSON TODD
☐ 32. AL WOODS
☐ 149. ALFREDO GRIFFIN
☐ 150. JERRY GARVIN
☐ 151. PAUL MIRABELLA
☐ 152. RICK BOSETTI
☐ 269. DAMASO GARCIA
☐ 270. TOM BUSKEY
☐ 271. JOEY MCLAUGHLIN
☐ 272. BARRY BONNELL
☐ 389. BOB BAILOR
☐ 390. ERNIE WHITT
☐ 391. OTTO VELEZ
☐ 392. ROY HOWELL
☐ 569. DANNY AINGE
☐ 570. BOBBY MATTICK(M)
☐ 582. DAVE STIEB

1982 DONRUSS (660)
2 1/2" X 3 1/2"

ATLANTA BRAVES

☐ 47. CHRIS CHAMBLISS
☐ 58. CLAUDELL WASHINGTON
☐ 97. AL HRABOSKY
☐ 123. GENE GARBER
☐ 149. MATT SINATRO
☐ 173. BOB HORNER
☐ 184. BRIAN ASSELSTINE
☐ 223. RICK CAMP
☐ 249. TOMMY BOGGS
☐ 275. BRETT BUTLER
☐ 299. DALE MURPHY
☐ 310. RUFINO LINARES
☐ 349. MICKEY MAHLER
☐ 375. BRUCE BENEDICT
☐ 401. STEVE BEDROSIAN
☐ 425. EDDIE MILLER
☐ 436. GLENN HUBBARD
☐ 475. PHIL NIEKRO
☐ 501. KEN DAYLEY
☐ 527. LARRY MCWILLIAMS
☐ 543. GAYLORD PERRY
☐ 546. RAFAEL RAMIREZ
☐ 553. LARRY BRADFORD
☐ 555. JERRY ROYSTER

BALTIMORE ORIOLES

☐ 27. EARL WEAVER(M)
☐ 77. RICK DEMPSEY
☐ 79. DENNIS MARTINEZ
☐ 105. KEN SINGLETON
☐ 131. TIM STODDARD
☐ 153. AL BUMBRY
☐ 203. JOSE MORALES
☐ 205. TIPPY MARTINEZ
☐ 231. JIM PALMER
☐ 257. RICH DAUER
☐ 279. DOUG DECINCES
☐ 329. MIKE FLANAGAN
☐ 331. SCOTT MCGREGOR
☐ 357. STEVE STONE
☐ 383. TERRY CROWLEY
☐ 405. CAL RIPKEN
☐ 455. DAN GRAHAM
☐ 457. SAMMY STEWART
☐ 483. EDDIE MURRAY

- ☐ 509. GARY ROENICKE
- ☐ 579. CAL RIPKEN, SR.(C)
- ☐ 581. BENNY AYALA
- ☐ 597. DAVE FORD
- ☐ 599. JOHN LOWENSTEIN
- ☐ 610. BOB BONNER
- ☐ 611. JIM DWYER
- ☐ 644. LENN SAKATA

BOSTON RED SOX

- ☐ 30. DENNIS ECKERSLEY
- ☐ 74. CARL YASTRZEMSKI
- ☐ 82. CARNEY LANSFORD
- ☐ 109. DWIGHT EVANS
- ☐ 134. BOB STANLEY
- ☐ 156. JERRY REMY
- ☐ 200. JIM RICE
- ☐ 208. DAVE STAPLETON
- ☐ 235. MIKE TORREZ
- ☐ 260. JOHN TUDOR
- ☐ 282. RALPH HOUK(M)
- ☐ 326. FRANK TANANA
- ☐ 334. RICK MILLER
- ☐ 361. TOM BURGMEIER
- ☐ 386. GARY ALLENSON
- ☐ 408. TONY PEREZ
- ☐ 452. MARK CLEAR
- ☐ 460. GLENN HOFFMAN
- ☐ 487. BILL CAMPBELL
- ☐ 512. RICH GEDMAN
- ☐ 540. BOB OJEDA
- ☐ 560. JULIO VALDEZ
- ☐ 564. STEVE CRAWFORD
- ☐ 586. JOE RUDI
- ☐ 608. GARRY HANCOCK
- ☐ 632. REID NICHOLS

CALIFORNIA ANGELS

- ☐ 38. STEVE RENKO
- ☐ 66. BRUCE KISON
- ☐ 90. BOBBY GRICH
- ☐ 115. BRIAN DOWNING
- ☐ 141. GENE MAUCH(M)
- ☐ 164. GEOFF ZAHN
- ☐ 192. ED OTT
- ☐ 216. ROD CAREW
- ☐ 241. FRED PATEK
- ☐ 267. DON AASE
- ☐ 290. DAVE FROST
- ☐ 318. BOB CLARK
- ☐ 342. RICK BURLESON
- ☐ 367. FRED LYNN
- ☐ 393. KEN FORSCH
- ☐ 416. MIKE WITT
- ☐ 444. JOHN HARRIS
- ☐ 468. DAN FORD
- ☐ 493. DON BAYLOR
- ☐ 519. ANDY HASSLER
- ☐ 577. BUTCH HOBSON
- ☐ 587. JUAN BENIQUEZ
- ☐ 593. BERT CAMPANERIS

CHICAGO CUBS

- ☐ 48. IVAN DEJESUS
- ☐ 57. HECTOR CRUZ
- ☐ 99. TIM BLACKWELL
- ☐ 126. RANDY MARTZ
- ☐ 151. LEON DURHAM
- ☐ 174. STEVE DILLARD
- ☐ 183. STEVE HENDERSON
- ☐ 225. JODY DAVIS
- ☐ 252. LEE SMITH
- ☐ 277. KEN REITZ
- ☐ 300. MIKE LUM
- ☐ 309. JERRY MORALES
- ☐ 351. MIKE KRUKOW
- ☐ 378. KEN KRAVEC
- ☐ 403. BILL BUCKNER
- ☐ 426. BILL CAUDILL
- ☐ 435. MIKE TYSON
- ☐ 477. DICK TIDROW
- ☐ 504. DOUG BIRD
- ☐ 529. PAT TABLER
- ☐ 533. MIKE GRIFFIN
- ☐ 554. SCOTT FLETCHER
- ☐ 633. DAVE GEISEL

CHICAGO WHITE SOX

- ☐ 39. MIKE SQUIRES
- ☐ 67. WAYNE NORDHAGEN
- ☐ 104. ROSS BAUMGARTEN
- ☐ 117. LAMARR HOYT
- ☐ 143. TONY BERNAZARD
- ☐ 165. RON LEFLORE
- ☐ 193. GREG LUZINSKI
- ☐ 230. BRITT BURNS
- ☐ 243. STEVE TROUT
- ☐ 269. LAMAR JOHNSON
- ☐ 291. CHET LEMON
- ☐ 319. TONY LARUSSA(M)
- ☐ 356. RICHARD DOTSON
- ☐ 369. JIM ESSIAN
- ☐ 395. JIM MORRISON
- ☐ 417. BOB MOLINARO
- ☐ 445. VADA PINSON(C)
- ☐ 482. ED FARMER
- ☐ 495. CARLTON FISK
- ☐ 521. GREG PRYOR
- ☐ 568. HAROLD BAINES
- ☐ 603. JERRY KOOSMAN
- ☐ 609. JERRY TURNER
- ☐ 619. DENNIS LAMP
- ☐ 631. KEVIN HICKEY
- ☐ 637. BILL ALMON

CINCINNATI REDS

- ☐ 43. LARRY BIITTNER
- ☐ 62. JOE NOLAN
- ☐ 103. MARIO SOTO
- ☐ 122. FRANK PASTORE
- ☐ 148. TOM SEAVER
- ☐ 169. DAVE COLLINS
- ☐ 188. JUNIOR KENNEDY
- ☐ 229. TOM HUME
- ☐ 248. DAN DRIESSEN
- ☐ 274. GEORGE FOSTER
- ☐ 295. SAM MEJIAS
- ☐ 314. PAUL HOUSEHOLDER
- ☐ 355. PAUL MOSKAU
- ☐ 374. RAY KNIGHT
- ☐ 400. JOHNNY BENCH
- ☐ 421. DAVE CONCEPCION
- ☐ 440. MIKE LACOSS
- ☐ 481. JOE PRICE
- ☐ 500. RON OESTER
- ☐ 526. JOHN MCNAMARA(M)
- ☐ 538. MIKE O'BERRY
- ☐ 634. KEN GRIFFEY

CLEVELAND INDIANS

- ☐ 33. RICK WAITS
- ☐ 72. TOBY HARRAH
- ☐ 85. RICK MANNING
- ☐ 111. BERT BLYLEVEN
- ☐ 137. LEN BARKER
- ☐ 159. ALAN BANNISTER
- ☐ 198. DUANE KUIPER
- ☐ 211. JORGE ORTA
- ☐ 237. VON HAYES
- ☐ 263. BO DIAZ
- ☐ 285. MIKE STANTON
- ☐ 324. ANDRE THORNTON
- ☐ 337. DAVE GARCIA(M)
- ☐ 363. JOE CHARBONEAU
- ☐ 389. MIKE HARGROVE
- ☐ 411. DAN SPILLNER
- ☐ 450. TOM VERYZER
- ☐ 463. RON HASSEY
- ☐ 489. WAYNE GARLAND
- ☐ 515. MIGUEL DILONE
- ☐ 551. CHRIS BANDO
- ☐ 572. JOHN DENNY
- ☐ 617. DAVE ROSELLO
- ☐ 620. SID MONGE
- ☐ 647. JERRY DYBZINSKI

DETROIT TIGERS

- ☐ 29. SPARKY ANDERSON(M)
- ☐ 76. ALAN TRAMMELL
- ☐ 81. CHAMP SUMMERS
- ☐ 107. JACK MORRIS
- ☐ 133. DAN PETRY
- ☐ 155. RICK PETERS
- ☐ 202. TOM BROOKENS
- ☐ 207. AL COWENS
- ☐ 233. MILT WILCOX
- ☐ 259. DAVE ROZEMA
- ☐ 281. LANCE PARRISH
- ☐ 328. RICHIE HEBNER
- ☐ 333. STAN PAPI
- ☐ 359. AURELIO LOPEZ
- ☐ 385. DAN SCHATZEDER
- ☐ 407. KIRK GIBSON
- ☐ 454. LOU WHITAKER
- ☐ 459. JOHN WOCKENFUSS
- ☐ 485. KEVIN SAUCIER
- ☐ 511. DAVE TOBIK
- ☐ 542. LYNN JONES
- ☐ 583. RICK LEACH
- ☐ 594. STEVE KEMP
- ☐ 601. MICK KELLEHER
- ☐ 602. RON JACKSON

HOUSTON ASTROS

- ☐ 41. BOB KNEPPER
- ☐ 65. JOE SAMBITO
- ☐ 92. ART HOWE
- ☐ 118. CESAR CEDENO
- ☐ 144. BILL VIRDON(M)
- ☐ 167. JOE NIEKRO
- ☐ 191. DAVE SMITH
- ☐ 218. JOE PITTMAN
- ☐ 244. JOSE CRUZ
- ☐ 270. FRANK LACORTE
- ☐ 293. VERN RUHLE
- ☐ 317. ALAN ASHBY
- ☐ 344. CRAIG REYNOLDS
- ☐ 370. TERRY PUHL
- ☐ 396. MIKE IVIE
- ☐ 419. NOLAN RYAN
- ☐ 443. DON SUTTON
- ☐ 470. KIKO GARCIA
- ☐ 496. DENNY WALLING
- ☐ 522. TONY SCOTT
- ☐ 544. PHIL GARNER
- ☐ 576. LUIS PUJOLS
- ☐ 625. DAVE W. ROBERTS

KANSAS CITY ROYALS

- ☐ 34. GEORGE BRETT
- ☐ 70. AMOS OTIS
- ☐ 86. JOHN WATHAN
- ☐ 112. DAN QUISENBERRY
- ☐ 138. RICH GALE
- ☐ 160. U.L. WASHINGTON
- ☐ 196. HAL MCRAE
- ☐ 212. JAMIE QUIRK
- ☐ 238. RENIE MARTIN
- ☐ 264. DENNIS LEONARD
- ☐ 286. FRANK WHITE
- ☐ 322. CESAR GERONIMO
- ☐ 338. LARRY GURA
- ☐ 364. KEN BRETT
- ☐ 390. DARRYL MOTLEY
- ☐ 412. WILLIE AIKENS
- ☐ 448. WILLIE WILSON
- ☐ 464. PAUL SPLITTORFF
- ☐ 490. JIM L. WRIGHT
- ☐ 516. CLINT HURDLE
- ☐ 570. LEE MAY
- ☐ 590. DAVE CHALK
- ☐ 630. RANCE MULLINIKS

LOS ANGELES DODGERS

- ☐ 32. BURT HOOTON
- ☐ 75. BOB WELCH
- ☐ 84. STEVE GARVEY
- ☐ 110. TOM LASORDA(M)
- ☐ 136. PEDRO GUERRERO
- ☐ 158. STEVE HOWE
- ☐ 201. STEVE YEAGER
- ☐ 210. RON CEY
- ☐ 236. BOBBY CASTILLO
- ☐ 262. JAY JOHNSTONE
- ☐ 284. JERRY REUSS
- ☐ 327. DAVEY LOPES
- ☐ 336. DUSTY BAKER
- ☐ 362. TERRY FORSTER
- ☐ 388. KEN LANDREAUX
- ☐ 410. DAVE STEWART
- ☐ 453. BILL RUSSELL

□ 462. FERNANDO VALENZUELA
□ 488. REGGIE SMITH
□ 514. RICK MONDAY
□ 537. DERREL THOMAS
□ 562. MIKE MARSHALL
□ 598. MIKE SCIOSCIA
□ 604. DAVE GOLTZ
□ 624. STEVE SAX

MILWAUKEE BREWERS

□ 28. ROLLIE FINGERS
□ 78. PAUL MOLITOR
□ 80. JIM SLATON
□ 106. TED SIMMONS
□ 132. GORMAN THOMAS
□ 154. MARK BROUHARD
□ 204. ROY HOWELL
□ 206. MOOSE HAAS
□ 232. BOB RODGERS(M)
□ 258. CECIL COOPER
□ 280. CHARLIE MOORE
□ 330. MIKE CALDWELL
□ 332. JERRY AUGUSTINE
□ 358. LARRY HISLE
□ 384. DON MONEY
□ 406. JIM GANTNER
□ 456. REGGIE CLEVELAND
□ 458. PETE VUCKOVICH
□ 484. BEN OGLIVIE
□ 510. ROBIN YOUNT
□ 536. EDDIE ROMERO
□ 578. HARVEY KUENN(C)
□ 592. SAL BANDO
□ 595. RANDY LERCH
□ 618. RICKEY KEETON
□ 623. JAMIE EASTERLY

MINNESOTA TWINS

□ 51. PETE REDFERN
□ 53. DOUG CORBETT
□ 102. DAVE ENGLE
□ 130. ROB WILFONG
□ 177. FERNANDO ARROYO
□ 179. DARRELL JACKSON
□ 228. HOSKEN POWELL
□ 256. JOHN CASTINO
□ 303. ROGER ERICKSON
□ 305. DANNY GOODWIN
□ 354. PETE MACKANIN
□ 382. BRAD HAVENS
□ 429. AL WILLIAMS
□ 431. GLENN ADAMS
□ 480. MICKEY HATCHER
□ 508. BUTCH WYNEGAR
□ 532. SAL BUTERA
□ 539. JACK O'CONNOR
□ 549. TIM LAUDNER
□ 557. KENT HRBEK
□ 566. JOHNNY PODRES(C)
□ 571. GARY WARD
□ 573. ROY SMALLEY
□ 591. BILLY GARDNER(M)

MONTREAL EXPOS

□ 36. STEVE ROGERS
□ 68. WOODIE FRYMAN
□ 88. ANDRE DAWSON
□ 114. GARY CARTER
□ 140. TIM WALLACH
□ 162. BILL GULLICKSON
□ 194. BILL LEE
□ 214. TIM RAINES
□ 240. RODNEY SCOTT
□ 266. JOHN MILNER
□ 288. SCOTT SANDERSON
□ 320. CHARLIE LEA
□ 340. WARREN CROMARTIE
□ 366. CHRIS SPEIER
□ 392. STAN BAHNSEN
□ 414. RAY BURRIS
□ 446. ELIAS SOSA
□ 466. LARRY PARRISH
□ 492. JIM FANNING(M)
□ 518. GRANT JACKSON
□ 547. JEFF REARDON
□ 621. JERRY WHITE
□ 627. TERRY FRANCONA
□ 650. FELIPE ALOU(C)

NEW YORK METS

□ 49. LEE MAZZILLI
□ 56. RUSTY STAUB
□ 98. FRANK TAVERAS
□ 128. MIKE SCOTT
□ 175. MOOKIE WILSON
□ 182. DAVE KINGMAN
□ 224. MIKE JORGENSEN
□ 254. PAT ZACHRY
□ 301. TOM HAUSMAN
□ 308. BOB BAILOR
□ 350. ALEX TREVINO
□ 380. PETE FALCONE
□ 427. DOUG FLYNN
□ 434. JOHN STEARNS
□ 476. HUBIE BROOKS
□ 506. NEIL ALLEN
□ 589. CRAIG SWAN
□ 605. ELLIS VALENTINE
□ 613. JOEL YOUNGBLOOD
□ 641. ED LYNCH
□ 646. JESSE OROSCO
□ 649. RON GARDENHIRE

NEW YORK YANKEES

□ 31. DAVE WINFIELD
□ 73. DAVE RIGHETTI
□ 83. BARRY FOOTE
□ 108. BOB WATSON
□ 135. LOU PINIELLA
□ 157. RICK REUSCHEL
□ 199. RICK CERONE
□ 209. BUCKY DENT
□ 234. DAVE REVERING
□ 261. JERRY MUMPHREY
□ 283. RICH GOSSAGE
□ 325. RUDY MAY
□ 335. GRAIG NETTLES
□ 360. OSCAR GAMBLE
□ 387. YOGI BERRA(C)
□ 409. TOMMY JOHN
□ 451. RON DAVIS
□ 461. WILLIE RANDOLPH
□ 486. BOBBY MURCER
□ 513. GENE NELSON
□ 535. REGGIE JACKSON
□ 548. RON GUIDRY
□ 552. BOBBY BROWN
□ 569. DAVE LAROCHE
□ 584. GEORGE FRAZIER
□ 614. LARRY MILBOURNE
□ 635. BOB LEMON(M)

OAKLAND A'S

□ 35. STEVE MCCATTY
□ 71. MATT KEOUGH
□ 87. BRIAN KINGMAN
□ 113. RICKEY HENDERSON
□ 139. WAYNE GROSS
□ 161. RICK LANGFORD
□ 197. MIKE NORRIS
□ 213. JEFF JONES
□ 239. DWAYNE MURPHY
□ 265. JIM SPENCER
□ 287. BOB OWCHINKO
□ 323. TOM UNDERWOOD
□ 339. CLIFF JOHNSON
□ 365. TONY ARMAS
□ 391. DAVE MCKAY
□ 413. MIKE HEATH
□ 449. FRED STANLEY
□ 465. ROB PICCIOLO
□ 491. BILLY MARTIN(M)
□ 517. JEFF NEWMAN
□ 534. KELVIN MOORE
□ 556. SHOOTY BABITT
□ 616. KEITH DRUMRIGHT
□ 626. RICK BOSETTI

PHILADELPHIA PHILLIES

□ 42. STEVE CARLTON
□ 63. LARRY BOWA
□ 93. MARTY BYSTROM
□ 119. KEITH MORELAND
□ 147. DICK DAVIS
□ 168. PETE ROSE
□ 189. SPARKY LYLE
□ 219. LARRY CHRISTENSON
□ 245. MANNY TRILLO
□ 273. DEL UNSER
□ 294. MIKE SCHMIDT
□ 315. GARRY MADDOX
□ 345. MIKE PROLY
□ 371. GREG GROSS
□ 399. RON REED
□ 420. TUG MCGRAW
□ 441. GARY MATTHEWS
□ 471. BOB BOONE
□ 497. BAKE MCBRIDE
□ 525. DICK RUTHVEN
□ 606. LONNIE SMITH
□ 622. LUIS AGUAYO

PITTSBURGH PIRATES

□ 45. STEVE NICOSIA
□ 59. ENRIQUE ROMO
□ 95. DAVE PARKER
□ 124. TONY PENA
□ 150. CHUCK TANNER(M)
□ 171. JIM BIBBY
□ 185. ROD SCURRY
□ 221. MIKE EASLER
□ 250. DALE BERRA
□ 276. LEE LACY
□ 297. JOHN CANDELARIA
□ 311. KENT TEKULVE
□ 347. OMAR MORENO
□ 376. TIM FOLI
□ 402. BILL ROBINSON
□ 423. RICK RHODEN
□ 437. EDDIE SOLOMON
□ 473. RANDY NIEMANN
□ 502. JASON THOMPSON
□ 528. JOHNNY RAY
□ 582. VANCE LAW
□ 639. WILLIE STARGELL
□ 651. HARVEY HADDIX(C)
□ 653. BILL MADLOCK

ST. LOUIS CARDINALS

□ 40. GEORGE HENDRICK
□ 64. SIXTO LEZCANO
□ 91. BOB FORSCH
□ 120. BOB SHIRLEY
□ 152. GENE TENACE
□ 166. DANE IORG
□ 190. WHITEY HERZOG(M)
□ 217. JIM KAAT
□ 246. LARY SORENSEN
□ 278. KEITH HERNANDEZ
□ 292. TITO LANDRUM
□ 316. MIKE RAMSEY
□ 343. JOHN MARTIN
□ 372. BRUCE SUTTER
□ 404. KEN OBERKFELL
□ 418. STEVE BRAUN
□ 442. MARK LITTELL
□ 469. SILVIO MARTINEZ
□ 498. DARRELL PORTER
□ 530. TOM HERR
□ 545. GARRY TEMPLETON
□ 588. LUIS DELEON
□ 607. JOAQUIN ANDUJAR
□ 615. GENE ROOF

1982 Donruss

☐ 636. ORLANDO SANCHEZ
☐ 640. BOB SYKES
☐ 645. JULIO GONZALEZ

SAN DIEGO PADRES

☐ 44. CHRIS WELSH
☐ 61. TIM FLANNERY
☐ 94. OZZIE SMITH
☐ 121. TERRY KENNEDY
☐ 145. JOHN LITTLEFIELD
☐ 170. RICK WISE
☐ 187. DANNY BOONE
☐ 220. JUAN BONILLA
☐ 247. DAVE EDWARDS
☐ 271. BARRY EVANS
☐ 296. GARY LUCAS
☐ 313. JOHN URREA
☐ 346. RUPPERT JONES
☐ 373. JOE LEFEBVRE
☐ 397. BRODERICK PERKINS
☐ 422. JUAN EICHELBERGER
☐ 439. RANDY BASS
☐ 472. LUIS SALAZAR
☐ 499. GENE RICHARDS
☐ 523. STEVE MURA

SAN FRANCISCO GIANTS

☐ 46. JACK CLARK
☐ 60. GARY LAVELLE
☐ 96. DOYLE ALEXANDER
☐ 125. ALLEN RIPLEY
☐ 146. DAVE BERGMAN
☐ 172. LARRY HERNDON
☐ 186. FRED BREINING
☐ 222. VIDA BLUE
☐ 251. EDDIE WHITSON
☐ 272. ENOS CABELL
☐ 298. JERRY MARTIN
☐ 312. JOE MORGAN
☐ 348. GREG MINTON
☐ 377. AL HOLLAND
☐ 398. DARRELL EVANS
☐ 424. FRANK ROBINSON(M)
☐ 438. JEFF LEONARD
☐ 474. TOM GRIFFIN
☐ 503. MILT MAY
☐ 524. JOHNNIE LEMASTER
☐ 563. RENNIE STENNETT
☐ 574. BOB BRENLY

SEATTLE MARINERS

☐ 50. JULIO CRUZ
☐ 55. JOE SIMPSON
☐ 100. FLOYD BANNISTER
☐ 127. RICHIE ZISK
☐ 176. DAN MEYER
☐ 181. JIM ANDERSON
☐ 226. MIKE PARROTT
☐ 253. TOM PACIOREK
☐ 302. GLENN ABBOTT
☐ 307. LENNY RANDLE
☐ 352. SHANE RAWLEY
☐ 379. JEFF BURROUGHS
☐ 428. LARRY ANDERSEN
☐ 433. JERRY NARRON
☐ 478. JIM BEATTIE
☐ 505. BRUCE BOCHTE
☐ 567. PAUL SERNA
☐ 596. BRYAN CLARK
☐ 600. RENE LACHEMANN(M)
☐ 612. TERRY BULLING
☐ 648. TOMMY DAVIS(C)

TEXAS RANGERS

☐ 37. BILL STEIN
☐ 69. BILLY SAMPLE
☐ 89. JIM KERN
☐ 116. AL OLIVER
☐ 142. GEORGE MEDICH
☐ 163. MARK WAGNER
☐ 195. DON ZIMMER(M)
☐ 215. JON MATLACK
☐ 242. MICKEY RIVERS
☐ 268. JIM SUNDBERG
☐ 289. BUMP WILLS
☐ 321. DANNY DARWIN
☐ 341. STEVE COMER
☐ 368. BUDDY BELL
☐ 394. MARIO MENDOZA
☐ 415. LEON ROBERTS
☐ 447. CHARLIE HOUGH
☐ 467. JOHN GRUBB
☐ 494. RICK HONEYCUTT
☐ 520. PAT PUTNAM
☐ 550. JOHN HENRY JOHNSON
☐ 565. BOB BABCOCK
☐ 642. JOHN ELLIS
☐ 643. FERGIE JENKINS

TORONTO BLUE JAYS

☐ 52. DAVE STIEB
☐ 54. JORGE BELL
☐ 101. ALFREDO GRIFFIN
☐ 129. LLOYD MOSEBY
☐ 178. JACKSON TODD
☐ 180. AL WOODS
☐ 227. JIM CLANCY
☐ 255. LUIS LEAL
☐ 304. OTTO VELEZ
☐ 306. JOHN MAYBERRY
☐ 353. GARTH IORG
☐ 381. ERNIE WHITT
☐ 430. JERRY GARVIN
☐ 432. BARRY BONNELL
☐ 479. DAMASO GARCIA
☐ 507. JOEY MCLAUGHLIN
☐ 541. ROY LEE JACKSON
☐ 559. MARK BOMBACK
☐ 561. BUCK MARTINEZ
☐ 580. JUAN BERENGUER
☐ 629. PAUL MIRABELLA
☐ 638. DANNY AINGE
☐ 652. WILLIE UPSHAW

1983 DONRUSS (660)
2 1/2" X 3 1/2"

ATLANTA BRAVES

☐ 47. DALE MURPHY
☐ 58. BOB HORNER
☐ 97. PHIL NIEKRO
☐ 123. CHRIS CHAMBLISS
☐ 149. RICK CAMP
☐ 173. STEVE BEDROSIAN
☐ 184. GLENN HUBBARD
☐ 223. GENE GARBER
☐ 249. CLAUDELL WASHINGTON
☐ 275. RUFINO LINARES
☐ 299. BRUCE BENEDICT
☐ 310. RAFAEL RAMIREZ
☐ 349. TOMMY BOGGS
☐ 375. KEN DAYLEY
☐ 401. BOB WALK
☐ 425. JERRY ROYSTER
☐ 436. BIFF POCOROBA
☐ 475. AL HRABOSKY
☐ 501. LARRY WHISENTON
☐ 527. RICK MAHLER
☐ 551. BOB WATSON
☐ 557. PASCUAL PEREZ
☐ 562. CARLOS DIAZ
☐ 607. TERRY HARPER
☐ 622. MATT SINATRO
☐ 628. JOE TORRE(M)
☐ 636. BRETT BUTLER

BALTIMORE ORIOLES

☐ 27. GARY ROENICKE
☐ 77. JIM PALMER
☐ 79. JOE NOLAN
☐ 105. MIKE FLANAGAN
☐ 131. GLENN GULLIVER
☐ 153. JOHN LOWENSTEIN
☐ 203. SAMMY STEWART
☐ 205. LENN SAKATA
☐ 231. DENNIS MARTINEZ
☐ 257. KEN SINGLETON
☐ 279. CAL RIPKEN
☐ 329. RICK DEMPSEY
☐ 331. BENNY AYALA
☐ 357. TIPPY MARTINEZ
☐ 383. AL BUMBRY
☐ 405. EDDIE MURRAY
☐ 455. RICH DAUER
☐ 457. TERRY CROWLEY
☐ 483. SCOTT MCGREGOR
☐ 509. DAN FORD
☐ 581. TIM STODDARD
☐ 583. JIM DWYER
☐ 619. STORM DAVIS

BOSTON RED SOX

☐ 30. GARY ALLENSON
☐ 74. JERRY REMY
☐ 82. RICK MILLER
☐ 109. LUIS APONTE
☐ 134. BRUCE HURST
☐ 156. RICH GEDMAN
☐ 200. DAVE STAPLETON
☐ 208. JIM RICE
☐ 235. TOM BURGMEIER
☐ 260. BOB OJEDA
☐ 282. GLENN HOFFMAN
☐ 326. CARL YASTRZEMSKI
☐ 334. CHUCK RAINEY
☐ 361. MARK CLEAR
☐ 386. BOB STANLEY
☐ 408. CARNEY LANSFORD
☐ 452. DWIGHT EVANS

- ☐ 460. REID NICHOLS
- ☐ 487. DENNIS ECKERSLEY
- ☐ 512. MIKE TORREZ
- ☐ 534. ROGER LAFRANCOIS
- ☐ 563. JOHN TUDOR
- ☐ 578. TONY PEREZ
- ☐ 586. WADE BOGGS

CALIFORNIA ANGELS

- ☐ 38. DON AASE
- ☐ 66. GEOFF ZAHN
- ☐ 90. ROD CAREW
- ☐ 115. REGGIE JACKSON
- ☐ 141. DARYL SCONIERS
- ☐ 164. KEN FORSCH
- ☐ 192. BOB BOONE
- ☐ 216. DOUG DECINCES
- ☐ 241. FRED LYNN
- ☐ 267. BRUCE KISON
- ☐ 290. ANDY HASSLER
- ☐ 318. RICK BURLESON
- ☐ 342. TIM FOLI
- ☐ 367. BRIAN DOWNING
- ☐ 393. STEVE RENKO
- ☐ 416. MIKE WITT
- ☐ 444. BOBBY CLARK
- ☐ 468. BOBBY GRICH
- ☐ 493. DON BAYLOR
- ☐ 519. LUIS SANCHEZ
- ☐ 542. LUIS TIANT
- ☐ 570. TOMMY JOHN
- ☐ 604. JOE FERGUSON
- ☐ 612. ROB WILFONG
- ☐ 639. RON JACKSON
- ☐ 640. JUAN BENIQUEZ

CHICAGO CUBS

- ☐ 48. DOUG BIRD
- ☐ 57. ALLEN RIPLEY
- ☐ 99. BILL BUCKNER
- ☐ 126. MEL HALL
- ☐ 151. RANDY MARTZ
- ☐ 174. WILLIE HERNANDEZ
- ☐ 183. JODY DAVIS
- ☐ 225. MIKE PROLY
- ☐ 252. STEVE HENDERSON
- ☐ 277. RYNE SANDBERG
- ☐ 300. FERGIE JENKINS
- ☐ 309. KEITH MORELAND
- ☐ 351. BUMP WILLS
- ☐ 378. SCOT THOMPSON
- ☐ 403. LEE SMITH
- ☐ 426. DICKIE NOLES
- ☐ 435. LARRY BOWA
- ☐ 477. LEON DURHAM
- ☐ 504. BILL CAMPBELL
- ☐ 529. JUNIOR KENNEDY
- ☐ 552. PAT TABLER
- ☐ 561. JAY JOHNSTONE
- ☐ 596. BOBBY MOLINARO
- ☐ 614. LEE ELIA(M)
- ☐ 631. GARY WOODS

CHICAGO WHITE SOX

- ☐ 39. JERRY KOOSMAN
- ☐ 67. SALOME BAROJAS
- ☐ 104. CARLTON FISK
- ☐ 117. VANCE LAW
- ☐ 143. HAROLD BAINES
- ☐ 165. DENNIS LAMP
- ☐ 193. BRITT BURNS
- ☐ 230. MARC HILL
- ☐ 243. TOM PACIOREK
- ☐ 269. STEVE KEMP
- ☐ 291. ERNESTO ESCARREGA
- ☐ 319. RICHARD DOTSON
- ☐ 356. BILL ALMON
- ☐ 369. AURELIO RODRIGUEZ
- ☐ 395. GREG LUZINSKI
- ☐ 417. STEVE TROUT
- ☐ 445. KEVIN HICKEY
- ☐ 482. TONY BERNAZARD
- ☐ 495. MIKE SQUIRES
- ☐ 521. RUDY LAW
- ☐ 543. RON LEFLORE
- ☐ 571. TONY LARUSSA(M)
- ☐ 616. JERRY HAIRSTON
- ☐ 632. LAMARR HOYT
- ☐ 652. MARVIS FOLEY

CINCINNATI REDS

- ☐ 43. CESAR CEDENO
- ☐ 62. FRANK PASTORE
- ☐ 103. BRUCE BERENYI
- ☐ 122. TOM SEAVER
- ☐ 148. DAVE CONCEPCION
- ☐ 169. EDDIE MILNER
- ☐ 188. DAVE VANGORDER
- ☐ 229. TOM HUME
- ☐ 248. MARIO SOTO
- ☐ 274. DAN DRIESSEN
- ☐ 295. GREG HARRIS
- ☐ 314. WAYNE KRENCHICKI
- ☐ 355. JIM KERN
- ☐ 374. ALEX TREVINO
- ☐ 400. TOM LAWLESS
- ☐ 421. CHARLIE LIEBRANDT
- ☐ 440. LARRY BIITTNER
- ☐ 481. JOE PRICE
- ☐ 500. JOHNNY BENCH
- ☐ 526. RON OESTER
- ☐ 547. BRAD LESLEY
- ☐ 566. PAUL HOUSEHOLDER
- ☐ 597. MIKE VAIL
- ☐ 624. DUANE WALKER

CLEVELAND INDIANS

- ☐ 33. CHRIS BANDO
- ☐ 72. RICK SUTCLIFFE
- ☐ 85. MIGUEL DILONE
- ☐ 111. LEN BARKER
- ☐ 137. DAN SPILLNER
- ☐ 159. RON HASSEY
- ☐ 198. RICK MANNING
- ☐ 211. ANDRE THORNTON
- ☐ 237. JOHN DENNY
- ☐ 263. RICK WAITS
- ☐ 285. ALAN BANNISTER
- ☐ 324. VON HAYES
- ☐ 337. TOBY HARRAH
- ☐ 363. LARY SORENSEN
- ☐ 389. ED WHITSON
- ☐ 411. LARRY MILBOURNE
- ☐ 450. MIKE HARGROVE
- ☐ 463. JACK PERCONTE
- ☐ 489. MIKE FISCHLIN
- ☐ 515. RODNEY CRAIG
- ☐ 537. ED GLYNN
- ☐ 576. JERRY DYBZINSKI
- ☐ 589. BERT BLYLEVEN

DETROIT TIGERS

- ☐ 29. PAT UNDERWOOD
- ☐ 76. JOHN WOCKENFUSS
- ☐ 81. RICK LEACH
- ☐ 107. JACK MORRIS
- ☐ 133. DAVE ROZEMA
- ☐ 155. MILT WILCOX
- ☐ 202. ENOS CABELL
- ☐ 207. ALAN TRAMMELL
- ☐ 233. LARRY PASHNICK
- ☐ 259. ELIAS SOSA
- ☐ 281. BILL FAHEY
- ☐ 328. HOWARD JOHNSON
- ☐ 333. LOU WHITAKER
- ☐ 359. DAN PETRY
- ☐ 385. DAVE TOBIK
- ☐ 407. LANCE PARRISH
- ☐ 454. TOM BROOKENS
- ☐ 459. KIRK GIBSON
- ☐ 485. MIKE IVIE
- ☐ 511. CHET LEMON
- ☐ 533. SPARKY ANDERSON(M)
- ☐ 580. GLEN WILSON
- ☐ 585. LARRY HERNDON
- ☐ 600. JERRY UJDUR
- ☐ 641. DAVE RUCKER

HOUSTON ASTROS

- ☐ 41. JOSE CRUZ
- ☐ 65. HARRY SPILMAN
- ☐ 92. BOB KNEPPER
- ☐ 118. NOLAN RYAN
- ☐ 144. ALAN ASHBY
- ☐ 167. TERRY PUHL
- ☐ 191. DICKIE THON
- ☐ 218. FRANK LACORTE
- ☐ 244. JOE SAMBITO
- ☐ 270. PHIL GARNER
- ☐ 293. TONY SCOTT
- ☐ 317. CRAIG REYNOLDS
- ☐ 344. MIKE LACOSS
- ☐ 370. DAVE SMITH
- ☐ 396. ART HOWE
- ☐ 419. DENNY WALLING
- ☐ 443. DANNY HEEP
- ☐ 470. JOE NIEKRO
- ☐ 496. BERT ROBERGE
- ☐ 522. RAY KNIGHT
- ☐ 545. RANDY MOFFITT
- ☐ 569. KIKO GARCIA
- ☐ 620. ALAN KNICELY
- ☐ 627. VERN RUHLE
- ☐ 642. LUIS PUJOLS

KANSAS CITY ROYALS

- ☐ 34. VIDA BLUE
- ☐ 70. DAN QUISENBERRY
- ☐ 86. JOHN WATHAN
- ☐ 112. WILLIE WILSON
- ☐ 138. JERRY MARTIN
- ☐ 160. LARRY GURA
- ☐ 196. DON SLAUGHT
- ☐ 212. WILLIE AIKENS
- ☐ 238. HAL MCRAE
- ☐ 264. GREG PRYOR
- ☐ 286. PAUL SPLITTORFF
- ☐ 322. BUD BLACK
- ☐ 338. GEORGE BRETT
- ☐ 364. AMOS OTIS
- ☐ 390. DON HOOD
- ☐ 412. DENNIS LEONARD
- ☐ 448. CESAR GERONIMO
- ☐ 464. FRANK WHITE
- ☐ 490. U.L. WASHINGTON
- ☐ 516. ONIX CONCEPCION
- ☐ 538. LEE MAY
- ☐ 574. KEITH CREEL
- ☐ 590. DICK HOWSER(M)

LOS ANGELES DODGERS

- ☐ 32. BURT HOOTON
- ☐ 75. MIKE SCIOSCIA
- ☐ 84. RON CEY
- ☐ 110. PEDRO GUERRERO
- ☐ 136. TOM LASORDA(M)
- ☐ 158. JERRY REUSS
- ☐ 201. STEVE YEAGER
- ☐ 210. BILL RUSSELL
- ☐ 236. KEN LANDREAUX
- ☐ 262. CANDY MALDONADO
- ☐ 284. FERNANDO VALENZUELA
- ☐ 327. RON ROENICKE
- ☐ 336. STEVE SAX
- ☐ 362. MIKE MARSHALL
- ☐ 388. JORGE ORTA
- ☐ 410. BOB WELCH
- ☐ 453. TERRY FORSTER
- ☐ 462. DUSTY BAKER
- ☐ 488. STEVE GARVEY
- ☐ 514. MARK BELANGER
- ☐ 536. TOM NIEDENFUER
- ☐ 579. GREG BROCK
- ☐ 588. DAVE STEWART
- ☐ 630. STEVE HOWE
- ☐ 643. RICK MONDAY

MILWAUKEE BREWERS

- ☐ 28. DWIGHT BERNARD
- ☐ 78. ROLLIE FINGERS
- ☐ 80. PETE VUCKOVICH
- ☐ 106. CECIL COOPER
- ☐ 132. DON MONEY
- ☐ 154. MIKE CALDWELL
- ☐ 204. MOOSE HAAS
- ☐ 206. CHARLIE MOORE
- ☐ 232. JIM GANTNER
- ☐ 258. ROBIN YOUNT
- ☐ 280. JAMIE EASTERLY
- ☐ 330. JIM SLATON
- ☐ 332. TED SIMMONS
- ☐ 358. ROY HOWELL
- ☐ 384. BEN OGLIVIE
- ☐ 406. MARSHALL EDWARDS
- ☐ 456. ROB PICCIOLO

- □ 458. NED YOST
- □ 484. PAUL MOLITOR
- □ 510. GORMAN THOMAS
- □ 531. DON SUTTON
- □ 532. MARK BROUHARD
- □ 582. BOB MCCLURE
- □ 584. ED ROMERO
- □ 608. HARVEY KUENN(M)

MINNESOTA TWINS

- □ 51. JACK O'CONNOR
- □ 53. GARY GAETTI
- □ 102. BOBBY CASTILLO
- □ 130. JOHN PACELLA
- □ 177. TIM LAUDNER
- □ 179. KENT HRBEK
- □ 228. RON DAVIS
- □ 256. PETE REDFERN
- □ 303. JOHN CASTINO
- □ 305. RANDY JOHNSON
- □ 354. TERRY FELTON
- □ 382. FRANK VIOLA
- □ 429. GARY WARD
- □ 431. RON WASHINGTON
- □ 480. BRAD HAVENS
- □ 508. AL WILLIAMS
- □ 555. TOM BRUNANSKY
- □ 615. MICKEY HATCHER
- □ 646. DAVE ENGLE
- □ 650. JESUS VEGA

MONTREAL EXPOS

- □ 36. RAY BURRIS
- □ 68. DAVID PALMER
- □ 88. BYRN SMITH
- □ 114. MIKE GATES
- □ 140. AL OLIVER
- □ 162. WOODIE FRYMAN
- □ 194. JEFF REARDON
- □ 214. TIM BLACKWELL
- □ 240. DOUG FLYNN
- □ 266. CHRIS SPEIER
- □ 288. BILL GULLICKSON
- □ 320. STEVE ROGERS
- □ 340. GARY CARTER
- □ 366. BRAD MILLS
- □ 392. TIM WALLACH
- □ 414. CHARLIE LEA
- □ 446. SCOTT SANDERSON
- □ 466. WARREN CROMARTIE
- □ 492. ROY JOHNSON
- □ 518. ANDRE DAWSON
- □ 540. TIM RAINES
- □ 572. JOEL YOUNGBLOOD
- □ 592. TERRY FRANCONA
- □ 602. JERRY WHITE

NEW YORK METS

- □ 49. HUBIE BROOKS
- □ 56. MOOKIE WILSON
- □ 98. NEIL ALLEN
- □ 128. CHARLIE PULEO
- □ 175. RON GARDENHIRE
- □ 182. PETE FALCONE
- □ 224. SCOTT HOLMAN
- □ 254. CRAIG SWAN
- □ 301. DAVE KINGMAN
- □ 308. ED LYNCH
- □ 350. RUSTY STAUB
- □ 380. JOHN STEARNS
- □ 427. GEORGE FOSTER
- □ 434. JESSE OROSCO
- □ 476. RON HODGES
- □ 506. BOB BAILOR
- □ 553. BRENT GAFF
- □ 560. PAT ZACHRY
- □ 599. GARY RAJSICH
- □ 618. WALLY BACKMAN
- □ 634. TERRY LEACH

NEW YORK YANKEES

- □ 31. RON GUIDRY
- □ 73. STEVE BALBONI
- □ 83. GRAIG NETTLES
- □ 108. MIKE MORGAN
- □ 135. RUDY MAY
- □ 157. RICH GOSSAGE
- □ 199. DAVE RIGHETTI
- □ 209. ROY SMALLEY
- □ 234. DAVE COLLINS
- □ 261. BOBBY MURCER
- □ 283. WILLIE RANDOLPH
- □ 325. BUTCH WYNEGAR
- □ 335. LOU PINIELLA
- □ 360. JERRY MUMPHREY
- □ 387. ANDRE ROBERTSON
- □ 409. DAVE WINFIELD
- □ 451. DOYLE ALEXANDER
- □ 461. OSCAR GAMBLE
- □ 486. KEN GRIFFEY
- □ 513. SHANE RAWLEY
- □ 535. GEORGE FRAZIER
- □ 577. RICK CERONE
- □ 587. JAY HOWELL
- □ 638. LEE MAZZILLI

OAKLAND A'S

- □ 35. RICKEY HENDERSON
- □ 71. TONY ARMAS
- □ 87. KELVIN MOORE
- □ 113. DAVE BEARD
- □ 139. MIKE NORRIS
- □ 161. DWAYNE MURPHY
- □ 197. FRED STANLEY
- □ 213. DAVE MCKAY
- □ 239. MATT KEOUGH
- □ 265. BOB OWCHINKO
- □ 287. JOE RUDI
- □ 323. JEFF BURROUGHS
- □ 339. DAVEY LOPES
- □ 365. RICK LANGFORD
- □ 391. TOM UNDERWOOD
- □ 413. DAN MEYER
- □ 449. JIMMY SEXTON
- □ 465. MICKEY KLUTTS
- □ 491. STEVE MCCATTY
- □ 517. MIKE HEATH
- □ 539. BOB KEARNEY
- □ 575. BILLY MARTIN(M)
- □ 591. WAYNE GROSS
- □ 601. CLIFF JOHNSON
- □ 635. JEFF NEWMAN
- □ 651. JEFF JONES

PHILADELPHIA PHILLIES

- □ 42. PETE ROSE
- □ 63. GARRY MADDOX
- □ 93. MARTY BYSTROM
- □ 119. MIKE KRUKOW
- □ 147. BO DIAZ
- □ 168. MIKE SCHMIDT
- □ 189. BOB DERNIER
- □ 219. STEVE CARLTON
- □ 245. SID MONGE
- □ 273. DAVE W. ROBERTS
- □ 294. MANNY TRILLO
- □ 315. GEORGE VUKOVICH
- □ 345. LARRY CHRISTENSON
- □ 371. TUG MCGRAW
- □ 399. IVAN DEJESUS
- □ 420. GARY MATTHEWS
- □ 441. GREG GROSS
- □ 471. ED FARMER
- □ 497. DICK RUTHVEN
- □ 525. JULIO FRANCO
- □ 546. LUIS AGUAYO
- □ 567. RON REED
- □ 606. OZZIE VIRGIL
- □ 626. PAT CORRALES(M)

PITTSBURGH PIRATES

- □ 45. LARRY MCWILLIAMS
- □ 59. TONY PENA
- □ 95. JASON THOMPSON
- □ 124. CHUCK TANNER(M)
- □ 150. JIM MORRISON
- □ 171. DON ROBINSON
- □ 185. DALE BERRA
- □ 221. MIKE EASLER
- □ 250. RICK RHODEN
- □ 276. LEE LACY
- □ 297. KENT TEKULVE
- □ 311. BILL MADLOCK
- □ 347. OMAR MORENO
- □ 376. ROD SCURRY
- □ 402. JIMMY SMITH
- □ 423. MATT GUANTE
- □ 437. JOHNNY RAY
- □ 473. DAVE PARKER
- □ 502. MANNY SARMIENTO
- □ 528. STEVE NICOSIA
- □ 549. JOHN CANDELARIA
- □ 610. WILLIE STARGELL
- □ 647. DICK DAVIS

ST. LOUIS CARDINALS

- □ 40. BRUCE SUTTER
- □ 64. BOB FORSCH
- □ 91. LONNIE SMITH
- □ 120. OZZIE SMITH
- □ 152. KEITH HERNANDEZ
- □ 166. DAVID GREEN
- □ 190. WILLIE MCGEE
- □ 217. TOM HERR
- □ 246. KEN OBERKFELL
- □ 278. DARRELL PORTER
- □ 292. STEVE MURA
- □ 316. JOAQUIN ANDUJAR
- □ 343. JIM KAAT
- □ 372. DOUG BAIR
- □ 404. GEORGE HENDRICK
- □ 418. GLENN BRUMMER
- □ 442. GENE TENACE
- □ 469. DANE IORG
- □ 498. TITO LANDRUM
- □ 530. WHITEY HERZOG(M)
- □ 544. DAVE LAPOINT
- □ 568. MIKE RAMSEY
- □ 617. JOHN MARTIN
- □ 621. JOHN STUPER

SAN DIEGO PADRES

- □ 44. FLOYD CHIFFER
- □ 61. TIM LOLLAR
- □ 94. CHRIS WELSH
- □ 121. BRODERICK PERKINS
- □ 145. GARRY TEMPLETON
- □ 170. JOHN CURTIS
- □ 187. GARY LUCAS
- □ 220. TERRY KENNEDY
- □ 247. JOE PITTMAN
- □ 271. GENE RICHARDS
- □ 296. LUIS DELEON
- □ 313. JOHN MONTEFUSCO
- □ 346. JUAN BONILLA
- □ 373. RUPPERT JONES
- □ 397. ALAN WIGGINS
- □ 422. JUAN EICHELBERGER
- □ 439. ERIC SHOW
- □ 472. TIM FLANNERY
- □ 499. SIXTO LEZCANO
- □ 523. JOE LEFEBVRE
- □ 548. LUIS SALAZAR
- □ 565. DAVE EDWARDS
- □ 598. TONY GWYNN
- □ 625. DICK WILLIAMS(M)
- □ 633. STEVE SWISHER

SAN FRANCISCO GIANTS

- □ 46. ALAN FOWLKES
- □ 60. GARY LAVELLE
- □ 96. TOM O'MALLEY
- □ 125. JOHNNIE LEMASTER
- □ 146. AL HOLLAND
- □ 172. RICH GALE
- □ 186. GREG MINTON
- □ 222. JACK CLARK
- □ 251. DARRELL EVANS
- □ 272. RENIE MARTIN
- □ 298. ATLEE HAMMAKER
- □ 312. MILT MAY
- □ 348. CHARLES DAVIS
- □ 377. BOB BRENLY
- □ 398. JIM BARR
- □ 424. BILL LASKEY
- □ 438. JOE MORGAN
- □ 474. JEFF LEONARD
- □ 503. FRED BREINING
- □ 524. JIM WOHLFORD
- □ 550. DAVE BERGMAN
- □ 564. FRANK ROBINSON(M)
- □ 605. GUY SULARZ
- □ 611. REGGIE SMITH

SEATTLE MARINERS

- □ 50. FLOYD BANNISTER
- □ 55. GENE NELSON
- □ 100. ED VANDEBERG
- □ 127. BRUCE BOCHTE
- □ 176. JIM BEATTIE
- □ 181. LARRY ANDERSEN
- □ 226. TERRY BULLING
- □ 253. MANNY CASTILLO
- □ 302. BILL CAUDILL
- □ 307. GAYLORD PERRY
- □ 352. RICK SWEET
- □ 379. JULIO CRUZ
- □ 428. MIKE MOORE
- □ 433. MIKE STANTON
- □ 478. JIM ESSIAN
- □ 505. TODD CRUZ
- □ 554. AL COWENS
- □ 559. RICHIE ZISK
- □ 603. BRYAN CLARK
- □ 637. GARY GRAY
- □ 649. AL CHAMBERS

TEXAS RANGERS

- □ 37. JOHN BUTCHER
- □ 69. CHARLIE HOUGH
- □ 89. DAVE HOSTETLER
- □ 116. GEORGE WRIGHT
- □ 142. LAMAR JOHNSON
- □ 163. STEVE COMER
- □ 195. JON MATLACK
- □ 215. BUDDY BELL
- □ 242. BILLY SAMPLE
- □ 268. MARK WAGNER
- □ 289. DANNY DARWIN
- □ 321. DAVE J. SCHMIDT
- □ 341. JOHN GRUBB
- □ 368. MIKE RICHARDT
- □ 394. MICKEY RIVERS
- □ 415. RICK HONEYCUTT
- □ 447. FRANK TANANA
- □ 467. LARRY PARRISH
- □ 494. BOBBY JOHNSON
- □ 520. TERRY BOGENER
- □ 541. PAUL MIRABELLA
- □ 573. WAYNE TOLLESON
- □ 593. DON WERNER
- □ 594. BILL STEIN
- □ 609. JIM SUNDBERG

TORONTO BLUE JAYS

- □ 52. STEVE SENTENEY
- □ 54. DAMASO GARCIA
- □ 101. JIM CLANCY
- □ 129. LUIS LEAL
- □ 178. BUCK MARTINEZ
- □ 180. ALFREDO GRIFFIN
- □ 227. JERRY GARVIN
- □ 255. JOEY MCLAUGHLIN
- □ 304. ERNIE WHITT
- □ 306. GARTH IORG
- □ 353. JIM GOTT
- □ 381. DALE MURRAY
- □ 430. BARRY BONNELL
- □ 432. RANCE MULLINIKS
- □ 479. ROY LEE JACKSON
- □ 507. DAVE STIEB
- □ 556. LLOYD MOSEBY
- □ 558. WILLIE UPSHAW
- □ 595. JESSE BARFIELD
- □ 623. GENE PETRALLI
- □ 629. ANTHONY JOHNSON
- □ 644. HOSKEN POWELL

1984 DONRUSS (660)
2 1/2" X 3 1/2"

ATLANTA BRAVES

- □ 36. BRAD KOMMINSK
- □ 66. DALE MURPHY
- □ 77. BIFF POCOROBA
- □ 141. BRETT BUTLER
- □ 165. RICK CAMP
- □ 188. PHIL NIEKRO
- □ 199. KEN DAYLEY
- □ 263. GERALD PERRY
- □ 287. GENE GARBER
- □ 310. CLAUDELL WASHINGTON
- □ 321. RANDY JOHNSON
- □ 385. PETE FALCONE
- □ 409. BRUCE BENEDICT
- □ 432. GLENN HUBBARD
- □ 443. LEN BARKER
- □ 507. PASCUAL PEREZ
- □ 531. JERRY ROYSTER
- □ 535. BOB HORNER
- □ 537. CHRIS CHAMBLISS
- □ 565. STEVE BEDROSIAN
- □ 589. RAFAEL RAMIREZ*
- □ 599. CRAIG MCMURTRY

*RAMIREZ IS SHOWN ON THIS CARD WITH THE A'S. HOWEVER HE WAS NEVER WITH THE A'S ORGANIZATION DURING THIS TIME PERIOD. THEREFORE IT IS THE FEELING OF THE AUTHORS THAT THIS CARD IS AN ERROR AND BELONGS IN THE ATLANTA BRAVES TEAM SET.

BALTIMORE ORIOLES

- □ 47. EDDIE MURRAY
- □ 88. JOE ALTOBELLI(M)
- □ 106. CAL RIPKEN
- □ 123. MIKE BODDICKER
- □ 148. TODD CRUZ
- □ 169. MIKE FLANAGAN
- □ 210. AL BUMBRY
- □ 228. JOHN LOWENSTEIN
- □ 245. TIM STODDARD
- □ 270. BENNY AYALA
- □ 291. JOHN SHELBY
- □ 332. ALLAN RAMIREZ
- □ 350. RICH DAUER
- □ 367. DAN FORD
- □ 392. GARY ROENICKE
- □ 413. RICK DEMPSEY
- □ 454. JIM DWYER
- □ 472. TIPPY MARTINEZ
- □ 489. JOE NOLAN
- □ 514. SAMMY STEWART
- □ 576. JIM PALMER
- □ 585. STORM DAVIS
- □ 594. SCOTT MCGREGOR
- □ 610. KEN SINGLETON
- □ 620. LENN SAKATA
- □ 621. MIKE YOUNG
- □ 622. JOHN STEFERO
- □ 633. DENNIS MARTINEZ

BOSTON RED SOX

- □ 50. JIM RICE
- □ 91. JOHN HENRY JOHNSON
- □ 127. ED JURAK
- □ 151. WADE BOGGS
- □ 172. JERRY REMY
- □ 213. BRUCE HURST
- □ 249. JEFF NEWMAN
- □ 273. DAVE STAPLETON
- □ 294. TONY ARMAS
- □ 335. GARY ALLENSON
- □ 371. LUIS APONTE
- □ 395. DWIGHT EVANS
- □ 416. JOHN TUDOR
- □ 457. DENNIS BOYD
- □ 493. RICK MILLER
- □ 517. MIKE BROWN
- □ 538. BOB OJEDA
- □ 579. RICH GEDMAN
- □ 606. GLENN HOFFMAN
- □ 611. MARK CLEAR
- □ 614. REID NICHOLS
- □ 639. DENNIS ECKERSLEY
- □ 644. BOB STANLEY

CALIFORNIA ANGELS

- □ 35. DICK SCHOFIELD
- □ 42. MIKE BROWN
- □ 57. REGGIE JACKSON
- □ 85. RICK ADAMS
- □ 108. FRED LYNN
- □ 133. RON JACKSON
- □ 158. BOB BOONE
- □ 179. BOBBY GRICH
- □ 207. JUAN BENIQUEZ
- □ 230. DOUG DECINCES
- □ 255. ANDY HASSLER
- □ 280. KEN FORSCH
- □ 301. TOMMY JOHN
- □ 329. ROB WILFONG
- □ 352. ROD CAREW
- □ 377. STEVE LUBRATICH
- □ 402. GEOFF ZAHN
- □ 423. BRIAN DOWNING
- □ 451. DARYL SCONIERS
- □ 474. TIM FOLI
- □ 499. BRUCE KISON
- □ 524. BOBBY CLARK
- □ 597. LUIS SANCHEZ
- □ 647. GARY PETTIS

CHICAGO CUBS

- □ 41. JOE CARTER
- □ 67. LEON DURHAM
- □ 76. CHUCK RAINEY
- □ 117. BILL BUCKNER
- □ 144. GARY WOODS
- □ 167. SCOT THOMPSON
- □ 189. FERGUSON JENKINS
- □ 198. STEVE LAKE
- □ 239. LARRY BOWA
- □ 266. DICKIE NOLES
- □ 289. LEE SMITH
- □ 311. RYNE SANDBERG
- □ 320. MIKE PROLY
- □ 361. RON CEY
- □ 388. CRAIG LEFFERTS
- □ 411. MEL HALL
- □ 433. JODY DAVIS
- □ 442. WARREN BRUSSTAR
- □ 483. KEITH MORELAND
- □ 510. DICK RUTHVEN
- □ 533. STEVE TROUT
- □ 540. JAY JOHNSTONE
- □ 555. BILL CAMPBELL
- □ 623. CARMELO MARTINEZ

CHICAGO WHITE SOX

- □ 27. JOEL SKINNER
- □ 58. HAROLD BAINES
- □ 86. JERRY HAIRSTON
- □ 122. GREG LUZINSKI
- □ 135. KEVIN HICKEY
- □ 160. JERRY DYBZINSKI
- □ 180. RICHARD DOTSON
- □ 208. JUAN AGOSTO
- □ 244. RON KITTLE
- □ 257. RUDY LAW
- □ 282. TOM PACIOREK
- □ 302. CARLTON FISK
- □ 330. MARC HILL
- □ 366. FLOYD BANNISTER
- □ 379. JULIO CRUZ
- □ 404. MIKE SQUIRES
- □ 424. BRITT BURNS
- □ 452. SCOTT FLETCHER
- □ 488. LAMARR HOYT
- □ 501. JERRY KOOSMAN
- □ 526. DENNIS LAMP
- □ 546. VANCE LAW
- □ 570. SALOME BAROJAS
- □ 609. GREG WALKER

CINCINNATI REDS

- □ 62. RON OESTER
- □ 81. TOM FOLEY
- □ 121. DAVE CONCEPCION
- □ 140. RICH GALE
- □ 164. FRANK PASTORE
- □ 184. GARY REDUS
- □ 203. BILL SCHERRER
- □ 243. DAN DRIESSEN
- □ 262. JEFF JONES
- □ 286. ALEX TREVINO
- □ 306. CESAR CEDENO
- □ 325. DUAN WALKER
- □ 365. EDDIE MILNER
- □ 384. KELLY PARIS
- □ 408. DANN BILARDELLO
- □ 428. MARIO SOTO
- □ 447. TED POWER
- □ 487. BRUCE BERENYI
- □ 506. JOE PRICE
- □ 530. CHARLIE PULEO
- □ 550. TOM HUME
- □ 569. JEFF RUSSELL
- □ 602. NICK ESASKY

CLEVELAND INDIANS

- □ 43. MIKE JEFFCOAT
- □ 94. ANDRE THORNTON
- □ 102. TOM BRENNAN
- □ 129. BERT BLYLEVEN
- □ 154. ALAN BANNISTER
- □ 216. JULIO FRANCO
- □ 224. CHRIS BANDO
- □ 251. TOBY HARRAH
- □ 276. BRODERICK PERKINS
- □ 338. RICH SUTCLIFFE
- □ 346. RICK BEHENNA
- □ 373. NEAL HEATON
- □ 398. JUAN EICHELBERGER
- □ 460. RON HASSEY
- □ 468. GEORGE VUKOVICH
- □ 495. MIKE HARGROVE
- □ 520. GERRY WILLARD
- □ 536. PAT TABLER
- □ 542. BROOK JACOBY
- □ 574. GORMAN THOMAS
- □ 582. DAN SPILLNER
- □ 590. BUD ANDERSON
- □ 608. RICHARD BARNES
- □ 629. JIM ESSIAN
- □ 635. LARY SORENSEN

DETROIT TIGERS

- □ 49. LANCE PARRISH
- □ 90. JOHN GRUBB
- □ 105. DAN PETRY
- □ 125. JUAN BERENGUER
- □ 150. JOHN WOCKENFUSS
- □ 171. CHET LEMON
- □ 212. HOWARD BAILEY
- □ 227. LOU WHITAKER
- □ 247. MARTY CASTILLO
- □ 272. DAVE ROZEMA
- □ 293. ALAN TRAMMELL
- □ 334. WAYNE KRENCHICKI
- □ 349. LARRY HERNDON
- □ 369. DOUG BAIR
- □ 394. LARRY PASHNICK
- □ 415. JACK MORRIS
- □ 456. ENOS CABELL
- □ 471. MILT WILCOX
- □ 491. MIKE LAGA
- □ 516. AURELIO LOPEZ
- □ 578. TOM BROOKENS
- □ 593. KIRK GIBSON
- □ 618. GLENN WILSON

HOUSTON ASTROS

- □ 60. NOLAN RYAN
- □ 84. BOB LILLIS(M)
- □ 110. JOE NIEKRO
- □ 136. MIKE SCOTT
- □ 161. MIKE MADDEN
- □ 182. JOSE CRUZ
- □ 206. MIKE LACOSS
- □ 232. RAY KNIGHT
- □ 258. HARRY SPILMAN
- □ 283. FRANK LACORTE
- □ 304. DICKIE THON
- □ 328. BILL DAWLEY
- □ 354. PHIL GARNER
- □ 380. JOHN MIZEROCK
- □ 405. CRAIG REYNOLDS
- □ 426. JERRY MUMPHREY
- □ 450. KEVIN BASS
- □ 476. TERRY PUHL
- □ 502. FRANK DIPINO
- □ 527. TONY SCOTT
- □ 539. ALAN ASHBY
- □ 548. DAVE SMITH
- □ 564. VERN RUHLE
- □ 572. BOB KNEPPER
- □ 580. BILL DORAN
- □ 641. DENNY WALLING

KANSAS CITY ROYALS

- □ 53. GEORGE BRETT
- □ 95. ONIX CONCEPCION
- □ 100. LARRY GURA
- □ 130. BUD BLACK
- □ 155. WILLIE AIKENS
- □ 175. WILLIE WILSON
- □ 217. MIKE ARMSTRONG
- □ 222. FRANK WHITE
- □ 252. CESAR GERONIMO
- □ 277. BUTCH DAVIS
- □ 297. HAL MCRAE
- □ 339. MARK HUISMANN
- □ 344. DARRYL MOTLEY
- □ 374. GREG PRYOR
- □ 399. LEON ROBERTS
- □ 419. DON SLAUGHT
- □ 461. DANNY JACKSON
- □ 466. JOHN WATHAN
- □ 496. JOE SIMPSON
- □ 521. PAUL SPLITTORFF
- □ 543. U.L. WASHINGTON
- □ 583. DAN QUISENBERRY
- □ 588. PAT SHERIDAN

LOS ANGELES DODGERS

- □ 44. SID FERNANDEZ
- □ 52. FERNANDO VALENZUELA
- □ 93. CANDY MALDONADO
- □ 104. STEVE SAX
- □ 128. TOM NIENDENFUER
- □ 153. BOB WELCH
- □ 174. PEDRO GUERRERO
- □ 215. PAT ZACHRY
- □ 226. DUSTY BAKER
- □ 250. ALEJANDRO PENA
- □ 275. JOSE MORALES
- □ 296. GREG BROCK
- □ 337. JOE BECKWITH
- □ 348. MIKE MARSHALL
- □ 372. JACK FIMPLE
- □ 397. DERREL THOMAS
- □ 418. JERRY REUSS
- □ 459. BURT HOOTON
- □ 470. KEN LANDREAUX
- □ 494. RICK HONEYCUTT
- □ 519. DAVE SAX
- □ 581. STEVE YEAGER
- □ 587. BILL RUSSELL
- □ 642. DAVE ANDERSON

MILWAUKEE BREWERS

- □ 31. DION JAMES
- □ 48. ROBIN YOUNT
- □ 89. ED ROMERO
- □ 107. PAUL MOLITOR
- □ 115. JIM GANTNER
- □ 124. PETE LADD
- □ 149. TOM TELLMANN
- □ 170. RICK MANNING
- □ 211. MARK BROUHARD
- □ 229. BEN OGLIVIE
- □ 237. MIKE CALDWELL
- □ 246. BOB GIBSON
- □ 271. NED YOST
- □ 292. CHARLIE MOORE
- □ 333. CHUCK PORTER
- □ 351. CECIL COOPER
- □ 359. BOB MCCLURE
- □ 368. MOOSE HAAS
- □ 393. TOM CANDIOTTI
- □ 414. DON SUTTON
- □ 455. ROB PICCIOLO
- □ 473. TED SIMMONS
- □ 481. JIM SLATON
- □ 490. MARSHALL EDWARDS
- □ 515. BILL SCHROEDER

MINNESOTA TWINS

- □ 37. TIM TEUFEL
- □ 39. GREG GAGNE
- □ 70. KENT HRBEK
- □ 72. KEN SCHROM
- □ 120. JOHN CASTINO
- □ 147. MICKEY HATCHER
- □ 192. GARY WARD
- □ 194. PETE FILSON
- □ 242. TOM BRUNANSKY
- □ 269. RON DAVIS
- □ 314. GARY GAETTI
- □ 316. AL WILLIAMS
- □ 364. FRANK VIOLA
- □ 391. RON WASHINGTON
- □ 436. BOBBY CASTILLO
- □ 438. SCOTT ULLGER
- □ 486. BRYAN OELKERS
- □ 513. RANDY BUSH
- □ 558. LEN WHITEHOUSE
- □ 560. RICK LYSANDER
- □ 598. DAVE ENGLE

MONTREAL EXPOS

- □ 29. MIKE STENHOUSE
- □ 33. ANGEL SALAZAR
- □ 40. MIKE FUENTES
- □ 55. GARY CARTER
- □ 87. BOB JAMES
- □ 97. ANDRE DAWSON
- □ 132. DAN SCHATZEDER

☐ 157. BRYAN LITTLE
☐ 177. AL OLIVER
☐ 209. BOBBY RAMOS
☐ 219. STEVE ROGERS
☐ 254. DOUG FLYNN
☐ 279. JEFF REARDON
☐ 299. TIM RAINES
☐ 331. RAY BURRIS
☐ 341. SCOTT SANDERSON
☐ 376. CHARLIE LEA
☐ 401. BILL GULLICKSON
☐ 421. TIM WALLACH
☐ 453. BRYN SMITH
☐ 463. TERRY FRANCONA
☐ 498. CHRIS WELSH
☐ 523. CHRIS SPEIER
☐ 575. MANNY TRILLO

NEW YORK METS

☐ 30. RON DARLING
☐ 68. DARRYL STRAWBERRY
☐ 75. ED LYNCH
☐ 116. TOM SEAVER
☐ 190. MOOKIE WILSON
☐ 197. JESSE OROSCO
☐ 238. KEITH HERNANDEZ
☐ 312. GEORGE FOSTER
☐ 319. JUNIOR ORTIZ
☐ 360. DAVE KINGMAN
☐ 434. DANNY HEEP
☐ 441. CRAIG SWAN
☐ 482. MIKE FITZGERALD
☐ 554. RUSTY STAUB
☐ 556. MIKE TORREZ
☐ 563. BRIAN GILES
☐ 595. BOB BAILOR
☐ 600. CARLOS DIAZ
☐ 603. RON HODGES
☐ 607. HUBIE BROOKS
☐ 615. DOUG SISK
☐ 640. WALT TERRELL
☐ 643. JOSE OQUENDO

NEW YORK YANKEES

☐ 45. BRIAN DAYETT
☐ 51. DAVE WINFIELD
☐ 92. JUAN ESPINO
☐ 103. DAVE RIGHETTI
☐ 126. JOHN MONTEFUSCO
☐ 152. DON BAYLOR
☐ 173. RON GUIDRY
☐ 214. BOB SHIRLEY
☐ 225. ROY SMALLEY
☐ 248. DON MATTINGLY
☐ 274. LOU PINIELLA
☐ 295. SHANE RAWLEY
☐ 336. BOB MEACHAM
☐ 347. ANDRE ROBERTSON
☐ 370. RAY FONTENOT
☐ 396. RICH GOSSAGE
☐ 417. WILLIE RANDOLPH
☐ 458. BUTCH WYNEGAR
☐ 469. STEVE KEMP
☐ 492. RICK CERONE
☐ 518. GRAIG NETTLES
☐ 577. DALE MURRAY
☐ 591. GEORGE FRAZIER
☐ 613. KEN GRIFFEY
☐ 626. RUDY MAY
☐ 627. MATT KEOUGH
☐ 637. OMAR MORENO

OAKLAND A'S

☐ 54. RICKEY HENDERSON
☐ 96. DON HILL
☐ 101. DWAYNE MURPHY
☐ 131. GORMAN HEIMUELLER
☐ 156. JEFF BURROUGHS
☐ 176. CARNEY LANSFORD
☐ 218. DAVE BEARD
☐ 223. MIKE HEATH
☐ 253. TOM UNDERWOOD
☐ 278. TONY PHILLIPS
☐ 298. MIKE DAVIS
☐ 340. TIM CONROY
☐ 345. CHRIS CODIROLI
☐ 375. WAYNE GROSS
☐ 400. DAVEY LOPES
☐ 420. STEVE MCCATTY
☐ 462. BOB KEARNEY
☐ 467. BILL ALMON
☐ 497. KEITH ATHERTON
☐ 522. TOM BURGMEIER
☐ 631. MIKE WARREN

PHILADELPHIA PHILLIES

☐ 61. PETE ROSE
☐ 82. JOE LEFEBVRE
☐ 111. STEVE CARLTON
☐ 137. BO DIAZ
☐ 163. WILLIE HERNANDEZ
☐ 183. MIKE SCHMIDT
☐ 204. AL HOLLAND
☐ 233. GARY MATTHEWS
☐ 259. MARTY BYSTROM
☐ 285. GREG GROSS
☐ 305. GARRY MADDOX
☐ 326. OZZIE VIRGIL
☐ 355. JOE MORGAN
☐ 381. KEVIN GROSS
☐ 407. JOHN DENNY
☐ 427. IVAN DEJESUS
☐ 448. CHARLIE HUDSON
☐ 477. VON HAYES
☐ 503. TONY PEREZ
☐ 529. RON REED
☐ 541. BOB DERNIER
☐ 545. KIKO GARCIA
☐ 547. TUG MCGRAW
☐ 549. LEN MATUSZEK

PITTISBURGH PIRATES

☐ 38. DOUG FROBEL
☐ 64. JASON THOMPSON
☐ 78. CECILIO GUANTE
☐ 113. BILL MADLOCK
☐ 142. BRIAN HARPER
☐ 166. LEE MAZZILLI
☐ 186. TONY PENA
☐ 200. MANNY SARMIENTO
☐ 235. ROD SCURRY
☐ 264. GENE TENACE
☐ 288. DAVE PARKER
☐ 308. JOHNNY RAY
☐ 322. JIM MORRISON
☐ 357. JOHN CANDELARIA
☐ 386. MILT MAY
☐ 410. KENT TEKULVE
☐ 430. DALE BERRA
☐ 444. MIKE EASLER
☐ 479. LEE LACY
☐ 508. MARVELL WYNNE
☐ 532. DON ROBINSON
☐ 552. RICK RHODEN
☐ 566. LARRY MCWILLIAMS
☐ 592. LEE TUNNELL
☐ 628. JOSE DELEON

ST. LOUIS CARDINALS

☐ 59. OZZIE SMITH
☐ 83. ANDY VAN SLYKE
☐ 109. NEIL ALLEN
☐ 138. GLENN BRUMMER
☐ 168. BOB FORSCH
☐ 181. JOAQUIN ANDUJAR
☐ 205. DAVID VON OHLEN
☐ 231. LONNIE SMITH
☐ 260. DAVE RUCKER
☐ 290. DAVE LAPOINT
☐ 303. DARRELL PORTER
☐ 327. JEFF LAHTI
☐ 353. WILLIE MCGEE
☐ 382. MIKE RAMSEY
☐ 412. JOHN STUPER
☐ 425. DAVID GREEN
☐ 449. DANNY COX
☐ 475. GEORGE HENDRICK
☐ 504. KEN OBERKFELL
☐ 534. BRUCE SUTTER
☐ 571. DANE IORG
☐ 596. TOM HERR

SAN DIEGO PADRES

☐ 34. KEVIN MCREYNOLDS
☐ 63. STEVE GARVEY
☐ 80. KURT BEVACQUA
☐ 112. TERRY KENNEDY
☐ 139. SID MONGE
☐ 162. LUIS DELEON
☐ 185. GARRY TEMPLETON
☐ 202. TIM FLANNERY
☐ 234. JUAN BONILLA
☐ 261. RUPPERT JONES
☐ 284. TIM LOLLAR
☐ 307. GARY LUCAS
☐ 324. TONY GWYNN
☐ 356. LUIS SALAZAR
☐ 383. DOUG GWOSDZ
☐ 406. ERIC SHOW
☐ 429. GENE RICHARDS
☐ 446. DENNIS RASMUSSEN
☐ 478. BOBBY BROWN
☐ 505. MARK THURMOND
☐ 528. ED WHITSON
☐ 551. DAVE DRAVECKY
☐ 568. ALAN WIGGINS

SAN FRANCISCO GIANTS

☐ 46. CHRIS SMITH
☐ 65. JACK CLARK
☐ 79. JIM BARR
☐ 114. CHILI DAVIS
☐ 143. JOHN RABB
☐ 187. GREG MINTON
☐ 201. MARK DAVIS
☐ 236. ATLEE HAMMAKER
☐ 265. BRAD WELLMAN
☐ 309. ANDY MCGAFFIGAN
☐ 323. MAX VENABLE
☐ 358. BILL LASKEY
☐ 387. FRED BREINING
☐ 431. DARRELL EVANS
☐ 445. RENIE MARTIN
☐ 480. JOEL YOUNGBLOOD
☐ 509. MIKE KRUKOW
☐ 553. DUAN KUIPER
☐ 567. JEFF LEONARD
☐ 573. GARY LAVELLE
☐ 601. TOM O'MALLEY
☐ 616. BOB BRENLY
☐ 624. DAVE BERGMAN
☐ 646. SCOTT GARRELTS
☐ 649. JOHNNIE LEMASTER

SEATTLE MARINERS

☐ 69. RICHIE ZISK
☐ 74. JOHN MOSES
☐ 118. BILL CAUDILL
☐ 145. PAT PUTNAM
☐ 191. JIM BEATTIE
☐ 196. RICK SWEET
☐ 240. TONY BERNAZARD
☐ 267. JAMIE ALLEN
☐ 313. SPIKE OWEN
☐ 318. ORLANDO MERCADO
☐ 362. MATT YOUNG
☐ 389. STEVE HENDERSON
☐ 435. EDWIN NÚNEZ

□ 440. DOMINGO RAMOS
□ 484. RON ROENICKE
□ 511. AL COWENS
□ 557. DAVE HENDERSON
□ 562. BRYAN CLARK
□ 604. ED VANDE BERG
□ 619. BOB STODDARD
□ 630. DARNELL COLES
□ 632. DEL CRANDALL(M)
□ 634. MIKE MOORE
□ 636. RICKY NELSON

TEXAS RANGERS

□ 28. TOM DUNBAR
□ 56. BUDDY BELL
□ 98. FRANK TANANA
□ 99. CURT WILKERSON
□ 134. TOM HENKE
□ 159. DAVE HOSTETLER
□ 178. JIM SUNDBERG
□ 220. JOHN BUTCHER
□ 221. MIKE SMITHSON
□ 256. ODELL JONES
□ 281. PETE O'BRIEN
□ 300. BUCKY DENT
□ 342. LARRY BITTNER
□ 343. DAVE STEWART
□ 378. JON MATLACK
□ 403. BILLY SAMPLE
□ 422. LARRY PARRISH
□ 464. WAYNE TOLLESON
□ 465. MICKEY RIVERS
□ 500. BOB JOHNSON
□ 525. GEORGE WRIGHT
□ 544. DANNY DARWIN
□ 586. DAVE SCHMIDT
□ 638. CHARLIE HOUGH

TORONTO BLUE JAYS

□ 32. TONY FERNANDEZ
□ 71. DAVE STIEB
□ 73. GEORGE BELL
□ 119. JIM CLANCY
□ 146. JIM ACKER
□ 193. JESSE BARFIELD
□ 195. ROY LEE JACKSON
□ 241. DAMASO GARCIA
□ 268. JIM GOTT
□ 315. WILLIE UPSHAW
□ 317. JORGE ORTA
□ 363. LLOYD MOSEBY
□ 390. RANDY MOFFITT
□ 437. ERNIE WHITT
□ 439. DOYLE ALEXANDER
□ 485. LUIS LEAL
□ 512. CLIFF JOHNSON
□ 559. BARRY BONNELL
□ 561. GARTH IORG
□ 584. RANCE MULLINIKS
□ 605. ALFREDO GRIFFIN
□ 612. BUCK MARTINEZ
□ 617. JOEY MCLAUGHLIN
□ 645. DAVE GEISEL
□ 650. DAVE COLLINS

1985 DONRUSS (660)
2 1/2" X 3 1/2"

ATLANTA BRAVES

□ 66. DALE MURPHY
□ 77. BOB HORNER
□ 141. RAFAEL RAMIREZ
□ 165. LEN BARKER
□ 188. CRAIG MCMURTRY
□ 199. GLENN HUBBARD
□ 263. BRUCE BENEDICT
□ 287. CHRIS CHAMBLISS
□ 310. CLAUDELL WASHINGTON
□ 321. BRAD KOMMINSK
□ 385. RICK MAHLER
□ 409. RICK CAMP
□ 432. KEN OBERKFELL
□ 443. GERALD PERRY
□ 507. PASCUAL PEREZ
□ 531. RANDY JOHNSON
□ 554. JEFF DEDMON
□ 565. ALEX TREVINO
□ 628. STEVE BEDROSIAN
□ 650. DONNIE MOORE

BALTIMORE ORIOLES

□ 36. LARRY SHEETS
□ 45. JIM TRABER
□ 47. EDDIE MURRAY
□ 88. MIKE FLANAGAN
□ 106. RICH DAUER
□ 123. GARY ROENICKE
□ 148. SAMMY STEWART
□ 169. CAL RIPKEN
□ 210. TIPPY MARTINEZ
□ 228. WAYNE GROSS
□ 245. JOHN LOWENSTEIN
□ 270. KEN DIXON
□ 291. MIKE BODDICKER
□ 332. RICK DEMPSEY
□ 350. AL BUMBRY
□ 367. MIKE YOUNG
□ 392. BILL SWAGGERTY
□ 413. SCOTT MCGREGOR
□ 454. STORM DAVIS
□ 472. JOHN SHELBY
□ 489. DAN FORD
□ 514. DENNIS MARTINEZ
□ 535. VIC RODRIGUEZ
□ 576. FLOYD RAYFORD
□ 594. JOE NOLAN

BOSTON RED SOX

□ 29. STEVE LYONS
□ 40. CHARLIE MITCHELL
□ 50. JIM RICE
□ 91. BOB STANLEY
□ 127. MARTY BARRETT
□ 151. DENNIS BOYD
□ 172. WADE BOGGS
□ 213. MIKE EASLER
□ 249. TONY ARMAS
□ 273. ROGER CLEMENS
□ 294. DWIGHT EVANS
□ 335. JACKIE GUTIERREZ
□ 371. BOB OJEDA
□ 395. STEVE CRAWFORD
□ 416. BILL BUCKNER
□ 457. RICH GEDMAN
□ 493. BRUCE HURST
□ 517. RICK MILLER
□ 538. MARK CLEAR
□ 579. ED JURAK
□ 614. AL NIPPER
□ 636. REID NICHOLS

CALIFORNIA ANGELS

□ 57. REGGIE JACKSON
□ 85. ROD CAREW
□ 108. MIKE WITT
□ 133. FRED LYNN
□ 158. BRIAN DOWNING
□ 179. DOUG DECINCES
□ 207. MIKE BROWN
□ 230. BOB BOONE
□ 255. DON AASE
□ 280. BOBBY GRICH
□ 301. GEOFF ZAHN
□ 329. DICK SCHOFIELD
□ 352. LUIS SANCHEZ
□ 377. BRUCE KISON
□ 402. ROB WILFONG
□ 423. TOMMY JOHN
□ 451. RON ROMANICK
□ 474. DOUG CORBETT
□ 499. GARY PETTIS
□ 524. CURT KAUFMAN
□ 545. JIM SLATON
□ 573. JUAN BENIQUEZ
□ 620. DARYL SCONIERS
□ 643. JERRY NARRON
□ 644. DARRELL MILLER

CHICAGO CUBS

□ 39. SHAWON DUNSTON
□ 41. BILLY HATCHER
□ 67. RYNE SANDBERG
□ 76. JODY DAVIS
□ 117. KEITH MORELAND
□ 144. TIM STODDARD
□ 167. GEORGE FRAZIER
□ 189. LEON DURHAM
□ 198. STEVE TROUT
□ 239. GARY MATTHEWS
□ 266. SCOTT SANDERSON
□ 289. RICH BORDI
□ 311. LEE SMITH
□ 320. RON CEY
□ 361. LARRY BOWA
□ 388. THAD BOSLEY
□ 411. HENRY COTTO
□ 433. RICK SUTCLIFFE
□ 442. DENNIS ECKERSLEY
□ 483. DAVE OWEN
□ 510. BOB DERNIER
□ 533. WARREN BRUSSTAR
□ 555. GARY WOODS
□ 564. RICH HEBNER
□ 604. DAVE LOPES

CHICAGO WHITE SOX

□ 33. DARYL BOSTON
□ 58. HAROLD BAINES
□ 86. LAMARR HOTY
□ 122. VANCE LAW
□ 135. JERRY HAIRSTON
□ 160. MARC HILL
□ 180. RON KITTLE
□ 208. CARLTON FISK
□ 244. RUDY LAW
□ 257. BRITT BURNS
□ 282. RON REED
□ 302. RICH DOTSON
□ 330. SCOTT FLETCHER
□ 366. GREG WALKER
□ 379. FLOYD BANNISTER
□ 404. AL JONES
□ 424. TOM SEAVER
□ 452. JULIO CRUZ
□ 488. TOM PACIOREK
□ 501. MIKE SQUIRES
□ 526. JUAN AGOSTO
□ 546. GREG LUZINSKI
□ 574. JOEL SKINNER

- □ 615. GENE NELSON
- □ 622. ROY SMALLEY
- □ 645. TIM HULETT

CINCINNATI REDS

- □ 62. DAVE PARKER
- □ 81. RON OESTER
- □ 121. NICK ESASKY
- □ 140. WAYNE KRENCHICKI
- □ 164. JOHN FRANCO
- □ 184. MARIO SOTO
- □ 203. DAVE CONCEPCION
- □ 243. DANN BILARDELLO
- □ 262. JAY TIBBS
- □ 286. TED POWER
- □ 306. GARY REDUS
- □ 325. ERIC DAVIS
- □ 365. BRAD GULDEN
- □ 384. DAVE VAN GORDER
- □ 408. TOM HUME
- □ 428. EDDIE MILNER
- □ 447. CESAR CEDENO
- □ 487. JEFF RUSSELL
- □ 506. BOB OWCHINKO
- □ 530. SKEETER BARNES
- □ 550. FRANK PASTORE
- □ 569. TOM FOLEY
- □ 608. DUANE WALKER
- □ 627. JOE PRICE
- □ 634. TOM BROWNING
- □ 641. PERE ROSS(M)
- □ 642. WADE ROWDON
- □ 646. ANDY MCGAFFIGAN
- □ 649. RON ROBINSON

CLEVELAND INDIANS

- □ 94. JULIO FRANCO
- □ 102. TONY BERNAZARD
- □ 129. ERNIE CAMACHO
- □ 154. BROOK JACOBY
- □ 216. BRETT BUTLER
- □ 224. BERT BLYLEVEN
- □ 251. MIKE JEFFCOAT
- □ 276. GEORGE VUKOVICH
- □ 338. MEL HALL
- □ 346. JERRY WILLARD
- □ 373. NEAL HEATON
- □ 398. MIKE HARGROVE
- □ 460. PAT TABLER
- □ 468. ANDRE THORNTON
- □ 495. MIKE FISCHLIN
- □ 520. CHRIS BANDO
- □ 582. TOM WADDELL
- □ 590. CARMEN CASTILLO
- □ 611. ROY SMITH
- □ 616. JOE CARTER
- □ 639. DON SCHULZE
- □ 653. STEVE FARR

DETROIT TIGERS

- □ 49. LANCE PARRISH
- □ 90. CHET LEMON
- □ 105. MILT WILCOX
- □ 125. DAVE ROZEMA
- □ 150. LARRY HERNDON
- □ 171. ALAN TRAMMELL
- □ 212. WILLIE HERNANDEZ
- □ 227. DARRELL EVANS
- □ 247. HOWARD JOHNSON
- □ 272. JUAN BERENGUER
- □ 293. LOU WHITAKER
- □ 334. DAN PETRY
- □ 349. AURELIO LOPEZ
- □ 369. DOUG BAIR
- □ 394. MARTY CASTILLO
- □ 415. JACK MORRIS
- □ 456. BARBARO GARBEY
- □ 471. KIRK GIBSON
- □ 491. SCOTTIE EARL
- □ 516. RUSTY KUNTZ
- □ 537. DAVE BERGMAN
- □ 578. JOHN GRUBB
- □ 593. TOM BROOKENS
- □ 612. RUPPERT JONES

HOUSTON ASTROS

- □ 60. NOLAN RYAN
- □ 84. BILL DORAN
- □ 110. ENOS CABELL
- □ 136. KEVIN BASS
- □ 161. PHIL GARNER
- □ 182. JOE NIEKRO
- □ 260. JERRY MUMPHREY
- □ 232. FRANK DIPINO
- □ 258. MIKE SCOTT
- □ 283. ALAN ASHBY
- □ 304. JOSE CRUZ
- □ 328. CRAIG REYNOLDS
- □ 354. BILL DAWLEY
- □ 380. VERN RUHLE
- □ 405. MIKE LACOSS
- □ 426. TERRY PUHL
- □ 450. MARK BAILEY
- □ 476. BOB KNEPPER
- □ 502. JIM PANKOVITZ
- □ 527. DENNY WALLING
- □ 548. DAVE SMITH
- □ 572. JOE SAMBITO

KANSAS CITY ROYALS

- □ 32. JOHN MORRIS
- □ 42. RUSS STEPHANS
- □ 53. GEORGE BRETT
- □ 95. DAN QUISENBERRY
- □ 100. BUD BLACK
- □ 130. JORGE ORTA
- □ 155. ONIX CONCEPCION
- □ 175. FRANK WHITE
- □ 217. LARRY GURA
- □ 222. BRET SABERHAGEN
- □ 252. DANE IORG
- □ 277. GREG PRYOR
- □ 297. WILLIE WILSON
- □ 339. PAT SHERIDAN
- □ 344. MARK GUBICZA
- □ 374. DANNY JACKSON
- □ 399. CHARLIE LEIBRANDT
- □ 419. STEVE BALBONI
- □ 461. DARRYL MOTLEY
- □ 466. JOHN WATHAN
- □ 496. DON SLAUGHT
- □ 521. U.L. WASHINGTON
- □ 541. JOE BECKWITH
- □ 583. MARK HUISMANN
- □ 588. HAL MCRAE
- □ 640. MIKE JONES

LOS ANGELES DODGERS

- □ 31. TONY BREWER
- □ 52. FERNANDO VALENZUELA
- □ 93. BILL RUSSELL
- □ 104. BURT HOOTON
- □ 128. R.J. REYNOLDS
- □ 153. TOM NIEDENFUER
- □ 174. PEDRO GUERRERO
- □ 215. RICK HONEYCUTT
- □ 226. JERRY REUSS
- □ 250. CANDY MALDONADO
- □ 275. DAVE ANDERSON
- □ 296. MIKE MARSHALL
- □ 337. ALEJANDRO PENA
- □ 348. FRANKLIN STUBBS
- □ 372. BOB WELCH
- □ 397. BOB BAILOR
- □ 418. STEVE SAX
- □ 459. MIKE SCIOSCIA
- □ 470. SID BREAM
- □ 494. KEN LANDREAUX
- □ 519. STEVE YEAGER
- □ 540. TERRY WHITFIELD
- □ 581. OREL HERSHISER
- □ 592. KEN HOWELL
- □ 638. GERMAN RIVERA

MILWAUKEE BREWERS

- □ 46. DOUG LOMAN
- □ 48. ROBIN YOUNT
- □ 89. JIM SUNDBERG
- □ 107. DON SUTTON
- □ 115. CHUCK PORTER
- □ 124. BILL SCHROEDER
- □ 149. MARK BROUHARD
- □ 170. CECIL COOPER
- □ 211. DION JAMES
- □ 229. JIM GANTNER
- □ 237. RICK MANNING
- □ 246. TOM TELLMANN
- □ 271. PETE LADD
- □ 292. ROLLIE FINGERS
- □ 333. BEN OGLIVIE
- □ 351. CHARLIE MOORE
- □ 359. PAUL MOLITOR
- □ 368. RICK WAITS
- □ 393. BOB GIBSON
- □ 414. TED SIMMONS
- □ 455. JAIME COCANOWER
- □ 473. MOOSE HAAS
- □ 481. BOBBY CLARK
- □ 490. MIKE CALDWELL
- □ 515. ED ROMERO
- □ 536. BOB MCCLURE
- □ 577. ROY HOWELL
- □ 595. WILLIE LOZADO

MINNESOTA TWINS

- □ 30. JEFF REED
- □ 70. KENT HRBEK
- □ 72. DAVE ENGLE
- □ 120. RON DAVIS
- □ 147. DAVE MEIER
- □ 192. TIM TEUFEL
- □ 194. MICKEY HATCHER
- □ 242. GARY GAETTI
- □ 269. HOUSTON JIMENEZ
- □ 314. JOHN BUTCHER
- □ 316. MIKE SMITHSON
- □ 364. TOM BRUNANSKY
- □ 391. RON WASHINGTON
- □ 436. FRANK VIOLA
- □ 438. KIRBY PUCKETT
- □ 486. KEN SCHROM
- □ 513. LEN WHITEHOUSE
- □ 558. DARRELL BROWN
- □ 560. RICK LYSANDER
- □ 607. PETE FILSON
- □ 633. RANDY BUSH
- □ 652. TIM LAUDNER

MONTREAL EXPOS

- □ 55. GARY CARTER
- □ 87. TIM WALLACH
- □ 97. BILL GULLICKSON

- ☐ 132. TERRY FRANCONA
- ☐ 157. JOE HESKETH
- ☐ 177. CHARLIE LEA
- ☐ 209. BRYN SMITH
- ☐ 219. STEVE ROGERS
- ☐ 254. PETE ROSE
- ☐ 279. BOB JAMES
- ☐ 299. TIM RAINES
- ☐ 331. JEFF REARDON
- ☐ 341. DAVID PALMER
- ☐ 376. MIKE STENHOUSE
- ☐ 401. RAZOR SHINES
- ☐ 421. ANDRE DAWSON
- ☐ 453. MIGUEL DILONE
- ☐ 463. DOUG FLYNN
- ☐ 498. GARY LUCAS
- ☐ 523. ANGEL SALAZAR
- ☐ 543. DAN SCHATZEDER
- ☐ 575. RANDY ST. CLAIRE
- ☐ 585. JIM WOHLFORD
- ☐ 619. DAN DRIESSEN

NEW YORK METS

- ☐ 38. CALVIN SCHIRALDI
- ☐ 68. KEITH HERNANDEZ
- ☐ 75. JESSE OROSCO
- ☐ 116. JOHN GIBBONS
- ☐ 190. DWIGHT GOODEN
- ☐ 197. HUBIE BROOKS
- ☐ 238. MIKE FITZGERALD
- ☐ 312. DARRYL STRAWBERRY
- ☐ 319. WALLY BACKMAN
- ☐ 360. RON GARDENHIRE
- ☐ 434. RON DARLING
- ☐ 441. DOUG SISK
- ☐ 482. MOOKIE WILSON
- ☐ 556. DANNY HEEP
- ☐ 563. SID FERNANDEZ
- ☐ 597. WALT TERRELL
- ☐ 603. GEORGE FOSTER
- ☐ 610. RAFAEL SANTANA
- ☐ 617. RAY KNIGHT
- ☐ 623. ED LYNCH
- ☐ 625. BRUCE BERENYI
- ☐ 626. KELVIN CHAPMAN

NEW YORK YANKEES

- ☐ 37. SCOTT BRADLEY
- ☐ 51. DAVE WINFIELD
- ☐ 92. WILLIE RANDOLPH
- ☐ 103. JAY HOWELL
- ☐ 126. BOBBY MEACHAM
- ☐ 152. BRIAN DAYETT
- ☐ 173. DON BAYLOR
- ☐ 214. RON GUIDRY
- ☐ 225. STEVE KEMP
- ☐ 248. RAY FONTENOT
- ☐ 274. RICK CERONE
- ☐ 295. DON MATTINGLY
- ☐ 336. DAVE RIGHETTI
- ☐ 347. KEN GRIFFEY
- ☐ 370. BOB SHIRLEY
- ☐ 396. CLAY CHRISTIANSEN
- ☐ 417. BUTCH WYNEGAR
- ☐ 458. PHIL NIEKRO
- ☐ 469. REX HUDLER
- ☐ 492. JOSE RIJO
- ☐ 518. DENNIS RASMUSSEN
- ☐ 539. MIKE PAGLIARULO
- ☐ 580. JOHN MONTEFUSCO
- ☐ 591. OMAR MORENO
- ☐ 602. MIKE ARMSTRONG
- ☐ 613. JOE COWLEY
- ☐ 629. VIC MATA
- ☐ 637. DAN PASQUA

OAKLAND A'S

- ☐ 35. STEVE KIEFER
- ☐ 54. DAVE KINGMAN
- ☐ 96. BILL CAUDILL
- ☐ 101. TONY PHILLIPS
- ☐ 131. LARY SORENSEN
- ☐ 156. TIM CONROY
- ☐ 176. RICKEY HENDERSON
- ☐ 218. RAY BURRIS
- ☐ 223. MIKE DAVIS
- ☐ 253. BRUCE BOCHTE
- ☐ 278. MIKE WARREN
- ☐ 298. MIKE HEATH
- ☐ 340. KEITH ATHERTON
- ☐ 345. CARNEY LANSFORD
- ☐ 375. DONNIE HILL
- ☐ 400. TOM BURGMEIER
- ☐ 420. DWAYNE MURPHY
- ☐ 462. CHRIS CODOROLI
- ☐ 467. BILL KRUEGER
- ☐ 497. STEVE MCCATTY
- ☐ 522. CURT YOUNG
- ☐ 542. JEFF BURROUGHS
- ☐ 584. JOE MORGAN
- ☐ 589. BILL ALMON
- ☐ 618. CHUCK RAINEY

PHILADELPHIA PHILLIES

- ☐ 44. STEVE JELTZ
- ☐ 61. MIKE SCHMIDT
- ☐ 82. OZZIE VIRGIL
- ☐ 111. JOHN DENNY
- ☐ 137. GARRY MADDOX
- ☐ 163. BILL CAMPBELL
- ☐ 183. JUAN SAMUEL
- ☐ 204. IVAN DEJESUS
- ☐ 233. JERRY KOOSMAN
- ☐ 259. LEN MATUSZEK
- ☐ 285. JOE LEFEBVRE
- ☐ 305. STEVE CARLTON
- ☐ 326. VON HAYES
- ☐ 355. CHARLIE HUDSON
- ☐ 381. TIM CORCORAN
- ☐ 407. GREG GROSS
- ☐ 427. AL HOLLAND
- ☐ 448. RICK SCHU
- ☐ 477. KEVIN GROSS
- ☐ 503. LUIS AGUAYO
- ☐ 529. SIXTO LEZCANO
- ☐ 549. JOHN WOCKENFUSS
- ☐ 570. LARRY ANDERSEN
- ☐ 598. AL OLIVER
- ☐ 599. SHANE RAWLEY
- ☐ 609. GLENN WILSON
- ☐ 624. JEFF STONE
- ☐ 648. JOHN RUSSELL

PITTSBURGH PIRATES

- ☐ 28. MIKE BIELECKI
- ☐ 34. ALFONSO PULIDO
- ☐ 64. TONY PENA
- ☐ 78. LARRY MCWILLIAMS
- ☐ 113. MARVELL WYNNE
- ☐ 142. ROD SCURRY
- ☐ 166. BENNY DISTEFANO
- ☐ 186. JOHNNY RAY
- ☐ 200. BILL MADLOCK
- ☐ 235. JOHN TUDOR
- ☐ 264. DON ROBINSON
- ☐ 288. LEE TUNNELL
- ☐ 308. JOSE DELEON
- ☐ 322. JASON THOMPSON
- ☐ 357. CECILIO GUANTE
- ☐ 386. LEE MAZZILLI
- ☐ 410. MILT MAY
- ☐ 430. JOHN CANDELARIA
- ☐ 444. DALE BERRA
- ☐ 479. KENT TEKULVE
- ☐ 508. LEE LACY
- ☐ 532. JIM MORRISON
- ☐ 552. RICK RHODEN
- ☐ 566. BRIAN HARPER
- ☐ 600. DENNY GONZALEZ

ST. LOUIS CARDINALS

- ☐ 59. OZZIE SMITH
- ☐ 83. RICKY HORTON
- ☐ 109. BRUCE SUTTER
- ☐ 138. DAVE LAPOINT
- ☐ 168. TITO LANDRUM
- ☐ 181. GEORGE HENDRICK
- ☐ 205. NEIL ALLEN
- ☐ 231. LONNIE SMITH
- ☐ 260. DAVE RUCKER
- ☐ 290. GLENN BRUMMER
- ☐ 303. DAVID GREEN
- ☐ 327. ANDY VAN SLYKE
- ☐ 353. DARRELL PORTER
- ☐ 382. KURT KEPSHIRE
- ☐ 412. DAVE VON OHLEN
- ☐ 425. TOM HERR
- ☐ 449. JOAQUIN ANDUJAR
- ☐ 475. WILLIE MCGEE
- ☐ 504. RALPH CITARELLA
- ☐ 534. TERRY PENDLETON
- ☐ 547. MARK SALAS
- ☐ 571. DANNY COX
- ☐ 596. TOM NIETO

SAN DIEGO PADRES

- ☐ 63. TONY GWYNN
- ☐ 80. ALAN WIGGINS
- ☐ 112. DAVE DRAVECKY
- ☐ 139. KEVIN MCREYNOLDS
- ☐ 162. JERRY DAVIS
- ☐ 185. RICH GOSSAGE
- ☐ 202. ERIC SHOW
- ☐ 234. GRAIG NETTLES
- ☐ 261. CRAIG LEFFERTS
- ☐ 284. MARK THURMOND
- ☐ 307. STEVE GARVEY
- ☐ 324. TIM LOLLAR
- ☐ 356. GARRY TEMPLETON
- ☐ 383. BOBBY BROWN
- ☐ 406. LUIS DELEON
- ☐ 429. TERRY KENNEDY
- ☐ 446. ED WHITSON
- ☐ 478. CARMELO MARTINEZ
- ☐ 505. BRUCE BOCHY
- ☐ 528. ANDY HAWKINS
- ☐ 551. TIM FLANNERY
- ☐ 568. LUIS SALAZAR
- ☐ 647. KURT BEVACQUA

SAN FRANCISCO GIANTS

- ☐ 43. ALEJANDRO SANCHEZ
- ☐ 65. JACK CLARK
- ☐ 79. JOEL YOUNGBLOOD
- ☐ 114. JOHNNIE LEMASTER
- ☐ 143. GREG MINTO
- ☐ 187. BOB BRENLY
- ☐ 201. JEFF ROBINSON
- ☐ 236. JOHN RABB
- ☐ 265. GARY LAVELLE
- ☐ 309. RANDY LERCH
- ☐ 323. FRANK WILLIAMS
- ☐ 358. JEFF LEONARD
- ☐ 387. BILL LASKEY
- ☐ 431. MANNY TRILLO
- ☐ 445. DUSTY BAKER
- ☐ 480. CHILI DAVIS
- ☐ 509. ATLEE HAMMAKER
- ☐ 553. MARK DAVIS
- ☐ 567. DAN GLADDEN
- ☐ 601. MARK GRANT
- ☐ 630. MIKE KRUKOW

SEATTLE MARINERS

- ☐ 27. DANNY TARTABULL
- ☐ 69. ALVIN DAVIS
- ☐ 74. JACK PERCONTE
- ☐ 118. DARNELL COLES
- ☐ 145. STEVE HENDERSON
- ☐ 191. BARRY BONNELL
- ☐ 196. AL COWENS
- ☐ 240. JIM PRESLEY
- ☐ 267. MATT YOUNG
- ☐ 313. JIM BEATTIE
- ☐ 318. KEN PHELPS
- ☐ 362. BOB KEARNEY
- ☐ 389. AL CHAMBERS
- ☐ 435. SPIKE OWEN
- ☐ 440. MIKE MOORE
- ☐ 484. EDWIN NUNEZ
- ☐ 511. ED VANDE BERG
- ☐ 557. MARK LANGSTON
- ☐ 562. MIKE STANTON
- ☐ 605. SALOME BAROJAS
- ☐ 631. PHIL BRADLEY

TEXAS RANGERS

- ☐ 56. BUDDY BELL
- ☐ 98. DANNY DARWIN
- ☐ 99. CURTIS WILKERSON
- ☐ 134. BOBBY JONES
- ☐ 159. TOMMY DUNBAR
- ☐ 178. PETE O'BRIEN
- ☐ 220. FRANK TANANA

☐ 221. NED YOST
☐ 256. GEORGE WRIGHT
☐ 281. MIKE MASON
☐ 300. LARRY PARRISH
☐ 342. GARY WARD
☐ 343. DAVE STEWART
☐ 378. WAYNE TOLLESON
☐ 403. TOM HENKE
☐ 422. CHARLIE HOUGH
☐ 464. BILLY SAMPLE
☐ 465. MICKEY RIVERS
☐ 500. MARVIS FOLEY
☐ 525. ODELL JONES
☐ 544. DONNIE SCOTT
☐ 586. DAVE SCHMIDT
☐ 587. JEFF KUNKEL
☐ 621. BILL STEIN

TORONTO BLUE JAYS

☐ 71. WILLIE UPSHAW
☐ 73. ALFREDO GRIFFIN
☐ 119. DENNIS LAMP
☐ 146. GEORGE BELL
☐ 193. DAVE STIEB
☐ 195. JESSE BARFIELD
☐ 241. DAVE COLLINS
☐ 268. ERNIE WHITT
☐ 315. DAMASO GARCIA
☐ 317. LUIS LEAL
☐ 363. GARTH IORG
☐ 390. TONY FERNANDEZ
☐ 437. LLOYD MOSEBY
☐ 439. JIM CLANCY
☐ 485. RANCE MULLINIKS
☐ 512. CLIFF JOHNSON
☐ 559. JIMMY KEY
☐ 561. DOYLE ALEXANDER
☐ 606. ROY LEE JACKSON
☐ 632. JIM GOTT

1986 DONRUSS (660)
2 1/2 X 3 1/2

ATLANTA BRAVES

☐ 36. MARTY CLARY
☐ 66. DALE MURPHY
☐ 77. RICK MAHLER
☐ 141. GLENN HUBBARD
☐ 165. GERALD PERRY
☐ 188. BOB HORNER
☐ 199. STEVE BEDROSIAN
☐ 263. RAFAEL RAMIREZ
☐ 287. CLAUDELL WASHINGTON
☐ 310. RICK CERONE
☐ 321. BRUCE SUTTER
☐ 385. RICK CAMP
☐ 409. LEN BARKER
☐ 432. TERRY FORSTER
☐ 443. JEFF DEDMON
☐ 507. MILT THOMPSON
☐ 531. KEN OBERKFELL
☐ 554. BRUCE BENEDICT
☐ 565. ZANE SMITH
☐ 618. CHRIS CHAMBLISS
☐ 624. JOE JOHNSON
☐ 627. TERRY HARPER

BALTIMORE ORIOLES

☐ 45. JOHN HABYAN
☐ 47. MIKE BODDICKER
☐ 88. EDDIE MURRAY
☐ 106. RICK DEMPSEY
☐ 123. MIKE YOUNG
☐ 148. KEN DIXON
☐ 169. STORM DAVIS
☐ 210. CAL RIPKEN
☐ 228. LEE LACY
☐ 245. FRED LYNN
☐ 270. SAMMY STEWART
☐ 291. SCOTT MCGREGOR
☐ 332. FLOYD RAYFORD
☐ 350. LARRY SHEETS
☐ 367. NATE SNELL
☐ 392. DON AASE
☐ 413. JIM DWYER
☐ 454. DENNIS MARTINEZ
☐ 472. GARY ROENICKE
☐ 489. AL PARDO
☐ 514. TIPPY MARTINEZ
☐ 535. WAYNE GROSS
☐ 576. MIKE FLANAGAN
☐ 594. BILL SWAGGERTY
☐ 599. BRAD HAVENS
☐ 607. ALAN WIGGINS
☐ 643. JOHN SHELBY

BOSTON RED SOX

☐ 50. OIL CAN BOYD
☐ 91. BOB STANLEY
☐ 127. TONY ARMAS
☐ 151. BILL BUCKNER
☐ 172. ROGER CLEMENS
☐ 213. JIM RICE
☐ 249. DWIGHT EVANS
☐ 273. RICH GEDMAN
☐ 294. MARTY BARRETT
☐ 335. JACKIE GUTIERREZ
☐ 371. WADE BOGGS
☐ 395. MIKE EASLER
☐ 416. STEVE CRAWFORD
☐ 457. GLENN HOFFMAN
☐ 493. MARK CLEAR
☐ 517. BRUCE HURST
☐ 538. AL NIPPER
☐ 579. STEVE LYONS
☐ 614. MARC SULLIVAN
☐ 616. BRUCE KISON
☐ 620. TIM LOLLAR
☐ 636. BOB OJEDA

CALIFORNIA ANGELS

☐ 35. MARK MCLEMORE
☐ 57. DOUG DECINCES
☐ 85. RON ROMANICK
☐ 108. BRIAN DOWNING
☐ 133. DICK SCHOFIELD
☐ 158. GARY PETTIS
☐ 179. MIKE WITT
☐ 207. BOBBY GRICH
☐ 230. BOB BOONE
☐ 255. DONNIE MOORE
☐ 280. ROD CAREW
☐ 301. STU CLIBURN
☐ 329. URBANO LUGO
☐ 352. JUAN BENIQUEZ
☐ 377. REGGIE JACKSON
☐ 402. JIM SLATON
☐ 423. RUPPERT JONES
☐ 451. JERRY NARRON
☐ 474. KIRK MCCASKILL
☐ 499. JOHN CANDELARIA
☐ 524. JACK HOWELL
☐ 545. CRAIG GERBER
☐ 573. AL HOLLAND
☐ 611. DON SUTTON

CHICAGO CUBS

☐ 32. JOHNNY ABREGO
☐ 67. RYNE SANDBERG
☐ 76. GARY MATTHEWS
☐ 117. STEVE TROUT
☐ 144. LEE SMITH
☐ 167. KEITH MORELAND
☐ 189. RICK SUTCLIFFE
☐ 198. RON CEY
☐ 239. DENNIS ECKERSLEY
☐ 266. BOB DERNIER
☐ 289. JODY DAVIS
☐ 311. SHAWON DUNSTON
☐ 320. LEON DURHAM
☐ 361. RAY FONTENOT
☐ 388. DAVEY LOPES
☐ 411. GEORGE FRAZIER
☐ 433. BILLY HATCHER
☐ 442. SCOTT SANDERSON
☐ 483. THAD BOSLEY
☐ 510. STEVE ENGEL
☐ 533. RON MERIDITH
☐ 555. WARREN BRUSSTAR
☐ 564. DICK RUTHVEN
☐ 613. JAY BALLER

CHICAGO WHITE SOX

☐ 58. BRITT BURNS
☐ 86. DARYL BOSTON
☐ 122. DAN SPILLNER
☐ 135. GREG WALKER
☐ 160. RICHARD DOTSON
☐ 180. HAROLD BAINES
☐ 208. OZZIE GUILLEN
☐ 244. FLOYD BANNISTER
☐ 257. JULIO CRUZ
☐ 282. SCOTT FLETCHER
☐ 302. LUIS SALAZAR
☐ 330. JOEL SKINNER
☐ 366. CARLTON FISK
☐ 379. BOB JAMES
☐ 404. TIM HULETT
☐ 424. JERRY HAIRSTON
☐ 452. BRYAN LITTLE
☐ 488. JUAN AGOSTO
☐ 501. GENE NELSON
☐ 526. RON KITTLE
☐ 546. JOE DESA
☐ 574. REID NICHOLS
☐ 609. TOM SEAVER
☐ 623. JOEL DAVIS
☐ 632. RUDY LAW

CINCINNATI REDS

☐ 27. KAL DANIELS
☐ 37. PAUL O'NEILL
☐ 62. PETE ROSE
☐ 81. RON OESTER
☐ 121. RON ROBINSON
☐ 140. WAYNE KRENCHICKI
☐ 164. ERIC DAVIS
☐ 184. MARIO SOTO
☐ 203. DAVE PARKER
☐ 243. DAVE CONCEPCION
☐ 262. JAY TIBBS
☐ 286. NICK ESASKY
☐ 306. GARY REDUS
☐ 325. EDDIE MILNER
☐ 365. TOM HUME
☐ 384. TOM BROWNING
☐ 408. TED POWER
☐ 428. TONY PEREZ
☐ 447. BUDDY BELL
☐ 487. JOHN FRANCO
☐ 506. JOE PRICE
☐ 530. BO DIAZ
☐ 550. DAVE VAN GORDER
☐ 569. TOM RUNNELLS
☐ 650. MAX VENABLE

CLEVELAND INDIANS

☐ 29. CORY SNYDER
☐ 94. TOM WADDELL
☐ 102. BRETT BUTLER
☐ 129. PAT TABLER
☐ 154. BROOK JACOBY
☐ 216. JULIO FRANCO
☐ 224. JOE CARTER
☐ 251. ANDRE THORNTON
☐ 276. MEL HALL
☐ 338. NEAL HEATON
☐ 346. GEORGE VUKOVICH
☐ 373. CHRIS BANDO
☐ 398. JERRY WILLARD
☐ 460. CARMEN CASTILLO

☐ 468. ROY SMITH
☐ 495. RAMON ROMERO
☐ 520. TONY BERNAZARD
☐ 582. JAMIE EASTERLY
☐ 590. MIKE HARGROVE

DETROIT TIGERS

☐ 49. LOU WHITAKER
☐ 90. CHET LEMON
☐ 105. JACK MORRIS
☐ 125. KIRK GIBSON
☐ 150. CHRIS PITTARO
☐ 171. ALAN TRAMMELL
☐ 212. DAN PETRY
☐ 227. WILLIE HERNANDEZ
☐ 247. WALT TERRELL
☐ 272. NELSON SIMMONS
☐ 293. AURELIO LOPEZ
☐ 334. LANCE PARRISH
☐ 349. BARBARO GARBEY
☐ 369. DARRELL EVANS
☐ 394. RANDY O'NEAL
☐ 415. ALEJANDRO SANCHEZ
☐ 456. BOB MELVIN
☐ 471. DAVE BERGMAN
☐ 491. FRANK TANANA
☐ 516. BILL SCHERRER
☐ 537. TOM BROOKENS
☐ 578. MIKE LAGA
☐ 593. LARRY HERNDON
☐ 615. JOHN GRUBB

HOUSTON ASTROS

☐ 31. TY GAINEY
☐ 60. JOSE CRUZ
☐ 84. JERRY MUMPHREY
☐ 110. BILL DORAN
☐ 136. DENNY WALLING
☐ 161. BOB KNEPPER
☐ 182. JEFF HEATHCOCK
☐ 206. TERRY PUHL
☐ 232. CRAIG REYNOLDS
☐ 258. NOLAN RYAN
☐ 283. BILL DAWLEY
☐ 304. FRANK DIPINO
☐ 328. DAVE SMITH
☐ 354. MARK BAILEY
☐ 380. GLENN DAVIS
☐ 405. ALAN ASHBY
☐ 426. JEFF CALHOUN
☐ 450. JIM PANKOVITS
☐ 476. MIKE SCOTT
☐ 502. JOHN MIZEROCK
☐ 527. PHIL GARNER
☐ 548. KEVIN BASS
☐ 572. DICKIE THON

KANSAS CITY ROYALS

☐ 53. GEORGE BRETT
☐ 95. DANNY JACKSON
☐ 100. BRET SABERHAGEN
☐ 130. FRANK WHITE
☐ 155. PAT SHERIDAN
☐ 175. WILLIE WILSON
☐ 217. DARRYL MOTLEY
☐ 222. STEVE BALONI
☐ 252. ONIX CONCEPCION
☐ 277. JIM SUNDBERG
☐ 297. CHARLIE LEIBRANDT
☐ 339. JORGE ORTA
☐ 344. GREG PRYOR
☐ 374. BUD BLACK
☐ 399. LONNIE SMITH
☐ 419. MIKE JONES
☐ 461. DAVE LEEPER
☐ 466. LYNN JONES
☐ 496. JOHN WATHAN
☐ 521. HAL MCRAE
☐ 541. DAN QUISENBERRY
☐ 583. MARK GUBICZA
☐ 588. STEVE FARR
☐ 605. BUDDY BIANCALANA

LOS ANGELES DODGERS

☐ 52. MIKE MARSHALL
☐ 93. MIKE SCIOSCIA
☐ 104. JERRY REUSS
☐ 128. MARIANO DUNCAN
☐ 153. BILL RUSSELL
☐ 174. PEDRO GUERRERO
☐ 215. FERNANDO VALENZUELA
☐ 226. OREL HERSHISER
☐ 250. DENNIS POWELL
☐ 275. KEN HOWELL
☐ 296. GREG BROCK
☐ 337. TERRY WHITFIELD
☐ 348. CARLOS DIAZ
☐ 372. RICK HONEYCUTT
☐ 397. TOM NIEDENFUER
☐ 418. ENOS CABELL
☐ 459. BOB WELCH
☐ 470. KEN LANDREAUX
☐ 494. LEN MATUSZEK
☐ 519. STEVE YEAGER
☐ 540. STEVE SAX
☐ 581. GILBERTO REYES
☐ 592. FRANKLIN STUBBS
☐ 617. BILL MADLOCK

MILWAUKEE BREWERS

☐ 40. JUAN NIEVES
☐ 48. ROBIN YOUNT
☐ 89. DION JAMES
☐ 107. RAY BURRIS
☐ 115. JIM GANTNER
☐ 124. PAUL MOLITOR
☐ 149. DANNY DARWIN
☐ 170. CECIL COOPER
☐ 211. BILL SCHROEDER
☐ 229. ROLLIE FINGERS
☐ 237. MOOSE HAAS
☐ 246. CHARLIE MOORE
☐ 271. BOB GIBSON
☐ 292. TED SIMMONS
☐ 333. BEN OGLIVIE
☐ 351. TED HIGUERA
☐ 359. EARNEST RILES
☐ 368. RICK MANNING
☐ 393. JAIME COCANOWER
☐ 414. PAUL HOUSEHOLDER
☐ 455. ED ROMERO
☐ 473. PETE VUCKOVICH
☐ 481. RANDY READY
☐ 490. BILL WEGMAN
☐ 515. BILLY JO ROBIDOUX
☐ 536. RAY SEARAGE
☐ 577. TIM LEARY
☐ 595. CARLOS PONCE
☐ 634. MIKE FELDER

MINNESOTA TWINS

☐ 70. KENT HRBEK
☐ 72. KIRBY PUCKETT
☐ 120. JOHN BUTCHER
☐ 147. MIKE SMITHSON
☐ 192. TOM BRUNANSKY
☐ 194. FRANK VIOLA
☐ 242. TIM TEUFEL
☐ 269. MICKEY HATCHER
☐ 314. GARY GAETTI
☐ 316. MARK SALAS
☐ 364. RON DAVIS
☐ 391. TIM LAUDNER
☐ 436. PETE FILSON
☐ 438. DAVE ENGLE
☐ 486. ROY SMALLEY
☐ 513. FRANK EUFEMIA
☐ 558. GREG GAGNE
☐ 560. RON WASHINGTON
☐ 598. STEVE LOMBARDOZZI
☐ 630. MARK FUNDERBURK
☐ 635. KEN SCHROM
☐ 649. BERT BLYLEVEN

MONTREAL EXPOS

☐ 33. ANDRES GALARRAGA
☐ 55. HUBIE BROOKS
☐ 87. ANDRE DAWSON
☐ 97. MIKE FITZGERALD
☐ 132. VANCE LAW
☐ 157. JIM WOHLFORD
☐ 177. TIM RAINES
☐ 209. JEFF REARDON
☐ 219. TIM WALLACH
☐ 254. DAVID PALMER
☐ 279. HERMAN WINNINGHAM
☐ 299. BRYN SMITH
☐ 331. BILL GULLICKSON
☐ 341. JOE HESKETH
☐ 376. CHARLIE LEA
☐ 401. TERRY FRANCONA
☐ 421. TIM BURKE
☐ 453. GARY LUCAS
☐ 463. RANDY ST. CLAIRE
☐ 498. U.L. WASHINGTON
☐ 523. MITCH WEBSTER
☐ 543. FLOYD YOUMANS
☐ 575. BERT ROBERGE
☐ 585. BILL LASKEY

NEW YORK METS

☐ 68. GARY CARTER
☐ 75. DWIGHT GOODEN
☐ 116. GEORGE FOSTER
☐ 190. KEITH HERNANDEZ
☐ 197. DARRYL STRAWBERRY
☐ 238. WALLY BACKMAN
☐ 312. HOWARD JOHNSON
☐ 319. RAFAEL SANTANA
☐ 360. JOHN CHRISTENSEN
☐ 434. CLINT HURDLE
☐ 441. RICK AGUILERA
☐ 482. LENNY DYKSTRA
☐ 556. DANNY HEEP
☐ 563. RON DARLING
☐ 597. RAY KNIGHT
☐ 604. MOOKIE WILSON
☐ 625. SID FERNANDEZ
☐ 629. ROGER MCDOWELL
☐ 631. ED LYNCH
☐ 646. JESSE OROSCO
☐ 647. BILLY BEANE
☐ 652. CALVIN SCHIRALDI

NEW YORK YANKEES

☐ 51. RICKEY HENDERSON
☐ 92. WILLIE RANDOLPH
☐ 103. RON GUIDRY
☐ 126. KEN GRIFFEY
☐ 152. MIKE PAGLIARULO
☐ 173. DON MATTINGLY
☐ 214. DAVE RIGHETTI
☐ 225. ED WHITSON
☐ 248. DAVE WINFIELD
☐ 274. BUTCH WYNEGAR
☐ 295. DALE BERRA
☐ 336. DENNIS RASMUSSEN
☐ 347. DON BAYLOR
☐ 370. RON HASSEY
☐ 396. SCOTT BRADLEY
☐ 417. DAN PASQUA
☐ 458. BOB SHIRLEY
☐ 469. ANDRE ROBERTSON
☐ 492. BRIAN FISHER
☐ 518. RICH BORDI
☐ 539. BILLY SAMPLE
☐ 580. PHIL NIEKRO
☐ 591. MARTY BYSTROM
☐ 601. JOE NIEKRO
☐ 608. JOE COWLEY
☐ 610. NEIL ALLEN
☐ 638. BOBBY MEACHAM

OAKLAND A'S

□ 39. JOSE CANSECO
□ 54. DAVE KINGMAN
□ 96. MIKE DAVIS
□ 101. ALFREDO GRIFFIN
□ 131. CARNEY LANSFORD
□ 156. MIKE GALLEGO
□ 176. DWAYNE MURPHY
□ 218. DAVE COLLINS
□ 223. JAY HOWELL
□ 253. MIKE HEATH
□ 278. CHRIS CODIROLI
□ 298. BILL KRUEGER
□ 340. DONNIE HILL
□ 345. MICKEY TETTLETON
□ 375. STEVE HENDERSON
□ 400. BRUCE BOCHTE
□ 420. STEVE KIEFER
□ 462. TIM BIRTSAS
□ 467. DUSTY BAKER
□ 497. ROB PICCIOLO
□ 522. JOSE RIJO
□ 542. TONY PHILLIPS
□ 584. STAN JAVIER
□ 589. STEVE ONTIVEROS

PHILADELPHIA PHILLIES

□ 34. DAVE SPIPANOFF
□ 61. MIKE SCHMIDT
□ 82. JOHN RUSSELL
□ 111. KENT TEKULVE
□ 137. OZZIE VIRGIL
□ 163. GREG GROSS
□ 183. STEVE CARLTON
□ 204. JOHN DENNY
□ 233. SHANE RAWLEY
□ 259. JEFF STONE
□ 285. GLENN WILSON
□ 305. VON HAYES
□ 326. JUAN SAMUEL
□ 355. LARRY ANDERSON
□ 381. TIM CORCORAN
□ 407. GARRY MADDOX
□ 427. DON CARMAN
□ 448. DAVE RUCKER
□ 477. DARREN DAULTON
□ 503. LUIS AGUAYO
□ 529. KEVIN GROSS
□ 549. TOM FOLEY
□ 570. RICK SCHU
□ 612. FRED TOLIVER
□ 619. DAVE STEWART
□ 622. CHARLES HUDSON

PITTSBURGH PIRATES

□ 44. BOB KIPPER
□ 64. TONY PENA
□ 78. BENNY DISTEFANO
□ 113. MARVELL WYNNE
□ 142. CECILIO GUANTE
□ 166. RICK RHODEN
□ 186. JOHNNY RAY
□ 200. STEVE KEMP
□ 235. JOSE DELEON
□ 264. LARRY MCWILLIAMS
□ 288. LEE MAZZILLI
□ 308. SAM KHALIFA
□ 322. JASON THOMPSON
□ 357. DON ROBINSON
□ 386. JIM MORRISON
□ 410. DENNY GONZALEZ
□ 430. BOB WALK
□ 444. JOE ORSULAK
□ 479. BILL ALMON
□ 508. JUNIOR ORTIZ
□ 532. RICK REUSCHEL
□ 552. R.J. REYNOLDS
□ 566. SID BREAM
□ 600. PAT CLEMENTS
□ 642. MIKE BROWN

ST. LOUIS CARDINALS

□ 43. TODD WORRELL
□ 59. OZZIE SMITH
□ 83. TOMMY HERR
□ 109. WILLIE MCGEE
□ 138. RICKY HORTON
□ 168. JACK CLARK
□ 181. VINCE COLEMAN
□ 205. TERRY PENDLETON
□ 231. JOAQUIN ANDUJAR
□ 260. JOHN TUDOR
□ 290. DARRELL PORTER
□ 303. KEN DAYLEY
□ 327. TOM NIETO
□ 353. BOB FORSCH
□ 382. DANNY COX
□ 412. ANDY VAN SLYKE
□ 425. TITO LANDRUM
□ 449. IVAN DEJESUS
□ 475. JEFF LAHTI
□ 504. KURT KEPSHIRE
□ 534. STEVE BRAUN
□ 547. BRIAN HARPER
□ 571. BILL CAMPBELL
□ 596. PAT PERRY
□ 648. CESAR CEDENO

SAN DIEGO PADRES

□ 41. LANCE MCCULLERS
□ 63. STEVE GARVEY
□ 80. KEVIN MCREYNOLDS
□ 112. TONY GWYNN
□ 139. LAMARR HOYT
□ 162. DAVE DRAVECKY
□ 185. GOOSE GOSSAGE
□ 202. GARRY TEMPLETON
□ 234. ERIC SHOW
□ 261. MARK THURMOND
□ 284. ANDY HAWKINS
□ 307. CRAIG LEFFERTS
□ 324. CARMELO MARTINEZ
□ 356. TERRY KENNEDY
□ 383. TIM FLANNERY
□ 406. TIM STODDARD
□ 429. JERRY DAVIS
□ 446 JERRY ROYSTER
□ 478. GRAIG NETTLES
□ 505. ED WOJNA
□ 528. KURT BEVACQUA
□ 551. BRUCE BOCHY
□ 568. MARIO RAMIREZ

SAN FRANCISCO GIANTS

□ 46. MIKE WOODARD
□ 65. CHILI DAVIS
□ 79. JEFF LEONARD
□ 114. DAVID GREEN
□ 143. MIKE KRUKOW
□ 187. DAN GLADDEN
□ 201. MANNY TRILLO
□ 236. JOSE URIBE
□ 265. MARK DAVIS
□ 309. SCOTT GARRELTS
□ 323. BOB BRENLY
□ 358. JIM GOTT
□ 387. DAVE LAPOINT
□ 431. BRAD WELLMAN
□ 445. ATLEE HAMMAKER
□ 480. GREG MINTON
□ 509. VIDA BLUE
□ 553. CHRIS BROWN
□ 567. JOEL YOUNGBLOOD
□ 633. ROGER MASON
□ 641. DAN DRIESSEN

SEATTLE MARINERS

□ 38. DANNY TARTABULL
□ 69. ALVIN DAVIS
□ 74. BOB KEARNEY
□ 118. MARK LANGSTON
□ 145. EDWIN NUNEZ
□ 191. PHIL BRADLEY
□ 196. JIM BEATTIE
□ 240. MIKE MOORE
□ 267. MATT YOUNG
□ 313. JIM PRESLEY
□ 318. DAVE HENDERSON
□ 362. SPIKE OWEN
□ 389. AL COWENS
□ 435. IVAN CALDERON
□ 440. GORMAN THOMAS
□ 484. HAROLD REYNOLDS
□ 511. KARL BEST
□ 557. DARNELL COLES
□ 562. BILLY SWIFT
□ 628. JACK LAZORKO
□ 637. ED VANDE BERG

TEXAS RANGERS

□ 30. JOSE GUZMAN
□ 42. RICK SURHOFF
□ 56. ODDIBE MCDOWELL
□ 98. GARY WARD
□ 99. PETE O'BRIEN
□ 134. WAYNE TOLLESON
□ 159. TOBY HARRAH
□ 178. LARRY PARRISH
□ 220. GEORGE WRIGHT
□ 221. TOMMY DUNBAR
□ 256. CURTIS WILKERSON
□ 281. DON SLAUGHT
□ 300. BURT HOOTON
□ 342. CHARLIE HOUGH
□ 343. DAVE ROZEMA
□ 378. DAVE SCHMIDT
□ 403. BILL STEIN
□ 422. MIKE MASON
□ 464. CHRIS WELSH
□ 465. GREG HARRIS
□ 500. DUANE WALKER
□ 525. ALAN BANNISTER
□ 544. STEVE BUECHELE
□ 586. JEFF RUSSELL
□ 587. DICKIE NOLES
□ 603. DWAYNE HENRY

TORONTO BLUE JAYS

□ 28. FRED MCGRIFF
□ 71. GEORGE BELL
□ 73. LLOYD MOSEBY
□ 119. TONY FERNANDEZ
□ 146. DAVE STIEB
□ 193. JESSE BARFIELD
□ 195. WILLIE UPSHAW
□ 241. DAMASO GARCIA
□ 268. JIM CLANCY
□ 315. LUIS LEAL
□ 317. BILL CAUDILL
□ 363. JIM ACKER
□ 390. DOYLE ALEXANDER
□ 437. TOM HENKE
□ 439. TOM FILER
□ 485. AL OLIVER
□ 512. CECIL FIELDER
□ 559. ERNIE WHITT
□ 561. JIMMY KEY
□ 606. RANCE MULLINIKS
□ 621. GARY LAVELLE
□ 626. DENNIS LAMP
□ 639. CLIFF JOHNSON
□ 640. GARTH IORG

1986 DONRUSS ROOKIES (56) 2 1/2 X 3 1/2

ATLANTA BRAVES

- ☐ 10. ANDRES THOMAS
- ☐ 28. PAUL ASSENMACHER

BALTIMORE ORIOLES

NO CARDS ISSUED

BOSTON RED SOX

- ☐ 29. JEFF SELLERS
- ☐ 48. REY QUINONEZ
- ☐ 53. ROB WOODWARD

CALIFORNIA ANGELS

- ☐ 1. WALLY JOYNER

CHICAGO CUBS

NO CARDS ISSUED

CHICAGO WHITE SOX

- ☐ 30. BOBBY BONILLA
- ☐ 51. JOHN CANGELOSI
- ☐ 55. JOE MCKEON

CINCINNATI REDS

- ☐ 2. TRACY JONES

CLEVELAND INDIANS

- ☐ 15. CORY SNYDER
- ☐ 25. SCOTT BAILES
- ☐ 43. ANDY ALLANSON

DETROIT TIGERS

- ☐ 27. ERIC KING

HOUSTON ASTROS

- ☐ 9. CHARLIE KERFELD
- ☐ 34. JIM DESHAIES

KANSAS CITY ROYALS

- ☐ 36. SCOTT BANKHEAD
- ☐ 38. BO JACKSON

LOS ANGELES DODGERS

- ☐ 5. REGGIE WILLIAMS

MILWAUKEE BREWERS

- ☐ 12. JUAN NIEVES
- ☐ 14. DAN PLESAC
- ☐ 37. DALE SVEUM

MINNESOTA TWINS

- ☐ 3. ALLAN ANDERSON
- ☐ 18. STEVE LOMBARDOZZI
- ☐ 44. MARK PORTUGAL

MONTREAL EXPOS

- ☐ 7. ANDRES GALARRAGA
- ☐ 9. AL NEWMAN

NEW YORK METS

- ☐ 17. KEVIN MITCHELL
- ☐ 54. ED HEARN

NEW YORK YANKEES

- ☐ 8. BOB TEWKSBURY
- ☐ 31. DOUG DRABEK

OAKLAND A'S

- ☐ 22. JOSE CANSECO
- ☐ 40. ERIC PLUNK
- ☐ 41. BILL BATHE
- ☐ 50. BILL MOONEYHAM

PHILADELPHIA PHILLIES

NO CARDS ISSUED

PITTSBURGH PIRATES

- ☐ 11. BARRY BONDS
- ☐ 46. BOB KIPPER

ST. LOUIS CARDINALS

- ☐ 21. TODD WORRELL
- ☐ 26. GREG MATHEWS
- ☐ 35. MIKE LAVALLIERE

SAN DIEGO PADRES

- ☐ 33. BIP ROBERTS
- ☐ 42. JOHN KRUK
- ☐ 47. GENE WALTER

SAN FRANCISCO GIANTS

- ☐ 32. WILL CLARK
- ☐ 39. ROB THOMPSON

SEATTLE MARINERS

- ☐ 45. DANNY TARTABULL

TEXAS RANGERS

- ☐ 4. ED CORREA
- ☐ 19. MITCH WILLIAMS
- ☐ 23. PETE INCAVIGLIA
- ☐ 24. JOSE GUZMAN
- ☐ 49. BOBBY WITT
- ☐ 52. RUBEN SIERRA

TORONTO BLUE JAYS

- ☐ 13. MARK EICHHORN
- ☐ 16. KELLY GRUBER
- ☐ 20. JOHN CERUTTI

1987 DONRUSS (660) 2 1/2 X 3 1/2

ATLANTA BRAVES

- ☐ 67. OZZIE VIRGIL
- ☐ 78. DALE MURPHY
- ☐ 143. BILLY SAMPLE
- ☐ 167. ZANE SMITH
- ☐ 190. RICK MAHLER
- ☐ 202. RAFAEL RAMIREZ
- ☐ 266. ANDRES THOMAS
- ☐ 290. PAUL ASSENMACHER
- ☐ 314. JEFF DEDMON
- ☐ 325. DAVID PALMER
- ☐ 389. BOB HORNER
- ☐ 414. GENE GARBER
- ☐ 437. KEN OBERKFELL
- ☐ 448. BRUCE BENEDICT
- ☐ 513. KEN GRIFFEY
- ☐ 537. TED SIMMONS
- ☐ 560. ED OLWINE
- ☐ 571. CLIFF SPECK
- ☐ 634. GLENN HUBBARD
- ☐ 657. DOYLE ALEXANDER
- ☐ 659. JIM ACKER

BALTIMORE ORIOLES

- ☐ 30. KEN GERHART
- ☐ 39. ERIC BELL
- ☐ 48. EDDIE MURRAY
- ☐ 89. CAL RIPKEN
- ☐ 108. FRED LYNN
- ☐ 125. MIKE BODDICKER
- ☐ 150. MIKE YOUNG
- ☐ 171. KEN DIXON
- ☐ 213. RICH BORDI
- ☐ 231. DON AASE
- ☐ 248. LARRY SHEETS
- ☐ 273. STORM DAVIS
- ☐ 294. RICK DEMPSEY
- ☐ 336. LEE LACY
- ☐ 354. JOHN SHELBY
- ☐ 371. JUAN BENIQUEZ

- ☐ 396. NATE SNELL
- ☐ 418. JIM DWYER
- ☐ 459. MIKE FLANAGAN
- ☐ 477. JIM TRABER
- ☐ 494. JOHN HABYAN
- ☐ 520. SCOTT MCGREGOR
- ☐ 541. JOHN STEFERO
- ☐ 582. ODELL JONES
- ☐ 601. JACKIE GUTIERREZ

BOSTON RED SOX

- ☐ 44. PAT DODSON
- ☐ 51. OIL CAN BOYD
- ☐ 92. JIM RICE
- ☐ 129. DWIGHT EVANS
- ☐ 153. RICH GEDMAN
- ☐ 174. BRUCE HURST
- ☐ 216. BOB STANLEY
- ☐ 252. WADE BOGGS
- ☐ 276. ROGER CLEMENS
- ☐ 297. AL NIPPER
- ☐ 339. DON BAYLOR
- ☐ 375. TOM SEAVER
- ☐ 399. STEVE CRAWFORD
- ☐ 421. JOE SAMBITO
- ☐ 462. BILL BUCKNER
- ☐ 498. TONY ARMAS
- ☐ 523. MARTY BARRETT
- ☐ 544. JEFF SELLERS
- ☐ 585. MIKE GREENWELL
- ☐ 606. ED ROMERO
- ☐ 622. DAVE HENDERSON
- ☐ 633. SPIKE OWEN
- ☐ 641. CALVIN SCHIRALDI
- ☐ 643. MARC SULLIVAN
- ☐ 647. DAVE SAX
- ☐ 652. ROB WOODWARD
- ☐ 658. SAMMY STEWART

CALIFORNIA ANGELS

- ☐ 38. DEVON WHITE
- ☐ 40. WILL FRASER
- ☐ 58. MIKE WITT
- ☐ 86. BRIAN DOWNING
- ☐ 110. DONNIE MOORE
- ☐ 135. WALLY JOYNER
- ☐ 160. GARY PETTIS
- ☐ 181. DON SUTTON
- ☐ 210. REGGIE JACKSON
- ☐ 233. BOB BOONE
- ☐ 258. ROB WILFONG
- ☐ 283. DICK SCHOFIELD
- ☐ 305. JACK HOWELL
- ☐ 333. DOUG CORBETT
- ☐ 356. DOUG DECINCES
- ☐ 381. KIRK MCCASKILL
- ☐ 407. CHUCK FINLEY
- ☐ 428. RUPPERT JONES
- ☐ 456. BOBBY GRICH
- ☐ 479. MARK MCLEMORE
- ☐ 505. RAY CHADWICK
- ☐ 530. STU CLIBURN
- ☐ 551. JOHN CANDELARIA
- ☐ 579. GUS POLIDOR
- ☐ 583. MARK RYAL
- ☐ 603. JERRY NARRON
- ☐ 618. GARY LUCAS

CHICAGO CUBS

- ☐ 36. GREG MADDUX
- ☐ 43. RAFAEL PALMEIRO
- ☐ 68. RICK SUTCLIFFE
- ☐ 77. RYNE SANDBERG
- ☐ 119. SHAWON DUNSTON
- ☐ 146. BOB DERNIER
- ☐ 169. KEITH MORELAND
- ☐ 191. THAD BOSLEY
- ☐ 201. STEVE TROUT
- ☐ 242. LEON DURHAM
- ☐ 269. JODY DAVIS
- ☐ 292. LEE SMITH
- ☐ 315. JAMIE MOYER
- ☐ 324. JERRY MUMPHREY
- ☐ 365. DENNIS ECKERSLEY
- ☐ 392. CHRIS SPEIER
- ☐ 416. FRANK DIPINO
- ☐ 438. RON DAVIS
- ☐ 447. SCOTT SANDERSON
- ☐ 488. DAVE MARTINEZ
- ☐ 516. ED LYNCH
- ☐ 539. CHICO WALKER
- ☐ 570. MANNY TRILLO
- ☐ 594. DREW HALL

CHICAGO WHITE SOX

- ☐ 59. GREG WALKER
- ☐ 87. OZZIE GUILLEN
- ☐ 124. JOEL DAVIS
- ☐ 137. DARYL BOSTON
- ☐ 162. JOHN CANGELOSI
- ☐ 182. DAVE SCHMIDT
- ☐ 211. FLOYD BANNISTER
- ☐ 247. CARLTON FISK
- ☐ 260. TIM HULETT
- ☐ 285. JERRY HAIRSTON
- ☐ 306. RUSS MORMAN
- ☐ 334. RON KARKOVICE
- ☐ 370. BOBBY THIGPEN
- ☐ 383. RICH DOTSON
- ☐ 409. STEVE LYONS
- ☐ 429. HAROLD BAINES
- ☐ 457. JOSE DELEON
- ☐ 493. BOB JAMES
- ☐ 507. NEIL ALLEN
- ☐ 532. RON HASSEY
- ☐ 552. JOE COWLEY
- ☐ 580. GENE NELSON
- ☐ 617. STEVE CARLTON
- ☐ 628. BILL DAWLEY

CINCINNATI REDS

- ☐ 63. TOM BROWNING
- ☐ 82. MARIO SOTO
- ☐ 123. KURT STILLWELL
- ☐ 142. KAL DANIELS
- ☐ 166. NICK ESASKY
- ☐ 186. PETE ROSE(M)
- ☐ 206. RON OESTER
- ☐ 246. BO DIAZ
- ☐ 265. ERIC DAVIS
- ☐ 289. JOHN FRANCO
- ☐ 310. RON ROBINSON
- ☐ 329. JOHN DENNY
- ☐ 369. BILL GULLICKSON
- ☐ 388. DAVE PARKER
- ☐ 413. TRACY JONES
- ☐ 433. EDDIE MILNER
- ☐ 452. ROB MURPHY
- ☐ 492. BARRY LARKIN
- ☐ 512. TERRY MCGRIFF
- ☐ 536. TED POWER
- ☐ 556. BUDDY BELL

CLEVELAND INDIANS

- ☐ 32. GREG SWINDELL
- ☐ 95. ANDY ALLANSON
- ☐ 104. BROOK JACOBY
- ☐ 131. JULIO FRANCO
- ☐ 156. JOE CARTER
- ☐ 219. BRETT BUTLER
- ☐ 227. SCOTT BAILES
- ☐ 254. PAT TABLER
- ☐ 279. ANDRE THORNTON
- ☐ 342. TOM CANDIOTTI
- ☐ 350. ERNIE CAMACHO
- ☐ 377. TONY BERNAZARD
- ☐ 403. KEN SCHROM
- ☐ 465. PHIL NIEKRO
- ☐ 473. MEL HALL
- ☐ 501. CHRIS BANDO
- ☐ 526. CORY SNYDER
- ☐ 588. CARMEN CASTILLO
- ☐ 596. BRYAN OELKERS
- ☐ 623. DAVE CLARK

DETROIT TIGERS

- ☐ 47. BRUCE FIELDS
- ☐ 50. KIRK GIBSON
- ☐ 91. LANCE PARRISH
- ☐ 107. LOU WHITAKER
- ☐ 127. ALAN TRAMMELL
- ☐ 152. FRANK TANANA
- ☐ 173. JACK MORRIS
- ☐ 215. DAVE COLLINS
- ☐ 230. DARNELL COLES
- ☐ 250. ERIC KING
- ☐ 275. WALT TERRELL
- ☐ 296. TOM BROOKENS
- ☐ 338. DWIGHT LOWRY
- ☐ 353. CHET LEMON
- ☐ 373. DAN PETRY
- ☐ 398. DARRELL EVANS
- ☐ 420. DAVE BERGMAN
- ☐ 461. CHUCK CARY
- ☐ 476. JOHNNY GRUBB
- ☐ 496. MIKE HEATH
- ☐ 522. WILLIE HERNANDEZ
- ☐ 543. MARK THURMOND
- ☐ 584. RANDY O'NEAL

HOUSTON ASTROS

- ☐ 61. GLENN DAVIS
- ☐ 85. JOSE CRUZ
- ☐ 112. BOB KNEPPER
- ☐ 138. NOLAN RYAN
- ☐ 163. MIKE SCOTT
- ☐ 184. JIM DESHAIES
- ☐ 209. CHARLIE KERFELD
- ☐ 235. MARK BAILEY
- ☐ 261. DICKIE THON
- ☐ 286. BILL DORAN
- ☐ 308. DAVE SMITH
- ☐ 332. ALAN ASHBY
- ☐ 358. PHIL GARNER
- ☐ 384. CRAIG REYNOLDS
- ☐ 410. KEVIN BASS
- ☐ 431. TERRY PUHL
- ☐ 455. DAVEY LOPES
- ☐ 481. BILLY HATCHER
- ☐ 508. DANNY DARWIN
- ☐ 533. TY GAINEY
- ☐ 554. DENNY WALLING
- ☐ 578. JEFF CALHOUN
- ☐ 605. JIM PANKOVITS
- ☐ 629. AURELIO LOPEZ
- ☐ 640. LARRY ANDERSEN
- ☐ 653. JOHN MIZEROCK

KANSAS CITY ROYALS

- ☐ 35. BO JACKSON
- ☐ 54. GEORGE BRETT
- ☐ 96. WILLIE WILSON
- ☐ 102. STEVE BALBONI
- ☐ 132. BRET SABERHAGEN
- ☐ 157. DANNY JACKSON
- ☐ 177. DAN QUISENBERRY
- ☐ 220. CHARLIE LEIBRANDT
- ☐ 225. LONNIE SMITH
- ☐ 255. FRANK WHITE
- ☐ 280. JIM SUNDBERG
- ☐ 301. STEVE FARR
- ☐ 343. RUDY LAW
- ☐ 348. JORGE ORTA
- ☐ 378. GREG PRYOR
- ☐ 404. BUD BLACK
- ☐ 424. MIKE KINGERY
- ☐ 466. MARK GUBICZA
- ☐ 471. HAL MCRAE
- ☐ 502. DAVID CONE
- ☐ 527. BUDDY BIANCALANA
- ☐ 624. ANGEL SALAZAR

LOS ANGELES DODGERS

□ 53. PEDRO GUERRERO
□ 94. FERNANDO VALENZUELA
□ 106. OREL HERSHISER
□ 130. MIKE SCIOSCIA
□ 155. BILL MADLOCK
□ 176. MIKE MARSHALL
□ 218. TOM NIEDENFUER
□ 229. KEN HOWELL
□ 253. MARIANO DUNCAN
□ 278. STEVE SAX
□ 299. FRANKLIN STUBBS
□ 341. REGGIE WILLIAMS
□ 352. KEN LANDREAUX
□ 376. ED VANDE BERG
□ 402. RICK HONEYCUTT
□ 423. LEN MATUSZEK
□ 464. JEFF HAMILTON
□ 475. BOB WELCH
□ 499. DENNIS POWELL
□ 525. JOSE GONZALEZ
□ 546. ALEX TREVINO
□ 587. RALPH BRYANT
□ 598. BRIAN HOLTON

MILWAUKEE BREWERS

□ 28. B.J. SURHOFF
□ 33. MIKE BIRKBECK
□ 49. TED HIGUERA
□ 90. JUAN NIEVES
□ 109. BILL WEGMAN
□ 117. PAUL MOLITOR
□ 126. ROBIN YOUNT
□ 151. ERNEST RILES
□ 172. JIM GANTNER
□ 214. DAN PLESAC
□ 232. TIM LEARY
□ 240. BILLY JO ROBIDOUX
□ 249. JUAN CASTILLO
□ 274. ROB DEER
□ 295. MIKE FELDER
□ 337. GLENN BRAGGS
□ 355. MARK CLEAR
□ 363. CECIL COOPER
□ 372. CHARLIE MOORE
□ 397. BRYAN CLUTTERBUCK
□ 419. BEN OGLIVIE
□ 460. JOEY MEYER
□ 478. CHRIS BOSIO
□ 486. BILL SCHROEDER
□ 495. JIM ADDUCI
□ 521. RICK MANNING
□ 542. DALE SVEUM

MINNESOTA TWINS

□ 71. BERT BLYLEVEN
□ 73. KENT HRBEK
□ 122. GARY GAETTI
□ 149. KIRBY PUCKETT
□ 194. TOM BRUNANSKY
□ 196. FRANK VIOLA
□ 245. MIKE SMITHSON
□ 272. KEITH ATHERTON
□ 318. STEVE LOMBARDOZZI
□ 320. TIM LAUDNER
□ 368. ALLAN ANDERSON
□ 395. GREG GAGNE
□ 441. RANDY BUSH
□ 443. ROY SMALLEY
□ 491. MICKEY HATCHER
□ 519. ANDRE DAVID
□ 564. GEORGE FRAZIER
□ 566. MARK PORTUGAL
□ 615. NEAL HEATON

MONTREAL EXPOS

□ 56. TIM RAINES
□ 88. HUBIE BROOKS
□ 98. JEFF REARDON
□ 134. JOE HESKETH
□ 159. BRYN SMITH
□ 179. TIM WALLACH
□ 212. VANCE LAW
□ 222. TIM BURKE
□ 257. FLOYD YOUMANS
□ 282. JAY TIBBS
□ 303. ANDRES GALARRAGA
□ 335. MITCH WEBSTER
□ 345. MIKE FITZGERALD
□ 380. ANDY MCGAFFIGAN
□ 406. WAYNE KRENCHICKI
□ 426. AL NEWMAN
□ 458. ANDRE DAWSON
□ 468. BOB SEBRA
□ 504. TOM FOLEY
□ 529. WILFREDO TEJADA
□ 549. CASEY CANDAELE
□ 625. RANDY HUNT

NEW YORK METS

□ 29. RANDY MYERS
□ 69. GARY CARTER
□ 76. KEITH HERNANDEZ
□ 118. DARRYL STRAWBERRY
□ 192. RON DARLING
□ 199. DWIGHT GOODEN
□ 241. ROGER MCDOWELL
□ 316. WALLY BACKMAN
□ 323. SID FERNANDEZ
□ 364. BOB OJEDA
□ 439. JESSE OROSCO
□ 446. ED HEARN
□ 487. MOOKIE WILSON
□ 562. LEE MAZZILLI
□ 569. RAFAEL SANTANA
□ 575. DAVE MAGADAN
□ 581. TIM TEUFEL
□ 586. RAY KNIGHT
□ 599. KEVIN MITCHELL
□ 611. LEN DYKSTRA
□ 620. RICK AGUILERA
□ 626. JOHN GIBBONS
□ 635. KEVIN ELSTER
□ 642. STAN JEFFERSON
□ 646. HOWARD JOHNSON
□ 649. DANNY HEEP

NEW YORK YANKEES

□ 52. DON MATTINGLY
□ 93. RON GUIDRY
□ 105. DAVE WINFIELD
□ 128. DAVE RIGHETTI
□ 154. WILLIE RANDOLPH
□ 175. DENNIS RASMUSSEN
□ 217. JOE NIEKRO
□ 228. RICKEY HENDERSON
□ 251. DOUG DRABEK
□ 277. MIKE EASLER
□ 298. MIKE PAGLIARULO
□ 340. BRIAN FISHER
□ 351. RON KITTLE
□ 374. ROD SCURRY
□ 401. PHIL LOMBARDI
□ 422. BOB TEWKSBURY
□ 463. BOB SHIRLEY
□ 474. DAN PASQUA
□ 497. TIM STODDARD
□ 524. WAYNE TOLLESON
□ 545. JOEL SKINNER
□ 597. SCOTT NIELSEN

OAKLAND A'S

□ 34. TERRY STEINBACH
□ 46. MARK MCGWIRE
□ 55. JOSE RIJO
□ 97. JOSE CANSECO
□ 103. TONY PHILLIPS
□ 133. MIKE DAVIS
□ 158. CARNEY LANSFORD
□ 178. ERIC PLUNK
□ 221. STEVE ONTIVEROS
□ 226. CHRIS CODIROLI
□ 256. ALFREDO GRIFFIN
□ 281. BILL BATHE
□ 302. BILL MOONEYHAM
□ 344. CURT YOUNG
□ 349. MICKEY TETTLETON
□ 379. DWAYNE MURPHY
□ 405. DONNIE HILL
□ 425. DAVE KINGMAN
□ 467. JERRY WILLARD
□ 472. DAVE LEIPER
□ 503. JAY HOWELL
□ 528. MOOSE HAAS
□ 548. JOAQUIN ANDUJAR
□ 590. STAN JAVIER
□ 595. ROB NELSON
□ 648. DAVE STEWART

PHILADELPHIA PHILLIES

□ 42. CHRIS JAMES
□ 62. GLENN WILSON
□ 83. SHANE RAWLEY
□ 113. VON HAYES
□ 139. MIKE SCHMIDT
□ 165. JUAN SAMUEL
□ 185. STEVE BEDROSIAN
□ 207. JOHN RUSSELL
□ 236. KEVIN GROSS
□ 262. DARREN DAULTON
□ 288. GARY REDUS
□ 309. JEFF STONE
□ 330. MILT THOMPSON
□ 359. STEVE JELTZ
□ 385. GREG GROSS
□ 412. RON ROENICKE
□ 432. DON CARMAN
□ 453. KENT TEKULVE
□ 482. DAN SCHATZEDER
□ 509. RICK SCHU
□ 535. MIKE MADDUX
□ 555. BRUCE RUFFIN
□ 576. MARVIN FREEMAN
□ 630. CHARLIE HUDSON

PITTSBURGH PIRATES

□ 65. R.J. REYNOLDS
□ 79. SID BREAM
□ 115. TONY PENA
□ 144. JOHNNY RAY
□ 168. MIKE BROWN
□ 188. RICK REUSCHEL
□ 203. BOB WALK
□ 238. CECILIO GUANTE
□ 267. MIKE DIAZ
□ 291. JOE ORSULAK
□ 312. JIM WINN
□ 326. BILL ALMON
□ 361. BARRY BONDS
□ 390. PAT CLEMENTS
□ 415. MIKE BIELECKI
□ 435. RICK RHODEN
□ 449. JUNIOR ORTIZ
□ 484. JIM MORRISON
□ 514. BENNY DISTEFANO
□ 538. RAFAEL BELLIARD
□ 558. BOBBY BONILLA
□ 572. BOB KIPPER
□ 602. BARRY JONES
□ 608. DON ROBINSON

ST. LOUIS CARDINALS

□ 37. JIM LINDEMAN
□ 60. OZZIE SMITH
□ 84. WILLIE MCGEE
□ 111. JACK CLARK
□ 140. TOMMY HERR
□ 170. JOHN TUDOR
□ 183. TERRY PENDLETON
□ 208. GREG MATHEWS
□ 234. RICKY HORTON
□ 263. VINCE COLEMAN

☐ 293. MIKE LAGA
☐ 307. TODD WORRELL
☐ 331. MIKE LAVALLIERE
☐ 357. KEN DAYLEY
☐ 386. TITO LANDRUM
☐ 417. ANDY VAN SLYKE
☐ 430. PAT PERRY
☐ 454. CURT FORD
☐ 480. JOHN MORRIS
☐ 510. JOSE OQUENDO
☐ 540. BOB FORSCH
☐ 553. DANNY COX
☐ 577. JEFF LAHTI
☐ 604. STEVE LAKE
☐ 631. RAY SOFF

SAN DIEGO PADRES

☐ 31. BENITO SANTIAGO
☐ 64. TONY GWYNN
☐ 81. STEVE GARVEY
☐ 114. LEON "BIP" ROBERTS
☐ 141. GARRY TEMPLETON
☐ 164. ERIC SHOW
☐ 187. DAVE DRAVECKY
☐ 205. TERRY KENNEDY
☐ 237. LANCE MCCULLERS
☐ 264. ANDY HAWKINS
☐ 287. TIM FLANNERY
☐ 311. BRUCE BOCHY
☐ 328. JOHN KRUK
☐ 360. ED WHITSON
☐ 387. CRAIG LEFFERTS
☐ 411. MARVELL WYNNE
☐ 434. LAMARR HOYT
☐ 451. KEVIN MCREYNOLDS
☐ 483. RICH GOSSAGE
☐ 511. GENE WALTER
☐ 534. JERRY ROYSTER
☐ 557. JIMMY JONES
☐ 574. RANDY ASADOOR
☐ 589. ED WOJNA
☐ 607. DAVE LAPOINT
☐ 632. RAY HAYWARD
☐ 654. TIM PYZNARSKI

SAN FRANCISCO GIANTS

☐ 66 WILL CLARK
☐ 80. CHRIS BROWN
☐ 116. SCOTT GARRELTS
☐ 145. ROB THOMPSON
☐ 189. DAN GLADDEN
☐ 204. ROGER MASON
☐ 239. BOB MELVIN
☐ 268. CHILI DAVIS
☐ 313. MARK DAVIS
☐ 327. CANDY MALDONADO
☐ 362. VIDA BLUE
☐ 391. JEFF LEONARD
☐ 436. JOSE URIBE
☐ 450. MIKE ALDRETE
☐ 485. BOB BRENLY
☐ 515. TERRY MULHOLLAND
☐ 547. RANDY KUTCHER
☐ 559. JEFF ROBINSON
☐ 573. KELLY DOWNS
☐ 609. MIKE KRUKOW
☐ 616. JUAN BERENGUER
☐ 636. MIKE LACOSS
☐ 644. MARK GRANT

SEATTLE MARINERS

☐ 70. MIKE MOORE
☐ 75. ALVIN DAVIS
☐ 120. JIM PRESLEY
☐ 147. DANNY TARTABULL
☐ 193. MATT YOUNG
☐ 198. KARL BEST
☐ 243. ED NUNEZ
☐ 270. PHIL BRADLEY
☐ 317. KEN PHELPS
☐ 322. LEE GUETTERMAN
☐ 366. MIKE MORGAN
☐ 393. JOHN MOSES
☐ 440. SCOTT BRADLEY
☐ 445. BOB KEARNEY
☐ 489. HAROLD REYNOLDS
☐ 517. BILL SWIFT
☐ 563. MIKE BROWN

☐ 568. MARK LANGSTON
☐ 610. DAVE VALLE
☐ 613. MIKE TRUJILLO
☐ 638. REY QUINONES
☐ 656. MICKEY BRANTLEY
☐ 660. PETE LADD

TEXAS RANGERS

☐ 41. JERRY BROWNE
☐ 57. ED CORREA
☐ 99. BOBBY WITT
☐ 101. JOSE GUZMAN
☐ 136. DON SLAUGHT
☐ 161. ODDIBE MCDOWELL
☐ 180. STEVE BUECHELE
☐ 223. CURTIS WILKERSON
☐ 224. PETE INCAVIGLIA
☐ 259. PETE O'BRIEN
☐ 284. MIKE MASON
☐ 304. SCOTT FLETCHER
☐ 346. RUBEN SIERRA
☐ 347. MITCH WILLIAMS
☐ 382. GREG HARRIS
☐ 408. TOBY HARRAH
☐ 427. GARY WARD
☐ 469. LARRY PARRISH
☐ 470. CHARLIE HOUGH
☐ 506. MIKE LOYND
☐ 531. DALE MOHORCIC
☐ 550. JEFF RUSSELL
☐ 592. MIKE STANLEY
☐ 593. DARRELL PORTER
☐ 619. GENO PETRALLI
☐ 627. KEVIN BROWN
☐ 637. DWAYNE HENRY
☐ 651. BOB BROWER

TORONTO BLUE JAYS

☐ 45. DUANE WARD
☐ 72. TONY FERNANDEZ
☐ 74. LLOYD MOSEBY
☐ 121. JESSE BARFIELD
☐ 148. ERNIE WHITT
☐ 195. DAVE STIEB
☐ 197. TOM HENKE
☐ 244. JIMMY KEY
☐ 271. GEORGE BELL
☐ 319. RANCE MULLINIKS
☐ 321. MARK EICHHORN
☐ 367. WILLIE UPSHAW
☐ 394. GARTH IORG
☐ 442. JOHN CERUTTI
☐ 444. KELLY GRUBER
☐ 490. JEFF HEARRON
☐ 518. MANNY LEE
☐ 561. GLENALLEN HILL
☐ 565. MIKE SHARPERSON
☐ 567. RICK LEACH
☐ 591. JEFF MUSSELMAN
☐ 614. DAMASO GARCIA
☐ 621. FRED MCGRIFF
☐ 639. JIM CLANCY
☐ 645. CLIFF JOHNSON
☐ 650. JOE JOHNSON
☐ 655. LUIS AQUINO

1987 DONRUSS ROOKIES (56) 2 1/2 X 3 1/2

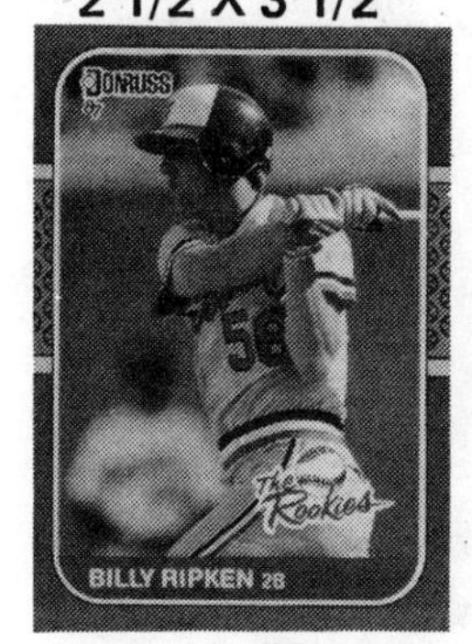

ATLANTA BRAVES

NO CARDS ISSUED

BALTIMORE ORIOLES

☐ 2. ERIC BELL
☐ 3. MARK WILLIAMSON
☐ 16. BILLY RIPKEN
☐ 24. KEN GERHART

BOSTON RED SOX

☐ 4. MIKE GREENWELL
☐ 5. ELLIS BURKS
☐ 30. TODD BENZINGER

CALIFORNIA ANGELS

☐ 6. DEWAYNE BUICE
☐ 7. MARK MCLEMORE
☐ 8. DEVON WHITE
☐ 9. WILLIE FRASER

CHICAGO CUBS

☐ 10. LESTER LANCASTER
☐ 47. RAFAEL PALMEIRO
☐ 51. PAUL NOCE
☐ 52. GREG MADDUX

CHICAGO WHITE SOX

☐ 11. KEN WILLIAMS
☐ 48. BILL LONG

CINCINNATI REDS

NO CARDS ISSUED

CLEVELAND INDIANS

NO CARDS ISSUED

DETROIT TIGERS

☐ 12. MATT NOKES
☐ 13. JEFF ROBINSON
☐ 32. MIKE HENNEMAN

HOUSTON ASTROS

☐ 46. DAVE MEADS
☐ 55. CHUCK JACKSON

KANSAS CITY ROYALS

☐ 14. BO JACKSON
☐ 15. KEVIN SEITZER

LOS ANGELES DODGERS

☐ 54. BRIAN HOLTON

MILWAUKEE BREWERS

☐ 17. B.J. SURHOFF
☐ 18. CHUCK CRIM
☐ 19. MIKE BIRKBECK
☐ 20. CHRIS BOSIO

MINNESOTA TWINS

- □ 21. LES STRAKER
- □ 22. MARK DAVIDSON
- □ 23. GENE LARKIN

MONTREAL EXPOS

- □ 33. CASEY CANDAELE

NEW YORK METS

- □ 34. DAVE MAGADAN
- □ 35. DAVID CONE
- □ 37. JOHN MITCHELL

NEW YORK YANKEES

NO CARDS ISSUED

OAKLAND A'S

- □ 1. MARK MCGWIRE
- □ 25. LUIS POLONIA
- □ 26. TERRY STEINBACH

PHILADELPHIA PHILLIES

- □ 36. MIKE JACKSON

PITTSBURGH PIRATES

- □ 38. MIKE DUNNE
- □ 39. JOHN SMILEY

ST. LOUIS CARDINALS

- □ 40. JOE MAGRANE
- □ 41. JIM LINDEMAN

SAN DIEGO PADRES

- □ 42. SHANE MACK
- □ 43. STAN JEFFERSON
- □ 44. BENITO SANTIAGO
- □ 50. JAMES STEELS

SAN FRANCISCO GIANTS

- □ 45. MATT WILLIAMS

SEATTLE MARINERS

- □ 27. MICKEY BRANTLEY

TEXAS RANGERS

- □ 28. MIKE STANLEY
- □ 29. JERRY BROWNE
- □ 49. BOB BROWER

TORONTO BLUE JAYS

- □ 31. FRED MCGRIFF
- □ 53. JEFF JUSSELMAN

1988 DONRUSS (660)
2 1/2 X 3 1/2

ATLANTA BRAVES

- □ 67. KEN OBERKFELL
- □ 78. DALE MURPHY
- □ 143. OZZIE VIRGIL
- □ 167. ZANE SMITH
- □ 190. DION JAMES
- □ 202. KEN GRIFFEY
- □ 266. DAVID PALMER
- □ 290. ALBERT HALL
- □ 314. GLENN HUBBARD
- □ 325. JEFF DEDMON
- □ 389. RICK MAHLER
- □ 414. DAMASO GARCIA
- □ 437. GERALD PERRY
- □ 448. RAFAEL RAMIREZ
- □ 513. JEFF BLAUSER
- □ 537. CHARLIE PULEO
- □ 560. TED SIMMONS
- □ 571. PETE SMITH
- □ 627. ANDRES THOMAS
- □ 644. TOM GLAVINE
- □ 654. RON GANT

BALTIMORE ORIOLES

- □ 48. KEN DIXON
- □ 89. MIKE BODDICKER
- □ 108. RAY KNIGHT
- □ 125. ERIC BELL
- □ 150. TERRY KENNEDY
- □ 171. CAL RIPKEN
- □ 213. KEN GERHART
- □ 231. EDDIE MURRAY
- □ 248. FRED LYNN
- □ 273. LARRY SHEETS
- □ 294. TOM NIEDENFUER
- □ 336. BILLY RIPKEN
- □ 354. JOHN HABYAN
- □ 371. DAVE SCHMIDT
- □ 396. MIKE YOUNG
- □ 418. MARK WILLIAMSON
- □ 459. JIM DWYER
- □ 477. CARL NICHOLS
- □ 494. MIKE GRIFFIN
- □ 520. JEFF BALLARD
- □ 541. PETE STANICEK
- □ 582. RENE GONZALES
- □ 601. JOSE MESA

BOSTON RED SOX

- □ 41. JODY REED
- □ 51. ROGER CLEMENS
- □ 92. BOB STANLEY
- □ 129. RICH GEDMAN
- □ 153. WADE BOGGS
- □ 174. ELLIS BURKS
- □ 216. DWIGHT EVANS
- □ 252. BRUCE HURST
- □ 276. MARTY BARRETT
- □ 297. TODD BENZINGER
- □ 339. MIKE GREENWELL
- □ 375. CALVIN SCHIRALDI
- □ 399. JIM RICE
- □ 421. JOHN MARZANO
- □ 462. OIL CAN BOYD
- □ 498. SAM HORN
- □ 523. AL NIPPER
- □ 544. SPIKE OWEN
- □ 585. JEFF SELLERS
- □ 623. ED ROMERO
- □ 634. WES GARDNER

CALIFORNIA ANGELS

- □ 58. DEWAYNE BUICE
- □ 86. MIKE WITT
- □ 110. WALLY JOYNER
- □ 135. WILLIE FRASER
- □ 160. JACK LAZORKO
- □ 181. MARK MCLEMORE
- □ 210. GARY PETTIS
- □ 233. DICK SCHOFIELD
- □ 258. BRIAN DOWNING
- □ 283. DEVON WHITE
- □ 305. BOB BOONE
- □ 333. JACK HOWELL
- □ 356. GUS POLIDOR
- □ 381. KIRK MCCASKILL
- □ 407. DON SUTTON
- □ 428. JOHNNY RAY
- □ 456. BILL BUCKNER
- □ 479. GEORGE HENDRICK
- □ 505. GREG MINTON
- □ 530. CHUCK FINLEY
- □ 551. DARRELL MILLER
- □ 579. GARY LUCAS
- □ 621. DONNIE MOORE

CHICAGO CUBS

- □ 40. MARK GRACE
- □ 68. RICK SUTCLIFFE
- □ 77. ED LYNCH
- □ 110. JODY DAVIS
- □ 146. SHAWON DUNSTON
- □ 169. JAMIE MOYER
- □ 191. LEON DURHAM
- □ 201. KEITH MORELAND
- □ 242. RYNE SANDBERG
- □ 269. ANDRE DAWSON
- □ 292. LEE SMITH
- □ 315. PAUL NOCE
- □ 324. RAFAEL PALMEIRO
- □ 365. LUIS QUINONES
- □ 392. BOB DERNIER
- □ 416. BRAIN DAYETT
- □ 438. DAVE MARTINEZ
- □ 447. JERRY MUMPHREY
- □ 488. JIM SUNDBERG
- □ 516. MANNY TRILLO
- □ 539. GREG MADDUX
- □ 561. LESTER LANCASTER
- □ 570. FRANK DIPINO
- □ 609. MIKE BRUMLEY
- □ 639. DAMON BERRYHILL
- □ 646. SCOTT SANDERSON

CHICAGO WHITE SOX

- □ 47. JACK MCDOWELL
- □ 59 JOSE DELEON
- □ 87. DONNIE HILL
- □ 124. RICHARD DOTSON
- □ 137. OZZIE GUILLEN
- □ 162. GREG WALKER
- □ 182. IVAN CALDERON
- □ 211. HAROLD BAINES
- □ 247. BOBBY THIGPEN
- □ 260. CARLTON FISK

- □ 285. JERRY HAIRSTON
- □ 306. BILL LONG
- □ 334. KEN WILLIAMS
- □ 370. GARY REDUS
- □ 383. FLOYD BANNISTER
- □ 409. JIM WINN
- □ 429. RAY SEARAGE
- □ 457. JOHN PAWLOWSKI
- □ 493. FRED MANRIQUE
- □ 507. BOB JAMES
- □ 532. STEVE LYONS
- □ 552. DAVE LAPOINT
- □ 580. RON HASSEY

CINCINNATI REDS

- □ 29. JEFF TREADWAY
- □ 63. TOM BROWNING
- □ 82. ROB MURPHY
- □ 123. JOHN FRANCO
- □ 142. TED POWER
- □ 166. RON ROBINSON
- □ 186. BO DIAZ
- □ 206. BUDDY BELL
- □ 246. RON OESTER
- □ 265. KURT STILLWELL
- □ 289. KAL DANIELS
- □ 310. TRACY JONES
- □ 329. DAVE CONCEPCION
- □ 369. ERIC DAVIS
- □ 388. DAVE PARKER
- □ 413. NICK ESASKY
- □ 433. PAUL O'NEILL
- □ 452. GUY HOFFMAN
- □ 492. BARRY LARKIN
- □ 512. FRANK WILLIAMS
- □ 536. PAT PACILLO
- □ 556. TERRY MCGRIFF
- □ 575. DENNIS RASMUSSEN
- □ 626. PAT PERRY

CLEVELAND INDIANS

- □ 42. JOHN FARRELL
- □ 46. EDDIE WILLIAMS
- □ 95. CHRIS BANDO
- □ 104. SCOTT BAILES
- □ 131. BROOK JACOBY
- □ 156. JULIO FRANCO
- □ 219. PAT TABLER
- □ 227. GREG SWINDELL
- □ 254. JOE CARTER
- □ 279. BRETT BUTLER
- □ 342. MEL HALL
- □ 350. CORY SNYDER
- □ 377. TOM CONDIOTTI
- □ 403. CARMEN CASTILLO
- □ 465. ANDY ALLANSON
- □ 473. DAVE CLARK
- □ 501. KEN SCHROM
- □ 526. TOMMY HINZO
- □ 588. DOUG JONES
- □ 596. SAMMY STEWART
- □ 637. JAY BELL

DETROIT TIGERS

- □ 50 ERIC KING
- □ 91. WALT TERRELL
- □ 107. TOM BROOKENS
- □ 127. JACK MORRIS
- □ 152. MATT NOKES
- □ 173. LOU WHITAKER
- □ 215. CHET LEMON
- □ 230. ALAN TRAMMELL
- □ 250. DARRELL EVANS
- □ 275. KIRK GIBSON
- □ 296. JEFF ROBINSON
- □ 338. MIKE HEATH
- □ 353. LARRY HERNDON
- □ 373. DAVE BERGMAN
- □ 398. WILLIE HERNANDEZ
- □ 420. MIKE HENNEMAN
- □ 461. FRANK TANANA
- □ 476. DAN PETRY
- □ 496. BILL MADLOCK
- □ 522. PAT SHERIDAN
- □ 543. JIM MORRISON
- □ 584. DOYLE ALEXANDER
- □ 599. MARK THURMOND
- □ 615. SCOTT LUSADER

HOUSTON ASTROS

- □ 61. NOLAN RYAN
- □ 85. JIM DESHAIES
- □ 112. MIKE SCOTT
- □ 138. BOB KNEPPER
- □ 163. ALAN ASHBY
- □ 184. GLENN DAVIS
- □ 209. CRAIG REYNOLDS
- □ 235. BILL DORAN
- □ 261. BILLY HATCHER
- □ 286. KEVIN BASS
- □ 308. KEN CAMINITI
- □ 332. LARRY ANDERSEN
- □ 358. DANNY DARWIN
- □ 384. DENNY WALLING
- □ 410. DAVE SMITH
- □ 431. GERALD YOUNG
- □ 455. DAVE MEADS
- □ 481. MANNY HERNANDEZ
- □ 508. ROBBIE WINE
- □ 533. TERRY PUHL
- □ 554. ROCKY CHILDRESS
- □ 578. TY GAINEY

KANSAS CITY ROYALS

- □ 44. GARY THURMAN
- □ 54. MARK GUBICZA
- □ 96. BRET SABERHAGEN
- □ 102. GEROGE BRETT
- □ 132. DANNY JACKSON
- □ 157. CHARLIE LEIBRANDT
- □ 177. DANNY TARTABULL
- □ 220. BO JACKSON
- □ 225. FRANK WHITE
- □ 255. WILLIE WILSON
- □ 280. KEVIN SEITZER
- □ 301. BUD BLACK
- □ 343. JIM EISENREICH
- □ 348. THAD BOSLEY
- □ 378. STEVE FARR
- □ 404. JAMIE QUIRK
- □ 424. STEVE BALBONI
- □ 466. BILL PECOTA
- □ 471. DAN QUISENBERRY
- □ 502. ANGEL SALAZAR
- □ 527. LONNIE SMITH
- □ 547. JERRY GLEATON
- □ 589. MELIDO PEREZ
- □ 584. JOHN DAVIS
- □ 618. GENE GARBER

LOS ANGELES DODGERS

- □ 35. SHAWN HILLEGAS
- □ 53. FERNANDO VALENZUELA
- □ 94. OREL HERSHIER
- □ 106. MIKE SCIOSCIA
- □ 130. KEN HOWELL
- □ 155. MARIANO DUNCAN
- □ 176. STEVE SAX
- □ 218. FRANKLIN STUBBS
- □ 229. MIKE MARSHALL
- □ 253. BOB WELCH
- □ 278. PEDRO GUERRERO
- □ 299. MICKEY HATCHER
- □ 341. JOSE GONZALEZ
- □ 352. JOHN SHELBY
- □ 376. ALEX TREVINO
- □ 402. BRIAN HOLTON
- □ 423. MATT YOUNG
- □ 464. TIM CREWS
- □ 475. DAVE ANDERSON
- □ 499. TRACY WOODSON
- □ 525. JEFF HAMILTON
- □ 546. MIKE DEVEREAUX
- □ 587. TIM BELCHER
- □ 598. ALEJANDRO PENA

MILWAUKEE BREWERS

- □ 36. JOEY MEYER
- □ 49. MIKE BIRKBECK
- □ 90. TED HIGUERA
- □ 109. DAN PLESAC
- □ 117. CHRIS BOSIO
- □ 126. JUAN NIEVES
- □ 151. BILL WEGMAN
- □ 172. B.J. SURHOFF
- □ 214. JIM GANTNER
- □ 232. DALE SVEUM
- □ 240. GLENN BRAGGS
- □ 249. PAUL MOLITOR
- □ 274. ROB DEER
- □ 295. ROBIN YOUNT
- □ 337. GREG BROCK
- □ 355. CHUCK CRIM
- □ 363. JUAN CASTILLO
- □ 372. MARK CLEAR
- □ 397. MIKE FELDER
- □ 419. BILL SCHROEDER
- □ 460. JAY ALRRICH
- □ 478. ERNEST RILES
- □ 486. RICK MANNING
- □ 495. MARK KNUDSON
- □ 521. DAVE STAPLETON
- □ 542. STEVE KIEFER
- □ 583. BRAD KOMMINSK
- □ 602. DON AUGUST

MINNESOTA TWINS

- □ 71. BERT BLYLEVEN
- □ 73. LES STRAKER
- □ 122. JEFF REARDON
- □ 149. FRANK VIOLA
- □ 194. GARY GAETTI
- □ 196. STEVE LOBARDOZZI
- □ 245. TOM BRUNANSKY
- □ 272. RANDY BUSH
- □ 318. KEITH ATHERTON
- □ 320. KENT HRBEK
- □ 368. KIRBY PUCKETT
- □ 395. JUAN BERENGUER
- □ 441. GREG GAGNE
- □ 443. GEORGE FRAZIER
- □ 491. DAN GLADDEN
- □ 519. MARK DAVISON
- □ 564. GENE LARKIN
- □ 566. ROY SMALLEY
- □ 612. TOM NIETO
- □ 631. TIM LAUDNER
- □ 645. AL NEWMAN

MONTREAL EXPOS

- □ 56. FLOYD YOUMANS
- □ 88. JEFF REED
- □ 98. TIM BURKE
- □ 134. NEAL HEATON
- □ 159. MIKE FITZGERALD
- □ 179. CASEY CANDAELE
- □ 212. VANCE LAW
- □ 222. TIM WALLACH
- □ 257. MITCH WEBSTER
- □ 282. ANDRES GALARRAGA
- □ 303. TOM FOLEY
- □ 335. BRYN SMITH
- □ 345. TIM RAINES
- □ 380. ANDY MCGAFFIGAN
- □ 406. JEFF PARRETT
- □ 426. RANDY ST. CLAIRE
- □ 458. BOB SEBRA
- □ 468. HUBIE BROOKS
- □ 504. JOE HESKETH
- □ 529. ROB MCCLURE
- □ 549. DENNIS MARTINEZ
- □ 581. HERM WINNINGHAM
- □ 591. PASCUAL PEREZ

NEW YORK METS

- □ 37. DEVIN ELSTER
- □ 69. DWIGHT GOODEN
- □ 76. RON DARLING
- □ 118. SID FERNANDEZ
- □ 192. JESSE OROSCO
- □ 199. GARY CARTER
- □ 241. WALLY BACKMAN
- □ 316. KEITH HERNANDEZ
- □ 323. DAVE MAGADAN
- □ 364. LEN DYKSTRA
- □ 439. DARRYL STRAWBERRY
- □ 446. RICH AGUILERA
- □ 487. BILL ALMON
- □ 562. KEITH MILLER
- □ 569. HOWARD JOHNSON
- □ 603. TERRY LEACH
- □ 608. JOHN CANDELARIA
- □ 614. LEE MAZZILLI
- □ 617. KEVIN MCREYNOLDS
- □ 619. BARRY LYONS

☐ 620. RANDY MYERS
☐ 632. BOB OJEDA
☐ 633. RAFAEL SANTANA
☐ 642. DOUG SISK
☐ 648. TIM TEUFEL
☐ 651. ROGER MCDOWELL
☐ 652. MOOKIE WILSON
☐ 653. DAVID CONE
☐ 657. GREGG JEFFERIES

NEW YORK YANKEES

☐ 43. AL LEITER
☐ 52. PAT CLEMENTS
☐ 93. DAVE RIGHETTI
☐ 105. MIKE PAGLIARULO
☐ 128. RICH RHODEN
☐ 154. WAYNE TOLLESON
☐ 175. RON GUIDRY
☐ 217. DON MATTINGLY
☐ 228. WILLIE RANDOLPH
☐ 251. GARY WARD
☐ 277. RICKEY HENDERSON
☐ 298. DAVE WINFIELD
☐ 340. CLAUDELL WASHINGTON
☐ 351. RICK CERONE
☐ 374. CHARLES HUDSON
☐ 401. TOMMY JOHN
☐ 422. RON KITTLE
☐ 463. DAN PASQUA
☐ 474. JOEL SKINNER
☐ 497. TIM STODDARD
☐ 524. STEVE TROUT
☐ 545. JAY BUHNER
☐ 586. BILL GULLICKSON
☐ 597. NEIL ALLEN
☐ 616. BOBBY MEACHAM
☐ 635. ROBERTO KELLY
☐ 660. JERRY ROYSTER

OAKLAND A'S

☐ 56. JAY HOWELL
☐ 97. CURT YOUNG
☐ 103. MICKEY TETTLETON
☐ 133. GENE NELSON
☐ 158. TERRY STEINBACH
☐ 178. CARNEY LANSFORD
☐ 221. TONY PHILLIPS
☐ 226. ALFREDO GRIFFIN
☐ 256. MARK MCGWIRE
☐ 281. MIKE DAVIS
☐ 302. JOSE CANSECO
☐ 344. TONY BERNAZARD
☐ 349. DENNIS ECKERSLEY
☐ 379. MIKE GALLEGO
☐ 405. DWAYNE MURPHY
☐ 425. LUIS POLONIA
☐ 467. STEVE ONTIVEROS
☐ 472. DAVE STEWART
☐ 503. ERIC PLUNK
☐ 528. GREG CARADET
☐ 548. JOSE RIJO
☐ 590. RICK HONEYCUTT
☐ 595. STORM DAVIS

PHILADELPHIA PHILLIES

☐ 62. STEVE BEDROSIAN
☐ 83. SHANE RAWLEY
☐ 113. KEVIN GROSS
☐ 139. MIKE JACKSON
☐ 165. BRUCE RUFFIN
☐ 185. LUIS AGUAYO
☐ 207. VON HAYES
☐ 236. MILT THOMPSON
☐ 262. GLENN WILSON
☐ 288. JUAN SAMUEL
☐ 309. DARREN DAULTON
☐ 330. MIKE SCHMIDT
☐ 359. LANCE PARRISH
☐ 385. DON CARMAN
☐ 412. GREG GROSS
☐ 432. RICK SCHU
☐ 453. CHRIS JAMES
☐ 482. JEFF STONE
☐ 509. JEFF CALHOUN
☐ 535. KENT TEKULVE
☐ 555. WALLY RITCHIE
☐ 576. STEVE JELTZ
☐ 604. TOM NEWELL
☐ 643. KEITH HUGHES

PITTSBURGH PIRATES

☐ 28. MACKEY SASSER
☐ 38. JOSE LIND
☐ 45. VICENTE PALACIOS
☐ 65. R. J. REYNOLDS
☐ 79. DOUG DRABEK
☐ 115. BOB KIPPER
☐ 144. FELIX FERMIN
☐ 168. JUNIOR ORTIZ
☐ 188. SID BREAM
☐ 203. TOMMY GREGG
☐ 238. BOBBY BONILLA
☐ 267. MIKE DIAZ
☐ 291. ANDY VAN SLYKE
☐ 312. MIKE LAVALLIER
☐ 326. BARRY BONDS
☐ 361. AL PEDRIQUE
☐ 390. MIKE DUNNE
☐ 415. BRIAN FISHER
☐ 435. JOHN CANGELOSI
☐ 449. JOHN SMILEY
☐ 484. MIKE BIELECKI
☐ 514. BOB WALK
☐ 538. TOM PRINCE
☐ 558. JEFF ROBINSON
☐ 572. DARNELL COLES
☐ 606. JIM GOTT

ST. LOUIS CARDINALS

☐ 31. LANCE JOHNSON
☐ 60. DANNY COX
☐ 84. GREG MATHEWS
☐ 111. BOB FORSCH
☐ 140. JOE MAGRANE
☐ 170. TONY PENA
☐ 183. JACK CLARK
☐ 208. TOMMY HERR
☐ 234. JOSE OQUENDO
☐ 263. OZZIE SMITH
☐ 293. VINCE COLEMAN
☐ 307. WILLIE MCGEE
☐ 331. BILL DAWLEY
☐ 357. KEN DAYLEY
☐ 386. TODD WORRELL
☐ 417. CURT FORD
☐ 430. RICKY HORTON
☐ 454. TERRY PENDLETON
☐ 480. JOHN MORRIS
☐ 510. STEVE LAKE
☐ 540. JIM LINDEMAN
☐ 553. JOHN TUDOR
☐ 577. TOM PAGNOZZI
☐ 647. SCOTT TERRY

SAN DIEGO PADRES

☐ 33. SHAWN ABNER
☐ 34. ROBERTO ALOMAR
☐ 64. MARK DAVIS
☐ 81. ED WHITSON
☐ 114. BENITO SANTIAGO
☐ 141. JIMMY JONES
☐ 164. TONY GWYNN
☐ 187. STAN JEFFERSON
☐ 205. JOHN KRUK
☐ 237. MARVELL WYNNE
☐ 264. RANDY READY
☐ 287. CARMELO MARTINEZ
☐ 311. GREG BOOKER
☐ 328. TIM FLANNERY
☐ 360. JAMES STEELS
☐ 387. ERIC SHOW
☐ 411. SHANE MACK
☐ 434. RICH GOSSAGE
☐ 451. LANCE MCCULLERS
☐ 483. CHRIS BROWN
☐ 511. MARK GRANT
☐ 534. ERIC NOLTE
☐ 557. DAVE LEIPER
☐ 574. ROB NELSON
☐ 605. RANDALL BYERS
☐ 649. GARRY TEMPLETON

SAN FRANCISCO GIANTS

☐ 39. KIRT MANWARING
☐ 66. KEVIN MITCHELL
☐ 80. SCOTT GARRELTS
☐ 116. MIKE KRUKOW
☐ 145. KELLY DOWNS
☐ 189. BOB BRENLY
☐ 204. WILL CLARK
☐ 239. CHRIS SPEIER
☐ 268. ROB THOMPSON
☐ 313. CHILI DAVIS
☐ 327. JEFFREY LEONARD
☐ 362. MIKE ALDRETE
☐ 391. CANDY MALDONADO
☐ 436. MIKE LACOSS
☐ 450. ATLEE HAMMAKER
☐ 485. DAVE DRAVECKY
☐ 515. CRAIG LEFFERTS
☐ 559. JOSE URIBE
☐ 573. DON ROBINSON
☐ 607. HARRY SPILMAN
☐ 613. RICK REUSCHEL
☐ 628. MATT WILLIAMS
☐ 638. BOB MELVIN
☐ 655. JOE PRICE

SEATTLE MARINERS

☐ 30. MIKE CAMPBELL
☐ 70. SCOTT BANKHEAD
☐ 75. MIKE MOORE
☐ 120. MIKE MORGAN
☐ 147. SCOTT BRADLEY
☐ 193. ALVIN DAVIS
☐ 198. REY QUINONES
☐ 243. PHIL BRADLEY
☐ 270. LEE GUETTERMAN
☐ 317. MARK LANGSTON
☐ 322. MIKE KINGERY
☐ 366. JIM PRESLEY
☐ 393. DAVE VALLE
☐ 440. JOHN MOSES
☐ 445. ED NUNEZ
☐ 489. KEN PHELPS
☐ 517. JERRY REED
☐ 563. HAROLD REYNOLDS
☐ 568. BILL WILKINSON
☐ 610. MICKEY BRANTLEY
☐ 622. DOMINGO RAMOS
☐ 629. DAVE HENGEL

TEXAS RANGERS

☐ 57. ED CORREA
☐ 99. CHARLIE HOUGH
☐ 101. BOBBY WITT
☐ 136. JOSE GUZMAN
☐ 161. MITCH WILLIAMS
☐ 180. SCOTT FLETCHER
☐ 223. RUBEN SIERRA
☐ 224. STEVE BUECHELE
☐ 259. MIKE STANLEY
☐ 284. PETE O'BRIEN
☐ 304. PETE INCAVIGLIA
☐ 346. BOB BROWER
☐ 347. LARRY PARRISH
☐ 382. ODDIBE MCDOWELL
☐ 408. JERRY BROWNE
☐ 427. GREG HARRIS
☐ 469. PAUL KILGUS
☐ 470. DALE MOHORCIC
☐ 506. GENO PETRALLI
☐ 531. JEFF RUSSELL
☐ 500. MIKE LOYND
☐ 592. CURT WILKERSON
☐ 593. STEVE HOWE

TORONTO BLUE JAYS

- ☐ 32. NELSON LIRIANO
- ☐ 72. JIMMY KEY
- ☐ 74. JIM CLANCY
- ☐ 121. MARK EICHHORN
- ☐ 148. DAVE STIEB
- ☐ 195. FRED MCGRIFF
- ☐ 197. RANCE MULLINIKS
- ☐ 244. KELLY GRUBER
- ☐ 271. WILLIE UPSHAW
- ☐ 319. TONY FERNANDEZ
- ☐ 321. JOHN CERUTTI
- ☐ 367. LLOYD MOSEBY
- ☐ 394. ERNIE WHITT
- ☐ 442. JESSE BARFIELD
- ☐ 444. GARTH IORG
- ☐ 490. TOM HENKE
- ☐ 518. RICK LEACH
- ☐ 565. CECIL FIELDER
- ☐ 567. DUANE WARD
- ☐ 611. JOSE NUNEZ
- ☐ 624. GREG MYERS
- ☐ 630. JEFF MUSSELMAN
- ☐ 636. MIKE FLANAGAN
- ☐ 640. DAVID WELLS
- ☐ 650. MANNY LEE
- ☐ 656. GEORGE BELL
- ☐ 658. TODD STOTTLEMYRE
- ☐ 659. GERONIMO BERROA

1988 DONRUSS ROOKIES (56)
2 1/2 X 3 1/2

ATLANTA BRAVES

- ☐ 10. PETE SMITH
- ☐ 47. RON GANT
- ☐ 49. KEVIN COFFMAN

BALTIMORE ORIOLES

- ☐ 15. PETE STANICEK
- ☐ 23. CRAIG WORTHINGTON
- ☐ 39. CARL NICHOLS
- ☐ 41. JOSE BAUTISTA

BOSTON RED SOX

- ☐ 14. BRADY ANDERSON
- ☐ 24. JOHN TRAUTWEIN
- ☐ 44. JODY REED
- ☐ 54. STEVE ELLSWORTH

CALIFORNIA ANGELS

- ☐ 53. BRYAN HARVEY

CHICAGO CUBS

- ☐ 1. MARK GRACE
- ☐ 31. DAMON BERRYHILL
- ☐ 45. DARRIN JACKSON
- ☐ 46. MIKE CAPEL

CHICAGO WHITE SOX

- ☐ 7. DAVE GALLAGHER
- ☐ 21. MELIDO PEREZ
- ☐ 40. JACK MCDOWELL
- ☐ 48. JOHN DAVIS

CINNINNATI REDS

- ☐ 17. JEFF TREADWAY
- ☐ 30. CHRIS SABO

CLEVELAND INDIANS

NO CARDS ISSUED

DETROIT TIGERS

- ☐ 19. PAUL GIBSON

HOUSTON ASTROS

NO CARDS ISSUED

KANSAS CITY ROYALS

- ☐ 33. GARY THURMAN
- ☐ 55. MIKE MACFARLANE

LOS ANGELES DODGERS

- ☐ 20. TIM CREWS
- ☐ 28. TIM BELCHER

MILWAUKEE BREWERS

- ☐ 4. DAVE STAPLETON
- ☐ 38. JOEY MEYER

MINNESOTA TWINS

NO CARDS ISSUED

MONTREAL EXPOS

- ☐ 29. JOHNNY PAREDES
- ☐ 43. JOHN DOPSON

NEW YORK METS

- ☐ 34. KEVIN ELSTER
- ☐ 51. MACKEY SASSER

NEW YORK YANKEES

- ☐ 11. JAY BUHNER
- ☐ 16. ROBERTO KELLY
- ☐ 27. AL LEITER

OAKLAND A'S

- ☐ 13. DOUG JENNINGS
- ☐ 18. WALT WEISS

PHILADELPHIA PHILLIES

- ☐ 3. TODD FROHWIRTH

PITTSBURGH PIRATES

- ☐ 32. RANDY MILLIGAN

ST. LOUIS CARDINALS

- ☐ 22. STEVE PETERS
- ☐ 50. CRIS CARPENTER
- ☐ 52. LUIS ALICEA

SAN DIEGO PADRES

- ☐ 5. SHAWN ABNER
- ☐ 8. MARK PARENT
- ☐ 35. ROBERTO ALOMAR

SAN FRANCISCO GIANTS

NO CARDS ISSUED

SEATTLE MARINERS

- ☐ 2. MIKE CAMPBELL
- ☐ 36. EDGAR MARTINEZ

TEXAS RANGERS

- ☐ 6. JOSE CECENA
- ☐ 9. CECIL ESPY
- ☐ 25. DEWAYNE VAUGHN

TORONTO BLUE JAYS

- ☐ 12. PAT BORDERS
- ☐ 26. DAVID WELLS
- ☐ 37. TODD STOTTLEMYRE
- ☐ 42. SIL CAMPUSANO

1989 DONRUSS (660)
2 1/2 X 3 1/2

ATLANTA BRAVES

- ☐ 50. RON GANT
- ☐ 104. DALE MURPHY
- ☐ 121. TOMMY GREGG
- ☐ 145. OZZIE VIRGIL
- ☐ 168. JOE BOEVER
- ☐ 222. RICK MAHLER
- ☐ 239. GERALD PERRY
- ☐ 263. PETE SMITH
- ☐ 286. CHARLIE PULEO
- ☐ 340. DION JAMES
- ☐ 357. PAUL ASSENMACHER
- ☐ 381. TOM GLAVINE
- ☐ 405. JOSE ALVAREZ
- ☐ 458. BRUCE SUTTER
- ☐ 475. BRUCE BENEDICT
- ☐ 499. ZANE SMITH

☐ 523. MARK LEMKE
☐ 576. ANDRES THOMAS
☐ 592. JEFF BLAUSER
☐ 616. ANDY NEZELEK
☐ 642. JOHN SMOLTZ
☐ 650. JODY DAVIS
☐ 653. DEREK LILLIQUIST

BALTIMORE ORIOLES

☐ 44. PETE HARNISCH
☐ 46. GREGG OLSON
☐ 51. CAL RIPKEN
☐ 96. EDDIE MURRAY
☐ 141. TERRY KENNEDY
☐ 164. MIKE MORGAN
☐ 169. PETE STANICEK
☐ 215. DAVE SCHMIDT
☐ 259. BILLY RIPKEN
☐ 282. TOM NIEDENFUER
☐ 287. JOEW ORSULAK
☐ 333. LARRY SHEETS
☐ 377. R. C. GONZALES
☐ 401. MICKEY TETTLETON
☐ 406. RICK SCHU
☐ 451. JOSE BAUTISTA
☐ 495. JEFF BALLARD
☐ 519. BRADY ANDERSON
☐ 524. OSWALD PERAZA
☐ 569. CRAIG WORTHINGTON
☐ 635. CURT SCHILLING
☐ 651. BOB MILACKI

BOSTON RED SOX

☐ 37. CARLOS QUINTANA
☐ 66. LEE SMITH
☐ 68. WADE BOGGS
☐ 122. JIM RICE
☐ 162. RICH GEDMAN
☐ 184. MARTY BARRETT
☐ 186. MIKE GREENWELL
☐ 240. DWIGHT EVANS
☐ 280. ROGER CLEMENS
☐ 303. ELLIS BURKS
☐ 305. JODY REED
☐ 358. TODD BENZINGER
☐ 398. RICK CERONE
☐ 421. BOB STANLEY
☐ 423. BRUCE HURST
☐ 476. OIL CAN BOYD
☐ 517. JEFF SELLERS
☐ 539. TOM BOLTON
☐ 541. WES GARDNER
☐ 593. SPIKE OWEN
☐ 612. MIKE BODDICKER
☐ 628. MIKE SMITHSON
☐ 633. DENNIS LAMP
☐ 660. ERIC HETZEL

CALIFORNIA ANGELS

☐ 52. WALLY JOYNER
☐ 94. MARK MCLEMORE
☐ 108. DICK SCHOFIELD
☐ 136. KIRK MCCASKILL
☐ 170. BOB BOONE
☐ 213. DEVON WHITE
☐ 226. CHUCK FINLEY
☐ 254. BRIAN DOWNING
☐ 288. JACK HOWELL
☐ 331. JOHNNY RAY
☐ 344. DAN PETRY
☐ 372. MIKE WITT
☐ 407. SHERMAN CORBETT
☐ 449. CHILI DAVIS
☐ 462. STEW CLIBURN
☐ 490. GREG MINTON
☐ 525. BRYAN HARVEY
☐ 567. WILLIE FRASER
☐ 580. TONY ARMAS
☐ 607. TERRY CLARK
☐ 634. DANTE BICHETTE

CHICAGO CUBS

☐ 43. MIKE HARKEY
☐ 49. RAFAEL PALMEIRO
☐ 105. RYNE SANDBERG
☐ 137. SHAWON DUNSTON
☐ 157. JAMIE MOYER
☐ 158. RICH GOSSAGE
☐ 167. ANDRE DAWSON
☐ 223. RICK SUTCLIFFE
☐ 255. MARK GRACE
☐ 275. DAMON BERRYHILL
☐ 276. VANCE LAW
☐ 285. CALVIN SCHIRALDI
☐ 341. LES LANCASTER
☐ 373. GREG MADDUX
☐ 393. FRANK DIPINO
☐ 384. AL NIPPER
☐ 404. PAT PERRY
☐ 459. MITCH WEBSTER
☐ 491. DOUG DASCENZO
☐ 512. MIKE BIELECKI
☐ 513. JEFF PICO
☐ 522. DREW HALL
☐ 577. ROLANDO ROOMES
☐ 608. MANNY TRILLO
☐ 629. SCOTT SANDERSON
☐ 658. KEVIN BLANKENSHIP

CHICAGO WHITE SOX

☐ 58. MELIDO PEREZ
☐ 101. CARLTON FISK
☐ 135. GREG WALKER
☐ 148. HAROLD BAINES
☐ 176. OZZIE GUILLEN
☐ 219. STEVE ROSENBERG
☐ 253. STEVE LYONS
☐ 266. BOBBY THIGPEN
☐ 294. DAN PASQUA
☐ 337. KEN WILLIAMS
☐ 371. IVAN CALDERON
☐ 384. DAVE GALLAGHER
☐ 413. JERRY REUSS
☐ 455. DARYL BOSTON
☐ 489. FRED MANRIQUE
☐ 503. SHAWN HILLEGAS
☐ 531. JACK MCDOWELL
☐ 573. BILL LONG
☐ 606. LANCE JOHNSON
☐ 619. ADAM PETERSON
☐ 647. BARRY JONES
☐ 655. MIKE DIAZ

CINCINNATI REDS

☐ 71. TOM BROWNING
☐ 80. ERIC DAVIS
☐ 115. KEITH BROWN
☐ 124. DANNY JACKSON
☐ 139. ROB MURPHY
☐ 189. NICK ESASKY
☐ 198. KAL DANIELS
☐ 233. JOHN FRANCO
☐ 242. BO DIAZ
☐ 257. BARRY LARKIN
☐ 308. RON ROBINSON
☐ 317. CHRIS SABO
☐ 351. JEFF TREADWAY
☐ 360. PAUL O'NEILL
☐ 375. JOSE RIJO
☐ 426. ROB DIBBLE
☐ 435. HERM WINNINGHAM
☐ 469. JEFF REED
☐ 478. FRANK WILLIAMS
☐ 493. JACK ARMSTRONG
☐ 544. NORM CHARLTON
☐ 553. RON OESTER
☐ 586. VAN SNIDER
☐ 595. LLOYD MCCLENDON

CLEVELAND INDIANS

☐ 36. LUIS MEDINA
☐ 73. MEL HALL
☐ 83. JOE CARTER
☐ 114. BROOK JACOBY
☐ 138. ANDY ALLANSON
☐ 191. CORY SNYDER
☐ 202. SCOTT BAILES
☐ 232. GREG SWINDELL
☐ 256. TOM CANDIOTTI
☐ 310. JULIO FRANCO
☐ 320. JOHN FARRELL
☐ 350. JAY BELL
☐ 374. CARMEN CASTILLO
☐ 428. RON KITTLE
☐ 438. DOUG JONES
☐ 468. RON WASHINGTON
☐ 492. WILLIE UPSHAW
☐ 546. RICH YETT
☐ 556. BUD BLACK
☐ 585. DAVE CLARK
☐ 609. SCOTT JORDAN
☐ 639. TOM LAMPKIN
☐ 649. ROD NICHOLS

DETROIT TIGERS

☐ 29. STEVE SEARCY
☐ 60. GARY PETTIS
☐ 62. GUILLERMO HERNANDEZ
☐ 90. FRANK TANANA
☐ 116. MATT NOKES
☐ 153. TED POWER
☐ 178. DOYLE ALEXANDER
☐ 180. ALAN TRAMMELL
☐ 209. CHET LEMON
☐ 234. JACK MORRIS
☐ 271. MIKE HEATH
☐ 296. WALT TERRELL
☐ 298. LOU WHITAKER
☐ 327. MIKE HENNEMAN
☐ 352. LUIS SALAZAR
☐ 389. DAVE BERGMAN
☐ 415. JIM WALEWANDER
☐ 417. PAT SHERIDAN
☐ 445. PAUL GIBSON
☐ 470. JEFF ROBINSON
☐ 508. TOM BROOKENS
☐ 533. DARRELL EVANS
☐ 535. ERIC KING
☐ 563. FRED LYNN

HOUSTON ASTROS

☐ 30. CAMERON DREW
☐ 69. MIKE SCOTT
☐ 88. ALAN ASHBY
☐ 118. BOB FORSCH
☐ 123. BOB KNEPPER
☐ 154. NOLAN RYAN
☐ 187. BILLY HATCHER
☐ 207. GERALD YOUNG
☐ 236. GLENN DAVIS
☐ 241. JIM DESHAIES
☐ 272. DAVE SMITH
☐ 306. BILL DORAN
☐ 325. KEVIN BASS
☐ 354. JUAN AGOSTO
☐ 359. LARRY ANDERSEN
☐ 390. DANNY DARWIN
☐ 424. DAVE MEADS
☐ 443. JOHN FISHEL
☐ 472. TERRY PUHL
☐ 477. CRAIG REYNOLDS
☐ 509. RAFAEL RAMIREZ
☐ 542. KEN CAMINITI
☐ 561. CRAIG BIGGIO
☐ 640. BRIAN MEYER

KANSAS CITY ROYALS

☐ 45. TOM GORDON
☐ 61. DANNY TARTABULL
☐ 85. FRANK WHITE
☐ 89. CHARLIE LEIBRANDT
☐ 120. WILLIE WILSON
☐ 144. BRET SABERHAGEN
☐ 179. MARK GUBICZA
☐ 204. GEORGE BRETT
☐ 208. BO JACKSON
☐ 238. KEVIN SEITZER
☐ 262. FLOYD BANNISTER
☐ 297. ED HEARN
☐ 322. KURT STILLWELL
☐ 326. PAT TABLER
☐ 356. STEVE FARR
☐ 380. BRAD WELLMAN
☐ 416. MIKE MACFARLANE
☐ 440. JEFF MONTGOMERY
☐ 444. JERRY DON GLEATON
☐ 474. ISRAEL SANCHEZ
☐ 498. GARY THURMAN
☐ 534. LUIS AQUINO
☐ 558. JOSE DEJESUS
☐ 562. LUIS DE LOS SANTOS

LOS ANGELES DODGERS

☐ 77. MIKE SCIOSCIA
☐ 79. ALFREDO GRIFFIN

□ 84. STEVE SAX
□ 110. MIKE MARSHALL
□ 132. KIRK GIBSON
□ 195. JOHN TUDOR
□ 197. OREL HERSHISER
□ 203. TIM BELCHER
□ 228. JESSE OROSCO
□ 250. FERNANDO VALENZUELA
□ 314. JOHN SHELBY
□ 316. MIKE DAVIS
□ 321. FRANKLIN STUBBS
□ 346. MICKEY HATCHER
□ 368. DANNY HEEP
□ 432. RICK DEMPSEY
□ 434. DAVE ANDERSON
□ 439. BRIAN HOLTON
□ 464. RAMON MARTINEZ
□ 486. TIM CREWS
□ 550. JEFF HAMILTON
□ 552. TIM LEARY
□ 557. ALEJANDRO PENA
□ 582. RICKY HORTON
□ 589. WILLIAM BRENNAN
□ 603. MIKE DEVEREAUX
□ 610. JAY HOWELL

MILWAUKEE BREWERS

□ 31. GARY SHEFFIELD
□ 55. ROBIN YOUNT
□ 57. GREG BROCK
□ 103. GLENN BRAGGS
□ 146. DALE SVEUM
□ 173. ROB DEER
□ 175. TED HIGUERA
□ 221. B. J. SURHOFF
□ 264. JIM GANTNER
□ 291. PAUL MOLITOR
□ 293. BILL WEGMAN
□ 339. JOEY MEYER
□ 382. DAN PLESAC
□ 410. DON AUGUST
□ 412. CHRIS BOSIO
□ 457. JEFFREY LEONARD
□ 501. MIKE BIRKBECK
□ 528. MARK CLEAR
□ 530. JUAN CASTILLO
□ 575. JUAN NIEVES
□ 617. CHUCK CRIM
□ 632. MIKE YOUNG
□ 644. BILL SCHROEDER
□ 654. PAUL MIRABELLA

MINNESOTA TWINS

□ 64. GARY GAETTI
□ 81. JUAN BERENGUER
□ 119. BERT BLYLEVEN
□ 155. JEFF REARDON
□ 182. KIRBY PUCKETT
□ 199. KENT HRBEK
□ 237. FRANK VIOLA
□ 273. KEITH ATHERTON
□ 301. TOMMY HERR
□ 318. GREG GAGNE
□ 355. GENE LARKIN
□ 391. DAN GLADDEN
□ 419. ALLAN ANDERSON
□ 436. AL NEWMAN
□ 473. CHARLIE LEA
□ 510. FRED TOLIVER
□ 537. RANDY BUSH
□ 554. STEVE LOMBARDOZZI
□ 590. GERMAN GONZALEZ
□ 615. TIM LAUDNER
□ 626. JOHN MOSES
□ 641. BRIAN HARPER

MONTREAL EXPOS

□ 42. RANDY JOHNSON
□ 97. TIM RAINES
□ 102. DAVE MARTINEZ
□ 106. DENNIS MARTINEZ
□ 130. ANDRES GALARRAGA
□ 156. TIM WALLACH
□ 216. BRYN SMITH
□ 220. HUBIE BROOKS
□ 224. NEAL HEATON
□ 248. PASCUAL PEREZ
□ 274. TIM BURKE
□ 234. JEFF PARRETT
□ 338. ANDY MCGAFFIGAN
□ 342. TOM FOLEY
□ 366. NELSON SANTOVENIA
□ 392. JOHN DOPSON
□ 452. REX HUDLER
□ 456. MIKE FITZGERALD
□ 460. JOE HESKETH
□ 484. WALLACE JOHNSON
□ 511. BRIAN HOLMAN
□ 570. JOHNNY PAREDES
□ 574. TRACY JONES
□ 578. LUIS RIVERA

NEW YORK METS

□ 35. GREGG JEFFERIES
□ 41. DAVE WEST
□ 53. GARY CARTER
□ 99. KEVIN MCREYNOLDS
□ 117. KEITH HERNANDEZ
□ 147. DARRYL STRAWBERRY
□ 152. MOOKIE WILSON
□ 171. RON DARLING
□ 218. BOB OJEDA
□ 235. HOWARD JOHNSON
□ 265. ROGER MCDOWELL
□ 270. DWIGHT GOODEN
□ 289. KEVIN ELSTER
□ 336. RANDY MYERS
□ 353. LENNY DYKSTRA
□ 383. WALLY BACKMAN
□ 388. DAVID CONE
□ 408. DAVE MAGADAN
□ 454. MACKEY SASSER
□ 471. SID FERNANDEZ
□ 502. TERRY LEACH
□ 507. TIM TEUFEL
□ 526. RICK AGUILERA
□ 572. BARRY LYONS
□ 618. JACK SAVAGE
□ 623. KEITH MILLER

NEW YORK YANKEES

□ 72. CLAUDELL WASHINGTON
□ 74. DON MATTINGLY
□ 78. DAVE RIGHETTI
□ 127. MIKE PAGLIARULO
□ 159. DAVE WINFIELD
□ 190. DON SLAUGHT
□ 192. JOHN CANDELARIA
□ 196. NEIL ALLEN
□ 245. RICKEY HENDERSON
□ 277. RICH DOTSON
□ 309. RAFAEL SANTANA
□ 311. JACK CLARK
□ 315. AL LEITER
□ 363. KEN PHELPS
□ 395. WILLIE RANDOLPH
□ 427. JOEL SKINNER
□ 429. RICK RHODEN
□ 433. ROBERTO KELLY
□ 481. DAVE EILAND
□ 514. CHARLES HUDSON
□ 545. HAL MORRIS
□ 547. HENSLEY MEULENS
□ 551. LOUIS AGUAYO
□ 598. HIPOLITO PENA
□ 630. DALE MOHORCIC
□ 659. WAYNE TOLLESON

OAKLAND A'S

□ 38. FELIX JOSE
□ 67. DENNIS ECKERSLEY
□ 91. JOSE CANSECO
□ 95. MARK MCGWIRE
□ 125. ERIC PLUNK
□ 150. DAVE PARKER
□ 185. STAN JAVIER
□ 210. STORM DAVIS
□ 214. DAVE STEWART
□ 243. CARNEY LANSFORD
□ 268. TERRY STEINBACH
□ 304. CURT YOUNG
□ 328. RICK HONEYCUTT
□ 332. BOB WELCH
□ 361. RON HASSEY
□ 386. LUIS POLONIA
□ 422. MIKE GALLEGO
□ 446. WALT WEISS
□ 450. DAVE HENDERSON
□ 479. GREG CADARET
□ 505. DOUG JENNINGS
□ 540. GENE NELSON
□ 564. TODD BURNS
□ 568. GLENN HUBBARD
□ 596. STEVE ONTIVEROS
□ 621. LANCE BLANKENSHIP

PHILADELPHIA PHILLIES

□ 40. RON JONES
□ 75. STEVE BEDROSIAN
□ 76. JUAN SAMUEL
□ 133. DAVID PALMER
□ 160. VON HAYES
□ 193. MIKE SCHMIDT
□ 194. KEVIN GROSS
□ 251. SHANE RAWLEY
□ 278. LANCE PARRISH
□ 312. CHRIS JAMES
□ 313. MILT THOMPSON
□ 369. PHIL BRADLEY
□ 396. DON CARMAN
□ 430. BOB DERNIER
□ 431. STEVE JELTZ
□ 487. MIKE MADDUX
□ 515. BRUCE RUFFIN
□ 548. GREG HARRIS
□ 549. DARREN DAULTON
□ 587. TODD FROHWIRTH
□ 604. ALEX MADRID
□ 624. RICKY JORDAN
□ 631. MARVIN FREEMAN

PITTSBURGH PIRATES

□ 54. ANDY VAN SLYKE
□ 92. BARRY BONDS
□ 126. BRIAN FISHER
□ 134. R. J. REYNOLDS
□ 151. BOBBY BONILLA
□ 172. BOB WALK
□ 211. DOUG DRABEK
□ 244. MIKE LAVALLIERE
□ 252. SID BREAM
□ 269. MIKE DUNNE
□ 290. JOSE LIND
□ 329. JOHN SMILEY
□ 362. JIM GOTT
□ 370. JEFF ROBINSON
□ 387. JUNIOR ORTIZ
□ 409. BOB KIPPER
□ 447. GLENN WILSON
□ 480. RANDY KRAMER
□ 488. DAVE LAPOINT
□ 506. KEN OBERKFELL
□ 527. TOM PRINCE
□ 565. FELIX FERMIN
□ 597. SCOTT MEDVIN
□ 605. GARY REDUX
□ 622. MIGUEL GARCIA

ST. LOUIS CARDINALS

□ 39. CRIS CARPENTER
□ 63. OZZIE SMITH
□ 82. TODD WORRELL
□ 112. TOM BRUNANSKY
□ 161. WILLIE MCGEE
□ 163. TONY PENA
□ 181. VINCE COLEMAN

- ☐ 201. JOE MAGRANE
- ☐ 230. TERRY PENDLETON
- ☐ 279. DENNY WALLING
- ☐ 281. GREG MATHEWS
- ☐ 299. KEN DAYLEY
- ☐ 319. JOSE OQUENDO
- ☐ 348. DANNY COX
- ☐ 397. SCOTT TERRY
- ☐ 399. TOM PAGNOZZI
- ☐ 418. PEDRO GUERRERO
- ☐ 437. JOSE DELEON
- ☐ 466. LOUIS ALICEA
- ☐ 516. LARRY MCWILLIAMS
- ☐ 518. JOHN COSTELLO
- ☐ 536. KEN HILL
- ☐ 555. TIM JONES

SAN DIEGO PADRES

- ☐ 28. SANDY ALOMAR JR.
- ☐ 34. GREG HARRIS
- ☐ 65. MARK DAVIS
- ☐ 86. JOHN KRUK
- ☐ 111. KEITH MORELAND
- ☐ 128. TONY GWYNN
- ☐ 129. LANCE MCCULLERS
- ☐ 183. CHRIS BROWN
- ☐ 205. BENITO SANTIAGO
- ☐ 229. ED WHITSON
- ☐ 246. ROBERTO ALOMAR
- ☐ 247. JIMMY JONES
- ☐ 302. MIKE BRUMLEY
- ☐ 323. SHAWN ABNER
- ☐ 347. MARVELL WYNNE
- ☐ 364. TIM FLANNERY
- ☐ 365. RANDY READY
- ☐ 420. MARK PARENT
- ☐ 441. DICKIE THON
- ☐ 465. DAVE LEIPER
- ☐ 482. ERIC SHOW
- ☐ 483. GARRY TEMPLETON
- ☐ 538. SHANE MACK
- ☐ 559. DENNIS RASMUSSEN
- ☐ 583. ANDY HAWKINS
- ☐ 599. JERALD CLARK
- ☐ 601. CARMELO MARTINEZ

SAN FRANCISCO GIANTS

- ☐ 59. CRAIG LEFFERTS
- ☐ 98. ROB THOMPSON
- ☐ 131. JOSE URIBE
- ☐ 140. MIKE ALDRETE
- ☐ 177. CANDY MALDONADO
- ☐ 217. BRETT BUTLER
- ☐ 249. WILL CLARK
- ☐ 258. MIKE KRUKOW
- ☐ 295. SCOTT GARRELTS
- ☐ 335. RICK REUSCHEL
- ☐ 367. KELLY DOWNS
- ☐ 376. JOE PRICE
- ☐ 414. ATLEE HAMMAKER
- ☐ 453. BOB BRENLY
- ☐ 485. KEVIN MITCHELL
- ☐ 494. KIRT MANWARING
- ☐ 532. CHRIS SPEIER
- ☐ 571. DON ROBINSON
- ☐ 594. MATT WILLIAMS
- ☐ 602. MIKE LACOSS
- ☐ 611. FRANCISCO MELENDEZ
- ☐ 625. ERNEST RILES
- ☐ 646. DENNIS COOK

SEATTLE MARINERS

- ☐ 32. ERIK HANSON
- ☐ 33. KEN GRIFFEY
- ☐ 93. HAROLD REYNOLDS
- ☐ 109. HENRY COTTO
- ☐ 143. STEVE BALBONI
- ☐ 212. MICKEY BRANTLEY
- ☐ 227. MARK LANGSTON
- ☐ 261. SCOTT BRADLEY
- ☐ 330. REY QUINONES
- ☐ 345. ALVIN DAVIS
- ☐ 379. JIM PRESLEY
- ☐ 448. MIKE MOORE
- ☐ 463. SCOTT BANKHEAD
- ☐ 497. MIKE CAMPBELL
- ☐ 566. DARNELL COLES
- ☐ 581. JAY BUHNER
- ☐ 614. DAVE VALLE
- ☐ 637. MIKE SCHOOLER
- ☐ 645. EDGAR MARTINEZ
- ☐ 652. MIKE JACKSON
- ☐ 657. JERRY REED

TEXAS RANGERS

- ☐ 48. RUBEN SIERRA
- ☐ 56. PETE INCAVIGLIA
- ☐ 107. PETE O'BRIEN
- ☐ 142. SCOTT FLETCHER
- ☐ 165. CHARLIE HOUGH
- ☐ 166. MIKE STANLEY
- ☐ 174. STEVE BUECHELE
- ☐ 225. MITCH WILLIAMS
- ☐ 260. CECILIO GUANTE
- ☐ 283. PAUL KILGUS
- ☐ 284. JOSE GUZMAN
- ☐ 292. CECIL ESPY
- ☐ 343. GENO PETRALLI
- ☐ 378. ODDIBE MCDOWELL
- ☐ 402. CURTIS WILKERSON
- ☐ 403. JEFF RUSSELL
- ☐ 411. BOB BROWER
- ☐ 461. BOBBY WITT
- ☐ 496. JEFF KUNKEL
- ☐ 520. CRAIG MCMURTRY
- ☐ 521. RAY HAYWARD
- ☐ 529. JERRY BROWNE
- ☐ 579. CHAD KREUTER
- ☐ 613. KEVIN BROWN
- ☐ 636. SCOTT MAY

TORONTO BLUE JAYS

- ☐ 47. ALEX SANCHEZ
- ☐ 70. FRED MCGRIFF
- ☐ 87. RANCE MULLINIKS
- ☐ 113. KELLY GRUBER
- ☐ 149. GEORGE BELL
- ☐ 188. JIMMY KEY
- ☐ 206. TONY FERNANDEZ
- ☐ 231. LLOYD MOSEBY
- ☐ 267. JIM CLANCY
- ☐ 307. DAVID WELLS
- ☐ 324. MIKE FLANAGAN
- ☐ 349. DAVE STIEB
- ☐ 385. TOM HENKE
- ☐ 425. JESSE BARFIELD
- ☐ 442. CECIL FIELDER
- ☐ 467. JOHN CERUTTI
- ☐ 504. MANNY LEE
- ☐ 543. DUANE WARD
- ☐ 560. PAT BORDERS
- ☐ 584. SIL CAMPUSANO
- ☐ 591. ERNIE WHITT
- ☐ 620. TODD STOTTLEMYRE
- ☐ 627. NELSON LIRIANO
- ☐ 638. RICK LEACH
- ☐ 656. JEFF MUSSELMAN

1989 DONRUSS TRADED (56)
2 1/2 X 3 1/2

ATLANTA BRAVES

NO CARDS ISSUED

BALTIMORE ORIOLES

- ☐ 20T. BRIAN HOLTON
- ☐ 30T. MIKE DEVEREAUX
- ☐ 41T. PHIL BRADLEY

BOSTON RED SOX

- ☐ 7T. JOHN DOPSON
- ☐ 15T. ROB MURPHY
- ☐ 18T. NICK ESASKY

CALIFORNIA ANGELS

- ☐ 35T. BERT BLYLEVEN
- ☐ 46T. CLAUDELL WASHINGTON

CHICAGO CUBS

- ☐ 34T. CURT WILKERSON
- ☐ 38T. MITCH WILLIAMS
- ☐ 42T. PAUL KILGUS

CHICAGO WHITE SOX

- ☐ 29T. EDDIE WILLIAMS
- ☐ 37T. ERIC KING
- ☐ 51T. RON KITTLE

CINCINNATI REDS

- ☐ 24T. RICK MAHLER
- ☐ 47T. TODD BENZINGER

CLEVELAND INDIANS

- ☐ 16T. PETE O'BRIEN
- ☐ 22T. JOEL SKINNER
- ☐ 26T. JESSE OROSCO
- ☐ 33T. FELIX FERMIN
- ☐ 44T. JERRY BROWNE
- ☐ 49T. ODDIBE MCDOWELL

DETROIT TIGERS

- ☐ 9T. CHRIS BROWN
- ☐ 17T. KEN WILLIAMS
- ☐ 50T. CHARLES HUDSON

HOUSTON ASTROS

- ☐ 32T. JIM CLANCY
- ☐ 40T. RICK RHODEN

KANSAS CITY ROYALS

- ☐ 5T. BOB BOONE

LOS ANGELES DODGERS

- ☐ 8T. WILLIE RANDOLPH
- ☐ 12T. EDDIE MURRAY

MILWAUKEE BREWERS

NO CARDS ISSUED

MINNESOTA TWINS

☐ 10T. WALLY BACKMAN

MONTREAL EXPOS

☐ 3T. KEVIN GROSS
☐ 14T. SPKIE OWEN
☐ 25T. MIKE ALDRETE

NEW YORK METS

NO CARDS ISSUED

NEW YORK YANKEES

☐ 13T. LANCE MCCULLERS
☐ 23T. STEVE SAX
☐ 27T. DAVE LAPOINT
☐ 36T. MEL HALL
☐ 48T. STEVE BALBONI
☐ 52T. ANDY HAWKINS
☐ 53T. TOM BROOKENS

OAKLAND A'S

☐ 21T. MIKE MOORE

PHILADELPHIA PHILLIES

☐ 4T. TOMMY HERR
☐ 11T. STEVE ONTIVEROS
☐ 55T. JEFF PARRETT

PITTSBURGH PIRATES

NO CARDS ISSUED

ST. LOUIS CARDINALS

☐ 43T. MILT THOMPSON

SAN DIEGO PADRES

☐ 2T. JACK CLARK
☐ 28T. WALT TERRELL
☐ 45T. BRUCE HURST

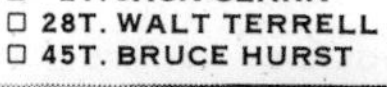

SAN FRANCISCO GIANTS

NO CARDS ISSUED

SEATTLE MARINERS

☐ 1T. JEFFREY LEONARD
☐ 54T. TOM NIEDENFUER

TEXAS RANGERS

☐ 6T. RAFAEL PALMEIRO
☐ 19T. NOLAN RYAN
☐ 31T. JULIO FRANCO
☐ 39T. JAMIE MOYER

TORONTO BLUE JAYS

NO CARDS ISSUED

1989 DONRUSS ROOKIES (56) 2 1/2 X 3 1/2

ATLANTA BRAVES

☐ 19. GERONIMO BERROA
☐ 54. DEREK LILLIQUIST

BALTIMORE ORIOLES

☐ 22. BOB MILACKI
☐ 25. CRAIG WORTHINGTON
☐ 35. GREGG OLSON
☐ 47. STEVE FINLEY
☐ 51. MIKE DEVEREAUX

BOSTON RED SOX

NO CARDS ISSUED

CALIFORNIA ANGELS

☐ 16. JIM ABBOTT
☐ 29. DANTE BICHETTE

CHICAGO CUBS

☐ 10. STEVE WILSON
☐ 23. JOE GIRARDI
☐ 26. JEROME WALTON
☐ 32. DWIGHT SMITH
☐ 36. PHIL STEPHENSON
☐ 38. RICK WRONA

CHICAGO WHITE SOX

☐ 7. DONN PALL
☐ 14. CARLOS MARTINEZ
☐ 37. KEN PATTERSON
☐ 50. MATT MERULLO

CINCINNATI REDS

NO CARDS ISSUED

CLEVELAND INDIANS

☐ 20. LUIS MEDINA

DETROIT TIGERS

☐ 17. TOREY LOVULLO
☐ 39. MIKE BRUMLEY

HOUSTON ASTROS

☐ 34. ERIC YELDING

KANSAS CITY ROYALS

☐ 4. TOM GORDON
☐ 33. LUIS DE LOS SANTOS

LOS ANGELES DODGERS

☐ 45. RAMON MARTINEZ

MILWAUKEE BREWERS

☐ 1. GARY SHEFFIELD
☐ 5. BILLY SPIERS

MINNESOTA TWINS

☐ 9. FRANCISCO OLIVERAS
☐ 24. GERMAN GONZALEZ
☐ 27. GARY WAYNE

MONTREAL EXPOS

☐ 43. RANDY JOHNSON

NEW YORK METS

☐ 2. GREGG JEFFERIES
☐ 18. MARK CARREON

NEW YORK YANKEES

☐ 6. DEION SANDERS
☐ 11. BOB GEREN
☐ 52. CLAY PARKER

OAKLAND A'S

NO CARDS ISSUED

PHILADELPHIA PHILLIES

☐ 42. RON JONES

PITTSBURGH PIRATES

☐ 8. STEVE CARTER
☐ 48. RANDY KRAMER

ST. LOUIS CARDINALS

☐ 28. TIM JONES
☐ 31. KEN HILL
☐ 40. CRIS CARPENTER

SAN DIEGO PADRES

☐ 21. SANDY ALOMAR, JR.
☐ 46. GREG HARRIS

SAN FRANCISCO GIANTS

☐ 41. JEFF BRANTLEY

SEATTLE MARINERS

- □ 3. KEN GRIFFEY, JR.
- □ 15. EDGAR MARTINEZ
- □ 49. ERIK HANSON
- □ 53. OMAR VIZQUEL

TEXAS RANGERS

- □ 13. KENNY ROGERS
- □ 44. KEVIN BROWN

TORONTO BLUE JAYS

- □ 12. TONY CASTILLO
- □ 30. ALEXIS INFANTE
- □ 55. JUNIOR FELIX

1990 DONRUSS (715)
2 1/2 X 3 1/2

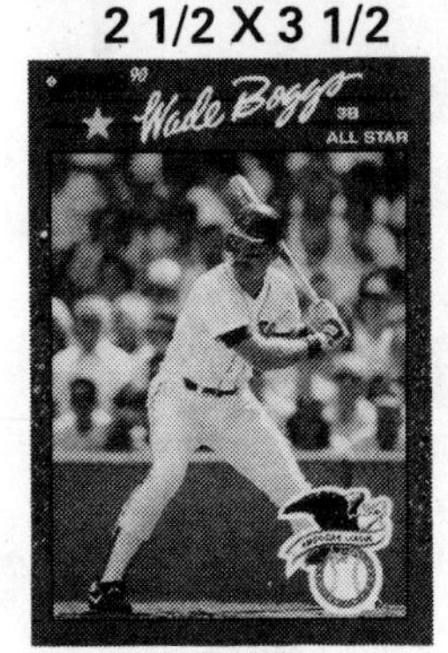

ATLANTA BRAVES

- □ 31. KENT MERCKER
- □ 39. STEVE AVERY
- □ 46. KELLY MANN
- □ 50. JEFF TREADWAY
- □ 104. GERONIMO BERROA
- □ 121. JOHN SMOLTZ
- □ 145. TOM GLAVINE
- □ 153. GERALD PERRY
- □ 168. DALE MURPHY
- □ 222. LONNIE SMITH
- □ 239. TOMMY GREGG
- □ 263. ANDRES THOMAS
- □ 271. JEFF BLAUSER
- □ 286. DEREK LILLIQUIST
- □ 340. ODDIBE MCDOWELL
- □ 357. JOE BOEVER
- □ 381. MARTY CLARY
- □ 389. JOSE ALVAREZ
- □ 405. SERGIO VALDEZ
- □ 458. JOHN RUSSELL
- □ 475. RON GANT
- □ 499. PETE SMITH
- □ 508. MIKE STANTON
- □ 523. ANDY NEZELEK
- □ 576. TOMMY GREENE
- □ 592. TONY CASTILLO
- □ 624. MARK LEMKE
- □ 646. FRANCISCO CABRERA
- □ 704. DAVE JUSTICE
- □ 713. GARY EAVE

BALTIMORE ORIOLES

- □ 32. BEN MCDONALD
- □ 51. JEFF BALLARD
- □ 96. CAL RIPKEN
- □ 141. CRAIG WORTHINGTON
- □ 164. BILLY RIPKEN
- □ 169. MICKEY TETTLETON
- □ 215. STEVE FINLEY
- □ 259. PHIL BRADLEY
- □ 282. MIKE DEVEREAUX
- □ 287. JOE ORSULAK
- □ 333. BOB MILACKI
- □ 377. GREGG OLSON
- □ 401. RENE GONZALES
- □ 406. MARK WILLIAMSON
- □ 451. BOB MELVIN
- □ 495. LARRY SHEETS
- □ 519. RANDY MILLIGAN
- □ 524. DAVE SCHMIDT
- □ 569. JIM TRABER
- □ 583. KEVIN HICKEY
- □ 596. PETE HARNISCH
- □ 612. MARK THURMOND
- □ 635. BRIAN HOLTON
- □ 638. BRADY ANDERSON
- □ 667. CURT SCHILLING
- □ 702. DAVE JOHNSON

BOSTON RED SOX

- □ 66. MIKE GREENWELL
- □ 68. WADE BOGGS
- □ 110. LEE SMITH
- □ 122. DWIGHT EVANS
- □ 162. JOHN DOPSON
- □ 184. ROGER CLEMENS
- □ 186. ROB MURPHY
- □ 228. ELLIS DURKS
- □ 240. MARTY BARRETT
- □ 280. MIKE BODDICKER
- □ 303. NICK ESASKY
- □ 305. RICK CERONE
- □ 346. RICH GEDMAN
- □ 358. DANNY HEEP
- □ 398. JODY REED
- □ 421. LUIS RIVERA
- □ 423. DENNIS LAMP
- □ 464. MIKE SMITHSON
- □ 476. KEVIN ROMINE
- □ 517. CARLOS QUINTANA
- □ 539. ERIC HETZEL
- □ 541. WES GARDNER
- □ 582. GREG HARRIS
- □ 633. OIL CAN BOYD

CALIFORNIA ANGELS

- □ 35. MIKE FETERS
- □ 52. CLAUDELL WASHINGTON
- □ 94. WALLY JOYNER
- □ 108. JIM ABBOTT
- □ 116. GREG MINTON
- □ 136. CHILI DAVIS
- □ 170. KIRK MCCASKILL
- □ 213. LANCE PARRISH
- □ 226. DEVON WHITE
- □ 234. JOHNNY RAY
- □ 254. JACK HOWELL
- □ 288. DICK SCHOFIELD
- □ 331. BERT BLYLEVEN
- □ 344. CHUCK FINLEY
- □ 352. BRIAN DOWNING
- □ 372. BRYAN HARVEY
- □ 407. GLENN HOFFMAN
- □ 449. LEE STEVENS
- □ 462. RICH MONTELEONE
- □ 470. BOB MCCLURE
- □ 490. KENT ANDERSON
- □ 525. TONY ARMAS
- □ 567. BILL SCHROEDER
- □ 580. MIKE WITT
- □ 587. WILLIE FRASER

CHICAGO CUBS

- □ 49. SHAWON DUNSTON
- □ 105. RYNE SANDBERG
- □ 137. MITCH WEBSTER
- □ 157. RICK SUTCLIFFE
- □ 158. GREG MADDUX
- □ 167. DAMON BERRYHILL
- □ 223. ANDRE DAWSON
- □ 255. MARVELL WYNNE
- □ 275. MITCH WILLIAMS
- □ 276. PAUL KILGUS
- □ 285. JEROME WALTON
- □ 341. LLOYD MCCLENDON
- □ 373. MIKE BIELECKI
- □ 393. DWIGHT SMITH
- □ 394. STEVE WILSON
- □ 404. JOE GIRARDI
- □ 459. PAUL ASSENMACHER
- □ 491. DOMINGO RAMOS
- □ 512. RICK WRONA
- □ 513. LUIS SALAZAR
- □ 522. MIKE HARKEY
- □ 577. MARK GRACE
- □ 585. JEFF PICO
- □ 608. CURT WILKERSON
- □ 628. LES LANCASTER
- □ 629. VANCE LAW
- □ 647. SCOTT SANDERSON

CHICAGO WHITE SOX

- □ 28. ROBIN VENTURA
- □ 58. CARLTON FISK
- □ 101. MELIDO PEREZ
- □ 135. OZZIE GUILLEN
- □ 148. RON KITTLE
- □ 176. DAN PASQUA
- □ 219. DAVE GALLAGHER
- □ 253. STEVE ROSENBERG
- □ 266. BOBBY THIGPEN
- □ 294. IVAN CALDERON
- □ 337. ERIC KING
- □ 371. KEN PATTERSON
- □ 384. GREG HIBBARD
- □ 413. RON KARKOVICE
- □ 455. SCOTT FLETCHER
- □ 489. SAMMY SOSA
- □ 503. JERRY KUTZLER
- □ 531. CARLOS MARTINEZ
- □ 573. LANCE JOHNSON
- □ 606. DONN PALL
- □ 619. SHAWN HILLEGAS
- □ 651. STEVE LYONS

CINCINNATI REDS

- □ 71. BARRY LARKIN
- □ 80. DANNY JACKSON
- □ 115. JOSE RIJO
- □ 124. JOHN FRANCO
- □ 139. BO DIAZ
- □ 189. ROB DIBBLE
- □ 198. PAUL O'NEILL
- □ 233. ERIC DAVIS
- □ 242. CHRIS SABO
- □ 257. TODD BENZINGER
- □ 308. TOM BROWNING
- □ 317. RON OESTER
- □ 351. JEFF REED
- □ 360. ROLANDO ROOMES
- □ 375. RICK MAHLER
- □ 426. NORM CHARLTON
- □ 435. SCOTT SCUDDER
- □ 469. KEN GRIFFEY
- □ 478. HERM WINNINGHAM
- □ 493. TIM BIRTSAS
- □ 544. JACK ARMSTRONG
- □ 553. RON ROBINSON
- □ 586. JOE OLIVER
- □ 595. LUIS QUINONES
- □ 670. TIM LEARY
- □ 684. MARIANO DUNCAN

CLEVELAND INDIANS

- □ 73. JOEL SKINNER
- □ 83. BROOK JACOBY
- □ 114. JOE CARTER
- □ 138. JERRY BROWNE
- □ 154. JESSE OROSCO
- □ 191. FELIX FERMIN
- □ 202. PETE O'BRIEN
- □ 232. JOHN FARRELL
- □ 256. TOM CANDIOTTI
- □ 272. CORY SNYDER
- □ 310. GREG SWINDELL
- □ 320. DOUG JONES
- □ 350. BRAD KOMMINSK
- □ 374. TOM MAGRANN
- □ 390. JOEY BELLE
- □ 428. DION JAMES
- □ 438. STEVE OLIN
- □ 468. SCOTT BAILES
- □ 492. DAVE CLARK
- □ 509. RICH YETT
- □ 546. ROD NICHOLS
- □ 556. BUD BLACK
- □ 691. BEAU ALLRED

DETROIT TIGERS

- □ 38. BRIAN DUBOIS
- □ 60. CHET LEMON
- □ 62. DOYLE ALEXANDER
- □ 90. ALAN TRAMMELL

☐ 178. MATT NOKES
☐ 180. FRANK TANANA
☐ 209. MIKE HEATH
☐ 296. MIKE HENNEMAN
☐ 298. LOU WHITAKER
☐ 327. FRANK WILLIAMS
☐ 415. KEVIN RITZ
☐ 417. JEFF ROBINSON
☐ 445. DAVE BERGMAN
☐ 533. MIKE BRUMLEY
☐ 535. DOUG STRANGE
☐ 563. EDWIN NUNEZ
☐ 599. RICK SCHU
☐ 610. GUILLERMO HERNANDEZ
☐ 621. GARY WARD
☐ 636. TRACY JONES
☐ 639. JACK MORRIS
☐ 657. PAUL GIBSON
☐ 661. GARY PETTIS
☐ 696. SCOTT LUSADER

HOUSTON ASTROS

☐ 34. ERIC ANTHONY
☐ 69. JIM CLANCY
☐ 88. DAVE SMITH
☐ 118. GLENN DAVIS
☐ 123. EIRC YELDING
☐ 187. JIM DESHAIES
☐ 207. MIKE SCOTT
☐ 236. BILL DORAN
☐ 241. RAFAEL RAMIREZ
☐ 306. CRAIG BIGGIO
☐ 325. GERALD YOUNG
☐ 354. TERRY PUHL
☐ 359. LARRY ANDERSEN
☐ 424. KEN CAMINITI
☐ 443. ALEX TREVINO
☐ 472. GLENN WILSON
☐ 477. JUAN AGOSTO
☐ 542. MARK PORTUGAL
☐ 561. DANNY DARWIN
☐ 589. KEVIN BASS
☐ 594. DAN SCHATZEDER
☐ 648. BRIAN MEYER
☐ 688. STEVE LOMBARDOZZI

KANSAS CITY ROYALS

☐ 61. BO JACKSON
☐ 85. KEVIN SEITZER
☐ 89. BRET SABERHAGEN
☐ 120. KURT STILLWELL
☐ 144. GEORGE BRETT
☐ 179. LUIS AQUINO
☐ 204. MARK GUBICZA
☐ 208. CHARLIE LEIBRANDT
☐ 238. JIM EISENREICH
☐ 262. FRANK WHITE
☐ 297. TOM GORDON
☐ 322. DANNY TARTABULL
☐ 326. BOB BOONE
☐ 356. STEVE FARR
☐ 380. JEFF MONTGOMERY
☐ 416. GARY THURMAN
☐ 440. WILLIE WILSON
☐ 444. PAT TABLER
☐ 474. BILL BUCKNER
☐ 498. MIKE MACFARLANE
☐ 534. TERRY LEACH
☐ 562. RICK LUECKEN
☐ 709. LARRY MCWILLIAMS

LOS ANGELES DODGERS

☐ 77. EDDIE MURRAY
☐ 79. TIM BELCHER
☐ 84. MIKE MARSHALL
☐ 132. MIKE MORGAN
☐ 195. ALFREDO GRIFFIN
☐ 197. OREL HERSHISER
☐ 203. JAY HOWELL
☐ 250. WILLIE RANDOLPH
☐ 314. JOSE GONZALEZ
☐ 316. MIKE SCIOSCIA
☐ 321. JEFF HAMILTON
☐ 368. KIRK GIBSON
☐ 432. KAL DANIELS
☐ 434. LENNY HARRIS
☐ 439. MICKEY HATCHER
☐ 486. DAVE ANDERSON
☐ 550. TIM CREWS
☐ 552. MIKE DAVIS
☐ 557. RICK DEMPSEY
☐ 603. MIKE SHARPERSON
☐ 615. FRANKLIN STUBBS
☐ 625. FERNANDO VALENZUELA
☐ 649. RAY SEARAGE
☐ 664. ALEJANDRO PENA
☐ 671. JOHN WETTELAND
☐ 685. RAMON MARTINEZ

MILWAUKEE BREWERS

☐ 37. GREG VAUGHN
☐ 55. ROB DEER
☐ 57. CHRIS BOSIO
☐ 103. PAUL MOLITOR
☐ 146. ROBIN YOUNT
☐ 173. B. J. SURHOFF
☐ 175. DAN PLESAC
☐ 221. CHUCK CRIM
☐ 264. GLENN BRAGGS
☐ 291. JIM GANTNER
☐ 293. GREG BROCK
☐ 339. TED HIGUERA
☐ 382. BILL SPIERS
☐ 410. CHARLIE O'BRIEN
☐ 412. GUS POLIDOR
☐ 457. TONY FOSSAS
☐ 501. GARY SHEFFIELD
☐ 528. JERRY REUSS
☐ 530. JEFF PETEREK
☐ 575. MARK KNUDSON
☐ 609. MIKE FELDER
☐ 617. DON AUGUST
☐ 640. JAIME NAVARRO
☐ 687. TOM FILER
☐ 699. GEORGE CANALE

MINNESOTA TWINS

☐ 64. ALLAN ANDERSON
☐ 81. KENT HRBEK
☐ 119. JEFF REARDON
☐ 151. GARY GAETTI
☐ 155. WALLY BACKMAN
☐ 182. DAN GLADDEN
☐ 199. RANDY BUSH
☐ 237. GREG GAGNE
☐ 269. KIRBY PUCKETT
☐ 273. ROY SMITH
☐ 301. JUAN BERENGUER
☐ 318. GARY WAYNE
☐ 355. BRIAN HARPER
☐ 387. DAVE WEST
☐ 391. RICK AGUILERA
☐ 419. TIM LAUDNER
☐ 436. GENE LARKIN
☐ 473. KEVIN TAPANI
☐ 506. AL NEWMAN
☐ 510. TIM DRUMMOND
☐ 537. SHANE RAWLEY
☐ 554. CARMEN CASTILLO
☐ 590. JOHN MOSES
☐ 622. MARK GUTHRIE
☐ 626. PAUL SORRENTO
☐ 642. MIKE DYER
☐ 690. CHIP HALE

MONTREAL EXPOS

☐ 36. MARQUIS GRISSOM
☐ 40. MARK GARDNER
☐ 42. DELINO DESHIELDS
☐ 97. ANDRES GALARRAGA
☐ 102. SPIKE OWEN
☐ 106. BRYN SMITH
☐ 130. HUBIE BROOKS
☐ 156. DENNIS MARTINEZ
☐ 216. TIM RAINES
☐ 220. TIM WALLACH
☐ 224. NELSON SANTOVENIA
☐ 248. KEVIN GROSS
☐ 274. TOM FOLEY
☐ 334. TIM BURKE
☐ 338. MARK LANGSTON
☐ 342. PASCUAL PEREZ
☐ 366. REX HUDLER
☐ 392. MIKE FITZGERALD
☐ 452. DAVE MARTINEZ
☐ 456. OTIS NIXON
☐ 460. ZANE SMITH
☐ 484. JIM DWYER
☐ 511. JOE HESKETH
☐ 570. WALLACE JOHNSON
☐ 574. ANDY MCGAFFIGAN
☐ 578. LARRY WALKER
☐ 693. JEFF HUSON

NEW YORK METS

☐ 47. JULIO MACHADO
☐ 53. JUAN SAMUEL
☐ 99. HOWARD JOHNSON
☐ 117. BOB OJEDA
☐ 147. GARY CARTER
☐ 152. KEVIN ELSTER
☐ 171. DWIGHT GOODEN
☐ 218. KEVIN MCREYNOLDS
☐ 235. DARRYL STRAWBERRY
☐ 265. DAVID CONE
☐ 270. GREGG JEFFERIES
☐ 289. RON DARLING
☐ 336. RANDY MYERS
☐ 353. FRANK VIOLA
☐ 383. DAVE MAGADAN
☐ 388. KEITH HERNANDEZ
☐ 408. JEFF INNIS
☐ 454. MARK CARREON
☐ 471. MACKEY SASSER
☐ 502. TERRY BROSS
☐ 507. KEITH MILLER
☐ 526. BARRY LYONS
☐ 572. SID FERNANDEZ
☐ 618. TIM TEUFEL
☐ 623. JEFF MUSSELMAN

NEW YORK YANKEES

☐ 72. DAVE LAPOINT
☐ 74. JESSE BARFIELD
☐ 78. STEVE SAX
☐ 127. LEE GUETTERMAN
☐ 159. ANDY HAWKINS
☐ 190. DON MATTINGLY
☐ 192. ROBERTO KELLY
☐ 196. ERIC PLUNK
☐ 245. ALVARO ESPINOZA
☐ 277. DON SLAUGHT
☐ 309. WALT TERRELL
☐ 311. DAVE RIGHETTI
☐ 315. STEVE BALBONI
☐ 363. CLAY PARKER
☐ 395. BOB GEREN
☐ 427. DEION SANDERS
☐ 429. CHUCK CARY
☐ 433. LANCE MCCULLERS
☐ 481. KEVIN MMAHAT
☐ 514. HAL MORRIS
☐ 545. GREG CADARET
☐ 547. LUIS POLONIA
☐ 551. DAVE WINFIELD
☐ 598. MEL HALL
☐ 630. RANDY VELARDE
☐ 656. MIKE BLOWERS
☐ 678. GOOSE GOSSAGE
☐ 689. BERNIE WILLIAMS

OAKLAND A'S

☐ 67. WALT WEISS
☐ 91. TONY PHILLIPS
☐ 95. CARNEY LANSFORD
☐ 125. JOSE CANSECO
☐ 150. DAVE STEWART
☐ 185. MARK MCGWIRE

- ☐ 210. DENNIS ECKERSLEY
- ☐ 214. MIKE MOORE
- ☐ 243. DAVE HENDERSON
- ☐ 268. TERRY STEINBACH
- ☐ 304. RICKEY HENDERSON
- ☐ 328. DAVE PARKER
- ☐ 332. BOB WELCH
- ☐ 361. MIKE GALLEGO
- ☐ 386. RICK HONEYCUTT
- ☐ 422. JIM CORSI
- ☐ 446. TODD BURNS
- ☐ 450. RON HASSEY
- ☐ 479. STORM DAVIS
- ☐ 505. CURT YOUNG
- ☐ 540. GENE NELSON
- ☐ 564. FELIX JOSE
- ☐ 568. STAN JAVIER
- ☐ 675. KEN PHELPS

PHILADELPHIA PHILLIES

- ☐ 44. PAT COMBS
- ☐ 75. TOMMY HERR
- ☐ 76. RICKY JORDAN
- ☐ 133. STEVE JELTZ
- ☐ 160. JOHN KRUK
- ☐ 193. DENNIS COOK
- ☐ 194. DARREN DAULTON
- ☐ 251. ROGER MCDOWELL
- ☐ 278. VON HAYES
- ☐ 312. MIKE MADDUX
- ☐ 313. LENNY DYKSTRA
- ☐ 369. JEFF PARRETT
- ☐ 396. RANDY READY
- ☐ 430. KEN HOWELL
- ☐ 431. STEVE LAKE
- ☐ 487. RON JONES
- ☐ 515. TERRY MULHOLLAND
- ☐ 548. CHARLIE HAYES
- ☐ 549. DICKIE THON
- ☐ 604. DON CARMAN
- ☐ 631. TODD FROHWIRTH
- ☐ 643. MIKE SCHMIDT
- ☐ 694. CURT FORD

PITTSBURGH PIRATES

- ☐ 54. JOHN SMILEY
- ☐ 92. DOUG DRABEK
- ☐ 126. BARRY BONDS
- ☐ 134. JEFF ROBINSON
- ☐ 172. JOSE LIND
- ☐ 211. MIKE LAVALLIERE
- ☐ 244. ANDY VAN SLYKE
- ☐ 252. RAFAEL BELLIARD
- ☐ 290. BOBBY BONILLA
- ☐ 329. SID BREAM
- ☐ 362. BOB KIPPER
- ☐ 370. BOB WALK
- ☐ 409. RANDY KRAMER
- ☐ 447. R. J. REYNOLDS
- ☐ 480. JEFF KING
- ☐ 488. JAY BELL
- ☐ 527. RICK REED
- ☐ 565. JOHN CANGELOSI
- ☐ 597. GARY REDUS
- ☐ 605. JIM GOTT
- ☐ 616. BILLY HATCHER
- ☐ 658. NEAL HEATON
- ☐ 668. BILL LANDRUM

ST. LOUIS CARDINALS

- ☐ 29. TODD ZEILE
- ☐ 63. PEDRO GUERRERO
- ☐ 82. MILT THOMPSON
- ☐ 161. JOSE OQUENDO
- ☐ 163. JOE MAGRANE
- ☐ 181. TONY PENA
- ☐ 201. OZZIE SMITH
- ☐ 279. VINCE COLEMAN
- ☐ 281. KEN DAYLEY
- ☐ 299. TERRY PENDLETON
- ☐ 319. TODD WORRELL
- ☐ 397. KEN HILL
- ☐ 399. TOM BRUNANSKY
- ☐ 418. SCOTT TERRY
- ☐ 437. DAN QUISENBERRY
- ☐ 516. JOHN MORRIS
- ☐ 518. FRANK DIPINO
- ☐ 536. JOSE DELEON
- ☐ 555. JOHN COSTELLO
- ☐ 591. TOM PAGNOZZI
- ☐ 632. WILLIE MCGEE
- ☐ 634. CRIS CARPENTER
- ☐ 653. TED POWER
- ☐ 666. RICKY HORTON
- ☐ 677. DENNY WALLING
- ☐ 686. TIM JONES
- ☐ 714. BOB TEWKSBURY

SAN DIEGO PADRES

- ☐ 30. SANDY ALOMAR, JR.
- ☐ 41. ANDY BENES
- ☐ 65. GREG HARRIS
- ☐ 86. TONY GWYNN
- ☐ 111. ROBERTO ALOMAR
- ☐ 128. JACK CLARK
- ☐ 183. BRUCE HURST
- ☐ 205. ED WHITSON
- ☐ 229. MARK PARENT
- ☐ 246. GARRY TEMPLETON
- ☐ 302. MARK DAVIS
- ☐ 323. CHRIS JAMES
- ☐ 347. BIP ROBERTS
- ☐ 364. MIKE PAGLIARULO
- ☐ 420. DENNIS RASMUSSEN
- ☐ 441. MARK GRANT
- ☐ 465. BENITO SANTIAGO
- ☐ 482. CARMELO MARTINEZ
- ☐ 538. JOEY CORA
- ☐ 559. ERIC SHOW
- ☐ 593. JERALD CLARK
- ☐ 641. DARRIN JACKSON
- ☐ 672. CALVIN SCHIRALDI

SAN FRANCISCO GIANTS

- ☐ 59. KIRT MANWARING
- ☐ 98. KEVIN MITCHELL
- ☐ 112. RICK REUSCHEL
- ☐ 131. ERNEST RILES
- ☐ 140. ROBBY THOMPSON
- ☐ 177. KELLY DOWNS
- ☐ 217. SCOTT GARRELTS
- ☐ 230. WILL CLARK
- ☐ 249. BRETT BUTLER
- ☐ 258. DON ROBINSON
- ☐ 295. STEVE BEDROSIAN
- ☐ 335. JOSE URIBE
- ☐ 348. MATT WILLIAMS
- ☐ 367. PAT SHERIDAN
- ☐ 376. CRAIG LEFFERTS
- ☐ 414. TREVOR WILSON
- ☐ 453. GREG LITTON
- ☐ 466. JEFF BRANTLEY
- ☐ 485. BOB KNEPPER
- ☐ 494. KEN OBERKFELL
- ☐ 532. ATLEE HAMMAKER
- ☐ 571. DONELL NIXON
- ☐ 602. TERRY KENNEDY
- ☐ 611. CANDY MALDONADO
- ☐ 652. MIKE LACOSS
- ☐ 680. BILL BATHE

SEATTLE MARINERS

- ☐ 93. JEFFREY LEONARD
- ☐ 109. ALVIN DAVIS
- ☐ 129. DAVE VALLE
- ☐ 143. BRIAN HOLMAN
- ☐ 212. DARNELL COLES
- ☐ 227. HAROLD REYNOLDS
- ☐ 247. GENE HARRIS
- ☐ 261. SCOTT BANKHEAD
- ☐ 330. MIKE SCHOOLER
- ☐ 345. ERIK HANSON
- ☐ 365. KEN GRIFFEY, JR.
- ☐ 379. RANDY JOHNSON
- ☐ 448. JAY BUHNER
- ☐ 463. GREG BRILEY
- ☐ 483. OMAR VIZQUEL
- ☐ 497. JIM PRESLEY
- ☐ 566. BILLY SWIFT
- ☐ 581. SCOTT BRADLEY
- ☐ 601. MIKE KINGERY
- ☐ 614. JERRY REED
- ☐ 644. HENRY COTTO
- ☐ 662. CLINT ZAVARAS

TEXAS RANGERS

- ☐ 33. JUAN GONZALEZ
- ☐ 43. SCOTT COOLBAUGH
- ☐ 48. PETE INCAVIGLIA
- ☐ 56. GENO PETRALLI
- ☐ 107. STEVE BUECHELE
- ☐ 142. JULIO FRANCO
- ☐ 165. FRED MANRIQUE
- ☐ 166. NOLAN RYAN
- ☐ 174. RUBEN SIERRA
- ☐ 225. RAFAEL PALMEIRO
- ☐ 260. CECIL ESPY
- ☐ 283. KENNY ROGERS
- ☐ 284. JEFF RUSSELL
- ☐ 292. BOBBY WITT
- ☐ 343. KEVIN BROWN
- ☐ 378. JAMIE MOYER
- ☐ 402. HAROLD BAINES
- ☐ 403. CECILIO GUANTE
- ☐ 411. CHARLIE HOUGH
- ☐ 461. JACK DAUGHERTY
- ☐ 496. JEFF JUNKEL
- ☐ 520. CHAD KREUTER
- ☐ 521. MIKE JEFFCOAT
- ☐ 529. DEAN PALMER
- ☐ 579. MIKE STANLEY
- ☐ 613. RICK LEACH
- ☐ 679. GARY MIELKE

TORONTO BLUE JAYS

- ☐ 45. ALEX SANCHEZ
- ☐ 70. JUNIOR FELIX
- ☐ 87. DAVE STIEB
- ☐ 113. KELLY GRUBER
- ☐ 149. TONY FERNANDEZ
- ☐ 188. FRED MCGRIFF
- ☐ 206. GEORGE BELL
- ☐ 231. JIMMY KEY
- ☐ 267. NELSON LIRIANO
- ☐ 307. DUANE WARD
- ☐ 324. MIKE FLANAGAN
- ☐ 349. TOM HENKE
- ☐ 385. ERNIE WHITT
- ☐ 425. DAVID WELLS
- ☐ 442. MOOKIE WILSON
- ☐ 467. JOSE NUNEZ
- ☐ 504. LLOYD MOSEBY
- ☐ 543. AL LEITER
- ☐ 558. JIM ACKER
- ☐ 560. PAT BORDERS
- ☐ 584. LEE MAZZILLI
- ☐ 607. RANCE MULLINIKS
- ☐ 620. MANNY LEE
- ☐ 627. GLENALLEN HILL
- ☐ 645. JOHN CERUTTI
- ☐ 655. MAURO GOZZO
- ☐ 669. TODD STOTTLEMYRE
- ☐ 681. TOM LAWLESS
- ☐ 682. XAVIER HERNANDEZ
- ☐ 698. STEVE CUMMINGS
- ☐ 706. GREG MYERS
- ☐ 711. JOHN OLERUD

1990 DONRUSS ROOKIES (56)
2 1/2 X 3 1/2

ATLANTA BRAVES

☐ 7. MIKE STANTON
☐ 14. DAVE JUSTICE
☐ 42. STEVE AVERY
☐ 43. MARK LEMKE
☐ 46. GREG OLSON

BALTIMORE ORIOLES

☐ 30. BEN MCDONALD
☐ 39. MARTY BROWN

BOSTON RED SOX

☐ 28. DANA KIECKER
☐ 54. JOHN ORTON

CALIFORNIA ANGELS

NO CARDS ISSUED

CHICAGO CUBS

☐ 10. JOE KRAEMER
☐ 18. SHAWN BOSKIE
☐ 22. MIKE HARKEY

CHICAGO WHITE SOX

☐ 9. CRAIG GREBECK
☐ 15. ROBIN VENTURA
☐ 17. WAYNE EDWARDS
☐ 25. JERRY KUTZLER
☐ 40. SCOTT RADINSKY

CINCINNATI REDS

☐ 23. TIM LAYANA

CLEVELAND INDIANS

☐ 1. SANDY ALOMAR
☐ 19. CARLOS BAERGA
☐ 36. KEVIN WICKANDER
☐ 53. JEFF SHAW

DETROIT TIGERS

☐ 4. BRIAN DUBOIS

HOUSTON ASTROS

☐ 33. XAVIER HERNANDEZ
☐ 49. ERIC ANTHONY

KANSAS CITY ROYALS

☐ 21. KEVIN APPIER
☐ 55. TERRY SHUMPERT

LOS ANGELES DODGERS

☐ 8. MIKE MUNOZ
☐ 34. MIKE HARTLEY
☐ 37. CARLOS HERNANDEZ
☐ 38. BRIAN TRAXLER

MILWAUKEE BREWERS

☐ 16. GREG VAUGHN

MINNESOTA TWINS

☐ 35. KEVIN TAPANI
☐ 50. TIM DRUMMOND

MONTREAL EXPOS

☐ 6. DELINO DESHIELDS
☐ 12. BILL SAMPEN
☐ 20. MARK GARDNER
☐ 45. MARQUIS GRISSOM

NEW YORK METS

☐ 41. JULIO MACHADO

NEW YORK YANKEES

☐ 26. MIKE BLOWERS
☐ 44. ALAN MILLS

OAKLAND A'S

☐ 5. FELIX JOSE

PHILADELPHIA PHILLIES

☐ 3. PAT COMBS
☐ 47. DAVE HOLLINS

PITTSBURGH PIRATES

☐ 27. SCOTT RUSKIN

ST. LOUIS CARDINALS

☐ 31. TODD ZEILE

SAN DIEGO PADRES

☐ 48. JERALD CLARK

SAN FRANCISCO GIANTS

☐ 51. JOHN BURKETT

SEATTLE MARINERS

☐ 52. BRENT KNACKERT

TEXAS RANGERS

☐ 11. JEFF HUSON
☐ 13. BRIAN BOHANON
☐ 32. SCOTT COOLBAUGH

TORONTO BLUE JAYS

☐ 2. JOHN OLERUD
☐ 24. GLENALLEN HILL
☐ 29. WILLIE BLAIR

1991 DONRUSS (770)
2 1/2 X 3 1/2

ATLANTA BRAVES

☐ 75. JOHN SMOLTZ
☐ 117. JEFF TREADWAY
☐ 132. TOM GLAVINE
☐ 173. JIM PRESLEY
☐ 187. STEVE AVERY
☐ 229. JEFF BLAUSER
☐ 244. TOMMY GREGG
☐ 285. GREG OLSON
☐ 299. KENT MERCKER
☐ 341. FRANCISCO CABRERA
☐ 361. MARK GRANT
☐ 364. LONNIE SMITH
☐ 413. PAUL MARAK
☐ 450. ODDIBE MCDOWELL
☐ 491. ANDRES THOMAS
☐ 507. RON GANT
☐ 548. DAVE JUSTICE
☐ 562. CHARLIE LEIBRANDT
☐ 604. MARK LEMKE
☐ 619. MARVIN FREEMAN
☐ 660. JEFF PARRETT
☐ 716. MIKE STANTON
☐ 736. KELLY MANN
☐ 739. JIMMY KREMERS
☐ 753. JIM VATCHER

BALTIMORE ORIOLES

☐ 35. LEO GOMEZ
☐ 69. BOB MILACKI
☐ 111. GREGG OLSON
☐ 126. DAVE JOHNSON
☐ 167. BILLY RIPKEN

- ☐ 181. PETE HARNISCH
- ☐ 223. CAL RIPKEN
- ☐ 238. MARK WILLIAMSON
- ☐ 279. JEFF BALLARD
- ☐ 293. CRAIG WORTHINGTON
- ☐ 335. BOB MELVIN
- ☐ 355. STEVE FINLEY
- ☐ 358. CHRIS HOILES
- ☐ 444. MIKE DEVEREAUX
- ☐ 485. BEN MCDONALD
- ☐ 501. ANTHONY TELFORD
- ☐ 542. RANDY MILLIGAN
- ☐ 556. CURT SCHILLING
- ☐ 597. MICKEY TETTLETON
- ☐ 613. RON KITTLE
- ☐ 654. JOE ORSULAK
- ☐ 668. BRADY ANDERSON
- ☐ 706. TIM HULETT
- ☐ 710. JOHN MITCHELL
- ☐ 730. DAVID SEGUI
- ☐ 733. SAM HORN
- ☐ 765. JOSE MESA

BOSTON RED SOX

- ☐ 37. KEVIN MORTON
- ☐ 41. PHIL PLANTIER
- ☐ 81. ROGER CLEMENS
- ☐ 122. DWIGHT EVANS
- ☐ 123. JODY REED
- ☐ 138. DENNIS LAMP
- ☐ 178. WADE BOGGS
- ☐ 193. JOHN DOPSON
- ☐ 234. LUIS RIVERA
- ☐ 235. ELLIS BURKS
- ☐ 250. ROB MURPHY
- ☐ 290. KEVIN ROMINE
- ☐ 306. GREG HARRIS
- ☐ 346. JOHN MARZANO
- ☐ 347. DANA KIECKER
- ☐ 367. TIM NAEHRING
- ☐ 369. JEFF REARDON
- ☐ 430. MO VAUGHN
- ☐ 456. TONY PENA
- ☐ 496. SCOTT COOPER
- ☐ 513. TOM BRUNANSKY
- ☐ 553. MIKE GREENWELL
- ☐ 568. CARLOS QUINTANA
- ☐ 609. TOM BOLTON
- ☐ 625. MIKE MARSHALL
- ☐ 665. LARRY ANDERSEN
- ☐ 721. JEFF GRAY

CALIFORNIA ANGELS

- ☐ 78. JIM ABBOTT
- ☐ 93. LUIS POLONIA
- ☐ 135. LANCE PARRISH
- ☐ 150. DEVON WHITE
- ☐ 190. MARK LANGSTON
- ☐ 206. BRYAN HARVEY
- ☐ 247. JACK HOWELL
- ☐ 262. DICK SCHOFIELD
- ☐ 303. DANTE BICHETTE
- ☐ 318. MARK EICHHORN
- ☐ 376. DONNIE HILL
- ☐ 379. WILLIE FRASER
- ☐ 453. BERT BLYLEVEN
- ☐ 468. DAVE WINFIELD
- ☐ 510. MAX VENABLE
- ☐ 525. KENT ANDERSON
- ☐ 565. MIKE FETTERS
- ☐ 580. CHILI DAVIS
- ☐ 622. JOHNNY RAY
- ☐ 637. KIRK MCCASKILL
- ☐ 677. WALLY JOYNER
- ☐ 692. CHUCK FINLEY
- ☐ 714. JOHN ORTON
- ☐ 737. JOE GRAHE
- ☐ 754. LEE STEVENS

CHICAGO CUBS

- ☐ 36. DERRICK MAY
- ☐ 72. JEROME WALTON
- ☐ 87. MIKE BIELECKI
- ☐ 129. ANDRE DAWSON
- ☐ 144. PAUL ASSENMACHER
- ☐ 184. JOE GIRARDI
- ☐ 199. MARK GRACE
- ☐ 241. SHAWN BOSKIE
- ☐ 256. LES LANCASTER
- ☐ 296. HECTOR VILLANUEVA
- ☐ 312. MITCH WILLIAMS
- ☐ 372. LUIS SALAZAR
- ☐ 374. GREG MADDUX
- ☐ 424. LANCE DICKSON
- ☐ 447. MIKE HARKEY
- ☐ 462. RICK SUTCLIFFE
- ☐ 504. RYNE SANDBERG
- ☐ 519. STEVE WILSON
- ☐ 559. DWIGHT SMITH
- ☐ 574. GREG SMITH
- ☐ 616. DAVE CLARK
- ☐ 631. DAMON BERRYHILL
- ☐ 671. GARY VARSHO
- ☐ 678. DANNY JACKSON
- ☐ 686. SHAWON DUNSTON
- ☐ 749. DOUG DASCENZO

CHICAGO WHITE SOX

- ☐ 57. JACK MCDOWELL
- ☐ 59. ALEX FERNANDEZ
- ☐ 90. BOBBY THIGPEN
- ☐ 103. DAN PASQUA
- ☐ 108. CARLTON FISK
- ☐ 147. SAMMY SOSA
- ☐ 159. GREG HIBBARD
- ☐ 164. MELIDO PEREZ
- ☐ 203. IVAN CALDERON
- ☐ 215. DONN PALL
- ☐ 220. RON KARKOVICE
- ☐ 259. LANCE JOHNSON
- ☐ 271. ERIC KING
- ☐ 276. SCOTT FLETCHER
- ☐ 315. ROBIN VENTURA
- ☐ 327. WAYNE EDWARDS
- ☐ 332. SCOTT RADINSKY
- ☐ 378. CRAIG GREBECK
- ☐ 465. CARLOS MARTINEZ
- ☐ 477. FRANK THOMAS
- ☐ 522. KEN PATTERSON
- ☐ 534. BARRY JONES
- ☐ 577. OZZIE GUILLEN
- ☐ 589. SHAWN HILLEGAS
- ☐ 634. JERRY WILLARD
- ☐ 646. PHIL BRADLEY
- ☐ 747. MATT STARK

CINCINNATI REDS

- ☐ 84. ERIC DAVIS
- ☐ 96. DANNY JACKSON
- ☐ 141. HAL MORRIS
- ☐ 153. CHRIS SABO
- ☐ 196. BILLY HATCHER
- ☐ 209. RANDY MYERS
- ☐ 253. GLENN BRAGGS
- ☐ 265. SCOTT SCUDDER
- ☐ 309. MARIANO DUNCAN
- ☐ 321. ROB DIBBLE
- ☐ 381. JOE OLIVER
- ☐ 384. NORM CHARLTON
- ☐ 459. LUIS QUINONES
- ☐ 471. BARRY LARKIN
- ☐ 516. TIM LAYANA
- ☐ 528. TOM BROWNING
- ☐ 571. JACK ARMSTRONG
- ☐ 583. PAUL O'NEILL
- ☐ 628. RON OESTER
- ☐ 640. TODD BENZINGER
- ☐ 695. HERM WINNINGHAM
- ☐ 722. JOSE RIJO
- ☐ 741. JEFF REED
- ☐ 752. TERRY LEE
- ☐ 756. BILL DORAN
- ☐ 759. CHRIS HAMMOND

CLEVELAND INDIANS

- ☐ 29. MARK LEWIS
- ☐ 61. MIKE WALKER
- ☐ 106. JOHN FARRELL
- ☐ 115. TOM CANDIOTTI
- ☐ 120. JOEL SKINNER
- ☐ 162. JERRY BROWNE
- ☐ 171. JESSE OROSCO
- ☐ 176. BROOK JACOBY
- ☐ 218. RUDY SEANEZ
- ☐ 227. CHRIS JAMES
- ☐ 232. DOUG JONES
- ☐ 274. CARLOS BAERGA
- ☐ 283. MITCH WEBSTER
- ☐ 288. CORY SNYDER
- ☐ 330. COLBY WARD
- ☐ 339. STEVE OLIN
- ☐ 344. SERGIO VALDEZ
- ☐ 348. DION JAMES
- ☐ 383. ALEX COLE
- ☐ 429. TURNER WARD
- ☐ 480. CANDY MALDONADO
- ☐ 489. SANDY ALOMAR
- ☐ 537. FELIX FERMIN
- ☐ 546. GREG SWINDELL
- ☐ 592. CHARLES NAGY
- ☐ 602. JEFF MANTO
- ☐ 649. KEVIN WICKANDER
- ☐ 658. TOM BROOKENS

DETROIT TIGERS

- ☐ 40. MILT CUYLER
- ☐ 65. MARK SALAS
- ☐ 76. MIKE HENNEMAN
- ☐ 118. ALAN TRAMMELL
- ☐ 133. LANCE MCCULLERS
- ☐ 174. LOU WHITAKER
- ☐ 188. LLOYD MOSEBY
- ☐ 230. MIKE HEATH
- ☐ 245. JEFF ROBINSON
- ☐ 286. TONY PHILLPS
- ☐ 301. CHET LEMON
- ☐ 342. DAVE BERGMAN
- ☐ 353. PAUL GIBSON
- ☐ 422. SCOTT ALDRED
- ☐ 451. CECIL FIELDER
- ☐ 492. JACK MORRIS
- ☐ 508. FRANK TANANA
- ☐ 549. STEVE SEARCY
- ☐ 563. JOHN SHELBY
- ☐ 605. CLAY PARKER
- ☐ 620. EDWIN NUNEZ
- ☐ 661. JERRY DON GLEATON
- ☐ 675. DAN PETRY
- ☐ 717. WALT TERRELL
- ☐ 728. GARY WARD
- ☐ 729. ROB DEER
- ☐ 768. TRAVIS FRYMAN

HOUSTON ASTROS

- ☐ 99. FRANKLIN STUBBS
- ☐ 109. KEN OBERKFELL
- ☐ 156. GLENN WILSON
- ☐ 165. DANNY DARWIN
- ☐ 212. DAVE SMITH
- ☐ 221. KEN CAMINITI
- ☐ 268. MARK PORTUGAL
- ☐ 277. ERIC YELDING
- ☐ 324. CASEY CANDAELE
- ☐ 333. ERIC ANTHONY
- ☐ 474. GLENN DAVIS
- ☐ 483. MIKE SCOTT
- ☐ 531. JUAN AGOSTO
- ☐ 540. MARK DAVIDSON
- ☐ 586. RAFAEL RAMIREZ
- ☐ 595. CRAIG BIGGIO
- ☐ 643. JAVIER ORTIZ
- ☐ 652. JIM DESHAIES
- ☐ 689. GERALD YOUNG

- ☐ 690. LUIS GONZALEZ
- ☐ 698. KARL RHODES
- ☐ 708. XAVIER HERNANDEZ
- ☐ 743. DAVE ROHDE

KANSAS CITY ROYALS

- ☐ 73. KEVIN SEITZER
- ☐ 88. BRET SABERHAGEN
- ☐ 130. GERALD PERRY
- ☐ 145. MARK GUBICZA
- ☐ 185. STORM DAVIS
- ☐ 201. GEORGE BRETT
- ☐ 242. TOM GORDON
- ☐ 257. MEL STOTTLEMYRE
- ☐ 297. TERRY SHUMPERT
- ☐ 313. MIKE MACFARLANE
- ☐ 356. BOB BOONE
- ☐ 365. STEVE FARR
- ☐ 427. JEFF CONINE
- ☐ 448. JIM EISENREICH
- ☐ 463. DANNY TARTABULL
- ☐ 505. JEFF MONTGOMERY
- ☐ 520. KURT STILLWELL
- ☐ 560. MARK DAVIS
- ☐ 575. BRIAN MCRAE
- ☐ 617. BRENT MAYNE
- ☐ 632. BO JACKSON
- ☐ 672. BILL PECOTA
- ☐ 680. MIKE BODDICKER
- ☐ 687. JEFF SCHULZ
- ☐ 718. LUIS AQUINO
- ☐ 740. KEVIN APPIER

LOS ANGELES DODGERS

- ☐ 33. JOSE OFFERMAN
- ☐ 45. DAVE HANSEN
- ☐ 62. JUAN SAMUEL
- ☐ 70. TIM BELCHER
- ☐ 112. MIKE SCIOSCIA
- ☐ 127. FERNANDO VALENZUELA
- ☐ 168. MIKE SHARPERSON
- ☐ 182. MIKE MORGAN
- ☐ 224. LENNY HARRIS
- ☐ 239. STAN JAVIER
- ☐ 280. OREL HERSHISER
- ☐ 294. TIM CREWS
- ☐ 336. KAL DANIELS
- ☐ 349. HUBIE BROOKS
- ☐ 445. KIRK GIBSON
- ☐ 486. JAY HOWELL
- ☐ 488. ALFREDO GRIFFIN
- ☐ 502. EDDIE MURRAY
- ☐ 543. JOSE GONZALEZ
- ☐ 545. MIKE HARTLEY
- ☐ 557. RAMON MARTINEZ
- ☐ 598. CHRIS GWYNN
- ☐ 601. JIM GOTT
- ☐ 614. JOHN WETTELAND
- ☐ 655. JIMMY POOLE
- ☐ 657. DENNIS COOK
- ☐ 669. DARREN HOLMES
- ☐ 696. DARRYL STRAWBERRY
- ☐ 711. CARLOS HERNANDEZ
- ☐ 713. JIM NEIDLINGER
- ☐ 724. JOSE VIZCAINO

MILWAUKEE BREWERS

- ☐ 85. PAUL MOLITOR
- ☐ 104. DAN PLESAC
- ☐ 142. DAVE PARKER
- ☐ 160. CHRIS BOSIO
- ☐ 197. EDGAR DIAZ
- ☐ 216. JAIME NAVARRO
- ☐ 254. RON ROBINSON
- ☐ 272. ROBIN YOUNT
- ☐ 310. BILL SPIERS
- ☐ 328. MARK KNUDSON
- ☐ 414. TIM MCINTOSH
- ☐ 460. B.J. SURHOFF
- ☐ 478. GREG VAUGHN
- ☐ 517. DARRYL HAMILTON
- ☐ 535. MIKE FELDER
- ☐ 572. GREG BROCK
- ☐ 590. TOM EDENS
- ☐ 629. TED HIGUERA
- ☐ 647. BILL KRUEGER
- ☐ 674. KEVIN BROWN
- ☐ 684. CHUCK CRIM
- ☐ 703. JIM GANTNER
- ☐ 751. GARY SHEFFIELD
- ☐ 755. RANDY VERES
- ☐ 764. JULIO MACHADO

MINNESOTA TWINS

- ☐ 64. MARK GUTHRIE
- ☐ 95. KENT HRBEK
- ☐ 116. KEVIN TAPANI
- ☐ 152. GENE LARKIN
- ☐ 172. RICK AGUILERA
- ☐ 208. AL NEWMAN
- ☐ 228. DAN GLADDEN
- ☐ 264. DAVID WEST
- ☐ 284. GREG GAGNE
- ☐ 320. SHANE MACK
- ☐ 340. JUAN BERENGUER
- ☐ 382. RANDY BUSH
- ☐ 420. RICH GARCES
- ☐ 421. CHUCK KNOBLAUCH
- ☐ 470. ROY SMITH
- ☐ 490. KIRBY PUCKETT
- ☐ 527. ALLAN ANDERSON
- ☐ 547. GARY GAETTI
- ☐ 582. BRIAN HARPER
- ☐ 603. NELSON LIRIANO
- ☐ 639. PAUL ABBOTT
- ☐ 659. JUNIOR ORTIZ
- ☐ 694. TIM DRUMMOND
- ☐ 715. TERRY LEACH
- ☐ 745. PAUL SORRENTO
- ☐ 757. GARY WAYNE
- ☐ 758. PEDRO MUNOZ
- ☐ 767. SCOTT ERICKSON

MONTREAL EXPOS

- ☐ 38. MOISES ALOU
- ☐ 68. ANDRES GALARRAGA
- ☐ 82. MIKE FITZGERALD
- ☐ 125. TIM BURKE
- ☐ 139. DENNIS MARTINEZ
- ☐ 180. TOM FOLEY
- ☐ 194. OIL CAN BOYD
- ☐ 237. DAVE MARTINEZ
- ☐ 251. SPIKE OWEN
- ☐ 292. STEVE FREY
- ☐ 307. MARQUIS GRISSOM
- ☐ 351. BILL SAMPEN
- ☐ 359. LARRY WALKER
- ☐ 415. BRIAN BARNES
- ☐ 425. GREG COLBRUNN
- ☐ 443. MARK GARDNER
- ☐ 457. TIM RAINES
- ☐ 499. JERRY GOFF
- ☐ 514. TIM WALLACH
- ☐ 555. DELINO DESHIELDS
- ☐ 569. KEVIN GROSS
- ☐ 612. SCOTT RUSKIN
- ☐ 626. OTIS NIXON
- ☐ 667. CHRIS NABHOLZ
- ☐ 681. MEL ROJAS
- ☐ 726. JUNIOR NOBOA
- ☐ 734. HOWARD FARMER

NEW YORK METS

- ☐ 34. TERRY BROSS
- ☐ 39. JULIO VALERA
- ☐ 79. GREGG JEFFERIES
- ☐ 97. SID FERNANDEZ
- ☐ 136. MACKEY SASSER
- ☐ 154. DAVID CONE
- ☐ 191. KEVIN MCREYNOLDS
- ☐ 210. DARYL BOSTON
- ☐ 248. KEITH MILLER
- ☐ 266. DWIGHT GOODEN
- ☐ 304. KEVIN ELSTER
- ☐ 322. JOHN FRANCO
- ☐ 362. DAVE MAGADAN
- ☐ 370. TIM TEUFEL
- ☐ 454. HOWARD JOHNSON
- ☐ 472. RON DARLING
- ☐ 497. DAN SCHATZEDER
- ☐ 511. WALLY WHITEHURST
- ☐ 529. FRANK VIOLA
- ☐ 566. ALEJANDRO PENA
- ☐ 584. BOB OJEDA
- ☐ 610. TOM HERR
- ☐ 623. CHARLIE O'BRIEN
- ☐ 641. TODD HUNDLEY
- ☐ 731. MARK CARREON

NEW YORK YANKEES

- ☐ 31. HENSLEY MEULENS
- ☐ 63. MIKE BLOWERS
- ☐ 67. TIM LEARY
- ☐ 107. DON MATTINGLY
- ☐ 114. BOB GEREN
- ☐ 124. LEE GUETTERMAN
- ☐ 163. STEVE SAX
- ☐ 170. MATT NOKES
- ☐ 179. CHUCK CARY
- ☐ 219. JIM LEYRITZ
- ☐ 226. ALVARO ESPINOZA
- ☐ 236. GREG CADARET
- ☐ 275. DAVE RIGHETTI
- ☐ 282. MIKE WITT
- ☐ 291. JEFF ROBINSON
- ☐ 331. OSCAR AZOCAR
- ☐ 338. ALAN MILLS
- ☐ 354. DAVE EILAND
- ☐ 442. MEL HALL
- ☐ 481. DAVE LAPOINT
- ☐ 498. JESSE BARFIELD
- ☐ 538. ROBERTO KELLY
- ☐ 554. KEVIN MAAS
- ☐ 593. ERIC PLUNK
- ☐ 611. ANDY HAWKINS
- ☐ 650. STEVE BALBONI

OAKLAND A'S

- ☐ 102. DAVE STEWART
- ☐ 105. MARK MCGWIRE
- ☐ 158. MIKE GALLEGO
- ☐ 161. MIKE MOORE
- ☐ 214. WALT WEISS
- ☐ 217. WILLIE RANDOLPH
- ☐ 270. DENNIS ECKERSLEY
- ☐ 273. CARNEY LANSFORD
- ☐ 326. DAVE HENDERSON
- ☐ 329. TERRY STEINBACH
- ☐ 373. RICK HONEYCUTT
- ☐ 385. GENE NELSON
- ☐ 431. STEVE CHITREN
- ☐ 476. RON HASSEY
- ☐ 479. TODD BURNS
- ☐ 533. SCOTT SANDERSON
- ☐ 536. JOSE CANSECO
- ☐ 588. JAMIE QUIRK
- ☐ 591. JOE KLINK
- ☐ 645. BOB WELCH
- ☐ 648. RICKEY HENDERSON
- ☐ 666. WILLIE MCGEE
- ☐ 701. LANCE BLANKENSHIP
- ☐ 704. REGGIE HARRIS
- ☐ 723. CURT YOUNG
- ☐ 748. HAROLD BAINES

PHILADELPHIA PHILLIES

- ☐ 44. MICKEY MORANDINI
- ☐ 47. DARRIN FLETCHER
- ☐ 60. PAT COMBS
- ☐ 91. DICKIE THON
- ☐ 110. DARREL AKERFELDS
- ☐ 148. RANDY READY
- ☐ 166. ROGER MCDOWELL
- ☐ 204. KEN HOWELL
- ☐ 222. VON HAYES
- ☐ 260. JOHN KRUK
- ☐ 278. CHARLIE HAYES
- ☐ 316. DARREN DAULTON
- ☐ 334. STEVE LAKE
- ☐ 377. DON CARMAN
- ☐ 423. WES CHAMBERLAIN
- ☐ 466. RICKY JORDAN
- ☐ 484. DALE MURPHY
- ☐ 523. LEN DYKSTRA
- ☐ 541. TERRY MULHOLLAND
- ☐ 578. JOE BOEVER
- ☐ 596. JOSE DEJESUS
- ☐ 635. TOMMY GREENE
- ☐ 653. JASON GRIMSLEY
- ☐ 709. CHUCK MCELROY

PITTSBURGH PIRATES

- ☐ 58. JOSE LIND

- ☐ 101. R.J. REYNOLDS
- ☐ 121. MIKE LAVALLIERE
- ☐ 157. BOB WALK
- ☐ 177. WALLY BACKMAN
- ☐ 213. DON SLAUGHT
- ☐ 233. JEFF KING
- ☐ 269. DOUG DRABEK
- ☐ 289. JAY BELL
- ☐ 325. BOBBY BONILLA
- ☐ 345. BOB PATTERSON
- ☐ 350. BILL LANDRUM
- ☐ 418. STEVE CARTER
- ☐ 475. NEAL HEATON
- ☐ 495. BARRY BONDS
- ☐ 532. ZANE SMITH
- ☐ 552. ANDY VAN SLYKE
- ☐ 587. GARY REDUS
- ☐ 608. TED POWER
- ☐ 644. SID BREAM
- ☐ 664. JOHN SMILEY
- ☐ 699. STAN BELINDA
- ☐ 720. BOB KIPPER
- ☐ 725. RANDY TOMLIN
- ☐ 732. VICENTE PALACIOS

ST. LOUIS CARDINALS

- ☐ 30. BERNARD GILKEY
- ☐ 43. RAY LANKFORD
- ☐ 66. TIM JONES
- ☐ 71. TODD ZEILE
- ☐ 113. BRYN SMITH
- ☐ 128. JOSE DELEON
- ☐ 169. LEE SMITH
- ☐ 183. BOB TEWKSBURY
- ☐ 225. MILT THOMPSON
- ☐ 240. OZZIE SMITH
- ☐ 281. JOSE OQUENDO
- ☐ 295. JOE MAGRANE
- ☐ 337. TOM PAGNOZZI
- ☐ 360. FRANK DIPINO
- ☐ 446. TERRY PENDLETON
- ☐ 487. VINCE COLEMAN
- ☐ 503. OMAR OLIVARES
- ☐ 544. CRAIG WILSON
- ☐ 558. PEDRO GUERRERO
- ☐ 599. REX HUDLER
- ☐ 615. MIKE PEREZ
- ☐ 656. FELIX JOSE
- ☐ 670. KEN HILL
- ☐ 712. GERONIMO PENA

SAN DIEGO PADRES

- ☐ 74. JERALD CLARK
- ☐ 83. BRUCE HURST
- ☐ 131. GREG HARRIS
- ☐ 140. MIKE PAGLIARULO
- ☐ 186. ED WHITSON
- ☐ 195. BIP ROBERTS
- ☐ 243. TONY GWYNN
- ☐ 252. GARRY TEMPLETON
- ☐ 298. JOE CARTER
- ☐ 308. CALVIN SCHIRALDI
- ☐ 449. BENITO SANTIAGO
- ☐ 458. DENNIS RASMUSSEN
- ☐ 506. MARK PARENT
- ☐ 515. CRAIG LEFFERTS
- ☐ 561. SHAWN ABNER
- ☐ 570. DEREK LILLIQUIST
- ☐ 618. JACK CLARK
- ☐ 627. ANDY BENES
- ☐ 673. FRED LYNN
- ☐ 682. ROBERTO ALOMAR
- ☐ 707. ATLEE HAMMAKER
- ☐ 746. THOMAS HOWARD
- ☐ 769. RICH RODRIGUEZ

SAN FRANCISCO GIANTS

- ☐ 86. WILL CLARK
- ☐ 94. TERRY KENNEDY
- ☐ 143. BRETT BUTLER
- ☐ 151. GARY CARTER
- ☐ 198. GREG LITTON
- ☐ 207. STEVE BEDROSIAN
- ☐ 255. KEVIN MITCHELL
- ☐ 263. TREVOR WILSON
- ☐ 311. SCOTT GARRELTS
- ☐ 319. JEFF BRANTLEY
- ☐ 363. ROBBY THOMPSON
- ☐ 375. JOSE URIBE
- ☐ 416. ERIC GUNDERSON
- ☐ 428. STEVE DECKER
- ☐ 432. MIKE BENJAMIN
- ☐ 461. ERNEST RILES
- ☐ 469. FRANCISCO OLIVERAS
- ☐ 518. RICK REUSCHEL
- ☐ 526. MARK LEONARD
- ☐ 573. MIKE KINGERY
- ☐ 581. DON ROBINSON
- ☐ 630. KEVIN BASS
- ☐ 638. JOHN BURKETT
- ☐ 685. MATT WILLIAMS
- ☐ 719. BUD BLACK
- ☐ 738. KELLY DOWNS

SEATTLE MARINERS

- ☐ 28. TINO MARTINEZ
- ☐ 77. KEN GRIFFEY, JR.
- ☐ 119. PETE O'BRIEN
- ☐ 134. RANDY JOHNSON
- ☐ 175. HAROLD REYNOLDS
- ☐ 189. SCOTT BANKHEAD
- ☐ 231. OMAR VIZQUEL
- ☐ 246. KEITH COMSTOCK
- ☐ 287. SCOTT BRADLEY
- ☐ 302. MIKE SCHOOLER
- ☐ 343. HENRY COTTO
- ☐ 352. GREG BRILEY
- ☐ 366. DAVE VALLE
- ☐ 417. MIKE GARDINER
- ☐ 426. RICH DELUCIA
- ☐ 452. KEN GRIFFEY
- ☐ 482. ALVIN DAVIS
- ☐ 493. MATT YOUNG
- ☐ 509. JAY BUHNER
- ☐ 539. BRIAN HOLMAN
- ☐ 550. ERIK HANSON
- ☐ 564. BILL SWIFT
- ☐ 594. TRACY JONES
- ☐ 606. EDGAR MARTINEZ
- ☐ 621. RUSS SWAN
- ☐ 651. GENE HARRIS
- ☐ 662. BRENT KNACKERT
- ☐ 676. MIKE JACKSON

TEXAS RANGERS

- ☐ 42. SCOTT CHIAMPARINO
- ☐ 46. KEVIN BELCHER
- ☐ 80. KEVIN REIMER
- ☐ 89. NOLAN RYAN
- ☐ 137. GENO PETRALLI
- ☐ 146. CHARLIE HOUGH
- ☐ 192. JULIO FRANCO
- ☐ 202. JEFF RUSSELL
- ☐ 249. BOBBY WITT
- ☐ 258. KENNY ROGERS
- ☐ 305. JEFF HUSON
- ☐ 314. KEVIN BROWN
- ☐ 357. STEVE BUECHELE
- ☐ 371. JUAN GONZALEZ
- ☐ 419. GERALD ALEXANDER
- ☐ 455. MONTY FARRIS
- ☐ 464. PETE INCAVIGLIA
- ☐ 512. GARY PETTIS
- ☐ 521. RAFAEL PALMEIRO
- ☐ 567. RUBEN SIERRA
- ☐ 576. JACK DAUGHERTY
- ☐ 624. JOE BITKER
- ☐ 633. BRAD ARNSBERG
- ☐ 679. BILL HASELMAN
- ☐ 688. JOHN BARFIELD

TORONTO BLUE JAYS

- ☐ 32. DEREK BELL
- ☐ 92. DUANE WARD
- ☐ 98. JIMMY KEY
- ☐ 149. KELLY GRUBER
- ☐ 155. TODD STOTTLEMYRE
- ☐ 205. TOM HENKE
- ☐ 211. MANNY LEE
- ☐ 261. FRED MCGRIFF
- ☐ 267. WILLIE BLAIR
- ☐ 317. PAT BORDERS
- ☐ 323. JUNIOR FELIX
- ☐ 368. JIM ACKER
- ☐ 380. GLENALLEN HILL
- ☐ 467. JOHN CERUTTI
- ☐ 473. DAVID WELLS
- ☐ 494. GREG MYERS
- ☐ 524. TONY FERNANDEZ
- ☐ 530. JOHN OLERUD
- ☐ 551. DAVE STIEB
- ☐ 579. LUIS SOJO
- ☐ 585. MOOKIE WILSON
- ☐ 607. MARK WHITEN
- ☐ 636. BOB MACDONALD
- ☐ 642. GEORGE BELL
- ☐ 663. RANCE MULLINIKS
- ☐ 691. FRANK WILLS
- ☐ 697. AL LEITER
- ☐ 705. ROB DUCEY
- ☐ 735. KEN DAYLEY

1991 DONRUSS ROOKIES (56)
2 1/2 X 3 1/2

ATLANTA BRAVES

- ☐ 9. BRIAN HUNTER

BALTIMORE ORIOLES

- ☐ 54. CHITO MARTINEZ

BOSTON RED SOX

- ☐ 36. MO VAUGHN
- ☐ 40. KEVIN MORTON
- ☐ 46. MIKE GARDINER

CALIFORNIA ANGELS

NO CARDS ISSUED

CHICAGO CUBS

- ☐ 11. CED LANDRUM
- ☐ 20. FRANK CASTILLO
- ☐ 25. HEATHCLIFF SLOCUMB
- ☐ 38. RICK WILKINS

1991 Donruss Rookies

- ☐ 49. CHUCK MCELROY

CHICAGO WHITE SOX

- ☐ 13. RAMON GARCIA
- ☐ 15. WARREN NEWSON

CINCINNATI REDS

- ☐ 19. CHRIS HAMMOND
- ☐ 50. CHRIS JONES

CLEVELAND INDIANS

- ☐ 18. CHARLES NAGY
- ☐ 32. MARK WHITEN
- ☐ 42. MARK LEWIS
- ☐ 45. DENIS BOUCHER
- ☐ 55. REGGIE JEFFERSON

DETROIT TIGERS

- ☐ 6. MILT CUYLER
- ☐ 29. MARK LEITER
- ☐ 53. RUSTY MEACHAM

HOUSTON ASTROS

- ☐ 5. DARRYL KILE
- ☐ 17. LUIS GONZALEZ
- ☐ 30. JEFF BAGWELL
- ☐ 52. AL OSUNA

KANSAS CITY ROYALS

- ☐ 31. BRIAN MCRAE
- ☐ 43. BRENT MAYNE

LOS ANGELES DODGERS

NO CARDS ISSUED

MILWAUKEE BREWERS

NO CARDS ISSUED

MINNESOTA TWINS

- ☐ 4. SCOTT LEIUS
- ☐ 21. PEDRO MUNOZ
- ☐ 39. CHUCK KNOBLAUCH

MONTREAL EXPOS

- ☐ 28. JEFF FASSERO
- ☐ 44. CHRIS HANEY

NEW YORK METS

- ☐ 26. DOUG SIMONS

NEW YORK YANKEES

- ☐ 1. PAT KELLY
- ☐ 34. WADE TAYLOR
- ☐ 41. CARLOS RODRIGUEZ
- ☐ 47. JEFF JOHNSON
- ☐ 51. SCOTT KAMIENIECKI

OAKLAND A'S

- ☐ 7. TODD VAN POPPEL
- ☐ 24. KIRK DRESSENDORFER

PHILADELPHIA PHILLIES

- ☐ 3. WES CHAMBERLAIN

PITTSBURGH PIRATES

- ☐ 22. ORLANDO MERCED

ST. LOUIS CARDINALS

- ☐ 8. RAY LANKFORD

SAN DIEGO PADRES

- ☐ 16. PAUL FARIES
- ☐ 23. JOSE MELENDEZ

SAN FRANCISCO GIANTS

- ☐ 10. TONY PEREZCHICA
- ☐ 35. DARREN LEWIS
- ☐ 37. MIKE REMLINGER

SEATTLE MARINERS

- ☐ 2. RICH DELUCIA

TEXAS RANGERS

- ☐ 12. DAVE BURBA
- ☐ 33. IVAN RODRIGUEZ
- ☐ 48. DEAN PALMER

TORONTO BLUE JAYS

- ☐ 14. ED SPRAGUE
- ☐ 27. MIKE TIMLIN

1992 DONRUSS (784)
2 1/2 X 3 1/2

ATLANTA BRAVES

- ☐ 1. MARK WOHLERS
- ☐ 13. RYAN KLESKO
- ☐ 41. OTIS NIXON
- ☐ 81. STEVE AVERY
- ☐ 84. CHARLIE LEIBRANDT
- ☐ 107. RAFAEL BELLIARD
- ☐ 116. KENT MERCKER
- ☐ 163. BRIAN HUNTER
- ☐ 202. SID BREAM
- ☐ 205. JUAN BERENGUER
- ☐ 228. JEFF BLAUSER
- ☐ 237. TERRY PENDLETON
- ☐ 284. RON GANT
- ☐ 324. JEFF TREADWAY
- ☐ 327. DAVE JUSTICE
- ☐ 386. GREG OLSON
- ☐ 442. JOHN SMOLTZ
- ☐ 482. FRANCISCO CABRERA
- ☐ 485. TOMMY GREGG
- ☐ 508. KEITH MITCHELL
- ☐ 517. LONNIE SMITH
- ☐ 564. DEION SANDERS
- ☐ 603. MARVIN FREEMAN
- ☐ 606. MARK LEMKE
- ☐ 629. TOM GLAVINE
- ☐ 639. JIM CLANCY
- ☐ 771. DAMON BERRYHILL
- ☐ 772. ALEJANDRO PENA
- ☐ 776. MIKE BIELECKI
- ☐ 780. MIKE STANTON

BALTIMORE ORIOLES

- ☐ 6. LUIS MERCEDES
- ☐ 35. CAL RIPKEN
- ☐ 74. JEFF BALLARD
- ☐ 77. JEFF ROBINSON
- ☐ 101. BOB MILACKI
- ☐ 110. GREGG OLSON
- ☐ 156. CHRIS HOILES
- ☐ 196. MIKE FLANAGAN
- ☐ 199. LEO GOMEZ
- ☐ 222. RANDY MILLIGAN
- ☐ 231. BOB MELVIN
- ☐ 278. SAM HORN
- ☐ 317. TODD FROHWIRTH
- ☐ 321. DAVID SEGUI
- ☐ 354. MIKE DEVEREAUX
- ☐ 436. BEN MCDONALD
- ☐ 475. JOE ORSULAK
- ☐ 479. JUAN BELL
- ☐ 502. DWIGHT EVANS
- ☐ 511. MARK WILLIAMSON
- ☐ 558. CHITO MARTINEZ
- ☐ 597. GLENN DAVIS
- ☐ 600. JIMMY POOLE
- ☐ 623. ANTHONY TELFORD
- ☐ 632. MIKE MUSSINA
- ☐ 727. ARTHUR RHODES
- ☐ 734. BILLY RIPKEN
- ☐ 773. JOSE MESA

BOSTON RED SOX

- ☐ 47. JODY REED
- ☐ 87. DANNY DARWIN
- ☐ 89. JEFF REARDON
- ☐ 113. GREG HARRIS
- ☐ 122. JEFF GRAY
- ☐ 169. JACK CLARK
- ☐ 208. TONY PENA
- ☐ 210. WADE BOGGS
- ☐ 234. ELLIS BURKS
- ☐ 244. ROGER CLEMENS
- ☐ 290. MIKE GARDINER
- ☐ 330. KEVIN MORTON
- ☐ 332. LUIS RIVERA
- ☐ 448. JOHN MARZANO
- ☐ 488. PHIL PLANTIER
- ☐ 490. TOM BRUNANSKY
- ☐ 514. MO VAUGHN
- ☐ 523. MIKE GREENWELL
- ☐ 570. SCOTT COOPER
- ☐ 609. CARLOS QUINTANA
- ☐ 611. JOE HESKETH
- ☐ 635. MATT YOUNG
- ☐ 645. TONY FOSSAS
- ☐ 720. BOB ZUPCIC
- ☐ 742. TIM NAEHRING
- ☐ 758. STEVE LYONS

CALIFORNIA ANGELS

- ☐ 3. KYLE ABBOTT
- ☐ 44. DICK SCHOFIELD
- ☐ 59. JEFF ROBINSON
- ☐ 90. BOBBY ROSE
- ☐ 96. GARY GAETTI
- ☐ 130. JIM ABBOTT
- ☐ 133. DAVE WINFIELD
- ☐ 166. LANCE PARRISH
- ☐ 181. MARK EICHHORN
- ☐ 211. BRYAN HARVEY
- ☐ 217. JUNIOR FELIX
- ☐ 252. LUIS POLONIA
- ☐ 255. CHUCK FINLEY
- ☐ 287. RON TINGLEY
- ☐ 302. LUIS SOJO
- ☐ 333. WALLY JOYNER
- ☐ 340. KIRK MCCASKILL
- ☐ 357. SCOTT BAILES
- ☐ 377. DAVE GALLAGHER
- ☐ 445. JOE GRAHE
- ☐ 460. LEE STEVENS
- ☐ 491. MIKE FETTERS
- ☐ 497. GARY DISARCINA
- ☐ 531. MARK LANGSTON
- ☐ 698. CHRIS CRON
- ☐ 733. RUBEN AMARO
- ☐ 736. SHAWN ABNER

CHICAGO CUBS

- ☐ 38. DOUG DASCENZO
- ☐ 53. DAVE SMITH
- ☐ 91. DANNY JACKSON
- ☐ 119. ANDRE DAWSON
- ☐ 127. GEORGE BELL
- ☐ 152. LUIS SALAZAR
- ☐ 159. PAUL ASSENMACHER
- ☐ 175. JOE GIRARDI
- ☐ 212. JOSE VIZCAINO
- ☐ 241. MIKE HARKEY
- ☐ 249. RICK WILKINS
- ☐ 281. MARK GRACE
- ☐ 296. LES LANCASTER
- ☐ 334. HEATHCLIFF SLOCUMB
- ☐ 412. REY SANCHEZ
- ☐ 421. LANCE DICKSON
- ☐ 439. CHICO WALKER
- ☐ 454. BOB SCANLAN
- ☐ 492. FRANK CASTILLO
- ☐ 520. GREG MADDUX
- ☐ 528. JEROME WALTON
- ☐ 561. DWIGHT SMITH
- ☐ 576. RYNE SANDBERG
- ☐ 613. SHAWON DUNSTON
- ☐ 642. RICK SUTCLIFFE
- ☐ 650. CHUCK MCELROY
- ☐ 662. CED LANDRUM
- ☐ 725. HECTOR VILLANUEVA
- ☐ 754. YORKIS PEREZ

CHICAGO WHITE SOX

- ☐ 19. ROBERTO HERNANDEZ
- ☐ 56. DONN PALL
- ☐ 69. CHARLIE HOUGH
- ☐ 108. JOEY CORA
- ☐ 142. DAN PASQUA
- ☐ 145. ROBIN VENTURA
- ☐ 178. GREG HIBBARD
- ☐ 191. ALEX FERNANDEZ
- ☐ 229. OZZIE GUILLEN
- ☐ 264. MATT MERULLO
- ☐ 267. LANCE JOHNSON
- ☐ 299. SCOTT RADINSKY
- ☐ 312. TIM RAINES
- ☐ 352. JACK MCDOWELL
- ☐ 374. RON KARKOVICE
- ☐ 457. KEN PATTERSON
- ☐ 470. BO JACKSON
- ☐ 509. MELIDO PEREZ
- ☐ 543. CARLTON FISK
- ☐ 546. CRAIG GREBECK
- ☐ 579. MIKE HUFF
- ☐ 592. FRANK THOMAS
- ☐ 630. WILSON ALVAREZ
- ☐ 658. RAMON GARCIA
- ☐ 668. WARREN NEWSON
- ☐ 708. BOBBY THIGPEN
- ☐ 740. SAMMY SOSA
- ☐ 743. STEVE WAPNICK

CINCINNATI REDS

- ☐ 50. CHRIS SABO
- ☐ 63. PAUL O'NEILL
- ☐ 102. NORM CHARLTON
- ☐ 136. TOM BROWNING
- ☐ 139. ROB DIBBLE
- ☐ 172. CHRIS HAMMOND
- ☐ 185. BARRY LARKIN
- ☐ 223. JOSE RIJO
- ☐ 258. HAL MORRIS
- ☐ 261. JOE OLIVER
- ☐ 293. BILL DORAN
- ☐ 306. SCOTT SCUDDER
- ☐ 363. GLENN BRAGGS
- ☐ 399. DAN WILSON
- ☐ 415. REGGIE SANDERS
- ☐ 417. MO SANFORD
- ☐ 420. STEVE FOSTER
- ☐ 451. JEFF REED
- ☐ 464. CHRIS JONES
- ☐ 483. GREG SWINDELL
- ☐ 503. ERIC DAVIS
- ☐ 537. BILLY HATCHER
- ☐ 540. MARIANO DUNCAN
- ☐ 573. FREDDIE BENAVIDES
- ☐ 586. TED POWER
- ☐ 624. RANDY MYERS
- ☐ 659. MILT HILL

CLEVELAND INDIANS

- ☐ 12. REGGIE JEFFERSON
- ☐ 18. EDDIE TAUBENSEE
- ☐ 72. SHAWN HILLEGAS
- ☐ 82. CHRIS JAMES
- ☐ 99. JOEL SKINNER
- ☐ 120. CARLOS BAERGA
- ☐ 151. STEVE OLIN
- ☐ 194. ROD NICHOLS
- ☐ 203. SANDY ALOMAR
- ☐ 220. ALEX COLE
- ☐ 242. FELIX FERMIN
- ☐ 273. MARK LEWIS
- ☐ 315. CHARLES NAGY
- ☐ 325. MARK WHITEN
- ☐ 406. JIM THOME
- ☐ 411. JEFF MUTIS
- ☐ 473. JESSE OROSCO
- ☐ 500. ALBERT BELLE
- ☐ 521. CARLOS MARTINEZ
- ☐ 552. RUDY SEANEZ
- ☐ 595. JEFF SHAW
- ☐ 604. DENIS BOUCHER
- ☐ 621. MIKE ALDRETE
- ☐ 643. GLENALLEN HILL
- ☐ 674. DOUG JONES
- ☐ 730. DAVE OTTO
- ☐ 762. JACK ARMSTRONG

DETROIT TIGERS

- ☐ 42. ANDY ALLANSON
- ☐ 85. MICKEY TETTLETON
- ☐ 111. FRANK TANANA
- ☐ 131. BILL GULLICKSON
- ☐ 164. ALAN TRAMMELL
- ☐ 206. CECIL FIELDER
- ☐ 232. MILT CUYLER
- ☐ 253. MIKE HENNEMAN
- ☐ 285. LOU WHITAKER
- ☐ 328. TONY PHILLIPS
- ☐ 349. TRAVIS FRYMAN
- ☐ 375. PAUL GIBSON
- ☐ 443. LLOYD MOSEBY
- ☐ 486. SCOTT ALDRED
- ☐ 512. MARK SALAS
- ☐ 532. ROB DEER
- ☐ 565. WALT TERRELL
- ☐ 607. JERRY DON GLEATON
- ☐ 633. MARK LEITER
- ☐ 675. SCOTT LIVINGSTONE
- ☐ 709. JOHN CERUTTI
- ☐ 749. SKEETER BARNES

HOUSTON ASTROS

- ☐ 5. KENNY LOFTON
- ☐ 66. KEN CAMINITI
- ☐ 75. CRAIG BIGGIO
- ☐ 114. DWAYNE HENRY
- ☐ 148. ERIC YELDING
- ☐ 150. CASEY CANDAELE
- ☐ 188. MARK PORTUGAL
- ☐ 197. STEVE FINLEY
- ☐ 235. PETE HARNISCH
- ☐ 270. LUIS GONZALEZ
- ☐ 272. JIMMY JONES
- ☐ 309. DARRYL KILE
- ☐ 318. AL OSUNA
- ☐ 358. JEFF BAGWELL
- ☐ 405. JEFF JUDEN
- ☐ 413. CHRIS GARDNER
- ☐ 416. BRIAN WILLIAMS
- ☐ 467. JIM CORSI
- ☐ 477. GERALD YOUNG
- ☐ 515. JIM DESHAIES
- ☐ 549. ANDUJAR CEDENO
- ☐ 551. JAVIER ORTIZ
- ☐ 589. JOSE TOLENTINO
- ☐ 598. ANDY MOTA
- ☐ 671. RYAN BOWEN
- ☐ 673. ROB MALLICOAT
- ☐ 747. MIKE SIMMS
- ☐ 757. CURT SCHILLING
- ☐ 763. SCOTT SERVAIS
- ☐ 774. GARY COOPER
- ☐ 782. XAVIER HERNANDEZ

KANSAS CITY ROYALS

- ☐ 39. KIRK GIBSON
- ☐ 54. MARK DAVIS
- ☐ 128. BRET SABERHAGEN
- ☐ 143. GEORGE BRETT
- ☐ 161. MIKE MACFARLANE
- ☐ 176. MIKE BODDICKER
- ☐ 250. TOM GORDON
- ☐ 265. BRENT MAYNE

- ☐ 282. MARK GUBICZA
- ☐ 297. JIM EISENREICH
- ☐ 346. GARY THURMAN
- ☐ 361. BILL PECOTA
- ☐ 387. BRIAN MCRAE
- ☐ 400. ARCHIE CORBIN
- ☐ 440. KURT STILLWELL
- ☐ 455. KEVIN APPIER
- ☐ 529. STORM DAVIS
- ☐ 536. TODD BENZINGER
- ☐ 544. LUIS AQUINO
- ☐ 562. TERRY SHUMPERT
- ☐ 567. DAVE HOWARD
- ☐ 577. KEVIN SEITZER
- ☐ 651. SEAN BERRY
- ☐ 654. RUSTY MEACHAM
- ☐ 666. JEFF MONTGOMERY
- ☐ 676. DANNY TARTABULL
- ☐ 689. TIM SPEHR
- ☐ 706. MIKE MAGNANTE

LOS ANGELES DODGERS

- ☐ 16. ERIC KARROS
- ☐ 36. GARY CARTER
- ☐ 78. TIM BELCHER
- ☐ 105. JUAN SAMUEL
- ☐ 125. JOHN CANDELARIA
- ☐ 157. BOBBY OJEDA
- ☐ 200. MIKE MORGAN
- ☐ 226. LENNY HARRIS
- ☐ 247. OREL HERSHISER
- ☐ 279. KEVIN GROSS
- ☐ 322. STAN JAVIER
- ☐ 343. KAL DANIELS
- ☐ 369. BRETT BUTLER
- ☐ 392. EDDIE MURRAY
- ☐ 395. JAY HOWELL
- ☐ 437. TIM CREWS
- ☐ 480. MIKE SCIOSCIA
- ☐ 506. DAVE HANSEN
- ☐ 526. MIKE SHARPERSON
- ☐ 559. DARRYL STRAWBERRY
- ☐ 601. JIM GOTT
- ☐ 627. JOHN WETTELAND
- ☐ 648. CHRIS GWYNN
- ☐ 656. RAMON MARTINEZ
- ☐ 692. ALFREDO GRIFFIN
- ☐ 710. STEVE WILSON
- ☐ 714. MITCH WEBSTER
- ☐ 721. JOSE OFFERMAN
- ☐ 750. ROGER MCDOWELL
- ☐ 778. CARLOS HERNANDEZ

MILWAUKEE BREWERS

- ☐ 4. DAVE NILSSON
- ☐ 51. PAUL MOLITOR
- ☐ 70. B.J. SURHOFF
- ☐ 103. CHUCK CRIM
- ☐ 140. DON AUGUST
- ☐ 173. ROBIN YOUNT
- ☐ 192. GARY SHEFFIELD
- ☐ 224. GREG VAUGHN
- ☐ 262. JULIO MACHADO
- ☐ 294. TED HIGUERA
- ☐ 313. MARK LEE
- ☐ 347. DANTE BICHETTE
- ☐ 364. BILL SPIERS
- ☐ 378. BILL WEGMAN
- ☐ 398. JOHN JAHA
- ☐ 452. DALE SVEUM
- ☐ 471. CHRIS BOSIO
- ☐ 504. DARREN HOLMES
- ☐ 541. EDWIN NUNEZ
- ☐ 574. JIM GANTNER
- ☐ 593. DARRYL HAMILTON
- ☐ 618. FRANKLIN STUBBS
- ☐ 625. WILLIE RANDOLPH
- ☐ 663. DOUG HENRY
- ☐ 682. DAN PLESAC
- ☐ 705. JAIME NAVARRO
- ☐ 718. CAL ELDRED
- ☐ 746. CHRIS GEORGE
- ☐ 766. JIM OLANDER

MINNESOTA TWINS

- ☐ 62. MIKE PAGLIARULO
- ☐ 83. BRIAN HARPER
- ☐ 95. RICK AGUILERA
- ☐ 115. CHILI DAVIS
- ☐ 184. STEVE BEDROSIAN
- ☐ 204. GREG GAGNE
- ☐ 216. JACK MORRIS
- ☐ 236. KEVIN TAPANI
- ☐ 305. PEDRO MUNOZ
- ☐ 326. KENT HRBEK
- ☐ 339. AL NEWMAN
- ☐ 345. SHANE MACK
- ☐ 359. SCOTT LEIUS
- ☐ 390. CHUCK KNOBLAUCH
- ☐ 403. PAT MAHOMES
- ☐ 463. SCOTT ERICKSON
- ☐ 484. TERRY LEACH
- ☐ 496. GENE LARKIN
- ☐ 516. RICH GARCES
- ☐ 585. DAN GLADDEN
- ☐ 605. DENNY NEAGLE
- ☐ 617. KIRBY PUCKETT
- ☐ 638. DAVE WEST
- ☐ 665. CARL WILLIS
- ☐ 684. JUNIOR ORTIZ
- ☐ 691. MARK GUTHRIE
- ☐ 728. RANDY BUSH
- ☐ 752. PAUL SORRENTO
- ☐ 760. WILLIE BANKS
- ☐ 770. JARVIS BROWN

MONTREAL EXPOS

- ☐ 2. WIL CORDERO
- ☐ 34. TIM WALLACH
- ☐ 48. IVAN CALDERON
- ☐ 117. BRIAN BARNES
- ☐ 137. MARQUIS GRISSOM
- ☐ 155. BARRY JONES
- ☐ 170. CHRIS NABHOLZ
- ☐ 238. MARK GARDNER
- ☐ 259. LARRY WALKER
- ☐ 277. DELINO DESHIELDS
- ☐ 291. CHRIS HANEY
- ☐ 355. ANDRES GALARRAGA
- ☐ 381. GILBERTO REYES
- ☐ 394. SCOTT RUSKIN
- ☐ 414. JOHN VANDERWAL
- ☐ 435. MEL ROJAS
- ☐ 449. BRET BARBERIE
- ☐ 518. SPIKE OWEN
- ☐ 538. TOM FOLEY
- ☐ 557. GREG COLBRUNN
- ☐ 571. BILL SAMPEN
- ☐ 640. DOUG PIATT
- ☐ 660. STEVE FREY
- ☐ 683. ERIC BULLOCK
- ☐ 686. DENNIS MARTINEZ
- ☐ 717. JEFF FASSERO
- ☐ 732. DAVE MARTINEZ
- ☐ 779. HOWARD FARMER

NEW YORK METS

- ☐ 20. D.J. DOZIER
- ☐ 45. DAVE MAGADAN
- ☐ 64. HUBIE BROOKS
- ☐ 97. DAVID CONE
- ☐ 134. WALLY WHITEHURST
- ☐ 186. JOHN FRANCO
- ☐ 218. VINCE COLEMAN
- ☐ 256. MACKEY SASSER
- ☐ 288. KEVIN MCREYNOLDS
- ☐ 307. KEVIN ELSTER
- ☐ 335. RICK CERONE
- ☐ 341. HOWARD JOHNSON
- ☐ 366. TIM BURKE
- ☐ 372. GREGG JEFFERIES
- ☐ 409. ANTHONY YOUNG
- ☐ 446. DWIGHT GOODEN
- ☐ 465. MARK CARREON
- ☐ 498. FRANK VIOLA
- ☐ 535. PETE SCHOUREK
- ☐ 568. TODD HUNDLEY
- ☐ 587. JEFF INNIS
- ☐ 612. DARYL BOSTON
- ☐ 619. CHRIS DONNELS
- ☐ 657. KEITH MILLER
- ☐ 688. DOUG SIMONS
- ☐ 719. SID FERNANDEZ
- ☐ 739. TONY CASTILLO
- ☐ 765. JUNIOR NOBOA
- ☐ 777. CHARLIE O'BRIEN

NEW YORK YANKEES

- ☐ 15. JOHN RAMOS
- ☐ 32. JOHN HABYAN
- ☐ 73. ROBERTO KELLY
- ☐ 106. STEVE HOWE
- ☐ 126. MATT NOKES
- ☐ 153. KEVIN MAAS
- ☐ 195. SCOTT KAMIENIECKI
- ☐ 227. SCOTT SANDERSON
- ☐ 248. MEL HALL
- ☐ 275. JEFF JOHNSON
- ☐ 316. JESSE BARFIELD
- ☐ 344. BERNIE WILLIAMS
- ☐ 370. PAT KELLY
- ☐ 407. SAM MILITELLO
- ☐ 433. TIM LEARY
- ☐ 474. ALVARO ESPINOZA
- ☐ 507. LEE GUETTERMAN
- ☐ 527. WADE TAYLOR
- ☐ 554. ERIC PLUNK
- ☐ 596. DON MATTINGLY
- ☐ 628. GREG CADARET
- ☐ 649. JIM LEYRITZ
- ☐ 679. RANDY VELARDE
- ☐ 695. PASCUAL PEREZ
- ☐ 697. GERALD WILLIAMS
- ☐ 711. HENSLEY MEULENS
- ☐ 729. STEVE SAX
- ☐ 735. STEVE FARR
- ☐ 745. DARRIN CHAPIN
- ☐ 769. MIKE HUMPHREYS

OAKLAND A'S

- ☐ 9. TODD VAN POPPEL
- ☐ 68. HAROLD BAINES
- ☐ 71. WALT WEISS
- ☐ 104. TERRY STEINBACH
- ☐ 147. DENNIS ECKERSLEY
- ☐ 183. JOE KLINK
- ☐ 190. BOB WELCH
- ☐ 193. RICKEY HENDERSON
- ☐ 225. DAVE STEWART
- ☐ 269. RICK HONEYCUTT
- ☐ 311. DAVE HENDERSON
- ☐ 314. MIKE GALLEGO
- ☐ 337. MIKE MOORE
- ☐ 348. MARK MCGWIRE
- ☐ 385. STEVE CHITREN
- ☐ 469. CURT YOUNG
- ☐ 472. JAMIE QUIRK
- ☐ 505. MIKE BORDICK
- ☐ 548. JOSE CANSECO
- ☐ 591. SCOTT BROSIUS
- ☐ 594. KIRK DRESSENDORFER
- ☐ 626. JOE SLUSARSKI
- ☐ 637. SCOTT HEMOND
- ☐ 670. BROOK JACOBY
- ☐ 696. GENE NELSON
- ☐ 723. RON DARLING
- ☐ 751. DANN HOWITT
- ☐ 768. LANCE BLANKENSHIP
- ☐ 775. CARNEY LANSFORD

☐ 781. REGGIE HARRIS

PHILADELPHIA PHILLIES

☐ 11. ANDY ASHBY
☐ 57. LENNY DYKSTRA
☐ 76. PAT COMBS
☐ 92. JOHN MORRIS
☐ 109. TOMMY GREENE
☐ 146. DALE MURPHY
☐ 179. RANDY READY
☐ 198. DARREN DAULTON
☐ 230. JOHN KRUK
☐ 268. TERRY MULHOLLAND
☐ 300. JOSE DEJESUS
☐ 319. DARRIN FLETCHER
☐ 353. MITCH WILLIAMS
☐ 384. WES CHAMBERLAIN
☐ 402. KIM BATISTE
☐ 458. RICKY JORDAN
☐ 478. WALLY BACKMAN
☐ 493. JOE BOEVER
☐ 510. DICKIE THON
☐ 547. CHARLIE HAYES
☐ 580. VON HAYES
☐ 599. JASON GRIMSLEY
☐ 614. DANNY COX
☐ 631. WALLY RITCHIE
☐ 669. MICKEY MORANDINI
☐ 680. BRUCE RUFFIN
☐ 685. DAVE HOLLINS
☐ 701. JIM LINDEMAN
☐ 722. CLIFF BRANTLEY
☐ 726. MIKE HARTLEY
☐ 738. RON JONES
☐ 753. BRAULIO CASTILLO

PITTSBURGH PIRATES

☐ 14. CARLOS GARCIA
☐ 67. GARY REDUS
☐ 88. BOB WALK
☐ 100. JAY BELL
☐ 121. MIKE LAVALLIERE
☐ 189. JOSE LIND
☐ 209. DOUG DRABEK
☐ 221. BILL LANDRUM
☐ 243. BARRY BONDS
☐ 310. ORLANDO MERCED
☐ 331. JOHN SMILEY
☐ 338. LLOYD MCCLENDON
☐ 360. ZANE SMITH
☐ 365. VICENTE PALACIOS
☐ 367. RANDY TOMLIN
☐ 383. ANDY VAN SLYKE
☐ 468. JEFF KING
☐ 489. CURTIS WILKERSON
☐ 501. STAN BELINDA
☐ 522. NEAL HEATON
☐ 590. BOB PATTERSON
☐ 610. BOBBY BONILLA
☐ 622. BOB KIPPER
☐ 644. GARY VARSHO
☐ 653. DON SLAUGHT
☐ 678. CECIL ESPY
☐ 699. STEVE BUECHELE
☐ 715. ROGER MASON
☐ 731. JOHN WEHNER
☐ 748. ROSARIO RODRIGUEZ

ST. LOUIS CARDINALS

☐ 31. KEN HILL
☐ 37. JUAN AGOSTO
☐ 79. CRIS CARPENTER
☐ 112. LEE SMITH
☐ 132. TODD ZEILE
☐ 158. PEDRO GUERRERO
☐ 201. BOB TEWKSBURY
☐ 233. FELIX JOSE
☐ 246. JOSE DELEON
☐ 254. TOM PAGNOZZI
☐ 280. JOSE OQUENDO
☐ 323. BRYN SMITH
☐ 350. RAY LANKFORD
☐ 376. BERNARD GILKEY
☐ 432. OZZIE SMITH
☐ 438. REX HUDLER
☐ 481. OMAR OLIVARES
☐ 513. MILT THOMPSON
☐ 533. GERONIMO PENA
☐ 553. RICH GEDMAN
☐ 560. LUIS ALICEA
☐ 602. STAN ROYER
☐ 634. GERALD PERRY
☐ 655. SCOTT TERRY
☐ 661. BOB MCCLURE
☐ 712. RHEAL CORMIER
☐ 744. CRAIG WILSON
☐ 755. WILLIE FRASER
☐ 764. RAY STEPHENS
☐ 767. JOE MAGRANE

SAN DIEGO PADRES

☐ 10. FRANK SEMINARA
☐ 40. BENITO SANTIAGO
☐ 49. GREG HARRIS
☐ 123. BRUCE HURST
☐ 144. JERALD CLARK
☐ 162. CRAIG LEFFERTS
☐ 171. TIM TEUFEL
☐ 245. DENNIS RASMUSSEN
☐ 266. THOMAS HOWARD
☐ 283. FRED MCGRIFF
☐ 292. DARRIN JACKSON
☐ 362. TONY FERNANDEZ
☐ 371. BIP ROBERTS
☐ 380. ED WHITSON
☐ 388. RICH RODRIGUEZ
☐ 441. TONY GWYNN
☐ 450. MIKE MADDUX
☐ 524. ANDY BENES
☐ 545. RICKY BONES
☐ 563. JIM VATCHER
☐ 572. JOSE MELENDEZ
☐ 646. JACK HOWELL
☐ 667. CRAIG SHIPLEY
☐ 687. LARRY ANDERSEN
☐ 756. JEREMY HERNANDEZ

SAN FRANCISCO GIANTS

☐ 52. ROBBY THOMPSON
☐ 60. WILLIE MCGEE
☐ 93. BUD BLACK
☐ 135. MATT WILLIAMS
☐ 174. DAVE RIGHETTI
☐ 182. MIKE FELDER
☐ 214. WILL CLARK
☐ 257. JOHN BURKETT
☐ 295. JEFF BRANTLEY
☐ 303. KELLY DOWNS
☐ 336. MIKE REMLINGER
☐ 373. KEVIN BASS
☐ 389. STEVE DECKER
☐ 397. ROYCE CLAYTON
☐ 453. JOSE URIBE
☐ 461. ROD BECK
☐ 494. KIRT MANWARING
☐ 575. TREVOR WILSON
☐ 583. KEVIN MITCHELL
☐ 615. DARREN LEWIS
☐ 681. TED WOOD
☐ 700. PAUL MCCLELLAN
☐ 702. FRANCISCO OLIVERAS
☐ 737. GIL HEREDIA
☐ 759. DAVE ANDERSON
☐ 761. MARK LEONARD
☐ 783. BRYAN HICKERSON

SEATTLE MARINERS

☐ 7. ROGER SALKELD
☐ 17. PAT LENNON
☐ 43. BRIAN HOLMAN
☐ 61. JAY BUHNER
☐ 86. PETE O'BRIEN
☐ 118. RICH DELUCIA
☐ 124. ALVIN DAVIS
☐ 138. ERIK HANSON
☐ 165. KEN GRIFFEY, JR.
☐ 207. RANDY JOHNSON
☐ 213. ALONZO POWELL
☐ 239. HAROLD REYNOLDS
☐ 260. BILLY SWIFT
☐ 286. EDGAR MARTINEZ
☐ 304. SCOTT BANKHEAD
☐ 329. ROB MURPHY
☐ 356. HENRY COTTO
☐ 382. RUSS SWAN
☐ 404. DAVE FLEMING
☐ 408. JEFF NELSON
☐ 410. TINO MARTINEZ
☐ 444. MIKE SCHOOLER
☐ 462. DAVE VALLE
☐ 487. GREG BRILEY
☐ 519. TRACY JONES
☐ 525. JEFF SCHAEFER
☐ 539. DAVE COCHRANE
☐ 566. DAVE BURBA
☐ 584. MIKE JACKSON
☐ 608. BRENT KNACKERT
☐ 641. OMAR VIZQUEL
☐ 647. JIM CAMPANIS
☐ 672. BILL KRUEGER
☐ 690. CALVIN JONES
☐ 713. SCOTT BRADLEY

TEXAS RANGERS

☐ 46. RAFAEL PALMEIRO
☐ 55. KEVIN BROWN
☐ 129. JEFF RUSSELL
☐ 149. MARIO DIAZ
☐ 167. BRIAN DOWNING
☐ 168. JOHN BARFIELD
☐ 177. DEAN PALMER
☐ 251. KEVIN REIMER
☐ 271. JOSE GUZMAN
☐ 289. IVAN RODRIGUEZ
☐ 298. RUBEN SIERRA
☐ 351. MIKE JEFFCOAT
☐ 368. KENNY ROGERS
☐ 391. BOBBY WITT
☐ 393. JUAN GONZALEZ
☐ 401. BARRY MANUEL
☐ 419. HECTOR FAJARDO
☐ 447. OIL CAN BOYD
☐ 456. JEFF HUSON
☐ 530. JOSE HERNANDEZ
☐ 550. GENO PETRALLI
☐ 569. JACK DAUGHERTY
☐ 578. GERALD ALEXANDER
☐ 582. MIKE STANLEY
☐ 652. DONALD HARRIS
☐ 694. TERRY MATHEWS
☐ 703. ROB MAURER
☐ 707. NOLAN RYAN
☐ 741. JULIO FRANCO

TORONTO BLUE JAYS

☐ 8. EDDIE ZOSKY
☐ 58. ROBERTO ALOMAR
☐ 65. KELLY GRUBER
☐ 98. JOHN OLERUD
☐ 141. TOM HENKE
☐ 180. DEVON WHITE
☐ 187. ED SPRAGUE
☐ 219. JIMMY KEY
☐ 263. TODD STOTTLEMYRE
☐ 274. RENE GONZALES
☐ 301. MIKE TIMLIN
☐ 308. DUANE WARD
☐ 342. GREG MYERS
☐ 379. PAT BORDERS
☐ 418. DAVID WEATHERS
☐ 459. TOM CANDIOTTI
☐ 466. ROB DUCEY
☐ 499. MANUEL LEE
☐ 534. JUAN GUZMAN
☐ 542. RANCE MULLINIKS
☐ 581. DEREK BELL
☐ 588. BOB MACDONALD
☐ 620. DAVID WELLS
☐ 664. CANDY MALDONADO
☐ 693. JOE CARTER
☐ 704. PAT HENTGEN
☐ 724. DAVE STIEB

1992 DONRUSS ROOKIES (132) 2 1/2" X 3 1/2"

ATLANTA BRAVES

- ☐ 86. DAVID NIED

BALTIMORE ORIOLES

- ☐ 108. STEVE SCARSONE
- ☐ 114. JEFF TACKETT

BOSTON RED SOX

- ☐ 37. JOHN FLAHERTY
- ☐ 56. PETER HOY
- ☐ 75. JEFF MCNEELY

CALIFORNIA ANGELS

- ☐ 30. CHAD CURTIS
- ☐ 32. GARY DISARCINA
- ☐ 38. TIM FORTUGNO
- ☐ 119. JULIO VALERA

CHICAGO CUBS

- ☐ 20. JIM BULLINGER
- ☐ 22. PEDRO CASTELLANO
- ☐ 49. RYAN HAWBLITZEL
- ☐ 70. DERRICK MAY

CHICAGO WHITE SOX

- ☐ 10. ESTABAN BELTRE
- ☐ 41. RAMON GARCIA
- ☐ 59. SHAWN JETER
- ☐ 107. JOHNNY RUFFIN

CINCINNATI REDS

- ☐ 2. TROY AFENIR
- ☐ 13. JEFF BRANSON
- ☐ 19. JACOB BRUMFIELD
- ☐ 29. TIM COSTO
- ☐ 52. CESAR HERNANDEZ
- ☐ 77. TONY MENENDEZ

CLEVELAND INDIANS

- ☐ 23. MIKE CHRISTOPHER
- ☐ 65. JESSE LEVIS
- ☐ 98. MANNY RAMIREZ

DETROIT TIGERS

- ☐ 17. RICO BROGNA
- ☐ 33. JOHN DOHERTY
- ☐ 44. BUDDY GROOM
- ☐ 48. SHAWN HARE
- ☐ 62. KURT KNUDSEN

HOUSTON ASTROS

- ☐ 46. JUAN GUERRERO
- ☐ 51. BUTCH HENRY
- ☐ 102. SHANE REYNOLDS
- ☐ 115. EDDIE TAUBENSEE
- ☐ 117. SCOOTER TUCKER

KANSAS CITY ROYALS

- ☐ 60. JOEL JOHNSTON
- ☐ 63. KEVIN KOSLOFSKI
- ☐ 76. RUSTY MEACHAM
- ☐ 82. DENNIS MOELLER
- ☐ 95. HIPOLITO PICHARDO
- ☐ 97. HARVEY PULLIAM
- ☐ 106. RICO ROSSY
- ☐ 110. STEVE SHIFFLETT

LOS ANGELES DODGERS

- ☐ 5. BILLY ASHLEY
- ☐ 6. PEDRO ASTACIO
- ☐ 43. TOM GOODWIN
- ☐ 69. PEDRO MARTINEZ
- ☐ 83. RAUL MONDESI
- ☐ 105. HENRY RODRIGUEZ
- ☐ 128. ERIC YOUNG

MILWAUKEE BREWERS

- ☐ 7. JIM AUSTIN
- ☐ 73. TIM MCINTOSH
- ☐ 113. WILLIAM SUERO

MINNESOTA TWINS

- ☐ 18. J.T. BRUETT
- ☐ 100. JEFF REBOULET
- ☐ 124. LENNY WEBSTER

MONTREAL EXPOS

- ☐ 12. KENT BOTTENFIELD
- ☐ 24. ARCHI CIANFROCCO
- ☐ 57. JON HURST
- ☐ 71. MATT MAYSEY
- ☐ 84. ROB NATAL
- ☐ 101. DARREN REED
- ☐ 103. BILL RISLEY
- ☐ 112. MATT STAIRS
- ☐ 130. PETE YOUNG

NEW YORK METS

- ☐ 9. KEVIN BAEZ
- ☐ 55. PAT HOWELL

NEW YORK YANKEES

- ☐ 34. MIKE DRAPER
- ☐ 58. MARK HUTTON
- ☐ 67. ED MARTEL
- ☐ 87. JERRY NIELSEN
- ☐ 111. DAVE SILVESTRI
- ☐ 125. BOB WICKMAN

OAKLAND A'S

- ☐ 15. JOHN BRISCOE
- ☐ 21. KEVIN CAMPBELL
- ☐ 39. ERIC FOX
- ☐ 42. BRENT GATES
- ☐ 47. JOHNNY GUZMAN
- ☐ 53. VINCE HORSMAN
- ☐ 78. HENRY MERCEDES
- ☐ 85. TROY NEEL
- ☐ 123. BRUCE WALTON

PHILADELPHIA PHILLIES

- ☐ 1. KYLE ABBOTT
- ☐ 4. RUBEN AMARO
- ☐ 8. ROBERT AYRAULT
- ☐ 14. BRAD BRINK
- ☐ 45. JEFF GROTEWOLD
- ☐ 66. TOM MARSH
- ☐ 80. JOE MILLETTE
- ☐ 104. BEN RIVERA
- ☐ 126. MIKE WILLIAMS

PITTSBURGH PIRATES

- ☐ 27. VICTOR COLE
- ☐ 28. STEVE COOKE
- ☐ 68. AL MARTIN
- ☐ 79. PAUL MILLER
- ☐ 81. BLAS MINOR
- ☐ 93. WILLIAM PENNYFEATHER
- ☐ 120. PAUL WAGNER
- ☐ 121. TIM WAKEFIELD
- ☐ 129. KEVIN YOUNG

ST. LOUIS CARDINALS

- ☐ 25. MARK CLARK
- ☐ 36. BIEN FIGUEROA
- ☐ 88. DONOVAN OSBORNE
- ☐ 94. MIKE PEREZ

SAN DIEGO PADRES

- ☐ 16. DOUG BROCAIL
- ☐ 109. TIM SCOTT

SAN FRANCISCO GIANTS

- ☐ 26. CRAIG COLBERT
- ☐ 54. STEVE HOSEY
- ☐ 74. JIM MCNAMARA
- ☐ 89. JOHN PATTERSON
- ☐ 92. JIM PENA
- ☐ 99. PAT RAPP

SEATTLE MARINERS

- ☐ 3. RICH AMARAL
- ☐ 50. BERT HEFFERMAN
- ☐ 96. GREG PIRKL
- ☐ 118. SHANE TURNER
- ☐ 122. MIKE WALKER
- ☐ 127. KERRY WOODSON

1992 Donruss Rookies

TEXAS RANGERS

☐ 11. BRIAN BOHANON
☐ 31. DOUG DAVIS
☐ 35. MONTY FARISS
☐ 40. JEFF FRYE
☐ 64. DANNY LEON
☐ 72. RUSS MCGINNIS
☐ 90. ROGER PAVLIK
☐ 91. DAN PELTIER

TORONTO BLUE JAYS

☐ 61. JEFF KENT
☐ 116. RICK TRLICEK

1993 DONRUSS (792)
2 1/2" X 3 1/2"

ATLANTA BRAVES

☐ 2. KENT MERCKER
☐ 26. STEVE AVERY
☐ 52. MARK DAVIS
☐ 78. DAMON BERRYHILL
☐ 102. VINNY CASTILLA
☐ 130. JOHN SMOLTZ
☐ 134. JEFF BLAUSER
☐ 158. DEION SANDERS
☐ 184. FRANCISCO CABRERA
☐ 210. RON GANT
☐ 234. TERRY PENDLETON
☐ 262. OTIS NIXON
☐ 266. PAT GOMEZ
☐ 290. BRIAN HUNTER
☐ 316. MARK LEMKE
☐ 320. MELVIN NIEVES
☐ 398. RAFAEL BELLIARD
☐ 422. RYAN KLESKO
☐ 448. JEFF TREADWAY
☐ 474. MIKE STANTON
☐ 498. PETE SMITH
☐ 526. SID BREAM
☐ 530. GREG OLSON
☐ 554. TOM GLAVINE
☐ 580. DAVID JUSTICE
☐ 606. MARK WOHLERS
☐ 630. CHARLIE LEIBRANDT
☐ 658. LONNIE SMITH
☐ 662. MARVIN FREEMAN
☐ 721. CHIPPER JONES
☐ 739. JEFF REARDON
☐ 782. JAVY LOPEZ

BALTIMORE ORIOLES

☐ 1. CRAIG LEFFERTS
☐ 11. MANNY ALEXANDER
☐ 31. LEO GOMEZ
☐ 59. BILLY RIPKEN
☐ 89. BRADY ANDERSON
☐ 117. GREGG OLSON
☐ 133. ARTHUR RHODES
☐ 163. GLENN DAVIS
☐ 191. RANDY MILLIGAN
☐ 221. CHITO MARTINEZ
☐ 249. BEN MCDONALD
☐ 265. RICHIE LEWIS
☐ 295. JIMMY POOLE
☐ 323. CHRIS HOILES
☐ 381. STEVE SCARSONE
☐ 397. DAVID SEGUI
☐ 427. MIKE MUSSINA
☐ 455. MIKE DEVEREAUX
☐ 485. MARK MCLEMORE
☐ 513. TODD FROHWIRTH
☐ 529. JEFF TACKETT
☐ 559. CAL RIPKEN, JR.
☐ 587. BOB MILACKI
☐ 617. SAM HORN
☐ 645. LUIS MERCEDES
☐ 661. TIM HULETT
☐ 691. ALAN MILLS
☐ 719. RICK SUTCLIFFE
☐ 751. MOE ORSULAK
☐ 769. STORM DAVIS
☐ 789. ANTHONY TELFORD

BOSTON RED SOX

☐ 3. PHIL PLANTIER
☐ 33. ELLIS BURKS
☐ 44. ERIC WEDGE
☐ 63. JACK CLARK
☐ 91. FRANK VIOLA
☐ 119. ROGER CLEMENS
☐ 135. SCOTT COOPER
☐ 165. JODY REED
☐ 195. TONY FOSSAS
☐ 223. MIKE GREENWELL
☐ 251. JOHN VALENTIN
☐ 267. SCOTT TAYLOR
☐ 297. MIKE TWARDOSKI
☐ 327. PAUL QUANTRILL
☐ 383. KEN RYAN
☐ 399. TIM NAEHRING
☐ 429. MO VAUGHN
☐ 459. MATT YOUNG
☐ 487. JOHN MARZANO
☐ 515. MIKE GARDINER
☐ 531. BOB ZUPCIC
☐ 561. JOHN FLAHERTY
☐ 591. LUIS RIVERA
☐ 619. WADE BOGGS
☐ 647. DANNY DARWIN
☐ 663. GREG HARRIS
☐ 693. TOM BRUNANSKY
☐ 754. BILLY HATCHER

CALIFORNIA ANGELS

☐ 5. JULIO VALERA
☐ 35. JIM ABBOTT
☐ 65. LEE STEVENS
☐ 93. CHAD CURTIS
☐ 121. GARY DISARCINA
☐ 137. LUIS SOJO
☐ 167. SCOTT LEWIS
☐ 176. TIM SALMON
☐ 197. JUNIOR FELIX
☐ 225. CHUCK FINLEY
☐ 253. REGGIE WILLIAMS
☐ 269. GREG MYERS
☐ 299. TIM FORTUGNO
☐ 329. HILLY HATHAWAY
☐ 401. JOE GRAHE
☐ 431. JOHN ORTON
☐ 457. DAMION EASLEY
☐ 461. LUIS POLONIA
☐ 489. ROB DUCEY
☐ 517. GARY GAETTI
☐ 533. STEVE FREY
☐ 563. HUBIE BROOKS
☐ 593. MARK LANGSTON
☐ 621. RON TINGLEY
☐ 649. CHUCK CRIM
☐ 665. MIKE BUTCHER
☐ 757. MIKE FITZGERALD
☐ 785. RENE GONZALES

CHICAGO CUBS

☐ 4. ALEX ARIAS
☐ 28. RICK WILKINS
☐ 54. PAUL ASSENMACHER
☐ 80. HECTOR VILLANUEVA
☐ 104. STEVE BUECHELE
☐ 136. DOUG STRANGE
☐ 160. JEFF HARTSOCK
☐ 186. SAMMY SOSA
☐ 212. DOUG DASCENZO
☐ 236. CHUCK MCELROY
☐ 268. SHAWON DUNSTON
☐ 292. BOB SCANLAN
☐ 318. DERRICK MAY
☐ 344. RYNE SANDBERG
☐ 368. JESSIE HOLLINS
☐ 394. MIKE MORGAN
☐ 400. FRANK CASTILLO
☐ 424. REY SANCHEZ
☐ 450. MIKE HARKEY
☐ 476. DWIGHT SMITH
☐ 500. SHAWN BOSKIE
☐ 532. MARK GRACE
☐ 539. FERNANDO RAMSEY
☐ 556. JIM BULLINGER
☐ 582. JOSE VIZCAINO
☐ 608. GREG MADDUX
☐ 632. ANDRE DAWSON
☐ 664. HEATHCLIFF SLOCUMB
☐ 742. KEN PATTERSON

CHICAGO WHITE SOX

☐ 7. FRANK THOMAS
☐ 37. WILSON ALVAREZ
☐ 67. BOBBY THIGPEN
☐ 95. GEORGE BELL
☐ 123. STEVE SAX
☐ 139. ALEX FERNANDEZ
☐ 169. SCOTT RADINSKY
☐ 199. CRAIG GREBECK
☐ 227. KIRK MCCASKILL
☐ 255. OZZIE GUILLEN
☐ 271. GREG HIBBARD
☐ 301. LANCE JOHNSON
☐ 331. RON KARKOVICE
☐ 403. ROBERTO HERNANDEZ
☐ 433. JACK MCDOWELL
☐ 463. WARREN NEWSON
☐ 491. DAN PASQUA
☐ 519. CARLTON FISK
☐ 535. ROBIN VENTURA
☐ 565. TIM RAINES
☐ 595. ESTE BELTRE
☐ 623. SCOTT HEMOND
☐ 651. SHAWN ABNER
☐ 667. DONN PALL
☐ 672. BRIAN DRAHMAN
☐ 697. JOEY CORA
☐ 720. TERRY LEACH
☐ 788. MICHAEL HUFF

CINCINNATI REDS

☐ 6. DAN WILSON
☐ 30. BOBBY AYALA
☐ 58. CHRIS SABO
☐ 82. TIM BELCHER
☐ 106. BIP ROBERTS
☐ 138. JEFF BRANSON
☐ 143. WILLIE GREENE
☐ 162. TIM PUGH
☐ 190. TOM BROWNING
☐ 214. GERONIMO BERROA
☐ 238. NORM CHARLTON
☐ 270. TIM COSTO
☐ 294. HAL MORRIS
☐ 322. ROB DIBBLE
☐ 346. CHRIS HAMMOND
☐ 370. BILL DORAN
☐ 402. REGGIE SANDERS
☐ 426. BARRY LARKIN
☐ 454. JOSE RIJO
☐ 478. DWAYNE HENRY
☐ 502. MILT HILL
☐ 534. DAVE MARTINEZ
☐ 558. CESAR HERNANDEZ
☐ 586. JOE OLIVER
☐ 610. GREG CADARET
☐ 634. GREG SWINDELL
☐ 666. STEVE FOSTER
☐ 690. SCOTT BANKHEAD

CLEVELAND INDIANS

☐ 9. DEREK LILLIQUIST
☐ 39. SANDY ALOMAR, JR.
☐ 69. JACK ARMSTRONG
☐ 97. MARK WHITEN
☐ 125. MARK LEWIS
☐ 141. CHARLES NAGY
☐ 171. JIM THOME
☐ 201. GLENALLEN HILL
☐ 229. PAUL SORRENTO
☐ 257. THOMAS HOWARD
☐ 273. DAVE MLICKI
☐ 303. REGGIE JEFFERSON
☐ 333. ALAN EMBREE
☐ 380. WAYNE KIRBY
☐ 389. KEVIN WICKANDER
☐ 405. CARLOS BAERGA
☐ 435. ALBERT BELLE
☐ 465. JOSE MESA
☐ 493. BROOK JACOBY
☐ 521. ROD NICHOLS
☐ 537. KENNY LOFTON
☐ 567. STEVE OLIN
☐ 597. FELIX FERMIN
☐ 625. DENNIS COOK
☐ 653. SCOTT SCUDDER
☐ 669. JESSE LEVIS
☐ 682. CARLOS MARTINEZ
☐ 699. JUNIOR ORTIZ
☐ 766. TED POWER

COLORADO ROCKIES

☐ 730. ERIC YOUNG
☐ 733. SCOTT ALDRED
☐ 736. JOE GIRARDI
☐ 740. WILLIE BLAIR
☐ 743. ANDY ASHBY
☐ 746. FREDDIE BENAVIDES
☐ 749. CALVIN JONES
☐ 752. ARMANDO REYNOSO
☐ 755. DENIS BOUCHER
☐ 758. RUDY SEANEZ
☐ 760. MO SANFORD
☐ 761. PEDRO CASTELLANO
☐ 764. ANDRES GALARRAGA
☐ 767. BUTCH HENRY
☐ 770. VINNY CASTILLA
☐ 773. BRAD AUSMUS
☐ 776. CHARLIE HAYES
☐ 779. DARREN HOLMES
☐ 783. DANTE BICHETTE
☐ 786. ALEX COLE
☐ 790. JERALD CLARK
☐ 792. DAVID NIED

DETROIT TIGERS

☐ 13. MICKEY TETTLETON
☐ 41. RICO BROGNA
☐ 71. MARK CARREON
☐ 77. RICH ROWLAND
☐ 99. KEVIN RITZ
☐ 127. TRAVIS FRYMAN
☐ 145. KURT KNUDSEN
☐ 173. MILT CUYLER
☐ 203. JOHN KIELY
☐ 231. ROB DEER
☐ 259. MIKE HENNEMAN
☐ 277. JOHN DOHERTY
☐ 305. SHAWN HARE
☐ 335. DAVE HAAS
☐ 391. PHIL CLARK
☐ 409. SCOTT LIVINGSTONE
☐ 437. SKEETER BARNES
☐ 467. DAN GLADDEN
☐ 495. MARK LEITER
☐ 523. BILL GULLICKSON
☐ 541. CECIL FIELDER
☐ 569. BUDDY GROOM
☐ 599. FRANK TANANA
☐ 605. GREG GOHR
☐ 627. MIKE MUNOZ
☐ 655. ALAN TRAMMELL
☐ 673. CHAD KREUTER
☐ 686. LOU WHITAKER
☐ 701. TONY PHILLIPS
☐ 772. WALT TERRELL

FLORIDA MARLINS

☐ 728. BRYAN HARVEY
☐ 731. DAVE WEATHERS
☐ 734. CRIS CARPENETER
☐ 737. NIGEL WILSON
☐ 738. SCOTT CHIAMPARINO
☐ 741. JIM CORSI
☐ 744. ROB NATAL
☐ 747. CHRIS DONNELS
☐ 750. GARY SCOTT
☐ 753. MONTY FARISS
☐ 756. WALT WEISS
☐ 759. BRET BARBERIE
☐ 762. CHUCK CARR
☐ 765. JEFF CONINE
☐ 768. STEVE DECKER
☐ 771. JUNIOR FELIX
☐ 774. JAMIE MCANDREW
☐ 777. JACK ARMSTRONG
☐ 780. ALEX ARIAS
☐ 784. JOHN JOHNSTONE

HOUSTON ASTROS

☐ 8. ERIC ANTHONY
☐ 32. MIKE SIMMS
☐ 60. SCOOTER TUCKER
☐ 84. CRAIG BIGGIO
☐ 108. SCOTT SERVAIS
☐ 140. KEN CAMINITI
☐ 164. SHANE REYNOLDS
☐ 192. STEVE FINLEY
☐ 216. AL OSUNA
☐ 240. JUAN GUERRERO
☐ 272. PETE HARNISCH
☐ 296. DOUG JONES
☐ 324. JIMMY JONES
☐ 348. BUTCH HENRY
☐ 372. RYAN BOWEN
☐ 404. LUIS GONZALEZ
☐ 428. JEFF BAGWELL
☐ 456. ANDUJAR CEDENO
☐ 480. PETE INCAVIGLIA
☐ 504. JOE BOEVER
☐ 536. CASEY CANDAELE
☐ 560. EDDIE TAUBENSEE
☐ 588. ROB MURPHY
☐ 612. MARK PRTUGAL
☐ 636. XAVIER HERNANDEZ
☐ 668. DARRYL KILE
☐ 692. BRIAN WILLIAMS
☐ 729. TOM EDENS

KANSAS CITY ROYALS

☐ 15. TIM SPEHR
☐ 43. KEVIN APPIER
☐ 73. STEVE SHIFFLETT
☐ 101. JEFF CONINE
☐ 129. WALLY JOYNER
☐ 147. EDDIE PIERCE
☐ 175. JEFF MONTGOMERY
☐ 205. KEVIN KOSLOFSKI
☐ 233. KEVIN MCREYNOLDS
☐ 261. BRENT MAYNE
☐ 279. CHRIS HANEY
☐ 307. GREGG JEFFERIES
☐ 337. BILL SAMPEN
☐ 393. PHIL HIATT
☐ 411. BRIAN MCRAE
☐ 439. RUSTY MEACHAM
☐ 469. MIKE BODDICKER
☐ 497. TOM GORDON
☐ 525. MIKE MACFARLANE
☐ 543. KEITH MILLER
☐ 571. HIPOLITO PICHARDO
☐ 601. TERRY SHUMPERT
☐ 629. GARY THURMAN
☐ 657. CHRIS GWYNN
☐ 675. JOSE LIND
☐ 703. MARK GUBICZA
☐ 722. JIM EISENREICH
☐ 778. DENNIS RASMUSSEN

LOS ANGELES DODGERS

☐ 10. RAFAEL BOURNIGAL
☐ 34. STEVE WILSON
☐ 56. BILLY ASHLEY
☐ 62. MITCH WEBSTER
☐ 86. BRETT BUTLER
☐ 112. DARRYL STRAWBERRY
☐ 142. TOM CANDIOTTI
☐ 166. MIKE SHARPERSON
☐ 194. KIP GROSS
☐ 209. MIKE PIAZZA
☐ 218. HENRY RODRIGUEZ
☐ 244. DAVE HANSEN
☐ 274. OREL HERSHISER
☐ 298. RAMON MARTINEZ
☐ 326. PEDRO MARTINEZ
☐ 350. ROGER MCDOWELL
☐ 376. JOSE OFFERMAN
☐ 406. CARLOS HERNANDEZ
☐ 407. PEDRO ASTACIO
☐ 430. ERIC KARROS
☐ 458. KEVIN GROSS
☐ 482. ERIC DAVIS
☐ 508. MIKE SCIOSCIA
☐ 538. JAY HOWELL
☐ 562. TODD BENZINGER
☐ 590. LENNY HARRIS
☐ 614. BOBBY OJEDA
☐ 640. TOM GOODWIN
☐ 670. JIM GOTT

MILWAUKEE BREWERS

☐ 17. BILL WEGMAN
☐ 45. DANTE BICHETTE
☐ 75. PAUL MOLITOR
☐ 103. GREG VAUGHN
☐ 131. CAL ELDRED
☐ 149. DARREN HOLMES
☐ 177. FRANKLIN STUBBS
☐ 207. JOHN JAHA
☐ 235. DAVE NILSSON
☐ 263. MARK KIEFER
☐ 281. JAIME NAVARRO
☐ 309. PAT LISTACH
☐ 341. JIM TATUM
☐ 367. JOSE VALENTIN
☐ 413. RICKY BONES
☐ 441. ROBIN YOUNT
☐ 471. DOUG HENRY
☐ 499. CHRIS BOSIO
☐ 527. DARRYL HAMILTON
☐ 545. B.J. SURHOFF
☐ 573. MIKE FETTERS
☐ 603. KEVIN SEITZER
☐ 631. SCOTT FLETCHER
☐ 659. JIM AUSTIN
☐ 677. DAN PLESAC

MINNESOTA TWINS

☐ 19. RICK AGUILERA
☐ 47. MIKE TROMBLEY
☐ 79. WILLIE BANKS
☐ 105. DARREN REED
☐ 151. TERRY JORGENSEN
☐ 179. JEFF REBOULET
☐ 211. SCOTT ERICKSON
☐ 237. DEREK PARKS
☐ 283. KENT HRBEK
☐ 311. PEDRO MUNOZ
☐ 343. LARRY CASIAN

- ☐ 357. PAT MAHOMES
- ☐ 369. SCOTT LEIUS
- ☐ 395. SHANE MACK
- ☐ 415. CHUCK KNOBLAUCH
- ☐ 443. KEVIN TAPANI
- ☐ 475. JOHN SMILEY
- ☐ 501. DAVE WEST
- ☐ 547. BRIAN HARPER
- ☐ 575. GENE LARKIN
- ☐ 607. KIRBY PUCKETT
- ☐ 633. GREG GAGNE
- ☐ 679. CHILI DAVIS
- ☐ 694. LENNY WEBSTER
- ☐ 707. MIKE PAGLIARULO
- ☐ 714. MARK GUTHRIE
- ☐ 781. RANDY BUSH

MONTREAL EXPOS

- ☐ 12. BRET BARBERIE
- ☐ 36. TIM WALLACH
- ☐ 64. MARK GARDNER
- ☐ 88. BRIAN BARNES
- ☐ 114. CHRIS NABHOLZ
- ☐ 144. JOHN VANDER WAL
- ☐ 168. DENNIS MARTINEZ
- ☐ 196. IVAN CALDERON
- ☐ 220. KEN HILL
- ☐ 246. ARCHI CIANFROCCO
- ☐ 275. SEAN BEERY
- ☐ 276. GIL HEREDIA
- ☐ 300. MARQUIS GRISSOM
- ☐ 328. GREG COLBRUNN
- ☐ 342. TODD HANEY
- ☐ 352. BILL KRUEGER
- ☐ 378. DARRIN FLETCHER
- ☐ 408. MEL ROJAS
- ☐ 432. WIL CORDERO
- ☐ 440. TIM LAKER
- ☐ 460. MATT STAIRS
- ☐ 484. KENT BOTTENFIELD
- ☐ 510. MOISES ALOU
- ☐ 540. LARRY WALKER
- ☐ 564. DELINO DESHIELDS
- ☐ 592. JOHN WETTELAND
- ☐ 616. PETE YOUNG
- ☐ 642. JEFF FASSERO
- ☐ 727. TOM FOLEY
- ☐ 732. SPIKE OWEN

NEW YORK METS

- ☐ 14. ANTHONY YOUNG
- ☐ 38. DARYL BOSTON
- ☐ 66. TODD HUNDLEY
- ☐ 90. D.J. DOZIER
- ☐ 116. PAT HOWELL
- ☐ 146. JOHN FRANCO
- ☐ 170. DAVE GALLAGHER
- ☐ 198. PETE SCHOUREK
- ☐ 222. BRET SABERHAGEN
- ☐ 242. RYAN THOMPSON
- ☐ 248. BILL PECOTA
- ☐ 278. EDDIE MURRAY
- ☐ 302. JEFF KENT
- ☐ 330. JEFF INNIS
- ☐ 354. JOE VITKO
- ☐ 361. KEVIN BAEZ
- ☐ 410. CHICO WALKER
- ☐ 434. HOWARD JOHNSON
- ☐ 462. DWIGHT GOODEN
- ☐ 486. DAVE MAGADAN
- ☐ 506. BUTCH HUSKEY
- ☐ 512. MACKEY SASSER
- ☐ 542. LEE GUETTERMAN
- ☐ 566. SID FERNANDEZ
- ☐ 594. BOBBY BONILLA
- ☐ 618. VINCE COLEMAN
- ☐ 644. WILLIE RANDOLPH
- ☐ 674. TONY FERNANDEZ
- ☐ 698. CHARLIE O'BRIEN
- ☐ 745. KEVIN BASS
- ☐ 787. JEROMY BURNITZ

NEW YORK YANKEES

- ☐ 21. STEVE FARR
- ☐ 49. GERALD WILLIAMS
- ☐ 81. MIKE GALLEGO
- ☐ 107. JOHN HABYAN
- ☐ 110. J.T. SLNOW
- ☐ 153. RANDY VELARDE
- ☐ 181. CHARLIE HAYES
- ☐ 213. ANDY STANKIEWICZ
- ☐ 239. MATT NOKES
- ☐ 285. RUSS SPRINGER
- ☐ 313. ROBERTO KELLY
- ☐ 345. STERLING HITCHCOCK
- ☐ 359. JERRY NIELSEN
- ☐ 371. SAM MILITELLO
- ☐ 417. BOB WICKMAN
- ☐ 445. RICH MONTELEONE
- ☐ 477. JIM LEYRITZ
- ☐ 503. PAT KELLY
- ☐ 549. DANNY TARTABULL
- ☐ 577. BERNIE WILLIAMS
- ☐ 609. DON MATTINGLY
- ☐ 635. KEVIN MAAS
- ☐ 671. MARK HUTTON
- ☐ 681. SCOTT KAMIENIECKI
- ☐ 696. PAUL O'NEILL
- ☐ 709. MELIDO PEREZ
- ☐ 718. MIKE STANLEY
- ☐ 726. SCOTT SANDERSON
- ☐ 735. DION JAMES
- ☐ 763. STEVE HOWE

OAKLAND A'S

- ☐ 23. LANCE BLANKENSHIP
- ☐ 51. BOBBY WITT
- ☐ 83. MIKE BORDICK
- ☐ 109. WALT WEISS
- ☐ 155. KEVIN CAMPBELL
- ☐ 183. MIKE RACZKA
- ☐ 215. DENNIS ECKERSLEY
- ☐ 241. JEFF PARRETT
- ☐ 287. ERIC FOX
- ☐ 308. TROY NEEL
- ☐ 315. RICKEY HENDERSON
- ☐ 347. VINCE HORSMAN
- ☐ 373. DAVE HENDERSON
- ☐ 419. SCOTT BROSIUS
- ☐ 447. JERRY BROWNE
- ☐ 479. MARK MCGWIRE
- ☐ 505. TERRY STEINBACH
- ☐ 551. HENRY MERCEDES
- ☐ 579. BOB WELCH
- ☐ 611. DAVE STEWART
- ☐ 637. RUBEN SIERRA
- ☐ 683. MIKE MOORE
- ☐ 700. RON DARLING
- ☐ 711. JEFF RUSSELL
- ☐ 725. HAROLD BAINES

PHILADELPHIA PHILLIES

- ☐ 16. BOB AYRAULT
- ☐ 40. MITCH WILLIAMS
- ☐ 68. DAVE HOLLINS
- ☐ 92. DARREN DAULTON
- ☐ 118. CURT SCHILLING
- ☐ 148. KIM BATISTE
- ☐ 172. TERRY MULHOLLAND
- ☐ 200. JUAN BELL
- ☐ 224. MICKEY MORANDINI
- ☐ 250. CLIFF BRANTLEY
- ☐ 280. STAN JAVIER
- ☐ 304. WES CHAMBERLAIN
- ☐ 332. KEITH SHEPHERD
- ☐ 356. JAY BALLER
- ☐ 382. MARIANO DUNCAN
- ☐ 386. BRAULIO CASTILLO
- ☐ 412. BEN RIVERA
- ☐ 436. JOHN KRUK
- ☐ 464. JOSE DELEON
- ☐ 488. RUBEN AMARO
- ☐ 514. RICKY JORDAN
- ☐ 544. LENNY DYKSTRA
- ☐ 568. TOMMY GREENE
- ☐ 596. MIKE HARTLEY
- ☐ 620. TODD PRATT
- ☐ 646. DALE MURPHY
- ☐ 676. KYLE ABBOTT

PITTSBURGH PIRATES

- ☐ 18. JAY BELL
- ☐ 42. GARY VARSHO
- ☐ 61. TIM WAKEFIELD
- ☐ 70. ALEX COLE
- ☐ 94. ZANE SMITH
- ☐ 120. VICTOR COLE
- ☐ 150. STEVE COOKE
- ☐ 174. BOB PATTERSON
- ☐ 202. DANNY JACKSON
- ☐ 226. DENNY NEAGLE
- ☐ 252. JEFF KING
- ☐ 282. ORLANDO MERCED
- ☐ 306. MIKE LAVALLIERE
- ☐ 334. PAUL WAGNER
- ☐ 358. ROGER MASON
- ☐ 384. LLOYD MCCLENDON
- ☐ 414. ANDY VAN SLYKE
- ☐ 438. DON SLAUGHT
- ☐ 452. KEVIN YOUNG
- ☐ 466. DANNY COX
- ☐ 490. STAN BELINDA
- ☐ 516. GARY REDUS
- ☐ 546. BOB WALK
- ☐ 570. RANDY TOMLIN
- ☐ 598. CARLOS GARCIA
- ☐ 622. DOUG DRABEK
- ☐ 648. DENNIS MOELLER
- ☐ 678. BARRY BONDS
- ☐ 702. WILLIAM PENNYFEATHER
- ☐ 716. AL MARTIN
- ☐ 791. JOEL JOHNSTON

ST. LOUIS CARDINALS

- ☐ 20. TODD ZEILE
- ☐ 46. JOSE OQUENDO
- ☐ 72. TODD WORRELL
- ☐ 96. REX HUDLER
- ☐ 124. CHUCK CARR
- ☐ 152. MARK CLARK
- ☐ 178. DONOVAN OSBORNE
- ☐ 204. BOB TEWKSBURY
- ☐ 228. RHEAL CORMIER
- ☐ 256. MIKE PEREZ
- ☐ 284. BERNARD GILKEY
- ☐ 310. GERONIMO PENA
- ☐ 336. OZZIE CANSECO
- ☐ 360. TOM PAGNOZZI
- ☐ 366. RAY LANKFORD
- ☐ 388. OMAR OLIVARES
- ☐ 416. LUIS ALICEA
- ☐ 442. BRIAN JORDAN
- ☐ 468. GERALD PERRY
- ☐ 492. JOE MAGRANE
- ☐ 520. OZZIE SMITH
- ☐ 548. LEE SMITH
- ☐ 572. RENE AROCHA
- ☐ 574. FELIX JOSE
- ☐ 600. PEDRO GUERRERO
- ☐ 624. TIM JONES
- ☐ 638. DMITRI YOUNG
- ☐ 652. TRACY WOODSON
- ☐ 680. STAN ROYER
- ☐ 775. MILT THOMPSON

SAN DIEGO PADRES

- ☐ 22. ANDY BENES
- ☐ 48. DAN WALTERS
- ☐ 74. JERALD CLARK
- ☐ 98. TIM TEUFEL
- ☐ 126. TONY GWYNN
- ☐ 154. GREG HARRIS
- ☐ 180. JEREMY HERNANDEZ
- ☐ 206. CRAIG SHIPLEY
- ☐ 230. DARRIN JACKSON
- ☐ 258. KURT STILLWELL
- ☐ 286. MIKE MADDUX
- ☐ 312. GUILLERMO VELASQUEZ
- ☐ 325. DAVE STATON
- ☐ 338. RICH RODRIGUEZ
- ☐ 362. TIM SCOTT
- ☐ 390. FRED MCGRIFF
- ☐ 418. DOUG BROCAIL
- ☐ 444. GARY SHEFFIELD
- ☐ 470. JEFF GARDNER
- ☐ 494. GENE HARRIS
- ☐ 522. BENITO SANTIAGO
- ☐ 550. FRANK SEMINARA
- ☐ 576. BRUCE HURST
- ☐ 602. WALLY WHITEHURST
- ☐ 626. JOSE MELENDEZ
- ☐ 654. TOM LAMPKIN

SAN FRANCISCO GIANTS

- ☐ 24. TED WOOD
- ☐ 50. BUD BLACK
- ☐ 76. LARRY CARTER
- ☐ 100. JEFF BRANTLEY
- ☐ 128. DAVE BURBA
- ☐ 156. JOHN BURKETT
- ☐ 182. MATT WILLIAMS
- ☐ 193. JOHN PATTERSON
- ☐ 208. ROYCE CLAYTON
- ☐ 232. BILL SWIFT
- ☐ 260. STEVE DECKER
- ☐ 288. MARK LEONARD
- ☐ 314. MIKE JACKSON
- ☐ 340. GREG LITTON
- ☐ 355. WILLIE MCGEE
- ☐ 364. KIRT MANWARING
- ☐ 375. STEVE REED
- ☐ 392. DARREN LEWIS
- ☐ 420. ROD BECK
- ☐ 446. WILL CLARK
- ☐ 472. MIKE BENJAMIN
- ☐ 496. BRYAN HICKERSON
- ☐ 524. ROBBY THOMPSON
- ☐ 552. DAVE RIGHETTI
- ☐ 578. TREVOR WILSON
- ☐ 604. CHRIS JAMES
- ☐ 628. JIM PENA
- ☐ 656. CORY SNYDER
- ☐ 704. STEVE HOSEY

SEATTLE MARINERS

- ☐ 25. OMAR VIZQUEL
- ☐ 53. SHAWN BARTON
- ☐ 85. LANCE PARRISH
- ☐ 111. JAY BUHNER
- ☐ 157. KEVIN MITCHELL
- ☐ 185. RICH DELUCIA
- ☐ 188. BRET BOONE
- ☐ 217. TINO MARTINEZ
- ☐ 243. DAVE FLEMING
- ☐ 289. TIM LEARY
- ☐ 317. ERIK HANSON
- ☐ 349. DANN HOWITT
- ☐ 385. BRIAN HOLMAN
- ☐ 421. EDGAR MARTINEZ
- ☐ 449. MIKE SCHOOLER
- ☐ 481. DAVE COCHRANE
- ☐ 507. DAVID VALLE
- ☐ 553. KEN GRIFFEY, JR.
- ☐ 581. RANDY JOHNSON
- ☐ 589. GREG PIRKL
- ☐ 613. PETE O'BRIEN
- ☐ 639. HAROLD REYNOLDS
- ☐ 685. JEFF NELSON
- ☐ 695. GREG BRILEY
- ☐ 705. HENRY COTTO
- ☐ 713. RUSS SWAN
- ☐ 748. KERRY WOODSON

TEXAS RANGERS

- ☐ 27. BRIAN BOHANON
- ☐ 55. KEVIN REIMER
- ☐ 113. ROGER PAVLIK
- ☐ 159. JOSE CANSECO
- ☐ 187. IVAN RODRIGUEZ
- ☐ 245. MONTY FARISS
- ☐ 291. DONALD HARRIS
- ☐ 319. GENO PETRALLI
- ☐ 339. DEAN PALMER
- ☐ 353. CRIS COLON
- ☐ 365. RAFAEL PALMEIRO
- ☐ 374. DAN SMITH
- ☐ 377. KEVIN BROWN
- ☐ 387. DANNY LEON
- ☐ 423. NOLAN RYAN
- ☐ 451. JULIO FRANCO
- ☐ 473. DAN PELTIER
- ☐ 509. KENNY ROGERS
- ☐ 555. JUAN GONZALEZ
- ☐ 583. JEFF HUSON
- ☐ 584. ROB MAURER
- ☐ 641. TODD BURNS
- ☐ 687. JOSE GUZMAN
- ☐ 706. DAVID HULSE
- ☐ 724. JEFF FRYE

TORONTO BLUE JAYS

- ☐ 29. DEVON WHITE
- ☐ 57. EDDIE ZOSKY
- ☐ 87. MIKE TIMLIN
- ☐ 115. PAT BORDERS
- ☐ 161. TOM QUINLAN
- ☐ 189. JUAN GUZMAN
- ☐ 219. ED SPRAGUE
- ☐ 247. PAT HENTGEN
- ☐ 293. TURNER WARD
- ☐ 321. DOUG LINTON
- ☐ 351. JACK MORRIS
- ☐ 363. DOMINGO MARTINEZ
- ☐ 379. MIKE MAKSUDIAN
- ☐ 425. ROBERTO ALOMAR
- ☐ 453. KELLY GRUBER
- ☐ 483. JOHN OLERUD
- ☐ 511. DAVID WELLS
- ☐ 557. DEREK BELL
- ☐ 585. TODD STOTTLEMYRE
- ☐ 615. JOE CARTER
- ☐ 643. DAVE WINFIELD
- ☐ 684. CANDY MALDONADO
- ☐ 688. MANUEL LEE
- ☐ 689. BOB MACDONALD
- ☐ 708. DAVE STIEB
- ☐ 710. JIMMY KEY
- ☐ 712. DAVID CONE
- ☐ 717. RANDY KNORR
- ☐ 723. TOM HENKE

1994 DONRUSS (660)
2 1/2" X 3 1/2"

ATLANTA BRAVES

- ☐ 25. DAVID JUSTICE
- ☐ 34. RON GANT
- ☐ 41. STEVE AVERY
- ☐ 58. DAMON BERRYHILL
- ☐ 88. JEFF BLAUSER
- ☐ 118. SID BREAM
- ☐ 147. MARK LEMKE
- ☐ 175. GREG MCMICHAEL
- ☐ 203. KENT MERCKER
- ☐ 232. OTIS NIXON
- ☐ 260. JOHN SMOLTZ
- ☐ 287. TONY TARASCO
- ☐ 309. MARK WOHLERS
- ☐ 342. FRED MCGRIFF
- ☐ 364. TOM GLAVINE
- ☐ 380. GREG MADDUX
- ☐ 382. GREG OLSON
- ☐ 430. DEION SANDERS
- ☐ 453. CHIPPER JONES
- ☐ 479. STEVE BEDROSIAN
- ☐ 506. MIKE STANTON
- ☐ 556. TERRY PENDLETON
- ☐ 613. JAVY LOPEZ
- ☐ 617. RYAN KLESKO
- ☐ 626. DAVE GALLAGHER

BALTIMORE ORIOLES

- ☐ 8. GREGG OLSON
- ☐ 40. CAL RIPKEN, JR.
- ☐ 69. MIKE DEVEREAUX
- ☐ 99. CHRIS HOILES
- ☐ 129. TIM HULETT
- ☐ 158. BEN MCDONALD
- ☐ 186. MARK MCLEMORE
- ☐ 214. ALAN MILLS
- ☐ 243. MIKE PAGLIARULO
- ☐ 271. HAROLD REYNOLDS
- ☐ 299. ARTHUR RHODES
- ☐ 317. BRAD PENNINGTON
- ☐ 331. MIKE MUSSINA
- ☐ 389. TODD FROHWIRTH
- ☐ 396. SID FERNANDEZ
- ☐ 408. FERNANDO VALENZUELA
- ☐ 427. JIMMY POOLE
- ☐ 465. PAUL CAREY
- ☐ 486. HAROLD BAINES
- ☐ 500. RICK SUTCLIFFE
- ☐ 547. JAMIE MOYER
- ☐ 576. LEO GOMEZ
- ☐ 592. BRADY ANDERSON
- ☐ 605. DAMON BUFORD
- ☐ 624. DAVID SEGUI
- ☐ 629. JEFFREY HAMMONDS

BOSTON RED SOX

- ☐ 42. MO VAUGHN
- ☐ 74. ROB DEER
- ☐ 104. JOHN DOPSON
- ☐ 134. SCOTT FLETCHER
- ☐ 163. MIKE GREENWELL
- ☐ 191. TONY PENA
- ☐ 219. CARLOS QUINTANA
- ☐ 248. JEFF RUSSELL
- ☐ 276. KEN RYAN
- ☐ 303. AARON SELE
- ☐ 321. FRANK VIOLA
- ☐ 356. ROGER CLEMENS
- ☐ 411. BOB ZUPCIC
- ☐ 417. SCOTT COOPER
- ☐ 429. SCOTT BANKHEAD
- ☐ 434. BILLY HATCHER
- ☐ 448. ANDRE DAWSON
- ☐ 469. DANNY DARWIN
- ☐ 484. NATE MINCHEY
- ☐ 512. GREG HARRIS
- ☐ 517. JOHN VALENTIN
- ☐ 596. JOHN FLAHERTY
- ☐ 609. JEFF MCNEELY
- ☐ 644. PAUL QUANTRILL

CALIFORNIA ANGELS

- ☐ 11. CHAD CURTIS
- ☐ 31. MARK LANGSTON
- ☐ 52. MIKE BUTCHER
- ☐ 82. CHILI DAVIS
- ☐ 112. DAMION EASLEY
- ☐ 142. STEVE FREY
- ☐ 170. HILLY HATHAWAY
- ☐ 198. GREG MYERS
- ☐ 227. EDUARDO PEREZ
- ☐ 255. LUIS POLONIA
- ☐ 283. J.T. SNOW
- ☐ 325. RUSS SPRINGER
- ☐ 353. TIM SALMON
- ☐ 363. CHUCK FINLEY

- ☐ 403. PHIL LEFTWICH
- ☐ 454. JOE GRAHE
- ☐ 478. GARY DISARCINA
- ☐ 567. CHRIS TURNER
- ☐ 583. MARK HOLZEMER
- ☐ 612. TOREY LOVULLO
- ☐ 640. RENE GONZALES

CHICAGO CUBS

- ☐ 18. RYNE SANDBERG
- ☐ 61. SHAWN BOSKIE
- ☐ 91. FRANK CASTILLO
- ☐ 121. MIKE HARKEY
- ☐ 150. GLENALLEN HILL
- ☐ 178. DERRICK MAY
- ☐ 206. MIKE MORGAN
- ☐ 235. KEVIN ROBERSON
- ☐ 263. BOB SCANLAN
- ☐ 291. JOSE VIZCAINO
- ☐ 312. TURK WENDELL
- ☐ 337. SAMMY SOSA
- ☐ 358. MARK GRACE
- ☐ 383. REY SANCHEZ
- ☐ 399. RANDY MYERS
- ☐ 444. RICK WILKINS
- ☐ 458. JOSE BAUTISTA
- ☐ 490. SHAWON DUNSTON
- ☐ 507. JOSE GUZMAN
- ☐ 542. GREG HIBBARD
- ☐ 555. STEVE BUECHELE
- ☐ 570. DWIGHT SMITH
- ☐ 636. STEVE TRACHSEL
- ☐ 639. CHUCK MCELROY
- ☐ 641. DAN PLESAC

CHICAGO WHITE SOX

- ☐ 20. JACK MCDOWELL
- ☐ 23. ROBIN VENTURA
- ☐ 56. TIM BELCHER
- ☐ 86. JASON BERE
- ☐ 116. ROBERTO HERNANDEZ
- ☐ 145. ELLIS BURKS
- ☐ 173. BO JACKSON
- ☐ 201. MIKE LAVALLIERE
- ☐ 230. SCOTT RADINSKY
- ☐ 258. TIM RAINES
- ☐ 286. STEVE SAX
- ☐ 341. FRANK THOMAS
- ☐ 359. OZZIE GUILLEN
- ☐ 416. RON KARKOVICE
- ☐ 441. TERRY LEACH
- ☐ 447. JOEY CORA
- ☐ 518. WILSON ALVAREZ
- ☐ 540. KIRK MCCASKILL
- ☐ 552. LANCE JOHNSON
- ☐ 582. ALEX FERNANDEZ
- ☐ 598. ROD BOLTON
- ☐ 619. SCOTT RUFFCORN

CINCINNATI REDS

- ☐ 45. BARRY LARKIN
- ☐ 75. BOBBY AYALA
- ☐ 105. JOHN SMILEY
- ☐ 135. JOHNNY RUFFIN
- ☐ 164. THOMAS HOWARD
- ☐ 192. LARRY LUEBBERS
- ☐ 221. HAL MORRIS
- ☐ 249. JOE OLIVER
- ☐ 277. TIM PUGH
- ☐ 304. BIP ROBERTS
- ☐ 330. CHRIS SABO
- ☐ 344. ROBERTO KELLY
- ☐ 361. JOSE RIJO
- ☐ 377. KEVIN MITCHELL
- ☐ 413. BRET BOONE
- ☐ 436. REGGIE SANDERS
- ☐ 451. ROB DIBBLE
- ☐ 473. JACOB BRUMFIELD
- ☐ 539. WILLIE GREENE
- ☐ 551. JOHN ROPER
- ☐ 561. TIM COSTO
- ☐ 579. JERRY SPRADLIN
- ☐ 642. JEFF BRANSON

CLEVELAND INDIANS

- ☐ 14. CARLOS BAERGA
- ☐ 39. KENNY LOFTON
- ☐ 65. SANDY ALOMAR, JR.
- ☐ 95. JEREMY HERNANDEZ
- ☐ 125. WAYNE KIRBY
- ☐ 154. DEREK LILLIQUIST
- ☐ 182. JOSE MESA
- ☐ 210. RANDY MILLIGAN
- ☐ 239. CHARLES NAGY
- ☐ 267. ERIC PLUNK
- ☐ 295. JEFF TREADWAY
- ☐ 322. MANNY RAMIREZ
- ☐ 351. ALBERT BELLE
- ☐ 384. TOM KRAMER
- ☐ 425. JUNIOR ORTIZ
- ☐ 464. MARK LEWIS
- ☐ 523. JIM THOME
- ☐ 536. PAUL SORRENTO
- ☐ 573. FELIX FERMIN
- ☐ 590. BILL WERTZ
- ☐ 627. JULIAN TAVAREZ
- ☐ 648. ALBIE LOPEZ
- ☐ 653. REGGIE JEFFERSON
- ☐ 656. MARK CLARK
- ☐ 659. CANDY MALDONADO

COLORADO ROCKIES

- ☐ 46. CHARLIE HAYES
- ☐ 76. FREDDIE BENAVIDES
- ☐ 106. DAVID NIED
- ☐ 136. JERALD CLARK
- ☐ 165. JOE GIRARDI
- ☐ 193. GREG HARRIS
- ☐ 222. DARREN HOLMES
- ☐ 250. ROBERTO MEJIA
- ☐ 278. JAYHAWK OWENS
- ☐ 305. BRUCE RUFFIN
- ☐ 323. GARY WAYNE
- ☐ 346. ANDRES GALARRAGA
- ☐ 412. ERIC YOUNG
- ☐ 418. DANTE BICHETTE
- ☐ 438. STEVE REED
- ☐ 449. PEDRO CASTELLANO
- ☐ 474. LANCE PAINTER
- ☐ 487. HOWARD JOHNSON
- ☐ 497. ARMANDO REYNOSO
- ☐ 510. CHRIS JONES
- ☐ 528. KENT BOTTENFIELD
- ☐ 549. VINNY CASTILLA
- ☐ 580. CURT LESKANIC
- ☐ 610. DANNY SHEAFFER
- ☐ 631. WILLIE BLAIR

DETROIT TIGERS

- ☐ 27. CECIL FIELDER
- ☐ 44. MICKEY TETTLETON
- ☐ 78. JOHN DOHERTY
- ☐ 108. KIRK GIBSON
- ☐ 138. DAN GLADDEN
- ☐ 167. GREG GOHR
- ☐ 195. BILL GULLICKSON
- ☐ 224. CHAD KREUTER
- ☐ 252. BILL KREUGER
- ☐ 280. ALAN TRAMMELL
- ☐ 307. DAVID WELLS
- ☐ 360. LOU WHITAKER
- ☐ 378. TRAVIS FRYMAN
- ☐ 415. BOB MACDONALD
- ☐ 442. DANNY BAUTISTA
- ☐ 445. TONY PHILLIPS
- ☐ 475. MILT CUYLER
- ☐ 496. MIKE HENNEMAN
- ☐ 554. MIKE MOORE
- ☐ 597. SCOTT LIVINGSTONE
- ☐ 618. ERIC DAVIS
- ☐ 628. CHRIS GOMEZ
- ☐ 637. BUDDY GROOM
- ☐ 645. RICH ROWLAND

FLORIDA MARLINS

- ☐ 5. GARY SHEFFIELD
- ☐ 67. LUIS AQUINO
- ☐ 97. ALEX ARIAS
- ☐ 127. BRET BARBERIE
- ☐ 156. JEFF CONINE
- ☐ 184. HENRY COTTO
- ☐ 212. ORESTES DESTRADE
- ☐ 241. CARL EVERETT
- ☐ 269. CHARLIE HOUGH
- ☐ 297. RICHIE LEWIS
- ☐ 315. CHRIS HAMMOND
- ☐ 348. BENITO SANTIAGO
- ☐ 374. BRYAN HARVEY
- ☐ 407. RYAN BOWEN
- ☐ 428. WALT WEISS
- ☐ 466. JACK ARMSTRONG
- ☐ 499. RICK RENTERIA
- ☐ 509. CHUCK CARR
- ☐ 537. NIGEL WILSON
- ☐ 593. MATT TURNER
- ☐ 625. ROBB NEN
- ☐ 635. RICH RODRIGUEZ
- ☐ 643. DARRELL WHITMORE
- ☐ 658. DAVE MAGADAN

HOUSTON ASTROS

- ☐ 12. CRAIG BIGGIO
- ☐ 32. DARRYL KILE
- ☐ 53. KEN CAMINITI
- ☐ 83. LUIS GONZALEZ
- ☐ 113. PETE HARNISCH
- ☐ 143. XAVIER HERNANDEZ
- ☐ 171. TODD JONES
- ☐ 199. MARK PORTUGAL
- ☐ 228. GREG SWINDELL
- ☐ 256. EDDIE TAUBENSEE
- ☐ 284. BRIAN WILLIAMS
- ☐ 365. JEFF BAGWELL
- ☐ 381. SCOTT SERVAIS
- ☐ 402. STEVE FINLEY
- ☐ 456. TOM EDENS
- ☐ 480. ERIC ANTHONY
- ☐ 519. ANDUJAR CEDENO
- ☐ 533. DOUG JONES
- ☐ 541. AL OSUNA
- ☐ 632. DOUG DRABEK

KANSAS CITY ROYALS

- ☐ 43. BRIAN MCRAE
- ☐ 47. KEVIN APPIER
- ☐ 77. STAN BELINDA
- ☐ 107. GEORGE BRETT
- ☐ 137. BILLY BREWER
- ☐ 166. HUBIE BROOKS
- ☐ 194. DAVID CONE
- ☐ 223. CHRIS GWYNN
- ☐ 251. CHRIS HANEY
- ☐ 279. PHIL HIATT
- ☐ 306. JOSE LIND
- ☐ 324. MIKE MACFARLANE
- ☐ 345. WALLY JOYNER
- ☐ 362. JEFF MONTGOMERY
- ☐ 391. HIPOLITO PICHARDO
- ☐ 435. BOB HAMELIN
- ☐ 450. TOM GORDON
- ☐ 502. GARY GAETTI
- ☐ 511. BRENT MAYNE
- ☐ 529. FELIX JOSE
- ☐ 562. JOHN HABYAN
- ☐ 565. KEVIN MCREYNOLDS
- ☐ 595. GREG GAGNE

LOS ANGELES DODGERS

- ☐ 2. MIKE PIAZZA

- ☐ 62. PEDRO ASTACIO
- ☐ 92. JIM GOTT
- ☐ 122. CARLOS HERNANDEZ
- ☐ 151. OREL HERSHISER
- ☐ 179. PEDRO MARTINEZ
- ☐ 207. ROGER MCDOWELL
- ☐ 236. JODY REED
- ☐ 264. HENRY RODRIGUEZ
- ☐ 292. DARRYL STRAWBERRY
- ☐ 313. RAUL MONDESI
- ☐ 326. TIM WALLACH
- ☐ 338. ERIC KARROS
- ☐ 350. DELINO DESHIELDS
- ☐ 368. RAMON MARTINEZ
- ☐ 397. TODD WORRELL
- ☐ 420. BILLY ASHLEY
- ☐ 457. MITCH WEBSTER
- ☐ 521. TOM CANDIOTTI
- ☐ 535. CORY SNYDER
- ☐ 543. BRETT BUTLER
- ☐ 587. KEVIN GROSS
- ☐ 616. DAVE HANSEN
- ☐ 623. JOSE OFFERMAN

MILWAUKEE BREWERS

- ☐ 15. ROBIN YOUNT
- ☐ 59. RICKY BONES
- ☐ 89. CAL ELDRED
- ☐ 119. DOUG HENRY
- ☐ 148. PAT LISTACH
- ☐ 176. GRAEME LLOYD
- ☐ 204. DAVE NILSSON
- ☐ 233. KEVIN REIMER
- ☐ 261. KEVIN SEITZER
- ☐ 288. BILL SPIERS
- ☐ 310. B.J.SURHOFF
- ☐ 339. GREG VAUGHN
- ☐ 398. DARRYL HAMILTON
- ☐ 459. TROY O'LEARY
- ☐ 488. ANGEL MIRANDA
- ☐ 522. MATT MIESKE
- ☐ 544. JOSE VALENTIN
- ☐ 569. JOHN JAHA
- ☐ 603. MIKE FETTERS
- ☐ 621. JAIME NAVARRO
- ☐ 633. BILL WEGMAN

MINNESOTA TWINS

- ☐ 28. CHUCK KNOBLAUCH
- ☐ 55. PEDRO MUNOZ
- ☐ 79. WILLIE BANKS
- ☐ 85. JEFF REBOULET
- ☐ 109. LARRY CASIAN
- ☐ 115. KEVIN TAPANI
- ☐ 139. EDDIE GUARDADO
- ☐ 168. CHIP HALE
- ☐ 196. BRIAN HARPER
- ☐ 225. MIKE HARTLEY
- ☐ 253. SHANE MACK
- ☐ 281. DAVE MCCARTY
- ☐ 336. DAVE WINFIELD
- ☐ 343. KIRBY PUCKETT
- ☐ 392. PAT MEARES
- ☐ 437. SCOTT ERICKSON
- ☐ 443. KENT HRBEK
- ☐ 477. DEREK PARKS
- ☐ 503. RICK AGUILERA
- ☐ 530. MARK GUTHRIE
- ☐ 563. TERRY JORGENSEN
- ☐ 581. CARL WILLIS
- ☐ 620. MIKE TROMBLEY

MONTREAL EXPOS

- ☐ 3. MOISES ALOU
- ☐ 37. MARQUIS GRISSOM
- ☐ 63. FRANK BOLICK
- ☐ 93. GREG COLBRUNN
- ☐ 123. JEFF FASSERO
- ☐ 152. DARRIN FLETCHER
- ☐ 180. KEN HILL
- ☐ 208. MIKE LANSING
- ☐ 237. KIRK RUETER
- ☐ 265. TIM SCOTT
- ☐ 293. JOHN WETTELAND
- ☐ 320. RONDELL WHITE
- ☐ 371. LARRY WALKER
- ☐ 422. DENNIS MARTINEZ
- ☐ 461. SEAN BERRY
- ☐ 491. MEL ROJAS
- ☐ 524. LOU FRAZIER
- ☐ 545. WIL CORDERO
- ☐ 571. JOHN VANDER WAL
- ☐ 589. CHRIS NABHOLZ
- ☐ 646. CURTIS PRIDE
- ☐ 651. CLIFF FLOYD

NEW YORK METS

- ☐ 17. DWIGHT GOODEN
- ☐ 68. KEVIN BAEZ
- ☐ 98. JOHN FRANCO
- ☐ 128. TODD HUNDLEY
- ☐ 157. RYAN THOMPSON
- ☐ 185. JEFF KENT
- ☐ 213. MIKE MADDUX
- ☐ 242. CHARLIE O'BRIEN
- ☐ 270. JOE ORSULAK
- ☐ 298. BRET SABERHAGEN
- ☐ 316. TIM BOGAR
- ☐ 347. BOBBY BONILLA
- ☐ 386. EDDIE MURRAY
- ☐ 405. ANTHONY YOUNG
- ☐ 426. BUTCH HUSKEY
- ☐ 467. DAVID TELGHEDER
- ☐ 501. BOBBY JONES
- ☐ 514. ERIC HILLMAN
- ☐ 575. JEROMY BURNITZ
- ☐ 585. PETE SMITH
- ☐ 634. JEFF MCKNIGHT
- ☐ 652. PETE SCHOUREK

NEW YORK YANKEES

- ☐ 30. JIMMY KEY
- ☐ 36. WADE BOGGS
- ☐ 50. PAUL O'NEILL
- ☐ 57. PAUL ASSENMACHER
- ☐ 80. SPIKE OWEN
- ☐ 87. MARK HUTTON
- ☐ 117. DOMINGO JEAN
- ☐ 146. JIM LEYRITZ
- ☐ 174. BOBBY MUNOZ
- ☐ 202. MIKE STANLEY
- ☐ 231. BOB WICKMAN
- ☐ 259. BERNIE WILLIAMS
- ☐ 340. DON MATTINGLY
- ☐ 357. JIM ABBOTT
- ☐ 390. GERALD WILLIAMS
- ☐ 414. DANNY TARTABULL
- ☐ 439. RANDY VELARDE
- ☐ 446. DION JAMES
- ☐ 476. MELIDO PEREZ
- ☐ 483. PAT KELLY
- ☐ 495. MIKE GALLEGO
- ☐ 531. STEVE FARR
- ☐ 553. SCOTT KAMIENIECKI
- ☐ 564. MATT NOKES
- ☐ 638. STERLING HITCHCOCK
- ☐ 650. LEE SMITH

OAKLAND A'S

- ☐ 16. DENNIS ECKERSLEY
- ☐ 33. RUBEN SIERRA
- ☐ 51. MARCOS ARMAS
- ☐ 81. MIKE BORDICK
- ☐ 111. BRENT GATES
- ☐ 141. SCOTT HEMOND
- ☐ 169. RICK HONEYCUTT
- ☐ 197. STEVE KARSAY
- ☐ 226. SCOTT LYDY
- ☐ 254. TERRY STEINBACH
- ☐ 282. BOB WELCH
- ☐ 308. BOBBY WITT
- ☐ 335. MARK MCGWIRE
- ☐ 401. LANCE BLANKENSHIP
- ☐ 421. ROGER SMITHBERG
- ☐ 452. RON DARLING
- ☐ 505. MIKE MOHLER
- ☐ 513. DAVE HENDERSON
- ☐ 520. TROY NEEL
- ☐ 532. CRAIG PAQUETTE
- ☐ 557. TODD VAN POPPEL
- ☐ 602. HENRY MERCEDES
- ☐ 630. SCOTT BROSIUS

PHILADELPHIA PHILLIES

- ☐ 7. JOHN KRUK
- ☐ 29. DAVE HOLLINS
- ☐ 71. LARRY ANDERSEN
- ☐ 101. WES CHAMBERLAIN
- ☐ 131. DANNY JACKSON
- ☐ 160. TERRY MULHOLLAND
- ☐ 188. TODD PRATT
- ☐ 216. BEN RIVERA
- ☐ 245. KEVIN STOCKER
- ☐ 273. BOBBY THIGPEN
- ☐ 301. MILT THOMPSON
- ☐ 319. MITCH WILLIAMS
- ☐ 333. DARREN DAULTON
- ☐ 373. LENNY DYKSTRA
- ☐ 394. RICKY JORDAN
- ☐ 409. DAVID WEST
- ☐ 433. TYLER GREEN
- ☐ 470. KIM BATISTE
- ☐ 482. TOMMY GREENE
- ☐ 498. MICKEY MORANDINI
- ☐ 548. JIM EISENREICH
- ☐ 577. CURT SCHILLING
- ☐ 594. PETE INCAVIGLIA
- ☐ 614. MARIANO DUNCAN

PITTSBURGH PIRATES

- ☐ 21. JAY BELL
- ☐ 72. STEVE COOKE
- ☐ 102. MARK DEWEY
- ☐ 132. TOM FOLEY
- ☐ 161. CARLOS GARCIA
- ☐ 189. BLAS MINOR
- ☐ 217. DON SLAUGHT
- ☐ 246. JOEL JOHNSTON
- ☐ 274. RANDY TOMLIN
- ☐ 329. ANDY TOMBERLIN
- ☐ 334. ORLANDO MERCED
- ☐ 375. ANDY VAN SLYKE
- ☐ 395. BOB WALK
- ☐ 431. SCOTT BULLETT
- ☐ 471. TIM WAKEFIELD
- ☐ 485. WILLIAM PENNYFEATHER
- ☐ 494. AL MARTIN
- ☐ 538. JEFF KING
- ☐ 559. ZANE SMITH
- ☐ 578. KEVIN YOUNG
- ☐ 608. MIDRE CUMMINGS
- ☐ 611. PAUL WAGNER

ST. LOUIS CARDINALS

- ☐ 9. GREGG JEFFERIES
- ☐ 35. OZZIE SMITH
- ☐ 60. RENE AROCHA
- ☐ 90. BERNARD GILKEY
- ☐ 120. OMAR OLIVARES
- ☐ 149. DONOVAN OSBORNE
- ☐ 177. TOM PAGNOZZI
- ☐ 205. ERIK PAPPAS
- ☐ 234. GERONIMO PENA
- ☐ 262. BOB TEWKSBURY
- ☐ 289. ALLEN WATSON
- ☐ 311. MARK WHITEN
- ☐ 367. RAY LANKFORD
- ☐ 400. ROD BREWER
- ☐ 419. TRIPP CROMER
- ☐ 460. TODD ZEILE
- ☐ 534. LUIS ALICEA
- ☐ 586. BRIAN JORDAN
- ☐ 599. MIKE PEREZ
- ☐ 622. RHEAL CORMIER
- ☐ 649. RICH BATCHELOR

SAN DIEGO PADRES

- ☐ 10. TONY GWYNN
- ☐ 70. ANDY ASHBY
- ☐ 100. BRAD AUSMUS
- ☐ 130. PHIL CLARK
- ☐ 159. RICKY GUTIERREZ
- ☐ 187. TREVOR HOFFMAN
- ☐ 215. TIM MAUSER
- ☐ 244. KERRY TAYLOR
- ☐ 272. TIM TEUFEL
- ☐ 300. GUILLERMO VELASQUEZ
- ☐ 318. TIM WORRELL
- ☐ 332. ANDY BENES

- □ 387. KEVIN HIGGINS
- □ 393. LUIS LOPEZ
- □ 406. JEFF GARDNER
- □ 468. GENE HARRIS
- □ 489. SCOTT SANDERS
- □ 493. ARCHI CIANFROCCO
- □ 516. CRAIG SHIPLEY
- □ 526. PEDRO MARTINEZ
- □ 566. PHIL PLANTIER
- □ 591. DEREK BELL
- □ 615. DOUG BROCAIL
- □ 657. MARK DAVIS

SAN FRANCISCO GIANTS

- □ 13. JOHN BURKETT
- □ 38. WILL CLARK
- □ 48. ROBBY THOMPSON
- □ 64. BUD BLACK
- □ 94. JEFF BRANTLEY
- □ 124. DAVE BURBA
- □ 153. ROYCE CLAYTON
- □ 181. BRYAN HICKERSON
- □ 209. KIRT MANWARING
- □ 238. WILLIE MCGEE
- □ 266. SCOTT SANDERSON
- □ 294. BILL SWIFT
- □ 327. SALOMON TORRES
- □ 349. BARRY BONDS
- □ 370. MATT WILLIAMS
- □ 424. DARREN LEWIS
- □ 463. DAVE MARTINEZ
- □ 508 KEVIN ROGERS
- □ 525. MIKE JACKSON
- □ 572. TREVOR WILSON
- □ 588. J.R.PHILLIPS
- □ 604. ROD BECK
- □ 655. STEVE HOSEY

SEATTLE MARINERS

- □ 4. KEN GRIFFEY, JR.
- □ 66. RICH AMARAL
- □ 96. NORM CHARLTON
- □ 126. JOHN CUMMINGS
- □ 155. MIKE FELDER
- □ 183. DAVE FLEMING
- □ 211. ERIK HANSON
- □ 240. TIM LEARY
- □ 268. EDGAR MARTINEZ
- □ 296. TINO MARTINEZ
- □ 314. BRIAN TURANG
- □ 328. OMAR VIZQUEL
- □ 352. RANDY JOHNSON
- □ 369. JAY BUHNER
- □ 385. DAVID VALLE
- □ 388. DAN WILSON
- □ 423. MIKE BLOWERS
- □ 462. BRAD HOLMAN
- □ 492. JEFF NELSON
- □ 546. CHRIS BOSIO
- □ 574. MARC NEWFIELD
- □ 647. ERIK PLANTENBERG
- □ 654. BILL HASELMAN

TEXAS RANGERS

- □ 1. NOLAN RYAN
- □ 22. KEVIN BROWN
- □ 26. RAFAEL PALMEIRO
- □ 49. JUAN GONZALEZ
- □ 73. MARIO DIAZ
- □ 103. BENJI GIL
- □ 133. DONALD HARRIS
- □ 162. TOM HENKE
- □ 190. CHARLIE LEIBRANDT
- □ 218. BOB PATTERSON
- □ 247. GENO PETRALLI
- □ 275. GARY REDUS
- □ 302. DOUG STRANGE
- □ 355. DEAN PALMER
- □ 372. JOSE CANSECO
- □ 376. IVAN RODRIGUEZ
- □ 410. KENNY ROGERS
- □ 432. JEFF HUSON
- □ 472. CRAIG LEFFERTS
- □ 481. JULIO FRANCO
- □ 515. DAN PELTIER
- □ 527. ROGER PAVLIK
- □ 560. DAVID HULSE
- □ 606. MATT WHITESIDE

TORONTO BLUE JAYS

- □ 6. ROBERTO ALOMAR
- □ 19. RICKEY HENDERSON
- □ 24. PAUL MOLITOR
- □ 54. PAT BORDERS
- □ 84. ED SPRAGUE
- □ 114. DANNY COX
- □ 144. MARK EICHHORN
- □ 172. TONY FERNANDEZ
- □ 200. PAT HENTGEN
- □ 229. AL LEITER
- □ 257. DAVE STEWART
- □ 285. DEVON WHITE
- □ 354. JOHN OLERUD
- □ 366. JOE CARTER
- □ 379. DUANE WARD
- □ 404. JUAN GUZMAN
- □ 455. DOMINGO CEDENO
- □ 504. TODD STOTTLEMYRE
- □ 558. ROB BUTLER
- □ 568. CARLOS DELGADO
- □ 584. DOMINGO MARTINEZ
- □ 601. TONY CASTILLO
- □ 607. SHAWN GREEN

1995 DONRUSS (550)
2 1/2" X 3 1/2"

ATLANTA BRAVES

- □ 1. DAVID JUSTICE
- □ 28. MIKE STANTON
- □ 54. KENT MERCKER
- □ 87. STEVE AVERY
- □ 124. JOSE OLIVA
- □ 146. MARK LEMKE
- □ 166. JAVY LOPEZ
- □ 191. GREG MCMICHAEL
- □ 248. TOM GLAVINE
- □ 253. RYAN KLESKO
- □ 299. MIKE KELLY
- □ 301. ROBERTO KELLY
- □ 331. GREG MADDUX
- □ 349. FRED MCGRIFF
- □ 363. JEFF BLAUSER
- □ 394. TERRY PENDLETON
- □ 437. CHARLIE O'BRIEN
- □ 461. JOHN SMOLTZ
- □ 468. TONY TARASCO
- □ 527. MARK WOHLERS

BALTIMORE ORIOLES

- □ 9. MIKE MUSSINA
- □ 41. LEO GOMEZ
- □ 66. JAMIE MOYER
- □ 83. CAL RIPKEN, JR.
- □ 133. LEE SMITH
- □ 201. BRADY ANDERSON
- □ 216. ARMANDO BENITEZ
- □ 231. JEFFREY HAMMONDS
- □ 270. SID FERNANDEZ
- □ 295. CHRIS HOILES
- □ 327. JACK VOIGT
- □ 357. RAFAEL PALMEIRO
- □ 368. MIKE DEVEREAUX
- □ 372. MARK SMITH
- □ 399. MARK MCLEMORE
- □ 412. BEN MCDONALD
- □ 475. MARK EICHHORN
- □ 538. HAROLD BAINES
- □ 540. DAMON BUFORD

BOSTON RED SOX

- □ 17. AARON SELE
- □ 44. KEN RYAN
- □ 52. MO VAUGHN
- □ 89. JOHN VALENTIN
- □ 144. CARLOS RODRIGUEZ
- □ 188. TIM NAEHRING
- □ 213. OTIS NIXON
- □ 229. JOE HESKETH
- □ 261. CHRIS HOWARD
- □ 283. GAR FINNVOLD
- □ 316. WES CHAMBERLAIN
- □ 344. CORY BAILEY
- □ 359. TOM BRUNANSKY
- □ 413. SCOTT COOPER
- □ 427. ROGER CLEMENS
- □ 449. SCOTT FLETCHER
- □ 487. ANDRE DAWSON
- □ 505. RICH ROWLAND
- □ 547. MIKE GREENWELL

CALIFORNIA ANGELS

- □ 7. DAMION EASLEY
- □ 32. SPIKE OWEN
- □ 72. BRIAN ANDERSON
- □ 99. CHAD CURTIS
- □ 139. J.T. SNOW
- □ 155. MARK LANGSTON
- □ 199. PHIL LEFTWICH
- □ 214. EDUARDO PEREZ
- □ 223. JIM EDMONDS
- □ 256. GARY DISARCINA
- □ 276. JORGE FABREGAS
- □ 281. GARRET ANDERSON
- □ 361. CHRIS TURNER
- □ 403. TIM SALMON
- □ 426. GREG MYERS
- □ 452. CHILI DAVIS
- □ 477. CHUCK FINLEY
- □ 507. BO JACKSON
- □ 524. ANDREW LORRAINE

CHICAGO CUBS

- □ 23. STEVE TRACHSEL
- □ 39. SHAWON DUNSTON
- □ 64. EDDIE ZAMBRANO
- □ 90. GLENALLEN HILL
- □ 122. SAMMY SOSA
- □ 158. RICK WILKINS
- □ 173. REY SANCHEZ
- □ 186. STEVE BUECHELE
- □ 239. JIM BULLINGER
- □ 243. JOSE BAUTISTA
- □ 296. KEVIN FOSTER
- □ 334. TUFFY RHODES
- □ 358. ANTHONY YOUNG
- □ 385. MIKE MORGAN

- ☐ 429. RANDY MYERS
- ☐ 441. DERRICK MAY
- ☐ 466. JOSE HERNANDEZ
- ☐ 515. WILLIE BANKS
- ☐ 519. MARK GRACE

CHICAGO WHITE SOX

- ☐ 33. JOEY CORA
- ☐ 57. WILSON ALVAREZ
- ☐ 75. TIM RAINES
- ☐ 126. JOSE DELEON
- ☐ 165. NORBERTO MARTIN
- ☐ 198. RON KARKOVICE
- ☐ 259. ALEX FERNANDEZ
- ☐ 275. FRANK THOMAS
- ☐ 279. ROBERTO HERNANDEZ
- ☐ 294. OZZIE GUILLEN
- ☐ 298. LANCE JOHNSON
- ☐ 328. JULIO FRANCO
- ☐ 332. JASON BERE
- ☐ 378. ROBIN VENTURA
- ☐ 384. DARRIN JACKSON
- ☐ 418. JACK MCDOWELL
- ☐ 425. KIRK MCCASKILL
- ☐ 504. SCOTT RUFFCORN
- ☐ 517. MIKE LAVALLIERE
- ☐ 521. SCOTT SANDERSON
- ☐ 535. CRAIG GREBECK

CINCINNATI REDS

- ☐ 11. JOHN SMILEY
- ☐ 26. BRET BOONE
- ☐ 100. THOMAS HOWARD
- ☐ 101. HECTOR CARRASCO
- ☐ 204. REGGIE SANDERS
- ☐ 210. WILLIE GREENE
- ☐ 234. HAL MORRIS
- ☐ 241. BARRY LARKIN
- ☐ 287. JOHNNY RUFFIN
- ☐ 290. CHUCK MCELROY
- ☐ 292. JOSE RIJO
- ☐ 323. EDDIE TAUBENSEE
- ☐ 415. DEION SANDERS
- ☐ 442. JOHN ROPER
- ☐ 469. KEVIN MITCHELL
- ☐ 500. LENNY HARRIS
- ☐ 508. JEFF BRANSON
- ☐ 523. JEFF BRANTLEY
- ☐ 549. BRIAN DORSETT

CLEVELAND INDIANS

- ☐ 3. SANDY ALOMAR, JR.
- ☐ 36. OMAR VIZQUEL
- ☐ 58. JOSE MESA
- ☐ 92. DENNIS MARTINEZ
- ☐ 134. CHARLES NAGY
- ☐ 156. MARK CLARK
- ☐ 164. JASON GRIMSLEY
- ☐ 200. JIM THOME
- ☐ 237. WAYNE KIRBY
- ☐ 264. ALBERT BELLE
- ☐ 303. ALVARO ESPINOZA
- ☐ 326. CARLOS BAERGA
- ☐ 370. MANNY RAMIREZ
- ☐ 371. KENNY LOFTON
- ☐ 396. ERIC PLUNK
- ☐ 435. EDDIE MURRAY
- ☐ 454. TONY PENA
- ☐ 479. PAUL SHUEY
- ☐ 510. PAUL SORRENTO

COLORADO ROCKIES

- ☐ 14. WALT WEISS
- ☐ 47. WILLIE BLAIR
- ☐ 73. JOHN VANDER WAL
- ☐ 96. MIKE KINGERY
- ☐ 120. DAVID NIED
- ☐ 123. STEVE REED
- ☐ 169. MARCUS MOORE
- ☐ 181. VINNY CASTILLA
- ☐ 226. MARVIN FREEMAN
- ☐ 252. CHARLIE HAYES
- ☐ 300. ELLIS BURKS
- ☐ 302. DANTE BICHETTE
- ☐ 342. ANDRES GALARRAGA
- ☐ 367. JOE GIRARDI

- ☐ 383. ROBERTO MEJIA
- ☐ 400. GREG HARRIS
- ☐ 476. BRUCE RUFFIN
- ☐ 533. CURT LESKANIC
- ☐ 544. ERIC YOUNG

DETROIT TIGERS

- ☐ 45. LOU WHITAKER
- ☐ 82. TRAVIS FRYMAN
- ☐ 109. CECIL FIELDER
- ☐ 137. JOSE LIMA
- ☐ 154. MIKE MOORE
- ☐ 172. CHRIS GOMEZ
- ☐ 219. CHAD KREUTER
- ☐ 249. DANNY BAUTISTA
- ☐ 257. KIRK GIBSON
- ☐ 274. MILT CUYLER
- ☐ 309. JUNIOR FELIX
- ☐ 312. JOHN DOHERTY
- ☐ 339. TIM BELCHER
- ☐ 362. JOE BOEVER
- ☐ 407. TONY PHILLIPS
- ☐ 434. BILL GULLICKSON
- ☐ 465. DAVID WELLS
- ☐ 502. ALAN TRAMMELL
- ☐ 506. JUAN SAMUEL
- ☐ 537. MICKEY TETTLETON

FLORIDA MARLINS

- ☐ 22. DARRELL WHITMORE
- ☐ 27. CHARLES JOHNSON
- ☐ 70. KURT ABBOTT
- ☐ 85. BRET BARBERIE
- ☐ 121. PAT RAPP
- ☐ 149. ROBB NEN
- ☐ 168. GARY SHEFFIELD
- ☐ 192. CHUCK CARR
- ☐ 236. RYAN BOWEN
- ☐ 255. MATIAS CARRILLO
- ☐ 306. DAVE WEATHERS
- ☐ 345. BRYAN HARVEY
- ☐ 366. JEREMY HERNANDEZ
- ☐ 392. JEFF CONINE
- ☐ 428. CHRIS HAMMOND
- ☐ 446. JERRY BROWNE
- ☐ 463. GREG COLBRUNN
- ☐ 484. BENITO SANTIAGO
- ☐ 489. DAVE MAGADAN

HOUSTON ASTROS

- ☐ 20. JEFF BAGWELL
- ☐ 25. STEVE FINLEY
- ☐ 60. TODD JONES
- ☐ 94. ORLANDO MILLER
- ☐ 119. PETE HARNISCH
- ☐ 145. LUIS GONZALEZ
- ☐ 170. JOHN HUDEK
- ☐ 184. BRIAN HUNTER
- ☐ 230. ROBERTO PETAGINE
- ☐ 246. JAMES MOUTON
- ☐ 307. SHANE REYNOLDS
- ☐ 313. SCOTT SERVAIS
- ☐ 347. GREG SWINDELL
- ☐ 398. DARRYL KILE
- ☐ 411. KEVIN BASS
- ☐ 445. TONY EUSEBIO

- ☐ 456. CRAIG BIGGIO
- ☐ 472. KEN CAMINITI
- ☐ 530. ANDUJAR CEDENO
- ☐ 532. DOUG DRABEK

KANSAS CITY ROYALS

- ☐ 80. MARK GUBICZA
- ☐ 95. FELIX JOSE
- ☐ 118. VINCE COLEMAN
- ☐ 141. BILLY BREWER
- ☐ 167. BRIAN MCRAE
- ☐ 176. TERRY SHUMPERT
- ☐ 195. GREG GAGNE
- ☐ 225. JOSE LIND
- ☐ 238. BRENT MAYNE
- ☐ 289. DAVID CONE
- ☐ 321. JEFF MONTGOMERY
- ☐ 376. HIPOLITO PICHARDO
- ☐ 386. RUSTY MEACHAM
- ☐ 439. MIKE MACFARLANE
- ☐ 447. WALLY JOYNER
- ☐ 494. TOM GORDON
- ☐ 520. BOB HAMELIN
- ☐ 542. KEVIN APPIER

LOS ANGELES DODGERS

- ☐ 5. MIKE PIAZZA
- ☐ 29. ISMAEL VALDES
- ☐ 71. DELINO DESHIELDS
- ☐ 77. JOSE OFFERMAN
- ☐ 116. TOM CANDIOTTI
- ☐ 131. DARREN DREIFORT
- ☐ 175. CHAN HO PARK
- ☐ 180. BILLY ASHLEY
- ☐ 245. OREL HERSHISER
- ☐ 258. GAREY INGRAM
- ☐ 280. HENRY RODRIGUEZ
- ☐ 337. PEDRO ASTACIO
- ☐ 390. BRETT BUTLER
- ☐ 424. KEVIN GROSS
- ☐ 474. TODD WORRELL
- ☐ 481. RAMON MARTINEZ
- ☐ 488. ERIC KARROS
- ☐ 539. TIM WALLACH
- ☐ 543. RAUL MONDESI

MILWAUKEE BREWERS

- ☐ 10. KEVIN SEITZER
- ☐ 56. BOB SCANLAN
- ☐ 68. JOSE VALENTIN
- ☐ 74. TURNER WARD
- ☐ 130. GREG VAUGHN
- ☐ 143. RICKY BONES
- ☐ 182. BILL SPIERS
- ☐ 189. MATT MIESKE
- ☐ 232. JOHN JAHA
- ☐ 250. JOSE MERCEDES
- ☐ 273. TROY O'LEARY
- ☐ 288. DAVE NILSSON
- ☐ 333. BILL WEGMAN
- ☐ 356. B.J. SURHOFF
- ☐ 410. PAT LISTACH
- ☐ 414. JODY REED
- ☐ 443. DARRYL HAMILTON
- ☐ 448. BRIAN HARPER
- ☐ 503. MIKE FETTERS
- ☐ 536. CAL ELDRED

MINNESOTA TWINS

- ☐ 53. RICK AGUILERA
- ☐ 88. RICH BECKER
- ☐ 106. STEVE DUNN
- ☐ 161. SCOTT ERICKSON
- ☐ 185. PAT MEARES
- ☐ 217. DAVE MCCARTY
- ☐ 247. SCOTT LEIUS
- ☐ 269. KEVIN TAPANI
- ☐ 272. DENNY HOCKING
- ☐ 286. CHUCK KNOBLAUCH
- ☐ 304. ALEX COLE
- ☐ 320. MATT WALBECK
- ☐ 353. CARLOS PULIDO
- ☐ 380. KIRBY PUCKETT
- ☐ 432. JEFF REBOULET
- ☐ 436. PEDRO MUNOZ
- ☐ 467. CHIP HALE

☐ 512. PAT MAHOMES
☐ 526. SHANE MACK

MONTREAL EXPOS

☐ 15. MIKE LANSING
☐ 40. DARRIN FLETCHER
☐ 115. JOEY EISCHEN
☐ 150. WIL CORDERO
☐ 208. TIM SCOTT
☐ 212. CLIFF FLOYD
☐ 227. KEN HILL
☐ 251. MARQUIS GRISSOM
☐ 293. SEAN BERRY
☐ 310. JEFF FASSERO
☐ 315. PEDRO MARTINEZ
☐ 322. MEL ROJAS
☐ 343. RONDELL WHITE
☐ 388. LOU FRAZIER
☐ 408. MOISES ALOU
☐ 455. BUTCH HENRY
☐ 486. KIRK RUETER
☐ 492. LARRY WALKER
☐ 516. JOHN WETTELAND
☐ 541. LENNY WEBSTER

NEW YORK METS

☐ 6. BOBBY JONES
☐ 65. TODD HUNDLEY
☐ 97. JEFF KENT
☐ 136. JASON JACOME
☐ 142. JEROMY BURNITZ
☐ 171. KELLY STINNETT
☐ 190. JOSIAS MANZANILLO
☐ 242. DAVID SEGUI
☐ 266. JOE ORSULAK
☐ 308. BOBBY BONILLA
☐ 325. JOSE VIZCAINO
☐ 346. JOHN FRANCO
☐ 430. ROGER MASON
☐ 431. BRET SABERHAGEN
☐ 451. PETE SMITH
☐ 458. RYAN THOMPSON
☐ 525. RICO BROGNA

NEW YORK YANKEES

☐ 34. ROBERT EENHOORN
☐ 51. STERLING HITCHCOCK
☐ 55. DON MATTINGLY
☐ 59. SCOTT KAMIENIECKI
☐ 62. MIKE STANLEY
☐ 78. JIMMY KEY
☐ 93. PAT KELLY
☐ 103. DANNY TARTABULL
☐ 152. GERALD WILLIAMS
☐ 277. MIKE GALLEGO
☐ 282. BOB WICKMAN
☐ 284. PAUL O'NEILL
☐ 355. WADE BOGGS
☐ 369. JIM ABBOTT
☐ 381. STEVE HOWE
☐ 397. MELIDO PEREZ
☐ 401. JIM LEYRITZ
☐ 404. TERRY MULHOLLAND
☐ 491. RANDY VELARDE
☐ 501. JOE AUSANIO
☐ 509. BERNIE WILLIAMS

☐ 514. LUIS POLONIA
☐ 545. RUSS DAVIS

OAKLAND A'S

☐ 13. RON DARLING
☐ 48. TODD VAN POPPEL
☐ 76. MARK ACRE
☐ 84. GERONIMO BERROA
☐ 112. TROY NEEL
☐ 148. MIKE BORDICK
☐ 177. STEVE ONTIVEROS
☐ 203. STEVE KARSAY
☐ 262. MIGUEL JIMENEZ
☐ 305. RICKEY HENDERSON
☐ 329. BRENT GATES
☐ 354. TERRY STEINBACH
☐ 377. BILL TAYLOR
☐ 391. BOBBY WITT
☐ 406. RUBEN SIERRA
☐ 460. MARK MCGWIRE
☐ 485. STAN JAVIER
☐ 511. DENNIS ECKERSLEY
☐ 548. SCOTT BROSIUS

PHILADELPHIA PHILLIES

☐ 21. CURT SCHILLING
☐ 61. JOHN KRUK
☐ 98. PETE INCAVIGLIA
☐ 105. DANNY JACKSON
☐ 125. RICKY BOTTALICO
☐ 159. BOBBY MUNOZ
☐ 209. LENNY DYKSTRA
☐ 211. JIM EISENREICH
☐ 240. MIKE LIEBERTHAL
☐ 263. HEATH SLOCUMB
☐ 278. MICKEY MORANDINI
☐ 291. KEVIN STOCKER
☐ 341. MARIANO DUNCAN
☐ 348. DAVID WEST
☐ 395. RICKY JORDAN
☐ 420. TONY LONGMIRE
☐ 453. DAVE HOLLINS
☐ 470. BILLY HATCHER
☐ 497. DARREN DAULTON
☐ 518. TOMMY GREENE

PITTSBURGH PIRATES

☐ 35. RICK WHITE
☐ 91. CARLOS GARCIA
☐ 108. JEFF KING
☐ 111. DENNY NEAGLE
☐ 129. MARK DEWEY
☐ 147. AL MARTIN
☐ 163. JON LIEBER
☐ 193. MIDRE CUMMINGS
☐ 196. STEVE COOKE
☐ 206. JAY BELL
☐ 265. DAVE CLARK
☐ 335. KEVIN YOUNG
☐ 351. ORLANDO MERCED
☐ 389. ANDY VAN SLYKE
☐ 421. PAUL WAGNER
☐ 444. DAN MICELI
☐ 457. ZANE SMITH
☐ 498. DON SLAUGHT

ST. LOUIS CARDINALS

☐ 2. RENE AROCHA
☐ 16. ALLEN WATSON
☐ 43. LUIS ALICEA
☐ 50. OZZIE SMITH
☐ 79. MARK WHITEN
☐ 102. TOM PAGNOZZI
☐ 221. BRIAN JORDAN
☐ 254. VICENTE PALACIOS
☐ 260. JOHN MABRY
☐ 317. BRYAN EVERSGERD
☐ 324. RAY LANKFORD
☐ 352. RHEAL CORMIER
☐ 379. BERNARD GILKEY
☐ 417. GREGG JEFFERIES
☐ 422. GERONIMO PENA
☐ 480. BOB TEWKSBURY
☐ 483. TODD ZEILE

SAN DIEGO PADRES

☐ 4. LUIS LOPEZ
☐ 38. EDDIE WILLIAMS
☐ 86. ANDY ASHBY
☐ 104. DONNIE ELLIOTT
☐ 117. RAY MCDAVID
☐ 135. PHIL PLANTIER
☐ 178. BRAD AUSMUS
☐ 202. PEDRO MARTINEZ
☐ 218. SCOTT LIVINGSTONE
☐ 224. TONY GWYNN
☐ 267. JOEY HAMILTON
☐ 318. TREVOR HOFFMAN
☐ 336. ANDY BENES
☐ 364. DEREK BELL
☐ 393. TIM HYERS
☐ 416. RICKY GUTIERREZ
☐ 450. BIP ROBERTS
☐ 482. MELVIN NIEVES
☐ 528. SCOTT SANDERS
☐ 534. CRAIG SHIPLEY

SAN FRANCISCO GIANTS

☐ 8. BARRY BONDS
☐ 12. WILLIAM VAN LANDINGHAM
☐ 30. SALOMON TORRES
☐ 113. ROD BECK
☐ 138. J.R. PHILLIPS
☐ 187. KIRT MANWARING
☐ 194. DARRYL STRAWBERRY
☐ 233. JOHN BURKETT
☐ 268. MARK PORTUGAL
☐ 285. ROYCE CLAYTON
☐ 311. DARREN LEWIS
☐ 319. JOHN PATTERSON
☐ 365. MATT WILLIAMS
☐ 387. BILL SWIFT
☐ 405. ROBBY THOMPSON
☐ 459. MIKE JACKSON
☐ 462. STEVE SCARSONE
☐ 495. DAVE BURBA
☐ 546. MIKE BENJAMIN

SEATTLE MARINERS

☐ 18. RANDY JOHNSON
☐ 24. DAN WILSON
☐ 31. ERIC ANTHONY
☐ 46. MIKE BLOWERS
☐ 63. TINO MARTINEZ
☐ 67. RICH AMARAL
☐ 107. ROGER SALKELD
☐ 114. ALEX RODRIGUEZ
☐ 151. EDGAR MARTINEZ
☐ 157. BOBBY AYALA
☐ 179. TIM DAVIS
☐ 205. BILL RISLEY
☐ 338. REGGIE JEFFERSON
☐ 340. KEN GRIFFEY, JR.
☐ 373. DAVE FLEMING
☐ 409. FELIX FERMIN
☐ 438. JEFF NELSON
☐ 471. JAY BUHNER
☐ 478. MARC NEWFIELD
☐ 496. DARREN BRAGG
☐ 529. CHRIS BOSIO

TEXAS RANGERS

☐ 19. DEAN PALMER
☐ 42. JUAN GONZALEZ
☐ 128. WILL CLARK
☐ 153. ESTEBAN BELTRE
☐ 207. KEVIN BROWN
☐ 215. MANUEL LEE
☐ 222. MATT WHITESIDE
☐ 228. DAVID HULSE
☐ 244. HECTOR FAJARDO
☐ 271. STEVE DREYER
☐ 297. JEFF FRYE
☐ 314. RICK HELLING
☐ 350. JOSE CANSECO
☐ 375. ROGER PAVLIK
☐ 402. DOUG STRANGE
☐ 423. IVAN RODRIGUEZ
☐ 473. TOM HENKE
☐ 493. CRIS CARPENTER
☐ 513. RUSTY GREER

- ☐ 531. KENNY ROGERS

TORONTO BLUE JAYS

- ☐ 37. CARLOS DELGADO
- ☐ 49. ROBERTO ALOMAR
- ☐ 69. ALEX GONZALEZ
- ☐ 81. DARREN HALL
- ☐ 127. PAT HENTGEN
- ☐ 132. ED SPRAGUE
- ☐ 140. MICHAEL HUFF
- ☐ 162. PAUL MOLITOR
- ☐ 174. JUAN GUZMAN
- ☐ 183. RANDY KNORR
- ☐ 197. WOODY WILLIAMS
- ☐ 235. TONY CASTILLO
- ☐ 360. TODD STOTTLEMYRE
- ☐ 374. DAVE STEWART
- ☐ 382. DEVON WHITE
- ☐ 419. AL LEITER
- ☐ 433. JOHN OLERUD
- ☐ 464. SHAWN GREEN
- ☐ 499. PAT BORDERS
- ☐ 522. JOE CARTER

DONRUSS-LEAF

1990 LEAF (528)
2 1/2" X 3 1/2"

ATLANTA BRAVES

- ☐ 13. TOM GLAVINE
- ☐ 33. ANDRES THOMAS
- ☐ 59. JOHN SMOLTZ
- ☐ 86. TOMMY GREGG
- ☐ 112. ODDIBE MCDOWELL
- ☐ 144. PETE SMITH
- ☐ 164. NICK ESASKY
- ☐ 191. JEFF BLAUSER
- ☐ 217. LONNIE SMITH
- ☐ 243. DALE MURPHY
- ☐ 277. JIM PRESLEY
- ☐ 297. DAVE JUSTICE
- ☐ 323. GREG OLSON
- ☐ 349. JOE BOEVER
- ☐ 376. RON GANT
- ☐ 408. ERNIE WHITT
- ☐ 428. CHARLIE LEIBRANDT
- ☐ 455. JEFF TREADWAY
- ☐ 481. STEVE AVERY
- ☐ 507. JOE HESKETH

BALTIMORE ORIOLES

- ☐ 7. GREGG OLSON
- ☐ 39. PETE HARNISCH
- ☐ 65. MICKEY TETTLETON
- ☐ 92. RANDY MILLIGAN
- ☐ 118. JEFF BALLARD
- ☐ 138. PHIL BRADLEY
- ☐ 170. CRAIG WORTHINGTON
- ☐ 197. CAL RIPKEN
- ☐ 223. MIKE DEVEREAUX
- ☐ 249. BEN MCDONALD
- ☐ 271. BILLY RIPKEN
- ☐ 303. BRAD KOMMINSK
- ☐ 329. STEVE FINLEY
- ☐ 355. JOE ORSULAK
- ☐ 382. BOB MELVIN
- ☐ 402. BOB MILACKI
- ☐ 434. DAVE JOHNSON
- ☐ 461. MARK WILLIAMSON
- ☐ 487. BRIAN HOLTON
- ☐ 513. CHRIS HOILES

BOSTON RED SOX

- ☐ 12. ROGER CLEMENS
- ☐ 19. MIKE BODDICKER
- ☐ 51. WADE BOGGS
- ☐ 104. TONY PENA
- ☐ 130. JOHN DOPSON
- ☐ 143. MIKE GREENWELL
- ☐ 150. JODY REED
- ☐ 183. ROB MURPHY
- ☐ 235. DWIGHT EVANS
- ☐ 261. ELLIS BURKS
- ☐ 276. JEFF REARDON
- ☐ 283. LUIS RIVERA
- ☐ 315. DENNIS LAMP
- ☐ 368. JERRY REED
- ☐ 394. CARLOS QUINTANA
- ☐ 407. WES GARDNER
- ☐ 414. KEVIN ROMINE
- ☐ 447. TOM BRUNANSKY
- ☐ 499. GREG HARRIS
- ☐ 525. DANA KIECKER

CALIFORNIA ANGELS

- ☐ 24. WALLY JOYNER
- ☐ 31. JIM ABBOTT
- ☐ 63. BERT BLYLEVEN
- ☐ 76. DEVON WHITE
- ☐ 116. BRYAN HARVEY
- ☐ 155. MARK LANGSTON
- ☐ 162. CHUCK FINLEY
- ☐ 195. LANCE PARRISH
- ☐ 208. JOHNNY RAY
- ☐ 247. KIRK MCCASKILL
- ☐ 288. CHILI DAVIS
- ☐ 295. LUIS POLONIA
- ☐ 327. JACK HOWELL
- ☐ 340. DANTE BICHETTE
- ☐ 380. SCOTT BAILES
- ☐ 419. DICK SCHOFIELD
- ☐ 426. DAVE WINFIELD
- ☐ 459. MAX VENABLE
- ☐ 472. MARK EICHHORN
- ☐ 511. JOHN ORTON

CHICAGO CUBS

- ☐ 6. RICK SUTCLIFFE
- ☐ 25. GREG MADDUX
- ☐ 45. MIKE BIELECKI
- ☐ 98. RYNE SANDBERG
- ☐ 124. JEROME WALTON
- ☐ 137. MARK GRACE
- ☐ 156. MITCH WILLIAMS
- ☐ 177. ANDRE DAWSON
- ☐ 229. SHAWON DUNSTON
- ☐ 255. DWIGHT SMITH
- ☐ 270. MARVELL WYNNE
- ☐ 289. JOE GIRARDI
- ☐ 309. MIKE HARKEY
- ☐ 361. LES LANCASTER
- ☐ 388. LUIS SALAZAR
- ☐ 401. HECTOR VILLANUEVA
- ☐ 420. STEVE WILSON
- ☐ 440. DOMINGO RAMOS
- ☐ 493. PAUL ASSENMACHER
- ☐ 519. SHAWN BOSKIE

CHICAGO WHITE SOX

- ☐ 10. CARLTON FISK
- ☐ 36. MELIDO PEREZ
- ☐ 43. ERIC KING
- ☐ 89. IVAN CALDERON
- ☐ 128. OZZIE GUILLEN
- ☐ 141. SCOTT FLETCHER
- ☐ 167. ROBIN VENTURA
- ☐ 175. BOBBY THIGPEN
- ☐ 220. SAMMY SOSA
- ☐ 259. LANCE JOHNSON
- ☐ 274. DAN PASQUA
- ☐ 300. FRANK THOMAS
- ☐ 307. RON KARKOVICE
- ☐ 352. WAYNE EDWARDS
- ☐ 392. DONN PALL
- ☐ 405. RON KITTLE
- ☐ 431. BARRY JONES
- ☐ 438. CARLOS MARTINEZ
- ☐ 484. SCOTT RADINSKY
- ☐ 523. GREG HIBBARD

CINCINNATI REDS

- ☐ 15. TODD BENZINGER
- ☐ 18. BARRY LARKIN
- ☐ 57. ROB DIBBLE
- ☐ 70. PAUL O'NEILL
- ☐ 110. TOM BROWNING
- ☐ 146. CHRIS SABO
- ☐ 149. RANDY MYERS
- ☐ 189. ERIC DAVIS
- ☐ 202. MARIANO DUNCAN
- ☐ 241. BILLY HATCHER
- ☐ 279. DANNY JACKSON
- ☐ 282. JOSE RIJO
- ☐ 321. HAL MORRIS
- ☐ 334. NORM CHARLTON
- ☐ 374. JACK ARMSTRONG
- ☐ 410. TIM LAYANA
- ☐ 413. SCOTT SCUDDER
- ☐ 453. JOE OLIVER
- ☐ 466. GLENN BRAGGS
- ☐ 505. JEFF REED

CLEVELAND INDIANS

- ☐ 22. JOHN FARRELL
- ☐ 48. JERRY BROWNE
- ☐ 55. TOM CANDIOTTI
- ☐ 74. BROOK JACOBY
- ☐ 101. JESSE OROSCO
- ☐ 153. DOUG JONES
- ☐ 180. JOEY BELLE
- ☐ 187. CORY SNYDER
- ☐ 206. GREG SWINDELL
- ☐ 232. SANDY ALOMAR
- ☐ 286. JOEL SKINNER
- ☐ 312. MITCH WEBSTER
- ☐ 319. CHRIS JAMES
- ☐ 338. CANDY MALDONADO
- ☐ 365. CECILIO GUANTE
- ☐ 417. RUDY SEANEZ
- ☐ 443. CARLOS BAERGA
- ☐ 451. BUD BLACK
- ☐ 470. KEITH HERNANDEZ
- ☐ 496. SERGIO VALDEZ

DETROIT TIGERS

- ☐ 2. MIKE HENNEMAN
- ☐ 34. LOU WHITAKER
- ☐ 60. MIKE HEATH
- ☐ 87. FRANK TANANA
- ☐ 113. GARY WARD
- ☐ 133. CHET LEMON
- ☐ 165. CECIL FIELDER
- ☐ 192. MATT NOKES
- ☐ 218. ALAN TRAMMELL
- ☐ 244. DAVE BERGMAN
- ☐ 266. BRIAN DUBOIS
- ☐ 298. PAUL GIBSON
- ☐ 324. TONY PHILLIPS
- ☐ 350. LARRY SHEETS
- ☐ 377. LLOYD MOSEBY
- ☐ 397. EDWIN NUNEZ
- ☐ 429. JEFF ROBINSON
- ☐ 456. LANCE MCCULLERS
- ☐ 482. JACK MORRIS
- ☐ 508. DAN PETRY

HOUSTON ASTROS

- ☐ 4. MIKE SCOTT
- ☐ 30. GLENN DAVIS
- ☐ 37. CRAIG BIGGIO
- ☐ 82. ERIC ANTHONY

☐ 122. DAVE SMITH
☐ 135. RAFAEL RAMIREZ
☐ 161. BILL DORAN
☐ 168. JIM DESHAIES
☐ 214. GERALD YOUNG
☐ 253. KEN CAMINITI
☐ 268. GLENN WILSON
☐ 294. KEN OBERKFELL
☐ 301. ERIC YELDING
☐ 346. DANNY DARWIN
☐ 386. LARRY ANDERSEN
☐ 399. MARK PORTUGAL
☐ 425. FRANKLIN STUBBS
☐ 432. ALEX TREVINO
☐ 478. RICH GEDMAN
☐ 517. XAVIER HERNANDEZ

KANSAS CITY ROYALS

☐ 14. TOM GORDON
☐ 46. BOB BOONE
☐ 72. BRET SABERHAGEN
☐ 99. DANNY TARTABULL
☐ 125. BO JACKSON
☐ 145. MARK GUBICZA
☐ 178. GEORGE BRETT
☐ 204. FRANK WHITE
☐ 230. KEVIN SEITZER
☐ 256. KURT STILLWELL
☐ 278. JIM EISENREICH
☐ 310. MEL STOTTLEMYRE
☐ 336. WILLIE WILSON
☐ 362. STORM DAVIS
☐ 389. MIKE MACFARLANE
☐ 409. TERRY SHUMPERT
☐ 441. GERALD PERRY
☐ 468. MARK DAVIS
☐ 494. STEVE CRAWFORD
☐ 520. JEFF MONTGOMERY

LOS ANGELES DODGERS

☐ 16. HUBIE BROOKS
☐ 42. JAY HOWELL
☐ 49. MIKE SCIOSCIA
☐ 68. FERNANDO VALENZUELA
☐ 95. ALFREDO GRIFFIN
☐ 147. RAMON MARTINEZ
☐ 173. KIRK GIBSON
☐ 181. EDDIE MURRAY
☐ 200. TIM BELCHER
☐ 226. JUAN SAMUEL
☐ 280. OREL HERSHISER
☐ 306. JEFF HAMILTON
☐ 313. KAL DANIELS
☐ 332. MICKEY HATCHER
☐ 358. MIKE MORGAN
☐ 411. CHRIS GWYNN
☐ 437. LENNY HARRIS
☐ 445. STAN JAVIER
☐ 464. JOSE OFFERMAN
☐ 490. MIKE SHARPERSON

MILWAUKEE BREWERS

☐ 26. CHRIS BOSIO
☐ 58. CHUCK CRIM
☐ 71. ROBIN YOUNT
☐ 85. JAMIE NAVARRO
☐ 111. GREG VAUGHN
☐ 157. GARY SHEFFIELD
☐ 190. DAVE PARKER
☐ 203. BILL SPIERS
☐ 216. DAN PLESAC
☐ 242. PAUL MOLITOR
☐ 290. B.J. SURHOFF
☐ 322. ROB DEER
☐ 335. EDGAR DIAZ
☐ 348. MARK KNUDSON
☐ 375. CHARLIE O'BRIEN
☐ 421. BILL KRUEGER
☐ 454. GREG BROCK
☐ 467. RON ROBINSON
☐ 480. MIKE FELDER
☐ 506. TED HIGUERA

MINNESOTA TWINS

☐ 5. ALLAN ANDERSON
☐ 38. RICK AGUILERA
☐ 83. RANDY BUSH
☐ 97. GARY GAETTI
☐ 123. KIRBY PUCKETT
☐ 136. SHANE MACK
☐ 169. JUAN BERENGUER
☐ 215. GENE LARKIN
☐ 228. KENT HRBEK
☐ 254. DAN GLADDEN
☐ 269. KEVIN TAPANI
☐ 302. GREG GAGNE
☐ 347. AL NEWMAN
☐ 360. TERRY LEACH
☐ 387. DAVID WEST
☐ 400. ROY SMITH
☐ 433. JOHN MOSES
☐ 479. BRIAN HARPER
☐ 492. JOHN CANDELARIA
☐ 518. FRED MANRIQUE

MONTREAL EXPOS

☐ 28. TIM BURKE
☐ 54. DENNIS MARTINEZ
☐ 61. KEVIN GROSS
☐ 80. TIM WALLACH
☐ 107. MARQUIS GRISSOM
☐ 159. DENNIS BOYD
☐ 186. SPIKE OWEN
☐ 193. DELINO DESHIELDS
☐ 212. TIM RAINES
☐ 238. ZANE SMITH
☐ 292. TOM FOLEY
☐ 318. DAVE MARTINEZ
☐ 325. LARRY WALKER
☐ 344. WALLACE JOHNSON
☐ 371. MARK GARDNER
☐ 423. DREW HALL
☐ 450. ANDRES GALARRAGA
☐ 457. DAVE SCHMIDT
☐ 476. JERRY GOFF
☐ 502. NELSON SANTOVENIA

NEW YORK METS

☐ 8. KEVIN ELSTER
☐ 40. DAVID CONE
☐ 66. SID FERNANDEZ
☐ 93. FRANK VIOLA
☐ 119. BARRY LYONS
☐ 139. DWIGHT GOODEN
☐ 171. GREGG JEFFERIES
☐ 198. KEVIN MCREYNOLDS
☐ 224. MIKE MARSHALL
☐ 250. DARRYL STRAWBERRY
☐ 272. HOWARD JOHNSON
☐ 304. RON DARLING
☐ 330. DAVE MAGADAN
☐ 356. JOHN FRANCO
☐ 383. TIM TEUFEL
☐ 403. ALEJANDRO PENA
☐ 435. MACKEY SASSER
☐ 462. KEITH MILLER
☐ 488. MARK CARREON
☐ 514. DARYL BOSTON

NEW YORK YANKEES

☐ 17. ROBERTO KELLY
☐ 50. CHUCK CARY
☐ 69. DON MATTINGLY
☐ 96. STEVE SAX
☐ 109. MIKE BLOWERS
☐ 148. TIM LEARY
☐ 182. BOB GEREN
☐ 201. JESSE BARFIELD
☐ 227. MEL HALL
☐ 240. ALVARO ESPINOZA
☐ 281. ANDY HAWKINS
☐ 314. MATT NOKES
☐ 333. LEE GUETTERMAN
☐ 359. DEION SANDERS
☐ 373. STEVE BALBONI
☐ 412. JEFF ROBINSON
☐ 446. KEVIN MAAS
☐ 465. JIM LEYRITZ
☐ 491. ALAN MILLS
☐ 504. ERIC PLUNK

OAKLAND A'S

☐ 29. DENNIS ECKERSLEY
☐ 62. MARK MCGWIRE
☐ 81. DAVE STEWART
☐ 108. JOSE CANSECO
☐ 121. MIKE GALLEGO
☐ 160. RICKEY HENDERSON
☐ 194. SCOTT SANDERSON
☐ 213. CARNEY LANSFORD
☐ 239. WALT WEISS
☐ 252. TERRY STEINBACH
☐ 293. MIKE MOORE
☐ 326. RON HASSEY
☐ 345. WILLIE RANDOLPH
☐ 372. RICK HONEYCUTT
☐ 385. FELIX JOSE
☐ 424. CURT YOUNG
☐ 458. TODD BURNS
☐ 477. GENE NELSON
☐ 503. JOE KLINK
☐ 516. OZZIE CANSECO

PHILADELPHIA PHILLIES

☐ 20. ROGER MCDOWELL
☐ 52. VON HAYES
☐ 78. PAT COMBS
☐ 105. DICKIE THON
☐ 131. CHARLIE HAYES
☐ 151. BRUCE RUFFIN
☐ 184. TOM HERR
☐ 210. JEFF PARRETT
☐ 236. RICKY JORDAN
☐ 262. LEN DYKSTRA
☐ 284. JOHN KRUK
☐ 316. KEN HOWELL
☐ 342. DENNIS COOK
☐ 369. DARREN DAULTON
☐ 395. STEVE LAKE
☐ 415. JOSE DEJESUS
☐ 448. CARMELO MARTINEZ
☐ 474. TERRY MULHOLLAND
☐ 500. RANDY READY
☐ 526. DARREL AKERFELDS

PITTSBURGH PIRATES

☐ 32. MIKE LAVALLIERE
☐ 64. BOB WALK
☐ 77. JOSE LIND
☐ 91. BARRY BONDS
☐ 117. ANDY VAN SLYKE
☐ 163. JEFF KING
☐ 196. BOBBY BONILLA
☐ 209. GARY REDUS
☐ 222. BILL LANDRUM
☐ 248. JAY BELL
☐ 296. DOUG DRABEK
☐ 328. JOHN SMILEY
☐ 341. WALLY BACKMAN
☐ 354. DON SLAUGHT
☐ 381. R.J. REYNOLDS
☐ 427. RICK REED
☐ 460. NEAL HEATON
☐ 473. TED POWER
☐ 486. STAN BELINDA
☐ 512. SCOTT RUSKIN

ST. LOUIS CARDINALS

- ☐ 11. JOE MAGRANE
- ☐ 44. PEDRO GUERRERO
- ☐ 90. VINCE COLEMAN
- ☐ 103. FRANK DIPINO
- ☐ 129. JOSE OQUENDO
- ☐ 142. OZZIE SMITH
- ☐ 176. JOHN TUDOR
- ☐ 221. TODD ZEILE
- ☐ 234. SCOTT TERRY
- ☐ 260. TERRY PENDLETON
- ☐ 275. KEN DAYLEY
- ☐ 308. MILT THOMPSON
- ☐ 353. BERNARD GILKEY
- ☐ 367. WILLIE MCGEE
- ☐ 393. BRYN SMITH
- ☐ 406. BOB TEWKSBURY
- ☐ 439. REX HUDLER
- ☐ 485. JOSE DELEON
- ☐ 498. TOM PAGNOZZI
- ☐ 524. LEE SMITH

SAN DIEGO PADRES

- ☐ 23. BRUCE HURST
- ☐ 56. ANDY BENES
- ☐ 75. ROBERTO ALOMAR
- ☐ 102. GARRY TEMPLETON
- ☐ 115. ERIC SHOW
- ☐ 154. TONY GWYNN
- ☐ 188. FRED LYNN
- ☐ 207. BENITO SANTIAGO
- ☐ 233. BIP ROBERTS
- ☐ 246. ED WHITSON
- ☐ 287. JACK CLARK
- ☐ 320. MIKE PAGLIARULO
- ☐ 339. CRAIG LEFFERTS
- ☐ 366. JOEY CORA
- ☐ 379. JOE CARTER
- ☐ 418. MIKE DUNNE
- ☐ 452. GREG HARRIS
- ☐ 471. DENNIS RASMUSSEN
- ☐ 497. MARK PARENT
- ☐ 510. JERALD CLARK

SAN FRANCISCO GIANTS

- ☐ 3. STEVE BEDROSIAN
- ☐ 41. SCOTT GARRELTS
- ☐ 67. TERRY KENNEDY
- ☐ 94. MATT WILLIAMS
- ☐ 120. KEVIN MITCHELL
- ☐ 134. GARY CARTER
- ☐ 172. WILL CLARK
- ☐ 199. ROBBY THOMPSON
- ☐ 225. JOSE URIBE
- ☐ 251. BRETT BUTLER
- ☐ 267. DON ROBINSON
- ☐ 305. KEVIN BASS
- ☐ 331. GREG LITTON
- ☐ 357. JEFF BRANTLEY
- ☐ 384. JOHN BURKETT
- ☐ 398. RICK PARKER
- ☐ 436. RICK LEACH
- ☐ 463. MIKE LACOSS
- ☐ 489. TREVOR WILSON
- ☐ 515. FRANCISCO OLIVERAS

SEATTLE MARINERS

- ☐ 9. PETE O'BRIEN
- ☐ 35. ALVIN DAVIS
- ☐ 88. OMAR VIZQUEL
- ☐ 114. JAY BUHNER
- ☐ 127. SCOTT BANKHEAD
- ☐ 140. HAROLD REYNOLDS
- ☐ 166. DAVE VALLE
- ☐ 219. JEFFREY LEONARD
- ☐ 245. KEN GRIFFEY, JR.
- ☐ 258. MIKE SCHOOLER
- ☐ 273. BRIAN HOLMAN
- ☐ 299. EDGAR MARTINEZ
- ☐ 351. MIKE JACKSON
- ☐ 378. GENE HARRIS
- ☐ 391. GREG BRILEY
- ☐ 404. SCOTT BRADLEY
- ☐ 430. ERIK HANSON
- ☐ 483. RANDY JOHNSON
- ☐ 509. MATT YOUNG
- ☐ 522. KEITH COMSTOCK

RAFAEL PALMEIRO 1B

TEXAS RANGERS

- ☐ 21. NOLAN RYAN
- ☐ 47. KEVIN BROWN
- ☐ 73. GENO PETRALLI
- ☐ 100. RAFAEL PALMEIRO
- ☐ 126. HAROLD BAINES
- ☐ 152. JEFF RUSSELL
- ☐ 179. STEVE BUCHELE
- ☐ 205. JULIO FRANCO
- ☐ 231. PETE INCAVIGLIA
- ☐ 257. RUBEN SIERRA
- ☐ 285. JEFF HUSON
- ☐ 311. KENNY ROGERS
- ☐ 337. BOBBY WITT
- ☐ 363. SCOTT COOLBAUGH
- ☐ 390. CHARLIE HOUGH
- ☐ 416. MIKE JEFFCOAT
- ☐ 442. JEFF RUSSELL
- ☐ 469. GARY PETTIS
- ☐ 495. BRAD ARNSBERG
- ☐ 521. JACK DAUGHERTY

TORONTO BLUE JAYS

- ☐ 27. JOHN CERUTTI
- ☐ 53. TONY FERNANDEZ
- ☐ 79. DAVE STEIB
- ☐ 106. KELLY GRUBER
- ☐ 132. FRED MCGRIFF
- ☐ 158. TOM HENKE
- ☐ 185. GEORGE BELL
- ☐ 211. JIMMY KEY
- ☐ 237. JOHN OLERUD
- ☐ 263. MOOKIE WILSON
- ☐ 291. LUIS SOJO
- ☐ 317. GLENALLEN HILL
- ☐ 343. PAT BORDERS
- ☐ 370. MANNY LEE
- ☐ 396. MARK WHITEN
- ☐ 422. JUNIOR FELIX
- ☐ 449. WILLIE BLAIR
- ☐ 475. TODD STOTTLEMYRE
- ☐ 501. DUANE WARD
- ☐ 527. GREG MYERS

1991 LEAF (528)
2 1/2" X 3 1/2"

STEVE LAKE C

ATLANTA BRAVES

- ☐ 13. LONNIE SMITH
- ☐ 27. JOHN SMOLTZ
- ☐ 41. KENT MERCKER
- ☐ 77. DAVE JUSTICE
- ☐ 115. JEFF BLAUSER
- ☐ 129. RON GANT
- ☐ 144. TOMMY GREGG
- ☐ 158. GREG OLSON
- ☐ 172. TOM GLAVINE
- ☐ 209. CHARLIE LEIBRANDT
- ☐ 246. JEFF TREADWAY
- ☐ 260. PAUL MARAK
- ☐ 304. TERRY PENDLETON
- ☐ 320. MIKE HEATH
- ☐ 379. SID BREAM
- ☐ 395. OTIS NIXON
- ☐ 436. DEION SANDERS
- ☐ 453. RAFAEL BELLIARD
- ☐ 491. MIKE STANTON
- ☐ 510. STEVE AVERY
- ☐ 526. JUAN BERENGUER

BALTIMORE ORIOLES

- ☐ 7. BILLY RIPKEN
- ☐ 21. MARK WILLIAMSON
- ☐ 35. LEO GOMEZ
- ☐ 109. RANDY MILLIGAN
- ☐ 117. BEN MCDONALD
- ☐ 131. CHRIS HOILES
- ☐ 138. MIKE DEVEREAUX
- ☐ 152. JOE ORSULAK
- ☐ 166. JOSE MESA
- ☐ 240. BOB MELVIN
- ☐ 248. DAVE JOHNSON
- ☐ 262. JUAN BELL
- ☐ 266. DWIGHT EVANS
- ☐ 298. CRAIG WORTHINGTON
- ☐ 332. SAM HORN
- ☐ 391. ERNIE WHITT
- ☐ 398. GLENN DAVIS
- ☐ 430. CAL RIPKEN
- ☐ 464. JEFF ROBINSON
- ☐ 479. MIKE FLANAGAN
- ☐ 519. GREGG OLSON
- ☐ 522. JEFF BALLARD

BOSTON RED SOX

- ☐ 19. MIKE GREENWELL
- ☐ 33. TONY PENA
- ☐ 47. TOM BOLTON
- ☐ 69. JODY REED
- ☐ 83. GREG HARRIS
- ☐ 121. ELLIS BURKS
- ☐ 150. TIM NAEHRING
- ☐ 164. TOM BRUNANSKY
- ☐ 179. JOHN MARZANO
- ☐ 201. JACK CLARK
- ☐ 215. MATT YOUNG
- ☐ 252. JEFF REARDON
- ☐ 273. WADE BOGGS

- ☐ 276. TONY FOSSAS
- ☐ 341. DANA KIECKER
- ☐ 356. JEFF GRAY
- ☐ 405. DANNY DARWIN
- ☐ 408. LUIS RIVERA
- ☐ 473. CARLOS QUINTANA
- ☐ 488. ROGER CLEMENS

CALIFORNIA ANGELS

- ☐ 31. WALLY JOYNER
- ☐ 45. CHUCK FINLEY
- ☐ 59. DICK SCHOFIELD
- ☐ 67. MARK LANGSTON
- ☐ 81. LUIS POLONIA
- ☐ 162. JIM ABBOTT
- ☐ 177. DONNIE HILL
- ☐ 191. JOHN ORTON
- ☐ 199. KIRK MCCASKILL
- ☐ 213. BRYAN HARVEY
- ☐ 303. GARY GAETTI
- ☐ 307. JEFF ROBINSON
- ☐ 334. DAVE PARKER
- ☐ 367. LUIS SOJO
- ☐ 368. LANCE PARRISH
- ☐ 435. JUNIOR FELIX
- ☐ 439. FLOYD BANNISTER
- ☐ 499. DAVE WINFIELD

CHICAGO CUBS

- ☐ 25. SHAWON DUNSTON
- ☐ 39. JEROME WALTON
- ☐ 53. PAUL ASSENMACHER
- ☐ 75. HECTOR VILLANUEVA
- ☐ 90. MIKE HARKEY
- ☐ 127. GREG MADDUX
- ☐ 156. DAMON BERRYHILL
- ☐ 170. MARK GRACE
- ☐ 185. LUIS SALAZAR
- ☐ 207. RYNE SANDBERG
- ☐ 221. SHAWN BOSKIE
- ☐ 258. JOE GIRARDI
- ☐ 268. DANNY JACKSON
- ☐ 323. JOSE VIZCAINO
- ☐ 370. HEATH SLOCUMB
- ☐ 389. GEORGE BELL
- ☐ 400. ANDRE DAWSON
- ☐ 483. DOUG DASCENZO
- ☐ 501. CHICO WALKER
- ☐ 520. BOB SCANLAN

CHICAGO WHITE SOX

- ☐ 271. ROBIN VENTURA
- ☐ 281. FRANK THOMAS
- ☐ 296. ALEX FERNANDEZ
- ☐ 306. SCOTT FLETCHER
- ☐ 321. SAMMY SOSA
- ☐ 331. OZZIE GUILLEN
- ☐ 336. BOBBY THIGPEN
- ☐ 340. JACK MCDOWELL
- ☐ 375. JOEY CORA
- ☐ 384. CARLTON FISK
- ☐ 403. LANCE JOHNSON
- ☐ 413. TIM RAINES
- ☐ 428. DAN PASQUA
- ☐ 438. GREG HIBBARD
- ☐ 454. WAYNE EDWARDS
- ☐ 463. SCOTT RADINSKY
- ☐ 468. DONN PALL
- ☐ 472. CHARLIE HOUGH
- ☐ 506. CORY SNYDER
- ☐ 515. RON KARKOVICE

CINCINNATI REDS

- ☐ 37. ERIC DAVIS
- ☐ 51. HAL MORRIS
- ☐ 65. CHRIS SABO
- ☐ 73. JOE OLIVER
- ☐ 88. TOM BROWNING
- ☐ 102. JEFF REED
- ☐ 168. BARRY LARKIN
- ☐ 183. SCOTT SCUDDER
- ☐ 197. BILL DORAN
- ☐ 205. BILLY HATCHER
- ☐ 219. PAUL O'NEILL
- ☐ 233. LUIS QUINONES
- ☐ 282. ROB DIBBLE
- ☐ 326. JOSE RIJO
- ☐ 362. GLENN BRAGGS
- ☐ 373. CHRIS HAMMOND
- ☐ 414. NORM CHARLTON
- ☐ 459. JACK ARMSTRONG
- ☐ 494. MARIANO DUNCAN
- ☐ 504. RANDY MYERS
- ☐ 514. REGGIE JEFFERSON

CLEVELAND INDIANS

- ☐ 6. GREG SWINDELL
- ☐ 43. JERRY BROWNE
- ☐ 57. DOUG JONES
- ☐ 79. TOM CANDIOTTI
- ☐ 94. STEVE OLIN
- ☐ 108. ALEX COLE
- ☐ 137. FELIX FERMIN
- ☐ 175. CHRIS JAMES
- ☐ 189. SANDY ALOMAR
- ☐ 211. JOEL SKINNER
- ☐ 225. CARLOS BAERGA
- ☐ 239. ALBERT BELLE
- ☐ 289. MARK LEWIS
- ☐ 316. BEAU ALLRED
- ☐ 382. ERIC KING
- ☐ 421. BROOK JACOBY
- ☐ 449. TURNER WARD
- ☐ 513. SHAWN HILLEGAS

DETROIT TIGERS

- ☐ 4. TONY PHILLIPS
- ☐ 18. MIKE HENNEMAN
- ☐ 55. PAUL GIBSON
- ☐ 92. DAVE BERGMAN
- ☐ 106. CECIL FIELDER
- ☐ 120. LOU WHITAKER
- ☐ 135. JERRY DON GLEATON
- ☐ 149. TRAVIS FRYMAN
- ☐ 187. STEVE SEARCY
- ☐ 223. LLOYD MOSEBY
- ☐ 237. ROB DEER
- ☐ 251. MILT CUYLER
- ☐ 270. JOHN CERUTTI
- ☐ 322. MICKEY TETTLETON
- ☐ 351. ALAN TRAMMELL
- ☐ 366. PETE INCAVIGLIA
- ☐ 402. BILL GULLICKSON
- ☐ 455. ANDY ALLANSON
- ☐ 497. FRANK TANANA

HOUSTON ASTROS

- ☐ 12. CRAIG BIGGIO
- ☐ 49. JIM DESHAIES
- ☐ 63. MARK PORTUGAL
- ☐ 86. MARK MCLEMORE
- ☐ 100. ERIC YELDING
- ☐ 114. CASEY CANDAELE
- ☐ 143. MARK DAVIDSON
- ☐ 181. ERIC ANTHONY
- ☐ 195. KARL RHODES
- ☐ 217. CARL NICHOLS
- ☐ 231. STEVE FINLEY
- ☐ 245. PETE HARNISCH
- ☐ 292. CURT SCHILLING
- ☐ 329. DWAYNE HENRY
- ☐ 371. JIMMY JONES
- ☐ 424. DAVE ROHDE
- ☐ 456. DAVE SMITH
- ☐ 462. XAVIER HERNANDEZ
- ☐ 492. AL OSUNA
- ☐ 502. KEN CAMINITI

KANSAS CITY ROYALS

- ☐ 2. KURT STILLWELL
- ☐ 16. MARK DAVIS
- ☐ 30. MIKE MACFARLANE
- ☐ 104. TERRY SHUMPERT
- ☐ 118. BRET SABERHAGEN
- ☐ 132. TOM GORDON
- ☐ 133. KEVIN SEITZER
- ☐ 147. DANNY TARTABULL
- ☐ 161. STORM DAVIS
- ☐ 235. BRIAN MCRAE
- ☐ 249. KIRK GIBSON
- ☐ 263. RUSS MORMAN
- ☐ 325. DAVE HOWARD
- ☐ 330. MIKE BODDICKER
- ☐ 335. GEORGE BRETT
- ☐ 458. WARREN CROMARTIE
- ☐ 467. CARMELO MARTINEZ

LOS ANGELES DODGERS

- ☐ 10. JUAN SAMUEL
- ☐ 24. MIKE SCOSCIA
- ☐ 61. RAMON MARTINEZ
- ☐ 98. JAY HOWELL
- ☐ 112. KAL DANIELS
- ☐ 126. EDDIE MURRAY
- ☐ 141. TIM CREWS
- ☐ 155. STAN JAVIER
- ☐ 193. MIKE MORGAN
- ☐ 229. JIM GOTT
- ☐ 243. OREL HERSHISER
- ☐ 257. DENNIS COOK
- ☐ 279. KEVIN GROSS
- ☐ 324. JOHN CANDELARIA
- ☐ 344. ALFREDO GRIFFIN
- ☐ 377. DARRYL STRAWBERRY
- ☐ 411. BRETT BUTLER
- ☐ 457. GARY CARTER
- ☐ 476. BOBBY OJEDA
- ☐ 508. TIM BELCHER
- ☐ 509. JEFF HAMILTON

MILWAUKEE BREWERS

- ☐ 14. RON ROBINSON
- ☐ 28. CHUCK CRIM
- ☐ 42. B.J. SURHOFF
- ☐ 111. BILL SPIERS
- ☐ 116. ROBIN YOUNT
- ☐ 145. JIM GANTNER
- ☐ 159. MARK KNUDSON
- ☐ 173. GARY SHEFFIELD
- ☐ 242. DANTE BICHETTE
- ☐ 247. JULIO MACHADO
- ☐ 277. FRANKLIN STUBBS
- ☐ 287. DAN PLESAC
- ☐ 302. PAUL MOLITOR
- ☐ 343. MARK LEE
- ☐ 352. EDWIN NUNEZ
- ☐ 387. DARREN HOLMES
- ☐ 409. JAMIE NAVARRO
- ☐ 419. WILLIE RANDOLPH
- ☐ 434. CANDY MALDONADO
- ☐ 475. KEVIN BROWN
- ☐ 484. RICK DEMPSEY
- ☐ 518. CHRIS BOSIO

MINNESOTA TWINS

- ☐ 26. RANDY BUSH
- ☐ 40. SHANE MACK
- ☐ 54. BRIAN HARPER
- ☐ 76. DAN GLADDEN
- ☐ 128. KEVIN TAPANI
- ☐ 157. GENE LARKIN
- ☐ 171. MARK GUTHRIE
- ☐ 186. PEDRO MUNOZ
- ☐ 208. KIRBY PUCKETT
- ☐ 259. ALLAN ANDERSON
- ☐ 294. JACK MORRIS
- ☐ 313. KENT HRBEK
- ☐ 339. MIKE PAGLIARULO
- ☐ 374. CHILI DAVIS
- ☐ 396. CHUCK KNOBLAUCH
- ☐ 426. GREG GAGNE
- ☐ 446. AL NEWMAN
- ☐ 466. DENNY NEAGLE
- ☐ 471. RICK AGUILERA
- ☐ 481. LARRY CASIAN
- ☐ 498. JUNIOR ORTIZ
- ☐ 505. STEVE BEDROSIAN
- ☐ 527. SCOTT ERICKSON

MONTREAL EXPOS

- ☐ 8. DAVE MARTINEZ
- ☐ 22. MARQUIS GRISSOM
- ☐ 36. SPIKE OWEN
- ☐ 110. ANDRES GALARRAGA
- ☐ 124. TIM BURKE
- ☐ 139. DELINO DESHIELDS
- ☐ 153. STEVE FREY
- ☐ 167. DENNIS BOYD

- ☐ 241. LARRY WALKER
- ☐ 255. JUNIOR NOBOA
- ☐ 274. DENNIS MARTINEZ
- ☐ 284. RICK MAHLER
- ☐ 318. BILL SAMPEN
- ☐ 338. IVAN CALDERON
- ☐ 359. RON HASSEY
- ☐ 388. TIM WALLACH
- ☐ 406. BARRY JONES
- ☐ 416. CHRIS NABHOLZ
- ☐ 451. GILBERTO REYES
- ☐ 470. ERIC BULLOCK

NEW YORK METS

- ☐ 20. DAVE MAGADAN
- ☐ 34. HOWARD JOHNSON
- ☐ 48. TOM HERR
- ☐ 70. ALEJANDRO PENA
- ☐ 122. CHARLIE O'BRIEN
- ☐ 151. KEVIN MCREYNOLDS
- ☐ 165. DWIGHT GOODEN
- ☐ 180. FRANK VIOLA
- ☐ 202. DARYL BOSTON
- ☐ 253. DAVID CONE
- ☐ 295. HUBIE BROOKS
- ☐ 305. KEVIN ELSTER
- ☐ 314. TIM TEUFEL
- ☐ 333. WALLY WHITEHURST
- ☐ 361. MACKEY SASSER
- ☐ 378. RON DARLING
- ☐ 427. VINCE COLEMAN
- ☐ 437. JOHN FRANCO
- ☐ 447. CHRIS DONNELS
- ☐ 465. GREGG JEFFERIES
- ☐ 493. RICK CERONE

NEW YORK YANKEES

- ☐ 38. ROBERTO KELLY
- ☐ 52. LEE GUETTERMAN
- ☐ 66. CHUCK CARY
- ☐ 74. MIKE WITT
- ☐ 89. MATT NOKES
- ☐ 169. SCOTT SANDERSON
- ☐ 184. DAVE EILAND
- ☐ 198. ALVARO ESPINOZA
- ☐ 206. TIM LEARY
- ☐ 220. STEVE SAX
- ☐ 283. MEL HALL
- ☐ 293. PASCUAL PEREZ
- ☐ 308. JESSE BARFIELD
- ☐ 348. STEVE FARR
- ☐ 349. HENSLEY MEULENS
- ☐ 393. KEVIN MAAS
- ☐ 415. GREG CADARET
- ☐ 425. DON MATTINGLY
- ☐ 440. STEVE HOWE
- ☐ 480. JOHN HABYAN

OAKLAND A'S

- ☐ 50. WALT WEISS
- ☐ 64. BOB WELCH
- ☐ 78. MIKE GALLEGO
- ☐ 87. TERRY STEINBACH
- ☐ 101. RICKEY HENDERSON
- ☐ 182. JOSE CANSECO
- ☐ 196. HAROLD BAINES
- ☐ 210. RICK HONEYCUTT
- ☐ 218. MIKE MOORE
- ☐ 232. DAVE HENDERSON
- ☐ 285. DENNIS ECKERSLEY
- ☐ 299. WILLIE WILSON
- ☐ 328. GENE NELSON
- ☐ 354. ERIC SHOW
- ☐ 355. VANCE LAW
- ☐ 358. ERNEST RILES
- ☐ 417. DAVE STEWART
- ☐ 431. JAMIE QUIRK
- ☐ 461. JOE KLINK
- ☐ 486. STEVE CHITREN
- ☐ 487. MARK MCGWIRE

PHILADELPHIA PHILLIES

- ☐ 32. PAT COMBS
- ☐ 46. TERRY MULHOLLAND
- ☐ 60. DICKIE THON
- ☐ 68. JOE BOEVER
- ☐ 82. RANDY READY
- ☐ 163. LEN DYKSTRA
- ☐ 178. WES CHAMBERLAIN
- ☐ 192. DARREN DAULTON
- ☐ 200. JOSE DEJESUS
- ☐ 214. CHARLIE HAYES
- ☐ 278. JOHN KRUK
- ☐ 280. VON HAYES
- ☐ 288. JASON GRIMSLEY
- ☐ 350. DANNY COX
- ☐ 383. MICKEY MORANDINI
- ☐ 385. STEVE LAKE
- ☐ 410. ROGER MCDOWELL
- ☐ 412. DALE MURPHY
- ☐ 420. MITCH WILLIAMS
- ☐ 482. WALLY BACKMAN
- ☐ 496. JOHN MORRIS
- ☐ 524. TOMMY GREENE

PITTSBURGH PIRATES

- ☐ 15. MIKE LAVALLIERE
- ☐ 29. DON SLAUGHT
- ☐ 71. JEFF KING
- ☐ 123. JOHN SMILEY
- ☐ 130. JAY BELL
- ☐ 146. JOSE LIND
- ☐ 160. CARMELO MARTINEZ
- ☐ 203. RANDY TOMLIN
- ☐ 254. GARY REDUS
- ☐ 261. BARRY BONDS
- ☐ 310. ANDY VAN SLYKE
- ☐ 317. CURTIS WILKERSON
- ☐ 357. BOBBY BONILLA
- ☐ 442. VINCENTE PALACIOS
- ☐ 450. BOB WALK
- ☐ 489. ORLANDO MERCED
- ☐ 495. ZANE SMITH
- ☐ 500. GARY VARSHO
- ☐ 516. DOUG DRABEK

ST. LOUIS CARDINALS

- ☐ 44. LEE SMITH
- ☐ 58. JOSE OQUENDO
- ☐ 72. TOM PAGNOZZI
- ☐ 80. OZZIE SMITH
- ☐ 95. CRAIG WILSON
- ☐ 176. MILT THOMPSON
- ☐ 190. JOSE DELEON
- ☐ 204. PEDRO GUERRERO
- ☐ 212. REX HUDDLER
- ☐ 226. BRYN SMITH
- ☐ 272. GERALD PERRY
- ☐ 286. BERNARD GILKEY
- ☐ 327. TODD ZEILE
- ☐ 376. KEN HILL
- ☐ 392. FELIX JOSE
- ☐ 404. JUAN AGOSTO
- ☐ 418. RICH GEDMAN
- ☐ 460. BOB TEWKSBURY
- ☐ 507. CRIS CARPENTER
- ☐ 523. RAY LANKFORD

SAN DIEGO PADRES

- ☐ 265. JERALD CLARK
- ☐ 275. ANDY BENES
- ☐ 290. TONY GWYNN
- ☐ 300. MIKE MADDUX
- ☐ 315. TONY FERNANDEZ
- ☐ 337. ED WHITSON
- ☐ 342. FRED MCGRIFF
- ☐ 346. DARRIN JACKSON
- ☐ 381. SHAWN ABNER
- ☐ 390. CRAIG LEFFERTS
- ☐ 397. SCOTT COOLBAUGH
- ☐ 407. LARRY ANDERSEN
- ☐ 422. GREG HARRIS
- ☐ 432. BENITO SANTIAGO
- ☐ 448. RICH RODRIGUEZ
- ☐ 469. BRUCE HURST
- ☐ 474. MARTY BARRETT
- ☐ 478. BIP ROBERTS
- ☐ 512. TOM LAMPKIN

SAN FRANCISCO GIANTS

- ☐ 5. SCOTT GARRELTS
- ☐ 56. JOHN BURKETT
- ☐ 85. KEVIN MITCHELL
- ☐ 93. MATT WILLIAMS
- ☐ 107. ROBBY THOMPSON
- ☐ 136. JEFF BRANTLEY
- ☐ 188. DON ROBINSON
- ☐ 216. TERRY KENNEDY
- ☐ 224. MIKE KINGERY
- ☐ 238. WILL CLARK
- ☐ 301. DAVE RIGHETTI
- ☐ 309. MIKE LACOSS
- ☐ 312. BUD BLACK
- ☐ 360. WILLIE MCGEE
- ☐ 365. KEVIN BASS
- ☐ 369. MARK LEONARD
- ☐ 433. JOSE URIBE
- ☐ 441. STEVE DECKER
- ☐ 445. MIKE FELDER

SEATTLE MARINERS

- ☐ 11. BRIAN HOLMAN
- ☐ 62. JAY BUHNER
- ☐ 91. OMAR VIZQUEL
- ☐ 99. SCOTT BRADLEY
- ☐ 113. HENRY COTTO
- ☐ 142. ERIK HANSON
- ☐ 194. GREG BRILEY
- ☐ 222. RICH DELUCIA
- ☐ 230. MIKE SCHOOLER
- ☐ 244. PETE O'BRIEN
- ☐ 297. HAROLD REYNOLDS
- ☐ 319. RANDY JOHNSON
- ☐ 345. SCOTT BANKHEAD
- ☐ 372. KEN GRIFFEY, JR.
- ☐ 380. BILL SWIFT
- ☐ 429. ALVIN DAVIS
- ☐ 452. MIKE JACKSON
- ☐ 477. EDGAR MARTINEZ
- ☐ 503. KEN GRIFFEY, SR.
- ☐ 511. DAVE VALLE
- ☐ 521. ALONZO POWELL

TEXAS RANGERS

- ☐ 3. BOBBY WITT
- ☐ 17. JACK DAUGHERTY
- ☐ 97. RUBEN SIERRA
- ☐ 105. KENNY ROGERS
- ☐ 119. JUAN GONZALEZ
- ☐ 134. JEFF HUSON
- ☐ 148. GENO PETRALLI
- ☐ 228. JULIO FRANCO
- ☐ 236. RICH GOSSAGE
- ☐ 250. KEVIN BROWN
- ☐ 269. BRIAN DOWNING
- ☐ 291. JEFF RUSSELL
- ☐ 347. RAFAEL PALMEIRO
- ☐ 363. MARIO DIAZ
- ☐ 386. MIKE JEFFCOAT
- ☐ 401. SCOTT CHIAMPARINO
- ☐ 423. NOLAN RYAN

TORONTO BLUE JAYS

- ☐ 9. KELLY GRUBER
- ☐ 23. PAT BORDERS
- ☐ 96. DAVE STEIB
- ☐ 103. JIMMY KEY
- ☐ 125. JOHN OLERUD

- ☐ 140. DAVID WELLS
- ☐ 154. DUANE WARD
- ☐ 227. TODD STOTTLEMYRE
- ☐ 234. MARK WHITEN
- ☐ 256. GREG MYERS
- ☐ 267. ROBERTO ALOMAR
- ☐ 311. GLENALLEN HILL
- ☐ 353. JOE CARTER
- ☐ 394. DEVON WHITE
- ☐ 399. MANNY LEE
- ☐ 443. PAT TABLER
- ☐ 485. ED SPRAGUE
- ☐ 490. RENE GONZALES
- ☐ 517. TOM HENKE
- ☐ 525. MIKE TIMLIN

1992 LEAF (528)
2 1/2" X 3 1/2"

ATLANTA BRAVES

- ☐ 15. RON GANT
- ☐ 59. STEVE AVERY
- ☐ 94. MARK LEMKE
- ☐ 110. MARVIN FREEMAN
- ☐ 113. CHARLIE LEIBRANDT
- ☐ 147. JEFF BLAUSER
- ☐ 191. JOHN SMOLTZ
- ☐ 226. GREG OLSON
- ☐ 242. SID BREAM
- ☐ 245. TERRY PENDLETON
- ☐ 279. TOM GLAVINE
- ☐ 310. RAFAEL BELLIARD
- ☐ 358. OTIS NIXON
- ☐ 374. BRIAN HUNTER
- ☐ 377. MIKE STANTON
- ☐ 404. DAVID JUSTICE
- ☐ 423. DAMON BERRYHILL
- ☐ 448. DEION SANDERS
- ☐ 480. LONNIE SMITH
- ☐ 489. ALEJANDRO PENA
- ☐ 505. MIKE BIELECKI

BALTIMORE ORIOLES

- ☐ 13. MIKE MUSSINA
- ☐ 36. JOE ORSULAK
- ☐ 52. CAL RIPKEN
- ☐ 79. MIKE DEVEREAUX
- ☐ 87. LEO GOMEZ
- ☐ 130. LUIS MERCEDES
- ☐ 145. BEN MCDONALD
- ☐ 184. BILLY RIPKEN
- ☐ 211. CHRIS HOILES
- ☐ 219. SAM HORN
- ☐ 262. BOB MILACKI
- ☐ 277. GREGG OLSON
- ☐ 300. CHITO MARTINEZ
- ☐ 316. GLENN DAVIS
- ☐ 343. BRADY ANDERSON
- ☐ 351. JOSE MESA
- ☐ 394. ARTHUR RHODES
- ☐ 411. JEFF TACKETT
- ☐ 427. MARK MCLEMORE
- ☐ 465. STORM DAVIS
- ☐ 508. RICK STUCLIFFE

BOSTON RED SOX

- ☐ 19. ROGER CLEMENS
- ☐ 22. JOE HESKETH
- ☐ 50. PHIL PLANTIER
- ☐ 89. MIKE GREENWELL
- ☐ 103. MO VAUGHN
- ☐ 151. JEFF REARDON
- ☐ 154. GREG HARRIS
- ☐ 182. SCOTT COOPER
- ☐ 221. FRANK VIOLA
- ☐ 235. TIM NAEHRING
- ☐ 286. WADE BOGGS
- ☐ 314. ELLIS BURKS
- ☐ 323. TONY PENA
- ☐ 355. LUIS RIVERA
- ☐ 366. JACK CLARK
- ☐ 413. JODY REED
- ☐ 439. JOHN FLAHERTY
- ☐ 482. MIKE GARDINER
- ☐ 515. PETER HOY

CALIFORNIA ANGELS

- ☐ 1. JIM ABBOTT
- ☐ 5. LUIS SOJO
- ☐ 45. LUIS POLONIA
- ☐ 48. GARY DISARCINA
- ☐ 97. MARK EICHHORN
- ☐ 107. GARY GAETTI
- ☐ 118. JUNIOR FELIX
- ☐ 137. JOE GRAHE
- ☐ 168. ALVIN DAVIS
- ☐ 177. VON HAYES
- ☐ 229. MARK LANGSTON
- ☐ 250. BOBBY ROSE
- ☐ 269. LANCE PARRISH
- ☐ 309. BRYAN HARVEY
- ☐ 312. CHUCK CRIM
- ☐ 361. LEE STEVENS
- ☐ 371. MIKE FITZGERALD
- ☐ 378. HUBIE BROOKS
- ☐ 418. STEVE FREY
- ☐ 450. CHUCK FINLEY
- ☐ 490. JULIO VALERA

CHICAGO CUBS

- ☐ 6. GARY SCOTT
- ☐ 26. MARK GRACE
- ☐ 30. DAVE SMITH
- ☐ 51. DOUG DASCENZO
- ☐ 72. JOE GIRARDI
- ☐ 117. PAUL ASSENMACHER
- ☐ 158. CHUCK MCELROY
- ☐ 162. SHAWN BOSKIE
- ☐ 183. ANDRE DAWSON
- ☐ 204. MIKE MORGAN
- ☐ 249. SHAWON DUNSTON
- ☐ 270. JOSE VIZCAINO
- ☐ 290. FRANK CASTILLO
- ☐ 294. GREG MADDUX
- ☐ 317. RYNE SANDBERG
- ☐ 336. RICK WILKINS
- ☐ 381. DANNY JACKSON
- ☐ 412. SAMMY SOSA
- ☐ 437. BOB SCANLAN
- ☐ 476. DOUG STRANGE
- ☐ 509. KEN PATTERSON

CHICAGO WHITE SOX

- ☐ 17. ROBIN VENTURA
- ☐ 37. TIM RAINES
- ☐ 39. CHARLIE HOUGH
- ☐ 78. WILSON ALVAREZ
- ☐ 85. ALEX FERNANDEZ
- ☐ 105. RON KARKOVICE
- ☐ 149. OZZIE GUILLEN
- ☐ 169. GREG HIBBARD
- ☐ 210. BOBBY THIGPEN
- ☐ 217. STEVE SAX
- ☐ 237. LANCE JOHNSON
- ☐ 281. SCOTT RADINSKY
- ☐ 303. CARLTON FISK
- ☐ 342. MICHAEL HUFF
- ☐ 344. CRAIG GREBECK
- ☐ 349. FRANK THOMAS
- ☐ 369. DAN PASQUA
- ☐ 422. JACK MCDOWELL
- ☐ 462. GEORGE BELL
- ☐ 486. TERRY LEACH
- ☐ 517. KIRK MCCASKILL

CINCINNATI REDS

- ☐ 7. JOE OLIVER
- ☐ 46. TOM BROWNING
- ☐ 69. ROB DIBBLE
- ☐ 73. BARRY LARKIN
- ☐ 99. PAUL O'NEILL
- ☐ 120. NORM CHARLTON
- ☐ 139. JOSE RIJO
- ☐ 178. CHRIS HAMMOND
- ☐ 205. HAL MORRIS
- ☐ 231. BILL DORAN
- ☐ 252. BIP ROBERTS
- ☐ 271. CHRIS SABO
- ☐ 360. REGGIE SANDERS
- ☐ 384. GREG SWINDELL
- ☐ 417. TIM BELCHER
- ☐ 433. DWAYNE HENRY
- ☐ 457. DAVE MARTINEZ
- ☐ 485. SCOTT BANKHEAD
- ☐ 499. JACOB BRUMFIELD
- ☐ 521. SCOTT RUSKIN
- ☐ 525. TROY AFENIR

CLEVELAND INDIANS

- ☐ 9. SANDY ALOMAR
- ☐ 49. MARK LEWIS
- ☐ 70. GLENALLEN HILL
- ☐ 84. THOMAS HOWARD
- ☐ 86. REGGIE JEFFERSON
- ☐ 115. CHARLES NAGY
- ☐ 141. STEVE OLIN
- ☐ 181. JOEL SKINNER
- ☐ 202. CARLOS BAERGA
- ☐ 218. DAVE OTTO
- ☐ 247. JACK ARMSTRONG
- ☐ 299. JIM THOME
- ☐ 307. ALEX COLE
- ☐ 334. MARK WHITEN

- ☐ 350. ALBERT BELLE
- ☐ 379. ERIC BELL
- ☐ 401. PAUL SORRENTO
- ☐ 429. SCOTT SCUDDER
- ☐ 451. DEREK LILLIQUIST
- ☐ 456. THOMAS HOWARD
- ☐ 503. DENNIS COOK

DETROIT TIGERS

- ☐ 21. FRANK TANANA
- ☐ 40. TONY PHILLIPS
- ☐ 61. BILL GULLICKSON
- ☐ 75. MILT CUYLER
- ☐ 127. SCOTT LIVINGSTONE
- ☐ 153. CECIL FIELDER
- ☐ 172. ALAN TRAMMELL
- ☐ 193. ROB DEER
- ☐ 207. MARK LEITER
- ☐ 239. DAN GLADDEN
- ☐ 259. MARK CARREON
- ☐ 285. MICKEY TETTLETON
- ☐ 304. TRAVIS FRYMAN
- ☐ 325. MIKE HENNEMAN
- ☐ 386. KEVIN RITZ
- ☐ 391. LOU WHITAKER
- ☐ 402. LES LANCASTER
- ☐ 496. CHAD KREUTER

HOUSTON ASTROS

- ☐ 8. CHRIS GARDNER
- ☐ 28. JEFF BAGWELL
- ☐ 66. STEVE FINLEY
- ☐ 77. PETE HARNISCH
- ☐ 121. SCOTT SERVAIS
- ☐ 140. KEN CAMINITI
- ☐ 160. LUIS GONZALEZ
- ☐ 198. DARRYL KILE
- ☐ 209. AL OSUNA
- ☐ 253. DOUG JONES
- ☐ 315. CRAIG BIGGIO
- ☐ 341. ANDUJAR CEDENO
- ☐ 385. RYAN BOWEN
- ☐ 428. JUAN GUERRERO
- ☐ 435. BUTCH HENRY
- ☐ 444. CHRIS JONES
- ☐ 458. PETE INCAVIGLIA
- ☐ 491. JOE BOEVER

KANSAS CITY ROYALS

- ☐ 4. DAVE HOWARD
- ☐ 31. KEVIN APPIER
- ☐ 68. TOM GORDON
- ☐ 83. MIKE MACFARLANE
- ☐ 123. BRIAN MCRAE
- ☐ 136. JEFF MONTGOMERY
- ☐ 163. MARK DAVIS
- ☐ 200. BRENT MAYNE
- ☐ 215. GREGG JEFFERIES
- ☐ 255. GEORGE BRETT
- ☐ 268. MIKE BODDICKER
- ☐ 295. JIM EISENREICH
- ☐ 332. MARK GUBICZA
- ☐ 347. TERRY SHUMPERT
- ☐ 387. CURTIS WILKERSON
- ☐ 438. WALLY JOYNER
- ☐ 459. KEITH MILLER
- ☐ 518. CHRIS GWYNN
- ☐ 522. KEVIN MCREYNOLDS

LOS ANGELES DODGERS

- ☐ 29. DARRYL STRAWBERRY
- ☐ 33. KEVIN GROSS
- ☐ 54. CARLOS HERNANDEZ
- ☐ 58. ROGER MCDOWELL
- ☐ 81. OREL HERSHISER
- ☐ 125. JUAN SAMUEL
- ☐ 161. STEVE WILSON
- ☐ 165. MIKE SCIOSCIA
- ☐ 186. BRETT BUTLER
- ☐ 213. LENNY HARRIS
- ☐ 257. TODD BENZINGER
- ☐ 293. ERIC KARROS
- ☐ 297. RAMON MARTINEZ
- ☐ 318. MIKE SHARPERSON
- ☐ 322. JOSE OFFERMAN

- ☐ 345. BOBBY OJEDA
- ☐ 389. DAVE HANSEN
- ☐ 409. TOM CANDIOTTI
- ☐ 430. ERIC DAVIS

MILWAUKEE BREWERS

- ☐ 2. CAL ELDRED
- ☐ 12. DARRYL HAMILTON
- ☐ 64. ROBIN YOUNT
- ☐ 80. DOUG HENRY
- ☐ 106. BILL SPIERS
- ☐ 134. DANTE BICHETTE
- ☐ 144. JAIME NAVARRO
- ☐ 196. BILL WEGMAN
- ☐ 212. B.J. SURHOFF
- ☐ 234. SCOTT FLETCHER
- ☐ 238. PAUL MOLITOR
- ☐ 266. CHRIS BOSIO
- ☐ 276. GREG VAUGHN
- ☐ 328. FRANKLIN STUBBS
- ☐ 370. PAT LISTACH
- ☐ 399. KEVIN SEITZER
- ☐ 414. BRUCE RUFFIN
- ☐ 460. MIKE FETTERS
- ☐ 475. WILLIAM SUERO
- ☐ 500. RICKY BONES
- ☐ 510. ANDY ALLANSON
- ☐ 524. JESSE OROSCO

MINNESOTA TWINS

- ☐ 14. KEVIN TAPANI
- ☐ 34. RICK AGUILERA
- ☐ 53. PEDRO MUNOZ
- ☐ 82. SHANE MACK
- ☐ 98. KIRBY PUCKETT
- ☐ 131. BRIAN HARPER
- ☐ 146. GREG GAGNE
- ☐ 166. SCOTT ERICKSON
- ☐ 214. SCOTT LEIUS
- ☐ 230. CHUCK KNOBLAUCH
- ☐ 263. MARK GUTHRIE
- ☐ 346. MIKE PAGLIARULO
- ☐ 362. KENT HRBEK
- ☐ 395. CHILI DAVIS
- ☐ 415. GENE LARKIN
- ☐ 424. GARY WAYNE
- ☐ 452. CARL WILLIS
- ☐ 467. RANDY BUSH
- ☐ 477. BILL KRUEGER
- ☐ 498. DONNIE HILL
- ☐ 506. BOB KIPPER
- ☐ 526. JOHN SMILEY

MONTREAL EXPOS

- ☐ 138. DELINO DESHIELDS
- ☐ 190. DENNIS MARTINEZ
- ☐ 201. LARRY WALKER
- ☐ 264. DARRIN FLETCHER
- ☐ 273. MARQUIS GRISSOM
- ☐ 283. IVAN CALDERON
- ☐ 288. BRET BARBERIE
- ☐ 298. TIM WALLACH
- ☐ 327. CHRIS NABHOLZ
- ☐ 333. BILL LANDRUM
- ☐ 372. TOM FOLEY
- ☐ 416. JOHN VANDERWAL

- ☐ 426. MOISES ALOU
- ☐ 442. GARY CARTER
- ☐ 455. SPIKE OWEN
- ☐ 468. KEN HILL
- ☐ 478. JOHN WETTELAND
- ☐ 493. ARCHI CIANFROCCO
- ☐ 512. MARK GARDNER
- ☐ 523. RICK CERONE

NEW YORK METS

- ☐ 42. VINCE COLEMAN
- ☐ 44. TIM BURKE
- ☐ 92. DAVID CONE
- ☐ 108. MACKEY SASSER
- ☐ 112. DWIGHT GOODEN
- ☐ 132. HOWARD JOHNSON
- ☐ 174. JOHN FRANCO
- ☐ 176. PETE SCHOUREK
- ☐ 224. DAVE GALLAGHER
- ☐ 240. WILLIE RANDOLPH
- ☐ 244. BILL PECOTA
- ☐ 306. DAVE MAGADAN
- ☐ 308. BOBBY BONILLA
- ☐ 356. ANTHONY YOUNG
- ☐ 376. BRET SABERHAGEN
- ☐ 396. EDDIE MURRAY
- ☐ 403. JUNIOR NOBOA
- ☐ 419. DICK SCHOFIELD
- ☐ 461. PAUL GIBSON
- ☐ 519. SID FERNANDEZ

NEW YORK YANKEES

- ☐ 20. STEVE FARR
- ☐ 24. GREG CADARET
- ☐ 57. DON MATTINGLY
- ☐ 88. MEL HALL
- ☐ 102. MATT NOKES
- ☐ 104. PAT KELLY
- ☐ 152. SCOTT SANDERSON
- ☐ 156. ROBERTO KELLY
- ☐ 189. JOHN HABYAN
- ☐ 220. CHARLIE HAYES
- ☐ 236. MIKE GALLEGO
- ☐ 284. KEVIN MAAS
- ☐ 320. LEE GUETTERMAN
- ☐ 352. RICH MONTELEONE
- ☐ 365. DION JAMES
- ☐ 367. MIKE STANLEY
- ☐ 368. RANDY VELARDE
- ☐ 406. DANNY TARTABULL
- ☐ 470. ANDY STANKIEWICZ
- ☐ 479. MELIDO PEREZ

OAKLAND A'S

- ☐ 16. MARK MCGWIRE
- ☐ 32. STEVE CHITREN
- ☐ 100. DENNIS ECKERSLEY
- ☐ 116. RICKEY HENDERSON
- ☐ 126. HAROLD BAINES
- ☐ 148. CARNEY LANSFORD
- ☐ 164. MIKE MOORE
- ☐ 232. DAVE HENDERSON
- ☐ 246. RANDY READY
- ☐ 248. TODD VAN POPPEL
- ☐ 258. DAVE STEWART
- ☐ 267. JOSE CANSECO
- ☐ 364. MIKE BORDICK
- ☐ 380. WALT WEISS
- ☐ 390. BOB WELCH
- ☐ 410. LANCE BLANKENSHIP
- ☐ 431. JOE SLUSARSKI
- ☐ 447. RON DARLING
- ☐ 474. RICH GOSSAGE
- ☐ 487. VINCE HORSMAN
- ☐ 501. TERRY STEINBACH
- ☐ 520. JEFF PARRETT

PHILADELPHIA PHILLIES

- ☐ 278. DAVE HOLLINS
- ☐ 292. TOMMY GREENE
- ☐ 301. MITCH WILLIAMS
- ☐ 311. MARIANO DUNCAN
- ☐ 313. JOHN KRUK
- ☐ 330. MICKEY MORANDINI
- ☐ 335. DARREN DAULTON
- ☐ 339. RUBEN AMARO

☐ 405. ANDY ASHBY
☐ 421. KIM BATISTE
☐ 434. CLIFF BRANTLEY
☐ 443. WALLY RITCHIE
☐ 453. WES CHAMBERLAIN
☐ 464. TERRY MULHOLLAND
☐ 473. DALE SVEUM
☐ 484. BARRY JONES
☐ 495. KYLE ABBOTT
☐ 504. LENNY DYKSTRA
☐ 516. CURT SCHILLING
☐ 527. DALE MURPHY

PITTSBURGH PIRATES

☐ 11. DOUG DRABEK
☐ 43. ANDY VAN SLYKE
☐ 91. STEVE BUECHELE
☐ 96. ZANE SMITH
☐ 124. DON SLAUGHT
☐ 143. JAY BELL
☐ 175. JOSE LIND
☐ 223. GARY REDUS
☐ 228. MIKE LAVALLIERE
☐ 256. RANDY TOMLIN
☐ 275. BARRY BONDS
☐ 287. STAN BELINDA
☐ 353. BOB WALK
☐ 363. ORLANDO MERCED
☐ 388. GARY VARSHO
☐ 420. JEFF KING
☐ 454. ROGER MASON
☐ 492. PAUL MILLER

ST. LOUIS CARDINALS

☐ 18. PEDRO GUERRERO
☐ 25. REX HUDLER
☐ 63. FELIX JOSE
☐ 95. BOB TEWKSBURY
☐ 122. GERALD PERRY
☐ 150. MILT THOMPSON
☐ 157. BRYN SMITH
☐ 195. RAY LANKFORD
☐ 227. JOSE DELEON
☐ 254. LEE SMITH
☐ 282. OMAR OLIVARES
☐ 289. JOSE OQUENDO
☐ 337. BRIAN JORDAN
☐ 359. TOM PAGNOZZI
☐ 400. OZZIE SMITH
☐ 432. TODD ZEILE
☐ 436. TODD WORRELL
☐ 449. ANDRES GALARRAGA
☐ 469. RHEAL CORMIER
☐ 502. BERNARD GILKEY

SAN DIEGO PADRES

☐ 10. GREG HARRIS
☐ 55. JERALD CLARK
☐ 74. ANDY BENES
☐ 129. DARRIN JACKSON
☐ 142. KURT STILLWELL
☐ 187. TONY FERNANDEZ
☐ 206. TONY GWYNN
☐ 216. BRUCE HURST
☐ 261. TIM TEUFEL
☐ 274. FRED MCGRIFF
☐ 319. RICH RODRIGUEZ
☐ 321. BENITO SANTIAGO
☐ 338. KEVIN WARD
☐ 348. DANN BILARDELLO
☐ 393. MIKE MADDUX
☐ 408. CRAIG LEFFERTS
☐ 446. GARY SHEFFIELD
☐ 466. GARY PETTIS
☐ 488. DAVE EILAND
☐ 507. JOSE MELENDEZ

SAN FRANCISCO GIANTS

☐ 3. BUD BLACK
☐ 47. WILLIE MCGEE
☐ 56. JEFF BRANTLEY
☐ 76. KEVIN BASS
☐ 109. ROBBY THOMPSON
☐ 135. DAVE RIGHETTI
☐ 179. JOHN BURKETT
☐ 188. CORY SNYDER
☐ 208. KIRT MANWARING
☐ 241. WILL CLARK
☐ 272. ROYCE CLAYTON
☐ 280. BRYAN HICKERSON
☐ 340. TREVOR WILSON
☐ 373. MATT WILLIAMS
☐ 407. BILL SWIFT
☐ 441. DARREN LEWIS
☐ 471. DAVE BURBA
☐ 481. MIKE JACKSON
☐ 497. CHRIS JAMES
☐ 514. JIM MCNAMARA

SEATTLE MARINERS

☐ 23. ERIK HANSON
☐ 38. HAROLD REYNOLDS
☐ 65. GREG BRILEY
☐ 71. CALVIN JONES
☐ 128. JAY BUHNER
☐ 155. RICH DELUCIA
☐ 170. DAVID VALLE
☐ 185. KEVIN MITCHELL
☐ 197. EDGAR MARTINEZ
☐ 203. RUSS SWAN
☐ 260. PETE O'BRIEN
☐ 265. OMAR VIZQUEL
☐ 302. RANDY JOHNSON
☐ 329. TINO MARTINEZ
☐ 392. KEN GRIFFEY, JR.
☐ 398. DAVE COCHRANE
☐ 472. HENRY COTTO
☐ 494. DAVE FLEMING
☐ 513. JEFF SCHAEFER

TEXAS RANGERS

☐ 41. NOLAN RYAN
☐ 62. JUAN GONZALEZ
☐ 90. JEFF RUSSELL
☐ 93. KEVIN REIMER
☐ 119. JULIO FRANCO
☐ 173. KENNY ROGERS
☐ 180. DICKIE THON
☐ 194. IVAN RODRIGUEZ
☐ 222. JOSE GUZMAN
☐ 225. DEAN PALMER
☐ 251. JEFF HUSON
☐ 296. RAFAEL PALMEIRO
☐ 305. BOBBY WITT
☐ 326. KEVIN BROWN
☐ 354. MONTY FARISS
☐ 357. GENO PETRALLI
☐ 383. RUBEN SIERRA
☐ 440. BRIAN DOWNING
☐ 511. AL NEWMAN

TORONTO BLUE JAYS

☐ 27. KELLY GRUBER
☐ 35. JUAN GUZMAN
☐ 60. JOHN OLERUD
☐ 101. DUANE WARD
☐ 111. JIMMY KEY
☐ 114. DEVON WHITE
☐ 159. TOM HENKE
☐ 167. TODD STOTTLEMYRE
☐ 171. DAVE WINFIELD
☐ 192. GREG MYERS
☐ 233. ROBERTO ALOMAR
☐ 243. DEREK BELL
☐ 291. DAVE STIEB
☐ 324. PAT BORDERS
☐ 375. JOE CARTER
☐ 382. MANUEL LEE
☐ 425. JACK MORRIS
☐ 445. JEFF KENT
☐ 483. DAVID WELLS

1993 LEAF (550)
2 1/2" X 3 1/2"

ATLANTA BRAVES

☐ 11. MARVIN FREEMAN
☐ 50. DAVID JUSTICE
☐ 68. MARK LEMKE
☐ 86. JEFF BLAUSER
☐ 104. JOHN SMOLTZ
☐ 121. STEVE AVERY
☐ 178. SID BREAM
☐ 180. OTIS NIXON
☐ 196. DAMON BERRYHILL
☐ 214. PETE SMITH
☐ 222. DEION SANDERS
☐ 225. RON GANT
☐ 295. TOM GLAVINE
☐ 326. GREG MADDUX
☐ 357. GREG OLSON
☐ 387. TERRY PENDLETON
☐ 398. MIKE STANTON
☐ 452. TONY TARASCO
☐ 469. RYAN KLESKO
☐ 489. GREG MCMICHAEL
☐ 519. MARK WOHLERS
☐ 521. KENT MERCKER

BALTIMORE ORIOLES

☐ 1. BEN MCDONALD
☐ 23. GREGG OLSON
☐ 45. GLENN DAVIS
☐ 67. MIKE DEVEREAUX
☐ 89. RICK SUTCLIFFE
☐ 111. ALAN MILLS
☐ 133. CHRIS HOILES
☐ 155. LEO GOMEZ
☐ 177. BRADY ANDERSON
☐ 249. HAROLD BAINES
☐ 274. CHITO MARTINEZ
☐ 306. DAVID SEGUL
☐ 343. MIKE MUSSINA
☐ 370. HAROLD REYNOLDS
☐ 397. ARTHUR RHODES
☐ 431. CAL RIPKEN, JR.
☐ 446. SHERMAN OBANDO
☐ 472. FERNANDO VALENZUELA
☐ 492. DAMON BUFORD
☐ 512. MARK MCLEMORE
☐ 526. BRAD PENNINGTON

BOSTON RED SOX

☐ 21. FRANK VIOLA
☐ 43. TONY PENA
☐ 65. BOB ZUPCIC
☐ 87. JOHN VALENTIN
☐ 109. BILLY HATCHER
☐ 131. GREG HARRIS
☐ 153. MATT YOUNG
☐ 175. SCOTT COOPER
☐ 197. MIKE GREENWELL
☐ 242. IVAN CALDERON
☐ 279. ROGER CLEMENS
☐ 310. ANDRE DAWSON
☐ 344. SCOTT FLETCHER

- ☐ 371. JOSE MELENDEZ
- ☐ 432. MO VAUGHN
- ☐ 437. CARLOS QUINTANA
- ☐ 455. DANNY DARWIN
- ☐ 494. JEFF RUSSELL
- ☐ 518. AARON SELE
- ☐ 544. PAUL QUANTRILL

CALIFORNIA ANGELS

- ☐ 227. CHAD CURTIS
- ☐ 254. CHILI DAVIS
- ☐ 260. GARY DISARCINA
- ☐ 286. DAMION EASLEY
- ☐ 292. CHUCK FINLEY
- ☐ 318. GREG MYERS
- ☐ 324. MARK LANGSTON
- ☐ 345. RENE GONZALES
- ☐ 372. JOE GRAHE
- ☐ 385. JOHN ORTON
- ☐ 399. LUIS POLONIA
- ☐ 419. SCOTT SANDERSON
- ☐ 430. JULIO VALERA
- ☐ 445. TIM SALMON
- ☐ 476. TOREY LOVULLO
- ☐ 483. EDUARDO PEREZ
- ☐ 488. STEVE FREY
- ☐ 500. J.T. SNOW
- ☐ 532. KELLY GRUBER
- ☐ 549. RUSS SPRINGER

CHICAGO CUBS

- ☐ 13. BOB SCANLAN
- ☐ 31. JIM BULLINGER
- ☐ 70. SAMMY SOSA
- ☐ 88. REY SANCHEZ
- ☐ 106. STEVE BUECHELE
- ☐ 123. MIKE MORGAN
- ☐ 141. FRANK CASTILLO
- ☐ 198. MARK GRACE
- ☐ 200. DERRICK MAY
- ☐ 216. RICK WILKINS
- ☐ 224. RYNE SANDBERG
- ☐ 266. JOSE GUZMAN
- ☐ 298. GREG HIBBARD
- ☐ 329. CANDY MALDONADO
- ☐ 358. RANDY MYERS
- ☐ 388. DAN PLESAC
- ☐ 413. WILLIE WILSON
- ☐ 458. KEVIN ROBERSON
- ☐ 499. JOSE VIZCAINO
- ☐ 533. MIKE HARKEY
- ☐ 547. DWIGHT SMITH

CHICAGO WHITE SOX

- ☐ 20. DAN PASQUA
- ☐ 41. ALEX FERNANDEZ
- ☐ 63. RON KARKOVICE
- ☐ 85. OZZIE GUILLEN
- ☐ 107. STEVE SAX
- ☐ 151. KIRK MCCASKILL
- ☐ 173. BOBBY THIGPEN
- ☐ 195. FRANK THOMAS
- ☐ 217. GEORGE BELL
- ☐ 252. ELLIS BURKS
- ☐ 284. CARLTON FISK
- ☐ 316. BO JACKSON
- ☐ 346. ROBERTO HERNANDEZ
- ☐ 373. LANCE JOHNSON
- ☐ 400. JACK MCDOWELL
- ☐ 420. TIM RAINES
- ☐ 439. ROBIN VENTURA
- ☐ 461. JOEY CORA
- ☐ 496. WILSON ALVAREZ
- ☐ 510. MIKE LAVALLIERE
- ☐ 524. JASON BERE

CINCINNATI REDS

- ☐ 243. TIM BELCHER
- ☐ 257. HAL MORRIS
- ☐ 263. JOE OLIVER
- ☐ 280. ROB DIBBLE
- ☐ 289. ROBERTO KELLY
- ☐ 311. BARRY LARKIN
- ☐ 321. KEVIN MITCHELL
- ☐ 331. TIM PUGH
- ☐ 359. TOM BROWNING
- ☐ 389. JEFF REARDON
- ☐ 411. JOSE RIJO
- ☐ 414. BIP ROBERTS
- ☐ 418. CHRIS SABO
- ☐ 428. REGGIE SANDERS
- ☐ 433. JOHN SMILEY
- ☐ 456. WILLIE GREENE
- ☐ 481. JEFF BRANSON
- ☐ 513. RANDY MILLIGAN
- ☐ 529. TIM COSTO

CLEVELAND INDIANS

- ☐ 18. ALBERT BELLE
- ☐ 40. KENNY LOFTON
- ☐ 61. TED POWER
- ☐ 83. SANDY ALOMAR, JR.
- ☐ 105. PAUL SORRENTO
- ☐ 128. GLENALLEN HILL
- ☐ 171. CHARLES NAGY
- ☐ 193. DENNIS COOK
- ☐ 215. FELIX FERMIN
- ☐ 233. CARLOS BAERGA
- ☐ 270. MIKE BIELECKI
- ☐ 302. REGGIE JEFFERSON
- ☐ 347. CARLOS MARTINEZ
- ☐ 374. JOSE MESA
- ☐ 444. DEREL LILLIQUIST
- ☐ 480. JEFF TREADWAY
- ☐ 502. JEREMY HERNANDEZ
- ☐ 528. WAYNE KIRBY

COLORADO ROCKIES

- ☐ 244. FREDDIE BENAVIDES
- ☐ 258. DANTE BICHETTE
- ☐ 281. DARYL BOSTON
- ☐ 290. JERALD CLARK
- ☐ 312. ALEX COLE
- ☐ 322. ANDRES GALARRAGA
- ☐ 332. JOE GIRARDI
- ☐ 360. CHARLIE HAYES
- ☐ 383. DARREN HOLMES
- ☐ 390. DAVID NIED
- ☐ 409. BRYN SMITH
- ☐ 415. ERIC YOUNG
- ☐ 454. ARMANDO REYNOSO
- ☐ 495. VINNY CASTILLA
- ☐ 505. J. OWENS
- ☐ 527. CURT LESKANIC

DETROIT TIGERS

- ☐ 16. TRAVIS FRYMAN
- ☐ 38. MILT CUYLER
- ☐ 60. DAN GLADDEN
- ☐ 81. MIKE HENNEMAN
- ☐ 103. BILL GULLICKSON
- ☐ 126. TONY PHILLIPS
- ☐ 148. LOU WHITAKER
- ☐ 191. MIKE MUNOZ
- ☐ 213. MICKEY TETTLETON
- ☐ 246. ROB DEER
- ☐ 283. CECIL FIELDER
- ☐ 314. KIRK GIBSON
- ☐ 348. BILL KRUEGER
- ☐ 375. SCOTT LIVINGSTONE
- ☐ 401. MIKE MOORE
- ☐ 421. ALAN TRAMMELL
- ☐ 463. CHAD KREUTER
- ☐ 484. DAVID WELLS
- ☐ 534. JOHN DOHERTY

FLORIDA MARLINS

- ☐ 235. JACK ARMSTRONG
- ☐ 256. BRET BARBERIE
- ☐ 272. SCOTT POSE
- ☐ 288. JEFF CONINE
- ☐ 304. ORESTES DESTRADE
- ☐ 320. MONTY FARISS
- ☐ 333. JUNIOR FELIX
- ☐ 361. BRYAN HARVEY
- ☐ 384. CHARLIE HOUGH
- ☐ 391. DAVE MAGADAN
- ☐ 410. BENITO SANTIAGO
- ☐ 416. WALT WEISS
- ☐ 462. ALEX ARIAS
- ☐ 475. CHRIS HAMMOND
- ☐ 509. LUIS AQUINO
- ☐ 541. CHUCK CARR

HOUSTON ASTROS

- ☐ 15. CASEY CANDAELE
- ☐ 33. SCOTT SERVAIS
- ☐ 51. PETE HARNISCH
- ☐ 90. LUIS GONZALEZ
- ☐ 108. ANDUJAR CEDENO
- ☐ 125. JEFF BAGWELL
- ☐ 143. DARRYL KILE
- ☐ 161. DOUG JONES
- ☐ 218. ERIC ANTHONY
- ☐ 223. CRAIG BIGGIO
- ☐ 261. KEN CAMINITI
- ☐ 293. DOUG DRABEK
- ☐ 325. STEVE FINLEY
- ☐ 334. GREG SWINDELL
- ☐ 362. EDDIE TAUBENSEE
- ☐ 467. MARK PORTUGAL
- ☐ 485. BRIAN WILLIAMS
- ☐ 543. XAVIER HERNANDEZ

KANSAS CITY ROYALS

- ☐ 14. RUSTY MEACHAM
- ☐ 36. BRENT MAYNE
- ☐ 58. BRIAN MCRAE
- ☐ 80. KEVIN MCREYNOLDS
- ☐ 101. KEVIN APPIER
- ☐ 124. JEFF MONTGOMERY
- ☐ 146. GEORGE BRETT
- ☐ 168. KEITH MILLER
- ☐ 211. TOM GORDON
- ☐ 250. DAVID CONE
- ☐ 282. GREG GAGNE
- ☐ 313. MARK GARDNER
- ☐ 349. FELIX JOSE
- ☐ 376. WALLY JOYNER
- ☐ 402. JOSE LIND
- ☐ 422. MIKE MACFARLANE
- ☐ 453. CHRIS GWYNN
- ☐ 514. GARY GAETTI
- ☐ 538. CHRIS HANEY

LOS ANGELES DODGERS

- ☐ 17. JOSE OFFERMAN
- ☐ 35. MIKE PIAZZA
- ☐ 53. OREL HERSHISER
- ☐ 71. PEDRO ASTACIO
- ☐ 100. BILLY ASHLEY
- ☐ 127. LENNY HARRIS
- ☐ 145. STEVE WILSON
- ☐ 163. PEDRO MARTINEZ
- ☐ 181. KEVIN GROSS
- ☐ 210. DARRYL STRAWBERRY
- ☐ 230. BRETT BUTLER
- ☐ 234. ERIC KARROS
- ☐ 267. ERIC DAVIS
- ☐ 299. JODY REED
- ☐ 335. RAMON MARTINEZ
- ☐ 363. TIM WALLACH
- ☐ 429. TODD WORRELL
- ☐ 436. CORY SNYDER
- ☐ 442. CARLOS HERNANDEZ
- ☐ 473. RAUL MONDESI
- ☐ 487. TOM CANDIOTTI
- ☐ 511. JIM GOTT
- ☐ 537. ROGER MCDOWELL

MILWAUKEE BREWERS

- ☐ 12. JIM AUSTIN
- ☐ 34. CAL ELDRED
- ☐ 56. GREG VAUGHN
- ☐ 78. TIM MCINTOSH
- ☐ 122. RICKY BONES
- ☐ 144. BILL WEGMAN
- ☐ 166. B.J. SURHOFF
- ☐ 188. ROBIN YOUNT
- ☐ 199. DARRYL HAMILTON
- ☐ 226. TOM BRUNANSKY
- ☐ 264. PAT LISTACH
- ☐ 296. JAIME NAVARRO
- ☐ 327. DAVE NILSSON
- ☐ 350. JOHN JAHA
- ☐ 377. KEVIN REIMER
- ☐ 403. BILL SPIERS
- ☐ 459. GRAEME LLOYD

- ☐ 482. DICKIE THON
- ☐ 530. DOUG HENRY

MINNESOTA TWINS

- ☐ 32. RICK AGUILERA
- ☐ 54. PAT MAHOMES
- ☐ 76. KENT HRBEK
- ☐ 98. CHUCK KNOBLAUCH
- ☐ 142. SCOTT ERICKSON
- ☐ 164. CARL WILLIS
- ☐ 186. BRIAN HARPER
- ☐ 208. SCOTT LEIUS
- ☐ 219. PEDRO MUNOZ
- ☐ 251. MARK GUTHRIE
- ☐ 315. SHANE MACK
- ☐ 351. WILLIE BANKS
- ☐ 378. KIRBY PUCKETT
- ☐ 404. KEVIN TAPANI
- ☐ 423. DAVE WINFIELD
- ☐ 451. PAT MEARES
- ☐ 474. MIKE PAGLIARULO
- ☐ 498. LARRY CASIAN
- ☐ 522. JIM DESHAIES

MONTREAL EXPOS

- ☐ 19. JOHN VANDER WAL
- ☐ 37. WIL CORDERO
- ☐ 55. GREG COLBRUNN
- ☐ 73. CHRIS NABHOLZ
- ☐ 91. JEFF FASSERO
- ☐ 129. MARQUIS GRISSOM
- ☐ 147. MOISES ALOU
- ☐ 165. DARRIN FLETCHER
- ☐ 183. JOHN WETTELAND
- ☐ 201. KEN HILL
- ☐ 231. FRANK BOLICK
- ☐ 268. DELINO DESHIELDS
- ☐ 300. DENNIS MARTINEZ
- ☐ 336. SEAN BERRY
- ☐ 364. MEL ROJAS
- ☐ 367. TIM LAKER
- ☐ 392. LARRY WALKER
- ☐ 464. MIKE LANSING
- ☐ 515. LOU FRAZIER

NEW YORK METS

- ☐ 2. SID FERNANDEZ
- ☐ 39. HOWARD JOHNSON
- ☐ 57. VINCE COLEMAN
- ☐ 75. TODD HUNDLEY
- ☐ 93. BRET SABERHAGEN
- ☐ 112. JOHN FRANCO
- ☐ 149. CHICO WALKER
- ☐ 167. EDDIE MURRAY
- ☐ 185. JEFF KENT
- ☐ 203. DWIGHT GOODEN
- ☐ 236. BOBBY BONILLA
- ☐ 273. TONY FERNANDEZ
- ☐ 305. MIKE MADDUX
- ☐ 337. JOE ORSULAK
- ☐ 365. FRANK TANANA
- ☐ 479. DAVE GALLAGHER
- ☐ 503. JEROMY BURNITZ
- ☐ 525. TIM BOGAR
- ☐ 545. ANTHONY YOUNG

NEW YORK YANKEES

- ☐ 9. ANDY STANKIEWICZ
- ☐ 52. SAM MILITELLO
- ☐ 74. MELIDO PEREZ
- ☐ 96. MIKE GALLEGO
- ☐ 119. DANNY TARTABULL
- ☐ 130. BERNIE WILLIAMS
- ☐ 162. JOHN HABYAN
- ☐ 184. MIKE STANLEY
- ☐ 206. KEVIN MAAS
- ☐ 237. DON MATTINGLY
- ☐ 253. JIM ABBOTT
- ☐ 285. WADE BOGGS
- ☐ 317. JIMMY KEY
- ☐ 352. MATT NOKES
- ☐ 379. PAUL O'NEILL
- ☐ 405. SPIKE OWEN
- ☐ 424. BOB WICKMAN
- ☐ 447. PAT KELLY
- ☐ 468. JIM LEYRITZ
- ☐ 504. STEVE FARR
- ☐ 520. SCOTT KAMIENIECKI
- ☐ 548. BOBBY MUNOZ

OAKLAND A'S

- ☐ 7. TERRY STEINBACH
- ☐ 29. RUBEN SIERRA
- ☐ 72. DENNIS ECKERSLEY
- ☐ 94. BOB WELCH
- ☐ 117. MIKE BORDICK
- ☐ 139. DAVE HENDERSON
- ☐ 150. JERRY BROWNE
- ☐ 182. RON DARLING
- ☐ 204. BOBBY WITT
- ☐ 221. LANCE BLANKENSHIP
- ☐ 259. STORM DAVIS
- ☐ 291. RICKEY HENDERSON
- ☐ 323. MARK MCGWIRE
- ☐ 353. KEVIN SEITZER
- ☐ 448. TODD VAN POPPEL
- ☐ 478. MARCOS ARMAS
- ☐ 506. CRAIG PAQUETTE
- ☐ 536. BRENT GATES

PHILADELPHIA PHILLIES

- ☐ 4. CURT SCHILLING
- ☐ 22. TERRY MULHOLLAND
- ☐ 59. LENNY DYKSTRA
- ☐ 77. MICKEY MORANDINI
- ☐ 95. DARREN DAULTON
- ☐ 114. MITCH WILLIAMS
- ☐ 132. TOMMY GREENE
- ☐ 169. RICKY JORDAN
- ☐ 187. MARIANO DUNCAN
- ☐ 205. JUAN BELL
- ☐ 239. DAVE HOLLINS
- ☐ 276. PETE INCAVIGLIA
- ☐ 308. DANNY JACKSON
- ☐ 338. WES CHAMBERLAIN
- ☐ 366. JOHN KRUK
- ☐ 393. BEN RIVERA
- ☐ 417. MILT THOMPSON
- ☐ 460. DAVID WEST
- ☐ 491. LARRY ANDERSEN
- ☐ 507. JIM EISENREICH
- ☐ 523. KEVIN STOCKER

PITTSBURGH PIRATES

- ☐ 6. DON SLAUGHT
- ☐ 24. RANDY TOMLIN
- ☐ 42. DENNY NEAGLE
- ☐ 79. ANDY VAN SLYKE
- ☐ 97. ORLANDO MERCED
- ☐ 116. JAY BELL
- ☐ 134. BOB WALK
- ☐ 152. ZANE SMITH
- ☐ 189. AL MARTIN
- ☐ 207. JEFF KING
- ☐ 240. STEVE COOKE
- ☐ 277. CARLOS GARCIA
- ☐ 339. STAN BELINDA
- ☐ 394. LONNIE SMITH
- ☐ 466. PAUL WAGNER
- ☐ 497. SCOTT BULLETT
- ☐ 539. BLAS MINOR

ST. LOUIS CARDINALS

- ☐ 8. TODD ZEILE
- ☐ 26. JOSE OQUENDO
- ☐ 44. BOB TEWKSBURY
- ☐ 62. DONOVAN OSBORNE
- ☐ 99. BERNARD GILKEY
- ☐ 118. GERONIMO PENA
- ☐ 136. TOM PAGNOZZI
- ☐ 154. LEE SMITH
- ☐ 172. MARK CLARK
- ☐ 209. RHEAL CORMIER
- ☐ 229. BRIAN JORDAN
- ☐ 265. GREGG JEFFERIES
- ☐ 297. RAY LANKFORD
- ☐ 328. OZZIE SMITH
- ☐ 438. OMAR OLIVARES
- ☐ 449. MARK WHITEN
- ☐ 535. ERIK PAPPAS

SAN DIEGO PADRES

- ☐ 10. TIM TEUFEL
- ☐ 28. TONY GWYNN
- ☐ 46. FRED MCGRIFF
- ☐ 64. FRANK SEMINARA
- ☐ 82. GREG HARRIS
- ☐ 138. KURT STILLWELL
- ☐ 140. DARRIN JACKSON
- ☐ 156. DAN WALTERS
- ☐ 174. TIM SCOTT
- ☐ 192. ANDY BENES
- ☐ 238. JEFF GARDNER
- ☐ 275. PHIL PLANTIER
- ☐ 307. GARY SHEFFIELD
- ☐ 341. BRUCE HURST
- ☐ 368. RICH RODRIGUEZ
- ☐ 395. CRAIG SHIPLEY
- ☐ 441. KEVIN HIGGINS
- ☐ 471. GUILLERMO VELASQUEZ
- ☐ 493. RICKY GUTIERREZ
- ☐ 517. GENE HARRIS
- ☐ 531. TREVOR HOFFMAN

SAN FRANCISCO GIANTS

- ☐ 30. ROBBY THOMPSON
- ☐ 48. STEVE HOSEY
- ☐ 66. KIRT MANWARING
- ☐ 84. MIKE JACKSON
- ☐ 102. JEFF BRANTLEY
- ☐ 158. MATT WILLIAMS
- ☐ 160. JOHN PATTERSON
- ☐ 176. ROYCE CLAYTON
- ☐ 194. BILL SWIFT
- ☐ 212. BUD BLACK
- ☐ 232. ROD BECK
- ☐ 247. WILL CLARK
- ☐ 269. BARRY BONDS
- ☐ 301. DAVE MARTINEZ
- ☐ 342. JOHN BURKETT
- ☐ 369. DARREN LEWIS
- ☐ 396. WILLIE MCGEE
- ☐ 477. TREVOR WILSON
- ☐ 501. BRYAN HICKERSON

SEATTLE MARINERS

- ☐ 248. MIKE FELDER

- ☐ 255. CHRIS BOSIO
- ☐ 271. JAY BUHNER
- ☐ 287. NORM CHARLTON
- ☐ 303. JOHN CUMMINGS
- ☐ 319. KEN GRIFFEY, JR.
- ☐ 354. ERIK HANSON
- ☐ 380. RANDY JOHNSON
- ☐ 386. EDGAR MARTINEZ
- ☐ 406. TINO MARTINEZ
- ☐ 412. PETE O'BRIEN
- ☐ 425. DAVID VALLE
- ☐ 434. OMAR VIZQUEL
- ☐ 457. MIKE BLOWERS
- ☐ 490. MARC NEWFIELD
- ☐ 516. RICH AMAHAL
- ☐ 546. BRET BOONE

TEXAS RANGERS

- ☐ 5. IVAN RODRIGUEZ
- ☐ 27. JULIO FRANCO
- ☐ 49. RAFAEL PALMEIRO
- ☐ 92. KENNY ROGERS
- ☐ 115. NOLAN RYAN
- ☐ 137. JEFF HUSON
- ☐ 159. DEAN PALMER
- ☐ 170. JUAN GONZALEZ
- ☐ 202. KEVIN BROWN
- ☐ 241. JOSE CANSECO
- ☐ 278. TOM HENKE
- ☐ 309. CRAIG LEFFERTS
- ☐ 355. DAVID HULSE
- ☐ 381. MANUEL LEE
- ☐ 407. CHARLIE LEIBRANDT
- ☐ 426. GARY REDUS
- ☐ 435. BILLY RIPKEN
- ☐ 443. DAN PELTIER
- ☐ 470. MARIO DIAZ
- ☐ 508. MATT WHITESIDE
- ☐ 542. DOUG STRANGE
- ☐ 550. ROGER PAVLIK

TORONTO BLUE JAYS

- ☐ 3. JUAN GUZMAN
- ☐ 25. TODD STOTTLEMYRE
- ☐ 47. JOHN OLERUD
- ☐ 69. DEVON WHITE
- ☐ 113. JACK MORRIS
- ☐ 135. DUANE WARD
- ☐ 157. PAT BORDERS
- ☐ 179. DEREK BELL
- ☐ 190. EDDIE ZOSKY
- ☐ 228. JOE CARTER
- ☐ 245. ROBERTO ALOMAR
- ☐ 262. PAUL MOLITOR
- ☐ 294. DAVE STEWART
- ☐ 356. DOMINGO MARTINEZ
- ☐ 382. DICK SCHOFIELD
- ☐ 408. ED SPRAGUE
- ☐ 427. TURNER WARD
- ☐ 465. MIKE TIMLIN
- ☐ 486. DOMINGO CEDENO
- ☐ 540. PAT HENTGEN

1994 LEAF (440)
2 1/2" X 3 1/2"

ATLANTA BRAVES

- ☐ 2. TONY TARASCO
- ☐ 20. MIKE STANTON
- ☐ 46. CHIPPER JONES
- ☐ 94. GREG MADDUX
- ☐ 101. DEION SANDERS
- ☐ 138. STEVE AVERY
- ☐ 189. TERRY PENDLETON
- ☐ 194. JEFF BLAUSER
- ☐ 207. GREG MCMICHAEL
- ☐ 235. TOM GLAVINE
- ☐ 263. DAVID JUSTICE
- ☐ 286. RYAN KLESKO
- ☐ 309. JOHN SMOLTZ
- ☐ 345. FRED MCGRIFF
- ☐ 392. MARK LEMKE
- ☐ 410. KENT MERCKER

BALTIMORE ORIOLES

- ☐ 1. CAL RIPKEN, JR.
- ☐ 36. MARK MCLEMORE
- ☐ 66. BRADY ANDERSON
- ☐ 84. HAROLD BAINES
- ☐ 105. MIKE MUSSINA
- ☐ 127. BEN MCDONALD
- ☐ 154. MIKE DEVEREAUX
- ☐ 177. BRAD PENNINGTON
- ☐ 195. CHRIS HOILES
- ☐ 215. JAMIE MOYER
- ☐ 246. SID FERNANDEZ
- ☐ 289. RAFAEL PALMEIRO
- ☐ 324. CHRIS SABO
- ☐ 357. LEE SMITH
- ☐ 403. JEFFREY HAMMONDS

BOSTON RED SOX

- ☐ 34. BILLY HATCHER
- ☐ 60. FRANK VIOLA
- ☐ 75. SCOTT COOPER
- ☐ 77. JOHN VALENTIN
- ☐ 114. DANNY DARWIN
- ☐ 142. ANDRE DAWSON
- ☐ 182. MIKE GREENWELL
- ☐ 199. AARON SELE
- ☐ 201. TIM NAEHRING
- ☐ 255. ROGER CLEMENS
- ☐ 285. MO VAUGHN
- ☐ 336. JEFF RUSSELL
- ☐ 375. OTIS NIXON
- ☐ 422. SCOTT FLETCHER
- ☐ 430. DAVID VALLE

CALIFORNIA ANGELS

- ☐ 19. CHAD CURTIS
- ☐ 33. GREG MYERS
- ☐ 69. JOE GRAHE
- ☐ 86. DAMION EASLEY
- ☐ 109. TIM SALMON
- ☐ 132. PHIL LEFTWICH
- ☐ 162. MARK LANGSTON
- ☐ 173. GARY DISARCINA
- ☐ 204. TOREY LOVULLO
- ☐ 258. CHILI DAVIS
- ☐ 291. CHRIS TURNER
- ☐ 307. BO JACKSON
- ☐ 341. EDUARDO PEREZ
- ☐ 394. CHUCK FINLEY
- ☐ 428. HAROLD REYNOLDS

CHICAGO CUBS

- ☐ 18. GLENALLEN HILL
- ☐ 43. MARK GRACE
- ☐ 68. JOSE VIZCAINO
- ☐ 88. JOSE BAUTISTA
- ☐ 98. SAMMY SOSA
- ☐ 139. DERRICK MAY
- ☐ 180. STEVE BUECHELE
- ☐ 186. JOSE GUZMAN
- ☐ 192. MIKE MORGAN
- ☐ 217. FRANK CASTILLO
- ☐ 245. WILLIE BANKS
- ☐ 287. RICK WILKINS
- ☐ 316. SHAWON DUNSTON
- ☐ 356. TUFFY RHODES
- ☐ 396. RANDY MYERS
- ☐ 425. RYNE SANDBERG

CHICAGO WHITE SOX

- ☐ 13. LANCE JOHNSON
- ☐ 26. ROBIN VENTURA
- ☐ 71. WILSON ALVAREZ
- ☐ 107. OZZIE GUILLEN
- ☐ 116. TIM RAINES
- ☐ 125. JACK MCDOWELL
- ☐ 167. ROBERTO HERNANDEZ
- ☐ 175. JOEY CORA
- ☐ 184. RON KARKOVICE
- ☐ 210. STEVE SAX
- ☐ 241. JASON BERE
- ☐ 268. ALEX FERNANDEZ
- ☐ 300. DARRIN JACKSON
- ☐ 364. JULIO FRANCO
- ☐ 400. FRANK THOMAS
- ☐ 406. SCOTT SANDERSON

CINCINNATI REDS

- ☐ 24. JOHN SMILEY
- ☐ 40. ROBERTO KELLY
- ☐ 53. TIM COSTO
- ☐ 91. TIM PUGH
- ☐ 106. REGGIE SANDERS
- ☐ 126. BARRY LARKIN
- ☐ 146. JOE OLIVER
- ☐ 166. ROB DIBBLE
- ☐ 233. BRET BOONE
- ☐ 266. TONY FERNANDEZ
- ☐ 305. JOHNNY RUFFIN
- ☐ 326. WILLIE GREENE
- ☐ 340. JOSE RIJO
- ☐ 370. KEVIN MITCHELL
- ☐ 426. ERIK HANSON
- ☐ 433. HAL MORRIS

CLEVELAND INDIANS

- ☐ 223. SANDY ALOMAR, JR.
- ☐ 247. CARLOS BAERGA
- ☐ 251. ALBERT BELLE
- ☐ 270. STEVE FARR
- ☐ 283. WAYNE KIRBY
- ☐ 297. CHARLES NAGY
- ☐ 310. DENNIS MARTINEZ
- ☐ 313. EDDIE MURRAY
- ☐ 331. OMAR VIZQUEL
- ☐ 350. KENNY LOFTON
- ☐ 361. PAUL SORRENTO
- ☐ 382. JIM THOME
- ☐ 401. JACK MORRIS
- ☐ 423. MARK LEWIS
- ☐ 438. JOSE MESA

COLORADO ROCKIES

- ☐ 3. JOE GIRARDI
- ☐ 44. ERIC YOUNG
- ☐ 63. ROBERTO MEJIA
- ☐ 81. DANTE BICHETTE
- ☐ 119. DARREN HOLMES
- ☐ 134. CHARLIE HAYES
- ☐ 148. ARMANDO REYNOSO
- ☐ 156. ANDRES GALARRAGA

- ☐ 214. VINNY CASTILLA
- ☐ 242. ELLIS BURKS
- ☐ 276. MIKE HARKEY
- ☐ 312. DAVID NIED
- ☐ 359. WALT WEISS
- ☐ 416. GREG HARRIS
- ☐ 432. HOWARD JOHNSON

DETROIT TIGERS

- ☐ 5. CHAD KREUTER
- ☐ 39. DAVID WELLS
- ☐ 50. CECIL FIELDER
- ☐ 80. LOU WHITAKER
- ☐ 120. ALAN TRAMMELL
- ☐ 147. BILL GULLICKSON
- ☐ 160. TONY PHILLIPS
- ☐ 183. MIKE HENNEMAN
- ☐ 197. MIKE MOORE
- ☐ 202. SCOTT LIVINGSTONE
- ☐ 232. TIM BELCHER
- ☐ 256. ERIC DAVIS
- ☐ 279. MICKEY TETTLETON
- ☐ 342. KIRK GIBSON
- ☐ 371. JOHN DOHERTY
- ☐ 405. TRAVIS FRYMAN

FLORIDA MARLINS

- ☐ 14. RICHIE LEWIS
- ☐ 41. JEFF CONINE
- ☐ 62. BRET BARBERIE
- ☐ 76. NIGEL WILSON
- ☐ 96. BENITO SANTIAGO
- ☐ 140. BRYAN HARVEY
- ☐ 188. CHARLIE HOUGH
- ☐ 191. ORESTES DESTRADE
- ☐ 212. ROBB NEN
- ☐ 238. RYAN BOWEN
- ☐ 284. CHRIS HAMMOND
- ☐ 319. GARY SHEFFIELD
- ☐ 346. KURT ABBOTT
- ☐ 386. DAVE MAGADAN
- ☐ 408. CHUCK CARR

HOUSTON ASTROS

- ☐ 221. JEFF BAGWELL
- ☐ 236. CRAIG BIGGIO
- ☐ 244. KEN CAMINITI
- ☐ 260. ANDUJAR CEDENO
- ☐ 271. DOUG DRABEK
- ☐ 292. LUIS GONZALEZ
- ☐ 314. DARRYL KILE
- ☐ 332. SCOTT SERVAIS
- ☐ 348. MIKE FELDER
- ☐ 365. ROBERTO PETAGINE
- ☐ 379. GREG SWINDELL
- ☐ 383. STEVE FINLEY
- ☐ 398. PETE HARNISCH
- ☐ 415. TODD JONES
- ☐ 431. MITCH WILLIAMS

KANSAS CITY ROYALS

- ☐ 25. JEFF MONTGOMERY
- ☐ 65. JOSE LIND
- ☐ 70. KEVIN APPIER
- ☐ 90. PHIL HIATT
- ☐ 122. GREG GAGNE
- ☐ 141. WALLY JOYNER
- ☐ 159. MIKE MACFARLANE
- ☐ 168. FELIX JOSE
- ☐ 209. CHRIS GWYNN
- ☐ 240. VINCE COLEMAN
- ☐ 274. DAVID CONE
- ☐ 306. BRIAN MCRAE
- ☐ 327. HIPOLITO PICHARDO
- ☐ 363. BOB HAMELIN
- ☐ 389. TOM GORDON
- ☐ 427. GARY GAETTI

LOS ANGELES DODGERS

- ☐ 16. OREL HERSHISER
- ☐ 21. TIM WALLACH
- ☐ 72. TOM CANDIOTTI
- ☐ 93. RAUL MONDESI
- ☐ 111. BILLY ASHLEY
- ☐ 123. JOSE OFFERMAN
- ☐ 153. KEVIN GROSS
- ☐ 171. ERIC KARROS
- ☐ 187. BRETT BUTLER
- ☐ 205. JIM GOTT
- ☐ 237. PEDRO ASTACIO
- ☐ 277. DELINO DESHIELDS
- ☐ 303. RAMON MARTINEZ
- ☐ 362. TODD WORRELL
- ☐ 385. HENRY RODRIGUEZ
- ☐ 436. MIKE PIAZZA

MILWAUKEE BREWERS

- ☐ 222. RICKY BONES
- ☐ 250. ALEX DIAZ
- ☐ 267. CAL ELDRED
- ☐ 281. DARRYL HAMILTON
- ☐ 290. BRIAN HARPER
- ☐ 302. DAVE NILSSON
- ☐ 317. JOHN JAHA
- ☐ 321. GREG VAUGHN
- ☐ 339. KEVIN SEITZER
- ☐ 351. GRAEME LLOYD
- ☐ 369. B.J. SURHOFF
- ☐ 376. JODY REED
- ☐ 393. DOUG HENRY
- ☐ 420. PAT LISTACH
- ☐ 439. JAIME NAVARRO

MINNESOTA TWINS

- ☐ 45. RICK AGUILERA
- ☐ 52. KEVIN TAPANI
- ☐ 64. CHUCK KNOBLAUCH
- ☐ 78. DAVE MCCARTY
- ☐ 115. CHIP HALE
- ☐ 137. DAVE WINFIELD
- ☐ 157. PAT MEARES
- ☐ 198. CARL WILLIS
- ☐ 227. SCOTT ERICKSON
- ☐ 269. KENT HRBEK
- ☐ 294. KIRBY PUCKETT
- ☐ 337. SCOTT LEIUS
- ☐ 360. PEDRO MUNOZ
- ☐ 413. PAT MAHOMES
- ☐ 435. SHANE MACK

MONTREAL EXPOS

- ☐ 8. KIRK RUETER
- ☐ 42. SEAN BARRY
- ☐ 47. MEL ROJAS
- ☐ 89. MIKE LANSING
- ☐ 103. WIL CORDERO
- ☐ 118. DARRIN FLETCHER
- ☐ 174. MARQUIS GRISSOM
- ☐ 181. JEFF FASSERO
- ☐ 219. TIM SCOTT
- ☐ 252. MOISES ALOU
- ☐ 282. KEN HILL
- ☐ 343. RANDY MILLIGAN
- ☐ 367. PEDRO MARTINEZ
- ☐ 397. LARRY WALKER
- ☐ 414. JOHN WETTELAND

NEW YORK METS

- ☐ 10. DWIGHT GOODEN
- ☐ 31. BOBBY BONILLA
- ☐ 48. RYAN THOMPSON
- ☐ 74. ANTHONY YOUNG
- ☐ 99. TIM BOGAR
- ☐ 112. JEFF KENT
- ☐ 124. JOE ORSULAK
- ☐ 144. JOHN FRANCO
- ☐ 230. JEROMY BURNITZ
- ☐ 280. KEVIN MCREYNOLDS
- ☐ 304. BOBBY JONES
- ☐ 323. TODD HUNDLEY
- ☐ 352. DAVID SEGUI
- ☐ 419. PETE SMITH
- ☐ 437. BRET SABERHAGEN

NEW YORK YANKEES

- ☐ 4. BERNIE WILLIAMS
- ☐ 38. JIM ABBOTT
- ☐ 51. PAT KELLY
- ☐ 108. PAUL O'NEILL
- ☐ 121. DON MATTINGLY
- ☐ 136. MIKE GALLEGO
- ☐ 158. JIM LEYRITZ
- ☐ 190. MELIDO PEREZ
- ☐ 206. BOB WICKMAN
- ☐ 257. WADE BOGGS
- ☐ 273. XAVIER HERNANDEZ
- ☐ 295. MIKE STANLEY
- ☐ 353. DANNY TARTABULL
- ☐ 373. TERRY MULHOLLAND
- ☐ 390. LUIS POLONIA
- ☐ 412. JIMMY KEY

OAKLAND A'S

- ☐ 6. TROY NEEL
- ☐ 27. SCOTT LYDY
- ☐ 57. RON DARLING
- ☐ 67. RUBEN SIERRA
- ☐ 102. BOBBY WITT
- ☐ 128. MIKE BORDICK
- ☐ 151. TODD VAN POPPEL
- ☐ 161. BRENT GATES
- ☐ 178. TERRY STEINBACH
- ☐ 208. SCOTT BROSIUS
- ☐ 234. DENNIS ECKERSLEY
- ☐ 259. RICKEY HENDERSON
- ☐ 296. CARLOS REYES
- ☐ 325. STAN JAVIER
- ☐ 354. BOB WELCH
- ☐ 391. MARK MCGWIRE

PHILADELPHIA PHILLIES

- ☐ 11. MARIANO DUNCAN
- ☐ 22. MILT THOMPSON
- ☐ 54. DAVE HOLLINS
- ☐ 83. DANNY JACKSON
- ☐ 97. LENNY DYKSTRA
- ☐ 133. TOMMY GREENE
- ☐ 170. DARREN DAULTON
- ☐ 176. JIM EISENREICH
- ☐ 213. BEN RIVERA
- ☐ 243. WES CHAMBERLAIN
- ☐ 265. PETE INCAVIGLIA
- ☐ 320. CURT SCHILLING
- ☐ 347. JOHN KRUK
- ☐ 377. DOUG JONES
- ☐ 417. KEVIN STOCKER
- ☐ 424. MICKEY MORANDINI

PITTSBURGH PIRATES

- ☐ 12. JAY BELL
- ☐ 23. KEVIN YOUNG
- ☐ 49. AL MARTIN
- ☐ 82. MARK DEWEY
- ☐ 135. DON SLAUGHT
- ☐ 145. JEFF KING
- ☐ 155. TIM WAKEFIELD
- ☐ 169. STEVE COOKE
- ☐ 220. PAUL WAGNER
- ☐ 248. CARLOS GARCIA
- ☐ 275. BRIAN HUNTER
- ☐ 335. TOM FOLEY
- ☐ 374. ZANE SMITH
- ☐ 388. ORLANDO MERCED
- ☐ 411. ANDY VAN SLYKE

ST. LOUIS CARDINALS

- ☐ 7. TOM PAGNOZZI
- ☐ 29. MARK WHITEN
- ☐ 56. GREGG JEFFERIES
- ☐ 61. TODD ZEILE
- ☐ 110. RHEAL CORMIER
- ☐ 130. MIKE PEREZ
- ☐ 152. BERNARD GILKEY
- ☐ 163. ALLEN WATSON
- ☐ 172. GERONIMO PENA
- ☐ 203. LUIS ALICEA
- ☐ 228. RENE AROCHA
- ☐ 272. BRIAN JORDAN
- ☐ 315. RICK SUTCLIFFE
- ☐ 333. BOB TEWKSBURY
- ☐ 384. RAY LANKFORD
- ☐ 409. OZZIE SMITH

SAN DIEGO PADRES

- ☐ 32. ANDY ASHBY
- ☐ 37. SCOTT SANDERS
- ☐ 59. PHIL PLANTIER
- ☐ 79. ARCHI CIANFROCCO
- ☐ 113. DEREK BELL
- ☐ 143. ANDY BENES
- ☐ 165. DOUG BROCAIL
- ☐ 196. RICKY GUTIERREZ
- ☐ 216. WALLY WHITEHURST
- ☐ 239. BRAD AUSMUS
- ☐ 254. TONY GWYNN
- ☐ 299. BIP ROBERTS
- ☐ 349. DAVE STATON
- ☐ 407. GENE HARRIS
- ☐ 421. TREVOR HOFFMAN

SAN FRANCISCO GIANTS

- ☐ 15. DAVE MARTINEZ
- ☐ 30. ROBBY THOMPSON
- ☐ 55. KIRT MANWARING
- ☐ 73. JOHN BURKETT
- ☐ 85. TODD BENZINGER
- ☐ 224. ROD BECK
- ☐ 264. BARRY BONDS
- ☐ 288. BILL SWIFT
- ☐ 301. MIKE JACKSON
- ☐ 318. SALOMON TORRES
- ☐ 334. MATT WILLIAMS
- ☐ 366. WILLIE MCGEE
- ☐ 381. ROYCE CLAYTON
- ☐ 399. DARREN LEWIS
- ☐ 429. MARK PORTUGAL

SEATTLE MARINERS

- ☐ 9. CHRIS BOSIO
- ☐ 35. BRAD HOLMAN
- ☐ 58. BILL HASELMAN
- ☐ 92. TINO MARTINEZ
- ☐ 104. RICH AMARAL
- ☐ 131. JAY BUHNER
- ☐ 149. DAVE FLEMING
- ☐ 164. RANDY JOHNSON
- ☐ 218. MIKE BLOWERS
- ☐ 229. ERIC ANTHONY
- ☐ 253. BOBBY AYALA
- ☐ 298. REGGIE JEFFERSON
- ☐ 329. DAN WILSON
- ☐ 344. EDGAR MARTINEZ
- ☐ 368. KEN GRIFFEY, JR.
- ☐ 402. GREG HIBBARD

TEXAS RANGERS

- ☐ 226. JACK ARMSTRONG
- ☐ 231. KEVIN BROWN
- ☐ 249. JOSE CANSECO
- ☐ 261. CRIS CARPENTER
- ☐ 278. DAVID HULSE
- ☐ 293. KENNY ROGERS
- ☐ 311. DEAN PALMER
- ☐ 322. JAY HOWELL
- ☐ 328. DOUG STRANGE
- ☐ 338. IVAN RODRIGUEZ
- ☐ 358. CHRIS JAMES
- ☐ 372. MANUEL LEE
- ☐ 387. GARY REDUS
- ☐ 404. WILL CLARK
- ☐ 418. JUAN GONZALEZ
- ☐ 434. TOM HENKE

TORONTO BLUE JAYS

- ☐ 17. ROB BUTLER
- ☐ 28. TODD STOTTLEMYRE
- ☐ 87. DANNY COX
- ☐ 95. AL LEITER
- ☐ 117. ED SPRAGUE
- ☐ 129. DEVON WHITE
- ☐ 179. PAT BORDERS
- ☐ 185. PAT HENTGEN
- ☐ 193. JOE CARTER
- ☐ 211. DICK SCHOFIELD
- ☐ 225. ROBERTO ALOMAR
- ☐ 262. JUAN GUZMAN
- ☐ 308. DAVE STEWART
- ☐ 355. DUANE WARD
- ☐ 378. JOHN OLERUD
- ☐ 395. PAUL MOLITOR

1994 LEAF LIMITED
(160)
2 1/2" X 3 1/2"

ATLANTA BRAVES

- ☐ 81. STEVE AVERY
- ☐ 82. TOM GLAVINE
- ☐ 83. DAVID JUSTICE
- ☐ 84. ROBERTO KELLY
- ☐ 85. RYAN KLESKO
- ☐ 86. JAVY LOPEZ
- ☐ 87. GREG MADDUX
- ☐ 88. FRED MCGRIFF

BALTIMORE ORIOLES

- ☐ 1. JEFFREY HAMMONDS
- ☐ 2. BEN MCDONALD
- ☐ 3. MIKE MUSSINA
- ☐ 4. RAFAEL PALMEIRO
- ☐ 5. CAL RIPKIN, JR.
- ☐ 6. LEE SMITH

BOSTON RED SOX

- ☐ 7. ROGER CLEMENS
- ☐ 8. SCOTT COOPER
- ☐ 9. ANDRE DAWSON
- ☐ 10. MIKE GREENWELL
- ☐ 11. AARON SELE
- ☐ 12. MO VAUGHN

CALIFORNIA ANGELS

- ☐ 13. BRIAN ANDERSON
- ☐ 14. CHAD CURTIS
- ☐ 15. CHILI DAVIS
- ☐ 16. GARY DISARCINA
- ☐ 17. MARK LANGSTON
- ☐ 18. TIM SALMON

CHICAGO CUBS

- ☐ 89. SHAWON DUNSTON
- ☐ 90. MARK GRACE
- ☐ 91. DERRICK MAY
- ☐ 92. SAMMY SOSA
- ☐ 93. RICK WILKINS

CHICAGO WHITE SOX

- ☐ 19. WILSON ALVAREZ
- ☐ 20. JASON BERE
- ☐ 21. JULIO FRANCO
- ☐ 22. JACK MCDOWELL
- ☐ 23. TIM RAINES
- ☐ 24. FRANK THOMAS
- ☐ 25. ROBIN VENTURA

CINCINNATI REDS

- ☐ 94. BRET BOONE
- ☐ 95. BARRY LARKIN
- ☐ 96. KEVIN MITCHELL
- ☐ 97. HAL MORRIS
- ☐ 98. DEION SANDERS
- ☐ 99. REGGIE SANDERS

CLEVELAND INDIANS

- ☐ 26. CARLOS BAERGA
- ☐ 27. ALBERT BELLE
- ☐ 28. KENNY LOFTON
- ☐ 29. EDDIE MURRAY
- ☐ 30. MANNY RAMIREZ

COLORADO ROCKIES

- ☐ 100. DANTE BICHETTE
- ☐ 101. ELLIS BURKS
- ☐ 102. ANDRES GALARRAGA
- ☐ 103. JOE GIRARDI
- ☐ 104. CHARLIE HAYES

DETROIT TIGERS

- ☐ 31. CECIL FIELDER
- ☐ 32. TRAVIS FRYMAN
- ☐ 33. MICKEY TETTLETON
- ☐ 34. ALAN TRAMMELL
- ☐ 35. LOU WHITAKER

FLORIDA MARLINS

- ☐ 105. CHUCK CARR
- ☐ 106. JEFF CONINE
- ☐ 107. BRYAN HARVEY
- ☐ 108. BENITO SANTIAGO
- ☐ 109. GARY SHEFFIELD

HOUSTON ASTROS

- ☐ 110. JEFF BAGWELL
- ☐ 111. CRAIG BIGGIO
- ☐ 112. KEN CAMINITI
- ☐ 113. ANDUJAR CEDENO
- ☐ 114. DOUG DRABEK
- ☐ 115. LUIS GONZALEZ

KANSAS CITY ROYALS

- ☐ 36. DAVID CONE
- ☐ 37. GARY GAETTI
- ☐ 38. GREG GAGNE
- ☐ 39. BOB HAMELIN
- ☐ 40. WALLY JOYNER
- ☐ 41. BRIAN MCRAE

LOS ANGELES DODGERS

- ☐ 116. BRETT BUTLER
- ☐ 117. DELINO DESHIELDS
- ☐ 118. ERIC KARROS
- ☐ 119. RAUL MONDESI
- ☐ 120. MIKE PIAZZA
- ☐ 121. HENRY RODRIGUEZ
- ☐ 122. TIM WALLACH

MILWAUKEE BREWERS

☐ 42. RICKY BONES
☐ 43. BRIAN HARPER
☐ 44. JOHN JAHA
☐ 45. PAT LISTACH
☐ 46. DAVE NILSSON
☐ 47. GREG VAUGHN

MINNESOTA TWINS

☐ 48. KENT HRBEK
☐ 49. CHUCK KNOBLAUCH
☐ 50. SHANE MACK
☐ 51. KIRBY PUCKETT
☐ 52. DAVE WINFIELD

MONTREAL EXPOS

☐ 123. MOISES ALOU
☐ 124. CLIFF FLOYD
☐ 125. MARQUIS GRISSOM
☐ 126. KEN HILL
☐ 127. LARRY WALKER
☐ 128. JOHN WETTELAND

NEW YORK METS

☐ 129. BOBBY BONILLA
☐ 130. JOHN FRANCO
☐ 131. JEFF KENT
☐ 132. BRET SABERHAGEN
☐ 133. RYAN THOMPSON

NEW YORK YANKEES

☐ 53. JIM ABBOTT
☐ 54. WADE BOGGS
☐ 55. JIMMY KEY
☐ 56. DON MATTINGLY
☐ 57. PAUL O'NEILL
☐ 58. DANNY TARTABULL

OAKLAND A'S

☐ 59. DENNIS ECKERSLEY
☐ 60. RICKEY HENDERSON
☐ 61. MARK MCGWIRE
☐ 62. TROY NEEL
☐ 63. RUBEN SIERRA

PHILADELPHIA PHILLIES

☐ 134. DARREN DAULTON
☐ 135. MARIANO DUNCAN
☐ 136. LENNY DYKSTRA
☐ 137. DANNY JACKSON
☐ 138. JOHN KRUK

PITTSBURGH PIRATES

☐ 139. JAY BELL
☐ 140. JEFF KING
☐ 141. AL MARTIN
☐ 142. ORLANDO MERCED
☐ 143. ANDY VAN SLYKE

ST. LOUIS CARDINALS

☐ 144. BERNARD GILKEY
☐ 145. GREGG JEFFERIES
☐ 146. RAY LANKFORD
☐ 147. OZZIE SMITH
☐ 148. MARK WHITEN
☐ 149. TODD ZEILE

SAN DIEGO PADRES

☐ 150. DEREK BELL
☐ 151. ANDY BENES
☐ 152. TONY GWYNN
☐ 153. PHIL PLANTIER
☐ 154. BIP ROBERTS

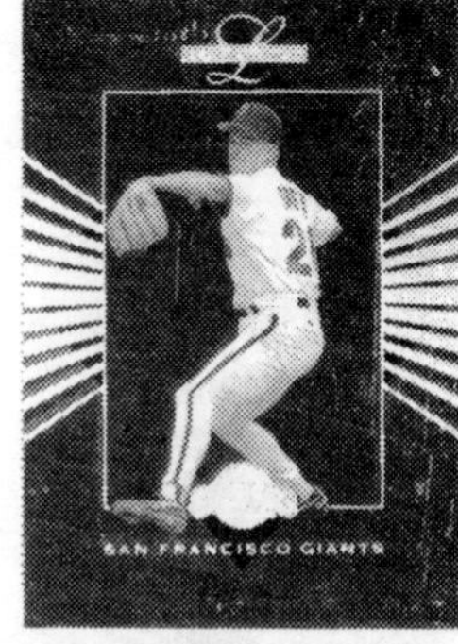

SAN FRANCISCO GIANTS

☐ 155. ROD BECK
☐ 156. BARRY BONDS
☐ 157. JOHN BURKETT
☐ 158. ROYCE CLAYTON
☐ 159. BILL SWIFT
☐ 160. MATT WILLIAMS

SEATTLE MARINERS

☐ 64. ERIC ANTHONY
☐ 65. JAY BUHNER
☐ 66. KEN GRIFFEY, JR.
☐ 67. RANDY JOHNSON
☐ 68. EDGAR MARTINEZ
☐ 69. TINO MARTINEZ

TEXAS RANGERS

☐ 70. JOSE CANSECO
☐ 71. WILL CLARK
☐ 72. JUAN GONZALEZ
☐ 73. DEAN PALMER
☐ 74. IVAN RODRIGUEZ

TORONTO BLUE JAYS

☐ 75. ROBERTO ALOMAR
☐ 76. JOE CARTER
☐ 77. CARLOS DELGADO
☐ 78. PAUL MOLITOR
☐ 79. JOHN OLERUD
☐ 80. DEVON WHITE

1994 LEAF LIMITED ROOKIES (80) 2 1/2" X 3 1/2"

ATLANTA BRAVES

☐ 48. JOSE OLIVA
☐ 60. MIKE KELLY
☐ 80. TONY TARASCO

BALTIMORE ORIOLES

☐ 64. MARK SMITH
☐ 74. ARMANDO BENITEZ

BOSTON RED SOX

☐ 30. GREG BLOSSER
☐ 55. CORY BAILEY
☐ 68. GAR FINNVOLD

CALIFORNIA ANGELS

☐ 49. JIM EDMONDS
☐ 62. GARRET ANDERSON
☐ 72. JORGE FABREGAS

CHICAGO CUBS

☐ 19. KEVIN FOSTER
☐ 25. STEVE TRACHSEL

CHICAGO WHITE SOX

☐ 10. SCOTT RUFFCORN
☐ 23. NORBERTO MARTIN

CINCINNATI REDS

☐ 8. HECTOR CARRASCO
☐ 18. JOHNNY RUFFIN

CLEVELAND INDIANS

☐ 7. PAUL SHUEY

COLORADO ROCKIES

☐ 61. MARCUS MOORE

DETROIT TIGERS

☐ 12. DANNY BAUTISTA
☐ 35. CHRIS GOMEZ

FLORIDA MARLINS

☐ 1. CHARLES JOHNSON
☐ 11. KURT ABBOTT
☐ 31. CARL EVERETT
☐ 36. JESUS TAVAREZ

1994 Leaf Limited Rookies

HOUSTON ASTROS

- ☐ 41. SHANE REYNOLDS
- ☐ 51. TONY EUSEBIO
- ☐ 57. JOHN HUDEK
- ☐ 63. BRIAN HUNTER
- ☐ 71. ORLANDO MILLER
- ☐ 76. JAMES MOUTON

KANSAS CITY ROYALS

NO CARDS ISSUED

LOS ANGELES DODGERS

- ☐ 43. ISMAEL VALDES
- ☐ 53. BILLY ASHLEY
- ☐ 59. DARREN DREIFORT
- ☐ 65. GAREY INGRAM
- ☐ 78. CHAN HO PARK

MILWAUKEE BREWERS

- ☐ 6. MATT MIESKE
- ☐ 21. TROY O'LEARY
- ☐ 33. JOSE VALENTIN

MINNESOTA TWINS

- ☐ 4. RICH BECKER
- ☐ 14. STEVE DUNN
- ☐ 26. DENNY HOCKING
- ☐ 39. MATT WALBECK

MONTREAL EXPOS

- ☐ 54. RONDELL WHITE

NEW YORK METS

- ☐ 2. RICO BROGNA
- ☐ 24. JASON JACOME

NEW YORK YANKEES

- ☐ 5. RUSS DAVIS
- ☐ 15. JOE AUSANIO
- ☐ 28. GERALD WILLIAMS

OAKLAND A'S

- ☐ 22. MARK ACRE
- ☐ 32. STEVE KARSAY
- ☐ 50. MIGUEL JIMENEZ
- ☐ 75. ERNIE YOUNG

PHILADELPHIA PHILLIES

- ☐ 17. RICKY BOTTALICO
- ☐ 27. MIKE LIEBERTHAL
- ☐ 37. TONY LONGMIRE

PITTSBURGH PIRATES

- ☐ 13. RICK WHITE
- ☐ 34. JON LIEBER
- ☐ 44. DANNY MICELI

ST. LOUIS CARDINALS

- ☐ 29. JOHN MABRY

SAN DIEGO PADRES

- ☐ 3. MELVIN NIEVES
- ☐ 38. LUIS LOPEZ
- ☐ 42. JOEY HAMILTON
- ☐ 70. RAY MCDAVID
- ☐ 73. RAY HOLBERT

SAN FRANCISCO GIANTS

- ☐ 9. J.R. PHILLIPS
- ☐ 16. SALOMON TORRES
- ☐ 20. W. VAN LANDINGHAM
- ☐ 40. RIKKERT FANEYTE

SEATTLE MARINERS

- ☐ 45. DARREN BRAGG
- ☐ 56. TIM DAVIS
- ☐ 67. MARC NEWFIELD
- ☐ 79. ROGER SALKELD

TEXAS RANGERS

- ☐ 47. RICK HELLING
- ☐ 66. RUSTY GREER

TORONTO BLUE JAYS

- ☐ 46. ALEX GONZALEZ
- ☐ 52. SHAWN GREEN
- ☐ 58. DARREN HALL
- ☐ 69. PAUL SPOLJARIC
- ☐ 77. ROBERT PEREZ

1995 LEAF SERIES 1 (200) 2 1/2" X 3 1/2"

ATLANTA BRAVES

- ☐ 18. JOHN SMOLTZ
- ☐ 25. MARK WOHLERS
- ☐ 62. DAVID JUSTICE
- ☐ 98. KENT MERCKER
- ☐ 115. GREG MADDUX
- ☐ 140. JAVY LOPEZ
- ☐ 174. MARK LEMKE

BALTIMORE ORIOLES

- ☐ 19. LEO GOMEZ
- ☐ 24. DAMON BUFORD
- ☐ 54. CHRIS HOILES
- ☐ 100. BRADY ANDERSON
- ☐ 129. RAFAEL PALMEIRO
- ☐ 134. CAL RIPKEN, JR.
- ☐ 197. BEN MCDONALD

BOSTON RED SOX

- ☐ 7. AARON SELE
- ☐ 12. JOHN VALENTIN
- ☐ 57. RICH ROWLAND
- ☐ 82. WES CHAMBERLAIN
- ☐ 130. GAR FINNVOLD
- ☐ 155. SCOTT COOPER
- ☐ 186. TIM NAEHRING

CALIFORNIA ANGELS

- ☐ 4. DAMION EASLEY
- ☐ 26. JIM EDMONDS
- ☐ 67. CHUCK FINLEY
- ☐ 93. CHILI DAVIS
- ☐ 118. BRIAN ANDERSON
- ☐ 145. EDUARDO PEREZ
- ☐ 199. CHRIS TURNER

CHICAGO CUBS

- ☐ 30. SHAWON DUNSTON
- ☐ 45. KEVIN FOSTER
- ☐ 71. STEVE BUECHELE
- ☐ 151. RANDY MYERS
- ☐ 160. REY SANCHEZ
- ☐ 163. STEVE TRACHSEL
- ☐ 180. RICK WILKINS

CHICAGO WHITE SOX

- ☐ 1. FRANK THOMAS
- ☐ 27. WILSON ALVAREZ
- ☐ 44. RON KARKOVICE
- ☐ 69. ALEX FERNANDEZ
- ☐ 117. OZZIE GUILLEN
- ☐ 164. ROBERTO HERNANDEZ
- ☐ 200. LANCE JOHNSON

CINCINNATI REDS

- ☐ 23. EDDIE TAUBENSEE
- ☐ 47. REGGIE SANDERS
- ☐ 72. WILLIE GREENE
- ☐ 94. DEION SANDERS
- ☐ 97. BRET BOONE

☐ 102. JOSE RIJO
☐ 109. JOHNNY RUFFIN

CLEVELAND INDIANS

☐ 8. KENNY LOFTON
☐ 43. PAUL SORRENTO
☐ 91. PAUL SHUEY
☐ 121. SANDY ALOMAR, JR.
☐ 158. CARLOS BAERGA
☐ 176. WAYNE KIRBY
☐ 195. DENNIS MARTINEZ

COLORADO ROCKIES

☐ 5. ROBERTO MEJIA
☐ 55. WALT WEISS
☐ 135. DANTE BICHETTE
☐ 159. JOE GIRARDI
☐ 175. MARCUS MOORE
☐ 188. ERIC YOUNG
☐ 192. DAVID NIED

DETROIT TIGERS

☐ 9. JOHN DOHERTY
☐ 35. CHRIS GOMEZ
☐ 63. CECIL FIELDER
☐ 78. KIRK GIBSON
☐ 113. JOSE LIMA
☐ 139. GREG GOHR
☐ 178. LOU WHITAKER

FLORIDA MARLINS

☐ 58. DAVE WEATHERS
☐ 95. DARRELL WHITMORE
☐ 116. GREG COLBRUNN
☐ 142. PAT RAPP
☐ 170. ROBB NEN
☐ 182. GARY SHEFFIELD
☐ 191. KURT ABBOTT

HOUSTON ASTROS

☐ 39. SCOTT SERVAIS
☐ 101. JAMES MOUTON
☐ 110. DARRYL KILE
☐ 119. JEFF BAGWELL
☐ 126. CRAIG BIGGIO
☐ 161. TODD JONES
☐ 187. JOHN HUDEK

KANSAS CITY ROYALS

☐ 29. JEFF MONTGOMERY
☐ 32. JOSE LIND
☐ 84. KEVIN APPIER
☐ 144. GREG GAGNE
☐ 157. MARK GUBICZA
☐ 194. WALLY JOYNER
☐ 198. BOB HAMELIN

LOS ANGELES DODGERS

☐ 13. ISMAEL VALDES
☐ 36. HENRY RODRIGUEZ
☐ 60. RAUL MONDESI
☐ 104. RAMON MARTINEZ
☐ 137. PEDRO ASTACIO
☐ 154. DELINO DESHIELDS
☐ 196. BILLY ASHLEY

MILWAUKEE BREWERS

☐ 34. CAL ELDRED
☐ 50. JOSE VALENTIN
☐ 73. DAVE NILSSON
☐ 86. KEVIN SEITZER
☐ 89. MATT MIESKE
☐ 120. PAT LISTACH
☐ 143. MARK KIEFER

MINNESOTA TWINS

☐ 14. DAVE MCCARTY
☐ 49. SCOTT LEIUS
☐ 52. DENNY HOCKING
☐ 66. RICK AGUILERA
☐ 125. PEDRO MUNOZ
☐ 173. KEVIN TAPANI
☐ 183. KIRBY PUCKETT

MONTREAL EXPOS

☐ 11. MIKE LANSING
☐ 48. RONDELL WHITE
☐ 53. JEFF FASSERO
☐ 88. PEDRO MARTINEZ
☐ 128. WIL CORDERO
☐ 133. DARRIN FLETCHER
☐ 184. CLIFF FLOYD

NEW YORK METS

☐ 3. TODD HUNDLEY
☐ 16. BOBBY JONES
☐ 74. BRET SABERHAGEN
☐ 83. RICO BROGNA
☐ 96. JOE ORSULAK
☐ 122. JOSE VIZCAINO
☐ 138. RYAN THOMPSON

NEW YORK YANKEES

☐ 40. WADE BOGGS
☐ 59. STERLING HITCHCOCK
☐ 75. JIMMY KEY
☐ 80. PAUL O'NEILL
☐ 105. BERNIE WILLIAMS
☐ 162. LUIS POLONIA
☐ 168. JIM LEYRITZ

OAKLAND A'S

☐ 22. RICKEY HENDERSON
☐ 46. MIGUEL JIMENEZ
☐ 56. GERONIMO BEROA
☐ 81. MIKE BORDICK
☐ 106. TROY NEEL
☐ 112. RON DARLING
☐ 148. TERRY STEINBACH
☐ 169. TODD VAN POPPEL

PHILADELPHIA PHILLIES

☐ 65. MIKE LIEBERTHAL
☐ 87. MICKEY MORANDINI
☐ 103. BOBBY MUNOZ
☐ 127. KEVIN STOCKER
☐ 132. HEATH SLOCUMB
☐ 141. LENNY DYKSTRA
☐ 149. JIM EISENREICH

PITTSBURGH PIRATES

☐ 2. CARLOS GARCIA
☐ 38. JON LIEBER
☐ 77. STEVE COOKE
☐ 136. DON SLAUGHT
☐ 152. RICK WHITE
☐ 171. MIDRE CUMMINGS
☐ 179. JAY BELL

ST. LOUIS CARDINALS

☐ 6. JOHN MABRY
☐ 31. TOM PAGNOZZI
☐ 64. BRIAN JORDAN
☐ 79. RAY LANKFORD
☐ 124. ALLEN WATSON
☐ 166. RENE AROCHA
☐ 193. TODD ZEILE

SAN DIEGO PADRES

☐ 15. MELVIN NIEVES
☐ 17. TREVOR HOFFMAN
☐ 42. EDDIE WILLIAMS
☐ 68. ANDY ASHBY
☐ 92. BIP ROBERTS
☐ 99. SCOTT LIVINGSTONE
☐ 114. JOEY HAMILTON
☐ 150. BRAD AUSMUS

SAN FRANCISCO GIANTS

☐ 28. MATT WILLIAMS
☐ 33. ROYCE CLAYTON
☐ 51. WILLIAM VAN LANDINGHA
☐ 76. DARREN LEWIS
☐ 108. SALOMON TORRES
☐ 153. MARK PORTUGAL
☐ 165. JOHN PATTERSON
☐ 190. KIRT MANWARING

SEATTLE MARINERS

☐ 37. DAVE FLEMING
☐ 90. TINO MARTINEZ
☐ 111. BOBBY AYALA
☐ 146. FELIX FERMIN
☐ 172. JAY BUHNER
☐ 177. RICH AMARAL
☐ 189. ROGER SALKELD

TEXAS RANGERS

☐ 20. ROGER PAVLIK
☐ 21. DEAN PALMER
☐ 61. RUSTY GREER
☐ 107. IVAN RODRIGUEZ
☐ 123. RICK HELLING
☐ 147. JEFF FRYE
☐ 167. WILL CLARK
☐ 185. DARREN OLIVER

TORONTO BLUE JAYS

☐ 10. JOE CARTER
☐ 41. JOHN OLERUD
☐ 70. ED SPRAGUE
☐ 85. JUAN GUZMAN
☐ 131. DARREN HALL
☐ 156. PAT HENTGEN
☐ 181. PAUL MOLITOR

DONRUSS-LEAF-STUDIO

1991 LEAF STUDIO (264)

2 1/2" X 3 1/2"

ATLANTA BRAVES

☐ 141. STEVE AVERY
☐ 142. SID BREAM
☐ 143. NICK ESASKY
☐ 144. RON GANT
☐ 145. TOM GLAVINE
☐ 146. DAVID JUSTICE
☐ 147. KELLY MANN
☐ 148. TERRY PENDLETON
☐ 149. JOHN SMOLTZ
☐ 150. JEFF TREADWAY

BALTIMORE ORIOLES

☐ 1. GLENN DAVIS
☐ 2. DWIGHT EVANS
☐ 3. LEO GOMEZ
☐ 4. CHRIS HOILES
☐ 5. SAM HORN
☐ 6. BEN MCDONALD
☐ 7. RANDY MILLIGAN
☐ 8. GREGG OLSON
☐ 9. CAL RIPKEN
☐ 10. DAVID SEGUI

BOSTON RED SOX

☐ 11. WADE BOGGS
☐ 12. ELLIS BURKS
☐ 13. JACK CLARK
☐ 14. ROGER CLEMENS
☐ 15. MIKE GREENWELL
☐ 16. TIM NAEHRING
☐ 17. TONY PENA
☐ 18. PHIL PLANTIER
☐ 19. JEFF REARDON
☐ 20. MO VAUGHN

CALIFORNIA ANGELS

☐ 21. JIMMIE REESE(C)
☐ 22. JIM ABBOTT
☐ 23. BERT BLYLEVEN
☐ 24. CHUCK FINLEY
☐ 25. GARY GAETTI
☐ 26. WALLY JOYNER
☐ 27. MARK LANGSTON
☐ 28. KIRK MCCASKILL
☐ 29. LANCE PARRISH
☐ 30. DAVE WINFIELD

CHICAGO CUBS

☐ 151. GEORGE BELL
☐ 152. SHAWN BOSKIE
☐ 153. ANDRE DAWSON
☐ 154. LANCE DICKSON
☐ 155. SHAWON DUNSTON
☐ 156. JOE GIRARDI
☐ 157. MARK GRACE
☐ 158. RYNE SANDBERG
☐ 159. GARY SCOTT
☐ 160. DAVE SMITH

CHICAGO WHITE SOX

☐ 31. ALEX FERNANDEZ
☐ 32. CARLTON FISK
☐ 33. SCOTT FLETCHER
☐ 34. GREG HIBBARD
☐ 35. CHARLIE HOUGH
☐ 36. JACK MCDOWELL
☐ 37. TIM RAINES
☐ 38. SAMMY SOSA
☐ 39. BOBBY THIGPEN
☐ 40. FRANK THOMAS

CINCINNATI REDS

☐ 161. TOM BROWNING
☐ 162. ERIC DAVIS
☐ 163. ROB DIBBLE
☐ 164. MARIANO DUNCAN
☐ 165. CHRIS HAMMOND
☐ 166. BILLY HATCHER
☐ 167. BARRY LARKIN
☐ 168. HAL MORRIS
☐ 169. PAUL O'NEILL
☐ 170. CHRIS SABO

CLEVELAND INDIANS

☐ 41. SANDY ALOMAR
☐ 42. JOHN FARRELL
☐ 43. GLENALLEN HILL
☐ 44. BROOK JACOBY
☐ 45. CHRIS JAMES
☐ 46. DOUG JONES
☐ 47. ERIC KING
☐ 48. MARK LEWIS
☐ 49. GREG SWINDELL
☐ 50. MARK WHITEN

DETROIT TIGERS

☐ 51. MILT CUYLER
☐ 52. ROB DEER
☐ 53. CECIL FIELDER
☐ 54. TRAVIS FRYMAN
☐ 55. BILL GULLICKSON
☐ 56. LLOYD MOSEBY
☐ 57. FRANK TANANA
☐ 58. MICKEY TETTLETON
☐ 59. ALAN TRAMMELL
☐ 60. LOU WHITAKER

HOUSTON ASTROS

☐ 171. ERIC ANTHONY
☐ 172. JEFF BAGWELL
☐ 173. CRAIG BIGGIO
☐ 174. KEN CAMINITI
☐ 175. JIM DESHAIES
☐ 176. STEVE FINLEY
☐ 177. PETE HARNISCH
☐ 178. DARRYL KILE
☐ 179. CURT SCHILLING
☐ 180. MIKE SCOTT

KANSAS CITY ROYALS

☐ 61. MIKE BODDICKER
☐ 62. GEORGE BRETT
☐ 63. JEFF CONINE
☐ 64. WARREN CROMARTIE
☐ 65. STORM DAVIS
☐ 66. KIRK GIBSON
☐ 67. MARK GUBICZA
☐ 68. BRIAN MCRAE
☐ 69. BRET SABERHAGEN
☐ 70. KURT STILLWELL

LOS ANGELES DODGERS

☐ 181. BRETT BUTLER
☐ 182. GARY CARTER
☐ 183. OREL HERSHISER
☐ 184. RAMON MARTINEZ
☐ 185. EDDIE MURRAY
☐ 186. JOSE OFFERMAN
☐ 187. BOB OJEDA
☐ 188. JUAN SAMUEL
☐ 189. MIKE SCIOSCIA
☐ 190. DARRYL STRAWBERRY

MILWAUKEE BREWERS

☐ 71. TIM MCINTOSH
☐ 72. CANDY MALDONADO
☐ 73. PAUL MOLITOR
☐ 74. WILLIE RANDOLPH
☐ 75. RON ROBINSON
☐ 76. GARY SHEFFIELD
☐ 77. FRANKLIN STUBBS
☐ 78. B.J. SURHOFF
☐ 79. GREG VAUGHN
☐ 80. ROBIN YOUNT

MINNESOTA TWINS

☐ 81. RICK AGUILERA
☐ 82. STEVE BEDROSIAN
☐ 83. SCOTT ERICKSON
☐ 84. GREG GAGNE
☐ 85. DAN GLADDEN
☐ 86. BRIAN HARPER
☐ 87. KENT HRBEK
☐ 88. SHANE MACK
☐ 89. JACK MORRIS
☐ 90. KIRBY PUCKETT

MONTREAL EXPOS

☐ 191. MOISES ALOU
☐ 192. BRIAN BARNES
☐ 193. DENNIS BOYD
☐ 194. IVAN CALDERON
☐ 195. DELINO DESHIELDS
☐ 196. MIKE FITZGERALD
☐ 197. ANDRES GALARRAGA

1991 Leaf Studio

- ☐ 198. MARQUIS GRISSOM
- ☐ 199. BILL SAMPEN
- ☐ 200. TIM WALLACH

NEW YORK METS

- ☐ 201. DARYL BOSTON
- ☐ 202. VINCE COLEMAN
- ☐ 203. JOHN FRANCO
- ☐ 204. DWIGHT GOODEN
- ☐ 205. TOM HERR
- ☐ 206. GREGG JEFFRIES
- ☐ 207. HOWARD JOHNSON
- ☐ 208. DAVE MAGADAN
- ☐ 209. KEVIN MCREYNOLDS
- ☐ 210. FRANK VIOLA

NEW YORK YANKEES

- ☐ 91. JESSE BARFIELD
- ☐ 92. STEVE FARR
- ☐ 93. STEVE HOWE
- ☐ 94. ROBERTO KELLY
- ☐ 95. TIM LEARY
- ☐ 96. KEVIN MAAS
- ☐ 97. DON MATTINGLY
- ☐ 98. HENSLEY MEULENS
- ☐ 99. SCOTT SANDERSON
- ☐ 100. STEVE SAX

OAKLAND A'S

- ☐ 101. JOSE CANSECO
- ☐ 102. DENNIS ECKERSLEY
- ☐ 103. DAVE HENDERSON
- ☐ 104. RICKEY HENDERSON
- ☐ 105. RICK HONEYCUTT
- ☐ 106. MARK MCGWIRE
- ☐ 107. DAVE STEWART
- ☐ 108. ERIC SHOW
- ☐ 109. TODD VAN POPPEL
- ☐ 110. BOB WELCH

PHILADELPHIA PHILLIES

- ☐ 211. WES CHAMBERLAIN
- ☐ 212. DARREN DAULTON
- ☐ 213. LENNY DYKSTRA
- ☐ 214. CHARLIE HAYES
- ☐ 215. RICKY JORDAN
- ☐ 216. STEVE LAKE
- ☐ 217. ROGER MCDOWELL
- ☐ 218. MICKEY MORANDINI
- ☐ 219. TERRY MULHOLLAND
- ☐ 220. DALE MURPHY

PITTSBURGH PIRATES

- ☐ 221. JAY BELL
- ☐ 222. BARRY BONDS
- ☐ 223. BOBBY BONILLA
- ☐ 224. DOUG DRABEK
- ☐ 225. BILL LANDRUM
- ☐ 226. MIKE LAVALLIERE
- ☐ 227. JOSE LIND
- ☐ 228. DON SLAUGHT
- ☐ 229. JOHN SMILEY
- ☐ 230. ANDY VAN SLYKE

ST. LOUIS CARDINALS

- ☐ 231. BERNARD GILKEY
- ☐ 232. PEDRO GUERRERO
- ☐ 233. REX HUDLER
- ☐ 234. RAY LANKFORD
- ☐ 235. JOE MAGRANE
- ☐ 236. JOSE OQUENDO
- ☐ 237. LEE SMITH
- ☐ 238. OZZIE SMITH
- ☐ 239. MILT THOMPSON
- ☐ 240. TODD ZEILE

SAN DIEGO PADRES

- ☐ 241. LARRY ANDERSEN
- ☐ 242. ANDY BENES
- ☐ 243. PAUL FARIES
- ☐ 244. TONY FERNANDEZ
- ☐ 245. TONY GWYNN
- ☐ 246. ATLEE HAMMAKER
- ☐ 247. FRED MCGRIFF
- ☐ 248. BIP ROBERTS
- ☐ 249. BENITO SANTIAGO
- ☐ 250. ED WHITSON

SAN FRANCISCO GIANTS

- ☐ 251. DAVE ANDERSON
- ☐ 252. MIKE BENJAMIN
- ☐ 253. JOHN BURKETT
- ☐ 254. WILL CLARK
- ☐ 255. SCOTT GARRELTS
- ☐ 256. WILLIE MCGEE
- ☐ 257. KEVIN MITCHELL
- ☐ 258. DAVE RIGHETTI
- ☐ 259. MATT WILLIAMS

SEATTLE MARINERS

- ☐ 111. ALVIN DAVIS
- ☐ 112. KEN GRIFFEY, JR.
- ☐ 113. KEN GRIFFEY, SR.
- ☐ 114. ERIC HANSON
- ☐ 115. BRIAN HOLMAN
- ☐ 116. RANDY JOHNSON
- ☐ 117. EDGAR MARTINEZ
- ☐ 118. TINO MARTINEZ
- ☐ 119. HAROLD REYNOLDS
- ☐ 120. DAVID VALLE

TEXAS RANGERS

- ☐ 121. KEVIN BELCHER
- ☐ 122. SCOTT CHIAMPARINO
- ☐ 123. JULIO FRANCO
- ☐ 124. JUAN GONZALEZ
- ☐ 125. RICH GOSSAGE
- ☐ 126. JEFF KUNKEL
- ☐ 127. RAFAEL PALMEIRO
- ☐ 128. NOLAN RYAN
- ☐ 129. RUBEN SIERRA
- ☐ 130. BOBBY WITT

TORONTO BLUE JAYS

- ☐ 131. ROBERTO ALOMAR
- ☐ 132. TOM CANDIOTTI
- ☐ 133. JOE CARTER
- ☐ 134. KEN DAYLEY
- ☐ 135. KELLY GRUBER
- ☐ 136. JOHN OLERUD
- ☐ 137. DAVE STIEB
- ☐ 138. TURNER WARD
- ☐ 139. DEVON WHITE
- ☐ 140. MOOKIE WILSON

1992 LEAF STUDIO
(264)
2 1/2" X 3 1/2"

ATLANTA BRAVES

- ☐ 1. STEVE AVERY
- ☐ 2. SID BREAM
- ☐ 3. RON GANT
- ☐ 4. TOM GLAVINE
- ☐ 5. DAVID JUSTICE
- ☐ 6. MARK LEMKE
- ☐ 7. GREG OLSON
- ☐ 8. TERRY PENDLETON
- ☐ 9. DEION SANDERS
- ☐ 10. JOHN SMOLTZ

BALTIMORE ORIOLES

- ☐ 121. BRADY ANDERSON
- ☐ 122. GLENN DAVIS
- ☐ 123. MIKE DEVEREAUX
- ☐ 124. CHRIS HOILES
- ☐ 125. SAM HORN
- ☐ 126. BEN MCDONALD
- ☐ 127. MIKE MUSSINA
- ☐ 128. GREGG OLSON
- ☐ 129. CAL RIPKEN, JR.
- ☐ 130. RICK SUTCLIFFE

BOSTON RED SOX

- ☐ 131. WADE BOGGS
- ☐ 132. ROGER CLEMENS
- ☐ 133. GREG HARRIS
- ☐ 134. TIM NAEHRING
- ☐ 135. TONY PENA
- ☐ 136. PHIL PLANTIER
- ☐ 137. JEFF REARDON
- ☐ 138. JODY REED
- ☐ 139. MO VAUGHN
- ☐ 140. FRANK VIOLA

CALIFORNIA ANGELS

- ☐ 141. JIM ABBOTT
- ☐ 142. HUBIE BROOKS
- ☐ 143. CHAD CURTIS
- ☐ 144. GARY DISARCINA
- ☐ 145. CHUCK FINLEY
- ☐ 146. BRYAN HARVEY
- ☐ 147. VON HAYES
- ☐ 148. MARK LANGSTON
- ☐ 149. LANCE PARRISH
- ☐ 150. LEE STEVENS

CHICAGO CUBS

- ☐ 11. DOUG DASCENZO
- ☐ 12. ANDRE DAWSON
- ☐ 13. JOE GIRARDI
- ☐ 14. MARK GRACE
- ☐ 15. GREG MADDUX
- ☐ 16. CHUCK MCELROY
- ☐ 17. MIKE MORGAN
- ☐ 18. RYNE SANDBERG
- ☐ 19. GARY SCOTT
- ☐ 20. SAMMY SOSA

CHICAGO WHITE SOX

- ☐ 151. GEORGE BELL
- ☐ 152. ALEX FERNANDEZ
- ☐ 153. GREG HIBBARD
- ☐ 154. LANCE JOHNSON

- ☐ 155. KIRK MCCASKILL
- ☐ 156. TIM RAINES
- ☐ 157. STEVE SAX
- ☐ 158. BOBBY THIGPEN
- ☐ 159. FRANK THOMAS
- ☐ 160. ROBIN VENTURA

CINCINNATI REDS

- ☐ 21. NORM CHARLTON
- ☐ 22. ROB DIBBLE
- ☐ 23. BARRY LARKIN
- ☐ 24. HAL MORRIS
- ☐ 25. PAUL O'NEILL
- ☐ 26. JOSE RIJO
- ☐ 27. BIP ROBERTS
- ☐ 28. CHRIS SABO
- ☐ 29. REGGIE SANDERS
- ☐ 30. GREG SWINDELL

CLEVELAND INDIANS

- ☐ 161. SANDY ALOMAR, JR.
- ☐ 162. JACK ARMSTONG
- ☐ 163. CARLOS BAERGA
- ☐ 164. ALBERT BELLE
- ☐ 165. ALEX COLE
- ☐ 166. GLENALLEN HILL
- ☐ 167. MARK LEWIS
- ☐ 168. KENNY LOFTON
- ☐ 169. PAUL SORRENTO
- ☐ 170. MARK WHITEN

DETROIT TIGERS

- ☐ 171. MILT CUYLER
- ☐ 172. ROB DEER
- ☐ 173. CECIL FIELDER
- ☐ 174. TRAVIS FRYMAN
- ☐ 175. MIKE HENNEMAN
- ☐ 176. TONY PHILLIPS
- ☐ 177. FRANK TANANA
- ☐ 178. MICKEY TETTLETON
- ☐ 179. ALAN TRAMMELL
- ☐ 180. LOU WHITAKER

HOUSTON ASTROS

- ☐ 31. JEFF BAGWELL
- ☐ 32. CRAIG BIGGIO
- ☐ 33. KEN CAMINITI
- ☐ 34. ANDUJAR CEDENO
- ☐ 35. STEVE FINLEY
- ☐ 36. PETE HARNISCH
- ☐ 37. BUTCH HENRY
- ☐ 38. DOUG JONES
- ☐ 39. DARRYL KILE
- ☐ 40. EDDIE TAUBENSEE

KANSAS CITY ROYALS

- ☐ 181. GEORGE BRETT
- ☐ 182. TOM GORDON
- ☐ 183. MARK GUBICZA
- ☐ 184. GREGG JEFFERIES
- ☐ 185. WALLY JOYNER
- ☐ 186. BRENT MAYNE
- ☐ 187. BRIAN MCRAE
- ☐ 188. KEVIN MCREYNOLDS
- ☐ 189. KEITH MILLER
- ☐ 190. JEFF MONTGOMERY

LOS ANGELES DODGERS

- ☐ 41. BRETT BUTLER
- ☐ 42. TOM CANDIOTTI
- ☐ 43. ERIC DAVIS
- ☐ 44. OREL HERSHISER
- ☐ 45. ERIC KARROS
- ☐ 46. RAMON MARTINEZ
- ☐ 47. JOSE OFFERMAN
- ☐ 48. MIKE SCIOSCIA
- ☐ 49. MIKE SHARPERSON
- ☐ 50. DARRYL STRAWBERRY

MILWAUKEE BREWERS

- ☐ 191. DANTE BICHETTE
- ☐ 192. RICKY BONES
- ☐ 193. SCOTT FLETCHER
- ☐ 194. PAUL MOLITOR
- ☐ 195. JAIME NAVARRO
- ☐ 196. FRANKLIN STUBBS
- ☐ 197. B.J. SURHOFF
- ☐ 198. GREG VAUGHN
- ☐ 199. BILL WEGMAN
- ☐ 200. ROBIN YOUNG

MINNESOTA TWINS

- ☐ 201. RICK AGUILERA
- ☐ 202. SCOTT ERICKSON
- ☐ 203. GREG GAGNE
- ☐ 204. BRIAN HARPER
- ☐ 205. KENT HRBEK
- ☐ 206. SCOTT LEIUS
- ☐ 207. SHANE MACK
- ☐ 208. PAT MAHOMES
- ☐ 209. KIRBY PUCKETT
- ☐ 210. JOHN SMILEY

MONTREAL EXPOS

- ☐ 51. BRET BARBERIE
- ☐ 52. IVAN CALDERON
- ☐ 53. GARY CARTER
- ☐ 54. DELINO DESHIELDS
- ☐ 55. MARQUIS GRISSOM
- ☐ 56. KEN HILL
- ☐ 57. DENNIS MARTINEZ
- ☐ 58. SPIKE OWEN
- ☐ 59. LARRY WALKER
- ☐ 60. TIM WALLACH

NEW YORK METS

- ☐ 61. BOBBY BONILLA
- ☐ 62. TIM BURKE
- ☐ 63. VINCE COLEMAN
- ☐ 64. JOHN FRANCO
- ☐ 65. DWIGHT GOODEN
- ☐ 66. TODD HUNDLEY
- ☐ 67. HOWARD JOHNSON
- ☐ 68. EDDIE MURRAY
- ☐ 69. BRET SABERHAGEN
- ☐ 70. ANTHONY YOUNG

NEW YORK YANKEES

- ☐ 211. MIKE GALLEGO
- ☐ 212. CHARLIE HAYES
- ☐ 213. PAT KELLY
- ☐ 214. ROBERTO KELLY
- ☐ 215. KEVIN MAAS
- ☐ 216. DON MATTINGLY
- ☐ 217. MATT NOKES
- ☐ 218. MELIDO PEREZ
- ☐ 219. SCOTT SANDERSON
- ☐ 220. DANNY TARTABULL

OAKLAND A'S

- ☐ 221. HAROLD BAINES
- ☐ 222. JOSE CANSECO
- ☐ 223. DENNIS ECKERSLEY
- ☐ 224. DAVE HENDERSON
- ☐ 225. CARNEY LANSFORD
- ☐ 226. MARK MCGWIRE
- ☐ 227. MIKE MOORE
- ☐ 228. RANDY READY
- ☐ 229. TERRY STEINBACH
- ☐ 230. DAVE STEWART

PHILADELPHIA PHILLIES

- ☐ 71. KIM BATISTE
- ☐ 72. WES CHAMBERLAIN
- ☐ 73. DARREN DAULTON
- ☐ 74. MARIANO DUNCAN
- ☐ 75. LENNY DYKSTRA
- ☐ 76. JOHN KRUK
- ☐ 77. MICKEY MORANDINI
- ☐ 78. TERRY MULHOLLAND
- ☐ 79. DALE MURPHY
- ☐ 80. MITCH WILLIAMS

PITTSBURGH PIRATES

- ☐ 81. JAY BELL
- ☐ 82. BARRY BONDS
- ☐ 83. STEVE BUECHELE
- ☐ 84. DOUG DRABEK
- ☐ 85. MIKE LAVALLIERE
- ☐ 86. JOSE LIND
- ☐ 87. DENNY NEAGLE
- ☐ 88. RANDY TOMLIN
- ☐ 89. ANDY VAN SLYKE
- ☐ 90. GARY VARSHO

ST. LOUIS CARDINALS

- ☐ 91. PEDRO GUERRERO
- ☐ 92. REX HUDLER
- ☐ 93. BRIAN JORDAN
- ☐ 94. FELIX JOSE
- ☐ 95. DONOVAN OSBORNE
- ☐ 96. TOM PAGNOZZI
- ☐ 97. LEE SMITH
- ☐ 98. OZZIE SMITH
- ☐ 99. TODD WORRELL
- ☐ 100. TODD ZEILE

SAN DIEGO PADRES

- ☐ 101. ANDY BENES
- ☐ 102. JERALD CLARK
- ☐ 103. TONY FERNANDEZ
- ☐ 104. TONY GWYNN
- ☐ 105. GREG HARRIS
- ☐ 106. FRED MCGRIFF
- ☐ 107. BENITO SANTIAGO
- ☐ 108. GARY SHEFFIELD
- ☐ 109. KURT STILLWELL
- ☐ 110. TIM TEUFEL

SAN FRANCISCO GIANTS

- ☐ 111. KEVIN BASS
- ☐ 112. JEFF BRANTLEY
- ☐ 113. JOHN BURKETT
- ☐ 114. WILL CLARK
- ☐ 115. ROYCE CLAYTON
- ☐ 116. MIKE JACKSON
- ☐ 117. DARREN LEWIS
- ☐ 118. BILL SWIFT
- ☐ 119. ROBBY THOMPSON
- ☐ 120. MATT WILLIAMS

SEATTLE MARINERS

- ☐ 231. JAY BUHNER
- ☐ 232. KEN GRIFFEY, JR.
- ☐ 233. ERIK HANSON
- ☐ 234. RANDY JOHNSON
- ☐ 235. EDGAR MARTINEZ
- ☐ 236. TINO MARTINEZ
- ☐ 237. KEVIN MITCHELL
- ☐ 238. PETE O'BRIEN
- ☐ 239. HAROLD REYNOLDS
- ☐ 240. DAVID VALLE

TEXAS RANGERS

- ☐ 241. JULIO FRANCO
- ☐ 242. JUAN GONZALEZ
- ☐ 243. JOSE GUZMAN
- ☐ 244. RAFAEL PALMEIRO
- ☐ 245. DEAN PALMER
- ☐ 246. IVAN RODRIGUEZ
- ☐ 247. JEFF RUSSELL
- ☐ 248. NOLAN RYAN
- ☐ 249. RUBEN SIERRA
- ☐ 250. DICKIE THON

TORONTO BLUE JAYS

- ☐ 251. ROBERTO ALOMAR
- ☐ 252. DEREK BELL
- ☐ 253. PAT BORDERS
- ☐ 254. JOE CARTER
- ☐ 255. KELLY GRUBER
- ☐ 256. JUAN GUZMAN
- ☐ 257. JACK MORRIS
- ☐ 258. JOHN OLERUD
- ☐ 259. DEVON WHITE
- ☐ 260. DAVE WINFIELD

1993 LEAF STUDIO (220) 2 1/2" X 3 1/2"

ATLANTA BRAVES

- ☐ 5. STEVE AVERY
- ☐ 38. SID BREAM
- ☐ 61. JOHN SMOLTZ
- ☐ 88. RON GANT
- ☐ 117. TERRY PENDLETON
- ☐ 145. TOM GLAVINE
- ☐ 173. DAVID JUSTICE
- ☐ 196. GREG MADDUX
- ☐ 216. OTIS NIXON

BALTIMORE ORIOLES

- ☐ 17. BRADY ANDERSON
- ☐ 55. MIKE DEVEREAUX
- ☐ 80. CAL RIPKEN, JR.
- ☐ 99. LEO GOMEZ
- ☐ 129. HAROLD REYNOLDS
- ☐ 156. CHRIS HOILES
- ☐ 190. HAROLD BAINES
- ☐ 202. MIKE MUSSINA

BOSTON RED SOX

- ☐ 22. ROGER CLEMENS
- ☐ 45. SCOTT COOPER
- ☐ 72. FRANK VIOLA
- ☐ 104. ANDRE DAWSON
- ☐ 134. MO VAUGHN
- ☐ 161. MIKE GREENWELL
- ☐ 186. BILLY HATCHER

CALIFORNIA ANGELS

- ☐ 2. CHAD CURTIS
- ☐ 15. SCOTT SANDERSON
- ☐ 32. CHILI DAVIS
- ☐ 58. J.T. SNOW
- ☐ 85. GARY DISARCINA
- ☐ 114. TIM SALMON
- ☐ 142. DAMION EASLEY
- ☐ 170. LUIS POLONIA

CHICAGO CUBS

- ☐ 8. STEVE BUECHELE
- ☐ 42. MARK GRACE
- ☐ 63. RICK WILKINS
- ☐ 91. JOSE GUZMAN
- ☐ 121. SAMMY SOSA
- ☐ 148. DERRICK MAY
- ☐ 176. RYNE SANDBERG
- ☐ 199. WILLIE WILSON
- ☐ 218. JOSE VIZCAINO

CHICAGO WHITE SOX

- ☐ 28. GEORGE BELL
- ☐ 33. ELLIS BURKS
- ☐ 78. ROBIN VENTURA
- ☐ 110. BO JACKSON
- ☐ 139. FRANK THOMAS
- ☐ 167. OZZIE GUILLEN
- ☐ 192. LANCE JOHNSON
- ☐ 200. JACK MCDOWELL
- ☐ 215. TIM RAINES

CINCINNATI REDS

- ☐ 23. ROBERTO KELLY
- ☐ 43. BARRY LARKIN
- ☐ 73. CHRIS SABO
- ☐ 105. RANDY MILLIGAN
- ☐ 135. BIP ROBERTS
- ☐ 162. KEVIN MITCHELL
- ☐ 187. JOE OLIVER
- ☐ 211. JOSE RIJO

CLEVELAND INDIANS

- ☐ 13. SANDY ALOMAR, JR.
- ☐ 50. CARLOS BAERGA
- ☐ 67. PAUL SORRENTO
- ☐ 95. ALBERT BELLE
- ☐ 125. CARLOS MARTINEZ
- ☐ 152. REGGIE JEFFERSON
- ☐ 180. KENNY LOFTON
- ☐ 203. CHARLES NAGY

COLORADO ROCKIES

- ☐ 24. DANTE BICHETTE
- ☐ 41. JERALD CLARK
- ☐ 74. DAVID NIED
- ☐ 106. ALEX COLE
- ☐ 136. CHARLIE HAYES
- ☐ 163. ANDRES GALARRAGA
- ☐ 188. JOE GIRARDI
- ☐ 212. VINNY CASTILLA

DETROIT TIGERS

- ☐ 26. ROB DEER
- ☐ 37. CECIL FIELDER
- ☐ 76. LOU WHITAKER
- ☐ 108. TRAVIS FRYMAN
- ☐ 138. MICKEY TETTLETON
- ☐ 165. KIRK GIBSON
- ☐ 213. TONY PHILLIPS

FLORIDA MARLINS

- ☐ 54. JEFF CONINE
- ☐ 69. WALT WEISS
- ☐ 97. ORESTES DESTRADE
- ☐ 127. BENITO SANTIAGO
- ☐ 154. DAVE MAGADAN
- ☐ 181. JUNIOR FELIX
- ☐ 205. CHARLIE HOUGH

HOUSTON ASTROS

- ☐ 3. ERIC ANTHONY
- ☐ 34. JEFF BAGWELL
- ☐ 59. GREG SWINDELL
- ☐ 86. CRAIG BIGGIO
- ☐ 115. DOUG JONES
- ☐ 143. KEN CAMINITI
- ☐ 171. LUIS GONZALEZ
- ☐ 194. DOUG DRABEK

KANSAS CITY ROYALS

- ☐ 25. GEORGE BRETT
- ☐ 39. GREG GAGNE
- ☐ 75. KEVIN MCREYNOLDS
- ☐ 107. PHIL HIATT
- ☐ 137. BRIAN MCRAE
- ☐ 164. WALLY JOYNER
- ☐ 189. JOSE LIND

LOS ANGELES DODGERS

- ☐ 9. BRETT BUTLER
- ☐ 64. TIM WALLACH
- ☐ 92. ERIC KARROS
- ☐ 122. DARRYL STRAWBERRY
- ☐ 149. RAMON MARTINEZ
- ☐ 177. JODY REED
- ☐ 182. JOSE OFFERMAN
- ☐ 201. MIKE PIAZZA

MILWAUKEE BREWERS

- ☐ 6. CAL ELDRED
- ☐ 40. DARRYL HAMILTON
- ☐ 89. JOHN JAHA
- ☐ 118. ROBIN YOUNT
- ☐ 146. PAT LISTACH
- ☐ 174. B.J. SURHOFF
- ☐ 197. GREG VAUGHN

MINNESOTA TWINS

- ☐ 27. BRIAN HARPER
- ☐ 35. KENT HRBEK
- ☐ 77. DAVE WINFIELD
- ☐ 109. CHUCK KNOBLAUCH
- ☐ 166. PEDRO MUNOZ
- ☐ 191. MIKE PAGLIARULO
- ☐ 214. KIRBY PUCKETT

MONTREAL EXPOS

- ☐ 11. MOISES ALOU
- ☐ 46. MIKE LANSING
- ☐ 65. JOHN WETTELAND
- ☐ 93. WIL CORDERO
- ☐ 123. LARRY WALKER
- ☐ 150. DELINO DESHIELDS
- ☐ 178. MARQUIS GRISSOM

NEW YORK METS

- ☐ 16. BOBBY BONILLA
- ☐ 56. VINCE COLEMAN
- ☐ 70. JOHN FRANCO

☐ 98. TONY FERNANDEZ
☐ 112. BRET SABERHAGEN
☐ 128. HOWARD JOHNSON
☐ 155. DWIGHT GOODEN
☐ 206. TODD HUNDLEY

NEW YORK YANKEES

☐ 29. JIM ABBOTT
☐ 31. WADE BOGGS
☐ 79. SPIKE OWEN
☐ 111. PAT KELLY
☐ 140. PAUL O'NEILL
☐ 168. JIMMY KEY
☐ 193. DON MATTINGLY

OAKLAND A'S

☐ 1. DENNIS ECKERSLEY
☐ 30. DAVE HENDERSON
☐ 57. TERRY STEINBACH
☐ 84. RICKEY HENDERSON
☐ 113. RUBEN SIERRA
☐ 141. MARK MCGWIRE
☐ 169. KEVIN SEITZER

PHILADELPHIA PHILLIES

☐ 10. TERRY MULHOLLAND
☐ 19. WES CHAMBERLAIN
☐ 51. DARREN DAULTON
☐ 82. MITCH WILLIAMS
☐ 101. LENNY DYKSTRA
☐ 131. CURT SCHILLING
☐ 158. DAVE HOLLINS
☐ 183. JOHN KRUK
☐ 208. MICKEY MORANDINI

PITTSBURGH PIRATES

☐ 20. JAY BELL
☐ 49. CARLOS GARCIA
☐ 83. TIM WAKEFIELD
☐ 102. JEFF KING
☐ 132. ANDY VAN SLYKE
☐ 159. AL MARTIN
☐ 184. ORLANDO MERCED
☐ 209. DON SLAUGHT
☐ 219. RANDY TOMLIN

ST. LOUIS CARDINALS

☐ 7. BERNARD GILKEY
☐ 62. TODD ZEILE
☐ 90. GREGG JEFFERIES
☐ 119. MARK WHITEN
☐ 147. LEE SMITH
☐ 175. RAY LANKFORD
☐ 198. TOM PAGNOZZI
☐ 217. OZZIE SMITH

SAN DIEGO PADRES

☐ 18. DEREK BELL
☐ 53. ANDY BENES
☐ 81. DAN WALTERS
☐ 100. TONY GWYNN
☐ 130. CRAIG SHIPLEY
☐ 157. FRED MCGRIFF
☐ 207. GARY SHEFFIELD

SAN FRANCISCO GIANTS

☐ 12. BARRY BONDS
☐ 44. JOHN BURKETT
☐ 48. WILL CLARK
☐ 66. MATT WILLIAMS
☐ 94. ROYCE CLAYTON
☐ 124. ROBBY THOMPSON
☐ 151. KIRT MANWARING
☐ 179. WILLIE MCGEE

SEATTLE MARINERS

☐ 14. CHRIS BOSIO
☐ 52. JAY BUHNER
☐ 68. DAVID VALLE
☐ 96. KEN GRIFFEY, JR.
☐ 126. EDGAR MARTINEZ
☐ 153. RANDY JOHNSON
☐ 204. TINO MARTINEZ

TEXAS RANGERS

☐ 21. KEVIN BROWN
☐ 47. JOSE CANSECO
☐ 71. NOLAN RYAN
☐ 103. JULIO FRANCO
☐ 133. IVAN RODRIGUEZ
☐ 160. JUAN GONZALEZ
☐ 185. RAFAEL PALMEIRO
☐ 210. DEAN PALMER

TORONTO BLUE JAYS

☐ 4. ROBERTO ALOMAR
☐ 36. PAT BORDERS
☐ 60. DEVON WHITE
☐ 87. JOE CARTER
☐ 116. ED SPRAGUE
☐ 144. JUAN GUZMAN
☐ 172. PAUL MOLITOR
☐ 195. JOHN OLERUD

1994 LEAF STUDIO (220) 2 1/2" X 3 1/2"

ATLANTA BRAVES

☐ 33. STEVE AVERY
☐ 34. TOM GLAVINE
☐ 35. DAVID JUSTICE
☐ 36. ROBERTO KELLY
☐ 37. RYAN KLESKO
☐ 38. JAVY LOPEZ
☐ 39. GREG MADDUX
☐ 40. FRED MCGRIFF
☐ 41. TERRY PENDLETON

BALTIMORE ORIOLES

☐ 121. HAROLD BAINES
☐ 122. MIKE DEVEREAUX
☐ 123. JEFFREY HAMMONDS
☐ 124. BEN MCDONALD
☐ 125. MIKE MUSSINA
☐ 126. RAFAEL PALMEIRO
☐ 127. CAL RIPKEN, JR.
☐ 128. LEE SMITH

BOSTON RED SOX

☐ 159. ROGER CLEMENS
☐ 160. SCOTT COOPER
☐ 161. ANDRE DAWSON
☐ 162. MIKE GREENWELL
☐ 163. OTIS NIXON
☐ 164. AARON SELE
☐ 165. JOHN VALENTIN
☐ 166. MO VAUGHN

CALIFORNIA ANGELS

☐ 8. CHAD CURTIS
☐ 9. CHILI DAVIS
☐ 10. GARY DISARCINA
☐ 11. DAMION EASLEY
☐ 12. BO JACKSON
☐ 13. MARK LANGSTON
☐ 14. EDUARDO PEREZ
☐ 15. TIM SALMON

CHICAGO CUBS

☐ 58. STEVE BUECHELE
☐ 59. SHAWON DUNSTON
☐ 60. MARK GRACE
☐ 61. DERRICK MAY
☐ 62. TUFFY RHODES
☐ 63. RYNE SANDBERG
☐ 64. SAMMY SOSA
☐ 65. RICK WILKINS

CHICAGO WHITE SOX

☐ 203. WILSON ALVAREZ
☐ 204. ALEX FERNANDEZ
☐ 205. JULIO FRANCO
☐ 206. OZZIE GUILLEN
☐ 207. JACK MCDOWELL
☐ 208. TIM RAINES
☐ 209. FRANK THOMAS
☐ 210. ROBIN VENTURA

CINCINNATI REDS

☐ 167. BRET BOONE
☐ 168. BARRY LARKIN
☐ 169. KEVIN MITCHELL
☐ 170. HAL MORRIS
☐ 171. JOSE RIJO
☐ 172. DEION SANDERS
☐ 173. REGGIE SANDERS
☐ 174. JOHN SMILEY

CLEVELAND INDIANS

☐ 90. SANDY ALOMAR, JR.
☐ 91. CARLOS BAERGA
☐ 92. ALBERT BELLE
☐ 93. KENNY LOFTON
☐ 94. EDDIE MURRAY
☐ 95. MANNY RAMIREZ
☐ 96. PAUL SORRENTO
☐ 97. JIM THOME

COLORADO ROCKIES

☐ 175. DANTE BICHETTE
☐ 176. ELLIS BURKS
☐ 177. ANDRES GALARRAGA
☐ 178. JOE GIRARDI
☐ 179. CHARLIE HAYES
☐ 180. ROBERTO MEJIA
☐ 181. WALT WEISS

DETROIT TIGERS

- ☐ 189. ERIC DAVIS
- ☐ 190. CECIL FIELDER
- ☐ 191. TRAVIS FRYMAN
- ☐ 192. TONY PHILLIPS
- ☐ 193. MICKEY TETTLETON
- ☐ 194. ALAN TRAMMELL
- ☐ 195. LOU WHITAKER

FLORIDA MARLINS

- ☐ 105. KURT ABBOTT
- ☐ 106. BRET BARBERIE
- ☐ 107. CHUCK CARR
- ☐ 108. JEFF CONINE
- ☐ 109. CHRIS HAMMOND
- ☐ 110. BRYAN HARVEY
- ☐ 111. BENITO SANTIAGO
- ☐ 112. GARY SHEFFIELD

HOUSTON ASTROS

- ☐ 16. JEFF BAGWELL
- ☐ 17. CRAIG BIGGIO
- ☐ 18. KEN CAMINITI
- ☐ 19. ANDUJAR CEDENO
- ☐ 20. DOUG DRABEK
- ☐ 21. STEVE FINLEY
- ☐ 22. LUIS GONZALEZ
- ☐ 23. DARRYL KILE

KANSAS CITY ROYALS

- ☐ 182. DAVID CONE
- ☐ 183. GARY GAETTI
- ☐ 184. GREG GAGNE
- ☐ 185. FELIX JOSE
- ☐ 186. WALLY JOYNER
- ☐ 187. MIKE MACFARLANE
- ☐ 188. BRIAN MCRAE

LOS ANGELES DODGERS

- ☐ 66. BRETT BUTLER
- ☐ 67. DELINO DESHIELDS
- ☐ 68. OREL HERSHISER
- ☐ 69. ERIC KARROS
- ☐ 70. RAUL MONDESI
- ☐ 71. JOSE OFFERMAN
- ☐ 72. MIKE PIAZZA
- ☐ 73. TIM WALLACH

MILWAUKEE BREWERS

- ☐ 42. RICKY BONES
- ☐ 43. DARRYL HAMILTON
- ☐ 44. BRIAN HARPER
- ☐ 45. JOHN JAHA
- ☐ 46. DAVE NILSSON
- ☐ 47. KEVIN SEITZER
- ☐ 48. GREG VAUGHN
- ☐ 49. TURNER WARD

MINNESOTA TWINS

- ☐ 196. KENT HRBEK
- ☐ 197. CHUCK KNOBLAUCH
- ☐ 198. SHANE MACK
- ☐ 199. PAT MEARES
- ☐ 200. KIRBY PUCKETT
- ☐ 201. MATT WALBECK
- ☐ 202. DAVE WINFIELD

MONTREAL EXPOS

- ☐ 74. MOISES ALOU
- ☐ 75. SEAN BERRY
- ☐ 76. WIL CORDERO
- ☐ 77. CLIFF FLOYD
- ☐ 78. MARQUIS GRISSOM
- ☐ 79. KEN HILL
- ☐ 80. LARRY WALKER
- ☐ 81. JOHN WETTELAND

NEW YORK METS

- ☐ 113. BOBBY BONILLA
- ☐ 114. DWIGHT GOODEN
- ☐ 115. TODD HUNDLEY
- ☐ 116. BOBBY JONES
- ☐ 117. JEFF KENT
- ☐ 118. KEVIN MCREYNOLDS
- ☐ 119. BRET SABERHAGEN
- ☐ 120. RYAN THOMPSON

NEW YORK YANKEES

- ☐ 211. JIM ABBOTT
- ☐ 212. WADE BOGGS
- ☐ 213. PAT KELLY
- ☐ 214. JIMMY KEY
- ☐ 215. DON MATTINGLY
- ☐ 216. PAUL O'NEILL
- ☐ 217. MIKE STANLEY
- ☐ 218. DANNY TARTABULL

OAKLAND A'S

- ☐ 1. DENNIS ECKERSLEY
- ☐ 2. BRENT GATES
- ☐ 3. RICKEY HENDERSON
- ☐ 4. MARK MCGWIRE
- ☐ 5. TROY NEEL
- ☐ 6. RUBEN SIERRA
- ☐ 7. TERRY STEINBACH

PHILADELPHIA PHILLIES

- ☐ 136. DARREN DAULTON
- ☐ 137. MARIANO DUNCAN
- ☐ 138. LENNY DYKSTRA
- ☐ 139. DAVE HOLLINS
- ☐ 140. PETE INCAVIGLIA
- ☐ 141. DANNY JACKSON
- ☐ 142. JOHN KRUK
- ☐ 143. KEVIN STOCKER

PITTSBURGH PIRATES

- ☐ 144. JAY BELL
- ☐ 145. CARLOS GARCIA
- ☐ 146. JEFF KING
- ☐ 147. AL MARTIN
- ☐ 148. ORLANDO MERCED
- ☐ 149. DON SLAUGHT
- ☐ 150. ANDY VAN SLYKE

ST. LOUIS CARDINALS

- ☐ 50. BERNARD GILKEY
- ☐ 51. GREGG JEFFERIES
- ☐ 52. RAY LANKFORD
- ☐ 53. TOM PAGNOZZI
- ☐ 54. OZZIE SMITH
- ☐ 55. BOB TEWKSBURY
- ☐ 56. MARK WHITEN
- ☐ 57. TODD ZEILE

SAN DIEGO PADRES

- ☐ 129. BRAD AUSMUS
- ☐ 130. DEREK BELL
- ☐ 131. ANDY BENES
- ☐ 132. TONY GWYNN
- ☐ 133. TREVOR HOFFMAN
- ☐ 134. SCOTT LIVINGSTONE
- ☐ 135. PHIL PLANTIER

SAN FRANCISCO GIANTS

- ☐ 82. ROD BECK
- ☐ 83. BARRY BONDS
- ☐ 84. ROYCE CLAYTON
- ☐ 85. DARREN LEWIS
- ☐ 86. WILLIE MCGEE
- ☐ 87. BILL SWIFT
- ☐ 88. ROBBY THOMPSON
- ☐ 89. MATT WILLIAMS

SEATTLE MARINERS

- ☐ 98. RICH AMARAL
- ☐ 99. ERIC ANTHONY
- ☐ 100. JAY BUHNER
- ☐ 101. KEN GRIFFEY, JR.
- ☐ 102. RANDY JOHNSON
- ☐ 103. EDGAR MARTINEZ

TEXAS RANGERS

- ☐ 151. KEVIN BROWN
- ☐ 152. JOSE CANSECO
- ☐ 153. WILL CLARK
- ☐ 154. JUAN GONZALEZ
- ☐ 155. DAVID HULSE
- ☐ 156. DEAN PALMER
- ☐ 157. IVAN RODRIGUEZ
- ☐ 158. KENNY ROGERS

TORONTO BLUE JAYS

- ☐ 24. ROBERTO ALOMAR
- ☐ 25. PAT BORDERS
- ☐ 26. JOE CARTER
- ☐ 27. CARLOS DELGADO
- ☐ 28. PAT HENTGEN
- ☐ 29. PAUL MOLITOR
- ☐ 30. JOHN OLERUD
- ☐ 31. ED SPRAGUE
- ☐ 32. DEVON WHITE

1963 FLEER (66)
2 1/2" X 3 1/2"

KEN BOYER
St. Louis Cardinals—Third Base

BALTIMORE ORIOLES

- ☐ 1. STEVE BARBER
- ☐ 2. RON HANSEN
- ☐ 3. MILT PAPPAS
- ☐ 4. BROOKS ROBINSON

BOSTON RED SOX

- ☐ 6. LOU CLINTON
- ☐ 7. BILL MONBOUQUETTE
- ☐ 8. CARL YASTRZEMSKI

CHICAGO CUBS

- ☐ 31. GLEN HOBBIE
- ☐ 32. RON SANTO

CHICAGO WHITE SOX

- ☐ 9. RAY HERBERT
- ☐ 10. JIM LANDIS

CINCINNATI REDS

- ☐ 33. GENE FREESE
- ☐ 34. VADA PINSON
- ☐ 35. BOB PURKEY

CLEVELAND INDIANS

- ☐ 11. DICK DONOVAN
- ☐ 12. TITO FRANCONA
- ☐ 13. JERRY KINDALL
- ☐ 46. JOE ADCOCK

DETROIT TIGERS

- ☐ 14. FRANK LARY

HOUSTON COLT .45'S

- ☐ 37. BOB ASPROMONTE
- ☐ 38. DICK FARRELL
- ☐ 39. AL SPANGLER

KANSAS CITY ATHLETICS

- ☐ 15. DICK HOWSER
- ☐ 16. JERRY LUMPE
- ☐ 17. NORM SIEBERN

LOS ANGELES ANGELS

- ☐ 18. DON LEE
- ☐ 19. ALBIE PEARSON
- ☐ 20. BOB RODGERS
- ☐ 21. LEON WAGNER

LOS ANGELES DODGERS

- ☐ 40. TOMMY DAVIS
- ☐ 41. DON DRYSDALE
- ☐ 42. SANDY KOUFAX
- ☐ 43. MAURY WILLS

WARREN SPAHN
Milwaukee Braves—Pitcher

MILWAUKEE BRAVES

- ☐ 44. FRANK BOLLING
- ☐ 45. WARREN SPAHN

MINNESOTA TWINS

- ☐ 22. JIM KAAT
- ☐ 23. VIC POWER
- ☐ 24. RICH ROLLINS

NEW YORK METS

- ☐ 47. ROGER CRAIG
- ☐ 48. AL JACKSON
- ☐ 49. ROD KANEHL

NEW YORK YANKEES

- ☐ 25. BOBBY RICHARDSON
- ☐ 26. RALPH TERRY

PHILADELPHIA PHILLIES

- ☐ 50. RUBEN AMARO
- ☐ 51. JOHN CALLISON
- ☐ 52. CLAY DALRYMPLE
- ☐ 53. DON DEMETER
- ☐ 54. ART MAHAFFEY

PITTSBURGH PIRATES

- ☐ 55. SMOKY BURGESS
- ☐ 56. ROBERTO CLEMENTE
- ☐ 57. ELROY FACE
- ☐ 58. VERNON LAW
- ☐ 59. BILL MAZEROSKI

ST. LOUIS CARDINALS

- ☐ 60. KEN BOYER
- ☐ 61. BOB GIBSON
- ☐ 62. GENE OLIVER
- ☐ 63. BILL WHITE

WILLIE MAYS
San Francisco Giants—Outfield

SAN FRANCISCO GIANTS

- ☐ 5. WILLIE MAYS
- ☐ 36. JOE AMALFITANO
- ☐ 64. ORLANDO CEPEDA
- ☐ 65. JIMMY DAVENPORT
- ☐ 66. BILLY O'DELL

WASHINGTON SENATORS

- ☐ 27. TOM CHENEY
- ☐ 28. CHUCK COTTIER
- ☐ 29. JIMMY PIERSALL
- ☐ 30. DAVE STENHOUSE

1981 FLEER (660)
2 1/2" X 3 1/2"

CHRIS CHAMBLISS
FIRST BASE

ATLANTA BRAVES

- ☐ 242. PHIL NIEKRO
- ☐ 243. DALE MURPHY
- ☐ 244. BOB HORNER
- ☐ 245. JEFF BURROUGHS
- ☐ 246. RICK CAMP
- ☐ 247. BOBBY COX(M)
- ☐ 248. BRUCE BENEDICT
- ☐ 249. GENE GARBER
- ☐ 250. JERRY ROYSTER
- ☐ 251. GARY MATTHEWS
- ☐ 252. CHRIS CHAMBLISS
- ☐ 253. LUIS GOMEZ
- ☐ 254. BILL NAHORODNY
- ☐ 255. DOYLE ALEXANDER
- ☐ 256. BRIAN ASSELSTINE
- ☐ 257. BIFF POCOROBA
- ☐ 258. MIKE LUM
- ☐ 259. CHARLIE SPIKES
- ☐ 260. GLENN HUBBARD
- ☐ 261. TOMMY BOGGS
- ☐ 262. AL HRABOSKY
- ☐ 263. RICK MATULA
- ☐ 264. PRESTON HANNA
- ☐ 265. LARRY BRADFORD
- ☐ 266. RAFAEL RAMIREZ
- ☐ 267. LARRY MCWILLIAMS
- ☐ 646. TEAM CHECKLIST(B)

BALTIMORE ORIOLES

- ☐ 169. JIM PALMER
- ☐ 170. STEVE STONE
- ☐ 171. MIKE FLANAGAN
- ☐ 172. AL BUMBRY
- ☐ 173. DOUG DECINCES
- ☐ 174. SCOTT MCGREGOR
- ☐ 175. MARK BELANGER
- ☐ 176. TIM STODDARD
- ☐ 177. RICK DEMPSEY
- ☐ 178. EARL WEAVER(M)
- ☐ 179. TIPPY MARTINEZ
- ☐ 180. DENNIS MARTINEZ
- ☐ 181. SAMMY STEWART
- ☐ 182. RICH DAUER
- ☐ 183. LEE MAY
- ☐ 184. EDDIE MURRAY
- ☐ 185. BENNY AYALA
- ☐ 186. JOHN LOWENSTEIN
- ☐ 187. GARY ROENICKE

- □ 188. KEN SINGLETON
- □ 189. DAN GRAHAM
- □ 190. TERRY CROWLEY
- □ 191. KIKO GARCIA
- □ 192. DAVE FORD
- □ 193. MARK COREY
- □ 194. LENN SAKATA
- □ 195. DOUG DECINCES
- □ 644. TEAM CHECKLIST(F)

BOSTON RED SOX

- □ 221. CARL YASTRZEMSKI
- □ 222. JIM RICE
- □ 223. FRED LYNN
- □ 224. CARLTON FISK
- □ 225. RICK BURLESON
- □ 226. DENNIS ECKERSLEY
- □ 227. BUTCH HOBSON
- □ 228. TOM BURGMEIER
- □ 229. GARRY HANCOCK
- □ 230. DON ZIMMER(M)
- □ 231. STEVE RENKO
- □ 232. DWIGHT EVANS
- □ 233. MIKE TORREZ
- □ 234. BOB STANLEY
- □ 235. JIM DWYER
- □ 236. DAVE STAPLETON
- □ 237. GLENN HOFFMAN
- □ 238. JERRY REMY
- □ 239. DICK DRAGO
- □ 240. BILL CAMPBELL
- □ 241. TONY PEREZ
- □ 638. CARL YASTRZEMSKI
- □ 646. TEAM CHECKLIST(F)

CALIFORNIA ANGELS

- □ 268. ROD CAREW
- □ 269. BOBBY GRICH
- □ 270. CARNEY LANSFORD
- □ 271. DON BAYLOR
- □ 272. JOE RUDI
- □ 273. DAN FORD
- □ 274. JIM FREGOSI(M)
- □ 275. DAVE FROST
- □ 276. FRANK TANANA
- □ 277. DICKIE THON
- □ 278. JASON THOMPSON
- □ 279. RICK MILLER
- □ 280. BERT CAMPANERIS
- □ 281. TOM DONOHUE
- □ 282. BRIAN DOWNING
- □ 283. FRED PATEK
- □ 284. BRUCE KISON
- □ 285. DAVE LAROCHE
- □ 286. DON AASE
- □ 287. JIM BARR
- □ 288. ALFREDO MARTINEZ
- □ 289. LARRY HARLOW
- □ 290. ANDY HASSLER
- □ 647. TEAM CHECKLIST(F)

CHICAGO CUBS

- □ 291. DAVE KINGMAN
- □ 292. BILL BUCKNER
- □ 293. RICK REUSCHEL
- □ 294. BRUCE SUTTER
- □ 295. JERRY MARTIN
- □ 296. SCOT THOMPSON
- □ 297. IVAN DEJUSUS
- □ 298. STEVE DILLARD
- □ 299. DICK TIDROW
- □ 300. RANDY MARTZ
- □ 301. LENNY RANDLE
- □ 302. LYNN MCGLOTHEN
- □ 303. CLIFF JOHNSON
- □ 304. TIM BLACKWELL
- □ 305. DENNIS LAMP
- □ 306. BILL CAUDILL
- □ 307. CARLOS LEZCANO
- □ 308. JIM TRACY
- □ 309. DOUG CAPILLA*
- □ 310. WILLIE HERNANDEZ
- □ 311. MIKE VAIL
- □ 312. MIKE KRUKOW
- □ 313. BARRY FOOTE
- □ 314. LARRY BIITTNER
- □ 315. MIKE TYSON
- □ 647. TEAM CHECKLIST(B)

CHICAGO WHITE SOX

- □ 339. ED FARMER
- □ 340. BOB MOLINARO
- □ 341. TODD CRUZ
- □ 342. BRITT BURNS
- □ 343. KEVIN BELL
- □ 344. TONY LARUSSA(M)
- □ 345. STEVE TROUT
- □ 346. HAROLD BAINES
- □ 347. RICH WORTHAM
- □ 348. WAYNE NORDHAGEN
- □ 349. MIKE SQUIRES
- □ 350. LAMAR JOHNSON
- □ 352. FRANCISCO BARRIOS
- □ 353. THAD BOSLEY
- □ 354. CHET LEMON
- □ 355. BRUCE KIMM
- □ 356. RICHARD DOTSON
- □ 357. JIM MORRISON
- □ 358. MIKE PROLY
- □ 359. GREG PRYOR
- □ 648. TEAM CHECKLIST(B)

CINCINNATI REDS

- □ 196. JOHNNY BENCH
- □ 197. DAVE CONCEPCION
- □ 198. RAY KNIGHT
- □ 199. KEN GRIFFEY
- □ 200. TOM SEAVER
- □ 201. DAVE COLLINS
- □ 202. GEORGE FOSTER
- □ 203. JUNIOR KENNEDY
- □ 204. FRANK PASTORE
- □ 205. DAN DRIESSEN
- □ 206. HECTOR CRUZ
- □ 207. PAUL MOSKAU
- □ 208. CHARLIE LEIBRANDT
- □ 209. HARRY SPILMAN
- □ 210. JOE PRICE
- □ 211. TOM HUME
- □ 212. JOE NOLAN
- □ 213. DOUG BAIR
- □ 214. MARIO SOTO
- □ 215. BILL BONHAM
- □ 216. GEORGE FOSTER
- □ 217. PAUL HOUSEHOLDER
- □ 218. RON OESTER
- □ 219. SAM MEJIAS
- □ 220. SHELDON BURNSIDE
- □ 644. TEAM CHECKLIST(B)

CLEVELAND INDIANS

- □ 387. MIKE HARGROVE
- □ 388. JORGE ORTA
- □ 389. TOBY HARRAH
- □ 390. TOM VERYZER
- □ 391. MIGUEL DILONE
- □ 392. DAN SPILLNER
- □ 393. JACK BROHAMER
- □ 394. WAYNE GARLAND
- □ 395. SID MONGE
- □ 396. RICK WAITS
- □ 397. JOE CHARBONEAU
- □ 398. GARY ALEXANDER
- □ 399. JERRY DYBZINSKI
- □ 400. MIKE STANTON
- □ 401. MIKE PAXTON
- □ 402. GARY GRAY
- □ 403. RICK MANNING
- □ 404. BO DIAZ
- □ 405. RON HASSEY
- □ 406. ROSS GRIMSLEY
- □ 407. VICTOR CRUZ
- □ 408. LEN BARKER
- □ 649. TEAM CHECKLIST(B)

DETROIT TIGERS

- □ 459. STEVE KEMP
- □ 460. SPARKY ANDERSON(M)
- □ 461. ALAN TRAMMELL
- □ 462. MARK FIDRYCH
- □ 463. LOU WHITAKER
- □ 464. DAVE ROZEMA
- □ 465. MILT WILCOX
- □ 466. CHAMP SUMMERS
- □ 467. LANCE PARRISH
- □ 468. DAN PETRY
- □ 469. PAT UNDERWOOD
- □ 470. RICK PETERS
- □ 471. AL COWENS
- □ 472. JOHN WOCKENFUSS
- □ 473. TOM BROOKENS
- □ 474. RICHIE HEBNER
- □ 475. JACK MORRIS
- □ 476. JIM LENTINE
- □ 477. BRUCE ROBBINS
- □ 478. MARK WAGNER
- □ 479. TIM CORCORAN
- □ 480. STAN PAPI
- □ 481. KIRK GIBSON
- □ 482. DAN SCHATZEDER
- □ 652. TEAM CHECKLIST(F)

HOUSTON ASTROS

- □ 51. ART HOWE
- □ 52. KEN FORSCH
- □ 53. VERN RUHLE
- □ 54. JOE NIEKRO
- □ 55. FRANK LACORTE
- □ 56. J.R. RICHARD
- □ 57. NOLAN RYAN
- □ 58. ENOS CABELL
- □ 59. CESAR CEDENO
- □ 60. JOSE CRUZ
- □ 61. BILL VIRDON(M)
- □ 62. TERRY PUHL
- □ 63. JOAQUIN ANDUJAR
- □ 64. ALAN ASHBY
- □ 65. JOE SAMBITO
- □ 66. DENNY WALLING
- □ 67. JEFF LEONARD
- □ 68. LUIS PUJOLS
- □ 69. BRUCE BOCHY
- □ 70. RAFAEL LANDESTOY
- □ 71. DAVE SMITH
- □ 72. DANNY HEEP
- □ 73. JULIO GONZALEZ
- □ 74. CRAIG REYNOLDS
- □ 75. GARY WOODS
- □ 76. DAVE BERGMAN
- □ 77. RANDY NIEMANN
- □ 78. JOE MORGAN
- □ 642. TEAM CHECKLIST(F)

KANSAS CITY ROYALS

- □ 28. GEORGE BRETT
- □ 29. WILLIE WILSON
- □ 30. PAUL SPLITTORFF
- □ 31. DAN QUISENBERRY
- □ 32. AMOS OTIS
- □ 33. STEVE BUSBY
- □ 34. U.L. WASHINGTON
- □ 35. DAVE CHALK
- □ 36. DARRELL PORTER
- □ 37. MARTY PATTIN
- □ 38. LARRY GURA
- □ 39. RENIE MARTIN
- □ 40. RICH GALE
- □ 41. HAL MCRAE
- □ 42. DENNIS LEONARD
- □ 43. WILLIE AIKENS
- □ 44. FRANK WHITE
- □ 45. CLINT HURDLE
- □ 46. JOHN WATHAN
- □ 47. PETE LACOCK
- □ 48. RANCE MULLINIKS
- □ 49. JEFF TWITTY
- □ 50. JAMIE QUIRK
- □ 483. AMOS OTIS
- □ 641. TEAM CHECKLIST(B)
- □ 653. WILLIE WILSON
- □ 655. GEORGE BRETT

LOS ANGELES DODGERS

- □ 110. STEVE GARVEY
- □ 111. REGGIE SMITH
- □ 112. DON SUTTON
- □ 113. BURT HOOTON
- □ 114. DAVE LOPES
- □ 115. DUSTY BAKER
- □ 116. TOM LASORDA(M)
- □ 117. BILL RUSSELL
- □ 118. JERRY REUSS
- □ 119. TERRY FORSTER

* Capilla appears with Braves on the back of his card. This notation is in error as Capilla did not play for the Braves. His card is not, therefore, listed with the Braves.

☐ 120. BOB WELCH
☐ 121. DON STANHOUSE
☐ 122. RICK MONDAY
☐ 123. DERREL THOMAS
☐ 124. JOE FERGUSON
☐ 125. RICK SUTCLIFFE
☐ 126. RON CEY
☐ 127. DAVE GOLTZ
☐ 128. JAY JOHNSTONE
☐ 129. STEVE YEAGER
☐ 130. GARY WEISS
☐ 131. MIKE SCIOSCIA
☐ 132. VIC DAVALILLO
☐ 133. DOUG RAU
☐ 134. PEPE FRIAS
☐ 135. MICKEY HATCHER
☐ 136. STEVE HOWE
☐ 137. BOBBY CASTILLO
☐ 138. GARY THOMASSON
☐ 139. RUDY LAW
☐ 140. FERNANDO VALENZUELA
☐ 141. MANNY MOTA
☐ 606. STEVE GARVEY
☐ 643. TEAM CHECKLIST(F)

MILWAUKEE BREWERS

☐ 507. GORMAN THOMAS
☐ 508. BEN OGLIVIE
☐ 509. LARRY HISLE
☐ 510. SAL BANDO
☐ 511. ROBIN YOUNT
☐ 512. MIKE CALDWELL
☐ 513. SIXTO LEZCANO
☐ 514. BILL TRAVERS
☐ 515. PAUL MOLITOR
☐ 516. MOSSE HAAS
☐ 517. BILL CASTRO
☐ 518. JIM SLATON
☐ 519. LARY SORENSEN
☐ 520. BOB MCCLURE
☐ 521. CHARLIE MOORE
☐ 522. JIM GANTNER
☐ 523. REGGIE CLEVELAND
☐ 524. DON MONEY
☐ 525. BILL TRAVERS
☐ 526. BUCK MARTINEZ
☐ 527. DICK DAVIS
☐ 639. CECIL COOPER
☐ 654. TEAM CHECKLIST(F)

MINNESOTA TWINS

☐ 551. ROY SMALLEY
☐ 552. JERRY KOOSMAN
☐ 553. KEN LANDREAUX
☐ 554. JOHN CASTINO
☐ 555. DOUG CORBETT
☐ 556. BOMBO RIVERA
☐ 557. RON JACKSON
☐ 558. BUTCH WYNEGAR
☐ 559. HOSKEN POWELL
☐ 560. PETE REDFERN
☐ 561. ROGER ERICKSON
☐ 562. GLENN ADAMS
☐ 563. RICK SOFIELD
☐ 564. GEOFF ZAHN
☐ 565. PETE MACKANIN
☐ 566. MIKE CUBBAGE
☐ 567. DARRELL JACKSON
☐ 568. DAVE EDWARDS
☐ 569. ROB WILFONG
☐ 570. SAL BUTERA
☐ 571. JOSE MORALES
☐ 656. TEAM CHECKLIST(F)

MONTREAL EXPOS

☐ 142. GARY CARTER
☐ 143. STEVE ROGERS
☐ 144. WARREN CROMARTIE
☐ 145. ANDRE DAWSON
☐ 146. LARRY PARRISH
☐ 147. ROWLAND OFFICE
☐ 148. ELLIS VALENTINE
☐ 149. DICK WILLIAMS(M)
☐ 150. BILL GULLICKSON
☐ 151. ELIAS SOSA
☐ 152. JOHN TAMARGO
☐ 153. CHRIS SPEIER
☐ 154. RON LEFLORE
☐ 155. RODNEY SCOTT
☐ 156. STAN BAHNSEN
☐ 157. BILL LEE
☐ 158. FRED NORMAN
☐ 159. WOODIE FRYMAN
☐ 160. DAVE PALMER
☐ 161. JERRY WHITE
☐ 162. ROBERTO RAMOS
☐ 163. JOHN D'ACQUISTO
☐ 164. TOMMY HUTTON
☐ 165. CHARLIE LEA
☐ 166. SCOTT SANDERSON
☐ 167. KEN MACHA
☐ 168. TONY BERNAZARD
☐ 643. TEAM CHECKLIST(B)

NEW YORK METS

☐ 316. LEE MAZZILLI
☐ 317. JOHN STEARNS
☐ 318. ALEX TREVINO
☐ 319. CRAIG SWAN
☐ 320. FRANK TAVERAS
☐ 321. STEVE HANDERSON
☐ 322. NEIL ALLEN
☐ 323. MARK BOMBACK
☐ 324. MIKE JORGENSEN
☐ 325. JOE TORRE(M)
☐ 326. ELLIOTT MADDOX
☐ 327. PETE FALCONE
☐ 328. RAY BURRIS
☐ 329. CLAUDELL WASHINGTON
☐ 330. DOUG FLYNN
☐ 331. JOEL YOUNGBLOOD
☐ 332. BILL ALMON
☐ 333. TOM HAUSMAN
☐ 334. PAT ZACHRY
☐ 335. JEFF REARDON
☐ 336. WALLY BACKMAN
☐ 337. DAN NORMAN
☐ 338. JERRY MORALES
☐ 648. TEAM CHECKLIST(F)

NEW YORK YANKEES

☐ 79. REGGIE JACKSON
☐ 80. BUCKY DENT
☐ 81. TOMMY JOHN
☐ 82. LUIS TIANT
☐ 83. RICK CERONE
☐ 84. DICK HOWSER(M)
☐ 85. LOU PINIELLA
☐ 86. RON DAVIS
☐ 87. GRAIG NETTLES
☐ 88. RON GUIDRY
☐ 89. RICH GOSSAGE
☐ 90. RUDY MAY
☐ 91. GAYLORD PERRY
☐ 92. ERIC SODERHOLM
☐ 93. BOB WATSON
☐ 94. BOBBY MURCER
☐ 95. BOBBY BROWN
☐ 96. JIM SPENCER
☐ 97. TOM UNDERWOOD
☐ 98. OSCAR GAMBLE
☐ 99. JOHNNY OATES
☐ 100. FRED STANLEY
☐ 101. RUPPERT JONES
☐ 102. DENNIS WERTH
☐ 103. JOE LEFEBVRE
☐ 104. BRIAN DOYLE
☐ 105. AURELIO RODRIGUEZ
☐ 106. DOUG BIRD
☐ 107. MIKE GRIFFIN
☐ 108. TIM LOLLAR
☐ 109. WILLIE RANDOLPH
☐ 642. TEAM CHECKLIST(B)
☐ 650. REGGIE JACKSON

OAKLAND A'S

☐ 351. RICKEY HENDERSON
☐ 572. RICK LANGFORD
☐ 573. MIKE NORRIS
☐ 574. RICKEY HENDERSON
☐ 575. TONY ARMAS
☐ 576. DAVE REVERING
☐ 577. JEFF NEWMAN
☐ 578. BOB LACEY
☐ 579. BRIAN KINGMAN
☐ 580. MITCHELL PAGE
☐ 581. BILLY MARTIN(M)
☐ 582. ROB PICCIOLO
☐ 583. MIKE HEATH
☐ 584. MICKEY KLUTTS
☐ 585. ORLANDO GONZALEZ
☐ 586. MIKE DAVIS
☐ 587. WAYNE GROSS
☐ 588. MATT KEOUGH
☐ 589. STEVE MCCATTY
☐ 590. DWAYNE MURPHY
☐ 591. MARIO GUERRERO
☐ 592. DAVE MCKAY
☐ 593. JIM ESSIAN
☐ 656. TEAM CHECKLIST(B)

PHILADELPHIA PHILLIES

☐ 1. PETE ROSE
☐ 2. LARRY BOWA
☐ 3. MANNY TRILLO
☐ 4. BOB BOONE
☐ 5. MIKE SCHMIDT
☐ 6. STEVE CARLTON
☐ 7. TUG MCGRAW
☐ 8. LARRY CHRISTENSON
☐ 9. BAKE MCBRIDE
☐ 10. GREG LUZINSKI
☐ 11. RON REED
☐ 12. DICKIE NOLES
☐ 13. KEITH MORELAND
☐ 14. BOB WALK
☐ 15. LONNIE SMITH
☐ 16. DICK RUTHVEN
☐ 17. SPARKY LYLE
☐ 18. GREG GROSS
☐ 19. GARRY MADDOX
☐ 20. NINO ESPINOSA
☐ 21. GEORGE VUKOVICH
☐ 22. JOHN VUKOVICH
☐ 23. RAMON AVILES
☐ 24. KEVIN SAUCIER
☐ 25. RANDY LERCH
☐ 26. DEL UNSER
☐ 27. TIM MCCARVER
☐ 640. MIKE SCHMIDT
☐ 641. TEAM CHECKLIST(F)
☐ 657. TUG MCGRAW
☐ 660. STEVE CARLTON

PITTSBURGH PIRATES

☐ 360. DAVE PARKER
☐ 361. OMAR MORENO
☐ 362. KENT TEKULVA
☐ 363. WILLIE STARGELL
☐ 364. PHIL GARNER
☐ 365. ED OTT
☐ 366. DON ROBINSON
☐ 367. CHUCK TANNER(M)
☐ 368. JIM ROOKER
☐ 369. DALE BERRA
☐ 370. JIM BIBBY
☐ 371. STEVE NICOSIA
☐ 372. MIKE EASLER
☐ 373. BILL ROBINSON
☐ 374. LEE LACY
☐ 375. JOHN CANDELARIA
☐ 376. MANNY SANGUILLEN
☐ 377. RICK RHODEN
☐ 378. GRANT JACKSON

- □ 379. TIM FOLI
- □ 380. ROD SCURRY
- □ 381. BILL MADLOCK
- □ 382. KURT BEVACQUA
- □ 383. BERT BLYLEVEN
- □ 384. EDDIE SOLOMON
- □ 385. ENRIQUE ROMO
- □ 386. JOHN MILNER
- □ 419. JESSE JEFFERSON(B)
- □ 649. TEAM CHECKLIST(F)

ST. LOUIS CARDINALS

- □ 528. TED SIMMONS
- □ 529. GARRY TEMPLETON
- □ 530. KEN REITZ
- □ 531. TONY SCOTT
- □ 532. KEN OBERKFELL
- □ 533. BOB SYKES
- □ 534. KEITH SMITH
- □ 535. JOHN LITTLEFIELD
- □ 536. JIM KAAT
- □ 537. BOB FORSCH
- □ 538. MIKE PHILLIPS
- □ 539. TERRY LANDRUM
- □ 540. LEON DURHAM
- □ 541. TERRY KENNEDY
- □ 542. GEORGE HENDRICK
- □ 543. DANE IORG
- □ 544. MARK LITTELL
- □ 545. KEITH HERNANDEZ
- □ 546. SILVIO MARTINEZ
- □ 547. DON HOOD
- □ 548. BOBBY BONDS
- □ 549. MIKE RAMSEY
- □ 550. TOM HERR
- □ 654. TEAM CHECKLIST(B)

SAN DIEGO PADRES

- □ 484. DAVE WINFIELD
- □ 485. ROLLIE FINGERS
- □ 486. GENE RICHARDS
- □ 487. RANDY JONES
- □ 488. OZZIE SMITH
- □ 489. GENE TENACE
- □ 490. BILL FAHEY
- □ 491. JOHN CURTIS
- □ 492. DAVE CASH
- □ 493. TIM FLANNERY
- □ 494. JERRY MUMPHREY
- □ 495. BOB SHIRLEY
- □ 496. STEVE MURA
- □ 497. ERIC RASMUSSEN
- □ 498. BRODERICK PERKINS
- □ 499. BARRY EVANS
- □ 500. CHUCK BAKER
- □ 501. LUIS SALAZAR
- □ 502. GARY LUCAS
- □ 503. MIKE ARMSTRONG
- □ 504. JERRY TURNER
- □ 505. DENNIS KINNEY
- □ 506. WILLIE MONTANEZ
- □ 652. TEAM CHECKLIST(B)

SAN FRANCISCO GIANTS

- □ 432. VIDA BLUE
- □ 433. JACK CLARK
- □ 434. WILLIE MCCOVEY
- □ 435. MIKE IVIE
- □ 436. DARRELL EVANS
- □ 437. TERRY WHITFIELD
- □ 438. RENNIE STENNETT
- □ 439. JOHN MONTEFUSCO
- □ 440. JIM WOHLFORD
- □ 441. BILL NORTH
- □ 442. MILT MAY
- □ 443. MAX VENABLE
- □ 444. ED WHITSON
- □ 445. AL HOLLAND
- □ 446. RANDY MOFFITT
- □ 447. BOB KNEPPER
- □ 448. GARY LAVELLE
- □ 449. GREG MINTON
- □ 450. JOHNNIE LEMASTER
- □ 451. LARRY HERNDON
- □ 452. RICH MURRAY
- □ 453. JOE PETTINI
- □ 454. ALLEN RIPLEY
- □ 455. DENNIS LITTLEJOHN
- □ 456. TOM GRIFFIN
- □ 457. ALAN HARGESHEIMER
- □ 458. JOE STRAIN
- □ 651. TEAM CHECKLIST(B)

SEATTLE MARINERS

- □ 594. DAVE HEAVERLO
- □ 595. MUARY WILLS(M)
- □ 596. JUAN BENIQUEZ
- □ 597. RODNEY CRAIG
- □ 598. JIM ANDERSON
- □ 599. FLOYD BANNISTER
- □ 600. BRUCE BOCHTE
- □ 601. JULIO CRUZ
- □ 602. TED COX
- □ 603. DAN MEYER
- □ 604. LARRY COX
- □ 605. BILL STEIN
- □ 607. DAVE A. ROBERTS
- □ 608. LEON ROBERTS
- □ 609. REGGIE WALTON
- □ 610. DAVE ELDER
- □ 611. LARRY MILBOURNE
- □ 612. KIM ALLEN
- □ 613. MARIO MENDOZA
- □ 614. TOM PACIOREK
- □ 615. GLENN ABBOTT
- □ 616. JOE SIMPSON
- □ 658. TEAM CHECKLIST(F)

TEXAS RANGERS

- □ 617. MICKEY RIVERS
- □ 618. JIM KERN
- □ 619. JIM SUNDBERG
- □ 620. RICHIE ZISK
- □ 621. JON MATLACK
- □ 622. FERGUSON JENKINS
- □ 623. PAT CORRALES(M)
- □ 624. ED FIGUEROA
- □ 625. BUDDY BELL
- □ 626. AL OLIVER
- □ 627. DOC MEDICH
- □ 628. BUMP WILLS
- □ 629. RUSTY STAUB
- □ 630. PAT PUTNAM
- □ 631. JOHN GRUBB
- □ 632. DANNY DARWIN
- □ 633. KEN CLAY
- □ 634. JIM NORRIS
- □ 635. JOHN BUTCHER
- □ 636. DAVE W. ROBERTS
- □ 637. BILLY SAMPLE
- □ 658. TEAM CHECKLIST(B)

TORONTO BLUE JAYS

- □ 409. BOB BAILOR
- □ 410. OTTO VELEZ
- □ 411. ERNIE WHITT
- □ 412. JIM CLANCY
- □ 413. BARRY BONNELL
- □ 414. DAVE STIEB
- □ 415. DAMASO GARCIA
- □ 416. JOHN MAYBERRY
- □ 417. ROY HOWELL
- □ 418. DANNY AINGE
- □ 419. JESSE JEFFERSON(F)
- □ 420. JOEY MCLAUGHLIN
- □ 421. LLOYD MOSEBY
- □ 422. AL WOODS
- □ 423. GARTH IORG
- □ 424. DOUG AULT
- □ 425. KEN SCHROM
- □ 426. MIKE WILLIS
- □ 427. STEVE BRAUN
- □ 428. BOB DAVIS
- □ 429. JERRY GARVIN
- □ 430. ALFREDO GRIFFIN
- □ 431. BOB MATTICK(M)
- □ 651. TEAM CHECKLIST(F)

1982 FLEER (660)
2 1/2" X 3 1/2"

ATLANTA BRAVES

- □ 428. BRIAN ASSELSTINE
- □ 429. BRUCE BENEDICT
- □ 430. TOM BOGGS
- □ 431. LARRY BRADFORD
- □ 432. RICK CAMP
- □ 433. CHRIS CHAMBLISS
- □ 434. GENE GARBER
- □ 435. PRESTON HANNA
- □ 436. BOB HORNER
- □ 437. GLENN HUBBARD
- □ 438. AL HRABOSKY
- □ 439. RUFINO LINARES
- □ 440. RICK MAHLER
- □ 441. ED MILLER
- □ 442. JOHN MONTEFUSCO
- □ 443. DALE MURPHY
- □ 444. PHIL NIEKRO
- □ 445. GAYLORD PERRY
- □ 446. BIFF POCOROBA
- □ 447. RAFAEL RAMIREZ
- □ 448. JERRY ROYSTER
- □ 449. CLAUDELL WASHINGTON
- □ 655. TEAM CHECKLIST(B)

BALTIMORE ORIOLES

- □ 157. BENNY AYALA
- □ 158. MARK BELANGER
- □ 159. AL BUMBRY
- □ 160. TERRY CROWLEY
- □ 161. RICH DAUER
- □ 162. DOUG DECINCES
- □ 163. RICK DEMPSEY
- □ 164. JIM DWYER
- □ 165. MIKE FLANAGAN
- □ 166. DAVE FORD
- □ 167. DAN GRAHAM
- □ 168. WAYNE KRENCHICKI
- □ 169. JOHN LOWENSTEIN
- □ 170. DENNIS MARTINEZ
- □ 171. TIPPY MARTINEZ
- □ 172. SCOTT MCGREGOR
- □ 173. JOSE MORALES
- □ 174. EDDIE MURRAY
- □ 175. JIM PALMER
- □ 176. CAL RIPKEN
- □ 177. GARY ROENICKE
- □ 178. LENN SAKATA
- □ 179. KEN SINGLETON
- □ 180. SAMMY STEWART

☐ 181. TIM STODDARD
☐ 182. STEVE STONE
☐ 650. TEAM CHECKLIST(F)

BOSTON RED SOX

☐ 287. GARY ALLENSON
☐ 288. TOM BURGMEIER
☐ 289. BILL CAMPBELL
☐ 290. MARK CLEAR
☐ 291. STEVE CRAWFORD
☐ 292. DENNIS ECKERSLEY
☐ 293. DWIGHT EVANS
☐ 294. RICH GEDMAN
☐ 295. GARRY HANCOCK
☐ 296. GLENN HOFFMAN
☐ 297. BRUCE HURST
☐ 298. CARNEY LANSFORD
☐ 299. RICK MILLER
☐ 300. REID NICHOLS
☐ 301. BOB OJEDA
☐ 302. TONY PEREZ
☐ 303. CHUCK RAINEY
☐ 304. JERRY REMY
☐ 305. JIM RICE
☐ 306. JOE RUDI
☐ 307. BOB STANLEY
☐ 308. DAVE STAPLETON
☐ 309. FRANK TANANA
☐ 310. MIKE TORREZ
☐ 311. JOHN TUDOR
☐ 312. CARL YASTRZEMSKI
☐ 652. TEAM CHECKLIST(B)

CALIFORNIA ANGELS

☐ 450. DON AASE
☐ 451. DON BAYLOR
☐ 452. JUAN BENIQUEZ
☐ 453. RICK BURLESON
☐ 454. BERT CAMPANERIS
☐ 455. ROD CAREW
☐ 456. BOB CLARK
☐ 457. BRIAN DOWNING
☐ 458. DAN FORD
☐ 459. KEN FORSCH
☐ 460. DAVE FROST
☐ 461. BOBBY GRICH
☐ 462. LARRY HARLOW
☐ 463. JOHN HARRIS
☐ 464. ANDY HASSLER
☐ 465. BUTCH HOBSON
☐ 466. JESSE JEFFERSON
☐ 467. BRUCE KISON
☐ 468. FRED LYNN
☐ 469. ANGEL MORENO
☐ 470. ED OTT
☐ 471. FRED PATEK
☐ 472. STEVE RENKO
☐ 473. MIKE WITT
☐ 474. GEOFF ZAHN
☐ 656. TEAM CHECKLIST(F)

CHICAGO CUBS

☐ 586. DOUG BIRD
☐ 587. TIM BLACKWELL
☐ 588. BOBBY BONDS
☐ 589. BILL BUCKNER
☐ 590. BILL CAUDILL
☐ 591. HECTOR CRUZ
☐ 592. JODY DAVID
☐ 593. IVAN DEJESUS
☐ 594. STEVE DILLARD
☐ 595. LEON DURHAM
☐ 596. RAWLY EASTWICK
☐ 597. STEVE HENDERSON
☐ 598. MIKE KRUKOW
☐ 599. MIKE LUM
☐ 600. RANDY MARTZ
☐ 601. JERRY MORALES
☐ 602. KEN REITZ
☐ 603. LEE SMITH
☐ 604. DICK TIDROW
☐ 605. JIM TRACY
☐ 606. MIKE TYSON
☐ 607. TY WALLER
☐ 659. TEAM CHECKLIST(F)

CHICAGO WHITE SOX

☐ 335. BILL ALMON
☐ 336. HAROLD BAINES
☐ 337. ROSS BAUMGARTEN
☐ 338. TONY BERNAZARD
☐ 339. BRITT BURNS
☐ 340. RICHARD DOTSON
☐ 341. JIM ESSIAN
☐ 342. ED FARMER
☐ 343. CARLTON FISK
☐ 344. KEVIN HICKEY
☐ 345. LAMARR HOYT
☐ 346. LAMAR JOHNSON
☐ 347. JERRY KOOSMAN
☐ 348. RUSTY KUNTZ
☐ 349. DENNIS LAMP
☐ 350. RON DEFLORE
☐ 351. CHET LEMON
☐ 352. GREG LUZINSKI
☐ 353. BOB MOLINARO
☐ 354. JIM MORRISON
☐ 355. WAYNE NORDHAGEN
☐ 356. GREG PRYOR
☐ 357. MIKE SQUIRES
☐ 358. STEVE TROUT
☐ 653. TEAM CHECKLIST(B)

CINCINNATI REDS

☐ 57. JOHNNY BENCH
☐ 58. BRUCE BERENYI
☐ 59. LARRY BIITTNER
☐ 60. SCOTT BROWN
☐ 61. DAVE COLLINS
☐ 62. GEOFF COMBE
☐ 63. DAVE CONCEPCION
☐ 64. DAN DRIESSEN
☐ 65. JOE EDELEN
☐ 66. GEORGE FÓSTER
☐ 67. KEN GRIFFEY
☐ 68. PAUL HOUSEHOLDER
☐ 69. TOM HUME
☐ 70. JUNIOR KENNEDY
☐ 71. RAY KNIGHT
☐ 72. MIKE LACOSS
☐ 73. RAFAEL LANDESTOY
☐ 74. CHARLIE LEIBRANDT
☐ 75. SAM MEJIAS
☐ 76. PAUL MOSKAU
☐ 77. JOE NOLAN
☐ 78. MIKE O'BERRY
☐ 79. RON OESTER
☐ 80. FRANK PASTORE
☐ 81. JOE PRICE
☐ 82. TOM SEAVER
☐ 83. MARIO SOTO
☐ 84. MIKE VAIL
☐ 648. TEAM CHECKLIST(F)

CLEVELAND INDIANS

☐ 359. ALAN BANNISTER
☐ 360. LEN BARKER
☐ 361. BERT BLYLEVEN
☐ 362. JOE CHARBONEAU
☐ 363. JOHN DENNY
☐ 364. BO DIAZ
☐ 365. MIGUEL DILONE
☐ 366. JERRY DYBZINSKI
☐ 367. WAYNE GARLAND
☐ 368. MIKE HARGROVE
☐ 369. TOBY HARRAH
☐ 370. RON HASSEY
☐ 371. VON HAYES
☐ 372. PAT KELLY
☐ 373. DUANE KUIPER
☐ 374. RICK MANNING
☐ 375. SID MONGE
☐ 376. JORGE ORTA
☐ 377. DAVE ROSELLO
☐ 378. DAN SPILLNER
☐ 379. MIKE STANTON
☐ 380. ANDRE THORNTON
☐ 381. TOM VERYZER
☐ 382. RICK WAITS
☐ 654. TEAM CHECKLIST(F)

DETROIT TIGERS

☐ 263. TOM BROOKENS
☐ 264. GEORGE CAPPUZZELLO
☐ 265. MARTY CASTILLO
☐ 266. AL COWENS
☐ 267. KIRK GIBSON
☐ 268. RICHIE HEBNER
☐ 269. RON JACKSON
☐ 270. LYNN JONES
☐ 271. STEVE KEMP
☐ 272. RICK LEACH
☐ 273. AURELIO LOPEZ
☐ 274. JACK MORRIS
☐ 275. KEVIN SAUCIER
☐ 276. LANCE PARRISH
☐ 277. RICK PETERS
☐ 278. DAN PETRY
☐ 279. DAVID ROZEMA
☐ 280. STAN PAPI
☐ 281. DAN SCHATZEDER
☐ 282. CHAMP SUMMERS
☐ 283. ALAN TRAMMELL
☐ 284. LOU WHITAKER
☐ 285. MILT WILCOX
☐ 286. JOHN WOCKENFUSS
☐ 652. TEAM CHECKLIST(F)

HOUSTON ASTROS

☐ 212. ALAN ASHBY
☐ 213. CESAR CEDENO
☐ 214. JOSE CRUZ
☐ 215. KIKO GARCIA
☐ 216. PHIL GARNER
☐ 217. DANNY HEEP
☐ 218. ART HOWE
☐ 219. BOB KNEPPER
☐ 220. FRANK LACORTE
☐ 221. JOE NIEKRO
☐ 222. JOE PITTMAN
☐ 223. TERRY PUHL
☐ 224. LUIS PUJOLS
☐ 225. CRAIG REYNOLDS
☐ 226. J.R. RICHARD
☐ 227. DAVE W. ROBERTS
☐ 228. VERN RUHLE
☐ 229. NOLAN RYAN
☐ 230. JOE SAMBITO
☐ 231. TONY SCOTT
☐ 232. DAVE SMITH
☐ 233. HARRY SPILMAN
☐ 234. DON SUTTON
☐ 235. DICKIE THON
☐ 236. DENNY WALLING
☐ 237. GARY WOODS
☐ 651. TEAM CHECKLIST(F)

KANSAS CITY ROYALS

☐ 404. WILLIE AIKENS
☐ 405. GEORGE BRETT
☐ 406. KEN BRETT
☐ 407. DAVE CHALK
☐ 408. RICH GALE
☐ 409. CESAR GERONIMO
☐ 410. LARRY GURA
☐ 411. CLINT HURDLE

- □ 412. MIKE JONES
- □ 413. DENNIS LEONARD
- □ 414. RENIE MARTIN
- □ 415. LEE MAY
- □ 416. HAL MCRAE
- □ 417. DARRYL MOTLEY
- □ 418. RANCE MULLINIKS
- □ 419. AMOS OTIS
- □ 420. KEN PHELPS
- □ 421. JAMIE QUIRK
- □ 422. DAN QUISENBERRY
- □ 423. PAUL SPLITTORFF
- □ 424. U.L. WASHINGTON
- □ 425. JOHN WATHAN
- □ 426. FRANK WHITE
- □ 427. WILLIE WILSON
- □ 655. TEAM CHECKLIST(F)

LOS ANGELES DODGERS

- □ 1. DUSTY BAKER
- □ 2. BOBBY CASTILLO
- □ 3. RON CEY
- □ 4. TERRY FORSTER
- □ 5. STEVE GARVEY
- □ 6. DAVE GOLTZ
- □ 7. PEDRO GUERRERO
- □ 8. BURT HOOTON
- □ 9. STEVE HOWE
- □ 10. JAY JOHNSTONE
- □ 11. KEN LANDREAUX
- □ 12. DAVEY LOPES
- □ 13. MIKE MARSHALL
- □ 14. BOBBY MITCHELL
- □ 15. RICK MONDAY
- □ 16. TOM NIEDENFUER
- □ 17. TED POWER
- □ 18. JERRY REUSS
- □ 19. RON ROENICKE
- □ 20. BILL RUSSELL
- □ 21. STEVE SAX
- □ 22. MIKE SCIOSCIA
- □ 23. REGGIE SMITH
- □ 24. DAVE STEWART
- □ 25. RICK SUTCLIFFE
- □ 26. DERREL THOMAS
- □ 27. FERNANDO VALENZUELA
- □ 28. BOB WELCH
- □ 29. STEVE YEAGER
- □ 647. TEAM CHECKLIST(F)

MILWAUKEE BREWERS

- □ 133. JERRY AUGUSTINE
- □ 134. SAL BANDO
- □ 135. MARK BROUHARD
- □ 136. MIKE CALDWELL
- □ 137. REGGIE CLEVELAND
- □ 138. CECIL COOPER
- □ 139. JAMIE EASTERLY
- □ 140. MARSHALL EDWARDS
- □ 141. ROLLIE FINGERS
- □ 142. JIM GANTNER
- □ 143. MOOSE HAAS
- □ 144. LARRY HISLE
- □ 145. ROY HOWELL
- □ 146. RICKEY KEETON
- □ 147. RANDY LERCH
- □ 148. PAUL MOLITOR
- □ 149. DON MONEY
- □ 150. CHARLIE MOORE
- □ 151. BEN OGLIVIE
- □ 152. TED SIMMONS
- □ 153. JIM SLATON
- □ 154. GORMAN THOMAS
- □ 155 ROBIN YOUNT
- □ 156. PETE VUCKOVICH
- □ 649. TEAM CHECKLIST(B)

MINNESOTA TWINS

- □ 545. GLENN ADAMS
- □ 546. FERNANDO ARROYO
- □ 547. JOHN VERHOEVEN
- □ 548. SAL BUTERA
- □ 549. JOHN CASTINO
- □ 550. DON COOPER
- □ 551. DOUG CORBETT
- □ 552. DAVE ENGLE
- □ 553. ROGER ERICKSON
- □ 554. DANNY GOODWIN
- □ 555. DARRELL JACKSON
- □ 556. PETE MACKANIN
- □ 557. JACK O'CONNOR
- □ 558. HOSKEN POWELL
- □ 559. PETE REDFERN
- □ 560. ROY SMALLEY
- □ 561. CHUCK BAKER
- □ 562. GARY WARD
- □ 563. ROB WILFONG
- □ 564. AL WILLIAMS
- □ 565. BUTCH WYNEGAR
- □ 658. TEAM CHECKLIST(F)

MONTREAL EXPOS

- □ 183. STAN BAHNSEN
- □ 184. RAY BURRIS
- □ 185. GARY CARTER
- □ 186. WARREN CROMARTIE
- □ 187. ANDRE DAWSON
- □ 188. TERRY FRANCONA
- □ 189. WOODIE FRYMAN
- □ 190. BILL GULLICKSON
- □ 191. GRANT JACKSON
- □ 192. WALLACE JOHNSON
- □ 193. CHARLIE LEA
- □ 194. BILL LEE
- □ 195. JERRY MANUEL
- □ 196. BRAD MILLS
- □ 197. JOHN MILNER
- □ 198. ROWLAND OFFICE
- □ 199. DAVID PALMER
- □ 200. LARRY PARRISH
- □ 201. MIKE PHILLIPS
- □ 202. TIM RAINES
- □ 203. BOBBY RAMOS
- □ 204. JEFF REARDON
- □ 205. STEVE ROGERS
- □ 206. SCOTT SANDERSON
- □ 207. RODNEY SCOTT
- □ 208. ELIAS SOSA
- □ 209. CHRIS SPEIER
- □ 210. TIM WALLACH
- □ 211. JERRY WHITE
- □ 630. TEAM CHECKLIST(B)

NEW YORK METS

- □ 520. NEIL ALLEN
- □ 521. BOB BAILOR
- □ 522. HUBIE BROOKS
- □ 523. MIKE CUBBAGE
- □ 524. PETE FALCONE
- □ 525. DOUG FLYNN
- □ 526. TOM HAUSMAN
- □ 527. RON HODGES
- □ 528. RANDY JONES
- □ 529. MIKE JORGENSEN
- □ 530. DAVE KINGMAN
- □ 531. ED LYNCH
- □ 532. MIKE MARSHALL
- □ 533. LEE MAZZILLI
- □ 534. DYAR MILLER
- □ 535. MIKE SCOTT
- □ 536. RUSTY STAUB
- □ 537. JOHN STEARNS
- □ 538. CRAIG SWAN
- □ 539. FRANK TAVERAS
- □ 540. ALEX TREVINO
- □ 541. ELLIS VALENTINE
- □ 542. MOOKIE WILSON
- □ 543. JOEL YOUNGBLOOD
- □ 544. PAT ZACHRY
- □ 657. TEAM CHECKLIST(B)

NEW YORK YANKEES

- □ 30. BOBBY BROWN
- □ 31. RICK CERONE
- □ 32. RON DAVIS
- □ 33. BUCKY DENT
- □ 34. BARRY FOOTE
- □ 35. GEORGE FRAZIER
- □ 36. OSCAR GAMBLE
- □ 37. RICH GOSSAGE
- □ 38. RON GUIDRY
- □ 39. REGGIE JACKSON
- □ 40. TOMMY JOHN
- □ 41. RUDY MAY
- □ 42. LARRY MILBOURNE
- □ 43. JERRY MUMPHREY
- □ 44. BOBBY MURCER
- □ 45. GENE NELSON
- □ 46. GRAIG NETTLES
- □ 47. JOHNNY OATES
- □ 48. LOU PINIELLA
- □ 49. WILLIE RANDOLPH
- □ 50. RICK REUSCHEL
- □ 51. DAVE REVERING
- □ 52. DAVE RIGHETTI
- □ 53. AURELIO RODRIGUEZ
- □ 54. BOB WATSON
- □ 55. DENNIS WERTH
- □ 56. DAVE WINFIELD
- □ 647. TEAM CHECKLIST(B)

OAKLAND A'S

- □ 85. TONY ARMAS
- □ 86. SHOOTY BABBIT
- □ 87. DAVE BEARD
- □ 88. RICK BOSETTI
- □ 89. KEITH DRUMRIGHT
- □ 90. WAYNE GROSS
- □ 91. MIKE HEATH
- □ 92. RICKEY HENDERSON
- □ 93. CLIFF JOHNSON
- □ 94. JEFF JONES
- □ 95. MATT KEOUGH
- □ 96. BRIAN KINGMAN
- □ 97. MICKEY KLUTTS
- □ 98. RICK LANGFORD
- □ 99. STEVE MCCATTY
- □ 100. DAVE MCKAY
- □ 101. DWAYNE MURPHY
- □ 102. JEFF NEWMAN
- □ 103. MIKE NORRIS
- □ 104. BOB OWCHINKO
- □ 105. MITCHELL PAGE
- □ 106. ROB PICCIOLO
- □ 107. JIM SPENCER
- □ 108. FRED STANLEY
- □ 109. TOM UNDERWOOD
- □ 648. TEAM CHECKLIST(B)

PHILADELPHIA PHILLIES

- □ 238. LUIS AGUAYO
- □ 239. RAMON AVILES
- □ 240. BOB BOONE
- □ 241. LARRY BOWA
- □ 242. WARREN BRUSSTAR
- □ 243. STEVE CARLTON
- □ 244. LARRY CHRISTENSON
- □ 245. DICK DAVIS
- □ 246. GREG GROSS
- □ 247. SPARKY LYLE
- □ 248. GARRY MADDOX
- □ 249. GARY MATTHEWS
- □ 250. BAKE MCBRIDE
- □ 251. TUG MCGRAW
- □ 252. KEITH MORELAND
- □ 253. DICKIE NOLES
- □ 254. MIKE PROLY
- □ 255. RON REED
- □ 256. PETE ROSE
- □ 257. DICK RUTHVEN
- □ 258. MIKE SCHMIDT
- □ 259. LONNIE SMITH

□ 260. MANNY TRILLO
□ 261. DEL UNSER
□ 262. GEORGE VUKOVICH
□ 651. TEAM CHECKLIST(B)

PITTSBURGH PIRATES

□ 475. GARY ALEXANDER
□ 476. DALE BERRA
□ 477. KURT BEVACQUA
□ 478. JIM BIBBY
□ 479. JOHN CANDELARIA
□ 480. VICTOR CRUZ
□ 481. MIKE EASLER
□ 482. TIM FOLI
□ 483. LEE LACY
□ 484. VANCE LAW
□ 485. BILL MADLOCK
□ 486. WILLIE MONTANEZ
□ 487. OMAR MORENO
□ 488. STEVE NICOSIA
□ 489. DAVE PARKER
□ 490. TONY PENA
□ 491. PASCUAL PEREZ
□ 492. JOHNNY RAY
□ 493. RICK RHODEN
□ 494. BILL ROBINSON
□ 495. DON ROBINSON
□ 496. ENRIQUE ROMO
□ 497. ROD SCURRY
□ 498. EDDIE SOLOMON
□ 499. WILLIE STARGELL
□ 500. KENT TEKULVE
□ 501. JASON THOMPSON
□ 656. TEAM CHECKLIST(B)

ST. LOUIS CARDINALS

□ 110. JOAQUIN ANDUJAR
□ 111. STEVE BRAUN
□ 112. BOB FORSCH
□ 113. GEORGE HENDRICK
□ 114. KEITH HERNANDEZ
□ 115. TOM HERR
□ 116. DANE IORG
□ 117. JIM KAAT
□ 118. TITO LANDRUM
□ 119. SIXTO LEZCANO
□ 120. MARK LITTELL
□ 121. JOHN MARTIN
□ 122. SILVIO MARTINEZ
□ 123. KEN OBERKFELL
□ 124. DARRELL PORTER
□ 125. MIKE RAMSEY
□ 126. ORLANDO SANCHEZ
□ 127. BOB SHIRLEY
□ 128. LARY SORENSEN
□ 129. BRUCE SUTTER
□ 130. BOB SYKES
□ 131. GARRY TEMPLETON
□ 132. GENE TENACE
□ 649. TEAM CHECKLIST(F)

SAN FRANCISCO GIANTS

□ 383. DOYLE ALEXANDER
□ 384. VIDA BLUE
□ 385. FRED BREINING
□ 386. ENOS CABELL
□ 387. JACK CLARK
□ 388. DARRELL EVANS
□ 389. TOM GRIFFIN
□ 390. LARRY HERNDON
□ 391. AL HOLLAND
□ 392. GARY LAVELLE
□ 393. JOHNNIE LEMASTER
□ 394. JERRY MARTIN
□ 395. MILT MAY
□ 396. GREG MINTON
□ 397. JOE MORGAN
□ 398. JOE PETTINI
□ 399. ALAN RIPLEY
□ 400. BILLY E. SMITH
□ 401. RENNIE STENNETT
□ 402. ED WHITSON
□ 403. JIM WOHLFORD
□ 654. TEAM CHECKLIST(B)

SAN DIEGO PADRES

□ 566. RANDY BASS
□ 567. JUAN BONILLA
□ 568. DANNY BOONE
□ 569. JOHN CURTIS
□ 570. JUAN EICHELBERGER
□ 571. BARRY EVANS
□ 572. TIM FLANNERY
□ 573. RUPPERT JONES
□ 574. TERRY KENNEDY
□ 575. JOE LEFEBVRE
□ 576. JOHN LITTLEFIELD
□ 577. GARY LUCAS
□ 578. STEVE MURA
□ 579. BRODERICK PERKINS
□ 580. GENE RICHARDS
□ 581. LUIS SALAZAR
□ 582. OZZIE SMITH
□ 583. JOHN URREA
□ 584. CHRIS WELSH
□ 585. RICK WISE
□ 658. TEAM CHECKLIST

SEATTLE MARINERS

□ 502. GLENN ABBOTT
□ 503. JIM ANDERSON
□ 504. FLOYD BANNISTER
□ 505. BRUCE BOCHTE
□ 506. JEFF BURROUGHS
□ 507. BRYAN CLARK
□ 508. KEN CLAY
□ 509. JULIO CRUZ
□ 510. DICK DRAGO
□ 511. GARY GRAY
□ 512. DAN MEYER
□ 513. JERRY NARRON
□ 514. TOM PACIOREK
□ 515. CASEY PARSONS
□ 516. LENNY RANDLE
□ 517. SHANE RAWLEY
□ 518. JOE SIMPSON
□ 519. RICHIE ZISK
□ 657. TEAM CHECKLIST(F)

TEXAS RANGERS

□ 313. BUDDY BELL
□ 314. STEVE COMER
□ 315. DANNY DARWIN
□ 316. JOHN ELLIS
□ 317. JOHN GRUBB
□ 318. RICK HONEYCUTT
□ 319. CHARLIE HOUGH
□ 320. FERGUSON JENKINS
□ 321. JOHN HENRY JOHNSON
□ 322. JIM KERN
□ 323. JON MATLACK
□ 324. DOC MEDICH
□ 325. MARIO MENDOZA
□ 326. AL OLIVER
□ 327. PAT PUTNAM
□ 328. MICKEY RIVERS
□ 329. LEON ROBERTS
□ 330. BILLY SAMPLE
□ 331. BILL STEIN
□ 332. JIM SUNDBERG
□ 333. MARK WAGNER
□ 334. BUMP WILLS
□ 653. TEAM CHECKLIST(F)

TORONTO BLUE JAYS

□ 608. DANNY AINGE
□ 609. JORGE BELL
□ 610. MARK BOMBACK
□ 611. BARRY BONNELL
□ 612. JIM CLANCY
□ 613. DAMASO GARCIA
□ 614. JERRY GARVIN
□ 615. ALFREDO GRIFFIN
□ 616. GARTH IORG
□ 617. LUIS LEAL
□ 618. KEN MACHA
□ 619. JOHN MAYBERRY
□ 620. JOEY MCLAUGHLIN
□ 621. LLOYD MOSEBY
□ 622. DAVE STIEB
□ 623. JACKSON TODD
□ 624. WILLIE UPSHAW
□ 625. OTTO VELEZ
□ 626. ERNIE WHITT
□ 627. AL WOODS
□ 659. TEAM CHECKLIST(B)

1983 FLEER (660)
2 1/2" X 3 1/2"

ATLANTA BRAVES

□ 129. STEVE BEDROSIAN
□ 130. BRUCE BENEDICT
□ 131. TOMMY BOGGS
□ 132. BRETT BUTLER
□ 133. RICK CAMP
□ 134. CHRIS CHAMBLISS
□ 135. KEN DAYLEY
□ 136. GENE GARBER
□ 137. TERRY HARPER
□ 138. BOB HORNER
□ 139. GLENN HUBBARD
□ 140. RUFINO LINARES
□ 141. RICK MAHLER
□ 142. DALE MURPHY
□ 143. PHIL NIEKRO
□ 144. PASCUAL PEREZ
□ 145. BIFF POCOROBA
□ 146. RAFAEL RAMIREZ
□ 147. JERRY ROYSTER
□ 148. KEN SMITH
□ 149. BOB WALK
□ 150. CLAUDELL WASHINGTON
□ 151. BOB WATSON
□ 152. LARRY WHISENTON
□ 649. TEAM CHECKLIST(B)

BALTIMORE ORIOLES

□ 52. BENNY AYALA
□ 53. BOB BONNER
□ 54. AL BUMBRY
□ 55. TERRY CROWLEY
□ 56. STORM DAVIS
□ 57. RICH DAUER
□ 58. RICK DEMPSEY
□ 59. JIM DWYER
□ 60. MIKE FLANAGAN
□ 61. DAN FORD
□ 62. GLENN GULLIVER
□ 63. JOHN LOWENSTEIN
□ 64. DENNIS MARTINEZ
□ 65. TIPPY MARTINEZ
□ 66. SCOTT MCGREGOR
□ 67. EDDIE MURRAY
□ 68. JOE NOLAN
□ 69. JIM PALMER
□ 70. CAL RIPKEN
□ 71. GARY ROENICKE
□ 72. LENN SAKATA
□ 73. KEN SINGLETON
□ 74. SAMMY STEWART
□ 75. TIM STODDARD
□ 648. TEAM CHECKLIST(F)

BOSTON RED SOX

- ☐ 177. GARY ALLENSON
- ☐ 178. LUIS APONTE
- ☐ 179. WADE BOGGS
- ☐ 180. TOM BURGMEIER
- ☐ 181. MARK CLEAR
- ☐ 182. DENNIS ECKERSLEY
- ☐ 183. DWIGHT EVANS
- ☐ 184. RICH GEDMAN
- ☐ 185. GLENN HOFFMAN
- ☐ 186. BRUCE HURST
- ☐ 187. CARNEY LANSFORD
- ☐ 188. RICK MILLER
- ☐ 189. REID NICHOLS
- ☐ 190. BOB OJEDA
- ☐ 191. TONY PEREZ
- ☐ 192. CHUCK RAINEY
- ☐ 193. JERRY REMY
- ☐ 194. JIM RICE
- ☐ 195. BOB STANLEY
- ☐ 196. DAVE STAPLETON
- ☐ 197. MIKE TORREZ
- ☐ 198. JOHN TUDOR
- ☐ 199. JULIO VALDEZ
- ☐ 200. CARL YASTRZEMSKI
- ☐ 650. TEAM CHECKLIST(B)

CALIFORNIA ANGELS

- ☐ 76. DON AASE
- ☐ 77. DON BAYLOR
- ☐ 78. JUAN BENIQUEZ
- ☐ 79. BOB BOONE
- ☐ 80. RICK BURLESON
- ☐ 81. ROD CAREW
- ☐ 82. BOBBY CLARK
- ☐ 83. DOUG CORBETT
- ☐ 84. JOHN CURTIS
- ☐ 85. DOUG DECINCES
- ☐ 86. BRIAN DOWNING
- ☐ 87. JOE FERGUSON
- ☐ 88. TIM FOLI
- ☐ 89. KEN FORSCH
- ☐ 90. DAVE GOLTZ
- ☐ 91. BOBBY GRICH
- ☐ 92. ANDY HASSLER
- ☐ 93. REGGIE JACKSON
- ☐ 94. RON JACKSON
- ☐ 95. TOMMY JOHN
- ☐ 96. BRUCE KISON
- ☐ 97. FRED LYNN
- ☐ 98. ED OTT
- ☐ 99. STEVE RENKO
- ☐ 100. LUIS SANCHEZ
- ☐ 101. ROB WILFONG
- ☐ 102. MIKE WITT
- ☐ 103. GEOFF ZAHN
- ☐ 648. TEAM CHECKLIST(B)

CHICAGO CUBS

- ☐ 490. DOUG BIRD
- ☐ 491. LARRY BOWA
- ☐ 492. BILL BUCKNER
- ☐ 493. BILL CAMPBELL
- ☐ 494. JODY DAVIS
- ☐ 495. LEON DURHAM
- ☐ 496. STEVE HENDERSON
- ☐ 497. WILLIE HERNANDEZ
- ☐ 498. FERGUSON JENKINS
- ☐ 499. JAY JOHNSTONE
- ☐ 500. JUNIOR KENNEDY
- ☐ 501. RANDY MARTZ
- ☐ 502. JERRY MORALES
- ☐ 503. KEITH MORELAND
- ☐ 504. DICKIE NOLES
- ☐ 505. MIKE PROLY
- ☐ 506. ALLEN RIPLEY
- ☐ 507. RYNE SANDBERG
- ☐ 508. LEE SMITH
- ☐ 509. PAT TABLER
- ☐ 510. DICK TIDROW
- ☐ 511. BUMP WILLS
- ☐ 512. GARY WOODS
- ☐ 657. TEAM CHECKLIST(F)

CHICAGO WHITE SOX

- ☐ 228. BILL ALMON
- ☐ 229. HAROLD BAINES
- ☐ 230. SALOME BAROJAS
- ☐ 231. TONY BERNAZARD
- ☐ 232. BRITT BURNS
- ☐ 233. RICHARD DOTSON
- ☐ 234. ERNESTO ESCARREGA
- ☐ 235. CARLTON FISK
- ☐ 236. JERRY HAIRSTON
- ☐ 237. KEVIN HICKEY
- ☐ 238. LEMARR HOYT
- ☐ 239. STEVE KEMP
- ☐ 240. JIM KERN
- ☐ 241. RON KITTLE
- ☐ 242. JERRY KOOSMAN
- ☐ 243. DENNIS LAMP
- ☐ 244. RUDY LAW
- ☐ 245. VANCE LAW
- ☐ 246. RON LEFLORE
- ☐ 247. GREG LUZINSKI
- ☐ 248. TOM PACIOREK
- ☐ 249. AURELIO RODRIGUEZ
- ☐ 250. MIKE SQUIRES
- ☐ 251. STEVE TROUT
- ☐ 651. TEAM CHECKLIST(B)

CINCINNATI REDS

- ☐ 584. JOHNNY BENCH
- ☐ 585. BRUCE BERENYI
- ☐ 586. LARRY BIITTNER
- ☐ 587. CESAR CEDENO
- ☐ 588. DAVE CONCEPCION
- ☐ 589. DAN DRIESSEN
- ☐ 590. GREG HARRIS
- ☐ 591. BEN HAYES
- ☐ 592. PAUL HOUSEHOLDER
- ☐ 593. TOM HUME
- ☐ 594. WAYNE KRENCHICKI
- ☐ 595. RAFAEL LANDESTOY
- ☐ 596. CHARLIE LEIBRANDT
- ☐ 597. EDDIE MILNER
- ☐ 598. RON OESTER
- ☐ 599. FRANK PASTORE
- ☐ 600. JOE PRICE
- ☐ 601. TOM SEAVER
- ☐ 602. BOB SHIRLEY
- ☐ 603. MARIO SOTO
- ☐ 604. ALEX TREVINO
- ☐ 605. MIKE VAIL
- ☐ 606. DUANE WALKER
- ☐ 659. TEAM CHECKLIST(F)

CLEVELAND INDIANS

- ☐ 400. CHRIS BANDO
- ☐ 401. ALAN BANNISTER
- ☐ 402. LEN BARKER
- ☐ 403. TOM BRENNAN
- ☐ 404. CARMELO CASTILLO
- ☐ 405. MIGUEL DILONE
- ☐ 406. JERRY DYBZINSKI
- ☐ 407. MIKE FISCHLIN
- ☐ 408. ED GLYNN
- ☐ 409. MIKE HARGROVE
- ☐ 410. TOBY HARRAH
- ☐ 411. RON HASSEY
- ☐ 412. VON HAYES
- ☐ 413. RICK MANNING
- ☐ 414. BAKE MCBRIDE
- ☐ 415. LARRY MILBOURNE
- ☐ 416. BILL NAHORODNY
- ☐ 417. JACK PERCONTE
- ☐ 418. LARY SORENSEN
- ☐ 419. DAN SPILLNER
- ☐ 420. RICK SUTCLIFFE
- ☐ 421. ANDRE THORNTON
- ☐ 422. RICK WAITS
- ☐ 423. EDDIE WHITSON
- ☐ 655. TEAM CHECKLIST(F)

DETROIT TIGERS

- ☐ 327. TOM BROOKENS
- ☐ 328. ENOS CABELL
- ☐ 329. KIRK GIBSON
- ☐ 330. LARRY HERNDON
- ☐ 331. MIKE IVIE
- ☐ 332. HOWARD JOHNSON
- ☐ 333. LYNN JONES
- ☐ 334. RICK LEACH
- ☐ 335. CHET LEMON
- ☐ 336. JACK MORRIS
- ☐ 337. LANCE PARRISH
- ☐ 338. LARRY PASHNICK
- ☐ 339. DAN PETRY
- ☐ 340. DAVE ROZEMA
- ☐ 341. DAVE RUCKER
- ☐ 342. ELIAS SOSA
- ☐ 343. DAVE TOBIK
- ☐ 344. ALAN TRAMMELL
- ☐ 345. JERRY TURNER
- ☐ 346. JERRY UJDUR
- ☐ 347. PAT UNDERWOOD
- ☐ 348. LOU WHITAKER
- ☐ 349. MILT WILCOX
- ☐ 350. GLENN WILSON
- ☐ 351. JOHN WOCKENFUSS
- ☐ 653. TEAM CHECKLIST(B)

HOUSTON ASTROS

- ☐ 445. ALAN ASHBY
- ☐ 446. JOSE CRUZ
- ☐ 447. KIKO GARCIA
- ☐ 448. PHIL GARNER
- ☐ 449. DANNY HEEP
- ☐ 450. ART HOWE
- ☐ 451. BOB KNEPPER
- ☐ 452. ALAN KNICELY
- ☐ 453. RAY KNIGHT
- ☐ 454. FRANK LACORTE
- ☐ 455. MIKE LACOSS
- ☐ 456. RANDY MOFFITT
- ☐ 457. JOE NIEKRO
- ☐ 458. TERRY PUHL
- ☐ 459. LUIS PUJOLS
- ☐ 460. CRAIG REYNOLDS
- ☐ 461. BERT ROBERGE
- ☐ 462. VERN RUHLE
- ☐ 463. NOLAN RYAN
- ☐ 464. JOE SAMBITO
- ☐ 465. TONY SCOTT
- ☐ 466. DAVE SMITH
- ☐ 467. HARRY SPILMAN
- ☐ 468. DICKIE THON
- ☐ 469. DENNY WALLING
- ☐ 656. TEAM CHECKLIST(F)

LOS ANGELES DODGERS

- ☐ 201. DUSTY BAKER
- ☐ 202. JOE BECKWITH
- ☐ 203. GREG BROCK
- ☐ 204. RON CEY
- ☐ 205. TERRY FORSTER
- ☐ 206. STEVE GARVEY
- ☐ 207. PEDRO GUERRERO
- ☐ 208. BURT HOOTON
- ☐ 209. STEVE HOWE
- ☐ 210. KEN LANDREAUX
- ☐ 211. MIKE MARSHALL
- ☐ 212. CANDY MALDONADO
- ☐ 213. RICK MONDAY
- ☐ 214. TOM NIEDENFUER
- ☐ 215. JORGE ORTA
- ☐ 216. JERRY REUSS
- ☐ 217. RON ROENICKE
- ☐ 218. VINCENTE ROMO
- ☐ 219. BILL RUSSELL
- ☐ 220. STEVE SAX
- ☐ 221. MIKE SCIOSCIA
- ☐ 222. DAVE STEWART
- ☐ 223. DERREL THOMAS
- ☐ 224. FERNANDO VALENZUELA
- ☐ 225. BOB WELCH
- ☐ 226. RICKY WRIGHT
- ☐ 227. STEVE YEAGER
- ☐ 651. TEAM CHECKLIST(F)

KANSAS CITY ROYALS

- ☐ 104. WILLIE AIKENS
- ☐ 105. MIKE ARMSTRONG
- ☐ 106. VIDA BLUE
- ☐ 107. BUD BLACK
- ☐ 108. GEORGE BRETT
- ☐ 109. BILL CASTRO
- ☐ 110. ONIX CONCEPCION
- ☐ 111. DAVE FROST
- ☐ 112. CESAR GERONIMO
- ☐ 113. LARRY GURA
- ☐ 114. STEVE HAMMOND
- ☐ 115. DON HOOD
- ☐ 116. DENNIS LEONARD
- ☐ 117. JERRY MARTIN

☐ 118. LEE MAY
☐ 119. HAL MCRAE
☐ 120. AMOS OTIS
☐ 121. GREG PRYOR
☐ 122. DAN QUISENBERRY
☐ 123. DON SLAUGHT
☐ 124. PAUL SPLITTORFF
☐ 125. U.L. WASHINGTON
☐ 126. JOHN WATHAN
☐ 127. FRANK WHITE
☐ 128. WILLIE WILSON
☐ 649. TEAM CHECKLIST(F)

MILWAUKEE BREWERS

☐ 26. JERRY AUGUSTINE
☐ 27. DWIGHT BERNARD
☐ 28. MARK BROUHARD
☐ 29. MIKE CALDWELL
☐ 30. CECIL COOPER
☐ 31. JAMIE EASTERLY
☐ 32. MARSHALL EDWARDS
☐ 33. ROLLIE FINGERS
☐ 34. JIM GANTNER
☐ 35. MOOSE HAAS
☐ 36. ROY HOWELL
☐ 37. PETER LADD
☐ 38. BOB MCCLURE
☐ 39. DOC MEDICH
☐ 40. PAUL MOLITOR
☐ 41. DON MONEY
☐ 42. CHARLIE MOORE
☐ 43. BEN OGLIVIE
☐ 44. ED ROMERO
☐ 45. TED SIMMONS
☐ 46. JIM SLATON
☐ 47. DON SUTTON
☐ 48. GORMAN THOMAS
☐ 49. PETE VUCKOVICH
☐ 50. NED YOST
☐ 51. ROBIN YOUNT
☐ 647. TEAM CHECKLIST(B)

MINNESOTA TWINS

☐ 607. TOM BRUNANSKY
☐ 608. BOBBY CASTILLO
☐ 609. JOHN CASTINO
☐ 610. RON DAVIS
☐ 611. LENNY FAEDO
☐ 612. TERRY FELTON
☐ 613. GARY GAETTI
☐ 614. MICKEY HATCHER
☐ 615. BRAD HAVENS
☐ 616. KENT HRBEK
☐ 617. RANDY JOHNSON
☐ 618. TIM LAUDNER
☐ 619. JEFF LITTLE
☐ 620. BOB MITCHELL
☐ 621. JACK O'CONNOR
☐ 622. JOHN PACELLA
☐ 623. PETE REDFERN
☐ 624. JESUS VEGA
☐ 625. FRANK VIOLA
☐ 626. RON WASHINGTON
☐ 627. GARY WARD
☐ 628. AL WILLIAMS
☐ 659. TEAM CHECKLIST(B)

MONTREAL EXPOS

☐ 277. RAY BURRIS
☐ 278. GARY CARTER
☐ 279. WARREN CROMARTIE
☐ 280. ANDRE DAWSON
☐ 281. TERRY FRANCONA
☐ 282. DOUG FLYNN
☐ 283. WOODY FRYMAN
☐ 284. BILL GULLICKSON
☐ 285. WALLACE JOHNSON
☐ 286. CHARLIE LEA
☐ 287. RANDY LERCH
☐ 288. BRAD MILLS
☐ 289. DAN NORMAN
☐ 290. AL OLIVER
☐ 291. DAVID PALMER
☐ 292. TIM RAINES
☐ 293. JEFF REARDON
☐ 294. STEVE ROGERS
☐ 295. SCOTT SANDERSON
☐ 296. DAN SCHATZEDER
☐ 297. BRYN SMITH
☐ 298. CHRIS SPEIER
☐ 299. TIM WALLACH
☐ 300. JERRY WHITE
☐ 301. JOEL YOUNGBLOOD
☐ 652. TEAM CHECKLIST(B)

NEW YORK METS

☐ 536. NEIL ALLEN
☐ 537. WALLY BACKMAN
☐ 538. BOB BAILOR
☐ 539. HUBIE BROOKS
☐ 540. CARLOS DIAZ
☐ 541. PETE FALCONE
☐ 542. GEORGE FOSTER
☐ 543. RON GARDENHIRE
☐ 544. BRIAN GILES
☐ 545. RON HODGES
☐ 546. RANDY JONES
☐ 547. MIKE JORGENSEN
☐ 548. DAVE KINGMAN
☐ 549. ED LYNCH
☐ 550. JESSE OROSCO
☐ 551. RICK OWNBEY
☐ 552. CHARLIE PULEO
☐ 553. GARY RAJSICH
☐ 554. MIKE SCOTT
☐ 555. RUSTY STAUB
☐ 556. JOHN STEARNS
☐ 557. CRAIG SWAN
☐ 558. ELLIS VALENTINE
☐ 559. TOM VERYZER
☐ 560. MOOKIE WILSON
☐ 561. PAT ZACHRY
☐ 658. TEAM CHECKLIST(F)

NEW YORK YANKEES

☐ 376. RICK CERONE
☐ 377. DAVE COLLINS
☐ 378. ROGER ERICKSON
☐ 379. GEORGE FRAZIER
☐ 380. OSCAR GAMBLE
☐ 381. RICH GOSSAGE
☐ 382. KEN GRIFFEY
☐ 383. RON GUIDRY
☐ 384. DAVE LAROCHE
☐ 385. RUDY MAY
☐ 386. JOHN MAYBERRY
☐ 387. LEE MAZZILLI
☐ 388. MIKE MORGAN
☐ 389. JERRY MUMPHREY
☐ 390. BOBBY MURCER
☐ 391. GRAIG NETTLES
☐ 392. LOU PINIELLA
☐ 393. WILLIE RANDOLPH
☐ 394. SHANE RAWLEY
☐ 395. DAVE RIGHETTI
☐ 396. ANDRE ROBERTSON
☐ 397. ROY SMALLEY
☐ 398. DAVE WINFIELD
☐ 399. BUTCH WYNEGAR
☐ 654. TEAM CHECKLIST(B)

OAKLAND A'S

☐ 513. TONY ARMAS
☐ 514. DAVE BEARD
☐ 515. JEFF BURROUGHS
☐ 516. JOHN D'ACQUISTO
☐ 517. WAYNE GROSS
☐ 518. MIKE HEATH
☐ 519. RICKEY HENDERSON
☐ 520. CLIFF JOHNSON
☐ 521. MATT KEOUGH
☐ 522. BRIAN KINGMAN
☐ 523. RICK LANGFORD
☐ 524. DAVEY LOPES
☐ 525. STEVE MCCATTY
☐ 526. DAVE MCKAY
☐ 527. DAN MEYER
☐ 528. DWAYNE MURPHY
☐ 529. JEFF NEWMAN
☐ 530. MIKE NORRIS
☐ 531. BOB OWCHINKO
☐ 532. JOE RUDI
☐ 533. JIMMY SEXTON
☐ 534. FRED STANLEY
☐ 535. TOM UNDERWOOD
☐ 657. TEAM CHECKLIST(B)

PHILADELPHIA PHILLIES

☐ 153. PORFIORIO ALTAMIRANO
☐ 154. MARTY BYSTROM
☐ 155. STEVE CARLTON
☐ 156. LARRY CHRISTENSON
☐ 157. IVAN DEJESUS
☐ 158. JOHN DENNY
☐ 159. BOB DERNIER
☐ 160. BO DIAZ
☐ 161. ED FARMER
☐ 162. GREG GROSS
☐ 163. MIKE KRUKOW
☐ 164. GARRY MADDOX
☐ 165. GARY MATTHEWS
☐ 166. TUG MCGRAW
☐ 167. BOB MOLINARO
☐ 168. SID MONGE
☐ 169. RON REED
☐ 170. BILL ROBINSON
☐ 171. PETE ROSE
☐ 172. DICK RUTHVEN
☐ 173. MIKE SCHMIDT
☐ 174. MANNY TRILLO
☐ 175. OZZIE VIRGIL
☐ 176. GEORGE VUKOVICH
☐ 650. TEAM CHECKLIST(F)

PITTSBURGH PIRATES

☐ 302. ROSS BAUMGARTEN
☐ 303. DALE BERRA
☐ 304. JOHN CANDELARIA
☐ 305. DICK DAVIS
☐ 306. MIKE EASLER
☐ 307. RICHIE HEBNER
☐ 308. LEE LACY
☐ 309. BILL MADLOCK
☐ 310. LARRY MCWILLIAMS
☐ 311. JOHN MILNER
☐ 312. OMAR MORENO
☐ 313. JIM MORRISON
☐ 314. STEVE NICOSIA
☐ 315. DAVE PARKER

- ☐ 316. TONY PENA
- ☐ 317. JOHNNY RAY
- ☐ 318. RICK RHODEN
- ☐ 319. DON ROBINSON
- ☐ 320. ENRIQUE ROMO
- ☐ 321. MANNY SARMIENTO
- ☐ 322. ROD SCURRY
- ☐ 323. JIM SMITH
- ☐ 324. WILLIE STARGELL
- ☐ 325. JASON THOMPSON
- ☐ 326. KENT TEKULVE
- ☐ 653. TEAM CHECKLIST(F)

ST. LOUIS CARDINALS

- ☐ 1. JOAQUIN ANDUJAR
- ☐ 2. DOUG BAIR
- ☐ 3. STEVE BRAUN
- ☐ 4. GLENN BRUMMER
- ☐ 5. BOB FORSCH
- ☐ 6. DAVID GREEN
- ☐ 7. GEORGE HENDRICK
- ☐ 8. KEITH HERNANDEZ
- ☐ 9. TOM HERR
- ☐ 10. DANE IORG
- ☐ 11. JIM KAAT
- ☐ 12. JEFF LAHTI
- ☐ 13. TITO LANDRUM
- ☐ 14. DAVE LAPOINT
- ☐ 15. WILLIE MCGEE
- ☐ 16. STEVE MURA
- ☐ 17. KEN OBERKFELL
- ☐ 18. DARRELL PORTER
- ☐ 19. MIKE RAMSEY
- ☐ 20. GENE ROOF
- ☐ 21. LONNIE SMITH
- ☐ 22. OZZIE SMITH
- ☐ 23. JOHN STUPER
- ☐ 24. BRUCE SUTTER
- ☐ 25. GENE TENACE
- ☐ 647. TEAM CHECKLIST(F)

SAN DIEGO PADRES

- ☐ 352. KURT BEVACQUA
- ☐ 353. JUAN BONILLA
- ☐ 354. FLOYD CHIFFER
- ☐ 355. LUIS DELEON
- ☐ 356. DAVE DRAVECKY
- ☐ 357. DAVE EDWARDS
- ☐ 358. JUAN EICHELBERGER
- ☐ 359. TIM FLANNERY
- ☐ 360. TONY GWYNN
- ☐ 361. RUPPERT JONES
- ☐ 362. TERRY KENNEDY
- ☐ 363. JOE LEFEBVRE
- ☐ 364. SIXTO LEZCANO
- ☐ 365. TIM LOLLAR
- ☐ 366. GARY LUCAS
- ☐ 367. JOHN MONTEFUSCO
- ☐ 368. BRODERICK PERKINS
- ☐ 369. JOE PITTMAN
- ☐ 370. GENE RICHARDS
- ☐ 371. LUIS SALAZAR
- ☐ 372. ERIC SHOW
- ☐ 373. GARRY TEMPLETON
- ☐ 374. CHRIS WELSH
- ☐ 375. ALAN WIGGINS
- ☐ 654. TEAM CHECKLIST(F)

SAN FRANCISCO GIANTS

- ☐ 252. JIM BARR
- ☐ 253. DAVE BERGMANN
- ☐ 254. FRED BREINING
- ☐ 255. BOB BRENLY
- ☐ 256. JACK CLARK
- ☐ 257. CHILI DAVIS
- ☐ 258. DARRELL EVANS
- ☐ 259. ALAN FOWLKES
- ☐ 260. RICH GALE
- ☐ 261. ATLEE HAMMAKER
- ☐ 262. AL HOLLAND
- ☐ 263. DUANE KUIPER
- ☐ 264. BILL LASKEY
- ☐ 265. GARY LAVELLE
- ☐ 266. JOHNNIE LEMASTER
- ☐ 267. RENIE MARTIN
- ☐ 268. MILT MAY
- ☐ 269. GREG MINTO
- ☐ 270. JOE MORGAN
- ☐ 271. TOM O'MALLEY
- ☐ 272. REGGIE SMITH
- ☐ 273. GUY SULARZ
- ☐ 274. CHAMP SUMMERS
- ☐ 275. MAX VENABLE
- ☐ 276. JIM WOHLFORD
- ☐ 652. TEAM CHECKLIST(F)

SEATTLE MARINERS

- ☐ 470. LARRY ANDERSEN
- ☐ 471. FLOYD BANNISTER
- ☐ 472. JIM BEATTIE
- ☐ 473. BRUCE BOCHTE
- ☐ 474. MANNY CASTILLO
- ☐ 475. BILL CAUDILL
- ☐ 476. BRYAN CLARK
- ☐ 477. AL COWENS
- ☐ 478. JULIO CRUZ
- ☐ 479. TODD CRUZ
- ☐ 480. GARY GRAY
- ☐ 481. DAVE HENDERSON
- ☐ 482. MIKE MOORE
- ☐ 483. GAYLORD PERRY
- ☐ 484. DAVE REVERING
- ☐ 485. JOE SIMPSON
- ☐ 486. MIKE STANTON
- ☐ 487. RICK SWEET
- ☐ 488. ED VANDEBERG
- ☐ 489. RICHIE ZISK
- ☐ 656. TEAM CHECKLIST(B)

TEXAS RANGERS

- ☐ 562. BUDDY BELL
- ☐ 563. JOHN BUTCHER
- ☐ 564. STEVE COMER
- ☐ 565. DANNY DARWIN
- ☐ 566. BUCKY DENT
- ☐ 567. JOHN GRUBB
- ☐ 568. RICK HONEYCUTT
- ☐ 569. DAVE HOSTETLER
- ☐ 570. CHARLIE HOUGH
- ☐ 571. LAMAR JOHNSON
- ☐ 572. JON MATLACK
- ☐ 573. PAUL MIRABELLA
- ☐ 574. LARRY PARRISH
- ☐ 575. MIKE RICHARDT
- ☐ 576. MICKEY RIVERS
- ☐ 577. BILLY SAMPLE
- ☐ 578. DAVE J. SCHMIDT
- ☐ 579. BILL STEIN
- ☐ 580. JIM SUNDBERG
- ☐ 581. FRANK TANANA
- ☐ 582. MARK WAGNER
- ☐ 583. GEORGE WRIGHT
- ☐ 658. TEAM CHECKLIST(B)

TORONTO BLUE JAYS

- ☐ 424 JESSIE BARFIELD
- ☐ 425. BARRY BONNELL
- ☐ 426. JIM CLANCY
- ☐ 427. DAMASO GARCIA
- ☐ 428. JERRY GARVIN
- ☐ 429. ALFREDO GRIFFIN
- ☐ 430. GARTH IORG
- ☐ 431. ROY LEE JACKSON
- ☐ 432. LUIS LEAL
- ☐ 433. BUCK MARTINEZ
- ☐ 434. JOE MCLAUGHLIN
- ☐ 435. LLOYD MOSEBY
- ☐ 436. RANCE MULLINIKS
- ☐ 437. DALE MURRAY
- ☐ 438. WAYNE NORDHAGEN
- ☐ 439. GENE PETRALLI
- ☐ 440. HOSKEN POWELL
- ☐ 441. DAVE STIEB
- ☐ 442. WILLIE UPSHAW
- ☐ 443. ERNIE WHITT
- ☐ 444. AL WOODS
- ☐ 655 TEAM CHECKLIST(B)

1984 FLEER (660)
2 1/2" X 3 1/2"

ATLANTA BRAVES

- ☐ 170. LEN BARKER
- ☐ 171. STEVE BEDROSIAN
- ☐ 172. BRUCE BENEDICT
- ☐ 173. BRETT BUTLER
- ☐ 174. RICK CAMP
- ☐ 175. CHRIS CHAMBLISS
- ☐ 176. KEN DAYLEY
- ☐ 177. PETE FALCONE
- ☐ 178. TERRY FORSTER
- ☐ 179. GENE GARBER
- ☐ 180. TERRY HARPER
- ☐ 181. BOB HORNER
- ☐ 182. GLENN HUBBARD
- ☐ 183. RANDY JOHNSON
- ☐ 184. CRAIG MCMURTRY
- ☐ 185. DONNIE MOORE
- ☐ 186. DALE MURPHY
- ☐ 187. PHIL NIEKRO
- ☐ 188. PASCUAL PEREZ
- ☐ 189. BIFF POCOROBA
- ☐ 190. RAFAEL RAMIREZ
- ☐ 191. JERRY ROYSTER
- ☐ 192. CLAUDELL WASHINGTON
- ☐ 193. BOB WATSON
- ☐ 654. TEAM(F) & TORRE(M)

BALTIMORE ORIOLES

- ☐ 1. MIKE BODDICKER
- ☐ 2. AL BUMBRY
- ☐ 3. TODD CRUZ
- ☐ 4. RICH DAUER
- ☐ 5. STORM DAVIS
- ☐ 6. RICK DEMPSEY
- ☐ 7. JIM DWYER
- ☐ 8. MIKE FLANAGAN
- ☐ 9. DAN FORD
- ☐ 10. JOHN LOWENSTEIN
- ☐ 11. DENNIS MARTINEZ
- ☐ 12. TIPPY MARTINEZ
- ☐ 13. SCOTT MCGREGOR
- ☐ 14. EDDIE MURRAY
- ☐ 15. JOE NOLAN
- ☐ 16. JIM PALMER
- ☐ 17. CAL RIPKEN
- ☐ 18. GARY ROENICKE
- ☐ 19. LENN SAKATA
- ☐ 20. JOHN SHELBY
- ☐ 21. KEN SINGLETON
- ☐ 22. SAMMY STEWARD
- ☐ 23. TIM STODDARD
- ☐ 647. TEAM(F) & ALTOBELLI(M)

BOSTON RED SOX

- ☐ 388. GARY ALLENSON
- ☐ 389. LUIS APONTE
- ☐ 390. TONY ARMAS
- ☐ 391. DOUG BIRD
- ☐ 392. WADE BOGGS
- ☐ 393. DENNIS BOYD
- ☐ 394. MIKE BROWN
- ☐ 395. MARK CLEAR
- ☐ 396. DENNIS ECKERSLEY

- ☐ 397. DWIGHT EVANS
- ☐ 398. RICH GEDMAN
- ☐ 399. GLENN HOFFMAN
- ☐ 400. BRUCE HURST
- ☐ 401. JOHN HENRY JOHNSON
- ☐ 402. ED JURAK
- ☐ 403. RICK MILLER
- ☐ 404. JEFF NEWMAN
- ☐ 405. REID NICHOLS
- ☐ 406. BOB OJEDA
- ☐ 407. JERRY REMY
- ☐ 408. JIM RICE
- ☐ 409. BOB STANELY
- ☐ 410. DAVE STAPLETON
- ☐ 411. JOHN TUDOR
- ☐ 412. CARL YASTRZMESKI
- ☐ 649. TEAM CHECKLIST(B)

CALIFORNIA ANGELS

- ☐ 508. JUAN BENIQUEZ
- ☐ 509. BOB BOONE
- ☐ 510. RICK BURLESON
- ☐ 511. ROD CAREW
- ☐ 512. BOBBY CLARK
- ☐ 513. JOHN CURTIS
- ☐ 514. DOUG DECINCES
- ☐ 515. BRIAN DOWNING
- ☐ 516. TIM FOLI
- ☐ 517. KEN FORSCH
- ☐ 518. BOBBY GRICH
- ☐ 519. ANDY HASSLER
- ☐ 520. REGGIE JACKSON
- ☐ 521. RON JACKSON
- ☐ 522. TOMMY JOHN
- ☐ 523. BRUCE KISON
- ☐ 524. STEVE LUBRATICH
- ☐ 525. FRED LYNN
- ☐ 526. GARY PETTIS
- ☐ 527. LUIS SANCHEZ
- ☐ 528. DARYL SCONIERS
- ☐ 529. ELLIS VALENTINE
- ☐ 530. ROB WILFONG
- ☐ 531. MIKE WITT
- ☐ 532. GEOFF ZAHN
- ☐ 654. TEAM CHECKLIST(B)

CHICAGO CUBS

- ☐ 486. LARRY BOWA
- ☐ 487. WARREN BRUSSTAR
- ☐ 488. BILL BUCKNER
- ☐ 489. BILL CAMPBELL
- ☐ 490. RON CEY
- ☐ 491. JODY DAVIS
- ☐ 492. LEON DURHAM
- ☐ 493. MEL HALL
- ☐ 494. FERGUSON JENKINS
- ☐ 495. JAY JOHNSTONE
- ☐ 496. CRAIG LEFFERTS
- ☐ 497. CARMELO MARTINEZ
- ☐ 498. JERRY MORALES
- ☐ 499. KEITH MORELAND
- ☐ 500. DICKIE NOLES
- ☐ 501. MIKE PROLY
- ☐ 502. CHUCK RAINEY
- ☐ 503. DICK RUTHVEN
- ☐ 504. RYNE SANDBERY
- ☐ 505. LEE SMITH
- ☐ 506. STEVE TROUT
- ☐ 507. GARY WOODS
- ☐ 653. TEAM CHECKLIST(B)

CHICAGO WHITE SOX

- ☐ 50. JUAN AGOSTO
- ☐ 51. HARROLD BAINES
- ☐ 52. FLOYD BANNISTER
- ☐ 53. SALOME BAROJAS
- ☐ 54. BRITT BURNS
- ☐ 55. JULIO CRUZ
- ☐ 56. RICHARD DOTSON
- ☐ 57. JERRY DYBZINSKI
- ☐ 58. CARLTON FISK
- ☐ 59. SCOTT FLETCHER
- ☐ 60. JERRY HAIRSTON
- ☐ 61. KEVIN HICKEY
- ☐ 62. MARC HILL
- ☐ 63. LA MARR HOYT
- ☐ 64. RON KITTLE
- ☐ 65. JERRY KOOSMAN
- ☐ 66. DENNIS LAMP
- ☐ 67. RUDY LAW
- ☐ 68. VANCE LAW
- ☐ 69. GREG LUZINSKI
- ☐ 70. TOM PACIOREK
- ☐ 71. MIKE SQUIRES
- ☐ 72. DICK TIDROW
- ☐ 73. GREG WALKER
- ☐ 649. TEAM(F) & LARUSSA(M)

CINCINNATI REDS

- ☐ 462. JOHNNY BENCY
- ☐ 463. BRUCE BERENYI
- ☐ 464. DANN BILARDELLO
- ☐ 465. CESAR CEDENO
- ☐ 466. DAVE CONCEPCION
- ☐ 467. DAN DRIESSEN
- ☐ 468. NICK ESASKY
- ☐ 469. RICH GALE
- ☐ 470. BEN HAYES
- ☐ 471. PAUL HOUSEHOLDER
- ☐ 471. TOM HUME
- ☐ 473. ALAN KNICELY
- ☐ 474. EDDIE MILNER
- ☐ 475. RON OESTER
- ☐ 476. KELLY PARIS
- ☐ 477. FRANK PASTORE
- ☐ 478. TED POWER
- ☐ 479. JOE PRICE
- ☐ 480. CHARLIE PULEO
- ☐ 481. GARY REDUS
- ☐ 482. BILL SCHERRER
- ☐ 483. MARIO SOTO
- ☐ 484. ALEX TREVINO
- ☐ 485. DUANE WALKER
- ☐ 652. TEAM CHECKLIST(B)

CLEVELAND INDIANS

- ☐ 533. BUD ANDERSON
- ☐ 534. CHRIS BANDO
- ☐ 535. ALAN BANNISTER
- ☐ 536. BERT BLYLEVEN
- ☐ 537. TOM BRENNAN
- ☐ 538. JAMIE EASTERLY
- ☐ 539. JUAN EICHELBERGER
- ☐ 540. JIM ESSIAN
- ☐ 541. MIKE FISCHLIN
- ☐ 542. JULIO FRANCO
- ☐ 543. MIKE HARGROVE
- ☐ 544. TOBY HARRAH
- ☐ 545. RON HASSEY
- ☐ 546. NEAL HEATON
- ☐ 547. BAKE MCBRIDE
- ☐ 548. BRODERICK PERKINS
- ☐ 549. LARY SORENSEN
- ☐ 550. DAN SPILLNER
- ☐ 551. RICK SUTCLIFFE
- ☐ 552. PAT TABLER
- ☐ 553. GORMAN THOMAS
- ☐ 554. ANDRE THORNTON
- ☐ 555. GEORGE VUKOVICH
- ☐ 655. TEAM CHECKLIST(B)

DETROIT TIGERS

- ☐ 74. GLENN ABBOTT
- ☐ 75. HOWARD BAILEY
- ☐ 76. DOUG BAIR
- ☐ 77. JUAN BERENGUER
- ☐ 78. TOM BROOKENS
- ☐ 79. ENOS CABELL
- ☐ 80. KIRK GIBSON
- ☐ 81. JOHN GRUBB
- ☐ 82. LARRY HERNDON
- ☐ 83. WAYNE KRENCHICKI
- ☐ 84. RICK LEACH
- ☐ 85. CHET LEMON
- ☐ 86. AURELIO LOPEZ
- ☐ 87. JACK MORRIS
- ☐ 88. LANCE PARRISH
- ☐ 89. DAN PETRY
- ☐ 90. DAVE ROZEMA
- ☐ 91. ALAN TRAMMELL
- ☐ 92. LOU WHITAKER
- ☐ 93. MILT WILCOX
- ☐ 94. GLENN WILSON
- ☐ 95. JOHN WOCKENFUSS
- ☐ 650. TEAM(F) & ANDERSON(M)

HOUSTON ASTROS

- ☐ 220. ALAN ASHBY
- ☐ 221. KEVIN BASS
- ☐ 222. JOSE CRUZ
- ☐ 223. BILL DAWLEY
- ☐ 224. FRANK DIPINO
- ☐ 225. BILL DORAN
- ☐ 226. PHIL GARNER
- ☐ 227. ART HOWE
- ☐ 228. BOB KNEPPER
- ☐ 229. RAY KNIGHT
- ☐ 230. FRANK LACORTE
- ☐ 231. MIKE LACOSS
- ☐ 232. MIKE MADDEN
- ☐ 233. JERRY MUMPHREY
- ☐ 234. JOE NIEKRO
- ☐ 235. TERRY PUHL
- ☐ 236. LUIS PUJOLS
- ☐ 237. CRAIG REYNOLDS
- ☐ 238. VERN RUHLE
- ☐ 239. NOLAN RYAN
- ☐ 240. MIKE SCOTT
- ☐ 241. TONY SCOTT
- ☐ 242. DAVE SMITH
- ☐ 243. DICKIE THON
- ☐ 244. DENNY WALLING
- ☐ 656. TEAM(F) & LILLIS(M)

KANSAS CITY ROYALS

- ☐ 341. WILLIE AIKENS
- ☐ 342. MIKE ARMSTRONG
- ☐ 343. BUD BLACK
- ☐ 344. GEORGE BRETT
- ☐ 345. ONIX CONCEPCION
- ☐ 346. KEITH CREEL
- ☐ 347. LARRY GURA
- ☐ 348. DON HOOD
- ☐ 349. DENNIS LEONARD
- ☐ 350. HAL MCRAE
- ☐ 351. AMOS OTIS
- ☐ 352. GAYLORD PERRY
- ☐ 353. GREG PRYOR
- ☐ 354. DAN QUISENBERRY
- ☐ 355. STEVE RENKO
- ☐ 356. LEON ROBERTS
- ☐ 357. PAT SHERIDAN
- ☐ 358. JOE SIMPSON
- ☐ 359. DON SLAUGHT
- ☐ 360. PAUL SPLITTORFF
- ☐ 361. U.L. WASHINGTON
- ☐ 362. JOHN WATHAN
- ☐ 363. FRANKE WHITE
- ☐ 364. WILLIE WILSON
- ☐ 647. TEAM CHECKLIST(B)

LOS ANGELES DODGERS

- ☐ 96. DUSTY BAKER
- ☐ 97. JOE BECKWITH
- ☐ 98. GREG BROCK
- ☐ 99. JACK FIMPLE
- ☐ 100. PEDRO GUERRERO
- ☐ 101. RICK HONEYCUTT
- ☐ 102. BURT HOOTON
- ☐ 103. STEVE HOWE
- ☐ 104. KEN LANDREAUX
- ☐ 105. MIKE MARSHALL
- ☐ 106. RICK MONDAY
- ☐ 107. JOSE MORALES
- ☐ 108. TOM NIENDENFUER
- ☐ 109. ALEJANDRO PENA
- ☐ 110. JERRY REUSS
- ☐ 111. BILL RUSSELL
- ☐ 112. STEVE SAX
- ☐ 113. MIKE SCIOSCIA
- ☐ 114. DERREL THOMAS
- ☐ 115. FERNANDO VALENZUELA
- ☐ 116. BOB WELCH
- ☐ 117. STEVE YEAGER
- ☐ 118. PAT ZACHRY
- ☐ 651. TEAM(F) & LASORDA(M)

MILWAUKEE BREWERS

- ☐ 194. JERRY AUGUSTINE
- ☐ 195. MARK BROUHARD
- ☐ 196. MIKE CALDWELL
- ☐ 197. TOM CANDIOTTI

□ 198. CECIL COOPER
□ 199. ROLLIE FINGERS
□ 200. JIM GANTNER
□ 201. BOB GIBSON
□ 202. MOOSE HAAS
□ 203. ROY HOWELL
□ 204. PETE LADD
□ 205. RICK MANNING
□ 206. BOB MCCLURE
□ 207. PAUL MOLITOR
□ 208. DON MONEY
□ 209. CHARLIE MOORE
□ 210. BEN OGLIVIE
□ 211. CHUCK PORTER
□ 212. ED ROMERO
□ 213. TED SIMMONS
□ 214. JIM SLATON
□ 215. DON SUTTON
□ 216. TOM TELLMANN
□ 217. PETE VUCKOVICH
□ 218. NED YOST
□ 219. ROBIN YOUNT
□ 655. TEAM(F) & LACHEMANN(M)

MINNESOTA TWINS

□ 556. DARRELL BROWN
□ 557. TOM BRUNANSKY
□ 558. RANDY BUSH
□ 559. BOBBY CASTILLO
□ 560. JOHN CASTINO
□ 561. RON DAVIS
□ 562. DAVE ENGLE
□ 563. LENNY FAEDO
□ 564. PETE FILSON
□ 565. GARY GAETTI
□ 566. MICKEY HATCHER
□ 567. KENT HRBEK
□ 568. RUSTY KUNTZ
□ 569. TIM LAUDNER
□ 570. RICK LYSANDER
□ 571. BOBBY MITCHELL
□ 572. KEN SCHROM
□ 573. RAY SMITH
□ 574. TIM TEUFEL
□ 575. FRANK VIOLA
□ 576. GARY WARD
□ 577. RON WASHINGTON
□ 578. LEN WHITEHOUSE
□ 579. AL WILLIAMS
□ 656. TEAM CHECKLIST(B)

MONTREAL EXPOS

□ 270. RAY BURRIS
□ 271. GARY CARTER
□ 272. WARREN CROMARTIE
□ 273. ANDRE DAWSON
□ 274. DOUG FLYNN
□ 275. TERRY FRANCONA
□ 276. BILL GULLICKSON
□ 277. BOB JAMES
□ 278. CHARLIE LEA
□ 279. BRYAN LITTLE
□ 280. AL OLIVER
□ 281. TIM RAINES
□ 282. BOBBY RAMOS
□ 283. JEFF REARDON
□ 284. STEVE ROGERS
□ 285. SCOTT SANDERSON
□ 286. DAN SCHATZEDER
□ 287. BRYN SMITH
□ 288. CHRIS SPEIER
□ 289. MANNY TRILLO
□ 290. MIKE VAIL
□ 291. TIM WALLACH
□ 292. CHRIS WELSH
□ 293. JIM WOHLFORD
□ 658. TEAM(F) & VIRDON(M)

NEW YORK METS

□ 580. BOB BAILOR
□ 581. MARK BRADLEY
□ 582. HUBIE BROOKS
□ 583. CARLOS DIAZ
□ 584. GEORGE FOSTER
□ 585. BRIAN GILES
□ 586. DANNY HEEP
□ 587. KEITH HERNANDEZ
□ 588. RON HODGES
□ 589. SCOTT HOLMAN
□ 590. DAVE KINGMAN
□ 591. ED LYNCH
□ 592. JOSE OQUENDO
□ 593. JESSE OROSCO
□ 594. JUNIOR ORTIZ
□ 595. TOM SEAVER
□ 596. DOUG SISK
□ 597. RUSTY STAUB
□ 598. JOHN STEARNS
□ 599. DARRYL STRAWBERRY
□ 600. CRAIG SWAN
□ 601. WALT TERRELL
□ 602. MIKE TORREZ
□ 603. MOOKIE WILSON
□ 657. TEAM CHECKLIST(B)

NEW YORK YANKEES

□ 119. DON BAYLOR
□ 120. BERT CAMPANERIS
□ 121. RICK CERONE
□ 122. RAY FONTENOT
□ 123. GEORGE FRAZIER
□ 124. OSCAR GAMBLE
□ 125. GOOSE GOSSAGE
□ 126. KEN GRIFFEY
□ 127. RON GUIDRY
□ 128. JAY HOWELL
□ 129. STEVE KEMP
□ 130. MATT KEOUGH
□ 131. DON MATTINGLY
□ 132. JOHN MONTEFUSCO
□ 133. OMAR MORENO
□ 134. DALE MURRAY
□ 135. GRAIG NETTLES
□ 136. LOU PINIELLA
□ 137. WILLIE RANDOLPH
□ 138. SHANE RAWLEY
□ 139. DAVE RIGHETTI
□ 140. ANDRE ROBERTSON
□ 141. BOB SHIRLEY
□ 142. ROY SMALLEY
□ 143. DAVE WINFIELD
□ 144. BUTCH WYNEGAR
□ 652. TEAM(F) & MARTIN(M)

OAKLAND A'S

□ 436. BILL ALMON
□ 437. KEITH ATHERTON
□ 438. DAVE BEARD
□ 439. TOM BURGMEIER
□ 440. JEFF BURROUGHS
□ 441. CHRIS CONDIROLI
□ 442. TIM CONROY
□ 443. MIKE DAVIS
□ 444. WAYNE GROSS
□ 445. GARRY HANCOCK
□ 446. MIKE HEATH
□ 447. RICKEY HENDERSON
□ 448. DON HILL
□ 449. BOB KEARNEY
□ 450. BILL KRUEGER
□ 451. RICK LANGFORD
□ 452. CARNEY LANSFORD
□ 453. DAVEY LOPES
□ 454. STEVE MCCATTY
□ 455. DAN MEYER
□ 456. DWAYNE MURPHY
□ 457. MIKE NORRIS
□ 458. RICKY PETERS
□ 459. TONY PHILLIPS
□ 460. TOM UNDERWOOD
□ 461. MIKE WARREN
□ 651. TEAM CHECKLIST(B)

PHILADELPHIA PHILLIES

□ 24. MARTY BYSTROM
□ 25. STEVE CARLTON
□ 26. IVAN DEJESUS
□ 27. JOHN DENNY
□ 28. BOB DERNIER
□ 29. BO DIAZ
□ 30. KIKO GARCIA
□ 31. GREG GROSS
□ 32. KEVIN GROSS
□ 33. VON HAYES
□ 34. WILLIE HERNANDEZ
□ 35. AL HOLLAND
□ 36. CHARLES HUDSON
□ 37. JOE LEFEBVRE
□ 38. SIXTON LEZCANO
□ 39. GARRY MADDOX
□ 40. GARY MATTHEWS
□ 41. LEN MATUSZEK
□ 42. TUG MCGRAW
□ 43. JOE MORGAN
□ 44. TONY PEREZ
□ 45. RON REED
□ 46. PETE ROSE
□ 47. JUAN SAMUEL
□ 48. MIKE SCHMIDT
□ 49. OZZIE VIRGIL
□ 648. TEAM(F) & OWENS(M)

PITTSBURGH PIRATES

□ 245. DALE BERRA
□ 246. JIM BIBBY
□ 247. JOHN CANDELARIA
□ 248. JOSE DELEON
□ 249. MIKE EASLER
□ 250. CECILIO GUANTE
□ 251. RICHIE HEBNER
□ 252. LEE LACY
□ 253. BILL MADLOCK
□ 254. MILT MAY
□ 255. LEE MAZZILLI
□ 256. LARRY MCWILLIAMS
□ 257. JIM MORRISON
□ 258. DAVE PARKER
□ 259. TONY PENA
□ 260. JOHNNY RAY
□ 261. RICK RHODEN
□ 262. DON ROBINSON
□ 263. MANNY SARMIENTO
□ 264. ROD SCURRY
□ 265. KENT TEKULVE
□ 266. GENE TENACE
□ 267. JASON THOMPSON
□ 268. LEE TUNNELL
□ 269. MARVELL WYNNE
□ 657. TEAM(F) & TANNER(M)

ST. LOUIS CARDINALS

□ 318. NEIL ALLEN
□ 319. JOAQUIN ANDUJAR
□ 320. STEVE BRAUN
□ 321. GLENN BRUMMER
□ 322. BOB FORSCH
□ 323. DAVID GREEN
□ 324. GEORGE HENDRICK
□ 325. TOM HERR
□ 326. DANE IORG
□ 327. JEFF LAHTI
□ 328. DAVE LAPOINT
□ 329. WILLIE MCGEE
□ 330. KEN OBERKFELL
□ 331. DARRELL PORTER
□ 332. JAMIE QUIRK
□ 333. MIKE RAMSEY
□ 334. FLOYD RAYFORD
□ 335. LONNIE SMITH
□ 336. OZZIE SMITH
□ 337. JOHN STUPER
□ 338. BRUCE SUTTER

- ☐ 339. ANDY VAN SLYKE
- ☐ 340. DAVE VON OHLEN
- ☐ 660. TEAM(F) & HERZOG(M)

SAN DIEGO PADRES

- ☐ 294. KURT BEVACQUA
- ☐ 295. JUAN BONILLA
- ☐ 296. BOBBY BROWN
- ☐ 297. LUIS DELEON
- ☐ 298. DAVE DRAVECKY
- ☐ 299. TIM FLANNERY
- ☐ 300. STEVE GARVEY
- ☐ 301. TONY GWYNN
- ☐ 302. ANDY HAWKINS
- ☐ 303. RUPPERT JONES
- ☐ 304. TERRY KENNEDY
- ☐ 305. TIM LOLLAR
- ☐ 306. GARY LUCAS
- ☐ 307. KEVIN MCREYNOLDS
- ☐ 308. SID MONGE
- ☐ 309. MARIO RAMIREZ
- ☐ 310. GENE RICHARDS
- ☐ 311. LUIS SALAZAR
- ☐ 312. ERIC SHOW
- ☐ 313. ELIAS SOSA
- ☐ 314. GARRY TEMPLETON
- ☐ 315. MARK THURMOND
- ☐ 316. ED WHITSON
- ☐ 317. ALAN WIGGINS
- ☐ 659. TEAM(F) & WILLIAMS(M)

SAN FRANCISCO GIANTS

- ☐ 365. JIM BARR
- ☐ 366. DAVE BERGMAN
- ☐ 367. FRED BREINING
- ☐ 368. BOB BRENLY
- ☐ 369. JACK CLARK
- ☐ 370. CHILI DAVIS
- ☐ 371. MARK DAVIS
- ☐ 372. DARRELL EVANS
- ☐ 373. ATLEE HAMMAKER
- ☐ 374. MIKE KRUKOW
- ☐ 375. DUANE KUIPER
- ☐ 376. BILL LASKEY
- ☐ 377. GARY LAVELL
- ☐ 378. JOHNNIE LEMASTER
- ☐ 379. JEFF LEONARD
- ☐ 380. RANDY LERCH
- ☐ 381. RENIE MARTIN
- ☐ 382. ANDY MCGAFFIGAN
- ☐ 383. GREG MINTON
- ☐ 384. TOM O'MALLEY
- ☐ 385. MAX VENABLE
- ☐ 386. BRAD WELLMAN
- ☐ 387. JOEL YOUNGBLOOD
- ☐ 648. TEAM CHECKLIST(B)

SEATTLE MARINERS

- ☐ 604. JAMIE ALLEN
- ☐ 605. JIM BEATTIE
- ☐ 606. TONY BERNAZARD
- ☐ 607. MANNY CASTILLO
- ☐ 608. BILL CAUDILL
- ☐ 609. BRYAN CLARK
- ☐ 610. AL COWENS
- ☐ 611. DAVE HENDERSON
- ☐ 612. STEVE HENDERSON
- ☐ 613. ORLANDO MERCADO
- ☐ 614. MIKE MOORE
- ☐ 615. RICKY NELSON
- ☐ 616. SPIKE OWEN
- ☐ 617. PAT PUTNAM
- ☐ 618. RON ROENICKE
- ☐ 619. MIKE STANTON
- ☐ 620. BOB STODDARD
- ☐ 621. RICK SWEET
- ☐ 622. ROY THOMAS
- ☐ 623. ED VANDEBERG
- ☐ 624. MATT YOUNG
- ☐ 625. RICHIE ZISK
- ☐ 658. TEAM CHECKLIST(B)

TEXAS RANGERS

- ☐ 413. BUDDY BELL
- ☐ 414. LARRY BITTNER
- ☐ 415. JOHN BUTCHER
- ☐ 416. DANNY DARWIN
- ☐ 417. BUCKY DENT
- ☐ 418. DAVE HOSTETLER
- ☐ 419. CHARLIE HOUGH
- ☐ 420. BOBBY JOHNSON
- ☐ 421. ODELL JONES
- ☐ 422. JON MATLACK
- ☐ 423. PETE O'BRIEN
- ☐ 424. LARRY PARRISH
- ☐ 425. MICKEY RIVERS
- ☐ 426. BILLY SAMPLE
- ☐ 427. DAVE SCHMIDT
- ☐ 428. MIKE SMITHSON
- ☐ 429. BILL STEIN
- ☐ 430. DAVE STEWART
- ☐ 431. JIM SUNDBERG
- ☐ 432. FRANK TANANA
- ☐ 433. DAVE TOBIK
- ☐ 434. WAYNE TOLLESON
- ☐ 435. GEORGE WRIGHT
- ☐ 650. TEAM CHECKLIST(B)

TORONTO BLUE JAYS

- ☐ 145. JIM ACKER
- ☐ 146. DOYLE ALEXANDER
- ☐ 147. JESSE BARFIELD
- ☐ 148. JORGE BELL
- ☐ 149. BARRY BONNELL
- ☐ 150. JIM CLANCY
- ☐ 151. DAVE COLLINS
- ☐ 152. TONY FERNANDEZ
- ☐ 153. DAMASO GARCIA
- ☐ 154. DAVE GEISEL
- ☐ 155. JIM GOTT
- ☐ 156. ALFREDO GRIFFIN
- ☐ 157. GARTH IORG
- ☐ 158. ROY LEE JACKSON
- ☐ 159. CLIFF JOHNSON
- ☐ 160. LUIS LEAL
- ☐ 161. BUCK MARTINEZ
- ☐ 162. JOEY MCLAUGHLIN
- ☐ 163. RANDY MOFFIT
- ☐ 164. LLOYD MOSEBY
- ☐ 165. RANCE MULLINIKS
- ☐ 166. JORGE ORTA
- ☐ 167. DAVE STIEB
- ☐ 168. WILLIE UPSHAW
- ☐ 169. ERNIE WHITT
- ☐ 653. TEAM(F) & COX(M)

1984 FLEER TRADED (132) 2 1/2" X 3 1/2"

ATLANTA BRAVES

- ☐ 63U. BRAD KOMMINSK
- ☐ 84U. KEN OBERKFELL
- ☐ 92U. GERALD PERRY
- ☐ 118U. ALEX TREVINO

BALTIMORE ORIOLES

- ☐ 45U. WAYNE GROSS
- ☐ 95U. FLOYD RAYFORD
- ☐ 121U. TOM UNDERWOOD
- ☐ 131U. MIKE YOUNG

BOSTON RED SOX

- ☐ 8U. MARTY BARRETT
- ☐ 18U. BILL BUCKNER
- ☐ 27U. ROGER CLEMENS
- ☐ 33U. MIKE EASLER
- ☐ 41U. RICH GALE
- ☐ 47U. JACKIE GUTIERREZ

CALIFORNIA ANGELS

- ☐ 17U. MIKE BROWN
- ☐ 67U. FRANK LACORTE
- ☐ 101U. RON ROMANICK
- ☐ 105U. DICK SCHOFIELD
- ☐ 107U. JIM SLATON
- ☐ 115U. CRAIG SWAN

CHICAGO CUBS

- ☐ 31U. BOB DERNIER
- ☐ 34U. DENNIS ECKERSLEY
- ☐ 40U. GEORGE FRAZIER
- ☐ 49U. RON HASSEY
- ☐ 50U. RICHIE HEBNER
- ☐ 77U. GARY MATTHEWS
- ☐ 104U. SCOTT SANDERSON
- ☐ 110U. TIM STODDARD
- ☐ 114U. RICK SUTCLIFFE

CHICAGO WHITE SOX

- ☐ 96U. RON REED
- ☐ 106U. TOM SEAVER

CINCINNATI REDS

- ☐ 39U. JOHN FRANCO
- ☐ 65U. WAYNE KRENCHICKI
- ☐ 88U. BOB OWCHINKO
- ☐ 89U. DAVE PARKER
- ☐ 91U. TONY PEREZ

CLEVELAND INDIANS

- ☐ 2U. LUIS APONTE
- ☐ 12U. TONY BERNAZARD
- ☐ 21U. BRETT BUTLER
- ☐ 56U. BROOK JACOBY
- ☐ 58U. MIKE JEFFCOAT
- ☐ 123U. TOM WADDELL

DETROIT TIGERS

- ☐ 11U. DAVE BERGMAN
- ☐ 36U. DARRELL EVANS
- ☐ 42U. BARBARO GARBEY
- ☐ 51U. WILLIE HERNANDEZ
- ☐ 59U. RUPPERT JONES
- ☐ 66U. RUSTY KUNTZ

HOUSTON ASTROS

- ☐ 3U. MARK BAILEY
- ☐ 22U. ENOS CABELL

KANSAS CITY ROYALS

- ☐ 6U. STEVE BALBONI
- ☐ 10U. JOE BECKWITH
- ☐ 46U. MARK GUBICZA
- ☐ 55U. DANE IORG
- ☐ 81U. DARRYL MOTLEY
- ☐ 86U. JORGE ORTA
- ☐ 103U. BRET SABERHAGEN

LOS ANGELES DODGERS

- ☐ 4U. BOB BAILOR
- ☐ 32U. CARLOS DIAZ
- ☐ 97U. R.J. REYNOLDS
- ☐ 122U. MIKE VAIL
- ☐ 125U. TERRY WHITFIELD

MILWAUKEE BREWERS

- ☐ 25U. BOBBY CLARK
- ☐ 28U. JAIME COCANOWER
- ☐ 57U. DION JAMES
- ☐ 113U. JIM SUNDBERG

MINNESOTA TWINS

- ☐ 20U. JOHN BUTCHER
- ☐ 52U. ED HODGE
- ☐ 93U. KIRBY PUCKETT
- ☐ 108U. MIKE SMITHSON

MONTREAL EXPOS

- ☐ 16U. FRED BREINING
- ☐ 73U. GARY LUCAS
- ☐ 78U. ANDY MCGAFFIGAN
- ☐ 102U. PETE ROSE
- ☐ 116U. DERREL THOMAS

NEW YORK METS

- ☐ 29U. RON DARLING
- ☐ 37U. MIKE FITZGERALD
- ☐ 43U. DWIGHT GOODEN
- ☐ 74U. JERRY MARTIN

NEW YORK YANKEES

- ☐ 38U. TIM FOLI
- ☐ 48U. TOBY HARRAH
- ☐ 83U. PHIL NIEKRO
- ☐ 99U. JOSE RIJO

OAKLAND A'S

- ☐ 13U. BRUCE BOCHTE
- ☐ 19U. RAY BURRIS
- ☐ 24U. BILL CAUDILL
- ☐ 35U. JIM ESSIAN
- ☐ 62U. DAVE KINGMAN
- ☐ 80U. JOE MORGAN
- ☐ 109U. LARY SORENSEN

PHILADELPHIA PHILLIES

- ☐ 23U. BILL CAMPBELL
- ☐ 64U. JERRY KOOSMAN
- ☐ 94U. SHANE RAWLEY
- ☐ 111U. JEFF STONE
- ☐ 128U. GLENN WILSON
- ☐ 129U. JOHN WOCKENFUSS

PITTSBURGH PIRATES

- ☐ 87U. AMOS OTIS
- ☐ 120U. JOHN TUDOR

ST. LOUIS CARDINALS

- ☐ 53U. RICKY HORTON
- ☐ 54U. ART HOWE
- ☐ 69U. TITO LANDRUM

SAN DIEGO PADRES

- ☐ 44U. RICH GOSSAGE
- ☐ 72U. CRAIG LEFFERTS
- ☐ 75U. CARMELO MARTINEZ
- ☐ 82U. GRAIG NETTLES
- ☐ 112U. CHAMP SUMMERS

SAN FRANCISCO GIANTS

- ☐ 5U. DUSTY BAKER
- ☐ 85U. AL OLIVER
- ☐ 98U. GENE RICHARDS
- ☐ 100U. JEFF ROBINSON
- ☐ 119U. MANNY TRILLO
- ☐ 127U. FRANK WILLIAMS

SEATTLE MARINERS

- ☐ 9U. DAVE BEARD
- ☐ 14U. BARRY BONNELL
- ☐ 15U. PHIL BRADLEY
- ☐ 30U. ALVIN DAVIS
- ☐ 60U. BOB KEARNEY
- ☐ 70U. MARK LANGSTON
- ☐ 90U. JACK PERCONTE
- ☐ 117U. GORMAN THOMAS

TEXAS RANGERS

- ☐ 7U. ALAN BANNISTER
- ☐ 76U. MIKE MASON
- ☐ 79U. JOEY MCLAUGHLIN
- ☐ 124U. CURTIS WILKERSON
- ☐ 130U. NED YOST

TORONTO BLUE JAYS

- ☐ 1U. WILLIE AIKENS
- ☐ 26U. BRYAN CLARK
- ☐ 61U. JIMMY KEY
- ☐ 68U. DENNIS LAMP
- ☐ 71U. RICH LEACH

1985 FLEER
2 1/2" X 3 1/2"

ATLANTA BRAVES

- ☐ 318. LEN BARKER
- ☐ 319. STEVE BEDROSIAN
- ☐ 320. BRUCE BENEDICT
- ☐ 321. RICK CAMP
- ☐ 322. CHRIS CHAMBLISS
- ☐ 323. JEFF DEDMON
- ☐ 324. TERRY FORSTER
- ☐ 325. GENE GARBER
- ☐ 326. ALBERT HALL
- ☐ 327. TERRY HARPER
- ☐ 328. BOB HORNER
- ☐ 329. GLENN HUBBARD
- ☐ 330. RANDY JOHNSON
- ☐ 331. BRAD KOMMINSK
- ☐ 332. RICK MAHLER
- ☐ 333. CRAIG MCMURTRY
- ☐ 334. DONNIE MOORE
- ☐ 335. DALE MURPHY
- ☐ 336. KEN OBERKFELL
- ☐ 337. PASCUAL PEREZ
- ☐ 338. GERALD PERRY
- ☐ 339. RAFAEL RAMIREZ
- ☐ 340. JERRY ROYSTER
- ☐ 341. ALEX TREVINO
- ☐ 342. CLAUDELL WASHINGTON
- ☐ 651. ZANE SMITH(P)
- ☐ 651. PAUL ZUVELLA(P)
- ☐ 657. TEAM CHECKLIST(F)

BALTIMORE ORIOLES

- ☐ 170. MIKE BODDICKER
- ☐ 171. AL BUMBRY
- ☐ 172. TODD CRUZ
- ☐ 173. RICH DAUER
- ☐ 174. STORM DAVIS
- ☐ 175. RICK DEMPSEY
- ☐ 176. JIM DWYER
- ☐ 177. MIKE FLANAGAN
- ☐ 178. DAN FORD
- ☐ 179. WAYNE GROSS
- ☐ 180. JOHN LOWENSTEIN
- ☐ 181. DENNIS MARTINEZ
- ☐ 182. TIPPY MARTINEZ
- ☐ 183. SCOTT MCGREGOR
- ☐ 184. EDDIE MURRAY
- ☐ 185. JOE NOLAN
- ☐ 186. FLOYD RAYFORD
- ☐ 187. CAL RIPKEN
- ☐ 188. GARY ROENICKE
- ☐ 189. LENN SAKATA
- ☐ 190. JOHN SHELBY
- ☐ 191. KEN SINGLETON
- ☐ 192. SAMMY STEWART
- ☐ 193. BILL SWAGGERTY
- ☐ 194. TOM UNDERWOOD
- ☐ 195. MIKE YOUNG
- ☐ 655. TEAM CHECKLIST(B)

BOSTON RED SOX

- ☐ 148. GARY ALLENSON
- ☐ 149. TONY ARMAS
- ☐ 150. MARTY BARRETT
- ☐ 151. WADE BOGGS
- ☐ 152. DENNIS BOYD
- ☐ 153. BILL BUCKNER
- ☐ 154. MARK CLEAR
- ☐ 155. ROGER CLEMENS
- ☐ 156. STEVE CRAWFORD
- ☐ 157. MIKE EASLER
- ☐ 158. DWIGHT EVANS
- ☐ 159. RICH GEDMAN
- ☐ 160. JACKIE GUTIERREZ
- ☐ 161. BRUCE HURST
- ☐ 162. JOHN HENRY JOHNSON
- ☐ 163. RICK MILLER
- ☐ 164. REID NICHOLS
- ☐ 165. AL NIPPER
- ☐ 166. BOB OJEDA
- ☐ 167. JERRY REMY
- ☐ 168. JIM RICE
- ☐ 169. BOB STANLEY
- ☐ 655. TEAM CHECKLIST(B)

CALIFORNIA ANGELS

- ☐ 293. DON AASE
- ☐ 294. JUAN BENIQUEZ
- ☐ 295. BOB BOONE
- ☐ 296. MIKE BROWN
- ☐ 297. ROD CAREW
- ☐ 298. DOUG CORBETT
- ☐ 299. DOUG DECINCES
- ☐ 300. BRIAN DOWNING
- ☐ 301. KEN FORSCH
- ☐ 302. BOBBY GRICH
- ☐ 303. REGGIE JACKSON
- ☐ 304. TOMMY JOHN
- ☐ 305. CURT KAUFMAN
- ☐ 306. BRUCE KISON
- ☐ 307. FRED LYNN
- ☐ 308. GARY PETTIS
- ☐ 309. RON ROMANICK
- ☐ 310. LUIS SANCHEZ
- ☐ 311. DICK SCHOFIELD
- ☐ 312. DARYL SCONIERS
- ☐ 313. JIM SLATON
- ☐ 314. DERREL THOMAS
- ☐ 315. ROB WILFONG
- ☐ 316. MIKE WITT
- ☐ 317. GEOFF ZAHN
- ☐ 657. TEAM CHECKLIST(F)

CHICAGO CUBS

- ☐ 49. RICH BORDI
- ☐ 50. LARRY BOWA
- ☐ 51. WARREN BRUSSTAR
- ☐ 52. RON CEY
- ☐ 53. HENRY COTTO
- ☐ 54. JODY DAVIS
- ☐ 55. BOB DERNIER
- ☐ 56. LEON DURHAM
- ☐ 57. DENNIS ECKERSLEY
- ☐ 58. GEORGE FRAZIER
- ☐ 59. RICHIE HEBNER
- ☐ 60. DAVE LOPES
- ☐ 61. GARY MATTHEWS
- ☐ 62. KEITH MORELAND
- ☐ 63. RICK REUSCHEL
- ☐ 64. DICK RUTHVEN
- ☐ 65. RYNE SANDBERG
- ☐ 66. SCOTT SANDERSON
- ☐ 67. LEE SMITH
- ☐ 68. TIM STODDARD
- ☐ 69. RICK SUTCLIFFE
- ☐ 70. STEVE TROUT
- ☐ 71. GARY WOODS
- ☐ 649. BILL HATCHER(P)
- ☐ 649. SHAWON DUNSTON(P)
- ☐ 654. TEAM CHECKLIST(B)

CHICAGO WHITE SOX

- ☐ 506. JUAN AGOSTO
- ☐ 507. HAROLD BAINES
- ☐ 508. FLOYD BANNISTER
- ☐ 509. BRITT BURNS
- ☐ 510. JULIO CRUZ
- ☐ 511. RICHARD DOTSON
- ☐ 512. JERRY DYBZINSKI
- ☐ 513. CARLTON FISK
- ☐ 514. SCOTT FLETCHER
- ☐ 515. JERRY HAIRSTON
- ☐ 516. MARC HILL
- ☐ 517. LAMARR HOYT
- ☐ 518. RON KITTLE
- ☐ 519. RUDY LAW
- ☐ 520. VANCE LAW
- ☐ 521. GREG LUZINSKI
- ☐ 522. GENE NELSON
- ☐ 523. TOM PACIOREK
- ☐ 524. RON REED
- ☐ 525. BERT ROBERGE
- ☐ 526. TOM SEAVER
- ☐ 527. ROY SMALLEY
- ☐ 528. DAN SPILLNER
- ☐ 529. MIKE SQUIRES
- ☐ 530. GREG WALKER
- ☐ 646. JOEL SKINNER(P)
- ☐ 659. TEAM CHECKLIST(F)

CINCINNATI REDS

- ☐ 531. CESAR CEDENO
- ☐ 532. DAVE CONCEPCION
- ☐ 533. ERIC DAVIS
- ☐ 534. NICK ESASKY
- ☐ 535. TOM FOLEY
- ☐ 536. JOHN FRANCO
- ☐ 537. BRAD GULDEN
- ☐ 538. TOM HUME
- ☐ 539. WAYNE KRENCHICKI
- ☐ 540. ANDY MCGAFFIGAN
- ☐ 541. EDDIE MILNER
- ☐ 542. RON OESTER
- ☐ 543. BOB OWCHINKO
- ☐ 544. DAVE PARKER
- ☐ 545. FRANK PASTORE
- ☐ 546. TONY PEREZ
- ☐ 547. TED POWER
- ☐ 548. JOE PRICE
- ☐ 549. GARY REDUS
- ☐ 550. PETE ROSE(M)
- ☐ 551. JEFF RUSSELL
- ☐ 552. MARIO SOTO
- ☐ 553. JAY TIBBS
- ☐ 554. DUANE WALKER
- ☐ 650. RON ROBINSON(P)
- ☐ 659. TEAM CHECKLIST(B)

CLEVELAND INDIANS

- ☐ 437. LUIS APONTE
- ☐ 438. CHRIS BANDO
- ☐ 439. TONY BERNAZARD
- ☐ 440. BERT BLYLEVEN
- ☐ 441. BRETT BUTLER
- ☐ 442. ERNIE CAMACHO
- ☐ 443. JOE CARTER
- ☐ 444. CARMELO CASTILLO
- ☐ 445. JAMIE EASTERLY
- ☐ 446. STEVE FARR
- ☐ 447. MIKE FISCHLIN
- ☐ 448. JULIO FRANCO
- ☐ 449. MEL HALL
- ☐ 450. MIKE HARGROVE
- ☐ 451. NEAL HEATON
- ☐ 452. BROOK JACOBY
- ☐ 453. MIKE JEFFCOAT
- ☐ 454. DON SCHULZE
- ☐ 455. ROY SMITH
- ☐ 456. PAT TABLER
- ☐ 457. ANDRE THORNTON
- ☐ 458. GEORGE VUKOVICH
- ☐ 459. TOM WADDELL
- ☐ 460. JERRY WILLARD
- ☐ 646. JOSE ROMAN(P)
- ☐ 658. TEAM CHECKLIST(B)

DETROIT TIGERS

- ☐ 1. DOUG BAIR
- ☐ 2. JUAN BERENGUER
- ☐ 3. DAVE BERGMAN
- ☐ 4. TOM BROOKENS
- ☐ 5. MARTY CASTILLO
- ☐ 6. DARRELL EVANS
- ☐ 7. BARBARO GARBEY
- ☐ 8. KIRK GIBSON
- ☐ 9. JOHN GRUBB
- ☐ 10. WILLIE HERNANDEZ
- ☐ 11. LARRY HERNDON
- ☐ 12. HOWARD JOHNSON
- ☐ 13. RUPPERT JONES
- ☐ 14. RUSTY KUNTZ
- ☐ 15. CHET LEMON
- ☐ 16. AURELIO LOPEZ
- ☐ 17. SID MONGE
- ☐ 18. JACK MORRIS
- ☐ 19. LANCE PARRISH
- ☐ 20. DAN PETRY
- ☐ 21. DAVE ROZEMA
- ☐ 22. BILL SCHERRER
- ☐ 23. ALAN TRAMMELL
- ☐ 24. LOU WHITAKER
- ☐ 25. MILT WILCOX
- ☐ 654. RANDY O'NEAL(P)
- ☐ 654. TEAM CHECKLIST(F)

HOUSTON ASTROS

- ☐ 343. ALAN ASHBY
- ☐ 344. MARK BAILEY
- ☐ 345. KEVIN BASS
- ☐ 346. ENOS CABELL
- ☐ 347. JOSE CRUZ
- ☐ 348. BILL DAWLEY
- ☐ 349. FRANK DIPINO
- ☐ 350. BILL DORAN
- ☐ 351. PHIL GARNER
- ☐ 352. BOB KNEPPER
- ☐ 353. MIKE LACOSS
- ☐ 354. JERRY MUMPHREY
- ☐ 355. JOE NIEKRO
- ☐ 356. TERRY PUHL
- ☐ 357. CRAIG REYNOLDS
- ☐ 358. VERN RUHLE
- ☐ 359. NOLAN RYAN
- ☐ 360. JOE SAMBITO
- ☐ 361. MIKE SCOTT
- ☐ 362. DAVE SMITH
- ☐ 363. JULIO SOLANO
- ☐ 364. DICKIE THON
- ☐ 365. DENNY WALLING
- ☐ 652. GLENN DAVIS(P)
- ☐ 657. TEAM CHECKLIST(B)

KANSAS CITY ROYALS

- ☐ 196. STEVE BALBONI
- ☐ 197. JOE BECKWITH
- ☐ 198. BUD BLACK
- ☐ 199. GEORGE BRETT
- ☐ 200. ONIX CONCEPCION
- ☐ 201. MARK GUBICZA
- ☐ 202. LARRY GURA
- ☐ 203. MARK HUISMANN
- ☐ 204. DANE IORG
- ☐ 205. DANNY JACKSON
- ☐ 206. CHARLIE LEIBRANDT
- ☐ 207. HAL MCRAE
- ☐ 208. DARRYL MOTLEY
- ☐ 209. JORGE ORTA
- ☐ 210. GREG PRYOR
- ☐ 211. DAN QUISENBERRY
- ☐ 212. BRET SABERHAGEN
- ☐ 213. PAT SHERIDAN

- □ 214. DON SLAUGHT
- □ 215. U.L. WASHINGTON
- □ 216. JOHN WATHAN
- □ 217. FRANK WHITE
- □ 218. WILLIE WILSON
- □ 656. TEAM CHECKLIST(F)

LOS ANGELES DODGERS

- □ 366. DAVE ANDERSON
- □ 367. BOB BAILOR
- □ 368. GREG BROCK
- □ 369. CARLOS DIAZ
- □ 370. PEDRO GUERRERO
- □ 371. OREL HERSHISER
- □ 372. RICK HONEYCUTT
- □ 373. BURT HOOTON
- □ 374. KEN HOWELL
- □ 375. KEN LANDREQUX
- □ 376. CANDY MALDONADO
- □ 377. MIKE MARSHALL
- □ 378. TOM NIEDENFUER
- □ 379. ALEJANDRO PENA
- □ 380. JERRY REUSS
- □ 381. R.J. REYNOLDS
- □ 382. GERMAN RIVERA
- □ 383. BILL RUSSELL
- □ 384. STEVE SAX
- □ 385. MIKE SCIOSCIA
- □ 386. FRANKLIN STUBBS
- □ 387. FERNANDO VALENZUELA
- □ 388. BOB WELCH
- □ 389. TERRY WHITFIELD
- □ 390. STEVE YEAGER
- □ 391. PAT ZACHRY
- □ 657. TEAM CHECKLIST(B)

MILWAUKEE BREWERS

- □ 576. MARK BROUHARD
- □ 577. MIKE CALDWELL
- □ 578. BOBBY CLARK
- □ 579. JAIME COCANOWER
- □ 580. CECIL COOPER
- □ 581. ROLLIE FINGERS
- □ 582. JIM GANTNER
- □ 583. MOOSE HAAS
- □ 584. DION JAMES
- □ 585. PETE LADD
- □ 586. RICK MANNING
- □ 587. BOB MCCLURE
- □ 588. PAUL MOLITOR
- □ 589. CHARLIE MOORE
- □ 590. BEN OGLIVIE
- □ 591. CHUCK PORTER
- □ 592. RANDY READY
- □ 593. ED ROMERO
- □ 594. BILL SCHROEDER
- □ 595. RAY SEARAGE
- □ 596. TED SIMMONS
- □ 597. JIM SUNDBERG
- □ 598. DON SUTTON
- □ 599. TOM TELLMAN
- □ 600. RICK WAITS
- □ 601. ROBIN YOUNT
- □ 644. WILLIE LOZADO(P)
- □ 660 TEAM CHECKLIST(F)

MINNESOTA TWINS

- □ 270. DARRELL BROWN
- □ 271. TOM BRUNANSKY
- □ 272. RANDY BUSH
- □ 273. JOHN BUTCHER
- □ 274. BOBBY CASTILLO
- □ 275. RON DAVIS
- □ 276. DAVE ENGLE
- □ 277. PETE FILSON
- □ 278. GARY GAETTI
- □ 279. MICKEY HATCHER
- □ 280. ED HODGE
- □ 281. KENT HRBEK
- □ 282. HOUSTON JIMENEZ
- □ 283. TIM LAUDNER
- □ 284. RICK LYSANDER
- □ 285. DAVE MEIER
- □ 286. KIRBY PUCKETT
- □ 287. PAT PUTNAM
- □ 288. KEN SCHROM
- □ 289. MIKE SMITHSON
- □ 290. TIM TEUFEL
- □ 291. FRANK VIOLA
- □ 292. RON WASHINGTON
- □ 656. TEAM CHECKLIST(B)

MONTREAL EXPOS

- □ 392. FRED BREINING
- □ 393. GARY CARTER
- □ 394. ANDRE DAWSON
- □ 395. MIGUEL DILONE
- □ 396. DAN DRIESSEN
- □ 397. DOUG FLYNN
- □ 398. TERRY FRANCONA
- □ 399. BILL GULLICKSON
- □ 400. BOB JAMES
- □ 401. CHARLIE LEA
- □ 402. BRYAN LITTLE
- □ 403. GARY LUCAS
- □ 404. DAVID PALMER
- □ 405. TIM RAINES
- □ 406. MIKE RAMSEY
- □ 407. JEFF REARDON
- □ 408. STEVE ROGERS
- □ 409. DAN SCHATZEDER
- □ 410. BRYN SMITH
- □ 411. MIKE STENHOUSE
- □ 412. TIM WALLACH
- □ 413. JIM WOHLFORD
- □ 652. JOE HESKETH(P)
- □ 658. TEAM CHECKLIST(F)

NEW YORK METS

- □ 72. WALLY BACKMAN
- □ 73. BRUCE BERENYI
- □ 74. HUBIE BROOKS
- □ 75. KELVIN CHAPMAN
- □ 76. RON DARLING
- □ 77. SID FERNANDEZ
- □ 78. MIKE FITZGERALD
- □ 79. GEORGE FOSTER
- □ 80. BRENT GAFF
- □ 81. RON GARDENHIRE
- □ 82. DWIGHT GOODEN
- □ 83. TOM GORMAN
- □ 84. DANNY HEEP
- □ 85. KEITH HERNANDEZ
- □ 86. RAY KNIGHT
- □ 87. ED LYNCH
- □ 88. JOSE OQUENDO
- □ 89. JESSE OROSCO
- □ 90. RAFAEL SANTANA
- □ 91. DOUG SISK
- □ 92. RUSTY STAUB
- □ 93. DARRYL STRAWBERRY
- □ 94. WALT TERRELL
- □ 95. MOOKIE WILSON
- □ 654. TEAM CHECKLIST(B)

NEW YORK YANKEES

- □ 120. MIKE ARMSTRONG
- □ 121. DON BAYLOR
- □ 122. MARTY BYSTROM
- □ 123. RICK CERONE
- □ 124. JOE COWLEY
- □ 125. BRIAN DAYETT
- □ 126. TIM FOLI
- □ 127. RAY FONTENOT
- □ 128. KEN GRIFFEY
- □ 129. RON GUIDRY
- □ 130. TOBY HARRAH
- □ 131. JAY HOWELL
- □ 132. STEVE KEMP
- □ 133. DON MATTINGLY
- □ 134. BOBBY MEACHAM
- □ 135. JOHN MONTEFUSCO
- □ 136. OMAR MORENO
- □ 137. DALE MURRAY
- □ 138. PHIL NIEKRO
- □ 139. MIKE PAGLIARULO
- □ 140. WILLIE RANDOLPH
- □ 141. DENNIS RASMUSSEN
- □ 142. DAVE RIGHETTI
- □ 143. JOSE RIJO
- □ 144. ANDRE ROBERTSON
- □ 145. BOB SHIRLEY
- □ 146. DAVE WINFIELD
- □ 147. BUTCH WYNEGAR
- □ 644. VIC MATA(P)
- □ 655. TEAM CHECKLIST(F)

OAKLAND A'S

- □ 414. BILL ALMON
- □ 415. KEITH ATHERTON
- □ 416. BRUCE BOCHTE
- □ 417. TOM BURGMEIER
- □ 418. RAY BURRIS
- □ 419. BILL CAUDILL
- □ 420. CHRIS CODIROLI
- □ 421. TIM CONROY
- □ 422. MIKE DAVIS
- □ 423. JIM ESSIAN
- □ 424. MIKE HEATH
- □ 425. RICKEY HENDERSON
- □ 426. DONNIE HILL
- □ 427. DAVE KINGMAN
- □ 428. BILL KRUEGER
- □ 429. CARNEY LANSFORD
- □ 430. STEVE MCCATTY
- □ 431. JOE MORGAN
- □ 432. DWAYNE MURPHY
- □ 433. TONY PHILLIPS
- □ 434. LARY SORENSEN
- □ 435. MIKE WARREN
- □ 436. CURT YOUNG
- □ 647. STEVE KIEFER(P)
- □ 658. TEAM CHECKLIST(F)

PHILADELPHIA PHILLIES

- □ 244. LARRY ANDERSON
- □ 245. BILL CAMPBELL
- □ 246. STEVE CARLTON
- □ 247. TIM CORCORAN
- □ 248. IVAN DEJESUS
- □ 249. JOHN DENNY
- □ 250. BO DIAZ
- □ 251. GREG GROSS
- □ 252. KEVIN GROSS
- □ 253. VON HAYES
- □ 254. AL HOLLAND
- □ 255. CHARLES HUDSON
- □ 256. JERRY KOOSMAN
- □ 257. JOE LEFEBVRE
- □ 258. SIXTO LEZCANO
- □ 259. GARRY MADDOX
- □ 260. LEN MATUSZEK
- □ 261. TUG MCGRAW
- □ 262. AL OLVIER
- □ 263. SHANE RAWLEY
- □ 264. JUAN SAMUEL
- □ 265. MIKE SCHMIDT
- □ 266. JEFF STONE
- □ 267. OZZIE VIRGIL
- □ 268. GLENN WILSON
- □ 269. JOHN WOCKENFUSS
- □ 653. JOHN RUSSELL(P)
- □ 653. STEVE JELTZ(P)
- □ 656. TEAM CHECKLIST(B)

PITTSBURGH PIRATES

- □ 461. DALE BERRA
- □ 462. JOHN CANDELARIA
- □ 463. JOSE DELEON
- □ 464. DOUG FROBEL
- □ 465. CECILLIO GUANTE

- ☐ 466. BRIAN HARPER
- ☐ 467. LEE LACY
- ☐ 468. BILL MADLOCK
- ☐ 469. LEE MAZZILLI
- ☐ 470. LARRY MCWILLIAMS
- ☐ 471. JIM MORRISON
- ☐ 472. TONY PENA
- ☐ 473. JOHNNY RAY
- ☐ 474. RICK RHODEN
- ☐ 475. DON ROBINSON
- ☐ 476. ROD SCURRY
- ☐ 477. KENT TEKULVE
- ☐ 478. JASON THOMPSON
- ☐ 479. JOHN TUDOR
- ☐ 480. LEE TUNNELL
- ☐ 481. MARVELL WYNNE
- ☐ 650. MIKE BIELECKI(P)
- ☐ 658. TEAM CHECKLIST(B)

ST. LOUIS CARDINALS

- ☐ 219. NEIL ALLEN
- ☐ 220. JOAQUIN ANDUJAR
- ☐ 221. STEVE BRAUN
- ☐ 222. DANNY COX
- ☐ 223. BOB FORSCH
- ☐ 224. DAVID GREEN
- ☐ 225. GEORGE HENDRICK
- ☐ 226. TOM HERR
- ☐ 227. RICKY HORTON
- ☐ 228. ART HOWE
- ☐ 229. MIKE JORGENSEN
- ☐ 230. KURT KEPSHIRE
- ☐ 231. JEFF LAHTI
- ☐ 232. TITO LANDRUM
- ☐ 233. DAVE LAPOINT
- ☐ 234. WILLIE MCGEE
- ☐ 235. TOM NIETO
- ☐ 236. TERRY PENDLETON
- ☐ 237. DARRELL PORTER
- ☐ 238. DAVE RUCKER
- ☐ 239. LONNIE SMITH
- ☐ 240. OZZIE SMITH
- ☐ 241. BRUCE SUTTER
- ☐ 242. ANDY VAN SLYKE
- ☐ 243. DAVE VON OHLEN
- ☐ 656. TEAM CHECKLIST(F)

SAN DIEGO PADRES

- ☐ 26. KURT BEVACQUA
- ☐ 27. GREG BOOKER
- ☐ 28. BOBBY BROWN
- ☐ 29. LUIS DELEON
- ☐ 30. DAVE DRAVECKY
- ☐ 31. TIM FLANNERY
- ☐ 32. STEVE GARVEY
- ☐ 33. GOOSE GOSSAGE
- ☐ 34. TONY GWYNN
- ☐ 35. GREG HARRIS
- ☐ 36. ANDY HAWKINS
- ☐ 37. TERRY KENNEDY
- ☐ 38. CRAIG LEFFERTS
- ☐ 39. TIM LOLLAR
- ☐ 40. CARMELO MARTINEZ
- ☐ 41. KEVIN MCREYNOLDS
- ☐ 42. GRAIG NETTLES
- ☐ 43. LUIS SALAZAR
- ☐ 44. ERIC SHOW
- ☐ 45. GARRY TEMPLETON
- ☐ 46. MARK THURMOND
- ☐ 47. ED WHITSON
- ☐ 48. ALAN WIGGINS
- ☐ 654. TEAM CHECKLIST(F)

SAN FRANCISCO GIANTS

- ☐ 602. DUSTY BAKER
- ☐ 603. BOB BRENLY
- ☐ 604. JACK CLARK
- ☐ 605. CHILI DAVIS
- ☐ 606. MARK DAVIS
- ☐ 607. DAN GLADDEN
- ☐ 608. ATLEE HAMMAKER
- ☐ 609. MIKE KRUKOW
- ☐ 610. DUANE KUIPER
- ☐ 611. BOB LACEY
- ☐ 612. BILL LASKEY
- ☐ 613. GARY LAVELLE
- ☐ 614. JOHNNIE LEMASTER
- ☐ 615. JEFF LEONARD
- ☐ 616. RANDY LERCH
- ☐ 617. GREG MINTON
- ☐ 618. STEVE NICOSIA
- ☐ 619. GENE RICHARDS
- ☐ 620. JEFF ROBINSON
- ☐ 621. SCOT THOMPSON
- ☐ 622. MANNY TRILLO
- ☐ 623. BRAD WELLMAN
- ☐ 624. FRANK WILLIAMS
- ☐ 625. JOEL YOUNGBLOOD
- ☐ 648. ROB DEER(P)
- ☐ 648. ALEJANDRO SANCHEZ(P)
- ☐ 660. TEAM CHECKLIST(F)

SEATTLE MARINERS

- ☐ 482. SALOME BAROJAS
- ☐ 483. DAVE BEARD
- ☐ 484. JIM BEATTIE
- ☐ 485. BARRY BONNELL
- ☐ 486. PHIL BRADLEY
- ☐ 487. AL COWENS
- ☐ 488. ALVIN DAVIS
- ☐ 489. DAVE HENDERSON
- ☐ 490. STEVE HENDERSON
- ☐ 491. BOB KEARNEY
- ☐ 492. MARK LANGSTON
- ☐ 493. LARRY MILBOURNE
- ☐ 494. PAUL MIRABELLA
- ☐ 495. MIKE MOORE
- ☐ 496. EDWIN NUNEZ
- ☐ 497. SPIKE OWEN
- ☐ 498. JACK PERCONTE
- ☐ 499. KEN PHELPS
- ☐ 500. JIM PRESLEY
- ☐ 501. MIKE STANTON
- ☐ 502. BOB STODDARD
- ☐ 503. GORMAN THOMAS
- ☐ 504. ED VANDE BERG
- ☐ 505. MATT YOUNG
- ☐ 647. DANNY TARTABULL(P)
- ☐ 659. TEAM CHECKLIST(F)

TEXAS RANGERS

- ☐ 555. ALAN BANNISTER
- ☐ 556. BUDDY BELL
- ☐ 557. DANNY DARWIN
- ☐ 558. CHARLIE HOUGH
- ☐ 559. BOBBY JONES
- ☐ 560. ODELL JONES
- ☐ 561. JEFF KUNKEL
- ☐ 562. MIKE MASON
- ☐ 563. PETE O'BRIEN
- ☐ 564. LARRY PARRISH
- ☐ 565. MICKEY RIVERS
- ☐ 566. BILLY SAMPLE
- ☐ 567. DAVE SCHMIDT
- ☐ 568. DONNIE SCOTT
- ☐ 569. DAVE STEWART
- ☐ 570. FRANK TANANA
- ☐ 571. WAYNE TOLLESON
- ☐ 572. GARY WARD
- ☐ 573. CURTIS WILKERSON
- ☐ 574. GEORGE WRIGHT
- ☐ 575. NED YOST
- ☐ 659. TEAM CHECKLIST(B)

TORONTO BLUE JAYS

- ☐ 96. JIM ACKER
- ☐ 97. WILLIE AIKENS
- ☐ 98. DOYLE ALEXANDER
- ☐ 99. JESSE BARFIELD
- ☐ 100. GEORGE BELL
- ☐ 101. JIM CLANCY
- ☐ 102. DAVE COLLINS
- ☐ 103. TONY FERNANDEZ
- ☐ 104. DAMASO GARCIA
- ☐ 105. JIM GOTT
- ☐ 106. ALFREDO GRIFFIN
- ☐ 107. GARTH IORG
- ☐ 108. ROY LEE JACKSON
- ☐ 109. CLIFF JOHNSON
- ☐ 110. JIMMY KEY
- ☐ 111. DENNIS LAMPE
- ☐ 112. RICK LEACH
- ☐ 113. LUIS LEAL
- ☐ 114. BUCK MARTINEZ
- ☐ 115. LLOYD MOSEBY
- ☐ 116. RANCE MULLINIKS
- ☐ 117. DAVE STIEB
- ☐ 118. WILLIE UPSHAW
- ☐ 119. ERNIE WHITT
- ☐ 645. KELLY GRUBER(P)
- ☐ 655 TEAM CHECKLIST(F)

1985 FLEER TRADED (132) 2 1/2 X 3 1/2

ATLANTA BRAVES

- ☐ 24U. RICK CERONE
- ☐ 114U. BRUCE SUTTER

BALTIMORE ORIOLES

- ☐ 1U. DON AASE
- ☐ 30U. FRITZ CONNALLY
- ☐ 36U. KEN DIXON
- ☐ 67U. LEE LACY
- ☐ 75U. FRED LYNN
- ☐ 101U. LARRY SHEETS
- ☐ 107U. NATE SNELL

BOSTON RED SOX

- ☐ 65U. BRUCE KISON
- ☐ 76U. STEVE LYONS

CALIFORNIA ANGELS

- ☐ 26U. PAT CLEMENTS
- ☐ 27U. STEWART CLIBURN
- ☐ 63U. RUPPERT JONES
- ☐ 74U. URBANO LUGO
- ☐ 82U. DONNIE MOORE

CHICAGO CUBS

- ☐ 35U. BRIAN DAYETT
- ☐ 42U. RAY FONTENOT
- ☐ 108U LARY SORENSEN
- ☐ 109U. CHRIS SPEIER

CHICAGO WHITE SOX

- ☐ 9U. DARYL BOSTON
- ☐ 39U. BOB FALLON
- ☐ 44U. OSCAR GAMBLE
- ☐ 48U. OZZIE GUILLEN
- ☐ 59U. TIM HULETT
- ☐ 60U. BOB JAMES
- ☐ 73U. TIM LOLLAR
- ☐ 95U. LUIS SALAZAR
- ☐ 116U. BRUCE TANNER

CINCINNATI REDS

- ☐ 12U. TOM BROWNING
- ☐ 112U. JOHN STUPER

CLEVELAND INDIANS

- ☐ 93U. VERN RUHLE
- ☐ 120U. RICH THOMPSON
- ☐ 126U. DAVE VON OHLEN

DETROIT TIGERS

- □ 87U. CHRIS PITTARO
- □ 98U. ALEX SANCHEZ
- □ 103U. NELSON SIMMONS
- □ 118U. WALT TERRELL

HOUSTON ASTROS

- □ 18U. JEFF CALHOUN
- □ 78U. RON MATHIS

KANSAS CITY ROYALS

- □ 66U. MIKE LACOSS
- □ 106U. LONNIE SMITH
- □ 113U. JIM SUNDBERG

LOS ANGELES DODGERS

- □ 22U. BOBBY CASTILLO
- □ 38U. MARIANO DUNCAN
- □ 84U. AL OLIVER

MILWAUKEE BREWERS

- □ 15U. RAY BURRIS
- □ 32U. DANNY DARWIN
- □ 54U. TEDDY HIGUERA
- □ 89U. EARNIE RILES

MINNESOTA TWINS

- □ 43U. GREG GAGNE
- □ 94U. MARK SALAS
- □ 105U. ROY SMALLEY
- □ 110U. MIKE STENHOUSE
- □ 127U. CURT WARDLE
- □ 131U. RICH YETT

MONTREAL EXPOS

- □ 10U. HUBIE BROOKS
- □ 14U. TIM BURKE
- □ 41U. MIKE FITZGERALD
- □ 70U. VANCE LAW
- □ 77U. MICKEY MAHLER
- □ 128U. U.L. WASHINGTON
- □ 130U. HERM WINNINGHAM

NEW YORK METS

- □ 21U. GARY CARTER
- □ 62U. HOWARD JOHNSON
- □ 81U. ROGER MCDOWELL
- □ 96U. JOE SAMBITO
- □ 99U. CALVIN SCHIRALDI

NEW YORK YANKEES

- □ 4U. DALE BERRA
- □ 8U. RICH BORDI
- □ 31U. HENRY COTTO
- □ 40U. BRIAN FISHER
- □ 50U. RON HASSEY
- □ 51U. RICKEY HENDERSON
- □ 86U. DAN PASQUA
- □ 97U. BILLY SAMPLE
- □ 129U. ED WHITSOM

OAKLAND A'S

- □ 3U. DUSTY BAKER
- □ 6U. TIM BIRTSAS
- □ 29U. DAVE COLLINS
- □ 47U. ALFREDO GRIFFIN
- □ 52U. STEVE HENDERSON
- □ 57U. JAY HOWELL
- □ 115U. DON SUTTON
- □ 119U. MICKEY TETTLETON

PHILADELPHIA PHILLIES

- □ 20U. DON CARMAN
- □ 33U. DARREN DAULTON
- □ 92U. DAVE RUCKER
- □ 100U. RICK SCHU
- □ 117U. KENT TEKULVE

PITTSBURGH PIRATES

- □ 2U. BILL ALMON
- □ 53U. GEORGE HENDRICK
- □ 55U. AL HOLLAND
- □ 64U. STEVE KEMP
- □ 72U. SIXTO LEZCANO
- □ 85U. JOE ORSULAK
- □ 88U. RICK REUSCHEL

ST. LOUIS CARDINALS

- □ 19U. BILL CAMPBELL
- □ 25U. JACK CLARK
- □ 28U. VINCE COLEMAN
- □ 123U. JOHN TUDOR

SAN DIEGO PADRES

- □ 13U. AL BUMBRY
- □ 34U. JERRY DAVIS
- □ 58U. LAMARR HOYT
- □ 90U JERRY ROYSTER
- □ 111U. TIM STODDARD

SAN FRANCISCO GIANTS

- □ 7U. VIDA BLUE
- □ 11U. CHRIS BROWN
- □ 45U. JIM GOTT
- □ 46U. DAVID GREEN
- □ 68U. DAVE LAPOINT
- □ 122U. ALEX TREVINO
- □ 124U. JOSE URIBE

SEATTLE MARINERS

- □ 5U. KARL BEST
- □ 17U. IVAN CALDERON
- □ 125U. DAVE VALLE

TEXAS RANGERS

- □ 37U. TOMMY DUNBAR
- □ 49U. TOBY HARRAH
- □ 56U. BURT HOOTON
- □ 61U. CLIFF JOHNSON
- □ 80U. ODDIBE MCDOWELL
- □ 91U. DAVE ROZEMA
- □ 104U. DON SLAUGHT

TORONTO BLUE JAYS

- □ 16U. JEFF BURROUGHS
- □ 23U. BILL CAUDILL
- □ 69U. GARY LAVELLE
- □ 71U. MANNY LEE
- □ 79U. LEN MATUSZEK
- □ 83U. RON MUSSELMAN
- □ 102U. RON SHEPHERD
- □ 121U. LOUIS THORNTON

1986 FLEER (660)
2 1/2 X 3 1/2

ATLANTA BRAVES

- □ 507. LEN BARKER
- □ 508. STEVE BEDROSIAN
- □ 509. BRUCE BENEDICT
- □ 510. RICK CAMP
- □ 511. RICK CERONE
- □ 512. CHRIS CHAMBLISS
- □ 513. JEFF DEDMON
- □ 514. TERRY FORSTER
- □ 515. GENE GARBER
- □ 516. TERRY HARPER
- □ 517. BOB HORNER
- □ 518. GLENN HUBBARD
- □ 519. JOE JOHNSON
- □ 520. BRAD KOMMINSK
- □ 521. RICK MAHLER
- □ 522. DALE MURPHY
- □ 523. KEN OBERKFELL
- □ 524. PASCUAL PEREZ
- □ 525. GERALD PERRY
- □ 526. RAFAEL RAMIREZ
- □ 527. STEVE SHIELDS
- □ 528. ZANE SMITH
- □ 529. BRUCE SUTTER
- □ 530. MILT THOMPSON
- □ 531. CLAUDELL WASHINGTON
- □ 532. PAUL ZUVELLA
- □ 659. TEAM CHECKLIST(F)

BALTIMORE ORIOLES

- □ 268. DON AASE
- □ 269. MIKE BODDICKER
- □ 270. RICH DAUER
- □ 271. STORM DAVIS
- □ 272. RICK DEMPSEY
- □ 273. KEN DIXON
- □ 274. JIM DWYER
- □ 275. MIKE FLANAGAN
- □ 276. WAYNE GROSS
- □ 277. LEE LACY
- □ 278. FRED LYNN
- □ 279. DENNIS MARTINEZ
- □ 280. TIPPY MARTINEZ
- □ 281. SCOTT MCGREGOR
- □ 282. EDDIE MURRAY
- □ 283. FLOYD RAYFORD
- □ 284. CAL RIPKEN
- □ 285. GARY ROENICKE
- □ 286. LARRY SHEETS
- □ 287. JOHN SHELBY
- □ 288. NATE SNELL
- □ 289. SAMMY STEWART
- □ 290. ALAN WIGGINS
- □ 291. MIKE YOUNG
- □ 656. TEAM CHECKLIST(B)

BOSTON RED SOX

- ☐ 339. TONY ARMAS
- ☐ 340. MARTY BARRETT
- ☐ 341. WADE BOGGS
- ☐ 342. DENNIS BOYD
- ☐ 343. BILL BUCKNER
- ☐ 344. MARK CLEAR
- ☐ 345. ROGER CLEMENS
- ☐ 346. STEVE CRAWFORD
- ☐ 347. MIKE EASLER
- ☐ 348. DWIGHT EVANS
- ☐ 349. RICH GEDMAN
- ☐ 350. JACKIE GUTIERREZ
- ☐ 351. GLENN HOFFMAN
- ☐ 352. BRUCE HURST
- ☐ 353. BRUCE KISON
- ☐ 354. TIM LOLLAR
- ☐ 355. STEVE LYONS
- ☐ 356. AL NIPPER
- ☐ 357. BOB OJEDA
- ☐ 358. JIM RICE
- ☐ 359. BOB STANLEY
- ☐ 360. MIKE TRUJILLO
- ☐ 651. ROB WOODWARD(P)
- ☐ 657. TEAM CHECKLIST(B)

CALIFORNIA ANGELS

- ☐ 148. JUAN BENIQUEZ
- ☐ 149. BOB BOONE
- ☐ 150. JOHN CANDELARIA
- ☐ 151. ROD CAREW
- ☐ 152. STEWARD CLIBURN
- ☐ 153. DOUG DECINCES
- ☐ 154. BRIAN DOWNING
- ☐ 155. KEN FORSCH
- ☐ 156. CRAIG GERBER
- ☐ 157. BOBBY GRICH
- ☐ 158. GEORGE HENDRICK
- ☐ 159. AL HOLLAND
- ☐ 160. REGGIE JACKSON
- ☐ 161. RUPPERT JONES
- ☐ 162. URBANO LUGO
- ☐ 163. KIRK MCCASKILL
- ☐ 164. DONNIE MOORE
- ☐ 165. GARY PETTIS
- ☐ 166. RON ROMANICK

CALIFORNIA ANGELS

- ☐ 148. JUAN BENIQUEZ
- ☐ 149. BOB BOONE
- ☐ 150. JOHN CANDELARIA
- ☐ 151. ROD CAREW
- ☐ 152. STEWART CLIBURN
- ☐ 153. DOUG DECINCES
- ☐ 154. BRIAN DOWNING
- ☐ 155. KEN FORSCH
- ☐ 156. CRAIG GERBER
- ☐ 157. BOBBY GRICH
- ☐ 158. GEORGE HENDRICK
- ☐ 159. AL HOLLAND
- ☐ 160. REGGIE JACKSON
- ☐ 161. RUPPERT JONES
- ☐ 162. URBANO LUGO
- ☐ 163. KIRK MCCASKILL
- ☐ 164. DONNIE MOORE
- ☐ 165. GARY PETTIS
- ☐ 166. RON ROMANICK
- ☐ 167. DICK SCHOFIELD
- ☐ 168. DARYL SCONIERS
- ☐ 169. JIM SLATON
- ☐ 170. DON SUTTON
- ☐ 171. MIKE WITT
- ☐ 650. GUS POLIDOR(P)
- ☐ 650. MARK MCLEMORE(P)
- ☐ 655. TEAM CHECKLIST(B)

CHICAGO CUBS

- ☐ 361. THAD BOSLEY
- ☐ 362. WARREN BRUSSTAR
- ☐ 363. RON CEY
- ☐ 364. JODY DAVIS
- ☐ 365. BOB DERNIER
- ☐ 366. SHAWON DUNSTON
- ☐ 367. LEON DURHAM
- ☐ 368. DENNIS ECKERSLEY
- ☐ 369. RAY FONTENOT
- ☐ 370. GEORGE FRAZIER
- ☐ 371. BILL HATCHER
- ☐ 372. DAVE LOPES
- ☐ 373. GARY MATTHEWS
- ☐ 374. RON MEREDITH
- ☐ 375. KEITH MORELAND
- ☐ 376. REGGIE PATTERSON
- ☐ 377. DICK RUTHVEN
- ☐ 378. RYNE SANDBERG
- ☐ 379. SCOTT SANDERSON
- ☐ 380. LEE SMITH
- ☐ 381. LARY SORENSEN
- ☐ 382. CHRIS SPEIER
- ☐ 383. RICK SUTCLIFFE
- ☐ 384. STEVE TROUT
- ☐ 385. GARY WOODS
- ☐ 657. TEAM CHECKLIST(B)

CHICAGO WHITE SOX

- ☐ 197. JUAN AGOSTO
- ☐ 198. HAROLD BAINES
- ☐ 199. FLOYD BANNISTER
- ☐ 200. BRITT BURNS
- ☐ 201. JULIO CRUZ
- ☐ 202. JOEL DAVIS
- ☐ 203. RICHARD DOTSON
- ☐ 204. CARLTON FISK
- ☐ 205. SCOTT FLETCHER
- ☐ 206. OZZIE GUILLEN
- ☐ 207. JERRY HAIRSTON
- ☐ 208. TIM HULETT
- ☐ 209. BOB JAMES
- ☐ 210. RON KITTLE
- ☐ 211. RUDY LAW
- ☐ 212. BRYAN LITTLE
- ☐ 213. GENE NELSON
- ☐ 214. REID NICHOLS
- ☐ 215. LUIS SALAZAR
- ☐ 216. TOM SEAVER
- ☐ 217. DAN SPILLNER
- ☐ 218. BRUCE TANNER
- ☐ 219. GREG WALKER
- ☐ 220. DAVE WEHRMEISTER
- ☐ 656. TEAM CHECKLIST(F)

CINCINNATI REDS

- ☐ 172. BUDDY BELL
- ☐ 173. TOM BROWNING
- ☐ 174. DAVE CONCEPCION
- ☐ 175. ERIC DAVIS
- ☐ 176. BO DIAZ
- ☐ 177. NICK ESASKY
- ☐ 178. JOHN FRANCO
- ☐ 179. TOM HUME
- ☐ 180. WAYNE KRENCHICKI
- ☐ 181. ANDY MCGAFFIGAN
- ☐ 182. EDDIE MILNER
- ☐ 183. RON OESTER
- ☐ 184. DAVE PARKER
- ☐ 185. FRANK PASTORE
- ☐ 186. TONY PEREZ
- ☐ 187. TED POWER
- ☐ 188. JOE PRICE
- ☐ 189. GARY REDUS
- ☐ 190. RON ROBINSON
- ☐ 191. PETE ROSE(M)
- ☐ 192. MARIO SOTO
- ☐ 193. JOHN STUPER
- ☐ 194. JAY TIBBS
- ☐ 195. DAVE VAN GORDER
- ☐ 196. MAX VENABLE
- ☐ 646. KAL DANIELS(P)
- ☐ 646. PAUL O'NEILL(P)
- ☐ 655. TEAM CHECKLIST(B)

CLEVELAND INDIANS

- ☐ 579. CHRIS BANDO
- ☐ 580. TONY BERNAZARD
- ☐ 581. BRETT BUTLER
- ☐ 582. ERNIE CAMACHO
- ☐ 583. JOE CARTER
- ☐ 584. CARMEN CASTILLO
- ☐ 585. JAMIE EASTERLY
- ☐ 586. JULIO FRANCO
- ☐ 587. MEL HALL
- ☐ 588. MIKE HARGROVE
- ☐ 589. NEAL HEATON
- ☐ 590. BROOK JACOBY
- ☐ 591. OTIS NIXON
- ☐ 592. JERRY REED
- ☐ 593. VERN RUHLE
- ☐ 594. PAT TABLER
- ☐ 595. RICH THOMPSON
- ☐ 596. ANDRE THORNTON
- ☐ 597. DAVE VON OHLEN
- ☐ 598. GEORGE VUKOVICH
- ☐ 599. TOM WADDELL
- ☐ 600. CURT WARDLE
- ☐ 601. JERRY WILLARD
- ☐ 653. CORY SNYDER(P)
- ☐ 660. TEAM CHECKLIST(F)

DETROIT TIGERS

- ☐ 221. JUAN BERENGUER
- ☐ 222. DAVE BERGMAN
- ☐ 223. TOM BROOKENS
- ☐ 224. DARRELL EVANS
- ☐ 225. BARBARO GARBEY
- ☐ 226. KIRK GIBSON
- ☐ 227. JOHN GRUBB
- ☐ 228. WILLIE HERNANDEZ
- ☐ 229. LARRY HERNDON
- ☐ 230. CHET LEMON
- ☐ 231. AURELIO LOPEZ
- ☐ 232. JACK MORRIS
- ☐ 233. RANDY O'NEAL
- ☐ 234. LANCE PARRISH
- ☐ 235. DAN PETRY
- ☐ 236. ALEX SANCHEZ
- ☐ 237. BILL SCHERRER
- ☐ 238. NELSON SIMMONS
- ☐ 239. FRANK TANANA
- ☐ 240. WALT TERRELL
- ☐ 241. ALAN TRAMMELL
- ☐ 242. LOU WHITAKER
- ☐ 243. MILT WILCOX
- ☐ 656. TEAM CHECKLIST(F)

HOUSTON ASTROS

- ☐ 292. ALAN ASHBY
- ☐ 293. MARK BAILEY
- ☐ 294. KEVIN BASS
- ☐ 295. JEFF CALHOUN
- ☐ 296. JOSE CRUZ
- ☐ 297. GLENN DAVIS
- ☐ 298. BILL DAWLEY
- ☐ 299. FRANK DIPINO
- ☐ 300. BILL DORAN
- ☐ 301. PHIL GARNER
- ☐ 302. JEFF HEATHCOCK
- ☐ 303. CHARLIE KERFELD
- ☐ 304. BOB KNEPPER
- ☐ 305. RON MATHIS
- ☐ 306. JERRY MUMPHREY
- ☐ 307. JIM PANKOVITS
- ☐ 308. TERRY PUHL
- ☐ 309. CRAIG REYNOLDS
- ☐ 310. NOLAN RYAN
- ☐ 311. MIKE SCOTT
- ☐ 312. DAVE SMITH
- ☐ 313. DICKIE THON
- ☐ 314. DENNY WALLING
- ☐ 657. TEAM CHECKLIST(F)

KANSAS CITY ROYALS

□ 1. STEVE BALBONI
□ 2. JOE BECKWITH
□ 3. BUDDY BIANCALANA
□ 4. BUD BLACK
□ 5. GEORGE BRETT
□ 6. ONIX CONCEPCION
□ 7. STEVE FARR
□ 8. MARK GUBICZA
□ 9. DANE IORG
□ 10. DANNY JACKSON
□ 11. LYNN JONES
□ 12. MIKE JONES
□ 13. CHARLIE LEIBRANDT
□ 14. HAL MCRAE
□ 15. OMAR MORENO
□ 16. DARRYL MOTLEY
□ 17. JORGE ORTA
□ 18. DAN QUISENBERRY
□ 19. BRET SABERHAGEN
□ 20. PAT SHERIDAN
□ 21. LONNIE SMITH
□ 22. JIM SUNDBERG
□ 23. JOHN WATHAN
□ 24. FRANK WHITE
□ 25. WILLIE WILSON
□ 654. TEAM CHECKLIST(F)

LOS ANGELES DODGERS

□ 123. DAVE ANDERSON
□ 124. BOB BAILOR
□ 125. GREG BROCK
□ 126. ENOS CABELL
□ 127. BOBBY CASTILLO
□ 128. CARLOS DIAZ
□ 129. MARIANO DUNCAN
□ 130. PEDRO GUERRERO
□ 131. OREL HERSHISER
□ 132. RICK HONEYCUTT
□ 133. KEN HOWELL
□ 134. KEN LANDREAUX
□ 135. BILL MADLOCK
□ 136. CANDY MALDONADO
□ 137. MIKE MARSHALL
□ 138. LEN MATUSZEK
□ 139. TOM NIEDENFUER
□ 140. ALEJANDRO PENA
□ 141. JERRY REUSS
□ 142. BILL RUSSELL
□ 143. STEVE SAX
□ 144. MIKE SCIOSCIA
□ 145. FERNANDO VALENZUELA
□ 146. BOB WELCH
□ 147. TERRY WHITFIELD
□ 655. TEAM CHECKLIST(F)

MILWAUKEE BREWERS

□ 482. RAY BURRIS
□ 483. JAIME COCANOWER
□ 484. CECIL COOPER
□ 485. DANNY DARWIN
□ 486. ROLLIE FINGERS
□ 487. JIM GANTNER
□ 488. BOB GIBSON
□ 489. MOOSE HAAS
□ 490. TEDDY HIGUERA
□ 491. PAUL HOUSEHOLDER
□ 492. PETE LADD
□ 493. RICK MANNING
□ 494. BOB MCCLURE
□ 495. PAUL MOLITOR
□ 496. CHARLIE MOORE
□ 497. BEN OGLIVIE
□ 498. RANDY READY
□ 499. EARNIE RILES
□ 500. ED ROMERO
□ 501. BILL SCHROEDER
□ 502. RAY SEARAGE
□ 503. TED SIMMONS
□ 504. PETE VUCKOVICH
□ 505. RICK WAITS
□ 506. ROBIN YOUNT
□ 652. BILLY JOE ROBIDOUX(P)
□ 659. TEAM CHECKLIST(F)

MINNESOTA TWINS

□ 386. BERT BLYLEVEN
□ 387. TOM BRUNANSKY
□ 388. RANDY BUSH
□ 389. JOHN BUTCHER
□ 390. RON DAVIS
□ 391. DAVE ENGLE
□ 392. FRANK EUFEMIA
□ 393. PETE FILSON
□ 394. GARY GAETTI
□ 395. GREG GAGNE
□ 396. MICKEY HATCHER
□ 397. KENT HRBEK
□ 398. TIM LAUDNER
□ 399. RICK LYSANDER
□ 400. DAVE MEIER
□ 401. KIRBY PUCKETT
□ 402. MARK SALAS
□ 403. KEN SCHROM
□ 404. ROY SMALLEY
□ 405. MIKE SMITHSON
□ 406. MIKE STENHOUSE
□ 407. TIM TEUFEL
□ 408. FRANK VIOLA
□ 409. RON WASHINGTON
□ 652. MARK FUNDERBURK(P)
□ 658. TEAM CHECKLIST(F)

MONTREAL EXPOS

□ 244. HUBIE BROOKS
□ 245. TIM BURKE
□ 246. ANDRE DAWSON
□ 247. MIKE FITZGERALD
□ 248. TERRY FRANCONA
□ 249. BILL GULLICKSON
□ 250. JOE HESKETH
□ 251. BILL LASKEY
□ 252. VANCE LAW
□ 253. CHARLIE LEA
□ 254. GARY LUCAS
□ 255. DAVID PALMER
□ 256. TIM RAINES
□ 257. JEFF REARDON
□ 258. BERT ROBERGE
□ 259. DAN SCHATZEDER
□ 260. BRYN SMITH
□ 261. RANDY ST. CLAIRE
□ 262. SCOT THOMPSON
□ 263. TIM WALLACH
□ 264. U.L. WASHINGTON
□ 265. MITCH WEBSTER
□ 266. HERM WINNINGHAM
□ 267. FLOYD YOUMANS
□ 647. ANDRES GALARRAGA(P)
□ 656. TEAM CHECKLIST(B)

NEW YORK METS

□ 74. RICK AGUILERA
□ 75. WALLY BACKMAN
□ 76. GARY CARTER
□ 77. RON DARLING
□ 78. LEN DYKSTRA
□ 79. SID FERNANDEZ
□ 80. GEORGE FOSTER
□ 81. DWIGHT GOODEN
□ 82. TOM GORMAN
□ 83. DANNY HEEP
□ 84. KEITH HERNANDEZ
□ 85. HOWARD JOHNSON
□ 86. RAY KNIGHT
□ 87. TERRY LEACH
□ 88. ED LYNCH
□ 89. ROGER MCDOWELL
□ 90. JESSE OROSCO
□ 91. TOM PACIOREK
□ 92. RONN REYNOLDS
□ 93. RAFAEL SANTANA
□ 94. DOUG SISK
□ 95. RUSTY STAUB
□ 96. DARRYL STRAWBERRY
□ 97. MOOKIE WILSON
□ 654. TEAM CHECKLIST

NEW YORK YANKEES

□ 98. NEIL ALLEN
□ 99. DON BAYLOR
□ 100. DALE BERRA
□ 101. RICH BORDI
□ 102. MARTY BYSTROM
□ 103. JOE COWLEY
□ 104. BRIAN FISHER
□ 105. KEN GRIFFEY
□ 106. RON GUIDRY
□ 107. RON HASSEY
□ 108. RICKEY HENDERSON
□ 109. DON MATTINGLY
□ 110. BOBBY MEACHAM
□ 111. JOHN MONTEFUSCO
□ 112. PHIL NIEKRO
□ 113. MIKE PAGLIARULO
□ 114. DAN PASQUA
□ 115. WILLIE RANDOLPH
□ 116. DAVE RIGHETTI
□ 117. ANDRE ROBERTSON
□ 118. BILLY SAMPLE
□ 119. BOB SHIRLEY
□ 120. ED WHITSON
□ 121. DAVE WINFIELD
□ 122. BUTCH WYNEGAR
□ 655. TEAM CHECKLIST(F)

OAKLAND A'S

□ 410. KEITH ATHERTON
□ 411. DUSTY BAKER
□ 412. TIM BIRTSAS
□ 413. BRUCE BOCHTE
□ 414. CHRIS CODIROLLI
□ 415. DAVE COLLINS
□ 416. MIKE DAVIS
□ 417. ALFREDO GRIFFIN
□ 418. MIKE HEATH
□ 419. STEVE HENDERSON
□ 420. DONNIE HILL
□ 421. JAY HOWELL
□ 422. TOMMY JOHN
□ 423. DAVE KINGMAN
□ 424. BILL KRUEGER
□ 425. RICK LANGFORD
□ 426. CARNEY LANSFORD
□ 427. STEVE MCCATTY
□ 428. DWAYNE MURPHY
□ 429. STEVE ONTIVEROS
□ 430. TONY PHILLIPS
□ 431. JOSE RIJO
□ 432. MICKEY TETTLETON
□ 649. ERIC PLUNK(P)
□ 649. JOSE CANSECO(P)
□ 658. TEAM CHECKLIST(F)

PHILADELPHIA PHILLIES

□ 433. LUIS AGUAYO
□ 434. LARRY ANDERSEN
□ 435. STEVE CARLTON
□ 436. DON CARMAN
□ 437. TIM CORCORAN
□ 438. DARREN DAULTON
□ 439. JOHN DENNY
□ 440. TOM FOLEY
□ 441. GREG GROSS
□ 442. KEVIN GROSS
□ 443. VON HAYES
□ 444. CHARLES HUDSON
□ 445. GARRY MADDOX
□ 446. SHANE RAWLEY

- ☐ 447. DAVE RUCKER
- ☐ 448. JOHN RUSSELL
- ☐ 449. JUAN SAMUEL
- ☐ 450. MIKE SCHMIDT
- ☐ 451. RICH SCHU
- ☐ 452. DAVE SHIPANOFF
- ☐ 453. DAVE STEWART
- ☐ 454. JEFF STONE
- ☐ 455. KENT TEKULVE
- ☐ 456. OZZIE VIRGIL
- ☐ 457. GLENN WILSON
- ☐ 647. FRED TOLIVER(P)
- ☐ 658. TEAM CHECKLIST(B)

PITTSBURGH PIRATES

- ☐ 602. BILL ALMON
- ☐ 603. MIKE BIELECKI
- ☐ 604. SID BREAM
- ☐ 605. MIKE BROWN
- ☐ 606. PAT CLEMENTS
- ☐ 607. JOSE DELEON
- ☐ 608. DENNY GONZALEZ
- ☐ 609. CECILIO GUANTE
- ☐ 610. STEVE KEMP
- ☐ 611. SAM KHALIFA
- ☐ 612. LEE MAZZILLI
- ☐ 613. LARRY MCWILLIAMS
- ☐ 614. JIM MORRISON
- ☐ 615. JOE ORSULAK
- ☐ 616. TONY PENA
- ☐ 617. JOHNNY RAY
- ☐ 618. RICK REUSCHEL
- ☐ 619. R.J. REYNOLDS
- ☐ 620. RICK RHODEN
- ☐ 621. DON ROBINSON
- ☐ 622. JASON THOMPSON
- ☐ 623. LEE TUNNELL
- ☐ 624. JIM WINN
- ☐ 625. MARVELL WYNNE
- ☐ 648. BOB KIPPER(P)
- ☐ 660. TEAM CHECKLIST(F)

ST. LOUIS CARDINALS

- ☐ 26. JOAQUIN ANDUJAR
- ☐ 27. STEVE BRAUN
- ☐ 28. BILL CAMPBELL
- ☐ 29. CESAR CEDENO
- ☐ 30. JACK CLARK
- ☐ 31. VINCE COLEMAN
- ☐ 32. DANNY COX
- ☐ 33. KEN DAYLEY
- ☐ 34. IVAN DEJESUS
- ☐ 35. BOB FORSCH
- ☐ 36. BRIAN HARPER
- ☐ 37. TOM HERR
- ☐ 38. RICKY HORTON
- ☐ 39. KURT KEPSHIRE
- ☐ 40. JEFF LAHTI
- ☐ 41. TITO LANDRUM
- ☐ 42. WILLIE MCGEE
- ☐ 43. TOM NIETO
- ☐ 44. TERRY PENDLETON
- ☐ 45. DARRELL PORTER
- ☐ 46. OZZIE SMITH
- ☐ 47. JOHN TUDOR
- ☐ 48. ANDY VAN SLYKE
- ☐ 49. TODD WORRELL
- ☐ 648. CURT FORD(P)
- ☐ 654. TEAM CHECKLIST(F)

SAN DIEGO PADRES

- ☐ 315. KURT BEVACQUA
- ☐ 316. AL BUMBRY
- ☐ 317. JERRY DAVIS
- ☐ 318. LUIS DELEON
- ☐ 319. DAVE DRAVECKY
- ☐ 320. TIM FLANNERY
- ☐ 321. STEVE GARVEY
- ☐ 322. GOOSE GOSSAGE
- ☐ 323. TONY GWYNN
- ☐ 324. ANDY HAWKINS
- ☐ 325. LAMARR HOYT
- ☐ 326. ROY LEE JACKSON
- ☐ 327. TERRY KENNEDY
- ☐ 328. CRAIG LEFFERTS
- ☐ 329. CARMELO MARTINEZ
- ☐ 330. LANCE MCCULLERS
- ☐ 331. KEVIN MCREYNOLDS
- ☐ 332. GRAIG NETTLES
- ☐ 333. JERRY ROYSTER
- ☐ 334. ERIC SHOW
- ☐ 335. TIM STODDARD
- ☐ 336. GARRY TEMPLETON
- ☐ 337. MARK THURMOND
- ☐ 338. ED WOJNA
- ☐ 644. BENITO SANTIAGO(P)
- ☐ 644. GENE WALTER(P)
- ☐ 651. TEAM CHECKLIST(F)

SAN FRANCISCO GIANTS

- ☐ 533. VIDA BLUE
- ☐ 534. BOB BRENLEY
- ☐ 535. CHRIS BROWN
- ☐ 536. CHILI DAVIS
- ☐ 537. MARK DAVIS
- ☐ 538. ROB DEER
- ☐ 539. DAN DRIESSEN
- ☐ 540. SCOTT GARRELTS
- ☐ 541. DAN GLADDEN
- ☐ 542. JIM GOTT
- ☐ 543. DAVID GREEN
- ☐ 544. ATLEE HAMMAKER
- ☐ 545. MIKE JEFFCOAT
- ☐ 546. MIKE KRUKOW
- ☐ 547. DAVE LAPOINT
- ☐ 548. JEFF LEONARD
- ☐ 549. GREG MINTON
- ☐ 550. ALEX TREVINO
- ☐ 551. MANNY TRILLO
- ☐ 552. JOSE URIBE
- ☐ 553. BRAD WELLMAN
- ☐ 554. FRANK WILLIAMS
- ☐ 555. JOEL YOUNGBLOOD
- ☐ 645. MIKE WOODARD(P)
- ☐ 645. COLIN WARD(P)
- ☐ 659. TEAM CHECKLIST(B)

SEATTLE MARINERS

- ☐ 458. JIM BEATTIE
- ☐ 459. KARL BEST
- ☐ 460. BARRY BONNELL
- ☐ 461. PHIL BRADLEY
- ☐ 462. IVAN CALDERON
- ☐ 463. AL COWENS
- ☐ 464. ALVIN DAVIS
- ☐ 465. DAVE HENDERSON
- ☐ 466. BOB KEARNEY
- ☐ 467. MARK LANGSTON
- ☐ 468. BOB LONG
- ☐ 469. MIKE MOORE
- ☐ 470. EDWIN NUNEZ
- ☐ 471. SPIKE OWEN
- ☐ 472. JACK PERCONTE
- ☐ 473. JIM PRESLEY
- ☐ 474. DONNIE SCOTT
- ☐ 475. BILL SWIFT
- ☐ 476. DANNY TARTABULL
- ☐ 477. GORMAN THOMAS
- ☐ 478. ROY THOMAS
- ☐ 479. ED VANDE BERG
- ☐ 480. FRANK WILLS
- ☐ 481. MATT YOUNG
- ☐ 651. MICKEY BRANTLEY(P)
- ☐ 658. TEAM CHECKLIST(B)

TEXAS RANGERS

- ☐ 556. ALAN BANNISTER
- ☐ 557. GLENN BRUMMER
- ☐ 558. STEVE BUECHELE
- ☐ 559. JOSE GUZMAN
- ☐ 560. TOBY HARRAH
- ☐ 561. GREG HARRIS
- ☐ 562. DWAYNE HENRY
- ☐ 563. BURT HOOTON
- ☐ 564. CHARLIE HOUGH
- ☐ 565. MIKE MASON
- ☐ 566. ODDIBE MCDOWELL
- ☐ 567. DICKIE NOLES
- ☐ 568. PETE O'BRIEN
- ☐ 569. LARRY PARRISH
- ☐ 570. DAVE ROZEMA
- ☐ 571. DAVE SCHMIDT
- ☐ 572. DON SLAUGHT
- ☐ 573. WAYNE TOLLESON
- ☐ 574. DUANE WALKER
- ☐ 575. GARY WARD
- ☐ 576. CHRIS WELSH
- ☐ 577. CURTIS WILKERSON
- ☐ 578. GEORGE WRIGHT
- ☐ 659. TEAM CHECKLIST(B)

TORONTO BLUE JAYS

- ☐ 50. JIM ACKER
- ☐ 51. DOYLE ALEXANDER
- ☐ 52. JESSE BARFIELD
- ☐ 53. GEORGE BELL
- ☐ 54. JEFF BURROUGHS
- ☐ 55. BILL CAUDILL
- ☐ 56. JIM CLANCY
- ☐ 57. TONY FERNANDEZ
- ☐ 58. TOM FILER
- ☐ 59. DAMASO GARCIA
- ☐ 60. TOM HENKE
- ☐ 61. GARTH IORG
- ☐ 62. CLIFF JOHNSON
- ☐ 63. JIMMY KEY
- ☐ 64. DENNIS LAMP
- ☐ 65. GARY LAVELLE
- ☐ 66. BUCK MARTINEZ
- ☐ 67. LLOYD MOSEBY
- ☐ 68. RANCE MULLINIKS
- ☐ 69. AL OLIVER
- ☐ 70. DAVE STIEB
- ☐ 71. LOUIS THORNTON
- ☐ 72. WILLIE UPSHAW
- ☐ 73. ERNIE WHITT
- ☐ 653. CECIL FIELDER(P)
- ☐ 654. TEAM CHECKLIST(B)

1986 FLEER TRADED (132) 2 1/2 X 3 1/2

ATLANTA BRAVES

- ☐ 5U. PAUL ASSENMACHER
- ☐ 78U. OMAR MORENO
- ☐ 87U. DAVID PALMER
- ☐ 102U. BILLY SAMPLE
- ☐ 106U. TED SIMMONS
- ☐ 112U. ANDRES THOMAS
- ☐ 122U. OZZIE VIRGIL
- ☐ 125U. DUANE WARD

BALTIMORE ORIOLES

- ☐ 13U. JUAN BENIQUEZ
- ☐ 16U. RICH BORDI
- ☐ 47U. JACKIE GUTIERREZ

BOSTON RED SOX

- ☐ 10U. DON BAYLOR
- ☐ 93U. REY QUINONEZ
- ☐ 101U. JOE SAMBITO
- ☐ 107U. SAMMY STEWART

CALIFORNIA ANGELS

- ☐ 42U. TERRY FORSTER
- ☐ 59U. WALLY JOYNER

CHICAGO CUBS

- □ 7U. JAY BALLER
- □ 43U. TERRY FRANCONA
- □ 51U. GUY HOFFMAN
- □ 79U. JERRY MUMPHREY
- □ 120U. MANNY TRILLO

CHICAGO WHITE SOX

- □ 3U. NEIL ALLEN
- □ 15U. BOBBY BONILLA
- □ 19U. JOHN CANGELOSI
- □ 31U. JOE COWLEY
- □ 32U. BILL DAWLEY
- □ 75U. JOEL MCKEON
- □ 103U. DAVE SCHMIDT
- □ 118U. WAYNE TOLLESON

CINCINNATI REDS

- □ 34U. JOHN DENNY
- □ 46U. BILL GULLICKSON
- □ 58U. TRACY JONES
- □ 108U. KURT STILLWELL

CLEVELAND INDIANS

- □ 2U. ANDY ALLANSON
- □ 6U. SCOTT BAILES
- □ 18U. TOM CANDIOTTI
- □ 81U. PHIL NIEKRO
- □ 104U. KEN SCHROM

DETROIT TIGERS

- □ 17U. BILL CAMPBELL
- □ 21U. CHUCK CARY
- □ 28U. DAVE COLLINS
- □ 27U. DARNELL COLES
- □ 39U. DAVE ENGLE
- □ 64U. DAVE LAPOINT

HOUSTON ASTROS

- □ 35U. JIM DESHAIES
- □ 49U. BILLY HATCHER
- □ 69U. AURELIO LOPEZ
- □ 123U. TONY WALKER

KANSAS CITY ROYALS

- □ 8U. SCOTT BANKHEAD
- □ 66U. RUDY LAW
- □ 67U. DENNIS LEONARD
- □ 100U. ANGEL SALAZAR

LOS ANGELS DODGERS

- □ 119U. ALEX TREVINO
- □ 121U. ED VANDE BERG
- □ 128U. REGGIE WILLIAMS

MILWAUKEE BREWERS

- □ 22U. JUAN CASTILLO
- □ 23U. RICK CERONE
- □ 26U. MARK CLEAR
- □ 33U. ROB DEER
- □ 83U. JUAN NIEVES
- □ 90U. DAN PLASAC
- □ 97U. BILLY JOE ROBIDOUX
- □ 109U. DALE SVEUM

MINNESOTA TWINS

- □ 11U. BILLY BEANE
- □ 68U. STEVE LOMBARDOZZI
- □ 95U. JEFF REED

MONTREAL EXPOS

- □ 44U. ANDRES GALARRAGA
- □ 60U. WAYNE KRENCHICKI
- □ 74U. ANDY MCGAFFIGAN
- □ 80U. AL NEWMAN
- □ 88U. JEFF PARRETT
- □ 113U. JASON THOMPSON
- □ 116U. JAY TIBBS

NEW YORK METS

- □ 76U. KEVIN MITCHELL
- □ 82U. RANDY NIEMANN
- □ 84U. BOB OJEDA
- □ 110U. TIM TEUFEL

NEW YORK YANKEES

- □ 36U. DOUG DRABEK
- □ 37U. MIKE EASLER
- □ 40U. MIKE FISCHLIN
- □ 57U. TOMMY JOHN
- □ 98U. GARY ROENICKE
- □ 111U. BOB TEWKSBURY

OAKLAND A'S

- □ 4U. JOAQUIN ANDUJAR
- □ 9U. BILL BATHE
- □ 20U. JOSE CANSECO
- □ 48U. MOOSE HAAS
- □ 56U. STAN JAVIER
- □ 77U. BILL MOONEYHAM
- □ 126U. JERRY WILLARD

PHILADELPHIA PHILLIES

- □ 12U. STEVE BEDROSIAN
- □ 52U. TOM HUME
- □ 55U. CHRIS JAMES
- □ 94U. GARY REDUS
- □ 99U. RON ROENICKE
- □ 114U. MILT THOMPSON
- □ 117U. FRED TOLIVER

PITTSBURGH PIRATES

- □ 14U. BARRY BONDS

ST. LOUIS CARDINALS

- □ 29U. TIM CONROY
- □ 50U. MIKE HEATH
- □ 65U. MIKE LA VALLIERE
- □ 73U. GREG MATHEWS
- □ 85U. RICK OWNBEY
- □ 89U. PAT PERRY

SAN DIEGO PADRES

- □ 54U. DANE IORG
- □ 61U. JOHN KRUK
- □ 96U. BIP ROBERTS
- □ 124U. GENE WALTER
- □ 130U. MARVELL WYNNE

SAN FRANCISCO GIANTS

- □ 1U. MIKE ALDRETE
- □ 25U. WILL CLARK
- □ 62U. MIKE LACOSS
- □ 71U. CANDY MALDONADO
- □ 72U. ROGER MASON
- □ 92U. LUIS QUINONES
- □ 115U. ROB THOMPSON

SEATTLE MARINERS

- □ 45U. LEE GUETTERMAN
- □ 63U. PETER LADD
- □ 131U. STEVE YEAGER

TEXAS RANGERS

- □ 30U. ED CORREA
- □ 41U. SCOTT FLETCHER
- □ 53U. PETE INCAVIGLIA
- □ 70U. MICKEY MAHLER
- □ 86U. TOM PACIOREK
- □ 91U. DARRELL PORTER
- □ 105U. RUBEN SIERRA
- □ 127U. MITCH WILLIAMS
- □ 129U. BOBBY WITT

TORONTO BLUE JAYS

- □ 24U. JOHN CERUTTI
- □ 38U. MARK EICHHORN

1987 FLEER (660)
2 1/2 X 3 1/2

ATLANTA BRAVES

- □ 509. JIM ACKER
- □ 510. DOYLE ALEXANDER
- □ 511. PAUL ASSENMACHER
- □ 512. BRUCE BENEDICT
- □ 513. CHRIS CHAMBLISS
- □ 514. JEFF DEDMON
- □ 515. GENE GARBER
- □ 516. KEN GRIFFEY
- □ 517. TERRY HARPER
- □ 518. BOB HORNER
- □ 519. GLENN HUBBARD
- □ 520. RICK MAHLER
- □ 521. OMAR MORENO
- □ 522. DALE MURPHY
- □ 523. KEN OBERKFELL
- □ 524. ED OLWINE
- □ 525. DAVID PALMER
- □ 526. RAFAEL RAMIREZ
- □ 527. BILLY SAMPLE
- □ 528. TED SIMMONS
- □ 529. ZANE SMITH
- □ 530. BRUCE SUTTER
- □ 531. ANDRES THOMAS
- □ 532. OZZIE VIRGIL
- □ 659. TEAM CHECKLIST(F)

BALTIMORE ORIOLES

- ☐ 461. DON AASE
- ☐ 462. JUAN BENIQUEZ
- ☐ 463. MIKE BODDICKER
- ☐ 464. JUAN BONILLA
- ☐ 465. RICH BORDI
- ☐ 466. STORM DAVIS
- ☐ 467. RICK DEMPSEY
- ☐ 468. KEN DIXON
- ☐ 469. JIM DWYER
- ☐ 470. MIKE FLANAGAN
- ☐ 471. JACKIE GUTIERREZ
- ☐ 472. BRAD HAVENS
- ☐ 473. LEE LACY
- ☐ 474. FRED LYNN
- ☐ 475. SCOTT MCGREGOR
- ☐ 476. EDDIE MURRAY
- ☐ 477. TOM O'MALLEY
- ☐ 478. CAL RIPKEN
- ☐ 479. LARRY SHEETS
- ☐ 480. JOHN SHELBY
- ☐ 481. NATE SNELL
- ☐ 482. JIM TRABER
- ☐ 483. MIKE YOUNG
- ☐ 652. JOHN STEFERO(P)
- ☐ 658. TEAM CHECKLIST(B)

BOSTON RED SOX

- ☐ 26. TONY ARMAS
- ☐ 27. MARTY BARRETT
- ☐ 28. DON BAYLOR
- ☐ 29. WADE BOGGS
- ☐ 30. OIL CAN BOYD
- ☐ 31. BILL BUCKNER
- ☐ 32. ROGER CLEMENS
- ☐ 33. STEVE CRAWFORD
- ☐ 34. DWIGHT EVANS
- ☐ 35. RICH GEDMAN
- ☐ 36. DAVE HENDERSON
- ☐ 37. BRUCE HURST
- ☐ 38. TIM LOLLAR
- ☐ 39. AL NIPPER
- ☐ 40. SPIKE OWEN
- ☐ 41. JIM RICE
- ☐ 42. ED ROMERO
- ☐ 43. JOE SAMBITO
- ☐ 44. CALVIN SCHIRALDI
- ☐ 45. TOM SEAVER
- ☐ 46. JEFF SELLERS
- ☐ 47. BOB STANLEY
- ☐ 48. SAMMY STEWART
- ☐ 654. TEAM CHECKLIST(F)

CALIFORNIA ANGELS

- ☐ 73. BOB BOONE
- ☐ 74. RICK BURLESON
- ☐ 75. JOHN CANDELARIA
- ☐ 76. DOUG CORBETT
- ☐ 77. DOUG DECINCES
- ☐ 78. BRIAN DOWNING
- ☐ 79. CHUCK FINLEY
- ☐ 80. TERRY FORSTER
- ☐ 81. BOBBY GRICH
- ☐ 82. GEORGE HENDRICK
- ☐ 83. JACK HOWELL
- ☐ 84. REGGIE JACKSON
- ☐ 85. RUPPERT JONES
- ☐ 86. WALLY JOYNER
- ☐ 87. GARY LUCAS
- ☐ 88. KIRK MCCASKILL
- ☐ 89. DONNIE MOORE
- ☐ 90. GARY PETTIS
- ☐ 91. VERN RUHLE
- ☐ 92. DICK SCHOFIELD
- ☐ 93. DON SUTTON
- ☐ 94. ROB WILFONG
- ☐ 95. MIKE WITT
- ☐ 646. WILLIE FRASER(P)
- ☐ 646. DEVON WHITE(P)
- ☐ 654. TEAM CHECKLIST(B)

CINCINNATI REDS

- ☐ 193. BUDDY BELL
- ☐ 194. TOM BROWNING
- ☐ 195. SAL BUTERA
- ☐ 196. DAVE CONCEPCION
- ☐ 197. KAL DANIELS
- ☐ 198. ERIC DAVIS
- ☐ 199. JOHN DENNY
- ☐ 200. BO DIAZ
- ☐ 201. NICK ESASKY
- ☐ 202. JOHN FRANCO
- ☐ 203. BILL GULLICKSON
- ☐ 204. BARRY LARKIN
- ☐ 205. EDDIE MILNER
- ☐ 206. ROB MURPHY
- ☐ 207. RON OESTER
- ☐ 208. DAVE PARKER
- ☐ 209. TONY PEREZ
- ☐ 210. TED POWER
- ☐ 211. JOE PRICE
- ☐ 212. RON ROBINSON
- ☐ 213. PETE ROSE(M)
- ☐ 214. MARIO SOTO
- ☐ 215. KURT STILLWELL
- ☐ 216. MAX VENABLE
- ☐ 217. CHRIS WELSH
- ☐ 218. CARL WILLIS
- ☐ 651. TRACY JONES(P)
- ☐ 656. TEAM CHECKLIST(F)

CLEVELAND INDIANS

- ☐ 241. ANDY ALLANSON
- ☐ 242. SCOTT BAILES
- ☐ 243. CHRIS BANDO
- ☐ 244. TONY BERNAZARD
- ☐ 245. JOHN BUTCHER
- ☐ 246. BRETT BUTLER
- ☐ 247. ERNIE CAMACHO
- ☐ 248. TOM CANDIOTTI
- ☐ 249. JOE CARTER
- ☐ 250. CARMEN CASTILLO
- ☐ 251. JULIO FRANCO
- ☐ 252. MEL HALL
- ☐ 253. BROOK JACOBY
- ☐ 254. PHIL NIEKRO
- ☐ 255. OTIS NIXON
- ☐ 256. DICKIE NOLES
- ☐ 257. BRYAN OELKERS
- ☐ 258. KEN SCHROM
- ☐ 259. DON SCHULZE
- ☐ 260. CORY SNYDER
- ☐ 261. PAT TABLER
- ☐ 262. ANDERE THORNTON
- ☐ 263. RICH YETT
- ☐ 644. DAVE CLARK(P)
- ☐ 644. GREG SWINDELL(P)
- ☐ 656. TEAM CHECKLIST(B)

CHICAGO CUBS

- ☐ 555. THAD BOSLEY
- ☐ 556. RON CEY
- ☐ 557. JODY DAVIS
- ☐ 558. RON DAVIS
- ☐ 559. BOB DERNIER
- ☐ 560. FRANK DIPINO
- ☐ 561. SHAWON DUNSTON
- ☐ 562. LEON DURHAM
- ☐ 563. DENNIS ECKERSLEY
- ☐ 564. TERRY FRANCONA
- ☐ 565. DAVE GUMPERT
- ☐ 566. GUY HOFFMAN
- ☐ 567. ED LYNCH
- ☐ 568. GARY MATTHEWS
- ☐ 569. KEITH MORELAND
- ☐ 570. JAMIE MOYER
- ☐ 571. JERRY MUMPHREY
- ☐ 572. RYNE SANDBERG
- ☐ 573. SCOTT SANDERSON
- ☐ 574. LEE SMITH
- ☐ 575. CHRIS SPEIER
- ☐ 576. RICK SUTCLIFFE
- ☐ 577. MANNY TRILLO
- ☐ 578. STEVE TROUT
- ☐ 659. TEAM CHECKLIST(B)

CHICAGO WHITE SOX

- ☐ 484. NEIL ALLEN
- ☐ 485. HAROLD BAINES
- ☐ 486. FLOYD BANNISTER
- ☐ 487. DARYL BOSTON
- ☐ 488. IVAN CALDERON
- ☐ 489. JOHN CANGELOSI
- ☐ 490. STEVE CARLTON
- ☐ 491. JOE COWLEY
- ☐ 492. JULIO CRUZ
- ☐ 493. BILL DAWLEY
- ☐ 494. JOSE DELEON
- ☐ 495. RICHARD DOTSON
- ☐ 496. CARLTON FISK
- ☐ 497. OZZIE GUILLEN
- ☐ 498. JERRY HAIRSTON
- ☐ 499. RON HASSEY
- ☐ 500. TIM HULETT
- ☐ 501. BOB JAMES
- ☐ 502. STEVE LYONS
- ☐ 503. JOEL MCKEON
- ☐ 504. GENE NELSON
- ☐ 505. DAVE SCHMIDT
- ☐ 506. RAY SEARAGE
- ☐ 507. BOBBY THIGPEN
- ☐ 508. GREG WALKER
- ☐ 645. RUSS MORMAN(P)
- ☐ 645. RON KARKOVICE(P)
- ☐ 659. TEAM CHECKLIST(F)

DETROIT TIGERS

- ☐ 144. DAVE BERGMAN
- ☐ 145. TOM BROOKENS
- ☐ 146. BILL CAMPBELL
- ☐ 147. CHUCK CARY
- ☐ 148. DARNELL COLES
- ☐ 149. DAVE COLLINS
- ☐ 150. DARRELL EVANS
- ☐ 151. KIRK GIBSON
- ☐ 152. JOHN GRUBB
- ☐ 153. WILLIE HERNANDEZ
- ☐ 154. LARRY HERNDON
- ☐ 155. ERIC KING
- ☐ 156. CHET LEMON
- ☐ 157. DWIGHT LOWRY
- ☐ 158. JACK MORRIS
- ☐ 159. RANDY O'NEAL
- ☐ 160. LANCE PARRIS
- ☐ 161. DAN PETRY
- ☐ 162. PAT SHERIDAN
- ☐ 163. JIM SLATON
- ☐ 164. FRANK TANANA
- ☐ 165. WALT TERRELL
- ☐ 166. MARK THURMOND
- ☐ 167. ALLAN TRAMMELL
- ☐ 168. LOU WHITAKER
- ☐ 655. TEAM CHECKLIST(B)

HOUSTON ASTROS

- ☐ 49. LARRY ANDERSON
- ☐ 50. ALAN ASHBY
- ☐ 51. KEVIN BASS
- ☐ 52. JEFF CALHOUN
- ☐ 53. JOSE CRUZ
- ☐ 54. DANNY DARWIN
- ☐ 55. GLENN DAVIS
- ☐ 56. JIM DESHAIES
- ☐ 57. BILL DORAN
- ☐ 58. PHIL GARNER
- ☐ 59. BILLY HATCHER
- ☐ 60. CHARLIE KERFELD
- ☐ 61. BOB KNEPPER
- ☐ 62. DAVE LOPES
- ☐ 63. AURELIO LOPEZ
- ☐ 64. JIM PANKOVITS
- ☐ 65. TERRY PUHL
- ☐ 66. CRAIG REYNOLDS
- ☐ 67. NOLAN RYAN

☐ 68. MIKE SCOTT
☐ 69. DAVE SMITH
☐ 70. DICKIE THON
☐ 71. TONY WALKER
☐ 72. DENNY WALLING
☐ 654. TEAM CHECKLIST(B)

KANSAS CITY ROYALS

☐ 362. STEVE BALBONI
☐ 363. SCOTT BANKHEAD
☐ 364. BUDDY BIANCALANA
☐ 365. BUD BLACK
☐ 366. GEORGE BRETT
☐ 367. STEVE FARR
☐ 368. MARK GUBICZA
☐ 369. BO JACKSON
☐ 370. DANNY JACKSON
☐ 371. MIKE KINGERY
☐ 372. RUDY LAW
☐ 373. CHARLIE LEIBRANDT
☐ 374. DENNIS LEONARD
☐ 375. HAL MCRAE
☐ 376. JORE ORTA
☐ 377. JAMIE QUIRK
☐ 378. DAN QUISENBERRY
☐ 379. BRET SABERHAGEN
☐ 380. ANGEL SALAZAR
☐ 381. LONNIE SMITH
☐ 382. JIM SUNDBERG
☐ 383. FRANK WHITE
☐ 384. WILLIE WILSON
☐ 652. KEVIN SEITZER(P)
☐ 657. TEAM CHECKLIST(B)

LOS ANGELES DODGERS

☐ 436. DAVE ANDERSON
☐ 437. GREG BROCK
☐ 438. ENOS CABELL
☐ 439. MARIANO DUNCAN
☐ 440. PEDRO GUERRERO
☐ 441. OREL HERSHISER
☐ 442. RICK HONEYCUTT
☐ 443. KEN HOWELL
☐ 444. KEN LANDREAUX
☐ 445. BILL MADLOCK
☐ 446. MIKE MARSHALL
☐ 447. LEN MATUSZEK
☐ 448. TOM NIEDENFUER
☐ 449. AJEJANDRO PENA
☐ 450. DENNIS POWELL
☐ 451. JERRY REUSS
☐ 452. BUD RUSSELL
☐ 453. STEVE SAX
☐ 454. MIKE SCIOSCIA
☐ 455. FRANKLIN STUBBS
☐ 456. ALEX TREVINO
☐ 457. FERNANDO VALENZUELA
☐ 458. ED VANDE BERG
☐ 459. BOB WELCH
☐ 460. REGGIE WILLIAMS
☐ 649. RALPH BRYANT(P)
☐ 649. JOSE GONZALEZ(P)
☐ 658. TEAM CHECKLIST(B)

MILWAUKEE BREWERS

☐ 338. CHRIS BOSIO
☐ 339. GLENN BRAGGS
☐ 340. RICK CERONE
☐ 341. MARK CLEAR
☐ 342. BRYAN CLUTTERBUCK
☐ 343. CECIL COOPER
☐ 344. ROB DEER
☐ 345. JIM GANTNER
☐ 346. TED HIGUERA
☐ 347. JOHN HENRY JOHNSON
☐ 348. TIM LEARY
☐ 349. RICK MANNING
☐ 350. PAUL MOLITOR
☐ 351. CHARLIE MOORE
☐ 352. JUAN NIEVES
☐ 353. BEN OGLIVIE
☐ 354. DAN PLESAC
☐ 355. ERNEST RILES
☐ 356. BILLY JOE ROBIDOUX
☐ 357. BILL SCHROEDER
☐ 358. DALE SVEUM
☐ 359. GORMAN THOMAS
☐ 360. BILL WEGMAN
☐ 361. ROBIN YOUNT
☐ 657. TEAM CHECKLIST(B)

MINNESOTA TWINS

☐ 533. ALLAN ANDERSON
☐ 534. KEITH ATHERTON
☐ 535. BILLY BEANE
☐ 536. BERT BLYLEVEN
☐ 537. TOM BRUNANSKY
☐ 538. RANDY BUSH
☐ 539. GEORGE FRAZIER
☐ 540. GARY GAETTI
☐ 541. GREG GAGNE
☐ 542. MICKEY HATCHER
☐ 543. NEAL HEATON
☐ 544. KENT HRBEK
☐ 545. ROY LEE JACKSON
☐ 546. TIM LAUDNER
☐ 547. STEVE LOMBARDOZZI
☐ 548. MARK PORTUGAL
☐ 549. KIRBY PUCKETT
☐ 550. JEFF REED
☐ 551. MARK SALAS
☐ 552. ROY SMALLEY
☐ 553. MIKE SMITHSON
☐ 554. FRANK VIOLA
☐ 659. TEAM CHECKLIST(B)

MONTREAL EXPOS

☐ 313. DANN BILARDELLO
☐ 314. HUBIE BROOKS
☐ 315. TIM BURKE
☐ 316. ANDRE DAWSON
☐ 317. MIKE FITZGERALD
☐ 318. TOM FOLEY
☐ 319. ANDRES GALARRAGA
☐ 320. JOE HESKETH
☐ 321. WALLACE JOHNSON
☐ 322. WAYNE KRENCHICKI
☐ 323. VANCE LAW
☐ 324. DENNIS MARTINEZ
☐ 325. BOB MCCLURE
☐ 326. ANDY MCGAFFIGAN
☐ 327. AL NEWMAN
☐ 328. TIM RAINES
☐ 329. JEFF REARDON
☐ 330. LUIS RIVERA
☐ 331. BOB SEBRA
☐ 332. BRYN SMITH
☐ 333. JAY TIBBS
☐ 334. TIM WALLACH
☐ 335. MITCH WEBSTER
☐ 336. JIM WOHLFORD
☐ 337. FLOYD YOUMANS
☐ 657. TEAM CHECKLIST(F)

NEW YORK METS

☐ 1. RICK AGUILERA
☐ 2. RICHARD ANDERSON
☐ 3. WALLY BACKMAN
☐ 4. GARY CARTER
☐ 5. RON DARLING
☐ 6. LEN DYKSTRA
☐ 7. KEVIN ELSTER
☐ 8. SID FERNANDEZ
☐ 9. DWIGHT GOODEN
☐ 10. ED HEARN
☐ 11. DANNY HEEP
☐ 12. KEITH HERNANDEZ
☐ 13. HOWARD JOHNSON
☐ 14. RAY KNIGHT
☐ 15. LEE MAZZILLI
☐ 16. ROGER MCDOWELL
☐ 17. KEVIN MITCHELL
☐ 18. RANDY NIEMANN
☐ 19. BOB OJEDA
☐ 20. JESSE OROSCO
☐ 21. RAFAEL SANTANA
☐ 22. DOUG SISK
☐ 23. DARRYL STRAWBERRY
☐ 24. TIM TEUFEL
☐ 25. MOOKIE WILSON
☐ 648. DAVE MAGADAN(P)
☐ 654. TEAM CHECKLIST(F)

NEW YORK YANKEES

☐ 96. DOUG DRABEK
☐ 97. MIKE EASLER
☐ 98. MIKE FISCHLIN
☐ 99. BRIAN FISHER
☐ 100. RON GUIDRY
☐ 101. RICKEY HENDERSON
☐ 102. TOMMY JOHN
☐ 103. RON KITTLE
☐ 104. DON MATTINGLY
☐ 105. BOBBY MEACHAM
☐ 106. JOE NIEKRO
☐ 107. MIKE PAGLIARULO
☐ 108. DAN PASQUA
☐ 109. WILLIE RANDOLPH
☐ 110. DENNIS RASMUSSEN
☐ 111. DAVE RIGHETTI
☐ 112. GARY ROENICKE
☐ 113. ROD SCURRY
☐ 114. BOB SHIRLEY
☐ 115. JOEL SKINNER
☐ 116. TIM STODDARD
☐ 117. BOB TEWKSBURY
☐ 118. WAYNE TOLLESON
☐ 119. CLAUDELL WASHINGTON
☐ 120. DAVE WINFIELD
☐ 648. PHIL LOMBARDI(P)
☐ 655. TEAM CHECKLIST(F)

OAKLAND A'S

☐ 385. JOAQUIN ANDUJAR
☐ 386. DOUG BAIR
☐ 387. DUSTY BAKER
☐ 388. BRUCE BOCHTE
☐ 389. JOSE CANSECO
☐ 390. CHRIS CONDIROLI
☐ 391. MIKE DAVIS
☐ 392. ALFREDO GRIFFIN
☐ 393. MOOSE HAAS
☐ 394. DONNIE HILL
☐ 395. JAY HOWELL
☐ 396. DAVE KINGMAN
☐ 397. CARNEY LANSFORD
☐ 398. DAVID LEIPER
☐ 399. BILL MOONEYHAM
☐ 400. DWAYNE MURPHY
☐ 401. STEVE ONTIVEROS
☐ 402. TONY PHILLIPS
☐ 403. ERIC PLUNK
☐ 404. JOSE RIJO
☐ 405. TERRY STEINBACH
☐ 406. DAVE STEWART
☐ 407. MICKEY TETTLETON
☐ 408. DAVE VON OHLEN
☐ 409. JERRY WILLARD
☐ 410. CURT YOUNG
☐ 653. ROB NELSON(P)
☐ 658. TEAM CHECKLIST(F)

PHILADELPHIA PHILLIES

☐ 169. LUIS AGUAYO
☐ 170. STEVE BEDROSIAN
☐ 171. DON CARMAN
☐ 172. DARREN DAULTON
☐ 173. GREG GROSS
☐ 174. KEVIN GROSS
☐ 175. VON HAYES

- ☐ 176. CHARLES HUDSON
- ☐ 177. TOM HUME
- ☐ 178. STEVE JELTZ
- ☐ 179. MIKE MADDUX
- ☐ 180. SHANE RAWLEY
- ☐ 181. GARY REDUS
- ☐ 182. RON ROENICKE
- ☐ 183. BRUCE RUFFIN
- ☐ 184. JOHN RUSSELL
- ☐ 185. JUAN SAMUEL
- ☐ 186. DAN SCHATZEDER
- ☐ 187. MIKE SCHMIDT
- ☐ 188. RICK SCHU
- ☐ 189. JEFF STONE
- ☐ 190. KENT TEKULVE
- ☐ 191. MILT THOMPSON
- ☐ 192. GLENN WILSON
- ☐ 651. MARVIN FREEMAN(P)
- ☐ 655 TEAM CHECKLIST(B)

PITTSBURGH PIRATES

- ☐ 601. BILL ALMON
- ☐ 602. RAFAEL BELLIARD
- ☐ 603. MIKE BIELECKI
- ☐ 604. BARRY BONDS
- ☐ 605. BOBBY BONILLA
- ☐ 606. SID BREAM
- ☐ 607. MIKE BROWN
- ☐ 608. PAT CLEMENTS
- ☐ 609. MIKE DIAZ
- ☐ 610. CECILIO GUANTE
- ☐ 611. BARRY JONES
- ☐ 612. BOB KIPPER
- ☐ 613. LARRY MCWILLIAMS
- ☐ 614. JIM MORRISON
- ☐ 615. JOE ORSULAK
- ☐ 616. JUNIOR ORTIZ
- ☐ 617. TONY PENA
- ☐ 618. JOHNNY RAY
- ☐ 619. RICK REUSCHEL
- ☐ 620. R. J. REYNOLDS
- ☐ 621. RICK RHODEN
- ☐ 622. DON ROBINSON
- ☐ 623. BOB WALK
- ☐ 624. JIM WINN
- ☐ 660. TEAM CHECKLIST(F)

ST. LOUIS CARDINALS

- ☐ 289. JACK CLARK
- ☐ 290. VINCE COLEMAN
- ☐ 291. TIM CONROY
- ☐ 292. DANNY COX
- ☐ 293. KEN DAYLEY
- ☐ 294. CURT FORD
- ☐ 295. BOB FORSCH
- ☐ 296. TOM HERR
- ☐ 297. RICKY HORTON
- ☐ 298. CLINT HURDLE
- ☐ 299. JEFF LAHTI
- ☐ 300. STEVE LAKE
- ☐ 301. TITO LANDRUM
- ☐ 302. MIKE LAVALLIERE
- ☐ 303. GREG MATHEWS
- ☐ 304. WILLIE MCGEE
- ☐ 305. JOSE OQUENDO
- ☐ 306. TERRY PENDLETON
- ☐ 307. PAT PERRY
- ☐ 308. OZZIE SMITH
- ☐ 309. RAY SOFF
- ☐ 310. JOHN TUDOR
- ☐ 311. ANDY VAN SLYKE
- ☐ 312. TODD WORRELL
- ☐ 657. TEAM CHECKLIST(F)

SAN DIEGO PADRES

- ☐ 411. BRUCE BOCHY
- ☐ 412. DAVE DRAVECKY
- ☐ 413. TIM FLANNERY
- ☐ 414. STEVE GARVEY
- ☐ 415. GOOSE GOSSAGE
- ☐ 416. TONY GWYNN
- ☐ 417. ANDY HAWKINS
- ☐ 418. LAMARR HOYT
- ☐ 419. TERRY KENNEDY
- ☐ 420. JOHN KRUK
- ☐ 421. DAVE LAPOINT
- ☐ 422. CRAIG LEFFERTS
- ☐ 423. CARMELO MARTINEZ
- ☐ 424. LANCE MCCULLERS
- ☐ 425. KEVIN MCREYNOLDS
- ☐ 426. GRAIG NETTLES
- ☐ 427. BIP ROBERTS
- ☐ 428. JERRY ROYSTER
- ☐ 429. BENITO SANTIAGO
- ☐ 430. ERIC SHOW
- ☐ 431. BOB STODDARD
- ☐ 432. GARRY TEMPLETON
- ☐ 433. GENE WALTER
- ☐ 434. ED WHITSON
- ☐ 435. MARVELL WYNNE
- ☐ 650. JIMMY JONES(P)
- ☐ 650. RANDY ASADOOR(P)
- ☐ 658. TEAM CHECKLIST(F)

SAN FRANCISCO GIANTS

- ☐ 264. MIKE ALDRETE
- ☐ 265. JUAN BERENGUER
- ☐ 266. VIDA BLUE
- ☐ 267. BOB BRENLY
- ☐ 268. CHRIS BROWN
- ☐ 269. WILL CLARK
- ☐ 270. CHILI DAVIS
- ☐ 271. MARK DAVIS
- ☐ 272. KELLY DOWNS
- ☐ 273. SCOTT GARRELTS
- ☐ 274. DAN GLADDEN
- ☐ 275. MIKE KRUKOW
- ☐ 276. RANDY KUTCHER
- ☐ 277. MIKE LACOSS
- ☐ 278. JEFF LEONARD
- ☐ 279. CANDY MALDONADO
- ☐ 280. ROGER MASON
- ☐ 281. BOB MELVIN
- ☐ 282. GREG MINTON
- ☐ 283. JEFF ROBINSON
- ☐ 284. HARRY SPILMAN
- ☐ 285. ROB THOMPSON
- ☐ 286. JOSE URIBE
- ☐ 287. FRANK WILLIAMS
- ☐ 288. JOEL YOUNGBLOOD
- ☐ 656 TEAM CHECKLIST(B)

SEATTLE MARINERS

- ☐ 579. KARL BEST
- ☐ 580. PHIL BRADLEY
- ☐ 581. SCOTT BRADLEY
- ☐ 582. MICKEY BRANTLEY
- ☐ 583. MIKE BROWN
- ☐ 584. ALVIN DAVIS
- ☐ 585. LEE GUETTERMAN
- ☐ 586. MARK HUISMANN
- ☐ 587. BOB KEARNEY
- ☐ 588. PETE LADD
- ☐ 589. MARK LANGSTON
- ☐ 590. MIKE MOORE
- ☐ 591. MIKE MORGAN
- ☐ 592. JOHN MOSES
- ☐ 593. KEN PHELPS
- ☐ 594. JIM PRESLEY
- ☐ 595. REY QUINONEZ
- ☐ 596. HAROLD REYNOLDS
- ☐ 597. BILLY SWIFT
- ☐ 598. DANNY TARTABULL
- ☐ 599. STEVE YEAGER
- ☐ 600. MATT YOUNG
- ☐ 653. STEVE FIREOVID(P)
- ☐ 660. TEAM CHECKLIST(F)

TEXAS RANGERS

- ☐ 121. STEVE BUECHELE
- ☐ 122. ED CORREA
- ☐ 123. SCOTT FLETCHER
- ☐ 124. JOSE GUZMAN
- ☐ 125. TOBY HARRAH
- ☐ 126. GREG HARRIS
- ☐ 127. CHARLIE HOUGH
- ☐ 128. PETE INCAVIGLIA
- ☐ 129. MIKE MASON
- ☐ 130. ODDIBE MCDOWELL
- ☐ 131. DALE MOHORCIC
- ☐ 132. PETE O'BRIEN
- ☐ 133. TOM PACIOREK
- ☐ 134. LARRY PARRISH
- ☐ 135. GENO PETRALLI
- ☐ 136. DARRELL PORTER
- ☐ 137. JEFF RUSSELL
- ☐ 138. RUBEN SIERRA
- ☐ 139. DON SLAUGHT
- ☐ 140. GARY WARD
- ☐ 141. CURTIS WILKERSON
- ☐ 142. MITCH WILLIAMS
- ☐ 143. BOBBY WITT
- ☐ 647. JERRY BROWNE(P)
- ☐ 647. MIKE STANLEY(P)
- ☐ 655. TEAM CHECKLIST(F)

TORONTO BLUE JAYS

- ☐ 219. JESSE BARFIELD
- ☐ 220. GEORGE BELL
- ☐ 221. BILL CAUDILL
- ☐ 222. JOHN CERUTTI
- ☐ 223. CLANCY
- ☐ 224. MARK EICHHORN
- ☐ 225. TONY FERNANDEZ
- ☐ 226. DAMASO GARCIA
- ☐ 227. KELLY GRUBER
- ☐ 228. TOM HENKE
- ☐ 229. GARTH IORG
- ☐ 230. CLIFF JOHNSON
- ☐ 231. JOE JOHNSON
- ☐ 232. JIMMY KEY
- ☐ 233. DENNIS LAMP
- ☐ 234. RICK LEACH
- ☐ 235. BUCK MARTINEZ
- ☐ 236. LLOYD MOSEBY
- ☐ 237. RANCE MULLINIKS
- ☐ 238. DAVE STIEB
- ☐ 239. WILLIE UPSHAW
- ☐ 240. ERNIE WHITT
- ☐ 656. TEAM CHECKLIST(F)

1987 FLEER TRADED (132) 2 1/2 X 3 1/2

ATLANTA BRAVES

- ☐ 39U. ALBERT HALL
- ☐ 51U. DION JAMES

BALTIMORE ORIOLES

- ☐ 2U. ERIC BELL
- ☐ 34U. KEN GERHART
- ☐ 56U. TERRY KENNEDY
- ☐ 58U. RAY KNIGHT
- ☐ 107U. DAVE SCHMIDT
- ☐ 124U. ALAN WIGGINS

BOSTON RED SOX

- ☐ 15U. ELLIS BURKS
- ☐ 37U. MIKE GREENWELL

CALIFORNIA ANGELS

- ☐ 14U. DEWAYNE BUICE
- ☐ 33U. WILLIE FRASER
- ☐ 61U. JACK LAZORKO
- ☐ 77U. MARK LEMORE
- ☐ 80U. GREG MINTON
- ☐ 123U. DEVON WHITE

CHICAGO CUBS

- ☐ 24U. ANDRE DAWSON
- ☐ 25U. BRIAN DAYETT
- ☐ 68U. GREG MADDUX
- ☐ 73U. MIKE MASON
- ☐ 91U. DICKIE NOLES
- ☐ 114U. JIM SUNDBERG

CHICAGO WHITE SOX

- ☐ 66U. BILL LONG
- ☐ 72U. FRED MANRIQUE
- ☐ 102U. GARY REDUS
- ☐ 126U. JIM WINN
- ☐ 128U. KEN WILLIAMS

CINCINNATI REDS

- ☐ 45U. GUY HOFFMAN
- ☐ 55U. TRACY JONES
- ☐ 74U. LLOYD MCCLENDON
- ☐ 94U. PAUL O'NEILL
- ☐ 127U. FRANK WILLIAMS

CLEVELAND INDIANS

- ☐ 17U. STEVE CARLTON
- ☐ 26U. RICK DEMPSEY
- ☐ 116U. GREG SWINDELL
- ☐ 120U. ED VANDEBERG

DETROIT TIGERS

- ☐ 42U. MIKE HEATH
- ☐ 44U. MIKE HENNEMAN
- ☐ 69U. BILL MADLOCK
- ☐ 90U. MATT NOKES
- ☐ 105U. JEFF ROBINSON

HOUSTON ASTROS

- ☐ 47U. CHUCK JACKSON
- ☐ 79U. DAVE MEADS

KANSAS CITY ROYALS

- ☐ 3U. JUAN BENIQUEZ
- ☐ 8U. THAD BOSLEY
- ☐ 97U. BILL PECOTA
- ☐ 108U. KEVIN SEITZER
- ☐ 117U. DANNY TARTABULL

LOS ANGELES DODGERS

- ☐ 13U. RALPH BRYANT
- ☐ 41U. MICKEY HATCHER
- ☐ 109U. JOHN SHELBY
- ☐ 131U. MATT YOUNG

MILWAUKEE BREWERS

- ☐ 5U. MIKE BIRKBECK
- ☐ 9U. GREG BROCK
- ☐ 18U. JUAN CASTILLO
- ☐ 19U. CHUCK CRIM
- ☐ 95U. JIM PACIOREK
- ☐ 115U. B. J. SURHOFF

MINNESOTA TWINS

- ☐ 4U. JUAN BERENGUER
- ☐ 20U. MARK DAVIDSON
- ☐ 36U. DAN GLADDEN
- ☐ 59U. GENE LARKIN
- ☐ 87U. JOE NIEKRO
- ☐ 88U. TOM NIETO
- ☐ 101U. JEFF REARDON

MONTREAL EXPOS

- ☐ 16U. CASEY CANDAELE
- ☐ 43U. NEAL HEATON
- ☐ 89U. REID NICHOLS
- ☐ 111U. LARY SORENSEN
- ☐ 113U. RANDY ST. CLAIRE
- ☐ 130U. HERM WINNINGHAM

NEW YORK METS

- ☐ 62U. TERRY LEACH
- ☐ 70U. DAVE MAGADAN
- ☐ 78U. KEVIN MCREYNOLDS
- ☐ 81U. JOHN MITCHELL
- ☐ 85U. RANDY MYERS

NEW YORK YANKEES

- ☐ 38U. CECILIO GUANTE
- ☐ 46U. CHARLES HUDSON
- ☐ 103U. RICK RHODEN
- ☐ 106U. MARK SALAS
- ☐ 122U. GARY WARD

OAKLAND A'S

- ☐ 30U. DENNIS ECKERSLEY
- ☐ 49U. REGGIE JACKSON
- ☐ 52U. STAN JAVIER
- ☐ 76U. MARK MCGWIRE
- ☐ 86U. GENE NELSON
- ☐ 99U. LUIS POLONIA

PHILADELPHIA PHILLIES

- ☐ 27U. KEN DOWELL
- ☐ 48U. MIKE JACKSON
- ☐ 50U. CHRIS JAMES
- ☐ 96U. LANCE PARRISH
- ☐ 104U. WALLY RITCHIE

PITTSBURGH PIRATES

- ☐ 29U. MIKE DUNNE
- ☐ 32U. BRIAN FISHER
- ☐ 60U. MIKE LAVALLIERE
- ☐ 110U. JOHN SMILEY
- ☐ 118U. DORN TAYLOR
- ☐ 121U. ANDY VAN SLYKE

ST. LOUIS CARDINALS

- ☐ 7U. ROD BOOKER
- ☐ 23U. BILL DAWLEY
- ☐ 65U. JIM LINDEMAN
- ☐ 71U. JOE MAGRANE
- ☐ 83U. JOHN MORRIS
- ☐ 98U. TONY PENA
- ☐ 119U. LEE TUNNELL

SAN DIEGO PADRES

- ☐ 11U. CHRIS BROWN
- ☐ 21U. MARK DAVIS
- ☐ 22U. STORM DAVIS
- ☐ 53U. STAN JEFFERSON
- ☐ 54U. JIMMY JONES
- ☐ 100U. RANDY READY

SAN FRANCISCO GIANTS

- ☐ 6U. RANDY BOCKUS
- ☐ 28U. DAVE DRAVECKY
- ☐ 35U. JIM GOTT
- ☐ 40U. ATLEE HAMMAKER
- ☐ 64U. CRAIG LEFFERTS
- ☐ 82U. KEVIN MITCHELL
- ☐ 112U. CHRIS SPEIER
- ☐ 129U. MATT WILLIAMS

SEATTLE MARINERS

- ☐ 1U. SCOTT BANKHEAD
- ☐ 57U. MIKE KINGERY
- ☐ 92U. EDWIN NUNEZ
- ☐ 125U. BILL WILKINSON

TEXAS RANGERS

- ☐ 10U. BOB BROWER
- ☐ 12U. JERRY BROWNE
- ☐ 67U. MIKE LOYND

TORONTO BLUE JAYS

- ☐ 31U. CECIL FIELDER
- ☐ 63U. RICK LEACH
- ☐ 75U. FRED MCGRIFF
- ☐ 84U. JEFF MUSSELMAN
- ☐ 93U. JOSE NUNEZ

1988 FLEER (660)
2 1/2 X 3 1/2

ATLANTA BRAVES

- ☐ 531. JIM ACKER
- ☐ 532. PAUL ASSENMACHER
- ☐ 533. JEFF BLAUSER
- ☐ 534. JOE BOEVER
- ☐ 535. MARTIN CLARY
- ☐ 536. KEVIN COFFMAN
- ☐ 537. JEFF DEDMON
- ☐ 538. RON GANT
- ☐ 539. TOM GLAVINE
- ☐ 540. KEN GRIFFEY
- ☐ 541. AL HALL
- ☐ 542. GLENN HUBBARD
- ☐ 543. DION JAMES
- ☐ 544. DALE MURPHY
- ☐ 545. KEN OBERKFELL
- ☐ 546. DAVID PALMER
- ☐ 547. GERALD PERRY
- ☐ 548. CHARLIE PULEO
- ☐ 549. TED SIMMONS
- ☐ 550. ZANE SMITH
- ☐ 551. ANDRES THOMAS
- ☐ 552. OZZIE VIRGIL
- ☐ 647. PETER SMITH (P)
- ☐ 659. TEAM CHECKLIST (B)

BALTIMORE ORIOLES

- ☐ 553. DON AASE
- ☐ 554. JEFF BALLARD
- ☐ 555. ERIC BELL
- ☐ 556. MIKE BODDICKER
- ☐ 557. KEN DIXON
- ☐ 558. JIM DWYER
- ☐ 559. KEN GERHART
- ☐ 560. RENE GONZALES
- ☐ 561. MIKE GRIFFIN
- ☐ 562. JOHN HAYBAN
- ☐ 563. TERRY KENNEDY
- ☐ 564. RAY KNIGHT
- ☐ 565. LEE LACY
- ☐ 566. FRED LYNN
- ☐ 567. EDDIE MURRAY
- ☐ 568. TOM NIEDENFUER
- ☐ 569. BILL RIPKEN
- ☐ 570. CAL RIPKEN, JR.
- ☐ 571. DAVE SCHMIDT
- ☐ 572. LARRY SHEETS
- ☐ 573. PETE STANICEK
- ☐ 574. MARK WILLIAMSON
- ☐ 575. MIKE YOUNG
- ☐ 659. TEAM CHECKLIST (B)

BOSTON RED SOX

- ☐ 343. MARTY BARRETT
- ☐ 344. TODD BENZINGER
- ☐ 345. WADE BOGGS
- ☐ 346. TOM BOLTON
- ☐ 347. OIL CAN BOYD
- ☐ 348. ELLIS BURKS
- ☐ 349. ROGER CLEMENS
- ☐ 350. STEVE CRAWFORD
- ☐ 351. DWIGHT EVANS
- ☐ 352. WES GARDNER
- ☐ 353. RICH GEDMAN
- ☐ 354. MIKE GREENWELL
- ☐ 355. SAM HORN
- ☐ 356. BRUCE HURST
- ☐ 357. JOHN MARZANO
- ☐ 358. AL NIPPER
- ☐ 359. SPIKE OWEN
- ☐ 360. JODY REED
- ☐ 361. JIM RICE
- ☐ 362. ED ROMERO
- ☐ 363. KEVIN ROMINE
- ☐ 364. JOE SAMBITO
- ☐ 365. CALVIN SCHIRALDI
- ☐ 366. JEFF SELLERS
- ☐ 367. BOB STANLEY
- ☐ 657. TEAM CHECKLIST (B)

CALIFORNIA ANGELS

- ☐ 484. TONY ARMAS
- ☐ 485. BOB BOONE
- ☐ 486. BILL BUCKNER
- ☐ 487. DEWAYNE BUICE
- ☐ 488. BRIAN DOWNING
- ☐ 489. CHUCK FINLEY
- ☐ 490. WILLIE FRASER
- ☐ 491. JACK HOWELL
- ☐ 492. RUPPERT JONES
- ☐ 493. WALLY JOYNER
- ☐ 494. JACK LAZORKO
- ☐ 495. GARY LUCAS
- ☐ 496. KIRK MCCASKILL
- ☐ 497. MARK MCLEMORE
- ☐ 498. DARRELL MILLER
- ☐ 499. GREG MINTON
- ☐ 500. DONNIE MOORE
- ☐ 501. GUS POLIDOR
- ☐ 502. JOHNNY RAY
- ☐ 503. MARK RYAL
- ☐ 504. DICK SCHOFIELD
- ☐ 505. DON SUTTON
- ☐ 506. DEVON WHITE
- ☐ 507. MIKE WITT
- ☐ 645. JIM EPPARD (P)
- ☐ 659. TEAM CHECKLIST (F)

CHICAGO CUBS

- ☐ 414. JODY DAVIS
- ☐ 415. ANDRE DAWSON
- ☐ 416. BRIAN DAYETT
- ☐ 417. BOB DERNIER
- ☐ 418. FRANK DIPINO
- ☐ 419. SHAWON DUNSTON
- ☐ 420. LEON DURHAM
- ☐ 421. LES LANCASTER
- ☐ 422. ED LYNCH
- ☐ 423. GREG MADDUX
- ☐ 424. DAVE MARTINEZ
- ☐ 425. KEITH MORELAND
- ☐ 426. JAMIE MOYER
- ☐ 427. JERRY MUMPHREY
- ☐ 428. PAUL NOCE
- ☐ 429. RAFAEL PALMEROI
- ☐ 430. WADE ROWDON
- ☐ 431. RYNE SANDBERG
- ☐ 432. SCOTT SANDERSON
- ☐ 433. LEE SMITH
- ☐ 434. JIM SUNDBERG
- ☐ 435. RICK SUTCLIFFE
- ☐ 436. MANNY TRILLO
- ☐ 641. MARK GRACE (P)
- ☐ 641. DARRIN JACKSON (P)
- ☐ 642. DAMON BERRYHILL (P)
- ☐ 658. TEAM CHECKLIST (F)

CHICAGO WHITE SOX

- ☐ 391. HAROLD BAINES
- ☐ 392. FLOYD BANNISTER
- ☐ 393. DARYL BOSTON
- ☐ 394. IVAN CALDERON
- ☐ 395. JOSE DELEON
- ☐ 396. RICHARD DOTSON
- ☐ 397. CARLTON FISK
- ☐ 398. OZZIE GUILLEN
- ☐ 399. RON HASSEY
- ☐ 400. DONNIE HILL
- ☐ 401. BOB JAMES
- ☐ 402. DAVE LAPOINT
- ☐ 403. BILL LINDSEY
- ☐ 404. BILL LONG
- ☐ 405. STEVE LYONS
- ☐ 406. FRED MANRIQUE
- ☐ 407. JACK MCDOWELL
- ☐ 408. GARY REDUS
- ☐ 409. RAY SEARAGE
- ☐ 410. BOBBY THIGPEN
- ☐ 411. GREG WALKER
- ☐ 412. KENNY WILLIAMS
- ☐ 413. JIM WINN
- ☐ 646. ADAM PETERSON (P)
- ☐ 658. TEAM CHECKLIST (F)

CINCINNATI REDS

- ☐ 227. BUDDY BELL
- ☐ 228. TOM BROWNING
- ☐ 229. DAVE CONCEPCION
- ☐ 230. KAL DANIELS
- ☐ 231. ERIC DAVIS
- ☐ 232. BO DIAZ
- ☐ 233. NICK ESASKY
- ☐ 234. JOHN FRANCO
- ☐ 235. GUY HOFFMAN
- ☐ 236. TOM HUME
- ☐ 237. TRACY JONES
- ☐ 238. BILL LANDRUM
- ☐ 239. BARRY LARKIN
- ☐ 240. TERRY MCGRIFF
- ☐ 241. ROB MURPHY
- ☐ 242. RON OESTER
- ☐ 243. DAVE PARKER
- ☐ 244. PAT PERRY
- ☐ 245. TED POWER
- ☐ 246. DENNIS RASMUSSEN
- ☐ 247. RON ROBINSON
- ☐ 248. KURT STILLWELL
- ☐ 249. JEFF TREADWAY
- ☐ 250. FRANK WILLIAMS
- ☐ 642. JEFF MONTGOMERY (P)
- ☐ 656. TEAM CHECKLIST (F)

CLEVELAND INDIANS

- ☐ 600. SCOTT BAILES
- ☐ 601. CHRIS BANDO
- ☐ 602. JAY BELL
- ☐ 603. BRETT BUTLER
- ☐ 604. TOM CANDIOTTI
- ☐ 605. JOE CARTER
- ☐ 606. CARMEN CASTILLO
- ☐ 607. BRIAN DORSETT
- ☐ 608. JOHN FARRELL
- ☐ 609. JULIO FRANCO
- ☐ 610. MEL HALL
- ☐ 611. TOMMY HINZO
- ☐ 612. BROOK JACOBY
- ☐ 613. DOUG JONES
- ☐ 614. KEN SCHROM
- ☐ 615. CORY SNYDER
- ☐ 616. SAMMY STEWART
- ☐ 617. GREG SWINDELL
- ☐ 618. PAT TABLER
- ☐ 619. ED VANDEBERG
- ☐ 620. EDDIE WILLIAMS
- ☐ 621. RICH YETT
- ☐ 660. TEAM CHECKLIST (F)

DETROIT TIGERS

- ☐ 51. DOYLE ALEXANDER
- ☐ 52. DAVE BERGMAN
- ☐ 53. TOM BROOKENS
- ☐ 54. DARRELL EVANS
- ☐ 55. KIRK GIBSON
- ☐ 56. MIKE HEATH
- ☐ 57. MIKE HENNEMAN
- ☐ 58. WILLIE HERNANDEZ
- ☐ 59. LARRY HERNDON
- ☐ 60. ERIC KING
- ☐ 61. CHET LEMON
- ☐ 62. SCOTT LUSADER
- ☐ 63. BILL MADLOCK
- ☐ 64. JACK MORRIS
- ☐ 65. JIM MORRISON
- ☐ 66. MATT NOKES
- ☐ 67. DAN PETRY
- ☐ 68. JEFF ROBINSON
- ☐ 69. PAT SHERIDAN
- ☐ 70. NATE SNELL
- ☐ 71. FRANK TANANA
- ☐ 72. WALT TERRELL
- ☐ 73. MARK THURMOND
- ☐ 74. ALAN TRAMMELL
- ☐ 75. LOU WHITAKER
- ☐ 654. TEAM CHECKLIST (B)

HOUSTON ASTROS

- ☐ 437. JUAN AGOSTO
- ☐ 438. LARRY ANDERSEN
- ☐ 439. ALAN ASHBY
- ☐ 440. KEVIN BASS
- ☐ 441. KEN CAMINITI
- ☐ 442. ROCKY CHILDRESS
- ☐ 443. JOSE CRUZ
- ☐ 444. DANNY DARWIN
- ☐ 445. GLENN DAVIS
- ☐ 446. JIM DESHAIES
- ☐ 447. BILL DORAN
- ☐ 448. TY GAINEY
- ☐ 449. BILLY HATCHER
- ☐ 450. JEFF HEATHCOCK
- ☐ 451. BOB KNEPPER
- ☐ 452. ROB MALLICOAT
- ☐ 453. DAVE MEADS
- ☐ 454. CRAIG REYNOLDS
- ☐ 455. NOLAN RYAN
- ☐ 456. MIKE SCOTT
- ☐ 457. DAVE SMITH
- ☐ 458. DENNY WALLING
- ☐ 459. ROBBIE WINE
- ☐ 460. GERALD YOUNG
- ☐ 658. TEAM CHECKLIST (B)

KANSAS CITY ROYALS

- □ 251. STEVE BALBONI
- □ 252. BUD BLACK
- □ 253. THAD BOSLEY
- □ 254. GEORGE BRETT
- □ 255. JOHN DAVIS
- □ 256. STEVE FARR
- □ 257. GENE GARBER
- □ 258. JERRY GLEATON
- □ 259. MARK GUBICZA
- □ 260. BO JACKSON
- □ 261. DANNY JACKSON
- □ 262. ROSS JONES
- □ 263. CHARLIE LEIBRANDT
- □ 264. BILL PECOTA
- □ 265. MELIDO PEREZ
- □ 266. JAMIE QUIRK
- □ 267. DAN QUISENBERRY
- □ 268. BRET SABERHAGEN
- □ 269. ANGEL SALAZAR
- □ 270. KEVIN SEITZER
- □ 271. DANNY TARTABULL
- □ 272. GARY THURMAN
- □ 273. FRANK WHITE
- □ 274. WILLIE WILSON
- □ 656. TEAM CHECKLIST

LOS ANGELES DODGERS

- □ 508. DAVE ANDERSON
- □ 509. TIM BELCHER
- □ 510. RALPH BRYANT
- □ 511. TIM CREWS
- □ 512. MIKE DEVEREAUX
- □ 513. MARIANO DUNCAN
- □ 514. PEDRO GUERRERO
- □ 515. JEFF HAMILTON
- □ 516. MICKEY HATCHER
- □ 517. BRAD HAVENS
- □ 518. OREL HERSHISER
- □ 519. SHAWN HILLEGAS
- □ 520. KEN HOWELL
- □ 521. TIM LEARY
- □ 522. MIKE MARSHALL
- □ 523. STEVE SAX
- □ 524. MIKE SCIOSCIA
- □ 525. MIKE SHARPERSON
- □ 526. JOHN SHELBY
- □ 527. FRANKLIN STUBBS
- □ 528. FERNANDO VALENZUELA
- □ 529. BOB WELCH
- □ 530. MATT YOUNG
- □ 647. CHRIS GWYNN (P)
- □ 650. JACK SAVAGE (P)
- □ 659. TEAM CHECKLIST (P)

MILWAUKEE BREWERS

- □ 155. JAY ALDRICH
- □ 156. CHRIS BOSIO
- □ 157. GLENN BRAGGS
- □ 158. GREG BROCK
- □ 159. JUAN CASTILLO
- □ 160. MARK CLEAR
- □ 161. CECIL COOPER
- □ 162. CHUCK CRIM
- □ 163. ROB DEER
- □ 164. MIKE FELDER
- □ 165. JIM GANTNER
- □ 166. TED HIGUERA
- □ 167. STEVE KIEFER
- □ 168. RICK MANNING
- □ 169. PAUL MOLITOR
- □ 170. JUAN NIEVES
- □ 171. DAN PLESAC
- □ 172. EARNEST RILES
- □ 173. BILL SCHROEDER
- □ 174. STEVE STANICEK
- □ 175. B. J. SURHOFF
- □ 176. DALE SVEUM
- □ 177. BILL WEGMAN
- □ 178. ROBIN YOUNT
- □ 645. JOEY MEYER (P)
- □ 655. TEAM CHECKLIST (B)

MINNESOTA TWINS

- □ 1. KEITH ATHERTON
- □ 2. DON BAYLOR
- □ 3. JUAN BERENGUER
- □ 4. BERT BLYLEVEN
- □ 5. TOM BRUNANSKY
- □ 6. RANDY BUSH
- □ 7. STEVE CARLTON
- □ 8. MARK DAVIDSON
- □ 9. GEORGE FRAZIER
- □ 10. GARY GAETTI
- □ 11. GREG GAGNE
- □ 12. DAN GLADDEN
- □ 13. KENT HRBEK
- □ 14. GENE LARKIN
- □ 15. TIM LAUDNER
- □ 16. STEVE LOMBARDOZZI
- □ 17. AL NEWMAN
- □ 18. JOE NIEKRO
- □ 19. KIRBY PUCKETT
- □ 20. JEFF REARDON
- □ 21. DAN SCHATZADER
- □ 22. ROY SMALLEY
- □ 23. MIKE SMITHSON
- □ 24. LES STRAKER
- □ 25. FRANK VIOLA
- □ 654. TEAM CHECKLIST (F)

MONTREAL EXPOS

- □ 179. HUBIE BROOKS
- □ 180. TIM BURKE
- □ 181. CASEY CANDAELE
- □ 182. MIKE FITZGERALD
- □ 183. TOM FOLEY
- □ 184. ANDRES GALARRAGA
- □ 185. NEAL HEATON
- □ 186. WALLACE JOHNSON
- □ 187. VANCE LAW
- □ 188. DENNIS MARTINEZ
- □ 189. BOB MCCLURE
- □ 190. ANDY MCGAFFIGAN
- □ 191. REID NICHOLS
- □ 192. PASCUAL PEREZ
- □ 193. TIM RAINES
- □ 194. JEFF REED
- □ 195. BOB SEBRA
- □ 196. BRYN SMITH
- □ 197. RANDY ST. CLAIRE
- □ 198. TIM WALLACH
- □ 199. MITCH WEBSTER
- □ 200. HERM WINNINGHAM
- □ 201. FLOYD YOUMANS
- □ 655. TEAM CHECKLIST (B)

NEW YORK METS

- □ 127. RICK AGUILERA
- □ 128. WALLY BACKMAN
- □ 129. MARK CARREON
- □ 130. GARY CARTER
- □ 131. DAVID CONE
- □ 132. RON DARLING
- □ 133. LEN DYKSTRA
- □ 134. SID FERNANDEZ
- □ 135. DWIGHT GOODEN
- □ 136. KEITH HERNANDEZ
- □ 137. GREGG JEFFERIES
- □ 138. HOWARD JOHNSON
- □ 139. TERRY LEACH
- □ 140. BARRY LYONS
- □ 141. DAVE MAGADAN
- □ 142. ROGER MCDOWELL
- □ 143. KEVIN MCREYNOLDS
- □ 144. KEITH MILLER
- □ 145. JOHN MITCHELL
- □ 146. RANDY MYERS
- □ 147. BOB OJEDA
- □ 148. JESSE OROSCO
- □ 149. RAFAEL SANTANA
- □ 150. DOUG SISK
- □ 151. DARRYL STRAWBERRY
- □ 152. TIM TEUFEL
- □ 153. GENE WALTER
- □ 154. MOOKIE WILSON
- □ 655. TEAM CHECKLIST (F)

NEW YORK YANKEES

- □ 202. BRAD ARNSBERG
- □ 203. RICK CERONE
- □ 204. PAT CLEMENTS
- □ 205. HENRY COTTO
- □ 206. MIKE EASLER
- □ 207. RON GUIDRY
- □ 208. BILL GULLICKSON
- □ 209. RICKEY HENDERSON
- □ 210. CHARLES HUDSON
- □ 211. TOMMY JOHN
- □ 212. ROBERTO KELLY
- □ 213. RON KITTLE
- □ 214. DON MATTINGLY
- □ 215. BOBBY MEACHAM
- □ 216. MIKE PAGLIARULO
- □ 217. DAN PASQUA
- □ 218. WILLIE RANDOLPH
- □ 219. RICK RHODEN
- □ 220. DAVE RIGHETTI
- □ 221. JERRY ROYSTER
- □ 222. TIM STODDARD
- □ 223. WAYNE TOLLESON
- □ 224. GARY WARD
- □ 225. CLAUDELL WASHINGTON
- □ 226. DAVE WINFIELD
- □ 646. RANDY VELARDE (P)
- □ 656. TEAM CHECKLIST (F)

OAKLAND A'S

- □ 275. TONY BERNAZARD
- □ 276. JOSE CANSECO
- □ 277. MIKE DAVIS
- □ 278. STORM DAVIS
- □ 279. DENNIS ECKERSLEY
- □ 280. ALFREDO GRIFFIN
- □ 281. RICK HONEYCUTT
- □ 282. JAY HOWELL
- □ 283. REGGIE JACKSON
- □ 284. DENNIS LAMP
- □ 285. CARNEY LANSFORD
- □ 286. MARK MCGWIRE
- □ 287. DWAYNE MURPHY
- □ 288. GENE NELSON
- □ 289. STEVE ONTIVEROS
- □ 290. TONY PHILLIPS
- □ 291. ERIC PLUNK
- □ 292. LUIS POLONIA
- □ 293. RICK RODRIGUEZ
- □ 294. TERRY STEINBACH
- □ 295. DAVE STEWART
- □ 296. CURT YOUNG
- □ 652. WALT WEISS (P)
- □ 652. DAVE OTTO (P)
- □ 656. TEAM CHECKLIST (B)

PHILADELPHIA PHILLIES

- □ 297. LUIS AGUAYO
- □ 298. STEVE BEDROSIAN
- □ 299. JEFF CALHOUN
- □ 300. DON CARMAN
- □ 301. TODD FROHWIRTH
- □ 302. GREG GROSS
- □ 303. KEVIN GROSS
- □ 304. VON HAYES
- □ 305. KEITH HUGHES
- □ 306. MIKE JACKSON
- □ 307. CHRIS JAMES
- □ 308. STEVE JELTZ
- □ 309. MIKE MADDUX
- □ 310. LANCE PARRISH
- □ 311. SHANE RAWLEY
- □ 312. WALLY RITCHIE
- □ 313. BRUCE RUFFIN
- □ 314. JUAN SAMUEL
- □ 315. MIKE SCHMIDT
- □ 316. RICK SCHU
- □ 317. JEFF STONE
- □ 318. KENT TEKULVE
- □ 319. MILT THOMPSON
- □ 320. GLENN WILSON
- □ 648. GREG JELKS (P)
- □ 648. TOM NEWELL (P)
- □ 657. TEAM CHECKLIST (F)

PITTSBURGH PIRATES

- □ 321. RAFAEL BELLIARD
- □ 322. BARRY BONDS
- □ 323. BOBBY BONILLA
- □ 324. SID BREAM
- □ 325. JOHN CANGELOSI
- □ 326. MIKE DIAZ
- □ 327. DOUG DRABEK
- □ 328. MIKE DUNNE
- □ 329. BRIAN FISHER
- □ 330. BRETT GIDEON

- □ 331. TERRY HARPER
- □ 332. BOB KIPPER
- □ 333. MIKE LAVALLIERE
- □ 334. JOSE LIND
- □ 335. JUNIOR ORTIZ
- □ 336. VINCENTE PALACIOS
- □ 337. BOB PATTERSON
- □ 338. AL PEDRIQUE
- □ 339. R. J. REYNOLDS
- □ 340. JOHN SMILEY
- □ 341. ANDY VAN SLYKE
- □ 342. BOB WALK
- □ 643. FELIX FERMIN (P)
- □ 653. JEFF KING (P)
- □ 657. TEAM CHECKLIST (F)

ST. LOUIS CARDINALS

- □ 26. JACK CLARK
- □ 27. VINCE COLEMAN
- □ 28. DANNY COX
- □ 29. BILL DAWLEY
- □ 30. KEN DAYLEY
- □ 31. DOUG DECINCES
- □ 32. CURT FORD
- □ 33. BOB FORSCH
- □ 34. DAVID GREEN
- □ 35. TOM HERR
- □ 36. RICKY HORTON
- □ 37. LANCE JOHNSON
- □ 38. STEVE LAKE
- □ 39. JIM LINDEMAN
- □ 40. JOE MAGRANE
- □ 41. GREG MATHEWS
- □ 42. WILLIE MCGEE
- □ 43. JOHN MORRIS
- □ 44. JOSE OQUENDO
- □ 45. TONY PENA
- □ 46. TERRY PENDLETON
- □ 47. OZZIE SMITH
- □ 48. JOHN TUDOR
- □ 49. LEE TUNNELL
- □ 50. TODD WORRELL
- □ 654. TEAM CHECKLIST (F)

SAN DIEGO PADRES

- □ 576. SHAWN ABNER
- □ 577. GREG BOOKER
- □ 578. CHRIS BROWN
- □ 579. KEITH COMSTOCK
- □ 580. JOEY CORA
- □ 581. MARK DAVIS
- □ 582. TIM FLANNERY
- □ 583. GOOSE GOSSAGE
- □ 584. MARK GRANT
- □ 585. TONY GWYNN
- □ 586. ANDY HAWKINS
- □ 587. STAN JEFFERSON
- □ 588. JIMMY JONES
- □ 589. JOHN KRUK
- □ 590. SHANE MACK
- □ 591. CARMELO MARTINEZ
- □ 592. LANCE MCCULLERS
- □ 593. ERIC NOLTE
- □ 594. RANDY READY
- □ 595. LUIS SALAZAR
- □ 596. BENITO SANTIAGO
- □ 597. ERIC SHOW
- □ 598. GARRY TEMPLETON
- □ 599. ED WHITSON
- □ 650. TODD SIMMONS (P)
- □ 653. RANDELL BYERS (P)
- □ 660. TEAM CHECKLIST (F)

SAN FRANCISCO GIANTS

- □ 76. MIKE ALDRETE
- □ 77. BOB BRENLY
- □ 78. WILL CLARK
- □ 79. CHILI DAVIS
- □ 80. KELLY DOWNS
- □ 81. DAVE DRAVECKY
- □ 82. SCOTT GARRELTS
- □ 83. ATLEE HAMMAKER
- □ 84. DAVE HENDERSON
- □ 85. MIKE KRUKOW
- □ 86. MIKE LACOSS
- □ 87. CRAIG LEFFERTS
- □ 88. JEFF LEONARD
- □ 89. CANDY MALDONADO
- □ 90. BOB MELVIN
- □ 91. ED MILNER
- □ 92. KEVIN MITCHELL
- □ 93. JON PERLMAN
- □ 94. RICK REUSCHEL
- □ 95. DON ROBINSON
- □ 96. CHRIS SPEIER
- □ 97. HARRY SPILMAN
- □ 98. ROBBIE THOMPSON
- □ 99. JOSE URIBE
- □ 100. MARK WASINGER
- □ 101. MATT WILLIAMS
- □ 643. JESSIE REID (P)
- □ 651. KIRT MANWARING (P)
- □ 651. JOHN BURKETT (P)
- □ 654 TEAM CHECKLIST (B)

SEATTLE MARINERS

- □ 368. SCOTT BANKHEAD
- □ 369. PHIL BRADLEY
- □ 370. SCOTT BRADLEY
- □ 371. MICKEY BRANTLEY
- □ 372. MIKE CAMPBELL
- □ 373. ALVIN DAVIS
- □ 374. LEE GUETTERMAN
- □ 375. DAVE HENGEL
- □ 376. MIKE KINGERY
- □ 377. MARK LANGSTON
- □ 378. EDGAR MARTINEZ
- □ 379. MIKE MOORE
- □ 380. MIKE MORGAN
- □ 381. JOHN MOSES
- □ 382. DONNELL NIXON
- □ 383. EDWIN NUNEZ
- □ 384. KEN PHELPS
- □ 385. JIM PRESLEY
- □ 386. REY QUINONES
- □ 387. JERRY REED
- □ 388. HAROLD REYNOLDS
- □ 389. DAVE VALLE
- □ 390. BILL WILKINSON
- □ 649. MARIO DIAZ (P)
- □ 649. CLAY PARKER (P)
- □ 657. TEAM CHECKLIST (B)

TEXAS RANGERS

- □ 461. BOB BROWER
- □ 462. JERRY BROWNE
- □ 463. STEVE BUECHELE
- □ 464. EDWIN CORREA
- □ 465. CECIL ESPY
- □ 466. SCOTT FLETCHER
- □ 467. JOSE GUZMAN
- □ 468. GREG HARRIS
- □ 469. CHARLIE HOUGH
- □ 470. PETE INCAVIGLIA
- □ 471. PAUL KILGUS
- □ 472. MIKE LOYND
- □ 473. ODDIBE MCDOWELL
- □ 474. DALE MOHORCIC
- □ 475. PETE O'BRIEN
- □ 476. LARRY PARRISH
- □ 477. GENO PETRALLI
- □ 478. JEFF RUSSELL
- □ 479. RUBEN SIERRA
- □ 480. MIKE STANLEY
- □ 481. CURTIS WILKERSON
- □ 482. MITCH WILLIAMS
- □ 483. BOBBY WITT
- □ 644. GREG TABOR (P)
- □ 658. TEAM CHECKLIST (B)

TORONTO BLUE JAYS

- □ 102. JESSE BARFIELD
- □ 103. GEORGE BELL
- □ 104. JUAN BENIQUEZ
- □ 105. JOHN CERUTTI
- □ 106. JIM CLANCY
- □ 107. ROB DUCEY
- □ 108. MARK EICHHORN
- □ 109. TONY FERNANDEZ
- □ 110. CECIL FIELDER
- □ 111. KELLY GRUBER
- □ 112. TOM HENKE
- □ 113. GARTH IORG
- □ 114. JIMMY KEY
- □ 115. RICK LEACH
- □ 116. MANNY LEE
- □ 117. NELSON LIRIANO
- □ 118. FRED MCGRIFF
- □ 119. LLOYD MOSEBY
- □ 120. RANCE MULLINIKS
- □ 121. JEFF MUSSELMAN
- □ 122. JOSE NUNEZ
- □ 123. DAVE STIEB
- □ 124. WILLIE UPSHAW
- □ 125. DUANE WARD
- □ 126. ERNIE WHITT
- □ 644. GREG MYERS (P)
- □ 655. TEAM CHECKLIST (F)

1988 FLEER TRADED (132) 2 1/2 X 3 1/2

ATLANTA BRAVES

- □ 70U. JOSE ALVAREZ
- □ 71U. PAUL RUNGE
- □ 72U. CESAR JIMENEZ
- □ 73U. PETE SMITH
- □ 74U. JOHN SMOLTZ

BALTIMORE ORIOLES

- □ 1U. JOSE BAUTISTA
- □ 2U. JOE ORSULAK
- □ 3U. DOUG SISK
- □ 4U. CRAIG WORTHINGTON

BOSTON RED SOX

- □ 5U. MIKE BODDICKER
- □ 6U. RICK CERONE
- □ 7U. LARRY PARRISH
- □ 8U. LEE SMITH
- □ 9U. MIKE SMITHSON
- □ 10U. JOHN TRAUTWEIN

CALIFORNIA ANGELS

- □ 11U. SHERMAN CORBETT
- □ 12U. CHILI DAVIS
- □ 13U. JIM EPPARD
- □ 14U. BRYAN HARVEY

CHICAGO CUBS

- □ 75U. DAMON BERRYHILL
- □ 76U. GOOSE GOSSAGE
- □ 77U. MARK GRACE

- ☐ 78U. DARRIN JACKSON
- ☐ 79U. VANCE LAW
- ☐ 80U. JEFF PICO
- ☐ 81U. GARY VARSHO

CHICAGO WHITE SOX

- ☐ 15U. JOHN DAVIS
- ☐ 16U. DAVE GALLAGHER
- ☐ 17U. RICKY HORTON
- ☐ 18U. DAN PASQUA
- ☐ 19U. MELIDO PEREZ
- ☐ 20U. JOSE SEGURA

CINCINNATI REDS

- ☐ 82U. TIM BIRTSAS
- ☐ 83U. ROB DIBBLE
- ☐ 84U. DANNY JACKSON
- ☐ 85U. PAUL O'NEILL
- ☐ 86U. JOSE RIJO
- ☐ 87U. CHRIS SABO

CLEVELAND INDIANS

- ☐ 21U. ANDY ALLANSON
- ☐ 22U. JON PERLMAN
- ☐ 23U. DOMINGO RAMOS
- ☐ 24U. RICK RODRIGUEZ
- ☐ 25U. WILLIE UPSHAW

DETROIT TIGERS

- ☐ 26U. PAUL GIBSON
- ☐ 27U. DON HEINKEL
- ☐ 28U. RAY KNIGHT
- ☐ 29U. GARY PETTIS
- ☐ 30U. LUIS SALAZAR

HOUSTON ASTROS

- ☐ 88U. JOHN FISHEL
- ☐ 89U. CRAIG BIGGIO
- ☐ 90U. TERRY PUHL
- ☐ 91U. RAFAEL RAMIREZ
- ☐ 92U. LOUIE MEADOWS

KANSAS CITY ROYALS

- ☐ 31U. MIKE MACFARLANE
- ☐ 32U. JEFF MONTGOMERY
- ☐ 33U. TED POWER
- ☐ 34U. ISRAEL SANCHEZ
- ☐ 35U. KURT STILLWELL
- ☐ 36U. PAT TABLER

LOS ANGELES DODGERS

- ☐ 93U. KIRK GIBSON
- ☐ 94U. ALFREDO GRIFFIN
- ☐ 95U. JAY HOWELL
- ☐ 96U. JESSE OROSCO
- ☐ 97U. ALEJANDRO PENA
- ☐ 98U. TRACY WOODSON

MILWAUKEE BREWERS

- ☐ 37U. DON AUGUST
- ☐ 38U. DARRYL HAMILTON
- ☐ 39U. JEFF LEONARD
- ☐ 40U. JOEY MEYER

MINNESOTA TWINS

- ☐ 41U. ALLAN ANDERSON
- ☐ 42U. BRIAN HARPER
- ☐ 43U. TOM HERR
- ☐ 44U. CHARLIE LEA
- ☐ 45U. JOHN MOSES

MONTREAL EXPOS

- ☐ 99U. JOHN DOPSON
- ☐ 100U. BRIAN HOLMAN
- ☐ 101U. REX HUDLER
- ☐ 102U. JEFF PARRETT
- ☐ 103U. NELSON SANTOVENIA

NEW YORK METS

- ☐ 104U. KEVIN ELSTER
- ☐ 105U. JEFF INNIS
- ☐ 106U. MACKEY SASSER

NEW YORK YANKEES

- ☐ 46U. JOHN CANDELARIA
- ☐ 47U. JACK CLARK
- ☐ 48U. RICHARD DOTSON
- ☐ 49U. AL LEITER
- ☐ 50U. RAFAEL SANTANA
- ☐ 51U. DON SLAUGHT

OAKLAND A'S

- ☐ 52U. TODD BURNS
- ☐ 53U. DAVE HENDERSON
- ☐ 54U. DOUG JENNINGS
- ☐ 55U. DAVE PARKER
- ☐ 56U. WALT WEISS
- ☐ 57U. BOB WELCH

PHILADELPHIA PHILLIES

- ☐ 107U. PHIL BRADLEY
- ☐ 108U. DANNY CLAY
- ☐ 109U. GREG HARRIS
- ☐ 110U. RICKY JORDAN
- ☐ 111U. DAVID PALMER

PITTSBURGH PIRATES

- ☐ 112U. JIM GOTT
- ☐ 113U. TOMMY GREGG
- ☐ 114U. BARRY JONES
- ☐ 115U. RANDY MILLIGAN

ST. LOUIS CARDINALS

- ☐ 116U. LUIS ALICEA
- ☐ 117U. TOM BRUNANSKY
- ☐ 118U. JOHN COSTELLO
- ☐ 119U. JOSE DELEON
- ☐ 120U. BOB HORNER
- ☐ 121U. SCOTT TERRY

SAN DIEGO PADRES

- ☐ 122U. ROBERTO ALOMAR
- ☐ 123U. DAVE LEIPER
- ☐ 124U. KEITH MORELAND
- ☐ 125U. MARK PARENT
- ☐ 126U. DENNIS RASMUSSEN

SAN FRANCISCO GIANTS

- ☐ 127U. RANDY BOCKUS
- ☐ 128U. BRETT BUTLER
- ☐ 129U. DONELL NIXON
- ☐ 130U. EARNEST RILES
- ☐ 131U. ROGER SAMUELS

SEATTLE MARINERS

- ☐ 58U. HENRY COTTO
- ☐ 59U. MARIO DIAZ
- ☐ 60U. MIKE JACKSON
- ☐ 61U. BILL SWIFT

TEXAS RANGERS

- ☐ 62U. JOSE CECENA
- ☐ 63U. RAY HAYWARD
- ☐ 64U. JIM STEELE

TORONTO BLUE JAYS

- ☐ 65U. PAT BORDERS
- ☐ 66U. SIL CAMPUSANO
- ☐ 67U. MIKE FLANAGAN
- ☐ 68U. TODD STOTTLEMYRE
- ☐ 69U. DAVID WELLS

1989 FLEER (660)
2 1/2 X 3 1/2

ATLANTA BRAVES

- ☐ 585. JOSE ALVAREZ
- ☐ 586. PAUL ASSENMACHER
- ☐ 587. BRUCE BENEDICT
- ☐ 588. JEFF BLAUSER
- ☐ 589. TERRY BLOCKER
- ☐ 590. RON GANT
- ☐ 591. TOM GLAVINE
- ☐ 592. TOMMY GREGG
- ☐ 593. ALBERT HALL
- ☐ 594. DION JAMES
- ☐ 595. RICH MAHLER
- ☐ 596. DALE MURPHY
- ☐ 597. GERALD PERRY
- ☐ 598. CHARLIE PULEO
- ☐ 599. TED SIMMONS
- ☐ 600. PETE SMITH
- ☐ 601. ZANE SMITH
- ☐ 602. JOHN SMOLTZ
- ☐ 603. BRUCE SUTTER
- ☐ 604. ANDRES THOMAS
- ☐ 605. OZZIE VIRGIL
- ☐ 660. TEAM CHECKLIST (F)

BALTIMORE ORIOLES

- ☐ 606. BRADY ANDERSON
- ☐ 607. JEFF BALLARD
- ☐ 608. JOSE BAUTISTA
- ☐ 609. KEN GERHART
- ☐ 610. TERRY KENNEDY
- ☐ 611. EDDIE MURRAY
- ☐ 612. CARL NICHOLS
- ☐ 613. TOM NIEDENFEUR
- ☐ 614. JOE ORSULAK
- ☐ 615. OSWALDO PERAZA
- ☐ 616. BILL RIPKEN

☐ 617. CAL RIPKEN, JR.
☐ 618. DAVE SCHMIDT
☐ 619. RICH SCHU
☐ 620. LARRY SHEETS
☐ 621. DOUGH SISK
☐ 622. PETE STANICEK
☐ 623. MICKEY TETTLETON
☐ 624. JAY TIBBS
☐ 625. JIM TRABER
☐ 626. MARK WILLIAMSON
☐ 627. CRAIG WORTHINGTON
☐ 649. BOB MILACKI (P)
☐ 660. TEAM CHECKLIST (F)

BOSTON RED SOX

☐ 78. MARTY BARRETT
☐ 79. TODD BENZINGER
☐ 80. MIKE BODDICKER
☐ 81. WADE BOGGS
☐ 82. OIL CAN BOYD
☐ 83. ELLIS BURKS
☐ 84. RICK CERONE
☐ 85. ROGER CLEMENS
☐ 86. STEVE CURRY
☐ 87. DWIGHT EVANS
☐ 88. WES GARDNER
☐ 89. RICH GEDMAN
☐ 90. MIKE GREENWELL
☐ 91. BRUCE HURST
☐ 92. DENNIS LAMP
☐ 93. SPIKE OWEN
☐ 94. LARRY PARRISH
☐ 95. CARLOS QUINTANA
☐ 96. JODY REED
☐ 97. JIM RICE
☐ 98. KEVIN ROMINE
☐ 99. LEE SMITH
☐ 100. MIKE SMITHSON
☐ 101. BOB STANLEY
☐ 650. MIKE ROCHFORD (P)
☐ 654. TEAM CHECKLIST (B)

GREG MINTON
PITCHER
FLEER

CALIFORNIA ANGELS

☐ 467. TONY ARMAS
☐ 468. DANTE BICHETTE
☐ 469. BOB BOONE
☐ 470. TERRY CLARK
☐ 471. STEW CLIBURN
☐ 472. MIKE COOK
☐ 473. SHERMAN CORBETT
☐ 474. CHILI DAVIS
☐ 475. BRIAN DOWNING
☐ 476. JIM EPPARD
☐ 477. CHUCK FINLEY
☐ 478. WILLIE FRASER
☐ 479. BRYAN HARVEY
☐ 480. JACK HOWELL
☐ 481. WALLY JOYNER
☐ 482. JACK LAZORKO
☐ 483. KIRK MCCASKILL
☐ 484. MARK MCLEMORE
☐ 485. GREG MINTON
☐ 486. DAN PETRY
☐ 487. JOHNNY RAY
☐ 488. DICK SCHOFIELD
☐ 489. DEVON WHITE
☐ 490. MIKE WITT
☐ 651. VANCE LOVELACE (P)
☐ 658. TEAM CHECKLIST (B)

CHICAGO CUBS

☐ 418. DAMON BERRYHILL
☐ 419. MIKE BIELECKI
☐ 420. DOUG DASCENZO
☐ 421. JODY DAVIS
☐ 422. ANDRE DAWSON
☐ 423. FRANK DIPINO
☐ 424. SHAWON DUNSTON
☐ 425. GOOSE GOSSAGE
☐ 426. MARK GRACE
☐ 427. MIKE HARKEY
☐ 428. DARRIN JACKSON
☐ 429. LES LANCASTER
☐ 430. VANCE LAW
☐ 431. GREG MADDUX
☐ 432. JAMIE MOYER
☐ 433. AL NIPPER
☐ 434. RAFAEL PALMEIRO
☐ 435. PAT PERRY
☐ 436. JEFF PICO
☐ 437. RYNE SANDBERG
☐ 438. CALVIN SCHIRALDI
☐ 439. RICK SUTCLIFFE
☐ 440. MANNY TRILLO
☐ 441. GARY VARSHO
☐ 442. MITCH WEBSTER
☐ 643. MIKE CAPEL (P)
☐ 643. DREW HALL (P)
☐ 644. JOE GIRARDI (P)
☐ 644. ROLANDO ROOMES (P)
☐ 658. TEAM CHECKLIST (F)

CHICAGO WHITE SOX

☐ 491. HAROLD BAINES
☐ 492. DARYL BOSTON
☐ 493. IVAN CALDERON
☐ 494. MIKE DIAZ
☐ 495. CARLTON FISK
☐ 496. DAVE GALLAGHER
☐ 497. OZZIE GUILLEN
☐ 498. SHAWN HILLEGAS
☐ 499. LANCE JOHNSON
☐ 500. BARRY JONES
☐ 501. BILL LONG
☐ 502. STEVE LYONS
☐ 503. FRED MANRIQUE
☐ 504. JACK MCDOWELL
☐ 505. DONN PALL
☐ 506. KELLY PARIS
☐ 507. DAN PASQUA
☐ 508. KEN PATTERSON
☐ 509. MELIDO PEREZ
☐ 510. JERRY REUSS
☐ 511. MARK SALAS
☐ 512. BOBBY THIGPEN
☐ 513. MIKE WOODARD
☐ 650. GRADY HALL (P)
☐ 659. TEAM CHECKLIST (F)

CINCINNATI REDS

☐ 152. TIM BIRTSAS
☐ 153. TOM BROWNING
☐ 154. KEITH BROWN
☐ 155. NORM CHARLTON
☐ 156. DAVE CONCEPCION
☐ 157. KAL DANIELS
☐ 158. ERIC DAVIS
☐ 159. BO DIAZ
☐ 160. ROB DIBBLE
☐ 161. NICK ESASKY
☐ 162. JOHN FRANCO
☐ 163. DANNY JACKSON
☐ 164. BARRY LARKIN
☐ 165. ROB MURPHY
☐ 166. PAUL O'NEILL
☐ 167. JEFF REED
☐ 168. JOSE RIJO
☐ 169. RON ROBINSON
☐ 170. CHRIS SABO
☐ 171. CANDY SIERRA
☐ 172. VAN SNIDER
☐ 173. JEFF TREADWAY
☐ 174. FRANK WILLIAMS
☐ 175. HERM WINNINGHAM
☐ 645. LENNY HARRIS (P)
☐ 645. MARTY BROWN (P)
☐ 655. TEAM CHECKLIST (B)

CLEVELAND INDIANS

☐ 396. ANDY ALLANSON
☐ 397. ROD ALLEN
☐ 398. SCOTT BAILES
☐ 399. TOM CANDIOTTI
☐ 400. JOE CARTER
☐ 401. CARMEN CASTILLO
☐ 402. DAVE CLARK
☐ 403. JOHN FARRELL
☐ 404. JULIO FRANCO
☐ 405. DON GORDON
☐ 406. MEL HALL
☐ 407. BRAD HAVENS
☐ 408. BROOK JACOBY
☐ 409. DOUG JONES
☐ 410. JEFF KAISER
☐ 411. LUIS MEDINA
☐ 412. CORY SNYDER
☐ 413. GREG SWINDELL
☐ 414. RON TINGLEY
☐ 415. WILLIE UPSHAW
☐ 416. RON WASHINGTON
☐ 417. RICH YETT
☐ 658. TEAM CHECKLIST (F)

DETROIT TIGERS

☐ 128. DOYLE ALEXANDER
☐ 129. DAVE BERGMAN
☐ 130. TOM BROOKENS
☐ 131. PAUL GIBSON
☐ 132. MIKE HEATH
☐ 133. DON HEINKEL
☐ 134. MIKE HENNEMAN
☐ 135. GUILLERMO HERNANDEZ
☐ 136. ERIC KING
☐ 137. CHET LEMON
☐ 138. FRED LYNN
☐ 139. JACK MORRIS
☐ 140. MATT NOKES
☐ 141. GARY PETTIS
☐ 142. TED POWER
☐ 143. JEFF M. ROBINSON
☐ 144. LUIS SALAZAR
☐ 145. STEVE SEARCY
☐ 146. PAT SHERIDAN
☐ 147. FRANK TANANA
☐ 148. ALAN TRAMMELL
☐ 149. WALT TERRELL
☐ 150. JIM WALEWANDER
☐ 151. LOU WHITAKER
☐ 648. TOREY LOVULLO (P)
☐ 655. TEAM CHICKLIST (F)

HOUSTON ASTROS

☐ 348. JUAN AGOSTO
☐ 349. LARRY ANDERSEN
☐ 350. ALAN ASHBY
☐ 351. KEVIN BASS
☐ 352. BUDDY BELL
☐ 353. CRAIG BIGGIO
☐ 354. DANNY DARWIN
☐ 355. GLENN DAVIS
☐ 356. JIM DESHAIES
☐ 357. BILL DORAN
☐ 358. JOHN FISHEL
☐ 359. BILLY HATCHER
☐ 360. BOB KNEPPER
☐ 361. LOUIE MEADOWS
☐ 362. DAVE MEADS
☐ 363. JIM PANKOVITS
☐ 364. TERRY PUHL
☐ 365. RAFAEL RAMIREZ
☐ 366. CRAIG REYNOLDS
☐ 367. NOLAN RYAN
☐ 368. MIKE SCOTT
☐ 369. DAVE SMITH
☐ 370. GERALD YOUNG
☐ 640. CAMERON DREW (P)
☐ 657. TEAM CHECKLIST (B)

KANSAS CITY ROYALS

☐ 275. LUIS AQUINO
☐ 276. FLOYD BANNISTER
☐ 277. GEORGE BRETT
☐ 278. BILL BUCKNER
☐ 279. NICK CAPRA
☐ 280. JOSE DEJESUS

☐ 281. STEVE FARR
☐ 282. JERRY GLEATON
☐ 283. MARK GUBICZA
☐ 284. TOM GORDON
☐ 285. BO JACKSON
☐ 286. CHARLIE LEIBRANDT
☐ 287. MIKE MACFARLANE
☐ 288. JEFF MONTGOMERY
☐ 289. BILL PECOTA
☐ 290. JAMIE QUIRK
☐ 291. BRET SABERHAGEN
☐ 292. KEVIN SEITZER
☐ 293. KURT STILLWELL
☐ 294. PAT TABLER
☐ 295. DANNY TARTABULL
☐ 296. GARY THURMAN
☐ 297. FRANK WHITE
☐ 298. WILLIE WILSON
☐ 646. LUIS DELOS SANTOS (P)
☐ 646. JIM CAMPBELL (P)
☐ 648. ROBERT PALACIOS (P)
☐ 656. TEAM CHECKLIST (B)

LOS ANGELES DODGERS

☐ 53. DAVE ANDERSON
☐ 54. TIM BELCHER
☐ 55. MIKE DAVIS
☐ 56. MIKE DEVEREAUX
☐ 57. KIRK GIBSON
☐ 58. ALFREDO GRIFFIN
☐ 59. CHRIS GWYNN
☐ 60. JEFF HAMILTON
☐ 61. DANNY HEEP
☐ 62. OREL HERSHISER
☐ 63. BRIAN HOLTON
☐ 64. JAY HOWELL
☐ 65. TIM LEARY
☐ 66. MIKE MARSHALL
☐ 67. RAMON MARTINEZ
☐ 68. JESS OROSCO
☐ 69. ALEJANDRO PENA
☐ 70. STEVE SAX
☐ 71. MIKE SCIOSCIA
☐ 72. MIKE SHARPERSON
☐ 73. JOHN SHELBY
☐ 74. FRANKLIN STUBBS
☐ 75. JOHN TUDOR
☐ 76. FERNANDO VALENZUELA
☐ 77. TRACY WOODSON
☐ 654. TEAM CHECKLIST (B)

MILWAUKEE BREWERS

☐ 176. JIM ADDUCI
☐ 177. DON AUGUST
☐ 178. MIKE BIRKBECK
☐ 179. CHRIS BOSLO
☐ 180. GLENN BRAGGS
☐ 181. GREG BROCK
☐ 182. MARK CLEAR
☐ 183. CHUCK CRIM
☐ 184. ROB DEER
☐ 185. TOM FILER
☐ 186. JIM GANTNER
☐ 187. DARRYL HAMILTON
☐ 188. TED HIGUERA
☐ 189. ODELL JONES
☐ 190. JEFFREY LEONARD
☐ 191. JOEY MEYER
☐ 192. PAUL MIRABELLA
☐ 193. PAUL MOLITOR
☐ 194. CHARLIE O'BRIEN
☐ 195. DAN PLESAC
☐ 196. GARY SHEFFIELD
☐ 197. B. J. SURHOFF
☐ 198. DALE SVEUM
☐ 199. BILL WEGMAN
☐ 200. ROBIN YOUNT
☐ 655. TEAM CHECKLIST (B)

MINNESOTA TWINS

☐ 102. ALLAN ANDERSON
☐ 103. KEITH ATHERTON
☐ 104. JUAN BERENGUER
☐ 105. BERT BLYLEVEN
☐ 106. ERIC BULLOCK
☐ 107. RANDY BUSH
☐ 108. JOHN CHRISTENSEN
☐ 109. MARK DAVIDSON
☐ 110. GARY GAETTI
☐ 111. GREG GAGNE
☐ 112. DAN GLADDEN
☐ 113. GERMAN GONZALEZ
☐ 114. BRIAN HARPER
☐ 115. TOM HERR
☐ 116. KENT HRBEK
☐ 117. GENE LARKIN
☐ 118. TIM LAUDNER
☐ 119. CHARLIE LEA
☐ 120. STEVE LOMBARDOZZI
☐ 121. JOHN MOSES
☐ 122. AL NEWMAN
☐ 123. MARK PORTUGAL
☐ 124. KIRBY PUCKETT
☐ 125. JEFF REARDON
☐ 126. FRED TOLIVER
☐ 127. FRANK VIOLA
☐ 655. TEAM CHECKLIST((F)

MONTREAL EXPOS

☐ 371. HUBIE BROOKS
☐ 372. TIM BURKE
☐ 373. JOHN DOPSON
☐ 374. MIKE FITZGERALD
☐ 375. TOM FOLEY
☐ 376. ANDRES GALARRAGA
☐ 377. NEAL HEATON
☐ 378. JOE HESKETH
☐ 379. BRIAN HOLMAN
☐ 380. REX HUDLER
☐ 381. RANDY JOHNSON
☐ 382. WALLACE JOHNSON
☐ 383. TRACY JONES
☐ 384. DAVE MARTINEZ
☐ 385. DENNIS MARTINEZ
☐ 386. ANDY MCGAFFIGAN
☐ 387. OTIS NIXON
☐ 388. JOHNNY PAREDES
☐ 389. JEFF PARRETT
☐ 390. PASCUAL PEREZ
☐ 391. TIM RAINES
☐ 392. LUIS RIVERA
☐ 393. NELSON SANTOVENIA
☐ 394. BRYN SMITH
☐ 395. TIM WALLACH
☐ 657. TEAM CHECKLIST (B)

NEW YORK METS

☐ 27. RICK AGUILERA
☐ 28. WALLY BACKMAN
☐ 29. MARK CARREON
☐ 30. GARY CARTER
☐ 31. DAVID CONE
☐ 32. RON DARLING
☐ 33. LEN DYKSTRA
☐ 34. KEVIN ELSTER
☐ 35. SID FERNANDEZ
☐ 36. DWIGHT GOODEN
☐ 37. KEITH HERNANDEZ
☐ 38. GREGG JEFFERIES
☐ 39. HOWARD JOHNSON
☐ 40. TERRY LEACH
☐ 41. DAVE MAGADAN
☐ 42. BOB MCCLURE
☐ 43. ROGER MCDOWELL
☐ 44. KEVIN MCREYNOLDS
☐ 45. KEITH MILLER
☐ 46. RANDY MYERS
☐ 47. BOB OJEDA
☐ 48. MACKEY SASSER
☐ 49. DARRYL STRAWBERRY
☐ 50. TIM TEUFEL
☐ 51. DAVE WEST
☐ 52. MOOKIE WILSON
☐ 654. TEAM CHECKLIST (F)

NEW YORK YANKEES

☐ 249. LUIS AGUAYO
☐ 250. NEIL ALLEN
☐ 251. JOHN CANDELARIA
☐ 252. JACK CLARK
☐ 253. RICHARD DOTSON
☐ 254. RICKEY HENDERSON
☐ 255. TOMMY JOHN
☐ 256. ROBERTO KELLY
☐ 257. AL LEITER
☐ 258. DON MATTINGLY
☐ 259. DALE MOHORCIC
☐ 260. HAL MORRIS
☐ 261. SCOTT NIELSEN
☐ 262. MIKE PAGLIARULO
☐ 263. HIPOLITO PENA
☐ 264. KEN PHELPS
☐ 265. WILLIE RANDOLPH
☐ 266. RICK RHODEN
☐ 267. DAVE RIGHETTI
☐ 268. RAFAEL SANTANA
☐ 269. STEVE SHIELDS
☐ 270. JOEL SKINNER
☐ 271. DON SLAUGHT
☐ 272. CLAUDELL WASHINGTON
☐ 273. GARY WARD
☐ 274. DAVE WINFIELD
☐ 656. TEAM CHECKLIST (B)

OAKLAND A'S

☐ 1. DON BAYLOR
☐ 2. LANCE BLANKENSHIP
☐ 3. TODD BURNS
☐ 4. GREG CADARET
☐ 5. JOSE CANSECO
☐ 6. STORM DAVIS
☐ 7. DENNIS ECKERSLEY
☐ 8. MIKE GALLEGO
☐ 9. RON HASSEY
☐ 10. DAVE HENDERSON
☐ 11. RICK HONEYCUTT
☐ 12. GLENN HUBBARD
☐ 13. STAN JAVIER
☐ 14. DOUG JENNINGS
☐ 15. FELIX JOSE
☐ 16. CARNEY LANSFORD
☐ 17. MARK MCGWIRE
☐ 18. GENE NELSON
☐ 19. DAVE PARKER
☐ 20. ERIC PLUNK
☐ 21. LUIS POLONIA
☐ 22. TERRY STEINBACH
☐ 23. DAVE STEWART
☐ 24. WALT WEISS
☐ 25. BOB WELCH
☐ 26. CURT YOUNG
☐ 649. JIM CORSI (P)
☐ 654. TEAM CHECKLIST (F)

PHILADELPHIA PHILLIES

☐ 562. STEVE BEDROSIAN
☐ 563. PHIL BRADLEY
☐ 564. DON CARMAN
☐ 565. BOB DERNIER
☐ 566. MARVIN FREEMAN
☐ 567. TODD FROHWIRTH
☐ 568. GREG GROSS
☐ 569. KEVIN GROSS
☐ 570. GREG HARRIS
☐ 571. VON HAYES
☐ 572. CHRIS JAMES
☐ 573. STEVE JELTZ
☐ 574. RON JONES
☐ 575. RICKY JORDAN
☐ 576. MIKE MADDUX
☐ 577. DAVID PALMER
☐ 578. LANCE PARRISH
☐ 579. SHANE RAWLEY
☐ 580. BRUCE RUFFIN
☐ 581. JUAN SAMUEL
☐ 582. MIKE SCHMIDT
☐ 583. KENT TEKULVE

- ☐ 584. MILT THOMPSON
- ☐ 653. SCOTT SERVICE (P)
- ☐ 653. SHANE TURNER (P)
- ☐ 659. TEAM CHECKLIST (B)

PITTSBURGH PIRATES

- ☐ 201. RAFAEL BELLIARD
- ☐ 202. BARRY BONDS
- ☐ 203. BOBBY BONILLA
- ☐ 204. SID BREAM
- ☐ 205. BENNY DISTEFANO
- ☐ 206. DOUG DRABEK
- ☐ 207. MIKE DUNNE
- ☐ 208. FELIX FERMIN
- ☐ 209. BRIAN FISHER
- ☐ 210. JIM GOTT
- ☐ 211. BOB KIPPER
- ☐ 212. DAVE LAPOINT
- ☐ 213. MIKE LAVALLIERE
- ☐ 214. JOSE LIND
- ☐ 215. JUNIOR ORIZ
- ☐ 216. VICENTE PALACIOS
- ☐ 217. TOM PRINCE
- ☐ 218. GARY REDUS
- ☐ 219. R. J. REYNOLDS
- ☐ 220. JEFF ROBINSON
- ☐ 221. JOHN SMILEY
- ☐ 222. ANDY VAN SLYKE
- ☐ 223. BOB WALK
- ☐ 224. GLENN WILSON
- ☐ 647. RANDY KRAMER (P)
- ☐ 647. MIGUEL GARCIA (P)
- ☐ 656. TEAM CHECKLIST (F)

ST. LOUIS CARDINALS

- ☐ 443. LUIS ALICEA
- ☐ 444. TOM BRUNANSKY
- ☐ 445. VINCE COLEMAN
- ☐ 446. JOHN COSTELLO
- ☐ 447. DANNY COX
- ☐ 448. KEN DAYLEY
- ☐ 449. JOSE DELEON
- ☐ 450. CURT FORD
- ☐ 451. PEDRO GUERRERO
- ☐ 452. BOB HORNER
- ☐ 453. TIM JONES
- ☐ 454. STEVE LAKE
- ☐ 455. JOE MAGRANE
- ☐ 456. GREG MATHEWS
- ☐ 457. WILLIE MCGEE
- ☐ 458. LARRY MCWILLIAMS
- ☐ 459. JOSE OQUENDO
- ☐ 460. TONY PENA
- ☐ 461. TERRY PENDLETON
- ☐ 462. STEVE PETERS
- ☐ 463. OZZIE SMITH
- ☐ 464. SCOTT TERRY
- ☐ 465. DENNY WALLING
- ☐ 466. TODD WORRELL
- ☐ 652. KEN HILL (P)
- ☐ 658. TEAM CHECKLIST (B)

SAN DIEGO PADRES

- ☐ 299. ROBERTO ALOMAR
- ☐ 300. SANDY ALOMAR, JR.
- ☐ 301. CHRIS BROWN
- ☐ 302. MIKE BRUMLEY
- ☐ 303. MARK DAVIS
- ☐ 304. MARK GRANT
- ☐ 305. TONY GWYNN
- ☐ 306. GREG W. HARRIS
- ☐ 307. ANDY HAWKINS
- ☐ 308. JIMMY JONES
- ☐ 309. JOHN KRUK
- ☐ 310. DAVE LEIPER
- ☐ 311. CARMELO MARTINEZ
- ☐ 312. LANCE MCCULLERS
- ☐ 313. KEITH MORELAND
- ☐ 314. DENNIS RASMUSSEN
- ☐ 315. RANDY READY
- ☐ 316. BENITO SANTIAGO
- ☐ 317. ERIC SHOW
- ☐ 318. TODD SIMMONS
- ☐ 319. GARRY TEMPLETON
- ☐ 320. DICKIE THON
- ☐ 321. ED WHITSON
- ☐ 322. MARVELL WYNNE
- ☐ 642. BRAD POUNDERS (P)
- ☐ 642. JERALD CLARK (P)
- ☐ 657. TEAM CHECKLIST (F)

SAN FRANCISCO GIANTS

- ☐ 323. MIKE ALDRETE
- ☐ 324. BRETT BUTLER
- ☐ 325. WILL CLARK
- ☐ 326. KELLY DOWNS
- ☐ 327. DAVE DRAVECKY
- ☐ 328. SCOTT GARRELTS
- ☐ 329. ATLEE HAMMAKER
- ☐ 330. CHARLIE HAYES
- ☐ 331. MIKE KRUKOW
- ☐ 332. CRAIG LEFFERTS
- ☐ 333. CANDY MALDONADO
- ☐ 334. KIRT MANWARING
- ☐ 335. BOB MELVIN
- ☐ 336. KEVIN MITCHELL
- ☐ 337. DONELL NIXON
- ☐ 338. TONY PEREZCHICA
- ☐ 339. JOE PRICE
- ☐ 340. RICK REUSCHEL
- ☐ 341. EARNEST RILES
- ☐ 342. DON ROBINSON
- ☐ 343. CHRIS SPEIER
- ☐ 344. ROBBY THOMPSON
- ☐ 345. JOSE URIBE
- ☐ 346. MATT WILLIAMS
- ☐ 347. TREVOR WILSON
- ☐ 652. DENNIS COOK (P)
- ☐ 657. TEAM CHECKLIST (F)

SEATTLE MARINERS

- ☐ 538. STEVE BALBONI
- ☐ 539. SCOTT BANKHEAD
- ☐ 540. SCOTT BRADLEY
- ☐ 541. MICKEY BRANTLEY
- ☐ 542. JAY BUHNER
- ☐ 543. MIKE CAMPBELL
- ☐ 544. DARNELL COLES
- ☐ 545. HENRY COTTO
- ☐ 546. ALVIN DAVIS
- ☐ 547. MARIO DIAZ
- ☐ 548. KEN GRIFFEY, JR.
- ☐ 549. ERIK HANSON
- ☐ 550. MIKE JACKSON
- ☐ 551. MARK LANGSTON
- ☐ 552. EDGAR MARTINEZ
- ☐ 553. BILL MCGUIRE
- ☐ 554. MIKE MOORE
- ☐ 555. JIM PRESLEY
- ☐ 556. REY QUINONES
- ☐ 557. JERRY REED
- ☐ 558. HAROLD REYNOLDS
- ☐ 559. MIKE SCHOOLER
- ☐ 560. BILL SWIFT
- ☐ 561. DAVE VALLE
- ☐ 651. TERRY TAYLOR (P)
- ☐ 659. TEAM CHECKLIST (B)

TEXAS RANGERS

- ☐ 514. BOB BROWER
- ☐ 515. STEVE BUECHELE
- ☐ 516. JOSE CECENA
- ☐ 517. CECIL ESPY
- ☐ 518. SCOTT FLETCHER
- ☐ 519. CECILIO GUANTE
- ☐ 520. JOSE GUZMAN
- ☐ 521. RAY HAYWARD
- ☐ 522. CHARLIE HOUGH
- ☐ 523. PETE INCAVIGLIA
- ☐ 524. MIKE JEFFCOAT
- ☐ 525. PAUL KILGUS
- ☐ 526. CHAD KREUTER
- ☐ 527. JEFF KUNKEL
- ☐ 528. ODDIBE MCDOWELL
- ☐ 529. PETE O'BRIEN
- ☐ 530. GENO PETRALLI
- ☐ 531. JEFF RUSSELL
- ☐ 532. RUBEN SIERRA
- ☐ 533. MIKE STANLEY
- ☐ 534. ED VANDEBERG
- ☐ 535. CURTIS WILKERSON
- ☐ 536. MITCH WILLIAMS
- ☐ 537. BOBBY WITT
- ☐ 640. STEVE WILSON (P)
- ☐ 641. KEVIN BROWN (P)
- ☐ 641. KEVIN REIMER (P)
- ☐ 659. TEAM CHECKLIST (F)

TORONTO BLUE JAYS

- ☐ 225. JESS BARFIELD
- ☐ 226. GEORGE BELL
- ☐ 227. PAT BORDERS
- ☐ 228. JOHN CERUTTI
- ☐ 229. JIM CLANCY
- ☐ 230. MARK EICHHORN
- ☐ 231. TONY FERNANDEZ
- ☐ 232. CECIL FIELDER
- ☐ 233. MIKE FLANAGAN
- ☐ 234. KELLY GRUBER
- ☐ 235. TOM HENKE
- ☐ 236. JIMMY KEY
- ☐ 237. RICK LEACH
- ☐ 238. MANNY LEE
- ☐ 239. NELSON LIRIANO
- ☐ 240. FRED MCGRIFF
- ☐ 241. LLOYD MOSEBY
- ☐ 242. RANCE MULLINIKS
- ☐ 243. JEFF MUSSELMAN
- ☐ 244. DAVE STIEB
- ☐ 245. TODD STOTTLEMYRE
- ☐ 246. DUANE WARD
- ☐ 247. DAVID WELLS
- ☐ 248. ERNIE WHITT
- ☐ 656. TEAM CHECKLIST (F)

1989 FLEER TRADED (132)
2 1/2 X 3 1/2

ATLANTA BRAVES

- ☐ 72U. GERONIMO BERROA
- ☐ 73U. DEREK LILLIQUIST
- ☐ 74U. LONNIE SMITH
- ☐ 75U. JEFF TREADWAY

BALTIMORE ORIOLES

- ☐ 1U. PHIL BRADLEY
- ☐ 2U. MIKE DEVEREAUX
- ☐ 3U. STEVE FINLEY
- ☐ 4U. KEVIN HICKEY
- ☐ 5U. BRIAN HOLTON
- ☐ 6U. BOB MILACKI
- ☐ 7U. RANDY MILLIGAN

BOSTON RED SOX

- ☐ 8U. JOHN DOPSON
- ☐ 9U. NICK ESASKY
- ☐ 10U. ROB MURPHY

CALIFORNIA ANGELS

- ☐ 11U. JIM ABBOTT
- ☐ 12U. BERT BLYLEVEN
- ☐ 13U. JEFF MANTO
- ☐ 14U. BOB MCCLURE
- ☐ 15U. LANCE PARRISH
- ☐ 16U. LEE STEVENS
- ☐ 17U. CLAUDELL WASHINGTON

CHICAGO CUBS

- □ 76U. PAUL KILGUS
- □ 77U. LLOYD MCCLENDON
- □ 78U. SCOTT SANDERSON
- □ 79U. DWIGHT SMITH
- □ 80U. JEROME WALTON
- □ 81U. MITCH WILLIAMS
- □ 82U. STEVE WILSON

CHICAGO WHITE SOX

- □ 18U. MARK DAVIS
- □ 19U. ERIC KING
- □ 20U. RON KITTLE
- □ 21U. MATT MERULLO
- □ 22U. STEVE ROSENBERG
- □ 23U. ROBIN VENTURA

CINCINNATI REDS

- □ 83U. TODD BENZINGER
- □ 84U. KEN GRIFFEY
- □ 85U. RICK MAHLER
- □ 86U. ROLANDO ROOMES
- □ 87U. SCOTT SCUDDER

CLEVELAND INDIANS

- □ 24U. KEITH ATHERTON
- □ 25U. JOEY BELLE
- □ 26U. JERRY BROWNE
- □ 27U. FELIX FERMIN
- □ 28U. BRAD KOMMINSK
- □ 29U. PETE O'BRIEN

DETROIT TIGERS

- □ 30U. MIKE BRUMLEY
- □ 31U. TRACY JONES
- □ 32U. MIKE SCHWABE
- □ 33U. GARY WARD
- □ 34U. FRANK WILLIAMS

HOUSTON ASTROS

- □ 88U. JIM CLANCY
- □ 89U. RICH RHODEN
- □ 90U. DAN SCHATZEDER

KANSAS CITY ROYALS

- □ 35U. KEVIN APPIER
- □ 36U. BOB BOONE
- □ 37U. LUIS DE LOS SANTOS
- □ 38U. JIM EISENREICH

LOS ANGELES DODGERS

- □ 91U. MIKE MORGAN
- □ 92U. EDDIE MURRAY
- □ 93U. WILLIE RANDOLPH
- □ 94U. RAY SEARAGE

MILWAUKEE BREWERS

- □ 39U. JAIME NAVARRO
- □ 40U. BILL SPIERS
- □ 41U. GREG VAUGHN
- □ 42U. RANDY VERES

MINNESOTA TWINS

- □ 43U. WALLY BACKMAN
- □ 44U. SHANE RAWLEY

MONTREAL EXPOS

- □ 95U. MIKE ALDRETE
- □ 96U. KEVIN GROSS
- □ 97U. MARK LANGSTON
- □ 98U. SPIKE OWEN
- □ 99U. ZANE SMITH

NEW YORK METS

- □ 100U. DON AASE
- □ 101U. BARRY LYONS
- □ 102U. JUAN SAMUEL
- □ 103U. WALLY WHITEHURST

NEW YORK YANKEES

- □ 45U. STEVE BALBONI
- □ 46U. JESSE BARFIELD
- □ 47U. ALVARO ESPINOZA
- □ 48U. BOB GEREN
- □ 49U. MEL HALL
- □ 50U. ANDY HAWKINS
- □ 51U. HENSLEY MEULENS
- □ 52U. STEVE SAX
- □ 53U. DEION SANDERS

OAKLAND A'S

- □ 54U. RICKEY HENDERSON
- □ 55U. MIKE MOORE
- □ 56U. TONY PHILLIPS

PHILADELPHIA PHILLIES

- □ 104U. DENNIS COOK
- □ 105U. LENNY DYKSTRA
- □ 106U. CHARLIE HAYES
- □ 107U. TOMMY HERR
- □ 108U. KEN HOWELL
- □ 109U. JOHN KRUK
- □ 110U. ROGER MCDOWELL
- □ 111U. TERRY MULHOLLAND
- □ 112U. JEFF PARRETT
- □ 131U. MIKE SCHMIDT

PITTSBURGH PIRATES

- □ 113U. NEAL HEATON
- □ 114U. JEFF KING
- □ 115U. RANDY KRAMER
- □ 116U. BILL LANDRUM

ST. LOUIS CARDINALS

- □ 117U. CRIS CARPENTER
- □ 118U. FRANK DIPINO
- □ 119U. KEN HILL
- □ 120U. DAN QUISENBERRY
- □ 121U. MILT THOMPSON
- □ 122U. TODD ZEILE

SAN DIEGO PADRES

- □ 123U. JACK CLARK
- □ 124U. BRUCE HURST
- □ 125U. MARK PARENT
- □ 126U. BIP ROBERTS

SAN FRANCISCO GIANTS

- □ 127U. JEFF BRANTLEY
- □ 128U. TERRY KENNEDY
- □ 129U. MIKE LACOSS
- □ 130U. GREG LITTON

SEATTLE MARINERS

- □ 57U. GREG BRILEY
- □ 58U. GENE HARRIS
- □ 59U. RANDY JOHNSON
- □ 60U. JEFFREY LWONARD
- □ 61U. DENNIS POWELL
- □ 62U. OMAR VIZQUEL

TEXAS RANGERS

- □ 63U. KEVIN BROWN
- □ 64U. JULIO FRANCO
- □ 65U. JAMIE MOYER
- □ 66U. RAFAEL PALMEIRO
- □ 67U. NOLAN RYAN

TORONTO BLUE JAYS

- □ 68U. FRANCISCO CABRERA
- □ 69U. JUNIOR FELIX
- □ 70U. AL LEITER
- □ 71U. ALEX SANCHEZ

1990 FLEER (660)
2 1/2 X 3 1/2

ATLANTA BRAVES

- □ 574. JOSE ALVAREZ
- □ 575. GERONIMO BERROA
- □ 576. JEFF BLAUSER
- □ 577. JOE BOEVER
- □ 578. MARTY CLARY
- □ 579. JODY DAVIS
- □ 580. MARK EICHHORN
- □ 581. DARRELL EVANS
- □ 582. RON GANT
- □ 583. TOM GLAVINE
- □ 584. TOMMY GREENE
- □ 585. TOMMY GREGG
- □ 586. DAVID JUSTICE
- □ 587. MARK LEMKE
- □ 588. DEREK LILLIQUIST
- □ 589. ODDIBE MCDOWELL
- □ 590. KENT MERCKER
- □ 591. DALE MURPHY
- □ 592. GERALD PERRY
- □ 593. LONNIE SMITH
- □ 594. PETE SMITH
- □ 595. JOHN SMOLTZ
- □ 596. MIKE STANTON
- □ 597. ANDRES THOMAS
- □ 598. JEFF TREADWAY
- □ 642. KELLY MANN (P)
- □ 660. TEAM CHECKLIST (F)

BALTIMORE ORIOLES

- ☐ 172. BRADY ANDERSON
- ☐ 173. JEFF BALLARD
- ☐ 174. PHIL BRADLEY
- ☐ 175. MIKE DEVEREAUX
- ☐ 176. STEVE FINLEY
- ☐ 177. PETE HARNISCH
- ☐ 178. KEVIN HICKEY
- ☐ 179. BRIAN HOLTON
- ☐ 180. BEN MCDONALD
- ☐ 181. BOB MELVIN
- ☐ 182. BOB MILACKI
- ☐ 183. RANDY MILLIGAN
- ☐ 184. GREGG OLSON
- ☐ 185. JOE ORSULAK
- ☐ 186. BILL RIPKEN
- ☐ 187. CAL RIPKEN, JR.
- ☐ 188. DAVE SCHMIDT
- ☐ 189. LARRY SHEETS
- ☐ 190. MICKEY TETTLETON
- ☐ 191. MARK THURMOND
- ☐ 192. JAY TIBBS
- ☐ 193. JIM TRABER
- ☐ 194. MARK WILLIAMSON
- ☐ 195. CRAIG WORTHINGTON
- ☐ 655. TEAM CHECKLIST (B)

BOSTON RED SOX

- ☐ 266. MARTY BARRETT
- ☐ 267. MIKE BODDICKER
- ☐ 268. WADE BOGGS
- ☐ 269. ELLIS BURKS
- ☐ 270. RICK CERONE
- ☐ 271. ROGER CLEMENS
- ☐ 272. JOHN DOPSON
- ☐ 273. NICK ESASKY
- ☐ 274. DWIGHT EVANS
- ☐ 275. WES GARDNER
- ☐ 276. RICH GEDMAN
- ☐ 277. MIKE GREENWELL
- ☐ 278. DANNY HEEP
- ☐ 279. ERIC HETZEL
- ☐ 280. DENNIS LAMP
- ☐ 281. ROB MURPHY
- ☐ 282. JOE PRICE
- ☐ 283. CARLOS QUINTANA
- ☐ 284. JODY REED
- ☐ 285. LUIS RIVERA
- ☐ 286. KEVIN ROMINE
- ☐ 287. LEE SMITH
- ☐ 288. MIKE SMITHSON
- ☐ 289. BOB STANLEY
- ☐ 648. DANA WILLIAMS (P)
- ☐ 656. TEAM CHECKLIST (B)

CALIFORNIA ANGELS

- ☐ 125. JIM ABBOTT
- ☐ 126. TONY ARMAS
- ☐ 127. DANTE BICHETTE
- ☐ 128. BERT BLYLEVEN
- ☐ 129. CHILI DAVIS
- ☐ 130. BRIAN DOWNING
- ☐ 131. MIKE FETTERS
- ☐ 132. CHUCK FINLEY
- ☐ 133. WILLIE FRASER
- ☐ 134. BRYAN HARVEY
- ☐ 135. JACK HOWELL
- ☐ 136. WALLY JOYNER
- ☐ 137. JEFF MANTO
- ☐ 138. KIRK MCCASKILL
- ☐ 139. BOB MCCLURE
- ☐ 140. GREG MINTON
- ☐ 141. LANCE PARRISH
- ☐ 142. DAN PETRY
- ☐ 143. JOHNNY RAY
- ☐ 144. DICK SCHOFIELD
- ☐ 145. LEE STEVENS
- ☐ 146. CLAUDELL WASHINGTON
- ☐ 147. DEVON WHITE
- ☐ 148. MIKE WITT
- ☐ 640. COLIN CHARLAND (P)
- ☐ 647. JOHN ORTON (P)
- ☐ 648. RICH MONTELEONE (P)
- ☐ 651. BOBBY ROSE (P)
- ☐ 655. TEAM CHECKLIST (F)

CHICAGO CUBS

- ☐ 25. PAUL ASSENMACHER
- ☐ 26. DAMON BERRYHILL
- ☐ 27. MIKE BIELECKI
- ☐ 28. KEVIN BLANKENSHIP
- ☐ 29. ANDRE DAWSON
- ☐ 30. SHAWON DUNSTON
- ☐ 31. JOE GIRARDI
- ☐ 32. MARK GRACE
- ☐ 33. MIKE HARKEY
- ☐ 34. PAUL KILGUS
- ☐ 35. LES LANCASTER
- ☐ 36. VANCE LAW
- ☐ 37. GREG MADDUX
- ☐ 38. LLOYD MCCLENDON
- ☐ 39. JEFF PICO
- ☐ 40. RYNE SANDBERG
- ☐ 41. SCOTT SANDERSON
- ☐ 42. DWIGHT SMITH
- ☐ 43. RICK SUTCLIFFE
- ☐ 44. JEROME WALTON
- ☐ 45. MITCH WEBSTER
- ☐ 46. CURT WILKERSON
- ☐ 47. DEAN WILKINS
- ☐ 48. MITCH WILLIAMS
- ☐ 49. STEVE WILSON
- ☐ 643. GREG SMITH (P)
- ☐ 645. DERRICK MAY (P)
- ☐ 654. TEAM CHECKLIST (F)

CHICAGO WHITE SOX

- ☐ 529. IVAN CALDERON
- ☐ 530. CARLTON FISK
- ☐ 531. SCOTT FLETCHER
- ☐ 532. DAVE GALLAGHER
- ☐ 533. OZZIE GUILLEN
- ☐ 534. GREG HIBBARD
- ☐ 535. SHAWN HILLEGAS
- ☐ 536. LANCE JOHNSON
- ☐ 537. ERIC KING
- ☐ 538. RON KITTLE
- ☐ 539. STEVE LYONS
- ☐ 540. CARLOS MARTINEZ
- ☐ 541. TOM MCCARTHY
- ☐ 542. MATT MERULLO
- ☐ 543. DONN PALL
- ☐ 544. DAN PASQUA
- ☐ 545. KEN PATTERSON
- ☐ 546. MELIDO PEREZ
- ☐ 547. STEVE ROSENBERG
- ☐ 548. SAMMY SOSA
- ☐ 549. BOBBY THIGPEN
- ☐ 550. ROBIN VENTURA
- ☐ 551. GREG WALKER
- ☐ 644. TOM DREES (P)
- ☐ 652. WAYNE EDWARDS (P)
- ☐ 659. TEAM CHECKLIST (B)

CINCINNATI REDS

- ☐ 412. JACK ARMSTRONG
- ☐ 413. TODD BENZINGER
- ☐ 414. TIM BIRTSAS
- ☐ 415. TOM BROWNING
- ☐ 416. NORM CHARLTON
- ☐ 417. ERIC DAVIS
- ☐ 418. ROB DIBBLE
- ☐ 419. JOHN FRANCO
- ☐ 420. KEN GRIFFEY
- ☐ 421. CHRIS HAMMOND
- ☐ 422. DANNY JACKSON
- ☐ 423. BARRY LARKIN
- ☐ 424. TIM LEARY
- ☐ 425. RICK MAHLER
- ☐ 426. JOE OLIVER
- ☐ 427. PAUL O'NEILL
- ☐ 428. LUIS QUINONES
- ☐ 429. JEFF REED
- ☐ 430. JOSE RIJO
- ☐ 431. RON ROBINSON
- ☐ 432. ROLANDO ROOMES
- ☐ 433. CHRIS SABO
- ☐ 434. SCOTT SCUDDER
- ☐ 435. HERM WINNINGHAM
- ☐ 645. MIKE ROESLER (P)
- ☐ 658. TEAM CHECKLIST (F)

CLEVELAND INDIANS

- ☐ 483. ANDY ALLANSON
- ☐ 484. SCOTT BAILES
- ☐ 485. JOEY BELLE
- ☐ 486. BUD BLACK
- ☐ 487. JERRY BROWNE
- ☐ 488. TOM CANDIOTTI
- ☐ 489. JOE CARTER
- ☐ 490. DAVID CLARK
- ☐ 491. JOHN FARRELL
- ☐ 492. FELIX FERMIN
- ☐ 493. BROOK JACOBY
- ☐ 494. DION JAMES
- ☐ 495. DOUG JONES
- ☐ 496. BRAD KOMMINSK
- ☐ 497. ROD NICHOLS
- ☐ 498. PETE O'BRIEN
- ☐ 499. STEVE OLIN
- ☐ 500. JESSE OROSCO
- ☐ 501. JOEL SKINNER
- ☐ 502. CORY SNYDER
- ☐ 503. GREG SWINDELL
- ☐ 504. RICH YETT
- ☐ 640. RUDY SEANEZ (P)
- ☐ 659. TEAM CHECKLIST (F)

DETROIT TIGERS

- ☐ 599. DOYLE ALEXANDER
- ☐ 600. DAVE BERGMAN
- ☐ 601. BRIAN DUBOIS
- ☐ 602. PAUL GIBSON
- ☐ 603. MIKE HEATH
- ☐ 604. MIKE HENNEMAN
- ☐ 605. GUILLERMO HERNANDEZ
- ☐ 606. SHAWN HOLMAN
- ☐ 607. TRACY JONES
- ☐ 608. CHET LEMON
- ☐ 609. FRED LYNN
- ☐ 610. JACK MORRIS
- ☐ 611. MATT NOKES
- ☐ 612. GARY PETTIS
- ☐ 613. KEVIN RITZ
- ☐ 614. JEFF ROBINSON
- ☐ 615. STEVE SEARCY
- ☐ 616. FRANK TANANA
- ☐ 617. ALAN TRAMMELL
- ☐ 618. GARY WARD
- ☐ 619. LOU WHITAKER
- ☐ 620. FRANK WILLIAMS
- ☐ 660. TEAM CHECKLIST (F)

HOUSTON ASTROS

- ☐ 220. JUAN AGOSTO
- ☐ 221. LARRY ANDERSEN
- ☐ 222. ERIC ANTHONY
- ☐ 223. KEVIN BASS
- ☐ 224. CRAIG BIGGIO
- ☐ 225. KEN CAMINITI
- ☐ 226. JIM CLANCY
- ☐ 227. DANNY DARWIN
- ☐ 228. GLENN DAVIS
- ☐ 229. JIM DESHAIES
- ☐ 230. BILL DORAN
- ☐ 231. BOB FORSCH
- ☐ 232. BRIAN MEYER
- ☐ 233. TERRY PUHL
- ☐ 234. RAFAEL RAMIREZ
- ☐ 235. RICK RHODEN
- ☐ 236. DAN SCHATZEDER
- ☐ 237. MIKE SCOTT
- ☐ 238. DAVE SMITH
- ☐ 239. ALEX TREVINO
- ☐ 240. GLENN WILSON
- ☐ 241. GERALD YOUNG
- ☐ 656. TEAM CHECKLIST (F)

KANSAS CITY ROYALS

- ☐ 100. KEVIN APPIER
- ☐ 101. LUIS AQUINO
- ☐ 102. BOB BOONE
- ☐ 103. GEORGE BRETT
- ☐ 104. JOSE DEJESUS
- ☐ 105. LUIS DE LOS SANTOS
- ☐ 106. JIM EISENREICH
- ☐ 107. STEVE FARR
- ☐ 108. TOM GORDON

- ☐ 109. MARK GUBICZA
- ☐ 110. BO JACKSON
- ☐ 111. TERRY LEACH
- ☐ 112. CHARLIE LEIBRANDT
- ☐ 113. RICH LUECKEN
- ☐ 114. MIKE MACFARLANE
- ☐ 115. JEFF MONTGOMERY
- ☐ 116. BRET SABERHAGEN
- ☐ 117. KEVIN SEITZER
- ☐ 118. KURT STILLWELL
- ☐ 119. PAT TABLER
- ☐ 120. DANNY TARTABULL
- ☐ 121. GARY THURMAN
- ☐ 122. FRANK WHITE
- ☐ 123. WILLIE WILSON
- ☐ 124. MATT WINTERS
- ☐ 655. TEAM CHECKLIST (F)

LOS ANGELES DODGERS

- ☐ 389. TIM BELCHER
- ☐ 390. TIM CREWS
- ☐ 391. MIKE DAVIS
- ☐ 392. RICK DEMPSEY
- ☐ 393. KIRK GIBSON
- ☐ 394. JOSE GONZALEZ
- ☐ 395. ALFREDO GRIFFIN
- ☐ 396. JEFF HAMILTON
- ☐ 397. LENNY HARRIS
- ☐ 398. MICKEY HATCHER
- ☐ 399. OREL HERSHISER
- ☐ 400. JAY HOWELL
- ☐ 401. MIKE MARSHALL
- ☐ 402. RAMON MARTINEZ
- ☐ 403. MIKE MORGAN
- ☐ 404. EDDIE MURRAY
- ☐ 405. ALEJANDRO PENA
- ☐ 406. WILLIE RANDOLPH
- ☐ 407. MIKE SCIOSCIA
- ☐ 408. RAY SEARAGE
- ☐ 409. FERNANDO VALENZUELA
- ☐ 410. JOSE VIZCAINO
- ☐ 411. JOHN WETTELAND
- ☐ 642. DAVE HANSEN (P)
- ☐ 649. MIKE HUFF (P)
- ☐ 651. MIKE HARTLEY (P)
- ☐ 658. TEAM CHECKLIST (F)

MILWAUKEE BREWERS

- ☐ 316. CHRIS BOSIO
- ☐ 317. GLENN BRAGGS
- ☐ 318. GREG BROCK
- ☐ 319. CHUCK CRIM
- ☐ 320. ROB DEER
- ☐ 321. MIKE FELDER
- ☐ 322. TOM FILER
- ☐ 323. TONY FOSSAS
- ☐ 324. JIM GANTNER
- ☐ 325. DARRYL HAMILTON
- ☐ 326. TED HIGUERA
- ☐ 327. MARK KNUDSON
- ☐ 328. BILL KRUEGER
- ☐ 329. TIM MCINTOSH
- ☐ 330. PAUL MOLITOR
- ☐ 331. JAIME NAVARRO
- ☐ 332. CHARLIE O'BRIEN
- ☐ 333. JEFF PETEREK
- ☐ 334. DAN PLESAC
- ☐ 335. JERRY REUSS
- ☐ 336. GARY SHEFFIELD
- ☐ 337. BILL SPIERS
- ☐ 338. B. J. SURHOFF
- ☐ 339. GREG VAUGHN
- ☐ 340. ROBIN YOUNT
- ☐ 641. GEORGE CANALE (P)
- ☐ 651. TEAM CHECKLIST (F)

MINNESOTA TWINS

- ☐ 365. RICK AGUILERA
- ☐ 366. ALLAN ANDERSON
- ☐ 367. WALLY BACKMAN
- ☐ 368. DOUG BAKER
- ☐ 369. JUAN BERENGUER
- ☐ 370. RANDY BUSH
- ☐ 371. CARMEN CASTILLO
- ☐ 372. MIKE DYER
- ☐ 373. GARY GAETTI
- ☐ 374. GREG GAGNE
- ☐ 375. DAN GLADDEN
- ☐ 376. GERMAN GONZALEZ
- ☐ 377. BRIAN HARPER
- ☐ 378. KENT HRBEK
- ☐ 379. GENE LARKIN
- ☐ 380. TIM LAUDNER
- ☐ 381. JOHN MOSES
- ☐ 382. AL NEWMAN
- ☐ 383. KIRBY PUCKETT
- ☐ 384. SHANE RAWLEY
- ☐ 385. JEFF REARDON
- ☐ 386. ROY SMITH
- ☐ 387. GARY WAYNE
- ☐ 388. DAVE WEST
- ☐ 647. SCOTT LEIUS (P)
- ☐ 657. TEAM CHECKLIST (B)

MONTREAL EXPOS

- ☐ 341. HUBIE BROOKS
- ☐ 342. TIM BURKE
- ☐ 343. MIKE FITZGERALD
- ☐ 344. TOM FOLEY
- ☐ 345. ANDRES GALARRAGA
- ☐ 346. DAMASO GARCIA
- ☐ 347. MARQUIS GRISSOM
- ☐ 348. KEVIN GROSS
- ☐ 349. JOE HESKETH
- ☐ 350. JEFF HUSON
- ☐ 351. WALLACE JOHNSON
- ☐ 352. MARK LANGSTON
- ☐ 353. DAVE MARTINEZ
- ☐ 354. DENNIS MARTINEZ
- ☐ 355. ANDY MCGAFFIGAN
- ☐ 356. OTIS NIXON
- ☐ 357. SPIKE OWEN
- ☐ 358. PASCUAL PEREZ
- ☐ 359. TIM RAINES
- ☐ 360. NELSON SANTOVENIA
- ☐ 361. BRYN SMITH
- ☐ 362. ZANE SMITH
- ☐ 363. LARRY WALKER
- ☐ 364. TIM WALLACH
- ☐ 646. MARK GARDNER (P)
- ☐ 649. STEVE FREY (P)
- ☐ 653. DELINO DESHIELDS (P)
- ☐ 657. TEAM CHECKLIST (B)

NEW YORK METS

- ☐ 196. DON AASE
- ☐ 197. BLAINE BEATTY
- ☐ 198. MARK CARREON
- ☐ 199. GARY CARTER
- ☐ 200. DAVID CONE
- ☐ 201. RON DARLING
- ☐ 202. KEVIN ELSTER
- ☐ 203. SID FERNANDEZ
- ☐ 204. DWIGHT GOODEN
- ☐ 205. KEITH HERNANDEZ
- ☐ 206. JEFF INNIS
- ☐ 207. GREGG JEFFERIES
- ☐ 208. HOWARD JOHNSON
- ☐ 209. BARRY LYONS
- ☐ 210. DAVE MAGADAN
- ☐ 211. KEVIN MCREYNOLDS
- ☐ 212. JEFF MUSSELMAN
- ☐ 213. RANDY MYERS
- ☐ 214. BOB OJEDA
- ☐ 215. JUAN SAMUEL
- ☐ 216. MACKEY SASSER
- ☐ 217. DARRYL STRAWBERRY
- ☐ 218. TIM TEUFEL
- ☐ 219. FRANK VIOLA
- ☐ 656. TEAM CHECKLIST (F)

NEW YORK YANKEES

- ☐ 436. STEVE BALBONI
- ☐ 437. JESSE BARFIELD
- ☐ 438. MIKE BLOWERS
- ☐ 439. TOM BROOKENS
- ☐ 440. GREG CADARET
- ☐ 441. ALVARO ESPINOZA
- ☐ 442. BOB GEREN
- ☐ 443. LEE GUETTERMAN
- ☐ 444. MEL HALL
- ☐ 445. ANDY HAWKINS
- ☐ 446. ROBERTO KELLY
- ☐ 447. DON MATTINGLY*
- ☐ 448. LANCE MCCULLERS
- ☐ 449. HENSLEY MEULENS
- ☐ 450. DALE MOHORCIC
- ☐ 451. CLAY PARKER
- ☐ 452. ERIC PLUNK
- ☐ 453. DAVE RIGHETTI
- ☐ 454. DEION SANDERS
- ☐ 455. STEVE SAX
- ☐ 456. DON SLAUGHT
- ☐ 457. WALT TERRELL
- ☐ 458. DAVE WINFIELD
- ☐ 641. KEVIN MAAS (P)
- ☐ 658. TEAM CHECKLIST (B)

OAKLAND A'S

- ☐ 1. LANCE BLANKENSHIP
- ☐ 2. TODD BURNS
- ☐ 3. JOSE CANSECO
- ☐ 4. JIM CORSI
- ☐ 5. STORM DAVIS
- ☐ 6. DENNIS ECKERSLEY
- ☐ 7. MIKE GALLEGO
- ☐ 8. RON HASSEY
- ☐ 9. DAVE HENDERSON
- ☐ 10. RICKEY HENDERSON
- ☐ 11. RICK HONEYCUTT
- ☐ 12. STAN JAVIER
- ☐ 13. FELIX JOSE
- ☐ 14. CARNEY LANSFORD
- ☐ 15. MARK MCGWIRE
- ☐ 16. MIKE MOORE
- ☐ 17. GENE NELSON
- ☐ 18. DAVE PARKER
- ☐ 19. TONY PHILLIPS
- ☐ 20. TERRY STEINBACH
- ☐ 21. DAVE STEWART
- ☐ 22. WALT WEISS
- ☐ 23. BOB WELCH
- ☐ 24. CURT YOUNG
- ☐ 644. DANN HOWITT (P)
- ☐ 646. SCOTT HEMOND (P)
- ☐ 654. TEAM CHECKLIST (F)

PHILADELPHIA PHILLIES

- ☐ 552. DON CARMAN
- ☐ 553. PAT COMBS
- ☐ 554. DENNIS COOK
- ☐ 555. DARREN DAULTON
- ☐ 556. LENNY DYKSTRA
- ☐ 557. CURT FORD
- ☐ 558. CHARLIE HAYES
- ☐ 559. VON HAYES
- ☐ 560. TOM HERR
- ☐ 561. KEN HOWELL
- ☐ 562. STEVE JELTZ
- ☐ 563. RON JONES
- ☐ 564. RICKY JORDAN
- ☐ 565. JOHN KRUK
- ☐ 566. STEVE LAKE
- ☐ 567. ROGER MCDOWELL
- ☐ 568. TERRY MULHOLLAND
- ☐ 569. DWAYNE MURPHY
- ☐ 570. JEFF PARRETT
- ☐ 571. RANDY READY
- ☐ 572. BRUCE RUFFIN
- ☐ 573. DICKIE THON
- ☐ 650. CHUCK MCELROY (P)
- ☐ 653. JASON GRIMSLEY (P)
- ☐ 659. TEAM CHECKLIST (B)

PITTSBURGH PIRATES

- ☐ 459. JAY BELL
- ☐ 460. RAFAEL BELLIARD
- ☐ 461. BARRY BONDS
- ☐ 462. BOBBY BONILLA
- ☐ 463. SID BREAM
- ☐ 464. BENNY DISTEFANO
- ☐ 465. DOUG DRABEK
- ☐ 466. JIM GOTT
- ☐ 467. BILLY HATCHER
- ☐ 468. NEAL HEATON
- ☐ 469. JEFF KING
- ☐ 470. BOB KIPPER
- ☐ 471. RANDY KRAMER
- ☐ 472. BILL LANDRUM
- ☐ 473. MIKE LAVALLIERE
- ☐ 474. JOSE LIND
- ☐ 475. JUNIOR ORTIZ
- ☐ 476. GARY REDUS
- ☐ 477. RICK REED
- ☐ 478. R.J. REYNOLDS
- ☐ 479. JEFF ROBINSON
- ☐ 480. JOHN SMILEY
- ☐ 481. ANDY VAN SLYKE
- ☐ 482. BOB WALK
- ☐ 650. MOISES ALOU(P)
- ☐ 658. TEAM CHECKLIST(B)

ST. LOUIS CARDINALS

- ☐ 242. TOM BRUNANSKY
- ☐ 243. CRIS CARPENTER
- ☐ 244. ALEX COLE
- ☐ 245. VINCE COLEMAN
- ☐ 246. JOHN COSTELLO
- ☐ 247. KEN DAYLEY
- ☐ 248. JOSE DELEON
- ☐ 249. FRANK DIPINO
- ☐ 250. PEDRO GUERRERO
- ☐ 251. KEN HILL
- ☐ 252. JOE MAGRANE
- ☐ 253. WILLIE MCGEE
- ☐ 254. JOHN MORRIS
- ☐ 255. JOSE OQUENDO
- ☐ 256. TONY PENA
- ☐ 257. TERRY PENDLETON
- ☐ 258. TED POWER
- ☐ 259. DAN QUISENBERRY
- ☐ 260. OZZIE SMITH
- ☐ 261. SCOTT TERRY
- ☐ 262. MILT THOMPSON
- ☐ 263. DENNY WALLING
- ☐ 264. TODD WORRELL
- ☐ 265. TODD ZEILE
- ☐ 652. MATT KINZER(P)
- ☐ 656. TEAM CHECKLIST(B)

SAN DIEGO PADRES

- ☐ 149. ROBERTO ALOMAR
- ☐ 150. SANDY ALOMAR, JR.
- ☐ 151. ANDY BENES
- ☐ 152. JACK CLARK
- ☐ 153. PAT CLEMENTS
- ☐ 154. JOEY CORA
- ☐ 155. MARK DAVIS
- ☐ 156. MARK GRANT
- ☐ 157. TONY GWYNN
- ☐ 158. GREG HARRIS
- ☐ 159. BRUCE HURST
- ☐ 160. DARRIN JACKSON
- ☐ 161. CHRIS JAMES
- ☐ 162. CARMELO MARTINEZ
- ☐ 163. MIKE PAGLIARULO
- ☐ 164. MARK PARENT
- ☐ 165. DENNIS RASMUSSEN
- ☐ 166. BIP ROBERTS
- ☐ 167. BENITO SANTIAGO
- ☐ 168. CALVIN SCHIRALDI
- ☐ 169. ERIC SHOW
- ☐ 170. GARRY TEMPLETON
- ☐ 171. ED WHITSON
- ☐ 655. TEAM CHECKLIST(B)

SAN FRANCISCO GIANTS

- ☐ 50. STEVE BEDROSIAN
- ☐ 51. MIKE BENJAMIN
- ☐ 52. JEFF BRANTLEY
- ☐ 53. BRETT BUTLER
- ☐ 54. WILL CLARK
- ☐ 55. KELLY DOWNS
- ☐ 56. SCOTT GARRELTS
- ☐ 57. ATLEE HAMMAKER
- ☐ 58. TERRY KENNEDY
- ☐ 59. MIKE LACOSS
- ☐ 60. CRAIG LEFFERTS
- ☐ 61. GREG LITTON
- ☐ 62. CANDY MALDONADO
- ☐ 63. KIRT MANWARING
- ☐ 64. RANDY MCCAMENT
- ☐ 65. KEVIN MITCHELL
- ☐ 66. DONELL NIXON
- ☐ 67. KEN OBERKFELL
- ☐ 68. RICK REUSCHEL
- ☐ 69. ERNEST RILES
- ☐ 70. DON ROBINSON
- ☐ 71. PAT SHERIDAN
- ☐ 72. CHRIS SPEIER
- ☐ 73. ROBBY THOMPSON
- ☐ 74. JOSE URIBE
- ☐ 75. MATT WILLIAMS
- ☐ 643. STU TATE(P)
- ☐ 654. TEAM CHECKLIST(B)

SEATTLE MARINERS

- ☐ 505. SCOTT BANKHEAD
- ☐ 506. SCOTT BRADLEY
- ☐ 507. GREG BRILEY
- ☐ 508. JAY BUHNER
- ☐ 509. DARNELL COLES
- ☐ 510. KEITH COMSTOCK
- ☐ 511. HENRY COTTO
- ☐ 512. ALVIN DAVIS
- ☐ 513. KEN GRIFFEY, JR.
- ☐ 514. ERIK HANSON
- ☐ 515. GENE HARRIS
- ☐ 516. BRIAN HOLMAN
- ☐ 517. MIKE JACKSON
- ☐ 518. RANDY JOHNSON
- ☐ 519. JEFFREY LEONARD
- ☐ 520. EDGAR MARTINEZ
- ☐ 521. DENNIS POWELL
- ☐ 522. JIM PRESLEY
- ☐ 523. JERRY REED
- ☐ 524. HAROLD REYNOLDS
- ☐ 525. MIKE SCHOOLER
- ☐ 526. BILL SWIFT
- ☐ 527. DAVID VALLE
- ☐ 528. OMAR VIZQUEL
- ☐ 659. TEAM CHECKLIST(F)

TEXAS RANGERS

- ☐ 290. HAROLD BAINES
- ☐ 291. KEVIN BROWN
- ☐ 292. STEVE BUECHELE
- ☐ 293. SCOTT COOLBAUGH
- ☐ 294. JACK DAUGHERTY
- ☐ 295. CECIL ESPY
- ☐ 296. JULIO FRANCO
- ☐ 297. JUAN GONZALEZ
- ☐ 298. CECILIO GUANTE
- ☐ 299. DREW HALL
- ☐ 300. CHARLIE HOUGH
- ☐ 301. PETE INCAVIGLIA
- ☐ 302. MIKE JEFFCOAT
- ☐ 303. CHAD KREUTER
- ☐ 304. JEFF KUNKEL
- ☐ 305. RICK LEACH
- ☐ 306. FRED MANRIQUE
- ☐ 307. JAMIE MOYER
- ☐ 308. RAFAEL PALMEIRO
- ☐ 309. GENO PETRALLI
- ☐ 310. KEVIN REIMER
- ☐ 311. KENNY ROGERS
- ☐ 312. JEFF RUSSELL
- ☐ 313. NOLAN RYAN
- ☐ 314. RUBEN SIERRA
- ☐ 315. BOBBY WITT
- ☐ 657. TEAM CHECKLIST(F)

TORONTO BLUE JAYS

- ☐ 76. GEORGE BELL
- ☐ 77. PAT BORDERS
- ☐ 78. JOHN CERUTTI
- ☐ 79. JUNIOR FELIX
- ☐ 80. TONY FERNANDEZ
- ☐ 81. MIKE FLANAGAN
- ☐ 82. MAURO GOZZO
- ☐ 83. KELLY GRUBER
- ☐ 84. TOM HENKE
- ☐ 85. JIMMY KEY
- ☐ 86. MANNY LEE
- ☐ 87. NELSON LIRIANO
- ☐ 88. LEE MAZZILLI
- ☐ 89. FRED MCGRIFF
- ☐ 90. LLOYD MOSEBY
- ☐ 91. RANCE MULLINIKS
- ☐ 92. ALEX SANCHEZ
- ☐ 93. DAVE STIEB
- ☐ 94. TODD STOTTLEMYRE
- ☐ 95. DUANE WARD
- ☐ 96. DAVID WELLS
- ☐ 97. ERNIE WHITT
- ☐ 98. FRANK WILLS
- ☐ 99. MOOKIE WILSON
- ☐ 654. TEAM CHECKLIST(B)

1990 FLEER TRADED (132) 2 1/2 X 3 1/2

ATLANTA BRAVES

- ☐ 1U. STEVE AVERY
- ☐ 2U. FRANCISCO CABRERA
- ☐ 3U. NICK ESASKY
- ☐ 4U. JIM KREMERS
- ☐ 5U. GREG OLSON
- ☐ 6U. JIM PRESLEY

BALTIMORE ORIOLES

- ☐ 65U. CHRIS HOILES
- ☐ 66U. TIM HULETT
- ☐ 67U. DAVE JOHNSON
- ☐ 68U. CURT SCHILLING
- ☐ 69U. DAVID SEGUI

BOSTON RED SOX

- ☐ 70U. TOM BRUNANSKY
- ☐ 71U. GREG HARRIS
- ☐ 72U. DANA KIECKER
- ☐ 73U. TIM NAEHRING
- ☐ 74U. TONY PENA
- ☐ 75U. JEFF REARDON
- ☐ 76U. JERRY REED

CALIFORNIA ANGELS

- ☐ 77U. MARK EICHHORN
- ☐ 78U. MARK LANGSTON
- ☐ 79U. JOHN ORTON
- ☐ 80U. LUIS POLONIA
- ☐ 81U. DAVE WINFIELD
- ☐ 82U. CLIFF YOUNG

1990 Fleer Traded

CHICAGO CUBS

- ☐ 7U. SHAWN BOSKIE
- ☐ 8U. JOE KRAEMER
- ☐ 9U. LUIS SALAZAR
- ☐ 10U. HECTOR VILLANUEVA

CHICAGO WHITE SOX

- ☐ 83U. WAYNE EDWARDS
- ☐ 84U. ALEX FERNANDEZ
- ☐ 85U. CRAIG GREBECK
- ☐ 86U. SCOTT RADINSKY
- ☐ 87U. FRANK THOMAS

CINCINNATI REDS

- ☐ 11U. GLENN BRAGGS
- ☐ 12U. MARIANO DUNCAN
- ☐ 13U. BILLY HATCHER
- ☐ 14U. TIM LAYANA
- ☐ 15U. HAL MORRIS

CLEVELAND INDIANS

- ☐ 88U. BEAU ALLRED
- ☐ 89U. SANDY ALOMAR
- ☐ 90U. CARLOS BAERGA
- ☐ 91U. KEVIN BEARSE
- ☐ 92U. CHRIS JAMES
- ☐ 93U. CANDY MALDONADO
- ☐ 94U. JEFF MANTO

DETROIT TIGERS

- ☐ 95U. CECIL FIELDER
- ☐ 96U. TRAVIS FRYMAN
- ☐ 97U. LLOYD MOSEBY
- ☐ 98U. EDWIN NUNEZ
- ☐ 99U. TONY PHILLIPS
- ☐ 100U. LARRY SHEETS

HOUSTON ASTROS

- ☐ 16U. JAVIER ORTIZ
- ☐ 17U. DAVE ROHDE
- ☐ 18U. ERIC YELDING

KANSAS CITY ROYALS

- ☐ 101U. MARK DAVIS
- ☐ 102U. STORM DAVIS
- ☐ 103U. GERALD PERRY
- ☐ 104U. TERRY SHUMPERT

LOS ANGELES DODGERS

- ☐ 19U. HUBIE BROOKS
- ☐ 20U. KAL DANIELS
- ☐ 21U. DAVE HANSEN
- ☐ 22U. MIKE HARTLEY
- ☐ 23U. STAN JAVIER
- ☐ 24U. JOSE OFFERMAN
- ☐ 25U. JUAN SAMUEL

MILWAUKEE BREWERS

- ☐ 105U. EDGAR DIAZ
- ☐ 106U. DAVE PARKER

MINNESOTA TWINS

- ☐ 107U. TIM DRUMMOND
- ☐ 108U. JUNIOR ORTIZ
- ☐ 109U. PARK PITTMAN
- ☐ 110U. KEVIN TAPANI

MONTREAL EXPOS

- ☐ 26U. DENNIS BOYD
- ☐ 27U. DELINO DESHIELDS
- ☐ 28U. STEVE FREY
- ☐ 29U. MARK GARDNER
- ☐ 30U. CHRIS NABHOLZ
- ☐ 31U. BILL SAMPEN
- ☐ 32U. DAVE SCHMIDT

NEW YORK METS

- ☐ 33U. DARYL BOSTON
- ☐ 34U. CHUCK CARR
- ☐ 35U. JOHN FRANCO
- ☐ 36U. TODD HUNDLEY
- ☐ 37U. JULIO MACHADO
- ☐ 38U. ALEJANDRO PENA
- ☐ 39U. DARREN REED
- ☐ 40U. KELVIN TORVE

NEW YORK YANKEES

- ☐ 111U. OSCAR AZOCAR
- ☐ 112U. JIM LEYRITZ
- ☐ 113U. KEVIN MAAS
- ☐ 114U. ALAN MILLS
- ☐ 115U. MATT NOKES
- ☐ 116U. PASCUAL PEREZ

OAKLAND A'S

- ☐ 117U. OZZIE CANSECO
- ☐ 118U. SCOTT SANDERSON

PHILADELPHIA PHILLIES

- ☐ 41U. DARREL AKERFELDS
- ☐ 42U. JOSE DEJESUS
- ☐ 43U. DANE HOLLINS
- ☐ 44U. CARMELO MARTINEZ
- ☐ 45U. BRAD MOORE
- ☐ 46U. DALE MURPHY

PITTSBURGH PIRATES

- ☐ 47U. WALLY BACKMAN
- ☐ 48U. STAN BELINDA
- ☐ 49U. BOB PATTERSON
- ☐ 50U. TED POWER
- ☐ 51U. DON SLAUGHT

ST. LOUIS CARDINALS

- ☐ 52U. GERONIMO PENA
- ☐ 53U. LEE SMITH
- ☐ 54U. JOHN TUDOR

SAN DIEGO PADRES

- ☐ 55U. JOE CARTER
- ☐ 56U. TOM HOWARD
- ☐ 57U. CRAIG LEFFERTS
- ☐ 58U. RAFAEL VALDEZ

SAN FRANCISCO GIANTS

- ☐ 59U. DAVE ANDERSON
- ☐ 60U. KEVIN BASS
- ☐ 61U. JOHN BURKETT
- ☐ 62U. GARY CARTER
- ☐ 63U. RICK PARKER
- ☐ 64U. TREVOR WILSON

SEATTLE MARINERS

- ☐ 119U. TINO MARTINEZ
- ☐ 120U. JEFF SCHAEFER
- ☐ 121U. MATT YOUNG

TEXAS RANGERS

- ☐ 122U. BRIAN BOHANON
- ☐ 123U. JEFF HUSON
- ☐ 124U. RAMON MANON

TORONTO BLUE JAYS

- ☐ 125U. GARY MIELKE
- ☐ 126U. WILLIE BLAIR
- ☐ 127U. GLENALLEN HILL
- ☐ 128U. JOHN OLERUD
- ☐ 129U. LUIS SOJO
- ☐ 130U. MARK WHITEN

1991 FLEER (720)
2 1/2 X 3 1/2

ATLANTA BRAVES

- ☐ 681. STEVE AVERY
- ☐ 682. MIKE BELL
- ☐ 683. JEFF BLAUSER
- ☐ 684. FRANCISCO CABRERA
- ☐ 685. TONY CASTILLO
- ☐ 686. MARTY CLARY
- ☐ 687. NICK ESASKY
- ☐ 688. RON GANT
- ☐ 689. TOM GLAVINE
- ☐ 690. MARK GRANT
- ☐ 691. TOMMY GREGG
- ☐ 692. DWAYNE HENRY
- ☐ 693. DAVE JUSTICE
- ☐ 694. JIMMY KREMERS
- ☐ 695. CHARLIE LEIBRANDT
- ☐ 696. MARK LEMKE
- ☐ 697. ODDIBE MCDOWELL
- ☐ 698. GREG OLSON
- ☐ 699. JEFF PARRETT
- ☐ 700. JIM PRESLEY
- ☐ 701. VICTOR ROSARIO
- ☐ 702. LONNIE SMITH
- ☐ 703. PETE SMITH
- ☐ 704. JOHN SMOLTZ
- ☐ 705. MIKE STANTON
- ☐ 706. ANDRES THOMAS

☐ 707. JEFF TREADWAY
☐ 708. JIM VATCHER
☐ 720. TEAM CHECKLIST(F)

BALTIMORE ORIOLES

☐ 466. BRADY ANDERSON
☐ 467. JEFF BALLARD
☐ 468. JUAN BELL
☐ 469. MIKE DEVEREAUX
☐ 470. STEVE FINLEY
☐ 471. DAVE GALLAGHER
☐ 472. LEO GOMEZ
☐ 473. RENE GONZALES
☐ 474. PETE HARNISCH
☐ 475. KEVIN HICKEY
☐ 476. CHRIS HOILES
☐ 477. SAM HORN
☐ 478. TIM HULETT
☐ 479. DAVE JOHNSON
☐ 480. RON KITTLE
☐ 481. BEN MCDONALD
☐ 482. BOB MELVIN
☐ 483. BOB MILACKI
☐ 484. RANDY MILLIGAN
☐ 485. JOHN MITCHELL
☐ 486. GREGG OLSON
☐ 487. JOE ORSULAK
☐ 488. JOE PRICE
☐ 489. BILLY RIPKEN
☐ 490. CAL RIPKEN, JR.
☐ 491. CURT SCHILLING
☐ 492. DAVID SEGUI
☐ 493. ANTHONY TELFORD
☐ 494. MICKEY TETTLETON
☐ 495. MARK WILLIAMSON
☐ 496. CRAIG WORTHINGTON
☐ 718. TEAM CHECKLIST(F)

BOSTON RED SOX

☐ 83. LARRY ANDERSEN
☐ 84. MARTY BARRETT
☐ 85. MIKE BODDICKER
☐ 86. WADE BOGGS
☐ 87. TOM BOLTON
☐ 88. TOM BRUNANSKY
☐ 89. ELLIS BURKS
☐ 90. ROGER CLEMENS
☐ 91. SCOTT COOPER
☐ 92. JOHN DOPSON
☐ 93. DWIGHT EVANS
☐ 94. WES GARDNER
☐ 95. JEFF GRAY
☐ 96. MIKE GREENWELL
☐ 97. GREG HARRIS
☐ 98. DARYL IRVINE
☐ 99. DANA KIECKER
☐ 100. RANDY KUTCHER
☐ 101. DENNIS LAMP
☐ 102. MIKE MARSHALL
☐ 103. JOHN MARZANO
☐ 104. ROB MURPHY
☐ 105. TIM NAEHRING
☐ 106. TONY PENA
☐ 107. PHIL PLANTIER
☐ 108. CARLOS QUINTANA
☐ 109. JEFF REARDON
☐ 110. JERRY REED
☐ 111. JODY REED
☐ 112. LUIS RIVERA
☐ 113. KEVIN ROMINE
☐ 714. TEAM CHECKLIST(B)

CALIFORNIA ANGELS

☐ 305. JIM ABBOTT
☐ 306. KENT ANDERSON
☐ 307. DANTE BICHETTE
☐ 308. BERT BLYLEVEN
☐ 309. CHILI DAVIS
☐ 310. BRIAN DOWNING
☐ 311. MARK EICHHORN
☐ 312. MIKE FETTERS
☐ 313. CHUCK FINLEY
☐ 314. WILLIE FRASER
☐ 315. BRYAN HARVEY
☐ 316. DONNIE HILL
☐ 317. WALLY JOYNER
☐ 318. MARK LANGSTON
☐ 319. KIRK MCCASKILL
☐ 320. JOHN ORTON
☐ 321. LANCE PARRISH
☐ 322. LUIS POLONIA
☐ 323. JOHNNY RAY
☐ 324. BOBBY ROSE
☐ 325. DICK SCHOFIELD
☐ 326. RICK SCHU
☐ 327. LEE STEVENS
☐ 328. DEVON WHITE
☐ 329. DAVE WINFIELD
☐ 330. CLIFF YOUNG
☐ 716. TEAM CHECKLIST(B)

CHICAGO CUBS

☐ 413. PAUL ASSENMACHER
☐ 414. DAMON BERRYHILL
☐ 415. MIKE BIELECKI
☐ 416. SHAWN BOSKIE
☐ 417. DAVE CLARK
☐ 418. DOUG DASCENZO
☐ 419. ANDRE DAWSON
☐ 420. SHAWON DUNSTON
☐ 421. JOE GIRARDI
☐ 422. MARK GRACE
☐ 423. MIKE HARKEY
☐ 424. LES LANCASTER
☐ 425. BILL LONG
☐ 426. GREG MADDUX
☐ 427. DERRICK MAY
☐ 428. JEFF PICO
☐ 429. DOMINGO RAMOS
☐ 430. LUIS SALAZAR
☐ 431. RYNE SANDBERG
☐ 432. DWIGHT SMITH
☐ 433. GREG SMITH
☐ 434. RICK SUTCLIFFE
☐ 435. GARY VARSHO
☐ 436. HECTOR VILLANUEVA
☐ 437. JEROME WALTON
☐ 438. CURTIS WILKERSON
☐ 439. MITCH WILLIAMS
☐ 440. STEVE WILSON
☐ 441. MARVELL WYNNE
☐ 717. TEAM CHECKLIST(B)

CHICAGO WHITE SOX

☐ 114. PHIL BRADLEY
☐ 115. IVAN CALDERON
☐ 116. WAYNE EDWARDS
☐ 117. ALEX FERNANDEZ
☐ 118. CARLTON FISK
☐ 119. SCOTT FLETCHER
☐ 120. CRAIG GREBECK
☐ 121. OZZIE GUILLEN
☐ 122. GREG HIBBARD
☐ 123. LANCE JOHNSON
☐ 124. BARRY JONES
☐ 125. RON KARKOVICE
☐ 126. ERIC KING
☐ 127. STEVE LYONS
☐ 128. CARLOS MARTINEZ
☐ 129. JACK MCDOWELL
☐ 130. DONN PALL
☐ 131. DAN PASQUA
☐ 132. KEN PATTERSON
☐ 133. MELIDO PEREZ
☐ 134. ADAM PETERSON
☐ 135. SCOTT RADINSKY
☐ 136. SAMMY SOSA
☐ 137. BOBBY THIGPEN
☐ 138. FRANK THOMAS
☐ 139. ROBIN VENTURA
☐ 715. TEAM CHECKLIST(F)

CINCINNATI REDS

☐ 55. JACK ARMSTRONG
☐ 56. TODD BENZINGER
☐ 57. GLENN BRAGGS
☐ 58. KEITH BROWN
☐ 59. TOM BROWNING
☐ 60. NORM CHARLTON
☐ 61. ERIC DAVIS
☐ 62. ROB DIBBLE
☐ 63. BILL DORAN
☐ 64. MARIANO DUNCAN
☐ 65. CHRIS HAMMOND
☐ 66. BILLY HATCHER
☐ 67. DANNY JACKSON
☐ 68. BARRY LARKIN
☐ 69. TIM LAYANA
☐ 70. TERRY LEE
☐ 71. RICK MAHLER
☐ 72. HAL MORRIS
☐ 73. RANDY MYERS
☐ 74. RON OESTER
☐ 75. JOE OLIVER
☐ 76. PAUL O'NEILL
☐ 77. LUIS QUINONES
☐ 78. JEFF REED
☐ 79. JOSE RIJO
☐ 80. CHRIS SABO
☐ 81. SCOTT SCUDDER
☐ 82. HERM WINNINGHAM
☐ 714. TEAM CHECKLIST(B)

CLEVELAND INDIANS

☐ 358. BEAU ALLRED
☐ 359. SANDY ALOMAR
☐ 360. CARLOS BAERGA
☐ 361. KEVIN BEARSE
☐ 362. TOM BROOKENS
☐ 363. JERRY BROWNE
☐ 364. TOM CANDIOTTI
☐ 365. ALEX COLE
☐ 366. JOHN FARRELL
☐ 367. FELIX FERMIN
☐ 368. KEITH HERNANDEZ
☐ 369. BROOK JACOBY
☐ 370. CHRIS JAMES
☐ 371. DION JAMES
☐ 372. DOUG JONES
☐ 373. CANDY MALDONADO
☐ 374. STEVE OLIN
☐ 375. JESSE OROSCO
☐ 376. RUDY SEANEZ
☐ 377. JOEL SKINNER
☐ 378. CORY SNYDER
☐ 379. GREG SWINDELL
☐ 380. SERGIO VALDEZ
☐ 381. MIKE WALKER
☐ 382. COLBY WARD
☐ 383. TURNER WARD
☐ 384. MITCH WEBSTER
☐ 385. KEVIN WICKANDER
☐ 717. TEAM CHECKLIST(B)

DETROIT TIGERS

☐ 331. DAVE BERGMAN
☐ 332. PHIL CLARK
☐ 333. DARNELL COLES

☐ 334. MILT CUYLER
☐ 335. CECIL FIELDER
☐ 336. TRAVIS FRYMAN
☐ 337. PAUL GIBSON
☐ 338. JERRY DON GLEATON
☐ 339. MIKE HEATH
☐ 340. MIKE HENNEMAN
☐ 341. CHET LEMON
☐ 342. LANCE MCCULLERS
☐ 343. JACK MORRIS
☐ 344. LLOYD MOSEBY
☐ 345. EDWIN NUNEZ
☐ 346. CLAY PARKER
☐ 347. DAN PETRY
☐ 348. TONY PHILLIPS
☐ 349. JEFF ROBINSON
☐ 350. MARK SALAS
☐ 351. MIKE SCHWABE
☐ 352. LARRY SHEETS
☐ 353. JOHN SHELBY
☐ 354. FRANK TANANA
☐ 355. ALAN TRAMMELL
☐ 356. GARY WARD
☐ 357. LOU WHITAKER
☐ 717. TEAM CHECKLIST(F)

HOUSTON ASTROS

☐ 497. JUAN AGOSTO
☐ 498. ERIC ANTHONY
☐ 499. CRAIG BIGGIO
☐ 500. KEN CAMINITI
☐ 501. CASEY CANDAELE
☐ 502. ANDUJAR CEDENO
☐ 503. DANNY DARWIN
☐ 504. MARK DAVIDSON
☐ 505. GLENN DAVIS
☐ 506. JIM DESHAIES
☐ 507. LUIS GONZALEZ
☐ 508. BILL GULLICKSON
☐ 509. XAVIER HERNANDEZ
☐ 510. BRIAN MEYER
☐ 511. KEN OBERKFELL
☐ 512. MARK PORTUGAL
☐ 513. RAFAEL RAMIREZ
☐ 514. KARL RHODES
☐ 515. MIKE SCOTT
☐ 516. MIKE SIMMS
☐ 517. DAVE SMITH
☐ 518. FRANKLIN STUBBS
☐ 519. GLENN WILSON
☐ 520. ERIC YELDING
☐ 521. GERALD YOUNG
☐ 718. TEAM CHECKLIST(B)

KANSAS CITY ROYALS

☐ 549. KEVIN APPIER
☐ 550. LUIS AQUINO
☐ 551. BOB BOONE
☐ 552. GEORGE BRETT
☐ 553. JEFF CONINE
☐ 554. STEVE CRAWFORD
☐ 555. MARK DAVIS
☐ 556. STORM DAVIS
☐ 557. JIM EISENREICH
☐ 558. STEVE FARR
☐ 559. TOM GORDON
☐ 560. MARK GUBICZA
☐ 561. BO JACKSON
☐ 562. MIKE MACFARLANE
☐ 563. BRIAN MCRAE
☐ 564. JEFF MONTGOMERY
☐ 565. BILL PECOTA
☐ 566. GERALD PERRY
☐ 567. BRET SABERHAGEN
☐ 568. JEFF SCHULZ
☐ 569. KEVIN SEITZER
☐ 570. TERRY SHUMPERT
☐ 571. KURT STILLWELL
☐ 572. DANNY TARTABULL
☐ 573. GARY THURMAN
☐ 574. FRANK WHITE
☐ 575. WILLIE WILSON
☐ 719. TEAM CHECKLIST(F)

LOS ANGELES DODGERS

☐ 193. DON AASE
☐ 194. TIM BELCHER
☐ 195. HUBIE BROOKS
☐ 196. DENNIS COOK
☐ 197. TIM CREWS
☐ 198. KAL DANIELS
☐ 199. KIRK GIBSON
☐ 200. JIM GOTT
☐ 201. ALFREDO GRIFFIN
☐ 202. CHRIS GWYNN
☐ 203. DAVE HANSEN
☐ 204. LENNY HARRIS
☐ 205. MIKE HARTLEY
☐ 206. MICKEY HATCHER
☐ 207. CAROLOS HERNANDEZ
☐ 208. OREL HERSHISER
☐ 209. JAY HOWELL
☐ 210. MIKE HUFF
☐ 211. STAN JAVIER
☐ 212. RAMON MARTINEZ
☐ 213. MIKE MORGAN
☐ 214. EDDIE MURRAY
☐ 215. JIM NEIDLINGER
☐ 216. JOSE OFFERMAN
☐ 217. JIM POOLE
☐ 218. JUAN SAMUEL
☐ 219. MIKE SCIOSCIA
☐ 220. RAY SEARAGE
☐ 221. MIKE SHARPERSON
☐ 222. FERNANDO VALENZUELA
☐ 223. JOSE VIZCAINO
☐ 715. TEAM CHECKLIST(B)

MILWAUKEE BREWERS

☐ 576. CHRIS BOSIO
☐ 577. GREG BROCK
☐ 578. GEORGE CANALE
☐ 579. CHUCK CRIM
☐ 580. ROB DEER
☐ 581. EDGAR DIAZ
☐ 582. TOM EDENS
☐ 583. MIKE FELDER
☐ 584. JIM GANTNER
☐ 585. DARRYL HAMILTON
☐ 586. TED HIGUERA
☐ 587. MARK KNUDSON
☐ 588. BILL KRUEGER
☐ 589. TIM MCINTOSH
☐ 590. PAUL MIRABELLA
☐ 591. PAUL MOLITOR
☐ 592. JAIME NAVARRO
☐ 593. DAVE PARKER
☐ 594. DAN PLESAC
☐ 595. RON ROBINSON
☐ 596. GARY SHEFFIELD
☐ 597. BILL SPIERS
☐ 598. B.J. SURHOFF
☐ 599. GREG VAUGHN
☐ 600. RANDY VERES
☐ 601. ROBIN YOUNT
☐ 719. TEAM CHECKLIST(F)

MINNESOTA TWINS

☐ 602. RICK AGUILERA
☐ 603. ALLAN ANDERSON
☐ 604. JUAN BERENGUER
☐ 605. RANDY BUSH
☐ 606. CARMEN CASTILLO
☐ 607. TIM DRUMMOND
☐ 608. SCOTT ERICKSON
☐ 609. GARY GAETTI
☐ 610. GREG GAGNE
☐ 611. DAN GLADDEN
☐ 612. MARK GUTHRIE
☐ 613. BRIAN HARPER
☐ 614. KENT HRBEK
☐ 615. GENE LARKIN
☐ 616. TERRY LEACH
☐ 617. NELSON LIRIANO
☐ 618. SHANE MACK
☐ 619. JOHN MOSES
☐ 620. PEDRO MUNOZ
☐ 621. AL NEWMAN
☐ 622. JUNIOR ORTIZ
☐ 623. KIRBY PUCKETT
☐ 624. ROY SMITH
☐ 625. KEVIN TAPANI
☐ 626. GARY WAYNE
☐ 627. DAVID WEST
☐ 719. TEAM CHECKLIST(B)

MONTREAL EXPOS

☐ 224. MIKE ALDRETE
☐ 225. SCOTT ANDERSON
☐ 226. DENNIS BOYD
☐ 227. TIM BURKE
☐ 228. DELINO DESHIELDS
☐ 229. MIKE FITZGERALD
☐ 230. TOM FOLEY
☐ 231. STEVE FREY
☐ 232. ANDRES GALARRAGA
☐ 233. MARK GARDNER
☐ 234. MARQUIS GRISSOM
☐ 235. KEVIN GROSS
☐ 236. DREW HALL
☐ 237. DAVE MARTINEZ
☐ 238. DENNIS MARTINEZ
☐ 239. DALE MOHORCIC
☐ 240. CHRIS NABHOLZ
☐ 241. OTIS NIXON
☐ 242. JUNIOR NOBOA
☐ 243. SPIKE OWEN
☐ 244. TIM RAINES
☐ 245. MEL ROJAS
☐ 246. SCOTT RUSKIN
☐ 247. BILL SAMPEN
☐ 248. NELSON SANTOVENIA
☐ 249. DAVE SCHMIDT
☐ 250. LARRY WALKER
☐ 251. TIM WALLACH
☐ 716. TEAM CHECKLIST(F)

NEW YORK METS

☐ 140. DARYL BOSTON
☐ 141. CHUCK CARR
☐ 142. MARK CARREON
☐ 143. DAVID CONE
☐ 144. RON DARLING
☐ 145. KEVIN ELSTER
☐ 146. SID FERNANDEZ
☐ 147. JOHN FRANCO
☐ 148. DWIGHT GOODEN
☐ 149. TOM HERR
☐ 150. TODD HUNDLEY
☐ 151. GREGG JEFFERIES
☐ 152. HOWARD JOHNSON
☐ 153. DAVE MAGADAN
☐ 154. KEVIN MCREYNOLDS
☐ 155. KEITH MILLER
☐ 156. BOB OJEDA
☐ 157. TOM O'MALLEY
☐ 158. ALEJANDRO PENA
☐ 159. DARREN REED
☐ 160. MACKEY SASSER
☐ 161. DARRYL STRAWBERRY
☐ 162. TIM TEUFEL
☐ 163. KELVIN TORVE
☐ 164. JULIO VALERA
☐ 165. FRANK VIOLA
☐ 166. WALLY WHITEHURST
☐ 715. TEAM CHECKLIST(F)

NEW YORK YANKEES

☐ 655. OSCAR AZOCAR
☐ 656. STEVE BALBONI
☐ 657. JESSE BARFIELD
☐ 658. GREG CADARET

- ☐ 659. CHUCK CARY
- ☐ 660. RICK CERONE
- ☐ 661. DAVID EILAND
- ☐ 662. ALVARO ESPINOZA
- ☐ 663. BOB GEREN
- ☐ 664. LEE GUETTERMAN
- ☐ 665. MEL HALL
- ☐ 666. ANDY HAWKINS
- ☐ 667. JIMMY JONES
- ☐ 668. ROBERTO KELLY
- ☐ 669. DAVE LAPOINT
- ☐ 670. TIM LEARY
- ☐ 671. JIM LEYRITZ
- ☐ 672. KEVIN MAAS
- ☐ 673. DON MATTINGLY
- ☐ 674. MATT NOKES
- ☐ 675. PASCUAL PEREZ
- ☐ 676. ERIC PLUNK
- ☐ 677. DAVE RIGHETTI
- ☐ 678. JEFF ROBINSON
- ☐ 679. STEVE SAX
- ☐ 680. MIKE WITT
- ☐ 720. TEAM CHECKLIST(F)

OAKLAND A'S

- ☐ 1. TROY AFENIR
- ☐ 2. HAROLD BAINES
- ☐ 3. LANCE BLANKENSHIP
- ☐ 4. TODD BURNS
- ☐ 5. JOSE CANSECO
- ☐ 6. DENNIS ECKERSLEY
- ☐ 7. MIKE GALLEGO
- ☐ 8. RON HASSEY
- ☐ 9. DAVE HENDERSON
- ☐ 10. RICKEY HENDERSON
- ☐ 11. RICK HONEYCUTT
- ☐ 12. DOUG JENNINGS
- ☐ 13. JOE KLINK
- ☐ 14. CARNEY LANSFORD
- ☐ 15. DARREN LEWIS
- ☐ 16. WILLIE MCGEE
- ☐ 17. MARK MCGWIRE
- ☐ 18. MIKE MOORE
- ☐ 19. GENE NELSON
- ☐ 20. DAVE OTTO
- ☐ 21. JAMIE QUIRK
- ☐ 22. WILLIE RANDOLPH
- ☐ 23. SCOTT SANDERSON
- ☐ 24. TERRY STEINBACH
- ☐ 25. DAVE STEWART
- ☐ 26. WALT WEISS
- ☐ 27. BOB WELCH
- ☐ 28. CURT YOUNG
- ☐ 714. TEAM CHECKLIST(F)

PHILADELPHIA PHILLIES

- ☐ 386. DARREL AKERFELDS
- ☐ 387. JOE BOEVER
- ☐ 388. ROD BOOKER
- ☐ 389. SIL CAMPUSANO
- ☐ 390. DON CARMAN
- ☐ 391. WES CHAMBERLAIN
- ☐ 392. PAT COMBS
- ☐ 393. DARREN DAULTON
- ☐ 394. JOSE DEJESUS
- ☐ 395. LEN DYKSTRA
- ☐ 396. JASON GRIMSLEY
- ☐ 397. CHARLIE HAYES
- ☐ 398. VON HAYES
- ☐ 399. DAVID HOLLINS
- ☐ 400. KEN HOWELL
- ☐ 401. RICKY JORDAN
- ☐ 402. JOHN KRUK
- ☐ 403. STEVE LAKE
- ☐ 404. CHUCK MALONE
- ☐ 405. ROGER MCDOWELL
- ☐ 406. CHUCK MCELROY
- ☐ 407. MICKEY MORANDINI
- ☐ 408. TERRY MULHOLLAND
- ☐ 409. DALE MURPHY
- ☐ 410. RANDY READY
- ☐ 411. BRUCE RUFFIN
- ☐ 412. DICKIE THON
- ☐ 717. TEAM CHECKLIST(B)

PITTSBURGH PIRATES

- ☐ 29. WALLY BACKMAN
- ☐ 30. STAN BELINDA
- ☐ 31. JAY BELL
- ☐ 32. RAFAEL BELLIARD
- ☐ 33. BARRY BONDS
- ☐ 34. BOBBY BONILLA
- ☐ 35. SID BREAM
- ☐ 36. DOUG DRABEK
- ☐ 37. CARLOS GARCIA
- ☐ 38. NEAL HEATON
- ☐ 39. JEFF KING
- ☐ 40. BOB KIPPER
- ☐ 41. BILL LANDRUM
- ☐ 42. MIKE LAVALLIERE
- ☐ 43. JOSE LIND
- ☐ 44. CARMELO MARTINEZ
- ☐ 45. BOB PATTERSON
- ☐ 46. TED POWER
- ☐ 47. GARY REDUS
- ☐ 48. R.J. REYNOLDS
- ☐ 49. DON SLAUGHT
- ☐ 50. JOHN SMILEY
- ☐ 51. ZANE SMITH
- ☐ 52. RANDY TOMLIN
- ☐ 53. ANDY VAN SLYKE
- ☐ 54. BOB WALK
- ☐ 714. TEAM CHECKLIST(F)

ST. LOUIS CARDINALS

- ☐ 628. CRIS CARPENTER
- ☐ 629. VINCE COLEMAN
- ☐ 630. KEN DAYLEY
- ☐ 631. JOSE DELEON
- ☐ 632. FRANK DIPINO
- ☐ 633. BERNARD GILKEY
- ☐ 634. PEDRO GUERRERO
- ☐ 635. KEN HILL
- ☐ 636. FELIX JOSE
- ☐ 637. RAY LANKFORD
- ☐ 638. JOE MAGRANE
- ☐ 639. TOM NIEDENFUER
- ☐ 640. JOSE OQUENDO
- ☐ 641. TOM PAGNOZZI
- ☐ 642. TERRY PENDLETON
- ☐ 643. MIKE PEREZ
- ☐ 644. BRYN SMITH
- ☐ 645. LEE SMITH
- ☐ 646. OZZIE SMITH
- ☐ 647. SCOTT TERRY
- ☐ 648. BOB TEWKSBURY
- ☐ 649. MILT THOMPSON
- ☐ 650. JOHN TUDOR
- ☐ 651. DENNY WALLING
- ☐ 652. CRAIG WILSON
- ☐ 653. TODD WORRELL
- ☐ 654. TODD ZEILE
- ☐ 719. TEAM CHECKLIST(B)

SAN DIEGO PADRES

- ☐ 522. SHAWN ABNER
- ☐ 523. ROBERTO ALOMAR
- ☐ 524. ANDY BENES
- ☐ 525. JOE CARTER
- ☐ 526. JACK CLARK
- ☐ 527. JOEY CORA
- ☐ 528. PAUL FARIES
- ☐ 529. TONY GWYNN
- ☐ 530. ATLEE HAMMAKER
- ☐ 531. GREG HARRIS
- ☐ 532. THOMAS HOWARD
- ☐ 533. BRUCE HURST
- ☐ 534. CRAIG LEFFERTS
- ☐ 535. DEREK LILLIQUIST
- ☐ 536. FRED LYNN
- ☐ 537. MIKE PAGLIARULO
- ☐ 538. MARK PARENT
- ☐ 539. DENNIS RASMUSSEN
- ☐ 540. BIP ROBERTS
- ☐ 541. RICHARD RODRIGUEZ
- ☐ 542. BENITO SANTIAGO
- ☐ 543. CALVIN SCHIRALDI
- ☐ 544. ERIC SHOW
- ☐ 545. PHIL STEPHENSON
- ☐ 546. GARRY TEMPLETON
- ☐ 547. ED WHITSON
- ☐ 548. EDDIE WILLIAMS
- ☐ 718. TEAM CHECKLIST(B)

SAN FRANCISCO GIANTS

- ☐ 252. DAVE ANDERSON
- ☐ 253. KEVIN BASS
- ☐ 254. STEVE BEDROSIAN
- ☐ 255. JEFF BRANTLEY
- ☐ 256. JOHN BURKETT
- ☐ 257. BRETT BUTLER
- ☐ 258. GARY CARTER
- ☐ 259. WILL CLARK
- ☐ 260. STEVE DECKER
- ☐ 261. KELLY DOWNS
- ☐ 262. SCOTT GARRELTS
- ☐ 263. TERRY KENNEDY
- ☐ 264. MIKE LACOSS
- ☐ 265. MARK LEONARD
- ☐ 266. GREG LITTON
- ☐ 267. KEVIN MITCHELL
- ☐ 268. RANDY O'NEAL
- ☐ 269. RICK PARKER
- ☐ 270. RICK REUSCHEL
- ☐ 271. ERNEST RILES
- ☐ 272. DON ROBINSON
- ☐ 273. ROBBY THOMPSON
- ☐ 274. MARK THURMOND
- ☐ 275. JOSE URIBE
- ☐ 276. MATT WILLIAMS
- ☐ 277. TREVOR WILSON
- ☐ 716. TEAM CHECKLIST(F)

SEATTLE MARINERS

- ☐ 442. SCOTT BANKHEAD
- ☐ 443. SCOTT BRADLEY
- ☐ 444. GREG BRILEY
- ☐ 445. MIKE BRUMLEY
- ☐ 446. JAY BUHNER
- ☐ 447. DAVE BURBA
- ☐ 448. HENRY COTTO
- ☐ 449. ALVIN DAVIS
- ☐ 450. KEN GRIFFEY, JR.
- ☐ 451. ERIK HANSON
- ☐ 452. GENE HARRIS
- ☐ 453. BRIAN HOLMAN
- ☐ 454. MIKE JACKSON
- ☐ 455. RANDY JOHNSON
- ☐ 456. JEFFREY LEONARD
- ☐ 457. EDGAR MARTINEZ
- ☐ 458. TINO MARTINEZ
- ☐ 459. PETE O'BRIEN
- ☐ 460. HAROLD REYNOLDS
- ☐ 461. MIKE SCHOOLER
- ☐ 462. BILL SWIFT
- ☐ 463. DAVE VALLE
- ☐ 464. OMAR VIZQUEL
- ☐ 465. MATT YOUNG
- ☐ 718. TEAM CHECKLIST(F)

TEXAS RANGERS

- ☐ 278. GERALD ALEXANDER
- ☐ 279. BRAD ARNSBERG
- ☐ 280. KEVIN BELCHER
- ☐ 281. JOE BITKER
- ☐ 282. KEVIN BROWN
- ☐ 283. STEVE BUECHELE
- ☐ 284. JACK DAUGHERTY
- ☐ 285. JULIO FRANCO
- ☐ 286. JUAN GONZALEZ
- ☐ 287. BILL HASELMAN
- ☐ 288. CHARLIE HOUGH
- ☐ 289. JEFF HUSON
- ☐ 290. PETE INCAVIGLIA
- ☐ 291. MIKE JEFFCOAT
- ☐ 292. JEFF KUNKEL
- ☐ 293. GARY MIELKE
- ☐ 294. JAMIE MOYER
- ☐ 295. RAFAEL PALMEIRO
- ☐ 296. GENO PETRALLI
- ☐ 297. GARY PETTIS
- ☐ 298. KEVIN REIMER
- ☐ 299. KENNY ROGERS
- ☐ 300. JEFF RUSSELL
- ☐ 301. JOHN RUSSELL
- ☐ 302. NOLAN RYAN
- ☐ 303. RUBEN SIERRA
- ☐ 304. BOBBY WITT
- ☐ 716. TEAM CHECKLIST(B)

TORONTO BLUE JAYS

- ☐ 167. JIM ACKER
- ☐ 168. DEREK BELL
- ☐ 169. GEORGE BELL

☐ 170. WILLIE BLAIR
☐ 171. PAT BORDERS
☐ 172. JOHN CERUTTI
☐ 173. JUNIOR FELIX
☐ 174. TONY FERNANDEZ
☐ 175. KELLY GRUBER
☐ 176. TOM HENKE
☐ 177. GLENALLEN HILL
☐ 178. JIMMY KEY
☐ 179. MANNY LEE
☐ 180. FRED MCGRIFF
☐ 181. RANCE MULLINIKS
☐ 182. GREG MYERS
☐ 183. JOHN OLERUD
☐ 184. LUIS SOJO
☐ 185. DAVE STIEB
☐ 186. TODD STOTTLEMYRE
☐ 187. DUANE WARD
☐ 188. DAVE WELLS
☐ 189. MARK WHITEN
☐ 190. KEN WILLIAMS
☐ 191. FRANK WILLS
☐ 192. MOOKIE WILSON
☐ 715. TEAM CHECKLIST(B)

1991 FLEER TRADED (132) 2 1/2 X 3 1/2

ATLANTA BRAVES

☐ 70U. RAFAEL BELLIARD
☐ 71U. JUAN BERENGUER
☐ 72U. SID BREAM
☐ 73U. MARVIN FREEMAN
☐ 74U. KENT MERCKER
☐ 75U. OTIS NIXON
☐ 76U. TERRY PENDLETON

BALTIMORE ORIOLES

☐ 1U. GLENN DAVIS
☐ 2U. DWIGHT EVANS
☐ 3U. JOSE MESA

BOSTON RED SOX

☐ 4U. JACK CLARK
☐ 5U. DANNY DARWIN
☐ 6U. STEVE LYONS
☐ 7U. MO VAUGHN

CALIFORNIA ANGELS

☐ 8U. FLOYD BANNISTER
☐ 9U. GARY GAETTI
☐ 10U. DAVE PARKER

CHICAGO CUBS

☐ 77U. GEORGE BELL
☐ 78U. DANNY JACKSON
☐ 79U. CHUCK MCELROY
☐ 80U. GARY SCOTT
☐ 81U. HEATHCLIFF SLOCUMB
☐ 82U. DAVE SMITH
☐ 83U. RICK WILKINS

CHICAGO WHITE SOX

☐ 11U. JOEY CORA
☐ 12U. CHARLIE HOUGH
☐ 13U. MATT MERULLO
☐ 14U. WARREN NEWSON
☐ 15U. TIM RAINES

CINCINNATI REDS

☐ 84U. FREDDIE BENAVIDES
☐ 85U. TED POWER
☐ 86U. MO SANFORD

CLEVELAND INDIANS

☐ 16U. ALBERT BELLE
☐ 17U. GLENALLEN HILL
☐ 18U. SHAWN HILLEGAS
☐ 19U. MARK LEWIS
☐ 20U. CHARLES NAGY
☐ 21U. MARK WHITEN

DETROIT TIGERS

☐ 22U. JOHN CERUTTI
☐ 23U. ROB DEER
☐ 24U. MICKEY TETTLETON

HOUSTON ASTROS

☐ 87U. JEFF BAGWELL
☐ 88U. STEVE FINLEY
☐ 89U. PETE HARNISCH
☐ 90U. DARRYL KILE

KANSAS CITY ROYALS

☐ 25U. WARREN CROMARTIE
☐ 26U. KIRK GIBSON
☐ 27U. DAVID HOWARD
☐ 28U. BRENT MAYNE

LOS ANGELES DODGERS

☐ 91U. BRETT BUTLER
☐ 92U. JOHN CANDELARIA
☐ 93U. GARY CARTER
☐ 94U. KEVIN GROSS
☐ 95U. BOB OJEDA
☐ 96U. DARRYL STRAWBERRY

MILWAUKEE BREWERS

☐ 29U. DANTE BICHETTE
☐ 30U. MARK LEE
☐ 31U. JULIO MACHADO
☐ 32U. EDWIN NUNEZ
☐ 33U. WILLIE RANDOLPH
☐ 34U. FRANKLIN STUBBS
☐ 35U. BILL WEGMAN

MINNESOTA TWINS

☐ 36U. CHILI DAVIS
☐ 37U. CHUCK KNOBLAUCH
☐ 38U. SCOTT LEIUS
☐ 39U. JACK MORRIS
☐ 40U. MIKE PAGLIARULO
☐ 41U. LENNY WEBSTER

MONTREAL EXPOS

☐ 97U. IVAN CALDERON
☐ 98U. RON HASSEY
☐ 99U. GILBERTO REYES

NEW YORK METS

☐ 100U. HUBIE BROOKS
☐ 101U. RICK CERONE
☐ 102U. VINCE COLEMAN
☐ 103U. JEFF INNIS
☐ 104U. PETE SCHOUREK

NEW YORK YANKEES

☐ 42U. JOHN HABYAN
☐ 43U. STEVE HOWE
☐ 44U. JEFF JOHNSON
☐ 45U. SCOTT KAMIENIECKI
☐ 46U. PAT KELLY
☐ 47U. HENSLEY MEULENS
☐ 48U. WADE TAYLOR
☐ 49U. BERNIE WILLIAMS

OAKLAND A'S

☐ 50U. KIRK DRESSENDORFER
☐ 51U. ERNEST RILES

PHILADELPHIA PHILLIES

☐ 105U. ANDY ASHBY
☐ 106U. WALLY BACKMAN
☐ 107U. DARRIN FLETCHER
☐ 108U. TOMMY GREENE
☐ 109U. JOHN MORRIS
☐ 110U. MITCH WILLIAMS

PITTSBURGH PIRATES

☐ 111U. LLOYD MCCLENDON
☐ 112U. ORLANDO MERCED
☐ 113U. VICENTE PALACIOS
☐ 114U. GARY VARSHO
☐ 115U. JOHN WEHNER

ST. LOUIS CARDINALS

☐ 116U. REX HUDLER
☐ 117U. TIM JONES
☐ 118U. GERONIMO PENA
☐ 119U. GERALD PERRY

SAN DEIGO PADRES

☐ 120U. LARRY ANDERSEN
☐ 121U. JERALD CLARK
☐ 122U. SCOTT COOLBAUGH
☐ 123U. TONY FERNANDEZ
☐ 124U. DARRIN JACKSON
☐ 125U. FRED MCGRIFF
☐ 126U. JOSE MOTA

- ☐ 127U. TIM TEUFEL

SAN FRANCISCO GIANTS

- ☐ 128U. BUD BLACK
- ☐ 129U. MIKE FELDER
- ☐ 130U. WILLIE MCGEE
- ☐ 131U. DAVE RIGHETTI

SEATTLE MARINERS

- ☐ 52U. RICH DELUCIA
- ☐ 53U. TRACY JONES
- ☐ 54U. BILL KRUEGER
- ☐ 55U. ALONZO POWELL
- ☐ 56U. JEFF SCHAEFER
- ☐ 57U. RUSS SWAN

TEXAS RANGERS

- ☐ 58U. JOHN BARFIELD
- ☐ 59U. RICH GOSSAGE
- ☐ 60U. JOSE GUZMAN
- ☐ 61U. DEAN PALMER
- ☐ 62U. IVAN RODRIGUEZ

TORONTO BLUE JAYS

- ☐ 63U. ROBERTO ALOMAR
- ☐ 64U. TOM CANDIOTTI
- ☐ 65U. JOE CARTER
- ☐ 66U. ED SPRAGUE
- ☐ 67U. PAT TABLER
- ☐ 68U. MIKE TIMLIN
- ☐ 69U. DEVON WHITE

1992 FLEER (720)
2 1/2 X 3 1/2

ATLANTA BRAVES

- ☐ 349. STEVE AVERY
- ☐ 350. MIKE BELL
- ☐ 351. RAFAEL BELLIARD
- ☐ 352. JUAN BERENGUER
- ☐ 353. JEFF BLAUSER
- ☐ 354. SID BREAM
- ☐ 355. FRANCISCO CABRERA
- ☐ 356. MARVIN FREEMAN
- ☐ 357. RON GANT
- ☐ 358. TOM GLAVINE
- ☐ 359. BRIAN HUNTER
- ☐ 360. DAVE JUSTICE
- ☐ 361. CHARLIE LEIBRANDT
- ☐ 362. MARK LEMKE
- ☐ 363. KENT MERCKER
- ☐ 364. KEITH MITCHELL
- ☐ 365. GREG OLSON
- ☐ 366. TERRY PENDLETON
- ☐ 367. ARMANDO REYNOSO
- ☐ 368. DEION SANDERS
- ☐ 369. LONNIE SMITH
- ☐ 370. PETE SMITH
- ☐ 371. JOHN SMOLTZ
- ☐ 372. MIKE STANTON
- ☐ 373. JEFF TREADWAY
- ☐ 374. MARK WOHLERS
- ☐ 666. VINNY CASTILLA
- ☐ 676. RICO ROSSY
- ☐ 717. TEAM CHECKLIST(B)

BALTIMORE ORIOLES

- ☐ 1. BRADY ANDERSON
- ☐ 2. JOSE BAUTISTA
- ☐ 3. JUAN BELL
- ☐ 4. GLENN DAVIS
- ☐ 5. MIKE DEVEREAUX
- ☐ 6. DWIGHT EVANS
- ☐ 7. MIKE FLANAGAN
- ☐ 8. LEO GOMEZ
- ☐ 9. CHRIS HOILES
- ☐ 10. SAM HORN
- ☐ 11. TIM HULETT
- ☐ 12. DAVE JOHNSON
- ☐ 13. CHITO MARTINEZ
- ☐ 14. BEN MCDONALD
- ☐ 15. BOB MELVIN
- ☐ 16. LUIS MERCEDES
- ☐ 17. JOSE MESA
- ☐ 18. BOB MILACKI
- ☐ 19. RANDY MILLIGAN
- ☐ 20. MIKE MUSSINA
- ☐ 21. GREGG OLSON
- ☐ 22. JOE ORSULAK
- ☐ 23. JIM POOLE
- ☐ 24. ARTHUR RHODES
- ☐ 25. BILLY RIPKEN
- ☐ 26. CAL RIPKEN, JR.
- ☐ 27. DAVID SEGUI
- ☐ 28. ROY SMITH
- ☐ 29. ANTHONY TELFORD
- ☐ 30. MARK WILLIAMSON
- ☐ 31. CRAIG WORTHINGTON
- ☐ 663. MIKE LINSKEY
- ☐ 714. TEAM CHECKLIST(F)

BOSTON RED SOX

- ☐ 32. WADE BOGGS
- ☐ 33. TOM BOLTON
- ☐ 34. TOM BRUNANSKY
- ☐ 35. ELLIS BURKS
- ☐ 36. JACK CLARK
- ☐ 37. ROGER CLEMENS
- ☐ 38. DANNY DARWIN
- ☐ 39. MIKE GREENWELL
- ☐ 40. JOE HESKETH
- ☐ 41. DARYL IRVINE
- ☐ 42. DENNIS LAMP
- ☐ 43. TONY PENA
- ☐ 44. PHIL PLANTIER
- ☐ 45. CARLOS QUINTANA
- ☐ 46. JEFF REARDON
- ☐ 47. JODY REED
- ☐ 48. LUIS RIVERA
- ☐ 49. MO VAUGHN
- ☐ 714. TEAM CHECKLIST(F)

CALIFORNIA ANGELS

- ☐ 50. JIM ABBOTT
- ☐ 51. KYLE ABBOTT
- ☐ 52. RUBEN AMARO, JR.
- ☐ 53. SCOTT BAILES
- ☐ 54. CHRIS BEASLEY
- ☐ 55. MARK EICHHORN
- ☐ 56. MIKE FETTERS
- ☐ 57. CHUCK FINLEY
- ☐ 58. GARY GAETTI
- ☐ 59. DAVE GALLAGHER
- ☐ 60. DONNIE HILL
- ☐ 61. BRYAN HARVEY
- ☐ 62. WALLY JOYNER
- ☐ 63. MARK LANGSTON
- ☐ 64. KIRK MCCASKILL
- ☐ 65. JOHN ORTON
- ☐ 66. LANCE PARRISH
- ☐ 67. LUIS POLONIA
- ☐ 68. BOBBY ROSE
- ☐ 69. DICK SCHOFIELD
- ☐ 70. LUIS SOJO
- ☐ 71. LEE STEVENS
- ☐ 72. DAVE WINFIELD
- ☐ 73. CLIFF YOUNG
- ☐ 656. CHRIS CRON
- ☐ 664. GARY DISARCINA
- ☐ 714. TEAM CHECKLIST(B)

CHICAGO CUBS

- ☐ 375. PAUL ASSENMACHER
- ☐ 376. GEORGE BELL
- ☐ 377. SHAWN BOSKIE
- ☐ 378. FRANK CASTILLO
- ☐ 379. ANDRE DAWSON
- ☐ 380. SHAWON DUNSTON
- ☐ 381. MARK GRACE
- ☐ 382. MIKE HARKEY
- ☐ 383. DANNY JACKSON
- ☐ 384. LES LANCASTER
- ☐ 385. CEDRIC LANDRUM
- ☐ 386. GREG MADDUX
- ☐ 387. DERRICK MAY
- ☐ 388. CHUCK MCELROY
- ☐ 389. RYNE SANDBERG
- ☐ 390. HEATHCLIFF SLOCUMB
- ☐ 391. DAVE SMITH
- ☐ 392. DWIGHT SMITH
- ☐ 393. RICK SUTCLIFFE
- ☐ 394. HECTOR VILLANUEVA
- ☐ 395. CHICO WALKER
- ☐ 396. JEROME WALTON
- ☐ 397. RICK WILKINS
- ☐ 717. TEAM CHECKLIST(B)

CHICAGO WHITE SOX

- ☐ 74. WILSON ALVAREZ
- ☐ 75. ESTEBAN BELTRE
- ☐ 76. JOEY CORA
- ☐ 77. BRIAN DRAHMAN
- ☐ 78. ALEX FERNANDEZ
- ☐ 79. CARLTON FISK
- ☐ 80. SCOTT FLETCHER
- ☐ 81. CRAIG GREBECK
- ☐ 82. OZZIE GUILLEN
- ☐ 83. GREG HIBBARD
- ☐ 84. CHARLIE HOUGH
- ☐ 85. MIKE HUFF
- ☐ 86. BO JACKSON
- ☐ 87. LANCE JOHNSON
- ☐ 88. RON KARKOVICE
- ☐ 89. JACK MCDOWELL
- ☐ 90. MATT MERULLO
- ☐ 91. WARREN NEWSON
- ☐ 92. DONN PALL
- ☐ 93. DAN PASQUA
- ☐ 94. KEN PATTERSON
- ☐ 95. MELIDO PEREZ
- ☐ 96. SCOTT RADINSKY
- ☐ 97. TIM RAINES
- ☐ 98. SAMMY SOSA
- ☐ 99. BOBBY THIGPEN
- ☐ 100. FRANK THOMAS
- ☐ 101. ROBIN VENTURA
- ☐ 677. ROBERTO HERNANDEZ
- ☐ 714. TEAM CHECKLIST(B)

CINCINNATI REDS

- ☐ 398. JACK ARMSTRONG
- ☐ 399. FREDDIE BENAVIDES
- ☐ 400. GLENN BRAGGS
- ☐ 401. TOM BROWNING
- ☐ 402. NORM CHARLTON
- ☐ 403. ERIC DAVIS
- ☐ 404. ROB DIBBLE
- ☐ 405. BILL DORAN
- ☐ 406. MARIANO DUNCAN
- ☐ 407. KIP GROSS
- ☐ 408. CHRIS HAMMOND
- ☐ 409. BILLY HATCHER
- ☐ 410. CHRIS JONES
- ☐ 411. BARRY LARKIN
- ☐ 412. HAL MORRIS
- ☐ 413. RANDY MYERS
- ☐ 414. JOE OLIVER
- ☐ 415. PAUL O'NEILL
- ☐ 416. TED POWER
- ☐ 417. LUIS QUINONES
- ☐ 418. JEFF REED
- ☐ 419. JOSE RIJO
- ☐ 420. CHRIS SABO
- ☐ 421. REGGIE SANDERS
- ☐ 422. SCOTT SCUDDER
- ☐ 423. GLENN SUTKO
- ☐ 718. TEAM CHECKLIST(F)

CLEVELAND INDIANS

☐ 102. MIKE ALDRETE
☐ 103. SANDY ALOMAR, JR.
☐ 104. CARLOS BAERGA
☐ 105. ALBERT BELLE
☐ 106. WILLIE BLAIR
☐ 107. JERRY BROWNE
☐ 108. ALEX COLE
☐ 109. FELIX FERMIN
☐ 110. GLENALLEN HILL
☐ 111. SHAWN HILLEGAS
☐ 112. CHRIS JAMES
☐ 113. REGGIE JEFFERSON
☐ 114. DOUG JONES
☐ 115. ERIC KING
☐ 116. MARK LEWIS
☐ 117. CARLOS MARTINEZ
☐ 118. CHARLES NAGY
☐ 119. ROD NICHOLS
☐ 120. STEVE OLIN
☐ 121. JESSE OROSCO
☐ 122. RUDY SEANEZ
☐ 123. JOEL SKINNER
☐ 124. GREG SWINDELL
☐ 125. JIM THOME
☐ 126. MARK WHITEN
☐ 670. WAYNE KIRBY
☐ 715. TEAM CHECKLIST(F)

DETROIT TIGERS

☐ 127. SCOTT ALDRED
☐ 128. ANDY ALLANSON
☐ 129. JOHN CERUTTI
☐ 130. MILT CUYLER
☐ 131. MIKE DALTON
☐ 132. ROB DEER
☐ 133. CECIL FIELDER
☐ 134. TRAVIS FRYMAN
☐ 135. DAN GAKELER
☐ 136. PAUL GIBSON
☐ 137. BILL GULLICKSON
☐ 138. MIKE HENNEMAN
☐ 139. PETE INCAVIGLIA
☐ 140. MARK LEITER
☐ 141. SCOTT LIVINGSTONE
☐ 142. LLOYD MOSEBY
☐ 143. TONY PHILLIPS
☐ 144. MARK SALAS
☐ 145. FRANK TANANA
☐ 146. WALT TERRELL
☐ 147. MICKEY TETTLETON
☐ 148. ALAN TRAMMELL
☐ 149. LOU WHITAKER
☐ 715. TEAM CHECKLIST(F)

HOUSTON ASTROS

☐ 424. ERIC ANTHONY
☐ 425. JEFF BAGWELL
☐ 426. CRAIG BIGGIO
☐ 427. KEN CAMINITI
☐ 428. CASEY CANDAELE
☐ 429. MIKE CAPEL
☐ 430. ANDUJAR CEDENO
☐ 431. JIM CORSI
☐ 432. MARK DAVIDSON
☐ 433. STEVE FINLEY
☐ 434. LUIS GONZALEZ
☐ 435. PETE HARNISCH
☐ 436. DWAYNE HENRY
☐ 437. XAVIER HERNANDEZ
☐ 438. JIMMY JONES
☐ 439. DARRYL KILE
☐ 440. ROB MALLICOAT
☐ 441. ANDY MOTA
☐ 442. AL OSUNA
☐ 443. MARK PORTUGAL
☐ 444. SCOTT SERVAIS
☐ 445. MIKE SIMMS
☐ 446. GERALD YOUNG
☐ 655. KENNY LOFTON
☐ 718. TEAM CHECKLIST(F)

KANSAS CITY ROYALS

☐ 150. KEVIN APPIER
☐ 151. LUIS AQUINO
☐ 152. TODD BENZINGER
☐ 153. MIKE BODDICKER
☐ 154. GEORGE BRETT
☐ 155. STORM DAVIS
☐ 156. JIM EISENREICH
☐ 157. KIRK GIBSON
☐ 158. TOM GORDON
☐ 159. MARK GUBICZA
☐ 160. DAVID HOWARD
☐ 161. MIKE MACFARLANE
☐ 162. BRENT MAYNE
☐ 163. BRIAN MCRAE
☐ 164. JEFF MONTGOMERY
☐ 165. BILL PECOTA
☐ 166. HARVEY PULLIAM
☐ 167. BRET SABERHAGEN
☐ 168. KEVIN SEITZER
☐ 169. TERRY SHUMPERT
☐ 170. KURT STILLWELL
☐ 171. DANNY TARTABULL
☐ 172. GARY THURMAN
☐ 672. BOB HAMELIN
☐ 673. JOEL JOHNSTON
☐ 674. TIM SPEHR
☐ 680. SEAN BERRY
☐ 715. TEAM CHECKLIST(B)

LOS ANGELES DODGERS

☐ 447. TIM BELCHER
☐ 448. BRETT BUTLER
☐ 449. JOHN CANDELARIA
☐ 450. GARY CARTER
☐ 451. DENNIS COOK
☐ 452. TIM CREWS
☐ 453. KAL DANIELS
☐ 454. JIM GOTT
☐ 455. ALFREDO GRIFFIN
☐ 456. KEVIN GROSS
☐ 457. CHRIS GWYNN
☐ 458. LENNY HARRIS
☐ 459. OREL HERSHISER
☐ 460. JAY HOWELL
☐ 461. STAN JAVIER
☐ 462. ERIC KARROS
☐ 463. RAMON MARTINEZ
☐ 464. ROGER MCDOWELL
☐ 465. MIKE MORGAN
☐ 466. EDDIE MURRAY
☐ 467. JOSE OFFERMAN
☐ 468. BOB OJEDA
☐ 469. JUAN SAMUEL
☐ 470. MIKE SCIOSCIA
☐ 471. DARRYL STRAWBERRY
☐ 652. TOM GOODWIN
☐ 654. MIKE CHRISTOPHER
☐ 661. HENRY RODRIGUEZ
☐ 718. TEAM CHECKLIST(B)

MILWAUKEE BREWERS

☐ 173. DANTE BICHETTE
☐ 174. KEVIN BROWN
☐ 175. CHUCK CRIM
☐ 176. JIM GANTNER
☐ 177. DARRYL HAMILTON
☐ 178. TED HIGUERA
☐ 179. DARREN HOLMES
☐ 180. MARK LEE
☐ 181. JULIO MACHADO
☐ 182. PAUL MOLITOR
☐ 183. JAIME NAVARRO
☐ 184. EDWIN NUNEZ
☐ 185. DAN PLESAC
☐ 186. WILLIE RANDOLPH
☐ 187. RON ROBINSON
☐ 188. GARY SHEFFIELD
☐ 189. BILL SPIERS
☐ 190. B.J. SURHOFF
☐ 191. DALE SVEUM
☐ 192. GREG VAUGHN
☐ 193. BILL WEGMAN
☐ 194. ROBIN YOUNT
☐ 679. CAL ELDRED
☐ 715. TEAM CHECKLIST(B)

MINNESOTA TWINS

☐ 195. RICK AGUILERA
☐ 196. ALLAN ANDERSON
☐ 197. STEVE BEDROSIAN
☐ 198. RANDY BUSH
☐ 199. LARRY CASIAN
☐ 200. CHILI DAVIS
☐ 201. SCOTT ERICKSON
☐ 202. GREG GAGNE
☐ 203. DAN GLADDEN
☐ 204. BRIAN HARPER
☐ 205. KENT HRBEK
☐ 206. CHUCK KNOBLAUCH
☐ 207. GENE LARKIN
☐ 208. TERRY LEACH
☐ 209. SCOTT LEIUS
☐ 210. SHANE MACK
☐ 211. JACK MORRIS
☐ 212. PEDRO MUNOZ
☐ 213. DENNY NEAGLE
☐ 214. AL NEWMAN
☐ 215. JUNIOR ORTIZ
☐ 216. MIKE PAGLIARULO
☐ 217. KIRBY PUCKETT
☐ 218. PAUL SORRENTO
☐ 219. KEVIN TAPANI
☐ 220. LENNY WEBSTER
☐ 657. WILLIE BANKS
☐ 667. PAUL ABBOTT
☐ 669. JARVIS BROWN
☐ 716. TEAM CHECKLIST(F)

MONTREAL EXPOS

☐ 472. BRET BARBERIE
☐ 473. BRIAN BARNES
☐ 474. ERIC BULLOCK
☐ 475. IVAN CALDERON
☐ 476. DELINO DESHIELDS
☐ 477. JEFF FASSERO
☐ 478. MIKE FITZGERALD
☐ 479. STEVE FREY
☐ 480. ANDRES GALARRAGA
☐ 481. MARK GARDNER
☐ 482. MARQUIS GRISSOM
☐ 483. CHRIS HANEY
☐ 484. BARRY JONES
☐ 485. DAVE MARTINEZ
☐ 486. DENNIS MARTINEZ
☐ 487. CHRIS NABHOLZ
☐ 488. SPIKE OWEN
☐ 489. GILBERTO REYES
☐ 490. MEL ROJAS
☐ 491. SCOTT RUSKIN
☐ 492. BILL SAMPEN
☐ 493. LARRY WALKER
☐ 494. TIM WALLACH
☐ 718. TEAM CHECKLIST(B)

NEW YORK METS

☐ 495. DARYL BOSTON
☐ 496. HUBIE BROOKS
☐ 497. TIM BURKE
☐ 498. MARK CARREON
☐ 499. TONY CASTILLO
☐ 500. VINCE COLEMAN
☐ 501. DAVID CONE
☐ 502. KEVIN ELSTER
☐ 503. SID FERNANDEZ
☐ 504. JOHN FRANCO
☐ 505. DWIGHT GOODEN
☐ 506. TODD HUNDLEY
☐ 507. JEFF INNIS

- ☐ 508. GREGG JEFFERIES
- ☐ 509. HOWARD JOHNSON
- ☐ 510. DAVE MAGADAN
- ☐ 511. TERRY MCDANIEL
- ☐ 512. KEVIN MCREYNOLDS
- ☐ 513. KEITH MILLER
- ☐ 514. CHARLIE O'BRIEN
- ☐ 515. MACKEY SASSER
- ☐ 516. PETE SCHOUREK
- ☐ 517. JULIO VALERA
- ☐ 518. FRANK VIOLA
- ☐ 519. WALLY WHITEHURST
- ☐ 520. ANTHONY YOUNG
- ☐ 653. TERRY BROSS
- ☐ 675. JEFF GARDNER
- ☐ 719. TEAM CHECKLIST(F)

NEW YORK YANKEES

- ☐ 221. JESSE BARFIELD
- ☐ 222. GREG CADARET
- ☐ 223. DAVE EILAND
- ☐ 224. ALVARO ESPINOZA
- ☐ 225. STEVE FARR
- ☐ 226. BOB GEREN
- ☐ 227. LEE GUETTERMAN
- ☐ 228. JOHN HABYAN
- ☐ 229. MEL HALL
- ☐ 230. STEVE HOWE
- ☐ 231. MIKE HUMPHREYS
- ☐ 232. SCOTT KAMIENIECKI
- ☐ 233. PAT KELLY
- ☐ 234. ROBERTO KELLY
- ☐ 235. TIM LEARY
- ☐ 236. KEVIN MAAS
- ☐ 237. DON MATTINGLY
- ☐ 238. HENSLEY MEULENS
- ☐ 239. MATT NOKES
- ☐ 240. PASCUAL PEREZ
- ☐ 241. ERIC PLUNK
- ☐ 242. JOHN RAMOS
- ☐ 243. SCOTT SANDERSON
- ☐ 244. STEVE SAX
- ☐ 245. WADE TAYLOR
- ☐ 246. RANDY VELARDE
- ☐ 247. BERNIE WILLIAMS
- ☐ 716. TEAM CHECKLIST(F)

OAKLAND A'S

- ☐ 248. TROY AFENIR
- ☐ 249. HAROLD BAINES
- ☐ 250. LANCE BLANKENSHIP
- ☐ 251. MIKE BORDICK
- ☐ 252. JOSE CANSECO
- ☐ 253. STEVE CHITREN
- ☐ 254. RON DARLING
- ☐ 255. DENNIS ECKERSLEY
- ☐ 256. MIKE GALLEGO
- ☐ 257. DAVE HENDERSON
- ☐ 258. RICKEY HENDERSON
- ☐ 259. RICK HONEYCUTT
- ☐ 260. BROOK JACOBY
- ☐ 261. CARNEY LANSFORD
- ☐ 262. MARK MCGWIRE
- ☐ 263. MIKE MOORE
- ☐ 264. GENE NELSON
- ☐ 265. JAMIE QUIRK
- ☐ 266. JOE SLUSARSKI
- ☐ 267. TERRY STEINBACH
- ☐ 268. DAVE STEWART
- ☐ 269. TODD VAN POPPEL
- ☐ 270. WALT WEISS
- ☐ 271. BOB WELCH
- ☐ 272. CURT YOUNG
- ☐ 671. SCOTT BROSIUS
- ☐ 716. TEAM CHECKLIST(B)

PHILADELPHIA PHILLIES

- ☐ 521. ANDY ASHBY
- ☐ 522. KIM BATISTE
- ☐ 523. JOE BOEVER
- ☐ 524. WES CHAMBERLAIN
- ☐ 525. PAT COMBS
- ☐ 526. DANNY COX
- ☐ 527. DARREN DAULTON
- ☐ 528. JOSE DEJESUS
- ☐ 529. LENNY DYKSTRA
- ☐ 530. DARRIN FLETCHER
- ☐ 531. TOMMY GREENE
- ☐ 532. JASON GRIMSLEY
- ☐ 533. CHARLIE HAYES
- ☐ 534. VON HAYES
- ☐ 535. DAVE HOLLINS
- ☐ 536. RICKY JORDAN
- ☐ 537. JOHN KRUK
- ☐ 538. JIM LINDEMAN
- ☐ 539. MICKEY MORANDINI
- ☐ 540. TERRY MULHOLLAND
- ☐ 541. DALE MURPHY
- ☐ 542. RANDY READY
- ☐ 543. WALLY RITCHIE
- ☐ 544. BRUCE RUFFIN
- ☐ 545. STEVE SEARCY
- ☐ 546. DICKIE THON
- ☐ 547. MITCH WILLIAMS
- ☐ 662. CLIFF BRANTLEY
- ☐ 719. TEAM CHECKLIST(F)

PITTSBURGH PIRATES

- ☐ 548. STAN BELINDA
- ☐ 549. JAY BELL
- ☐ 550. BARRY BONDS
- ☐ 551. BOBBY BONILLA
- ☐ 552. STEVE BUECHELE
- ☐ 553. DOUG DRABEK
- ☐ 554. NEAL HEATON
- ☐ 555. JEFF KING
- ☐ 556. BOB KIPPER
- ☐ 557. BILL LANDRUM
- ☐ 558. MIKE LAVALLIERE
- ☐ 559. JOSE LIND
- ☐ 560. LLOYD MCCLENDON
- ☐ 561. ORLANDO MERCED
- ☐ 562. BOB PATTERSON
- ☐ 563. JOE REDFIELD
- ☐ 564. GARY REDUS
- ☐ 565. ROSARIO RODRIGUEZ
- ☐ 566. DON SLAUGHT
- ☐ 567. JOHN SMILEY
- ☐ 568. ZANE SMITH
- ☐ 569. RANDY TOMLIN
- ☐ 570. ANDY VAN SLYKE
- ☐ 571. GARY VARSHO
- ☐ 572. BOB WALK
- ☐ 573. JOHN WEHNER
- ☐ 719. TEAM CHECKLIST(B)

ST. LOUIS CARDINALS

- ☐ 574. JUAN AGOSTO
- ☐ 575. CRIS CARPENTER
- ☐ 576. JOSE DELEON
- ☐ 577. RICH GEDMAN
- ☐ 578. BERNARD GILKEY
- ☐ 579. PEDRO GUERRERO
- ☐ 580. KEN HILL
- ☐ 581. REX HUDLER
- ☐ 582. FELIX JOSE
- ☐ 583. RAY LANKFORD
- ☐ 584. OMAR OLIVARES
- ☐ 585. JOSE OQUENDO
- ☐ 586. TOM PAGNOZZI
- ☐ 587. GERONIMO PENA
- ☐ 588. MIKE PEREZ
- ☐ 589. GERALD PERRY
- ☐ 590. BRYN SMITH
- ☐ 591. LEE SMITH
- ☐ 592. OZZIE SMITH
- ☐ 593. SCOTT TERRY
- ☐ 594. BOB TEWKSBURY
- ☐ 595. MILT THOMPSON
- ☐ 596. TODD ZEILE
- ☐ 719. TEAM CHECKLIST(B)

SAN DIEGO PADRES

- ☐ 597. LARRY ANDERSEN
- ☐ 598. OSCAR AZOCAR
- ☐ 599. ANDY BENES
- ☐ 600. RICKY BONES
- ☐ 601. JERALD CLARK
- ☐ 602. PAT CLEMENTS
- ☐ 603. PAUL FARIES
- ☐ 604. TONY FERNANDEZ
- ☐ 605. TONY GWYNN
- ☐ 606. GREG HARRIS
- ☐ 607. THOMAS HOWARD
- ☐ 608. BRUCE HURST
- ☐ 609. DARRIN JACKSON
- ☐ 610. TOM LAMPKIN
- ☐ 611. CRAIG LEFFERTS
- ☐ 612. JIM LEWIS
- ☐ 613. MIKE MADDUX
- ☐ 614. FRED MCGRIFF
- ☐ 615. JOSE MELENDEZ
- ☐ 616. JOSE MOTA
- ☐ 617. DENNIS RASMUSSEN
- ☐ 618. BIP ROBERTS
- ☐ 619. RICH RODRIGUEZ
- ☐ 620. BENITO SANTIAGO
- ☐ 621. CRAIG SHIPLEY
- ☐ 622. TIM TEUFEL
- ☐ 623. KEVIN WARD
- ☐ 624. ED WHITSON
- ☐ 720. TEAM CHECKLIST(F)

SAN FRANCISCO GIANTS

- ☐ 625. DAVE ANDERSON
- ☐ 626. KEVIN BASS
- ☐ 627. ROD BECK
- ☐ 628. BUD BLACK
- ☐ 629. JEFF BRANTLEY
- ☐ 630. JOHN BURKETT
- ☐ 631. WILL CLARK
- ☐ 632. ROYCE CLAYTON
- ☐ 633. STEVE DECKER
- ☐ 634. KELLY DOWNS
- ☐ 635. MIKE FELDER
- ☐ 636. SCOTT GARRELTS
- ☐ 637. ERIC GUNDERSON
- ☐ 638. BRYAN HICKERSON
- ☐ 639. DARREN LEWIS
- ☐ 640. GREG LITTON
- ☐ 641. KIRT MANWARING
- ☐ 642. PAUL MCCLELLAN
- ☐ 643. WILLIE MCGEE
- ☐ 644. KEVIN MITCHELL
- ☐ 645. FRANCISCO OLIVERAS
- ☐ 646. MIKE REMLINGER
- ☐ 647. DAVE RIGHETTI
- ☐ 648. ROBBY THOMPSON
- ☐ 649. JOSE URIBE
- ☐ 650. MATT WILLIAMS
- ☐ 651. TREVOR WILSON
- ☐ 665. GIL HEREDIA
- ☐ 678. TED WOOD
- ☐ 720. TEAM CHECKLIST(F)

SEATTLE MARINERS

- ☐ 273. SCOTT BRADLEY
- ☐ 274. GREG BRILEY
- ☐ 275. JAY BUHNER
- ☐ 276. HENRY COTTO
- ☐ 277. ALVIN DAVIS
- ☐ 278. RICH DELUCIA
- ☐ 279. KEN GRIFFEY, JR.
- ☐ 280. ERIK HANSON
- ☐ 281. BRIAN HOLMAN
- ☐ 282. MIKE JACKSON
- ☐ 283. RANDY JOHNSON
- ☐ 284. TRACY JONES
- ☐ 285. BILL KRUEGER
- ☐ 286. EDGAR MARTINEZ
- ☐ 287. TINO MARTINEZ
- ☐ 288. ROB MURPHY
- ☐ 289. PETE O'BRIEN
- ☐ 290. ALONZO POWELL
- ☐ 291. HAROLD REYNOLDS
- ☐ 292. MIKE SCHOOLER
- ☐ 293. RUSS SWAN
- ☐ 294. BILL SWIFT
- ☐ 295. DAVE VALLE
- ☐ 296. OMAR VIZQUEL
- ☐ 658. PAT RICE
- ☐ 716. TEAM CHECKLIST(B)

TEXAS RANGERS

- ☐ 297. GERALD ALEXANDER
- ☐ 298. BRAD ARNSBERG
- ☐ 299. KEVIN BROWN
- ☐ 300. JACK DAUGHERTY
- ☐ 301. MARIO DIAZ
- ☐ 302. BRIAN DOWNING
- ☐ 303. JULIO FRANCO
- ☐ 304. JUAN GONZALEZ
- ☐ 305. RICH GOSSAGE
- ☐ 306. JOSE GUZMAN
- ☐ 307. JOSE HERNANDEZ
- ☐ 308. JEFF HUSON
- ☐ 309. MIKE JEFFCOAT
- ☐ 310. TERRY MATHEWS
- ☐ 311. RAFAEL PALMEIRO
- ☐ 312. DEAN PALMER
- ☐ 313. GENO PETRALLI
- ☐ 314. GARY PETTIS
- ☐ 315. KEVIN REIMER
- ☐ 316. IVAN RODRIGUEZ
- ☐ 317. KENNY ROGERS
- ☐ 318. WAYNE ROSENTHAL
- ☐ 319. JEFF RUSSELL
- ☐ 320. NOLAN RYAN
- ☐ 321. RUBEN SIERRA
- ☐ 659. ROB MAURER
- ☐ 660. DON HARRIS
- ☐ 668. MONTY FARISS
- ☐ 717. TEAM CHECKLIST(F)

TORONTO BLUE JAYS

- ☐ 322. JIM ACKER
- ☐ 323. ROBERTO ALOMAR
- ☐ 324. DEREK BELL
- ☐ 325. PAT BORDERS
- ☐ 326. TOM CANDIOTTI
- ☐ 327. JOE CARTER
- ☐ 328. ROB DUCEY
- ☐ 329. KELLY GRUBER
- ☐ 330. JUAN GUZMAN
- ☐ 331. TOM HENKE
- ☐ 332. JIMMY KEY
- ☐ 333. MANNY LEE
- ☐ 334. AL LEITER
- ☐ 335. BOB MACDONALD
- ☐ 336. CANDY MALDONADO
- ☐ 337. RANCE MULLINIKS
- ☐ 338. GREG MYERS
- ☐ 339. JOHN OLERUD
- ☐ 340. ED SPRAGUE
- ☐ 341. DAVE STIEB
- ☐ 342. TODD STOTTLEMYRE
- ☐ 343. MIKE TIMLIN
- ☐ 344. DUANE WARD
- ☐ 345. DAVID WELLS
- ☐ 346. DEVON WHITE
- ☐ 347. MOOKIE WILSON
- ☐ 348. EDDIE ZOSKY
- ☐ 717. TEAM CHECKLIST(F)

1992 FLEER UPDATE (132) 2 1/2" X 3 1/2"

ATLANTA BRAVES

- ☐ 68U. DAVID NIED
- ☐ 69U. OTIS NIXON
- ☐ 70U. ALEJANDRO PENA
- ☐ 71U. JEFF REARDON

BALTIMORE ORIOLES

- ☐ 1U. TODD FROHWIRTH
- ☐ 2U. ALAN MILLS
- ☐ 3U. RICK SUTCLIFFE

BOSTON RED SOX

- ☐ 4U. JOHN VALENTIN
- ☐ 5U. FRANK VIOLA
- ☐ 6U. BOB ZUPCIC

CALIFORNIA ANGELS

- ☐ 7U. MIKE BUTCHER
- ☐ 8U. CHAD CURTIS
- ☐ 9U. DAMION EASLEY
- ☐ 10U. TIM SALMON
- ☐ 11U. JULIO VALERA

CHICAGO CUBS

- ☐ 72U. ALEX ARIAS
- ☐ 73U. JIM BULLINGER
- ☐ 74U. MIKE MORGAN
- ☐ 75U. REY SANCHEZ
- ☐ 76U. BOB SCANLAN
- ☐ 77U. SAMMY SOSA

CHICAGO WHITE SOX

- ☐ 12U. GEORGE BELL
- ☐ 13U. ROBERTO HERNANDEZ
- ☐ 14U. SHAWN JETER

CINCINNATI REDS

- ☐ 78U. SCOTT BANKHEAD
- ☐ 79U. TIM BELCHER
- ☐ 80U. STEVE FOSTER
- ☐ 81U. WILLIE GREENE
- ☐ 82U. BIP ROBERTS
- ☐ 83U. SCOTT RUSKIN
- ☐ 84U. GREG SWINDELL

CLEVELAND INDIANS

- ☐ 15U. THOMAS HOWARD
- ☐ 16U. JESSE LEVIS
- ☐ 17U. KENNY LOFTON
- ☐ 18U. PAUL SORRENTO

DETROIT TIGERS

- ☐ 19U. RICO BROGNA
- ☐ 20U. JOHN DOHERTY
- ☐ 21U. DAN GLADDEN
- ☐ 22U. BUDDY GROOM
- ☐ 23U. SHAWN HARE
- ☐ 24U. JOHN KIELY
- ☐ 25U. KURT KNUDSEN

HOUSTON ASTROS

- ☐ 85U. JUAN GUERRERO
- ☐ 86U. BUTCH HENRY
- ☐ 87U. DOUG JONES
- ☐ 88U. BRIAN WILLIAMS

KANSAS CITY ROYALS

- ☐ 26U. GREGG JEFFERIES
- ☐ 27U. WALLY JOYNER
- ☐ 28U. KEVIN KOSLOFSKI
- ☐ 29U. KEVIN MCREYNOLDS
- ☐ 30U. RUSTY MEACHAM
- ☐ 31U. KEITH MILLER
- ☐ 32U. HIPOLITO PICHARDO

LOS ANGELES DODGERS

- ☐ 89U. TOM CANDIOTTI
- ☐ 90U. ERIC DAVIS
- ☐ 91U. CARLOS HERNANDEZ
- ☐ 92U. MIKE PIAZZA
- ☐ 93U. MIKE SHARPERSON
- ☐ 94U. ERIC YOUNG

MILWAUKEE BREWERS

- ☐ 33U. JAMES AUSTIN
- ☐ 34U. SCOTT FLETCHER
- ☐ 35U. JOHN JAHA
- ☐ 36U. PAT LISTACH
- ☐ 37U. DAVE NILSSON
- ☐ 38U. KEVIN SEITZER

MINNESOTA TWINS

- ☐ 39U. TOM EDENS

1992 Fleer Update

☐ 40U. PAT MAHOMES
☐ 41U. JOHN SMILEY

MONTREAL EXPOS

☐ 95U. MOISES ALOU
☐ 96U. GREG COLBRUNN
☐ 97U. WIL CORDERO
☐ 98U. KEN HILL
☐ 99U. JOHN VANDER WAL
☐ 100U. JOHN WETTELAND

NEW YORK METS

☐ 101U. BOBBY BONILLA
☐ 102U. ERIC HILLMAN
☐ 103U. PAT HOWELL
☐ 104U. JEFF KENT
☐ 105U. DICK SCHOFIELD
☐ 106U. RYAN THOMPSON
☐ 107U. CHICO WALKER

NEW YORK YANKEES

☐ 42U. CHARLIE HAYES
☐ 43U. SAM MILITELLO
☐ 44U. ANDY STANKIEWICZ
☐ 45U. DANNY TARTABULL
☐ 46U. BOB WICKMAN

OAKLAND A'S

☐ 47U. JERRY BROWNE
☐ 48U. KEVIN CAMPBELL
☐ 49U. VINCE HORSMAN
☐ 50U. TROY NEEL
☐ 51U. RUBEN SIERRA
☐ 52U. BRUCE WALTON
☐ 53U. WILLIE WILSON

PHILADELPHIA PHILLIES

☐ 108U. JUAN BELL
☐ 109U. MARIANO DUNCAN
☐ 110U. JEFF GROTEWOLD
☐ 111U. BEN RIVERA
☐ 112U. CURT SCHILLING

PITTSBURGH PIRATES

☐ 113U. VICTOR COLE
☐ 114U. ALBERT MARTIN
☐ 115U. ROGER MASON
☐ 116U. BLAS MINOR
☐ 117U. TIM WAKEFIELD

ST. LOUIS CARDINALS

☐ 118U. MARK CLARK
☐ 119U. RHEAL CORMIER
☐ 120U. DONOVAN OSBORNE
☐ 121U. TODD WORRELL

SAN DIEGO PADRES

☐ 122U. JEREMY HERNANDEZ
☐ 123U. RANDY MYERS
☐ 124U. FRANK SEMINARA
☐ 125U. GARY SHEFFIELD
☐ 126U. DAN WALTERS

SAN FRANCISCO GIANTS

☐ 127U. STEVE HOSEY
☐ 128U. MIKE JACKSON
☐ 129U. JIM PENA
☐ 130U. CORY SNYDER
☐ 131U. BILL SWIFT

SEATTLE MARINERS

☐ 54U. BRET BOONE
☐ 55U. DAVE FLEMING
☐ 56U. KEVIN MITCHELL
☐ 57U. JEFF NELSON
☐ 58U. SHANE TURNER

TEXAS RANGERS

☐ 59U. JOSE CANSECO
☐ 60U. JEFF FRYE
☐ 61U. DANILO LEON
☐ 62U. ROGER PAVLIK

TORONTO BLUE JAYS

☐ 63U. DAVID CONE
☐ 64U. PAT HENTGEN
☐ 65U. RANDY KNORR
☐ 66U. JACK MORRIS
☐ 67U. DAVE WINFIELD

1993 FLEER (720)
2 1/2" X 3 1/2"

ATLANTA BRAVES

☐ 1. STEVE AVERY
☐ 2. SID BREAM
☐ 3. RON GANT
☐ 4. TOM GLAVINE
☐ 5. BRIAN HUNTER
☐ 6. RYAN KLESKO
☐ 7. CHARLIE LEIBRANDT
☐ 8. KENT MERCKER
☐ 9. DAVID NIED
☐ 10. OTIS NIXON
☐ 11. GREG OLSON
☐ 12. TERRY PENDLETON
☐ 13. DEION SANDERS
☐ 14. JOHN SMOLTZ
☐ 15. MIKE STANTON
☐ 16. MARK WOHLERS
☐ 361. RAFAEL BELLIARD
☐ 362. DAMON BERRYHILL
☐ 363. MIKE BIELECKI
☐ 364. JEFF BLAUSER
☐ 365. FRANCISCO CABRERA
☐ 366. MARVIN FREEMAN
☐ 367. DAVID JUSTICE
☐ 368. MARK LEMKE
☐ 369. ALEJANDRO PENA
☐ 370. JEFF REARDON
☐ 371. LONNIE SMITH
☐ 372. PETE SMITH

BALTIMORE ORIOLES

☐ 163. BRADY ANDERSON
☐ 164. GLENN DAVIS
☐ 165. MIKE DEVEREAUX
☐ 166. TOOD FROHWIRTH
☐ 167. LEO GOMEZ
☐ 168. CHRIS HOILES
☐ 169. BEN MCDONALD
☐ 170. RANDY MILLIGAN
☐ 171. ALAN MILLS
☐ 172. MIKE MUSSINA
☐ 173. GREGG OLSON
☐ 174. ARTHUR RHODES
☐ 175. DAVID SEGUI
☐ 541. STORM DAVIS
☐ 542. SAM HORN
☐ 543. TIM HULETT
☐ 544. CARIG LEFFERTS
☐ 545. CHITO MARTINEZ
☐ 546. MARK MCLEMORE
☐ 547. LUIS MERCEDES
☐ 548. BOB MILACKI
☐ 549. JOE ORSULAK
☐ 550. BILLY RIPKEN
☐ 551. CAL RIPKEN, JR.
☐ 552. RICK SUTCLIFFE
☐ 553. JEFF TACKETT

BOSTON RED SOX

☐ 176. ELLIS BURKS
☐ 177. ROGER CLEMENS
☐ 178. SCOTT COOPER
☐ 179. DANNY DARWIN
☐ 180. TONY FOSSAS
☐ 181. PAUL QUANTRILL
☐ 182. JODY REED
☐ 183. JOHN VALENTIN
☐ 184. MO VAUGHN
☐ 185. FRANK VIOLA
☐ 186. BOB ZUPCIC
☐ 554. WADE BOGGS
☐ 555. TOM BRUNANSKY
☐ 556. JACK CLARK
☐ 557. JOHN DOPSON
☐ 558. MIKE GARDINER
☐ 559. MIKE GREENWELL
☐ 560. GREG HARRIS
☐ 561. BILLY HATCHER
☐ 562. JOE HESKETH
☐ 563. TONY PENA
☐ 564. PHIL PLANTIER
☐ 565. LUIS RIVERA
☐ 566. HERM WINNINGHAM
☐ 567. MATT YOUNG

CALIFORNIA ANGELS

☐ 187. JIM ABBOTT
☐ 188. GARY DISARCINA
☐ 189. DAMION EASLEY
☐ 190. JUNIOR FELIX
☐ 191. CHUCK FINLEY
☐ 192. JOE GRAHE
☐ 193. BRYAN HARVEY
☐ 194. MARK LANGSTON
☐ 195. JOHN ORTON
☐ 196. LUIS POLONIA
☐ 197. TIM SALMON
☐ 198. LUIS SOJO
☐ 568. BERT BLYLEVEN
☐ 569. MIKE BUTCHER
☐ 570. CHUCK CRIM
☐ 571. CHAD CURTIS
☐ 572. TIM FORTUGNO
☐ 573. STEVE FREY
☐ 574. GARY GAETTI
☐ 575. SCOTT LEWIS
☐ 576. LEE STEVENS
☐ 577. RON TINGLEY
☐ 578. JULIO VALERA

CHICAGO CUBS

- ☐ 17. PAUL ASSENMACHER
- ☐ 18. STEVE BUECHELE
- ☐ 19. SHAWON DUNSTON
- ☐ 20. MARK GRACE
- ☐ 21. DERRICK MAY
- ☐ 22. CHUCK MCELROY
- ☐ 23. MIKE MORGAN
- ☐ 24. REY SANCHEZ
- ☐ 25. RYNE SANDBERG
- ☐ 26. BOB SCANLAN
- ☐ 27. SAMMY SOSA
- ☐ 28. RICK WILKINS
- ☐ 373. SHAWN BOSKIE
- ☐ 374. JIM BULLINGER
- ☐ 375. FRANK CASTILLO
- ☐ 376. DOUG DASCENZO
- ☐ 377. ANDRE DAWSON
- ☐ 378. MIKE HARKEY
- ☐ 379. GREG HIBBARD
- ☐ 380. GREG MADDUX
- ☐ 381. KEN PATTERSON
- ☐ 382. JEFF ROBINSON
- ☐ 383. LUIS SALAZAR
- ☐ 384. DWIGHT SMITH
- ☐ 385. JOSE VIZCAINO

CHICAGO WHITE SOX

- ☐ 199. WILSON ALVAREZ
- ☐ 200. GEORGE BELL
- ☐ 201. ALEX FERNANDEZ
- ☐ 202. CRAIG GREBECK
- ☐ 203. OZZIE GUILLEN
- ☐ 204. LANCE JOHNSON
- ☐ 205. RON KARKOVICE
- ☐ 206. KIRK MCCASKILL
- ☐ 207. JACK MCDOWELL
- ☐ 208. SCOTT RADINSKY
- ☐ 209. TIM RAINES
- ☐ 210. FRANK THOMAS
- ☐ 211. ROBIN VENTURA
- ☐ 579. SHAWN ABNER
- ☐ 580. JOEY CORA
- ☐ 581. CHRIS CRON
- ☐ 582. CARLTON FISK
- ☐ 583. ROBERTO HERNANDEZ
- ☐ 584. CHARLIE HOUGH
- ☐ 585. TERRY LEACH
- ☐ 586. DONN PALL
- ☐ 587. DAN PASQUA
- ☐ 588. STEVE SAX
- ☐ 589. BOBBY THIGPEN

CINCINNATI REDS

- ☐ 29. BOBBY AYALA
- ☐ 30. TIM BELCHER
- ☐ 31. JEFF BRANSON
- ☐ 32. NORM CHARLTON
- ☐ 33. STEVE FOSTER
- ☐ 34. WILLIE GREENE
- ☐ 35. CHRIS HAMMOND
- ☐ 36. MILT HILL
- ☐ 37. HAL MORRIS
- ☐ 38. JOE OLIVER
- ☐ 39. PAUL O'NEILL
- ☐ 40. TIM PUGH
- ☐ 41. JOSE RIJO
- ☐ 42. BIP ROBERTS
- ☐ 43. CHRIS SABO
- ☐ 44. REGGIE SANDERS
- ☐ 386. SCOTT BANKHEAD
- ☐ 387. TOM BROWNING
- ☐ 388. DARNELL COLES
- ☐ 389. ROB DIBBLE
- ☐ 390. BILL DORAN
- ☐ 391. DWAYNE HENRY
- ☐ 392. CESAR HERNANDEZ
- ☐ 393. ROBERTO KELLY
- ☐ 394. BARRY LARKIN
- ☐ 395. DAVE MARTINEZ
- ☐ 396. KEVIN MITCHELL
- ☐ 397. JEFF REED
- ☐ 398. SCOTT RUSKIN
- ☐ 399. GREG SWINDELL
- ☐ 400. DAN WILSON

CLEVELAND INDIANS

- ☐ 212. SANDY ALOMAR, JR.
- ☐ 213. CARLOS BAERGA
- ☐ 214. DENNIS COOK
- ☐ 215. THOMAS HOWARD
- ☐ 216. MARK LEWIS
- ☐ 217. DEREK LILLIQUIST
- ☐ 218. KENNY LOFTON
- ☐ 219. CHARLES NAGY
- ☐ 220. STEVE OLIN
- ☐ 221. PAUL SORRENTO
- ☐ 222. JIM THOME
- ☐ 223. MARK WHITEN
- ☐ 590. ALBERT BELLE
- ☐ 591. FELIX FERMIN
- ☐ 592. GLENALLEN HILL
- ☐ 593. BROOK JACOBY
- ☐ 594. REGGIE JEFFERSON
- ☐ 595. CARLOS MARTINEZ
- ☐ 596. JOSE MESA
- ☐ 597. ROD NICHOLS
- ☐ 598. JUNOR ORTIZ
- ☐ 599. ERIC PLUNK
- ☐ 600. TED POWER
- ☐ 601. SCOTT SCUDDER
- ☐ 602. KEVIN WICKANDER

COLORADO ROCKIES

- ☐ 401. ANDY ASHBY
- ☐ 402. FREDDIE BENAVIDES
- ☐ 403. DANTE BICHETTE
- ☐ 404. WILLIE BLAIR
- ☐ 405. DENIS BOUCHER
- ☐ 406. VINNY CASTILLA
- ☐ 407. BRAULIO CASTILLO
- ☐ 408. ALEX COLE
- ☐ 409. ANDRES GALARRAGA
- ☐ 410. JOE GIRARDI
- ☐ 411. BUTCH HENRY
- ☐ 412. DARREN HOLMES
- ☐ 413. CALVIN JONES
- ☐ 414. STEVE REED
- ☐ 415. KEVIN RITZ
- ☐ 416. JIM TATUM

DETROIT TIGERS

- ☐ 224. MILT CUYLER
- ☐ 225. ROB DEER
- ☐ 226. JOHN DOHERTY
- ☐ 227. CECIL FIELDER
- ☐ 228. TRAVIS FRYMAN
- ☐ 229. MIKE HENNEMAN
- ☐ 230. JOHN KIELY
- ☐ 231. KURT KNUDSEN
- ☐ 232. SCOTT LIVINGSTONE
- ☐ 233. TONY PHILLIPS
- ☐ 234. MICKEY TETTLETON
- ☐ 603. SKEETER BARNES
- ☐ 604. MARK CARREON
- ☐ 605. DAN GLADDEN
- ☐ 606. BILL GULLICKSON
- ☐ 607. CHAD KREUTER
- ☐ 608. MARK LEITER
- ☐ 609. MIKE MUNOZ
- ☐ 610. RICH ROWLAND
- ☐ 611. FRANK TANANA
- ☐ 612. WALT TERRELL
- ☐ 613. ALAN TRAMMELL
- ☐ 614. LOU WHITAKER

FLORIDA MARLINS

- ☐ 417. JACK ARMSTRONG
- ☐ 418. BRET BARBERIE
- ☐ 419. RYAN BOWEN
- ☐ 420. CRIS CARPENTER
- ☐ 421. CHUCK CARR
- ☐ 422. SCOTT CHIAMPARINO
- ☐ 423. JEFF CONINE
- ☐ 424. JIM CORSI
- ☐ 425. STEVE DECKER
- ☐ 426. CHRIS DONNELS
- ☐ 427. MONTY FARISS
- ☐ 428. BOB NATAL
- ☐ 429. PAT RAPP
- ☐ 430. DAVE WEATHERS
- ☐ 431. NIGEL WILSON

HOUSTON ASTROS

- ☐ 45. ERIC ANTHONY
- ☐ 46. JEFF BAGWELL
- ☐ 47. CRAIG BIGGIO
- ☐ 48. JOE BOEVER
- ☐ 49. CASEY CANDAELE
- ☐ 50. STEVE FINLEY
- ☐ 51. LUIS GONZALEZ
- ☐ 52. PETE HARNISCH
- ☐ 53. XAVIER HERNANDEZ
- ☐ 54. DOUG JONES
- ☐ 55. EDDIE TAUBENSEE
- ☐ 56. BRIAN WILLIAMS
- ☐ 432. KEN CAMINITI
- ☐ 433. ANDUJAR CEDENO
- ☐ 434. TOM EDENS
- ☐ 435. JUAN GUERRERO
- ☐ 436. PETE INCAVIGLIA
- ☐ 437. JIMMY JONES
- ☐ 438. DARRYL KILE
- ☐ 439. ROB MURPHY
- ☐ 440. AL OSUNA
- ☐ 441. MARK PORTUGAL
- ☐ 442. SCOTT SERVAIS

KANSAS CITY ROYALS

- ☐ 235. KEVIN APPIER
- ☐ 236. GEORGE BRETT
- ☐ 237. TOM GORDON
- ☐ 238. GREGG JEFFERIES
- ☐ 239. WALLY JOYNER
- ☐ 240. KEVIN KOSLOFSKI
- ☐ 241. MIKE MACFARLANE
- ☐ 242. BRIAN MCRAE
- ☐ 243. RUSTY MEACHAM
- ☐ 244. KEITH MILLER
- ☐ 245. JEFF MONTGOMERY
- ☐ 246. HIPOLITO PICHARDO
- ☐ 615. LUIS AQUINO
- ☐ 616. MIKE BODDICKER
- ☐ 617. JIM EISENREICH
- ☐ 618. MARK GUBICZA
- ☐ 619. DAVID HOWARD
- ☐ 620. MIKE MAGNANTE
- ☐ 621. BRENT MAYNE
- ☐ 622. KEVIN MCREYNOLDS
- ☐ 623. ED PIERCE
- ☐ 624. BILL SAMPEN
- ☐ 625. STEVE SHIFFLETT
- ☐ 626. GARY THURMAN
- ☐ 627. CURTIS WILKERSON

LOS ANGELES DODGERS

- ☐ 57. PEDRO ASTACIO
- ☐ 58. TODD BENZINGER
- ☐ 59. BRETT BUTLER
- ☐ 60. TOM CANDIOTTI
- ☐ 61. LENNY HARRIS
- ☐ 62. CARLOS HERNANDEZ
- ☐ 63. OREL HERSHISER
- ☐ 64. ERIC KARROS
- ☐ 65. RAMON MARTINEZ
- ☐ 66. JOSE OFFERMAN
- ☐ 67. MIKE SCIOSCIA
- ☐ 68. MIKE SHARPERSON
- ☐ 69. ERIC YOUNG
- ☐ 443. JOHN CANDELARIA
- ☐ 444. TIM CREWS
- ☐ 445. ERIC DAVIS
- ☐ 446. TOM GOODWIN
- ☐ 447. JIM GOTT
- ☐ 448. KEVIN GROSS
- ☐ 449. DAVE HANSEN
- ☐ 450. JAY HOWELL
- ☐ 451. ROGER MCDOWELL
- ☐ 452. BOB OJEDA
- ☐ 453. HENRY RODRIGUEZ
- ☐ 454. DARRYL STRAWBERRY
- ☐ 455. MITCH WEBSTER
- ☐ 456. STEVE WILSON

MILWAUKEE BREWERS

- ☐ 247. RICKY BONES
- ☐ 248. CAL ELDRED
- ☐ 249. MIKE FETTERS
- ☐ 250. DARRYL HAMILTON
- ☐ 251. DOUG HENRY

☐ 252. JOHN JAHA
☐ 253. PAT LISTACH
☐ 254. PAUL MOLITOR
☐ 255. JAIME NAVARRO
☐ 256. KEVIN SEITZER
☐ 257. B.J. SURHOFF
☐ 258. GREG VAUGHN
☐ 259. BILL WEGMAN
☐ 260. ROBIN YOUNT
☐ 628. CHRIS BOSIO
☐ 629. SCOTT FLETCHER
☐ 630. JIM GANTNER
☐ 631. DAVE NILSSON
☐ 632. JESSE OROSCO
☐ 633. DAN PLESAC
☐ 634. RON ROBINSON
☐ 635. BILL SPIERS
☐ 636. FRANKLIN STUBBS

MINNESOTA TWINS

☐ 261. RICK AGUILERA
☐ 262. CHILI DAVIS
☐ 263. SCOTT ERICKSON
☐ 264. GREG GAGNE
☐ 265. MARK GUTHRIE
☐ 266. BRIAN HARPER
☐ 267. KENT HRBEK
☐ 268. TERRY JORGENSEN
☐ 269. GENE LARKIN
☐ 270. SCOTT LEIUS
☐ 271. PAT MAHOMES
☐ 272. PEDRO MUNOZ
☐ 273. KIRBY PUCKETT
☐ 274. KEVIN TAPANI
☐ 275. CARL WILLIS
☐ 637. WILLIE BANKS
☐ 638. RANDY BUSH
☐ 639. CHUCK KNOBLAUCH
☐ 640. SHANE MACK
☐ 641. MIKE PAGLIARULO
☐ 642. JEFF REBOULET
☐ 643. JOHN SMILEY
☐ 644. MIKE TROMBLEY
☐ 645. GARY WAYNE
☐ 646. LENNY WEBSTER

MONTREAL EXPOS

☐ 70. MOISES ALOU
☐ 71. IVAN CALDERON
☐ 72. ARCHI CIANFROCCO
☐ 73. WIL CORDERO
☐ 74. DELINO DESHIELDS
☐ 75. MARK GARDNER
☐ 76. KEN HILL
☐ 77. TIM LAKER
☐ 78. CHRIS NABHOLZ
☐ 79. MEL ROJAS
☐ 80. JOHN VANDER WAL
☐ 81. LARRY WALKER
☐ 82. TIM WALLACH
☐ 83. JOHN WETTELAND
☐ 457. BRIAN BARNES
☐ 458. SEAN BERRY
☐ 459. JEFF FASSERO
☐ 460. DARRIN FLETCHER
☐ 461. MARQUIS GRISSOM
☐ 462. DENNIS MARTINEZ
☐ 463. SPIKE OWEN
☐ 464. MATT STAIRS
☐ 465. SERGIO VALDEZ

NEW YORK METS

☐ 84. BOBBY BONILLA
☐ 85. DARYL BOSTON
☐ 86. SIDE FERNANDEZ
☐ 87. ERIC HILLMAN
☐ 88. TODD HUNDLEY
☐ 89. HOWARD JOHNSON
☐ 90. JEFF KENT
☐ 91. EDDIE MURRAY
☐ 92. BILL PECOTA
☐ 93. BRET SABERHAGEN
☐ 94. DICK SCHOFIELD
☐ 95. PETE SCHOUREK
☐ 96. ANTHONY YOUNG
☐ 466. KEVIN BASS
☐ 467. VINCE COLEMAN

☐ 468. MARK DEWEY
☐ 469. KEVIN ELSTER
☐ 470. TONY FERNANDEZ
☐ 471. JOHN FRANCO
☐ 472. DAVE GALLAGHER
☐ 473. PAUL GIBSON
☐ 474. DWIGHT GOODEN
☐ 475. LEE GUETTERMAN
☐ 476. JEFF INNIS
☐ 477. DAVE MAGADAN
☐ 478. CHARLIE O'BRIEN
☐ 479. WILLIE RANDOLPH
☐ 480. MACKEY SASSER
☐ 481. RYAN THOMPSON
☐ 482. CHICO WALKER

NEW YORK YANKEES

☐ 276. STEVE FARR
☐ 277. JOHN HABYAN
☐ 278. MEL HALL
☐ 279. CHARLIE HAYES
☐ 280. PAT KELLY
☐ 281. DON MATTINGLY
☐ 282. SAM MILITELLO
☐ 283. MATT NOKES
☐ 284. MELIDO PEREZ
☐ 285. ANDY STANKIEWICZ
☐ 286. DANNY TARTABULL
☐ 287. RANDY VELARDE
☐ 288. BOB WICKMAN
☐ 289. BERNIE WILLIAMS
☐ 647. TIM BURKE
☐ 648. MIKE GALLEGO
☐ 649. DION JAMES
☐ 650. JEFF JOHNSON
☐ 651. SCOTT KAMIENIECKI
☐ 652. KEVIN MAAS
☐ 653. RICH MONTELEONE
☐ 654. JERRY NIELSEN
☐ 655. SCOTT SANDERSON
☐ 656. MIKE STANLEY
☐ 657. GERALD WILLIAMS
☐ 658. CURT YOUNG

OAKLAND A'S

☐ 290. LANCE BLANKENSHIP
☐ 291. MIKE BORDICK
☐ 292. JERRY BROWNE
☐ 293. DENNIS ECKERSLEY
☐ 294. RICKEY HENDERSON
☐ 295. VINCE HORSMAN
☐ 296. MARK MCGWIRE
☐ 297. JEFF PARRETT
☐ 298. RUBEN SIERRA
☐ 299. TERRY STEINBACH
☐ 300. WALT WEISS
☐ 301. BOB WELCH
☐ 302. WILLIE WILSON
☐ 303. BOBBY WITT
☐ 659. HAROLD BAINES
☐ 660. KEVIN CAMPBELL
☐ 661. RON DARLING
☐ 662. KELLY DOWNS
☐ 663. ERIC FOX
☐ 664. DAVE HENDERSON
☐ 665. RICK HONEYCUTT
☐ 666. MIKE MOORE
☐ 667. JAMIE QUIRK
☐ 668. JEFF RUSSELL
☐ 669. DAVE STEWART

PHILADELPHIA PHILLIES

☐ 97. RUBEN AMARO, JR.
☐ 98. JUAN BELL
☐ 99. WES CHAMBERLAIN
☐ 100. DARREN DAULTON
☐ 101. MARIANO DUNCAN
☐ 102. MIKE HARTLEY
☐ 103. RICKY JORDAN
☐ 104. JOHN KRUK
☐ 105. MICKEY MORANDINI
☐ 106. TERRY MULHOLLAND
☐ 107. BEN RIVERA
☐ 108. CURT SCHILLING
☐ 109. KEITH SHEPHERD
☐ 483. KYLE ABBOTT
☐ 484. BOB AYRAULT
☐ 485. KIM BATISTE
☐ 486. CLIFF BRANTLEY
☐ 487. JOSE DELEON
☐ 488. LENNY DYKSTRA
☐ 489. TOMMY GREENE
☐ 490. JEFF GROTEWOLD
☐ 491. DAVE HOLLINS
☐ 492. DANNY JACKSON
☐ 493. STAN JAVIER
☐ 494. TOM MARSH
☐ 495. GREG MATHEWS
☐ 496. DALE MURPHY
☐ 497. TODD PRATT
☐ 498. MITCH WILLIAMS

PITTSBURGH PIRATES

☐ 110. STAN BELINDA
☐ 111. JAY BELL
☐ 112. BARRY BONDS
☐ 113. JEFF KING
☐ 114. MIKE LAVALLIERE
☐ 115. JOSE LIND
☐ 116. ROGER MASON
☐ 117. ORLANDO MERCED
☐ 118. BOB PATTERSON
☐ 119. DON SLAUGHT
☐ 120. ZANE SMITH
☐ 121. RANDY TOMLIN
☐ 122. ANDY VAN SLYKE
☐ 123. TIM WAKEFIELD
☐ 499. DANNY COX
☐ 500. DOUG DRABEK
☐ 501. CARLOS GARCIA
☐ 502. LLOYD MCCLENDON
☐ 503. DENNY NEAGLE
☐ 504. GARY REDUS
☐ 505. BOB WALK
☐ 506. JOHN WEHNER

ST. LOUIS CARDINALS

☐ 124. RHEAL CORMIER
☐ 125. BERNARD GILKEY
☐ 126. FELIX JOSE
☐ 127. RAY LANKFORD
☐ 128. BOB MCCLURE
☐ 129. DONOVAN OSBORNE
☐ 130. TOM PAGNOZZI
☐ 131. GERONIMO PENA
☐ 132. MIKE PEREZ
☐ 133. LEE SMITH
☐ 134. BOB TEWKSBURY
☐ 135. TODD WORRELL
☐ 136. TODD ZEILE
☐ 507. LUIS ALICEA
☐ 508. MARK CLARK
☐ 509. PEDRO GUERRERO
☐ 510. REX HUDLER
☐ 511. BRIAN JORDAN
☐ 512. OMAR OLIVARES
☐ 513. JOSE OQUENDO
☐ 514. GERALD PERRY
☐ 515. BRYN SMITH
☐ 516. CRAIG WILSON
☐ 517. TRACY WOODSON

SAN DIEGO PADRES

- ☐ 137. JERALD CLARK
- ☐ 138. TONY GWYNN
- ☐ 139. GREG HARRIS
- ☐ 140. JEREMY HERNANDEZ
- ☐ 141. DARRIN JACKSON
- ☐ 142. MIKE MADDUX
- ☐ 143. FRED MCGRIFF
- ☐ 144. JOSE MELENDEZ
- ☐ 145. RICH RODRIGUEZ
- ☐ 146. FRANK SEMINARA
- ☐ 147. GARY SHEFFIELD
- ☐ 148. KURT STILLWELL
- ☐ 149. DAN WALTERS
- ☐ 518. LARRY ANDERSEN
- ☐ 519. ANDY BENES
- ☐ 520. JIM DESHAIES
- ☐ 521. BRUCE HURST
- ☐ 522. RANDY MYERS
- ☐ 523. BENITO SANTIAGO
- ☐ 524. TIM SCOTT
- ☐ 525. TIM TEUFEL

SAN FRANCISCO GIANTS

- ☐ 150. ROD BECK
- ☐ 151. BUD BLACK
- ☐ 152. JEFF BRANTLEY
- ☐ 153. JOHN BURKETT
- ☐ 154. WILL CLARK
- ☐ 155. ROYCE CLAYTON
- ☐ 156. MIKE JACKSON
- ☐ 157. DARREN LEWIS
- ☐ 158. KIRT MANWARING
- ☐ 159. WILLIE MCGEE
- ☐ 160. CORY SNYDER
- ☐ 161. BILL SWIFT
- ☐ 162. TREVOR WILSON
- ☐ 526. MIKE BENJAMIN
- ☐ 527. DAVE BURBA
- ☐ 528. CRAIG COLBERT
- ☐ 529. MIKE FELDER
- ☐ 530. BRYAN HICKERSON
- ☐ 531. CHRIS JAMES
- ☐ 532. MARK LEONARD
- ☐ 533. GREG LITTON
- ☐ 534. FRANCISCO OLIVERAS
- ☐ 535. JOHN PATTERSON
- ☐ 536. JIM PENA
- ☐ 537. DAVE RIGHETTI
- ☐ 538. ROBBY THOMPSON
- ☐ 539. JOSE URIBE
- ☐ 540. MATT WILLIAMS

SEATTLE MARINERS

- ☐ 304. BRET BOONE
- ☐ 305. JAY BUHNER
- ☐ 306. DAVE FLEMING
- ☐ 307. KEN GRIFFEY, JR.
- ☐ 308. ERIK HANSON
- ☐ 309. EDGAR MARTINEZ
- ☐ 310. TINO MARTINEZ
- ☐ 311. JEFF NELSON
- ☐ 312. DENNIS POWELL
- ☐ 313. MIKE SCHOOLER
- ☐ 314. RUSS SWAN
- ☐ 315. DAVE VALLE
- ☐ 316. OMAR VIZQUEL
- ☐ 670. GREG BRILEY
- ☐ 671. DAVE COCHRANE
- ☐ 672. HENRY COTTO
- ☐ 673. RICH DELUCIA
- ☐ 674. BRIAN FISHER
- ☐ 675. MARK GRANT
- ☐ 676. RANDY JOHNSON
- ☐ 677. TIM LEARY
- ☐ 678. PETE O'BRIEN
- ☐ 679. LANCE PARRISH
- ☐ 680. HAROLD REYNOLDS
- ☐ 681. SHANE TURNER

TEXAS RANGERS

- ☐ 317. KEVIN BROWN
- ☐ 318. TODD BURNS
- ☐ 319. JOSE CANSECO
- ☐ 320. JULIO FRANCO
- ☐ 321. JEFF FRYE
- ☐ 322. JUAN GONZALEZ
- ☐ 323. JOSE GUZMAN
- ☐ 324. JEFF HUSON
- ☐ 325. DEAN PALMER
- ☐ 326. KEVIN REIMER
- ☐ 327. IVAN RODRIGUEZ
- ☐ 328. KENNY ROGERS
- ☐ 329. DAN SMITH
- ☐ 682. JACK DAUGHERTY
- ☐ 683. DAVID HULSE
- ☐ 684. TERRY MATHEWS
- ☐ 685. AL NEWMAN
- ☐ 686. EDWIN NUNEZ
- ☐ 687. RAFAEL PALMEIRO
- ☐ 688. ROGER PAVLIK
- ☐ 689. GENO PETRALLI
- ☐ 690. NOLAN RYAN

TORONTO BLUE JAYS

- ☐ 330. ROBERTO ALOMAR
- ☐ 331. DEREK BELL
- ☐ 332. PAT BORDERS
- ☐ 333. JOE CARTER
- ☐ 334. KELLY GRUBER
- ☐ 335. TOM HENKE
- ☐ 336. JIMMY KEY
- ☐ 337. MANUEL LEE
- ☐ 338. CANDY MALDONADO
- ☐ 339. JOHN OLERUD
- ☐ 340. TODD STOTTLEMYRE
- ☐ 341. DUANE WARD
- ☐ 342. DEVON WHITE
- ☐ 343. DAVE WINFIELD
- ☐ 691. DAVID CONE
- ☐ 692. ALFREDO GRIFFIN
- ☐ 693. JUAN GUZMAN
- ☐ 694. PAT HENTGEN
- ☐ 695. RANDY KNORR
- ☐ 696. BOB MACDONALD
- ☐ 697. JACK MORRIS
- ☐ 698. ED SPRAGUE
- ☐ 699. DAVE STIEB
- ☐ 700. PAT TABLER
- ☐ 701. MIKE TIMLIN
- ☐ 702. DAVID WELLS
- ☐ 703. EDDIE ZOSKY

1993 FLEER FINAL EDITION (300) 2 1/2" X 3 1/2"

ATLANTA BRAVES

- ☐ 1F. STEVE BEDROSIAN
- ☐ 2F. JAY HOWELL
- ☐ 3F. GREG MADDUX
- ☐ 4F. GREG MCMICHAEL
- ☐ 5F. TONY TARASCO

BALTIMORE ORIOLES

- ☐156F. HAROLD BAINES
- ☐157F. DAMON BUFORD
- ☐158F. PAUL CAREY
- ☐159F. JEFFREY HAMMONDS
- ☐160F. JAMIE MOYER
- ☐161F. SHERMAN OBANDO
- ☐162F. JOHN O'DONOGHUE
- ☐163F. BRAD PENNINGTON
- ☐164F. JIM POOLE
- ☐165F. HAROLD RENOLDS
- ☐166F. F. VALENZUELA
- ☐167F. JACK VOIGT
- ☐168F. MARK WILLIAMSON

BOSTON RED SOX

- ☐169F. SCOTT BANKHEAD
- ☐170F. GREG BLOSSER
- ☐171F. JIM BYRD
- ☐172F. IVAN CALDERON
- ☐173F. ANDRE DAWSON
- ☐174F. SCOTT FLETCHER
- ☐175F. JOSE MELENDEZ
- ☐176F. CARLOS QUNITANA
- ☐177F. JEFF RUSSELL
- ☐178F. AARON SELE

CALIFORNIA ANGELS

- ☐179F. ROD CORREIA
- ☐180F. CHILI DAVIS
- ☐181F. JIM EDMONDS
- ☐182F. RENE GONZALES
- ☐183F. HILLY HATHAWAY
- ☐184F. TOREY LOVULLO
- ☐185F. GREG MYERS
- ☐186F. GENE NELSON
- ☐187F. TROY PERCIVAL
- ☐188F. SCOTT SANDERSON
- ☐189F. .DARRYL SCOTT
- ☐190F. J.T. SNOW
- ☐191F. RUS SPRINGER

CHICAGO CUBS

- ☐ 6F. JOSE BAUTISTA
- ☐ 7F. JOSE GUZMAN
- ☐ 8F. GREG HIBBARD
- ☐ 9F. CANDY MALDONADO
- ☐ 10F. RANDY MYERS
- ☐ 11F. MATT WALBECK
- ☐ 12F. TURK WENDELL
- ☐ 13F. WILLIE WILSON

CHICAGO WHITE SOX

- ☐192F. JASON BERE
- ☐193F. RODNEY BOLTON
- ☐194F. ELLIS BURKS
- ☐195F. BO JACKSON
- ☐196F. MIKE LAVALLIERE
- ☐197F. SCOTT RUFFCORN
- ☐198F. JEFF SCHWARTZ

CINCINNATI REDS

- ☐ 14F. GREG CADARET
- ☐ 15F. ROBERTO KELLY
- ☐ 16F. RANDY MILLIGAN
- ☐ 17F. KEVIN MITCHELL
- ☐ 18F. JEFF REARDON
- ☐ 19F. JOHN ROPER
- ☐ 20F. JOHN SMILEY

CLEVELAND INDIANS

- ☐199F. JERRY DIPOTO
- ☐200F. ALVARO ESPINOZA
- ☐201F. WAYNE KIRBY
- ☐202F. TOM KRAMER
- ☐203F. JESSE LEVIS
- ☐204F. MANNY RAMIREZ
- ☐205F. JEFF TREADWAY
- ☐206F. BILL WERTZ
- ☐207F. CLIFF YOUNG
- ☐208F. MATT YOUNG

COLORADO ROCKIES

- ☐ 21F. ANDY ASHBY
- ☐ 22F. DANTE BICHETTE
- ☐ 23F. WILLIE BLAIR
- ☐ 24F. PEDRO CASTELLANO
- ☐ 25F. VINNY CASTILLA
- ☐ 26F. JERALD CLARK
- ☐ 27F. ALEX COLE
- ☐ 28F. SCOTT FREDRICKSON
- ☐ 29F. JAY GAINER
- ☐ 30F. ANDRES GALARRAGA
- ☐ 31F. JOE GIRARDI
- ☐ 32F. RYAN HAWBLITZEL
- ☐ 33F. CHARLIE HAYES
- ☐ 34F. DARREN HOLMES
- ☐ 35F. CHRIS JONES
- ☐ 36F. DAVID NIED
- ☐ 37F. J. OWENS
- ☐ 38F. LANCE PAINTER
- ☐ 39F. JEFF PARRETT
- ☐ 40F. STEVE REED
- ☐ 41F. ARMONDO REYNOSO
- ☐ 42F. BRUCE RUFFIN
- ☐ 43F. DANNY SHEAFFER
- ☐ 44F. KEITH SHEPHERD
- ☐ 45F. JIM TATUM
- ☐ 46F. GARY WAYNE
- ☐ 47F. ERIC YOUNG

DETROIT TIGERS

- ☐209F. KIRK GIBSON
- ☐210F. GREG GOHR
- ☐211F. BILL KRUEGER
- ☐212F. BOB MACDONALD
- ☐213F. MIKE MOORE
- ☐214F. DAVID WELLS

FLORIDA MARLINS

- ☐ 48F. LUIS AQUINO
- ☐ 49F. ALEX ARIAS
- ☐ 50F. JACK ARMSTRONG
- ☐ 51F. BRET BARBERIE
- ☐ 52F. GERONIMO BERROA
- ☐ 53F. RYAN BOWEN
- ☐ 54F. GREG BRILEY
- ☐ 55F. CRIS CARPENTER
- ☐ 56F. CHUCK CARR
- ☐ 57F. JEFF CONINE
- ☐ 58F. JIM CORSI
- ☐ 59F. ORESTES DESTRADE
- ☐ 60F. JUNIOR FELIX
- ☐ 61F. CHRIS HAMMOND
- ☐ 62F. BRYAN HARVEY
- ☐ 63F. CHARLIE HOUGH
- ☐ 64F. JOE KLINK
- ☐ 65F. RICHIE LEWIS
- ☐ 66F. MITCH LYDEN
- ☐ 67F. BOB NATAL
- ☐ 68F. SCOTT POSE
- ☐ 69F. RICH BENTERIA
- ☐ 70F. BENITO SANTIAGO
- ☐ 71F. GARY SHEFFIELD
- ☐ 72F. MATT TURNER
- ☐ 73F. WALT WEISS
- ☐ 74F. DARRELL WHITMORE
- ☐ 75F. NIGEL WILSON

HOUSTON ASTROS

- ☐ 76F. KEVIN BASS
- ☐ 77F. DOUG DRABEK
- ☐ 78F. TOM EDENS
- ☐ 79F. CHRIS JAMES
- ☐ 80F. GREG SWINDELL

KANSAS CITY ROYALS

- ☐215F. BILLY BREWER
- ☐216F. DAVID CONE
- ☐217F. GREG GAGNE
- ☐218F. MARK GARDNER
- ☐219F. CHRIS HANEY
- ☐220F. PHIL HIATT
- ☐221F. JOSE LIND

LOS ANGELES DODGERS

- ☐ 81F. OMAR DAAL
- ☐ 82F. RAUL MONDESI
- ☐ 83F. JODY REED
- ☐ 84F. CORY SNYDER
- ☐ 85F. RICK TRLICEK
- ☐ 86F. TIM WALLACH
- ☐ 87F. TODD WORRELL

MILWAUKEE BREWERS

- ☐222F. JUAN BELL
- ☐223F. TOM BRUNANSKY
- ☐224F. MIKE IGNASIAK
- ☐225F. JOE KMAK
- ☐226F. TOM LAMPKIN
- ☐227F. GRAEME LLOYD
- ☐228F. CARLOS MALDONADO
- ☐229F. MATT MIESKE
- ☐230F. ANGEL MIRANDA
- ☐231F. TROY O'LEARY
- ☐232F. KEVIN REIMER

MINNESOTA TWINS

- ☐233F. LARRY CASIAN
- ☐234F. JIM DESHAIES
- ☐235F. EDDIE GUARDADO
- ☐236F. CHIP HALE
- ☐237F. MIKE MAKSUDIAN
- ☐238F. DAVID MCCARTY
- ☐239F. PAT MEARES
- ☐240F. GEORGE TSAMIS
- ☐241F. DAVE WINFIELD

MONTREAL EXPOS

- ☐ 88F. TAVO ALVAREZ
- ☐ 89F. FRANK BOLICK
- ☐ 90F. KENT BOTTENFIELD
- ☐ 91F. GREG COLBRUNN
- ☐ 92F. CLIFF FLOYD
- ☐ 93F. LOU FRAZIER
- ☐ 94F. MIKE GARDINER
- ☐ 95F. MIKE LANSING
- ☐ 96F. BILL RISLEY
- ☐ 97F. JEFF SHAW

NEW YORK METS

- ☐ 98F. KEVIN BAEZ
- ☐ 99F. TIM BOGAR
- ☐100F. JEROMY BURNITZ
- ☐101F. MIKE DRAPER
- ☐102F. DARRIN JACKSON
- ☐103F. MIKE MADDUX
- ☐104F. JOE ORSULAK
- ☐105F. DOUG SAUNDERS
- ☐106F. FRANK TANANA
- ☐107F. DAVE TELGHEDER

NEW YORK YANKEES

- ☐242F. JIM ABBOTT
- ☐243F. WADE BOGGS
- ☐244F. ANDY COOK
- ☐245F. RUSS DAVIS
- ☐246F. MIKE HUMPHREYS
- ☐247F. JIMMY KEY
- ☐248F. JIM LEYRITZ
- ☐249F. BOBBY MUNOZ
- ☐250F. PAUL O'NEILL
- ☐251F. SPIKE OWEN
- ☐252F. DAVE SILVERSTRI

OAKLAND A'S

- ☐253F. MARCOS ARMAS
- ☐254F. BRENT GATES
- ☐255F. GOOSE GOSSAGE
- ☐256F. SCOTT LYDY
- ☐257F. HENRY MERCEDES
- ☐258F. MIKE MOHLER
- ☐259F. TROY NEEL
- ☐260F. EDWIN NUNEZ
- ☐261F. CRAIG PAQUETTE
- ☐262F. KEVIN SEITZER

PHILADELPHIA PHILLIES

- ☐108F. LARRY ANDERSEN
- ☐109F. JIM EISENRIECH
- ☐110F. PETE INCAVIGLIA
- ☐111F. DANNY JACKSON
- ☐112F. DAVID WEST

PITTSBURGH PIRATES

- ☐113F. AL MARTIN
- ☐114F. BLAS MINOR
- ☐115F. DENNIS MOELLER
- ☐116F. WILL PENNYFEATHER
- ☐117F. RICH ROBERTSON
- ☐118F. BEN SHELTON
- ☐119F. LONNIE SMITH
- ☐120F. FREDDIE TOLIVER
- ☐121F. PAUL WAGNER
- ☐122F. KEVIN YOUNG

ST. LOUIS CARDINALS

- ☐123F. RENE AROCHA
- ☐124F. GREGG JEFFERIES
- ☐125F. PAUL KILGUS
- ☐126F. LES LANCASTER
- ☐127F. JOE MAGRANE
- ☐128F. ROB MURPHY
- ☐129F. ERIK PAPPAS
- ☐130F. STAN ROYER
- ☐131F. OZZIE SMITH
- ☐132F. TOM URBANI
- ☐133F. MARK WHITEN

SAN DIEGO PADRES

- ☐134F. DEREK BELL
- ☐135F. DOUG BROCAIL
- ☐136F. PHIL CLARK
- ☐137F. MARK ETTLES
- ☐138F. JEFF GARDNER
- ☐139F. PAT GOMEZ
- ☐140F. RICKY GUTIERREZ
- ☐141F. GENE HARRIS
- ☐142F. KEVIN HIGGINS
- ☐143F. TREVOR HOFFMAN
- ☐144F. PHIL PLANTIER

□145F. KERRY TAYLOR
□146F. GUILLERMO VELASQUEX
□147F. WALLY WHITEHURST
□148F. TIM WORRELL

SAN FRANCISCO GIANTS

□149F. TODD BENZINGER
□150F. BARRY BONDS
□151F. GREG BRUMMETT
□152F. MARK CARREON
□153F. DAVE MARTINEZ
□154F. JEFF REED
□155F. KEVIN ROGERS

SEATTLE MARINERS

□263F. RICH AMARAL
□264F. MIKE BLOWERS
□265F. CHRIS BOSIO
□266F. NORM CHARLTON
□267F. JIM CONVERSE
□268F. JOHN CUMMNGS
□269F. MIKE FELDER
□270F. MIKE HAMPTON
□271F. BILL HASELMAN
□272F. DWAYNE HENRY
□273F. GREG LITTON
□274F. MACKEY SASSER
□275F. LEE TINSLEY
□276F. DAVID WAINHOUSE

TEXAS RANGERS

□277F. JEFF BRONKEY
□278F. BENJI GIL
□279F. TOM HENKE
□280F. CHARLIE LEIBRANDT
□281F. ROBB NEN
□282F. BILL RIPKEN
□283F. JON SHAVE
□284F. DOUG STRANGE
□285F. MATT WHITESIDE

TORONTO BLUE JAYS

□286F. SCOTT BROW
□287F. WILLIE CANATE
□288F. TONY CASTILLO
□289F. DOMINGO CEDENO
□290F. DARNELL COLES
□291F. DANNY COX
□292F. MARK EICHHORN
□293F. TONY FERNANDEZ
□294F. AL LEITER
□295F. PAUL MOLITOR
□296F. DAVE STEWART
□297F. WODDY WILLIAMS

1994 FLEER (720)
2 1/2" X 3 1/2"

ATLANTA BRAVES

□ 350. STEVE AVERY
□ 351. STEVE BEDROSIAN
□ 352. RAFAEL BELLIARD
□ 353. DAMON BERRYHILL
□ 354. JEFF BLAUSER
□ 355. SID BREAM
□ 356. FRANCISCO CABRERA
□ 357. MARVIN FREEMAN
□ 358. RON GANT
□ 359. TOM GLAVINE
□ 360. JAY HOWELL
□ 361. DAVID JUSTICE
□ 362. RYAN KLESKO
□ 363. MARK LEMKE
□ 364. JAVIER LOPEZ
□ 365. GREG MADDUX
□ 366. FRED MCGRIFF
□ 367. GREG MCMICHAEL
□ 368. KENT MERCKER
□ 369. OTIS NIXON
□ 370. GREG OLSON
□ 371. BILL PECOTA
□ 372. TERRY PENDLETON
□ 373. DEION SANDERS
□ 374. PETE SMITH
□ 375. JOHN SMOLTZ
□ 376. MIKE STANTON
□ 377. TONY TARASCO
□ 378. MARK WOHLERS

BALTIMORE ORIOLES

□ 1. BRADY ANDERSON
□ 2. HAROLD BAINES
□ 3. MIKE DEVEREAUX
□ 4. TODD FROHWIRTH
□ 5. JEFFREY HAMMONDS
□ 6. CHRIS HOILES
□ 7. TIM HULETT
□ 8. BEN MCDONALD
□ 9. MARK MCLEMORE
□ 10. ALAN MILLS
□ 11. JAMIE MOYER
□ 12. MIKE MUSSINA
□ 13. GREGG OLSON
□ 14. MIKE PAGLIARULO
□ 15. BRAD PENNINGTON
□ 16. JIM POOLE
□ 17. HAROLD REYNOLDS
□ 18. ARTHUR RHODES
□ 19. CAL RIPKEN, JR.
□ 20. DAVID SEGUI
□ 21. RICK SUTCLIFFE
□ 22. FERNANDO VALENZUELA
□ 23. JACK VOIGT
□ 24. MARK WILLIAMSON

BOSTON RED SOX

□ 25. SCOTT BANKHEAD
□ 26. ROGER CLEMENS
□ 27. SCOTT COOPER
□ 28. DANNY DARWIN
□ 29. ANDRE DAWSON
□ 30. ROB DEER
□ 31. JOHN DOPSON
□ 32. SCOTT FLETCHER
□ 33. MIKE GREENWELL
□ 34. GREG HARRIS
□ 35. BILLY HATCHER
□ 36. BOB MELVIN
□ 37. TONY PENA
□ 38. PAUL QUANTRILL
□ 39. CARLOS QUINTANA
□ 40. ERNEST RILES
□ 41. JEFF RUSSELL
□ 42. KEN RYAN
□ 43. AARON SELE
□ 44. JOHN VALENTIN
□ 45. MO VAUGHN
□ 46. FRANK VIOLA
□ 47. BOB ZUPCIC

CALIFORNIA ANGELS

□ 48. MIKE BUTCHER
□ 49. ROD CORREIA
□ 50. CHAD CURTIS
□ 51. CHILI DAVIS
□ 52. GARY DISARCINA
□ 53. DAMION EASLEY
□ 54. JIM EDMONDS
□ 55. CHUCK FINLEY
□ 56. STEVE FREY
□ 57. RENE GONZALES
□ 58. JOE GRAHE
□ 59. HILLY HATHAWAY
□ 60. STAN JAVIER
□ 61. MARK LANGSTON
□ 62. PHIL LEFTWICH
□ 63. TOREY LOVULLO
□ 64. JOE MAGRANE
□ 65. GREG MYERS
□ 66. KEN PATTERSON
□ 67. EDUARDO PEREZ
□ 68. LUIS POLONIA
□ 69. TIM SALMON
□ 70. J.T. SNOW
□ 71. RON TINGLEY
□ 72. JULIO VALERA

CHICAGO CUBS

□ 379. JOSE BAUTISTA
□ 380. SHAWN BOSKIE
□ 381. STEVE BUECHELE
□ 382. FRANK CASTILLO
□ 383. MARK GRACE
□ 384. JOSE GUZMAN
□ 385. MIKE HARKEY
□ 386. GREG HIBBARD
□ 387. GLENALLEN HILL
□ 388. STEVE LAKE
□ 389. DERRICK MAY
□ 390. CHUCK MCELROY
□ 391. MIKE MORGAN
□ 392. RANDY MYERS
□ 393. DAN PLESAC
□ 394. KEVIN ROBERSON
□ 395. REY SANCHEZ
□ 396. RYNE SANDBERG
□ 397. BOB SCANLAN
□ 398. DWIGHT SMITH
□ 399. SAMMY SOSA
□ 400. JOSE VIZCAINO
□ 401. RICK WILKINS
□ 402. WILLIE WILSON
□ 403. ERIC YELDING

CHICAGO WHITE SOX

□ 73. WILSON ALVAREZ
□ 74. TIM BELCHER
□ 75. GEORGE BELL
□ 76. JASON BERE
□ 77. ROD BOLTON
□ 78. ELLIS BURKS
□ 79. JOEY CORA
□ 80. ALEX FERNANDEZ
□ 81. CRAIG GREBECK
□ 82. OZZIE GUILLEN
□ 83. ROBERTO HERNANDEZ
□ 84. BO JACKSON
□ 85. LANCE JOHNSON
□ 86. RON KARKOVICE
□ 87. MIKE LAVALLIERE
□ 88. KIRK MCCASKILL
□ 89. JACK MCDOWELL
□ 90. WARREN NEWSON
□ 91. DAN PASQUA
□ 92. SCOTT RADINSKY
□ 93. TIM RAINES
□ 94. STEVE SAX
□ 95. JEFF SCHWARZ
□ 96. FRANK THOMAS
□ 97. ROBIN VENTURA

CINCINNATI REDS

□ 404. BOBBY AYALA
□ 405. JEFF BRANSON
□ 406. TOM BROWNING
□ 407. JACOB BRUMFIELD
□ 408. TIM COSTO
□ 409. ROB DIBBLE
□ 410. WILLIE GREENE
□ 411. THOMAS HOWARD
□ 412. ROBERTO KELLY
□ 413. BILL LANDRUM
□ 414. BARRY LARKIN
□ 415. LARRY LUEBBERS
□ 416. KEVIN MITCHELL

- ☐ 417. HAL MORRIS
- ☐ 418. JOE OLIVER
- ☐ 419. TIM PUGH
- ☐ 420. JEFF REARDON
- ☐ 421. JOSE RIJO
- ☐ 422. BIP ROBERTS
- ☐ 423. JOHN ROPER
- ☐ 424. JOHNNY RUFFIN
- ☐ 425. CHRIS SABO
- ☐ 426. JUAN SAMUEL
- ☐ 427. REGGIE SANDERS
- ☐ 428. SCOTT SERVICE
- ☐ 429. JOHN SMILEY
- ☐ 430. JERRY SPRADLIN
- ☐ 431. KEVIN WICKANDER

CLEVELAND INDIANS

- ☐ 98. SANDY ALOMAR, JR.
- ☐ 99. CARLOS BAERGA
- ☐ 100. ALBERT BELLE
- ☐ 101. MARK CLARK
- ☐ 102. JERRY DIPOTO
- ☐ 103. ALVARO ESPINOZA
- ☐ 104. FELIX FERMIN
- ☐ 105. JEREMY HERNANDEZ
- ☐ 106. REGGIE JEFFERSON
- ☐ 107. WAYNE KIRBY
- ☐ 108. TOM KRAMER
- ☐ 109. MARK LEWIS
- ☐ 110. DEREK LILLIQUIST
- ☐ 111. KENNY LOFTON
- ☐ 112. CANDY MALDONADO
- ☐ 113. JOSE MESA
- ☐ 114. JEFF MUTIS
- ☐ 115. CHARLES NAGY
- ☐ 116. BOB OJEDA
- ☐ 117. JUNIOR ORTIZ
- ☐ 118. ERIC PLUNK
- ☐ 119. MANNY RAMIEREZ
- ☐ 120. PAUL SORRENTO
- ☐ 121. JIM THOME
- ☐ 122. JEFF TREADWAY
- ☐ 123. BILL WERTZ

COLORADO ROCKIES

- ☐ 432. FREDDIE BENAVIDES
- ☐ 433. DANTE BICHETTE
- ☐ 434. WILLIE BLAIR
- ☐ 435. DARYL BOSTON
- ☐ 436. KENT BOTTENFIELD
- ☐ 437. VINNY CASTILLA
- ☐ 438. JERALD CLARK
- ☐ 439. ALEX COLE
- ☐ 440. ANDRES GALARRAGA
- ☐ 441. JOE GIRARDI
- ☐ 442. GREG HARRIS
- ☐ 443. CHARLIE HAYES
- ☐ 444. DARREN HOLMES
- ☐ 445. CHRIS JONES
- ☐ 446. ROBERTO MEJIA
- ☐ 447. DAVID NIED
- ☐ 448. J. OWENS
- ☐ 449. JEFF PARRETT
- ☐ 450. STEVE REED
- ☐ 451. ARMANDO REYNOSO
- ☐ 452. BRUCE RUFFIN
- ☐ 453. MO SANFORD
- ☐ 454. DANNY SHEAFFER
- ☐ 455. JIM TATUM
- ☐ 456. GARY WAYNE
- ☐ 457. ERIC YOUNG

DETROIT TIGERS

- ☐ 124. SKEETER BARNES
- ☐ 125. MILT CUYLER
- ☐ 126. ERIC DAVIS
- ☐ 127. JOHN DOHERTY
- ☐ 128. CECIL FIELDER
- ☐ 129. TRAVIS FRYMAN
- ☐ 130. KIRK GIBSON
- ☐ 131. DAN GLADDEN
- ☐ 132. GREG GOHR
- ☐ 133. CHRIS GOMEZ
- ☐ 134. BILL GULLICKSON
- ☐ 135. MIKE HENNEMAN
- ☐ 136. KURT KNUDSEN
- ☐ 137. CHAD KREUTER
- ☐ 138. BILL KRUEGER
- ☐ 139. SCOTT LIVINGSTONE
- ☐ 140. BOB MACDONALD
- ☐ 141. MIKE MOORE
- ☐ 142. TONY PHILLIPS
- ☐ 143. MICKEY TETTLETON
- ☐ 144. ALAN TRAMMELL
- ☐ 145. DAVID WELLS
- ☐ 146. LOU WHITAKER

FLORIDA MARLINS

- ☐ 458. LUIS AQUINO
- ☐ 459. ALEX ARIAS
- ☐ 460. JACK ARMSTRONG
- ☐ 461. BRET BARBERIE
- ☐ 462. RYAN BOWEN
- ☐ 463. CHUCK CARR
- ☐ 464. JEFF CONINE
- ☐ 465. HENRY COTTO
- ☐ 466. ORESTES DESTRADE
- ☐ 467. CHRIS HAMMOND
- ☐ 468. BRYAN HARVEY
- ☐ 469. CHARLIE HOUGH
- ☐ 470. JOE KLINK
- ☐ 471. RICHIE LEWIS
- ☐ 472. BOB NATAL
- ☐ 473. PAT RAPP
- ☐ 474. RICH RENTERIA
- ☐ 475. RICH RODRIGUEZ
- ☐ 476. BENITO SANTIAGO
- ☐ 477. GARY SHEFFIELD
- ☐ 478. MATT TURNER
- ☐ 479. DAVID WEATHERS
- ☐ 480. WALT WEISS
- ☐ 481. DARRELL WHITMORE

HOUSTON ASTROS

- ☐ 482. ERIC ANTHONY
- ☐ 483. JEFF BAGWELL
- ☐ 484. KEVIN BASS
- ☐ 485. CRAIG BIGGIO
- ☐ 486. KEN CAMINITI
- ☐ 487. ANDUJAR CEDENO
- ☐ 488. CHRIS DONNELS
- ☐ 489. DOUG DRABEK
- ☐ 490. STEVE FINLEY
- ☐ 491. LUIS GONZALEZ
- ☐ 492. PETE HARNISCH
- ☐ 493. XAVIER HERNANDEZ
- ☐ 494. DOUG JONES
- ☐ 495. TODD JONES
- ☐ 496. DARRYL KILE
- ☐ 497. AL OSUNA
- ☐ 498. MARK PORTUGAL
- ☐ 499. SCOTT SERVAIS
- ☐ 500. GREG SWINDELL
- ☐ 501. EDDIE TAUBENSEE
- ☐ 502. JOSE URIBE
- ☐ 503. BRIAN WILLIAMS

KANSAS CITY ROYALS

- ☐ 147. KEVIN APPIER
- ☐ 148. STAN BELINDA
- ☐ 149. GEORGE BRETT
- ☐ 150. BILLY BREWER
- ☐ 151. HUBIE BROOKS
- ☐ 152. DAVID CONE
- ☐ 153. GARY GAETTI
- ☐ 154. GREG GAGNE
- ☐ 155. TOM GORDON
- ☐ 156. MARK GUBICZA
- ☐ 157. CHRIS GWYNN
- ☐ 158. JOHN HABYAN
- ☐ 159. CHRIS HANEY
- ☐ 160. PHIL HIATT
- ☐ 161. FELIX JOSE
- ☐ 162. WALLY JOYNER
- ☐ 163. JOSE LIND
- ☐ 164. MIKE MACFARLANE
- ☐ 165. MIKE MAGNANTE
- ☐ 166. BRENT MAYNE
- ☐ 167. BRIAN MCRAE
- ☐ 168. KEVIN MCREYNOLDS
- ☐ 169. KEITH MILLER
- ☐ 170. JEFF MONTGOMERY
- ☐ 171. HIPOLITO PICHARDO
- ☐ 172. RICO ROSSY

LOS ANGELES DODGERS

- ☐ 504. BILLY ASHLEY
- ☐ 505. PEDRO ASTACIO
- ☐ 506. BRETT BUTLER
- ☐ 507. TOM CANDIOTTI
- ☐ 508. OMAR DAAL
- ☐ 509. JIM GOTT
- ☐ 510. KEVIN GROSS
- ☐ 511. DAVE HANSEN
- ☐ 512. CARLOS HERNANDEZ
- ☐ 513. OREL HERSHISER
- ☐ 514. ERIC KARROS
- ☐ 515. PEDRO MARTINEZ
- ☐ 516. RAMON MARTINEZ
- ☐ 517. ROGER MCDOWELL
- ☐ 518. RAUL MONDESI
- ☐ 519. JOSE OFFERMAN
- ☐ 520. MIKE PIAZZA
- ☐ 521. JODY REED
- ☐ 522. HENRY RODRIGUEZ
- ☐ 523. MIKE SHARPERSON
- ☐ 524. CORY SNYDER
- ☐ 525. DARRYL STRAWBERRY
- ☐ 526. RICK TRLICEK
- ☐ 527. TIM WALLACH
- ☐ 528. MITCH WEBSTER
- ☐ 529. STEVE WILSON
- ☐ 530. TODD WORRELL

MILWAUKEE BREWERS

- ☐ 173. JUAN BELL
- ☐ 174. RICKY BONES
- ☐ 175. CAL ELDRED
- ☐ 176. MIKE FETTERS
- ☐ 177. DARRYL HAMILTON
- ☐ 178. DOUG HENRY
- ☐ 179. MIKE IGNASIAK
- ☐ 180. JOHN JAHA
- ☐ 181. PAT LISTACH
- ☐ 182. GRAEME LLOYD
- ☐ 183. MATT MIESKE
- ☐ 184. ANGEL MIRANDA
- ☐ 185. JAIME NAVARRO
- ☐ 186. DAVE NILSSON
- ☐ 187. TROY O'LEARY
- ☐ 188. JESSE OROSCO
- ☐ 189. KEVIN REIMER
- ☐ 190. KEVIN SEITZER
- ☐ 191. BILL SPIERS
- ☐ 192. B.J. SURHOFF
- ☐ 193. DICKIE THON
- ☐ 194. JOSE VALENTIN
- ☐ 195. GREG VAUGHN
- ☐ 196. BILL WEGMAN
- ☐ 197. ROBIN YOUNT

MINNESOTA TWINS

- ☐ 198. RICK AGUILERA
- ☐ 199. WILLIE BANKS
- ☐ 200. BERNARDO BRITO
- ☐ 201. LARRY CASIAN
- ☐ 202. SCOTT ERICKSON
- ☐ 203. EDDIE GUARDADO
- ☐ 204. MARK GUTHRIE
- ☐ 205. CHIP HALE
- ☐ 206. BRIAN HARPER
- ☐ 207. MIKE HARTLEY
- ☐ 208. KENT HRBEK
- ☐ 209. TERRY JORGENSEN
- ☐ 210. CHUCK KNOBLAUCH
- ☐ 211. GENE LARKIN
- ☐ 212. SHANE MACK
- ☐ 213. DAVID MCCARTY
- ☐ 214. PAT MEARES
- ☐ 215. PEDRO MUNOZ
- ☐ 216. DEREK PARKS
- ☐ 217. KIRBY PUCKETT
- ☐ 218. JEFF REBOULET
- ☐ 219. KEVIN TAPANI
- ☐ 220. MIKE TROMBLEY
- ☐ 221. GEORGE TSAMIS
- ☐ 222. CARL WILLIS
- ☐ 223. DAVE WINFIELD

MONTREAL EXPOS

- ☐ 531. MOISES ALOU
- ☐ 532. BRIAN BARNES
- ☐ 533. SEAN BERRY
- ☐ 534. GREG COLBRUNN
- ☐ 535. DELINO DESHIELDS
- ☐ 536. JEFF FASSERO
- ☐ 537. DARRIN FLETCHER
- ☐ 538. CLIFF FLOYD
- ☐ 539. LOU FRAZIER
- ☐ 540. MARQUIS GRISSOM
- ☐ 541. BUTCH HENRY
- ☐ 542. KEN HILL
- ☐ 543. MIKE LANSING
- ☐ 544. BRIAN LOONEY
- ☐ 545. DENNIS MARTINEZ
- ☐ 546. CHRIS NABHOLZ
- ☐ 547. RANDY READY
- ☐ 548. MEL ROJAS
- ☐ 549. KIRK RUETER
- ☐ 550. TIM SCOTT
- ☐ 551. JEFF SHAW
- ☐ 552. TIM SPEHR
- ☐ 553. JOHN VANDER WAL
- ☐ 554. LARRY WALKER
- ☐ 555. JOHN WETTELAND
- ☐ 556. RONDELL WHITE

NEW YORK METS

- ☐ 557. TIM BOGAR
- ☐ 558. BOBBY BONILLA
- ☐ 559. JEROMY BURNITZ
- ☐ 560. SID FERNANDEZ
- ☐ 561. JOHN FRANCO
- ☐ 562. DAVE GALLAGHER
- ☐ 563. DWIGHT GOODEN
- ☐ 564. ERIC HILLMAN
- ☐ 565. TODD HUNDLEY
- ☐ 566. JEFF INNIS
- ☐ 567. DARRIN JACKSON
- ☐ 568. HOWARD JOHNSON
- ☐ 569. BOBBY JONES
- ☐ 570. JEFF KENT
- ☐ 571. MIKE MADDUX
- ☐ 572. JEFF MCKNIGHT
- ☐ 573. EDDIE MURRAY
- ☐ 574. CHARLIE O'BRIEN
- ☐ 575. JOE ORSULAK
- ☐ 576. BRET SABERHAGEN
- ☐ 577. PETE SCHOUREK
- ☐ 578. DAVE TELGHEDER
- ☐ 579. RYAN THOMPSON
- ☐ 580. ANTHONY YOUNG

NEW YORK YANKEES

- ☐ 224. JIM ABBOTT
- ☐ 225. PAU ASSENMACHER
- ☐ 226. WADE BOGGS
- ☐ 227. RUSS DAVIS
- ☐ 228. STEVE FARR
- ☐ 229. MIKE GALLEGO
- ☐ 230. PAUL GIBSON
- ☐ 231. STEVE HOWE
- ☐ 232. DION JAMES
- ☐ 233. DOMINGO JEAN
- ☐ 234. SCOTT KAMIENIECKI
- ☐ 235. PAT KELLY
- ☐ 236. JIMMY KEY
- ☐ 237. JIM LEYRITZ
- ☐ 238. KEVIN MAAS
- ☐ 239. DON MATTINGLY
- ☐ 240. RICH MONTELEONE
- ☐ 241. BOBBY MUNOZ
- ☐ 242. MATT NOKES
- ☐ 243. PAUL O'NEILL
- ☐ 244. SPIKE OWEN
- ☐ 245. MELIDO PEREZ
- ☐ 246. LEE SMITH
- ☐ 247. MIKE STANLEY
- ☐ 248. DANNY TARTABULL
- ☐ 249. RANDY VELARDE
- ☐ 250. BOB WICKMAN
- ☐ 251. BERNIE WILLIAMS

OAKLAND A'S

- ☐ 252. MIKE ALDRETE
- ☐ 253. MARCOS ARMAS
- ☐ 254. LANCE BLANKENSHIP
- ☐ 255. MIKE BORDICK
- ☐ 256. SCOTT BROSIUS
- ☐ 257. JERRY BROWNE
- ☐ 258. RON DARLING
- ☐ 259. KELLY DOWNS
- ☐ 260. DENNIS ECKERSLEY
- ☐ 261. BRENT GATES
- ☐ 262. GOOSE GOSSAGE
- ☐ 263. SCOTT HEMOND
- ☐ 264. DAVE HENDERSON
- ☐ 265. RICK HONEYCUTT
- ☐ 266. VINCE HORSMAN
- ☐ 267. SCOTT LYDY
- ☐ 268. MARK MCGWIRE
- ☐ 269. MIKE MOHLER
- ☐ 270. TROY NEEL
- ☐ 271. EDWIN NUNEZ
- ☐ 272. CRAIG PAQUETTE
- ☐ 273. RUBEN SIERRA
- ☐ 274. TERRY STEINBACH
- ☐ 275. TODD VAN POPPEL
- ☐ 276. BOB WELCH
- ☐ 277. BOBBY WITT

PHILADELPHIA PHILLIES

- ☐ 581. RUBEN AMARO
- ☐ 582. LARRY ANDERSEN
- ☐ 583. KIM BATISTE
- ☐ 584. WES CHAMBERLAIN
- ☐ 585. DARREN DAULTON
- ☐ 586. MARIANO DUNCAN
- ☐ 587. LENNY DYKSTRA
- ☐ 588. JIM EISENREICH
- ☐ 589. TOMMY GREENE
- ☐ 590. DAVE HOLLINS
- ☐ 591. PETE INCAVIGLIA
- ☐ 592. DANNY JACKSON
- ☐ 593. RICKY JORDAN
- ☐ 594. JOHN KRUK
- ☐ 595. ROGER MASON
- ☐ 596. MICKEY MORANDINI
- ☐ 597. TERRY MULHOLLAND
- ☐ 598. TODD PRATT
- ☐ 599. BEN RIVERA
- ☐ 600. CURT SCHILLING
- ☐ 601. KEVIN STOCKER
- ☐ 602. MILT THOMPSON
- ☐ 603. DAVID WEST
- ☐ 604. MITCH WILLIAMS

PITTSBURGH PIRATES

- ☐ 605. JAY BELL
- ☐ 606. DAVE CLARK
- ☐ 607. STEVE COOKE
- ☐ 608. TOM FOLEY
- ☐ 609. CARLOS GARCIA
- ☐ 610. JOEL JOHNSTON
- ☐ 611. JEFF KING
- ☐ 612. AL MARTIN
- ☐ 613. LLOYD MCCLENDON
- ☐ 614. ORLANDO MERCED
- ☐ 615. BLAS MINOR
- ☐ 616. DENNY NEAGLE
- ☐ 617. MARK PETKOVSEK
- ☐ 618. TOM PRINCE
- ☐ 619. DON SLAUGHT
- ☐ 620. ZANE SMITH
- ☐ 621. RANDY TOMLIN
- ☐ 622. ANDY VAN SLYKE
- ☐ 623. PAUL WAGNER
- ☐ 624. TIM WAKEFIELD
- ☐ 625. BOB WALK
- ☐ 626. KEVIN YOUNG

ST. LOUIS CARDINALS

- ☐ 627. LUIS ALICEA
- ☐ 628. RENE AROCHA
- ☐ 629. ROD BREWER
- ☐ 630. RHEAL CORMIER
- ☐ 631. BERNARD GILKEY
- ☐ 632. LEE GUETTERMAN
- ☐ 633. GREGG JEFFERIES
- ☐ 634. BRIAN JORDAN
- ☐ 635. LES LANCASTER
- ☐ 636. RAY LANKFORD
- ☐ 637. ROB MURPHY
- ☐ 638. OMAR OLIVARES
- ☐ 639. JOSE OQUENDO
- ☐ 640. DONOVAN OSBORNE
- ☐ 641. TOM PAGNOZZI
- ☐ 642. ERIK PAPPAS
- ☐ 643. GERONIMO PENA
- ☐ 644. MIKE PEREZ
- ☐ 645. GERALD PERRY
- ☐ 646. OZZIE SMITH
- ☐ 647. BOB TEWKSBURY
- ☐ 648. ALLEN WATSON
- ☐ 649. MARK WHITEN
- ☐ 650. TRACY WOODSON
- ☐ 651. TODD ZEILE

SAN DIEGO PADRES

- ☐ 652. ANDY ASHBY
- ☐ 653. BRAD AUSMUS
- ☐ 654. BILLY BEAN
- ☐ 655. DEREK BELL
- ☐ 656. ANDY BENES
- ☐ 657. DOUG BROCAIL
- ☐ 658. JARVIS BROWN
- ☐ 659. ARCHI CIANFROCCO
- ☐ 660. PHIL CLARK
- ☐ 661. MARK DAVIS
- ☐ 662. JEFF GARDNER
- ☐ 663. PAT GOMEZ
- ☐ 664. RICKY GUTIERREZ
- ☐ 665. TONY GWYNN
- ☐ 666. GENE HARRIS
- ☐ 667. KEVIN HIGGINS
- ☐ 668. TREVOR HOFFMAN
- ☐ 669. PEDRO MARTINEZ
- ☐ 670. TIM MAUSER
- ☐ 671. MELVIN NIEVES
- ☐ 672. PHIL PLANTIER
- ☐ 673. FRANK SEMINARA
- ☐ 674. CRAIG SHIPLEY
- ☐ 675. KERRY TAYLOR
- ☐ 676. TIM TEUFEL
- ☐ 677. GUILLERMO VELASQUEZ
- ☐ 678. WALLY WHITEHURST
- ☐ 679. TIM WORRELL

SAN FRANCISCO GIANTS

- ☐ 680. ROD BECK
- ☐ 681. MIKE BENJAMIN
- ☐ 682. TODD BENZINGER
- ☐ 683. BUD BLACK
- ☐ 684. BARRY BONDS
- ☐ 685. JEFF BRANTLEY
- ☐ 686. DAVE BURBA
- ☐ 687. JOHN BURKETT
- ☐ 688. MARK CARREON
- ☐ 689. WILL CLARK
- ☐ 690. ROYCE CLAYTON
- ☐ 691. BRYAN HICKERSON
- ☐ 692. MIKE JACKSON
- ☐ 693. DARREN LEWIS
- ☐ 694. KIRT MANWARING
- ☐ 695. DAVE MARTINEZ
- ☐ 696. WILLIE MCGEE
- ☐ 697. JOHN PATTERSON
- ☐ 698. JEFF REED
- ☐ 699. KEVIN ROGERS

☐ 700. SCOTT SANDERSON
☐ 701. STEVE SCARSONE
☐ 702. BILLY SWIFT
☐ 703. ROBBY THOMPSON
☐ 704. MATT WILLIAMS
☐ 705. TREVOR WILSON

SEATTLE MARINERS

☐ 278. RICH AMARAL
☐ 279. MIKE BLOWERS
☐ 280. BRET BOONE
☐ 281. CHRIS BOSIO
☐ 282. JAY BUHNER
☐ 283. NORM CHARLTON
☐ 284. MIKE FELDER
☐ 285. DAVE FLEMING
☐ 286. KEN GRIFFEY, JR.
☐ 287. ERIK HANSON
☐ 288. BILL HASELMAN
☐ 289. BRAD HOLMAN
☐ 290. RANDY JOHNSON
☐ 291. TIM LEARY
☐ 292. GREG LITTON
☐ 293. DAVE MAGADAN
☐ 294. EDGAR MARTINEZ
☐ 295. TINO MARTINEZ
☐ 296. JEFF NELSON
☐ 297. ERIK PLANTENBERG
☐ 298. MACKEY SASSER
☐ 299. BRIAN TURANG
☐ 300. DAVE VALLE
☐ 301. OMAR VIZQUEL

TEXAS RANGERS

☐ 302. BRIAN BOHANON
☐ 303. KEVIN BROWN
☐ 304. JOSE CANSECO
☐ 305. MARIO DIAZ
☐ 306. JULIO FRANCO
☐ 307. JUAN GONZALEZ
☐ 308. TOM HENKE
☐ 309. DAVID HULSE
☐ 310. MANUEL LEE
☐ 311. CRAIG LEFFERTS
☐ 312. CHARLIE LEIBRANDT
☐ 313. RAFAEL PALMEIRO
☐ 314. DEAN PALMER
☐ 315. ROGER PAVLIK
☐ 316. DAN PELTIER
☐ 317. GENO PETRALLI
☐ 318. GARY REDUS
☐ 319. IVAN RODRIGUEZ
☐ 320. KENNY ROGERS
☐ 321. NOLAN RYAN
☐ 322. DOUG STRANGE
☐ 323. MATT WHITESIDE

TORONTO BLUE JAYS

☐ 324. ROBERTO ALOMAR
☐ 325. PAT BORDERS
☐ 326. JOE CARTER
☐ 327. TONY CASTILLO
☐ 328. DARNELL COLES
☐ 329. DANNY COX
☐ 330. MARK EICHHORN
☐ 331. TONY FERNANDEZ
☐ 332. ALFREDO GRIFFIN
☐ 333. JUAN GUZMAN
☐ 334. RICKEY HENDERSON
☐ 335. PAT HENTGEN
☐ 336. RANDY KNORR
☐ 337. AL LEITER
☐ 338. PAUL MOLITOR
☐ 339. JACK MORRIS
☐ 340. JOHN OLERUD
☐ 341. DICK SCHOFIELD
☐ 342. ED SPRAGUE
☐ 343. DAVE STEWART
☐ 344. TODD STOTTLEMYRE
☐ 345. MIKE TIMLIN
☐ 346. DUANE WARD
☐ 347. TURNER WARD
☐ 348. DEVON WHITE
☐ 349. WOODY WILLIAMS

1994 FLEER UPDATE (200) 2 1/2" X 3 1/2"

ATLANTA BRAVES

☐ 101U. MIKE KELLY
☐ 102U. ROBERTO KELLY
☐ 103U. CHARLIE O'BRIEN
☐ 104U. JOSE OLIVA
☐ 105U. GREGG OLSON

BALTIMORE ORIOLES

☐ 1U. MARK EICHHORN
☐ 2U. SID FERNANDEZ
☐ 3U. LEO GOMEZ
☐ 4U. MIKE OQUIST
☐ 5U. RAFAEL PALMEIRO
☐ 6U. CHRIS SABO
☐ 7U. DWIGHT SMITH
☐ 8U. LEE SMITH

BOSTON RED SOX

☐ 9U. DAMON BERRYHILL
☐ 10U. WES CHAMERLAIN
☐ 11U. GAR FINNVOLD
☐ 12U. CHRIS HOWARD
☐ 13U. TIM NAEHRING
☐ 14U. OTIS NIXON

CALIFORNIA ANGELS

☐ 15U. BRIAN ANDERSON
☐ 16U. JORGE FABREGAS
☐ 17U. REX HUDLER
☐ 18U. BO JACKSON
☐ 19U. MARK LEITER
☐ 20U. SPIKE OWEN
☐ 21U. HAROLD REYNOLDS
☐ 22U. CHRIS TURNER

CHICAGO CUBS

☐ 106U. WILLIE BANKS
☐ 107U. JIM BULLINGER
☐ 108U. CHUCK CRIM
☐ 109U. SHAWON DUNSTON
☐ 110U. KARL RHODES
☐ 111U. STEVE TRACHSEL
☐ 112U. ANTHONY YOUNG
☐ 113U. EDDIE ZAMBRANO

CHICAGO WHITE SOX

☐ 23U. DENNIS COOK
☐ 24U. JOSE DELEON
☐ 25U. JULIO FRANCO
☐ 26U. JOE HALL
☐ 27U. DARRIN JACKSON
☐ 28U. DANE JOHNSON
☐ 29U. NORBERTO MARTIN
☐ 30U. SCOTT SANDERSON

CINCINNATI REDS

☐ 114U. BRET BOONE
☐ 115U. JEFF BRANTLEY
☐ 116U. HECTOR CARRASCO
☐ 117U. TONY FERNANDEZ
☐ 118U. TIM FORTUGNO
☐ 119U. ERIK HANSON
☐ 120U. CHUCK MCELROY
☐ 121U. DEION SANDERS

CLEVELAND INDIANS

☐ 31U. JASON GRIMSLEY
☐ 32U. DENNIS MARTINEZ
☐ 33U. JACK MORRIS
☐ 34U. EDDIE MURRAY
☐ 35U. CHAD OGEA
☐ 36U. TONY PENA
☐ 37U. PAUL SHUEY
☐ 38U. OMAR VIZQUEL

COLORADO ROCKIES

☐ 122U. ELLIS BURKS
☐ 123U. MARVIN FREEMAN
☐ 124U. MIKE HARKEY
☐ 125U. HOWARD JOHNSON
☐ 126U. MIKE KINGERY
☐ 127U. NELSON LIRIANO
☐ 128U. MARCUS MOORE
☐ 129U. MIKE MUNOZ
☐ 130U. KEVIN RITZ
☐ 131U. WALT WEISS

DETROIT TIGERS

☐ 39U. DANNY BAUTISTA
☐ 40U. TIM BELCHER
☐ 41U. JOE BOEVER
☐ 42U. STORM DAVIS
☐ 43U. JUNIOR FELIX
☐ 44U. MIKE GARDINER
☐ 45U. BUDDY GROOM
☐ 46U. JUAN SAMUEL

FLORIDA MARLINS

☐ 132U. KURT ABBOTT
☐ 133U. JERRY BROWNE
☐ 134U. GREG COLBRUNN
☐ 135U. JEREMY HERNANDEZ
☐ 136U. DAVE MAGADAN
☐ 137U. KURT MILLER
☐ 138U. ROBB NEN
☐ 139U. JESUS TAVAREZ

HOUSTON ASTROS

☐ 140U. SID BREAM
☐ 141U. TOM EDENS
☐ 142U. TONY EUSEBIO
☐ 143U. JOHN HUDEK
☐ 144U. BRIAN HUNTER
☐ 145U. ORLANDO MILLER
☐ 146U. JAMES MOUTON

1994 Fleer Update

□147U. SHANE REYNOLDS

KANSAS CITY ROYALS

□ 47U. VINCE COLEMAN
□ 48U. BOB HAMELIN
□ 49U. DAVE HENDERSON
□ 50U. RUSTY MEACHAM
□ 51U. TERRY SHUMPERT

LOS ANGELES DODGERS

□148U. RAFAEL BOURNIGAL
□149U. DELINO DESHIELDS
□150U. GAREY INGRAM
□151U. CHAN HO PARK

MILWAUKEE BREWERS

□ 52U. JEFF BRONKEY
□ 53U. ALEX DIAZ
□ 54U. BRIAN HARPER
□ 55U. JOSE MERCEDES
□ 56U. JODY REED
□ 57U. BOB SCANLAN
□ 58U. TURNER WARD

MINNESOTA TWINS

□ 59U. RICH BECKER
□ 60U. ALEX COLE
□ 61U. DENNY HOCKING
□ 62U. SCOTT LEIUS
□ 63U. PAT MAHOMES
□ 64U. CARLOS PULIDO
□ 65U. DAVE STEVENS
□ 66U. MATT WALBECK

MONTREAL EXPOS

□152U. WIL CORDERO
□153U. PEDRO MARTINEZ
□154U. RANDY MILLIGAN
□155U. LENNY WEBSTER

NEW YORK METS

□156U. RICO BROGNA
□157U. JOSIAS MANZANILLO
□158U. KEVIN MCREYNOLDS
□159U. MIKE REMLINGER
□160U. DAVID SEGUI
□161U. PETE SMITH
□162U. KELLY STINNETT
□163U. JOSE VIZCAINO

NEW YORK YANKEES

□ 67U. XAVIER HERNANDEZ
□ 68U. STERLING HITCHCOCK
□ 69U. TERRY MULHOLLAND
□ 70U. LUIS POLONIA
□ 71U. GERALD WILLIAMS

OAKLAND A'S

□ 72U. MARK ACRE

□ 73U. GERONIMO BERROA
□ 74U. RICKEY HENDERSON
□ 75U. STAN JAVIER
□ 76U. STEVE KARSAY
□ 77U. CARLOS REYES
□ 78U. BILL TAYLOR

PHILADELPHIA PHILLIES

□164U. BILLY HATCHER
□165U. DOUG JONES
□166U. MIKE LIEBERTHAL
□167U. TONY LONGMIRE
□168U. BOBBY MUNOZ
□169U. PAUL QUANTRILL
□170U. HEATHCLIFF SLOCUMB
□171U. FERNANDO VALENZUELA

PITTSBURGH PIRATES

□172U. MARK DEWEY
□173U. BRIAN HUNTER
□174U. JON LIEBER
□175U. RAVELO MANZANILLO
□176U. DAN MICELI
□177U. RICK WHITE

ST. LOUIS CARDINALS

□178U. BRYAN EVERSGERD
□179U. JOHN HABYAN
□180U. TERRY MCGRIFF
□181U. VICENTE PALACIOS
□182U. RICH RODRIGUEZ
□183U. RICK SUTCLIFFE

SAN DIEGO PADRES

□184U. DONNIE ELLIOTT
□185U. JOEY HAMILTON
□186U. TIM HYERS
□187U. LUIS LOPEZ
□188U. RAY MCDAVID
□189U. BIP ROBERTS
□190U. SCOTT SANDERS
□191U. EDDIE WILLIAMS

SAN FRANCISCO GIANTS

□192U. STEVE FREY
□193U. PAT GOMEZ
□194U. RICH MONTELEONE
□195U. MARK PORTUGAL
□196U. DARRYL STRAWBERRY
□197U. SALOMON TORRES
□198U. BILL VAN LANDINGHAM

SEATTLE MARINERS

□ 79U. ERIC ANTHONY
□ 80U. BOBBY AYALA
□ 81U. TIM DAVIS
□ 82U. FELIX FERMIN
□ 83U. REGGIE JEFFERSON
□ 84U. KEITH MITCHELL
□ 85U. BILL RISLEY
□ 86U. ALEX RODRIGUEZ
□ 87U. ROGER SALKELD
□ 88U. DAN WILSON

TEXAS RANGERS

□ 89U. CRIS CARPENTER
□ 90U. WILL CLARK
□ 91U. JEFF FRYE
□ 92U. RICK HELLING
□ 93U. CHRIS JAMES
□ 94U. ODDIBE MCDOWELL

TORONTO BLUE JAYS

□ 96U. CARLOS DELGADO
□ 97U. ALEX GONZALEZ
□ 98U. SHAWN GREEN
□ 99U. DARREN HALL
□100U. MIKE HUFF

1995 FLEER (600)
2 1/2" X 3 1/2"

ATLANTA BRAVES

□ 299. STEVE AVERY
□ 300. STEVE BEDROSIAN
□ 301. RAFAEL BELLIARD
□ 302. JEFF BLAUSER
□ 303. DAVE GALLAGHER
□ 304. TOM GLAVINE
□ 305. DAVID JUSTICE
□ 306. MIKE KELLY
□ 307. ROBERTO KELLY
□ 308. RYAN KLESKO
□ 309. MARK LEMKE
□ 310. JAVIER LOPEZ
□ 311. GREG MADDUX
□ 312. FRED MCGRIFF
□ 313. GREG MCMICHAEL
□ 314. KENT MERCKER
□ 315. CHARLIE O'BRIEN
□ 316. JOSE OLIVA
□ 317. TERRY PENDLETON
□ 318. JOHN SMOLTZ
□ 319. MIKE STANTON
□ 320. TONY TARASCO
□ 321. TERRELL WADE
□ 322. MARK WOHLERS

BALTIMORE ORIOLES

□ 1. BRADY ANDERSON
□ 2. HAROLD BAINES
□ 3. DAMON BUFORD
□ 4. MIKE DEVEREAUX
□ 5. MARK EICHHORN
□ 6. SID FERNANDEZ
□ 7. LEO GOMEZ
□ 8. JEFFREY HAMMONDS
□ 9. CHRIS HOILES
□ 10. RICK KRIVDA
□ 11. BEN MCDONALD
□ 12. MARK MCLEMORE

☐ 13. ALAN MILLS
☐ 14. JAMIE MOYER
☐ 15. MIKE MUSSINA
☐ 16. MIKE OQUIST
☐ 17. RAFAEL PALMEIRO
☐ 18. ARTHUR RHODES
☐ 19. CAL RIPKEN, JR.
☐ 20. CHRIS SABO
☐ 21. LEE SMITH
☐ 22. JACK VOIGT

BOSTON RED SOX

☐ 23. DAMON BERRYHILL
☐ 24. TOM BRUNANSKY
☐ 25. WES CHAMBERLAIN
☐ 26. ROGER CLEMENS
☐ 27. SCOTT COOPER
☐ 28. ANDRE DAWSON
☐ 29. GAR FINNVOLD
☐ 30. TONY FOSSAS
☐ 31. MIKE GREENWELL
☐ 32. JOE HESKETH
☐ 33. CHRIS HOWARD
☐ 34. CHRIS NABHOLZ
☐ 35. TIM NAEHRING
☐ 36. OTIS NIXON
☐ 37. CARLOS RODRIGUEZ
☐ 38. RICH ROWLAND
☐ 39. KEN RYAN
☐ 40. AARON SELE
☐ 41. JOHN VALENTIN
☐ 42. MO VAUGHN
☐ 43. FRANK VIOLA

CALIFORNIA ANGELS

☐ 218. BRIAN ANDERSON
☐ 219. CHAD CURTIS
☐ 220. CHILI DAVIS
☐ 221. GARY DISARCINA
☐ 222. DAMION EASLEY
☐ 223. JIM EDMONDS
☐ 224. CHUCK FINLEY
☐ 225. JOE GRAHE
☐ 226. REX HUDLER
☐ 227. BO JACKSON
☐ 228. MARK LANGSTON
☐ 229. PHIL LEFTWICH
☐ 230. MARK LEITER
☐ 231. SPIKE OWEN
☐ 232. BOB PATTERSON
☐ 233. TROY PERCIVAL
☐ 234. EDUARDO PEREZ
☐ 235. TIM SALMON
☐ 236. J.T. SNOW
☐ 237. CHRIS TURNER

CHICAGO CUBS

☐ 408. WILLIE BANKS
☐ 409. JOSE BAUTISTA
☐ 410. STEVE BUECHELE
☐ 411. JIM BULLINGER
☐ 412. CHUCK CRIM
☐ 413. SHAWON DUNSTON
☐ 414. KEVIN FOSTER
☐ 415. MARK GRACE
☐ 416. JOSE HERNANDEZ
☐ 417. GLENALLEN HILL
☐ 418. BROOKS KIESCHNICK
☐ 419. DERRICK MAY
☐ 420. RANDY MYERS
☐ 421. DAN PLESAC
☐ 422. KARL RHODES
☐ 423. REY SANCHEZ
☐ 424. SAMMY SOSA
☐ 425. STEVE TRACHSEL
☐ 426. RICK WILKINS
☐ 427. ANTHONY YOUNG
☐ 428. EDDIE ZAMBRANO

CHICAGO WHITE SOX

☐ 109. WILSON ALVAREZ
☐ 110. PAUL ASSENMACHER
☐ 111. JASON BERE
☐ 112. DENNIS COOK
☐ 113. JOEY CORA
☐ 114. JOSE DELEON
☐ 115. ALEX FERNANDEZ
☐ 116. JULIO FRANCO
☐ 117. CRAIG GREBECK
☐ 118. OZZIE GUILLEN
☐ 119. ROBERTO HERNANDEZ
☐ 120. DARRIN JACKSON
☐ 121. LANCE JOHNSON
☐ 122. RON KARKOVICE
☐ 123. MIKE LAVALLIERE
☐ 124. NORBERTO MARTIN
☐ 125. KIRK MCCASKILL
☐ 126. JACK MCDOWELL
☐ 127. TIM RAINES
☐ 128. FRANK THOMAS
☐ 129. ROBIN VENTURA

CINCINNATI REDS

☐ 429. BRET BOONE
☐ 430. JEFF BRANSON
☐ 431. JEFF BRANTLEY
☐ 432. HECTOR CARRASCO
☐ 433. BRIAN DORSETT
☐ 434. TONY FERNANDEZ
☐ 435. TIM FORTUGNO
☐ 436. ERIK HANSON
☐ 437. THOMAS HOWARD
☐ 438. KEVIN JARVIS
☐ 439. BARRY LARKIN
☐ 440. CHUCK MCELROY
☐ 441. KEVIN MITCHELL
☐ 442. HAL MORRIS
☐ 443. JOSE RIJO
☐ 444. JOHN ROPER
☐ 445. JOHNNY RUFFIN
☐ 446. DEION SANDERS
☐ 447. REGGIE SANDERS
☐ 448. PETE SCHOUREK
☐ 449. JOHN SMILEY
☐ 450. EDDIE TAUBENSEE

CLEVELAND INDIANS

☐ 130. SANDY ALOMAR, JR.
☐ 131. CARLOS BAERGA
☐ 132. ALBERT BELLE
☐ 133. MARK CLARK
☐ 134. ALVARO ESPINOZA
☐ 135. JASON GRIMSLEY
☐ 136. WAYNE KIRBY
☐ 137. KENNY LOFTON
☐ 138. ALBIE LOPEZ
☐ 139. DENNIS MARTINEZ
☐ 140. JOSE MESA
☐ 141. EDDIE MURRAY
☐ 142. CHARLES NAGY
☐ 143. TONY PENA
☐ 144. ERIC PLUNK
☐ 145. MANNY RAMIREZ
☐ 146. JEFF RUSSELL
☐ 147. PAUL SHUEY
☐ 148. PAUL SORRENTO
☐ 149. JIM THOME
☐ 150. OMAR VIZQUEL
☐ 151. DAVE WINFIELD

COLORADO ROCKIES

☐ 514. DANTE BICHETTE
☐ 515. WILLIE BLAIR
☐ 516. ELLIS BURKS
☐ 517. MARVIN FREEMAN
☐ 518. ANDRES GALARRAGA
☐ 519. JOE GIRARDI
☐ 520. GREG HARRIS
☐ 521. CHARLIE HAYES
☐ 522. MIKE KINGERY
☐ 523. NELSON LIRIANO
☐ 524. MIKE MUNOZ
☐ 525. DAVID NIED
☐ 526. STEVE REED
☐ 527. KEVIN RITZ
☐ 528. BRUCE RUFFIN
☐ 529. JOHN VANDER WAL
☐ 530. WALT WEISS
☐ 531. ERIC YOUNG

DETROIT TIGERS

☐ 44. DANNY BAUTISTA
☐ 45. JOE BOEVER
☐ 46. MILT CUYLER
☐ 47. STORM DAVIS
☐ 48. JOHN DOHERTY
☐ 49. JUNIOR FELIX
☐ 50. CECIL FIELDER
☐ 51. TRAVIS FRYMAN
☐ 52. MIKE GARDINER
☐ 53. KIRK GIBSON
☐ 54. CHRIS GOMEZ
☐ 55. BUDDY GROOM
☐ 56. MIKE HENNEMAN
☐ 57. CHAD KREUTER
☐ 58. MIKE MOORE
☐ 59. TONY PHILLIPS
☐ 60. JUAN SAMUEL
☐ 61. MICKEY TETTLETON
☐ 62. ALAN TRAMMELL
☐ 63. DAVID WELLS
☐ 64. LOU WHITAKER

FLORIDA MARLINS

☐ 323. KURT ABBOTT
☐ 324. LUIS AQUINO
☐ 325. BRET BARBERIE
☐ 326. RYAN BOWEN
☐ 327. JERRY BROWNE
☐ 328. CHUCK CARR
☐ 329. MATIAS CARRILLO
☐ 330. GREG COLBRUNN
☐ 331. JEFF CONINE
☐ 332. MARK GARDNER
☐ 333. CHRIS HAMMOND
☐ 334. BRYAN HARVEY
☐ 335. RICHIE LEWIS
☐ 336. DAVE MAGADAN
☐ 337. TERRY MATHEWS
☐ 338. ROBB NEN
☐ 339. YORKIS PEREZ
☐ 340. PAT RAPP
☐ 341. BENITO SANTIAGO
☐ 342. GARY SHEFFIELD
☐ 343. DAVE WEATHERS

HOUSTON ASTROS

☐ 451. JEFF BAGWELL
☐ 452. KEVIN BASS
☐ 453. CRAIG BIGGIO
☐ 454. KEN CAMINITI
☐ 455. ANDUJAR CEDENO
☐ 456. DOUG DRABEK
☐ 457. TONY EUSEBIO
☐ 458. MIKE FELDER
☐ 459. STEVE FINLEY
☐ 460. LUIS GONZALEZ
☐ 461. MIKE HAMPTON
☐ 462. PETE HARNISCH
☐ 463. JOHN HUDEK
☐ 464. TODD JONES
☐ 465. DARRYL KILE
☐ 466. JAMES MOUTON
☐ 467. SHANE REYNOLDS
☐ 468. SCOTT SERVAIS
☐ 469. GREG SWINDELL
☐ 470. DAVE VERES
☐ 471. BRIAN WILLIAMS

KANSAS CITY ROYALS

☐ 152. KEVIN APPIER
☐ 153. BILLY BREWER
☐ 154. VINCE COLEMAN
☐ 155. DAVID CONE
☐ 156. GARY GAETTI
☐ 157. GREG GAGNE
☐ 158. TOM GORDON
☐ 159. MARK GUBICZA
☐ 160. BOB HAMELIN
☐ 161. DAVE HENDERSON
☐ 162. FELIX JOSE
☐ 163. WALLY JOYNER
☐ 164. JOSE LIND
☐ 165. MIKE MACFARLANE
☐ 166. MIKE MAGNANTE
☐ 167. BRENT MAYNE
☐ 168. BRIAN MCRAE
☐ 169. RUSTY MEACHAM
☐ 170. JEFF MONTGOMERY
☐ 171. HIPOLITO PICHARDO
☐ 172. TERRY SHUMPERT
☐ 173. MICHAEL TUCKER

LOS ANGELES DODGERS

☐ 532. BILLY ASHLEY
☐ 533. PEDRO ASTACIO
☐ 534. RAFAEL BOURNIGAL
☐ 535. BRETT BUTLER
☐ 536. TOM CANDIOTTI
☐ 537. OMAR DAAL
☐ 538. DELINO DESHIELDS
☐ 539. DARREN DREIFORT
☐ 540. KEVIN GROSS
☐ 541. OREL HERSHISER
☐ 542. GAREY INGRAM
☐ 543. ERIC KARROS
☐ 544. RAMON MARTINEZ
☐ 545. RAUL MONDESI
☐ 546. CHAN HO PARK
☐ 547. MIKE PIAZZA
☐ 548. HENRY RODRIGUEZ
☐ 549. RUDY SEANEZ
☐ 550. ISMAEL VALDES
☐ 551. TIM WALLACH
☐ 552. TODD WORRELL

MILWAUKEE BREWERS

☐ 174. RICKY BONES
☐ 175. JEFF CIRILLO
☐ 176. ALEX DIAZ
☐ 177. CAL ELDRED
☐ 178. MIKE FETTERS
☐ 179. DARRYL HAMILTON
☐ 180. BRIAN HARPER
☐ 181. JOHN JAHA
☐ 182. PAT LISTACH
☐ 183. GRAEME LLOYD
☐ 184. JOSE MERCEDES
☐ 185. MATT MIESKE
☐ 186. DAVE NILSSON
☐ 187. JODY REED
☐ 188. BOB SCANLAN
☐ 189. KEVIN SEITZER
☐ 190. BILL SPIERS
☐ 191. B.J. SURHOFF
☐ 192. JOSE VALENTIN
☐ 193. GREG VAUGHN
☐ 194. TURNER WARD
☐ 195. BILL WEGMAN

MINNESOTA TWINS

☐ 196. RICK AGUILERA
☐ 197. RICH BECKER
☐ 198. ALEX COLE
☐ 199. MARTY CORDOVA
☐ 200. STEVE DUNN
☐ 201. SCOTT ERICKSON
☐ 202. MARK GUTHRIE
☐ 203. CHIP HALE
☐ 204. LATROY HAWKINS
☐ 205. DENNY HOCKING
☐ 206. CHUCK KNOBLAUCH
☐ 207. SCOTT LEIUS
☐ 208. SHANE MACK
☐ 209. PAT MAHOMES

☐ 210. PAT MEARES
☐ 211. PEDRO MUNOZ
☐ 212. KIRBY PUCKETT
☐ 213. JEFF REBOULET
☐ 214. DAVE STEVENS
☐ 215. KEVIN TAPANI
☐ 216. MATT WALBECK
☐ 217. CARL WILLIS

MONTREAL EXPOS

☐ 344. MOISES ALOU
☐ 345. SEAN BERRY
☐ 346. WIL CORDERO
☐ 347. JOEY EISCHEN
☐ 348. JEFF FASSERO
☐ 349. DARRIN FLETCHER
☐ 350. CLIFF FLOYD
☐ 351. MARQUIS GRISSOM
☐ 352. BUTCH HENRY
☐ 353. GIL HEREDIA
☐ 354. KEN HILL
☐ 355. MIKE LANSING
☐ 356. PEDRO MARTINEZ
☐ 357. MEL ROJAS
☐ 358. KIRK RUETER
☐ 359. TIM SCOTT
☐ 360. JEFF SHAW
☐ 361. LARRY WALKER
☐ 362. LENNY WEBSTER
☐ 363. JOHN WETTELAND
☐ 364. RONDELL WHITE

NEW YORK METS

☐ 365. BOBBY BONILLA
☐ 366. RICO BROGNA
☐ 367. JEROMY BURNITZ
☐ 368. JOHN FRANCO
☐ 369. DWIGHT GOODEN
☐ 370. TODD HUNDLEY
☐ 371. JASON JACOME
☐ 372. BOBBY JONES
☐ 373. JEFF KENT
☐ 374. JIM LINDEMAN
☐ 375. JOSIAS MANZANILLO
☐ 376. ROGER MASON
☐ 377. KEVIN MCREYNOLDS
☐ 378. JOE ORSULAK
☐ 379. BILL PULSIPHER
☐ 380. BRET SABERHAGEN
☐ 381. DAVID SEGUI
☐ 382. PETE SMITH
☐ 383. KELLY STINNETT
☐ 384. RYAN THOMPSON
☐ 385. JOSE VIZCAINO

NEW YORK YANKEES

☐ 65. JIM ABBOTT
☐ 66. JOE AUSANIO
☐ 67. WADE BOGGS
☐ 68. MIKE GALLEGO
☐ 69. XAVIER HERNANDEZ
☐ 70. STERLING HITCHCOCK
☐ 71. STEVE HOWE
☐ 72. SCOTT KAMIENIECKI
☐ 73. PAT KELLY
☐ 74. JIMMY KEY
☐ 75. JIM LEYRITZ
☐ 76. DON MATTINGLY
☐ 77. TERRY MULHOLLAND
☐ 78. PAUL O'NEILL
☐ 79. MELIDO PEREZ
☐ 80. LUIS POLONIA
☐ 81. MIKE STANLEY
☐ 82. DANNY TARTABULL
☐ 83. RANDY VELARDE
☐ 84. BOB WICKMAN
☐ 85. BERNIE WILLIAMS
☐ 86. GERALD WILLIAMS

OAKLAND A'S

☐ 238. MARK ACRE
☐ 239. GERONIMO BERROA
☐ 240. MIKE BORDICK
☐ 241. JOHN BRISCOE
☐ 242. SCOTT BROSIUS
☐ 243. RON DARLING
☐ 244. DENNIS ECKERSLEY
☐ 245. BRENT GATES
☐ 246. RICKEY HENDERSON
☐ 247. STAN JAVIER
☐ 248. STEVE KARSAY
☐ 249. MARK MCGWIRE
☐ 250. TROY NEEL
☐ 251. STEVE ONTIVEROS
☐ 252. CARLOS REYES
☐ 253. RUBEN SIERRA
☐ 254. TERRY STEINBACH
☐ 255. BILL TAYLOR
☐ 256. TODD VAN POPPEL
☐ 257. BOBBY WITT

PHILADELPHIA PHILLIES

☐ 386. TOBY BORLAND
☐ 387. RICKY BOTTALICO
☐ 388. DARREN DAULTON
☐ 389. MARIANO DUNCAN
☐ 390. LENNY DYKSTRA
☐ 391. JIM EISENREICH
☐ 392. TOMMY GREENE
☐ 393. DAVE HOLLINS
☐ 394. PETE INCAVIGLIA
☐ 395. DANNY JACKSON
☐ 396. DOUG JONES
☐ 397. RICKY JORDAN
☐ 398. JOHN KRUK
☐ 399. MIKE LIEBERTHAL
☐ 400. TONY LONGMIRE
☐ 401. MICKEY MORANDINI
☐ 402. BOBBY MUNOZ
☐ 403. CURT SCHILLING
☐ 404. HEATHCLIFF SLOCUMB
☐ 405. KEVIN STOCKER
☐ 406. FERNANDO VALENZUELA
☐ 407. DAVID WEST

PITTSBURGH PIRATES

☐ 472. JAY BELL
☐ 473. JACOB BRUMFIELD
☐ 474. DAVE CLARK
☐ 475. STEVE COOKE
☐ 476. MIDRE CUMMNGS
☐ 477. MARK DEWEY
☐ 478. TOM FOLEY
☐ 479. CARLOS GARCIA
☐ 480. JEFF KING
☐ 481. JON LIEBER
☐ 482. RAVELO MANZANILLO
☐ 483. AL MARTIN
☐ 484. ORLANDO MERCED
☐ 485. DANNY MICELI
☐ 486. DENNY NEAGLE
☐ 487. LANCE PARRISH
☐ 488. DON SLAUGHT
☐ 489. ZANE SMITH
☐ 490. ANDY VAN SLYKE
☐ 491. PAUL WAGNER
☐ 492. RICK WHITE

ST. LOUIS CARDINALS

☐ 493. LUIS ALICEA
☐ 494. RENE AROCHA

- ☐ 495. RHEAL CORMIER
- ☐ 496. BRYAN EVERSGERD
- ☐ 497. BERNARD GILKEY
- ☐ 498. JOHN HABYAN
- ☐ 499. GREGG JEFFERIES
- ☐ 500. BRIAN JORDAN
- ☐ 501. RAY LANKFORD
- ☐ 502. JOHN MABRY
- ☐ 503. TERRY MCGRIFF
- ☐ 504. TOM PAGNOZZI
- ☐ 505. VICENTE PALACIOS
- ☐ 506. GERONIMO PENA
- ☐ 507. GERALD PERRY
- ☐ 508. RICH RODRIGUEZ
- ☐ 509. OZZIE SMITH
- ☐ 510. BOB TEWKSBURY
- ☐ 511. ALLEN WATSON
- ☐ 512. MARK WHITEN
- ☐ 513. TODD ZEILE

SAN DIEGO PADRES

- ☐ 553. ANDY ASHBY
- ☐ 554. BRAD AUSMUS
- ☐ 555. DEREK BELL
- ☐ 556. ANDY BENES
- ☐ 557. PHIL CLARK
- ☐ 558. DONNIE ELLIOTT
- ☐ 559. RICKY GUTIERREZ
- ☐ 560. TONY GWYNN
- ☐ 561. JOEY HAMILTON
- ☐ 562. TREVOR HOFFMAN
- ☐ 563. LUIS LOPEZ
- ☐ 564. PEDRO MARTINEZ
- ☐ 565. TIM MAUSER
- ☐ 566. PHIL PLANTIER
- ☐ 567. BIP ROBERTS
- ☐ 568. SCOTT SANDERS
- ☐ 569. CRAIG SHIPLEY
- ☐ 570. JEFF TABAKA
- ☐ 571. EDDIE WILLIAMS

SAN FRANCISCO GIANTS

- ☐ 572. ROD BECK
- ☐ 573. MIKE BENJAMIN
- ☐ 574. BARRY BONDS
- ☐ 575. DAVE BURBA
- ☐ 576. JOHN BURKETT
- ☐ 577. MARK CARREON
- ☐ 578. ROYCE CLAYTON
- ☐ 579. STEVE FREY
- ☐ 580. BRYAN HICKERSON
- ☐ 581. MIKE JACKSON
- ☐ 582. DARREN LEWIS
- ☐ 583. KIRT MANWARING
- ☐ 584. RICH MONTELEONE
- ☐ 585. JOHN PATTERSON
- ☐ 586. J.R. PHILLIPS
- ☐ 587. MARK PORTUGAL
- ☐ 588. JOE ROSSELLI
- ☐ 589. DARRYL STRAWBERRY
- ☐ 590. BILL SWIFT
- ☐ 591. ROBBY THOMPSON
- ☐ 592. BILL VAN LANDINGHAM
- ☐ 593. MATT WILLIAMS

SEATTLE MARINERS

- ☐ 258. RICH AMARAL
- ☐ 259. ERIC ANTHONY
- ☐ 260. BOBBY AYALA
- ☐ 261. MIKE BLOWERS
- ☐ 262. CHRIS BOSIO
- ☐ 263. JAY BUHNER
- ☐ 264. JOHN CUMMINGS
- ☐ 265. TIM DAVIS
- ☐ 266. FELIX FERMIN
- ☐ 267. DAVE FLEMING
- ☐ 268. GOOSE GOSSAGE
- ☐ 269. KEN GRIFFEY, JR
- ☐ 270. REGGIE JEFFERSON
- ☐ 271. RANDY JOHNSON
- ☐ 272. EDGAR MARTINEZ
- ☐ 273. TINO MARTINEZ
- ☐ 274. GREG PIRKL
- ☐ 275. BILL RISLEY
- ☐ 276. ROGER SALKELD
- ☐ 277. LUIS SOJO
- ☐ 278. MAC SUZUKI
- ☐ 279. DAN WILSON

TEXAS RANGERS

- ☐ 280. KEVIN BROWN
- ☐ 281. JOSE CANSECO
- ☐ 282. CRIS CARPENTER
- ☐ 283. WILL CLARK
- ☐ 284. JEFF FRYE
- ☐ 285. JUAN GONZALEZ
- ☐ 286. RICK HELLING
- ☐ 287. TOM HENKE
- ☐ 288. DAVID HULSE
- ☐ 289. CHRIS JAMES
- ☐ 290. MANUEL LEE
- ☐ 291. ODDIBE MCDOWELL
- ☐ 292. DEAN PALMER
- ☐ 293. ROGER PAVLIK
- ☐ 294. BILL RIPKEN
- ☐ 295. IVAN RODRIGUEZ
- ☐ 296. KENNY ROGERS
- ☐ 297. DOUG STRANGE
- ☐ 298. MATT WHITESIDE

TORONTO BLUE JAYS

- ☐ 87. ROBERTO ALOMAR
- ☐ 88. PAT BORDERS
- ☐ 89. JOE CARTER
- ☐ 90. TONY CASTILLO
- ☐ 91. BRAD CORNETT
- ☐ 92. CARLOS DELGADO
- ☐ 93. ALEX GONZALEZ
- ☐ 94. SHAWN GREEN
- ☐ 95. JUAN GUZMAN
- ☐ 96. DARREN HALL
- ☐ 97. PAT HENTGEN
- ☐ 98. MIKE HUFF
- ☐ 99. RANDY KNORR
- ☐ 100. AL LEITER
- ☐ 101. PAUL MOLITOR
- ☐ 102. JOHN OLERUD
- ☐ 103. DICK SCHOFIELD
- ☐ 104. ED SPRAGUE
- ☐ 105. DAVE STEWART
- ☐ 106. TODD STOTTLEMYRE
- ☐ 107. DEVON WHITE
- ☐ 108. WOODY WILLIAMS

Suzy "Scrump" Sevcik
Computer Design Specialist

FLEER-ULTRA

1991 FLEER ULTRA
(400)
2 1/2 x 3 1/2

ATLANTA BRAVES

- ☐ 1. STEVE AVERY
- ☐ 2. JEFF BLAUSER
- ☐ 3. FRANCISCO CABRERA
- ☐ 4. RON GANT
- ☐ 5. TOM GLAVINE
- ☐ 6. TOMMY GREGG
- ☐ 7. DAVE JUSTICE
- ☐ 8. ODDIBE MCDOWELL
- ☐ 9. GREG OLSON
- ☐ 10. TERRY PENDLETON
- ☐ 11. LONNIE SMITH
- ☐ 12. JOHN SMOLTZ
- ☐ 13. JEFF TREADWAY

BALTIMORE ORIOLES

- ☐ 14. GLENN DAVIS
- ☐ 15. MIKE DEVEREAUX
- ☐ 16. LEO GOMEZ
- ☐ 17. CHRIS HOILES
- ☐ 18. DAVE JOHNSON
- ☐ 19. BEN MCDONALD
- ☐ 20. RANDY MILLIGAN
- ☐ 21. GREGG OLSON
- ☐ 22. JOE ORSULAK
- ☐ 23. BILL RIPKEN
- ☐ 24. CAL RIPKEN, JR.
- ☐ 25. DAVID SEGUI
- ☐ 26. CRAIG WORTHINGTON

BOSTON RED SOX

- ☐ 27. WADE BOGGS
- ☐ 28. TOM BOLTON
- ☐ 29. TOM BRUNANSKY
- ☐ 30. ELLIS BURKS
- ☐ 31. ROGER CLEMENS
- ☐ 32. MIKE GREENWELL
- ☐ 33. GREG HARRIS
- ☐ 34. DARYL IRVINE
- ☐ 35. MIKE MARSHALL
- ☐ 36. TIM NAEHRING
- ☐ 37. TONY PENA
- ☐ 38. PHIL PLANTIER
- ☐ 39. CARLOS QUINTANA
- ☐ 40. JEFF REARDON
- ☐ 41. JODY REED
- ☐ 42. LUIS RIVERA
- ☐ 387. MO VAUGHN

CALIFORNIA ANGELS

- ☐ 43. JIM ABBOTT
- ☐ 44. CHUCK FINLEY
- ☐ 45. BRYAN HARVEY
- ☐ 46. DONNIE HILL
- ☐ 47. JACK HOWELL
- ☐ 48. WALLY JOYNER
- ☐ 49. MARK LANGSTON
- ☐ 50. KIRK MCCASKILL
- ☐ 51. LANCE PARRISH
- ☐ 52. DICK SCHOFIELD
- ☐ 53. LEE STEVENS
- ☐ 54. DAVE WINFIELD

CHICAGO CUBS

- ☐ 55. GEORGE BELL
- ☐ 56. DAMON BERRYHILL
- ☐ 57. MIKE BIELECKI
- ☐ 58. ANDRE DAWSON
- ☐ 59. SHAWON DUNSTON
- ☐ 60. JOE GIRARDI
- ☐ 61. MARK GRACE
- ☐ 62. MIKE HARKEY
- ☐ 63. LES LANCASTER
- ☐ 64. GREG MADDUX
- ☐ 65. DERRICK MAY
- ☐ 66. RYNE SANDBERG
- ☐ 67. LUIS SALAZAR
- ☐ 68. DWIGHT SMITH
- ☐ 69. HECTOR VILLANUEVA
- ☐ 70. JEROME WALTON
- ☐ 71. MITCH WILLIAMS

CHICAGO WHITE SOX

- ☐ 72. CARLTON FISK
- ☐ 73. SCOTT FLETCHER
- ☐ 74. OZZIE GUILLEN
- ☐ 75. GREG HIBBARD
- ☐ 76. LANCE JOHNSON
- ☐ 77. STEVE LYONS
- ☐ 78. JACK MCDOWELL
- ☐ 79. DAN PASQUA
- ☐ 80. MELIDO PEREZ
- ☐ 81. TIM RAINES
- ☐ 82. SAMMY SOSA
- ☐ 83. CORY SNYDER
- ☐ 84. BOBBY THIGPEN
- ☐ 85. FRANK THOMAS
- ☐ 86. ROBIN VENTURA

CINCINNATI REDS

- ☐ 87. TODD BENZINGER
- ☐ 88. GLENN BRAGGS
- ☐ 89. TOM BROWNING
- ☐ 90. NORM CHARLTON
- ☐ 91. ERIC DAVIS
- ☐ 92. ROB DIBBLE
- ☐ 93. BILL DORAN
- ☐ 94. MARIANO DUNCAN
- ☐ 95. BILLY HATCHER
- ☐ 96. BARRY LARKIN
- ☐ 97. RANDY MYERS
- ☐ 98. HAL MORRIS
- ☐ 99. JOE OLIVER
- ☐ 100. PAUL O'NEILL
- ☐ 101. JEFF REED
- ☐ 102. JOSE RIJO
- ☐ 103. CHRIS SABO
- ☐ 379. REGGIE JEFFERSON

CLEVELAND INDIANS

- ☐ 101. BEAU ALLRED
- ☐ 103. CARLOS BAERGA
- ☐ 105. SANDY ALOMAR
- ☐ 107. ALBERT BELLE
- ☐ 108. JERRY BROWNE
- ☐ 109. TOM CANDIOTTI
- ☐ 110. ALEX COLE
- ☐ 111. JOHN FARRELL
- ☐ 111. CHRIS JAMES
- ☐ 112. FELIX FERMIN
- ☐ 113. BROOK JACOBY
- ☐ 115. DOUG JONES
- ☐ 116. STEVE OLIN
- ☐ 116. MITCH WEBSTER
- ☐ 117. GREG SWINDELL
- ☐ 118. TURNER WARD

DETROIT TIGERS

- ☐ 120. DAVE BERGMAN
- ☐ 121. CECIL FIELDER
- ☐ 122. TRAVIS FRYMAN
- ☐ 123. MIKE HENNEMAN
- ☐ 124. LLOYD MOSEBY
- ☐ 125. DAN PETRY
- ☐ 126. TONY PHILLIPS
- ☐ 127. MARK SALAS
- ☐ 128. FRANK TANANA
- ☐ 129. ALAN TRAMMELL
- ☐ 130. LOU WHITAKER

HOUSTON ASTROS

- ☐ 131. ERIC ANTHONY
- ☐ 132. CRAIG BIGGIO
- ☐ 133. KEN CAMINITI
- ☐ 134. CASEY CANDAELE
- ☐ 135. ANDUJAR CEDENO
- ☐ 136. MARK DAVIDSON
- ☐ 137. JIM DESHAIES
- ☐ 138. MARK PORTUGAL
- ☐ 139. RAFAEL RAMIREZ
- ☐ 140. MIKE SCOTT
- ☐ 141. ERIC YELDING
- ☐ 142. GERALD YOUNG

KANSAS CITY ROYALS

- ☐ 143. KEVIN APPIER
- ☐ 144. GEORGE BRETT
- ☐ 145. JEFF CONINE
- ☐ 146. JIM EISENREICH
- ☐ 147. TOM GORDON
- ☐ 148. MARK GUBICZA
- ☐ 149. BO JACKSON
- ☐ 150. BRENT MAYNE
- ☐ 151. MIKE MACFARLANE
- ☐ 152. BRIAN MCRAE
- ☐ 153. JEFF MONTGOMERY
- ☐ 154. BRET SABERHAGEN
- ☐ 155. KEVIN SEITZER
- ☐ 156. TERRY SHUMPERT
- ☐ 157. KURT STILLWELL
- ☐ 158. DANNY TARTABULL

LOS ANGELES DODGERS

- ☐ 159. TIM BELCHER
- ☐ 160. KAL DANIELS
- ☐ 161. ALFREDO GRIFFIN
- ☐ 162. LENNY HARRIS
- ☐ 163. JAY HOWELL
- ☐ 164. RAMON MARTINEZ
- ☐ 165. MIKE MORGAN
- ☐ 166. EDDIE MURRAY
- ☐ 167. JOSE OFFERMAN
- ☐ 168. JUAN SAMUEL
- ☐ 169. MIKE SCIOSCIA
- ☐ 170. MIKE SHARPERSON
- ☐ 171. DARRYL STRAWBERRY
- ☐ 380. ERIC KARROS
- ☐ 384. DAN OPPERMAN
- ☐ 386. HENRY RODRIGUEZ

MILWAUKEE BREWERS

- ☐ 172. GREG BROCK
- ☐ 173. CHUCK CRIM
- ☐ 174. JIM GANTNER
- ☐ 175. TED HIGUERA
- ☐ 176. MARK KNUDSON
- ☐ 177. TIM MCINTOSH
- ☐ 178. PAUL MOLITOR
- ☐ 179. DAN PLESAC
- ☐ 180. GARY SHEFFIELD
- ☐ 181. BILL SPIERS
- ☐ 182. B.J. SURHOFF
- ☐ 183. GREG VAUGHN
- ☐ 184. ROBIN YOUNT

MINNESOTA TWINS

- ☐ 185. RICK AGUILERA
- ☐ 186. GREG GAGNE
- ☐ 187. DAN GLADDEN
- ☐ 188. BRIAN HARPER
- ☐ 189. KENT HRBEK
- ☐ 190. GENE LARKIN
- ☐ 191. SHANE MACK
- ☐ 192. PEDRO MUNOZ
- ☐ 193. AL NEWMAN
- ☐ 194. JUNIOR ORTIZ
- ☐ 195. KIRBY PUCKETT
- ☐ 196. KEVIN TAPANI
- ☐ 373. WILLIE BANKS
- ☐ 378. RICH GARCES
- ☐ 382. CHUCK KNOBLAUCH
- ☐ 383. DENNY NEAGLE

MONTREAL EXPOS

- ☐ 197. DENNIS BOYD
- ☐ 198. TIM BURKE
- ☐ 199. IVAN CALDERON
- ☐ 200. DELINO DESHIELDS
- ☐ 201. MIKE FITZGERALD
- ☐ 202. STEVE FREY
- ☐ 203. ANDRES GALARRAGA
- ☐ 204. MARQUIS GRISSOM
- ☐ 205. DAVE MARTINEZ
- ☐ 206. DENNIS MARTINEZ
- ☐ 207. JUNIOR NOBOA
- ☐ 208. SPIKE OWEN
- ☐ 209. SCOTT RUSKIN
- ☐ 210. TIM WALLACH

NEW YORK METS

- ☐ 211. DARYL BOSTON
- ☐ 212. VINCE COLEMAN
- ☐ 213. DAVID CONE
- ☐ 214. RON DARLING
- ☐ 215. KEVIN ELSTER
- ☐ 216. SID FERNANDEZ
- ☐ 217. JOHN FRANCO
- ☐ 218. DWIGHT GOODEN
- ☐ 219. TOM HERR
- ☐ 220. TODD HUNDLEY
- ☐ 221. GREGG JEFFERIES
- ☐ 222. HOWARD JOHNSON
- ☐ 223. DAVE MAGADAN
- ☐ 224. KEVIN MCREYNOLDS
- ☐ 225. KEITH MILLER
- ☐ 226. MACKEY SASSER
- ☐ 227. FRANK VIOLA

NEW YORK YANKEES

- ☐ 228. JESSE BARFIELD
- ☐ 229. GREG CADARET
- ☐ 230. ALVARO ESPINOZA
- ☐ 231. BOB GEREN
- ☐ 232. LEE GUETTERMAN
- ☐ 233. MEL HALL
- ☐ 234. ANDY HAWKINS
- ☐ 235. ROBERTO KELLY
- ☐ 236. TIM LEARY
- ☐ 237. JIM LEYRITZ
- ☐ 238. KEVIN MAAS
- ☐ 239. DON MATTINGLY
- ☐ 240. HENSLEY MEULENS
- ☐ 241. ERIC PLUNK
- ☐ 242. STEVE SAX
- ☐ 381. PAT KELLY
- ☐ 385. JOHN RAMOS
- ☐ 388. GERALD WILLIAMS

OAKLAND A'S

- ☐ 243. TODD BURNS
- ☐ 244. JOSE CANSECO
- ☐ 245. DENNIS ECKERSLEY
- ☐ 246. MIKE GALLEGO
- ☐ 247. DAVE HENDERSON
- ☐ 248. RICKEY HENDERSON
- ☐ 249. RICK HONEYCUTT
- ☐ 250. CARNEY LANSFORD
- ☐ 251. MARK MCGWIRE
- ☐ 252. MIKE MOORE
- ☐ 253. TERRY STEINBACH
- ☐ 254. DAVE STEWART
- ☐ 255. WALT WEISS
- ☐ 256. BOB WELCH
- ☐ 257. CURT YOUNG
- ☐ 376. STEVE CHITREN

PHILADELPHIA PHILLIES

- ☐ 258. WES CHAMBERLAIN
- ☐ 259. PAT COMBS
- ☐ 260. DARREN DAULTON
- ☐ 261. JOSE DEJESUS
- ☐ 262. LEN DYKSTRA
- ☐ 263. CHARLIE HAYES
- ☐ 264. VON HAYES
- ☐ 265. KEN HOWELL
- ☐ 266. JOHN KRUK
- ☐ 267. ROGER MCDOWELL
- ☐ 268. MICKEY MORANDINI
- ☐ 269. TERRY MULHOLLAND
- ☐ 270. DALE MURPHY
- ☐ 271. RANDY READY
- ☐ 272. DICKIE THON
- ☐ 377. DARRIN FLETCHER

PITTSBURGH PIRATES

- ☐ 273. STAN BELINDA
- ☐ 274. JAY BELL
- ☐ 275. BARRY BONDS
- ☐ 276. BOBBY BONILLA
- ☐ 277. DOUG DRABEK
- ☐ 278. CARLOS GARCIA
- ☐ 279. NEAL HEATON
- ☐ 280. JEFF KING
- ☐ 281. BILL LANDRUM
- ☐ 282. MIKE LAVALLIERE
- ☐ 283. JOSE LIND
- ☐ 284. ORLANDO MERCED
- ☐ 285. GARY REDUS
- ☐ 286. DON SLAUGHT
- ☐ 287. ANDY VAN SLYKE
- ☐ 374. STEVE CARTER
- ☐ 389. MIKE YORK

ST. LOUIS CARDINALS

- ☐ 288. JOSE DELEON
- ☐ 289. PEDRO GUERRERO
- ☐ 290. RAY LANKFORD
- ☐ 291. JOE MAGRANE
- ☐ 292. JOSE OQUENDO
- ☐ 293. TOM PAGNOZZI
- ☐ 294. BRYN SMITH
- ☐ 295. LEE SMITH
- ☐ 296. OZZIE SMITH
- ☐ 297. MILT THOMPSON
- ☐ 298. CRAIG WILSON
- ☐ 299. TODD ZEILE

SAN DIEGO PADRES

- ☐ 300. SHAWN ABNER
- ☐ 301. ANDY BENES
- ☐ 302. PAUL FARIES
- ☐ 303. TONY GWYNN
- ☐ 304. GREG HARRIS
- ☐ 305. THOMAS HOWARD
- ☐ 306. BRUCE HURST
- ☐ 307. CRAIG LEFFERTS
- ☐ 308. FRED MCGRIFF
- ☐ 309. DENNIS RASMUSSEN
- ☐ 310. BIP ROBERTS
- ☐ 311. BENITO SANTIAGO
- ☐ 312. GARRY TEMPLETON
- ☐ 313. ED WHITSON

SAN FRANCISCO GIANTS

- ☐ 314. DAVE ANDERSON
- ☐ 315. KEVIN BASS
- ☐ 316. JEFF BRANTLEY
- ☐ 317. JOHN BURKETT
- ☐ 318. WILL CLARK
- ☐ 319. STEVE DECKER
- ☐ 320. SCOTT GARRELTS
- ☐ 321. TERRY KENNEDY
- ☐ 322. MARK LEONARD
- ☐ 323. DARREN LEWIS
- ☐ 324. GERG LITTON
- ☐ 325. WILLIE MCGEE
- ☐ 326. KEVIN MITCHELL
- ☐ 327. DON ROBINSON
- ☐ 328. ANDRES SANTANA
- ☐ 329. ROBBY THOMPSON
- ☐ 330. JOSE URIBE
- ☐ 331. MATT WILLIAMS

SEATTLE MARINERS

- ☐ 332. SCOTT BRADLEY
- ☐ 333. HENRY COTTO
- ☐ 334. ALVIN DAVIS
- ☐ 335. KEN GRIFFEY, SR.
- ☐ 336. KEN GRIFFEY, JR.
- ☐ 337. ERIK HANSON
- ☐ 338. BRIAN HOLMAN
- ☐ 339. RANDY JOHNSON
- ☐ 340. EDGAR MARTINEZ
- ☐ 341. TINO MARTINEZ
- ☐ 342. PETE O'BRIEN
- ☐ 343. HAROLD REYNOLDS
- ☐ 344. DAVID VALLE
- ☐ 345. OMAR VIZQUEL

TEXAS RANGERS

- ☐ 346. BRAD ARNSBERG
- ☐ 347. KEVIN BROWN
- ☐ 348. JULIO FRANCO
- ☐ 349. JEFF HUSON
- ☐ 350. RAFAEL PALMEIRO
- ☐ 351. GENO PETRALLI
- ☐ 352. GARY PETTIS
- ☐ 353. KENNY ROGERS
- ☐ 354. JEFF RUSSELL
- ☐ 355. NOLAN RYAN
- ☐ 356. RUBEN SIERRA
- ☐ 357. BOBBY WITT
- ☐ 375. SCOTT CHIAMPARINO

TORONTO BLUE JAYS

- ☐ 358. ROBERTO ALOMAR
- ☐ 359. PAT BORDERS
- ☐ 360. JOE CARTER
- ☐ 361. KELLY GRUBER
- ☐ 362. TOM HENKE
- ☐ 363. GLENALLEN HILL
- ☐ 364. JIMMY KEY

- ☐ 365. MANNY LEE
- ☐ 366. RANCE MULLINIKS
- ☐ 367. JOHN OLERUD
- ☐ 368. DAVE STIEB
- ☐ 369. DUANE WARD
- ☐ 370. DAVID WELLS
- ☐ 371. MARK WHITEN
- ☐ 372. MOOKIE WILSON
- ☐ 390. EDDIE ZOSKY

1991 FLEER ULTRA TRADED (120)
2 1/2 X 3 1/2

ATLANTA BRAVES

- ☐ 65U. RAFAEL BELLIARD
- ☐ 66U. JUAN BERENGUER
- ☐ 67U. BRIAN HUNTER
- ☐ 68U. KENT MERCKER
- ☐ 69U. OTIS NIXON

BALTIMORE ORIOLES

- ☐ 1U. DWIGHT EVANS
- ☐ 2U. CHITO MARTINEZ
- ☐ 3U. BOB MELVIN
- ☐ 4U. MIKE MUSSINA

BOSTON RED SOX

- ☐ 5U. JACK CLARK
- ☐ 6U. DANA KIECKER
- ☐ 7U. STEVE LYONS

CALIFORNIA ANGELS

- ☐ 8U. GARY GAETTI
- ☐ 9U. DAVE GALLAGHER
- ☐ 10U. DAVE PARKER
- ☐ 11U. LUIS POLONIA
- ☐ 12U. LUIS SOJO

CHICAGO CUBS

- ☐ 70U. DANNY JACKSON
- ☐ 71U. CHUCK MCELROY
- ☐ 72U. GARY SCOTT
- ☐ 73U. HEATHCLIFF SLOCUMB
- ☐ 74U. CHICO WALKER
- ☐ 75U. RICK WILKINS

CHICAGO WHITE SOX

- ☐ 13U. WILSON ALVAREZ
- ☐ 14U. ALEX FERNANDEZ
- ☐ 15U. CRAIG GREBECK
- ☐ 16U. RON KARKOVICE
- ☐ 17U. WARREN NEWSON
- ☐ 18U. SCOTT RADINSKY

CINCINNATI REDS

- ☐ 76U. CHRIS HAMMOND
- ☐ 77U. LUIS QUINONES
- ☐ 78U. HERM WINNINGHAM

CLEVELAND INDIANS

- ☐ 19U. GLENALLEN HILL
- ☐ 20U. CHARLES NAGY
- ☐ 21U. MARK WHITEN

DETROIT TIGERS

- ☐ 22U. MILT CUYLER
- ☐ 23U. PAUL GIBSON
- ☐ 24U. MICKEY TETTLETON

HOUSTON ASTROS

- ☐ 79U. JEFF BAGWELL
- ☐ 80U. JIM CORSI
- ☐ 81U. STEVE FINLEY
- ☐ 82U. LUIS GONZALEZ
- ☐ 83U. PETE HARNISCH
- ☐ 84U. DARRYL KILE

KANSAS CITY ROYALS

- ☐ 25U. TODD BENZINGER
- ☐ 26U. STORM DAVIS
- ☐ 27U. KIRK GIBSON
- ☐ 28U. BILL PECOTA
- ☐ 29U. GARY THURMAN

LOS ANGELES DODGERS

- ☐ 85U. BRETT BUTLER
- ☐ 86U. GARY CARTER
- ☐ 87U. TIM CREWS
- ☐ 88U. OREL HERSHISER
- ☐ 89U. BOB OJEDA

MILWAUKEE BREWERS

- ☐ 30U. DARRYL HAMILTON
- ☐ 31U. JAIME NAVARRO
- ☐ 32U. WILLIE RANDOLPH
- ☐ 33U. BILL WEGMAN

MINNESOTA TWINS

- ☐ 34U. RANDY BUSH
- ☐ 35U. CHILI DAVIS
- ☐ 36U. SCOTT ERICKSON
- ☐ 37U. CHUCK KNOBLAUCH
- ☐ 38U. SCOTT LEIUS
- ☐ 39U. JACK MORRIS

MONTREAL EXPOS

- ☐ 90U. BRET BARBERIE
- ☐ 91U. BARRY JONES
- ☐ 92U. GILBERTO REYES
- ☐ 93U. LARRY WALKER

NEW YORK METS

- ☐ 94U. HUBIE BROOKS
- ☐ 95U. TIM BURKE
- ☐ 96U. RICK CERONE
- ☐ 97U. JEFF INNIS

NEW YORK YANKEES

- ☐ 40U. JOHN HABYAN
- ☐ 41U. PAT KELLY
- ☐ 42U. MATT NOKES
- ☐ 43U. SCOTT SANDERSON
- ☐ 44U. BERNIE WILLIAMS

OAKLAND A'S

- ☐ 45U. HAROLD BAINES
- ☐ 46U. BROOK JACOBY
- ☐ 47U. ERNEST RILES
- ☐ 48U. WILLIE WILSON

PHILADELPHIA PHILLIES

- ☐ 98U. WALLY BACKMAN
- ☐ 99U. TOMMY GREENE
- ☐ 100U. RICKY JORDAN
- ☐ 101U. MITCH WILLIAMS

PITTSBURGH PIRATES

- ☐ 102U. JOHN SMILEY
- ☐ 103U. RANDY TOMLIN
- ☐ 104U. GARY VARSHO

ST. LOUIS CARDINALS

- ☐ 105U. CRIS CARPENTER
- ☐ 106U. KEN HILL
- ☐ 107U. FELIX JOSE
- ☐ 108U. OMAR OLIVARES
- ☐ 109U. GERALD PERRY

SAN DIEGO PADRES

- ☐ 110U. JERALD CLARK
- ☐ 111U. TONY FERNANDEZ
- ☐ 112U. DARRIN JACKSON
- ☐ 113U. MIKE MADDUX
- ☐ 114U. TIM TEUFEL

SAN FRANCISCO GIANTS

- ☐ 115U. BUD BLACK
- ☐ 116U. KELLY DOWNS
- ☐ 117U. MIKE FELDER
- ☐ 118U. WILLIE MCGEE
- ☐ 119U. TREVOR WILSON

SEATTLE MARINERS

- ☐ 49U. JAY BUHNER
- ☐ 50U. RICH DELUCIA
- ☐ 51U. MIKE JACKSON
- ☐ 52U. BILL KRUEGER
- ☐ 53U. BILL SWIFT

TEXAS RANGERS

- ☐ 54U. BRIAN DOWNING
- ☐ 55U. JUAN GONZALEZ
- ☐ 56U. DEAN PALMER
- ☐ 57U. KEVIN REIMER
- ☐ 58U. IVAN RODRIGUEZ

TORONTO BLUE JAYS

- ☐ 59U. TOM CANDIOTTI
- ☐ 60U. JUAN GUZMAN
- ☐ 61U. BOB MACDONALD

- ☐ 62U. GREG MYERS
- ☐ 63U. ED SPRAGUE
- ☐ 64U. DEVON WHITE

1992 ULTRA (600)
2 1/2" X 3 1/2"

ATLANTA BRAVES

- ☐ 157. STEVE AVERY
- ☐ 158. RAFAEL BELLIARD
- ☐ 159. JEFF BLAUSER
- ☐ 160. SID BREAM
- ☐ 161. RON GANT
- ☐ 162. TOM GLAVINE
- ☐ 163. BRIAN HUNTER
- ☐ 164. DAVE JUSTICE
- ☐ 165. MARK LEMKE
- ☐ 166. GREG OLSON
- ☐ 167. TERRY PENDLETON
- ☐ 168. LONNIE SMITH
- ☐ 169. JOHN SMOLTZ
- ☐ 170. MIKE STANTON
- ☐ 171. JEFF TREADWAY
- ☐ 455. JUAN BERENGUER
- ☐ 456. DAMON BERRYHILL
- ☐ 457. MIKE BIELECKI
- ☐ 458. MARVIN FREEMAN
- ☐ 459. CHARLIE LEIBRANDT
- ☐ 460. KENT MERCKER
- ☐ 461. OTIS NIXON
- ☐ 462. ALEJANDRO PENA
- ☐ 463. BEN RIVERA
- ☐ 464. DEION SANDERS
- ☐ 465. MARK WOHLERS

BALTIMORE ORIOLES

- ☐ 1. GLENN DAVIS
- ☐ 2. MIKE DEVEREAUX
- ☐ 3. DWIGHT EVANS
- ☐ 4. LEO GOMEZ
- ☐ 5. CHRIS HOILES
- ☐ 6. SAM HORN
- ☐ 7. CHITO MARTINEZ
- ☐ 8. RANDY MILLIGAN
- ☐ 9. MIKE MUSSINA
- ☐ 10. BILLY RIPKEN
- ☐ 11. CAL RIPKEN, JR.
- ☐ 301. BRADY ANDERSON
- ☐ 302. TODD FROHWIRTH
- ☐ 303. BEN MCDONALD
- ☐ 304. MARK MCLEMORE
- ☐ 305. JOSE MESA
- ☐ 306. BOB MILACKI
- ☐ 307. GREGG OLSON
- ☐ 308. DAVID SEGUI
- ☐ 309. RICK SUTCLIFFE
- ☐ 310. JEFF TACKETT

BOSTON RED SOX

- ☐ 12. TOM BRUNANSKY
- ☐ 13. ELLIS BURKS
- ☐ 14. JACK CLARK
- ☐ 15. ROGER CLEMENS
- ☐ 16. MIKE GREENWELL
- ☐ 17. JOE HESKETH
- ☐ 18. TONY PENA
- ☐ 19. CARLOS QUINTANA
- ☐ 20. JEFF REARDON
- ☐ 21. JODY REED
- ☐ 22. LUIS RIVERA
- ☐ 23. MO VAUGHN
- ☐ 311. WADE BOGGS
- ☐ 312. SCOTT COOPER
- ☐ 313. JOHN FLAHERTY
- ☐ 314. WAYNE HOUSIE
- ☐ 315. PETER HOY
- ☐ 316. JOHN MARZANO
- ☐ 317. TIM NAEHRING
- ☐ 318. PHIL PLANTIER
- ☐ 319. FRANK VIOLA
- ☐ 320. MATT YOUNG

CALIFORNIA ANGELS

- ☐ 24. GARY DISARCINA
- ☐ 25. CHUCK FINLEY
- ☐ 26. GARY GAETTI
- ☐ 27. BRYAN HARVEY
- ☐ 28. LANCE PARRISH
- ☐ 29. LUIS POLONIA
- ☐ 30. DICK SCHOFIELD
- ☐ 31. LUIS SOJO
- ☐ 321. JIM ABBOTT
- ☐ 322. HUBIE BROOKS
- ☐ 323. CHAD CURTIS
- ☐ 324. ALVIN DAVIS
- ☐ 325. JUNIOR FELIX
- ☐ 326. VON HAYES
- ☐ 327. MARK LANGSTON
- ☐ 328. SCOTT LEWIS
- ☐ 329. DON ROBINSON
- ☐ 330. BOBBY ROSE
- ☐ 331. LEE STEVENS

CHICAGO CUBS

- ☐ 172. PAUL ASSENMACHER
- ☐ 173. GEORGE BELL
- ☐ 174. SHAWON DUNSTON
- ☐ 175. MARK GRACE
- ☐ 176. DANNY JACKSON
- ☐ 177. LES LANCASTER
- ☐ 178. GREG MADDUX
- ☐ 179. LUIS SALAZAR
- ☐ 180. REY SANCHEZ
- ☐ 181. RYNE SANDBERG
- ☐ 182. JOSE VIZCAINO
- ☐ 183. CHICO WALKER
- ☐ 184. JEROME WALTON
- ☐ 466. SHAWN BOSKIE
- ☐ 467. FRANK CASTILLO
- ☐ 468. ANDRE DAWSON
- ☐ 469. JOE GIRARDI
- ☐ 470. CHUCK MCELROY
- ☐ 471. MIKE MORGAN
- ☐ 472. KEN PATTERSON
- ☐ 473. BOB SCANLAN
- ☐ 474. GARY SCOTT
- ☐ 475. DAVE SMITH
- ☐ 476. SAMMY SOSA
- ☐ 477. HECTOR VILLANUEVA

CHICAGO WHITE SOX

- ☐ 32. WILSON ALVAREZ
- ☐ 33. CARLTON FISK
- ☐ 34. CRAIG GREBECK
- ☐ 35. OZZIE GUILLEN
- ☐ 36. GREG HIBBARD
- ☐ 37. CHARLIE HOUGH
- ☐ 38. LANCE JOHNSON
- ☐ 39. RON KARKOVICE
- ☐ 40. JACK MCDOWELL
- ☐ 41. DONN PALL
- ☐ 42. MELIDO PEREZ
- ☐ 43. TIM RAINES
- ☐ 44. FRANK THOMAS
- ☐ 332. GEORGE BELL
- ☐ 333. ESTEBAN BELTRE
- ☐ 334. JOEY CORA
- ☐ 335. ALEX FERNANDEZ
- ☐ 336. ROBERTO HERNANDEZ
- ☐ 337. MIKE HUFF
- ☐ 338. KIRK MCCASKILL
- ☐ 339. DAN PASQUA
- ☐ 340. SCOTT RADINSKY
- ☐ 341. STEVE SAX
- ☐ 342. BOBBY THIGPEN
- ☐ 343. ROBIN VENTURA

CINCINNATI REDS

- ☐ 185. GLENN BRAGGS
- ☐ 186. TOM BROWNING
- ☐ 187. ROB DIBBLE
- ☐ 188. BILL DORAN
- ☐ 189. CHRIS HAMMOND
- ☐ 190. BILLY HATCHER
- ☐ 191. BARRY LARKIN
- ☐ 192. HAL MORRIS
- ☐ 193. JOE OLIVER
- ☐ 194. PAUL O'NEILL
- ☐ 195. JEFF REED
- ☐ 196. JOSE RIJO
- ☐ 197. CHRIS SABO
- ☐ 478. SCOTT BANKHEAD
- ☐ 479. TIM BELCHER
- ☐ 480. FREDDIE BENAVIDES
- ☐ 481. JACO BRUMFIELD
- ☐ 482. NORM CHARLTON
- ☐ 483. DWAYNE HENRY
- ☐ 484. DAVE MARTINEZ
- ☐ 485. BIP ROBERTS
- ☐ 486. REGGIE SANDERS
- ☐ 487. GREG SWINDELL

CLEVELAND INDIANS

- ☐ 45. SANDY ALOMAR, JR.
- ☐ 46. CARLOS BAERGA
- ☐ 47. ALBERT BELLE
- ☐ 48. JERRY BROWNE
- ☐ 49. FELIX FERMIN
- ☐ 50. REGGIE JEFFERSON
- ☐ 51. MARK LEWIS
- ☐ 52. CARLOS MARTINEZ
- ☐ 53. STEVE OLIN
- ☐ 54. JIM THOME
- ☐ 55. MARK WHITEN
- ☐ 344. JACK ARMSTRONG
- ☐ 345. ALEX COLE
- ☐ 346. DENNIS COOK
- ☐ 347. GLENALLEN HILL
- ☐ 348. THOMAS HOWARD
- ☐ 349. BROOK JACOBY
- ☐ 350. KENNY LOFTON
- ☐ 351. CHARLES NAGY
- ☐ 352. ROD NICHOLS
- ☐ 353. JUNIOR ORTIZ
- ☐ 354. DAVE OTTO
- ☐ 355. TONY PEREZCHICA
- ☐ 356. SCOTT SCUDDER
- ☐ 357. PAUL SORRENTO

DETROIT TIGERS

- ☐ 56. DAVE BERGMAN
- ☐ 57. MILT CUYLER
- ☐ 58. ROB DEER
- ☐ 59. CECIL FIELDER
- ☐ 60. TRAVIS FRYMAN
- ☐ 61. SCOTT LIVINGSTONE

- □ 62. TONY PHILLIPS
- □ 63. MICKEY TETTLETON
- □ 64. ALAN TRAMMELL
- □ 65. LOU WHITAKER
- □ 358. SKEETER BARNES
- □ 359. MARK CARREON
- □ 360. JOHN DOHERTY
- □ 361. DAN GLADDEN
- □ 362. BILL GULLICKSON
- □ 363. SHAWN HARE
- □ 364. MIKE HENNEMAN
- □ 365. CHAD KREUTER
- □ 366. MARK LEITER
- □ 367. MIKE MUNOZ

HOUSTON ASTROS

- □ 198. JEFF BAGWELL
- □ 199. CRAIG BIGGIO
- □ 200. KEN CAMINITI
- □ 201. ANDUJAR CEDENO
- □ 202. STEVE FINLEY
- □ 203. LUIS GONZALEZ
- □ 204. PETE HARNISCH
- □ 205. XAVIER HERNANDEZ
- □ 206. DARRYL KILE
- □ 207. AL OSUNA
- □ 208. CURT SCHILLING
- □ 488. RYAN BOWEN
- □ 489. CASEY CANDAELE
- □ 490. JUAN GUERRERO
- □ 491. PETE INCAVIGLIA
- □ 492. JEFF JUDEN
- □ 493. ROB MURPHY
- □ 494. MARK PORTUGAL
- □ 495. RAFAEL RAMIREZ
- □ 496. SCOTT SERVAIS
- □ 497. ED TAUBENSEE
- □ 498. BRIAN WILLIAMS

KANSAS CITY ROYALS

- □ 66. KEVIN APPIER
- □ 67. MIKE BODDICKER
- □ 68. GEORGE BRETT
- □ 69. JIM EISENREICH
- □ 70. MARK GUBICZA
- □ 71. DAVID HOWARD
- □ 72. JOEL JOHNSTON
- □ 73. MIKE MACFARLANE
- □ 74. BRENT MAYNE
- □ 75. BRIAN MCRAE
- □ 76. JEFF MONTGOMERY
- □ 77. TERRY SHUMPERT
- □ 369. MARK DAVIS
- □ 370. TOM GORDON
- □ 371. CHRIS GWYNN
- □ 372. GREGG JEFFERIES
- □ 373. WALLY JOYNER
- □ 374. KEVIN MCREYNOLDS
- □ 375. KEITH MILLER
- □ 376. RICO ROSSY
- □ 377. CURTIS WILKERSON

LOS ANGELES DODGERS

- □ 209. BRETT BUTLER
- □ 210. KAL DANIELS
- □ 211. LENNY HARRIS
- □ 212. STAN JAVIER
- □ 213. RAMON MARTINEZ
- □ 214. ROGER MCDOWELL
- □ 215. JOSE OFFERMAN
- □ 216. JUAN SAMUEL
- □ 217. MIKE SCIOSCIA
- □ 218. MIKE SHARPERSON
- □ 219. DARRYL STRAWBERRY
- □ 499. TODD BENZINGER
- □ 500. JOHN CANDELARIA
- □ 501. TOM CANDIOTTI
- □ 502. TIM CREWS
- □ 503. ERIC DAVIS
- □ 504. JIM GOTT
- □ 505. DAVE HANSEN
- □ 506. CARLOS HERNANDEZ
- □ 507. OREL HERSHISER
- □ 508. ERIC KARROS
- □ 509. BOB OJEDA
- □ 510. STEVE WILSON

MILWAUKEE BREWERS

- □ 78. DON AUGUST
- □ 79. DANTE BICHETTE
- □ 80. TED HIGUERA
- □ 81. PAUL MOLITOR
- □ 82. JAMIE NAVARRO
- □ 83. GARY SHEFFIELD
- □ 84. BILL SPIERS
- □ 85. B.J.SURHOFF
- □ 86. GREG VAUGHN
- □ 87. ROBIN YOUNT
- □ 378. RICKY BONES
- □ 379. CHRIS BOSIO
- □ 380. CAL ELDRED
- □ 381. SCOTT FLETCHER
- □ 382. JIM GANTNER
- □ 383. DARRYL HAMILTON
- □ 384. DOUG HENRY
- □ 385. PAT LISTACH
- □ 386. TIM MCINTOSH
- □ 387. EDWIN NUNEZ
- □ 388. DAN PLESAC
- □ 389. KEVIN SEITZER
- □ 390. FRANKLIN STUBBS
- □ 391. WILLIAM SUERO
- □ 392. BILL WEGMAN

MINNESOTA TWINS

- □ 88. RICK AGUILERA
- □ 89. CHILI DAVIS
- □ 90. SCOTT ERICKSON
- □ 91. BRIAN HARPER
- □ 92. KENT HRBEK
- □ 93. CHUCK KNOBLAUCH
- □ 94. SCOTT LEIUS
- □ 95. SHANE MACK
- □ 96. MIKE PAGLIARULO
- □ 97. KIRBY PUCKETT
- □ 98. KEVIN TAPANI
- □ 393. WILLIE BANKS
- □ 394. JARVIS BROWN
- □ 395. GREG GAGNE
- □ 396. MARK GUTHRIE
- □ 397. BILL KRUEGER
- □ 398. PAT MAHOMES
- □ 399. PEDRO MUNOZ
- □ 400. JOHN SMILEY
- □ 401. GARY WAYNE
- □ 402. LENNY WEBSTER
- □ 403. CARL WILLIS

MONTREAL EXPOS

- □ 220. DELINO DESHIELDS
- □ 221. TOM FOLEY
- □ 222. STEVE FREY
- □ 223. DENNIS MARTINEZ
- □ 224. SPIKE OWEN
- □ 225. GILBERTO REYES
- □ 226. TIM WALLACH
- □ 511. MOISES ALOU
- □ 512. BRET BARBERIE
- □ 513. IVAN CALDERON
- □ 514. GARY CARTER
- □ 515. ARCHI CIANFROCCO
- □ 516. JEFF FASSERO
- □ 517. DARRIN FLETCHER
- □ 518. MARQUIS GRISSOM
- □ 519. CHRIS HANEY
- □ 520. KEN HILL
- □ 521. CHRIS NABHOLZ
- □ 522. BILL SAMPEN
- □ 523. JOHN VANDER WAL
- □ 524. DAVID WAINHOUSE
- □ 525. LARRY WALKER
- □ 526. JOHN WETTELAND

NEW YORK METS

- □ 227. DARYL BOSTON
- □ 228. TIM BURKE
- □ 229. VINCE COLEMAN
- □ 230. DAVID CONE
- □ 231. KEVIN ELSTER
- □ 232. DWIGHT GOODEN
- □ 233. TODD HUNDLEY
- □ 234. JEFF INNIS
- □ 235. HOWARD JOHNSON
- □ 236. DAVE MAGADAN
- □ 237. MACKEY SASSER
- □ 238. ANTHONY YOUNG
- □ 527. BOBBY BONILLA
- □ 528. SID FERNANDEZ
- □ 529. JOHN FRANCO
- □ 530. DAVE GALLAGHER
- □ 531. PAUL GIBSON
- □ 532. EDDIE MURRAY
- □ 533. JUNIOR NOBOA
- □ 534. CHARLIE O'BRIEN
- □ 535. BILL PECOTA
- □ 536. WILLIE RANDOLPH
- □ 537. BRET SABERHAGEN
- □ 538. DICK SCHOFIELD
- □ 539. PETE SCHOUREK

NEW YORK YANKEES

- □ 99. JESSE BARFIELD
- □ 100. ALVARO ESPINOZA
- □ 101. MEL HALL
- □ 102. PAT KELLY
- □ 103. ROBERTO KELLY
- □ 104. KEVIN MAAS
- □ 105. DON MATTINGLY
- □ 106. HENSLEY MEULENS
- □ 107. MATT NOKES
- □ 108. STEVE SAX
- □ 404. GREG CADARET
- □ 405. STEVE FARR
- □ 406. MIKE GALLEGO
- □ 407. CHARLIE HAYES
- □ 408. STEVE HOWE
- □ 409. DION JAMES
- □ 410. JEFF JOHNSON
- □ 411. TIM LEARY
- □ 412. JIM LEYRITZ
- □ 413. MELIDO PEREZ
- □ 414. SCOTT SANDERSON
- □ 415. ANDY STANKIEWICZ
- □ 416. MIKE STANLEY
- □ 417. DANNY TARTABULL

OAKLAND A'S

- □ 109. HAROLD BAINES
- □ 110. JOSE CANSECO
- □ 111. RON DARLING
- □ 112. MIKE GALLEGO
- □ 113. DAVE HENDERSON
- □ 114. RICKEY HENDERSON
- □ 115. MARK MCGWIRE
- □ 116. TERRY STEINBACH
- □ 117. DAVE STEWART
- □ 118. TODD VAN POPPEL
- □ 119. BOB WELCH
- □ 418. LANCE BLANKENSHIP
- □ 419. MIKE BORDICK
- □ 420. SCOTT BROSIUS
- □ 421. DENNIS ECKERSLEY
- □ 422. SCOTT HEMOND
- □ 423. CARNEY LANSFORD
- □ 424. HENRY MERCEDES
- □ 425. MIKE MOORE
- □ 426. GENE NELSON
- □ 427. RANDY READY
- □ 428. BRUCE WALTON

☐ 429. WILLIE WILSON

PHILADELPHIA PHILLIES

☐ 239. WES CHAMBERLAIN
☐ 240. DARREN DAULTON
☐ 241. LENNY DYKSTRA
☐ 242. TOMMY GREENE
☐ 243. CHARLIE HAYES
☐ 244. DAVE HOLLINS
☐ 245. RICKY JORDAN
☐ 246. JOHN KRUK
☐ 247. MICKEY MORANDINI
☐ 248. TERRY MULHOLLAND
☐ 249. DALE MURPHY
☐ 540. RUBEN AMARO
☐ 541. ANDY ASHBY
☐ 542. KIM BATISTE
☐ 543. CLIFF BRANTLEY
☐ 544. MARIANO DUNCAN
☐ 545. JEFF GROTEWOLD
☐ 546. BARRY JONES
☐ 547. JULIO PEGUERO
☐ 548. CURT SCHILLING
☐ 549. MITCH WILLIAMS

PITTSBURGH PIRATES

☐ 250. JAY BELL
☐ 251. BARRY BONDS
☐ 252. STEVE BUECHELE
☐ 253. DOUG DRABEK
☐ 254. MIEK LAVALLIERE
☐ 255. JOSE LIND
☐ 256. LLOYD MCCLENDON
☐ 257. ORLANDO MERCED
☐ 258. DON SLAUGHT
☐ 259. JOHN SMILEY
☐ 260. ZANE SMITH
☐ 261. RANDY TOMLIN
☐ 262. ANDY VAN SLYKE
☐ 550. STAN BELINDA
☐ 551. SCOTT BULLETT
☐ 552. CECIL ESPY
☐ 553. JEFF KING
☐ 554. ROGER MASON
☐ 555. PAUL MILLER
☐ 556. DENNY NEAGLE
☐ 557. VICENTE PALACIOS
☐ 558. BOB PATTERSON
☐ 559. TOM PRINCE
☐ 560. GARY REDUS
☐ 561. GARY VARSHO

ST. LOUIS CARDINALS

☐ 263. PEDRO GUERERRO
☐ 264. FELIX JOSE
☐ 265. RAY LANKFORD
☐ 266. OMAR OLIVARES
☐ 267. JOSE OQUENDO
☐ 268. TOM PAGNOZZI
☐ 269. BRYN SMITH
☐ 270. LEE SMITH
☐ 271. OZZIE SMITH
☐ 272. MILT THOMPSON
☐ 273. TODD ZEILE
☐ 562. JUAN AGOSTO
☐ 563. CRIS CARPENTER
☐ 564. MARK CLARK
☐ 565. JOSE DELEON
☐ 566. RICH GEDMAN
☐ 567. BERNARD GILKEY
☐ 568. REX HUDLER
☐ 569. TIM JONES
☐ 570. DONOVAN OSBORNE
☐ 571. MIKE PEREZ
☐ 572. GERALD PERRY
☐ 573. BOB TEWKSBURY
☐ 574. TODD WORRELL

SAN DIEGO PADRES

☐ 274. ANDY BENES
☐ 275. JERALD CLARK
☐ 276. TONY FERNANDEZ
☐ 277. TONY GWYNN
☐ 278. GREG HARRIS
☐ 279. THOMAS HOWARD
☐ 280. BRUCE HURST
☐ 281. MIKE MADDUX
☐ 282. FRED MCGRIFF
☐ 283. BENITO SANTIAGO
☐ 575. DAVE EILAND
☐ 576. JEREMY HERNANDEZ
☐ 577. CRAIG LEFFERTS
☐ 578. JOSE MELENDEZ
☐ 579. RANDY MYERS
☐ 580. GARY PETTIS
☐ 581. RICH RODRIGUEZ
☐ 582. GARY SHEFFIELD
☐ 583. CRAIG SHIPLEY
☐ 584. KURT STILLWELL
☐ 585. TIM TEUFEL

SAN FRANCISCO GIANTS

☐ 284. KEVIN BASS
☐ 285. JEFF BRANTLEY
☐ 286. JOHN BURKETT
☐ 287. WILL CLARK
☐ 288. ROYCE CLAYTON
☐ 289. STEVE DECKER
☐ 290. KELLY DOWNS
☐ 291. MIKE FEIDER
☐ 292. DARREN LEWIS
☐ 293. KIRT MANWARING
☐ 294. WILLIE MCGEE
☐ 295. ROBBY THOMPSON
☐ 296. MATT WILLIAMS
☐ 297. TREVOR WILSON
☐ 586. ROD BECK
☐ 587. DAVE BURBA
☐ 588. CRAIG COLBERT
☐ 589. BRYAN HICKERSON
☐ 590. MIKE JACKSON
☐ 591. MARK LEONARD
☐ 592. JIM MCNAMARA
☐ 593. JOHN PATTERSON
☐ 594. DAVE RIGHETTI
☐ 595. CORY SNYDER
☐ 596. BILL SWIFT
☐ 597. TED WOOD

SEATTLE MARINERS

☐ 120. GREG BRILEY
☐ 121. JAY BUHNER
☐ 122. RICH DELUCIA
☐ 123. KEN GRIFFEY, JR.
☐ 124. ERIK HANSON
☐ 125. RANDY JOHNSON
☐ 126. EDGAR MARTINEZ
☐ 127. TINO MARTINEZ
☐ 128. PETE O'BRIEN
☐ 129. HAROLD REYNOLDS
☐ 130. DAVE VALLE
☐ 430. RICH AMARAL
☐ 431. DAVE COCHRANE
☐ 432. HENRY COTTO
☐ 433. CALVIN JONES
☐ 434. KEVIN MITCHELL
☐ 435. CLAY PARKER
☐ 436. OMAR VIZQUEL

TEXAS RANGERS

☐ 131. JULIO FRANCO
☐ 132. JUAN GONZALEZ
☐ 133. JEFF HUSON
☐ 134. MIKE JEFFCOAT
☐ 135. TERRY MATHEWS
☐ 136. RAFAEL PALMEIRO
☐ 137. DEAN PALMER
☐ 138. GENO PETRALLI
☐ 139. IVAN RODRIGUEZ
☐ 140. JEFF RUSSELL
☐ 141. NOLAN RYAN
☐ 142. RUBEN SIERRA
☐ 437. FLOYD BANNISTER
☐ 438. KEVIN BROWN
☐ 439. JOHN CANGELOSI
☐ 440. BRIAN DOWNING
☐ 441. MONTY FARISS
☐ 442. JOSE GUZMAN
☐ 443. DONALD HARRIS
☐ 444. KEVIN REIMER
☐ 445. KENNY ROGERS
☐ 446. WAYNE ROSENTHAL
☐ 447. DICKIE THON

TORONTO BLUE JAYS

☐ 143. ROBERTO ALOMAR
☐ 144. PAT BORDERS
☐ 145. JOE CARTER
☐ 146. KELLY GRUBER
☐ 147. JIMMY KEY
☐ 148. MANNY LEE
☐ 149. RANCE MULLINIKS
☐ 150. GREG MYERS
☐ 151. JOHN OLERUD
☐ 152. DAVE STIEB
☐ 153. TODD STOTTLEMYRE
☐ 154. DUANE WARD
☐ 155. DEVON WHITE
☐ 156. EDDIE ZOSKY
☐ 448. DEREK BELL
☐ 449. JUAN GUZMAN
☐ 450. TOM HENKE
☐ 451. CANDY MALDONADO
☐ 452. JACK MORRIS
☐ 453. DAVID WELLS
☐ 454. DAVE WINFIELD

1993 ULTRA (650)
2 1/2" X 3 1/2"

ATLANTA BRAVES

☐ 1. STEVE AVERY
☐ 2. RAFAEL BELLIARD
☐ 3. DAMON BERRYHILL
☐ 4. SID BREAM
☐ 5. RON GANT
☐ 6. TOM GLAVINE
☐ 7. RYAN KLESKO
☐ 8. MARK LEMKE
☐ 9. JAVIER LOPEZ
☐ 10. GREG OLSON
☐ 11. TERRY PENDLETON
☐ 12. DEION SANDERS
☐ 13. MIKE STANTON
☐ 301. STEVE BEDROSIAN
☐ 302. JEFF BLAUSER
☐ 303. FRANCISCO CABRERA
☐ 304. MARVIN FREEMAN
☐ 305. BRIAN HUNTER
☐ 306. DAVID JUSTICE
☐ 307. GREG MADDUX
☐ 308. GREG MCMICHAEL
☐ 309. KENT MERCKER
☐ 310. OTIS NIXON
☐ 311. PETE SMITH
☐ 312. JOHN SMOLTZ

BALTIMORE ORIOLES

☐ 138. BRADY ANDERSON
☐ 139. GLENN DAVIS
☐ 140. LEO GOMEZ
☐ 141. CHITO MARTINEZ
☐ 142. BEN MCDONALD
☐ 143. ALAN MILLS
☐ 144. MIKE MUSSINA

☐ 145. GREGG OLSON
☐ 146. DAVID SEGUI
☐ 147. JEFF TACKETT
☐ 492. HAROLD BAINES
☐ 493. MIKE DEVEREAUX
☐ 494. TODD FROHWIRTH
☐ 495. CHRIS HOILES
☐ 496. LUIS MERCEDES
☐ 497. SHERMAN OBANDO
☐ 498. BRAD PENNINGTON
☐ 499. HAROLD REYNOLDS
☐ 500. ARTHUR RHODES
☐ 501. CAL RIPKEN, JR.
☐ 502. RICK SUTCLIFFE
☐ 503. FERNANDO VALENZUELA
☐ 504. MARK WILLIAMSON

BOSTON RED SOX

☐ 148. JACK CLARK
☐ 149. SCOTT COOPER
☐ 150. DANNY DARWIN
☐ 151. JOHN DOPSON
☐ 152. MIKE GREENWELL
☐ 153. TIM NAEHRING
☐ 154. TONY PENA
☐ 155. PAUL QUANTRILL
☐ 156. MO VAUGHN
☐ 157. FRANK VIOLA
☐ 158. BOB ZUPCIC
☐ 505. SCOTT BANKHEAD
☐ 506. GREG BLOSSER
☐ 507. IVAN CALDERON
☐ 508. ROGER CLEMENS
☐ 509. ANDRE DAWSON
☐ 510. SCOTT FLETCHER
☐ 511. GREG HARRIS
☐ 512. BILLY HATCHER
☐ 513. BOB MELVIN
☐ 514. CARLOS QUINTANA
☐ 515. LUIS RIVERA
☐ 516. JEFF RUSSELL
☐ 517. KEN RYAN

CALIFORNIA ANGELS

☐ 159. CHAD CURTIS
☐ 160. GARY DISARCINA
☐ 161. DAMION EASLEY
☐ 162. CHUCK FINLEY
☐ 163. TIM FORTUGNO
☐ 164. RENE GONZALES
☐ 165. JOE GRAHE
☐ 166. MARK LANGSTON
☐ 167. JOHN ORTON
☐ 168. LUIS POLONIA
☐ 169. JULIO VALERA
☐ 518. CHILI DAVIS
☐ 519. JIM EDMONDS
☐ 520. GARY GAETTI
☐ 521. TOREY LOVULLO
☐ 522. TROY PERCIVAL
☐ 523. TIM SALMON
☐ 524. SCOTT SANDERSON
☐ 525. J.T. SNOW
☐ 526. JEROME WALTON

CHICAGO CUBS

☐ 14. PAUL ASSENMACHER
☐ 15. STEVE BUECHELE
☐ 16. FRANK CASTILLO
☐ 17. SHAWON DUNSTON
☐ 18. MARK GRACE
☐ 19. DERRICK MAY
☐ 20. CHUCK MCELROY
☐ 21. MIKE MORGAN
☐ 22. BOB SCANLAN
☐ 23. DWIGHT SMITH
☐ 24. SAMMY SOSA
☐ 25. RICK WILKINS
☐ 313. JOSE GUZMAN
☐ 314. MIKE HARKEY
☐ 315. GREG HIBBARD
☐ 316. CANDY MALDONADO
☐ 317. RANDY MYERS
☐ 318. DAN PLESAC
☐ 319. REY SANCHEZ
☐ 320. RYNE SANDBERG
☐ 321. TOMMY SHIELDS

☐ 322. JOSE VIZCAINO
☐ 323. MATT WALBECK
☐ 324. WILLIE WILSON

CHICAGO WHITE SOX

☐ 170. WILSON ALVAREZ
☐ 171. GEORGE BELL
☐ 172. JOEY CORA
☐ 173. ALEX FERNANDEZ
☐ 174. LANCE JOHNSON
☐ 175. RON KARKOVICE
☐ 176. JACK MCDOWELL
☐ 177. SCOTT RADINSKY
☐ 178. TIM RAINES
☐ 179. STEVE SAX
☐ 180. BOBBY THIGPEN
☐ 181. FRANK THOMAS
☐ 527. JASON BERE
☐ 528. ROD BOLTON
☐ 529. ELLIS BURKS
☐ 530. CARLTON FISK
☐ 531. CRAIG GREBECK
☐ 532. OZZIE GUILLEN
☐ 533. ROBERTO HERNANDEZ
☐ 534. BO JACKSON
☐ 535. KIRK MCCASKILL
☐ 536. DAVE STIEB
☐ 537. ROBIN VENTURA

CINCINNATI REDS

☐ 26. TIM BELCHER
☐ 27. JEFF BRANSON
☐ 28. BILL DORAN
☐ 29. CHRIS HAMMOND
☐ 30. BARRY LARKIN
☐ 31. HAL MORRIS
☐ 32. JOE OLIVER
☐ 33. JOSE RIJO
☐ 34. BIP ROBERTS
☐ 35. CHRIS SABO
☐ 36. REGGIE SANDERS
☐ 325. TOM BROWNING
☐ 326. TIM COSTO
☐ 327. ROB DIBBLE
☐ 328. STEVE FOSTER
☐ 329. ROBERTO KELLY
☐ 330. RANDY MILLIGAN
☐ 331. KEVIN MITCHELL
☐ 332. TIM PUGH
☐ 333. JEFF REARDON
☐ 334. JOHN ROPER
☐ 335. JUAN SAMUEL
☐ 336. JOHN SMILEY
☐ 337. DAN WILSON

CLEVELAND INDIANS

☐ 182. SANDY ALOMAR, JR.
☐ 183. CARLOS BAERGA
☐ 184. FELIX FERMIN
☐ 185. THOMAS HOWARD
☐ 186. MARK LEWIS
☐ 187. DEREK LILLIQUIST
☐ 188. CARLOS MARTINEZ
☐ 189. CHARLES NAGY
☐ 190. SCOTT SCUDDER
☐ 191. PAUL SORRENTO
☐ 192. JIM THOME
☐ 193. MARK WHITEN
☐ 538. ALBERT BELLE
☐ 539. MIKE BIELECKI
☐ 540. GLENALLEN HILL
☐ 541. REGGIE JEFFERSON
☐ 542. KENNY LOFTON
☐ 543. JEFF MUTIS
☐ 544. JUNIOR ORTIZ
☐ 545. MANNY RAMIREZ
☐ 546. JEFF TREADWAY
☐ 547. KEVIN WICKANDER

COLORADO ROCKIES

☐ 338. SCOTT ALDRED
☐ 339. ANDY ASHBY
☐ 340. FREDDIE BENAVIDES
☐ 341. DANTE BICHETTE
☐ 342. WILLIE BLAIR
☐ 343. DARYL BOSTON
☐ 344. VINNY CASTILLA
☐ 345. JERALD CLARK
☐ 346. ALEX COLE
☐ 347. ANDRES GALARRAGA
☐ 348. JOE GIRARDI
☐ 349. RYAN HAWBLITZEL
☐ 350. CHARLIE HAYES
☐ 351. BUTCH HENRY
☐ 352. DARREN HOLMES
☐ 353. DALE MURPHY
☐ 354. DAVID NIED
☐ 355. JEFF PARRETT
☐ 356. STEVE REED
☐ 357. BRUCE RUFFIN
☐ 358. DANNY SHEAFFER
☐ 359. BRYN SMITH
☐ 360. JIM TATUM
☐ 361. ERIC YOUNG
☐ 362. GERALD YOUNG

DETROIT TIGERS

☐ 194. MILT CUYLER
☐ 195. ROB DEER
☐ 196. JOHN DOHERTY
☐ 197. TRAVIS FRYMAN
☐ 198. DAN GLADDEN
☐ 199. MIKE HENNEMAN
☐ 200. JOHN KIELY
☐ 201. CHAD KREUTER
☐ 202. SCOTT LIVINGSTONE
☐ 203. TONY PHILLIPS
☐ 204. ALAN TRAMMELL
☐ 548. CECIL FIELDER
☐ 549. KIRK GIBSON
☐ 550. GREG GOHR
☐ 551. DAVID HAAS
☐ 552. BILL KRUEGER
☐ 553. MIKE MOORE
☐ 554. MICKEY TETTLETON
☐ 555. LOU WHITAKER

FLORIDA MARLINS

☐ 363. LUIS AQUINO
☐ 364. ALEX ARIAS
☐ 365. JACK ARMSTRONG
☐ 366. BRET BARBERIE
☐ 367. RYAN BOWEN
☐ 368. GREG BRILEY
☐ 369. CRIS CARPENTER
☐ 370. CHUCK CARR
☐ 371. JEFF CONINE
☐ 372. STEVE DECKER
☐ 373. ORESTES DESTRADE
☐ 374. MONTY FARISS
☐ 375. JUNIOR FELIX
☐ 376. CHRIS HAMMOND
☐ 377. BRYAN HARVEY
☐ 378. TREVOR HOFFMAN
☐ 379. CHARLIE HOUGH
☐ 380. JOE KLINK
☐ 381. RICHIE LEWIS
☐ 382. DAVE MAGADAN
☐ 383. BOB MCCLURE
☐ 384. SCOTT POSE
☐ 385. RICH RENTERIA
☐ 386. BENITO SANTIAGO

☐ 387. WALT WEISS
☐ 388. NIGEL WILSON

HOUSTON ASTROS

☐ 37. CRAIG BIGGIO
☐ 38. KEN CAMINITI
☐ 39. STEVE FINLEY
☐ 40. LUIS GONZALEZ
☐ 41. JUAN GUERRERO
☐ 42. PETE HARNISCH
☐ 43. XAVIER HERNANDEZ
☐ 44. DOUG JONES
☐ 45. AL OSUNA
☐ 46. EDDIE TAUBENSEE
☐ 47. SCOOTER TUCKER
☐ 48. BRIAN WILLIAMS
☐ 389. ERIC ANTHONY
☐ 390. JEFF BAGWELL
☐ 391. ANDUJAR CEDENO
☐ 392. DOUG DRABEK
☐ 393. DARRYL KILE
☐ 394. MARK PORTUGAL
☐ 395. KARL RHODES
☐ 396. SCOTT SERVAIS
☐ 397. GREG SWINDELL

KANSAS CITY ROYALS

☐ 205. MIKE BODDICKER
☐ 206. GEORGE BRETT
☐ 207. TOM GORDON
☐ 208. MARK GUBICZA
☐ 209. GREGG JEFFERIES
☐ 210. WALLY JOYNER
☐ 211. KEVIN KOSLOFSKI
☐ 212. BRENT MAYNE
☐ 213. BRIAN MCRAE
☐ 214. KEVIN MCREYNOLDS
☐ 215. RUSTY MEACHAM
☐ 216. STEVE SHIFFLETT
☐ 556. KEVIN APPIER
☐ 557. BILLY BREWER
☐ 558. DAVID CONE
☐ 559. GREG GAGNE
☐ 560. MARK GARDNER
☐ 561. PHIL HIATT
☐ 562. FELIX JOSE
☐ 563. JOSE LIND
☐ 564. MIKE MACFARLANE
☐ 565. KEITH MILLER
☐ 566. JEFF MONTGOMERY
☐ 567. HIPOLITO PICHARDO

LOS ANGELES DODGERS

☐ 49. PEDRO ASTACIO
☐ 50. RAFAEL BOURNIGAL
☐ 51. BRETT BUTLER
☐ 52. TOM CANDIOTTI
☐ 53. ERIC DAVIS
☐ 54. LENNY HARRIS
☐ 55. OREL HERSHISER
☐ 56. ERIC KARROS
☐ 57. PEDRO MARTINEZ
☐ 58. ROGER MCDOWELL
☐ 59. JOSE OFFERMAN
☐ 60. MIKE PIAZZA
☐ 398. TOM GOODWIN
☐ 399. KEVIN GROSS
☐ 400. CARLOS HERNANDEZ
☐ 401. RAMON MARTINEZ
☐ 402. RAUL MONDESI
☐ 403. JODY REED
☐ 404. MIKE SHARPERSON
☐ 405. CORY SNYDER
☐ 406. DARRYL STRAWBERRY
☐ 407. RICK TRLICEK
☐ 408. TIM WALLACH
☐ 409. TOOD WORRELL

MILWAUKEE BREWERS

☐ 217. JAMES AUSTIN
☐ 218. CAL ELDRED
☐ 219. DARRYL HAMILTON
☐ 220. DOUG HENRY
☐ 221. JOHN JAHA
☐ 222. DAVE NILSSON
☐ 223. JESSE OROSCO
☐ 224. B.J. SURHOFF
☐ 225. GREG VAUGHN
☐ 226. BILL WEGMAN
☐ 227. ROBIN YOUNT
☐ 568. RICKY BONES
☐ 569. TOM BRUNANSKY
☐ 570. JOE KMAK
☐ 571. PAT LISTACH
☐ 572. GRAEME LLOYD
☐ 573. CARLOS MALDONADO
☐ 574. JOSIAS MANZANILLO
☐ 575. MATT MIESKE
☐ 576. KEVIN REIMER
☐ 577. BILL SPIERS
☐ 578. DICKIE THON

MINNESOTA TWINS

☐ 228. RICK AGUILERA
☐ 229. J.T. BRUETT
☐ 230. SCOTT ERICKSON
☐ 231. KENT HRBEK
☐ 232. TERRY JORGENSEN
☐ 233. SCOTT LEIUS
☐ 234. PAT MAHOMES
☐ 235. PEDRO MUNOZ
☐ 236. KIRBY PUCKETT
☐ 237. KEVIN TAPANI
☐ 238. LENNY WEBSTER
☐ 239. CARL WILLIS
☐ 579. WILLIE BANKS
☐ 580. JIM DESHAIES
☐ 581. MARK GUTHRIE
☐ 582. BRIAN HARPER
☐ 583. CHUCK KNOBLAUCH
☐ 584. GENE LARKIN
☐ 585. SHANE MACK
☐ 586. DAVID MCCARTY
☐ 587. MIKE PAGLIARULO
☐ 588. MIKE TROMBLEY
☐ 589. DAVE WINFIELD

MONTREAL EXPOS

☐ 61. MOISES ALOU
☐ 62. KENT BOTTENFIELD
☐ 63. ARCHI CIANFROCCO
☐ 64. GREG COLBRUNN
☐ 65. WIL CORDERO
☐ 66. DELINO DESHIELDS
☐ 67. DARRIN FLETCHER
☐ 68. KEN HILL
☐ 69. CHRIS NABHOLZ
☐ 70. MEL ROJAS
☐ 71. LARRY WALKER
☐ 410. TAVO ALVAREZ
☐ 411. SEAN BERRY
☐ 412. FRANK BOLICK
☐ 413. CLIFF FLOYD
☐ 414. MIKE GARDINER
☐ 415. MARQUIS GRISSOM
☐ 416. TIM LAKER
☐ 417. MIKE LANSING
☐ 418. DENNIS MARTINEZ
☐ 419. JOHN VANDER WAL
☐ 420. JOHN WETTELAND
☐ 421. RONDELL WHITE

NEW YORK METS

☐ 72. SID FERNANDEZ
☐ 73. JOHN FRANCO
☐ 74. DAVE GALLAGHER
☐ 75. TODD HUNDLEY
☐ 76. HOWARD JOHNSON
☐ 77. JEFF KENT
☐ 78. EDDIE MURRAY
☐ 79. BRET SABERHAGEN
☐ 80. CHICO WALKER
☐ 81. ANTHONY YOUNG
☐ 422. BOBBY BONILLA
☐ 423. JEROMY BURNITZ
☐ 424. VINCE COLEMAN
☐ 425. MIKE DRAPER
☐ 426. TONY FERNANDEZ
☐ 427. DWIGHT GOODEN
☐ 428. JEFF INNIS
☐ 429. BOBBY JONES
☐ 430. MIKE MADDUX
☐ 431. CHARLIE O'BRIEN
☐ 432. JOE ORSULAK
☐ 433. PETE SCHOUREK
☐ 434. FRANK TANANA
☐ 435. RYAN THOMPSON

NEW YORK YANKEES

☐ 240. MIKE GALLEGO
☐ 241. JOHN HABYAN
☐ 242. PAT KELLY
☐ 243. KEVIN MAAS
☐ 244. DON MATTINGLY
☐ 245. HENSLEY MEULENS
☐ 246. SAM MILITELLO
☐ 247. MATT NOKES
☐ 248. MELIDO PEREZ
☐ 249. ANDY STANKIEWICZ
☐ 250. RANDY VELARDE
☐ 251. BOB WICKMAN
☐ 252. BERNIE WILLIAMS
☐ 590. JIM ABBOTT
☐ 591. WADE BOGGS
☐ 592. RUSS DAVIS
☐ 593. STEVE FARR
☐ 594. STEVE HOWE
☐ 595. MIKE HUMPHREYS
☐ 596. JIMMY KEY
☐ 597. JIM LEYRITZ
☐ 598. BOBBY MUNOZ
☐ 599. PAUL O'NEILL
☐ 600. SPIKE OWEN
☐ 601. MIKE STANLEY
☐ 602. DANNY TARTABULL

OAKLAND A'S

☐ 253. LANCE BLANKENSHIP
☐ 254. MIKE BORDICK
☐ 255. JERRY BROWNE
☐ 256. RON DARLING
☐ 257. DENNIS ECKERSLEY
☐ 258. RICKEY HENDERSON
☐ 259. VINCE HORSMAN
☐ 260. TROY NEEL
☐ 261. JEFF PARRETT
☐ 262. TERRY STEINBACH
☐ 263. BOB WELCH
☐ 264. BOBBY WITT
☐ 603. SCOTT BROSIUS
☐ 604. STORM DAVIS
☐ 605. ERIC FOX
☐ 606. GOOSE GOSSAGE
☐ 607. SCOTT HEMOND
☐ 608. DAVE HENDERSON
☐ 609. MARK MCGWIRE
☐ 610. MIKE MOHLER
☐ 611. EDWIN NUNEZ
☐ 612. KEVIN SEITZER
☐ 613. RUBEN SIERRA

PHILADELPHIA PHILLIES

☐ 82. KYLE ABBOTT
☐ 83. RUBEN AMARO, JR.
☐ 84. JUAN BELL
☐ 85. WES CHAMBERLAIN
☐ 86. DARREN DAULTON
☐ 87. MARIANO DUNCAN
☐ 88. DAVE HOLLINS

☐ 89. RICKY JORDAN
☐ 90. JOHN KRUK
☐ 91. MICKEY MORANDINI
☐ 92. TERRY MULHOLLAND
☐ 93. BEN RIVERA
☐ 94. MIKE WILLIAMS
☐ 436. KIM BATISTE
☐ 437. MARK DAVIS
☐ 438. JOSE DELEON
☐ 439. LENNY DYKSTRA
☐ 440. JIM EISENREICH
☐ 441. TOMMY GREENE
☐ 442. PETE INCAVIGLIA
☐ 443. DANNY JACKSON
☐ 444. TODD PRATT
☐ 445. CURT SCHILLING
☐ 446. MILT THOMPSON
☐ 447. DAVID WEST
☐ 448. MITCH WILLIAMS

PITTSBURGH PIRATES

☐ 95. STAN BELINDA
☐ 96. JAY BELL
☐ 97. JEFF KING
☐ 98. MIKE LAVALLIERE
☐ 99. LLOYD MCCLENDON
☐ 100. ORLANDO MERCED
☐ 101. ZANE SMITH
☐ 102. RANDY TOMLIN
☐ 103. ANDY VAN SLYKE
☐ 104. TIM WAKEFIELD
☐ 105. JOHN WEHNER
☐ 449. STEVE COOKE
☐ 450. CARLOS GARCIA
☐ 451. AL MARTIN
☐ 452. BLAS MINOR
☐ 453. DENNIS MOELLER
☐ 454. DENNY NEAGLE
☐ 455. DON SLAUGHT
☐ 456. LONNIE SMITH
☐ 457. PAUL WAGNER
☐ 458. BOB WALK
☐ 459. KEVIN YOUNG

ST. LOUIS CARDINALS

☐ 106. BERNARD GILKEY
☐ 107. BRIAN JORDAN
☐ 108. RAY LANKFORD
☐ 109. DONOVAN OSBORNE
☐ 110. TOM PAGNOZZI
☐ 111. MIKE PEREZ
☐ 112. LEE SMITH
☐ 113. OZZIE SMITH
☐ 114. BOB TEWKSBURY
☐ 115. TODD ZEILE
☐ 460. RENE AROCHA
☐ 461. BRIAN BARBER
☐ 462. RHEAL CORMIER
☐ 463. GREGG JEFFERIES
☐ 464. JOE MAGRANE
☐ 465. OMAR OLIVARES
☐ 466. GERONIMO PENA
☐ 467. ALLEN WATSON
☐ 468. MARK WHITEN

SAN DIEGO PADRES

☐ 116. ANDY BENES
☐ 117. GREG HARRIS
☐ 118. DARRIN JACKSON
☐ 119. FRED MCGRIFF
☐ 120. RICH RODRIGUEZ
☐ 121. FRANK SEMINARA
☐ 122. GARY SHEFFIELD
☐ 123. CRAIG SHIPLEY
☐ 124. KURT STILLWELL
☐ 125. DAN WALTERS
☐ 469. DEREK BELL
☐ 470. PHIL CLARK
☐ 471. PAT GOMEZ
☐ 472. TONY GWYNN
☐ 473. JEREMY HERNANDEZ
☐ 474. BRUCE HURST
☐ 475. PHIL PLANTIER
☐ 476. SCOTT SANDERS
☐ 477. TIM SCOTT
☐ 478. DARRELL SHERMAN
☐ 479. GUILLERMO VELASQUEZ
☐ 480. TIM WORRELL

SAN FRANCISCO GIANTS

☐ 126. ROD BECK
☐ 127. MIKE BENJAMIN
☐ 128. JEFF BRANTLEY
☐ 129. JOHN BURKETT
☐ 130. WILL CLARK
☐ 131. ROYCE CLAYTON
☐ 132. STEVE HOSEY
☐ 133. MIKE JACKSON
☐ 134. DARREN LEWIS
☐ 135. KIRT MANWARING
☐ 136. BILL SWIFT
☐ 137. ROBBY THOMPSON
☐ 481. TODD BENZINGER
☐ 482. BUD BLACK
☐ 483. BARRY BONDS
☐ 484. DAVE BURBA
☐ 485. BRYAN HICKERSON
☐ 486. DAVE MARTINEZ
☐ 487. WILLIE MCGEE
☐ 488. JEFF REED
☐ 489. KEVIN ROGERS
☐ 490. MATT WILLIAMS
☐ 491. TREVOR WILSON

SEATTLE MARINERS

☐ 265. RICH AMARAL
☐ 266. BRET BOONE
☐ 267. JAY BUHNER
☐ 268. DAVE FLEMING
☐ 269. RANDY JOHNSON
☐ 270. EDGAR MARTINEZ
☐ 271. MIKE SCHOOLER
☐ 272. RUSS SWAN
☐ 273. DAVE VALLE
☐ 274. OMAR VIZQUEL
☐ 275. KERRY WOODSON
☐ 614. CHRIS BOSIO
☐ 615. NORM CHARLTON
☐ 616. JIM CONVERSE
☐ 617. JOHN CUMMINGS
☐ 618. MIKE FELDER
☐ 619. KEN GRIFFEY, JR.
☐ 620. MIKE HAMPTON
☐ 621. ERIK HANSON
☐ 622. BILL HASELMAN
☐ 623. TINO MARTINEZ
☐ 624. LEE TINSLEY
☐ 625. FERNANDO VINA
☐ 626. DAVID WAINHOUSE

TEXAS RANGERS

☐ 276. KEVIN BROWN
☐ 277. JULIO FRANCO
☐ 278. JEFF FRYE
☐ 279. JUAN GONZALEZ
☐ 280. JEFF HUSON
☐ 281. RAFAEL PALMEIRO
☐ 282. DEAN PALMER
☐ 283. ROGER PAVLIK
☐ 284. IVAN RODRIGUEZ
☐ 285. KENNY ROGERS
☐ 627. JOSE CANSECO
☐ 628. BENJI GIL
☐ 629. TOM HENKE
☐ 630. DAVID HULSE
☐ 631. MANUEL LEE
☐ 632. CRAIG LEFFERTS
☐ 633. ROBB NEN
☐ 634. GARY REDUS
☐ 635. BILL RIPKEN
☐ 636. NOLAN RYAN
☐ 637. DAN SMITH
☐ 638. MATT WHITESIDE

TORONTO BLUE JAYS

☐ 286. DEREK BELL
☐ 287. PAT BORDERS
☐ 288. JOE CARTER
☐ 289. BOB MACDONALD
☐ 290. JACK MORRIS
☐ 291. JOHN OLERUD
☐ 292. ED SPRAGUE
☐ 293. TODD STOTTLEMYRE
☐ 294. MIKE TIMLIN
☐ 295. DUANE WARD
☐ 296. DAVID WELLS
☐ 297. DEVON WHITE
☐ 639. ROBERTO ALOMAR
☐ 640. JUAN GUZMAN
☐ 641. PAT HENTGEN
☐ 642. DARRIN JACKSON
☐ 643. RANDY KNORR
☐ 644. DOMINGO MARTINEZ
☐ 645. PAUL MOLITOR
☐ 646. DICK SCHOFIELD
☐ 647. DAVE STEWART

1994 ULTRA (600)
2 1/2" X 3 1/2"

ATLANTA BRAVES

☐ 147. STEVE AVERY
☐ 148. STEVE BEDROSIAN
☐ 149. DAMON BERRYHILL
☐ 150. JEFF BLAUSER
☐ 151. TOM GLAVINE
☐ 152. CHIPPER JONES
☐ 153. MARK LEMKE
☐ 154. FRED MCGRIFF
☐ 155. GREG MCMICHAEL
☐ 156. DEION SANDERS
☐ 157. JOHN SMOLTZ
☐ 158. MARK WOHLERS
☐ 443. DAVID JUSTICE
☐ 444. MIKE KELLY
☐ 445. RYAN KLESKO
☐ 446. JAVIER LOPEZ
☐ 447. GREG MADDUX
☐ 448. KENT MERCKER
☐ 449. CHARLIE O'BRIEN
☐ 450. TERRY PENDLETON
☐ 451. MIKE STANTON
☐ 452. TONY TARASCO
☐ 453. TERRELL WADE

BALTIMORE ORIOLES

☐ 1. JEFFREY HAMMONDS
☐ 2. CHRIS HOILES
☐ 3. BEN MCDONALD
☐ 4. MARK MCLEMORE
☐ 5. ALAN MILLS
☐ 6. JAMIE MOYER
☐ 7. BRAD PENNINGTON
☐ 8. JIM POOLE
☐ 9. CAL RIPKEN, JR.
☐ 10. JACK VOIGT
☐ 301. BRADY ANDERSON
☐ 302. HAROLD BAINES
☐ 303. DAMON BUFORD
☐ 304. MIKE DEVEREAUX
☐ 305. SID FERNANDEZ
☐ 306. RICK KRIVDA
☐ 307. MIKE MUSSINA
☐ 308. RAFAEL PALMEIRO
☐ 309. CHRIS SABO
☐ 310. LEE SMITH
☐ 311. GREGG ZAUN

1994 Ultra

BOSTON RED SOX

- ☐ 11. ROGER CLEMENS
- ☐ 12. DANNY DARWIN
- ☐ 13. ANDRE DAWSON
- ☐ 14. SCOTT FLETCHER
- ☐ 15. GREG HARRIS
- ☐ 16. BILLY HATCHER
- ☐ 17. JEFF RUSSELL
- ☐ 18. AARON SELE
- ☐ 19. MO VAUGHN
- ☐ 312. SCOTT COOPER
- ☐ 313. MIKE GREENWELL
- ☐ 314. TIM NAEHRING
- ☐ 315. OTIS NIXON
- ☐ 316. PAUL QUANTRILL
- ☐ 317. JOHN VALENTIN
- ☐ 318. DAVE VALLE
- ☐ 319. FRANK VIOLA

CALIFORNIA ANGELS

- ☐ 20. MIKE BUTCHER
- ☐ 21. ROD CORREIA
- ☐ 22. STEVE FREY
- ☐ 23. PHIL LEFTWICH
- ☐ 24. TOREY LOVULLO
- ☐ 25. KEN PATTERSON
- ☐ 26. EDUARDO PEREZ
- ☐ 27. TIM SALMON
- ☐ 28. J.T. SNOW
- ☐ 29. CHRIS TURNER
- ☐ 320. BRIAN ANDERSON
- ☐ 321. GARRET ANDERSON
- ☐ 322. CHAD CURTIS
- ☐ 323. CHILI DAVIS
- ☐ 324. GARY DISARCINA
- ☐ 325. DAMION EASLEY
- ☐ 326. JIM EDMONDS
- ☐ 327. CHUCK FINLEY
- ☐ 328. JOE GRAHE
- ☐ 329. BO JACKSON
- ☐ 330. MARK LANGSTON
- ☐ 331. HAROLD REYNOLDS

CHICAGO CUBS

- ☐ 159. JOSE BAUTISTA
- ☐ 160. STEVE BUECHELE
- ☐ 161. MIKE HARKEY
- ☐ 162. GREG HIBBARD
- ☐ 163. CHUCK MCELROY
- ☐ 164. MIKE MORGAN
- ☐ 165. KEVIN ROBERSON
- ☐ 166. RYNE SANDBERG
- ☐ 167. JOSE VIZCAINO
- ☐ 168. RICK WILKINS
- ☐ 169. WILLIE WILSON
- ☐ 454. SHAWON DUNSTON
- ☐ 455. MARK GRACE
- ☐ 456. JOSE GUZMAN
- ☐ 457. JOSE HERNANDEZ
- ☐ 458. GLENALLEN HILL
- ☐ 459. BLAISE ILSLEY
- ☐ 460. BROOKS KIESCHNICK
- ☐ 461. DERRICK MAY
- ☐ 462. RANDY MYERS
- ☐ 463. KARL RHODES
- ☐ 464. SAMMY SOSA
- ☐ 465. STEVE TRACHSEL
- ☐ 466. EDDIE ZAMBRANO

CHICAGO WHITE SOX

- ☐ 30. WILSON ALVAREZ
- ☐ 31. JASON BERE
- ☐ 32. JOEY CORA
- ☐ 33. ALEX FERNANDEZ
- ☐ 34. ROBERTO HERNANDEZ
- ☐ 35. LANCE JOHNSON
- ☐ 36. RON KARKOVICE
- ☐ 37. KIRK MCCASKILL
- ☐ 38. JEFF SCHWARZ
- ☐ 39. FRANK THOMAS
- ☐ 332. JAMES BALDWIN
- ☐ 333. RAY DURHAM
- ☐ 334. JULIO FRANCO
- ☐ 335. CRAIG GREBECK
- ☐ 336. OZZIE GUILLEN
- ☐ 337. JOE HALL
- ☐ 338. DARRIN JACKSON
- ☐ 339. JACK MCDOWELL
- ☐ 340. TIM RAINES
- ☐ 341. ROBIN VENTURA

CINCINNATI REDS

- ☐ 170. WILLIE GREENE
- ☐ 171. ROBERTO KELLY
- ☐ 172. LARRY LUEBBERS
- ☐ 173. KEVIN MITCHELL
- ☐ 174. JOE OLIVER
- ☐ 175. JOHN ROPER
- ☐ 176. JOHNNY RUFFIN
- ☐ 177. REGGIE SANDERS
- ☐ 178. JOHN SMILEY
- ☐ 179. JERRY SPRADLIN
- ☐ 467. BRET BOONE
- ☐ 468. TOM BROWNING
- ☐ 469. HECTOR CARRASCO
- ☐ 470. ROB DIBBLE
- ☐ 471. ERIK HANSON
- ☐ 472. THOMAS HOWARD
- ☐ 473. KEVIN JARVIS
- ☐ 474. BARRY LARKIN
- ☐ 475. HAL MORRIS
- ☐ 476. JOSE RIJO

CLEVELAND INDIANS

- ☐ 40. SANDY ALOMAR, JR.
- ☐ 41. ALBERT BELLE
- ☐ 42. FELIX FERMIN
- ☐ 43. WAYNE KIRBY
- ☐ 44. TOM KRAMER
- ☐ 45. KENNY LOFTON
- ☐ 46. JOSE MESA
- ☐ 47. ERIC PLUNK
- ☐ 48. PAUL SORRENTO
- ☐ 49. JIM THOME
- ☐ 50. BILL WERTZ
- ☐ 342. CARLOS BAERGA
- ☐ 343. DEREK LILLIQUIST
- ☐ 344. DENNIS MARTINEZ
- ☐ 345. JACK MORRIS
- ☐ 346. EDDIE MURRAY
- ☐ 347. CHRIS NABHOLZ
- ☐ 348. CHARLES NAGY
- ☐ 349. CHAD OGEA
- ☐ 350. MANNY RAMIREZ
- ☐ 351. OMAR VIZQUEL

COLORADO ROCKIES

- ☐ 180. FREDDIE BENAVIDES
- ☐ 181. DANTE BICHETTE
- ☐ 182. WILLIE BLAIR
- ☐ 183. KENT BOTTENFIELD
- ☐ 184. JERALD CLARK
- ☐ 185. JOE GIRARDI
- ☐ 186. ROBERTO MEJIA
- ☐ 187. STEVE REED
- ☐ 188. ARMANDO REYNOSO
- ☐ 189. BRUCE RUFFIN
- ☐ 190. ERIC YOUNG
- ☐ 477. JOHN BURKE
- ☐ 478. ELLIS BURKS
- ☐ 479. MARVIN FREEMAN
- ☐ 480. ANDRES GALARRAGA
- ☐ 481. GREG HARRIS
- ☐ 482. CHARLIE HAYES
- ☐ 483. DARREN HOLMES
- ☐ 484. HOWARD JOHNSON
- ☐ 485. MARCUS MOORE
- ☐ 486. DAVID NIED
- ☐ 487. MARK THOMPSON
- ☐ 488. WALT WEISS

DETROIT TIGERS

- ☐ 51. JOHN DOHERTY
- ☐ 52. CECIL FIELDER
- ☐ 53. TRAVIS FRYMAN
- ☐ 54. CHRIS GOMEZ
- ☐ 55. MIKE HENNEMAN
- ☐ 56. CHAD KREUTER
- ☐ 57. BOB MACDONALD
- ☐ 58. MIKE MOORE
- ☐ 59. TONY PHILLIPS
- ☐ 60. LOU WHITAKER
- ☐ 352. DANNY BAUTISTA
- ☐ 353. TIM BELCHER
- ☐ 354. ERIC DAVIS
- ☐ 355. RICK GREENE
- ☐ 356. MICKEY TETTLETON
- ☐ 357. ALAN TRAMMELL
- ☐ 358. DAVID WELLS

FLORIDA MARLINS

- ☐ 191. LUIS AQUINO
- ☐ 192. BRET BARBERIE
- ☐ 193. RYAN BOWEN
- ☐ 194. CHUCK CARR
- ☐ 195. ORESTES DESTRADE
- ☐ 196. RICHIE LEWIS
- ☐ 197. DAVE MAGADAN
- ☐ 198. BOB NATAL
- ☐ 199. GARY SHEFFIELD
- ☐ 200. MATT TURNER
- ☐ 201. DARRELL WHITMORE
- ☐ 489. KURT ABBOTT
- ☐ 490. MATIAS CARRILLO
- ☐ 491. JEFF CONINE
- ☐ 492. CHRIS HAMMOND
- ☐ 493. BRYAN HARVEY
- ☐ 494. CHARLIE HOUGH
- ☐ 495. YORKIS PEREZ
- ☐ 496. PAT RAPP
- ☐ 497. BENITO SANTIAGO
- ☐ 498. DAVID WEATHERS

HOUSTON ASTROS

- ☐ 202. ERIC ANTHONY
- ☐ 203. JEFF BAGWELL
- ☐ 204. ANDUJAR CEDENO
- ☐ 205. LUIS GONZALEZ
- ☐ 206. XAVIER HERNANDEZ
- ☐ 207. DOUG JONES
- ☐ 208. DARRYL KILE
- ☐ 209. SCOTT SERVAIS
- ☐ 210. GREG SWINDELL
- ☐ 211. BRIAN WILLIAMS
- ☐ 499. CRAIG BIGGIO
- ☐ 500. KEN CAMINITI
- ☐ 501. DOUG DRABEK
- ☐ 502. TONY EUSEBIO
- ☐ 503. STEVE FINLEY
- ☐ 504. PETE HARNISCH
- ☐ 505. BRIAN HUNTER
- ☐ 506. DOMINGO JEAN
- ☐ 507. TODD JONES
- ☐ 508. ORLANDO MILLER
- ☐ 509. JAMES MOUTON
- ☐ 510. ROBERTO PETAGINE
- ☐ 511. SHANE REYNOLDS
- ☐ 512. MITCH WILLIAMS

KANSAS CITY ROYALS

- ☐ 61. KEVIN APPIER
- ☐ 62. GREG GAGNE
- ☐ 63. CHRIS GWYNN
- ☐ 64. BOB HAMELIN
- ☐ 65. CHRIS HANEY
- ☐ 66. PHIL HIATT
- ☐ 67. FELIX JOSE
- ☐ 68. JOSE LIND

☐ 69. MIKE MACFARLANE
☐ 70. JEFF MONTGOMERY
☐ 71. HIPOLITO PICHARDO
☐ 359. STAN BELINDA
☐ 360. VINCE COLEMAN
☐ 361. DAVID CONE
☐ 362. GARY GAETTI
☐ 363. TOM GORDON
☐ 364. DAVE HENDERSON
☐ 365. WALLY JOYNER
☐ 366. BRENT MAYNE
☐ 367. BRIAN MCRAE
☐ 368. MICHAEL TUCKER

LOS ANGELES DODGERS

☐ 212. PEDRO ASTACIO
☐ 213. BRETT BUTLER
☐ 214. OMAR DAAL
☐ 215. JIM GOTT
☐ 216. RAUL MONDESI
☐ 217. JOSE OFFERMAN
☐ 218. MIKE PIAZZA
☐ 219. CORY SNYDER
☐ 220. TIM WALLACH
☐ 221. TODD WORRELL
☐ 513. BILLY ASHLEY
☐ 514. TOM CANDIOTTI
☐ 515. DELINO DESHIELDS
☐ 516. DARREN DREIFORT
☐ 517. KEVIN GROSS
☐ 518. OREL HERSHISER
☐ 519. ERIC KARROS
☐ 520. RAMON MARTINEZ
☐ 521. CHAN HO PARK
☐ 522. HENRY RODRIGUEZ

MILWAUKEE BREWERS

☐ 72. JUAN BELL
☐ 73. CAL ELDRED
☐ 74. DARRYL HAMILTON
☐ 75. DOUG HENRY
☐ 76. MIKE IGNASIAK
☐ 77. JOHN JAHA
☐ 78. GRAEME LLOYD
☐ 79. ANGEL MIRANDA
☐ 80. DAVE NILSSON
☐ 81. TROY O'LEARY
☐ 82. KEVIN REIMER
☐ 369. RICKY BONES
☐ 370. BRIAN HARPER
☐ 371. TYRONE HILL
☐ 372. MARK KIEFER
☐ 373. PAT LISTACH
☐ 374. MIKE MATHENY
☐ 375. JOSE MERCEDES
☐ 376. KEVIN SEITZER
☐ 377. B.J. SURHOFF
☐ 378. GREG VAUGHN
☐ 379. TURNER WARD
☐ 380. WES WEGER
☐ 381. BILL WEGMAN

MINNESOTA TWINS

☐ 83. WILLIE BANKS
☐ 84. LARRY CASIAN
☐ 85. SCOTT ERICKSON
☐ 86. EDDIE GUARDADO
☐ 87. KENT HRBEK
☐ 88. TERRY JORGENSEN
☐ 89. CHUCK KNOBLAUCH
☐ 90. PAT MEARES
☐ 91. MIKE TROMBLEY
☐ 92. DAVE WINFIELD
☐ 382. RICK AGUILERA
☐ 383. RICH BECKER
☐ 384. STEVE DUNN
☐ 385. KEITH GARAGOZZO
☐ 386. LATROY HAWKINS
☐ 387. SHANE MACK
☐ 388. DAVID MCCARTY
☐ 389. PEDRO MUNOZ
☐ 390. DEREK PARKS
☐ 391. KIRBY PUCKETT
☐ 392. KEVIN TAPANI
☐ 393. MATT WALBECK

MONTREAL EXPOS

☐ 222. MOISES ALOU
☐ 223. SEAN BERRY
☐ 224. WIL CORDERO
☐ 225. JEFF FASSERO
☐ 226. DARRIN FLETCHER
☐ 227. CLIFF FLOYD
☐ 228. MARQUIS GRISSOM
☐ 229. KEN HILL
☐ 230. MIKE LANSING
☐ 231. KIRK RUETER
☐ 232. JOHN WETTELAND
☐ 233. RONDELL WHITE
☐ 523. JOEY EISCHEN
☐ 524. ROD HENDERSON
☐ 525. PEDRO MARTINEZ
☐ 526. MEL ROJAS
☐ 527. LARRY WALKER
☐ 528. GABE WHITE

NEW YORK METS

☐ 234. TIM BOGAR
☐ 235. JEROMY BURNITZ
☐ 236. DWIGHT GOODEN
☐ 237. TODD HUNDLEY
☐ 238. JEFF KENT
☐ 239. JOSIAS MANZANILLO
☐ 240. JOE ORSULAK
☐ 241. RYAN THOMPSON
☐ 529. BOBBY BONILLA
☐ 530. JONATHAN HURST
☐ 531. BOBBY JONES
☐ 532. KEVIN MCREYNOLDS
☐ 533. BILL PULSIPHER
☐ 534. BRET SABERHAGEN
☐ 535. PETE SMITH
☐ 536. KELLY STINNETT
☐ 537. DAVE TELGHEDER
☐ 538. QUILVIO VERAS
☐ 539. JOSE VIZCAINO
☐ 540. PETE WALKER

NEW YORK YANKEES

☐ 93. WADE BOGGS
☐ 94. SCOTT KAMIENIECKI
☐ 95. PAT KELLY
☐ 96. JIMMY KEY
☐ 97. JIM LEYRITZ
☐ 98. BOBBY MUNOZ
☐ 99. PAUL O'NEILL
☐ 100. MELIDO PEREZ
☐ 101. MIKE STANLEY
☐ 102. DANNY TARTABULL
☐ 103. BERNIE WILLIAMS
☐ 394. JIM ABBOTT
☐ 395. MIKE GALLEGO
☐ 396. XAVIER HERNANDEZ
☐ 397. DON MATTINGLY
☐ 398. TERRY MULHOLLAND
☐ 399. MATT NOKES
☐ 400. LUIS POLONIA
☐ 401. BOB WICKMAN

OAKLAND A'S

☐ 104. KURT ABBOTT
☐ 105. MIKE BORDICK
☐ 106. RON DARLING
☐ 107. BRENT GATES
☐ 108. MIGUEL JIMENEZ
☐ 109. STEVE KARSAY
☐ 110. SCOTT LYDY
☐ 111. MARK MCGWIRE
☐ 112. TROY NEEL
☐ 113. CRAIG PAQUETTE
☐ 114. BOB WELCH
☐ 115. BOBBY WITT
☐ 402. MARK ACRE
☐ 403. GERONIMO BERROA
☐ 404. FAUSTO CRUZ
☐ 405. DENNIS ECKERSLEY
☐ 406. RICKEY HENDERSON
☐ 407. STAN JAVIER
☐ 408. CARLOS REYES
☐ 409. RUBEN SIERRA
☐ 410. TERRY STEINBACH
☐ 411. BILL TAYLOR
☐ 412. TODD VAN POPPEL

PHILADELPHIA PHILLIES

☐ 242. KIM BATISTE
☐ 243. DARREN DAULTON
☐ 244. TOMMY GREENE
☐ 245. DAVE HOLLINS
☐ 246. PETE INCAVIGLIA
☐ 247. DANNY JACKSON
☐ 248. RICKY JORDAN
☐ 249. JOHN KRUK
☐ 250. MICKEY MORANDINI
☐ 251. TERRY MULHOLLAND
☐ 252. BEN RIVERA
☐ 253. KEVIN STOCKER
☐ 541. RICKY BOTTALICO
☐ 542. WES CHAMERLAIN
☐ 543. MARIANO DUNCAN
☐ 544. LENNY DYKSTRA
☐ 545. JIM EISENREICH
☐ 546. PHIL GEISLER
☐ 547. WAYNE GOMES
☐ 548. DOUG JONES
☐ 549. JEFF JUDEN
☐ 550. MIKE LIEBERTHAL
☐ 551. TONY LONGMIRE
☐ 552. TOM MARSH
☐ 553. BOBBY MUNOZ
☐ 554. CURT SCHILLING

PITTSBURGH PIRATES

☐ 254. JAY BELL
☐ 255. STEVE COOKE
☐ 256. JEFF KING
☐ 257. AL MARTIN
☐ 258. DANNY MICELI
☐ 259. BLAS MINOR
☐ 260. DON SLAUGHT
☐ 261. PAUL WAGNER
☐ 262. TIM WAKEFIELD
☐ 263. KEVIN YOUNG
☐ 555. CARLOS GARCIA
☐ 556. RAVELO MANZANILLO
☐ 557. ORLANDO MERCED
☐ 558. WILL PENNYFEATHER
☐ 559. ANDY VAN SLYKE
☐ 560. RICK WHITE

ST. LOUIS CARDINALS

☐ 264. RENE AROCHA
☐ 265. RICHARD BATCHELOR
☐ 266. GREGG JEFFERIES
☐ 267. BRIAN JORDAN
☐ 268. JOSE OQUENDO
☐ 269. DONOVAN OSBORNE
☐ 270. ERIK PAPPAS
☐ 271. MIKE PEREZ
☐ 272. BOB TEWKSBURY
☐ 273. MARK WHITEN
☐ 274. TODD ZEILE
☐ 561. LUIS ALICEA
☐ 562. BRIAN BARBER
☐ 563. CLINT DAVIS
☐ 564. BERNARD GILKEY
☐ 565. RAY LANKFORD
☐ 566. TOM PAGNOZZI
☐ 567. OZZIE SMITH
☐ 568. RICK SUTCLIFFE
☐ 569. ALLEN WATSON
☐ 570. DMITRI YOUNG

SAN DIEGO PADRES

☐ 275. ANDY ASHBY
☐ 276. BRAD AUSMUS
☐ 277. PHIL CLARK
☐ 278. JEFF GARDNER
☐ 279. RICKY GUTIERREZ
☐ 280. TONY GWYNN
☐ 281. TIM MAUSER
☐ 282. SCOTT SANDERS
☐ 283. FRANK SEMINARA
☐ 284. WALLY WHITEHURST
☐ 571. DEREK BELL
☐ 572. ANDY BENES
☐ 573. ARCHI CIANFROCCO
☐ 574. JOEY HAMILTON

☐ 575. GENE HARRIS
☐ 576. TREVOR HOFFMAN
☐ 577. TIM HYERS
☐ 578. BRIAN JOHNSON
☐ 579. KEITH LOCKHART
☐ 580. PEDRO MARTINEZ
☐ 581. RAY MCDAVID
☐ 582. PHIL PLANTIER
☐ 583. BIP ROBERTS
☐ 584. A.J. SAGER
☐ 585. DAVE STATON

SAN FRANCISCO GIANTS

☐ 285. ROD BECK
☐ 286. BARRY BONDS
☐ 287. DAVE BURBA
☐ 288. MARK CARREON
☐ 289. ROYCE CLAYTON
☐ 290. MIKE JACKSON
☐ 291. DARREN LEWIS
☐ 292. KIRT MANWARING
☐ 293. DAVE MARTINEZ
☐ 294. BILLY SWIFT
☐ 295. SALOMON TORRES
☐ 296. MATT WILLIAMS
☐ 586. TODD BENZINGER
☐ 587. JOHN BURKETT
☐ 588. BRYAN HICKERSON
☐ 589. WILLIE MCGEE
☐ 590. JOHN PATTERSON
☐ 591. MARK PORTUGAL
☐ 592. KEVIN ROGERS
☐ 593. JOE ROSSELLI
☐ 594. STEVE SODERSTROM
☐ 595. ROBBY THOMPSON

SEATTLE MARINERS

☐ 116. RICH AMARAL
☐ 117. MIKE BLOWERS
☐ 118. JAY BUHNER
☐ 119. DAVE FLEMING
☐ 120. KEN GRIFFEY, JR.
☐ 121. TINO MARTINEZ
☐ 122. MARC NEWFIELD
☐ 123. TED POWER
☐ 124. MACKEY SASSER
☐ 125. OMAR VIZQUEL
☐ 413. ERIC ANTHONY
☐ 414. BOBBY AYALA
☐ 415. CHRIS BOSIO
☐ 416. DARREN BRAGG
☐ 417. TIM DAVIS
☐ 418. RANDY JOHNSON
☐ 419. KEVIN KING
☐ 420. ANTHONY MANAHAN
☐ 421. EDGAR MARTINEZ
☐ 422. KEITH MITCHELL
☐ 423. MAC SUZUKI
☐ 424. DAN WILSON

TEXAS RANGERS

☐ 126. KEVIN BROWN
☐ 127. JUAN GONZALEZ
☐ 128. TOM HENKE
☐ 129. DAVID HULSE
☐ 130. DEAN PALMER
☐ 131. ROGER PAVLIK
☐ 132. IVAN RODRIGUEZ
☐ 133. KENNY ROGERS
☐ 134. DOUG STRANGE
☐ 425. DUFF BRUMLEY
☐ 426. JOSE CANSECO
☐ 427. WILL CLARK
☐ 428. STEVE DREYER
☐ 429. RICK HELLING
☐ 430. JAMES HURST
☐ 431. CHRIS JAMES
☐ 432. DARREN OLIVER
☐ 433. MATT WHITESIDE

TORONTO BLUE JAYS

☐ 135. PAT BORDERS
☐ 136. JOE CARTER
☐ 137. DARNELL COLES
☐ 138. PAT HENTGEN
☐ 139. AL LEITER
☐ 140. PAUL MOLITOR
☐ 141. JOHN OLERUD
☐ 142. ED SPRAGUE
☐ 143. DAVE STEWART
☐ 144. MIKE TIMLIN
☐ 145. DUANE WARD
☐ 146. DEVON WHITE
☐ 434. ROBERTO ALOMAR
☐ 435. SCOTT BROW
☐ 436. DOMINGO CEDENO
☐ 437. CARLOS DELGADO
☐ 438. ALEX GONZALEZ
☐ 439. JUAN GUZMAN
☐ 440. PAUL SPOLJARIC
☐ 441. TODD STOTTLEMYRE
☐ 442. WOODY WILLIAMS

1995 ULTRA SERIES 1 (250) 2 1/2" X 3 1/2"

ATLANTA BRAVES

☐ 125. TOM GLAVINE
☐ 126. DAVID JUSTICE
☐ 127. ROBERTO KELLY
☐ 128. MARK LEMKE
☐ 129. GREG MADDUX
☐ 130. GREG MCMICHAEL
☐ 131. KENT MERCKER
☐ 132. CHARLIE O'BRIEN
☐ 133. JOHN SMOLTZ

BALTIMORE ORIOLES

☐ 1. BRADY ANDERSON
☐ 2. SID FERNANDEZ
☐ 3. JEFFREY HAMMONDS
☐ 4. CHRIS HOILES
☐ 5. BEN MCDONALD
☐ 6. MIKE MUSSINA
☐ 7. RAFAEL PALMEIRO
☐ 8. JACK VOIGT

BOSTON RED SOX

☐ 9. WES CHAMBERLAIN
☐ 10. ROGER CLEMENS
☐ 11. CHRIS HOWARD
☐ 12. TIM NAEHRING
☐ 13. OTIS NIXON
☐ 14. RICH ROWLAND
☐ 15. KEN RYAN
☐ 16. JOHN VALENTIN
☐ 17. MO VAUGHN

CALIFORNIA ANGELS

☐ 18. BRIAN ANDERSON
☐ 19. CHILI DAVIS
☐ 20. DAMION EASLEY
☐ 21. JIM EDMONDS
☐ 22. MARK LANGSTON
☐ 23. TIM SALMON
☐ 24. J.T. SNOW
☐ 25. CHRIS TURNER

CHICAGO CUBS

☐ 134. WILLIE BANKS
☐ 135. STEVE BUECHELE
☐ 136. KEVIN FOSTER
☐ 137. GLENALLEN HILL
☐ 138. REY SANCHEZ
☐ 139. SAMMY SOSA
☐ 140. STEVE TRACHSEL
☐ 141. RICK WILKINS

CHICAGO WHITE SOX

☐ 26. WILSON ALVAREZ
☐ 27. JOEY CORA
☐ 28. ALEX FERNANDEZ
☐ 29. ROBERTO HERNANDEZ
☐ 30. LANCE JOHNSON
☐ 31. RON KARKOVICE
☐ 32. KIRK MCCASKILL
☐ 33. TIM RAINES
☐ 34. FRANK THOMAS

CINCINNATI REDS

☐ 142. JEFF BRANTLEY
☐ 143. HECTOR CARRASCO
☐ 144. KEVIN JARVIS
☐ 145. BARRY LARKIN
☐ 146. CHUCK MCELROY
☐ 147. JOSE RIJO
☐ 148. JOHNNY RUFFIN
☐ 149. DEION SANDERS
☐ 150. EDDIE TAUBENSEE

CLEVELAND INDIANS

☐ 35. SANDY ALOMAR, JR.
☐ 36. ALBERT BELLE
☐ 37. MARK CLARK
☐ 38. KENNY LOFTON
☐ 39. EDDIE MURRAY
☐ 40. ERIC PLUNK

- ☐ 41. MANNY RAMIREZ
- ☐ 42. JIM THOME
- ☐ 43. OMAR VIZQUEL

COLORADO ROCKIES

- ☐ 151. DANTE BICHETTE
- ☐ 152. ELLIS BURKS
- ☐ 153. JOE GIRARDI
- ☐ 154. CHARLIE HAYES
- ☐ 155. MIKE KINGERY
- ☐ 156. STEVE REED
- ☐ 157. KEVIN RITZ
- ☐ 158. BRUCE RUFFIN
- ☐ 159. ERIC YOUNG

DETROIT TIGERS

- ☐ 44. DANNY BAUTISTA
- ☐ 45. JUNIOR FELIX
- ☐ 46. CECIL FIELDER
- ☐ 47. CHRIS GOMEZ
- ☐ 48. CHAD KREUTER
- ☐ 49. MIKE MOORE
- ☐ 50. TONY PHILLIPS
- ☐ 51. ALAN TRAMMELL
- ☐ 52. DAVID WELLS

FLORIDA MARLINS

- ☐ 160. KURT ABBOTT
- ☐ 161. CHUCK CARR
- ☐ 162. CHRIS HAMMOND
- ☐ 163. BRYAN HARVEY
- ☐ 164. TERRY MATHEWS
- ☐ 165. YORKIS PEREZ
- ☐ 166. PAT RAPP
- ☐ 167. GARY SHEFFIELD
- ☐ 168. DAVE WEATHERS

HOUSTON ASTROS

- ☐ 169. JEFF BAGWELL
- ☐ 170. KEN CAMINITI
- ☐ 171. DOUG DRABEK
- ☐ 172. STEVE FINLEY
- ☐ 173. JOHN HUDEK
- ☐ 174. TODD JONES
- ☐ 175. JAMES MOUTON
- ☐ 176. SHANE REYNOLDS
- ☐ 177. SCOTT SERVAIS

KANSAS CITY ROYALS

- ☐ 53. KEVIN APPIER
- ☐ 54. BILLY BREWER
- ☐ 55. DAVID CONE
- ☐ 56. GREG GAGNE
- ☐ 57. BOB HAMELIN
- ☐ 58. JOSE LIND
- ☐ 59. BRENT MAYNE
- ☐ 60. BRIAN MCRAE
- ☐ 61. TERRY SHUMPERT

LOS ANGELES DODGERS

- ☐ 178. TOM CANDIOTTI
- ☐ 179. OMAR DAAL
- ☐ 180. DARREN DREIFORT
- ☐ 181. ERIC KARROS
- ☐ 182. RAMON MARTINEZ
- ☐ 183. RAUL MONDESI
- ☐ 184. HENRY RODRIGUEZ
- ☐ 185. TODD WORRELL

MILWAUKEE BREWERS

- ☐ 62. RICKY BONES
- ☐ 63. MIKE FETTERS
- ☐ 64. DARRYL HAMILTON
- ☐ 65. JOHN JAHA
- ☐ 66. GRAEME LLOYD
- ☐ 67. MATT MIESKE
- ☐ 68. KEVIN SEITZER
- ☐ 69. JOSE VALENTIN
- ☐ 70. TURNER WARD

MINNESOTA TWINS

- ☐ 71. RICK AGUILERA
- ☐ 72. RICH BECKER
- ☐ 73. ALEX COLE
- ☐ 74. SCOTT LEIUS
- ☐ 75. PAT MEARES
- ☐ 76. KIRBY PUCKETT
- ☐ 77. DAVE STEVENS
- ☐ 78. KEVIN TAPANI
- ☐ 79. MATT WALBECK

MONTREAL EXPOS

- ☐ 186. MOISES ALOU
- ☐ 187. SEAN BERRY
- ☐ 188. WIL CORDERO
- ☐ 189. JEFF FASSERO
- ☐ 190. DARRIN FLETCHER
- ☐ 191. BUTCH HENRY
- ☐ 192. KEN HILL
- ☐ 193. MEL ROJAS
- ☐ 194. JOHN WETTELAND

NEW YORK METS

- ☐ 195. BOBBY BONILLA
- ☐ 196. RICO BROGNA
- ☐ 197. BOBBY JONES
- ☐ 198. JEFF KENT
- ☐ 199. JOSIAS MANZANILLO
- ☐ 200. KELLY STINNETT
- ☐ 201. RYAN THOMPSON
- ☐ 202. JOSE VIZCAINO

NEW YORK YANKEES

- ☐ 80. WADE BOGGS
- ☐ 81. SCOTT KAMIENIECKI
- ☐ 82. PAT KELLY
- ☐ 83. JIMMY KEY
- ☐ 84. PAUL O'NEILL
- ☐ 85. LUIS POLONIA
- ☐ 86. MIKE STANLEY
- ☐ 87. DANNY TARTABULL
- ☐ 88. BOB WICKMAN

OAKLAND A'S

- ☐ 89. MARK ACRE
- ☐ 90. GERONIMO BERROA
- ☐ 91. MIKE BORDICK
- ☐ 92. RON DARLING
- ☐ 93. STAN JAVIER
- ☐ 94. MARK MCGWIRE
- ☐ 95. TROY NEEL
- ☐ 96. RUBEN SIERRA
- ☐ 97. TERRY STEINBACH

PHILADELPHIA PHILLIES

- ☐ 203. LENNY DYKSTRA
- ☐ 204. JIM EISENREICH
- ☐ 205. DAVE HOLLINS
- ☐ 206. MIKE LIEBERTHAL
- ☐ 207. MICKEY MORANDINI
- ☐ 208. BOBBY MUNOZ
- ☐ 209. CURT SCHILLING
- ☐ 210. HEATHCLIFF SLOCUMB
- ☐ 211. DAVID WEST

PITTSBURGH PIRATES

- ☐ 212. DAVE CLARK
- ☐ 213. STEVE COOKE
- ☐ 214. MIDRE CUMMINGS
- ☐ 215. CARLOS GARCIA
- ☐ 216. JEFF KING
- ☐ 217. JON LIEBER
- ☐ 218. ORLANDO MERCED
- ☐ 219. DON SLAUGHT
- ☐ 220. RICK WHITE

ST. LOUIS CARDINALS

- ☐ 221. RENE AROCHA
- ☐ 222. BERNARD GILKEY
- ☐ 223. BRIAN JORDAN
- ☐ 224. TOM PAGNOZZI
- ☐ 225. VICENTE PALACIOS
- ☐ 226. GERONIMO PENA
- ☐ 227. OZZIE SMITH
- ☐ 228. ALLEN WATSON
- ☐ 229. MARK WHITEN

SAN DIEGO PADRES

- ☐ 230. BRAD AUSMUS
- ☐ 231. DEREK BELL
- ☐ 232. ANDY BENES
- ☐ 233. TONY GWYNN
- ☐ 234. JOEY HAMILTON
- ☐ 235. LUIS LOPEZ
- ☐ 236. PEDRO MARTINEZ
- ☐ 237. SCOTT SANDERS
- ☐ 238. EDDIE WILLIAMS

SAN FRANCISCO GIANTS

- ☐ 239. ROD BECK
- ☐ 240. DAVE BURBA
- ☐ 241. DARREN LEWIS
- ☐ 242. KIRT MANWARING
- ☐ 243. MARK PORTUGAL
- ☐ 244. DARRYL STRAWBERRY
- ☐ 245. ROBBY THOMPSON
- ☐ 246. BILL VAN LANDINGHAM
- ☐ 247. MATT WILLIAMS

SEATTLE MARINERS

- ☐ 98. ERIC ANTHONY
- ☐ 99. CHRIS BOSIO
- ☐ 100. DAVE FLEMING
- ☐ 101. KEN GRIFFEY, JR.
- ☐ 102. REGGIE JEFFERSON
- ☐ 103. RANDY JOHNSON
- ☐ 104. EDGAR MARTINEZ
- ☐ 105. BILL RISLEY
- ☐ 106. DAN WILSON

TEXAS RANGERS

- ☐ 107. CRIS CARPENTER
- ☐ 108. WILL CLARK
- ☐ 109. JUAN GONZALEZ
- ☐ 110. RUSTY GREER
- ☐ 111. DAVID HULSE
- ☐ 112. ROGER PAVLIK
- ☐ 113. IVAN RODRIGUEZ
- ☐ 114. DOUG STRANGE
- ☐ 115. MATT WHITESIDE

TORONTO BLUE JAYS

- ☐ 116. ROBERTO ALOMAR
- ☐ 117. BRAD CORNETT
- ☐ 118. CARLOS DELGADO
- ☐ 119. ALEX GONZALEZ
- ☐ 120. DARREN HALL
- ☐ 121. PAT HENTGEN
- ☐ 122. PAUL MOLITOR
- ☐ 123. ED SPRAGUE
- ☐ 124. DEVON WHITE

FLEER-FLAIR

1993 FLAIR (300)
2 1/2" X 3 1/2"

ATLANTA BRAVES

- ☐ 1. STEVE AVERY
- ☐ 2. JEFF BLAUSER
- ☐ 3. RON GANT
- ☐ 4. TOM GLAVINE
- ☐ 5. DAVID JUSTICE
- ☐ 6. MARK LEMKE
- ☐ 7. GREG MADDUX
- ☐ 8. FRED MCGRIFF
- ☐ 9. TERRY PENDLETON
- ☐ 10. DEION SANDERS
- ☐ 11. JOHN SMOLTZ
- ☐ 12. MIKE STANTON

BALTIMORE ORIOLES

- ☐ 149. BRADY ANDERSON
- ☐ 150. MIKE DEVEREAUX
- ☐ 151. CHRIS HOILES
- ☐ 152. BEN MCDONALD
- ☐ 153. MARK MCLEMORE
- ☐ 154. MIKE MUSSINA
- ☐ 155. GREGG OLSON
- ☐ 156. HAROLD REYNOLDS
- ☐ 157. CAL RIPKEN, JR.
- ☐ 158. RICK SUTCLIFFE
- ☐ 159. FERNANDO VALENZUELA

BOSTON RED SOX

- ☐ 160. ROGER CLEMENS
- ☐ 161. SCOTT COOPER
- ☐ 162. ANDRE DAWSON
- ☐ 163. SCOTT FLETCHER
- ☐ 164. MIKE GREENWELL
- ☐ 165. GREG HARRIS
- ☐ 166. BILLY HATCHER
- ☐ 167. JEFF RUSSELL
- ☐ 168. MO VAUGHN
- ☐ 169. FRANK VIOLA

CALIFORNIA ANGELS

- ☐ 170. CHAD CURTIS
- ☐ 171. CHILI DAVIS
- ☐ 172. GARY DISARCINA
- ☐ 173. DAMION EASLEY
- ☐ 174. CHUCK FINLEY
- ☐ 175. MARK LANGSTON
- ☐ 176. LUIS POLONIA
- ☐ 177. TIM SALMON
- ☐ 178. SCOTT SANDERSON
- ☐ 179. J.T. SNOW

CHICAGO CUBS

- ☐ 13. STEVE BUECHELE
- ☐ 14. MARK GRACE
- ☐ 15. GREG HIBBARD
- ☐ 16. DERRICK MAY
- ☐ 17. CHUCK MCELROY
- ☐ 18. MIKE MORGAN
- ☐ 19. RANDY MYERS
- ☐ 20. RYNE SANDBERG
- ☐ 21. DWIGHT SMITH
- ☐ 22. SAMMY SOSA
- ☐ 23. JOSE VIZCAINO

CHICAGO WHITE SOX

- ☐ 180. WILSON ALVAREZ
- ☐ 181. ELLIS BURKS
- ☐ 182. JOEY CORA
- ☐ 183. ALEX FERNANDEZ
- ☐ 184. OZZIE GUILLEN
- ☐ 185. ROBERTO HERNANDEZ
- ☐ 186. BO JACKSON
- ☐ 187. LANCE JOHNSON
- ☐ 188. JACK MCDOWELL
- ☐ 189. FRANK THOMAS
- ☐ 190. ROBIN VENTURA

CINCINNATI REDS

- ☐ 24. TIM BELCHER
- ☐ 25. ROB DIBBLE
- ☐ 26. ROBERTO KELLY
- ☐ 27. BARRY LARKIN
- ☐ 28. KEVIN MITCHELL
- ☐ 29. HAL MORRIS
- ☐ 30. JOE OLIVER
- ☐ 31. JOSE RIJO
- ☐ 32. BIP ROBERTS
- ☐ 33. CHRIS SABO
- ☐ 34. REGGIE SANDERS

CLEVELAND INDIANS

- ☐ 191. CARLOS BAERGA
- ☐ 192. ALBERT BELLE
- ☐ 193. WAYNE KIRBY
- ☐ 194. DEREK LILLIQUIST
- ☐ 195. KENNY LOFTON
- ☐ 196. CARLOS MARTINEZ
- ☐ 197. JOSE MESA
- ☐ 198. ERIC PLUNK
- ☐ 199. PAUL SORRENTO

COLORADO ROCKIES

- ☐ 35. DANTE BICHETTE
- ☐ 36. WILLIE BLAIR
- ☐ 37. JERALD CLARK
- ☐ 38. ALEX COLE
- ☐ 39. ANDRES GALARRAGA
- ☐ 40. JOE GIRARDI
- ☐ 41. CHARLIE HAYES
- ☐ 42. CHRIS JONES
- ☐ 43. DAVID NIED
- ☐ 44. ERIC YOUNG

DETROIT TIGERS

- ☐ 200. JOHN DOHERTY
- ☐ 201. CECIL FIELDER
- ☐ 202. TRAVIS FRYMAN
- ☐ 203. KIRK GIBSON
- ☐ 204. MIKE HENNEMAN
- ☐ 205. CHAD KREUTER
- ☐ 206. SCOTT LIVINGSTONE
- ☐ 207. TONY PHILLIPS
- ☐ 208. MICKEY TETTLETON
- ☐ 209. ALAN TRAMMELL
- ☐ 210. DAVID WELLS
- ☐ 211. LOU WHITAKER

FLORIDA MARLINS

- ☐ 45. ALEX ARIAS
- ☐ 46. JACK ARMSTRONG
- ☐ 47. BRET BARBERIE
- ☐ 48. CHUCK CARR
- ☐ 49. JEFF CONINE
- ☐ 50. ORESTES DESTRADE
- ☐ 51. CHRIS HAMMOND
- ☐ 52. BRYAN HARVEY
- ☐ 53. BENITO SANTIAGO
- ☐ 54. GARY SHEFFIELD
- ☐ 55. WALT WEISS

HOUSTON ASTROS

- ☐ 56. ERIC ANTHONY
- ☐ 57. JEFF BAGWELL
- ☐ 58. CRAIG BIGGIO
- ☐ 59. KEN CAMINITI
- ☐ 60. ANDUJAR CEDENO
- ☐ 61. DOUG DRABEK
- ☐ 62. STEVE FINLEY
- ☐ 63. LUIS GONZALEZ
- ☐ 64. PETE HARNISCH
- ☐ 65. DOUG JONES
- ☐ 66. DARRYL KILE
- ☐ 67. GREG SWINDELL

KANSAS CITY ROYALS

- ☐ 212. KEVIN APPIER
- ☐ 213. GEORGE BRETT
- ☐ 214. DAVID CONE
- ☐ 215. TOM GORDON
- ☐ 216. PHIL HIATT
- ☐ 217. FELIX JOSE
- ☐ 218. WALLY JOYNER
- ☐ 219. JOSE LIND
- ☐ 220. MIKE MACFARLANE
- ☐ 221. BRIAN MCRAE
- ☐ 222. JEFF MONTGOMERY

LOS ANGELES DODGERS

- ☐ 68. BRETT BUTLER
- ☐ 69. JIM GOTT
- ☐ 70. OREL HERSHISER
- ☐ 71. ERIC KARROS
- ☐ 72. PEDRO MARTINEZ
- ☐ 73. RAMON MARTINEZ
- ☐ 74. ROGER MCDOWELL
- ☐ 75. MIKE PIAZZA
- ☐ 76. JODY REED
- ☐ 77. TIM WALLACH

MILWAUKEE BREWERS

- ☐ 223. CAL ELDRED
- ☐ 224. DARRYL HAMILTON
- ☐ 225. JOHN JAHA
- ☐ 226. PAT LISTACH
- ☐ 227. GRAEME LLOYD
- ☐ 228. KEVIN REIMER
- ☐ 229. BILL SPIERS
- ☐ 230. B.J. SURHOFF
- ☐ 231. GREG VAUGHN
- ☐ 232. ROBIN YOUNT

MINNESOTA TWINS

- ☐ 233. RICK AGUILERA
- ☐ 234. JIM DESHAIES
- ☐ 235. BRIAN HARPER
- ☐ 236. KENT HRBEK
- ☐ 237. CHUCK KNOBLAUCH
- ☐ 238. SHANE MACK
- ☐ 239. DAVID MCCARTY
- ☐ 240. PEDRO MUNOZ
- ☐ 241. MIKE PAGLIARULO

☐ 242. KIRBY PUCKETT
☐ 243. DAVE WINFIELD

MONTREAL EXPOS

☐ 78. MOISES ALOU
☐ 79. GREG COLBRUNN
☐ 80. WIL CORDERO
☐ 81. DELINO DESHIELDS
☐ 82. JEFF FASSERO
☐ 83. MARQUIS GRISSOM
☐ 84. KEN HILL
☐ 85. MIKE LANSING
☐ 86. DENNIS MARTINEZ
☐ 87. LARRY WALKER
☐ 88. JOHN WETTELAND

NEW YORK METS

☐ 89. BOBBY BONILLA
☐ 90. VINCE COLEMAN
☐ 91. DWIGHT GOODEN
☐ 92. TODD HUNDLEY
☐ 93. HOWARD JOHNSON
☐ 94. EDDIE MURRAY
☐ 95. JOE ORSULAK
☐ 96. BRET SABERHAGEN

NEW YORK YANKEES

☐ 244. JIM ABBOTT
☐ 245. WADE BOGGS
☐ 246. PAT KELLY
☐ 247. JIMMY KEY
☐ 248. JIM LEYRITZ
☐ 249. DON MATTINGLY
☐ 250. MATT NOKES
☐ 251. PAUL O'NEILL
☐ 252. MIKE STANLEY
☐ 253. DANNY TARTABULL
☐ 254. BOB WICKMAN
☐ 255. BERNIE WILLIAMS

OAKLAND A'S

☐ 256. MIKE BORDICK
☐ 257. DENNIS ECKERSLEY
☐ 258. BRENT GATES
☐ 259. GOOSE GOSSAGE
☐ 260. RICKEY HENDERSON
☐ 261. MARK MCGWIRE
☐ 262. RUBEN SIERRA
☐ 263. TERRY STEINBACH
☐ 264. BOB WELCH
☐ 265. BOBBY WITT

PHILADELPHIA PHILLIES

☐ 97. DARREN DAULTON
☐ 98. MARIANO DUNCAN
☐ 99. LENNY DYKSTRA
☐ 100. JIM EISENREICH
☐ 101. TOMMY GREENE
☐ 102. DAVE HOLLINS
☐ 103. PETE INCAVIGLIA
☐ 104. DANNY JACKSON
☐ 105. JOHN KRUK
☐ 106. TERRY MULHOLLAND
☐ 107. CURT SCHILLING
☐ 108. MITCH WILLIAMS

PITTSBURGH PIRATES

☐ 109. STAN BELINDA
☐ 110. JAY BELL
☐ 111. STEVE COOKE
☐ 112. CARLOS GARCIA
☐ 113. JEFF KING
☐ 114. AL MARTIN
☐ 115. ORLANDO MERCED
☐ 116. DON SLAUGHT
☐ 117. ANDY VAN SLYKE
☐ 118. TIM WAKEFIELD

ST. LOUIS CARDINALS

☐ 119. RENE AROCHA
☐ 120. BERNARD GILKEY
☐ 121. GREGG JEFFERIES
☐ 122. RAY LANKFORD
☐ 123. DONOVAN OSBORNE
☐ 124. TOM PAGNOZZI
☐ 125. ERIK PAPPAS
☐ 126. GERONIMO PENA
☐ 127. LEE SMITH
☐ 128. OZZIE SMITH
☐ 129. BOB TEWKSBURY
☐ 130. MARK WHITEN

SAN DIEGO PADRES

☐ 131. DEREK BELL
☐ 132. ANDY BENES
☐ 133. TONY GWYNN
☐ 134. GENE HARRIS
☐ 135. TREVOR HOFFMAN
☐ 136. PHIL PLANTIER

SAN FRANCISCO GIANTS

☐ 137. ROD BECK
☐ 138. BARRY BONDS
☐ 139. JOHN BURKETT
☐ 140. WILL CLARK
☐ 141. ROYCE CLAYTON
☐ 142. MIKE JACKSON
☐ 143. DARREN LEWIS
☐ 144. KIRT MANWARING
☐ 145. WILLIE MCGEE
☐ 146. BILL SWIFT
☐ 147. ROBBY THOMPSON
☐ 148. MATT WILLIAMS

SEATTLE MARINERS

☐ 266. RICH AMARAL
☐ 267. CHRIS BOSIO
☐ 268. JAY BUHNER
☐ 269. NORM CHARLTON
☐ 270. KEN GRIFFEY, JR.
☐ 271. ERIK HANSON
☐ 272. RANDY JOHNSON
☐ 273. EDGAR MARTINEZ
☐ 274. TINO MARTINEZ
☐ 275. DAVE VALLE
☐ 276. OMAR VIZQUEL

TEXAS RANGERS

☐ 277. KEVIN BROWN
☐ 278. JOSE CANSECO
☐ 279. JULIO FRANCO
☐ 280. JUAN GONZALEZ
☐ 281. TOM HENKE
☐ 282. DAVID HULSE
☐ 283. RAFAEL PALMEIRO
☐ 284. DEAN PALMER
☐ 285. IVAN RODRIGUEZ
☐ 286. NOLAN RYAN

TORONTO BLUE JAYS

☐ 287. ROBERTO ALOMAR
☐ 288. PAT BORDERS
☐ 289. JOE CARTER
☐ 290. JUAN GUZMAN
☐ 291. PAT HENTGEN
☐ 292. PAUL MOLITOR
☐ 293. JOHN OLERUD
☐ 294. ED SPRAGUE
☐ 295. DAVE STEWART
☐ 296. DUANE WARD
☐ 297. DEVON WHITE

1994 FLAIR (450)
2 1/2"X 3 1/2"

ATLANTA BRAVES

☐ 124. JEFF BLAUSER
☐ 125. TOM GLAVINE
☐ 126. DAVID JUSTICE
☐ 127. MIKE KELLY
☐ 128. RYAN KLESKO
☐ 129. JAVIER LOPEZ
☐ 130. GREG MADDUX
☐ 131. FRED MCGRIFF
☐ 132. KENT MERCKER
☐ 133. MARK WOHLERS
☐ 352. STEVE AVERY
☐ 353. ROBERTO KELLY
☐ 354. MARK LEMKE
☐ 355. GREG MCMICHAEL
☐ 356. TERRY PENDLETON
☐ 357. JOHN SMOLTZ
☐ 358. MIKE STANTON
☐ 359. TONY TARASCO

BALTIMORE ORIOLES

☐ 1. HAROLD BAINES
☐ 2. JEFFREY HAMMONDS
☐ 3. CHRIS HOILES
☐ 4. BEN MCDONALD
☐ 5. MARK MCLEMORE
☐ 6. JAMIE MOYER
☐ 7. JIM POOLE
☐ 8. CAL RIPKEN, JR.
☐ 9. CHRIS SABO
☐ 251. BRADY ANDERSON
☐ 252. MIKE DEVEREAUX
☐ 253. SID FERNANDEZ
☐ 254. LEO GOMEZ
☐ 255. MIKE MUSSINA
☐ 256. MIKE OQUIST
☐ 257. RAFAEL PALMEIRO
☐ 258. LEE SMITH

BOSTON RED SOX

☐ 10. SCOTT BANKHEAD
☐ 11. SCOTT COOPER
☐ 12. DANNY DARWIN
☐ 13. ANDRE DAWSON
☐ 14. BILLY HATCHER
☐ 15. AARON SELE
☐ 16. JOHN VALENTIN
☐ 17. DAVE VALLE
☐ 18. MO VAUGHN
☐ 259. DAMON BERRYHILL
☐ 260. WES CHAMBERLAIN

- ☐ 261. ROGER CLEMENS
- ☐ 262. GAR FINNVOLD
- ☐ 263. MIKE GREENWELL
- ☐ 264. TIM NAEHRING
- ☐ 265. OTIS NIXON
- ☐ 266. KEN RYAN

CALIFORNIA ANGELS

- ☐ 19. BRIAN ANDERSON
- ☐ 20. GARY DISARCINA
- ☐ 21. JIM EDMONDS
- ☐ 22. CHUCK FINLEY
- ☐ 23. BO JACKSON
- ☐ 24. MARK LEITER
- ☐ 25. GREG MYERS
- ☐ 26. EDUARDO PEREZ
- ☐ 27. TIM SALMON
- ☐ 267. CHAD CURTIS
- ☐ 268. CHILI DAVIS
- ☐ 269. DAMION EASLEY
- ☐ 270. JORGE FABREGAS
- ☐ 271. MARK LANGSTON
- ☐ 272. PHIL LEFTWICH
- ☐ 273. HAROLD REYNOLDS
- ☐ 274. J.T. SNOW

CHICAGO CUBS

- ☐ 134. WILLIE BANKS
- ☐ 135. STEVE BUECHELE
- ☐ 136. SHAWON DUNSTON
- ☐ 137. JOSE GUZMAN
- ☐ 138. GLENALLEN HILL
- ☐ 139. RANDY MYERS
- ☐ 140. KARL RHODES
- ☐ 141. RYNE SANDBERG
- ☐ 142. STEVE TRACHSEL
- ☐ 360. MARK GRACE
- ☐ 361. DERRICK MAY
- ☐ 362. REY SANCHEZ
- ☐ 363. SAMMY SOSA
- ☐ 364. RICK WILKINS

CHICAGO WHITE SOX

- ☐ 28. WILSON ALVAREZ
- ☐ 29. JASON BERE
- ☐ 30. ALEX FERNANDEZ
- ☐ 31. OZZIE GUILLEN
- ☐ 32. JOE HALL
- ☐ 33. DARRIN JACKSON
- ☐ 34. KIRK MCCASKILL
- ☐ 35. TIM RAINES
- ☐ 36. FRANK THOMAS
- ☐ 275. JOEY CORA
- ☐ 276. JULIO FRANCO
- ☐ 277. ROBERTO HERNANDEZ
- ☐ 278. LANCE JOHNSON
- ☐ 279. RON KARKOVICE
- ☐ 280. JACK MCDOWELL
- ☐ 281. ROBIN VENTURA

CINCINNATI REDS

- ☐ 143. BRET BOONE
- ☐ 144. TOM BROWNING
- ☐ 145. HECTOR CARRASCO
- ☐ 146. BARRY LARKIN
- ☐ 147. HAL MORRIS
- ☐ 148. JOSE RIJO
- ☐ 149. REGGIE SANDERS
- ☐ 150. JOHN SMILEY
- ☐ 365. JEFF BRANTLEY
- ☐ 366. TONY FERNANDEZ
- ☐ 367. CHUCK MCELROY
- ☐ 368. KEVIN MITCHELL
- ☐ 369. JOHN ROPER
- ☐ 370. JOHNNY RUFFIN
- ☐ 371. DEION SANDERS

CLEVELAND INDIANS

- ☐ 37. CARLOS BAERGA
- ☐ 38. ALBERT BELLE
- ☐ 39. MARK CLARK
- ☐ 40. WAYNE KIRBY
- ☐ 41. DENNIS MARTINEZ
- ☐ 42. CHARLES NAGY
- ☐ 43. MANNY RAMIREZ
- ☐ 44. PAUL SORRENTO
- ☐ 45. JIM THOME
- ☐ 282. SANDY ALOMAR, JR.
- ☐ 283. KENNY LOFTON
- ☐ 284. JOSE MESA
- ☐ 285. JACK MORRIS
- ☐ 286. EDDIE MURRAY
- ☐ 287. CHAD OGEA
- ☐ 288. ERIC PLUNK
- ☐ 289. PAUL SHUEY
- ☐ 290. OMAR VIZQUEL

COLORADO ROCKIES

- ☐ 151. DANTE BICHETTE
- ☐ 152. ELLIS BURKS
- ☐ 153. JOE GIRARDI
- ☐ 154. MIKE HARKEY
- ☐ 155. ROBERTO MEJIA
- ☐ 156. MARCUS MOORE
- ☐ 157. ARMANDO REYNOSO
- ☐ 158. BRUCE RUFFIN
- ☐ 159. ERIC YOUNG
- ☐ 372. MARVIN FREEMAN
- ☐ 373. ANDRES GALARRAGA
- ☐ 374. CHARLIE HAYES
- ☐ 375. NELSON LIRIANO
- ☐ 376. DAVID NIED
- ☐ 377. WALT WEISS

DETROIT TIGERS

- ☐ 46. ERIC DAVIS
- ☐ 47. JOHN DOHERTY
- ☐ 48. JUNIOR FELIX
- ☐ 49. CECIL FIELDER
- ☐ 50. KIRK GIBSON
- ☐ 51. MIKE MOORE
- ☐ 52. TONY PHILLIPS
- ☐ 53. ALAN TRAMMELL
- ☐ 291. DANNY BAUTISTA
- ☐ 292. TRAVIS FRYMAN
- ☐ 293. GREG GOHR
- ☐ 294. CHRIS GOMEZ
- ☐ 295. MICKEY TETTLETON
- ☐ 296. LOU WHITAKER

FLORIDA MARLINS

- ☐ 160. KURT ABBOTT
- ☐ 161. JEFF CONINE
- ☐ 162. ORESTES DESTRADE
- ☐ 163. CHRIS HAMMOND
- ☐ 164. BRYAN HARVEY
- ☐ 165. DAVE MAGADAN
- ☐ 166. GARY SHEFFIELD
- ☐ 167. DAVID WEATHERS
- ☐ 378. BRET BARBERIE
- ☐ 379. JERRY BROWNE
- ☐ 380. CHUCK CARR
- ☐ 381. GREG COLBRUNN
- ☐ 382. CHARLIE HOUGH
- ☐ 383. KURT MILLER
- ☐ 384. BENITO SANTIAGO

HOUSTON ASTROS

- ☐ 168. ANDUJAR CEDENO
- ☐ 169. TOM EDENS
- ☐ 170. LUIS GONZALEZ
- ☐ 171. PETE HARNISCH
- ☐ 172. TODD JONES
- ☐ 173. DARRYL KILE
- ☐ 174. JAMES MOUTON
- ☐ 175. SCOTT SERVAIS
- ☐ 176. MITCH WILLIAMS
- ☐ 385. JEFF BAGWELL
- ☐ 386. CRAIG BIGGIO
- ☐ 387. KEN CAMINITI
- ☐ 388. DOUG DRABEK
- ☐ 389. STEVE FINLEY
- ☐ 390. JOHN HUDEK
- ☐ 391. ORLANDO MILLER
- ☐ 392. SHANE REYNOLDS

KANSAS CITY ROYALS

- ☐ 54. KEVIN APPIER
- ☐ 55. STAN BELINDA
- ☐ 56. VINCE COLEMAN
- ☐ 57. GREG GAGNE
- ☐ 58. BOB HAMELIN
- ☐ 59. DAVE HENDERSON
- ☐ 60. WALLY JOYNER
- ☐ 61. MIKE MACFARLANE
- ☐ 62. JEFF MONTGOMERY
- ☐ 297. DAVID CONE
- ☐ 298. GARY GAETTI
- ☐ 299. TOM GORDON
- ☐ 300. FELIX JOSE
- ☐ 301. JOSE LIND
- ☐ 302. BRIAN MCRAE

LOS ANGELES DODGERS

- ☐ 177. PEDRO ASTACIO
- ☐ 178. OREL HERSHISER
- ☐ 179. RAUL MONDESI
- ☐ 180. JOSE OFFERMAN
- ☐ 181. CHAN HO PARK
- ☐ 182. MIKE PIAZZA
- ☐ 183. CORY SNYDER
- ☐ 184. TIM WALLACH
- ☐ 185. TODD WORRELL
- ☐ 393. BRETT BUTLER
- ☐ 394. TOM CANDIOTTI
- ☐ 395. DELINO DESHIELDS
- ☐ 396. KEVIN GROSS
- ☐ 397. ERIC KARROS
- ☐ 398. RAMON MARTINEZ
- ☐ 399. HENRY RODRIGUEZ

MILWAUKEE BREWERS

- ☐ 63. RICKY BONES
- ☐ 64. JEFF BRONKEY
- ☐ 65. ALEX DIAZ
- ☐ 66. CAL ELDRED
- ☐ 67. DARRYL HAMILTON
- ☐ 68. JOHN JAHA
- ☐ 69. MARK KIEFER
- ☐ 70. KEVIN SEITZER
- ☐ 71. TURNER WARD

☐ 303. MIKE FETTERS
☐ 304. BRIAN HARPER
☐ 305. PAT LISTACH
☐ 306. MATT MIESKE
☐ 307. DAVE NILSSON
☐ 308. JODY REED
☐ 309. GREG VAUGHN
☐ 310. BILL WEGMAN

MINNESOTA TWINS

☐ 72. RICH BECKER
☐ 72. SCOTT ERICKSON
☐ 74. KEITH GARAGOZZO
☐ 75. KENT HRBEK
☐ 76. SCOTT LEIUS
☐ 77. KIRBY PUCKETT
☐ 78. MATT WALBECK
☐ 79. DAVE WINFIELD
☐ 311. RICK AGUILERA
☐ 312. ALEX COLE
☐ 313. DENNY HOCKING
☐ 314. CHUCK KNOBLAUCH
☐ 315. SHANE MACK
☐ 316. PAT MEARES
☐ 317. KEVIN TAPANI

MONTREAL EXPOS

☐ 186. SEAN BERRY
☐ 187. WIL CORDERO
☐ 188. DARRIN FLETCHER
☐ 189. CLIFF FLOYD
☐ 190. MARQUIS GRISSOM
☐ 191. ROD HENDERSON
☐ 192. KEN HILL
☐ 193. PEDRO MARTINEZ
☐ 194. KIRK RUETER
☐ 400. MOISES ALOU
☐ 401. JEFF FASSERO
☐ 402. MIKE LANSING
☐ 403. MEL ROJAS
☐ 404. LARRY WALKER
☐ 405. JOHN WETTELAND
☐ 406. GABE WHITE

NEW YORK METS

☐ 195. JEROMY BURNITZ
☐ 196. JOHN FRANCO
☐ 197. DWIGHT GOODEN
☐ 198. TODD HUNDLEY
☐ 199. BOBBY JONES
☐ 200. JEFF KENT
☐ 201. MIKE MADDUX
☐ 202. RYAN THOMPSON
☐ 203. JOSE VIZCAINO
☐ 407. BOBBY BONILLA
☐ 408. JOSIAS MANZANILLO
☐ 409. BRET SABERHAGEN
☐ 410. DAVID SEGUI

NEW YORK YANKEES

☐ 80. MIKE GALLEGO
☐ 81. XAVIER HERNANDEZ
☐ 82. JIMMY KEY
☐ 83. JIM LEYRITZ
☐ 84. DON MATTINGLY
☐ 85. MATT NOKES
☐ 86. PAUL O'NEILL
☐ 87. MELIDO PEREZ
☐ 88. DANNY TARTABULL
☐ 318. JIM ABBOTT
☐ 319. WADE BOGGS
☐ 320. STERLING HITCHCOCK
☐ 321. PAT KELLY
☐ 322. TERRY MULHOLLAND
☐ 323. LUIS POLONIA
☐ 324. MIKE STANLEY
☐ 325. BOB WICKMAN
☐ 326. BERNIE WILLIAMS

OAKLAND A'S

☐ 89. MIKE BORDICK
☐ 90. RON DARLING
☐ 91. DENNIS ECKERSLEY
☐ 92. STAN JAVIER
☐ 93. STEVE KARSAY
☐ 94. MARK MCGWIRE
☐ 95. TROY NEEL
☐ 96. TERRY STEINBACH
☐ 97. BILL TAYLOR
☐ 327. MARK ACRE
☐ 328. GERONIMO BERROA
☐ 329. SCOTT BROSIUS
☐ 330. BRENT GATES
☐ 331. RICKEY HENDERSON
☐ 332. CARLOS REYES
☐ 333. RUBEN SIERRA
☐ 334. BOBBY WITT

PHILADELPHIA PHILLIES

☐ 204. DARREN DAULTON
☐ 205. LENNY DYKSTRA
☐ 206. JIM EISENREICH
☐ 207. DAVE HOLLINS
☐ 208. DANNY JACKSON
☐ 209. DOUG JONES
☐ 210. JEFF JUDEN
☐ 211. BEN RIVERA
☐ 212. KEVIN STOCKER
☐ 213. MILT THOMPSON
☐ 411. MARIANO DUNCAN
☐ 412. TOMMY GREENE
☐ 413. BILLY HATCHER
☐ 414. RICKY JORDAN
☐ 415. JOHN KRUK
☐ 416. BOBBY MUNOZ
☐ 417. CURT SCHILLING
☐ 418. FERNANDO VALENZUELA
☐ 419. DAVID WEST

PITTSBURGH PIRATES

☐ 214. JAY BELL
☐ 215. STEVE COOKE
☐ 216. MARK DEWEY
☐ 217. AL MARTIN
☐ 218. ORLANDO MERCED
☐ 219. DON SLAUGHT
☐ 220. ZANE SMITH
☐ 221. RICK WHITE
☐ 222. KEVIN YOUNG
☐ 420. CARLOS GARCIA
☐ 421. BRIAN HUNTER
☐ 422. JEFF KING
☐ 423. JON LIEBER
☐ 424. RAVELO MANZANILLO
☐ 425. DENNY NEAGLE
☐ 426. ANDY VAN SLYKE

ST. LOUIS CARDINALS

☐ 223. RENE AROCHA
☐ 224. RHEAL CORMIER
☐ 225. BRIAN JORDAN
☐ 226. RAY LANKFORD
☐ 227. MIKE PEREZ
☐ 228. OZZIE SMITH
☐ 229. MARK WHITEN
☐ 230. TODD ZEILE
☐ 427. BRYAN EVERSGERD
☐ 428. BERNARD GILKEY
☐ 429. GREGG JEFFERIES
☐ 430. TOM PAGNOZZI
☐ 431. BOB TEWKSBURY
☐ 432. ALLEN WATSON

SAN DIEGO PADRES

☐ 231. DEREK BELL
☐ 232. ARCHI CIANFROCCO
☐ 233. RICKY GUTIERREZ
☐ 234. TREVOR HOFFMAN
☐ 235. PHIL PLANTIER
☐ 236. DAVE STATON
☐ 237. WALLY WHITEHURST
☐ 433. ANDY ASHBY
☐ 434. ANDY BENES
☐ 435. DONNIE ELLIOTT
☐ 436. TONY GWYNN
☐ 437. JOEY HAMILTON
☐ 438. TIM HYERS
☐ 439. LUIS LOPEZ
☐ 440. BIP ROBERTS
☐ 441. SCOTT SANDERS

SAN FRANCISCO GIANTS

☐ 238. TODD BENZINGER
☐ 239. BARRY BONDS
☐ 240. JOHN BURKETT
☐ 241. ROYCE CLAYTON
☐ 242. BRYAN HICKERSON
☐ 243. MIKE JACKSON
☐ 244. DARREN LEWIS
☐ 245. KIRT MANWARING
☐ 246. MARK PORTUGAL
☐ 247. SALOMON TORRES
☐ 442. ROD BECK
☐ 443. DAVE BURBA
☐ 444. DARRYL STRAWBERRY
☐ 445. BILL SWIFT
☐ 446. ROBBY THOMPSON
☐ 447. BILL VAN LANDINGHAM
☐ 448. MATT WILLIAMS

SEATTLE MARINERS

☐ 98. ERIC ANTHONY
☐ 99. CHRIS BOSIO
☐ 100. TIM DAVIS
☐ 101. FELIX FERMIN
☐ 102. DAVE FLEMING
☐ 103. KEN GRIFFEY, JR.
☐ 104. GREG HIBBARD
☐ 105. REGGIE JEFFERSON
☐ 106. TINO MARTINEZ
☐ 335. BOBBY AYALA
☐ 336. JAY BUHNER
☐ 337. RANDY JOHNSON
☐ 338. EDGAR MARTINEZ
☐ 339. BILL RISLEY
☐ 340. ALEX RODRIGUEZ
☐ 341. ROGER SALKELD
☐ 342. DAN WILSON

TEXAS RANGERS

☐ 107. JACK ARMSTRONG
☐ 108. WILL CLARK
☐ 109. JUAN GONZALEZ
☐ 110. RICK HELLING
☐ 111. TOM HENKE
☐ 112. DAVID HULSE
☐ 113. MANUEL LEE
☐ 114. DOUG STRANGE
☐ 343. KEVIN BROWN
☐ 344. JOSE CANSECO
☐ 345. DEAN PALMER
☐ 346. IVAN RODRIGUEZ
☐ 347. KENNY ROGERS

TORONTO BLUE JAYS

☐ 115. ROBERTO ALOMAR
☐ 116. JOE CARTER
☐ 117. CARLOS DELGADO
☐ 118. PAT HENTGEN
☐ 119. PAUL MOLITOR
☐ 120. JOHN OLERUD
☐ 121. DAVE STEWART
☐ 122. TODD STOTTLEMYRE
☐ 123. MIKE TIMLIN
☐ 348. PAT BORDERS
☐ 349. JUAN GUZMAN
☐ 350. ED SPRAGUE
☐ 351. DEVON WHITE

1995 FLAIR SERIES 1
(216)
2 1/2" X 3 1/2"

ATLANTA BRAVES

- ☐ 102. ROBERTO KELLY
- ☐ 103. RYAN KLESKO
- ☐ 104. JAVIER LOPEZ
- ☐ 105. GREG MADDUX
- ☐ 106. FRED MCGRIFF
- ☐ 107. JOSE OLIVA
- ☐ 108. JOHN SMOLTZ
- ☐ 109. TONY TARASCO
- ☐ 110. MARK WOHLERS

BALTIMORE ORIOLES

- ☐ 1. BRADY ANDERSON
- ☐ 2. HAROLD BAINES
- ☐ 3. LEO GOMEZ
- ☐ 4. ALAN MILLS
- ☐ 5. JAMIE MOYER
- ☐ 6. MIKE MUSSINA
- ☐ 7. MIKE OQUIST
- ☐ 8. ARTHUR RHODES
- ☐ 9. CAL RIPKEN, JR.

BOSTON RED SOX

- ☐ 10. ROGER CLEMENS
- ☐ 11. SCOTT COOPER
- ☐ 12. MIKE GREENWELL
- ☐ 13. AARON SELE
- ☐ 14. JOHN VALENTIN
- ☐ 15. MO VAUGHN

CALIFORNIA ANGELS

- ☐ 16. CHAD CURTIS
- ☐ 17. GARY DISARCINA
- ☐ 18. CHUCK FINLEY
- ☐ 19. ANDREW LORRAINE
- ☐ 20. SPIKE OWEN
- ☐ 21. TIM SALMON
- ☐ 22. J.T. SNOW

CHICAGO CUBS

- ☐ 111. JIM BULLINGER
- ☐ 112. SHAWON DUNSTON
- ☐ 113. DERRICK MAY
- ☐ 114. RANDY MYERS
- ☐ 115. KARL RHODES
- ☐ 116. REY SANCHEZ
- ☐ 117. STEVE TRACHSEL
- ☐ 118. EDDIE ZAMBRANO

CHICAGO WHITE SOX

- ☐ 23. WILSON ALVAREZ
- ☐ 24. JASON BERE
- ☐ 25. OZZIE GUILLEN
- ☐ 26. MIKE LAVALLIERE
- ☐ 27. FRANK THOMAS
- ☐ 28. ROBIN VENTURA

CINCINNATI REDS

- ☐ 119. BRET BOONE
- ☐ 120. BRIAN DORSETT
- ☐ 121. HAL MORRIS
- ☐ 122. JOSE RIJO
- ☐ 123. JOHN ROPER
- ☐ 124. REGGIE SANDERS
- ☐ 125. PETE SCHOUREK
- ☐ 126. JOHN SMILEY

CLEVELAND INDIANS

- ☐ 29. CARLOS BAERGA
- ☐ 30. ALBERT BELLE
- ☐ 31. JASON GRIMSLEY
- ☐ 32. DENNIS MARTINEZ
- ☐ 33. EDDIE MURRAY
- ☐ 34. CHARLES NAGY
- ☐ 35. MANNY RAMIREZ
- ☐ 36. PAUL SORRENTO

COLORADO ROCKIES

- ☐ 127. ELLIS BURKS
- ☐ 128. VINNY CASTILLA
- ☐ 129. MARVIN FREEMAN
- ☐ 130. ANDRES GALARRAGA
- ☐ 131. MIKE MUNOZ
- ☐ 132. DAVID NIED
- ☐ 133. BRUCE RUFFIN
- ☐ 134. WALT WEISS
- ☐ 135. ERIC YOUNG

DETROIT TIGERS

- ☐ 37. JOHN DOHERTY
- ☐ 38. CECIL FIELDER
- ☐ 39. TRAVIS FRYMAN
- ☐ 40. CHRIS GOMEZ
- ☐ 41. TONY PHILLIPS
- ☐ 42. LOU WHITAKER

FLORIDA MARLINS

- ☐ 136. GREG COLBRUNN
- ☐ 137. JEFF CONINE
- ☐ 138. JEREMY HERNANDEZ
- ☐ 139. CHARLES JOHNSON
- ☐ 140. ROBB NEN
- ☐ 141. GARY SHEFFIELD
- ☐ 142. DAVE WEATHERS

HOUSTON ASTROS

- ☐ 143. JEFF BAGWELL
- ☐ 144. CRAIG BIGGIO
- ☐ 145. TONY EUSEBIO
- ☐ 146. LUIS GONZALEZ
- ☐ 147. JOHN HUDEK
- ☐ 148. DARRYL KILE
- ☐ 149. DAVE VERES

KANSAS CITY ROYALS

- ☐ 43. DAVID CONE
- ☐ 44. GARY GAETTI
- ☐ 45. MARK GUBICZA
- ☐ 46. BOB HAMELIN
- ☐ 47. WALLY JOYNER
- ☐ 48. RUSTY MEACHAM
- ☐ 49. JEFF MONTGOMERY

LOS ANGELES DODGERS

- ☐ 150. BILLY ASHLEY
- ☐ 151. PEDRO ASTACIO
- ☐ 152. RAFAEL BOURNIGAL
- ☐ 153. DELINO DESHIELDS
- ☐ 154. RAUL MONDESI
- ☐ 155. MIKE PIAZZA
- ☐ 156. RUDY SEANEZ
- ☐ 157. ISMAEL VALDES
- ☐ 158. TIM WALLACH
- ☐ 159. TODD WORRELL

MILWAUKEE BREWERS

- ☐ 50. RICKY BONES
- ☐ 51. CAL ELDRED
- ☐ 52. PAT LISTACH
- ☐ 53. MATT MIESKE
- ☐ 54. DAVE NILSSON
- ☐ 55. GREG VAUGHN
- ☐ 56. BILL WEGMAN

MINNESOTA TWINS

- ☐ 57. CHUCK KNOBLAUCH
- ☐ 58. SCOTT LEIUS
- ☐ 59. PAT MAHOMES
- ☐ 60. PAT MEARES
- ☐ 61. PEDRO MUNOZ
- ☐ 62. KIRBY PUCKETT

MONTREAL EXPOS

- ☐ 160. MOISES ALOU
- ☐ 161. CLIFF FLOYD
- ☐ 162. GIL HEREDIA
- ☐ 163. MIKE LANSING
- ☐ 164. PEDRO MARTINEZ
- ☐ 165. KIRK RUETER
- ☐ 166. TIM SCOTT
- ☐ 167. JEFF SHAW
- ☐ 168. RONDELL WHITE

NEW YORK METS

- ☐ 169. BOBBY BONILLA
- ☐ 170. RICO BROGNA
- ☐ 171. TODD HUNDLEY
- ☐ 172. JEFF KENT
- ☐ 173. JIM LINDEMAN
- ☐ 174. JOE ORSULAK
- ☐ 175. BRET SABERHAGEN

NEW YORK YANKEES

- ☐ 63. WADE BOGGS
- ☐ 64. JIMMY KEY
- ☐ 65. JIM LEYRITZ
- ☐ 66. DON MATTINGLY
- ☐ 67. PAUL O'NEILL
- ☐ 68. MELIDO PEREZ
- ☐ 69. DANNY TARTABULL

OAKLAND A'S

- ☐ 70. JOHN BRISCOE
- ☐ 71. SCOTT BROSIUS
- ☐ 72. RON DARLING
- ☐ 73. BRENT GATES
- ☐ 74. RICKEY HENDERSON
- ☐ 75. STAN JAVIER
- ☐ 76. MARK MCGWIRE
- ☐ 77. TODD VAN POPPEL

PHILADELPHIA PHILLIES

- ☐ 176. TOBY BORLAND
- ☐ 177. DARREN DAULTON
- ☐ 178. LENNY DYKSTRA
- ☐ 179. JIM EISENREICH
- ☐ 180. TOMMY GREENE
- ☐ 181. TONY LONGMIRE
- ☐ 182. BOBBY MUNOZ
- ☐ 183. KEVIN STOCKER

PITTSBURGH PIRATES

- ☐ 184. JAY BELL
- ☐ 185. STEVE COOKE
- ☐ 186. RAVELO MANZANILLO
- ☐ 187. AL MARTIN
- ☐ 188. DENNY NEAGLE
- ☐ 189. DON SLAUGHT
- ☐ 190. PAUL WAGNER

ST. LOUIS CARDINALS

- ☐ 191. RENE AROCHA
- ☐ 192. BERNARD GILKEY

- ☐ 193. JOSE OQUENDO
- ☐ 194. TOM PAGNOZZI
- ☐ 195. OZZIE SMITH
- ☐ 196. ALLEN WATSON
- ☐ 197. MARK WHITEN

SAN DIEGO PADRES

- ☐ 198. ANDY ASHBY
- ☐ 199. DONNIE ELLIOTT
- ☐ 200. BRYCE FLORIE
- ☐ 201. TONY GWYNN
- ☐ 202. TREVOR HOFFMAN
- ☐ 203. BRIAN JOHNSON
- ☐ 204. TIM MAUSER
- ☐ 205. BIP ROBERTS

SAN FRANCISCO GIANTS

- ☐ 206. ROD BECK
- ☐ 207. BARRY BONDS
- ☐ 208. ROYCE CLAYTON
- ☐ 209. DARREN LEWIS
- ☐ 210. MARK PORTUGAL
- ☐ 211. KEVIN ROGERS
- ☐ 212. BILL VAN LANDINGHAM
- ☐ 213. MATT WILLIAMS

SEATTLE MARINERS

- ☐ 78. BOBBY AYALA
- ☐ 79. MIKE BLOWERS
- ☐ 80. JAY BUHNER
- ☐ 81. KEN GRIFFEY, JR.
- ☐ 82. RANDY JOHNSON
- ☐ 83. TINO MARTINEZ
- ☐ 84. JEFF NELSON
- ☐ 85. ALEX RODRIGUEZ

TEXAS RANGERS

- ☐ 86. WILL CLARK
- ☐ 87. JEFF FRYE
- ☐ 88. JUAN GONZALEZ
- ☐ 89. RUSTY GREER
- ☐ 90. DARREN OLIVER
- ☐ 91. DEAN PALMER
- ☐ 92. IVAN RODRIGUEZ
- ☐ 93. MATT WHITESIDE

TORONTO BLUE JAYS

- ☐ 94. ROBERTO ALOMAR
- ☐ 95. JOE CARTER
- ☐ 96. TONY CASTILLO
- ☐ 97. JUAN GUZMAN
- ☐ 98. PAT HENTGEN
- ☐ 99. MIKE HUFF
- ☐ 100. JOHN OLERUD
- ☐ 101. WOODY WILLIAMS

1933 GOUDEY (240)
2 3/8" X 2 7/8"

BOSTON BRAVES

- ☐ 24. HORACE FORD
- ☐ 30. FRANK HOGAN
- ☐ 50. ED BRANDT
- ☐ 69. RANDY MOORE
- ☐ 91. TOM ZACHARY
- ☐ 98. WALTER BERGER
- ☐ 117. RABBIT MARANVILLE
- ☐ 131. FRED FRANKHOUSE
- ☐ 139. BEN CANTWELL
- ☐ 161. AL SPOHRER
- ☐ 162. LEO MANGUM
- ☐ 172. BILLY HARGRAVE
- ☐ 179. FRED LEACH
- ☐ 185. BOB SMITH
- ☐ 212. BILLY URBANSKI

BOSTON RED SOX

- ☐ 8. ROY JOHNSON
- ☐ 14. HENRY JOHNSON
- ☐ 42. EDDIE COLLINS
- ☐ 48. MARTY MCMANUS
- ☐ 93. JOHN WELCH
- ☐ 105. BERNIE FRIBERG
- ☐ 197. RICK FERRELL
- ☐ 221. DALE ALEXANDER

BROOKLYN DODGERS

- ☐ 2. DAZZY VANCE(F)
- ☐ 13. LAFAYETTE THOMPSON
- ☐ 17. WATSON CLARK
- ☐ 32. JOHN CLANCY
- ☐ 58. LEFTY O'DOUL
- ☐ 72. OWEN CARROLL
- ☐ 78. JACK QUINN
- ☐ 99. TONY CUCCINELLO
- ☐ 118. VAL PICINICH
- ☐ 141. RAY BENGE
- ☐ 143. GLENN WRIGHT
- ☐ 151. JAKE FLOWERS
- ☐ 155. JOE JUDGE
- ☐ 211. HACK WILSON

CHICAGO CUBS

- ☐ 5. BABE HERMAN
- ☐ 23. KIKI CUYLER
- ☐ 39. MARK KOENIG
- ☐ 51. CHARLIE GRIMM
- ☐ 55. PAT MALONE
- ☐ 64. BURLEIGH GRIMES
- ☐ 67. GUY BUSH
- ☐ 135. WOODY ENGLISH
- ☐ 152. ZACK TAYLOR
- ☐ 186. JOHN SCHULTE(C)
- ☐ 202. GABBY HARTNETT
- ☐ 203. LON WARNEKE
- ☐ 204. RIGGS STEPHENSON
- ☐ 224. FRANK DEMAREE
- ☐ 225. BILL JURGES
- ☐ 226. CHARLEY ROOT
- ☐ 227. BILL HERMAN

CHICAGO WHITE SOX

- ☐ 6. JIMMY DYKES
- ☐ 7. TED LYONS
- ☐ 33. RALPH KRESS
- ☐ 35. AL SIMMONS
- ☐ 43. LEW FONSECA
- ☐ 65. MILTON GASTON
- ☐ 79. RED FABER
- ☐ 81. SAM JONES
- ☐ 184. CHARLEY BERRY
- ☐ 195. EVAR SWANSON
- ☐ 219. MULE HAAS

CINCINNATI REDS

- ☐ 40. TAYLOR DOUTHIT
- ☐ 44. JIM BOTTOMLEY
- ☐ 45. LARRY BENTON
- ☐ 66. GEORGE GRANTHAM
- ☐ 74. EPPA RIXEY
- ☐ 80. CLYDE MANION
- ☐ 97. JOE MORRISSEY
- ☐ 137. FRED LUCAS
- ☐ 150. RAY KOLP
- ☐ 213. EARL ADAMS

CLEVELAND INDIANS

- ☐ 10. GLENN MYATT
- ☐ 26. CHALMER CISSELL
- ☐ 27. GEORGE CONNALLY
- ☐ 75. WILLIE KAMM
- ☐ 96. WILLIS HUDLIN
- ☐ 116. EDDIE MORGAN
- ☐ 171. CHARLEY JAMIESON
- ☐ 194. EARL AVERILL
- ☐ 218. WESLEY FERRELL

DETROIT TIGERS

- ☐ 4. HEINIE SCHUBLE
- ☐ 11. BILLY ROGELL
- ☐ 15. VICTOR SORRELL
- ☐ 100. GEORGE UHLE
- ☐ 104. FRED MARBERRY
- ☐ 199. TOM BRIDGES
- ☐ 222. CHARLEY GEHRINGER

NEW YORK GIANTS

- ☐ 3. HUGH GRITZ
- ☐ 20. BILLY TERRY
- ☐ 41. GUS MANCUSO
- ☐ 52. ANDY COHEN
- ☐ 84. GLENN SPENCER
- ☐ 102. TRAVIS JACKSON
- ☐ 125. BILL TERRY (M)
- ☐ 126. JOE MOORE
- ☐ 127. MEL OTT
- ☐ 129. HAROLD SCHUMACHER
- ☐ 130. FRED FITZSIMMONS
- ☐ 142. PAUL RICHARDS
- ☐ 207. MEL OTT
- ☐ 208. BERNIE JAMES
- ☐ 209. ADOLFO LUQUE
- ☐ 230. CARL HUBBELL
- ☐ 231. JOE MOORE
- ☐ 232. LEFTY O'DOUL
- ☐ 233. JOHNNY VERGEZ
- ☐ 234. CARL HUBBELL
- ☐ 235. FRED FITZSIMMONS
- ☐ 236. GEORGE DAVIS
- ☐ 237. GUS MANCUSO
- ☐ 238. HUGH CRITZ
- ☐ 239. LEROY PARMELEE
- ☐ 240. HAROLD SCHUMACHER

NEW YORK YANKEES

- ☐ 12. GEORGE PIPGRAS
- ☐ 19. BILL DICKEY
- ☐ 31. TONY LAZZERI
- ☐ 53. BABE RUTH
- ☐ 56. RED RUFFING
- ☐ 83. PETE JABLONOWSKI
- ☐ 92. LOU GEHRIG
- ☐ 103. EARLE COMBS
- ☐ 138. HERB PENNOCK
- ☐ 144. BABE RUTH
- ☐ 148. EDDIE FARRELL
- ☐ 149. BABE RUTH
- ☐ 156. DANNY MACFAYDEN
- ☐ 157. SAM BYRD
- ☐ 160. LOU GEHRIG
- ☐ 165. JOE SEWELL
- ☐ 181. BABE RUTH
- ☐ 191. BEN CHAPMAN
- ☐ 192. WALTER BROWN
- ☐ 193. LYNFORD LARY
- ☐ 215. RUSSELL VAN ATTA
- ☐ 216. LEFTY GOMEZ
- ☐ 217. FRANK CROSETTI

PHILADELPHIA ATHLETICS

- ☐ 29. JIMMY FOXX
- ☐ 59. BING MILLER
- ☐ 61. MAX BISHOP
- ☐ 76. MICKEY COCHRANE
- ☐ 82. DIB WILLIAMS
- ☐ 145. GEORGE WALBERT
- ☐ 154. JIMMY FOXX
- ☐ 183. GEORGE WALBERG
- ☐ 196. LEROY MAHAFFEY
- ☐ 220. LEFTY GROVE

PHILADELPHIA PHILLIES

- ☐ 21. PHIL COLLINS
- ☐ 28. DICK BARTELL
- ☐ 38. FRED BRICKELL
- ☐ 115. CLIFF HEATHCOTE
- ☐ 128. CHUCK KLEIN
- ☐ 132. JIM ELLIOTT
- ☐ 136. FLINT RHEM
- ☐ 170. HARRY MCCURDY
- ☐ 178. JACKIE WARNER
- ☐ 210. VIRGIL DAVIS

PITTSBURGH PIRATES

- ☐ 22. PIE TRAYNOR
- ☐ 25. PAUL WANER
- ☐ 36. TOMMY THEVENOW
- ☐ 54. RAY KREMER
- ☐ 60. WAITE HOYT
- ☐ 77. ADAM COMOROSKY
- ☐ 133. FRED LINDSTROM
- ☐ 164. LLOYD WANER
- ☐ 205. HEINIE MEINE
- ☐ 206. GUS SUHR
- ☐ 228. TONY PIET
- ☐ 229. FLOYD VAUGHAN

ST. LOUIS BROWNS

- ☐ 1. BENNY BENGOUGH
- ☐ 16. GEORGE BLAEHOLDER
- ☐ 18. MUDDY RUEL
- ☐ 101. DICK COFFMAN
- ☐ 120. CARL REYNOLDS
- ☐ 140. IRVING HADLEY
- ☐ 166. SAM WEST
- ☐ 188. ROGERS HORNSBY(M)
- ☐ 198. IRVING BURNS

ST. LOUIS CARDINALS

- ☐ 2. DAZZY VANCE(B)
- ☐ 34. BOB O'FARRELL
- ☐ 37. JIMMY WILSON
- ☐ 46. ETHAN ALLEN
- ☐ 49. FRANK FRISCH
- ☐ 62. PEPPER MARTIN
- ☐ 73. JESSE HAINES
- ☐ 94. BILL WALKER
- ☐ 119. ROGERS HORNSBY
- ☐ 147. LEO DUROCHER
- ☐ 173. ROSCOE HOLM
- ☐ 200. BILL HALLAHAN
- ☐ 201. ERNIE ORSATTI
- ☐ 223. DIZZY DEAN

WASHINGTON SENATORS

- ☐ 9. DAVE HARRIS
- ☐ 47. HEINIE MANUSH
- ☐ 63. JOE CRONIN(M)
- ☐ 71. ROBERT BURKE
- ☐ 95. ALVIN CROWDER
- ☐ 107. HEINIE MANUSH
- ☐ 108. JOE KUHEL
- ☐ 109. JOE CRONIN(M)
- ☐ 110. GOOSE GOSLIN
- ☐ 111. MONTE WEAVER
- ☐ 112. FRED SCHULTE
- ☐ 113. OSWALD BLUEGE
- ☐ 114. LUKE SEWELL
- ☐ 121. WALTER STEWART
- ☐ 122. ALVIN CROWDER
- ☐ 123. JACK RUSSELL
- ☐ 124. EARL WHITEHILL
- ☐ 134. SAM RICE
- ☐ 146. WALTER STEWART
- ☐ 153. BUDDY MYER
- ☐ 158. MOE BERG
- ☐ 159. OSWALD BLUEGE
- ☐ 163. LUKE SEWELL
- ☐ 167. JACK RUSSELL
- ☐ 168. GOOSE GOSLIN
- ☐ 169. AL THOMAS
- ☐ 187. HEINIE MANUSH
- ☐ 189. JOE CRONIN(M)
- ☐ 190. FRED SCHULTE
- ☐ 214. JOHN KERR

1934 GOUDEY (96)
2 3/8" X 2 7/8"

BOSTON BRAVES

- ☐ 5. ED BRANDT
- ☐ 20. FRANK HOGAN
- ☐ 31. BAXTER JORDAN
- ☐ 36. WALTER BETTS
- ☐ 59. JOE MOWRY
- ☐ 80. MARTY MCMANUS
- ☐ 81. BOB BROWN

BOSTON RED SOX

- ☐ 19. LEFTY GROVE
- ☐ 30. JULIUS SOLTERS
- ☐ 75. BILL WERBER
- ☐ 93. FRED OSTERMUELLER

BROOKLYN DODGERS

- ☐ 24. RAY BENGE
- ☐ 46. JOE STRIPP
- ☐ 47. JOHN FREDERICK
- ☐ 49. SAM LESLIE
- ☐ 50. WALTER BECK
- ☐ 89. LINUS FREY

CHICAGO CUBS

- ☐ 3. CHARLIE GRIMM(M)
- ☐ 4. WOODY ENGLISH
- ☐ 10. CHUCK KLEIN
- ☐ 60. LYNN NELSON
- ☐ 71. LYLE TINNING
- ☐ 90. KI KI CUYLER

CHICAGO WHITE SOX

- ☐ 27. LUKE APPLING
- ☐ 41. GEORGE EARNSHAW(B)
- ☐ 63. MINTER HAYES
- ☐ 74. BOB BOKEN
- ☐ 79. EDDIE DURHAM

CINCINNATI REDS

- ☐ 8. TONY PIET
- ☐ 34. CHICK HAFEY
- ☐ 35. ERNIE LOMBARDI
- ☐ 54. WESLEY SCHULMERICH(B)
- ☐ 56. MARK KOENIG
- ☐ 84. PAUL DERRINGER
- ☐ 85. ADAM COMOROSKY

CLEVELAND INDIANS

- ☐ 14. WILLIE KAMM
- ☐ 38. ORAL HILDEBRAND
- ☐ 43. DICK PORTER
- ☐ 66. MEL HARDER
- ☐ 67. BOB WEILAND
- ☐ 76. HAL TROSKY
- ☐ 77. JOE VOSMIK

DETROIT TIGERS

- ☐ 2. MICKEY COCHRANE(M)
- ☐ 23. CHARLEY GEHRINGER
- ☐ 26. GERALD WALKER
- ☐ 44. TOM BRIDGES
- ☐ 62. HANK GREENBERG
- ☐ 70. PETE FOX
- ☐ 92. STEVE LARKIN

NEW YORK GIANTS

- ☐ 12. CARL HUBBELL
- ☐ 17. HUGH CRITZ
- ☐ 21. BILL TERRY(M)
- ☐ 32. BLONDY RYAN
- ☐ 52. HERMAN BELL
- ☐ 53. GEORGE WATKINS
- ☐ 88. HOMER PEEL

NEW YORK YANKEES

- ☐ 9. BEN CHAPMAN
- ☐ 37. LOU GEHRIG
- ☐ 39. FRED WALKER
- ☐ 42. JOHN ALLEN
- ☐ 61. LOU GEHRIG
- ☐ 72. ARNDT JORGENS
- ☐ 94. RED ROLFE
- ☐ 95. MYRIL HOAG
- ☐ 96. JIM DESHONG

PHILADELPHIA ATHLETICS

- ☐ 1. JIMMY FOXX
- ☐ 25. ROGER CRAMER
- ☐ 28. ED COLEMAN
- ☐ 41. GEORGE EARNSHAW(F)
- ☐ 68. BOB JOHNSON
- ☐ 69. JOHN MARCUM
- ☐ 78. PINKEY HIGGINS

PHILADELPHIA PHILLIES

- ☐ 33. FRANK HURST
- ☐ 54. WESLEY SCHULMERICH(F)
- ☐ 55. ED HOLLEY
- ☐ 87. GEORGE DARROW
- ☐ 91. DOLPH CAMILLI

PITTSBURGH PIRATES

- ☐ 11. PAUL WANER
- ☐ 22. FLOYD VAUGHAN
- ☐ 29. LARRY FRENCH
- ☐ 57. BILL SWIFT
- ☐ 58. EARL GRACE
- ☐ 86. LLOYD JOHNSON

ST. LOUIS BROWNS

- ☐ 45. OSCAR MELILLO
- ☐ 64. FRANK GRUBE
- ☐ 73. ED WELLS

ST. LOUIS CARDINALS

- ☐ 6. DIZZY DEAN
- ☐ 7. LEO DUROCHER
- ☐ 13. FRANK FRISCH
- ☐ 48. TEX CARLETON
- ☐ 51. RIP COLLINS
- ☐ 82. BILL HALLAHAN
- ☐ 83. JIM MOONEY

WASHINGTON SENATORS

- ☐ 15. ALVIN CROWDER
- ☐ 16. JOE KUHEL
- ☐ 18. HEINIE MANUSH
- ☐ 40. JOHN STONE
- ☐ 65. CLIFF BOLTON

1935 GOUDEY PUZZLE (36)
2 3/8" X 2 7/8"

Each of the 1935 Goudey cards has four players depicted on the card. While most cards portray four players from the same team, several cards portray players from different teams. Players in parentheses are not on the same team as the subject player(s), but are on the same card.

BOSTON BRAVES

- ☐ MOORE, HOGAN, FRANKHOUSE, BRANDT
- ☐ RUTH, MCMANUS, BRANDT, MARANVILLE
- ☐ SPOHRER, RHEM, CANTWELL, BENTON

BOSTON RED SOX

- ☐ CRONIN, REYNOLDS, BISHOP, CISSELL
- ☐ WERBER, R. FERRELL, W. FERRELL, OSTERMUELLER

BROOKLYN DODGERS

- ☐ LESLIE, FREY, STRIPP, W. CLARK
- ☐ BENGE, ZACHARY (KOENIG, FITZSIMMONS)
- ☐ VANCE (BERRY, BURKE, KRESS)

CHICAGO CUBS

- ☐ GRIMES, KLEIN, CUYLER, ENGLISH

CHICAGO WHITE SOX

- ☐ EARNSHAW, DYKES, L. SEWELL, APPLINE
- ☐ HAYES, LYONS, HAAS, BONURA
- ☐ RUEL, SIMMONS (KAMM, COCHRANE)
- ☐ WRIGHT (TRAYNOR, LUCAS THEVENOW

CINCINNATI REDS

- ☐ CAMPBELL, MEYERS, GOODMAN, KAMPOURIS
- ☐ PIET, COMORDSKY, BOTTOMLEY, ADAMS
- ☐ BYRD, MACFAYDEN (MARTIN, O'FARRELL)
- ☐ COMOROSKY, BOTTOMLEY (HUDLIN, MYATT)

CLEVELAND INDIANS

- ☐ KAMM, HILDEBRAND, AVERILL, TROSKY
- ☐ VOSMIK, KNICKERBOCKER, HARDER, STEWART
- ☐ HUDLIN, MYATT (COMOROSKY, BOTTOMLEY
- ☐ KAMM (RUEL, SIMMONS, COCHRANE)

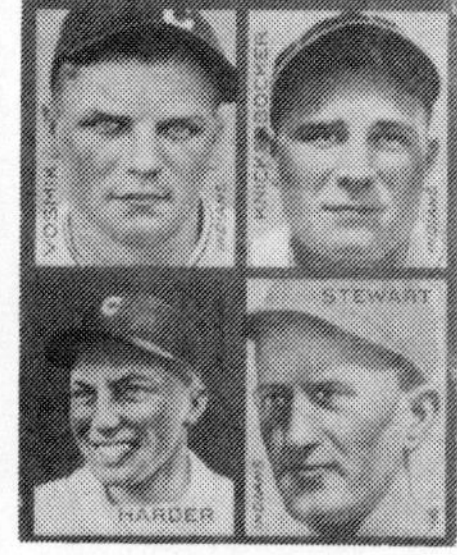

DETROIT TIGERS

- ☐ COCHRANE, GEHRINGER, BRIDGES, ROGELL
- ☐ FOX, GREENBERG, WALKER, ROWE
- ☐ SCHUBLE, MARBERRY, GOSLIN, CROWDER
- ☐ COCHRANE (RUEL, SIMMONS, KAMM)

NEW YORK GIANTS

- ☐ CRITZ, BARTELL, OTT, MANCUSO
- ☐ TERRY, SCHUMACHER, MANCUSO, JACKSON
- ☐ KOENIG FITZSIMMONS (BENGE, ZACHARY)

NEW YORK YANKEES

- ☐ DESHONG, ALLEN, ROLFE, WALKER
- ☐ RUFFING, MALONE, LAZZERI, DICKEY

PHILADELPHIA ATHLETICS

- ☐ JOHNSON, COLEMAN, MARCUM, CRAMER
- ☐ MAHAFFEY, FOXX, WILLIAMS, HIGGINS
- ☐ BERRY (VANCE, BURKE, KRESS)

PHILADELPHIA PHILLIES

- ☐ WILSON, ALLEN, JONNARD, BRICKELL

PITTSBURGH PIRATES

- ☐ HERMAN, SUHR, PADDEN, BLANTON
- ☐ P. WANER, BUSH, W. HOYT, L. WANER
- ☐ TRAYNOR, LUCAS, THEVENOW (WRIGHT)

ST. LOUIS BROWNS

- ☐ BURNS, HEMSLEY, GRUBE, WEILAND
- ☐ WEST, MELILLO, BLAEHOLDER, COFFMAN

ST. LOUIS CARDINALS

- ☐ FRISCH, J. DEAN, ORSATTI, TEX CARLETON
- ☐ MARTIN, O'FARRELL (BYRD, MACFAYDEN

WASHINGTON SENATORS

- ☐ KUHEL, WHITEHILL, MEYER, STONE
- ☐ MANUSH, LARY, M. WEAVER, HADLEY
- ☐ BURKE, KRESS (BERRY, VANCE)

1936 GOUDEY GAME (25) 2 3/8" X 2 7/8" BLACK & WHITE

BOSTON BRAVES

- ☐ 1. WALLY BERGER
- ☐ 8. JOE COSCARART

BOSTON RED SOX

- ☐ 13. RICK FERRELL
- ☐ 25. BILL WERBER

BROOKLYN DODGERS

- ☐ 3. FRENCHI BORDAGARA

CHICAGO CUBS

- ☐ 20. CHUCK KLEIN

CHICAGO WHITE SOX

- ☐ 2. ZEKE BONURA
- ☐ 12. JIMMY DYKES

CINCINNATI REDS

- ☐ 10. KIKI CUYLER
- ☐ 11. PAUL DERRINGER

CLEVELAND INDIANS

- ☐ 19. ORAL HILDEBRAND
- ☐ 23. JOE VOSMIK

DETROIT TIGERS

- ☐ 7. MICKEY COCHRANE
- ☐ 15. HANK GREENBERG

NEW YORK GIANTS

- ☐ 6. CLYDE CASTLEMAN

NEW YORK YANKEES

- ☐ 9. FRANK CROSETTI
- ☐ 14. LEFTY GOMEZ

PHILADELPHIA ATHLETICS

- ☐ 18. PINKY HIGGINS

PHILADELPHIA PHILLIES

- ☐ 5. DOLPH CAMILLI

PITTSBURGH PIRATES

- ☐ 4. BILL BRUBAKER
- ☐ 24. PAUL WANER

ST. LOUIS BROWNS

- ☐ 17. ROLLIE HEMSLEY

ST. LOUIS CARDINALS

□ 21. PEPPER MARTIN

WASHINGTON SENATORS

□ 16. BUCKY HARRIS
□ 22. BOBO NEWSOM

1938 GOUDEY HEADS UP (48) 2 3/8" X 2 7/8"

BOSTON BEES

□ 257. AL LOPEZ
□ 281. AL LOPEZ

BOSTON RED SOX

□ 247. JOE VOSMIK
□ 249. JIMMIE FOXX
□ 258. BOBBY DOERR
□ 271. JOE VOSMIK
□ 273. JIMMIE FOXX
□ 282. BOBBY DOERR

BROOKLYN DODGERS

□ 254. VAN LINGLE MUNGO
□ 278. VAN LINGLE MUNGO

CHICAGO CUBS

□ 244. FRANK DEMAREE
□ 268. FRANK DEMAREE

CHICAGO WHITE SOX

□ 243. JOE KUHEL
□ 261. RIP RADCLIFF
□ 263. MARVIN OWEN
□ 267. JOE KUHEL
□ 285. RIP RADCLIFF
□ 287. MARVIN OWEN

CINCINNATI REDS

□ 246. ERNIE LOMBARDI
□ 270. ERNIE LOMBARDI

CLEVELAND INDIANS

□ 245. FRANK PYTLAK
□ 255. MOOSE SOLTERS
□ 264. BOB FELLER
□ 269. FRANK PYTLAK
□ 279. MOOSE SOLTERS
□ 288. BOB FELLER

DETROIT TIGERS

□ 241. CHARLIE GEHRINGER
□ 242. PETE FOX
□ 253. HANK GREENBERG
□ 256. VERNON KENNEDY
□ 260. RUDY YORK
□ 265. CHARLIE GEHRINGER
□ 266. PETE FOX
□ 277. HANK GREENBERG
□ 280. VERNON KENNEDY
□ 284. RUDY YORK

NEW YORK GIANTS

□ 248. DICK BARTELL
□ 272. DICK BARTELL

NEW YORK YANKEES

□ 250. JOE DIMAGGIO
□ 251. BUMP HADLEY
□ 274. JOE DIMAGGIO
□ 275. BUMP HADLEY

PHILADELPHIA ATHLETICS

□ 259. BILL WERBER
□ 283. BILL WERBER

PHILADELPHIA PHILLIES

NO CARDS ISSUED

PITTSBURGH PIRATES

NO CARDS ISSUED

ST. LOUIS BROWNS

NO CARDS ISSUED

ST. LOUIS CARDINALS

□ 262. JOE MEDWICK
□ 286. JOE MEDWICK

WASHINGTON SENATORS

□ 252. ZEKE BONURA
□ 276. ZEKE BONURA

1941 GOUDEY (33) 2 3/8" X 2 7/8"

BOSTON BEES

□ 19. BILL POSEDEL
□ 22. JOE SULLIVAN
□ 24. STANLEY ANDREWS
□ 30. JIM TOBIN
□ 31. CHESTER ROSS

BOSTON RED SOX

□ 6. EMERSON DICKMAN

BROOKLYN DODGERS

□ 18. WHITLOW WYATT

CHICAGO CUBS

□ 21. HAROLD WARSTLER
□ 28 AL TODD

CHICAGO WHITE SOX

□ 9. BILL DIETRICH
□ 10. TAFT WRIGHT
□ 15. DARIO LODIGIANI

CINCINNATI REDS

□ 7. WAYNE AMBLER

CLEVELAND INDIANS

NO CARDS ISSUED

DETROIT TIGERS

□ 32. GEORGE COFFMAN

NEW YORK GIANTS

□ 3. LOUIS CHIOZZA
□ 20. CARL HUBBELL
□ 23. BABE YOUNG
□ 25. MORRIS ARNOVICH
□ 33. MELT OTT

NEW YORK YANKEES

□ 4. BUDDY ROSAR

PHILADELPHIA ATHLETICS

□ 13. FRANK HAYES

PHILADELPHIA PHILLIES

□ 1. HUGH MULCAHY
□ 17. VITO TAMULIS
□ 27. BILL CROUCH

PITTSBURGH PIRATES

- ☐ 26. ELBERT FLETCHER
- ☐ 29. DEBS GARMS

ST. LOUIS BROWNS

- ☐ 2. HARLAND CLIFT
- ☐ 5. GEORGE MCQUINN
- ☐ 8. BOB MUNCRIEF
- ☐ 11. DON HEFFNER
- ☐ 12. FRITZ OSTERMUELLER
- ☐ 14. JACK KRAMER

ST. LOUIS CARDINALS

NO CARDS ISSUED

WASHINGTON SENATORS

- ☐ 16. GEORGE CASE

1939 PLAY BALL AMERICA (162) 2 1/2" X 3 1/8" BLACK & WHITE

BOSTON BEES

- ☐ 49. EDDIE MILLER
- ☐ 57. BUDDY HASSETT
- ☐ 61. TONY CUCCINELLO
- ☐ 69. ELBIE FLETCHER
- ☐ 70. FRED FRANKHOUSE
- ☐ 72. DEBS GARMS
- ☐ 85. JOHN COONEY
- ☐ 87. MILBURN SHOFFNER
- ☐ 120. RABBIT WARSTLER
- ☐ 121. BILL POSEDEL
- ☐ 149. MAX WEST
- ☐ 155. JIM OUTLAW

BOSTON RED SOX

- ☐ 4. ELDEN AUKER
- ☐ 7. BOBBY DOERR
- ☐ 14. JIM TABOR
- ☐ 16. JOHN PEACOCK
- ☐ 17. EMERSON DICKMAN
- ☐ 20. JOE HEVING
- ☐ 27. FRED OSTERMUELLER
- ☐ 29. JACK WILSON
- ☐ 40. JIM BAGBY
- ☐ 62. TOM CAREY
- ☐ 92. TED WILLIAMS
- ☐ 101. ROGER CRAMER
- ☐ 103. MOE BERG
- ☐ 107. JOE VOSMIK
- ☐ 116. GENE DESAUTELS

BROOKLYN DODGERS

- ☐ 6. LEO DUROCHER(M)
- ☐ 13. LUKE HAMLIN
- ☐ 68. FRED SINGTON
- ☐ 74. COOKIE LAVAGETTO
- ☐ 76. GOODY ROSEN
- ☐ 86. DOLPH CAMILLI
- ☐ 95. WHIT WYATT
- ☐ 96. BABE PHELPS
- ☐ 110. FRED FITZSIMMONS
- ☐ 111. VAN LINGLE MUNGO
- ☐ 134. FORREST PRESSNELL
- ☐ 139. VITO TAMULIS
- ☐ 140. RAY HAYWORTH
- ☐ 141. PETE COSCARART
- ☐ 142. IRA HUTCHINSON
- ☐ 151. HUGH CASEY
- ☐ 154. JOHN HUDSON
- ☐ 159. RED EVANS
- ☐ 160. GENE MOORE

CHICAGO CUBS

NO CARDS ISSUED

CHICAGO WHITE SOX

- ☐ 91. JOHN KNOTT
- ☐ 105. ERIC MCNAIR

CINCINNATI REDS

- ☐ 2. LEE GRISSOM
- ☐ 15. PAUL DERRINGER
- ☐ 22. BUCKY WALTERS
- ☐ 36. FRANK MCCORMICK
- ☐ 38. BILL MYERS
- ☐ 65. HARRY CRAFT
- ☐ 67. ED JOOST
- ☐ 75. STAN BORDAGARAY
- ☐ 77. LEW RIGGS
- ☐ 99. WALLY BERGER
- ☐ 119. BILL HERSHBERGER
- ☐ 123. RAY DAVIS
- ☐ 161. LONNIE FREY
- ☐ 162. WHITEY MOORE

CLEVELAND INDIANS

- ☐ 5. LUKE SEWELL
- ☐ 78. JAKE SOLTERS
- ☐ 143. EARL AVERILL
- ☐ 152. ROY WEATHERLY

DETROIT TIGERS

- ☐ 50. CHARLIE GEHRINGER
- ☐ 56. HANK GREENBERG
- ☐ 60. SCHOOLBOY ROWE
- ☐ 80. PETE FOX
- ☐ 104. TOM BRIDGES
- ☐ 115. RALPH KRESS
- ☐ 136. ROY BELL
- ☐ 147. GEORGE COFFMAN
- ☐ 150. JIM WALKUP
- ☐ 153. DIZZY TROUT
- ☐ 158. BUD THOMAS

NEW YORK GIANTS

- ☐ 18. HARRY DANNING
- ☐ 23. BURGESS WHITEHEAD
- ☐ 24. RICHARD COFFMAN
- ☐ 32. BOB SEEDS
- ☐ 34. FRANK DEMAREE
- ☐ 35. BILL JURGES
- ☐ 51. MEL OTT
- ☐ 53. CARL HUBBELL
- ☐ 54. HARRY GUMBERT
- ☐ 58. LOU CHIOZZA
- ☐ 66. JIM RIPPLE
- ☐ 73. HAL SCHUMACHER
- ☐ 79. JOJO MOORE
- ☐ 124. WALTER BROWN
- ☐ 125. CLIFF MELTON
- ☐ 144. ZEKE BONURA

NEW YORK YANKEES

- ☐ 1. JAKE POWELL
- ☐ 3. RED RUFFING
- ☐ 25. GEORGE SELKIRK
- ☐ 26. JOE DIMAGGIO
- ☐ 30. BILL DICKEY
- ☐ 42. ARNDT JORGENS
- ☐ 48. LEFTY GOMEZ
- ☐ 52. TOMMY HENRICH
- ☐ 71. MONTE PEARSON
- ☐ 81. BABE DAHLGREN
- ☐ 88. CHARLIE KELLER

PHILADELPHIA PHILLIES

- ☐ 12. HERSHEL MARTIN
- ☐ 28. SYLVESTER JOHNSON
- ☐ 33. DEL YOUNG
- ☐ 37. VIRGIL DAVIS
- ☐ 45. MERRILL MAY
- ☐ 46. MORRIS ARNOVICH
- ☐ 63. EMMETT MUELLER
- ☐ 82. CHUCK KLEIN(F)
- ☐ 98. PINKEY WHITNEY
- ☐ 127. GIL BRACK
- ☐ 145. HUGH MULCAHY

PHILADELPHIA ATHLETCS

- ☐ 8. HENRY PIPPEN
- ☐ 64. WALLY MOSES
- ☐ 84. SKEETER NEWSOME
- ☐ 97. BOB JOHNSON
- ☐ 108. FRANK HAYES
- ☐ 117. WAYNE AMBLER
- ☐ 118. LYNN NELSON

PITTSBURGH PIRATES

- ☐ 9. JIM TOBIN
- ☐ 11. JOHN RIZZO
- ☐ 55. ARKIE VAUGHAN
- ☐ 82. CHUCK KLEIN(B)
- ☐ 83. GUS SUHR
- ☐ 89. LLOYD WANER
- ☐ 90. BOB KLINGER
- ☐ 94. HEINIE MANUSH
- ☐ 102. PEP YOUNG
- ☐ 112. PAUL WANER
- ☐ 128. JOE BOWMAN
- ☐ 129. BILL SWIFT
- ☐ 130. BILL BRUBAKER
- ☐ 156. RAY BERRES

ST. LOUIS BROWNS

- ☐ 43. MELO ALMADA
- ☐ 44. DON HEFFNER
- ☐ 109. MYRIL HOAG
- ☐ 122. GEORGE MCQUINN
- ☐ 148. BILL TROTTER

ST. LOUIS CARDINALS

- ☐ 19. DAFFY DEAN
- ☐ 41. LON WARNEKE
- ☐ 131. MORT COOPER

□ 132. JIM BROWN
□ 133. LYNN MYERS
□ 135. MICKEY OWEN
□ 146. TOM SUNKEL
□ 157. DON PADGETT

WASHINGTON SENATORS

□ 10. JIM DESHONG
□ 21. DUTCH LEONARD
□ 31. SAM WEST
□ 39. RICK FERRELL
□ 47. BUDDY LEWIS
□ 59. KEN CHASE
□ 93. CHARLIE GELBERT
□ 100. BUDDY MYER
□ 114. CECIL TRAVIS
□ 137. PETE APPLETON
□ 138. GEORGE CASE

1940 PLAY BALL (240)
2 1/2" X 3 1/8"
BLACK & WHITE

BOSTON BEES

□ 56. EDDIE MILLER
□ 57. MAX WEST
□ 58. BILL POSEDEL
□ 59. RABBITT WARTSLER
□ 60. JOHN COONEY
□ 61. TONY CUCCINELLO
□ 62. BUDDY HASSETT
□ 140. DICK COFFMAN
□ 141. CASEY STENGEL(M)
□ 142. GEORGE KELLY(C)
□ 143. GENE MOORE(B)

BOSTON RED SOX

□ 27. TED WILLIAMS
□ 28. GENE DESAUTELS
□ 29. ROGER CRAMER
□ 30. MOE BERG(C)
□ 31. JACK WILSON
□ 32. JIM BAGBY
□ 33. FRED OSTERMUELLER
□ 34. JOHN PEACOCK
□ 35. JOE HEVING
□ 36. JIM TABOR
□ 37. EMERSON DICKMAN
□ 38. BOBBY DOERR
□ 39. TOM CAREY
□ 133. JIMMIE FOXX
□ 134. JOE CRONIN(M)
□ 196. LEO NONNENKAMP
□ 197. LOU FINNEY
□ 198. DENNY GALEHOUSE

BROOKLYN DODGERS

□ 63. PETE COSCARART
□ 64. VAN LINGO MUNGO
□ 65. FRED FITZSIMMONS
□ 66. BABE PHELPS
□ 67. WHIT WYATT
□ 68. DOLPH CAMILLI
□ 69. COOKIE LAVAGETTO
□ 70. LUKE HAMLIN
□ 71. MELO ALMADA
□ 72. CHUCK DRESSEN(C)
□ 143. GENE MOORE(F)
□ 144. JOE VOSMIK
□ 145. VITO TAMULIS
□ 146. FORREST PRESSNELL
□ 147. JOHN HUDSON
□ 148. HUGH CASEY
□ 207. GUS MANCUSO

CHICAGO CUBS

□ 239. GEORGE UHLE(C)

CHICAGO WHITE SOX

□ 13. JOHN KNOTT
□ 14. ERIC MCNAIR
□ 126. JAKE SOLTERS
□ 127. MUDDY RUEL(C)
□ 128. PETE APPLETON
□ 184. MULE HAAS(C)
□ 185. JOE JUHEL
□ 186. TAFT WRIGHT
□ 187. JIMMY DYKES(M)

CINCINNATI REDS

□ 73. BUCKY WALTERS
□ 74. PAUL DERRINGER
□ 75. FRANK MCCORMICK
□ 76. LONNIE FREY
□ 77. BILL HERSHBERGER
□ 78. LEW RIGGS
□ 79. HARRY CRAFT
□ 80. BILL MYERS
□ 81. WALLY BERGER
□ 82. HANK GOWDY(C)
□ 149. MILBURN SHOFFNER
□ 150. WHITEY MOORE
□ 151. ED JOOST
□ 152. JIMMY WILSON(C)
□ 153. BILL MCKECHNIE(M)
□ 208. LEE GAMBLE

CLEVELAND INDIANS

□ 47. OSCAR VITT(M)
□ 48. LUKE SEWELL(C)
□ 49. ROY WEATHERLY
□ 50. HAL TROSKY
□ 138. BEAU BELL
□ 202. AL MILNAR
□ 203. ODELL HALE
□ 204. HARRY EISENSTAT
□ 205. ROLLIE HEMSLEY

DETROIT TIGERS

□ 40. HANK GREENBERG
□ 41. CHARLIE GEHRINGER
□ 42. BUD THOMAS
□ 43. PETE FOX
□ 44. DIZZY TROUT
□ 45. RALPH KRESS
□ 46. EARL AVERILL
□ 135. LYNN NELSON
□ 136. COTTON PIPPEN
□ 137. BING MILLER(C)
□ 199. PINKY HIGGINS
□ 200. BRUCE CAMPBELL
□ 201. BARNEY MCCOSKY

NEW YORK GIANTS

□ 83. CLIFF MELTON
□ 84. JOJO MOORE
□ 85. HAL SCHUMACHER
□ 86. HARRY GUMBERT
□ 87. CARL HUBBELL
□ 88. MEL OTT
□ 89. BILL JURGES
□ 90. FRANK DEMAREE
□ 91. BOB SEEDS
□ 92. BURGESS WHITEHEAD
□ 93. HARRY DANNING
□ 154. WALTER BROWN
□ 155. RAY HAYWORTH
□ 156. DAFFY DEAN
□ 157. LOU CHIOZZA
□ 158. TRAVIS JACKSON(C)
□ 159. FRANK SNYDER(C)
□ 209. HY VANDENBERG
□ 210. BILL LOHRMAN
□ 211. ROY JOINER
□ 212. BABE YOUNG
□ 213. JOHN RUCKER
□ 214. KEN O'DEA
□ 215. JOHNNIE MCCARTHY

NEW YORK YANKEES

□ 1. JOE DIMAGGIO
□ 2. ARNDT JORGENS
□ 3. BABE DAHLGREN
□ 4. TOMMY HENRICH
□ 5. MONTE PEARSON
□ 6. LEFTY GOMEZ
□ 7. BILL DICKEY
□ 8. GEORGE SELKIRK
□ 9. CHARLIE KELLER
□ 10. RED RUFFING
□ 11. JAKE POWELL
□ 12. JOHNNY SCHULTE(C)
□ 121. ATLEY DONALD
□ 122. STEVE SUNDRA
□ 123. ORAL HILDEBRAND
□ 124. EARLE COMBS(C)
□ 125. ART FLETCHER(C)
□ 181. SPUD CHANDLER
□ 182. BILL KNICKERBOCKER
□ 183. MARVIN BREUER

PHILADELPHIA ATHLETICS

□ 24. FRANK HAYES
□ 25. BOB JOHNSON
□ 26. WALLY MOSES
□ 132. CONNIE MACK(M)
□ 190. CHARLEY BERRY(C)
□ 191. JOHNNY BABICH
□ 192. DICK SIEBERT
□ 193. CHUBBY DEAN
□ 194. SAM CHAPMAN
□ 195. DEE MILES

PHILADELPHIA PHILLIES

□ 94. GUS SUHR
□ 95. HUGH MULCAHY
□ 96. EMMETT MUELLER
□ 97. MORRIS ARNOVICH
□ 98. MERRILL MAY
□ 99. SYLVESTER JOHNSON
□ 100. HERSHEL MARTIN
□ 101. DEL YOUNG
□ 102. CHUCK KLEIN
□ 160. HANS LOBERT(C)
□ 216. JOE MARTY

- ☐ 217. WALTER BECK
- ☐ 218. WALTER MILLIES
- ☐ 240. BILL ATWOOD

PITTSBURGH PIRATES

- ☐ 103. ELBIE FLETCHER
- ☐ 104. PAUL WANER
- ☐ 105. LLOYD WANER
- ☐ 106. PEP YOUNG
- ☐ 107. ARKY VAUGHAN
- ☐ 108. JOHN RIZZO
- ☐ 161. DEBS GARMS
- ☐ 162. JOE BOWMAN
- ☐ 163. SPUD DAVIS
- ☐ 164. RAY BERRES
- ☐ 165. BOB KLINGER
- ☐ 166. BILL BRUBAKER
- ☐ 167. FRANK FRISCH(M)
- ☐ 168. HONUS WAGNER(C)
- ☐ 219. RUSS BAUERS
- ☐ 220. MACE BROWN
- ☐ 221. LEE HANDLEY
- ☐ 222. MAX BUTCHER

ST. LOUIS BROWNS

- ☐ 51. DON HEFFNER
- ☐ 52. MYRIL HOAG
- ☐ 53. GEORGE MCQUINN
- ☐ 54. BILL TROTTER
- ☐ 55. GEORGE COFFMAN
- ☐ 139. ELDEN AUKER
- ☐ 206. CHET LAABS

ST. LOUIS CARDINALS

- ☐ 109. DON PADGETT
- ☐ 110. TOM SUNKEL
- ☐ 111. MICKEY OWEN
- ☐ 112. JIM BROWN
- ☐ 113. MORT COOPER
- ☐ 114. LON WARNEKE
- ☐ 115. MIKE GONZALES(C)

WASHINGTON SENATORS

- ☐ 15. GEORGE CASE
- ☐ 16. CECIL TRAVIS
- ☐ 17. BUDDY MYER
- ☐ 18. CHARLIE GELBERT
- ☐ 19. KEN CHASE
- ☐ 20. BUDDY LEWIS
- ☐ 21. RICK FERRELL
- ☐ 22. SAM WEST
- ☐ 23. DUTCH LEONARD
- ☐ 129. BUCKY HARRIS(M)
- ☐ 130. CLYDE MILAN(C)
- ☐ 131. ZEKE BONURA
- ☐ 188. JOE KRAKAUSKAS
- ☐ 189. JIM BLOODWORTH

1941 PLAY BALL SPORTS HALL OF FAME (72) 2 1/2" X 3 1/8"

BARNEY McCOSKY

BOSTON BRAVES

- ☐ 1. EDDIE MILLER*
- ☐ 2. MAX WEST*
- ☐ 25. GENE MOORE

* Nos. 1 and 2 appear with Boston Bees on the back of the card.

- ☐ 49. BABE DAHLGREN
- ☐ 50. JOHN COONEY
- ☐ 58. FRANK DEMAREE

BOSTON RED SOX

- ☐ 13. JIMMIE FOXX
- ☐ 14. TED WILLIAMS
- ☐ 15. JOE CRONIN(M)
- ☐ 29. JACK WILSON
- ☐ 30. LOU FINNEY
- ☐ 63. DOM DIMAGGIO
- ☐ 64. BOBBY DOERR

BROOKLYN DODGERS

- ☐ 51. DOLPH CAMILLI
- ☐ 52. KIRBY HIGBE
- ☐ 53. LUKE HAMLIN
- ☐ 54. PEE WEE REESE
- ☐ 55. WHIT WYATT

CHICAGO CUBS

NO CARDS ISSUED

CHICAGO WHITE SOX

- ☐ 31. JOE KUHEL
- ☐ 32. TAFT WRIGHT

CLEVELAND INDIANS

- ☐ 16. HAL TROSKY
- ☐ 17. ROY WEATHERLY
- ☐ 33. AL MILNAR
- ☐ 34. ROLLIE HEMSLEY

DETROIT TIGERS

- ☐ 18. HANK GREENBERG
- ☐ 19. CHARLIE GEHRINGER
- ☐ 35. PINKY HIGGINS
- ☐ 36. BARNEY MCCOSKY
- ☐ 37. BRUCE CAMPBELL
- ☐ 65. TOMMY BRIDGES

CARL HUBBELL

NEW YORK GIANTS

- ☐ 6. CARL HUBBELL
- ☐ 7. HARRY DANNING
- ☐ 8. MEL OTT
- ☐ 26. HARRY GUMBERT
- ☐ 27. BABE YOUNG
- ☐ 57. MORRIS ARNOVICH
- ☐ 59. BILL JURGES

NEW YORK YANKEES

- ☐ 20. RED RUFFING
- ☐ 21. CHARLIE KELLER
- ☐ 38. ATLEY DONALD
- ☐ 39. TOMMY HENRICH
- ☐ 70. BILL DICKEY
- ☐ 71. JOE DIMAGGIO
- ☐ 72. LEFTY GOMEZ

PHILADELPHIA ATHLETICS

- ☐ 22. BOB JOHNSON
- ☐ 40. JOHN BABICH
- ☐ 41. FRANK HAYES
- ☐ 42. WALLY MOSES
- ☐ 43. AL BRANCATO
- ☐ 44. SAM CHAPMAN
- ☐ 68. JOHN KNOTT

"PINKY" MAY

PHILADELPHIA PHILLIES

- ☐ 9. MERRILL MAY
- ☐ 28. JOE MARTY
- ☐ 60. CHUCK KLEIN

PITTSBURGH PIRATES

- ☐ 10. ARKY VAUGHAN
- ☐ 11. DEBS GARMS
- ☐ 61. VINCE DIMAGGIO
- ☐ 62. ELBIE FLETCHER

ST. LOUIS BROWNS

- ☐ 23. GEORGE MCQUINN
- ☐ 45. ELDEN AUKER
- ☐ 66. HARLAND CLIFT
- ☐ 67. WALT JUDNICH

ST. LOUIS CARDINALS

- ☐ 12. JIM BROWN

WASHINGTON SENATORS

- ☐ 24. DUTCH LEONARD
- ☐ 46. SID HUDSON
- ☐ 47. BUDDY LEWIS
- ☐ 48. CECIL TRAVIS*
- ☐ 69. GEORGE CASE

1988 SCORE (660)
2 1/2 X 3 1/2

ATLANTA BRAVES

- □ 111. GLENN HUBBARD
- □ 129. OZZIE VIRGIL
- □ 136. GERALD PERRY
- □ 148. ALBERT HALL
- □ 245. KEN OBERKFELL
- □ 285. TED SIMMONS
- □ 299. ANDRES THOMAS
- □ 319. RICK MAHLER
- □ 379. ED OLWINE
- □ 390. KEN GRIFFEY
- □ 395. DION JAMES
- □ 410. ZANE SMITH
- □ 423. BRUCE BENEDICT
- □ 426. RAFAEL RAMIREZ
- □ 440. GRAIG NETTLES
- □ 450. DALE MURPHY
- □ 454. CHARLIE PULEO
- □ 457. DAVID PALMER
- □ 482. GARY ROENICKE
- □ 498. JEFF DEDMON
- □ 542. JOE BOEVER
- □ 555. PHIL NIEKRO
- □ 562. JEFF BLAUSER
- □ 576. JIM ACKER
- □ 638. TOM GLAVINE
- □ 647. RON GANT

BALTIMORE ORIOLES

- □ 18. EDDIE MURRAY
- □ 42. FRED LYNN
- □ 58. KEN GERHART
- □ 67. MIKE BODDICKER
- □ 96. RAY KNIGHT
- □ 101. ERIC BELL
- □ 103. DAVE SCHMIDT
- □ 123. TERRY KENNEDY
- □ 173. LEE LACY
- □ 200. BILL RIPKEN
- □ 219. LARRY SHEETS
- □ 229. JIM DWYER
- □ 261. TOM NIEDENFUER
- □ 291. ALAN WIGGINS
- □ 315. SCOTT MCGREGOR
- □ 353. JOHN HABYAN
- □ 359. FLOYD RAYFORD
- □ 393. MIKE YOUNG
- □ 411. KEN DIXON
- □ 427. MIKE FLANAGAN (F)
- □ 434. JACK O'CONNOR
- □ 518. DON AASE
- □ 550. CAL RIPKEN
- □ 628. PETE STANICEK

BOSTON RED SOX

- □ 2. WADE BOGGS
- □ 14. JIM RICE
- □ 65. DWIGHT EVANS
- □ 110. ROGER CLEMENS
- □ 121. DENNIS BOYD
- □ 155. MARTY BARRETT
- □ 175. MIKE GREENWELL
- □ 201. SAME HORN
- □ 218. CALVIN SCHIRALDI
- □ 228. DAVE HENDERSON (F)
- □ 241. RICH GEDMAN
- □ 250. DON BAYLOR (F)
- □ 259. ED ROMERO
- □ 271. MARC SULLIVAN
- □ 289. STEVE CRAWFORD
- □ 300. BOB STANLEY
- □ 314. JOE SAMBITO
- □ 352. PAT DODSON
- □ 372. SPIKE OWEN
- □ 380. BRUCE HURST
- □ 403. ROB WOODWARD
- □ 472. ELLIS BURKS
- □ 527. AL NIPPER
- □ 541. JEFF SELLERS
- □ 546. TODD BENZINGER
- □ 584. JOHN MARZANO
- □ 625. JODY REED
- □ 644. KEVIN ROMINE

CALIFORNIA ANGELS

- □ 7. WALLY JOYNER
- □ 44. BRIAN DOWNING
- □ 63. BOB BOONE
- □ 81. MIKE WITT
- □ 105. DON SUTTON
- □ 124. JACK HOWELL
- □ 152. MARK MCLEMORE
- □ 176. GREG MINTON
- □ 195. DONNIE MOORE
- □ 212. DEVON WHITE
- □ 239. DOUG DECINCES
- □ 254. JOHNNY RAY
- □ 255. GARY PETTIS
- □ 270. JERRY REUSS
- □ 274. DICK SCHOFIELD
- □ 293. JOHN CANDELARIA
- □ 308. GEORGE HENDRICK
- □ 333. RUPPERT JONES
- □ 341. GUS POLIDOR
- □ 355. BUTCH WYNEGAR
- □ 376. DEWAYNE BUICE
- □ 394. WILLIE FRASER
- □ 437. JACK LAZORKO
- □ 463. DARRELL MILLER
- □ 487. TONY ARMAS
- □ 552. KIRK MCCASKILL
- □ 591. BILL BUCKNER

CHICAGO CUBS

- □ 4. ANDRE DAWSON
- □ 26. RYNE SANDBERG
- □ 31. LEE SMITH
- □ 50. RICK SUTCLIFFE
- □ 71. KEITH MORELAND
- □ 186. RAFAEL PALMEIRO
- □ 205. BRIAN DAYETT
- □ 223. DAVE MARTINEZ
- □ 244. JIM SUNDBERG
- □ 329. PAUL NOCE
- □ 378. LEON DURHAM
- □ 413. FRANK DIPINO
- □ 451. BOB DERNIER
- □ 467. JERRY MUMPHREY
- □ 506. ED LYNCH
- □ 524. MANNY TRILLO
- □ 529. SHAWON DUNSTON
- □ 544. SCOTT SANDERSON
- □ 551. JODY DAVIS
- □ 573. JAMIE MOYER
- □ 602. LES LANCASTER

CHICAGO WHITE SOX

- □ 93. GREG WALKER
- □ 112. KEN WILLIAMS
- □ 139. FRED MANRIQUE
- □ 307. BOBBY THIGPEN
- □ 374. RON KARKOVICE
- □ 443. GARY REDUS
- □ 462. JIM WINN
- □ 480. RICHARD DOTSON
- □ 508. JOSE DELEON
- □ 539. BILL LONG
- □ 572. DONNIE HILL
- □ 582. DARYL BOSTON
- □ 589. DAVE LAPOINT
- □ 590. HAROLD BAINES
- □ 592. CARLTON FISK
- □ 603. OZZIE GUILLEN
- □ 607. IVAN CALDERON
- □ 622. FLOYD BANNISTER

CINNINNATI REDS

- □ 10. ERIC DAVIS
- □ 17. DAVE PARKER
- □ 72. BARRY LARKIN
- □ 86. KAL DANIELS
- □ 99. BUDDY BELL
- □ 132. TOM BROWNING
- □ 163. NICK ESASKY
- □ 183. RON OESTER
- □ 206. BO DIAZ
- □ 210. DAVE CONCEPCION
- □ 221. KURT STILLWELL
- □ 242. TED POWER
- □ 281. TERRY MCGRIFF
- □ 297. TERRY FRANCONA
- □ 304. PAUL O'NEILL
- □ 317. FRANK WILLIAMS
- □ 326. TRACY JONES
- □ 371. DAVE COLLINS
- □ 476. RON ROBINSON
- □ 494. TOM HUME (B)
- □ 497. JEFF MONTGOMERY
- □ 535. JOHN FRANCO
- □ 557. PAT PERRY
- □ 559. ROB MURPHY
- □ 560. DENNIS RASMUSSEN
- □ 609. GUY HOFFMAN
- □ 646. JEFF TREADWAY

CLEVELAND INDIANS

- □ 23. PAT TABLER
- □ 39. BROOK JACOBY
- □ 60. JULIO FRANCO
- □ 80. JOE CARTER
- □ 92. CORY SNYDER
- □ 122. BRETT BUTLER
- □ 154. GREG SWINDELL
- □ 172. CHRIS BANDO
- □ 231. ANDRE THORNTON
- □ 262. RICK DEMPSEY
- □ 441. MEL HALL
- □ 484. RICH YETT
- □ 567. TOMMY HINZO
- □ 574. KEN SCHROM
- □ 581. CARMEN CASTILLO
- □ 586. ANDY ALLANSON
- □ 594. DOUG JONES
- □ 595. TOM CANDIOTTI
- □ 620. JOHN FARRELL
- □ 623. DARRELL AKERFELDS
- □ 633. DAVE CLARK

DETROIT TIGERS

- □ 15. MATT NOKES
- □ 37. ALAN TRAMMELL
- □ 56. LOU WHITAKER
- □ 75. DARRELL EVANS
- □ 119. CHET LEMON
- □ 138. LARRY HERNDON
- □ 156. MIKE HEATH
- □ 171. PAT SHERIDAN
- □ 199. JOHN GRUBB
- □ 217. DAVE BERGMAN
- □ 233. TOM BROOKENS
- □ 272. JIM MORRISON
- □ 382. MARK THURMOND
- □ 445. BILL MADLOCK
- □ 461. DAN PETRY
- □ 471. ERIC KING
- □ 490. FRANK TANANA
- □ 507. WILLIE HERNANDEZ
- □ 620. MIKE HENNEMAN
- □ 525. KIRK GIBSON
- □ 538. WALT TERRELL
- □ 545. JACK MORRIS
- □ 549. JEFF ROBINSON
- □ 571. JIM WALEWANDER
- □ 610. DOYLE ALEXANDER

HOUSTON ASTROS

- □ 28. JOSE CRUZ
- □ 33. KEVIN BASS
- □ 52. BILL DORAN
- □ 73. ALAN ASHBY
- □ 133. LARRY ANDERSEN

- □ 145. DENNIS WALLING
- □ 164. KEN CAMINITI
- □ 184. DANNY DARWIN
- □ 207. CRAIG REYNOLDS
- □ 222. CHUCK JACKSON
- □ 243. DAVE MEADS
- □ 282. TERRY PUHL
- □ 335. MIKE SCOTT
- □ 344. BOB KNEPPER
- □ 354. JIM DESHAIES
- □ 365. DAVE SMITH
- □ 383. BUDDY BIANCALANA
- □ 442. GERALD YOUNG
- □ 460. GLENN DAVIS
- □ 479. CHARLIE KERFELD
- □ 489. DAVEY LOPES
- □ 496. ROBBIE WINE
- □ 505. BILLY HATCHER
- □ 558. JUAN AGOSTO
- □ 575. NOLAN RYAN

KANSAS CITY ROYALS

- □ 6. KEVIN SEITZER
- □ 11. GEORGE BRETT
- □ 61. CHARLIE LEIBRANDT
- □ 79. FRANK WHITE
- □ 89. BRET SABERHAGEN
- □ 102. WILLIE WILSON
- □ 106. DANNY TARTABULL
- □ 180. BO JACKSON
- □ 230. LARRY OWEN
- □ 263. LONNIE SMITH
- □ 273. STEVE BALBONI
- □ 290. DAN QUISENBERRY
- □ 313. BUD BLACK
- □ 330. ANGEL SALAZAR
- □ 343. JERRY DON GLEATON
- □ 377. BILL PECOTA
- □ 398. DANNY JACKSON
- □ 456. JIM EISENREICH
- □ 466. STEVE FARR
- □ 516. MARK GUBICZA
- □ 565. GENE GARBER
- □ 569. ED HEARN
- □ 577. JAMIE QUIRK
- □ 598. ROSS JONES
- □ 631. GARY THURMAN
- □ 636. JOHN DAVIS

LOS ANGELES DODGERS

- □ 9. PEDRO GUERRERO
- □ 35. STEVE SAX
- □ 53. MIKE SCIOSCIA
- □ 87. RICK HONEYCUTT (F)
- □ 135. MIKE MARSHALL
- □ 147. FRANKLIN STUBBS
- □ 166. DAVE ANDERSON
- □ 182. ALEX TREVINO
- □ 208. BRIAN HOLTON
- □ 224. TIM LEARY
- □ 247. KEN LANDREAUX
- □ 267. MIKE RAMSEY
- □ 286. JOHN SHELBY
- □ 298. MICKEY HATCHER
- □ 321. MARIANO DUNCAN
- □ 357. MATT YOUNG
- □ 364. JOSE GONZALEZ
- □ 406. KEN HOWELL
- □ 417. DANNY HEEP
- □ 424. LEN MATUSZEK
- □ 431. PHIL GARNER
- □ 470. OREL HERSHISER
- □ 510. BOB WELCH
- □ 600. FERNANDO VALENZUELA
- □ 612. SHAWN HILLEGAS
- □ 637. MIKE DEVEREAUX
- □ 640. CHRIS GWYNN
- □ 641. TIM CREWS

MILWAUKEE BREWERS

- □ 22. B. J. SURHOFF
- □ 38. CHRIS BOSIO
- □ 59. GLENN BRAGGS
- □ 77. DAN PLESAC
- □ 95. ROB DEER
- □ 120. DALE SVEUM
- □ 160. ROBIN YOUNT
- □ 169. CECIL COOPER
- □ 197. JIM GANTNER
- □ 234. GREG BROCK
- □ 280. TEDDY HIGUERA
- □ 296. BILL WEGMAN
- □ 311. BILL SCHROEDER
- □ 334. BILLY JO ROBIDOUX
- □ 340. PAUL MOLITOR
- □ 349. ERNEST RILES
- □ 369. MIKE BIRKBECK
- □ 388. MIKE FELDER
- □ 402. CHUCK CRIM
- □ 429. JUAN CASTILLO
- □ 446. MARK CLEAR
- □ 513. JUAN NIEVES
- □ 578. JAY ALDRICH
- □ 593. RICK MANNING
- □ 630. STEVE KIEFER

MINNESOTA TWINS

- □ 24. KIRBY PUCKETT
- □ 43. KENT HRBEK
- □ 62. GARY GAETTI
- □ 90. BERT BLYLEVEN
- □ 91. JEFF REARDON
- □ 108. LES STRAKER
- □ 153. TOM LAUDNER
- □ 174. STEVE LOMBARDOZZI
- □ 194. TOM BRUNANSKY
- □ 214. GREG GAGNE
- □ 237. JOE NIEKRO
- □ 250. DON BAYLOR (B)
- □ 252. AL NEWMAN
- □ 276. GENE LARKIN
- □ 292. RANDY BUSH
- □ 324. DAN GLADDEN
- □ 332. GEORGE FRAZIER
- □ 361. SAL BUTERA
- □ 475. FRANK VIOLA
- □ 570. MARK DAVIDSOÑ
- □ 606. ROY SMALLEY
- □ 613. KEITH ATHERTON

MONTREAL EXPOS

- □ 3. TIM RAINES
- □ 19. ANDRES GALARRAGA
- □ 70. TIM WALLACH
- □ 85. VANCE LAW
- □ 97. CASEY CANDAELE
- □ 142. HERM WINNINGHAM
- □ 159. TOM FOLEY
- □ 187. TIM BURKE
- □ 305. HUBIE BROOKS
- □ 318. MIKE FITZGERALD
- □ 327. FLOYD YOUMANS
- □ 337. BOB SEBRA
- □ 345. MITCH WEBSTER
- □ 356. BRYN SMITH
- □ 366. ANDY MCGAFFIGAN
- □ 381. BOB MCCLURE
- □ 397. RANDY ST. CLAIRE
- □ 408. JEFF REED
- □ 430. NEAL HEATON
- □ 433. WALLACE JOHNSON
- □ 459. PASCUAL PEREZ
- □ 601. DENNIS MARTINEZ
- □ 608. JAY TIBBS
- □ 617. DAVE ENGLE

OAKLAND A'S

- □ 5. MARK MCGWIRE
- □ 45. JOSE CANSECO
- □ 64. LUIS POLONIA
- □ 82. TERRY STEINBACH
- □ 87. RICK HONEYCUTT (B)
- □ 88. ALFREDO GRIFFIN
- □ 104. DENNIS ECKERSLEY
- □ 125. CURT YOUNG
- □ 177. MOOSE HAAS
- □ 193. JOAQUIN ANDUJAR
- □ 211. MIKE DAVIS
- □ 253. CARNEY LANSFORD
- □ 269. MICKEY TETTLETON
- □ 294. TONY PHILLIPS
- □ 348. DAVE LEIPER (F)
- □ 367. STAN JAVIER
- □ 392. JOSE RIJO
- □ 428. MIKE GALLEGO
- □ 455. DWAYNE MURPHY
- □ 458. DAVE STEWART
- □ 504. REGGIE JACKSON
- □ 511. STEVE ONTIVEROS
- □ 522. JAY HOWELL
- □ 547. STEVE HENDERSON
- □ 588. GENE NELSON
- □ 604. TONY BERNAZARD
- □ 614. ERIC PLUNK
- □ 616. DENNIS LAMP

PHILADELPHIA PHILLIES

- □ 16. MIKE SCHMIDT
- □ 32. JUAN SAMUEL
- □ 115. MILT THOMPSON
- □ 131. LANCE PARRISH
- □ 144. MIKE JACKSON
- □ 161. STEVE BEDROSIAN
- □ 375. SHANE RAWLEY
- □ 386. GREG GROSS
- □ 401. DAN CARMAN
- □ 405. GLENN WILSON
- □ 409. CHRIS JAMES
- □ 425. KENT TEKULVE
- □ 435. STEVE JELTZ
- □ 448. RICK SCHU
- □ 468. KEVIN GROSS
- □ 473. DARREN DAULTON
- □ 492. BRUCE RUFFIN
- □ 494. TOM HUME (F)
- □ 499. LUIS AGUAYO
- □ 515. VON HAYES
- □ 526. WALLY RITCHIE
- □ 566. RON ROENICKE
- □ 635. KEITH HUGHES

PITTSBURGH PIRATES

- □ 34. R. J. REYNOLDS
- □ 51. DOUG DRABEK
- □ 116. BOBBY BONILLA
- □ 130. BRIAN FISHER
- □ 143. MIKE DIAZ
- □ 162. BOB WALK
- □ 260. SID BREAM
- □ 265. BARRY BONDS
- □ 287. JOHN SMILEY
- □ 301. AL PEDRIQUE
- □ 320. JIM GOTT
- □ 404. JUNIOR ORTIZ
- □ 416. ANDY VAN SLYKE
- □ 418. JOHN CANGELOSI
- □ 421. MIKE LAVALLIERE
- □ 432. MIKE DUNNE
- □ 439. JEFF ROBINSON
- □ 453. RAFAEL BELLIARD
- □ 554. DARNELL COLES
- □ 597. JOSE LIND
- □ 611. MIKE BIELECKI
- □ 642. MACKEY SASSER
- □ 643. VINCENTE PALACIOS

NEW YORK METS

- □ 21. KEVIN MCREYNOLDS
- □ 41. DAVE MAGADAN
- □ 49. DAVID CONE
- □ 69. HOWARD JOHNSON
- □ 128. TIM TEUFEL
- □ 141. RON DARLING
- □ 158. LEE MAZZILLI
- □ 188. ROGER MCDOWELL
- □ 203. TERRY LEACH
- □ 227. DOUG SISK

- ☐ 249. JOHN MITCHELL
- ☐ 303. WALLY BACKMAN
- ☐ 316. RAFAEL SANTANA
- ☐ 325. GARY CARTER
- ☐ 336. RANDY MYERS
- ☐ 350. DWIGHT GOODEN
- ☐ 360. DARRYL STRAWBERRY
- ☐ 370. LEN DYKSTRA
- ☐ 387. BARRY LYONS
- ☐ 400. KEITH HERNANDEZ
- ☐ 474. MOOKIE WILSON
- ☐ 495. JESSE OROSCO
- ☐ 521. RICK AGUILERA
- ☐ 563. BOB OJEDA
- ☐ 615. SID FERNANDEZ
- ☐ 623. RANDY MILLIGAN
- ☐ 624. KEVIN ELSTER
- ☐ 639. KEITH MILLER
- ☐ 645. GREGG JEFFERIES

NEW YORK YANKEES

- ☐ 1. DON MATTINGLY
- ☐ 13. RICKEY HENDERSON
- ☐ 55. DAVE WINFIELD
- ☐ 74. RICK RHODEN
- ☐ 117. WAYNE TOLLESON
- ☐ 137. BOBBY MEACHAM
- ☐ 157. GARY WARD
- ☐ 170. MIKE PAGLIARULO
- ☐ 196. DAN PASQUA
- ☐ 220. MIKE EASLER
- ☐ 232. MARK SALAS
- ☐ 240. TOMMY JOHN
- ☐ 258. TIM STODDARD
- ☐ 266. WILLIE RANDOLPH
- ☐ 310. RON GUIDRY
- ☐ 342. STEVE TROUT
- ☐ 351. DAVE RIGHETTI
- ☐ 368. HENRY COTTO
- ☐ 389. PAT CLEMENTS
- ☐ 449. RON KITTLE
- ☐ 486. RICK CERONE
- ☐ 532. JOEL SKINNER
- ☐ 579. CLAUDELL WASHINGTON
- ☐ 585. BILL GULLICKSON
- ☐ 634. ROBERTO KELLY

ST. LOUIS CARDINALS

- ☐ 12. OZZIE SMITH
- ☐ 40. WILLIE MCGEE
- ☐ 48. TONY PENA
- ☐ 68. VINCE COLEMAN
- ☐ 84. TOM HERR
- ☐ 94. JOE MAGRANE
- ☐ 100. JACK CLARK
- ☐ 190. TERRY PENDLETON
- ☐ 202. TODD WORRELL
- ☐ 226. GREG MATHEWS
- ☐ 248. JOSE OQUENDO
- ☐ 264. BOB FORSCH
- ☐ 275. JOHN TUDOR
- ☐ 288. CURT FORD
- ☐ 302. JIM LINDEMAN
- ☐ 328. BILL DAWLEY
- ☐ 346. JOHN MORRIS
- ☐ 358. TOM PAGNOZZI
- ☐ 384. TIM CONROY
- ☐ 412. RICK HORTON
- ☐ 415. DANNY COX
- ☐ 517. KEN DAYLEY
- ☐ 587. LEE TUNNELL
- ☐ 596. STEVE LAKE

SAN DIEGO PADRES

- ☐ 26. BENNY SANTIAGO
- ☐ 36. JOHN KRUK
- ☐ 114. STAN JEFFERSON
- ☐ 150. LANCE MCCULLERS
- ☐ 167. ED WHITSON
- ☐ 181. CARMELO MARTINEZ
- ☐ 189. GARRY TEMPLETON
- ☐ 209. MARVELL WYNNE
- ☐ 225. STEVE GARVEY
- ☐ 246. JIMMY JONES
- ☐ 284. LUIS SALAZAR
- ☐ 331. GOOSE GOSSAGE
- ☐ 338. ERIC SHOW
- ☐ 347. ANDY HAWKINS
- ☐ 348. DAVE LEIPER (B)
- ☐ 363. CHRIS BROWN
- ☐ 385. TONY GWYNN
- ☐ 391. MARK DAVIS
- ☐ 414. SHANE MACK
- ☐ 420. JOEY CORA
- ☐ 438. KEITH COMSTOCK
- ☐ 447. GREG BOOKER
- ☐ 469. BRUCE BOCHY
- ☐ 483. TIM FLANNERY
- ☐ 512. RANDY READY
- ☐ 568. ERIC NOTLE
- ☐ 626. SHAWN ABNER

SAN FRANCISCO GIANTS

- ☐ 27. KELLY DOWNS
- ☐ 54. CANDY MALDONADO
- ☐ 78. WILL CLARK
- ☐ 118. MATT WILLIAMS
- ☐ 134. BOB BRENLY
- ☐ 146. ROBBY THOMPSON
- ☐ 165. JOSE URIBE
- ☐ 185. MIKE KRUKOW
- ☐ 228. DAVE HENDERSON (B)
- ☐ 283. MARK WASINGER
- ☐ 465. MIKE LACOSS
- ☐ 477. BOB MELVIN
- ☐ 481. KEVIN MITCHELL
- ☐ 493. CHRIS SPEIER
- ☐ 509. JOEL YOUNGBLOOD
- ☐ 519. RICK REUSCHEL
- ☐ 528. ATLEE HAMMAKER
- ☐ 533. SCOTT GARRELTS
- ☐ 548. EDDIE MILNER
- ☐ 553. CRAIG LEFFERTS
- ☐ 556. MIKE ALDRETE
- ☐ 564. DAVE DRAVECKY
- ☐ 580. JEFFREY LEONARD
- ☐ 605. CHILI DAVIS
- ☐ 618. HARRY SPILMAN
- ☐ 619. DON ROBINSON
- ☐ 627. KIRT MANWARING

SEATTLE MARINERS

- ☐ 30. MARK LANGSTON
- ☐ 46. JIM PRESLEY
- ☐ 66. PHIL BRADLEY
- ☐ 83. ALVIN DAVIS
- ☐ 126. DAVE VALLE
- ☐ 151. SCOTT BRADLEY
- ☐ 178. MIKE KINGERY
- ☐ 192. REY QUINONES
- ☐ 213. MICKEY BRANTLEY
- ☐ 238. SCOTT BANKHEAD
- ☐ 256. KEN PHELPS
- ☐ 277. HAROLD REYNOLDS
- ☐ 295. MIKE MORGAN
- ☐ 309. JOHN MOSES
- ☐ 323. LEE GUETTERMAN
- ☐ 362. DOMINGO RAMOS
- ☐ 396. STEVE SHIELDS
- ☐ 419. JOHN CHRISTENSEN
- ☐ 436. DONELL NIXON
- ☐ 464. MIKE MOORE
- ☐ 488. JERRY REED
- ☐ 599. GARY MATTHEWS

TEXAS RANGERS

- ☐ 29. PETE O'BRIEN
- ☐ 47. MIKE STANLEY
- ☐ 113. RUBEN SIERRA
- ☐ 127. CURT WILKERSON
- ☐ 140. CHARLIE HOUGH
- ☐ 149. BOBBY WITT
- ☐ 179. GREG HARRIS
- ☐ 191. LARRY PARRISH
- ☐ 215. ODDIBE MCDOWELL
- ☐ 236. BOB BROWER
- ☐ 251. SCOTT FLETCHER
- ☐ 268. DON SLAUGHT
- ☐ 278. JERRY BROWNE
- ☐ 306. STEVE BUECHELE
- ☐ 322. JOSE GUZMAN
- ☐ 339. MITCH WILLIAMS
- ☐ 373. GENO PETRALLI
- ☐ 407. JEFF KUNKEL
- ☐ 452. DALE MOHORCIC
- ☐ 485. PETE INCAVIGLIA
- ☐ 491. MIKE LOYND
- ☐ 514. JEFF RUSSELL
- ☐ 523. ED CORREA
- ☐ 531. TOM PACIOREK
- ☐ 534. TOM O'MALLEY
- ☐ 536. PAUL KILGUS
- ☐ 537. DARRELL PORTER
- ☐ 543. STEVE HOWE

TORONTO BLUE JAYS

- ☐ 8. JESSE BARFIELD
- ☐ 20. TONY FERNANDEZ
- ☐ 57. TOM HENKE
- ☐ 76. DAVE STIEB
- ☐ 98. JOHN CERUTTI
- ☐ 107. FRED MCGRIFF
- ☐ 109. LLOYD MOSEBY
- ☐ 168. ERNIE WHITT
- ☐ 198. MARK EICHHORN
- ☐ 204. GARTH IORG
- ☐ 216. JIMMY KEY
- ☐ 235. RANCE MULLINIKS
- ☐ 257. RICK LEACH
- ☐ 279. WILLIE UPSHAW
- ☐ 312. JOSE NUNEZ
- ☐ 399. CECIL FIELDER
- ☐ 422. KELLY GRUBER
- ☐ 427. MIKE FLANAGAN (B)
- ☐ 444. CHARLIE MOORE
- ☐ 478. JEFF MUSSELMAN
- ☐ 530. JIM CLANCY
- ☐ 540. GEORGE BELL
- ☐ 561. MANNY LEE
- ☐ 583. JEFF DEWILLIS
- ☐ 621. NELSON LIRIANO
- ☐ 629. ROB DUCEY

1988 SCORE ROOKIE & TRADED (11
2 1/2 X 3 1/2

ATLANTA BRAVES

- ☐ 84T. PETE SMITH

BALTIMORE ORIOLES

- ☐ 31T. MICKEY TETTLETON
- ☐ 41T. JOE ORSULAK
- ☐ 70T. BRADY ANDERSON
- ☐ 77T. OSWALD PERAZA

BOSTON RED SOX

- ☐ 6T. DENNIS LAMP
- ☐ 20T. LEE SMITH
- ☐ 21T. RICK CERONE
- ☐ 59T. MIKE SMITHSON
- ☐ 65T. LARRY PARRISH
- ☐ 81T. STEVE CURRY
- ☐ 83T. STEVE ELLSWORTH

CALIFORNIA ANGELS

- ☐ 26T. DAN PETRY
- ☐ 28T. CHILI DAVIS
- ☐ 87T. BRYAN HARVEY

CHICAGO CUBS

- ☐ 14T. GOOSE GOSSAGE
- ☐ 16T. VANCE LAW
- ☐ 39T. CALVIN SCHIRALDI
- ☐ 80T. MARK GRACE
- ☐ 82T. DAMON BERRYHILL
- ☐ 94T. JEFF PICO
- ☐ 109T. DARRIN JACKSON

CHICAGO WHITE SOX

- ☐ 24T. RICK HORTON
- ☐ 52T. MARK SALAS
- ☐ 56T. DAN PASQUA
- ☐ 61T. JERRY REUSS
- ☐ 66T. JEFF BITTIGER
- ☐ 85T. JACK MCDOWELL
- ☐ 89T. DAVE GALLAGHER
- ☐ 108T. MELIDO PEREZ

CINCINNATI REDS

- ☐ 2T. DANNY JACKSON
- ☐ 27T. JOSE RIJO
- ☐ 43T. HERM WINNINGHAM
- ☐ 78T. JACK ARMSTRONG
- ☐ 86T. ROB DIBBLE
- ☐ 100T. CHRIS SABO

CLEVELAND INDIANS

- ☐ 11T. BUD BLACK
- ☐ 42T. WILLIE UPSHAW
- ☐ 44T. RON KITTLE
- ☐ 92T. DON GORDON

DETROIT TIGERS

- ☐ 13T. LUIS SALAZAR
- ☐ 17T. RAY KNIGHT
- ☐ 38T. GARY PETTIS
- ☐ 79T. DON HEINKEL

HOUSTON ASTROS

- ☐ 12T. RAFAEL RAMIREZ
- ☐ 103T. CRAIG BIGGIO

KANSAS CITY ROYALS

- ☐ 4T. KURT STILLWELL
- ☐ 22T. PAT TABLER
- ☐ 36T. BILL BUCKNER
- ☐ 63T. FLOYD BANNISTER
- ☐ 71T. JEFF MONTGOMERY
- ☐ 76T. MIKE MACFARLANE

LOS ANGELES DODGERS

- ☐ 10T. KIRK GIBSON
- ☐ 32T. RICK DEMPSEY
- ☐ 35T. JAY HOWELL
- ☐ 37T. ALFREDO GRIFFIN
- ☐ 53T. MIKE DAVIS
- ☐ 64T. JESSE OROSCO
- ☐ 101T. TIM BELCHER

MILWAUKEE BREWERS

- ☐ 72T. DARRYL HAMILTON
- ☐ 75T. JOEY MEYER
- ☐ 104T. DON AUGUST

MINNESOTA TWINS

- ☐ 8T. TOM HERR

MONTREAL EXPOS

- ☐ 25T. GRAIG NETTLES
- ☐ 88T. JOHN DOPSON
- ☐ 96T. NELSON SANTOVENIA

NEW YORK METS

- ☐ 30T. MACKEY SASSER

NEW YORK YANKEES

- ☐ 1T. JACK CLARK
- ☐ 19T. DON SLAUGHT
- ☐ 40T. JOHN CANDELARIA
- ☐ 47T. STEVE SHIELDS
- ☐ 54T. RAFAEL SANTANA
- ☐ 60T. RICHARD DOTSON
- ☐ 97T. AL LEITER

OAKLAND A'S

- ☐ 15T. BOB WELCH
- ☐ 33T. RON HASSEY
- ☐ 49T. DAVE HENDERSON
- ☐ 50T. DAVE PARKER
- ☐ 55T. DON BAYLOR
- ☐ 58T. GLENN HUBBARD
- ☐ 102T. WALT WEISS
- ☐ 106T. TODD BURNS

PHILADELPHIA PHILLIES

- ☐ 34T. PHIL BRADLEY
- ☐ 45T. BOB DERNIER
- ☐ 51T. MIKE YOUNG
- ☐ 68T. RICKY JORDAN

PITTSBURGH PIRATES

- ☐ 69T. TOMMY GREGG
- ☐ 110T. ORESTES DESTRADE

ST. LOUIS CARDINALS

- ☐ 5T. TOM BRUNANSKY
- ☐ 7T. JOSE DELEON
- ☐ 18T. DAN QUISENBERRY
- ☐ 23T. LARRY MCWILLIAMS
- ☐ 98T. LUIS ALICEA
- ☐ 107T. JOHN COSTELLO

SAN DIEGO PADRES

- ☐ 9T. KEITH MORELAND
- ☐ 29T. DICKIE THON
- ☐ 105T. ROBERTO ALOMAR

SAN FRANCISCO GIANTS

- ☐ 3T. BRETT BUTLER
- ☐ 57T. ERNEST RILES

SEATTLE MARINERS

- ☐ 46T. STEVE BALBONI
- ☐ 48T. HENRY COTTO
- ☐ 62T. MIKE JACKSON
- ☐ 74T. GREG BRILEY
- ☐ 91T. MIKE SCHOOLER
- ☐ 95T. JAY BUHNER

TEXAS RANGERS

- ☐ 67T. RAY HAYWARD
- ☐ 73T. CECIL ESPY

TORONTO BLUE JAYS

- ☐ 90T. TODD STOTTLEMYRE
- ☐ 93T. SIL CAMPUSANO
- ☐ 99T. PAT BORDERS

1989 SCORE (660)
2 1/2 X 3 1/2

ATLANTA BRAVES

- ☐ 30. DALE MURPHY
- ☐ 74. ALBERT HALL
- ☐ 101. GERALD PERRY
- ☐ 111. OZZIE VIRGIL
- ☐ 139. KEN OBERKFELL
- ☐ 163. DION JAMES
- ☐ 207. PETE SMITH
- ☐ 229. RICK MAHLER
- ☐ 372. RON GANT
- ☐ 373. PAUL ASSENMACHER
- ☐ 406. ANDRES THOMAS
- ☐ 425. BRUCE SUTTER
- ☐ 442. TOM GLAVINE
- ☐ 448. CHARLIE PULEO
- ☐ 492. ZANE SMITH
- ☐ 502. BRUCE BENEDICT
- ☐ 589. JEFF BLAUSER
- ☐ 605. TERRY BLOCKER
- ☐ 611. TED SIMMONS
- ☐ 616. JOHN SMOLTZ
- ☐ 631. DEREK LILLIQUIST

BALTIMORE ORIOLES

- ☐ 15. CAL RIPKEN, JR.
- ☐ 18. BILL RIPKEN
- ☐ 81. LARRY SHEETS
- ☐ 94. EDDIE MURRAY
- ☐ 123. TERRY KENNEDY
- ☐ 126. FRED LYNN
- ☐ 236. PETE STANICEK
- ☐ 247. JOE ORSULAK
- ☐ 252. TOM NIEDENFUER
- ☐ 262. JAY TIBBS
- ☐ 264. DOUG SISK

☐ 292. DAVE SCHMIDT
☐ 358. MICKEY TETTLETON
☐ 452. RICK SCHU
☐ 506. KEN GERHART
☐ 524. DON AASE
☐ 551. JEFF BALLARD
☐ 563. BRADY ANDERSON
☐ 571. OSWALD PERAZA
☐ 573. JOSE BAUTISTA
☐ 585. RENE GONZALES
☐ 590. JIM TRABER
☐ 592. MARK WILLIAMSON
☐ 636. CRAIG WORTHINGTON
☐ 651. BOB MILACKI

BOSTON RED SOX

☐ 9. ELLIS BURKS
☐ 63. MARTY BARRETT
☐ 66. MIKE GREENWELL
☐ 85. JIM RICE
☐ 150. LEE SMITH
☐ 175. WADE BOGGS
☐ 193. DWIGHT EVANS
☐ 218. SPIKE OWEN
☐ 238. DENNIS BOYD
☐ 325. BRUCE HURST
☐ 345. RICH GEDMAN
☐ 350. ROGER CLEMENS
☐ 371. TODD BENZINGER
☐ 383. BOB STANLEY
☐ 396. RICK CERONE
☐ 403. MIKE SMITHSON
☐ 412. WES GARDNER
☐ 486. JODY REED
☐ 491. JEFF SELLERS
☐ 495. LARRY PARRISH
☐ 508. DENNIS LAMP
☐ 531. TOM BOLTON
☐ 541. KEVIN ROMINE
☐ 549. MIKE BODDICKER
☐ 623. CARLOS QUINTANA

CALIFORNIA ANGELS

☐ 14. JOHNNY RAY
☐ 16. DICK SCHOFIELD
☐ 54. CHILI DAVIS
☐ 65. WALLY JOYNER
☐ 76. BRIAN DOWNING
☐ 122. DAN PETRY
☐ 140. BUTCH WYNEGAR
☐ 153. DEWAYNE BUICE
☐ 157. WILLIS FRASER
☐ 181. KIRK MCCASKILL
☐ 182. TONY ARMAS
☐ 185. BRYAN HARVEY
☐ 208. MARK MCLEMORE
☐ 233. BOB BOONE
☐ 261. JACK HOWELL
☐ 298. MIKE WITT
☐ 323. DEVON WHITE
☐ 445. STEWART CLIBURN
☐ 499. DARRELL MILLER
☐ 503. CHUCK FINLEY
☐ 535. DONNIE MOORE
☐ 543. GREG MINTON
☐ 566. TERRY CLARK

CHICAGO CUBS

☐ 2. ANDRE DAWSON
☐ 13. JEFF PICO
☐ 35. RYNE SANDBERG
☐ 60. LES LANCASTER
☐ 71. MITCH WEBSTER
☐ 77. DAVE MARTINEZ
☐ 102. VANCE LAW
☐ 119. GREG MADDUX
☐ 146. FRANK DIPINO
☐ 173. JODY DAVIS
☐ 199. RAFAEL PALMEIRO
☐ 223. RICH GOSSAGE
☐ 235. SHAWON DUNSTON
☐ 263. JAMIE MOYER
☐ 288. JERRY MUMPHREY
☐ 321. CALVIN SCHIRALDI
☐ 336. DAMON BERRYHILL
☐ 360. DARRIN JACKSON
☐ 362. MARK GRACE
☐ 364. PAT PERRY
☐ 407. RICK SUTCLIFFE
☐ 446. MANNY TRILLO
☐ 527. ANGEL SALAZAR
☐ 532. AL NIPPER
☐ 604. GARY VARSHO
☐ 621. DOUG DASCENZO
☐ 624. MIKE HARKEY
☐ 642. DWIGHT SMITH

CHICAGO WHITE SOX

☐ 37. GREG WALKER
☐ 67. KEN WILLIAMS
☐ 128. HAROLD BAINES
☐ 145. RICK HORTON
☐ 177. GARY REDUS
☐ 289. JACK MCDOWELL
☐ 331. IVAN CALDERON
☐ 338. DAN PASQUA
☐ 351. BILL LONG
☐ 384. DAVE LAPOINT
☐ 386. MELIDO PEREZ
☐ 388. STEVE LYONS
☐ 399. BOBBY THIGPEN
☐ 433. OZZIE GUILLEN
☐ 443. DARYL BOSTON
☐ 449. CARLTON FISK
☐ 455. DAVE GALLAGHER
☐ 457. FRED MANRIQUE
☐ 489. JERRY REUSS
☐ 512. JEFF BITTIGER
☐ 542. MARK SALAS
☐ 583. DONNIE HILL
☐ 603. MIKE DIAZ
☐ 607. JIM EPPARD
☐ 608. JOHN DAVIS

CINCINNATI REDS

☐ 7. KAL DANIELS
☐ 31. BARRY LARKIN
☐ 64. NICK ESASKY
☐ 86. JEFF TREADWAY
☐ 104. CHRIS SABO
☐ 109. ERIC DAVIS
☐ 141. ROB MURPHY
☐ 166. DAVE CONCEPCION
☐ 187. BO DIAZ
☐ 206. PAUL O'NEILL
☐ 267. DAVE COLLINS
☐ 454. TIM BIRTSAS
☐ 462. JACK ARMSTRONG
☐ 485. FRANK WILLIAMS
☐ 496. HERM WINNINGHAM
☐ 521. LLOYD MCCLENDON
☐ 552. JOSE RIJO
☐ 554. TOM BROWNING
☐ 555. DANNY JACKSON
☐ 559. RON ROBINSON
☐ 575. JOHN FRANCO
☐ 609. KEN GRIFFEY, SR.
☐ 615. RON OESTER
☐ 618. ROB DIBBLE
☐ 640. VAN SNIDER
☐ 646. NORM CHARLTON

CLEVELAND INDIANS

☐ 11. JULIO FRANCO
☐ 17. MEL HALL
☐ 19. BROOK JACOBY
☐ 46. ANDY ALLANSON
☐ 52. CORY SNYDER
☐ 96. RON KITTLE
☐ 188. WILLIE UPSHAW
☐ 213. JOE CARTER
☐ 239. TOM CANDIOTTI
☐ 266. JOHN FARRELL
☐ 282. GREG SWINDELL
☐ 352. JAY BELL
☐ 387. DOUG JONES
☐ 404. BUD BLACK
☐ 424. SCOTT BAILES
☐ 467. RICH YETT
☐ 497. CARMEN CASTILLO
☐ 547. DON GORDON
☐ 591. JON PERLMAN
☐ 597. TERRY FRANCONA
☐ 598. PAUL ZUVELLA
☐ 633. LUIS MEDINA

DETROIT TIGERS

☐ 43. MATT NOKES
☐ 26. GARY PETTIS
☐ 44. CHET LEMON
☐ 110. ALAN TRAMMELL
☐ 112. FRANK TANANA
☐ 129. DOYLE ALEXANDER
☐ 131. MIKE HEATH
☐ 135. RAY KNIGHT
☐ 168. DON HEINKEL
☐ 171. DARRELL EVANS
☐ 204. PAT SHERIDAN
☐ 230. LOU WHITAKER
☐ 250. JACK MORRIS
☐ 269. TOM BROOKENS
☐ 275. GUILLERMO HERNANDEZ
☐ 279. LARRY HERNDON
☐ 284. JEFF ROBINSON
☐ 293. MIKE HENNEMAN
☐ 311. JIM WALEWANDER
☐ 314. WALT TERRELL
☐ 316. LUIS SALAZAR
☐ 469. DAVE BERGMAN
☐ 471. ERIC KING
☐ 545. DWAYNE MURPHY
☐ 595. PAUL GIBSON
☐ 627. STEVE SEARCY

HOUSTON ASTROS

☐ 12. BILL DORAN
☐ 49. DENNY WALLING
☐ 61. BILLY HATCHER
☐ 97. GERALD YOUNG
☐ 113. RAFAEL RAMIREZ
☐ 164. GLENN DAVIS
☐ 192. JIM PANKOVITS
☐ 226. KEVIN BASS
☐ 237. CRAIG BIGGIO
☐ 245. DAVE SMITH
☐ 273. BOB KNEPPER
☐ 283. JUAN AGOSTO
☐ 300. NOLAN RYAN
☐ 366. ALAN ASHBY
☐ 468. CRAIG REYNOLDS
☐ 472. JOAQUIN ANDUJAR
☐ 523. LARRY ANDERSEN
☐ 546. JIM DESHAIES
☐ 550. MIKE SCOTT
☐ 553. DANNY DARWIN
☐ 567. TERRY PUHL
☐ 574. ALEX TREVINO
☐ 584. CHUCK JACKSON
☐ 593. DAVE MEADS
☐ 610. BUDDY BELL
☐ 643. CAMERON DREW

KANSAS CITY ROYALS

☐ 28. WILLIE WILSON
☐ 55. KEVIN SEITZER
☐ 75. GEORGE BRETT
☐ 105. DANNY TARTABULL
☐ 133. CHARLIE LEIBRANDT
☐ 162. KURT STILLWELL
☐ 183. STEVE FARR
☐ 214. BILL BUCKNER
☐ 249. FLOYD BANNISTER
☐ 251. BRET SABERHAGEN
☐ 291. MARK GUBICZA
☐ 319. MIKE MACFARLANE
☐ 330. BO JACKSON

□ 339. BILL PECOTA
□ 348. TED POWER
□ 367. JEFF MONTGOMERY
□ 390. FRANK WHITE
□ 391. PAT TABLER
□ 423. JERRY DON GLEATON
□ 441. RICK ANDERSON
□ 461. JAMIE QUIRK
□ 504. BRAD WELLMAN
□ 594. JIM EISENREICH
□ 634. TOM GORDON
□ 648. LUIS DE LOS SANTOS

LOS ANGELES DODGERS

□ 69. STEVE SAX
□ 103. JOHN SHELBY
□ 121. MIKE SCIOSCIA
□ 167. ALFREDO GRIFFIN
□ 186. MIKE MARSHALL
□ 210. KIRK GIBSON
□ 332. MICKEY HATCHER
□ 343. DANNY HEEP
□ 356. JESSE OROSCO
□ 370. OREL HERSHISER
□ 376. MIKE DAVIS
□ 378. JAY HOWELL
□ 389. ALEJANDRO PENA
□ 400. DON SUTTON
□ 418. TIM BELCHER
□ 429. TIM LEARY
□ 437. FERNANDO VALENZUELA
□ 478. DAVE ANDERSON
□ 488. SHAWN HILLEGAS
□ 505. TIM CREWS
□ 507. BRIAN HOLTON
□ 556. RICK DEMPSEY
□ 560. JOHN TUDOR
□ 570. JEFF HAMILTON
□ 586. TRACY WOODSON
□ 588. MARIO SOTO
□ 599. FRANKLIN STUBBS
□ 602. MIKE SHARPERSON
□ 622. BILL BRENNAN
□ 635. RAMON MARTINEZ

MILWAUKEE BREWERS

□ 72. ROB DEER
□ 132. TEDDY HIGUERA
□ 147. GLENN BRAGGS
□ 151. ROBIN YOUNT
□ 154. B. J. SURHOFF
□ 243. CHRIS BOSIO
□ 256. DALE SVEUM
□ 272. CHUCK CRIM
□ 307. GREG BROCK
□ 313. JIM GANTNER
□ 320. DAN PLESAC
□ 335. BILL WEGMAN
□ 374. JOEY MEYER
□ 410. JUAN NIEVES
□ 419. DON AUGUST
□ 430. MARK CLEAR
□ 557. JEFFREY LEONARD
□ 565. PAUL MOLITOR
□ 569. PAUL MIRABELLA
□ 579. ODELL JONES
□ 581. DAVE STAPLETON
□ 587. JIM ADDUCI
□ 596. MIKE BIRKBECK
□ 606. CHARLIE O'BRIEN
□ 625. GARY SHEFFIELD

MINNESOTA TWINS

□ 8. GARY GAETTI
□ 20. KIRBY PUCKETT
□ 62. DAN GLADDEN
□ 107. MARK DAVIDSON
□ 134. TIM LAUDNER
□ 159. GREG GAGNE
□ 191. TOMMY HERR
□ 212. RANDY BUSH
□ 215. BERT BLYLEVEN
□ 244. LES STRAKER
□ 280. GENE LARKIN
□ 290. FRANK VIOLA
□ 305. JEFF REARDON
□ 381. KEITH ATHERTON
□ 382. KENT HRBEK
□ 394. ALLAN ANDERSON

□ 408. BRIAN HARPER
□ 414. JUAN BERENGUER
□ 421. STEVE LOMBARDOZZI
□ 432. JOHN MOSES
□ 479. FRED TOLIVER
□ 482. MARK PORTUGAL
□ 493. AL NEWMAN
□ 501. CHARLIE LEA

MONTREAL EXPOS

□ 40. TIM RAINES
□ 53. HUBIE BROOKS
□ 99. JEFF REED
□ 114. DENNIS MARTINEZ
□ 138. ANDY MCGAFFIGAN
□ 144. ANDRES GALARRAGA
□ 169. LUIS RIVERA
□ 196. WALLACE JOHNSON
□ 220. TIM WALLACH
□ 228. TIM BURKE
□ 253. NEAL HEATON
□ 277. GRAIG NETTLES
□ 299. PASCUAL PEREZ
□ 346. NELSON SANTOVENIA
□ 377. JEFF PARRETT
□ 405. TOM FOLEY
□ 428. BRYN SMITH
□ 451. OTIS NIXON
□ 466. JOHN DOPSON
□ 470. REX HUDLER
□ 498. JOE HESKETH
□ 510. TRACY JONES
□ 511. MIKE FITZGERALD
□ 645. RANDY JOHNSON

NEW YORK METS

□ 10. DARRYL STRAWBERRY
□ 41. KEITH HERNANDEZ
□ 58. TIM TEUFEL
□ 84. LEN DYKSTRA
□ 93. KEVIN MCREYNOLDS
□ 116. BOB OJEDA
□ 130. KEVIN ELSTER
□ 136. HOWARD JOHNSON
□ 180. RON DARLING
□ 200. DOC GOODEN
□ 217. LEE MAZZILLI
□ 221. DAVID CONE
□ 240. GARY CARTER
□ 268. SID FERNANDEZ
□ 281. ROGER MCDOWELL
□ 302. MOOKIE WILSON
□ 303. MACKEY SASSER
□ 306. RANDY MYERS
□ 312. DAVE MAGADAN
□ 315. WALLY BACKMAN
□ 327. RICK AGUILERA
□ 431. TERRY LEACH
□ 456. BARRY LYONS
□ 464. KEITH MILLER
□ 572. BOB MCCLURE
□ 600. GREGG JEFFERIES
□ 650. DAVE WEST

NEW YORK YANKEES

□ 25. JACK CLARK
□ 45. WILLIE RANDOLPH
□ 50. DAVE WINFIELD
□ 70. RICKEY HENDERSON
□ 100. DON MATTINGLY
□ 189. MIKE PAGLIARULO
□ 211. CLAUDELL WASHINGTON
□ 225. DAVE RIGHETTI
□ 246. JOHN CANDELARIA
□ 278. RICH DOTSON
□ 296. RAFAEL SANTANA
□ 317. RICK RHODEN
□ 342. RON GUIDRY
□ 375. NEIL ALLEN
□ 415. CHARLES HUDSON
□ 435. GARY WARD
□ 436. LUIS AGUAYO
□ 439. CECILIO GUANTE
□ 447. JOEL SKINNER
□ 477. TOMMY JOHN
□ 487. ROBERTO KELLY
□ 509. BOBBY MEACHAM
□ 561. DON SLAUGHT
□ 578. STEVE SHIELDS

□ 580. AL LEITER
□ 582. WAYNE TOLLESON

OAKLAND A'S

□ 1. JOSE CANESCO
□ 3. MARK MCGWIRE
□ 29. CURT YOUNG
□ 32. DAVE STEWART
□ 34. GLENN HUBBARD
□ 108. DAVE PARKER
□ 156. TONY PHILLIPS
□ 165. WALT WEISS
□ 179. CARNEY LANSFORD
□ 205. DON BAYLOR
□ 248. STORM DAVIS
□ 276. DENNIS ECKERSLEY
□ 308. BOB WELCH
□ 322. STAN JAVIER
□ 334. RON HASSEY
□ 337. STEVE ONTIVEROS
□ 340. GREG CADARET
□ 365. TERRY STEINBACH
□ 380. LUIS POLONIA
□ 392. ERIC PLUNK
□ 416. RICK HONEYCUTT
□ 434. GENE NELSON
□ 459. DOUG JENNINGS
□ 465. TODD BURNS
□ 533. DAVE HENDERSON
□ 537. MIKE GALLEGO
□ 629. FELIX JOSE
□ 641. LANCE BLANKENSHIP

PHILADELPHIA PHILLIES

□ 39. VON HAYES
□ 79. PHIL BRADLEY
□ 92. MILT THOMPSON
□ 95. LANCE PARRISH
□ 125. GREG GROSS
□ 149. MIKE SCHMIDT
□ 170. SHANE RAWLEY
□ 202. CHRIS JAMES
□ 222. DON CARMAN
□ 227. KEVIN GROSS
□ 255. JUAN SAMUEL
□ 260. STEVE BEDROSIAN
□ 287. KENT TEKULVE
□ 328. BRUCE RUFFIN
□ 355. STEVE JELTZ
□ 357. BOB DERNIER
□ 393. MIKE MADDUX
□ 413. DARREN DAULTON
□ 476. GREG HARRIS
□ 494. MIKE YOUNG
□ 544. DAVE PALMER
□ 548. RICKY JORDAN
□ 639. RON JONES
□ 647. TODD FROHWIRTH

PITTSBURGH PIRATES

□ 24. BRIAN FISHER
□ 33. MIKE LAVALLIERE
□ 48. SID BREAM
□ 83. DARNELL COLES
□ 87. JOSE LIND
□ 91. R. J. REYNOLDS
□ 117. DOUG DRABEK
□ 127. BARRY BONDS
□ 174. ANDY VAN SLYKE
□ 195. BOBBY BONILLA
□ 224. BOB WALK
□ 257. JIM GOTT
□ 285. MIKE DUNNE
□ 309. JEFF ROBINSON
□ 333. BARRY JONES
□ 354. BOB KIPPER
□ 379. RAFAEL BELLIARD
□ 402. JUNIOR ORTIZ
□ 409. JOHN SMILEY
□ 601. JOHN CANGELOSI
□ 614. AL PEDRIQUE
□ 620. FELIX FERMIN
□ 626. TOM PRINCE

ST. LOUIS CARDINALS

□ 36. TONY PENA
□ 68. BOB HORNER
□ 80. OZZIE SMITH

- 88. WILLIE MCGEE
- 115. JOSE DELEON
- 137. TERRY PENDLETON
- 155. VINCE COLEMAN
- 184. TOM BRUNANSKY
- 231. LUIS ALICEA
- 259. LARRY MCWILLIAMS
- 265. TODD WORRELL
- 286. GREG MATHEWS
- 363. STEVE LAKE
- 397. SCOTT TERRY
- 460. JOE MARGRANE
- 483. TOM PAGNOZZI
- 520. DAN QUISENBERRY
- 525. BOB FORSCH
- 529. JOSE OQUENDO
- 534. JOHN COSTELLO
- 536. MIKE LAGA
- 564. PEDRO GUERRERO
- 613. DANNY COX
- 649. TIM JONES

SAN DIEGO PADRES

- 4. BENNY SANTIAGO
- 42. KEITH MORELAND
- 90. TONY GWYNN
- 118. ANDY HAWKINS
- 148. JOHN KRUK
- 158. LANCE MCCULLERS
- 176. GARRY TEMPLETON
- 203. MARVELL WYNNE
- 232. ROBERTO ALOMAR
- 234. DICKIE THON
- 254. ERIC SHOW
- 270. SHANE MACK
- 294. JIMMY JONES
- 329. ED WHITSON
- 349. MARK GRANT
- 369. CHRIS BROWN
- 411. SHAWN ABNER
- 417. GREG BOOKER
- 426. RANDY READY
- 490. MARK DAVIS
- 513. TIM FLANNERY
- 515. DAVE LEIPER
- 517. CARMELO MARTINEZ
- 519. STAN JEFFERSON
- 562. DENNIS RASMUSSEN
- 576. MARK PARENT
- 630. SANDY ALOMAR
- 644. JERALD CLARK

SAN FRANCISCO GIANTS

- 5. RICK REUSCHEL
- 39. KEVIN MITCHELL
- 47. CANDY MALDONADO
- 56. JOSE URIBE
- 82. MIKE ALDRETE
- 124. KELLY DOWNS
- 172. ROBBY THOMPSON
- 178. CRAIG LEFFERTS
- 190. MIKE KRUKOW
- 216. BRETT BUTLER
- 258. SCOTT GARRELTS
- 297. CHRIS SPEIER
- 395. BOB BRENLY
- 422. ATLEE HAMMAKER
- 440. DON ROBINSON
- 444. JOE PRICE
- 450. WILL CLARK
- 458. ERNEST RILES
- 474. TERRY MULHOLLAND
- 481. DONELL NIXON
- 500. MIKE LACOSS
- 539. JOEL YOUNGBLOOD
- 612. MATT WILLIAMS
- 617. BOB MELVIN
- 619. KIRT MANWARING
- 628. CHARLIE HAYES

SEATTLE MARINERS

- 27. DAVE VALLE
- 51. ALVIN DAVIS
- 73. JIM PRESLEY
- 89. MICKEY BRANTLEY
- 106. GLENN WILSON
- 142. RICH RENTERIA
- 161. MARK LANGSTON
- 209. HENRY COTTO
- 219. BILL SWIFT
- 242. KEN PHELPS
- 274. MIKE MOORE
- 310. HAROLD REYNOLDS
- 324. SCOTT BRADLEY
- 341. SCOTT BANKHEAD
- 353. STEVE BALBONI
- 361. REY QUINONES
- 398. MIKE JACKSON
- 427. JERRY REED
- 516. ROD SCURRY
- 522. STEVE TROUT
- 528. MIKE SCHOOLER
- 530. JAY BUHNER
- 568. MIKE CAMPBELL
- 637. EDGAR MARTINEZ

TEXAS RANGERS

- 22. PETE O'BRIEN
- 43. RUBEN SIERRA
- 59. ODDIBE MCDOWELL
- 78. SCOTT FLETCHER
- 143. JOSE GUZMAN
- 201. PETE INCAVIGLIA
- 241. MIKE STANLEY
- 271. PAUL KILGUS
- 295. CHARLIE HOUGH
- 301. MITCH WILLIAMS
- 344. BOB BROWER
- 368. STEVE BUECHELE
- 401. CECIL ESPY
- 420. DALE MOHORCIC
- 438. JEFF RUSSELL
- 463. BOBBY WITT
- 484. JEFF KUNKEL
- 514. RAY HAYWARD
- 518. CURTIS WILKERSON
- 526. GENO PETRALLI
- 638. CHAD KRUETER

TORONTO BLUE JAYS

- 6. FRED MCGRIFF
- 12. LLOYD MOSEBY
- 57. TONY FERNANDEZ
- 98. ERNIE WHITT
- 120. CECIL FIELDER
- 152. MARK EICHHORN
- 160. JESSE BARFIELD
- 194. KELLY GRUBER
- 197. DAVE STIEB
- 198. PAT BORDERS
- 304. JOHN CERUTTI
- 318. TOM HENKE
- 326. MANNY LEE
- 347. GEORGE BELL
- 359. DUANE WARD
- 385. RANCE MULLINIKS
- 453. TODD STOTTLEMYRE
- 473. SIL CAMPUSANO
- 475. MIKE FLANAGAN
- 480. JIMMY KEY
- 538. JIM CLANCY
- 540. RICK LEACH
- 558. JEFF MUSSELMAN
- 577. NELSON LIRIANO
- 632. GERONIMO BERROA

1989 SCORE ROOKIE & TRADED (11(
2 1/2 X 3 1/2

ATLANTA BRAVES

- 18T. JEFF TREADWAY
- 64T. JODY DAVIS
- 65T. DARRELL EVANS
- 72T. ODDIBE MCDOWELL

BALTIMORE ORIOLES

- 29T. KEITH MORELAND
- 44T. PHIL BRADLEY
- 59T. BRIAN HOLTON
- 61T. BOB MELVIN
- 95T. STEVE FINLEY
- 96T. GREGG OLSON
- 110T. PETE HARNISCH

BOSTON RED SOX

- 8T. ROB MURPHY
- 37T. NICK ESASKY
- 40T. JOHN DOPSON
- 57T. DANNY HEEP

CALIFORNIA ANGELS

- 10T. CLAUDELL WASHINGTON
- 17T. BERT BLYLEVEN
- 36T. LANCE PARRISH
- 58T. BOB MCCLURE
- 88T. JIM ABBOTT
- 92T. RICH MONTELEONE

CHICAGO CUBS

- 32T. MITCH WILLIAMS
- 84T. JOE GIRARDI
- 85T. JEROME WALTON

CHICAGO WHITE SOX

- 26T. ERIC KING
- 47T. SCOTT FLETCHER
- 80T. RICHARD DOTSON
- 97T. KEN PATTERSON
- 102T. DONN PALL
- 103T. CARLOS MARTINEZ

CINCINNATI REDS

- 15T. TODD BENZINGER
- 52T. TIM LEARY
- 66T. JOEL YOUNGBLOOD
- 79T. RICK MAHLER
- 99T. SCOTT SCUDDER
- 104T. JOE OLIVER
- 109T. ROLANDO ROOMES

CLEVELAND INDIANS

- 6T. PETE O'BRIEN
- 51T. DION JAMES
- 76T. JOEL SKINNER
- 78T. FELIX FERMIN
- 106T. JOEY BELLE

DETROIT TIGERS

☐ 43T. TRACY JONES

HOUSTON ASTROS

☐ 42T. JIM CLANCY

KANSAS CITY ROYALS

☐ 24T. TERRY LEACH
☐ 74T. BOB BOONE

LOS ANGELES DODGERS

☐ 31T. EDDIE MURRAY
☐ 41T. WILLIE RANDOLPH
☐ 48T. KAL DANIELS
☐ 90T. JOHN WETTELAND

MILWAUKEE BREWERS

☐ 82T. BILL SPIERS

MINNESOTA TWINS

☐ 23T. CARMELO CASTILLO
☐ 34T. WALLY BACKMAN
☐ 91T. GARY WAYNE

MONTREAL EXPOS

☐ 13T. SPIKE OWEN
☐ 25T. MARK LANGSTON
☐ 39T. KEVIN GROSS
☐ 56T. ZANE SMITH
☐ 68T. MIKE ALDRETE

NEW YORK METS

☐ 21T. JUAN SAMUEL
☐ 67T. FRANK VIOLA
☐ 108T. MARK CARREON

NEW YORK YANKEES

☐ 4T. DAVE LAPOINT
☐ 14T. ANDY HAWKINS
☐ 20T. STEVE SAX
☐ 22T. JESSE BARFIELD
☐ 27T. STEVE BALBONI
☐ 38T. LUIS POLONIA
☐ 54T. MEL HALL
☐ 63T. LANCE MCCULLERS
☐ 69T. GREG CADARET
☐ 73T. TOM BROOKENS
☐ 75T. WALT TERRELL
☐ 93T. BOB GEREN
☐ 94T. CLAY PARKER

OAKLAND A'S

☐ 5T. MIKE MOORE
☐ 50T. RICKEY HENDERSON

PHILADELPHIA PHILLIES

☐ 9T. TOM HERR
☐ 12T. STEVE LAKE
☐ 28T. LENNY DYKSTRA
☐ 33T. JEFF PARRETT
☐ 53T. ROGER MCDOWELL
☐ 55T. DICKIE THON
☐ 60T. RANDY READY
☐ 70T. JOHN KRUK

PITTSBURGH PIRATES

NO CARDS ISSUED

ST. LOUIS CARDINALS

☐ 45T. MILT THOMPSON
☐ 81T. CRIS CARPENTER
☐ 98T. KEN HILL

SAN DIEGO PADRES

☐ 3T. JACK CLARK
☐ 11T. MIKE PAGLIARULO
☐ 19T. BRUCE HURST
☐ 46T. CHRIS JAMES
☐ 87T. GREG HARRIS

SAN FRANCISCO GIANTS

☐ 30T. TERRY KENNEDY
☐ 49T. STEVE BEDROSIAN
☐ 71T. PAT SHERIDAN
☐ 86T. GREG LITTON
☐ 101T. JEFF BRANTLEY

SEATTLE MARINERS

☐ 7T. JEFFREY LEONARD
☐ 77T. RANDY JOHNSON
☐ 100T. KEN GRIFFEY, JR.
☐ 105T. OMAR VIZQUEL

TEXAS RANGERS

☐ 1T. RAFAEL PALMEIRO
☐ 2T. NOLAN RYAN
☐ 35T. JULIO FRANCO
☐ 62T. HAROLD BAINES
☐ 89T. KEVIN BROWN
☐ 107T. KENNY ROGERS

TORONTO BLUE JAYS

☐ 16T. MOOKIE WILSON
☐ 83T. JUNIOR FELIX

1990 SCORE (704)
2 1/2 X 3 1/2

ATLANTA BRAVES

☐ 66. DALE MURPHY
☐ 78. TOMMY GREGG
☐ 81. JOE BOEVER
☐ 95. JEFF TREADWAY
☐ 99. ANDRES THOMAS
☐ 148. JOSE ALVAREZ
☐ 151. GERONIMO BERROA
☐ 178. JEFF BLAUSER
☐ 225. PETE SMITH
☐ 243. DEREK LILLIQUIST
☐ 249. GERALD PERRY
☐ 302. DARRELL EVANS
☐ 328. JODY DAVIS
☐ 370. JOHN SMOLTZ
☐ 399. LONNIE SMITH
☐ 476. ODDIBE MCDOWELL
☐ 481. TOM GLAVINE
☐ 540. JEFF WETHERBY
☐ 593. MARK LEMKE
☐ 609. MIKE STANTON
☐ 621. GARY EAVE
☐ 627. KELLY MANN
☐ 640. TOMMY GREENE
☐ 644. ED WHITED
☐ 650. DAVE JUSTICE
☐ 677. TYLER HOUSTON

BALTIMORE ORIOLES

☐ 2. CAL RIPKEN
☐ 24. PHIL BRADLEY
☐ 30. DAVE SCHMIDT
☐ 33. BRADY ANDERSON
☐ 41. JOE ORSULAK
☐ 63. GREGG OLSON
☐ 111. LARRY SHEETS
☐ 118. RENE GONZALES
☐ 174. BILL RIPKEN
☐ 177. BRIAN HOLTON
☐ 214. KEVIN HICKEY
☐ 232. MIKE DEVEREAUX
☐ 234. CRAIG WORTHINGTON
☐ 239. BOB MILACKI
☐ 252. RANDY MILLIGAN
☐ 322. MICKEY TETTLETON
☐ 332. MARK WILLIAMSON
☐ 339. STEVE FINLEY
☐ 349. JEFF BALLARD
☐ 350. MARK THURMOND
☐ 355. PETE HARNISCH
☐ 444. KEITH MORELAND
☐ 453. BOB MELVIN
☐ 480. JAY TIBBS
☐ 528. DAVE JOHNSON
☐ 581. CURT SCHILLING
☐ 603. JUAN BELL
☐ 616. MICKEY WESTON
☐ 635. MIKE SMITH
☐ 680. BEN MCDONALD

BOSTON RED SOX

☐ 3. DWIGHT EVANS
☐ 11. JODY REED
☐ 15. MARTY BARRETT
☐ 31. MIKE BODDICKER
☐ 37. LEE SMITH
☐ 91. NICK ESASKY
☐ 113. DANNY HEEP
☐ 137. DENNIS BOYD
☐ 139. RICK CERONE
☐ 173. RICH GEDMAN
☐ 181. ROB MURPHY
☐ 245. WADE BOGGS
☐ 310. ROGER CLEMENS
☐ 331. JOHN DOPSON
☐ 340. ELLIS BURKS
☐ 345. MIKE GREENWELL
☐ 348. WES GARDNER
☐ 458. KEVIN ROMINE
☐ 471. DENNIS LAMP
☐ 512. MIKE SMITHSON
☐ 543. ERIC HETZEL
☐ 551. RANDY KUTCHER
☐ 651. SCOTT COOPER
☐ 658. CARLOS QUINTANA
☐ 675. MAURICE VAUGHN
☐ 681. GREG BLOSSER

CALIFORNIA ANGELS

- ☐ 8. BRYAN HARVEY
- ☐ 26. BRIAN DOWNING
- ☐ 35. LANCE PARRISH
- ☐ 44. DICK SCHOFIELD
- ☐ 48. GREG MINTON
- ☐ 117. BOB MCCLURE
- ☐ 120. WALLY JOYNER
- ☐ 180. BERT BLYLEVEN
- ☐ 206. JACK HOWELL
- ☐ 211. DAN PETRY
- ☐ 217. KIRK MCCASKILL
- ☐ 226. MIKE WITT
- ☐ 293. JOHNNY RAY
- ☐ 298. CLAUDELL WASHINGTON
- ☐ 312. DEVON WHITE
- ☐ 326. CHILI DAVIS
- ☐ 330. JIM ABBOTT
- ☐ 358. WILLIE FRASER
- ☐ 362. BILL SCHROEDER
- ☐ 378. TONY ARMAS
- ☐ 380. CHUCK FINLEY
- ☐ 412. KENT ANDERSON
- ☐ 565. RICH MONTELEONE
- ☐ 582. JOHN ORTON
- ☐ 604. BOBBY ROSE
- ☐ 673. KYLE ABBOTT

CHICAGO CUBS

- ☐ 73. VANCE LAW
- ☐ 85. MITCH WEBSTER
- ☐ 90. RYNE SANDBERG
- ☐ 92. LUIS SALAZAR
- ☐ 150. MARK GRACE
- ☐ 163. DAMON BERRYHILL
- ☐ 169. SHAWON DUNSTON
- ☐ 176. LLOYD MCCLENDON
- ☐ 196. PAUL KILGUS
- ☐ 229. JEROME WALTON
- ☐ 240. DWIGHT SMITH
- ☐ 262. MITCH WILLIAMS
- ☐ 265. ANDRE DAWSON
- ☐ 337. MARVELL WYNNE
- ☐ 403. GRED MADDUX
- ☐ 413. LES LANCASTER
- ☐ 428. JEFF PICO
- ☐ 436. PAT PERRY
- ☐ 450. RICK SUTCLIFFE
- ☐ 474. CURTIS WILKERSON
- ☐ 484. MIKE BIELECKI
- ☐ 488. SCOTT SANDERSON
- ☐ 489. DOMINGO RAMOS
- ☐ 531. STEVE WILSON
- ☐ 535. JOE GIRARDI
- ☐ 557. RICK WRONA
- ☐ 614. GREG SMITH
- ☐ 630. DEAN WILKINS
- ☐ 646. KEVIN BLANKENSHIP
- ☐ 670. EARL CUNNINGHAM

CHICAGO WHITE SOX

- ☐ 6. OZZIE GUILLEN
- ☐ 19. RICHARD DOTSON
- ☐ 22. RON KARKOVICE
- ☐ 28. ERIC KING
- ☐ 58. SCOTT FLETCHER
- ☐ 88. STEVE LYONS
- ☐ 94. IVAN CALDERON
- ☐ 115. DAVE GALLAGHER
- ☐ 152. BARRY JONES
- ☐ 207. KEN PATTERSON
- ☐ 213. DARYL BOSTON
- ☐ 290. CARLTON FISK
- ☐ 304. DONN PALL
- ☐ 306. DAN PASQUA
- ☐ 311. MELIDO PEREZ
- ☐ 314. CARLOS MARTINEZ
- ☐ 329. SHAWN HILLEGAS
- ☐ 335. BOBBY THIGPEN
- ☐ 354. GREG WALKER
- ☐ 369. GREG HIBBARD
- ☐ 523. STEVE ROSENBERG
- ☐ 526. BILL LONG
- ☐ 529. RON KITTLE
- ☐ 558. SAMMY SOSA
- ☐ 570. LANCE JOHNSON
- ☐ 595. ROBIN VENTURA
- ☐ 605. MATT MERULLO
- ☐ 617. JOHN PAWLOWSKI
- ☐ 663. FRANK THOMAS

CINCINNATI REDS

- ☐ 38. HERM WINNINGHAM
- ☐ 59. RON OESTER
- ☐ 65. TODD BENZINGER
- ☐ 70. CHRIS SABO
- ☐ 87. RICK MAHLER
- ☐ 147. JEFF REED
- ☐ 155. BARRY LARKIN
- ☐ 165. TOM BROWNING
- ☐ 185. ERIC DAVIS
- ☐ 248. NORM CHARLTON
- ☐ 273. JOHN FRANCO
- ☐ 277. ROB DIBBLE
- ☐ 289. DANNY JACKSON
- ☐ 295. PAUL O'NEILL
- ☐ 338. KEN GRIFFEY
- ☐ 344. JOEL YOUNGBLOOD
- ☐ 408. TIM BIRTSAS
- ☐ 417. ROLANDO ROOMES
- ☐ 434. BO DIAZ
- ☐ 495. RON ROBINSON
- ☐ 499. LUIS QUINONES
- ☐ 504. TIM LEARY
- ☐ 506. MARIANO DUNCAN
- ☐ 511. JOSE RIJO
- ☐ 518. SCOTT SCUDDER
- ☐ 576. JOE OLIVER
- ☐ 629. CHRIS HAMMOND
- ☐ 648. MIKE ROESLER
- ☐ 667. SCOTT BRYANT

CLEVELAND INDIANS

- ☐ 10. CORY SNYDER
- ☐ 52. JERRY BROWNE
- ☐ 56. BROOK JACOBY
- ☐ 103. JOHN FARRELL
- ☐ 130. DOUG JONES
- ☐ 141. DAVE CLARK
- ☐ 175. PETE O'BRIEN
- ☐ 187. STEVE DAVIS
- ☐ 197. BUD BLACK
- ☐ 218. SCOTT BAILES
- ☐ 230. GREG SWINDELL
- ☐ 256. FELIX FERMIN
- ☐ 269. TOM CANDIOTTI
- ☐ 274. RICH YETT
- ☐ 319. JOE CARTER
- ☐ 353. JESSE OROSCO
- ☐ 452. ANDY ALLANSON
- ☐ 496. BRAD KOMMINSK
- ☐ 508. JOEY BELLE
- ☐ 514. DION JAMES
- ☐ 590. STEVE OLIN
- ☐ 611. CHARLES NAGY
- ☐ 618. JOE SKALSKI

DETROIT TIGERS

- ☐ 9. ALAN TRAMMELL
- ☐ 55. MATT NOKES
- ☐ 57. FRANK TANANA
- ☐ 75. LOU WHITAKER
- ☐ 106. CHET LEMON
- ☐ 131. FRED LYNN
- ☐ 136. GARY PETTIS
- ☐ 172. MIKE HEATH
- ☐ 184. MIKE HENNEMAN
- ☐ 203. JACK MORRIS
- ☐ 237. DOYLE ALEXANDER
- ☐ 254. DAVE BERGMAN
- ☐ 261. PAUL GIBSON
- ☐ 267. GUILLERMO HERNANDEZ
- ☐ 291. TRACY JONES
- ☐ 333. JEFF ROBINSON
- ☐ 341. FRANK WILLIAMS
- ☐ 513. GARY WARD
- ☐ 572. KEVIN RITZ
- ☐ 575. SCOTT LUSADER
- ☐ 583. MILT CUYLER
- ☐ 607. RANDY NOSEK
- ☐ 620. SHAWN HOLMAN
- ☐ 626. PAT AUSTIN
- ☐ 657. BRIAN DUBOIS
- ☐ 679. GREG GOHR

HOUSTON ASTROS

- ☐ 40. MIKE SCOTT
- ☐ 42. RAFAEL RAMIREZ
- ☐ 43. GERALD YOUNG
- ☐ 45. DAVE SMITH
- ☐ 76. KEN CAMINITI
- ☐ 154. JIM DESHAIES
- ☐ 182. BILL DORAN
- ☐ 219. BOB FORSCH
- ☐ 272. GLENN DAVIS
- ☐ 275. CRAIG BIGGIO
- ☐ 279. KEVIN BASS
- ☐ 282. LARRY ANDERSEN
- ☐ 284. JUAN AGOSTO
- ☐ 346. GLENN WILSON
- ☐ 402. DANNY DARWIN
- ☐ 411. ERIC YELDING
- ☐ 418. DAN SCHATZEDER
- ☐ 424. JIM CLANCY
- ☐ 473. TERRY PUHL
- ☐ 552. MARK PORTUGAL
- ☐ 584. ERIC ANTHONY

KANSAS CITY ROYALS

- ☐ 60. BOB BOONE
- ☐ 82. CHARLIE LEIBRANDT
- ☐ 96. KURT STILLWELL
- ☐ 104. WILLIE WILSON
- ☐ 121. MARK GUBICZA
- ☐ 140. GEORGE BRETT
- ☐ 179. JIM EISENREICH
- ☐ 195. BRET SABERHAGEN
- ☐ 199. KEVIN SEITZER
- ☐ 242. PAT TABLER
- ☐ 244. DANNY TARTABULL
- ☐ 280. BO JACKSON
- ☐ 356. STEVE FARR
- ☐ 365. JEFF MONTGOMERY
- ☐ 372. FRANK WHITE
- ☐ 396. BILL BUCKNER
- ☐ 432. LUIS AQUINO
- ☐ 472. TOM GORDON
- ☐ 502. TERRY LEACH
- ☐ 587. JOSE DEJESUS
- ☐ 625. KEVIN APPIER
- ☐ 659. LUIS DE LOS SANTOS
- ☐ 664. BRENT MAYNE

LOS ANGELES DODGERS

- ☐ 23. LENNY HARRIS
- ☐ 39. ALEJANDRO PENA
- ☐ 50. OREL HERSHISER
- ☐ 54. FERNANDO VALENZUELA
- ☐ 80. EDDIE MURRAY
- ☐ 126. TIM BELCHER
- ☐ 132. JEFF HAMILTON
- ☐ 156. ALFREDO GRIFFIN
- ☐ 164. TIM CREWS
- ☐ 227. JAY HOWELL
- ☐ 238. DAVE ANDERSON
- ☐ 342. MIKE MORGAN
- ☐ 359. MICKEY HATCHER
- ☐ 368. JOSE GONZALEZ
- ☐ 384. MIKE MARSHALL
- ☐ 388. JOHN WETTELAND
- ☐ 395. WILLIE RANDOLPH
- ☐ 398. MIKE SCIOSCIA
- ☐ 414. RICK DEMPSEY
- ☐ 437. MIKE DAVIS
- ☐ 461. RAMON MARTINEZ

☐ 478. FRANKLIN STUBBS
☐ 487. KIRK GIBSON
☐ 490. KAL DANIELS
☐ 597. MIKE HUFF
☐ 613. JOSE VIZCAINO
☐ 622. DARRIN FLETCHER
☐ 641. MIKE HARTLEY
☐ 653. MIKE MUNOZ
☐ 654. JEFF FISCHER
☐ 668. TOM GOODWIN
☐ 676. KEITH JONES

MILWAUKEE BREWERS

☐ 74. B. J. SURHOFF
☐ 86. DAN PLESAC
☐ 97. GARY SHEFFIELD
☐ 105. GLENN BRAGGS
☐ 108. CHUCK CRIM
☐ 144. DON AUGUST
☐ 188. BILL WEGMAN
☐ 216. TERRY FRANCONA
☐ 268. MIKE FELDER
☐ 283. CHRIS BOSIO
☐ 305. TEDDY HIGUERA
☐ 320. ROBIN YOUNT
☐ 366. BILL KRUEGER
☐ 382. JIM GANTNER
☐ 390. ROB DEER
☐ 449. BILL SPIERS
☐ 460. PAUL MOLITOR
☐ 485. GREG BROCK
☐ 532. JOEY MEYER
☐ 539. MARK KNUDSON
☐ 567. TONY FOSSAS
☐ 569. JAIME NAVARRO
☐ 585. GREG VAUGHN
☐ 608. BILLY BATES
☐ 656. GEORGE CANALE
☐ 669. CAL ELDRED

MINNESOTA TWINS

☐ 61. DAN GLADDEN
☐ 71. SHANE RAWLEY
☐ 102. GREG GAGNE
☐ 123. CARMELO CASTILLO
☐ 128. AL NEWMAN
☐ 133. GERMAN GONZALEZ
☐ 145. GARY GAETTI
☐ 189. BRIAN HARPER
☐ 223. JUAN BERENGUER
☐ 276. GENE LARKIN
☐ 278. RANDY BUSH
☐ 281. WALLY BACKMAN
☐ 292. ALLAN ANDERSON
☐ 318. TIM LAUDNER
☐ 381. KENT HRBEK
☐ 391. JOHN MOSES
☐ 400. KIRBY PUCKETT
☐ 519. RICK AGUILERA
☐ 522. JEFF REARDON
☐ 527. GARY WAYNE
☐ 568. ROY SMITH
☐ 571. MIKE DYER
☐ 573. DAVE WEST
☐ 588. CHIP HALE
☐ 638. LENNY WEBSTER
☐ 647. PAUL SORRENTO
☐ 655. TERRY JORGENSEN
☐ 672. CHUCK KNOBLAUCH

MONTREAL EXPOS

☐ 25. ANDRES GALARRAGA
☐ 27. DAVE MARTINEZ
☐ 32. TOM FOLEY
☐ 47. DENNIS MARTINEZ
☐ 127. TIM BURKE
☐ 192. TIM WALLACH
☐ 220. MIKE ALDRETE
☐ 224. ANDY MCGAFFIGAN
☐ 241. OTIS NIXON
☐ 247. SPIKE OWEN
☐ 251. KEVIN GROSS
☐ 287. REX HUDLER
☐ 299. HUBIE BROOKS
☐ 361. MIKE FITZGERALD
☐ 401. MARK LANGSTON
☐ 409. TIM RAINES
☐ 419. BRYN SMITH

☐ 451. NELSON SANTOVENIA
☐ 477. ZANE SMITH
☐ 479. WALLACE JOHNSON
☐ 483. JOE HESKETH
☐ 486. PASCUAL PEREZ
☐ 591. MARQUIS GRISSOM
☐ 615. JEFF HUSON
☐ 631. LARRY WALKER
☐ 639. MARK GARDNER
☐ 645. DELINO DESHIELDS

NEW YORKS METS

☐ 5. KEVIN MCREYNOLDS
☐ 18. SID FERNANDEZ
☐ 29. BARRY LYONS
☐ 46. DAVE MAGADAN
☐ 53. BOB OJEDA
☐ 124. HOWARD JOHNSON
☐ 193. KEITH HERNANDEZ
☐ 198. JUAN SAMUEL
☐ 200. DARRYL STRAWBERRY
☐ 313. DWIGHT GOODEN
☐ 351. RANDY MYERS
☐ 363. MARK CARREON
☐ 377. DON AASE
☐ 416. GARY CARTER
☐ 430. DAVID CONE
☐ 443. KEVIN ELSTER
☐ 446. RON DARLING
☐ 468. GREGG JEFFERIES
☐ 500. FRANK VIOLA
☐ 501. TIM TEUFEL
☐ 510. MACKEY SASSER
☐ 525. JEFF MUSSELMAN
☐ 559. KEITH MILLER
☐ 599. WALLY WHITEHURST
☐ 632. BLAINE BEATTY
☐ 671. ALAN ZINTER

NEW YORK YANKEES

☐ 1. DON MATTINGLY
☐ 79. DON SLAUGHT
☐ 100. ROBERTO KELLY
☐ 101. ALVARO ESPINOZA
☐ 125. STEVE SAX
☐ 186. LANCE MCCULLERS
☐ 191. DALE MOHORCIC
☐ 194. DAVE RIGHETTI
☐ 222. JESSE BARFIELD
☐ 294. LEE GUETTERMAN
☐ 297. TOM BROOKENS
☐ 307. DAVE WINFIELD
☐ 316. CLAY PARKER
☐ 327. STEVE BALBONI
☐ 357. DAVE LAPOINT
☐ 383. MEL HALL
☐ 386. WAYNE TOLLESON
☐ 393. CHUCK CARY
☐ 442. LUIS POLONIA
☐ 463. WALT TERRELL
☐ 464. BOB GEREN
☐ 524. RANDY VELARDE
☐ 586. DEION SANDERS
☐ 602. HAL MORRIS
☐ 606. KEVIN MAAS
☐ 619. BERNIE WILLIAMS
☐ 624. MIKE BLOWERS
☐ 636. HENSLEY MEULENS
☐ 643. KEVIN MMAHAT
☐ 652. DAVE EILAND

OAKLAND A'S

☐ 64. TODD BURNS
☐ 84. TONY PHILLIPS
☐ 110. WALT WEISS
☐ 135. DAVE PARKER
☐ 159. BOB WELCH
☐ 162. TERRY STEINBACH
☐ 168. RON HASSEY
☐ 190. MIKE MOORE
☐ 266. STORM DAVIS
☐ 296. CARNEY LANSFORD
☐ 315. DENNIS ECKERSLEY
☐ 317. RICK HONEYCUTT
☐ 321. FELIX JOSE
☐ 323. MIKE GALLEGO
☐ 325. DAVE HENDERSON
☐ 360. RICKEY HENDERSON
☐ 375. JOSE CANSECO
☐ 385. MARK MCGWIRE
☐ 394. STAN JAVIER
☐ 410. DAVE STEWART
☐ 441. GENE NELSON
☐ 533. CURT YOUNG
☐ 536. LANCE BLANKENSHIP
☐ 553. JIM CORSI
☐ 598. SCOTT HEMOND

PHILADELPHIA PHILLIES

☐ 16. RICKY JORDAN
☐ 36. VON HAYES
☐ 142. DICKIE THON
☐ 171. TOM HERR
☐ 183. CURT FORD
☐ 364. RON JONES
☐ 376. RANDY READY
☐ 389. DARREN DAULTON
☐ 421. STEVE JELTZ
☐ 427. LENNY DYKSTRA
☐ 435. STEVE LAKE
☐ 445. ROGER MCDOWELL
☐ 467. JOHN KRUK
☐ 507. CHARLIE HAYES
☐ 542. TERRY MULHOLLAND
☐ 545. DENNIS COOK
☐ 623. PAT COMBS
☐ 633. TOM BARRETT
☐ 649. JASON GRIMSLEY
☐ 678. JEFF JACKSON

PITTSBURGH PIRATES

☐ 4. BARRY BONDS
☐ 14. GARY REDUS
☐ 21. BOB WALK
☐ 83. JOSE LIND
☐ 116. MIKE LAVALLIERE
☐ 143. JUNIOR ORTIZ
☐ 170. BOBBY BONILLA
☐ 334. JOHN SMILEY
☐ 367. JOHN CANGELOSI
☐ 423. SID BREAM
☐ 440. ANDY VAN SLYKE
☐ 456. BILL LANDRUM
☐ 469. R. J. REYNOLDS
☐ 505. DOUG DRABEK
☐ 515. JIM GOTT
☐ 517. DOUG BAIR
☐ 520. RAFAEL BELLIARD
☐ 544. RICK REED
☐ 547. BRIAN FISHER
☐ 549. JEFF KING
☐ 562. BILLY HATCHER
☐ 563. JAY BELL
☐ 592. MOISES ALOU
☐ 634. STAN BELINDA
☐ 682. WILLIE GREEN

ST. LOUIS CARDINALS

☐ 13. PEDRO GUERRERO
☐ 17. JOE MAGRANE
☐ 49. MILT THOMPSON
☐ 68. JOSE OQUENDO
☐ 72. TOM BRUNANSKY
☐ 122. TONY PENA
☐ 134. JOHN MORRIS
☐ 208. TERRY PENDLETON
☐ 233. KEN HILL
☐ 235. SCOTT TERRY

- ☐ 260. VINCE COLEMAN
- ☐ 285. OZZIE SMITH
- ☐ 309. JOSE DELEON
- ☐ 347. JOHN COSTELLO
- ☐ 374. WILLIE MCGEE
- ☐ 392. TODD WORRELL
- ☐ 462. FRANK DIPINO
- ☐ 475. DAN QUISENBERRY
- ☐ 537. GREG MATHEWS
- ☐ 556. KEN DAYLEY
- ☐ 579. TIM JONES
- ☐ 600. TODD ZEILE
- ☐ 628. MATT KINZER
- ☐ 662. PAUL COLEMAN

SAN DIEGO PADRES

- ☐ 12. ROBERTO ALOMAR
- ☐ 20. JACK CLARK
- ☐ 51. BIP ROBERTS
- ☐ 114. CARMELO MARTINEZ
- ☐ 119. MARK PARENT
- ☐ 129. DENNIS RASMUSSEN
- ☐ 212. DAVE LEIPER
- ☐ 255. TONY GWYNN
- ☐ 257. GREG HARRIS
- ☐ 259. MARK DAVIS
- ☐ 270. BRUCE HURST
- ☐ 336. GARRY TEMPLETON
- ☐ 352. SHAWN ABNER
- ☐ 373. ED WHITSON
- ☐ 434. BENNY SANTIAGO
- ☐ 466. MARK GRANT
- ☐ 493. ERIC SHOW
- ☐ 494. MIKE PAGLIARULO
- ☐ 498. CHRIS JAMES
- ☐ 541. DARRIN JACKSON
- ☐ 577. SANDY ALOMAR
- ☐ 578. ANDY BENES
- ☐ 642. PHIL STEPHENSON
- ☐ 660. JERALD CLARK

SAN FRANCISCO GIANTS

- ☐ 7. TERRY KENNEDY
- ☐ 112. DON ROBINSON
- ☐ 138. CANDY MALDONADO
- ☐ 146. KIRT MANWARING
- ☐ 209. CRAIG LEFFERTS
- ☐ 215. MIKE KRUKOW
- ☐ 231. ATLEE HAMMAKER
- ☐ 236. BRETT BUTLER
- ☐ 246. SCOTT GARRELTS
- ☐ 253. MIKE LACOSS
- ☐ 300. WILL CLARK
- ☐ 343. KEVIN MITCHELL
- ☐ 371. JEFF BRANTLEY
- ☐ 379. STEVE BEDROSIAN
- ☐ 397. ROBBY THOMPSON
- ☐ 422. KEN OBERKFELL
- ☐ 447. ERNEST RILES
- ☐ 455. JOSE URIBE
- ☐ 465. RICK REUSCHEL
- ☐ 497. GREG LITTON
- ☐ 503. MATT WILLIAMS
- ☐ 509. PAT SHERIDAN
- ☐ 534. KELLY DOWNS
- ☐ 538. DONELL NIXON
- ☐ 550. DAVE DRAVECKY
- ☐ 580. RANDY MCCAMENT
- ☐ 666. STEVE HOSEY

SEATTLE MARINERS

- ☐ 34. JIM PRESLEY
- ☐ 62. DARNELL COLES
- ☐ 98. JEFFREY LEONARD
- ☐ 109. DAVE VALLE
- ☐ 149. MIKE SCHOOLER
- ☐ 161. HENRY COTTO
- ☐ 167. HAROLD REYNOLDS
- ☐ 205. ALVIN DAVIS
- ☐ 228. SCOTT BRADLEY
- ☐ 264. OMAR VIZQUEL
- ☐ 303. GREG BRILEY
- ☐ 308. DENNIS POWELL
- ☐ 324. EDGAR MARTINEZ
- ☐ 387. BRIAN HOLMAN
- ☐ 415. RANDY JOHNSON
- ☐ 492. JERRY REED
- ☐ 521. JAY BUHNER
- ☐ 530. ERIK HANSON
- ☐ 546. MIKE JACKSON
- ☐ 548. GENE HARRIS
- ☐ 555. SCOTT BANKHEAD
- ☐ 560. KEN GRIFFEY, JR.
- ☐ 596. TINO MARTINEZ
- ☐ 674. ROGER SALKELD

TEXAS RANGERS

- ☐ 69. CECIL ESPY
- ☐ 93. PETE INCAVIGLIA
- ☐ 107. JAMIE MOYER
- ☐ 153. GENO PETRALLI
- ☐ 158. MIKE JEFFCOAT
- ☐ 160. JULIO FRANCO
- ☐ 166. FRED MANRIQUE
- ☐ 202. CHARLIE HOUGH
- ☐ 210. KEVIN BROWN
- ☐ 221. STEVE BUECHELE
- ☐ 250. NOLAN RYAN
- ☐ 263. JEFF RUSSELL
- ☐ 301. KENNY ROGERS
- ☐ 405. RAFAEL PALMEIRO
- ☐ 406. CHAD KREUTER
- ☐ 420. RUBEN SIERRA
- ☐ 426. RICK LEACH
- ☐ 431. JEFF KUNKEL
- ☐ 438. CECILIO GUANTE
- ☐ 457. BOBBY WITT
- ☐ 470. HAROLD BAINES
- ☐ 516. DREW HALL
- ☐ 564. JACK DAUGHERTY
- ☐ 574. GARY MIELKE
- ☐ 594. DEAN PALMER
- ☐ 612. SCOTT COOLBAUGH
- ☐ 637. JUAN GONZALEZ
- ☐ 661. DONALD HARRIS

TORONTO BLUE JAYS

- ☐ 67. MIKE FLANAGAN
- ☐ 77. NELSON LIRIANO
- ☐ 89. TONY FERNANDEZ
- ☐ 157. TOM HENKE
- ☐ 201. DAVE STIEB
- ☐ 204. RANCE MULLINIKS
- ☐ 258. JUNIOR FELIX
- ☐ 271. FRED MCGRIFF
- ☐ 286. GEORGE BELL
- ☐ 288. PAT BORDERS
- ☐ 404. LLOYD MOSEBY
- ☐ 407. JIMMY KEY
- ☐ 425. KELLY GRUBER
- ☐ 429. JOHN CERUTTI
- ☐ 433. ERNIE WHITT
- ☐ 439. DUANE WARD
- ☐ 448. MOOKIE WILSON
- ☐ 459. LEE MAZZILLI
- ☐ 482. MANNY LEE
- ☐ 491. DAVID WELLS
- ☐ 554. TODD STOTTLEMYRE
- ☐ 589. JOHN OLERUD
- ☐ 601. GLENALLEN HILL
- ☐ 610. GOOSE GOZZO
- ☐ 665. EDDIE ZOSKY

1990 SCORE ROOKIE & TRADED (110) 2 1/2 X 3 1/2

ATLANTA BRAVES

- ☐ 3T. NICK ESASKY
- ☐ 30T. ERNIE WHITT
- ☐ 36T. JIM PRESLEY
- ☐ 67T. FRANCISCO CABRERA
- ☐ 69T. GREG OLSON
- ☐ 72T. KENT MERCKER
- ☐ 109T. STEVE AVERY

BALTIMORE ORIOLES

- ☐ 53T. BRAD KOMMINSK
- ☐ 95T. DAVID SEGUI
- ☐ 96T. CHRIS HOILES

BOSTON RED SOX

- ☐ 7T. TONY PENA
- ☐ 17T. JEFF REARDON
- ☐ 49T. TOM BRUNANSKY
- ☐ 87T. TIM NAEHRING
- ☐ 102T. DANA KIECKER
- ☐ 104T. MICKEY PINA

CALIFORNIA ANGELS

- ☐ 1T. DAVE WINFIELD
- ☐ 11T. MARK LANGSTON
- ☐ 46T. LUIS POLONIA
- ☐ 64T. SCOTT BAILES
- ☐ 68T. GARY DISARCINA

CHICAGO CUBS

- ☐ 62T. BILL LONG
- ☐ 94T. SHAWN BOSKIE
- ☐ 98T. HECTOR VILLANUEVA

CHICAGO WHITE SOX

- ☐ 44T. PHIL BRADLEY
- ☐ 80T. JERRY KUTZLER
- ☐ 85T. WAYNE EDWARDS
- ☐ 86T. FRANK THOMAS
- ☐ 90T. SCOTT RADINSKY
- ☐ 105T. CRAIG GREBECK

CINCINNATI REDS

- ☐ 16T. RANDY MYERS
- ☐ 42T. BILLY HATCHER
- ☐ 56T. GLENN BRAGGS
- ☐ 107T. TIM LAYANA

1990 Score Rookie & Traded

CLEVELAND INDIANS

- ☐ 4T. MITCH WEBSTER
- ☐ 8T. CANDY MALDONADO
- ☐ 18T. SANDY ALOMAR
- ☐ 57T. KEITH HERNANDEZ
- ☐ 60T. CHRIS JAMES
- ☐ 70T. BEAU ALLRED
- ☐ 74T. CARLOS BAERGA

DETROIT TIGERS

- ☐ 9T. CECIL FIELDER
- ☐ 14T. TONY PHILLIPS
- ☐ 25T. LLOYD MOSEBY
- ☐ 39T. DAN PETRY
- ☐ 65T. LARRY SHEETS

HOUSTON ASTROS

- ☐ 40T. FRANKLIN STUBBS
- ☐ 58T. KEN OBERKFELL

KANSAS CITY ROYALS

- ☐ 21T. STORM DAVIS
- ☐ 26T. MARK DAVIS
- ☐ 28T. GERALD PERRY
- ☐ 59T. STEVE JELTZ
- ☐ 110T. TERRY SHUMPERT

LOS ANGELES DODGERS

- ☐ 29T. DON AASE
- ☐ 33T. JUAN SAMUEL
- ☐ 34T. HUBIE BROOKS
- ☐ 52T. STAN JAVIER

MILWAUKEE BREWERS

- ☐ 12T. DAVE PARKER

MINNESOTA TWINS

- ☐ 43T. TERRY LEACH
- ☐ 66T. JUNIOR ORTIZ
- ☐ 82T. KEVIN TAPANI
- ☐ 103T. TIM DRUMMOND

MONTREAL EXPOS

- ☐ 24T. DENNIS BOYD
- ☐ 79T. BILL SAMPEN
- ☐ 91T. HOWARD FARMER

NEW YORK METS

- ☐ 15T. JOHN FRANCO
- ☐ 32T. ALEJANDRO PENA
- ☐ 47T. DARYL BOSTON
- ☐ 76T. TODD HUNDLEY
- ☐ 92T. JULIO MACHADO
- ☐ 97T. D.J. DOZIER

NEW YORK YANKEES

- ☐ 5T. PASCUAL PEREZ
- ☐ 27T. TIM LEARY
- ☐ 38T. MATT NOKES
- ☐ 45T. CLAUDELL WASHINGTON
- ☐ 50T. MIKE WITT
- ☐ 63T. RICK CERONE
- ☐ 71T. OSCAR AZOCAR
- ☐ 83T. JIM LEYRITZ
- ☐ 89T. ALAN MILLS

OAKLAND A'S

- ☐ 51T. WILLIE RANDOLPH
- ☐ 61T. SCOTT SANDERSON
- ☐ 101T. DAVE OTTO
- ☐ 108T. SCOTT CHIAMPARINO

PHILADELPHIA PHILLIES

- ☐ 10T. CARMELO MARTINEZ
- ☐ 31T. DALE MURPHY
- ☐ 75T. DAVE HOLLINS

PITTSBURGH PIRATES

- ☐ 13T. DON SLAUGHT
- ☐ 37T. WALLY BACKMAN

ST. LOUIS CARDINALS

- ☐ 48T. LEE SMITH
- ☐ 55T. BRYN SMITH
- ☐ 84T. RAY LANKFORD
- ☐ 106T. BERNARD GILKEY

SAN DIEGO PADRES

- ☐ 19T. JOE CARTER
- ☐ 20T. FRED LYNN
- ☐ 22T. CRAIG LEFFERTS
- ☐ 93T. RAFAEL VALDEZ

SAN FRANCISCO GIANTS

- ☐ 2T. KEVIN BASS
- ☐ 35T. GARY CARTER
- ☐ 73T. JOH BURKETT
- ☐ 77T. RICK PARKER
- ☐ 99T. ERIC GUNDERSON

SEATTLE MARINERS

- ☐ 23T. PETE O'BRIEN

TEXAS RANGERS

- ☐ 6T. GARY PETTIS
- ☐ 41T. JEFF HUSON

TORONTO BLUE JAYS

- ☐ 54T. JOHN CANDELARIA
- ☐ 78T. STEVE CUMMINGS
- ☐ 81T. DEREK BELL
- ☐ 88T. WILLIE BLAIR
- ☐ 100T. ERIC LINDROS

1991 SCORE (893)
2 1/2 X 3 1/2

ATLANTA BRAVES

- ☐ 52. JEFF BLAUSER
- ☐ 55. DAVE JUSTICE
- ☐ 56. GREG OLSON
- ☐ 63. FRANCISCO CABRERA
- ☐ 79. KENT MERCKER
- ☐ 80. STEVE AVERY
- ☐ 121. ODDIBE MCDOWELL
- ☐ 205. PETE SMITH
- ☐ 206. TOM GLAVINE
- ☐ 208. JOHN SMOLTZ
- ☐ 219. JEFF TREADWAY
- ☐ 341. JIM VATCHER
- ☐ 375. MIKE BELL
- ☐ 448. RON GANT
- ☐ 468. MIKE STANTON
- ☐ 536. CHARLIE LEIBRANDT
- ☐ 543. LONNIE SMITH
- ☐ 565. JEFF PARRETT
- ☐ 582. TONY CASTILLO
- ☐ 606. TOMMY GREGG
- ☐ 613. ANDRES THOMAS
- ☐ 671. CHIPPER JONES
- ☐ 712. PAUL MARAK
- ☐ 736. JIMMY KREMERS
- ☐ 771. JIM PRESLEY
- ☐ 779. MARK LEMKE
- ☐ 824. MARK GRANT

BALTIMORE ORIOLES

- ☐ 86. RANDY MILLIGAN
- ☐ 95. CAL RIPKEN
- ☐ 243. JEFF BALLARD
- ☐ 249. BRADY ANDERSON
- ☐ 258. MIKE DEVEREAUX
- ☐ 259. BRAD KOMMINSK
- ☐ 266. STEVE FINLEY
- ☐ 270. MICKEY TETTLETON
- ☐ 334. CHRIS HOILES
- ☐ 354. ANTHONY TELFORD
- ☐ 362. DAVID SEGUI
- ☐ 369. JEFF MCKNIGHT
- ☐ 383. MIKE MUSSINA
- ☐ 487. BILL RIPKEN
- ☐ 490. GREGG OLSON
- ☐ 492. PETE HARNISCH
- ☐ 498. MARK WILLIAMSON
- ☐ 503. CRAIG WORTHINGTON
- ☐ 506. DAVE JOHNSON
- ☐ 508. JOE ORSULAK
- ☐ 512. BOB MILACKI
- ☐ 569. JOHN MITCHELL
- ☐ 605. SAM HORN
- ☐ 632. TIM HULETT
- ☐ 638. RENE GONZALES
- ☐ 645. BEN MCDONALD
- ☐ 715. DAN BOONE
- ☐ 725. LEO GOMEZ
- ☐ 788. CURT SCHILLING

1991 Score

BOSTON RED SOX

□ 8. ELLIS BURKS
□ 12. WADE BOGGS
□ 77. DANA KIECKER
□ 109. GREG HARRIS
□ 116. KEVIN ROMINE
□ 130. MIKE GREENWELL
□ 149. CARLOS QUINTANA
□ 164. JEFF REARDON
□ 173. JODY REED
□ 183. ROB MURPHY
□ 225. DWIGHT EVANS
□ 228. MARTY BARRETT
□ 232. MIKE BODDICKER
□ 245. TOM BRUNANSKY
□ 271. LUIS RIVERA
□ 333. DARYL IRVINE
□ 348. PHIL PLANTIER
□ 356. TIM NAEHRING
□ 586. JEFF GRAY
□ 592. WES GARDNER
□ 612. DENNIS LAMP
□ 617. MIKE MARSHALL
□ 655. ROGER CLEMENS
□ 739. MIKE ROCHFORD
□ 750. MO VAUGHN
□ 772. JOHN DOPSON
□ 781. TOM BOLTON
□ 790. TONY PENA
□ 827. DANNY HEEP
□ 831. JOHN MARZANO
□ 837. RANDY KUTCHER
□ 848. LARRY ANDERSEN

CALIFORNIA ANGELS

□ 21. MARK LANGSTON
□ 31. JOHNNY RAY
□ 37. LANCE PARRISH
□ 67. LEE STEVENS
□ 83. DAVE WINFIELD
□ 96. WILLIE FRASER
□ 100. CHUCK FINLEY
□ 104. BRIAN DOWNING
□ 105. JIM ABBOTT
□ 108. BRYAN HARVEY
□ 224. KENT ANDERSON
□ 235. BERT BLYLEVEN
□ 344. PETE COACHMAN
□ 367. JOE GRAHE
□ 463. DANTE BICHETTE
□ 466. DEVON WHITE
□ 467. JOHN ORTON
□ 470. WALLY JOYNER
□ 497. MIKE FETTERS
□ 504. MARK EICHHORN
□ 535. SCOTT BAILES
□ 587. LUIS POLONIA
□ 590. KIRK MCCASKILL
□ 759. SCOTT LEWIS
□ 768. GARY DISARCINA
□ 776. DICK SCHOFIELD
□ 803. CHILI DAVIS
□ 823. GREG MINTON
□ 842. JACK HOWELL

CHICAGO CUBS

□ 3. RYNE SANDBERG
□ 13. JEROME WALTON
□ 59. SHAWN BOSKIE
□ 71. HECTOR VILLANUEVA
□ 147. PAUL ASSENMACHER
□ 175. MARK GRACE
□ 201. SHAWON DUNSTON
□ 207. LUIS SALAZAR
□ 209. DOUG DASCENZO
□ 220. MITCH WILLIAMS
□ 293. LES LANCASTER
□ 301. DWIGHT SMITH
□ 306. STEVE WILSON
□ 317. GREG MADDUX
□ 322. MIKE HARKEY
□ 326. JEFF PICO
□ 378. DAVE PAVLAS
□ 379. DERRICK MAY
□ 385. LANCE DICKSON
□ 445. ANDRE DAWSON
□ 453. MIKE BIELECKI
□ 519. RICK WRONA
□ 531. MARVELL WYNNE
□ 542. DAVE CLARK
□ 559. BILL LONG
□ 585. JOE GIRARDI
□ 603. CURTIS WILKERSON
□ 755. JOE KRAEMER
□ 785. RICK SUTCLIFFE
□ 881. DAMON BERRYHILL

CHICAGO WHITE SOX

□ 11. OZZIE GUILLEN
□ 27. JACK MCDOWELL
□ 36. SCOTT FLETCHER
□ 62. SCOTT RADINSKY
□ 66. WAYNE EDWARDS
□ 69. CRAIG GREBECK
□ 85. DAN PASQUA
□ 115. BARRY JONES
□ 124. ERIC KING
□ 128. GREG HIBBARD
□ 132. DONN PALL
□ 157. LANCE JOHNSON
□ 179. MELIDO PEREZ
□ 254. IVAN CALDERON
□ 256. SAMMY SOSA
□ 265. CARLTON FISK
□ 269. STEVE LYONS
□ 274. CARLOS MARTINEZ
□ 280. BOBBY THIGPEN
□ 320. ROBIN VENTURA
□ 382. ALEX FERNANDEZ
□ 560. PHIL BRADLEY
□ 604. ADAM PETERSON
□ 749. JERRY KUTZLER
□ 751. MATT STARK
□ 763. RODNEY MCCRAY
□ 833. RON KARKOVICE
□ 840. FRANK THOMAS

CINCINNATI REDS

□ 17. ROB DIBBLE
□ 18. GLENN BRAGGS
□ 64. TIM LAYANA
□ 90. TODD BENZINGER
□ 137. ERIC DAVIS
□ 227. PAUL O'NEILL
□ 229. TOM BROWNING
□ 231. JACK ARMSTRONG
□ 373. ROSARIO RODRIGUEZ
□ 462. CHRIS SABO
□ 464. RICK MAHLER
□ 469. BILLY HATCHER
□ 479. MARIANO DUNCAN
□ 501. RANDY MYERS
□ 505. BARRY LARKIN
□ 530. NORM CHARLTON
□ 601. DANNY JACKSON
□ 620. JOE OLIVER
□ 642. SCOTT SCUDDER
□ 647. HAL MORRIS
□ 648. TIM BIRTSAS
□ 651. RON OESTER
□ 656. HERM WINNINGHAM
□ 658. JOSE RIJO
□ 681. DAN WILSON

□ 767. GLENN SUTKO
□ 775. BILL DORAN
□ 822. LUIS QUINONES

CLEVELAND INDIANS

□ 19. CORY SNYDER
□ 45. DOUG JONES
□ 50. JOHN FARRELL
□ 74. CARLOS BAERGA
□ 75. CHARLES NAGY
□ 89. KEITH HERNANDEZ
□ 93. CANDY MALDONADO
□ 106. TOM BROOKENS
□ 110. GREG SWINDELL
□ 131. DION JAMES
□ 139. FELIX FERMIN
□ 162. BROOK JACOBY
□ 337. JEFF MANTO
□ 338. BEAU ALLRED
□ 355. KEVIN WICKANDER
□ 481. JERRY BROWNE
□ 488. TOM CANDIOTTI
□ 491. CHRIS JAMES
□ 496. STEVE OLIN
□ 555. ALEX COLE
□ 578. JESSE OROSCO
□ 594. MITCH WEBSTER
□ 680. TIM COSTO
□ 723. EFRAIN VALDEZ
□ 732. TURNER WARD
□ 746. JEFF SHAW
□ 793. SANDY ALOMAR
□ 809. JOEL SKINNER
□ 843. MAURO GOZZO

DETROIT TIGERS

□ 38. TONY PHILLIPS
□ 40. ALAN TRAMMELL
□ 112. MIKE HEATH
□ 114. JACK MORRIS
□ 129. JEFF ROBINSON
□ 133. LLOYD MOSEBY
□ 142. MIKE HENNEMAN
□ 152. PAUL GIBSON
□ 168. CECIL FIELDER
□ 176. LARRY SHEETS
□ 297. LOU WHITAKER
□ 313. LANCE MCCULLERS
□ 316. JERRY DON GLEATON
□ 328. FRANK TANANA
□ 434. DAN PETRY
□ 557. CHET LEMON
□ 562. DAVE BERGMAN
□ 570. TRAVIS FRYMAN
□ 609. JOHN SHELBY
□ 629. DARNELL COLES
□ 637. GARY WARD
□ 649. STEVE SEARCY
□ 740. SCOTT ALDRED
□ 741. RICO BROGNA
□ 756. PHIL CLARK
□ 801. WALT TERRELL

HOUSTON ASTROS

□ 46. MIKE SCOTT
□ 51. DANNY DARWIN
□ 146. ERIC ANTHONY
□ 161. CRAIG BIGGIO
□ 177. BILL GULLICKSON
□ 186. KEN CAMINITI
□ 193. JIM DESHAIES
□ 214. KEN OBERKFELL
□ 298. GLENN WILSON
□ 305. RAFAEL RAMIREZ
□ 308. FRANKLIN STUBBS
□ 314. DAVE SMITH
□ 319. MARK PORTUGAL
□ 329. ERIC YELDING
□ 365. KARL RHODES
□ 387. TOM NEVERS
□ 564. XAVIER HERNANDEZ
□ 577. CASEY CANDAELE
□ 591. JUAN AGOSTO
□ 752. RANDY HENNIS
□ 753. ANDUJAR CEDENO
□ 766. MIKE SIMMS
□ 830. GLENN DAVIS
□ 844. GERALD YOUNG

KANSAS CITY ROYALS

- ☐ 5. BO JACKSON
- ☐ 6. BRET SABERHAGEN
- ☐ 120. GEORGE BRETT
- ☐ 136. MARK DAVIS
- ☐ 143. JEFF MONTGOMERY
- ☐ 154. JIM EISENREICH
- ☐ 172. STEVE FARR
- ☐ 197. TOM GORDON
- ☐ 212. MARK GUBICZA
- ☐ 268. KEVIN APPIER
- ☐ 272. STEVE JELTZ
- ☐ 279. KEVIN SEITZER
- ☐ 286. GERALD PERRY
- ☐ 287. STEVE CRAWFORD
- ☐ 295. KURT STILLWELL
- ☐ 331. BRIAN MCRAE
- ☐ 336. JEFF SCHULZ
- ☐ 349. TERRY SHUMPERT
- ☐ 361. MEL STOTTLEMYRE
- ☐ 511. STORM DAVIS
- ☐ 513. BILL PECOTA
- ☐ 515. DANNY TARTABULL
- ☐ 619. ANDY MCGAFFIGAN
- ☐ 722. JEFF CONINE
- ☐ 730. HECTOR WAGNER
- ☐ 764. SEAN BERRY
- ☐ 765. BRENT MAYNE
- ☐ 839. MIKE MACFARLANE

LOS ANGELES DODGERS

- ☐ 20. KAL DANIELS
- ☐ 29. JAY HOWELL
- ☐ 144. LENNY HARRIS
- ☐ 153. MICKEY HATCHER
- ☐ 178. CHRIS GWYNN
- ☐ 187. TIM BELCHER
- ☐ 196. HUBIE BROOKS
- ☐ 252. MIKE HARTLEY
- ☐ 267. JOHN WETTELAND
- ☐ 276. MIKE MORGAN
- ☐ 281. STAN JAVIER
- ☐ 289. DON AASE
- ☐ 300. RAMON MARTINEZ
- ☐ 302. TIM CREWS
- ☐ 310. EDDIE MURRAY
- ☐ 343. JOSE OFFERMAN
- ☐ 351. DAVID WALSH
- ☐ 357. JIM POOLE
- ☐ 359. TERRY WELLS
- ☐ 442. ALFREDO GRIFFIN
- ☐ 446. JUAN SAMUEL
- ☐ 449. FERNANDO VALENZUELA
- ☐ 520. MIKE SCIOSCIA
- ☐ 527. PAT PERRY
- ☐ 546. MIKE SHARPERSON
- ☐ 550. OREL HERSHISER
- ☐ 614. JOSE GONZALEZ
- ☐ 621. JIM GOTT
- ☐ 679. RON WALDEN
- ☐ 787. JOSE VIZCAINO
- ☐ 794. JIM NEIDLINGER
- ☐ 800. KIRK GIBSON
- ☐ 816. RICK DEMPSEY

MILWAUKEE BREWERS

- ☐ 43. CHRIS BOSIO
- ☐ 49. PAUL MOLITOR
- ☐ 78. TOM EDENS
- ☐ 84. BILL SPIERS
- ☐ 97. MIKE FELDER
- ☐ 99. CHUCK CRIM
- ☐ 102. JAIME NAVARRO
- ☐ 107. DARRYL HAMILTON
- ☐ 239. MARK KNUDSON
- ☐ 248. ROB DEER
- ☐ 260. TEDDY HIGUERA
- ☐ 275. DAN PLESAC
- ☐ 347. TIM MCINTOSH
- ☐ 372. MARK LEE
- ☐ 473. GARY SHEFFIELD
- ☐ 477. B.J. SURHOFF
- ☐ 483. BILL WEGMAN
- ☐ 484. DAVE PARKER
- ☐ 517. RON ROBINSON
- ☐ 522. GREG BROCK
- ☐ 525. ROBIN YOUNT
- ☐ 528. GREG VAUGHN
- ☐ 532. JIM GANTNER
- ☐ 558. PAUL MIRABELLA
- ☐ 576. EDGAR DIAZ
- ☐ 598. BILL KRUEGER
- ☐ 634. TONY FOSSAS
- ☐ 814. DALE SVEUM

MINNESOTA TWINS

- ☐ 60. KEVIN TAPANI
- ☐ 76. TIM DRUMMOND
- ☐ 111. JUAN BERENGUER
- ☐ 135. ALLAN ANDERSON
- ☐ 151. ROY SMITH
- ☐ 158. DAVE WEST
- ☐ 163. DAN GLADDEN
- ☐ 170. RICK AGUILERA
- ☐ 200. KIRBY PUCKETT
- ☐ 211. GREG GAGNE
- ☐ 283. GARY WAYNE
- ☐ 284. SHANE MACK
- ☐ 288. NELSON LIRIANO
- ☐ 292. KENT HRBEK
- ☐ 312. BRIAN HARPER
- ☐ 325. GARY GAETTI
- ☐ 332. PEDRO MUNOZ
- ☐ 363. PAUL ABBOTT
- ☐ 370. SCOTT LEIUS
- ☐ 424. AL NEWMAN
- ☐ 429. JOHN MOSES
- ☐ 438. JUNIOR ORTIZ
- ☐ 471. GENE LARKIN
- ☐ 556. TERRY LEACH
- ☐ 574. RANDY BUSH
- ☐ 608. CARMELO CASTILLO
- ☐ 678. TODD RITCHIE
- ☐ 778. MARK GUTHRIE
- ☐ 796. PAUL SORRENTO
- ☐ 812. SCOTT ERICKSON

MONTREAL EXPOS

- ☐ 22. KEVIN GROSS
- ☐ 35. TIM RAINES
- ☐ 68. BILL SAMPEN
- ☐ 82. DAVE MARTINEZ
- ☐ 156. DAVE SCHMIDT
- ☐ 181. TIM BURKE
- ☐ 198. MIKE FITZGERALD
- ☐ 202. DENNIS BOYD
- ☐ 210. TIM WALLACH
- ☐ 234. MARQUIS GRISSOM
- ☐ 241. LARRY WALKER
- ☐ 390. RONDELL WHITE
- ☐ 423. JUNIOR NOBOA
- ☐ 431. OTIS NIXON
- ☐ 436. STEVE FREY
- ☐ 443. ANDRES GALARRAGA
- ☐ 447. MIKE ALDRETE
- ☐ 452. SPIKE OWEN
- ☐ 454. DENNIS MARTINEZ
- ☐ 518. MARK GARDNER
- ☐ 526. TOM FOLEY
- ☐ 545. DELINO DESHIELDS
- ☐ 581. DREW HALL
- ☐ 596. DALE MOHORCIC
- ☐ 674. SHANE ANDREWS
- ☐ 708. BRIAN BARNES
- ☐ 718. HOWARD FARMER
- ☐ 729. MEL ROJAS
- ☐ 734. SCOTT ANDERSON
- ☐ 777. NELSON SANTOVENIA
- ☐ 799. SCOTT RUSKIN
- ☐ 804. CHRIS NABHOLZ
- ☐ 813. MOISES ALOU
- ☐ 834. JERRY GOFF

NEW YORK METS

- ☐ 14. JOHN FRANCO
- ☐ 165. MARK CARREON
- ☐ 180. SID FERNANDEZ
- ☐ 185. HOWARD JOHNSON
- ☐ 190. DAVE MAGADAN
- ☐ 204. ALEJANDRO PENA
- ☐ 294. JEFF MUSSELMAN
- ☐ 307. MACKEY SASSER
- ☐ 318. KEITH MILLER
- ☐ 321. BOB OJEDA
- ☐ 327. KEVIN MCREYNOLDS
- ☐ 340. TODD HUNDLEY
- ☐ 353. JULIO VALERA
- ☐ 368. DARREN REED
- ☐ 380. JEROMY BURNITZ
- ☐ 427. TIM TEUFEL
- ☐ 439. TOM O'MALLEY
- ☐ 456. RON DARLING
- ☐ 460. FRANK VIOLA
- ☐ 529. WALLY WHITEHURST
- ☐ 540. DWIGHT GOODEN
- ☐ 549. DAVID CONE
- ☐ 618. DARYL BOSTON
- ☐ 633. KEVIN ELSTER
- ☐ 640. DARRYL STRAWBERRY
- ☐ 660. GREGG JEFFERIES
- ☐ 754. KELVIN TORVE
- ☐ 811. PAT TABLER
- ☐ 820. TOM HERR
- ☐ 829. CHARLIE O'BRIEN

NEW YORK YANKEES

- ☐ 23. DON MATTINGLY
- ☐ 24. DAVE RIGHETTI
- ☐ 32. STEVE SAX
- ☐ 34. LEE GUETTERMAN
- ☐ 47. ANDY HAWKINS
- ☐ 65. JIM LEYRITZ
- ☐ 72. OSCAR AZOCAR
- ☐ 73. ALAN MILLS
- ☐ 119. ROBERTO KELLY
- ☐ 127. ALVARO ESPINOZA
- ☐ 134. RANDY VELARDE
- ☐ 148. JESSE BARFIELD
- ☐ 159. STEVE BALBONI
- ☐ 166. MEL HALL
- ☐ 188. GREG CADARET
- ☐ 192. JEFF ROBINSON
- ☐ 218. DAVE LAPOINT
- ☐ 386. CARL EVERETT
- ☐ 428. ERIC PLUNK
- ☐ 430. MIKE WITT
- ☐ 435. BOB GEREN
- ☐ 551. MATT NOKES
- ☐ 566. CHUCK CARY
- ☐ 580. RICK CERONE
- ☐ 583. JIMMY JONES
- ☐ 600. KEVIN MAAS
- ☐ 631. TIM LEARY
- ☐ 716. STEVE ADKINS
- ☐ 727. MARK LEITER
- ☐ 826. DAVE EILAND
- ☐ 828. HENSLEY MEULENS
- ☐ 838. MIKE BLOWERS

OAKLAND A'S

- ☐ 1. JOSE CANSECO
- ☐ 10. RICKEY HENDERSON
- ☐ 41. TODD BURNS
- ☐ 118. SCOTT SANDERSON
- ☐ 150. DAVE STEWART
- ☐ 171. WALT WEISS
- ☐ 194. WILLIE RANDOLPH
- ☐ 236. CURT YOUNG
- ☐ 291. HAROLD BAINES
- ☐ 303. LANCE BLANKENSHIP
- ☐ 311. BOB WELCH
- ☐ 324. MARK MCGWIRE
- ☐ 339. MIKE BORDICK
- ☐ 346. OZZIE CANSECO
- ☐ 350. DARREN LEWIS
- ☐ 364. STEVE HOWARD
- ☐ 381. DON PETERS
- ☐ 389. TODD VAN POPPEL
- ☐ 476. MIKE GALLEGO
- ☐ 478. GENE NELSON
- ☐ 485. DENNIS ECKERSLEY
- ☐ 516. MIKE MOORE
- ☐ 539. RICK HONEYCUTT
- ☐ 588. JOE KLINK
- ☐ 597. WILLIE MCGEE
- ☐ 630. CARNEY LANSFORD
- ☐ 643. REGGIE HARRIS
- ☐ 644. DAVE HENDERSON
- ☐ 745. TROY AFENIR
- ☐ 760. STEVE CHITREN
- ☐ 761. RAY YOUNG
- ☐ 780. TERRY STEINBACH
- ☐ 806. RON HASSEY
- ☐ 819. DOUG JENNINGS

PHILADELPHIA PHILLIES

- ☐ 15. RICKY JORDAN
- ☐ 33. TERRY MULHOLLAND
- ☐ 61. DAVE HOLLINS
- ☐ 94. JOHN KRUK
- ☐ 103. DICKIE THON
- ☐ 223. DARREL AKERFELDS
- ☐ 237. DON CARMAN
- ☐ 238. CHARLIE HAYES
- ☐ 246. DARREN DAULTON
- ☐ 250. LENNY DYKSTRA
- ☐ 374. CHUCK MCELROY
- ☐ 376. MICKEY MORANDINI
- ☐ 426. VON HAYES
- ☐ 440. PAT COMBS
- ☐ 458. KEN HOWELL
- ☐ 524. BRUCE RUFFIN
- ☐ 537. ROGER MCDOWELL
- ☐ 572. STEVE LAKE
- ☐ 615. RANDY READY
- ☐ 623. JOSE DEJESUS
- ☐ 650. DALE MURPHY
- ☐ 653. RON JONES
- ☐ 683. MIKE LIEBERTHAL
- ☐ 713. WES CHAMBERLAIN
- ☐ 724. CHUCK MALONE
- ☐ 808. TOMMY GREENE
- ☐ 818. JASON GRIMSLEY
- ☐ 832. STEVE ONTIVEROS
- ☐ 847. SIL CAMPUSANO

PITTSBURGH PIRATES

- ☐ 16. WALLY BACKMAN
- ☐ 98. BILL LANDRUM
- ☐ 222. MIKE LAVALLIERE
- ☐ 226. GARY REDUS
- ☐ 233. NEAL HEATON
- ☐ 244. JEFF KING
- ☐ 255. TED POWER
- ☐ 273. R.J. REYNOLDS
- ☐ 296. STAN BELINDA
- ☐ 304. SID BREAM
- ☐ 315. BOBBY BONILLA
- ☐ 323. JAY BELL
- ☐ 330. BARRY BONDS
- ☐ 461. JOSE LIND
- ☐ 465. JOHN SMILEY
- ☐ 472. DOUG DRABEK
- ☐ 475. ANDY VAN SLYKE
- ☐ 584. RICK REED
- ☐ 599. BOB WALK
- ☐ 610. DON SLAUGHT
- ☐ 636. BOB PATTERSON
- ☐ 646. BOB KIPPER
- ☐ 659. DANN BILARDELLO
- ☐ 682. KURT MILLER
- ☐ 738. MIKE YORK
- ☐ 747. ORLANDO MERCED
- ☐ 782. RANDY TOMLIN
- ☐ 792. CARMELO MARTINEZ
- ☐ 845. ZANE SMITH

ST. LOUIS CARDINALS

- ☐ 53. JOHN TUDOR
- ☐ 54. MILT THOMPSON
- ☐ 81. LEE SMITH
- ☐ 140. PEDRO GUERRERO
- ☐ 217. TOM NIEDENFUER
- ☐ 221. JOSE DELEON
- ☐ 230. TERRY PENDLETON
- ☐ 240. TODD ZEILE
- ☐ 247. SCOTT TERRY
- ☐ 444. BRYN SMITH
- ☐ 450. VINCE COLEMAN
- ☐ 499. BOB TEWKSBURY
- ☐ 553. FRANK DIPINO
- ☐ 567. KEN HILL
- ☐ 575. JOE MAGRANE
- ☐ 589. REX HUDLER
- ☐ 607. KEN DAYLEY
- ☐ 622. JOSE OQUENDO
- ☐ 676. AARON HOLBERT
- ☐ 677. DONOVAN OSBORNE
- ☐ 709. BERNARD GILKEY
- ☐ 717. GERONIMO PENA
- ☐ 731. RAY LANKFORD
- ☐ 743. RAY STEPHENS
- ☐ 748. OMAR OLIVARES
- ☐ 758. MIKE PEREZ
- ☐ 784. FELIX JOSE
- ☐ 797. TOM PAGNOZZI
- ☐ 807. TODD WORRELL
- ☐ 825. OZZIE SMITH

SAN DIEGO PADRES

- ☐ 9. JOE CARTER
- ☐ 25. ROBERTO ALOMAR
- ☐ 28. BIP ROBERTS
- ☐ 117. GARRY TEMPLETON
- ☐ 138. PHIL STEPHENSON
- ☐ 145. BRUCE HURST
- ☐ 169. DARRIN JACKSON
- ☐ 184. CRAIG LEFFERTS
- ☐ 199. MIKE PAGLIARULO
- ☐ 213. MARK PARENT
- ☐ 242. JERALD CLARK
- ☐ 251. GREG HARRIS
- ☐ 253. JOEY CORA
- ☐ 261. SHAWN ABNER
- ☐ 335. THOMAS HOWARD
- ☐ 360. RAFAEL VALDEZ
- ☐ 457. DENNIS RASMUSSEN
- ☐ 500. TONY GWYNN
- ☐ 523. JACK CLARK
- ☐ 538. ANDY BENES
- ☐ 552. EDDIE WILLIAMS
- ☐ 554. FRED LYNN
- ☐ 563. ERIC SHOW
- ☐ 571. DEREK LILLIQUIST
- ☐ 593. RICH RODRIGUEZ
- ☐ 611. CALVIN SCHIRALDI
- ☐ 673. ROBBIE BECKETT
- ☐ 711. PAUL FARIES
- ☐ 720. TOM LAMPKIN
- ☐ 789. ED WHITSON
- ☐ 810. BENNY SANTIAGO

SAN FRANCISCO GIANTS

- ☐ 7. WILL CLARK
- ☐ 26. ROBBY THOMPSON
- ☐ 58. RICK PARKER
- ☐ 70. JOHN BURKETT
- ☐ 101. KIRT MANWARING
- ☐ 160. JEFF BRANTLEY
- ☐ 189. MATT WILLIAMS
- ☐ 215. GARY CARTER
- ☐ 345. MIKE BENJAMIN
- ☐ 366. RAFAEL NOVOA
- ☐ 371. MARK DEWEY
- ☐ 388. ADAM HYZDU
- ☐ 451. KEVIN MITCHELL
- ☐ 455. BRETT BUTLER
- ☐ 459. STEVE BEDROSIAN
- ☐ 533. GREG LITTON
- ☐ 541. SCOTT GARRELTS
- ☐ 544. RICK REUSCHEL
- ☐ 547. MIKE KINGERY
- ☐ 548. TERRY KENNEDY
- ☐ 616. KEVIN BASS
- ☐ 626. ERNEST RILES
- ☐ 628. JOSE URIBE
- ☐ 635. FRANCISCO OLIVERAS
- ☐ 639. DON ROBINSON
- ☐ 641. DAVE ANDERSON
- ☐ 652. MIKE LACOSS
- ☐ 654. KELLY DOWNS
- ☐ 657. TREVOR WILSON
- ☐ 672. ERIC CHRISTOPHERSON
- ☐ 710. STEVE DECKER
- ☐ 719. MARK LEONARD
- ☐ 726. PAUL MCCLELLAN
- ☐ 735. TONY PEREZCHICA
- ☐ 744. ERIC GUNDERSON
- ☐ 757. ED VOSBERG
- ☐ 762. ANDRES SANTANA

SEATTLE MARINERS

- ☐ 2. KEN GRIFFEY, JR.
- ☐ 44. JEFFREY LEONARD
- ☐ 48. HAROLD REYNOLDS
- ☐ 87. TRACY JONES
- ☐ 91. MIKE JACKSON
- ☐ 113. SCOTT BRADLEY
- ☐ 123. BILL SWIFT
- ☐ 125. JAY BUHNER
- ☐ 126. MATT YOUNG
- ☐ 262. DAVE VALLE
- ☐ 264. EDGAR MARTINEZ
- ☐ 282. HENRY COTTO
- ☐ 285. BRIAN HOLMAN
- ☐ 290. RANDY JOHNSON
- ☐ 299. OMAR VIZQUEL
- ☐ 391. MARC NEWFIELD
- ☐ 482. ALVIN DAVIS
- ☐ 486. ERIK HANSON
- ☐ 489. MIKE SCHOOLER
- ☐ 494. GREG BRILEY
- ☐ 502. KEITH COMSTOCK
- ☐ 509. PETE O'BRIEN
- ☐ 624. MIKE BRUMLEY
- ☐ 627. GENE HARRIS
- ☐ 721. MIKE GARDINER
- ☐ 728. RICH DELUCIA
- ☐ 742. DAVE BURBA
- ☐ 774. BRENT KNACKERT
- ☐ 798. TINO MARTINEZ
- ☐ 817. SCOTT BANKHEAD
- ☐ 835. KEN GRIFFEY

TEXAS RANGERS

- ☐ 4. NOLAN RYAN
- ☐ 92. MIKE STANLEY
- ☐ 141. CHARLIE HOUGH
- ☐ 155. KENNY ROGERS
- ☐ 167. GARY MIELKE
- ☐ 174. MIKE JEFFCOAT
- ☐ 182. GARY PETTIS
- ☐ 191. GENO PETRALLI
- ☐ 216. RAFAEL PALMEIRO
- ☐ 257. STEVE BUECHELE
- ☐ 263. JEFF HUSON
- ☐ 277. JEFF RUSSELL
- ☐ 278. PETE INCAVIGLIA
- ☐ 309. JACK DAUGHERTY
- ☐ 352. SCOTT CHIAMPARINO
- ☐ 377. BILL HASELMAN
- ☐ 384. DAN SMITH
- ☐ 437. JAMIE MOYER
- ☐ 493. JULIO FRANCO
- ☐ 495. RUBEN SIERRA
- ☐ 507. BOBBY WITT
- ☐ 510. BRAD ARNSBERG
- ☐ 573. JOHN BARFIELD
- ☐ 602. CRAIG MCMURTRY
- ☐ 714. KEVIN BELCHER
- ☐ 733. GERALD ALEXANDER
- ☐ 783. JEFF KUNKEL
- ☐ 802. JOHN RUSSELL
- ☐ 805. JUAN GONZALEZ
- ☐ 836. KEVIN REIMER
- ☐ 846. KEVIN BROWN

TORONTO BLUE JAYS

- ☐ 30. DAVE STIEB
- ☐ 39. TODD STOTTLEMYRE
- ☐ 42. MOOKIE WILSON
- ☐ 57. WILLIE BLAIR
- ☐ 88. GREG MYERS
- ☐ 122. JIM ACKER
- ☐ 195. GEORGE BELL
- ☐ 203. JUNIOR FELIX
- ☐ 342. LUIS SOJO
- ☐ 358. MARK WHITEN

- ☐ 422. JIMMY KEY
- ☐ 425. PAT BORDERS
- ☐ 432. TONY FERNANDEZ
- ☐ 433. RANCE MULLINIKS
- ☐ 474. DAVID WELLS
- ☐ 480. FRED MCGRIFF
- ☐ 514. GLENALLEN HILL
- ☐ 521. FRANK WILLS
- ☐ 534. MANNY LEE
- ☐ 561. DUANE WARD
- ☐ 579. TOM HENKE
- ☐ 595. KELLY GRUBER
- ☐ 625. JOHN OLERUD
- ☐ 675. STEVE KARSAY
- ☐ 786. JOHN CERUTTI
- ☐ 791. JOHN CANDELARIA
- ☐ 821. ROB DUCEY

1991 SCORE ROOKIE & TRADED (110) 2 1/2 X 3 1/2

ATLANTA BRAVES

- ☐ 12T. SID BREAM
- ☐ 29T. OTIS NIXON
- ☐ 34T. DEION SANDERS
- ☐ 50T. TERRY PENDLETON
- ☐ 69T. MIKE HEATH
- ☐ 73T. JUAN BERENGUER
- ☐ 76T. RAFAEL BELLIARD

BALTIMORE ORIOLES

- ☐ 2T. MIKE FLANAGAN
- ☐ 7T. GLENN DAVIS
- ☐ 62T. DWIGHT EVANS

BOSTON RED SOX

- ☐ 4T. JACK CLARK
- ☐ 24T. DANNY DARWIN
- ☐ 54T. MATT YOUNG

CALIFORNIA ANGELS

- ☐ 20T. JUNIOR FELIX
- ☐ 39T. GARY GAETTI
- ☐ 49T. LUIS SOJO

CHICAGO CUBS

- ☐ 9T. DAVE SMITH
- ☐ 13T. GEORGE BELL
- ☐ 17T. DANNY JACKSON
- ☐ 84T. HEATH SLOCUMB
- ☐ 90T. GARY SCOTT
- ☐ 95T. ERIK PAPPAS
- ☐ 102T. BOB SCANLAN
- ☐ 103T. RICK WILKINS

CHICAGO WHITE SOX

- ☐ 1T. BO JACKSON
- ☐ 10T. TIM RAINES
- ☐ 52T. MIKE HUFF
- ☐ 81T. BRIAN DRAHMAN

CINCINNATI REDS

- ☐ 92T. CHRIS JONES
- ☐ 98T. FREDDIE BENAVIDES

CLEVELAND INDIANS

- ☐ 60T. ERIC KING
- ☐ 65T. SHAWN HILLEGAS
- ☐ 106T. MARK LEWIS
- ☐ 109T. LUIS LOPEZ

DETROIT TIGERS

- ☐ 3T. PETE INCAVIGLIA
- ☐ 25T. MICKEY TETTLETON
- ☐ 40T. JOHN CERUTTI
- ☐ 47T. ROB DEER
- ☐ 56T. BILL GULLICKSON

HOUSTON ASTROS

- ☐ 36T. PETE HARNISCH
- ☐ 80T. CURT SCHILLING
- ☐ 86T. DARRYL KILE
- ☐ 89T. AL OSUNA
- ☐ 96T. JEFF BAGWELL
- ☐ 99T. LUIS GONZALEZ

KANSAS CITY ROYALS

- ☐ 18T. KIRK GIBSON
- ☐ 45T. MIKE BODDICKER
- ☐ 83T. DAVID HOWARD

LOS ANGELES DODGERS

- ☐ 16T. DARRYL STRAWBERRY
- ☐ 23T. BRETT BUTLER
- ☐ 26T. GARY CARTER
- ☐ 32T. JOHN CANDELARIA
- ☐ 51T. KEVIN GROSS
- ☐ 68T. MITCH WEBSTER
- ☐ 79T. BOB OJEDA

MILWAUKEE BREWERS

- ☐ 35T. WILLIE RANDOLPH
- ☐ 37T. DANTE BICHETTE
- ☐ 59T. FRANKLIN STUBBS

MINNESOTA TWINS

- ☐ 14T. STEVE BEDROSIAN
- ☐ 42T. MIKE PAGLIARULO
- ☐ 70T. CHILI DAVIS
- ☐ 74T. JACK MORRIS
- ☐ 93T. CHUCK KNOBLAUCH

MONTREAL EXPOS

- ☐ 6T. IVAN CALDERON
- ☐ 43T. RON HASSEY
- ☐ 75T. BARRY JONES

NEW YORK METS

- ☐ 5T. HUBIE BROOKS
- ☐ 38T. GARRY TEMPLETON
- ☐ 41T. RICK CERONE
- ☐ 57T. VINCE COLEMAN
- ☐ 87T. PETE SCHOUREK
- ☐ 91T. DOUG SIMONS
- ☐ 104T. CHRIS DONNELS

NEW YORK YANKEES

- ☐ 21T. STEVE FARR
- ☐ 78T. SCOTT SANDERSON
- ☐ 100T. WADE TAYLOR
- ☐ 107T. PAT KELLY
- ☐ 110T. JEFF JOHNSON

OAKLAND A'S

- ☐ 15T. WILLIE WILSON
- ☐ 55T. ERNEST RILES
- ☐ 64T. ERIC SHOW
- ☐ 88T. BRUCE WALTON
- ☐ 94T. DANA ALLISON
- ☐ 97T. KIRK DRESSENDORFER
- ☐ 105T. JOE SLUSARSKI
- ☐ 108T. JOHN BRISCOE

PHILADELPHIA PHILLIES

- ☐ 8T. WALLY BACKMAN
- ☐ 27T. MITCH WILLIAMS

PITTSBURGH PIRATES

- ☐ 72T. GARY VARSHO
- ☐ 77T. STEVE BUECHELE

ST. LOUIS CARDINALS

- ☐ 63T. GERALD PERRY

SAN DIEGO PADRES

- ☐ 58T. FRED MCGRIFF
- ☐ 66T. TONY FERNANDEZ
- ☐ 67T. TIM TEUFEL
- ☐ 71T. LARRY ANDERSEN

SAN FRANCISCO GIANTS

- ☐ 19T. WILLIE MCGEE
- ☐ 46T. BUD BLACK
- ☐ 53T. DAVE RIGHETTI

SEATTLE MARINERS

- ☐ 33T. ROB MURPHY

TEXAS RANGERS

- ☐ 30T. BRIAN DOWNING
- ☐ 82T. IVAN RODRIGUEZ

TORONTO BLUE JAYS

- ☐ 11T. JOE CARTER
- ☐ 22T. PAT TABLER
- ☐ 28T. CANDY MALDONADO
- ☐ 31T. TOM CANDIOTTI
- ☐ 44T. ROBERTO ALOMAR
- ☐ 48T. DEVON WHITE
- ☐ 61T. CORY SNYDER
- ☐ 85T. MIKE TIMLIN
- ☐ 101T. ED SPRAGUE

1992 SCORE (893)
2 1/2 X 3 1/2

ATLANTA BRAVES

- ☐ 4. DAVE JUSTICE
- ☐ 13. LONNIE SMITH
- ☐ 18. TERRY PENDLETON
- ☐ 25. RON GANT
- ☐ 105. CHARLIE LEIBRANDT
- ☐ 116. RAFAEL BELLIARD
- ☐ 131. SID BREAM
- ☐ 142. JEFF TREADWAY
- ☐ 178. KENT MERCKER
- ☐ 188. JERRY WILLARD
- ☐ 216. JUAN BERENGUER
- ☐ 241. STEVE AVERY
- ☐ 249. MIKE BELL
- ☐ 287. JOHN SMOLTZ
- ☐ 307. MARVIN FREEMAN
- ☐ 344. MIKE HEATH
- ☐ 362. JEFF BLAUSER
- ☐ 386. MARK LEMKE
- ☐ 417. BRIAN HUNTER
- ☐ 443. OTIS NIXON
- ☐ 450. TOM GLAVINE
- ☐ 464. PETE SMITH
- ☐ 474. GREG OLSON
- ☐ 498. MIKE STANTON
- ☐ 571. DEION SANDERS
- ☐ 581. FRANCISCO CABRERA
- ☐ 623. TOMMY GREGG
- ☐ 627. JIM CLANCY
- ☐ 691. ALEJANDRO PENA
- ☐ 708. RANDY ST. CLAIRE
- ☐ 748. KEITH MITCHELL
- ☐ 759. MARK WOHLERS
- ☐ 817. RICO ROSSY
- ☐ 860. VINNY CASTILLA
- ☐ 877. ARMANDO REYNOSO

BALTIMORE ORIOLES

- ☐ 36. MIKE DEVEREAUX
- ☐ 71. GREGG OLSON
- ☐ 87. RANDY MILLIGAN
- ☐ 97. BILLY RIPKEN
- ☐ 129. JEFF BALLARD
- ☐ 150. DWIGHT EVANS
- ☐ 186. JEFF ROBINSON
- ☐ 208. BOB MELVIN
- ☐ 240. LEO GOMEZ
- ☐ 256. ROY SMITH
- ☐ 268. PAUL KILGUS
- ☐ 290. SAM HORN
- ☐ 314. BOB MILACKI
- ☐ 333. MIKE FLANAGAN
- ☐ 365. BRADY ANDERSON
- ☐ 391. TIM HULETT
- ☐ 400. CHITO MARTINEZ
- ☐ 487. MARK WILLIAMSON
- ☐ 534. TODD FROHWIRTH
- ☐ 540. CAL RIPKEN
- ☐ 551. JOE ORSULAK
- ☐ 554. DAVID SEGUI
- ☐ 604. DAVE JOHNSON
- ☐ 615. GLENN DAVIS
- ☐ 641. CHRIS HOILES
- ☐ 646. JUAN BELL
- ☐ 658. BEN MCDONALD
- ☐ 693. JIM POOLE
- ☐ 707. JOSE MESA
- ☐ 724. CRAIG WORTHINGTON
- ☐ 736. ARTHUR LEE RHODES
- ☐ 755. MIKE MUSSINA
- ☐ 826. LUIS MERCEDES
- ☐ 832. STACY JONES
- ☐ 853. ANTHONY TELFORD

BOSTON RED SOX

- ☐ 21. ROGER CLEMENS
- ☐ 46. TOM BRUNANSKY
- ☐ 58. JEFF REARDON
- ☐ 85. JODY REED
- ☐ 99. TOM BOLTON
- ☐ 138. DANNY DARWIN
- ☐ 156. GREG HARRIS
- ☐ 159. LUIS RIVERA
- ☐ 187. JEFF GRAY
- ☐ 189. CARLOS QUINTANA
- ☐ 259. TIM NAEHRING
- ☐ 270. ELLIS BURKS
- ☐ 294. STEVE LYONS
- ☐ 318. JACK CLARK
- ☐ 335. DENNIS LAMP
- ☐ 359. JOE HESKETH
- ☐ 363. MIKE BRUMLEY
- ☐ 389. TONY FOSSAS
- ☐ 406. PHIL PLANTIER
- ☐ 420. KEVIN MORTON
- ☐ 446. TONY PENA
- ☐ 539. JOHN MARZANO
- ☐ 545. MIKE GREENWELL
- ☐ 556. MO VAUGHN
- ☐ 660. WADE BOGGS
- ☐ 668. MATT YOUNG
- ☐ 694. MIKE GARDINER
- ☐ 705. DAN PETRY
- ☐ 726. DARYL IRVINE
- ☐ 732. DANA KIECKER
- ☐ 809. AARON SELE
- ☐ 823. JEFF PLYMPTON
- ☐ 836. WAYNE HOUSIE
- ☐ 838. JOSIAS MANZANILLO
- ☐ 850. ROBERT ZUPCIC
- ☐ 876. SCOTT COOPER

CALIFORNIA ANGELS

- ☐ 12. MARK LANGSTON
- ☐ 32. DAVE WINFIELD
- ☐ 39. GARY GAETTI
- ☐ 68. LUIS POLONIA
- ☐ 79. KIRK MCCASKILL
- ☐ 127. LUIS SOJO
- ☐ 165. SCOTT LEWIS
- ☐ 183. DONNIE HILL
- ☐ 221. MARK EICHHORN
- ☐ 239. DAVE GALLAGHER
- ☐ 274. JEFF ROBINSON
- ☐ 298. LANCE PARRISH
- ☐ 322. BRYAN HARVEY
- ☐ 331. SCOTT BAILES
- ☐ 372. LEE STEVENS
- ☐ 477. MAX VENABLE
- ☐ 519. JUNIOR FELIX
- ☐ 535. WALLY JOYNER
- ☐ 552. DICK SCHOFIELD
- ☐ 558. BOBBY ROSE
- ☐ 585. CHUCK FINLEY
- ☐ 606. MIKE FETTERS
- ☐ 616. SHAWN ABNER
- ☐ 620. JIM ABBOTT
- ☐ 674. JOE GRAHE
- ☐ 712. JOHN ORTON
- ☐ 757. RON TINGLEY
- ☐ 847. CHRIS CRON
- ☐ 849. KYLE ABBOTT

CHICAGO CUBS

- ☐ 45. GEORGE BELL
- ☐ 67. MIKE HARKEY
- ☐ 75. ANDRE DAWSON
- ☐ 98. DAVE SMITH
- ☐ 120. DANNY JACKSON
- ☐ 169. JOSE VIZCAINO
- ☐ 200. RYNE SANDBERG
- ☐ 213. HEATH SLOCUMB
- ☐ 269. GREG MADDUX
- ☐ 285. BOB SCANLAN
- ☐ 319. DOUG DASCENZO
- ☐ 348. LES LANCASTER
- ☐ 360. PAUL ASSENMACHER
- ☐ 366. CHUCK MCELROY
- ☐ 399. FRANK CASTILLO
- ☐ 418. CED LANDRUM
- ☐ 445. MARK GRACE
- ☐ 457. JEROME WALTON
- ☐ 483. RICK WILKINS
- ☐ 508. LUIS SALAZAR
- ☐ 578. CHICO WALKER
- ☐ 612. DWIGHT SMITH
- ☐ 634. SHAWON DUNSTON
- ☐ 657. DAVE CLARK
- ☐ 665. RICK SUTCLIFFE
- ☐ 677. HECTOR VILLANUEVA
- ☐ 701. JOE GIRARDI
- ☐ 713. SHAWN BOSKIE
- ☐ 812. STEVE WILSON
- ☐ 875. LADDIE RENFROE

CHICAGO WHITE SOX

- ☐ 29. MELIDO PEREZ
- ☐ 62. JACK MCDOWELL
- ☐ 72. CARLTON FISK
- ☐ 82. ALEX FERNANDEZ
- ☐ 92. OZZIE GUILLEN
- ☐ 122. ROBIN VENTURA
- ☐ 146. LANCE JOHNSON
- ☐ 203. SCOTT FLETCHER
- ☐ 237. DAN PASQUA
- ☐ 258. SAMMY SOSA
- ☐ 266. GREG HIBBARD
- ☐ 302. CHARLIE HOUGH
- ☐ 326. JOEY CORA
- ☐ 347. KEN PATTERSON
- ☐ 361. BO JACKSON
- ☐ 367. MATT MERULLO
- ☐ 398. WARREN NEWSON
- ☐ 444. SCOTT RADINSKY
- ☐ 484. DONN PALL
- ☐ 505. FRANK THOMAS
- ☐ 517. RODNEY MCCRAY
- ☐ 532. RON KARKOVICE
- ☐ 561. CRAIG GREBECK
- ☐ 570. BOBBY THIGPEN
- ☐ 635. TIM RAINES
- ☐ 664. MIKE HUFF
- ☐ 734. BRIAN DRAHMAN
- ☐ 745. RAMON GARCIA

- ☐ 760. WILSON ALVAREZ
- ☐ 766. ESTEBAN BELTRE
- ☐ 770. JEFF CARTER
- ☐ 806. SCOTT RUFFCORN
- ☐ 814. DON WAKAMATSU
- ☐ 863. STEVE WAPNICK
- ☐ 874. ROBERTO HERNANDEZ

CINCINNATI REDS

- ☐ 44. ERIC DAVIS
- ☐ 57. PAUL O'NEILL
- ☐ 70. CHRIS SABO
- ☐ 77. BILL DORAN
- ☐ 100. BARRY LARKIN
- ☐ 113. TED POWER
- ☐ 125. HAL MORRIS
- ☐ 155. RANDY MYERS
- ☐ 209. SCOTT SCUDDER
- ☐ 232. JOSE RIJO
- ☐ 267. NORM CHARLTON
- ☐ 311. JEFF REED
- ☐ 352. MARIANO DUNCAN
- ☐ 370. JOE OLIVER
- ☐ 393. GLENN BRAGGS
- ☐ 408. GINO MINUTELLI
- ☐ 447. BILLY HATCHER
- ☐ 455. ROB DIBBLE
- ☐ 488. JACK ARMSTRONG
- ☐ 513. CHRIS HAMMOND
- ☐ 574. HERM WINNINGHAM
- ☐ 628. TIM LAYANA
- ☐ 638. LUIS QUINONES
- ☐ 642. TOM BROWNING
- ☐ 686. CARMELO MARTINEZ
- ☐ 740. KIP GROSS
- ☐ 769. MO SANFORD
- ☐ 811. CHRIS JONES
- ☐ 813. FREDDIE BENAVIDES
- ☐ 820. MILT HILL
- ☐ 829. REGGIE SANDERS

CLEVELAND INDIANS

- ☐ 31. ALBERT BELLE
- ☐ 53. DOUG JONES
- ☐ 93. SHAWN HILLEGAS
- ☐ 128. CARLOS BAERGA
- ☐ 144. ERIC KING
- ☐ 148. FELIX FERMIN
- ☐ 227. JOEL SKINNER
- ☐ 262. CHRIS JAMES
- ☐ 330. CHARLES NAGY
- ☐ 351. MIKE ALDRETE
- ☐ 371. GREG SWINDELL
- ☐ 409. REGGIE JEFFERSON
- ☐ 448. GLENALLEN HILL
- ☐ 463. ALEX COLE
- ☐ 496. JERRY BROWNE
- ☐ 510. SANDY ALOMAR
- ☐ 528. MARK LEWIS
- ☐ 547. JESSE OROSCO
- ☐ 559. ROD NICHOLS
- ☐ 587. MARK WHITEN
- ☐ 593. CARLOS MARTINEZ
- ☐ 624. JEFF SHAW
- ☐ 644. STEVE OLIN
- ☐ 666. JEFF MANTO
- ☐ 696. RUDY SEANEZ
- ☐ 702. TONY PEREZCHICA
- ☐ 716. LUIS LOPEZ
- ☐ 730. WILLIE BLAIR
- ☐ 751. BRUCE EGLOFF
- ☐ 800. MANNY RAMIREZ
- ☐ 848. DENIS BOUCHER
- ☐ 859. JIM THOME
- ☐ 871. EDDIE TAUBENSEE

DETROIT TIGERS

- ☐ 26. MILT CUYLER
- ☐ 50. CECIL FIELDER
- ☐ 56. ROB DEER
- ☐ 65. TRAVIS FRYMAN
- ☐ 134. MICKEY TETTLETON
- ☐ 179. JOHN CERUTTI
- ☐ 217. MIKE HENNEMAN
- ☐ 242. BILL GULLICKSON
- ☐ 255. LOU WHITAKER
- ☐ 261. PAUL GIBSON
- ☐ 271. FRANK TANANA
- ☐ 306. PETE INCAVIGLIA
- ☐ 355. WALT TERRELL
- ☐ 375. JERRY DON GLEATON
- ☐ 394. MARK SALAS
- ☐ 395. RUSTY MEACHAM
- ☐ 414. SCOTT LIVINGSTONE
- ☐ 453. TONY PHILLIPS
- ☐ 468. LLOYD MOSEBY
- ☐ 515. ALAN TRAMMELL
- ☐ 537. ANDY ALLANSON
- ☐ 543. DAVE BERGMAN
- ☐ 569. SKEETER BARNES
- ☐ 626. MARK LEITER
- ☐ 729. SCOTT ALDRED
- ☐ 825. DAVID HAAS
- ☐ 828. SHAWN HARE
- ☐ 831. DAN GAKELER

HOUSTON ASTROS

- ☐ 33. JIMMY JONES
- ☐ 69. KEN CAMINITI
- ☐ 147. CASEY CANDAELE
- ☐ 176. STEVE FINLEY
- ☐ 197. ERIC YELDING
- ☐ 204. DWAYNE HENRY
- ☐ 210. LUIS GONZALEZ
- ☐ 224. PETE HARNISCH
- ☐ 243. MARK PORTUGAL
- ☐ 289. MARK DAVIDSON
- ☐ 315. ERIC ANTHONY
- ☐ 346. GERALD YOUNG
- ☐ 364. JIM DESHAIES
- ☐ 388. RAFAEL RAMIREZ
- ☐ 403. JAVIER ORTIZ
- ☐ 452. AL OSUNA
- ☐ 460. CRAIG BIGGIO
- ☐ 494. DARRYL KILE
- ☐ 524. JIM CORSI
- ☐ 576. JEFF BAGWELL
- ☐ 599. ANDUJAR CEDENO
- ☐ 632. MIKE SIMMS
- ☐ 671. CURT SCHILLING
- ☐ 687. MIKE CAPEL
- ☐ 762. RYAN BOWEN
- ☐ 816. SCOTT SERVAIS
- ☐ 819. ROB MALLICOAT
- ☐ 840. GARY COOPER
- ☐ 845. KENNY LOFTON
- ☐ 858. TONY EUSEBIO
- ☐ 872. ANDY MOTA

KANSAS CITY ROYALS

- ☐ 6. BRET SABERHAGEN
- ☐ 14. JEFF MONTGOMERY
- ☐ 27. MIKE MACFARLANE
- ☐ 84. BRENT MAYNE
- ☐ 102. MIKE BODDICKER
- ☐ 130. TOM GORDON
- ☐ 145. DANNY TARTABULL
- ☐ 158. JIM EISENREICH
- ☐ 236. KURT STILLWELL
- ☐ 248. TERRY SHUMPERT
- ☐ 252. BILL PECOTA
- ☐ 264. STORM DAVIS
- ☐ 310. KEVIN SEITZER
- ☐ 349. STEVE CRAWFORD
- ☐ 369. LUIS AQUINO
- ☐ 416. TIM SPEHR
- ☐ 459. MARK GUBICZA
- ☐ 478. BRIAN MCRAE
- ☐ 512. GARY THURMAN
- ☐ 520. KIRK GIBSON
- ☐ 542. KEVIN APPIER
- ☐ 563. TODD BENZINGER
- ☐ 637. WARREN CROMARTIE
- ☐ 650. GEORGE BRETT
- ☐ 678. SEAN BERRY
- ☐ 704. DAVID HOWARD
- ☐ 718. MARK DAVIS
- ☐ 739. MIKE MAGNANTE
- ☐ 761. HARVEY PULLIAM
- ☐ 764. JOEL JOHNSTON
- ☐ 844. JORGE PEDRE

LOS ANGELES DODGERS

- ☐ 9. DARRYL STRAWBERRY
- ☐ 34. KEVIN GROSS
- ☐ 73. JUAN SAMUEL
- ☐ 110. KAL DANIELS
- ☐ 119. JAY HOWELL
- ☐ 171. MIKE MORGAN
- ☐ 172. JIM GOTT
- ☐ 195. EDDIE MURRAY
- ☐ 226. MIKE SCIOSCIA
- ☐ 238. TIM CREWS
- ☐ 254. ALFREDO GRIFFIN
- ☐ 291. LENNY HARRIS
- ☐ 350. JOHN CANDELARIA
- ☐ 368. TIM BELCHER
- ☐ 449. CHRIS GWYNN
- ☐ 465. BRETT BUTLER
- ☐ 489. GARY CARTER
- ☐ 527. BOB OJEDA
- ☐ 583. STAN JAVIER
- ☐ 592. MIKE SHARPERSON
- ☐ 597. ROGER MCDOWELL
- ☐ 610. RAMON MARTINEZ
- ☐ 643. MITCH WEBSTER
- ☐ 653. OREL HERSHISER
- ☐ 684. JEFF HAMILTON
- ☐ 699. JOSE OFFERMAN
- ☐ 733. JOSE GONZALEZ
- ☐ 754. DAVE HANSEN
- ☐ 827. ERIC KARROS
- ☐ 830. TOM GOODWIN

MILWAUKEE BREWERS

- ☐ 22. CHUCK CRIM
- ☐ 30. WILLIE RANDOLPH
- ☐ 37. CHRIS BOSIO
- ☐ 61. PAUL MOLITOR
- ☐ 78. B.J. SURHOFF
- ☐ 126. TEDDY HIGUERA
- ☐ 181. DALE SVEUM
- ☐ 218. BILL SPIERS
- ☐ 231. JAIME NAVARRO
- ☐ 246. JIM GANTNER
- ☐ 277. MARK LEE
- ☐ 292. FRANKLIN STUBBS
- ☐ 316. DANTE BICHETTE
- ☐ 353. JULIO MACHADO
- ☐ 373. MARK KNUDSON
- ☐ 374. BILL WEGMAN
- ☐ 421. DOUG HENRY
- ☐ 469. TIM MCINTOSH
- ☐ 497. DARRYL HAMILTON
- ☐ 525. ROBIN YOUNT
- ☐ 533. DON AUGUST
- ☐ 567. DAN PLESAC
- ☐ 589. GARY SHEFFIELD
- ☐ 639. GREG VAUGHN
- ☐ 676. EDWIN NUNEZ
- ☐ 741. JIM HUNTER
- ☐ 747. JIM AUSTIN
- ☐ 753. DARREN HOLMES
- ☐ 807. TYRONE HILL
- ☐ 834. CAL ELDRED
- ☐ 835. CHRIS GEORGE
- ☐ 837. MIKE IGNASIAK
- ☐ 839. JIM OLANDER

MINNESOTA TWINS

- ☐ 17. STEVE BEDROSIAN
- ☐ 28. DAN GLADDEN
- ☐ 42. RICK AGUILERA

- ☐ 60. SCOTT ERICKSON
- ☐ 94. CHILI DAVIS
- ☐ 164. MARK GUTHRIE
- ☐ 173. MIKE PAGLIARULO
- ☐ 182. GREG GAGNE
- ☐ 215. BRIAN HARPER
- ☐ 272. GENE LARKIN
- ☐ 284. SHANE MACK
- ☐ 296. TERRY LEACH
- ☐ 320. SCOTT LEIUS
- ☐ 357. AL NEWMAN
- ☐ 377. RANDY BUSH
- ☐ 473. JUNIOR ORTIZ
- ☐ 482. CARL WILLIS
- ☐ 507. KEVIN TAPANI
- ☐ 514. PEDRO MUNOZ
- ☐ 530. KENT HRBEK
- ☐ 572. CHUCK KNOBLAUCH
- ☐ 600. KIRBY PUCKETT
- ☐ 652. JACK MORRIS
- ☐ 663. LENNY WEBSTER
- ☐ 669. DAVE WEST
- ☐ 697. PAUL ABBOTT
- ☐ 720. TOM EDENS
- ☐ 731. ALLAN ANDERSON
- ☐ 870. JARVIS BROWN

MONTREAL EXPOS

- ☐ 16. DELINO DESHIELDS
- ☐ 35. ANDRES GALARRAGA
- ☐ 66. MARQUIS GRISSOM
- ☐ 83. IVAN CALDERON
- ☐ 121. SCOTT RUSKIN
- ☐ 140. CHRIS NABHOLZ
- ☐ 166. BILL SAMPEN
- ☐ 199. LARRY WALKER
- ☐ 229. GILBERTO REYES
- ☐ 273. RON HASSEY
- ☐ 297. BARRY JONES
- ☐ 323. SPIKE OWEN
- ☐ 354. KEN WILLIAMS
- ☐ 419. BRET BARBERIE
- ☐ 422. DOUG PIATT
- ☐ 470. DENNIS MARTINEZ
- ☐ 486. TOM FOLEY
- ☐ 501. DAVE MARTINEZ
- ☐ 586. MARK GARDNER
- ☐ 595. TIM WALLACH
- ☐ 661. ERIC BULLOCK
- ☐ 667. MIKE FITZGERALD
- ☐ 715. BRIAN BARNES
- ☐ 725. MEL ROJAS
- ☐ 738. JEFF FASSERO
- ☐ 801. CLIFF FLOYD
- ☐ 873. CHRIS HANEY

NEW YORK METS

- ☐ 10. DWIGHT GOODEN
- ☐ 19. MARK CARREON
- ☐ 95. VINCE COLEMAN
- ☐ 103. KEVIN ELSTER
- ☐ 107. HUBIE BROOKS
- ☐ 168. KEVIN MCREYNOLDS
- ☐ 192. GREGG JEFFERIES
- ☐ 201. DAVE MAGADAN
- ☐ 212. CHRIS DONNELS
- ☐ 220. FRANK VIOLA
- ☐ 276. DARYL BOSTON
- ☐ 299. WALLY WHITEHURST
- ☐ 327. JEFF INNIS
- ☐ 332. PETE SCHOUREK
- ☐ 462. KEITH MILLER
- ☐ 472. MACKEY SASSER
- ☐ 479. DOUG SIMONS
- ☐ 550. HOWARD JOHNSON
- ☐ 588. GARRY TEMPLETON
- ☐ 602. TODD HUNDLEY
- ☐ 605. JOHN FRANCO
- ☐ 621. CHARLIE O'BRIEN
- ☐ 651. TIM BURKE
- ☐ 675. SID FERNANDEZ
- ☐ 680. DAVID CONE
- ☐ 682. TONY CASTILLO
- ☐ 756. ANTHONY YOUNG
- ☐ 763. TERRY BROSS
- ☐ 765. TERRY MCDANIEL
- ☐ 802. AL SHIRLEY
- ☐ 843. BLAINE BEATTY
- ☐ 857. CHUCK CARR
- ☐ 869. JEFF GARDNER

NEW YORK YANKEES

- ☐ 23. DON MATTINGLY
- ☐ 41. ALVARO ESPINOZA
- ☐ 47. STEVE FARR
- ☐ 88. PASCUAL PEREZ
- ☐ 89. HENSLEY MEULENS
- ☐ 154. MEL HALL
- ☐ 170. BOB GEREN
- ☐ 185. PAT KELLY
- ☐ 211. SCOTT SANDERSON
- ☐ 244. LEE GUETTERMAN
- ☐ 275. STEVE HOWE
- ☐ 286. TIM LEARY
- ☐ 324. ROBERTO KELLY
- ☐ 337. RANDY VELARDE
- ☐ 379. ERIC PLUNK
- ☐ 401. BERNIE WILLIAMS
- ☐ 411. CARLOS RODRIGUEZ
- ☐ 415. SCOTT KAMIENIECKI
- ☐ 451. JOHN HABYAN
- ☐ 454. GREG CADARET
- ☐ 475. STEVE SAX
- ☐ 523. JEFF JOHNSON
- ☐ 565. JESSE BARFIELD
- ☐ 573. MATT NOKES
- ☐ 613. KEVIN MAAS
- ☐ 631. WADE TAYLOR
- ☐ 679. DAVE EILAND
- ☐ 690. RICH MONTELEONE
- ☐ 815. MIKE HUMPHREYS
- ☐ 818. JOHN RAMOS

OAKLAND A'S

- ☐ 5. DAVE HENDERSON
- ☐ 20. MARK MCGWIRE
- ☐ 43. MIKE GALLEGO
- ☐ 51. WALT WEISS
- ☐ 91. MIKE MOORE
- ☐ 137. HAROLD BAINES
- ☐ 151. JOE KLINK
- ☐ 190. DENNIS ECKERSLEY
- ☐ 202. STEVE CHITREN
- ☐ 222. ERNEST RILES
- ☐ 279. LANCE BLANKENSHIP
- ☐ 300. BOB WELCH
- ☐ 309. JOE SLUSARSKI
- ☐ 328. WILLIE WILSON
- ☐ 341. TODD BURNS
- ☐ 383. GENE NELSON
- ☐ 407. TROY AFENIR
- ☐ 456. RICK HONEYCUTT
- ☐ 480. RICKEY HENDERSON
- ☐ 500. JOSE CANSECO
- ☐ 526. JAMIE QUIRK
- ☐ 577. BROOK JACOBY
- ☐ 580. DAVE STEWART
- ☐ 617. SCOTT HEMOND
- ☐ 633. TERRY STEINBACH
- ☐ 648. CARNEY LANSFORD
- ☐ 662. ERIC SHOW
- ☐ 681. MIKE BORDICK
- ☐ 710. RON DARLING
- ☐ 722. CURT YOUNG
- ☐ 728. KIRK DRESSENDORFER
- ☐ 735. BRAD KOMMINSK
- ☐ 805. BRENT GATES
- ☐ 846. SCOTT BROSIUS
- ☐ 855. KEVIN CAMPBELL
- ☐ 861. DANN HOWITT
- ☐ 865. TODD VAN POPPEL

PHILADELPHIA PHILLIES

- ☐ 24. DICKIE THON
- ☐ 59. RANDY READY
- ☐ 80. DALE MURPHY
- ☐ 106. PAT COMBS
- ☐ 118. TERRY MULHOLLAND
- ☐ 143. MICKEY MORANDINI
- ☐ 161. BRUCE RUFFIN
- ☐ 177. WALLY BACKMAN
- ☐ 193. DARRIN FLETCHER
- ☐ 207. VON HAYES
- ☐ 235. JOHN KRUK
- ☐ 301. CHARLIE HAYES
- ☐ 321. JIM LINDEMAN
- ☐ 336. TOMMY GREENE
- ☐ 342. RON JONES
- ☐ 356. MITCH WILLIAMS
- ☐ 380. JOSE DEJESUS
- ☐ 384. WES CHAMBERLAIN
- ☐ 396. ANDY ASHBY
- ☐ 467. STEVE LAKE
- ☐ 476. RICKY JORDAN
- ☐ 506. DARREN DAULTON
- ☐ 553. DAVE HOLLINS
- ☐ 560. LENNY DYKSTRA
- ☐ 568. DANNY COX
- ☐ 619. WALLY RITCHIE
- ☐ 647. JOE BOEVER
- ☐ 670. MIKE HARTLEY
- ☐ 698. STEVE SEARCY
- ☐ 711. JASON GRIMSLEY
- ☐ 744. TIM MAUSER
- ☐ 810. TYLER GREEN
- ☐ 824. BRAULIO CASTILLO
- ☐ 833. KIM BATISTE
- ☐ 854. CLIFF BRANTLEY
- ☐ 867. AMALIO CARRENO

PITTSBURGH PIRATES

- ☐ 38. MIKE LAVALLIERE
- ☐ 54. BOB WALK
- ☐ 86. RANDY TOMLIN
- ☐ 109. VICENTE PALACIOS
- ☐ 115. DOUG DRABEK
- ☐ 153. ORLANDO MERCED
- ☐ 180. JAY BELL
- ☐ 196. BILL LANDRUM
- ☐ 225. BOBBY BONILLA
- ☐ 265. JOSE LIND
- ☐ 280. DON SLAUGHT
- ☐ 303. GARY REDUS
- ☐ 325. STAN BELINDA
- ☐ 340. BOB KIPPER
- ☐ 382. CURTIS WILKERSON
- ☐ 412. JOE REDFIELD
- ☐ 481. GARY VARSHO
- ☐ 493. ZANE SMITH
- ☐ 511. JEFF KING
- ☐ 548. BOB PATTERSON
- ☐ 555. BARRY BONDS
- ☐ 566. LLOYD MCCLENDON
- ☐ 618. TOM PRINCE
- ☐ 655. ANDY VAN SLYKE
- ☐ 659. JOHN SMILEY
- ☐ 673. CECIL ESPY
- ☐ 695. STEVE BUECHELE
- ☐ 723. NEAL HEATON
- ☐ 727. ROGER MASON
- ☐ 752. JOHN WEHNER
- ☐ 804. JON FARRELL
- ☐ 821. CARLOS GARCIA

ST. LOUIS CARDINALS

- ☐ 40. FELIX JOSE
- ☐ 52. TODD ZEILE
- ☐ 81. JOSE DELEON
- ☐ 104. KEN HILL
- ☐ 114. MILT THOMPSON
- ☐ 136. TOM PAGNOZZI
- ☐ 160. CRIS CARPENTER
- ☐ 184. REX HUDLER
- ☐ 219. SCOTT TERRY
- ☐ 223. RAY LANKFORD
- ☐ 282. BOB TEWKSBURY
- ☐ 305. JOSE OQUENDO
- ☐ 329. JUAN AGOSTO
- ☐ 334. OMAR OLIVARES
- ☐ 376. PEDRO GUERRERO
- ☐ 404. TIM SHERRILL
- ☐ 491. GERALD PERRY
- ☐ 516. GERONIMO PENA
- ☐ 529. BRYN SMITH
- ☐ 544. BERNARD GILKEY
- ☐ 557. CRAIG WILSON
- ☐ 590. OZZIE SMITH
- ☐ 607. LUIS ALICEA
- ☐ 630. LEE SMITH
- ☐ 689. RICH GEDMAN
- ☐ 717. BOB MCCLURE
- ☐ 721. WILLIE FRASER
- ☐ 799. ALLEN WATSON
- ☐ 803. BRIAN BARBER
- ☐ 822. STAN ROYER
- ☐ 851. RHEAL CORMIER

☐ 864. ROD BREWER

SAN DIEGO PADRES

☐ 7. FRED MCGRIFF
☐ 111. BRUCE HURST
☐ 123. BIP ROBERTS
☐ 133. ANDY BENES
☐ 149. RICH RODRIGUEZ
☐ 175. CRAIG LEFFERTS
☐ 205. SCOTT COOLBAUGH
☐ 233. ATLEE HAMMAKER
☐ 234. TIM TEUFEL
☐ 245. BENNY SANTIAGO
☐ 257. JERALD CLARK
☐ 263. LARRY ANDERSEN
☐ 293. THOMAS HOWARD
☐ 313. MIKE MADDUX
☐ 338. TOM LAMPKIN
☐ 378. GREG HARRIS
☐ 397. JOSE MELENDEZ
☐ 509. PAUL FARIES
☐ 521. DARRIN JACKSON
☐ 536. DENNIS RASMUSSEN
☐ 564. ED WHITSON
☐ 614. JOHN COSTELLO
☐ 625. TONY GWYNN
☐ 645. TONY FERNANDEZ
☐ 692. OSCAR AZOCAR
☐ 706. JACK HOWELL
☐ 714. PAT CLEMENTS
☐ 719. DANN BILARDELLO
☐ 742. JOSE MOTA
☐ 758. RICKY BONES
☐ 852. JIM LEWIS
☐ 856. CRAIG SHIPLEY
☐ 862. KEVIN WARD

SAN FRANCISCO GIANTS

☐ 3. WILL CLARK
☐ 112. WILLIE MCGEE
☐ 117. SCOTT GARRELTS
☐ 139. KEVIN BASS
☐ 157. JEFF BRANTLEY
☐ 167. DAVE ANDERSON
☐ 191. KELLY DOWNS
☐ 230. MATT WILLIAMS
☐ 247. ROBBY THOMPSON
☐ 251. MIKE FELDER
☐ 260. DAVE RIGHETTI
☐ 278. JOSE SEGURA
☐ 295. FRANCISCO OLIVERAS
☐ 317. STEVE DECKER
☐ 358. BUD BLACK
☐ 410. MIKE REMLINGER
☐ 499. MARK LEONARD
☐ 503. TERRY KENNEDY
☐ 522. JOHN BURKETT
☐ 546. JOSE URIBE
☐ 562. DARREN LEWIS
☐ 601. RICK PARKER
☐ 603. GREG LITTON
☐ 608. TREVOR WILSON
☐ 636. KIRT MANWARING
☐ 640. KEVIN MITCHELL
☐ 649. MIKE BENJAMIN
☐ 703. PAUL MCCLELLAN
☐ 746. ROD BECK
☐ 750. BRYAN HICKERSON
☐ 768. TED WOOD
☐ 771. GIL HEREDIA
☐ 841. ROYCE CLAYTON

SEATTLE MARINERS

☐ 1. KEN GRIFFEY, JR.
☐ 8. ERIK HANSON
☐ 64. JAY BUHNER
☐ 76. ALVIN DAVIS
☐ 135. RICH DELUCIA
☐ 141. PETE O'BRIEN
☐ 162. OMAR VIZQUEL
☐ 194. MIKE JACKSON
☐ 206. TRACY JONES
☐ 228. BRIAN HOLMAN
☐ 250. HAROLD REYNOLDS
☐ 253. BILL KRUEGER
☐ 281. RUSS SWAN
☐ 304. SCOTT BRADLEY
☐ 343. DAVE VALLE
☐ 387. GREG BRILEY
☐ 390. HENRY COTTO
☐ 413. ALONZO POWELL
☐ 423. PAT RICE
☐ 461. DAVE COCHRANE
☐ 485. EDGAR MARTINEZ
☐ 492. ROB MURPHY
☐ 541. BILL SWIFT
☐ 584. RANDY JOHNSON
☐ 594. SCOTT BANKHEAD
☐ 596. TINO MARTINEZ
☐ 611. DAVE BURBA
☐ 629. JEFF SCHAEFER
☐ 654. MIKE SCHOOLER
☐ 868. CALVIN JONES

TEXAS RANGERS

☐ 2. NOLAN RYAN
☐ 11. JUAN GONZALEZ
☐ 55. RAFAEL PALMEIRO
☐ 101. KENNY ROGERS
☐ 108. JULIO FRANCO
☐ 124. JEFF RUSSELL
☐ 152. KEVIN REIMER
☐ 163. GERALD ALEXANDER
☐ 174. MIKE JEFFCOAT
☐ 283. GENO PETRALLI
☐ 308. GARY PETTIS
☐ 339. JOHN RUSSELL
☐ 381. BOBBY WITT
☐ 392. DEAN PALMER
☐ 466. JEFF HUSON
☐ 490. RUBEN SIERRA
☐ 502. JOSE GUZMAN
☐ 531. DENNIS BOYD
☐ 538. GOOSE GOOSAGE
☐ 549. MIKE STANLEY
☐ 579. BRIAN DOWNING
☐ 622. JACK DAUGHERTY
☐ 672. BRIAN BOHANON
☐ 683. JOHN BARFIELD
☐ 688. SCOTT CHIAMPARINO
☐ 700. IVAN RODRIGUEZ
☐ 709. KEVIN BROWN
☐ 737. TERRY MATHEWS
☐ 743. JOE BITKER
☐ 749. WAYNE ROSENTHAL
☐ 767. ROB MAURER
☐ 772. MONTY FARISS
☐ 808. BENJI GIL
☐ 842. HECTOR FAJARDO
☐ 866. JOSE HERNANDEZ

TORONTO BLUE JAYS

☐ 15. ROBERTO ALOMAR
☐ 48. DUANE WARD
☐ 49. DAVID WELLS
☐ 63. JIM ACKER
☐ 74. TODD STOTTLEMYRE
☐ 90. JOE CARTER
☐ 96. JIMMY KEY
☐ 132. RANCE MULLINIKS
☐ 198. DEVON WHITE
☐ 214. MIKE TIMLIN
☐ 288. PAT BORDERS
☐ 312. PAT TABLER
☐ 345. JOHN OLERUD
☐ 385. TOM HENKE
☐ 402. DEREK BELL
☐ 405. ROB MACDONALD
☐ 424. JUAN GUZMAN
☐ 458. MOOKIE WILSON
☐ 471. GREG MYERS
☐ 495. KELLY GRUBER
☐ 504. ED SPRAGUE
☐ 518. MANNY LEE
☐ 575. TOM CANDIOTTI
☐ 582. RENE GONZALES
☐ 591. CANDY MALDONADO
☐ 598. CORY SNYDER
☐ 609. ROB DUCEY
☐ 656. DAVE STIEB
☐ 685. KEN DAYLEY

1992 SCORE ROOKIE & TRADED (110) 2 1/2" X 3 1/2"

ATLANTA BRAVES

☐ 46. JEFF REARDON

BALTIMORE ORIOLES

☐ 8. RICK SUTCLIFFE
☐ 34. STORM DAVIS
☐ 86. JEFF TACKETT

BOSTON RED SOX

☐ 6. FRANK VIOLA
☐ 43. HERM WINNINGHAM
☐ 72. BILLY HATCHER

CALIFORNIA ANGELS

☐ 53. CHUCK CRIM
☐ 69. HUBIE BROOKS
☐ 75. RENE GONZALES
☐ 87. CHAD CURTIS
☐ 93. TIM SALMON

CHICAGO CUBS

☐ 21. STEVE BUECHELE
☐ 23. SAMMY SOSA
☐ 66. MIKE MORGAN
☐ 70. KAL DANIELS
☐ 101. JIM BULLINGER

CHICAGO WHITE SOX

☐ 4. STEVE SAX
☐ 24. GEORGE BELL
☐ 29. KIRK MCCASKILL

CINCINNATI REDS

☐ 10. GREG SWINDELL
☐ 33. DAVE MARTINEZ
☐ 47. SCOTT BANKHEAD
☐ 57. SCOTT RUSKIN
☐ 65. TIM BELCHER
☐ 77. TOM BOLTON
☐ 79. BIP ROBERTS

CLEVELAND INDIANS

☐ 14. KENNY LOFTON
☐ 44. DEREK LILLIQUIST
☐ 58. JACK ARMSTRONG
☐ 67. SCOTT SCUDDER

DETROIT TIGERS

☐ 28. DAN GLADDEN
☐ 37. MARK CARREON
☐ 42. ERIC KING
☐ 81. JOHN DOHERTY

HOUSTON ASTROS

☐ 17. PETE INCAVIGLIA
☐ 38. DOUG JONES
☐ 108. BRIAN WILLIAMS

KANSAS CITY ROYALS

☐ 13. WALLY JOYNER
☐ 31. KEVIN MCREYNOLDS
☐ 39. GREGG JEFFERIES
☐ 50. KEITH MILLER
☐ 56. CHRIS GWYNN
☐ 73. BOB MELVIN
☐ 103. HIPOLITO PICHARDO

LOS ANGELES DODGERS

☐ 45. DAVE ANDERSON
☐ 62. ERIC DAVIS
☐ 68. TOM CANDIOTTI
☐ 91. CARLOS HERNANDEZ

MILWAUKEE BREWERS

☐ 2. KEVIN SEITZER
☐ 71. BRUCE RUFFIN
☐ 80. PAT LISTACH
☐ 94. DAVE NILSSON
☐ 107. JAMES AUSTIN

MINNESOTA TWINS

☐ 22. JOHN SMILEY
☐ 102. PAT MAHOMES

MONTREAL EXPOS

☐ 59. GARY CARTER
☐ 61. KEN HILL
☐ 64. DARRIN FLETCHER
☐ 78. JOHN WETTELAND
☐ 99. ARCHI CIANFROCCO
☐ 105. JOHN VANDER WAL
☐ 110. WIL CORDERO

NEW YORK METS

☐ 5. BOBBY BONILLA
☐ 11. EDDIE MURRAY
☐ 20. BRET SABERHAGEN
☐ 26. DICK SCHOFIELD
☐ 35. WILLIE RANDOLPH
☐ 52. BILL PECOTA
☐ 55. DAVE GALLAGHER
☐ 74. LEE GUETTERMAN
☐ 76. KEVIN BASS
☐ 84. JEFF KENT

NEW YORK YANKEES

☐ 3. DANNY TARTABULL
☐ 16. CHARLIE HAYES
☐ 30. MIKE GALLEGO
☐ 36. MELIDO PEREZ
☐ 82. SAM MILITELLO
☐ 100. ANDY STANKIEWICZ

OAKLAND A'S

☐ 63. RUBEN SIERRA
☐ 88. ERIC FOX
☐ 106. VINCE HORSMAN

PHILADELPHIA PHILLIES

☐ 25. CURT SCHILLING
☐ 54. MARIANO DUNCAN
☐ 98. RUBEN AMARO, JR

PITTSBURGH PIRATES

☐ 89. DENNY NEAGLE
☐ 92. TIM WAKEFIELD

ST. LOUIS CARDINALS

☐ 60. ANDRES GALARRAGA
☐ 83. BRIAN JORDAN
☐ 90. DONOVAN OSBORNE
☐ 95. MIKE PEREZ

SAN DIEGO PADRES

☐ 1. GARY SHEFFIELD
☐ 12. RANDY MYERS
☐ 19. KURT STILLWELL
☐ 97. FRANK SEMINARA
☐ 109. DAN WALTERS

SAN FRANCISCO GIANTS

☐ 32. BILL SWIFT
☐ 40. MIKE JACKSON
☐ 48. CORY SNYDER
☐ 51. DAVE BURBA

SEATTLE MARINERS

☐ 18. KEVIN MITCHELL
☐ 85. DAVE FLEMING
☐ 104. BRET BOONE

TEXAS RANGERS

☐ 9. JOSE CANSECO
☐ 41. DICKIE THON
☐ 49. AL NEWMAN

TORONTO BLUE JAYS

☐ 7. DAVE WINFIELD
☐ 15. JACK MORRIS
☐ 27. DAVID CONE
☐ 96. PAT HENTGEN

1993 SCORE (660)
2 1/2" X 3 1/2"

ATLANTA BRAVES

☐ 15. TOM GLAVINE
☐ 36. TERRY PENDLETON
☐ 61. JOHN SMOLTZ
☐ 87. OTIS NIXON
☐ 107. DAVE JUSTICE
☐ 123. DEION SANDERS
☐ 142. JEFF BLAUSER
☐ 147. MARK LEMKE
☐ 169. STEVE AVERY
☐ 193. MARK WOHLERS
☐ 209. GREG OLSON
☐ 220. RON GANT
☐ 248. MELVIN NIEVES
☐ 294. RYAN KLESKO
☐ 310. PAT GOMEZ
☐ 317. MIKE STANTON
☐ 373. DAMON BERRYHILL
☐ 393. CHARLIE LEIBRANDT
☐ 396. SID BREAM
☐ 408. PETE SMITH
☐ 431. LONNIE SMITH
☐ 457. MIKE BIELECKI
☐ 461. JEFF TREADWAY
☐ 472. FRANCISCO CABRERA
☐ 478. RAFAEL BELLIARD
☐ 487. JAMIE ARNOLD
☐ 549. BRIAN HUNTER
☐ 564. JEFF REARDON
☐ 625. ALEJANDRO PENA

BALTIMORE ORIOLES

☐ 6. CAL RIPKEN, JR.
☐ 27. MIKE MUSSINA
☐ 54. CHRIS HOILES
☐ 80. GREGG OLSON
☐ 104. LEO GOMEZ
☐ 112. RANDY MILLIGAN
☐ 140. BRADY ANDERSON
☐ 170. MIKE DEVEREAUX
☐ 202. BEN MCDONALD
☐ 234. MANNY ALEXANDER
☐ 355. JEFF TACKETT
☐ 360. ARTHUR RHODES
☐ 383. GLENN DAVIS
☐ 435. CRAIG LEFFERTS
☐ 440. ALAN MILLS
☐ 449. STORM DAVIS
☐ 563. RICK SUTCLIFFE
☐ 590. JOE ORSULAK
☐ 610. DAVID SEGUI
☐ 638. CHITO MARTINEZ

BOSTON RED SOX

☐ 7. ROGER CLEMENS
☐ 55. FRANK VIOLA
☐ 78. ELLIS BURKS
☐ 132. MO VAUGHN
☐ 176. PHIL PLANTIER
☐ 198. SCOTT COOPER
☐ 221. PAUL QUANTRILL

☐ 230. PETER HOY
☐ 243. JOHN VALENTIN
☐ 261. TONY PENA
☐ 278. JOHN FLAHERTY
☐ 329. KEN RYAN
☐ 362. BOB ZUPCIC
☐ 385. MIKE GREENWELL
☐ 414. JODY REED
☐ 452. TIM NAEHRING
☐ 467. JOE HESKETH
☐ 592. WADE BOGGS
☐ 612. TOM BRUNANSKY
☐ 640. GREG HARRIS
☐ 657. BILLY HATCHER

CALIFORNIA ANGELS

☐ 39. LUIS POLONIA
☐ 66. MARK LANGSTON
☐ 124. LUIS SOJO
☐ 158. CHUCK FINLEY
☐ 188. JOE GRAHE
☐ 222. DAMION EASLEY
☐ 262. TIM FORTUGNO
☐ 277. MIKE BUTCHER
☐ 346. TIM SALMON
☐ 354. CHAD CURTIS
☐ 374. GARY DISARCINA
☐ 425. JUNIOR FELIX
☐ 427. JULIO VALERA
☐ 453. JOHN ORTON
☐ 455. CHUCK CRIM
☐ 468. GREG MYERS
☐ 500. PETE JANICKI
☐ 501. JEFF SCHMIDT
☐ 577. BERT BLYLEVEN
☐ 604. RENE GONZALES
☐ 644. GARY GAETTI
☐ 646. JIM ABBOTT

CHICAGO CUBS

☐ 4. RYNE SANDBERG
☐ 26. SHAWON DUNSTON
☐ 50. MARK GRACE
☐ 73. MIKE MORGAN
☐ 97. STEVE BUECHELE
☐ 111. MIKE HARKEY
☐ 143. SAMMY SOSA
☐ 185. RICK WILKINS
☐ 213. DERRICK MAY
☐ 324. REY SANCHEZ
☐ 339. JIM BULLINGER
☐ 361. BOB SCANLAN
☐ 389. CHUCK MCELROY
☐ 446. DOUG DASCENZO
☐ 462. FRANK CASTILLO
☐ 492. DEREK WALLACE
☐ 547. GARY SCOTT
☐ 552. ANDRE DAWSON
☐ 565. ALEX ARIAS
☐ 576. GREG MADDUX
☐ 637. DWIGHT SMITH

CHICAGO WHITE SOX

☐ 3. FRANK THOMAS
☐ 41. ROBIN VENTURA
☐ 70. JACK MCDOWELL
☐ 94. OZZIE GUILLEN
☐ 109. LANCE JOHNSON
☐ 126. CRAIG GREBECK
☐ 152. RON KARKOVICE
☐ 182. SCOTT RADINSKY
☐ 210. DAN PASQUA
☐ 223. CHARLIE HOUGH
☐ 376. ROBERTO HERNANDEZ
☐ 387. GEORGE BELL
☐ 412. ALEX FERNANDEZ
☐ 418. STEVE SAX
☐ 437. SHAWN ABNER
☐ 454. JOEY CORA
☐ 469. KIRK MCCASKILL
☐ 479. TERRY LEACH
☐ 579. CARLTON FISK
☐ 582. BOBBY THIGPEN
☐ 609. WILSON ALVAREZ
☐ 622. GREG HIBBARD
☐ 658. TIM RAINES

CINCINNATI REDS

☐ 16. BARRY LARKIN
☐ 38. HAL MORRIS
☐ 85. BIP ROBERTS
☐ 105. JOSE RIJO
☐ 125. JOE OLIVER
☐ 149. CHRIS SABO
☐ 171. REGGIE SANDERS
☐ 195. CHRIS HAMMOND
☐ 229. DAN WILSON
☐ 247. TIM PUGH
☐ 250. WILLIE GREENE
☐ 265. TIM COSTO
☐ 284. STEVE FOSTER
☐ 292. JACOB BRUMFIELD
☐ 302. CESAR HERNANDEZ
☐ 308. JEFF BRANSON
☐ 375. NORM CHARLTON
☐ 404. TOM BROWNING
☐ 416. DARNELL COLES
☐ 423. TIM BELCHER
☐ 439. PAUL O'NEILL
☐ 474. DWAYNE HENRY
☐ 566. GREG SWINDELL
☐ 584. SCOTT BANKHEAD
☐ 601. DAVE MARTINEZ
☐ 627. FREDDIE BENAVIDES
☐ 651. ROB DIBBLE

CLEVELAND INDIANS

☐ 9. CARLOS BAERGA
☐ 29. CHARLES NAGY
☐ 58. KENNY LOFTON
☐ 84. ALBERT BELLE
☐ 106. MARK WHITEN
☐ 116. SANDY ALOMAR, JR.
☐ 164. MARK LEWIS
☐ 194. PAUL SORRENTO
☐ 285. DAVE MLICKI
☐ 328. WAYNE KIRBY
☐ 330. JESSE LEVIS
☐ 358. KEVIN WICKANDER
☐ 364. JIM THOME
☐ 388. STEVE OLIN
☐ 398. GLENALLEN HILL
☐ 424. JOSE MESA
☐ 426. THOMAS HOWARD
☐ 433. REGGIE JEFFERSON
☐ 548. DEREK LILLIQUIST
☐ 567. BROOK JACOBY
☐ 594. ERIC PLUNK
☐ 655. JACK ARMSTRONG

COLORADO ROCKIES

☐ 405. JERALD CLARK
☐ 419. JOE GIRARDI
☐ 428. DANTE BICHETTE
☐ 553. DAVID NIED
☐ 561. ERIC WEDGE

DETROIT TIGERS

☐ 11. TRAVIS FRYMAN
☐ 31. CECIL FIELDER
☐ 60. MICKEY TETTLETON
☐ 82. MILT CUYLER
☐ 114. RICO BROGNA
☐ 166. MIKE HENNEMAN
☐ 196. SCOTT LIVINGSTONE
☐ 207. DAN GLADDEN
☐ 215. DAVID HAAS
☐ 228. MIKE MUNOZ
☐ 264. KURT KNUDSEN
☐ 283. RICH ROWLAND
☐ 313. ALAN TRAMMELL
☐ 353. JOHN DOHERTY
☐ 366. MARK CARREON
☐ 442. GARY PETTIS
☐ 596. LOU WHITAKER
☐ 614. TONY PHILLIPS
☐ 636. ROB DEER
☐ 643. BILL GULLICKSON
☐ 652. FRANK TANANA

FLORIDA MARLINS

☐ 558. BRYAN HARVEY
☐ 631. DAVE MAGADAN
☐ 653. STEVE DECKER
☐ 659. WALT WEISS

HOUSTON ASTROS

☐ 18. CRAIG BIGGIO
☐ 40. KEN CAMINITI
☐ 65. STEVE FINLEY
☐ 89. JEFF BAGWELL
☐ 108. EDDIE TAUBENSEE
☐ 127. ANDUJAR CEDENO
☐ 151. LUIS GONZALES
☐ 173. ERIC ANTHONY
☐ 197. DOUG JONES
☐ 237. SCOOTER TUCKER
☐ 253. ROB MALLICOAT
☐ 259. JUAN GUERRERO
☐ 282. SHANE REYNOLDS
☐ 333. BRIAN WILLIAMS
☐ 395. PETE HARNISCH
☐ 417. XAVIER HERNANDEZ
☐ 430. DARRYL KILE
☐ 463. JIMMY JONES
☐ 475. AL OSUNA
☐ 568. PETE INCAVIGLIA
☐ 569. BUTCH HENRY

KANSAS CITY ROYALS

☐ 17. GREGG JEFFERIES
☐ 43. WALLY JOYNER
☐ 57. GEORGE BRETT
☐ 69. KEVIN MCREYNOLDS
☐ 96. KEITH MILLER
☐ 128. BRIAN MCRAE
☐ 154. KEVIN APPIER
☐ 184. TOM GORDON
☐ 212. JEFF MONTGOMERY
☐ 226. KEVIN KOSLOFSKI
☐ 266. STEVE SHIFFLETT
☐ 323. MIKE MACFARLANE
☐ 336. HIPOLITO PICHARDO
☐ 378. RUSTY MEACHAM
☐ 392. DENNIS RASMUSSEN
☐ 402. JEFF CONINE
☐ 498. MICHAEL TUCKER
☐ 551. JIM EISENREICH
☐ 581. MARK GUBICZA
☐ 611. JUAN SAMUEL
☐ 645. DAVID HOWARD

LOS ANGELES DODGERS

☐ 20. BRETT BUTLER
☐ 42. DARRYL STRAWBERRY
☐ 63. ERIC KARROS
☐ 90. OREL HERSHISER
☐ 129. JOSE OFFERMAN
☐ 175. TOM CANDIOTTI
☐ 199. RAMON MARTINEZ
☐ 231. PEDRO ASTACIO
☐ 244. HENRY RODRIGUEZ
☐ 267. BILLY ASHLEY
☐ 286. MIKE PIAZZA

- ☐ 307. RAFAEL BOURNIGAL
- ☐ 321. PEDRO MARTINEZ
- ☐ 348. CARLOS HERNANDEZ
- ☐ 422. JIM GOTT
- ☐ 429. MIKE SHARPERSON
- ☐ 448. JOHN CANDELARIA
- ☐ 546. LENNY HARRIS
- ☐ 570. ERIC DAVIS
- ☐ 586. ERIC YOUNG
- ☐ 589. BOB OJEDA
- ☐ 605. ROGER MCDOWELL
- ☐ 623. MIKE SCIOSCIA

MILWAUKEE BREWERS

- ☐ 33. B.J. SURHOFF
- ☐ 47. ROBIN YOUNT
- ☐ 88. BILL SPIERS
- ☐ 118. DARRYL HAMILTON
- ☐ 160. GREG VAUGHN
- ☐ 177. DOUG HENRY
- ☐ 190. BILL WEGMAN
- ☐ 218. JAIME NAVARRO
- ☐ 236. JOHN JAHA
- ☐ 258. WILLIAM SUERO
- ☐ 331. JAMES AUSTIN
- ☐ 344. DAVE NILSSON
- ☐ 357. PAT LISTACH
- ☐ 368. CAL ELDRED
- ☐ 420. MIKE FETTERS
- ☐ 456. DAN PLESAC
- ☐ 470. RICKY BONES
- ☐ 571. KEVIN SEITZER
- ☐ 598. PAUL MOLITOR
- ☐ 600. DARREN HOLMES
- ☐ 616. CHRIS BOSIO
- ☐ 632. SCOTT FLETCHER

MINNESOTA TWINS

- ☐ 19. SHANE MACK
- ☐ 45. KEVIN TAPANI
- ☐ 64. RICK AGUILERA
- ☐ 72. BRIAN HARPER
- ☐ 98. KENT HRBEK
- ☐ 130. PEDRO MUNOZ
- ☐ 148. CHUCK KNOBLAUCH
- ☐ 178. SCOTT LEIUS
- ☐ 206. SCOTT ERICKSON
- ☐ 233. JEFF REBOULET
- ☐ 235. WILLIE BANKS
- ☐ 245. DEREK PARKS
- ☐ 275. J.T. BRUETT
- ☐ 287. MIKE TROMBLEY
- ☐ 306. BERNARDO BRITO
- ☐ 337. PAT MAHOMES
- ☐ 444. GENE LARKIN
- ☐ 450. TOM EDENS
- ☐ 458. TERRY JORGENSEN
- ☐ 471. LENNY WEBSTER
- ☐ 497. DAN SERAFINI
- ☐ 555. GREG GAGNE
- ☐ 583. CHILI DAVIS
- ☐ 606. KIRBY PUCKETT
- ☐ 624. JOHN SMILEY

MONTREAL EXPOS

- ☐ 5. LARRY WALKER
- ☐ 28. MARQUIS GRISSOM
- ☐ 48. KEN HILL
- ☐ 75. DENNIS MARTINEZ
- ☐ 95. IVAN CALDERON
- ☐ 145. DELINO DESHIELDS
- ☐ 165. JOHN WETTELAND
- ☐ 187. MOISES ALOU
- ☐ 211. TIM WALLACH
- ☐ 216. DARRIN FLETCHER
- ☐ 232. MATT STAIRS
- ☐ 269. PETE YOUNG
- ☐ 271. GREG COLBRUNN
- ☐ 299. JONATHAN HURST
- ☐ 312. KENT BOTTENFIELD
- ☐ 316. MATT MAYSEY
- ☐ 334. WIL CORDERO
- ☐ 340. ARCHI CIANFROCCO
- ☐ 359. JOHN VANDER WAL
- ☐ 363. MEL ROJAS
- ☐ 390. MARK GARDNER
- ☐ 477. CHRIS NABHOLZ
- ☐ 488. B.J. WALLACE
- ☐ 543. SEAN BERRY
- ☐ 554. SPIKE OWEN
- ☐ 617. BRET BARBERIE

NEW YORK METS

- ☐ 8. BOBBY BONILLA
- ☐ 53. DOC GOODEN
- ☐ 62. HOWARD JOHNSON
- ☐ 77. EDDIE MURRAY
- ☐ 113. ANTHONY YOUNG
- ☐ 115. BRET SABERHAGEN
- ☐ 139. JOHN FRANCO
- ☐ 167. TODD HUNDLEY
- ☐ 189. JEFF KENT
- ☐ 227. RYAN THOMPSON
- ☐ 280. ERIC HILLMAN
- ☐ 365. BILL PECOTA
- ☐ 399. CHICO WALKER
- ☐ 409. JEFF INNIS
- ☐ 447. DARYL BOSTON
- ☐ 499. CHRIS ROBERTS
- ☐ 556. SID FERNANDEZ
- ☐ 578. KEVIN BASS
- ☐ 613. WILLIE RANDOLPH
- ☐ 650. VINCE COLEMAN

NEW YORK YANKEES

- ☐ 23. DON MATTINGLY
- ☐ 35. DANNY TARTABULL
- ☐ 86. MELIDO PEREZ
- ☐ 120. BERNIE WILLIAMS
- ☐ 162. STEVE FARR
- ☐ 192. MATT NOKES
- ☐ 219. RANDY VELARDE
- ☐ 238. RUSS SPRINGER
- ☐ 252. DAVE SILVESTRI
- ☐ 260. J.T. SNOW
- ☐ 268. JERRY NIELSEN
- ☐ 291. BOB WICKMAN
- ☐ 298. GERALD WILLIAMS
- ☐ 311. STERLING HITCHCOCK
- ☐ 338. ANDY STANKIEWICZ
- ☐ 351. SAM MILITELLO
- ☐ 370. PAT KELLY
- ☐ 377. SCOTT KAMIENIECKI
- ☐ 411. CHARLIE HAYES
- ☐ 438. ROBERTO KELLY
- ☐ 459. JOHN HABYAN
- ☐ 489. DEREK JETER
- ☐ 595. HENSLEY MEULENS
- ☐ 618. SCOTT SANDERSON
- ☐ 634. KEVIN MAAS

OAKLAND A'S

- ☐ 21. DENNIS ECKERSLEY
- ☐ 71. RICKEY HENDERSON
- ☐ 100. MIKE BORDICK
- ☐ 134. DAVE HENDERSON
- ☐ 150. BOBBY WITT
- ☐ 180. JEFF PARRETT
- ☐ 208. BOB WELCH
- ☐ 270. JOHNNY GUZMAN
- ☐ 290. HENRY MERCEDES
- ☐ 326. TROY NEEL
- ☐ 352. ERIC FOX
- ☐ 382. JERRY BROWNE
- ☐ 406. VINCE HORSMAN
- ☐ 413. JEFF RUSSELL
- ☐ 495. BENJI GRIGSBY
- ☐ 557. MARK MCGWIRE
- ☐ 585. HAROLD BAINES
- ☐ 608. RUBEN SIERRA
- ☐ 619. RON DARLING
- ☐ 626. TERRY STEINBACH
- ☐ 641. MIKE MOORE
- ☐ 647. WILLIE WILSON
- ☐ 656. DAVE STEWART

PHILADELPHIA PHILLIES

- ☐ 10. DARREN DAULTON
- ☐ 30. LENNY DYKSTRA
- ☐ 52. CURT SCHILLING
- ☐ 79. JOHN KRUK
- ☐ 99. DAVE HOLLINS
- ☐ 117. TERRY MULHOLLAND
- ☐ 141. RICKY JORDAN
- ☐ 168. WES CHAMBERLAIN
- ☐ 191. KIM BATISTE
- ☐ 201. MARIANO DUNCAN
- ☐ 224. BRAD BRINK
- ☐ 242. BEN RIVERA
- ☐ 263. TOM MARSH
- ☐ 276. TODD PRATT
- ☐ 289. BOB AYRAULT
- ☐ 305. JEFF GROTEWALD
- ☐ 341. RUBEN AMARO, JR.
- ☐ 367. MITCH WILLIAMS
- ☐ 403. KYLE ABBOTT
- ☐ 415. MICKEY MORANDINI
- ☐ 443. STEVE LAKE
- ☐ 464. TOMMY GREENE
- ☐ 588. JUAN BELL
- ☐ 597. DALE MURPHY
- ☐ 629. BRAULIO CASTILLO

PITTSBURGH PIRATES

- ☐ 12. .ANDY VAN SLYKE
- ☐ 32. JAY BELL
- ☐ 83. MIKE LAVALLIERE
- ☐ 101. RANDY TOMLIN
- ☐ 121. ZANE SMITH
- ☐ 137. ORLANDO MERCED
- ☐ 144. BOB WALK
- ☐ 159. JEFF KING
- ☐ 181. DON SLAUGHT
- ☐ 239. PAUL MILLER
- ☐ 246. CARLOS GARCIA
- ☐ 273. KEVIN YOUNG
- ☐ 296. STEVE COOKE
- ☐ 301. WILLIAM PENNYFEATHER
- ☐ 304. BLAS MINOR
- ☐ 315. PAUL WAGNER
- ☐ 322. AL MARTIN
- ☐ 347. TIM WAKEFIELD
- ☐ 350. DENNY NEAGLE
- ☐ 369. STAN BELINDA
- ☐ 400. ALEX COLE
- ☐ 421. DANNY JACKSON
- ☐ 441. ROGER MASON
- ☐ 490. JASON KENDALL
- ☐ 560. BARRY BONDS
- ☐ 580. DOUG DRABEK
- ☐ 660. JOSE LIND
- ☐ 380. LLOYD MCCLENDON

ST. LOUIS CARDINALS

- ☐ 34. BOB TEWKSBURY
- ☐ 56. RAY LANKFORD
- ☐ 81. BERNARD GILKEY
- ☐ 103. LEE SMITH
- ☐ 110. FELIX JOSE
- ☐ 119. TODD ZEILE
- ☐ 135. TOM PAGNOZZI
- ☐ 161. GERONIMO PENA
- ☐ 163. JOSE OQUENDO
- ☐ 183. LUIS ALICEA
- ☐ 217. BRIAN JORDAN
- ☐ 241. OZZIE CANSECO
- ☐ 281. BIEN FIGUEROA
- ☐ 320. MARK CLARK
- ☐ 345. MIKE PEREZ
- ☐ 349. DONOVAN OSBORN
- ☐ 371. RHEAL CORMIER
- ☐ 397. MILT THOMPSON
- ☐ 434. BOB MCCLURE
- ☐ 465. TRACY WOODSON
- ☐ 476. CRAIG WILSON
- ☐ 493. SEAN LOWE
- ☐ 545. CHUCK CARR
- ☐ 562. OZZIE SMITH
- ☐ 633. CRIS CARPENTER
- ☐ 635. TODD WORRELL
- ☐ 649. ANDRES GALARRAGA

SAN DIEGO PADRES

- ☐ 2. GARY SHEFFIELD
- ☐ 24. TONY GWYNN
- ☐ 44. FRED MCGRIFF
- ☐ 91. ANDY BENES
- ☐ 133. BRUCE HURST
- ☐ 155. DARRIN JACKSON
- ☐ 251. TIM SCOTT

- ☐ 332. DAN WALTERS
- ☐ 342. FRANK SEMINARA
- ☐ 379. KURT STILLWELL
- ☐ 445. LARRY ANDERSEN
- ☐ 451. MIKE MADDUX
- ☐ 466. RICH RODRIGUEZ
- ☐ 480. TIM TEUFEL
- ☐ 572. TONY FERNANDEZ
- ☐ 591. BENITO SANTIAGO
- ☐ 599. GREG W. HARRIS
- ☐ 607. RANDY MYERS

SAN FRANCISCO GIANTS

- ☐ 22. WILL CLARK
- ☐ 46. MATT WILLIAMS
- ☐ 67. BILL SWIFT
- ☐ 93. WILLIE MCGEE
- ☐ 131. BUD BLACK
- ☐ 153. JEFF BRANTLEY
- ☐ 157. ROYCE CLAYTON
- ☐ 174. JOHN BURKETT
- ☐ 179. KIRT MANWARING
- ☐ 203. DARREN LEWIS
- ☐ 255. CRAIG COLBERT
- ☐ 279. JOHN PATTERSON
- ☐ 288. JIM PENA
- ☐ 300. LARRY CARTER
- ☐ 303. STEVE HOSEY
- ☐ 319. KEVIN ROGERS
- ☐ 381. MARK LEONARD
- ☐ 391. ROD BECK
- ☐ 401. TREVOR WILSON
- ☐ 573. STEVE REED
- ☐ 574. CORY SNYDER
- ☐ 593. ROBBY THOMPSON
- ☐ 603. MIKE BENJAMIN
- ☐ 621. MIKE FELDER

SEATTLE MARINERS

- ☐ 1. KEN GRIFFEY, JR
- ☐ 49. EDGAR MARTINEZ
- ☐ 76. TINO MARTINEZ
- ☐ 102. OMAR VIZQUEL
- ☐ 136. ERIK HANSON
- ☐ 172. JAY BUHNER
- ☐ 200. DAVE VALLE
- ☐ 249. RICH AMARAL
- ☐ 272. JEFF NELSON
- ☐ 327. KERRY WOODSON
- ☐ 335. BRET BOONE
- ☐ 356. DAVE FLEMING
- ☐ 384. RANDY JOHNSON
- ☐ 407. KEVIN MITCHELL
- ☐ 460. PETE O'BRIEN
- ☐ 544. MIKE SCHOOLER
- ☐ 559. HAROLD REYNOLDS
- ☐ 587. LANCE PARRISH

TEXAS RANGERS

- ☐ 13. JOSE CANSECO
- ☐ 25. IVAN RODRIGUEZ
- ☐ 51. JUAN GONZALEZ
- ☐ 59. NOLAN RYAN
- ☐ 74. RAFAEL PALMEIRO
- ☐ 138. DEAN PALMER
- ☐ 146. KEVIN BROWN
- ☐ 204. KENNY ROGERS
- ☐ 225. BARRY MANUEL
- ☐ 240. DAN PELTIER
- ☐ 254. DONALD HARRIS
- ☐ 256. JOSE GUZMAN
- ☐ 274. JEFF FRYE
- ☐ 293. DAVID HULSE
- ☐ 314. CRIS COLON
- ☐ 325. ROGER PAVLIK
- ☐ 386. SCOTT CHIAMPARINO
- ☐ 394. JULIO FRANCO
- ☐ 432. MONTY FARISS
- ☐ 491. RICK HELLING
- ☐ 628. KEVIN REIMER

TORONTO BLUE JAYS

- ☐ 14. ROBERTO ALOMAR
- ☐ 37. JACK MORRIS
- ☐ 68. JOHN OLERUD

- ☐ 92. DEVON WHITE
- ☐ 122. DEREK BELL
- ☐ 156. KELLY GRUBER
- ☐ 186. TODD STOTTLEMYRE
- ☐ 205. MANUEL LEE
- ☐ 214. ED SPRAGUE
- ☐ 257. DOMINGO MARTINEZ
- ☐ 295. DOUG LINTON
- ☐ 297. EDDIE ZOSKY
- ☐ 309. TOM QUINLAN
- ☐ 318. RICK TRLICEK
- ☐ 343. PAT HENTGEN
- ☐ 372. JUAN GUZMAN
- ☐ 410. MIKE TIMLIN
- ☐ 436. DUANE WARD
- ☐ 473. TURNER WARD
- ☐ 494. SHANNON STEARTS
- ☐ 496. TODD STEVERSON
- ☐ 575. JOE CARTER
- ☐ 602. TOM HENKE
- ☐ 615. CANDY MALDONADO
- ☐ 620. DAVE WINFIELD
- ☐ 630. DAVE STIEB
- ☐ 639. JIMMY KEY
- ☐ 642. PAT BORDERS
- ☐ 648. DAVID WELLS
- ☐ 654. DAVID CONE

1994 SCORE (660)
2 1/2" X 3 1/2"

ATLANTA BRAVES

- ☐ 30. TOM GLAVINE
- ☐ 54. JEFF BLAUSER
- ☐ 72. TERRY PENDLETON
- ☐ 82. FRED MCGRIFF
- ☐ 106. OTIS NIXON
- ☐ 126. KENT MERCKER
- ☐ 144. BILL PECOTA
- ☐ 166. STEVE AVERY
- ☐ 205. MIKE STANTON
- ☐ 222. FRANCISCO CABRERA
- ☐ 247. STEVE BEDROSIAN
- ☐ 275. DAMON BERRYHILL
- ☐ 303. RAFAEL BELLIARD
- ☐ 332. RON GANT
- ☐ 366. JOHN SMOLTZ
- ☐ 392. MARK LEMKE
- ☐ 422. DAVE JUSTICE
- ☐ 442. GREG OLSON
- ☐ 464. RYAN KLESKO
- ☐ 496. DEION SANDERS
- ☐ 524. GREG MADDUX
- ☐ 551. GREG MCMICHAEL
- ☐ 572. CHIPPER JONES
- ☐ 617. TONY TARASCO
- ☐ 620. JAVIER LOPEZ
- ☐ 647. TEAM CHECKLIST

BALTIMORE ORIOLES

- ☐ 9. MIKE MUSSINA
- ☐ 55. LEO GOMEZ
- ☐ 85. CAL RIPKEN, JR.
- ☐ 111. BEN MCDONALD
- ☐ 112. JIM POOLE
- ☐ 136. JEFF TACKETT
- ☐ 157. MARK WILLIAMSON
- ☐ 165. TIM HULETT
- ☐ 190. FERNANDO VALENZUELA
- ☐ 226. TODD FROHWIRTH
- ☐ 258. BRAD PENNINGTON
- ☐ 270. JAMIE MOYER
- ☐ 317. TEAM CHECKLIST
- ☐ 335. BRADY ANDERSON
- ☐ 357. CHRIS HOILES
- ☐ 361. DAVID SEGUI
- ☐ 386. MIKE DEVEREAUX
- ☐ 415. MARK MCLEMORE
- ☐ 441. HAROLD REYNOLDS
- ☐ 462. LONNIE SMITH
- ☐ 469. HAROLD BAINES
- ☐ 489. MIKE PAGLIARULO
- ☐ 497. RICK SUTCLIFFE
- ☐ 525. GREGG OLSON
- ☐ 560. JEFFREY HAMMONDS
- ☐ 575. JAY POWELL
- ☐ 580. JACK VOIGT
- ☐ 582. DAMON BUFORD
- ☐ 593. JOHN O'DONOGHUE
- ☐ 597. SHERMAN OBANDO

BOSTON RED SOX

- ☐ 25. ROGER CLEMENS
- ☐ 57. MO VAUGHN
- ☐ 83. MIKE GREENWELL
- ☐ 113. JOHN DOPSON
- ☐ 139. SCOTT BANKHEAD
- ☐ 192. DANNY DARWIN
- ☐ 221. BOB ZUPCIC
- ☐ 272. GREG HARRIS
- ☐ 313. JOHN FLAHERTY
- ☐ 318. TEAM CHECKLIST
- ☐ 331. FRANK VIOLA
- ☐ 363. TONY PENA
- ☐ 367. SCOTT FLETCHER
- ☐ 388. SCOTT COOPER
- ☐ 417. JOHN VALENTIN
- ☐ 429. TIM NAEHRING
- ☐ 443. BILLY HATCHER
- ☐ 471. ANDRE DAWSON
- ☐ 475. ROB DEER
- ☐ 486. TROT NIXON
- ☐ 499. CARLOS QUINTANA
- ☐ 529. JEFF RUSSELL
- ☐ 561. AARON SELE
- ☐ 583. PAUL QUANTRILL
- ☐ 592. KEN RYAN
- ☐ 602. LUIS ORTIZ
- ☐ 646. JEFF MCNEELY

CALIFORNIA ANGELS

- ☐ 17. DAMION EASLEY
- ☐ 45. LUIS POLONIA
- ☐ 71. MARK LANGSTON
- ☐ 95. CHAD CURTIS
- ☐ 121. GREG MYERS
- ☐ 151. CHUCK FINLEY
- ☐ 179. TOREY LOVULLO
- ☐ 202. JOE GRAHE
- ☐ 223. JULIO VALERA

- ☐ 250. STEVE FREY
- ☐ 252. STAN JAVIER
- ☐ 274. GENE NELSON
- ☐ 307. EDUARDO PEREZ
- ☐ 319. TEAM CHECKLIST
- ☐ 345. CHILI DAVIS
- ☐ 377. GARY DISARCINA
- ☐ 455. RENE GONZALES
- ☐ 468. BRIAN ANDERSON
- ☐ 500. CHRIS TURNER
- ☐ 511. J.T. SNOW
- ☐ 539. TIM SALMON
- ☐ 562. RUSS SPRINGER
- ☐ 594. ROD CORREIA
- ☐ 612. HILLY HATHAWAY

CHICAGO CUBS

- ☐ 20. RYNE SANDBERG
- ☐ 42. MARK GRACE
- ☐ 68. DERRICK MAY
- ☐ 96. MIKE HARKEY
- ☐ 134. WILLIE WILSON
- ☐ 178. JOSE GUZMAN
- ☐ 214. MIKE MORGAN
- ☐ 249. JOSE BAUTISTA
- ☐ 346. STEVE BUECHELE
- ☐ 370. JOSE VIZCAINO
- ☐ 385. EDDIE ZAMBRANO
- ☐ 408. DWIGHT SMITH
- ☐ 432. GREG HIBBARD
- ☐ 447. KARL RHODES
- ☐ 450. RICK WILKINS
- ☐ 454. JON RATLIFF
- ☐ 482. REY SANCHEZ
- ☐ 510. SAMMY SOSA
- ☐ 517. BROOKS KIESCHNICK
- ☐ 534. RANDY MYERS
- ☐ 604. KEVIN ROBERSON
- ☐ 616. TURK WENDELL
- ☐ 648. TEAM CHECKLIST

CHICAGO WHITE SOX

- ☐ 6. JACK MCDOWELL
- ☐ 41. FRANK THOMAS
- ☐ 69. LANCE JOHNSON
- ☐ 93. OZZIE GUILLEN
- ☐ 153. ALEX FERNANDEZ
- ☐ 181. MIKE LAVALLIERE
- ☐ 220. WILSON ALVAREZ
- ☐ 254. STEVE SAX
- ☐ 276. SCOTT RADINSKY
- ☐ 320. TEAM CHECKLIST
- ☐ 347. ROBIN VENTURA
- ☐ 379. TIM RAINES
- ☐ 403. RON KARKOVICE
- ☐ 431. ELLIS BURKS
- ☐ 457. ROBERTO HERNANDEZ
- ☐ 470. TIM BELCHER
- ☐ 485. JOEY CORA
- ☐ 513. BO JACKSON
- ☐ 541. GEORGE BELL
- ☐ 548. SCOTT CHRISTMAN
- ☐ 553. RODNEY BOLTON
- ☐ 563. JASON BERE
- ☐ 588. JEFF SCHWARZ
- ☐ 611. SCOTT RUFFCORN

CINCINNATI REDS

- ☐ 24. KEVIN MITCHELL
- ☐ 52. JOSE RIJO
- ☐ 74. BARRY LARKIN
- ☐ 108. BIP ROBERTS
- ☐ 114. ROB DIBBLE
- ☐ 146. JACK DAUGHERTY
- ☐ 168. TOM BROWNING
- ☐ 225. JEFF BRANSON
- ☐ 251. JEFF REARDON
- ☐ 334. ROBERTO KELLY
- ☐ 355. DAN WILSON
- ☐ 360. CHRIS SABO
- ☐ 394. REGGIE SANDERS
- ☐ 424. JOHN SMILEY
- ☐ 444. JOE OLIVER
- ☐ 501. THOMAS HOWARD
- ☐ 526. HAL MORRIS
- ☐ 552. TIM COSTO
- ☐ 589. ROSS POWELL
- ☐ 603. LARRY LUEBBERS
- ☐ 621. KEITH KESSINGER
- ☐ 623. JOHN ROPER
- ☐ 649. TEAM CHECKLIST

CLEVELAND INDIANS

- ☐ 7. ALBERT BELLE
- ☐ 53. CARLOS BAERGA
- ☐ 81. KENNY LOFTON
- ☐ 107. FELIX FERMIN
- ☐ 115. JEFF TREADWAY
- ☐ 131. ERIC PLUNK
- ☐ 141. ALVARO ESPINOZA
- ☐ 154. CANDY MALDONADO
- ☐ 167. JIM THOME
- ☐ 194. DEREK LILLIQUIST
- ☐ 204. JEREMY HERNANDEZ
- ☐ 230. WAYNE KIRBY
- ☐ 262. JUNIOR ORTIZ
- ☐ 278. JERRY DIPOTO
- ☐ 314. TOM KRAMER
- ☐ 321. TEAM CHECKLIST
- ☐ 333. CHARLES NAGY
- ☐ 391. REGGIE JEFFERSON
- ☐ 419. JOSE MESA
- ☐ 445. SANDY ALOMAR, JR.
- ☐ 473. PAUL SORRENTO
- ☐ 483. MARK LEWIS
- ☐ 498. RANDY MILLIGAN
- ☐ 527. DARON KIRKREIT
- ☐ 543. SAM HORN
- ☐ 645. MANNY RAMINREZ

COLORADO ROCKIES

- ☐ 8. ANDRES GALARRAGA
- ☐ 50. CHARLIE HAYES
- ☐ 76. JOE GIRARDI
- ☐ 110. DANTE BICHETTE
- ☐ 118. WILLIE BLAIR
- ☐ 148. CHRIS JONES
- ☐ 170. STEVE REED
- ☐ 197. DANNY SHEAFFER
- ☐ 207. DARREN HOLMES
- ☐ 227. ARMANDO REYNOSO
- ☐ 229. FREDDIE BENAVIDES
- ☐ 253. MO SANFORD
- ☐ 305. VINNY CASTILLA
- ☐ 311. JIM TATUM
- ☐ 336. ALEX COLE
- ☐ 362. JERALD CLARK
- ☐ 374. GREG W. HARRIS
- ☐ 396. DARYL BOSTON
- ☐ 472. ERIC YOUNG
- ☐ 528. DAVID NIED
- ☐ 573. JAMEY WRIGHT
- ☐ 595. DARRELL SHERMAN
- ☐ 615. ROBERTO MEJIA
- ☐ 643. ERIC WEDGE
- ☐ 650. TEAM CHECKLIST

DETROIT TIGERS

- ☐ 11. TRAVIS FRYMAN
- ☐ 51. MICKEY TETTLETON
- ☐ 79. LOU WHITAKER
- ☐ 103. TONY PHILLIPS
- ☐ 117. MIKE HENNEMAN
- ☐ 143. MIKE MOORE
- ☐ 171. SCOTT LIVINGSTONE
- ☐ 198. BILL GULLICKSON
- ☐ 215. DAN GLADDEN
- ☐ 228. RICH ROWLAND
- ☐ 232. SKEETER BARNES
- ☐ 268. GARY THURMAN
- ☐ 286. BOB MACDONALD
- ☐ 309. CHRIS GOMEZ
- ☐ 322. TEAM CHECKLIST
- ☐ 337. ALAN TRAMMELL
- ☐ 369. DAVID WELLS
- ☐ 393. CECIL FIELDER
- ☐ 421. KIRK GIBSON
- ☐ 503. CHAD KREUTER
- ☐ 504. ERIC DAVIS
- ☐ 531. JOHN DOHERTY
- ☐ 532. MATT BRUNSON
- ☐ 559. DANNY BAUTISTA

FLORIDA MARLINS

- ☐ 40. BENITO SANTIAGO
- ☐ 66. BRYAN HARVEY
- ☐ 98. WALT WEISS
- ☐ 100. GARY SHEFFIELD
- ☐ 124. CHRIS HAMMOND
- ☐ 142. RYAN BOWEN
- ☐ 161. HENRY COTTO
- ☐ 199. ALEX ARIAS
- ☐ 255. LUIS AQUINO
- ☐ 280. RICHIE LEWIS
- ☐ 283. JOE KLINK
- ☐ 295. RICH RODRIGUEZ
- ☐ 306. MATT TURNER
- ☐ 310. PAT RAPP
- ☐ 372. ORESTES DESTRADE
- ☐ 410. JACK ARMSTONG
- ☐ 434. BRET BARBERIE
- ☐ 452. CHARLIE HOUGH
- ☐ 484. JEFF CONINE
- ☐ 512. CHUCK CARR
- ☐ 555. MARC VALDES
- ☐ 556. DARRELL WHITMORE
- ☐ 598. KURT ABBOTT
- ☐ 601. CARL EVERETT
- ☐ 639. NIGEL WILSON
- ☐ 651. TEAM CHECKLIST

HOUSTON ASTROS

- ☐ 4. JEFF BAGWELL
- ☐ 48. CRAIG BIGGIO
- ☐ 78. PETE HARNISCH
- ☐ 104. ANDUJAR CEDENO
- ☐ 128. KEVIN BASS
- ☐ 150. BRIAN WILLIAMS
- ☐ 172. CHRIS DONNELS
- ☐ 193. MARK PORTUGAL
- ☐ 231. DARRYL KILE
- ☐ 246. TODD JONES
- ☐ 257. SCOTT SERVAIS
- ☐ 285. CASEY CANDAELE
- ☐ 342. KEN CAMINITI
- ☐ 364. STEVE FINLEY
- ☐ 400. ERIC ANTHONY
- ☐ 426. DOUG DRABEK
- ☐ 456. EDDIE TAUBENSEE
- ☐ 474. LUIS GONZALEZ
- ☐ 502. GREG SWINDELL
- ☐ 536. BILLY WAGNER
- ☐ 544. DOUG JONES
- ☐ 586. SHANE REYNOLDS
- ☐ 652. TEAM CHECKLIST

KANSAS CITY ROYALS

- ☐ 19. BRIAN MCRAE
- ☐ 39. JOSE LIND
- ☐ 67. WALLY JOYNER
- ☐ 91. GREG GAGNE
- ☐ 125. HUBIE BROOKS
- ☐ 155. JEFF MONTGOMERY
- ☐ 160. STAN BELINDA
- ☐ 183. BRENT MAYNE
- ☐ 206. DAVID HOWARD
- ☐ 218. HIPOLITO PICHARDO
- ☐ 234. TOM GORDON
- ☐ 279. CHRIS HANEY
- ☐ 294. JOHN HABYAN

- ☐ 300. GARY GAETTI
- ☐ 323. TEAM CHECKLIST
- ☐ 359. KEVIN APPIER
- ☐ 381. CHRIS GWYNN
- ☐ 405. DAVID CONE
- ☐ 433. FELIX JOSE
- ☐ 459. MIKE MACFARLANE
- ☐ 487. KEVIN MCREYNOLDS
- ☐ 515. PHIL HIATT
- ☐ 564. BILLY BREWER
- ☐ 574. JEFF GRANGER
- ☐ 622. BOB HAMELIN

LOS ANGELES DODGERS

- ☐ 26. ERIC KARROS
- ☐ 46. BRETT BUTLER
- ☐ 80. CORY SNYDER
- ☐ 102. OREL HERSHISER
- ☐ 130. MITCH WEBSTER
- ☐ 152. LENNY HARRIS
- ☐ 174. CARLOS HERNANDEZ
- ☐ 203. TOM CANDIOTTI
- ☐ 233. RAMON MARTINEZ
- ☐ 259. DAVE HANSEN
- ☐ 287. MIKE SHARPERSON
- ☐ 340. JOSE OFFERMAN
- ☐ 368. JODY REED
- ☐ 402. JIM GOTT
- ☐ 428. DARRYL STRAWBERRY
- ☐ 446. TIM WALLACH
- ☐ 476. MIKE PIAZZA
- ☐ 530. KEVIN GROSS
- ☐ 554. PEDRO MARTINEZ
- ☐ 600. RICK TRLICEK
- ☐ 618. RAUL MONDESI
- ☐ 653. TEAM CHECKLIST

MILWAUKEE BREWERS

- ☐ 13. ROBIN YOUNT
- ☐ 49. GREG VAUGHN
- ☐ 77. B.J. SURHOFF
- ☐ 105. BILL SPIERS
- ☐ 119. DOUG HENRY
- ☐ 145. JAIME NAVARRO
- ☐ 173. JOHN JAHA
- ☐ 200. MIKE FETTERS
- ☐ 236. RICKY BONES
- ☐ 282. JUAN BELL
- ☐ 284. GRAEME LLOYD
- ☐ 299. JESSE OROSCO
- ☐ 324. TEAM CHECKLIST
- ☐ 341. BILL WEGMAN
- ☐ 348. TEDDY HIGUERA
- ☐ 371. PAT LISTACH
- ☐ 395. DARRYL HAMILTON
- ☐ 423. TOM BRUNANSKY
- ☐ 449. CAL ELDRED
- ☐ 477. KEVIN REIMER
- ☐ 505. DICKIE THON
- ☐ 519. KEVIN SEITZER
- ☐ 533. DAVE NILSSON
- ☐ 610. MATT MAYSEY

MINNESOTA TWINS

- ☐ 21. KIRBY PUCKETT
- ☐ 37. BRIAN HARPER
- ☐ 65. KENT HRBEK
- ☐ 89. CHUCK KNOBLAUCH
- ☐ 129. RICK AGUILERA
- ☐ 185. WILLIE BANKS
- ☐ 238. PAT MEARES
- ☐ 288. GENE LARKIN
- ☐ 290. DAVID MCCARTY
- ☐ 325. TEAM CHECKLIST
- ☐ 351. KEVIN TAPANI
- ☐ 383. SHANE MACK
- ☐ 407. DAVE WINFIELD
- ☐ 435. PEDRO MUNOZ
- ☐ 461. SCOTT ERICKSON
- ☐ 545. SCOTT LEIUS
- ☐ 591. MIKE TROMBLEY
- ☐ 609. CHIP HALE
- ☐ 640. TORII HUNTER

MONTREAL EXPOS

- ☐ 38. DELINO DESHIELDS
- ☐ 64. KEN HILL
- ☐ 90. MOISES ALOU
- ☐ 162. MEL ROJAS
- ☐ 180. JOHN VANDER WAL
- ☐ 261. JEFF FASSERO
- ☐ 289. BRIAN BARNES
- ☐ 312. KIRK RUETER
- ☐ 352. MARQUIS GRISSOM
- ☐ 376. LARRY WALKER
- ☐ 390. JOHN WETTELAND
- ☐ 412. WIL CORDERO
- ☐ 436. DARRIN FLETCHER
- ☐ 488. MIKE LANSING
- ☐ 514. DENNIS MARTINEZ
- ☐ 577. LOU FRAZIER
- ☐ 587. CLIFF FLOYD
- ☐ 638. RONDELL WHITE
- ☐ 654. TEAM CHECKLIST

NEW YORK METS

- ☐ 22. DOC GOODEN
- ☐ 36. EDDIE MURRAY
- ☐ 92. BRET SABERHAGEN
- ☐ 122. JOHN FRANCO
- ☐ 182. SID FERNANDEZ
- ☐ 195. CHARLIE O'BRIEN
- ☐ 235. DAVE GALLAGHER
- ☐ 263. ANTHONY YOUNG
- ☐ 291. JEFF INNIS
- ☐ 378. BOBBY BONILLA
- ☐ 398. JOE ORSULAK
- ☐ 414. HOWARD JOHNSON
- ☐ 458. TODD HUNDLEY
- ☐ 516. JEFF KENT
- ☐ 518. KIRK PRESLEY
- ☐ 557. TIM BOGAR
- ☐ 570. JEROMY BURNITZ
- ☐ 576. RYAN THOMPSON
- ☐ 599. DAVE TELGHEDER
- ☐ 605. BUTCH HUSKEY
- ☐ 655. TEAM CHECKLIST

NEW YORK YANKEES

- ☐ 15. PAUL O'NEILL
- ☐ 23. DON MATTINGLY
- ☐ 75. JIMMY KEY
- ☐ 101. WADE BOGGS
- ☐ 127. JIM ABBOTT
- ☐ 147. BOB WICKMAN
- ☐ 175. DION JAMES
- ☐ 196. MATT NOKES
- ☐ 213. JIM LEYRITZ
- ☐ 216. RANDY VELARDE
- ☐ 224. PUAL ASSENMACHER
- ☐ 244. MIKE GALLEGO
- ☐ 245. LEE SMITH
- ☐ 256. DOMINGO JEAN
- ☐ 326. TEAM CHECKLIST
- ☐ 339. BERNIE WILLIAMS
- ☐ 350. SCOTT KAMIENIECKI
- ☐ 373. DANNY TARTABULL
- ☐ 397. PAT KELLY
- ☐ 425. KEVIN MAAS
- ☐ 451. MIKE STANLEY
- ☐ 479. MELIDO PEREZ
- ☐ 506. MATT DREWS
- ☐ 507. SPIKE OWEN
- ☐ 535. STEVE FARR
- ☐ 538. FRANK TANANA
- ☐ 565. STERLING HITCHCOCK
- ☐ 566. BOBBY MUNOZ
- ☐ 590. GERALD WILLIAMS
- ☐ 608. MARK HUTTON

OAKLAND A'S

- ☐ 47. TERRY STEINBACH
- ☐ 109. DENNIS ECKERSLEY
- ☐ 159. RON DARLING
- ☐ 187. BRENT GATES
- ☐ 208. RICK HONEYCUTT
- ☐ 248. TROY NEEL
- ☐ 260. GOOSE GOSSAGE
- ☐ 277. MIKE ALDRETE
- ☐ 296. EDWIN NUNEZ
- ☐ 327. TEAM CHECKLIST
- ☐ 349. JERRY BROWNE
- ☐ 409. RUBEN SIERRA
- ☐ 437. BOBBY WITT
- ☐ 463. DAVE HENDERSON
- ☐ 491. MIKE BORDICK
- ☐ 547. BOB WELCH
- ☐ 550. MARK MCGWIRE
- ☐ 558. STEVE KARSAY
- ☐ 567. CRAIG PAQUETTE
- ☐ 571. JOHN WASDIN
- ☐ 607. TODD VAN POPPEL

PHILADELPHIA PHILLIES

- ☐ 28. JOHN KRUK
- ☐ 34. DARREN DAULTON
- ☐ 60. LENNY DYKSTRA
- ☐ 88. CURT SCHILLING
- ☐ 116. RICKY JORDAN
- ☐ 123. ROGER MASON
- ☐ 156. DAVID WEST
- ☐ 158. MILT THOMPSON
- ☐ 184. TERRY MULHOLLAND
- ☐ 209. DANNY JACKSON
- ☐ 217. MITCH WILLIAMS
- ☐ 237. LARRY ANDERSEN
- ☐ 265. RUBEN AMARO, JR.
- ☐ 293. BEN RIVERA
- ☐ 354. DAVE HOLLINS
- ☐ 380. TOMMY GREENE
- ☐ 416. PETE INCAVIGLIA
- ☐ 438. WES CHAMBERLAIN
- ☐ 460. MICKEY MORANDINI
- ☐ 490. MARIANO DUNCAN
- ☐ 494. WAYNE GOMES
- ☐ 540. KIM BATISTE
- ☐ 619. KEVIN STOCKER
- ☐ 656. TEAM CHECKLIST

PITTSBURGH PIRATES

- ☐ 18. ANDY VAN SLYKE
- ☐ 32. JAY BELL
- ☐ 58. ORLANDO MERCED
- ☐ 86. DON SLAUGHT
- ☐ 186. STEVE COOKE
- ☐ 211. BLAS MNOR
- ☐ 239. ZANE SMITH
- ☐ 267. DAVE CLARK
- ☐ 308. JOEL JOHNSTON
- ☐ 356. BOB WALK
- ☐ 382. JEFF KING
- ☐ 418. TIM WAKEFIELD
- ☐ 492. KEVIN YOUNG
- ☐ 520. CARLOS GARCIA
- ☐ 546. AL MARTIN
- ☐ 578. PAUL WAGNER
- ☐ 657. TEAM CHECKLIST

ST. LOUIS CARDINALS

- ☐ 16. RAY LANKFORD
- ☐ 29. GREGG JEFFERIES
- ☐ 56. BOB TEWKSBURY
- ☐ 63. DONOVAN OSBORNE
- ☐ 84. MIKE PEREZ
- ☐ 120. GERALD PERRY
- ☐ 164. RENE AROCHA
- ☐ 188. ERIK PAPPAS
- ☐ 201. BRIAN JORDAN
- ☐ 269. LES LANCASTER

☐ 297. ROD BREWER
☐ 358. TODD ZEILE
☐ 384. OZZIE SMITH
☐ 420. BERNARD GILKEY
☐ 440. MARK WHITEN
☐ 466. TOM PAGNOZZI
☐ 522. LUIS ALICEA
☐ 613. ALLEN WATSON
☐ 658. TEAM CHECKLIST

SAN DIEGO PADRES

☐ 12. TONY GWYNN
☐ 44. ANDY BENES
☐ 138. GENE HARRIS
☐ 241. PHIL CLARK
☐ 271. RICKY GUTIERREZ
☐ 281. JARVIS BROWN
☐ 338. DEREK BELL
☐ 404. PHIL PLANTIER
☐ 478. JEFF GARDNER
☐ 579. BRAD AUSMUS
☐ 585. DERREK LEE
☐ 642. KEVIN HIGGINS
☐ 659. TEAM CHECKLIST

SAN FRANCISCO GIANTS

☐ 1. BARRY BONDS
☐ 5. JOHN BURKETT
☐ 10. WILL CLARK
☐ 70. WILLIE MCGEE
☐ 94. MATT WILLIAMS
☐ 132. MARK CARREON
☐ 140. TREVOR WILSON
☐ 176. BUD BLACK
☐ 219. DAVE BURBA
☐ 243. MIKE JACKSON
☐ 273. MIKE BENJAMIN
☐ 301. TODD BENZINGER
☐ 344. KIRT MANWARING
☐ 401. SCOTT SANDERSON
☐ 406. ROBBY THOMPSON
☐ 430. BILL SWIFT
☐ 448. ROYCE CLAYTON
☐ 480. DARREN LEWIS
☐ 508. ROD BECK
☐ 581. KEVIN ROGERS
☐ 596. STEVE SCARSONE
☐ 641. SALOMON TORRES
☐ 660. TEAM CHECKLIST

SEATTLE MARINERS

☐ 3. KEN GRIFFEY, JR.
☐ 14. DAVE MAGADAN
☐ 33. RANDY JOHNSON
☐ 59. TINO MARTINEZ
☐ 87. OMAR VIZQUEL
☐ 135. DAVE FLEMING
☐ 189. BILL HASELMAN
☐ 210. RICH AMARAL
☐ 240. TIM LEARY
☐ 264. CHRIS BOSIO
☐ 302. JEFF NELSON
☐ 328. TEAM CHECKLIST
☐ 353. JAY BUHNER
☐ 387. ERIK HANSON
☐ 411. MIKE FELDER
☐ 439. MACKEY SASSER
☐ 465. EDGAR MARTINEZ
☐ 493. DAVE VALLE
☐ 521. MIKE BLOWERS
☐ 549. NORM CHARLTON
☐ 568. BRET BOONE
☐ 584. MARC NEWFIELD
☐ 637. BRIAN TURANG
☐ 644. ROGER SALKELD

TEXAS RANGERS

☐ 27. JUAN GONZALEZ
☐ 31. IVAN RODRIGUEZ
☐ 61. JOSE CANSECO
☐ 99. KEVIN BROWN
☐ 137. GENO PETRALLI
☐ 163. DOUG STRANGE
☐ 169. MARIO DIAZ
☐ 191. GARY REDUS
☐ 212. KENNY ROGERS
☐ 292. BOB PATTERSON
☐ 304. MATT WHITESIDE
☐ 329. TEAM CHECKLIST
☐ 365. ROGER PAVLIK
☐ 389. DEAN PALMER
☐ 413. JULIO FRANCO
☐ 467. CHARLIE LEIBRANDT
☐ 495. RAFAEL PALMEIRO
☐ 523. DAVID HULSE
☐ 542. TOM HENKE
☐ 569. DAN PELTIER
☐ 606. BENJI GIL

TORONTO BLUE JAYS

☐ 2. JOHN OLERUD
☐ 35. RICKEY HENDERSON
☐ 43. ROBERTO ALOMAR
☐ 62. TONY FERNANDEZ
☐ 73. JOE CARTER
☐ 97. DEVON WHITE
☐ 133. DAVE STEWART
☐ 149. TODD STOTTLEMYRE
☐ 177. TONY CASTILLO
☐ 242. DANNY COX
☐ 266. MARK EICHHORN
☐ 298. MIKE TIMLIN
☐ 330. TEAM CHECKLIST
☐ 343. PAT BORDERS
☐ 375. JUAN GUZMAN
☐ 399. ED SPRAGUE
☐ 427. PAUL MOLITOR
☐ 453. JACK MORRIS
☐ 481. DUANE WARD
☐ 509. PAT HENTGEN
☐ 537. DARNELL COLES
☐ 614. CARLOS DELGADO

1994 SCORE ROOKIE & TRADED (165) 2 1/2" X 3 1/2"

ATLANTA BRAVES

☐ 65RT. ROBERTO KELLY
☐ 75RT. RYAN KLESKO
☐ 78RT. JAVIER LOPEZ
☐ 90RT. TONY TARASCO
☐ 159RT. MIKE KELLY

BALTIMORE ORIOLES

☐ 2RT. LEE SMITH
☐ 8RT. RAFAEL PALMEIRO
☐ 17RT. CHRIS SABO
☐ 51RT. SID FERNANDEZ
☐ 77RT. JEFFREY HAMMONDS
☐ 108RT. MARK SMITH
☐ 129RT. MIKE OQUIST

BOSTON RED SOX

☐ 25RT. WES CHAMBERLAIN
☐ 26RT. OTIS NIXON
☐ 98RT. RICH ROWLAND
☐ 121RT. NATE MINCHEY
☐ 127RT. TOM BRUNANSKY
☐ 135RT. LEE TINSLEY
☐ 162RT. GREG BLOSSER

CALIFORNIA ANGELS

☐ 3RT. BO JACKSON
☐ 20RT. HAROLD REYNOLDS
☐ 56RT. REX HUDLER
☐ 66RT. SPIKE OWEN
☐ 85RT. CHRIS TURNER
☐ 110RT. JORGE FABREGAS
☐ 125RT. BRIAN ANDERSON
☐ 160RT. JIM EDMONDS

CHICAGO CUBS

☐ 31RT. ANTHONY YOUNG
☐ 41RT. WILLIE BANKS
☐ 89RT. TURK WENDELL
☐ 93RT. EDDIE ZAMBRANO
☐ 161RT. STEVE TRACHSEL

CHICAGO WHITE SOX

☐ 29RT. JULIO FRANCO
☐ 38RT. DARRIN JACKSON
☐ 54RT. SCOTT SANDERSON
☐ 131RT. NORBERTO MARTIN
☐ 143RT. JOE HALL

CINCINNATI REDS

☐ 7RT. ERIK HANSON
☐ 33RT. LENNY HARRIS
☐ 34RT. EDDIE TAUBENSEE
☐ 39RT. TONY FERNANDEZ
☐ 57RT. DEION SANDERS
☐ 60RT. BRET BOONE
☐ 80RT. HECTOR CARRASCO
☐ 144RT. JOHNNY RUFFIN

CLEVELAND INDIANS

☐ 5RT. EDDIE MURRAY
☐ 10RT. OMAR VIZQUEL
☐ 21RT. JACK MORRIS
☐ 24RT. DENNIS MARTINEZ
☐ 59RT. TONY PENA
☐ 70RT. STEVE FARR
☐ 72RT. MANNY RAMIREZ
☐ 109RT. PAUL SHUEY

COLORADO ROCKIES

☐ 4RT. ELLIS BURKS
☐ 16RT. WALT WEISS
☐ 48RT. MARVIN FREEMAN
☐ 63RT. HOWARD JOHNSON
☐ 68RT. MIKE HARKEY
☐ 157RT. MARCUS MOORE

DETROIT TIGERS

- ☐ 44RT. JUNIOR FELIX
- ☐ 84RT. DANNY BAUTISTA
- ☐ 95RT. CHRIS GOMEZ
- ☐158RT. JOSE LIMA

FLORIDA MARLINS

- ☐ 11RT. KURT ABBOTT
- ☐ 23RT. DAVE MAGADAN
- ☐ 47RT. JERRY BROWNE
- ☐ 92RT. GREG COLBRUNN
- ☐120RT. CHARLES JOHNSON
- ☐138RT. MATIAS CARRILLO

HOUSTON ASTROS

- ☐ 58RT. SID BREAM
- ☐ 86RT. SHANE REYNOLDS
- ☐ 99RT. JAMES MOUTON
- ☐104RT. JOHN HUDEK
- ☐116RT. TONY EUSEBIO
- ☐142RT. BRIAN HUNTER

KANSAS CITY ROYALS

- ☐ 12RT. VINCE COLEMAN
- ☐ 18RT. DAVE HENDERSON
- ☐ 73RT. BOB HAMELIN

LOS ANGELES DODGERS

- ☐ 6RT. DELINO DESHIELDS
- ☐ 67RT. JEFF TREADWAY
- ☐ 82RT. RAUL MONDESI
- ☐136RT. CHAN HO PARK

MILWAUKEE BREWERS

- ☐ 32RT. BRIAN HARPER
- ☐ 49RT. JODY REED
- ☐ 55RT. TURNER WARD
- ☐101RT. JOSE VALENTIN
- ☐114RT. TROY O'LEARY
- ☐119RT. ALEX DIAZ
- ☐139RT. MARK KIEFER
- ☐156RT. MATT MIESKE

MINNESOTA TWINS

- ☐ 50RT. ALEX COLE
- ☐ 94RT. RICH BECKER
- ☐ 97RT. DEREK PARKS
- ☐106RT. DENNY HOCKING
- ☐154RT. MATT WALBECK

MONTREAL EXPOS

- ☐ 28RT. RANDY MILLIGAN
- ☐ 62RT. PEDRO MARTINEZ
- ☐ 76RT. CLIFF FLOYD
- ☐ 87RT. RONDELL WHITE

NEW YORK METS

- ☐ 30RT. KEVIN MCREYNOLDS
- ☐ 35RT. DAVID SEGUI
- ☐ 40RT. JOSE VIZCAINO
- ☐ 52RT. PETE SMITH
- ☐134RT. FERNANDO VINA
- ☐151RT. KELLY STINNETT

NEW YORK YANKEES

- ☐ 9RT. LUIS POLONIA
- ☐ 14RT. TERRY MULHOLLAND
- ☐ 53RT. XAVIER HERNANDEZ
- ☐ 81RT. GERALD WILLIAMS
- ☐ 83RT. STERLING HITCHCOCK
- ☐103RT. ROBERT EENHOORN
- ☐123RT. DARYL BOSTON
- ☐133RT. MARK HUTTON

OAKLAND A'S

- ☐ 13RT. RICKEY HENDERSON
- ☐ 36RT. STAN JAVIER
- ☐ 71RT. BILLY TAYLOR
- ☐ 74RT. STEVE KARSAY
- ☐117RT. CARLOS REYES
- ☐152RT. MIGUEL JIMENEZ
- ☐163RT. MARK ACRE

PHILADELPHIA PHILLIES

- ☐ 69RT. DOUG JONES
- ☐147RT. TOM MARSH
- ☐148RT. TONY LONGMIRE
- ☐153RT. JEFF JUDEN

PITTSBURGH PIRATES

- ☐ 42RT. BRIAN HUNTER
- ☐126RT. DAN MICELI

ST. LOUIS CARDINALS

- ☐ 19RT. RICK SUTCLIFFE
- ☐130RT. JOHN MABRY
- ☐140RT. STAN ROYER
- ☐141RT. BRYAN EVERSGERD

SAN DIEGO PADRES

- ☐ 46RT. BIP ROBERTS
- ☐100RT. TIM HYERS
- ☐122RT. SCOTT SANDERS
- ☐124RT. JOEY HAMILTON
- ☐128RT. DAVE STATON
- ☐146RT. KEITH LOCKHART
- ☐150RT. MELVIN NIEVES

SAN FRANCISCO GIANTS

- ☐ 64RT. MARK PORTUGAL
- ☐ 88RT. SALOMON TORRES
- ☐ 96RT. JOHN PATTERSON
- ☐111RT. RIKKERT FANEYTE
- ☐118RT. J.R. PHILLIPS

SEATTLE MARINERS

- ☐ 15RT. GREG HIBBARD
- ☐ 22RT. DAN WILSON
- ☐ 27RT. ERIC ANTHONY
- ☐ 37RT. FELIX FERMIN
- ☐ 43RT. REGGIE JEFFERSON
- ☐ 61RT. BOBBY AYALA
- ☐ 79RT. ROGER SALKELD
- ☐107RT. GREG PIRKL
- ☐149RT. KEITH MITCHELL
- ☐155RT. MARC NEWFIELD

TEXAS RANGERS

- ☐ 1RT. WILL CLARK
- ☐ 45RT. JACK ARMSTRONG
- ☐113RT. DARREN OLIVER
- ☐132RT. HECTOR FAJARDO

TORONTO BLUE JAYS

- ☐ 91RT. SHAWN GREEN
- ☐102RT. CARLOS DELGADO
- ☐105RT. DOMINGO CEDENO
- ☐112RT. ROB BUTLER
- ☐115RT. SCOTT BROW
- ☐137RT. PAUL SPOLJARIC
- ☐145RT. ALEX GONZALEZ

1995 SCORE SERIES 1 (330) 2 1/2" X 3 1/2"

ATLANTA BRAVES

- ☐ 10. RAFAEL BELLIARD
- ☐ 32. GREG MADDUX
- ☐ 59. ROBERTO KELLY
- ☐ 87. MARK LEMKE
- ☐ 119. JAVIER LOPEZ
- ☐ 145. TONY TARASCO
- ☐ 185. STEVE AVERY
- ☐ 215. BILL PECOTA
- ☐ 250. GREG MCMICHAEL
- ☐ 271. DAVE JUSTICE
- ☐ 283. MIKE KELLY
- ☐ 295. JOSE OLIVA
- ☐ 317. TEAM CHECKLIST

BALTIMORE ORIOLES

- ☐ 3. CAL RIPKEN, JR
- ☐ 31. LEO GOMEZ
- ☐ 57. HAROLD BAINES
- ☐ 75. LONNIE SMITH
- ☐ 91. LEE SMITH
- ☐ 114. JAMIE MOYER
- ☐ 162. MARK MCLEMORE
- ☐ 182. SID FERNANDEZ
- ☐ 200. MIKE OQUIST
- ☐ 249. JACK VOIGT
- ☐ 273. BEN MCDONALD
- ☐ 284. MARK SMITH
- ☐ 299. ARMANDO BENITEZ
- ☐ 317. TEAM CHECKLIST

BOSTON RED SOX

- ☐ 8. JOHN VALENTIN
- ☐ 12. MO VAUGHN
- ☐ 33. MIKE GREENWELL
- ☐ 62. RICH ROWLAND
- ☐ 86. TOM BRUNANDKY
- ☐ 118. ROGER CLEMENS
- ☐ 166. SCOTT FLETCHER
- ☐ 186. STEVE FARR
- ☐ 208. DANNY DARWIN
- ☐ 251. DAMON BERRYHILL
- ☐ 276. LUIS ORTIZ
- ☐ 286. GREG BLOSSER
- ☐ 318. TEAM CHECKLIST

CALIFORNIA ANGELS

- ☐ 14. CHILI DAVIS
- ☐ 55. CHRIS TURNER

☐ 66. REX HUDLER
☐ 88. SPIKE OWEN
☐ 126. MARK LANGSTON
☐ 134. CHUCK FINLEY
☐ 164. J.T. SNOW
☐ 184. GREG MYERS
☐ 225. MARK LEITER
☐ 253. JIM EDMONDS
☐ 278. MARK DALESANDRO
☐ 288. JORGE FABREGAS
☐ 310. GARRET ANDERSON
☐ 319. TEAM CHECKLIST

CHICAGO CUBS

☐ 9. GLENALLEN HILL
☐ 11. RANDY MYERS
☐ 34. SAMMY SOSA
☐ 63. REY SANCHEZ
☐ 89. SHAWON DUNSTON
☐ 121. KARL RHODES
☐ 191. WILLIE BANKS
☐ 202. EDDIE ZAMBRANO
☐ 285. TURK WENDELL
☐ 289. BLAISE ILSLEY
☐ 318. TEAM CHECKLIST

CHICAGO WHITE SOX

☐ 1. FRANK THOMAS
☐ 16. DARRIN JACKSON
☐ 53. SCOTT SANDERSON
☐ 70. JULIO FRANCO
☐ 90. WILSON ALVAREZ
☐ 112. TIM RAINES
☐ 136. CRAIG GREBECK
☐ 168. MIKE LAVALLIERE
☐ 188. DAN PASQUA
☐ 227. ROBIN VENTURA
☐ 255. JACK MCDOWELL
☐ 290. JOE HALL
☐ 320. TEAM CHECKLIST

CINCINNATI REDS

☐ 13. HECTOR CARRASCO
☐ 67. JOHNNY RUFFIN
☐ 93. JACOB BRUMFIELD
☐ 123. TONY FERNANDEZ
☐ 153. EDDIE TAUBENSEE
☐ 197. TOM BROWNING
☐ 207. JEROME WALTON
☐ 226. HAL MORRIS
☐ 252. BRIAN DORSETT
☐ 254. BARRY LARKIN
☐ 266. DEION SANDERS
☐ 270. JOSE RIJO
☐ 319. TEAM CHECKLIST

CLEVELAND INDIANS

☐ 51. CARLOS BAERGA
☐ 132. MARK CLARK
☐ 138. PAUL SHUEY
☐ 196. JOSE MESA
☐ 223. ALBERT BELLE
☐ 229. JIM THOME
☐ 257. EDDIE MURRAY
☐ 277. JULIAN TAVAREZ
☐ 321. TEAM CHECKLIST

COLORADO ROCKIES

☐ 15. DANTE BICHETTE
☐ 58. CHARLIE HAYES
☐ 71. ERIC YOUNG
☐ 95. JOE GIRARDI
☐ 139. DAVID NIED
☐ 156. MIKE KINGERY
☐ 189. BRUCE RUFFIN
☐ 198. JOHN VANDER WAL
☐ 228. MIKE MUNOZ
☐ 320. TEAM CHECKLIST

DETROIT TIGERS

☐ 18. JUNIOR FELIX
☐ 49. TONY PHILLIPS
☐ 78. MICKEY TETTLETON
☐ 94. KIRK GIBSON
☐ 116. CHRIS GOMEZ
☐ 148. MIKE HENNEMAN
☐ 174. MIKE MOORE
☐ 203. JOE BOEVER
☐ 231. JOHN DOHERTY
☐ 259. MILT CUYLER
☐ 292. JOSE LIMA
☐ 322. TEAM CHECKLIST

FLORIDA MARLINS

☐ 54. JEFF CONINE
☐ 97. GREG COLBRUNN
☐ 141. DAVE WEATHERS
☐ 158. BENITO SANTIAGO
☐ 159. MATIAS CARRILLO
☐ 187. ROBB NEN
☐ 224. CHUCK CARR
☐ 230. MARIO DIAZ
☐ 293. GREG O'HALLORAN
☐ 311. JOHN JOHNSTON
☐ 321. TEAM CHECKLIST

HOUSTON ASTROS

☐ 56. KEN CAMINITI
☐ 79. LUIS GONZALEZ
☐ 125. JAMES MOUTON
☐ 133. TONY EUSEBIO
☐ 177. DARRYL KILE
☐ 201. GREG SWINDELL
☐ 221. JEFF BAGWELL
☐ 240. SID BREAM
☐ 291. ORLANDO MILLER
☐ 305. ROBERTO PETAGINE
☐ 322. TEAM CHECKLIST

KANSAS CITY ROYALS

☐ 20. MARK GUBICZA
☐ 47. GREG GAGNE
☐ 82. FELIX JOSE
☐ 83. RUSTY MEACHAM
☐ 96. MIKE MACFARLANE
☐ 140. BILLY BREWER
☐ 172. JOSE LIND
☐ 206. DAVID HOWARD
☐ 256. WALLY JOYNER
☐ 261. VINCE COLEMAN
☐ 323. TEAM CHECKLIST

LOS ANGELES DODGERS

☐ 17. MIKE PIAZZA
☐ 52. HENRY RODRIGUEZ
☐ 99. DELINO DESHIELDS
☐ 169. DAVE HANSEN
☐ 205. CHRIS GWYNN
☐ 213. TODD WORRELL
☐ 233. RAUL MONDESI
☐ 238. OREL HERSHISER
☐ 268. JIM GOTT
☐ 272. ISMAEL VALDES
☐ 287. GAREY INGRAM
☐ 300. DARREN DREIFORT
☐ 323. TEAM CHECKLIST

MILWAUKEE BREWERS

☐ 25. BRIAN HARPER
☐ 45. KEVIN SEITZER
☐ 84. DARRYL HAMILTON
☐ 98. RICKY BONES
☐ 120. DAVE NILSSON
☐ 176. JODY REED
☐ 190. JOSE VALENTIN
☐ 235. JOHN JAHA
☐ 263. TURNER WARD
☐ 275. GRAEME LLOYD
☐ 294. MARK KIEFER
☐ 324. TEAM CHECKLIST

MINNESOTA TWINS

☐ 27. SCOTT ERICKSON
☐ 43. SHANE MACK
☐ 80. DAVE WINFIELD
☐ 100. PAT MEARES
☐ 122. RICK AGUILERA
☐ 142. SCOTT LEIUS
☐ 178. CARL WILLIS
☐ 237. KIRBY PUCKETT
☐ 265. MATT WALBECK
☐ 279. BRETT MERRIMAN
☐ 296. RICH BECKER
☐ 325. TEAM CHECKLIST

MONTREAL EXPOS

☐ 19. MOISES ALOU
☐ 50. KEN HILL
☐ 85. JOHN WETTELAND
☐ 101. JEFF FASSERO
☐ 127. MIKE LANSING
☐ 135. LOU FRAZIER
☐ 147. RONDELL WHITE
☐ 155. RAMON MARTINEZ
☐ 170. PEDRO MARTINEZ
☐ 171. KIRK RUETER
☐ 193. RANDY MILLIGAN
☐ 246. MARQUIS GRISSOM
☐ 258. LENNY WEBSTER
☐ 324. TEAM CHECKLIST

NEW YORK METS

☐ 21. BRET SABERHAGEN
☐ 48. JEFF KENT
☐ 81. RYAN THOMPSON
☐ 105. KEVIN MCREYNOLDS
☐ 129. JOE ORSULAK
☐ 137. KELLY STINNETT
☐ 179. JEROMY BURNITZ
☐ 216. JIM LINDEMAN
☐ 220. FERNANDO VINA
☐ 232. BOBBY JONES
☐ 297. BRIAN HUNTER
☐ 307. JONATHON HURST
☐ 325. TEAM CHECKLIST

NEW YORK YANKEES

☐ 23. STEVE HOWE
☐ 41. PAUL O'NEILL
☐ 76. JIMMY KEY
☐ 92. SCOTT KAMIENIECKI
☐ 102. JIM LEYRITZ
☐ 124. BERNIE WILLIAMS
☐ 144. MELIDO PEREZ
☐ 180. MIKE GALLEGO
☐ 195. MIKE STANLEY
☐ 239. DON MATTINGLY
☐ 267. GERALD WILLIAMS
☐ 281. ROBERT EENHOORN
☐ 298. DAVE SILVESTRI
☐ 326. TEAM CHECKLIST

OAKLAND A'S

☐ 29. BOB WELCH
☐ 38. STEVE ONTIVEROS
☐ 39. STAN JAVIER
☐ 72. MIKE BORDICK
☐ 104. TERRY STEINBACH
☐ 152. BOBBY WITT
☐ 160. SCOTT BROSIUS

☐ 192. MIKE ALDRETE
☐ 194. STEVE KARSAY
☐ 210. TODD VAN POPPEL
☐ 241. BRENT GATES
☐ 327. TEAM CHECKLIST

PHILADELPHIA PHILLIES

☐ 22. LENNY DYKSTRA
☐ 36. TOMMY GREENE
☐ 77. DAVE HOLLINS
☐ 107. DANNY JACKSON
☐ 131. PETE INCAVIGLIA
☐ 163. CURT SCHILLING
☐ 183. KIM BATISTE
☐ 234. RICKY JORDAN
☐ 242. TONY LONGMIRE
☐ 280. RICKY BOTTALACIO
☐ 309. MIKE LIEBERTHAL
☐ 326. TEAM CHECKLIST

PITTSBURGH PIRATES

☐ 24. MARK DEWEY
☐ 44. ORLANDO MERCED
☐ 73. DON SLAUGHT
☐ 109. JEFF KING
☐ 157. ZANE SMITH
☐ 161. DAVE CLARK
☐ 204. GARY VARSHO
☐ 217. RICK WHITE
☐ 236. CARLOS GARCIA
☐ 327. TEAM CHECKLIST

ST. LOUIS CARDINALS

☐ 26. OZZIE SMITH
☐ 69. TOM PAGNOZZI
☐ 111. GERALD PERRY
☐ 143. BRIAN JORDAN
☐ 167. BOB TEWKSBURY
☐ 173. LUIS ALICEA
☐ 218. JOSE OQUENDO
☐ 244. RICK SUTCLIFFE
☐ 264. RAY LANKFORD
☐ 301. JOHN MABRY
☐ 330. TEAM CHECKLIST

SAN DIEGO PADRES

☐ 28. TONY GWYNN
☐ 40. BIP ROBERTS
☐ 46. TREVOR HOFFMAN
☐ 65. RICKY GUTIERREZ
☐ 113. EDDIE WILLIAMS
☐ 117. LUIS LOPEZ
☐ 149. BRIAN JOHNSON
☐ 175. ANDY ASHBY
☐ 211. SCOTT LIVINGSTONE
☐ 306. KEITH LOCKHART
☐ 328. TEAM CHECKLIST

SAN FRANCISCO GIANTS

☐ 5. MATT WILLIAMS
☐ 30. BARRY BONDS
☐ 115. BUD BLACK
☐ 151. JOHN PATTERSON
☐ 165. ROD BECK
☐ 181. BILL VAN LANDINGHAM
☐ 209. DARRYL STRAWBERRY
☐ 243. ROBBY THOMPSON
☐ 248. MARK CARREON
☐ 260. TODD BENZINGER
☐ 274. DARREN LEWIS
☐ 282. RIKKERT FANEYTE
☐ 303. J.R. PHILLIPS
☐ 329. TEAM CHECKLIST

SEATTLE MARINERS

☐ 42. BILL HASELMAN
☐ 61. TIM DAVIS
☐ 68. JAY BUHNER
☐ 74. GOOSE GOSSAGE
☐ 106. FELIX FERMIN
☐ 128. TINO MARTINEZ
☐ 146. DAN WILSON
☐ 212. DAVE FLEMING

☐ 222. RANDY JOHNSON
☐ 302. GREG PIRKL
☐ 312. ALEX RODRIGUEZ
☐ 328. TEAM CHECKLIST

TEXAS RANGERS

☐ 4. JOSE CANSECO
☐ 6. ESTEBAN BELTRE
☐ 37. WILL CLARK
☐ 64. JUNIOR ORTIZ
☐ 103. GARY REDUS
☐ 108. CHRIS JAMES
☐ 130. DAVID HULSE
☐ 150. TOM HENKE
☐ 199. KEVIN BROWN
☐ 245. DEAN PALMER
☐ 269. JEFF FRYE
☐ 329. TEAM CHECKLIST

TORONTO BLUE JAYS

☐ 2. ROBERTO ALOMAR
☐ 7. DOMINGO CEDENO
☐ 35. DARNELL COLES
☐ 60. JOHN OLERUD
☐ 110. PAT HENTGEN
☐ 154. PAT BORDERS
☐ 214. CARLOS DELGADO
☐ 219. TONY CASTILLO
☐ 247. PAUL MOLITOR
☐ 262. TODD SOTTLEMYRE
☐ 304. SHAWN GREEN
☐ 308. PAUL SPOLJARIC
☐ 330. TEAM CHECKLIST

SCORE-PINNACLE

1992 PINNACLE (620)
2 1/2" X 3 1/2"

ATLANTA BRAVES

☐ 18. TERRY PENDLETON
☐ 55. MARK WOHLERS
☐ 75. TOM GLAVINE
☐ 100. DAVE JUSTICE
☐ 128. RON GANT
☐ 149. GREG OLSON
☐ 158. JEFF REARDON
☐ 170. DEION SANDERS
☐ 191. JOHN SMOLTZ
☐ 231. STEVE AVERY
☐ 258. KEITH MITCHELL
☐ 350. MIKE STANTON
☐ 357. RAFAEL BELLIARD
☐ 390. DAMON BERRYHILL
☐ 412. BRIAN HUNTER
☐ 423. CHARLIE LEIBRANDT
☐ 426. MARK LEMKE
☐ 446. SID BREAM
☐ 465. LONNIE SMITH
☐ 477. JEFF BLAUSER
☐ 515. JUAN BERENGUER
☐ 519. OTIS NIXON
☐ 528. ALEJANDRO PENA
☐ 566. MIKE BIELECKI

BALTIMORE ORIOLES

☐ 44. BEN MCDONALD
☐ 61. GREGG OLSON
☐ 83. CHRIS HOILES
☐ 138. GLENN DAVIS
☐ 165. MIKE DEVEREAUX
☐ 179. RANDY MILLIGAN
☐ 185. DAVID SEGUI
☐ 200. CAL RIPKEN, JR.
☐ 204. MIKE MUSSINA
☐ 221. SAM HORN
☐ 248. LUIS MERCEDES
☐ 251. ARTHUR RHODES
☐ 312. STORM DAVIS
☐ 336. BILLY RIPKEN
☐ 339. BOB MILACKI
☐ 356. LEO GOMEZ
☐ 362. JOE ORSULAK
☐ 380. CHITO MARTINEZ
☐ 398. RICK SUTCLIFFE
☐ 411. TODD FROHWIRTH
☐ 452. BRADY ANDERSON
☐ 475. MIKE FLANAGAN
☐ 478. CRAIG LEFFERTS

BOSTON RED SOX

☐ 26. ELLIS BURKS
☐ 33. TONY PENA
☐ 51. PHIL PLANTIER
☐ 85. JACK CLARK
☐ 95. ROGER CLEMENS
☐ 131. MIKE GREENWELL
☐ 175. WADE BOGGS
☐ 205. MO VAUGHN
☐ 222. JODY REED
☐ 242. TIM NAEHRING
☐ 252. SCOTT COOPER
☐ 314. TOM BRUNANSKY
☐ 346. LUIS RIVERA
☐ 358. CARLOS QUINTANA
☐ 407. FRANK VIOLA
☐ 415. JOE HESKETH
☐ 460. BILLY HATCHER
☐ 505. MIKE GARDINER
☐ 518. MATT YOUNG
☐ 526. PETER HOY
☐ 569. SCOTT HATTEBERG
☐ 576. BOB ZUPCIC
☐ 577. J.J. JOHNSON

CALIFORNIA ANGELS

☐ 42. CHUCK FINLEY
☐ 52. GARY DISARCINA
☐ 81. GARY GAETTI
☐ 132. MARK LANGSTON
☐ 166. LUIS POLONIA
☐ 220. JUNIOR FELIX
☐ 223. LUIS SOJO
☐ 267. JULIO VALERA
☐ 324. GREG MYERS

☐ 326. VON HAYES
☐ 353. MARK EICHHORN
☐ 371. JOE GRAHE
☐ 449. HUBIE BROOKS
☐ 453. LEE STEVENS
☐ 467. ALVIN DAVIS
☐ 523. CHAD CURTIS
☐ 539. JIM ABBOTT

CHICAGO CUBS

☐ 10. RYNE SANDBERG
☐ 65. GREG MADDUX
☐ 94. DAVE SMITH
☐ 115. ANDRE DAWSON
☐ 136. MARK GRACE
☐ 160. DOUG DASCENZO
☐ 197. MIKE HARKEY
☐ 224. JEROME WALTON
☐ 244. SHAWON DUNSTON
☐ 269. GARY SCOTT
☐ 272. LANCE DICKSON
☐ 329. CHUCK MCELROY
☐ 369. SAMMY SOSA
☐ 372. LUIS SALAZAR
☐ 374. KAL DANIELS
☐ 414. MIKE MORGAN
☐ 419. HECTOR VILLANUEVA
☐ 430. STEVE BUECHELE
☐ 466. PAUL ASSENMACHER
☐ 504. FRANK CASTILLO
☐ 527. SHAWN BOSKIE
☐ 534. DERRICK MAY
☐ 550. REY SANCHEZ

CHICAGO WHITE SOX

☐ 1. FRANK THOMAS
☐ 30. ALEX FERNANDEZ
☐ 37. GEORGE BELL
☐ 79. OZZIE GUILLEN
☐ 107. JACK MCDOWELL
☐ 121. ROBIN VENTURA
☐ 178. TIM RAINES
☐ 192. WILSON ALVAREZ
☐ 214. BOBBY THIGPEN
☐ 227. DAN PASQUA
☐ 253. ROBERTO HERNANDEZ
☐ 280. JEFF CARTER
☐ 300. SCOTT RUFFCORN
☐ 328. STEVE SAX
☐ 334. CRAIG GREBECK
☐ 361. CARLTON FISK
☐ 364. GREG HIBBARD
☐ 373. LANCE JOHNSON
☐ 389. SCOTT RADINSKY
☐ 391. KIRK MCCASKILL
☐ 413. RON KARKOVICE
☐ 422. CHARLIE HOUGH
☐ 485. MIKE HUFF
☐ 535. ESTEBAN BELTRE

CINCINNATI REDS

☐ 5. BARRY LARKIN
☐ 22. HAL MORRIS
☐ 47. BILL DORAN
☐ 101. TOM BROWNING
☐ 135. CHRIS SABO
☐ 154. PAUL O'NEILL
☐ 180. ROB DIBBLE
☐ 216. NORM CHARLTON
☐ 254. MO SANFORD
☐ 261. GINO MINUTELLI
☐ 278. FREDDIE BENAVIDES
☐ 327. GREG SWINDELL
☐ 331. JOE OLIVER
☐ 335. CHRIS HAMMOND
☐ 384. TIM BELCHER
☐ 397. DAVE MARTINEZ
☐ 404. BIP ROBERTS
☐ 440. REGGIE SANDERS
☐ 502. GLENN BRAGGS
☐ 508. JOSE RIJO
☐ 533. JEFF BRANSON
☐ 553. JACOB BRUMFIELD
☐ 580. SCOTT BANKHEAD

CLEVELAND INDIANS

☐ 3. CARLOS BAERGA
☐ 31. ALBERT BELLE
☐ 91. MARK LEWIS
☐ 120. STEVE OLIN
☐ 152. FELIX FERMIN
☐ 247. JIM THOME
☐ 295. MANNY RAMIREZ
☐ 316. DAVE OTTO
☐ 355. MARK WHITEN
☐ 376. BROOK JACOBY
☐ 383. CHARLES NAGY
☐ 420. GLENALLEN HILL
☐ 436. SANDY ALOMAR, JR.
☐ 476. REGGIE JEFFERSON
☐ 480. SCOTT SCUDDER
☐ 496. JOSE MESA
☐ 525. ROD NICHOLS
☐ 582. KENNY LOFTON

COLORADO ROCKIES

☐ 48. JERALD CLARK
☐ 498. JOE GIRARDI
☐ 514. DANTE BICHETTE

DETROIT TIGERS

☐ 4. CECIL FIELDER
☐ 29. LOU WHITAKER
☐ 87. BILL GULLICKSON
☐ 110. TRAVIS FRYMAN
☐ 113. ALAN TRAMMELL
☐ 164. MIKE HENNEMAN
☐ 174. MILT CUYLER
☐ 190. WALT TERRELL
☐ 198. FRANK TANANA
☐ 218. SKEETER BARNES
☐ 226. MICKEY TETTLETON
☐ 243. TONY PHILLIPS
☐ 318. DAN GLADDEN
☐ 348. ROB DEER
☐ 354. SCOTT ALDRED
☐ 441. MARK CARREON
☐ 490. SCOTT LIVINGSTONE
☐ 503. ERIC KING
☐ 513. JOHN DOHERTY
☐ 579. TREVER MILLER
☐ 598. SHAWN HARE

FLORIDA MARLINS

☐ 56. WALT WEISS
☐ 63. STEVE DECKER
☐ 145. BRYAN HARVEY
☐ 201. DAVE MAGADAN

HOUSTON ASTROS

☐ 19. STEVE FINLEY
☐ 43. KEN CAMINITI
☐ 70. JEFF BAGWELL
☐ 84. ANDUJAR CEDENO
☐ 140. CRAIG BIGGIO
☐ 163. LUIS GONZALEZ
☐ 189. MARK PORTUGAL
☐ 196. PETE HARNISCH
☐ 225. DARRYL KILE
☐ 255. SCOTT SERVAIS
☐ 257. ANDY MOTA
☐ 325. PETE INCAVIGLIA
☐ 347. AL OSUNA
☐ 363. ERIC ANTHONY
☐ 458. GERALD YOUNG
☐ 473. RYAN BOWEN
☐ 499. DOUG JONES
☐ 538. EDDIE TAUBENSEE
☐ 540. BRIAN WILLIAMS
☐ 543. MIKE GROPPUSO
☐ 545. SHAWN LIVSEY
☐ 552. JUAN GUERRERO
☐ 567. BUTCH HENRY
☐ 599. CHRIS GARDNER

KANSAS CITY ROYALS

☐ 60. GEORGE BRETT
☐ 86. DAVID HOWARD
☐ 99. JUAN SAMUEL
☐ 102. MARK GUBICZA
☐ 117. BRIAN MCRAE
☐ 142. MIKE BODDICKER
☐ 173. JEFF MONTGOMERY
☐ 203. TERRY SHUMPERT
☐ 238. TOM GORDON
☐ 259. JOEL JOHNSTON
☐ 279. HARVEY PULLIAM
☐ 330. GREGG JEFFERIES
☐ 359. MARK DAVIS
☐ 403. KEITH MILLER
☐ 427. KEVIN MCREYNOLDS
☐ 434. KEVIN APPIER
☐ 454. LUIS AQUINO
☐ 468. JIM EISENREICH
☐ 469. BRENT MAYNE
☐ 517. MIKE MACFARLANE
☐ 537. WALLY JOYNER
☐ 600. RUSTY MEACHAM

LOS ANGELES DODGERS

☐ 21. OREL HERSHISER
☐ 57. LENNY HARRIS
☐ 80. DARRYL STRAWBERRY
☐ 133. BRETT BUTLER
☐ 153. JOSE OFFERMAN
☐ 167. MIKE SHARPERSON
☐ 210. MIKE SCIOSCIA
☐ 228. JIM GOTT
☐ 256. ERIC KARROS
☐ 323. ERIC DAVIS
☐ 344. KEVIN GROSS
☐ 429. RAMON MARTINEZ
☐ 438. TODD BENZINGER
☐ 444. JAY HOWELL
☐ 445. ROGER MCDOWELL
☐ 456. CARLOS HERNANDEZ
☐ 459. TOM CANDIOTTI
☐ 493. DENNIS COOK
☐ 512. BOB OJEDA
☐ 551. PEDRO ASTACIO

MILWAUKEE BREWERS

☐ 8. PAUL MOLITOR
☐ 11. KEVIN SEITZER
☐ 38. ROBIN YOUNT
☐ 71. JIM GANTNER
☐ 92. GREG VAUGHN
☐ 118. B.J. SURHOFF
☐ 151. DARRYL HAMILTON
☐ 162. DAN PLESAC
☐ 177. BILL SPIERS
☐ 212. JAIME NAVARRO
☐ 249. CAL ELDRED
☐ 301. TYRONE HILL
☐ 320. FRANKLIN STUBBS
☐ 367. CHRIS BOSIO
☐ 396. BILL WEGMAN
☐ 439. TEDDY HIGUERA
☐ 562. PAT LISTACH
☐ 568. DAVE NILSSON

MINNESOTA TWINS

☐ 20. KIRBY PUCKETT
☐ 46. CHILI DAVIS
☐ 68. KENT HRBEK

- ☐ 73. BRIAN HARPER
- ☐ 106. SCOTT ERICKSON
- ☐ 119. CHUCK KNOBLAUCH
- ☐ 139. PEDRO MUNOZ
- ☐ 176. KEVIN TAPANI
- ☐ 184. JOHN SMILEY
- ☐ 211. RICK AGUILERA
- ☐ 230. SHANE MACK
- ☐ 246. MIKE PAGLIARULO
- ☐ 262. GREG GAGNE
- ☐ 276. LENNY WEBSTER
- ☐ 333. DAVID WEST
- ☐ 365. SCOTT LEIUS
- ☐ 435. GENE LARKIN
- ☐ 472. PAT MAHOMES
- ☐ 491. CARL WILLIS
- ☐ 495. BOB KIPPER
- ☐ 511. MARK GUTHRIE
- ☐ 544. JARVIS BROWN
- ☐ 575. WILLIE BANKS

MONTREAL EXPOS

- ☐ 24. DELINO DESHIELDS
- ☐ 58. IVAN CALDERON
- ☐ 77. DENNIS MARTINEZ
- ☐ 93. BRET BARBERIE
- ☐ 129. MARQUIS GRISSOM
- ☐ 161. TIM WALLACH
- ☐ 194. LARRY WALKER
- ☐ 215. MARK GARDNER
- ☐ 234. SPIKE OWEN
- ☐ 271. SEAN BERRY
- ☐ 296. CLIFF FLOYD
- ☐ 321. GARY CARTER
- ☐ 360. CHRIS NABHOLZ
- ☐ 428. GILBERTO REYES
- ☐ 461. JOHN WETTELAND
- ☐ 486. KEN HILL
- ☐ 501. BILL KRUEGER
- ☐ 510. ARCHI CIANFROCCO
- ☐ 521. CHRIS HANEY
- ☐ 559. JOHN VANDER WAL
- ☐ 572. MOISES ALOU
- ☐ 583. MATT STAIRS

NEW YORK METS

- ☐ 15. HOWARD JOHNSON
- ☐ 39. VINCE COLEMAN
- ☐ 53. KEVIN BASS
- ☐ 64. JOHN FRANCO
- ☐ 89. KEVIN ELSTER
- ☐ 111. DOC GOODEN
- ☐ 141. PETE SCHOUREK
- ☐ 168. CHRIS DONNELS
- ☐ 297. AL SHIRLEY
- ☐ 319. BILL PECOTA
- ☐ 338. DICK SCHOFIELD
- ☐ 343. DARYL BOSTON
- ☐ 382. WILLIE RANDOLPH
- ☐ 395. BOBBY BONILLA
- ☐ 424. EDDIE MURRAY
- ☐ 442. BRET SABERHAGEN
- ☐ 447. MACKEY SASSER
- ☐ 471. TIM BURKE
- ☐ 488. CHARLIE O'BRIEN
- ☐ 509. SID FERNANDEZ
- ☐ 522. JEFF KENT
- ☐ 548. BOBBY JONES
- ☐ 558. ANTHONY YOUNG
- ☐ 571. TODD HUNDLEY

NEW YORK YANKEES

- ☐ 23. DON MATTINGLY
- ☐ 54. PAT KELLY
- ☐ 72. MATT NOKES
- ☐ 90. KEVIN MAAS
- ☐ 114. ROBERTO KELLY
- ☐ 144. MEL HALL
- ☐ 182. PASCUAL PEREZ
- ☐ 206. STEVE FARR
- ☐ 229. BERNIE WILLIAMS
- ☐ 277. MIKE HUMPHREYS
- ☐ 322. MELIDO PEREZ
- ☐ 337. SCOTT SANDERSON
- ☐ 349. TIM LEARY
- ☐ 366. HENSLEY MEULENS
- ☐ 387. MIKE GALLEGO
- ☐ 402. GREG CADARET
- ☐ 425. JESSE BARFIELD
- ☐ 433. JOHN HABYAN
- ☐ 464. JEFF JOHNSON
- ☐ 497. CHARLIE HAYES
- ☐ 507. STEVE HOWE
- ☐ 531. DAVE SILVESTRI
- ☐ 547. DANNY TARTABULL
- ☐ 561. RUSS SPRINGER
- ☐ 564. ANDY STANKIEWICZ

OAKLAND A'S

- ☐ 14. RUBEN SIERRA
- ☐ 16. DAVE HENDERSON
- ☐ 25. DENNIS ECKERSLEY
- ☐ 41. HAROLD BAINES
- ☐ 76. TERRY STEINBACH
- ☐ 109. MIKE MOORE
- ☐ 157. DAVE STEWART
- ☐ 187. JOE SLUSARSKI
- ☐ 208. JERRY BROWNE
- ☐ 209. JEFF RUSSELL
- ☐ 217. MARK MCGWIRE
- ☐ 236. STEVE CHITREN
- ☐ 270. KIRK DRESSENDORFER
- ☐ 274. SCOTT BROSIUS
- ☐ 378. RON DARLING
- ☐ 401. RICKEY HENDERSON
- ☐ 409. BOB WELCH
- ☐ 443. GENE NELSON
- ☐ 451. BOBBY WITT
- ☐ 455. CARNEY LANSFORD
- ☐ 462. MIKE BORDICK
- ☐ 524. VINCE HORSMAN
- ☐ 574. TODD VAN POPPEL

PHILADELPHIA PHILLIES

- ☐ 12. LENNY DYKSTRA
- ☐ 36. WES CHAMBERLAIN
- ☐ 67. DAVE HOLLINS
- ☐ 103. MICKEY MORANDINI
- ☐ 124. DALE MURPHY
- ☐ 147. JOHN KRUK
- ☐ 155. TOMMY GREENE
- ☐ 172. JOSE DEJESUS
- ☐ 199. TERRY MULHOLLAND
- ☐ 241. DARREN DAULTON
- ☐ 265. ANDY ASHBY
- ☐ 266. KIM BATISTE
- ☐ 303. TYLER GREEN
- ☐ 377. MARIANO DUNCAN
- ☐ 406. MITCH WILLIAMS
- ☐ 432. KYLE ABBOTT
- ☐ 463. DON ROBINSON
- ☐ 530. RICKY JORDAN
- ☐ 554. BEN RIVERA
- ☐ 557. CLIFF BRANTLEY
- ☐ 570. RUBEN AMARO, JR.

PITTSBURGH PIRATES

- ☐ 9. ANDY VAN SLYKE
- ☐ 34. JAY BELL
- ☐ 49. JOSE LIND
- ☐ 62. ORLANDO MERCED
- ☐ 66. ALEX COLE
- ☐ 96. DOUG DRABEK
- ☐ 116. BILL LANDRUM
- ☐ 146. MIKE LAVALLIERE
- ☐ 213. RANDY TOMLIN
- ☐ 237. ZANE SMITH
- ☐ 260. JOHN WEHNER
- ☐ 264. CARLOS GARCIA
- ☐ 299. JON FARRELL
- ☐ 317. JEFF KING
- ☐ 370. STAN BELINDA
- ☐ 386. VICENTE PALACIOS
- ☐ 410. BOB WALK
- ☐ 416. DON SLAUGHT
- ☐ 457. DANNY JACKSON
- ☐ 481. KIRK GIBSON
- ☐ 500. BARRY BONDS
- ☐ 556. DENNY NEAGLE

ST. LOUIS CARDINALS

- ☐ 6. OZZIE SMITH
- ☐ 32. TODD ZEILE
- ☐ 69. TOM PAGNOZZI
- ☐ 88. BERNARD GILKEY
- ☐ 126. RAY LANKFORD
- ☐ 159. FELIX JOSE
- ☐ 186. OMAR OLIVARES
- ☐ 195. LEE SMITH
- ☐ 219. BOB TEWKSBURY
- ☐ 239. JOSE OQUENDO
- ☐ 263. STAN ROYER
- ☐ 298. BRIAN BARBER
- ☐ 304. ALLEN WATSON
- ☐ 315. REX HUDLER
- ☐ 341. JOSE DELEON
- ☐ 345. MILT THOMPSON
- ☐ 381. ANDRES GALARRAGA
- ☐ 392. PEDRO GUERRERO
- ☐ 474. BRYN SMITH
- ☐ 479. TODD WORRELL
- ☐ 487. GERONIMO PENA
- ☐ 494. JOE MAGRANE
- ☐ 541. DONOVAN OSBORNE
- ☐ 555. BRIAN JORDAN
- ☐ 565. MIKE PEREZ

SAN DIEGO PADRES

- ☐ 2. BENITO SANTIAGO
- ☐ 40. BRUCE HURST
- ☐ 74. ANDY BENES
- ☐ 104. ED WHITSON
- ☐ 112. FRED MCGRIFF
- ☐ 137. TONY FERNANDEZ
- ☐ 169. GREG W. HARRIS
- ☐ 207. DARRIN JACKSON
- ☐ 235. GARY SHEFFIELD
- ☐ 313. TIM TEUFEL
- ☐ 332. PAUL FARIES
- ☐ 399. LARRY ANDERSEN
- ☐ 400. TONY GWYNN
- ☐ 418. KURT STILLWELL
- ☐ 489. MIKE MADDUX
- ☐ 536. JOSE MELENDEZ

SAN FRANCISCO GIANTS

- ☐ 7. WILLIE MCGEE
- ☐ 28. MATT WILLIAMS
- ☐ 82. DAVE RIGHETTI
- ☐ 122. WILL CLARK
- ☐ 143. ROBBY THOMPSON
- ☐ 181. KIRT MANWARING
- ☐ 202. BUD BLACK
- ☐ 233. MARK LEONARD
- ☐ 268. ROYCE CLAYTON
- ☐ 311. MIKE FELDER
- ☐ 352. TREVOR WILSON
- ☐ 408. DARREN LEWIS
- ☐ 437. MIKE JACKSON
- ☐ 448. BILL SWIFT
- ☐ 470. JEFF BRANTLEY
- ☐ 492. KELLY DOWNS
- ☐ 506. CORY SNYDER
- ☐ 529. DAVE BURBA
- ☐ 532. JOHN PATTERSON
- ☐ 578. JOHN BURKETT
- ☐ 613. ROD BECK

SEATTLE MARINERS

- ☐ 13. EDGAR MARTINEZ
- ☐ 27. JAY BUHNER
- ☐ 59. HAROLD REYNOLDS
- ☐ 97. OMAR VIZQUEL
- ☐ 105. LANCE PARRISH
- ☐ 123. TINO MARTINEZ
- ☐ 125. PETE O'BRIEN
- ☐ 171. MIKE SCHOOLER
- ☐ 188. ERIK HANSON
- ☐ 232. DAVE VALLE
- ☐ 275. DAVE FLEMING
- ☐ 342. HENRY COTTO
- ☐ 379. RANDY JOHNSON
- ☐ 388. RICH DELUCIA
- ☐ 393. KEVIN MITCHELL
- ☐ 484. RUSS SWAN
- ☐ 520. BRIAN HOLMAN
- ☐ 542. PATRICK LENNON
- ☐ 549. KEN GRIFFEY, JR.
- ☐ 581. RICH AMARAL

TEXAS RANGERS

- ☐ 35. RAFAEL PALMEIRO
- ☐ 50. NOLAN RYAN
- ☐ 98. JOSE GUZMAN
- ☐ 127. JUAN GONZALEZ
- ☐ 130. JOSE CANSECO
- ☐ 150. JULIO FRANCO
- ☐ 156. IVAN RODRIGUEZ
- ☐ 273. ROB MAURER
- ☐ 302. BENJI GIL
- ☐ 340. KEVIN REIMER
- ☐ 351. DEAN PALMER
- ☐ 368. BRIAN DOWNING
- ☐ 394. DICKIE THON
- ☐ 405. KEVIN BROWN
- ☐ 482. KENNY ROGERS
- ☐ 516. JEFF ROBINSON
- ☐ 560. MONTY FARISS
- ☐ 573. HECTOR FAJARDO
- ☐ 597. DONALD HARRIS

TORONTO BLUE JAYS

- ☐ 17. DEVON WHITE
- ☐ 45. ROBERTO ALOMAR
- ☐ 78. JOHN OLERUD
- ☐ 108. DAVE STIEB
- ☐ 134. KELLY GRUBER
- ☐ 148. JOE CARTER
- ☐ 183. JUAN GUZMAN
- ☐ 193. JIMMY KEY
- ☐ 240. TODD STOTTLEMYRE
- ☐ 245. MANUEL LEE
- ☐ 250. DEREK BELL
- ☐ 375. DAVE WINFIELD
- ☐ 385. DUANE WARD
- ☐ 417. TOM HENKE
- ☐ 421. PAT BORDERS
- ☐ 431. DAVID WELLS
- ☐ 450. DAVID CONE
- ☐ 483. JACK MORRIS
- ☐ 546. JEFF WARE
- ☐ 563. PAT HENTGEN

1993 PINNACLE (620)
2 1/2" X 3 1/2"

ATLANTA BRAVES

- ☐ 4. DEION SANDERS
- ☐ 35. OTIS NIXON
- ☐ 60. TERRY PENDLETON
- ☐ 71. FRED MCGRIFF
- ☐ 90. TOM GLAVINE
- ☐ 143. JOHN SMOLTZ
- ☐ 173. GREG OLSON
- ☐ 204. SID BREAM
- ☐ 251. RYAN KLESKO
- ☐ 315. STEVE AVERY
- ☐ 344. DAVE JUSTICE
- ☐ 368. MARK LEMKE
- ☐ 379. MARK WOHLERS
- ☐ 392. DAMON BERRYHILL
- ☐ 414. BRIAN HUNTER
- ☐ 418. KENT MERCKER
- ☐ 432. JEFF BLAUSER
- ☐ 445. RON GANT
- ☐ 455. JAMIE ARNOLD
- ☐ 494. RAFAEL BELLIARD
- ☐ 517. GREG MADDUX
- ☐ 541. PETE SMITH
- ☐ 569. MIKE STANTON

BALTIMORE ORIOLES

- ☐ 20. CAL RIPKEN, JR.
- ☐ 44. MIKE MUSSINA
- ☐ 70. BRADY ANDERSON
- ☐ 72. BEN MCDONALD
- ☐ 97. GREGG OLSON
- ☐ 111. HAROLD BAINES
- ☐ 184. MARK MCLEMORE
- ☐ 186. CHRIS HOILES
- ☐ 214. CHITO MARTINEZ
- ☐ 217. GLENN DAVIS
- ☐ 244. MANNY ALEXANDER
- ☐ 325. DAVID SEGUI
- ☐ 326. ARTHUR RHODES
- ☐ 351. LEO GOMEZ
- ☐ 376. LUIS MERCEDES
- ☐ 400. MIKE DEVEREAUX
- ☐ 454. LONNIE SMITH
- ☐ 508. MIKE PAGLIARULO
- ☐ 530. HAROLD REYNOLDS
- ☐ 532. RICK SUTCLIFFE

BOSTON RED SOX

- ☐ 25. ROGER CLEMENS
- ☐ 76. FRANK VIOLA
- ☐ 102. MIKE GREENWELL
- ☐ 159. LUIS RIVERA
- ☐ 167. ROB DEER
- ☐ 175. PAUL QUANTRILL
- ☐ 189. MO VAUGHN
- ☐ 224. JOHN VALENTIN
- ☐ 278. KEN RYAN
- ☐ 330. SCOTT COOPER
- ☐ 382. TIM NAEHRING
- ☐ 404. BOB ZUPCIC
- ☐ 444. JEFF RUSSELL
- ☐ 448. JOE HESKETH
- ☐ 495. SCOTT FLETCHER
- ☐ 497. ANDRE DAWSON
- ☐ 506. TONY PENA
- ☐ 564. CARLOS QUINTANA

CALIFORNIA ANGELS

- ☐ 31. LUIS POLONIA
- ☐ 55. RENE GONZALES
- ☐ 56. MARK LANGSTON
- ☐ 139. JULIO VALERA
- ☐ 197. JOHN ORTON
- ☐ 198. KELLY GRUBER
- ☐ 201. CHUCK FINLEY
- ☐ 227. DAMION EASLEY
- ☐ 262. MIKE BUTCHER
- ☐ 276. TIM SALMON
- ☐ 337. GARY DISARCINA
- ☐ 342. JOE MAGRANE
- ☐ 411. CHAD CURTIS
- ☐ 412. JOE GRAHE
- ☐ 468. PETE JANICKI
- ☐ 469. JEFF SCHMIDT
- ☐ 536. CHILI DAVIS
- ☐ 609. J.T. SNOW

CHICAGO CUBS

- ☐ 15. RYNE SANDBERG
- ☐ 34. MARK GRACE
- ☐ 63. MIKE MORGAN
- ☐ 89. SHAWON DUNSTON
- ☐ 123. GLENALLEN HILL
- ☐ 141. WILLIE WILSON
- ☐ 145. SAMMY SOSA
- ☐ 176. STEVE BUECHELE
- ☐ 206. RICK WILKINS
- ☐ 208. FRANK CASTILLO
- ☐ 273. FERNANDO RAMSEY
- ☐ 317. REY SANCHEZ
- ☐ 341. CHUCK MCELROY
- ☐ 371. DERRICK MAY
- ☐ 395. MIKE HARKEY
- ☐ 417. BOB SCANLAN
- ☐ 433. DAN PLESAC
- ☐ 460. DEREK WALLACE
- ☐ 505. JOSE GUZMAN
- ☐ 527. GREG HIBBARD
- ☐ 549. RANDY MYERS
- ☐ 607. MATT WALBECK

CHICAGO WHITE SOX

- ☐ 28. ROBIN VENTURA
- ☐ 46. ELLIS BURKS
- ☐ 53. TIM RAINES
- ☐ 80. JACK MCDOWELL
- ☐ 108. FRANK THOMAS
- ☐ 129. ROBERTO HERNANDEZ
- ☐ 137. LANCE JOHNSON
- ☐ 150. IVAN CALDERON
- ☐ 166. OZZIE GUILLEN
- ☐ 195. RON KARKOVICE
- ☐ 219. MIKE LAVALLIERE
- ☐ 265. SHAWN JETER
- ☐ 335. STEVE SAX
- ☐ 354. DAN PASQUA
- ☐ 357. TIM BELCHER
- ☐ 362. CRAIG GREBECK
- ☐ 383. ALEX FERNANDEZ
- ☐ 387. GEORGE BELL
- ☐ 421. CARLTON FISK
- ☐ 441. WILSON ALVAREZ
- ☐ 451. SCOTT RADINSKY
- ☐ 524. BO JACKSON
- ☐ 552. DAVE STIEB
- ☐ 560. KIRK MCCASKILL
- ☐ 580. RODNEY BOLTON

CINCINNATI REDS

- ☐ 22. BARRY LARKIN
- ☐ 47. CHRIS SABO
- ☐ 77. JOSE RIJO
- ☐ 101. ROB DIBBLE
- ☐ 158. REGGIE SANDERS
- ☐ 190. JOE OLIVER
- ☐ 222. HAL MORRIS
- ☐ 255. DAN WILSON

- 270. TIM PUGH
- 285. WILLIE GREENE
- 358. BIP ROBERTS
- 405. TOM BROWNING
- 520. ROBERTO KELLY
- 535. JEFF REARDON
- 543. JOHN SMILEY
- 551. KEVIN MITCHELL
- 582. TIM COSTO
- 591. CESAR HERNANDEZ

CLEVELAND INDIANS

- 6. CARLOS BAERGA
- 40. KENNY LOFTON
- 65. CHARLES NAGY
- 93. ALBERT BELLE
- 128. SAM HORN
- 157. RANDY MILLIGAN
- 211. SANDY ALOMAR, JR.
- 275. DAVE MLICKI
- 288. JESSE LEVIS
- 320. PAUL SORRENTO
- 331. FELIX FERMIN
- 348. JIM THOME
- 374. MARK LEWIS
- 399. THOMAS HOWARD
- 410. STEVE OLIN
- 422. CANDY MALDONADO
- 436. JOSE MESA
- 537. BOB OJEDA
- 550. REGGIE JEFFERSON
- 554. TIM CREWS
- 585. TOM KRAMER
- 593. ALAN EMBREE

COLORADO ROCKIES

- 230. MO SANFORD
- 232. DANTE BICHETTE
- 234. JERALD CLARK
- 236. JOE GIRARDI
- 238. DAVID NIED
- 239. ERIC WEDGE
- 327. BRUCE HURST
- 431. JEFF PARRETT
- 434. ANDRES GALARRAGA
- 447. CHARLIE HAYES
- 503. DALE MURPHY
- 511. BUTCH HENRY
- 518. ERIC YOUNG
- 521. DARREN HOLMES
- 545. DARYL BOSTON
- 548. FREDDIE BENAVIDES
- 556. ALEX COLE
- 572. ANDY ASHBY
- 584. STEVE REED
- 587. JIM TATUM
- 617. KENT BOTTENFIELD

DETROIT TIGERS

- 26. CECIL FIELDER
- 52. MICKEY TETTLETON
- 79. TRAVIS FRYMAN
- 106. SCOTT LIVINGSTONE
- 114. DAVID WELLS
- 193. MILT CUYLER
- 202. MIKE MOORE
- 240. RICO BROGNA
- 264. RICH ROWLAND
- 287. PHIL CLARK
- 333. DAN GLADDEN
- 352. BILL GULLICKSON
- 353. ALAN TRAMMELL
- 385. MIKE HENNEMAN
- 406. TONY PHILLIPS
- 407. JOHN DOHERTY
- 429. ERIC DAVIS
- 509. LOU WHITAKER
- 547. BILL KRUEGER
- 615. GREG GOHR

FLORIDA MARLINS

- 1. GARY SHEFFIELD
- 231. WALT WEISS
- 233. STEVE DECKER
- 235. BRYAN HARVEY
- 449. CHRIS HAMMOND
- 502. BENITO SANTIAGO
- 513. JACK ARMSTRONG
- 515. JUNIOR FELIX
- 523. CHARLIE HOUGH
- 526. ORESTES DESTRADE
- 553. BRET BARBERIE
- 571. RYAN BOWEN
- 576. SCOTT POSE
- 601. JEFF CONINE
- 602. TREVOR HOFFMAN
- 608. RICHIE LEWIS
- 612. ALEX ARIAS
- 618. CHUCK CARR

HOUSTON ASTROS

- 10. JEFF BAGWELL
- 32. ANDUJAR CEDENO
- 50. CRAIG BIGGIO
- 59. KEN CAMINITI
- 84. ERIC ANTHONY
- 113. PETE HARNISCH
- 120. CHRIS JAMES
- 140. EDDIE TAUBENSEE
- 172. STEVE FINLEY
- 245. SCOOTER TUCKER
- 254. SHANE REYNOLDS
- 312. LUIS GONZALEZ
- 339. BRIAN WILLIAMS
- 366. MARK PORTUGAL
- 423. DOUG DRABEK
- 430. DARRYL KILE
- 443. DOUG JONES
- 453. XAVIER HERNANDEZ
- 507. GREG SWINDELL

KANSAS CITY ROYALS

- 36. FELIX JOSE
- 51. WALLY JOYNER
- 81. MARK GUBICZA
- 103. JOSE LIND
- 105. TOM GORDON
- 112. GARY GAETTI
- 131. GEORGE BRETT
- 133. KEVIN APPIER
- 142. STAN BELINDA
- 149. RUSTY MEACHAM
- 164. KEVIN MCREYNOLDS
- 194. CHRIS HANEY
- 332. MIKE MACFARLANE
- 336. JEFF MONTGOMERY
- 359. BRENT MAYNE
- 367. BRIAN MCRAE
- 384. KEITH MILLER
- 409. JOHN HABYAN
- 450. HIPOLITO PICHARDO
- 466. MICHAEL TUCKER
- 510. GREG GAGNE
- 544. DAVID CONE
- 606. BILLY BREWER
- 611. PHIL HIATT

LOS ANGELES DODGERS

- 14. ERIC KARROS
- 37. MIKE SHARPERSON
- 64. DARRYL STRAWBERRY
- 91. BRETT BUTLER
- 119. LENNY HARRIS
- 146. CARLOS HERNANDEZ
- 147. TOM CANDIOTTI
- 177. KEVIN GROSS
- 178. TIM WALLACH
- 182. HENRY RODRIGUEZ
- 209. DAVE HANSEN
- 229. BOB AYRAULT
- 252. MIKE PIAZZA
- 259. PEDRO MARTINEZ
- 279. RAFAEL BOURNIGAL
- 281. BILLY ASHLEY
- 284. RICK TRLICEK
- 319. OREL HERSHISER
- 345. JOSE OFFERMAN
- 377. RAMON MARTINEZ
- 396. PEDRO ASTACIO
- 435. JIM GOTT
- 519. JODY REED
- 528. ROGER MCDOWELL
- 529. CORY SNYDER

MILWAUKEE BREWERS

- 2. CAL ELDRED
- 33. PAT LISTACH
- 61. DAVE NILSSON
- 87. B.J. SURHOFF
- 117. KEVIN SEITZER
- 118. ROBIN YOUNT
- 144. DARRYL HAMILTON
- 207. JIM GANTNER
- 228. JOHN JAHA
- 271. WILLIAM SUERO
- 318. GREG VAUGHN
- 343. JAIME NAVARRO
- 369. BILL WEGMAN
- 393. RICKY BONES
- 415. DOUG HENRY
- 525. BILL SPIERS
- 531. KEVIN REIMER
- 534. TOM BRUNANSKY
- 566. JUAN BELL
- 575. JOE KMAK
- 616. GRAEME LLOYD

MINNESOTA TWINS

- 27. KENT HRBEK
- 54. BRIAN HARPER
- 78. SHANE MACK
- 83. BERT BLYLEVEN
- 107. CHUCK KNOBLAUCH
- 135. PEDRO MUNOZ
- 163. SCOTT ERICKSON
- 192. SCOTT LEIUS
- 241. J.T. BRUETT
- 267. DEREK PARKS
- 274. BERNARDO BRITO
- 334. KEVIN TAPANI
- 361. MARK GUTHRIE
- 372. CARL WILLIS
- 386. RICK AGUILERA
- 408. PAT MAHOMES
- 426. KIRBY PUCKETT
- 438. DAVE WINFIELD
- 465. DAN SERAFINI
- 578. MIKE TROMBLEY
- 594. TERRY JORGENSEN

MONTREAL EXPOS

- 3. LARRY WALKER
- 38. DENNIS MARTINEZ
- 66. KEN HILL
- 92. MOISES ALOU
- 121. DELINO DESHIELDS
- 169. LEE STEVENS
- 212. SEAN BERRY
- 221. JACK CLARK
- 242. JONATHAN HURST
- 280. WIL CORDERO
- 322. JOHN VANDER WAL
- 346. MARQUIS GRISSOM
- 373. CHRIS NABHOLZ
- 397. JOHN WETTELAND
- 419. MEL ROJAS
- 456. B.J. WALLACE
- 538. GREG COLBRUNN
- 583. TIM LAKER
- 588. FRANK BOLICK

☐ 620. MIKE LANSING

NEW YORK METS

☐ 18. EDDIE MURRAY
☐ 43. BOBBY BONILLA
☐ 69. VINCE COLEMAN
☐ 96. DOC GOODEN
☐ 125. DARRIN JACKSON
☐ 126. TODD HUNDLEY
☐ 155. JEFF KENT
☐ 185. BRET SABERHAGEN
☐ 216. JOHN FRANCO
☐ 249. RYAN THOMPSON
☐ 324. PETE SCHOUREK
☐ 350. ANTHONY YOUNG
☐ 389. HOWARD JOHNSON
☐ 467. CHRIS ROBERTS
☐ 500. SID FERNANDEZ
☐ 501. JOE ORSULAK
☐ 557. JEFF INNIS

NEW YORK YANKEES

☐ 7. BERNIE WILLIAMS
☐ 9. JIMMY KEY
☐ 11. JIM ABBOTT
☐ 23. DON MATTINGLY
☐ 82. MATT NOKES
☐ 109. MELIDO PEREZ
☐ 124. HENSLEY MEULENS
☐ 134. PAT KELLY
☐ 165. KEVIN MAAS
☐ 168. DANNY TARTABULL
☐ 180. DAVE SILVESTRI
☐ 196. STEVE FARR
☐ 225. SAM MILITELLO
☐ 226. BOB WICKMAN
☐ 266. GERALD WILLIAMS
☐ 314. RANDY VELARDE
☐ 363. ANDY STANKIEWICZ
☐ 388. MIKE GALLEGO
☐ 416. LEE SMITH
☐ 424. WADE BOGGS
☐ 446. PAUL O'NEILL
☐ 457. DEREK JETER
☐ 499. SPIKE OWEN
☐ 542. FRANK TANANA
☐ 559. STEVE HOWE
☐ 563. MIKE STANLEY
☐ 570. SCOTT KAMIENIECKI
☐ 579. STERLING HITCHCOCK

OAKLAND A'S

☐ 12. TERRY STEINBACH
☐ 58. MARK MCGWIRE
☐ 85. MIKE BORDICK
☐ 100. DENNIS ECKERSLEY
☐ 170. DAVE HENDERSON
☐ 199. RON DARLING
☐ 200. RUBEN SIERRA
☐ 246. TROY NEEL
☐ 261. JOHNNY GUZMAN
☐ 268. HENRY MERCEDES
☐ 277. MIKE RACZKA
☐ 338. LANCE BLANKENSHIP
☐ 365. BOBBY WITT
☐ 391. JERRY BROWNE
☐ 463. BENJI GRIGSBY
☐ 567. ERIC FOX
☐ 573. BOB WELCH
☐ 592. MIKE MOHLER

PHILADELPHIA PHILLIES

☐ 8. JOHN KRUK
☐ 45. LENNY DYKSTRA
☐ 73. TERRY MULHOLLAND
☐ 99. DARREN DAULTON
☐ 127. DAVE HOLLINS
☐ 156. MICKEY MORANDINI
☐ 187. RICKY JORDAN
☐ 218. MARIANO DUNCAN
☐ 256. TOM MARSH
☐ 313. TOMMY GREENE
☐ 328. WES CHAMBERLAIN
☐ 378. KYLE ABBOTT
☐ 390. KIM BATISTE
☐ 402. CURT SCHILLING
☐ 437. BEN RIVERA
☐ 452. BOBBY THIGPEN
☐ 492. PETE INCAVIGLIA
☐ 514. DANNY JACKSON
☐ 516. MILT THOMPSON
☐ 565. MITCH WILLIAMS
☐ 581. TYLER GREEN
☐ 598. TODD PRATT

PITTSBURGH PIRATES

☐ 19. ANDY VAN SLYKE
☐ 48. JAY BELL
☐ 74. RANDY TOMLIN
☐ 160. ORLANDO MERCED
☐ 188. DON SLAUGHT
☐ 258. PAUL MILLER
☐ 260. STEVE COOKE
☐ 282. PAUL WAGNER
☐ 283. BLAS MINOR
☐ 355. JEFF KING
☐ 380. BOB WALK
☐ 401. TIM WAKEFIELD
☐ 403. ZANE SMITH
☐ 458. JASON KENDALL
☐ 558. CARLOS GARCIA
☐ 589. KEVIN YOUNG
☐ 600. DENNIS MOELLER
☐ 614. AL MARTIN

ST. LOUIS CARDINALS

☐ 13. BOB TEWKSBURY
☐ 24. GREGG JEFFERIES
☐ 62. TOM PAGNOZZI
☐ 88. BERNARD GILKEY
☐ 116. RAY LANKFORD
☐ 162. MIKE PEREZ
☐ 174. GERONIMO PENA
☐ 205. TODD ZEILE
☐ 263. BIEN FIGUEROA
☐ 272. OZZIE CANSECO
☐ 316. JOSE OQUENDO
☐ 329. OZZIE SMITH
☐ 360. RHEAL CORMIER
☐ 370. DONOVAN OSBORNE
☐ 394. OMAR OLIVARES
☐ 420. MARK WHITEN
☐ 461. SEAN LOWE
☐ 540. BRIAN JORDAN
☐ 599. RENE AROCHA

SAN DIEGO PADRES

☐ 42. ANDY BENES
☐ 98. TONY GWYNN
☐ 130. VICENTE PALACIOS
☐ 154. KURT STILLWELL
☐ 171. DEREK BELL
☐ 183. TIM TEUFEL
☐ 215. DAN WALTERS
☐ 248. MELVIN NIEVES
☐ 349. ARCHI CIANFROCCO
☐ 425. MARK DAVIS
☐ 498. MIKE SCIOSCIA
☐ 539. PHIL PLANTIER
☐ 561. FRANK SEMINARA
☐ 577. RICKY GUTIERREZ
☐ 610. PAT GOMEZ
☐ 619. DARRELL SHERMAN

SAN FRANCISCO GIANTS

☐ 16. WILL CLARK
☐ 39. WILLIE MCGEE
☐ 67. MATT WILLIAMS
☐ 94. DARREN LEWIS
☐ 122. KIRT MANWARING
☐ 132. DAVE MARTINEZ
☐ 136. MARK CARREON
☐ 181. BUD BLACK
☐ 210. TREVOR WILSON
☐ 253. STEVE HOSEY
☐ 286. TED WOOD
☐ 321. ROYCE CLAYTON
☐ 347. BILL SWIFT
☐ 375. JOHN BURKETT
☐ 398. ROD BECK
☐ 413. JOHN PATTERSON
☐ 490. WILLIE MCGEE
☐ 491. ROBBY THOMPSON
☐ 504. BARRY BONDS
☐ 512. JEFF BRANTLEY
☐ 574. SCOTT SANDERSON
☐ 613. KEVIN ROGERS

SEATTLE MARINERS

☐ 5. DAVE FLEMING
☐ 17. EDGAR MARTINEZ
☐ 41. RANDY JOHNSON
☐ 68. JAY BUHNER
☐ 95. OMAR VIZQUEL
☐ 110. KEN GRIFFEY, JR.
☐ 148. MIKE FELDER
☐ 151. PETE O'BRIEN
☐ 152. ERIK HANSON
☐ 179. DAVE VALLE
☐ 213. TINO MARTINEZ
☐ 237. DAVE MAGADAN
☐ 243. BRET BOONE
☐ 250. SHAWN BARTON
☐ 323. HENRY COTTO
☐ 439. NORM CHARLTON
☐ 440. CHRIS BOSIO
☐ 595. JOHN CUMMINGS
☐ 604. LEE TINSLEY

TEXAS RANGERS

☐ 21. IVAN RODRIGUEZ
☐ 49. JOSE CANSECO
☐ 75. NOLAN RYAN
☐ 104. JULIO FRANCO
☐ 115. CHARLIE LEIBRANDT
☐ 153. BILLY RIPKEN
☐ 161. DEAN PALMER
☐ 191. JUAN GONZALEZ
☐ 220. RAFAEL PALMEIRO
☐ 257. BARRY MANUEL
☐ 269. DAVID HULSE
☐ 356. KEVIN BROWN
☐ 381. KENNY ROGERS
☐ 459. RICK HELLING
☐ 493. MANUEL LEE
☐ 496. JEFF FRYE
☐ 522. CRAIG LEFFERTS
☐ 546. TOM HENKE
☐ 555. DOUG DASCENZO
☐ 562. CRIS CARPENTER
☐ 586. ROBB NEN
☐ 590. MATT WHITESIDE
☐ 597. BENJI GIL
☐ 603. DANIEL SMITH
☐ 605. DAN PELTIER

TORONTO BLUE JAYS

☐ 29. RICKEY HENDERSON
☐ 30. ROBERTO ALOMAR
☐ 57. JACK MORRIS
☐ 86. JOHN OLERUD
☐ 138. DEVON WHITE
☐ 203. PAT BORDERS
☐ 223. ED SPRAGUE
☐ 247. EDDIE ZOSKY
☐ 311. TODD SOTTLEMYRE
☐ 340. DUANE WARD
☐ 364. JUAN GUZMAN

- ☐ 427. JOE CARTER
- ☐ 428. PAUL MOLITOR
- ☐ 442. DAVE STEWART
- ☐ 462. SHANNON STEWART
- ☐ 464. TODD STEVERSON
- ☐ 533. TONY FERNANDEZ
- ☐ 568. AL LEITER
- ☐ 596. DOMINGO MARTINEZ

1994 PINNACLE (540)
2 1/2" X 3 1/2"

ATLANTA BRAVES

- ☐ 8. STEVE AVERY
- ☐ 11. GREG MADDUX
- ☐ 40. DAVE JUSTICE
- ☐ 69. GREG MCMICHAEL
- ☐ 98. JEFF BLAUSER
- ☐ 157. RYAN KLESKO
- ☐ 174. DEION SANDERS
- ☐ 236. CHIPPER JONES
- ☐ 239. JAVIER LOPEZ
- ☐ 256. TONY TARASCO
- ☐ 260. RAMON CARABALLO
- ☐ 284. TOM GLAVINE
- ☐ 342. JOHN SMOLTZ
- ☐ 371. TERRY PENDLETON
- ☐ 384. FRED MCGRIFF
- ☐ 440. KENT MERCKER
- ☐ 444. MARK WOHLERS
- ☐ 447. MARK LEMKE
- ☐ 461. MIKE STANTON
- ☐ 498. OTIS NIXON
- ☐ 524. KEITH MITCHELL
- ☐ 534. MIKE KELLY

BALTIMORE ORIOLES

- ☐ 13. MIKE DEVEREAUX
- ☐ 35. MANNY ALEXANDER
- ☐ 50. CAL RIPKEN, JR.
- ☐ 112. CHRIS HOILES
- ☐ 131. DAVID SEGUI
- ☐ 165. BRADY ANDERSON
- ☐ 180. LEO GOMEZ
- ☐ 184. BEN MCDONALD
- ☐ 224. MIKE OQUIST
- ☐ 253. JOHN O'DONOGHUE
- ☐ 277. GREGG OLSON
- ☐ 295. MIKE MUSSINA
- ☐ 379. MARK MCLEMORE
- ☐ 403. PAUL CAREY
- ☐ 408. HAROLD BAINES
- ☐ 417. JEFFREY HAMMONDS
- ☐ 423. DAMON BUFORD
- ☐ 435. JAY POWELL
- ☐ 442. JAMIE MOYER
- ☐ 475. HAROLD REYNOLDS

BOSTON RED SOX

- ☐ 17. MO VAUGHN
- ☐ 25. ROGER CLEMENS
- ☐ 46. JEFF RUSSELL
- ☐ 65. TIM NAEHRING
- ☐ 72. SCOTT COOPER
- ☐ 95. AARON SELE
- ☐ 126. JOHN VALENTIN
- ☐ 146. SCOTT FLETCHER
- ☐ 175. CARLOS QUINTANA
- ☐ 231. JEFF MCNEELY
- ☐ 243. LUIS ORTIZ
- ☐ 245. GREG BLOSSER
- ☐ 270. TROT NIXON
- ☐ 285. MIKE GREENWELL
- ☐ 303. DANNY DARWIN
- ☐ 320. ANDRE DAWSON
- ☐ 348. FRANK VIOLA
- ☐ 362. BILLY HATCHER
- ☐ 406. NATE MINCHEY
- ☐ 420. CORY BAILEY
- ☐ 443. JOHN FLAHERTY
- ☐ 476. GREG HARRIS

CALIFORNIA ANGELS

- ☐ 9. TIM SALMON
- ☐ 38. CHUCK FINLEY
- ☐ 68. J.T. SNOW
- ☐ 97. GARY DISARCINA
- ☐ 114. JOE MAGRANE
- ☐ 127. HILLY HATHAWAY
- ☐ 156. GREG MYERS
- ☐ 185. STEVE FREY
- ☐ 202. EDUARDO PEREZ
- ☐ 225. DARRYL SCOTT
- ☐ 282. CHAD CURTIS
- ☐ 311. MARK LANGSTON
- ☐ 313. STAN JAVIER
- ☐ 340. DAMION EASLEY
- ☐ 364. RENE GONZALES
- ☐ 394. JIM EDMONDS
- ☐ 405. CHRIS TURNER
- ☐ 432. BRIAN ANDERSON
- ☐ 441. PHIL LEFTWICH
- ☐ 458. CHILI DAVIS
- ☐ 512. LUIS POLONIA

CHICAGO CUBS

- ☐ 3. SAMMY SOSA
- ☐ 6. RYNE SANDBERG
- ☐ 55. JOSE GUZMAN
- ☐ 66. DWIGHT SMITH
- ☐ 84. RICK WILKINS
- ☐ 113. MIKE MORGAN
- ☐ 141. JOSE VIZCAINO
- ☐ 171. MIKE HARKEY
- ☐ 196. DERRICK MAY
- ☐ 200. STEVE BUECHELE
- ☐ 237. EDDIE ZAMBRANO
- ☐ 254. TURK WENDELL
- ☐ 262. BROOKS KIESCHNICK
- ☐ 271. RANDY MYERS
- ☐ 336. MARK GRACE
- ☐ 437. JON RATLIFF
- ☐ 445. JOSE BAUTISTA
- ☐ 480. GREG HIBBARD
- ☐ 487. MATT WALBECK
- ☐ 497. KARL RHODES
- ☐ 523. SHAWON DUNSTON
- ☐ 536. STEVE TRACHSEL

CHICAGO WHITE SOX

- ☐ 1. FRANK THOMAS
- ☐ 29. ROBIN VENTURA
- ☐ 57. JACK MCDOWELL
- ☐ 86. LANCE JOHNSON
- ☐ 116. RON KARKOVICE
- ☐ 128. WILSON ALVAREZ
- ☐ 130. RODNEY BOLTON
- ☐ 135. SCOTT RADINSKY
- ☐ 164. ROBERTO HERNANDEZ
- ☐ 192. IVAN CALDERON
- ☐ 228. NORBERTO MARTIN
- ☐ 241. DREW DENSON
- ☐ 255. SCOTT RUFFCORN
- ☐ 266. SCOTT CHRISTMAN
- ☐ 289. ALEX FERNANDEZ
- ☐ 318. JOEY CORA
- ☐ 347. JASON BERE
- ☐ 428. OZZIE GUILLEN
- ☐ 462. TIM RAINES
- ☐ 491. TIM BELCHER
- ☐ 496. ELLIS BURKS
- ☐ 509. BO JACKSON

CINCINNATI REDS

- ☐ 12. BARRY LARKIN
- ☐ 41. ROB DIBBLE
- ☐ 70. KEVIN MITCHELL
- ☐ 99. JOHN SMILEY
- ☐ 137. JOHN ROPER
- ☐ 251. KEITH KESSINGER
- ☐ 286. ROBERTO KELLY
- ☐ 314. HAL MORRIS
- ☐ 322. JOSE RIJO
- ☐ 335. TOM BROWNING
- ☐ 360. REGGIE SANDERS
- ☐ 401. ROSS POWELL
- ☐ 402. JOE OLIVER
- ☐ 410. JOHNNY RUFFIN
- ☐ 481. TIM PUGH
- ☐ 490. CHRIS SABO
- ☐ 500. BIP ROBERTS
- ☐ 515. DAN WILSON
- ☐ 521. JEFF REARDON
- ☐ 522. WILLIE GREENE

CLEVELAND INDIANS

- ☐ 2. CARLOS BAERGA
- ☐ 15. ALBERT BELLE
- ☐ 44. SANDY ALOMAR, JR.
- ☐ 73. JIM THOME
- ☐ 102. FELIX FERMIN
- ☐ 132. WAYNE KIRBY
- ☐ 161. REGGIE JEFFERSON
- ☐ 170. SAM HORN
- ☐ 179. KENNY LOFTON
- ☐ 219. DEREK LILLIQUIST
- ☐ 244. MANNY RAMIREZ
- ☐ 263. DARON KIRKREIT
- ☐ 308. PAUL SORRENTO
- ☐ 337. JOSE MESA
- ☐ 366. ERIC PLUNK
- ☐ 385. CHRALES NAGY
- ☐ 411. JULIAN TAVAREZ
- ☐ 426. ALBIE LOPEZ
- ☐ 485. RANDY MILLIGAN
- ☐ 507. BOB OJEDA

COLORADO ROCKIES

- ☐ 14. CHARLIE HAYES
- ☐ 43. DAVID NIED
- ☐ 74. JOE GIRARDI
- ☐ 103. JERALD CLARK
- ☐ 133. ERIC YOUNG
- ☐ 181. ROBERTO MEJIA
- ☐ 191. VINNY CASTILLA
- ☐ 220. ARMANDO REYNOSO
- ☐ 229. PEDRO CASTELLANO
- ☐ 268. JAMEY WRIGHT
- ☐ 346. DANTE BICHETTE
- ☐ 375. DARREN HOLMES
- ☐ 418. JAYHAWK OWENS
- ☐ 446. ANDRES GALARRAGA
- ☐ 467. ALEX COLE
- ☐ 470. GREG W. HARRIS
- ☐ 504. BRUCE HURST

DETROIT TIGERS

- ☐ 10. CECIL FIELDER
- ☐ 67. MICKEY TETTLETON
- ☐ 96. JOHN DOHERTY
- ☐ 125. CHAD KREUTER
- ☐ 154. MIKE HENNEMAN
- ☐ 183. TRAVIS FRYMAN
- ☐ 212. MIKE MOORE
- ☐ 234. DANNY BAUTISTA
- ☐ 281. LOU WHITAKER
- ☐ 330. TONY PHILLIPS
- ☐ 359. MILT CUYLER
- ☐ 388. ERIC DAVIS
- ☐ 414. CHRIS GOMEZ
- ☐ 429. ALAN TRAMMELL
- ☐ 433. MATT BRUNSON
- ☐ 453. KIRK GIBSON
- ☐ 464. DAVID WELLS

FLORIDA MARLINS

- ☐ 30. JEFF CONINE
- ☐ 59. CHRIS HAMMOND
- ☐ 88. GARY SHEFFIELD
- ☐ 117. RYAN BOWEN
- ☐ 136. BRET BARBERIE
- ☐ 166. JACK ARMSTRONG
- ☐ 173. ROB NATAL
- ☐ 189. PAT RAPP
- ☐ 195. CHUCK CARR
- ☐ 223. LUIS AQUINO
- ☐ 226. KURT ABBOTT
- ☐ 240. NIGEL WILSON
- ☐ 252. CARL EVERETT
- ☐ 279. ROBB NEN
- ☐ 288. CHARLIE HOUGH
- ☐ 305. BENITO SANTIAGO
- ☐ 344. BRYAN HARVEY
- ☐ 373. ORESTES DESTRADE
- ☐ 387. GERONIMO BERROA
- ☐ 390. ALEX ARIAS
- ☐ 399. DARRELL WHITMORE
- ☐ 431. MARC VALDES
- ☐ 474. GREG COLBRUNN
- ☐ 486. WALT WEISS

HOUSTON ASTROS

- ☐ 20. CRAIG BIGGIO
- ☐ 45. PETE HARNISCH
- ☐ 75. ERIC ANTHONY
- ☐ 104. DOUG DRABEK
- ☐ 134. SCOTT SERVAIS
- ☐ 163. GREG SWINDELL
- ☐ 193. KEN CAMINITI
- ☐ 222. DOUG JONES
- ☐ 264. BILLY WAGNER
- ☐ 290. JEFF BAGWELL
- ☐ 292. ANDUJAR CEDENO
- ☐ 321. DARRYL KILE
- ☐ 323. LUIS GONZALEZ
- ☐ 351. STEVE FINLEY
- ☐ 409. BRIAN WILLIAMS
- ☐ 471. XAVIER HERNANDEZ
- ☐ 506. MARK PORTUGAL
- ☐ 535. JAMES MOUTON
- ☐ 537. TONY EUSEBIO

KANSAS CITY ROYALS

- ☐ 18. BRIAN MCRAE
- ☐ 48. KEVIN APPIER
- ☐ 77. FELIX JOSE
- ☐ 106. JEFF MONTGOMERY
- ☐ 199. JOSE LIND
- ☐ 269. JEFF GRANGER
- ☐ 275. HIPOLITO PICHARDO
- ☐ 291. WALLY JOYNER
- ☐ 297. CHRIS GWYNN
- ☐ 317. TOM GORDON
- ☐ 325. DAVID CONE
- ☐ 327. PHIL HIATT
- ☐ 354. GREG GAGNE
- ☐ 404. BOB HAMELIN
- ☐ 488. MIKE MACFARLANE

LOS ANGELES DODGERS

- ☐ 28. MIKE PIAZZA
- ☐ 58. OREL HERSHISER
- ☐ 87. ERIC KARROS
- ☐ 115. TOM CANDIOTTI
- ☐ 190. JOSE OFFERMAN
- ☐ 242. RUAL MONDESI
- ☐ 294. DARRYL STRAWBERRY
- ☐ 307. JIM GOTT
- ☐ 324. BILLY ASHLEY
- ☐ 339. ROGER MCDOWELL
- ☐ 353. RAMON MARTINEZ
- ☐ 369. BRETT BUTLER
- ☐ 454. PEDRO ASTACIO
- ☐ 466. CORY SNYDER
- ☐ 484. TIM WALLACH
- ☐ 501. PEDRO MARTINEZ
- ☐ 519. JODY REED
- ☐ 527. CHAN HO PARK
- ☐ 540. DARREN DREIFORT

MILWAUKEE BREWERS

- ☐ 19. CAL ELDRED
- ☐ 37. GREG VAUGHN
- ☐ 94. DARRYL HAMILTON
- ☐ 123. RICKY BONES
- ☐ 152. B.J. SURHOFF
- ☐ 210. DAVE NILSSON
- ☐ 249. JOSE VALENTIN
- ☐ 258. MATT MIESKE
- ☐ 283. DOUG HENRY
- ☐ 312. JOHN JAHA
- ☐ 341. ANGEL MIRANDA
- ☐ 370. BILL SPIERS
- ☐ 416. ALEX DIAZ
- ☐ 424. TROY O'LEARY
- ☐ 449. PAT LISTACH
- ☐ 473. JESSE OROSCO
- ☐ 526. MARK KIEFER

MINNESOTA TWINS

- ☐ 21. KIRBY PUCKETT
- ☐ 54. KEVIN TAPANI
- ☐ 83. CHUCK KNOBLAUCH
- ☐ 148. SHANE MACK
- ☐ 177. WILLIE BANKS
- ☐ 206. KENT HRBEK
- ☐ 248. SCOTT STAHOVIAK
- ☐ 267. TORII HUNTER
- ☐ 293. RICK AGUILERA
- ☐ 304. PAT MEARES
- ☐ 332. DAVE WINFIELD
- ☐ 333. DAVID MACCARTY
- ☐ 356. PEDRO MUNOZ
- ☐ 361. SCOTT ERICKSON
- ☐ 378. CARL WILLIS
- ☐ 421. DENNY HOCKING
- ☐ 494. BRIAN HARPER
- ☐ 529. RICH BECKER

MONTREAL EXPOS

- ☐ 7. MOISES ALOU
- ☐ 60. CHRIS NABHOLZ
- ☐ 89. WIL CORDERO
- ☐ 119. JOHN WETTELAND
- ☐ 147. DELINO DESHIELDS
- ☐ 176. MEL ROJAS
- ☐ 205. DARRIN FLETCHER
- ☐ 230. CURTIS PRIDE
- ☐ 246. RONDELL WHITE
- ☐ 310. LARRY WALKER
- ☐ 355. KEN HILL
- ☐ 358. MARQUIS GRISSOM
- ☐ 382. KIRK RUETER
- ☐ 392. CLIFF FLOYD
- ☐ 455. MIKE LANSING
- ☐ 456. SEAN BERRY
- ☐ 465. TIM LAKER
- ☐ 516. DENNIS MARTINEZ

NEW YORK METS

- ☐ 33. BOBBY BONILLA
- ☐ 62. DOC GOODEN
- ☐ 92. JOE ORSULAK
- ☐ 122. JEFF KENT
- ☐ 155. TODD HUNDLEY
- ☐ 203. BRET SABERHAGEN
- ☐ 235. BUTCH HUSKEY
- ☐ 368. JOHN FRANCO
- ☐ 380. BOBBY JONES
- ☐ 395. JEROMY BURNITZ
- ☐ 400. RYAN THOMPSON
- ☐ 436. KIRK PRESLEY
- ☐ 483. SID FERNANDEZ
- ☐ 495. EDDIE MURRAY
- ☐ 518. HOWARD JOHNSON
- ☐ 531. DARRIN JACKSON
- ☐ 538. KELLY STINNETT

NEW YORK YANKEES

- ☐ 23. DON MATTINGLY
- ☐ 31. WADE BOGGS
- ☐ 52. JIMMY KEY
- ☐ 81. DANNY TARTABULL
- ☐ 110. JIM ABBOTT
- ☐ 139. BERNIE WILLIAMS
- ☐ 142. GERALD WILLIAMS
- ☐ 168. MELIDO PEREZ
- ☐ 188. BOBBY MUNOZ
- ☐ 197. PAT KELLY
- ☐ 213. STERLING HITCHCOCK
- ☐ 238. DOMINGO JEAN
- ☐ 257. ANDY COOK
- ☐ 265. MATT DREWS
- ☐ 273. BOB WICKMAN
- ☐ 280. PAUL O'NEILL
- ☐ 309. SCOTT KAMIENIECKI
- ☐ 338. MIKE STANLEY
- ☐ 383. RANDY VELARDE
- ☐ 412. MARK HUTTON
- ☐ 451. MIKE GALLEGO
- ☐ 492. SPIKE OWEN
- ☐ 499. LEE SMITH
- ☐ 517. JIM LEYRITZ

OAKLAND A'S

- ☐ 32. DENNIS ECKERSLEY
- ☐ 61. RUBEN SIERRA
- ☐ 90. RON DARLING
- ☐ 120. TERRY STEINBACH
- ☐ 150. TROY NEEL
- ☐ 232. SCOTT LYDY
- ☐ 247. STEVE KARSAY
- ☐ 276. BOBBY WITT
- ☐ 299. BRENT GATES
- ☐ 300. MARK MCGWIRE
- ☐ 328. CRAIG PAQUETTE
- ☐ 329. BOB WELCH
- ☐ 357. TODD VAN POPPEL
- ☐ 398. MARCOS ARMAS
- ☐ 430. JOHN WASDIN
- ☐ 463. MIKE BORDICK
- ☐ 489. JERRY BROWNE
- ☐ 508. DAVE HENDERSON

PHILADELPHIA PHILLIES

- ☐ 34. LENNY DYKSTRA
- ☐ 47. TERRY MULHOLLAND
- ☐ 63. JOHN KRUK
- ☐ 78. TOMMY GREENE
- ☐ 91. DARREN DAULTON
- ☐ 105. CURT SCHILLING
- ☐ 121. DAVE HOLLINS
- ☐ 144. DANNY JACKSON
- ☐ 149. JIM EISENREICH
- ☐ 159. MICKEY MORANDINI
- ☐ 178. BEN RIVERA
- ☐ 201. WES CHAMBERLAIN
- ☐ 207. KIM BATISTE
- ☐ 218. MITCH WILLIAMS
- ☐ 434. WAYNE GOMES
- ☐ 460. KEVIN STOCKER
- ☐ 468. PETE INCAVIGLIA
- ☐ 479. MARIANO DUNCAN
- ☐ 503. TYLER GREEN
- ☐ 528. TONY LONGMIRE

PITTSBURGH PIRATES

- ☐ 16. ANDY VAN SLYKE
- ☐ 49. RANDY TOMLIN
- ☐ 76. ORLANDO MERCED

☐ 93. STEVE COOKE
☐ 108. CARLOS GARCIA
☐ 151. JAY BELL
☐ 160. BLAS MINOR
☐ 186. KEVIN YOUNG
☐ 208. JEFF KING
☐ 211. AL MARTIN
☐ 217. DON SLAUGHT
☐ 227. ANDY TOMBERLIN
☐ 448. TIM WAKEFIELD
☐ 457. BOB WALK
☐ 502. BRIAN HUNTER
☐ 533. RICK WHITE

ST. LOUIS CARDINALS

☐ 36. RAY LANKFORD
☐ 79. BERNARD GILKEY
☐ 107. RENE AROCHA
☐ 124. BRIAN JORDAN
☐ 145. ALLEN WATSON
☐ 153. MARK WHITEN
☐ 182. MIKE PEREZ
☐ 204. GREGG JEFFERIES
☐ 209. DONOVAN OSBORNE
☐ 214. GERONIMO PENA
☐ 319. LUIS ALICEA
☐ 367. TODD ZEILE
☐ 389. OZZIE SMITH
☐ 407. LONNIE MACLIN
☐ 425. TRIPP CROMER
☐ 439. TOM PAGNOZZI
☐ 452. BOB TEWKSBURY

SAN DIEGO PADRES

☐ 4. TONY GWYNN
☐ 22. DEREK BELL
☐ 51. ANDY BENES
☐ 80. PHIL PLANTIER
☐ 109. WALLY WHITEHURST
☐ 138. RICKY GUTIERREZ
☐ 167. PHIL CLARK
☐ 215. KEVIN HIGGINS
☐ 259. LUIS LOPEZ
☐ 272. TREVOR HOFFMAN
☐ 296. JEFF GARDNER
☐ 331. ARCHI CIANFROCCO
☐ 363. GENE HARRIS
☐ 381. SCOTT SANDERS
☐ 391. BRAD AUSMUS
☐ 396. DAVE STATON
☐ 438. DERREK LEE
☐ 478. MELVIN NIEVES

SAN FRANCISCO GIANTS

☐ 24. JOHN BURKETT
☐ 26. BARRY BONDS
☐ 39. TODD BENZINGER
☐ 53. KIRT MANWARING
☐ 82. TREVOR WILSON
☐ 111. ROYCE CLAYTON
☐ 118. ROD BECK
☐ 140. BUD BLACK
☐ 169. DARREN LEWIS
☐ 198. JEFF BRANTLEY
☐ 261. SALOMON TORRES
☐ 274. WILLIE MCGEE
☐ 298. MATT WILLIAMS
☐ 301. JIM DESHAIES
☐ 315. ROBBY THOMPSON
☐ 326. BILL SWIFT
☐ 365. KEVIN ROGERS
☐ 419. J.R. PHILLIPS
☐ 513. WILL CLARK

SEATTLE MARINERS

☐ 64. OMAR VIZQUEL
☐ 100. KEN GRIFFEY, JR.
☐ 129. TINO MARTINEZ
☐ 158. DAVE FLEMING
☐ 187. DAVE MAGADAN
☐ 216. NORM CHARLTON
☐ 250. MARC NEWFIELD
☐ 278. RANDY JOHNSON
☐ 302. EDGAR MARTINEZ
☐ 343. JAY BUHNER
☐ 352. MIKE FELDER
☐ 372. CHRIS BOSIO
☐ 377. BRIAN TURANG
☐ 386. RICH AMARAL
☐ 393. ROGER SALKELD
☐ 415. MIKE HAMPTON
☐ 472. ERIK HANSON
☐ 482. BOBBY AYALA
☐ 510. BRET BOONE
☐ 514. DAVE VALLE

TEXAS RANGERS

☐ 42. TOM HENKE
☐ 71. KEVIN BROWN
☐ 101. DEAN PALMER
☐ 162. DAVID HULSE
☐ 194. BENJI GIL
☐ 221. KENNY ROGERS
☐ 233. DARREN OLIVER
☐ 306. JOSE CANSECO
☐ 349. IVAN RODRIGUEZ
☐ 350. JUAN GONZALEZ
☐ 376. DOUG STRANGE
☐ 422. JON SHAVE
☐ 469. ROGER PAVLIK
☐ 493. RAFAEL PALMEIRO
☐ 520. JULIO FRANCO
☐ 525. RICK HELLING

TORONTO BLUE JAYS

☐ 5. JOHN OLERUD
☐ 27. PAUL MOLITOR
☐ 56. TODD STOTTLEMYRE
☐ 85. DEVON WHITE
☐ 143. DUANE WARD
☐ 172. JUAN GUZMAN
☐ 287. ROBERTO ALOMAR
☐ 316. PAT HENTGEN
☐ 334. AL LEITER
☐ 345. JOE CARTER
☐ 374. DAVE STEWART
☐ 397. ROB BUTLER
☐ 413. CARLOS DELGADO
☐ 427. TONY FERNANDEZ
☐ 450. RICKEY HENDRESON
☐ 459. ED SPRAGUE
☐ 477. PAT BORDERS
☐ 505. ALEX GONZALEZ
☐ 511. MARK EICHHORN
☐ 530. TIM HYERS
☐ 532. JACK MORRIS
☐ 539. PAUL SPOLJARIC

1995 PINNACLE SERIES 1 (225) 2 1/2" X 3 1/2"

ATLANTA BRAVES

☐ 12. FRED MCGRIFF
☐ 25. JOHN SMOLTZ
☐ 50. DAVE JUSTICE
☐ 111. CHIPPER JONES
☐ 126. MARK LEMKE
☐ 140. JOSE OLIVA
☐ 172. JACOB SHUMATE
☐ 185. STEVE AVERY
☐ 212. TONY TARASCO
☐ 224. RYAN KLESKO

BALTIMORE ORIOLES

☐ 10. JEFFREY HAMMONDS
☐ 14. MIKE MUSSINA
☐ 38. CHRIS HOILES
☐ 64. LEE SMITH
☐ 88. SID FERNANDEZ
☐ 103. LEO GOMEZ
☐ 120. BEN MCDONALD
☐ 134. ARMANDO BENITEZ
☐ 166. MARK SMITH
☐ 188. BRADY ANDERSON
☐ 204. CAL RIPKEN, JR.

BOSTON RED SOX

☐ 2. ROGER CLEMENS
☐ 19. LUIS ORTIZ
☐ 40. MIKE GREENWELL
☐ 67. SCOTT COOPER
☐ 75. JOHN VALENTIN
☐ 105. TIM NAEHRING
☐ 106. OTIS NIXON
☐ 216. MO VAUGHN

CALIFORNIA ANGELS

☐ 17. CHUCK FINLEY
☐ 65. JIM EDMONDS
☐ 133. GARRET ANDERSON
☐ 136. JORGE FABREGAS
☐ 167. MCKAY CHRISTENSEN
☐ 181. BRIAN ANDERSON
☐ 208. BO JACKSON
☐ 215. J.T. SNOW
☐ 220. CHAD CURTIS
☐ 225. MARK LANGSTON

CHICAGO CUBS

☐ 4. SHAWON DUNSTON
☐ 28. DERRICK MAY
☐ 53. RICK WILKINS
☐ 78. TURK WENDELL
☐ 131. STEVE TRACHSEL
☐ 176. JAYSON PETERSON

☐ 182. STEVE BUECHELE
☐ 213. KARL RHODES

CHICAGO WHITE SOX

☐ 41. LANCE JOHNSON
☐ 66. DARRIN JACKSON
☐ 68. RON KARKOVICE
☐ 107. OZZIE GUILLEN
☐ 123. WILSON ALVAREZ
☐ 174. MARK JOHNSON

CINCINNATI REDS

☐ 26. HECTOR CARRASCO
☐ 51. JOHN SMILEY
☐ 76. REGGIE SANDERS
☐ 168. C.J. NITKOWSKI
☐ 223. JOSE RIJO

CLEVELAND INDIANS

☐ 18. JIM THOME
☐ 39. SANDY ALOMAR, JR.
☐ 84. PAUL SORRENTO
☐ 89. CHARLES NAGY
☐ 129. OMAR VIZQUEL
☐ 155. PAUL SHUEY
☐ 183. MARK CLARK
☐ 189. KENNY LOFTON
☐ 200. CARLOS BAERGA

COLORADO ROCKIES

☐ 20. WALT WEISS
☐ 29. MIKE KINGERY
☐ 54. ELLIS BURKS
☐ 79. CHARLIE HAYES
☐ 95. DAVID NIED

DETROIT TIGERS

☐ 15. DANNY BAUTISTA
☐ 42. JUNIOR FELIX
☐ 69. CHRIS GOMEZ
☐ 117. LOU WHITAKER
☐ 124. TRAVIS FRYMAN
☐ 130. MILT CUYLER
☐ 148. JOSE LIMA
☐ 184. CECIL FIELDER
☐ 209. TONY PHILLIPS

FLORIDA MARLINS

☐ 11. JEFF CONINE
☐ 30. CHUCK CARR
☐ 55. DAVE WEATHERS
☐ 80. BRET BARBERIE
☐ 96. CHRIS HAMMOND
☐ 119. GARY SHEFFIELD
☐ 158. CHARLES JOHNSON
☐ 161. KURT MILLER
☐ 198. PAT RAPP
☐ 202. KURT ABBOTT
☐ 206. GREG COLBRUNN

HOUSTON ASTROS

☐ 1. JEFF BAGWELL
☐ 33. LUIS GONZALEZ
☐ 58. JAMES MOUTON
☐ 72. DOUG DRABEK
☐ 82. KEN CAMINITI
☐ 83. MILT THOMPSON
☐ 114. STEVE FINLEY
☐ 121. PETE HARNISCH
☐ 137. ORLANDO MILLER
☐ 145. ROBERTO PETAGINE
☐ 149. JOHN HUDEK
☐ 164. BRIAN HUNTER
☐ 171. SCOTT ELARTON

KANSAS CITY ROYALS

☐ 22. BOB HAMELIN
☐ 43. FELIX JOSE
☐ 70. KEVIN APPIER
☐ 77. WALLY JOYNER
☐ 90. JEFF MONTGOMERY
☐ 108. JOSE LIND
☐ 113. MIKE MACFARLANE
☐ 217. GREG GAGNE

LOS ANGELES DODGERS

☐ 7. ERIC KARROS
☐ 31. BILLY ASHLEY
☐ 56. PEDRO ASTACIO
☐ 102. DELINO DESHIELDS
☐ 139. ISMAEL VALDES
☐ 154. GAREY INGRAM
☐ 170. PAUL KONERKO

MILWAUKEE BREWERS

☐ 46. KEVIN SEITZER
☐ 73. MATT MIESKE
☐ 110. GREG VAUGHN
☐ 127. JOSE VALENTIN
☐ 144. MIKE MATHENY
☐ 150. DUANE SINGLETON
☐ 165. JEFF CIRILLO
☐ 169. ANTONE WILLIAMSON
☐ 207. DARRYL HAMILTON
☐ 218. RICKY BONES

MINNESOTA TWINS

☐ 6. KEVIN TAPANI
☐ 44. SCOTT LEIUS
☐ 91. CHUCK KNOBLAUCH
☐ 125. PEDRO MUNOZ
☐ 157. STEVE DUNN
☐ 163. DAVE STEVENS
☐ 190. ALEX COLE
☐ 211. RICH BECKER

MONTREAL EXPOS

☐ 8. CLIFF FLOYD
☐ 34. MARQUIS GRISSOM
☐ 59. MEL ROJAS
☐ 99. JEFF FASSERO
☐ 115. KEN HILL
☐ 162. JOEY EISCHEN

NEW YORK METS

☐ 5. BOBBY BONILLA
☐ 32. TODD HUNDLEY
☐ 57. RYAN THOMPSON
☐ 71. BOBBY JONES
☐ 173. TERRENCE LONG

NEW YORK YANKEES

☐ 9. PAT KELLY
☐ 21. DON MATTINGLY
☐ 23. MELIDO PEREZ
☐ 47. WADE BOGGS
☐ 74. STERLING HITCHCOCK
☐ 152. ROBERT EENHOORN

OAKLAND A'S

☐ 45. RUBEN SIERRA
☐ 81. TROY NEEL
☐ 109. STAN JAVIER
☐ 146. FAUSTO CRUZ
☐ 159. ERNIE YOUNG
☐ 175. BEN GRIEVE
☐ 191. BRENT GATES
☐ 196. MARK MCGWIRE
☐ 201. RICKEY HENDERSON
☐ 210. GERONIMO BERROA
☐ 219. MIKE BORDICK

PHILADELPHIA PHILLIES

☐ 16. MICKEY MORANDINI
☐ 98. KEVIN STOCKER
☐ 100. CURT SCHILLING
☐ 104. DAVE HOLLINS
☐ 143. RICKY BOTTALACIO
☐ 156. MIKE LIEBERTHAL
☐ 205. DARREN DAULTON

PITTSBURGH PIRATES

☐ 35. JEFF KING
☐ 60. ORLANDO MERCED
☐ 86. JAY BELL
☐ 101. DAVE CLARK
☐ 116. CARLOS GARCIA
☐ 153. JON LIEBER
☐ 194. STEVE COOKE

ST. LOUIS CARDINALS

☐ 3. MARK WHITEN
☐ 37. TOM PAGNOZZI
☐ 62. BERNARD GILKEY
☐ 118. TODD ZEILE
☐ 151. JOHN MABRY
☐ 195. RAY LANKFORD

SAN DIEGO PADRES

☐ 36. EDDIE WILLIAMS
☐ 85. TREVOR HOFFMAN
☐ 93. TONY GWYNN
☐ 147. BRYCE FLORIE
☐ 160. JOSE MARTINEZ
☐ 187. CRAIG SHIPLEY
☐ 214. PHIL PLANTIER

SAN FRANCISCO GIANTS

☐ 61. MATT WILLIAMS
☐ 63. J.R. PHILLIPS
☐ 87. MARK PORTUGAL
☐ 138. RIKKERT FANEYTE
☐ 199. DARREN LEWIS
☐ 203. KIRT MANWARING
☐ 221. ROYCE CLAYTON

SEATTLE MARINERS

☐ 13. CHRIS BOSIO
☐ 24. KEITH MITCHELL

- ☐ 48. REGGIE JEFFERSON
- ☐ 97. EDGAR MARTINEZ
- ☐ 128. KEN GRIFFEY, JR.
- ☐ 132. ALEX RODRIGUEZ
- ☐ 142. TIM DAVIS
- ☐ 197. MARC NEWFIELD

TEXAS RANGERS

- ☐ 49. JOSE CANSECO
- ☐ 92. JEFF FRYE
- ☐ 122. IVAN RODRIGUEZ
- ☐ 192. DEAN PALMER

TORONTO BLUE JAYS

- ☐ 27. PAT HENTGEN
- ☐ 52. JOE CARTER
- ☐ 94. JOHN OLERUD
- ☐ 112. ED SPRAGUE
- ☐ 135. SHAWN GREEN
- ☐ 141. AARON SMALL
- ☐ 186. DEVON WHITE
- ☐ 193. ALEX GONZALEZ
- ☐ 222. ROBERTO ALOMAR

SCORE-SELECT

1993 SELECT (405)
2 1/2" X 3 1/2"

ATLANTA BRAVES

- ☐ 7. TOM GLAVINE
- ☐ 17. TERRY PENDLETON
- ☐ 39. DAVE JUSTICE
- ☐ 84. DEION SANDERS
- ☐ 109. STEVE AVERY
- ☐ 133. RON GANT
- ☐ 159. OTIS NIXON
- ☐ 161. MARK LEMKE
- ☐ 177. JOHN SMOLTZ
- ☐ 189. BRIAN HUNTER
- ☐ 209. CHARLIE LEIBRANDT
- ☐ 233. GREG OLSON
- ☐ 267. RAFAEL BELLIARD
- ☐ 282. MARK WOHLERS
- ☐ 303. JAMIE ARNOLD
- ☐ 362. JEFF REARDON
- ☐ 382. SID BREAM
- ☐ 405. RYAN KLESKO

BALTIMORE ORIOLES

- ☐ 18. CAL RIPKEN, JR.
- ☐ 46. GREGG OLSON
- ☐ 56. BRADY ANDERSON
- ☐ 66. LEO GOMEZ
- ☐ 92. MIKE MUSSINA
- ☐ 144. CHRIS HOILES
- ☐ 170. MIKE DEVEREAUX
- ☐ 182. RICK SUTCLIFFE
- ☐ 212. RANDY MILLIGAN
- ☐ 224. BEN MCDONALD
- ☐ 234. JOE ORSULAK
- ☐ 294. JEFF TACKETT
- ☐ 300. ARTHUR RHODES
- ☐ 331. LUIS MERCEDES
- ☐ 367. ALAN MILLS
- ☐ 373. CRAIG LEFFERTS
- ☐ 378. GLENN DAVIS
- ☐ 391. MANNY ALEXANDER

BOSTON RED SOX

- ☐ 14. ROGER CLEMENS
- ☐ 48. WADE BOGGS
- ☐ 68. ELLIS BURKS
- ☐ 94. FRANK VIOLA
- ☐ 120. JODY REED
- ☐ 148. TONY PENA
- ☐ 188. JACK CLARK
- ☐ 210. TOM BRUANSKY
- ☐ 214. MO VAUGHN
- ☐ 225. BILLY HATCHER
- ☐ 228. MIKE GREENWELL
- ☐ 242. PHIL PLANTIER
- ☐ 292. BOB ZUPCIC
- ☐ 302. SCOTT COOPER
- ☐ 344. JOHN VALENTIN

CALIFORNIA ANGELS

- ☐ 28. JUNIOR FELIX
- ☐ 52. MARK LANGSTON
- ☐ 74. LUIS POLONIA
- ☐ 77. LUIS SOJO
- ☐ 98. JIM ABBOTT
- ☐ 198. CHUCK FINLEY
- ☐ 252. BERT BLYLEVEN
- ☐ 262. GARY GAETTI
- ☐ 281. GARY DISARCINA
- ☐ 288. JULIO VALERA
- ☐ 290. CHAD CURTIS
- ☐ 328. DAMION EASLEY
- ☐ 339. TIM SALMON
- ☐ 374. JOE GRAHE
- ☐ 379. RENE GONZALES

CHICAGO CUBS

- ☐ 9. ANDRE DAWSON
- ☐ 31. GREG MADDUX
- ☐ 73. MARK GRACE
- ☐ 97. RYNE SANDBERG
- ☐ 121. SHAWON DUNSTON
- ☐ 129. STEVE BUECHELE
- ☐ 145. MIKE MORGAN
- ☐ 165. SAMMY SOSA
- ☐ 181. KAL DANIELS
- ☐ 285. JIM BULLINGER
- ☐ 357. DEREK WALLACE
- ☐ 390. RICK WILKINS
- ☐ 397. MIKE HARKEY
- ☐ 402. DERRICK MAY

CHICAGO WHITE SOX

- ☐ 6. FRANK THOMAS
- ☐ 30. ROBIN VENTURA
- ☐ 76. CARLTON FISK
- ☐ 100. GEORGE BILL
- ☐ 128. OZZIE GUILLEN
- ☐ 160. STEVE SAX
- ☐ 196. JACK MCDOWELL
- ☐ 216. GREG HIBBARD
- ☐ 232. BOBBY THIGPEN
- ☐ 236. TIM RAINES
- ☐ 266. LANCE JOHNSON
- ☐ 311. ROBERTO HERNANDEZ
- ☐ 381. RON KARKOVICE
- ☐ 387. KIRK MCCASKILL
- ☐ 389. CRAIG GREBECK

CINCINNATI REDS

- ☐ 23. BARRY LARKIN
- ☐ 45. HAL MORRIS
- ☐ 65. ROB DIBBLE
- ☐ 86. PAUL O'NEILL
- ☐ 111. BIP ROBERTS
- ☐ 135. CHRIS SABO
- ☐ 163. JOSE RIJO
- ☐ 179. GREG SWINDELL
- ☐ 191. TIM BELCHER
- ☐ 207. NORM CHARLTON
- ☐ 235. JOE OLIVER
- ☐ 249. TOM BROWNING
- ☐ 265. SCOTT BANKHEAD
- ☐ 274. REGGIE SANDERS
- ☐ 345. DAN WILSON
- ☐ 348. WILLIE GREENE

CLEVELAND INDIANS

- ☐ 26. SANDY ALOMAR, JR.
- ☐ 50. ALBERT BELLE
- ☐ 70. CHARLES NAGY
- ☐ 122. CARLOS BEARGA
- ☐ 146. MARK WHITEN
- ☐ 150. MARK LEWIS
- ☐ 226. PAUL SORRENTO
- ☐ 256. FELIX FERMIN
- ☐ 275. KENNY LOFTON
- ☐ 304. JIM THOME
- ☐ 330. REGGIE JEFFERSON
- ☐ 377. STEVE OLIN

COLORADO ROCKIES

- ☐ 53. JOE GIRARDI
- ☐ 114. DANTE BICHETTE
- ☐ 401. ERIC WEDGE

DETROIT TIGERS

- ☐ 20. CECIL FIELDER
- ☐ 44. TRAVIS FRYMAN
- ☐ 60. MICKEY TETTLETON
- ☐ 85. BILL GULLICKSON
- ☐ 112. LOU WHITAKER
- ☐ 138. MIKE HENNEMAN
- ☐ 166. MILT CUYLER
- ☐ 186. ROB DEER
- ☐ 218. TONY PHILLIPS
- ☐ 230. ALAN TRAMMELL
- ☐ 244. DAN GLADDEN
- ☐ 298. JOHN DOHERTY
- ☐ 306. KURT KNUDSEN
- ☐ 320. SCOTT LIVINGSTONE
- ☐ 335. PHIL CLARK
- ☐ 398. FRANK TANANA

FLORIDA MARLINS

- ☐ 126. BRYAN HARVEY
- ☐ 149. DAVE MAGADAN
- ☐ 192. WALT WEISS

HOUSTON ASTROS

- ☐ 25. CRAIG BIGGIO
- ☐ 47. KEN CAMNITI
- ☐ 67. DOUG JONES
- ☐ 88. STEVE FINLEY
- ☐ 113. JEFF BAGWELL
- ☐ 137. ERIC ANTHONY
- ☐ 205. LUIS GONZALEZ
- ☐ 219. PETE HARNISCH
- ☐ 287. BRIAN WILLIAMS
- ☐ 333. EDDIE TAUBENSEE

KANSAS CITY ROYALS

- ☐ 34. WALLY JOYNER
- ☐ 54. KEITH MILLER
- ☐ 78. GEORGE BRETT
- ☐ 102. KEVIN APPIER
- ☐ 152. GREGG JEFFERIES
- ☐ 176. KEVIN MCREYNOLDS
- ☐ 227. MARK GUBICZA
- ☐ 237. JUAN SAMUEL
- ☐ 241. JIM EISENREICH
- ☐ 250. BRIAN MCRAE
- ☐ 264. JEFF MONTGOMERY
- ☐ 277. RUSTY MEACHAM
- ☐ 291. MICHAEL TUCKER
- ☐ 312. HIPOLITO PICHARDO
- ☐ 321. JEFF CONINE
- ☐ 394. KEVIN KOSLOFSKI

LOS ANGELES DODGERS

- ☐ 21. DARRYL STRAWBERRY
- ☐ 49. OREL HERSHISER
- ☐ 69. MIKE SCIOSCIA
- ☐ 91. ERIC DAVIS
- ☐ 115. BRETT BUTLER
- ☐ 143. TOM CANDIOTTI
- ☐ 157. MIKE SHARPERSON
- ☐ 197. JOSE OFFERMAN
- ☐ 213. RAMON MARTINEZ
- ☐ 263. BOB OJEDA
- ☐ 278. ERIC KARROS
- ☐ 317. CARLOS HERNANDEZ
- ☐ 325. PEDRO ASTACIO
- ☐ 342. ERIC YOUNG
- ☐ 347. MIKE PIAZZA
- ☐ 349. TOM GOODWIN
- ☐ 375. ROGER MCDOWELL
- ☐ 384. LENNY HARRIS
- ☐ 404. HENRY RODRIGUEZ

MILWAUKEE BREWERS

- ☐ 22. ROBIN YOUNT
- ☐ 42. PAUL MOLITOR
- ☐ 62. B.J. SURHOFF
- ☐ 87. KEVIN SEITZER
- ☐ 140. SCOTT FLETCHER
- ☐ 168. DARRYL HAMILTON
- ☐ 174. MIKE FETTERS
- ☐ 184. BILL WEGMAN
- ☐ 222. GREG VAUGHN
- ☐ 259. BILL SPIERS
- ☐ 260. JAIME NAVARRO
- ☐ 273. PAT LISTACH
- ☐ 283. DAVE NILSSON
- ☐ 296. CAL ELDRED
- ☐ 308. JOHN JAHA
- ☐ 322. JAMES AUSTIN
- ☐ 334. TIM MCINTOSH
- ☐ 399. DOUG HENRY

MINNESOTA TWINS

- ☐ 4. KIRBY PUCKETT
- ☐ 36. CHUCK KNOBLAUCH
- ☐ 75. JOHN SMILEY
- ☐ 80. KENT HRBEK
- ☐ 104. SHANE MACK
- ☐ 130. KEVIN TAPANI
- ☐ 154. BRIAN HARPER
- ☐ 178. GREG GAGNE
- ☐ 206. RICK AGUILERA
- ☐ 238. CHILI DAVIS
- ☐ 251. SCOTT LEIUS
- ☐ 253. SCOTT ERICKSON
- ☐ 314. WILLIE BANKS
- ☐ 324. PAT MAHOMES
- ☐ 352. DAN SERAFINI
- ☐ 370. PEDRO MUNOZ

MONTREAL EXPOS

- ☐ 27. LARRY WALKER
- ☐ 43. DELINO DESHIELDS
- ☐ 55. GARY CARTER
- ☐ 99. MARQUIS GRISSOM
- ☐ 125. IVAN CALDERON
- ☐ 147. DENNIS MARTINEZ
- ☐ 169. KEN HILL
- ☐ 185. MARK GARDNER
- ☐ 190. TIM WALLACH
- ☐ 201. JOHN WETTELAND
- ☐ 239. SPIKE OWEN
- ☐ 272. MOISES ALOU
- ☐ 295. GREG COLBRUNN
- ☐ 310. B.J. WALLACE
- ☐ 323. JOHN VANDER WAL
- ☐ 327. MATT STAIRS
- ☐ 336. WIL CORDERO

NEW YORK METS

- ☐ 11. BOBBY BONILLA
- ☐ 29. EDDIE MURRAY
- ☐ 57. DOC GOODEN
- ☐ 101. HOWARD JOHNSON
- ☐ 123. BRET SABERHAGEN
- ☐ 167. JOHN FRANCO
- ☐ 175. VINCE COLEMAN
- ☐ 195. WILLIE RANDOLPH
- ☐ 243. SID FERNANDEZ
- ☐ 284. ANTHONY YOUNG
- ☐ 293. TODD HUNDLEY
- ☐ 297. CHRIS ROBERTS
- ☐ 318. JEFF KENT
- ☐ 350. ERIC HILLMAN

NEW YORK YANKEES

- ☐ 12. DANNY TARTABULL
- ☐ 24. DON MATTINGLY
- ☐ 64. ROBERTO KELLY
- ☐ 89. MEL HALL
- ☐ 116. MELIDO PEREZ
- ☐ 142. KEVIN MAAS
- ☐ 172. STEVE FARR
- ☐ 194. CHARLIE HAYES
- ☐ 220. MIKE GALLEGO
- ☐ 255. PAT KELLY
- ☐ 261. SCOTT SANDERSON
- ☐ 279. ANDY STANKIEWICZ
- ☐ 315. SAM MILITELLO
- ☐ 337. RUSS SPRINGER
- ☐ 343. BOB WICKMAN
- ☐ 360. DEREK JETER
- ☐ 368. MATT NOKES
- ☐ 383. GERALD WILLIAMS
- ☐ 385. J.T. SNOW
- ☐ 393. BERNIE WILLIAMS

OAKLAND A'S

- ☐ 10. RON DARLING
- ☐ 16. MARK MCGWIRE
- ☐ 38. DENNIS ECKERSLEY
- ☐ 106. RICKEY HENDERSON
- ☐ 132. TERRY STEINBACH
- ☐ 156. CARNEY LANSFORD
- ☐ 208. MIKE BORDICK
- ☐ 240. DAVE STEWART
- ☐ 254. BOB WELCH
- ☐ 257. HAROLD BAINES
- ☐ 270. MIKE MOORE
- ☐ 313. ERIC FOX
- ☐ 316. VINCE HORSMAN
- ☐ 354. BENJI GRIGSBY
- ☐ 363. BOBBY WITT
- ☐ 365. JEFF RUSSELL
- ☐ 366. RUBEN SIERRA
- ☐ 395. WILLIE WILSON
- ☐ 396. JEFF PARRETT

PHILADELPHIA PHILLIES

- ☐ 13. DARREN DAULTON
- ☐ 33. JOHN KRUK
- ☐ 59. LENNY DYKSTRA
- ☐ 79. MITCH WILLIAMS
- ☐ 103. DALE MURPHY
- ☐ 127. TERRY MULHOLLAND
- ☐ 151. MARIANO DUNCAN
- ☐ 187. DAVE HOLLINS
- ☐ 217. WES CHAMBERLAIN
- ☐ 229. CURT SCHILLING
- ☐ 245. MICKEY MORANDINI
- ☐ 329. BEN RIVERA
- ☐ 332. KYLE ABBOTT
- ☐ 340. BRAULIO CASTILLO

PITTSBURGH PIRATES

- ☐ 1. BARRY BONDS
- ☐ 35. ANDY VAN SLYKE
- ☐ 61. RANDY TOMLIN
- ☐ 81. JAY BELL
- ☐ 105. JOSE LIND
- ☐ 153. DOUG DRABEK
- ☐ 171. DON SLAUGHT
- ☐ 183. ORLANDO MERCED
- ☐ 203. MIKE LAVALLIERE
- ☐ 231. ZANE SMITH
- ☐ 299. DENNY NEAGLE
- ☐ 307. TIM WAKEFIELD
- ☐ 359. JASON KENDALL
- ☐ 371. DANNY JACKSON
- ☐ 403. CARLOS GARCIA

ST. LOUIS CARDINALS

- ☐ 15. OZZIE SMITH
- ☐ 37. TOM PAGNOZZI
- ☐ 63. TODD ZEILE
- ☐ 83. LEE SMITH
- ☐ 107. BOB TEWKSBURY
- ☐ 131. FELIX JOSE
- ☐ 155. RAY LANKFORD
- ☐ 173. BERNARD GILKEY
- ☐ 223. MILT THOMPSON
- ☐ 276. DONOVAN OSBORNE
- ☐ 280. BRIAN JORDAN
- ☐ 301. MARK CLARK
- ☐ 319. MIKE PEREZ
- ☐ 356. SEAN LOWE
- ☐ 372. GERONIMO PENA

SAN DIEGO PADRES

- ☐ 5. TONY GWYNN
- ☐ 19. FRED MCGRIFF
- ☐ 41. GARY SHEFFIELD
- ☐ 93. TONY FERNANDEZ
- ☐ 117. ANDY BENES
- ☐ 141. BRUCE HURST
- ☐ 193. KURT STILLWELL
- ☐ 199. DARRIN JACKSON
- ☐ 215. RANDY MYERS
- ☐ 269. BENITO SANTIAGO
- ☐ 289. DAN WALTERS
- ☐ 305. FRANK SEMINARA

SAN FRANCISCO GIANTS

- ☐ 3. WILL CLARK
- ☐ 51. BILL SWIFT
- ☐ 71. CORY SNYDER
- ☐ 95. MATT WILLIAMS
- ☐ 119. WILLIE MCGEE
- ☐ 139. ROBBY THOMPSON
- ☐ 221. BUD BLACK
- ☐ 247. KIRT MANWARING
- ☐ 338. CRAIG COLBERT
- ☐ 346. STEVE HOSEY
- ☐ 351. STEVE REED
- ☐ 400. ROYCE CLAYTON

SEATTLE MARINERS

- ☐ 2. KEN GRIFFEY, JR
- ☐ 82. EDGAR MARTINEZ
- ☐ 108. KEVIN MITCHELL
- ☐ 118. RANDY JOHNSON
- ☐ 134. HAROLD REYNOLDS
- ☐ 164. OMAR VIZQUEL
- ☐ 202. JAY BUHNER
- ☐ 246. TINO MARTINEZ
- ☐ 271. DAVE FLEMING
- ☐ 326. BRET BOONE
- ☐ 388. LANCE PARRISH
- ☐ 392. MIKE SCHOOLER

TEXAS RANGERS

- ☐ 40. JUAN GONZALEZ
- ☐ 58. JULIO FRANCO
- ☐ 90. NOLAN RYAN
- ☐ 136. IVAN RODRIGUEZ
- ☐ 162. RAFAEL PALMEIRO
- ☐ 204. KEVIN BROWN

- ☐ 248. DEAN PALMER
- ☐ 268. KEVIN REIMER
- ☐ 341. DONALD HARRIS
- ☐ 358. RICK HELLING
- ☐ 364. JOSE CANSECO

TORONTO BLUE JAYS

- ☐ 8. ROBERTO ALOMAR
- ☐ 32. DAVE WINFIELD
- ☐ 72. DEVON WHITE
- ☐ 96. JOE CARTER
- ☐ 110. CANDY MALDONADO
- ☐ 124. JOHN OLERUD
- ☐ 158. JACK MORRIS
- ☐ 180. JUAN GUZMAN
- ☐ 200. KELLY GRUBER
- ☐ 211. TOM HENKE
- ☐ 258. DUANE WARD
- ☐ 286. DEREK BELL
- ☐ 309. PAT HENTGEN
- ☐ 353. TODD STEVERSON
- ☐ 355. SHANNON STEWART
- ☐ 361. DAVID CONE
- ☐ 369. PAT BORDERS
- ☐ 376. JIMMY KEY
- ☐ 380. MANUEL LEE
- ☐ 386. DAVE STIEB

1993 SELECT ROOKIE & TRADED (150) 2 1/2" X 3 1/2"

ATLANTA BRAVES

- ☐ 5T. FRED MCGRIFF
- ☐ 59T. GREG MCMICHAEL
- ☐ 123T. GREG MADDUX

BALTIMORE ORIOLES

- ☐ 8T. HAROLD BAINES
- ☐ 14T. HAROLD REYNOLDS
- ☐ 70T. SHERMAN OBANDO
- ☐ 75T. BRAD PENNINGTON
- ☐ 82T. JEFFREY HAMMONDS
- ☐ 115T. MIKE PAGLIARULO
- ☐ 141T. JACK VOIGT
- ☐ 149T. DAMON BUFORD

BOSTON RED SOX

- ☐ 2T. ROB DEER
- ☐ 7T. JEFF RUSSELL
- ☐ 11T. ANDRE DAWSON
- ☐ 46T. PAUL QUANTRILL
- ☐ 65T. KEN RYAN
- ☐ 86T. AARON SELE
- ☐ 98T. SCOTT FLETCHER
- ☐ 122T. SCOTT BANKHEAD

CALIFORNIA ANGELS

- ☐ 44T. J.T. SNOW
- ☐ 50T. EDUARDO PEREZ
- ☐ 55T. HILLY HATHAWAY
- ☐ 124T. CHILI DAVIS
- ☐ 142T. ROD CORREIA

CHICAGO CUBS

- ☐ 25T. RANDY MYERS
- ☐ 89T. KEVIN ROBERSON
- ☐ 103T. GREG HIBBARD
- ☐ 107T. JOSE GUZMAN

CHICAGO WHITE SOX

- ☐ 3T. TIM BELCHER
- ☐ 10T. ELLIS BURKS
- ☐ 43T. RODNEY BOLTON
- ☐ 81T. JASON BERE
- ☐ 118T. IVAN CALDERON

CINCINNATI REDS

- ☐ 20T. ROBERTO KELLY
- ☐ 29T. KEVIN MITCHELL
- ☐ 34T. JOHN ROPER
- ☐ 100T. JOHN SMILEY
- ☐ 129T. JUAN SAMUEL
- ☐ 135T. JEFF REARDON

CLEVELAND INDIANS

- ☐ 56T. WAYNE KIRBY
- ☐ 73T. TOM KRAMER
- ☐ 121T. BOB OJEDA

COLORADO ROCKIES

- ☐ 33T. MO SANFORD
- ☐ 38T. ARMANDO REYNOSO
- ☐ 48T. LANCE PAINTER
- ☐ 78T. DAVID NIED
- ☐ 87T. ROBERTO MEJIA
- ☐ 102T. ANDRES GALARRAGA
- ☐ 130T. ERIC YOUNG

DETROIT TIGERS

- ☐ 80T. CHRIS GOMEZ
- ☐ 92T. ERIC DAVIS
- ☐ 113T. DAVID WELLS

FLORIDA MARLINS

- ☐ 4T. GARY SHEFFIELD
- ☐ 26T. BENITO SANTIAGO
- ☐ 37T. CHUCK CARR
- ☐ 77T. DARRELL WHITMORE
- ☐ 104T. CHRIS HAMMOND
- ☐ 117T. CHARLIE HOUGH
- ☐ 139T. RICHIE LEWIS

HOUSTON ASTROS

- ☐ 97T. DOUG DRABEK
- ☐ 99T. GREG SWINDELL

KANSAS CITY ROYALS

- ☐ 18T. DAVID CONE
- ☐ 22T. JOSE LIND
- ☐ 28T. GREG GAGNE
- ☐ 66T. PHIL HIATT
- ☐ 95T. GARY GAETTI
- ☐ 110T. FELIX JOSE
- ☐ 143T. BILLY BREWER

LOS ANGELES DODGERS

- ☐ 27T. TIM WALLACH
- ☐ 36T. PEDRO MARTINEZ
- ☐ 93T. JODY REED
- ☐ 111T. CORY SNYDER
- ☐ 138T. RICK TRLICEK

MILWAUKEE BREWERS

- ☐ 72T. ANGEL MIRANDA
- ☐ 76T. GRAEME LLOYD
- ☐ 101T. KEVIN REIMER
- ☐ 134T. TOM BRUNANSKY

MINNESOTA TWINS

- ☐ 9T. DAVE WINFIELD
- ☐ 45T. DAVID MCCARTY
- ☐ 52T. MIKE TROMBLEY
- ☐ 67T. PAT MEARES
- ☐ 74T. CHIP HALE
- ☐ 144T. TERRY JORGENSEN

MONTREAL EXPOS

- ☐ 49T. LOU FRAZIER
- ☐ 60T. MIKE LANSING
- ☐ 88T. KIRK RUETER
- ☐ 146T. SEAN BERRY
- ☐ 150T. WIL CORDERO

NEW YORK METS

- ☐ 39T. RYAN THOMPSON
- ☐ 54T. TIM BOGAR
- ☐ 85T. JEROMY BURNITZ
- ☐ 131T. JOE ORSULAK
- ☐ 133T. DARRIN JACKSON

NEW YORK YANKEES

- ☐ 13T. JIMMY KEY
- ☐ 17T. WADE BOGGS
- ☐ 21T. PAUL O'NEILL
- ☐ 30T. JIM ABBOTT
- ☐ 31T. LEE SMITH
- ☐ 32T. BOBBY MUNOZ
- ☐ 53T. STERLING HITCHCOCK
- ☐ 109T. SPIKE OWEN
- ☐ 127T. FRANK TANANA

OAKLAND A'S

- ☐ 57T. CRAIG PAQUETTE
- ☐ 61T. BRENT GATES
- ☐ 68T. TROY NEEL
- ☐ 79T. TODD VAN POPPEL

PHILADELPHIA PHILLIES

- □ 84T. KEVIN STOCKER
- □ 94T. DANNY JACKSON
- □114T. PETE INCAVIGLIA
- □125T. MILT THOMPSON

PITTSBURGH PIRATES

- □ 40T. CARLOS GARCIA
- □ 47T. AL MARTIN
- □ 51T. KEVIN YOUNG
- □ 69T. STEVE COOKE
- □ 71T. BLAS MINOR
- □137T. JOEL JOHNSTON
- □148T. PAUL WAGNER

ST. LOUIS CARDINALS

- □ 6T. MARK WHITEN
- □ 12T. GREGG JEFFERIES
- □ 62T. RENE AROCHA
- □ 90T. ALLEN WATSON

SAN DIEGO PADRES

- □ 63T. RICKY GUTIERREZ
- □ 83T. BRAD AUSMUS
- □128T. PHIL PLANTIER
- □132T. DEREK BELL
- □136T. KEVIN HIGGINS
- □140T. JEFF GARDNER

SAN FRANCISCO GIANTS

- □ 23T. BARRY BONDS
- □ 64T. KEVIN ROGERS
- □126T. DAVE MARTINEZ

SEATTLE MARINERS

- □ 58T. BRET BOONE
- □ 96T. NORM CHARLTON
- □106T. MIKE FELDER
- □108T. CHRIS BOSIO
- □116T. DAVE MAGADAN
- □145T. RICH AMARAL

TEXAS RANGERS

- □ 15T. TOM HENKE
- □ 35T. DAVID HULSE
- □ 41T. MATT WHITESIDE
- □ 42T. BENJI GIL
- □ 91T. CHARLIE LEIBRANDT
- □112T. CRAIG LEFFERTS
- □119T. MANUEL LEE
- □120T. BOB PATTERSON
- □147T. DAN PELTIER

TORONTO BLUE JAYS

- □ 1T. RICKEY HENDERSON
- □ 16T. PAUL MOLITOR
- □ 19T. TONY FERNANDEZ
- □ 24T. DAVE STEWART
- □105T. DARNELL COLES

1994 SELECT (420)
2 1/2" X 3 1/2"

ATLANTA BRAVES

- □ 2. GREG MADDUX
- □ 14. JEFF BLAUSER
- □ 34. TERRY PENDLETON
- □ 60. MARK LEMKE
- □ 87. STEVE AVERY
- □ 174. JOHN SMOLTZ
- □ 188. JAVIER OPEZ
- □ 197. RYAN KLESKO
- □ 236. DAVE JUSTICE
- □ 247. GREG MCMICHAEL
- □ 250. TOM GLAVINE
- □ 268. FRED MCGRIFF
- □ 312. ROBERTO KELLY
- □ 381. TONY TARASCO
- □ 386. MIKE KELLY

BALTIMORE ORIOLES

- □ 15. CHRIS HOILES
- □ 31. HAROLD BAINES
- □ 36. MIKE MUSSINA
- □ 55. BRADY ANDERSON
- □ 80. MARK MCLEMORE
- □ 105. JACK VOIGT
- □ 117. BEN MCDONALD
- □ 131. MIKE DEVEREAUX
- □ 180. JEFFREY HAMMONDS
- □ 217. LEE SMITH
- □ 249. CAL RIPKEN, JR.
- □ 314. CHRIS SABO
- □ 317. RAFAEL PALMEIRO
- □ 338. LEO GOMEZ
- □ 353. SID FERNANDEZ
- □ 408. MARK SMITH

BOSTON RED SOX

- □ 10. MIKE GREENWELL
- □ 39. SCOTT COOPER
- □ 49. JOHN VALENTIN
- □ 61. ROGER CLEMENS
- □ 93. ANDRE DAWSON
- □ 96. BILLY HATCHER
- □ 110. DANNY DARWIN
- □ 116. MO VAUGHN
- □ 151. TIM NAEHRING
- □ 190. GREG BLOSSER
- □ 228. OTIS NIXON
- □ 241. DAVE VALLE
- □ 272. JEFF RUSSELL
- □ 337. AARON SELE
- □ 392. RICH ROWLAND

CALIFORNIA ANGELS

- □ 198. JIM EDMONDS
- □ 205. CHRIS TURNER
- □ 222. DAMION EASLEY
- □ 226. GARY DISARCINA
- □ 283. CHILI DAVIS
- □ 291. CHUCK FINLEY
- □ 309. TIM SALMON
- □ 313. HAROLD REYNOLDS
- □ 325. SPIKE OWEN
- □ 345. CHAD CURTIS
- □ 351. MARK LANGSTON
- □ 356. BO JACKSON
- □ 360. EDUARDO PEREZ
- □ 367. REX HUDLER
- □ 383. BRIAN ANDERSON
- □ 398. JORGE FABREGAS

CHICAGO CUBS

- □ 16. RICK WILKINS
- □ 22. RANDY MYERS
- □ 32. RYNE SANDBERG
- □ 38. DERRICK MAY
- □ 58. SAMMY SOSA
- □ 90. JOSE GUZMAN
- □ 121. MIKE MORGAN
- □ 136. SHAWON DUNSTON
- □ 141. KARL RHODES
- □ 166. STEVE BUECHELE
- □ 230. MARK GRACE
- □ 372. GLENALLEN HILL
- □ 389. STEVE TRACHSEL
- □ 400. EDDIE ZAMBRANO

CHICAGO WHITE SOX

- □ 6. FRANK THOMAS
- □ 13. LANCE JOHNSON
- □ 25. OZZIE GUILLEN
- □ 33. RON KARKOVICE
- □ 41. ROBIN VENTURA
- □ 92. TIM RAINES
- □ 97. JACK MCDOWELL
- □ 111. WILSON ALVAREZ
- □ 132. JOEY CORA
- □ 259. JASON BERE
- □ 277. ROBERTO HERNANDEZ
- □ 288. JULIO FRANCO
- □ 311. ALEX FERNANDEZ
- □ 352. DARRIN JACKSON
- □ 404. JOE HALL

CINCINNATI REDS

- □ 7. BARRY LARKIN
- □ 40. JOSE RIJO
- □ 71. REGGIE SANDERS
- □ 102. WILLIE GREENE
- □ 112. KEVIN MITCHELL
- □ 149. JOE OLIVER
- □ 158. HAL MORRIS
- □ 169. JOHN SMILEY
- □ 265. BRET BOONE
- □ 290. ERIK HANSON
- □ 305. DEION SANDERS
- □ 310. TONY FERNANDEZ
- □ 334. EDDIE TAUBENSEE
- □ 340. ROB DIBBLE
- □ 385. HECTOR CARRASCO
- □ 394. JOHNNY RUFFIN

CLEVELAND INDIANS

- □ 181. MANNY RAMIREZ
- □ 231. KENNY LOFTON
- □ 235. ALBERT BELLE
- □ 264. CHARLES NAGY
- □ 279. CARLOS BAERGA
- □ 289. JACK MORRIS
- □ 299. JIM THOME
- □ 321. OMAR VIZQUEL
- □ 329. EDDIE MURRAY
- □ 342. WAYNE KIRBY
- □ 346. DENNIS MARTINEZ
- □ 358. PAUL SORRENTO
- □ 366. SANDY ALOMAR, JR.
- □ 411. PAUL SHUEY

COLORADO ROCKIES

- □ 42. CHARLIE HAYES
- □ 63. ANDRES GALARRAGA
- □ 70. JOE GIRARDI
- □ 75. ROBERTO MEJIA
- □ 113. DAVID NIED

☐ 127. WALT WEISS
☐ 145. ERIC YOUNG
☐ 147. DANTE BICHETTE
☐ 287. ELLIS BURKS
☐ 315. HOWARD JOHNSON
☐ 344. ARMANDO REYNOSO

DETROIT TIGERS

☐ 186. DANNY BAUTISTA
☐ 194. CHRIS GOMEZ
☐ 215. TONY PHILLIPS
☐ 224. MIKE MOORE
☐ 233. CECIL FIELDER
☐ 248. TIM BELCHER
☐ 266. KIRK GIBSON
☐ 273. ERIC DAVIS
☐ 285. ALAN TRAMMELL
☐ 295. TRAVIS FRYMAN
☐ 323. LOU WHITAKER
☐ 327. CHAD KREUTER
☐ 331. MICKEY TETTLETON
☐ 335. JOHN DOHERTY
☐ 357. DAVID WELLS
☐ 368. MIKE HENNEMAN

FLORIDA MARLINS

☐ 11. CHUCK CARR
☐ 26. JEFF CONINE
☐ 59. RYAN BOWEN
☐ 103. BRYAN HARVEY
☐ 133. BRET BARBERIE
☐ 137. ALEX ARIAS
☐ 143. DAVE MAGADAN
☐ 150. ORESTES DESTRADE
☐ 187. KURT ABBOTT
☐ 256. GARY SHEFFIELD
☐ 354. BENITO SANTIAGO
☐ 387. GREG COLBRUNN
☐ 393. CARL EVERETT
☐ 407. CHARLES JOHNSON

HOUSTON ASTROS

☐ 184. JAMES MOUTON
☐ 192. TONY EUSEBIO
☐ 196. SHANE REYNOLDS
☐ 234. JEFF BAGWELL
☐ 243. GREG SWINDELL
☐ 284. PETE HARNISCH
☐ 296. CRAIG BIGGIO
☐ 308. ANDUJAR CEDENO
☐ 326. DARRYL KILE
☐ 348. LUIS GONZALEZ
☐ 349. DOUG DRABEK
☐ 359. KEN CAMINITI
☐ 362. STEVE FINLEY
☐ 405. JOHN HUDEK
☐ 406. ROBERTO PETAGINE

KANSAS CITY ROYALS

☐ 27. MIKE MACFARLANE
☐ 35. WALLY JOYNER
☐ 37. FELIX JOSE
☐ 47. BRIAN MCRAE
☐ 51. JOSE LIND
☐ 64. KEVIN APPIER
☐ 76. DAVID CONE
☐ 109. JEFF MONTGOMERY
☐ 118. TOM GORDON

☐ 191. BOB HAMELIN
☐ 270. GREG GAGNE
☐ 298. DAVE HENDERSON
☐ 369. VINCE COLEMAN
☐ 399. JEFF GRANGER

LOS ANGELES DODGERS

☐ 4. MIKE PIAZZA
☐ 44. ERIC KARROS
☐ 82. PEDRO ASTACIO
☐ 99. DARRYL STRAWBERRY
☐ 107. RAMON MARTINEZ
☐ 134. OREL HERSHISER
☐ 139. TIM WALLACH
☐ 157. KEVIN GROSS
☐ 170. CORY SNYDER
☐ 177. CHAN HO PARK
☐ 183. RAUL MONDESI
☐ 219. DAVE HANSEN
☐ 227. DELINO DESHIELDS
☐ 246. JOSE OFFERMAN
☐ 258. BRETT BUTLER
☐ 320. HENRY ROERIGUEZ

MILWAUKEE BREWERS

☐ 204. MIKE MATHENY
☐ 206. MATT MIESKE
☐ 216. JOHN JAHA
☐ 220. PAT LISTACH
☐ 225. BRIAN HARPER
☐ 262. GRAEME LLOYD
☐ 303. GREG VAUGHN
☐ 307. DARRYL HAMILTON
☐ 330. B.J. SURHOFF
☐ 336. JODY REED
☐ 339. DAVE NILSSON
☐ 347. CAL ELDRED
☐ 355. KEVIN SEITZER
☐ 380. MARK KIEFER

MINNESOTA TWINS

☐ 17. KIRBY PUCKETT
☐ 29. CHUCK KNOBLAUCH
☐ 84. DAVE WINFIELD
☐ 122. PAT MEARES
☐ 144. KEVIN TAPANI
☐ 154. DAVID MCCARTY
☐ 160. RICK AGUILERA
☐ 162. CHIP HALE
☐ 171. SCOTT ERICKSON
☐ 203. MATT WALBECK
☐ 261. KENT HRBEK
☐ 274. SHANE MACK
☐ 301. PEDRO MUNOZ
☐ 379. DENNY HOCKING
☐ 390. RICH BECKER
☐ 410. CARLOS PULIDO

MONTREAL EXPOS

☐ 18. LARRY WALKER
☐ 69. JOHN WETTELAND
☐ 81. WIL CORDERO
☐ 88. MIKE LANSING
☐ 124. JEFF FASSERO
☐ 159. MOISES ALOU
☐ 168. DARRIN FLETCHER
☐ 172. KIRK RUETER
☐ 185. CLIFF FLOYD
☐ 201. RONDELL WHITE
☐ 242. MARQUIS GRISSOM
☐ 263. LOU FRAZIER
☐ 332. PEDRO MARTINEZ
☐ 371. KEN HILL
☐ 373. SEAN BERRY

NEW YORK METS

☐ 46. RYAN THOMPSON
☐ 54. DOC GOODEN
☐ 73. TODD HUNDLEY
☐ 85. JEFF KENT
☐ 94. JOE ORSULAK
☐ 101. BRET SABERHAGEN
☐ 104. TIM BOGAR
☐ 167. BOBBY JONES

☐ 195. KELLY STINNETT
☐ 238. BOBBY BONILLA
☐ 275. JOSE VIZCAINO
☐ 282. JEROMY BURNITZ
☐ 293. KEVIN MCREYNOLDS
☐ 318. PETE SMITH
☐ 322. DAVID SEGUI
☐ 384. FERNANDO VINA

NEW YORK YANKEES

☐ 8. PAUL O'NEILL
☐ 23. DON MATTINGLY
☐ 43. JIMMY KEY
☐ 53. MIKE GALLEGO
☐ 78. JIM ABBOTT
☐ 100. MIKE STANLEY
☐ 140. BERNIE WILLIAMS
☐ 142. PAT KELLY
☐ 156. WADE BOGGS
☐ 251. LUIS POLONIA
☐ 255. TERRY MULHOLLAND
☐ 306. DANNY TARTABULL
☐ 350. JIM LEYRITZ
☐ 397. STERLING HITCHCOCK
☐ 402. GERALD WILLIAMS

OAKLAND A'S

☐ 45. RUBEN SIERRA
☐ 57. MARK MCGWIRE
☐ 68. TROY NEEL
☐ 86. TODD VAN POPPEL
☐ 115. STAN JAVIER
☐ 126. BOB WELCH
☐ 128. BOBBY WITT
☐ 176. MIKE BORDICK
☐ 179. STEVE KARSAY
☐ 245. DENNIS ECKERSLEY
☐ 254. RICKEY HENDERSON
☐ 257. TERRY STEINBACH
☐ 281. BRENT GATES
☐ 374. GERONIMO BERROA
☐ 391. BILLY TAYLOR
☐ 413. MARK ACRE

PHILADELPHIA PHILLIES

☐ 9. DARREN DAULTON
☐ 24. JOHN KRUK
☐ 28. DAVE HOLLINS
☐ 52. KEVIN STOCKER
☐ 67. WES CHAMBERLAIN
☐ 89. LENNY DYKSTRA
☐ 95. RICKY JORDAN
☐ 155. TOMMY GREENE
☐ 161. CURT SCHILLING
☐ 213. JIM EISENREICH
☐ 271. MARIANO DUNCAN
☐ 280. PETE INCAVIGLIA
☐ 382. TONY LONGMIRE
☐ 409. JEFF JUDEN

PITTSBURGH PIRATES

☐ 5. JAY BELL
☐ 50. AL MARTIN
☐ 56. JEFF KING
☐ 65. DON SLAUGHT
☐ 91. BRIAN HUNTER
☐ 119. CARLOS GARCIA
☐ 123. KEVIN YOUNG

- ☐ 129. ANDY VAN SLYKE
- ☐ 130. STEVE COOKE
- ☐ 361. ORLANDO MERCED
- ☐ 378. DAN MICELI

ST. LOUIS CARDINALS

- ☐ 20. BERNARD GILKEY
- ☐ 30. OZZIE SMITH
- ☐ 62. BRIAN JORDAN
- ☐ 83. BOB TEWKSBURY
- ☐ 98. TOM PAGNOZZI
- ☐ 108. MIKE PEREZ
- ☐ 148. GERONIMO PENA
- ☐ 152. RAY LANKFORD
- ☐ 164. MARK WHITEN
- ☐ 232. GREGG JEFFERIES
- ☐ 244. TODD ZEILE
- ☐ 300. RENE AROCHA
- ☐ 376. ALLEN WATSON

SAN DIEGO PADRES

- ☐ 77. TONY GWYNN
- ☐ 106. BRAD AUSMUS
- ☐ 120. PHIL PLANTIER
- ☐ 125. GENE HARRIS
- ☐ 138. ARCHI CIANFROCCO
- ☐ 146. DEREK BELL
- ☐ 153. PHIL CLARK
- ☐ 175. RICKY GUTIERREZ
- ☐ 200. DAVE STATON
- ☐ 218. BIP ROBERTS
- ☐ 363. ANDY BENES
- ☐ 395. KEITH LOCKHART
- ☐ 403. JOEY HAMILTON
- ☐ 415. MELVIN NIEVES
- ☐ 416. TIM HYERS

SAN FRANCISCO GIANTS

- ☐ 182. SALOMON TORRES
- ☐ 189. JOHN PATTERSON
- ☐ 211. BARRY BONDS
- ☐ 221. WILLIE MCGEE
- ☐ 240. ROBBY THOMPSON
- ☐ 252. BILL SWIFT
- ☐ 269. MATT WILLIAMS
- ☐ 278. ROYCE CLAYTON
- ☐ 304. DARREN LEWIS
- ☐ 316. MARK PORTUGAL
- ☐ 328. ROD BECK
- ☐ 341. JOHN BURKETT
- ☐ 365. TODD BENZINGER
- ☐ 370. KIRT MANWARING
- ☐ 396. J.R. PHILLIPS
- ☐ 401. RIKKERT FANEYTE

SEATTLE MARINERS

- ☐ 1. KEN GRIFFEY, JR
- ☐ 19. RANDY JOHNSON
- ☐ 66. MIKE BLOWERS
- ☐ 72. EDGAR MARTINEZ
- ☐ 79. JAY BUHNER
- ☐ 114. RICH AMARAL
- ☐ 163. TINO MARTINEZ
- ☐ 173. DAVE FLEMING
- ☐ 202. KEITH MITCHELL
- ☐ 286. ERIC ANTHONY
- ☐ 292. REGGIE JEFFERSON
- ☐ 294. GREG HIBBARD
- ☐ 324. FELIX FERMIN
- ☐ 343. DAN WILSON
- ☐ 377. MARC NEWFIELD
- ☐ 388. ROGER SALKELD
- ☐ 414. GREG PIRKL

TEXAS RANGERS

- ☐ 199. JAMES HURST
- ☐ 212. JUAN GONZALEZ
- ☐ 214. IVAN RODRIGUEZ
- ☐ 223. DEAN PALMER
- ☐ 237. TOM HENKE
- ☐ 260. DOUG STRANGE
- ☐ 267. KEVIN BROWN
- ☐ 276. JOSE CANSECO
- ☐ 297. KENNY ROGERS
- ☐ 302. DAVID HULSE
- ☐ 319. WILL CLARK
- ☐ 333. ROGER PAVLIK
- ☐ 364. MANUEL LEE

TORONTO BLUE JAYS

- ☐ 3. PAUL MOLITOR
- ☐ 12. JOE CARTER
- ☐ 21. DEVON WHITE
- ☐ 48. PAT HENTGEN
- ☐ 74. PAT BORDERS
- ☐ 135. ED SPRAGUE
- ☐ 165. DAVE STEWART
- ☐ 178. ALEX GONZALEZ
- ☐ 193. CARLOS DELGADO
- ☐ 229. ROBERTO ALOMAR
- ☐ 239. JOHN OLERUD
- ☐ 253. JUAN GUZMAN
- ☐ 375. DUANE WARD
- ☐ 412. ROB BUTLER

1951 TOPPS TEAM CARDS DATED (9) 2 1/16" X 5 1/4"

- ☐ BOSTON RED SOX
- ☐ BROOKLYN DODGERS
- ☐ CHICAGO WHITE SOX
- ☐ CINCINNATI REDS
- ☐ NEW YORK GIANTS
- ☐ PHILADELPHIA ATHLETICS
- ☐ PHILADELPHIA PHILLIES
- ☐ ST. LOUIS CARDINALS
- ☐ WASHINGTON SENATORS

1951 TOPPS TEAM CARDS UNDATED (9) 2 1/16" X 5 1/4"

- ☐ BOSTON RED SOX
- ☐ BROOKLYN DODGERS
- ☐ CHICAGO WHITE SOX
- ☐ CINCINNATI REDS
- ☐ NEW YORK GIANTS
- ☐ PHILADELPHIA ATHLETICS
- ☐ PHILADELPHIA PHILLIES
- ☐ ST. LOUIS CARDINALS
- ☐ WASHINGTON SENATORS

1951 TOPPS RED BACKS (52) 2" X 2 5/8"

BOSTON BRAVES

- ☐ 2. SID GORDON
- ☐ 30. WARREN SPAHN
- ☐ 52. TOMMY HOLMES

BOSTON RED SOX

- ☐ 4. VERN STEPHENS
- ☐ 10. MEL PARNELL
- ☐ 20. DOM DIMAGGIO
- ☐ 42. RAY SCARBOROUGH
- ☐ 43. MICKEY MCDERMOTT
- ☐ 46. BILLY GOODMAN

BROOKLYN DODGERS

- ☐ 11. GENE HERMANSKI
- ☐ 16. PREACHER ROE
- ☐ 31. GIL HODGES
- ☐ 38. DUKE SNIDER

CHICAGO CUBS

- ☐ 14. WAYNE TERWILLIGER

CHICAGO WHITE SOX

- ☐ 36. GUS ZERNIAL
- ☐ 49. AL ZARILLA
- ☐ 51. EDDIE ROBINSON

CINCINNATI REDS

- ☐ 34. GRADY HATTON
- ☐ 39. TED KLUSZEWSKI

CLEVELAND INDIANS

- ☐ 8. EARLY WYNN
- ☐ 12. JIM HEGAN
- ☐ 13. DALE MITCHELL
- ☐ 22. BOB FELLER
- ☐ 23. RAY BOONE
- ☐ 26. LUKE EASTER
- ☐ 29. BOB KENNEDY
- ☐ 35. AL ROSEN
- ☐ 40. MIKE GARCIA

DETROIT TIGERS

NO CARDS ISSUED

NEW YORK GIANTS

- ☐ 21. LARRY JANSEN
- ☐ 32. HENRY THOMPSON
- ☐ 37. WES WESTRUM
- ☐ 41. WHITEY LOCKMAN
- ☐ 48. EDDIE STANKY
- ☐ 50. MONTE IRVIN

NEW YORK YANKEES

- ☐ 1. YOGI BERRA
- ☐ 5. PHIL RIZZUTO
- ☐ 6. ALLIE REYNOLDS
- ☐ 18. GERRY COLEMAN
- ☐ 24. HANK BAUER

PHILADELPHIA ATHLETICS

- ☐ 3. FERRIS FAIN
- ☐ 28. ELMER VALO
- ☐ 36. GUS ZERNIAL

PHILADELPHIA PHILLIES

- ☐ 45. ANDY SEMINICK

PITTSBURGH PIRATES

- ☐ 15. RALPH KINER
- ☐ 17. GUS BELL
- ☐ 25. CLIFF CHAMBERS
- ☐ 27. WALLY WESTLAKE
- ☐ 33. BILL WERLE

ST. LOUIS BROWNS

- ☐ 9. ROY SIEVERS
- ☐ 19. DICK KOKOS

ST. LOUIS CARDINALS

- ☐ 7. HOWIE POLLET
- ☐ 47. TOMMY GLAVIANO

WASHINGTON SENATORS

- ☐ 44. SID HUDSON

1951 TOPPS BLUE BACKS (52) 2" X 2 5/8"

BOSTON BRAVES

- ☐ 9. JOHNNY SAIN
- ☐ 12. SAM JETHROE
- ☐ 32. BOB ELLIOTT
- ☐ 34. EARL TORGESON

BOSTON RED SOX

- ☐ 5. JOHNNY PESKY
- ☐ 37. BOBBY DOERR

BROOKLYN DODGERS

- ☐ 20. RALPH BRANCA
- ☐ 42. BRUCE EDWARDS
- ☐ 48. BILLY COX

CHICAGO CUBS

- ☐ 17. ROY SMALLEY
- ☐ 27. ANDY PAFKO
- ☐ 41. JOHNNY SCHMITZ
- ☐ 49. HANK SAUER

CHICAGO WHITE SOX

- ☐ 2. HANK MAJESKI
- ☐ 19. PHIL MASI
- ☐ 26. CHICO CARRASQUEL
- ☐ 45. BILLY PIERCE

CINCINNATI REDS

- ☐ 44. JOHNNY WYROSTEK
- ☐ 47. HERM WEHMEIER

CLEVELAND INDIANS

- ☐ 31. LOU BRISSIE
- ☐ 52. SAM CHAPMAN

DETROIT TIGERS

- ☐ 11. JOHNNY GROTH
- ☐ 23. DIZZY TROUT
- ☐ 40. VIC WERTZ
- ☐ 46. GERRY PRIDDY

NEW YORK GIANTS

NO CARDS ISSUED

NEW YORK YANKEES

- ☐ 10. JOE PAGE
- ☐ 35. TOMMY BYRNE
- ☐ 39. ED LOPAT
- ☐ 50. JOHNNY MIZE

PHILADELPHIA ATHLETICS

- ☐ 15. EDDIE JOOST

PHILADELPHIA PHILLIES

- ☐ 3. RICHIE ASHBURN
- ☐ 4. DEL ENNIS
- ☐ 8. DICK SISLER
- ☐ 29. GRANNY HAMNER
- ☐ 43. WILLIE JONES
- ☐ 51. EDDIE WAITKUS

PITTSBURGH PIRATES

- ☐ 16. MURRY DICKSON

ST. LOUIS BROWNS

- ☐ 18. NED GARVER
- ☐ 24. SHERMAN LOLLAR
- ☐ 33. DON LENHARDT
- ☐ 36. CLIFF FANNIN

ST. LOUIS CARDINALS

- ☐ 6. RED SCHOENDIENST
- ☐ 7. GERRY STALEY
- ☐ 14. GEORGE MUNGER
- ☐ 21. BILLY JOHNSON
- ☐ 28. HARRY BRECHEEN
- ☐ 30. ENOS SLAUGHTER

WASHINGTON SENATORS

- ☐ 1. EDDIE YOST
- ☐ 13. MICKEY VERNON
- ☐ 22. BOB KUZAVA
- ☐ 25. SAM MELE
- ☐ 38. IRV NOREN

1952 TOPPS (407) 2 5/8" X 3 3/4"

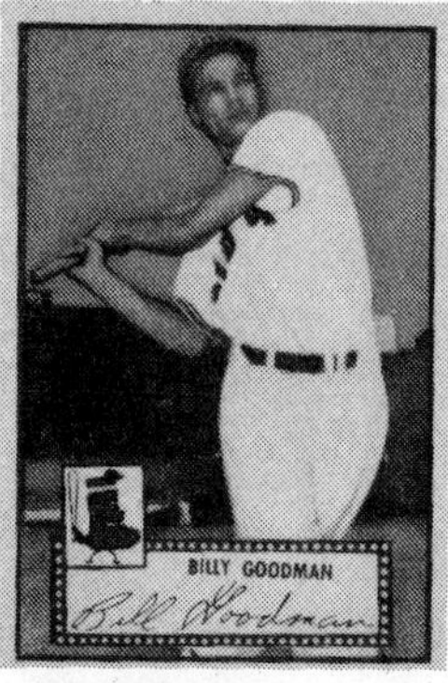

BOSTON BRAVES

- ☐ 14. BOB ELLIOTT
- ☐ 27. SAM JETHROE
- ☐ 33. WARREN SPAHN
- ☐ 96. WILLARD MARSHALL
- ☐ 97. EARL TORGESON
- ☐ 140. JOHN ANTONELLI
- ☐ 162. DEL CRANDALL
- ☐ 252. VERN BICKFORD
- ☐ 264. ROY HARTSFIELD
- ☐ 267. SID GORDON
- ☐ 276. JIM WILSON
- ☐ 288. CHET NICHOLS
- ☐ 289. TOMMY HOLMES(M)
- ☐ 293. SIBBY SISTI
- ☐ 294. WALKER COOPER
- ☐ 302. MAX SURKONT
- ☐ 360. GEORGE CROWE
- ☐ 367. BOB THORPE
- ☐ 388. BOB CHIPMAN
- ☐ 393. EBBA ST. CLAIRE
- ☐ 407. ED MATHEWS

BOSTON RED SOX

- ☐ 4. DON LENHARDT
- ☐ 15. JOHNNY PESKY
- ☐ 22. DOM DIMAGGIO
- ☐ 23. BILLY GOODMAN
- ☐ 30. MEL PARNELL
- ☐ 43. RAY SCARBOROUGH
- ☐ 54. LEO KIELY
- ☐ 72. KARL OLSON
- ☐ 78. ELLIS KINDER
- ☐ 84. VERN STEPHENS
- ☐ 119. MICKEY MCDERMOTT
- ☐ 121. GUS NIARHOS
- ☐ 139. KEN WOOD
- ☐ 152. AL EVANS

☐ 177. BILL WIGHT
☐ 180. CHARLEY MAXWELL
☐ 186. WALT MASTERSON
☐ 235. WALT DROPO
☐ 247. RANDY GUMPERT
☐ 255. CLYDE VOLLMER
☐ 269. WILLARD NIXON
☐ 327. ARCHIE WILSON
☐ 329. IVAN DELOCK
☐ 335. TED LEPCIO
☐ 343. DICK GERNERT
☐ 345. SAM WHITE
☐ 374. AL BENTON
☐ 376. FAYE THRONEBERRY
☐ 383. DEL WILBER
☐ 404. DICK BRODOWSKI

BROOKLYN DODGERS

☐ 1. ANDY PAFKO
☐ 7. WAYNE TERWILLIGER
☐ 20. BILLY LOES
☐ 36. GIL HODGES
☐ 37. DUKE SNIDER
☐ 51. JIM RUSSEL
☐ 53. CHRIS VAN CUYK
☐ 66. PREACHER ROE
☐ 136. JOHNNY SCHMITZ
☐ 188. CLARENCE PODBIELAN
☐ 198. PHIL HAUGSTAD
☐ 205. CLYDE KING
☐ 232. BILLY COX
☐ 239. ROCKY BRIDGES
☐ 250. CARL ERSKINE
☐ 273. ERV PALICA
☐ 274. RALPH BRANCA
☐ 312. JACKIE ROBINSON
☐ 314. ROY CAMPANELLA
☐ 319. RUBE WALKER
☐ 320. JOHN RUTHERFORD
☐ 321. JOE BLACK
☐ 326. GEORGE SHUBA
☐ 333. PEE WEE REESE
☐ 342. CLEM LABINE
☐ 355. BOBBY MORGAN
☐ 365. COOKIE LAVAGETTO(C)
☐ 377. CHUCK DRESSEN(M)
☐ 389. BEN WADE
☐ 390. ROCKY NELSON
☐ 394. BILLY HERMAN(C)
☐ 395. JAKE PITLER(C)
☐ 396. DICK WILLIAMS

CHICAGO CUBS

☐ 16. GENE HERMANSKI
☐ 35. HANK SAUER
☐ 105. JOHN PRAMESA
☐ 110. DUTCH LEONARD
☐ 114. WILLARD RAMSDELL
☐ 127. PAUL MINNER
☐ 148. JOHNNY KLIPPSTEIN
☐ 153. BOB RUSH
☐ 157. BOB USHER
☐ 164. WALT DUBIEL
☐ 172. EDDIE MIKSIS
☐ 173. ROY SMALLEY
☐ 184. BOB RAMAZZOTTI
☐ 194. JOE HATTEN
☐ 204. RON NORTHEY
☐ 224. BRUCE EDWARDS
☐ 225. FRANK BAUMHOLTZ
☐ 259. BOB ADDIS
☐ 295. PHIL CAVARRETTA(M)
☐ 322. RANDY JACKSON
☐ 324. WARREN HACKER
☐ 325. BILL SERENA
☐ 330. TURK LOWN
☐ 341. HAL JEFFCOAT
☐ 348. BOB KELLY
☐ 356. TOBY ATWELL
☐ 359. DEE FONDY
☐ 401. BOB SCHULTZ

CHICAGO WHITE SOX

☐ 32. EDDIE ROBINSON
☐ 42. LOU KRETLOW
☐ 50. MARV RICKERT
☐ 62. CHUCK STOBBS
☐ 70. AL ZARILLA
☐ 95. KEN HOLCOMBE
☐ 98. BILL PIERCE
☐ 102. BILL KENNEDY(B)
☐ 117. SHERMAN LOLLAR
☐ 133. AL WIDMAR
☐ 159. SAUL ROGOVIN
☐ 169. HOWIE JUDSON
☐ 195. MINNIE MINOSO
☐ 211. RAY COLEMAN
☐ 251. CHICO CARRASQUEL

☐ 254. JOE DOBSON
☐ 279. ED STEWART
☐ 283. PHIL MASI
☐ 303. HARRY DORISH
☐ 304. SAM DENTE
☐ 305. PAUL RICHARDS(M)
☐ 308. LUIS ALOMA

CINCINNATI REDS

☐ 6. GRADY HATTON
☐ 13. JOHNNY WYROSTEK
☐ 29. TED KLUSZEWSKI
☐ 69. VIRGIL STALLCUP
☐ 80. HERM WEHMEIER
☐ 113. DICK SISLER
☐ 118. KEN RAFFENSBERGER
☐ 135. DIXIE HOWELL
☐ 137. ROY MCMILLAN
☐ 142. HARRY PERKOWSKI
☐ 144. ED BLAKE
☐ 151. WALLY POST
☐ 156. FRANK HILLER
☐ 161. BUD BYERLY
☐ 171. ED ERAUTT
☐ 176. HANK EDWARDS
☐ 179. FRANK SMITH
☐ 249. BOBBY ADAMS
☐ 297. ANDY SEMINICK
☐ 323. BUBBA CHURCH
☐ 328. BOB BORKOWSKI
☐ 344. EWELL BLACKWELL
☐ 347. JOE ADCOCK
☐ 350. CAL ABRAMS
☐ 379. JOE ROSSI
☐ 391. BEN CHAPMAN(C)
☐ 405. ED PELLAGRINI
☐ 406. JOE NUXHALL

CLEVELAND INDIANS

☐ 10. AL ROSEN
☐ 17. JIM HEGAN
☐ 18. MERRILL COMBS
☐ 24. LUKE EASTER
☐ 55. RAY BOONE
☐ 77. BOB KENNEDY
☐ 88. BOB FELLER
☐ 92. DALE MITCHELL
☐ 120. BOB CHAKALES
☐ 189. PETE REISER
☐ 193. HARRY SIMPSON
☐ 199. GEORGE ZUVERINK
☐ 207. MICKEY HARRIS
☐ 217. GEORGE STIRNWEISS
☐ 243. LARRY DOBY
☐ 253. JOHN BERARDINO
☐ 257. BOBBY AVILA
☐ 258. STEVE GROMEK
☐ 268. BOB LEMON
☐ 270. LOU BRISSIE
☐ 272. MIKE GARCIA
☐ 277. EARLY WYNN
☐ 282. BIRDIE TEBBETTS
☐ 300. BARNEY MCCOSKY
☐ 363. DICK ROZEK
☐ 382. SAM JONES
☐ 399. JIM FRIDLEY

DETROIT TIGERS

☐ 25. JOHN GROTH
☐ 28. JERRY PRIDDY
☐ 39. DIZZY TROUT
☐ 86. TED GRAY
☐ 89. JOHNNY LIPON
☐ 103. CLIFF MAPES
☐ 104. DON KOLLOWAY
☐ 126. FRED HUTCHINSON
☐ 146. FRANK HOUSE
☐ 181. BOB SWIFT
☐ 192. MYRON GINSBERG
☐ 208. MARLIN STUART
☐ 222. HOOT EVERS
☐ 230. MATT BATTS
☐ 234. STEVE SOUCHOCK
☐ 238. ART HOUTTEMAN
☐ 244. VIC WERTZ
☐ 246. GEORGE KELL
☐ 262. VIRGIL TRUCKS
☐ 275. PAT MULLIN
☐ 296. RED ROLFE(M)
☐ 354. FRED HATFIELD
☐ 370. BILLY HOEFT

NEW YORK GIANTS

☐ 3. HANK THOMPSON
☐ 5. LARRY JANSEN
☐ 26. MONTY IRVIN
☐ 52. DON MUELLER
☐ 61. TOOKIE GILBERT
☐ 75. WES WESTRUM
☐ 101. MAX LANIER
☐ 124. MONTE KENNEDY
☐ 125. BILL RIGNEY
☐ 130. SHELDON JONES
☐ 141. CLINT HARTUNG
☐ 261. WILLIE MAYS
☐ 265. CHUCK DIERING
☐ 313. BOBBY THOMSON
☐ 315. LEO DUROCHER(M)
☐ 316. DAVEY WILLIAMS
☐ 318. HAL GREGG
☐ 336. DAVE KOSLO
☐ 337. JIM HEARN
☐ 338. SAL YVARS
☐ 346. GEORGE SPENCER
☐ 351. AL DARK
☐ 371. BOB HOFMAN
☐ 385. HERMAN FRANKS(C)
☐ 392. HOYT WILHELM

NEW YORK YANKEES

☐ 9. BOB HOGUE
☐ 11. PHIL RIZZUTO
☐ 48. JOE PAGE
☐ 49. JOHNNY SAIN
☐ 57. ED LOPAT
☐ 67. ALLIE REYNOLDS
☐ 85. BOB KUZAVA
☐ 99. GENE WOODLING
☐ 122. JACK JENSEN
☐ 128. DON BOLLWEG
☐ 129. JOHNNY MIZE
☐ 155. FRANK OVERMIRE
☐ 168. CHARLIE SILVERA
☐ 175. BILLY MARTIN
☐ 191. YOGI BERRA
☐ 200. RALPH HOUK
☐ 202. JOE COLLINS
☐ 206. JOE OSTROWSKI
☐ 214. JOHNNY HOPP
☐ 215. HANK BAUER
☐ 237. JERRY COLEMAN
☐ 248. FRANK SHEA(F)
☐ 311. MICKEY MANTLE
☐ 331. TOM MORGAN
☐ 372. GIL MCDOUGALD
☐ 373. JIM TURNER(C)
☐ 384. FRANK CROSETTI(C)
☐ 400. BILL DICKEY(C)
☐ 403. BILL MILLER

PHILADELPHIA ATHLETICS

☐ 21. FERRIS FAIN
☐ 31. GUS ZERNIAL
☐ 34. ELMER VALO
☐ 41. BOB WELLMAN
☐ 45. EDDIE JOOST
☐ 112. HENRY MAJESKI
☐ 116. CARL SCHEIB
☐ 131. MORRIE MARTIN
☐ 134. JOE TIPTON
☐ 182. BILLY HITCHCOCK
☐ 201. ALEX KELLNER
☐ 210. DICK FOWLER
☐ 219. BOBBY SHANTZ
☐ 226. DAVE PHILLEY
☐ 231. SAM ZOLDAK
☐ 256. PETE SUDER
☐ 278. AL CLARK
☐ 290. JOE ASTROTH
☐ 299. RAY MURRAY
☐ 340. BOB HOOPER
☐ 358. JOHN KUCAB
☐ 368. ED WRIGHT

PHILADELPHIA PHILLIES

□ 44. CON DEMPSEY
□ 47. WILLIE JONES
□ 59. ROBIN ROBERTS
□ 74. ANDY HANSEN
□ 107. CONNIE RYAN
□ 108. JIM KONSTANTY
□ 158. EDDIE WAITKUS
□ 185. BILL NICHOLSON
□ 187. BOB J. MILLER
□ 203. CURT SIMMONS
□ 209. HOWIE FOX
□ 213. NIPPY JONES
□ 216. RICHIE ASHBURN
□ 221. GRANNY HAMNER
□ 223. DEL ENNIS
□ 281. TOMMY BROWN
□ 339. RUSS MEYER
□ 352. KARL DREWS
□ 357. SMOKY BURGESS
□ 362. KEN HEINTZELMAN

PITTSBURGH PIRATES

□ 12. MONTY BASGALL
□ 63. HOWIE POLLET
□ 73. BILL WERLE
□ 81. VERNON LAW
□ 87. DALE COOGAN
□ 109. TED WILKS
□ 138. BILL MACDONALD
□ 150. TED BEARD
□ 154. JOE MUIR
□ 166. PAUL LEPALME
□ 167. BILL HOWERTON
□ 170. GUS BELL
□ 183. ERV DUSAK
□ 197. GEORGE STRICKLAND
□ 218. CLYDE MCCULLOUGH
□ 227. JOE GARAGIOLA
□ 233. BOB FRIEND
□ 236. ED FITZ GERALD
□ 240. JACK PHILLIPS
□ 260. PETE CASTIGLIONE
□ 266. MURRY DICKSON
□ 310. GEORGE METKOVICH
□ 332. TONY BARTIROME
□ 353. BOBBY DEL GRECO
□ 361. BILL POSEDEL(C)
□ 364. CLYDE SUKEFORTH(C)
□ 369. DICK GROAT
□ 375. JACK MERSON
□ 380. CLEM KOSHOREK
□ 381. MILT STOCK(C)
□ 387. BILLY MEYER(M)
□ 397. FORREST MAIN

ST. LOUIS BROWNS

□ 8. FRED MARSH
□ 46. GORDON GOLDSBERRY
□ 58. BOB MAHONEY
□ 64. ROY SIEVERS
□ 82. DUANE PILLETTE
□ 102. BILLY KENNEDY(F)
□ 143. LES MOSS
□ 147. BOB YOUNG
□ 149. DICK KRYHOSKI
□ 160. OWEN FRIEND
□ 163. STAN ROJEK
□ 174. CLARENCE MARSHALL
□ 212. NED GARVER
□ 229. GENE BEARDEN
□ 241. TOMMY BYRNE
□ 271. JIM DELSING
□ 284. HANK ARFT
□ 285. CLIFF FANNIN
□ 286. JOE DEMAESTRI
□ 349. BOB CAIN
□ 366. DAVE MADISON
□ 402. EARL HARRIST

ST. LOUIS CARDINALS

□ 19. JOHNNY BUCHA
□ 38. WALLY WESTLAKE
□ 56. TOMMY GLAVIANO
□ 65. ENOS SLAUGHTER
□ 68. CLIFF CHAMBERS
□ 76. EDDIE STANKY
□ 79. GERRY STALEY
□ 83. BILLY JOHNSON
□ 91. RED SCHOENDIENST
□ 100. DEL RICE
□ 111. HARRY LOWREY
□ 115. GEORGE MUNGER
□ 165. EDDIE KAZAK
□ 196. SOLLY HEMUS
□ 220. JOE PRESKO
□ 228. AL BRAZLE
□ 242. TOM POHOLSKY
□ 263. HARRY BRECHEEN
□ 280. CLOYD BOYER
□ 287. STEVE BILKO
□ 334. WILMER MIZELL
□ 378. LES FUSSELMAN
□ 386. EDDIE YUHAS
□ 398. HAL RICE

WASHINGTON SENATORS

□ 2. PETE RUNNELS
□ 40. IRV NOREN
□ 60. SID HUDSON
□ 71. TOM UPTON
□ 90. MICKEY GRASSO
□ 93. AL SIMA
□ 94. SAM MELE
□ 106. MICKEY VERNON
□ 123. EDDIE YOST
□ 132. CLYDE KLUTTZ
□ 145. JOE HAYNES
□ 178. CASS MICHAELS
□ 190. DON JOHNSON
□ 245. SHERRY ROBERTSON
□ 248. FRANK SHEA(B)
□ 291. GIL COAN
□ 292. FLOYD BAKER
□ 298. BOB ROSS
□ 301. BOB PORTERFIELD
□ 306. LOU SLEATER
□ 307. FRANK CAMPOS
□ 309. JIM BUSBY
□ 317. CONNIE MARRERO

1953 TOPPS (274)
2 5/8" X 3 3/4"

BOSTON RED SOX

□ 18. TED LEPCIO
□ 19. MEL PARNELL
□ 30. WILLARD NIXON
□ 32. CLYDE VOLLMER
□ 40. JOHN LIPON
□ 44. ELLIS KINDER
□ 49. FAYE THRONEBERRY
□ 55. MICKEY MCDERMOTT
□ 63. GUS NIARHOS
□ 69. DICK BRODOWSKI
□ 94. BILL KENNEDY
□ 138. GEORGE KELL
□ 139. SAMMY WHITE
□ 149. DOM DIMAGGIO
□ 169. DIZZY TROUT
□ 170. BILL WERLE
□ 181. AL ZARILLA
□ 184. HAL BROWN
□ 248. GENE STEPHENS
□ 251. SID HUDSON
□ 280. MILT BOLLING

BROOKLYN DODGERS

□ 1. JACKIE ROBINSON
□ 4. BEN WADE
□ 14. CLEM LABINE
□ 27. ROY CAMPANELLA
□ 34. GEORGE SHUBA
□ 50. CHUCK DRESSEN(M)
□ 76. PEE WEE REESE
□ 81. JOE BLACK
□ 85. BOBBY MORGAN
□ 125. DICK WILLIAMS
□ 134. RUBE WALKER
□ 137. JOHN RUTHERFORD
□ 174. BILLY LOES
□ 176. DON HOAK
□ 216. JIM HUGHES
□ 221. BOB MILLIKEN
□ 254. PREACHER ROE
□ 255. DIXIE HOWELL
□ 258. JIM GILLIAM
□ 263. JOHN PODRES
□ 272. BILL ANTONELLO

CHICAGO CUBS

□ 23. TOBY ATWELL
□ 29. HAL JEFFCOAT
□ 39. EDDIE MIKSIS
□ 46. JOHNNY KLIPPSTEIN
□ 92. PAUL MINNER
□ 111. HANK SAUER
□ 130. TURK LOWN
□ 144. BOB SCHULTZ
□ 155. DUTCH LEONARD
□ 157. BOB ADDIS
□ 173. PRESTON WARD
□ 179. GENE HERMANSKI
□ 202. CARL SAWATSKI

CHICAGO WHITE SOX

□ 5. JOE DOBSON
□ 53. SHERMAN LOLLAR
□ 66. MINNIE MINOSO
□ 73. EDDIE ROBINSON
□ 123. TOMMY BYRNE
□ 143. BILLY PIERCE
□ 156. JIM RIVERA
□ 196. BOB KEEGAN
□ 229. ROCKY KRSNICH
□ 240. FRED MARSH
□ 250. BOB WILSON
□ 257. BOB BOYD
□ 270. VERN STEPHENS

CINCINNATI REDS

□ 7. BOB BORKOWSKI
□ 12. HOWIE JUDSON
□ 28. EDDIE PELLAGRINI
□ 45. GRADY HATTON
□ 47. BUBBA CHURCH
□ 95. WILLARD MARSHALL
□ 105. JOE NUXHALL
□ 110. HERM WEHMEIER
□ 116. FRANK SMITH
□ 118. GUS BELL
□ 152. BOB ADAMS
□ 153. ANDY SEMINICK
□ 162. TED KLUSZEWSKI
□ 206. ED BAILEY
□ 209. JIM GREENGRASS
□ 226. ED ERAUTT
□ 236. HARRY PERKOWSKI
□ 237. BUD PODBIELAN
□ 252. HANK FOILES
□ 259. ROY MCMILLAN
□ 276. KEN RAFFENSBERGER

CLEVELAND INDIANS

□ 2. LUKE EASTER
□ 6. SAM JONES
□ 25. RAY BOONE
□ 26. DALE MITCHELL

☐ 33. BOB KENNEDY
☐ 54. BOB FELLER
☐ 61. EARLY WYNN
☐ 75. MIKE GARCIA
☐ 80. JIM HEGAN
☐ 84. BOB HOOPER
☐ 101. TED WILKS
☐ 135. AL ROSEN
☐ 150. HARRY SIMPSON
☐ 171. BILL GLYNN
☐ 187. JIM FRIDLEY
☐ 192. WALLY WESTLAKE
☐ 233. AL ABER

DETROIT TIGERS

☐ 52. TED GRAY
☐ 72. FRED HUTCHINSON(M)
☐ 99. DAVE MADISON
☐ 112. NED GARVER
☐ 113. JERRY PRIDDY
☐ 121. WALT DROPO
☐ 163. FRED HATFIELD
☐ 165. BILLY HOEFT
☐ 194. EDDIE KAZAK
☐ 211. J. W. PORTER
☐ 228. HAL NEWHOUSER
☐ 239. JIM DELSING
☐ 277. DON LUND

MILWAUKEE BRAVES

☐ 3. GEORGE CROWE*
☐ 37. ED MATHEWS*
☐ 91. EBBA ST. CLAIRE*
☐ 106. JOHNNY ANTONELLI*
☐ 117. SID GORDON*
☐ 124. SIBBY SISTI*
☐ 147. WARREN SPAHN*
☐ 158. JOHN LOGAN*
☐ 161. VERN BICKFORD*
☐ 185. JIM PENDLETON
☐ 197. DEL CRANDALL
☐ 208. JIM WILSON
☐ 212. JACK DITTMER
☐ 214. BILL BRUTON
☐ 215. GENE CONLEY
☐ 217. MURRAY WALL

NEW YORK GIANTS

☐ 11. SAL YVARS
☐ 20. HANK THOMPSON
☐ 38. JIM HEARN
☐ 62. MONTE IRVIN
☐ 109. AL DARK
☐ 115. GEORGE SPENCER
☐ 120. DAVEY WILLIAMS
☐ 126. BILL CONNELLY
☐ 151. HOYT WILHELM
☐ 182. BOBBY HOFMAN
☐ 244. WILLIE MAYS
☐ 260. SAM CALDERONE

NEW YORK YANKEES

☐ 9. JOE COLLINS
☐ 31. EWELL BLACKWELL
☐ 35. IRV NOREN
☐ 43. GIL MCDOUGALD
☐ 77. JOHNNY MIZE
☐ 82. MICKEY MANTLE
☐ 86. BILLY MARTIN
☐ 87. ED LOPAT
☐ 100. BILL MILLER
☐ 104. YOGI BERRA
☐ 114. PHIL RIZZUTO
☐ 119. JOHNNY SAIN
☐ 132. TOM MORGAN
☐ 141. ALLIE REYNOLDS
☐ 167. ART SCHULT
☐ 188. ANDY CAREY
☐ 207. WHITEY FORD
☐ 210. BOB CERV
☐ 213. RAY SCARBOROUGH
☐ 242. CHARLIE SILVERA
☐ 264. GENE WOODLING

PHILADELPHIA ATHLETICS

☐ 15. BOBO NEWSOM
☐ 17. BILLY HITCHCOCK
☐ 24. FERRIS FAIN
☐ 42. GUS ZERNIAL
☐ 57. CARL SCHEIB
☐ 64. DAVE PHILLEY
☐ 97. DON KOLLOWAY
☐ 103. JOE ASTROTH
☐ 122. ELMER VALO
☐ 129. KEITH THOMAS
☐ 131. HARRY BYRD
☐ 186. CHARLIE BISHOP
☐ 195. ED MCGHEE
☐ 199. MARION FRICANO
☐ 225. BOBBY SHANTZ
☐ 227. MORRIS MARTIN
☐ 234. RAY MURRAY
☐ 279. JOE COLEMAN

PHILADELPHIA PHILLIES

☐ 10. SMOKY BURGESS
☐ 22. HOWIE FOX
☐ 59. KARL DREWS
☐ 79. JOHNNY WYROSTEK
☐ 88. WILLIE JONES
☐ 102. CONNIE RYAN
☐ 136. KEN HEINTZELMAN
☐ 140. TOMMY GLAVIANO
☐ 146. GRANNY HAMNER

PITTSBURGH PIRATES

☐ 8. CLEM KOSHOREK
☐ 48. BOB DEL GRECO
☐ 58. GEORGE METKOVICH
☐ 71. TONY BARTIROME
☐ 74. JOE ROSSI
☐ 83. HOWIE POLLET
☐ 98. CAL ABRAMS
☐ 107. DANNY O'CONNELL
☐ 154. DICK GROAT
☐ 175. RON KLINE
☐ 178. JIM WAUGH
☐ 191. RALPH KINER
☐ 198. FORREST MAIN
☐ 201. PAUL LA PALME
☐ 222. VIC JANOWICZ
☐ 223. JOHN O'BRIEN
☐ 230. JOHNNY LINDELL
☐ 235. JOHN HETKI
☐ 238. CAL HOGUE
☐ 243. CARLOS BERNIER
☐ 246. ROY FACE
☐ 247. MIKE SANDLOCK
☐ 249. ED O'BRIEN

ST. LOUIS BROWNS

☐ 36. JOHNNY GROTH
☐ 65. EARL HARRIST
☐ 67. ROY SIEVERS
☐ 90. HANK EDWARDS
☐ 96. VIRGIL TRUCKS
☐ 127. CLINT COURTNEY
☐ 142. VIC WERTZ
☐ 160. BOB YOUNG
☐ 166. BILL HUNTER
☐ 177. JIM DYCK
☐ 200. GORDON GOLDSBERRY
☐ 203. CLIFF FANNIN
☐ 220. SATCHEL PAIGE
☐ 232. DICK KOKOS
☐ 245. BILL NORMAN(C)
☐ 266. BOB CAIN
☐ 269. DUANE PILLETTE
☐ 278. WILLIE MIRANDA

ST. LOUIS CARDINALS

☐ 16. HARRY LOWREY
☐ 21. BILLY JOHNSON
☐ 41. ENOS SLAUGHTER
☐ 56. GERALD STALEY
☐ 60. CLOYD BOYER
☐ 68. DEL RICE
☐ 70. ED YUHAS
☐ 78. RED SCHOENDIENST
☐ 93. HAL RICE
☐ 128. WILMER MIZELL
☐ 168. WILLARD SCHMIDT
☐ 172. RIP REPULSKI
☐ 180. VIRGIL STALLCUP
☐ 183. STU MILLER
☐ 189. RAY JABLONSKI
☐ 190. DIXIE WALKER(C)
☐ 193. MIKE CLARK
☐ 204. DICK BOKELMANN
☐ 205. VERN BENSON
☐ 218. LES FUSSELMAN
☐ 231. SOLLY HEMUS
☐ 273. HARVEY HADDIX
☐ 274. JOHN RIDDLE(C)

WASHINGTON SENATORS

☐ 13. CONNIE MARRERO
☐ 51. FRANK CAMPOS
☐ 89. CHUCK STOBBS
☐ 108. BOB PORTERFIELD
☐ 133. GIL COAN
☐ 148. MICKEY GRASSO
☐ 159. WAYNE TERWILLIGER
☐ 164. FRANK SHEA
☐ 219. PETE RUNNELS
☐ 224. LOU SLEATER
☐ 241. AL SIMA
☐ 256. LES PEDEN
☐ 262. BOB OLDIS
☐ 265. JACKIE JENSEN

1954 TOPPS (250)
2 5/8" X 3 3/4"

BALTIMORE ORIOLES

☐ 8. BOB YOUNG
☐ 19. JOHNNY LIPON(F)
☐ 48. BILLY HUNTER
☐ 54. VERN STEPHENS
☐ 85. BOB TURLEY
☐ 106. DICK KOKOS
☐ 107. DUANE PILLETTE
☐ 150. DICK KRYHOSKI

* Nos. 3, 37, 91, 106, 117, 124, 147, 158 & 161 appear with Boston Braves on the front of the card.

- □ 152. MIKE BLYZKA
- □ 156. JOE COLEMAN
- □ 157. DON LENHARDT
- □ 203. HARRY BRECHEEN(C)
- □ 207. TOM OLIVER(C)
- □ 226. JEHOSIE HEARD
- □ 240. SAM MELE
- □ 246. HOWIE FOX

BOSTON RED SOX

- □ 1. TED WILLIAMS
- □ 40. MEL PARNELL
- □ 47. ELLIS KINDER
- □ 66. TED LEPCIO
- □ 80. JACKIE JENSEN
- □ 82. MILT BOLLING
- □ 93. SID HUDSON
- □ 133. DEL BAKER(C)
- □ 144. BILL WERLE
- □ 171. LEO KIELY
- □ 172. HAL BROWN
- □ 186. KARL OLSON
- □ 195. BILL CONSOLO
- □ 217. PAUL SCHREIBER(C)
- □ 221. DICK BRODOWSKI
- □ 227. BUSTER MILLS(C)
- □ 250. TED WILLIAMS

BROOKLYN DODGERS

- □ 10. JACKIE ROBINSON
- □ 14. PREACHER ROE
- □ 32. DUKE SNIDER
- □ 35. JIM GILLIAM
- □ 86. BILLY HERMAN(C)
- □ 98. JOE BLACK
- □ 102. GIL HODGES
- □ 121. CLEM LABINE
- □ 126. BEN WADE
- □ 132. TOM LASORDA
- □ 153. RUBE WALKER
- □ 166. JOHNNY PODRES
- □ 169. JIM HUGHES
- □ 177. BOB MILLIKEN
- □ 209. CHARLIE THOMPSON
- □ 211. DON HOAK

CHICAGO CUBS

- □ 4. HANK SAUER
- □ 28. PAUL MINNER
- □ 31. JOHNNY KLIPPSTEIN
- □ 55. PHIL CAVARRETTA(M)
- □ 60. FRANK BAUMHOLTZ
- □ 67. JIM WILLIS
- □ 76. BOB SCHEFFING(C)
- □ 89. HOWIE POLLET
- □ 94. ERNIE BANKS
- □ 229. BOB TALBOT
- □ 243. RAY BLADES(C)

CHICAGO WHITE SOX

- □ 19. JOHNNY LIPON(B)
- □ 27. FERRIS FAIN
- □ 34. JIM RIVERA
- □ 39. SHERM LOLLAR
- □ 57. LUIS ALOMA
- □ 58. BOB WILSON
- □ 100. BOB KEEGAN
- □ 110. HARRY DORISH
- □ 113. BOB BOYD
- □ 146. DON JOHNSON
- □ 154. MIKE FORNIELES
- □ 173. JACK HARSHMAN
- □ 198. CARL SAWATSKI
- □ 216. AL SIMA
- □ 218. FRED MARSH
- □ 222. BILL WILSON

CINCINNATI REDS

- □ 7. TED KLUSZEWSKI
- □ 22. JIM GREENGRASS
- □ 46. KEN RAFFENSBERGER
- □ 69. BUD PODBIELAN
- □ 71. FRANK SMITH
- □ 120. ROY MCMILLAN
- □ 123. BOBBY ADAMS
- □ 125. HARRY PERKOWSKI
- □ 136. CONNIE RYAN
- □ 138. BOB BORKOWSKI
- □ 162. HERMAN WEHMEIER
- □ 182. CHUCK HARMON
- □ 184. ED BAILEY
- □ 208. GRADY HATTON

CLEVELAND INDIANS

- □ 15. AL ROSEN
- □ 23. LUKE EASTER
- □ 29. JIM HEGAN
- □ 70. LARRY DOBY
- □ 81. DAVE HOSKINS
- □ 92. WALLY WESTLAKE
- □ 103. JIM LEMON
- □ 155. BOB KENNEDY
- □ 159. DAVE PHILLEY
- □ 160. RALPH KRESS(C)
- □ 178. BILL GLYNN
- □ 199. ROCKY NELSON
- □ 248. AL SMITH

DETROIT TIGERS

- □ 18. WALT DROPO
- □ 25. HARVEY KUENN
- □ 44. NED GARVER
- □ 63. JOHNNY PESKY
- □ 65. BOB SWIFT(C)
- □ 77. RAY BOONE
- □ 88. MATT BATTS
- □ 111. JIM DELSING
- □ 131. RENO BERTOIA
- □ 163. FRANK HOUSE
- □ 167. DON LUND
- □ 190. RAY HERBERT
- □ 193. JOHNNY HOPP(C)
- □ 197. SCHOOLBOY ROWE(C)
- □ 201. AL KALINE
- □ 219. CHUCK KRESS
- □ 224. DICK WEIK
- □ 238. AL ABER
- □ 241. BOB G. MILLER

MILWAUKEE BRAVES

- □ 12. DEL CRANDALL
- □ 20. WARREN SPAHN
- □ 30. ED MATHEWS
- □ 53. JACK DITTMER
- □ 59. GENE CONLEY
- □ 68. SAMMY CALDERONE
- □ 79. ANDY PAFKO
- □ 109. BILL BRUTON
- □ 122. JOHNNY LOGAN
- □ 128. HANK AARON
- □ 141. JOEY JAY
- □ 165. JIM PENDLETON
- □ 176. BOB KEELY(C)
- □ 181. MEL ROACH
- □ 188. DAVE JOLLY
- □ 206. RAY CRONE
- □ 210. BOB BUHL
- □ 231. ROY SMALLEY

NEW YORK GIANTS

- □ 3. MONTE IRVIN
- □ 36. HOYT WILHELM
- □ 42. DON MUELLER
- □ 64. HANK THOMPSON
- □ 74. BILL TAYLOR
- □ 90. WILLIE MAYS
- □ 99. BOB HOFMAN
- □ 119. JOHNNY ANTONELLI
- □ 170. DUSTY RHODES
- □ 180. WES WESTRUM
- □ 200. LARRY JANSEN
- □ 220. RUBEN GOMEZ
- □ 225. DON LIDDLE

NEW YORK YANKEES

- □ 5. ED LOPAT
- □ 13. BILLY MARTIN
- □ 17. PHIL RIZZUTO
- □ 37. WHITEY FORD
- □ 50. YOGI BERRA
- □ 56. WILLIE MIRANDA
- □ 62. EDDIE ROBINSON
- □ 83. JOE COLLINS
- □ 96. CHARLIE SILVERA
- □ 101. GENE WOODLING
- □ 105. ANDY CAREY
- □ 130. HANK BAUER
- □ 175. FRANK LEJA
- □ 205. JOHNNY SAIN
- □ 230. BOB KUZAVA
- □ 239. BILL SKOWRON

PHILADELPHIA ATHLETICS

- □ 2. GUS ZERNIAL
- □ 21. BOBBY SHANTZ
- □ 49. RAY MURRAY
- □ 52. VIC POWER
- □ 61. BOB CAIN
- □ 112. BILL RENNA
- □ 118. CARL SCHEIB
- □ 124. MARION FRICANO
- □ 129. FORREST JACOBS
- □ 143. ROLLIE HEMSLEY(C)
- □ 145. ELMER VALO
- □ 148. BOB TRICE
- □ 149. JIM ROBERTSON
- □ 168. MORRIE MARTIN
- □ 214. ARNOLD PORTOCARRERO
- □ 215. ED MCGHEE
- □ 232. LOU LIMMER
- □ 233. AUGIE GALAN(C)
- □ 244. LEROY WHEAT

PHILADELPHIA PHILLIES

- □ 24. GRANNY HAMNER
- □ 41. WILLIE JONES
- □ 45. RICHIE ASHBURN
- □ 51. JOHNNY LINDELL
- □ 78. TED KAZANSKI
- □ 104. MIKE SANDLOCK
- □ 108. THORNTON KIPPER
- □ 127. STEVE O'NEILL(M)
- □ 174. TOM QUALTERS
- □ 183. EARLE COMBS(C)
- □ 196. STAN JOK
- □ 212. BOB MICELOTTA
- □ 236. PAUL PENSON
- □ 247. ED MAYO(C)

PITTSBURGH PIRATES

- □ 11. PAUL SMITH
- □ 16. VIC JANOWICZ
- □ 43. DICK GROAT
- □ 72. PRESTON WARD
- □ 75. FRED HANEY(M)
- □ 84. DICK COLE
- □ 87. ROY FACE
- □ 95. HAL RICE
- □ 134. CAL HOGUE
- □ 139. ED O'BRIEN
- □ 139. JOHN O'BRIEN
- □ 161. JOHN HETKI
- □ 179. GAIR ALLIE
- □ 202. BOB PURKEY
- □ 213. JOHN FITZPATRICK(C)
- □ 228. GENE HERMANSKI
- □ 234. JERRY LYNCH
- □ 235. VERN LAW
- □ 242. CURT ROBERTS

ST. LOUIS CARDINALS

- ☐ 9. HARVEY HADDIX
- ☐ 26. RAY JABLONSKI
- ☐ 38. EDDIE STANKY(M)
- ☐ 115. RIP REPULSKI
- ☐ 116. STEVE BILKO
- ☐ 117. SOLLY HEMUS
- ☐ 135. JOE PRESKO
- ☐ 137. WALLY MOON
- ☐ 142. TOM POHOLSKY
- ☐ 147. JOHN RIDDLE(C)
- ☐ 151. ALEX GRAMMAS
- ☐ 158. PEANUTS LOWREY
- ☐ 164. STU MILLER
- ☐ 191. DICK SCHOFIELD
- ☐ 192. COT DEAL
- ☐ 194. BILL SARNI
- ☐ 237. MIKE RYBA(C)
- ☐ 249. WILMER MIZELL

WASHINGTON SENATORS

- ☐ 6. PETE RUNNELS
- ☐ 33. JOHNNY SCHMITZ
- ☐ 73. WAYNE TERWILLIGER
- ☐ 91. BOB OLDIS
- ☐ 97. JERRY LANE
- ☐ 114. DEAN STONE
- ☐ 140. TOM WRIGHT
- ☐ 185. CHUCK STOBBS
- ☐ 187. HEINIE MANUSH(C)
- ☐ 189. BOB ROSS
- ☐ 204. ANGEL SCULL
- ☐ 223. JOE HAYNES(C)
- ☐ 245. ROY SIEVERS

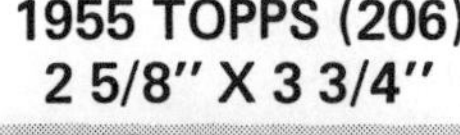

1955 TOPPS (206)
2 5/8" X 3 3/4"

BALTIMORE ORIOLES

- ☐ 8. HAL W. SMITH
- ☐ 13. FRED MARSH
- ☐ 48. BOB KENNEDY
- ☐ 57. BILLY O'DELL
- ☐ 64. GUS TRIANDOS
- ☐ 105. CHUCK DIERING
- ☐ 113. HARRY BRECHEEN(C)
- ☐ 154. WILLIE MIRANDA
- ☐ 162. JOE COLEMAN
- ☐ 165. DON JOHNSON
- ☐ 168. DUANE PILLETTE
- ☐ 185. DON FERRARESE
- ☐ 190. GENE WOODLING
- ☐ 208. RAY MOORE

BOSTON RED SOX

- ☐ 2. TED WILLIAMS
- ☐ 18. RUSS KEMMERER
- ☐ 36. LEO KIELY
- ☐ 72. KARL OLSON
- ☐ 83. TOM BREWER
- ☐ 91. MILT BOLLING
- ☐ 106. FRANK SULLIVAN
- ☐ 115. ELLIS KINDER
- ☐ 116. TOM HURD
- ☐ 128. TED LEPCIO
- ☐ 131. GRADY HATTON
- ☐ 140. MEL PARNELL
- ☐ 148. HAL BROWN
- ☐ 150. MIKE HIGGINS(M)
- ☐ 152. HARRY AGGANIS
- ☐ 163. FAYE THRONEBERRY
- ☐ 171. DICK BRODOWSKI
- ☐ 176. NORM ZAUCHIN
- ☐ 200. JACK JENSEN
- ☐ 206. PETE DALEY
- ☐ 207. BILL CONSOLO

BROOKLYN DODGERS

- ☐ 5. JIM GILLIAM
- ☐ 19. BILLY HERMAN(C)
- ☐ 25. JOHNNY PODRES
- ☐ 40. DON HOAK
- ☐ 50. JACKIE ROBINSON
- ☐ 51. JIM HUGHES
- ☐ 75. SANDY AMOROS
- ☐ 90. KARL SPOONER
- ☐ 92. DON ZIMMER
- ☐ 108. RUBE WALKER
- ☐ 111. BOB MILLIKEN
- ☐ 123. SANDY KOUFAX
- ☐ 156. JOE BLACK
- ☐ 180. CLEM LABINE
- ☐ 187. GIL HODGES
- ☐ 195. ED ROEBUCK
- ☐ 199. BERT HAMRIC
- ☐ 210. DUKE SNIDER

CHICAGO CUBS

- ☐ 6. STAN HACK(M)
- ☐ 28. ERNIE BANKS
- ☐ 45. HANK SAUER
- ☐ 52. BILL TREMEL
- ☐ 68. JIM DAVIS
- ☐ 76. HOWIE POLLET
- ☐ 93. STEVE BILKO
- ☐ 129. ELVIN TAPPE
- ☐ 172. FRANK BAUMHOLTZ
- ☐ 179. JIM BOLGER
- ☐ 184. HARRY PERKOWSKI
- ☐ 196. GALE WADE

CHICAGO WHITE SOX

- ☐ 10. BOB KEEGAN
- ☐ 32. ED MCGHEE
- ☐ 58. JIM RIVERA
- ☐ 66. RON JACKSON
- ☐ 104. JACK HARSHMAN
- ☐ 122. CARL SAWATSKI
- ☐ 146. DICK DONOVAN
- ☐ 201. SHERM LOLLAR

CINCINNATI REDS

- ☐ 3. ART FOWLER
- ☐ 44. CORKY VALENTINE
- ☐ 56. RAY JABLONSKI
- ☐ 69. ED BAILEY
- ☐ 74. BOB BORKOWSKI
- ☐ 82. CHUCK HARMON
- ☐ 120. TED KLUSZEWSKI
- ☐ 153. BUD PODBIELAN
- ☐ 170. JIM PEARCE
- ☐ 174. RUDY MINARCIN
- ☐ 178. BOBBY ADAMS
- ☐ 181. ROY MCMILLAN

CLEVELAND INDIANS

- ☐ 7. JIM HEGAN
- ☐ 24. HAL NEWHOUSER
- ☐ 39. BILLY GLYNN
- ☐ 70. AL ROSEN
- ☐ 85. DON MOSSI
- ☐ 102. WALLY WESTLAKE
- ☐ 133. DAVE HOSKINS
- ☐ 151. RED KRESS(C)
- ☐ 160. RAY NARLESKI
- ☐ 197. AL SMITH

DETROIT TIGERS

- ☐ 4. AL KALINE
- ☐ 9. BOB G. MILLER
- ☐ 11. FERRIS FAIN
- ☐ 49. J.W. PORTER
- ☐ 65. RAY BOONE
- ☐ 87. FRANK HOUSE
- ☐ 94. RENO BERTOIA
- ☐ 138. RAY HERBERT
- ☐ 192. JIM DELSING

KANSAS CITY ATHLETICS

- ☐ 14. JIM FINIGAN
- ☐ 30. VIC POWER
- ☐ 54. LOU LIMMER
- ☐ 61. SPOOK JACOBS
- ☐ 77. ARNOLD PORTOCARRERO
- ☐ 86. BILL WILSON
- ☐ 96. CHARLIE BISHOP
- ☐ 101. JOHNNY GRAY
- ☐ 110. GUS ZERNIAL
- ☐ 121. BILL RENNA
- ☐ 132. BOB TRICE
- ☐ 145. ELMER VALO
- ☐ 177. JIM ROBERTSON

MILWAUKEE BRAVES

- ☐ 15. JIM PENDLETON
- ☐ 23. JACK PARKS
- ☐ 31. WARREN SPAHN
- ☐ 35. DAVE JOLLY
- ☐ 47. HANK AARON
- ☐ 81. GENE CONLEY
- ☐ 103. CHARLIE WHITE
- ☐ 117. MEL ROACH
- ☐ 134. JOE JAY
- ☐ 149. RAY CRONE
- ☐ 155. ED MATHEWS
- ☐ 161. CHUCK TANNER
- ☐ 182. HUMBERTO ROBINSON

NEW YORK GIANTS

- ☐ 1. DUSTY RHODES
- ☐ 17. BOBBY HOFMAN
- ☐ 27. BILLY GARDNER
- ☐ 42. WINDY MCCALL
- ☐ 53. BILL TAYLOR
- ☐ 71. RUBEN GOMEZ
- ☐ 100. MONTE IRVIN
- ☐ 119. BOB LENNON
- ☐ 144. JOE AMALFITANO
- ☐ 194. WILLIE MAYS

NEW YORK YANKEES

- ☐ 20. ANDY CAREY
- ☐ 22. BILL SKOWRON
- ☐ 38. BOB TURLEY
- ☐ 63. JOE COLLINS
- ☐ 80. BOB GRIM
- ☐ 99. FRANK LEJA
- ☐ 109. ED LOPAT
- ☐ 139. STEVE KRALY
- ☐ 158. TOM CARROLL
- ☐ 166. HANK BAUER
- ☐ 188. CHARLIE SILVERA
- ☐ 189. PHIL RIZZUTO
- ☐ 193. JOHNNY SAIN
- ☐ 198. YOGI BERRA

PHILADELPHIA PHILLIES

- ☐ 29. HERMAN WEHMEIER
- ☐ 33. TOM QUALTERS
- ☐ 46. TED KAZANSKI
- ☐ 62. THORNTON KIPPER
- ☐ 79. DANNY SCHELL
- ☐ 114. LOU ORTIZ
- ☐ 130. MAYO SMITH(M)
- ☐ 157. BOB J. MILLER
- ☐ 167. TOM CASAGRANDE
- ☐ 202. JIM OWENS

PITTSBURGH PIRATES

- ☐ 12. JAKE THIES
- ☐ 26. DICK GROAT
- ☐ 59. GAIR ALLIE
- ☐ 73. JACK SHEPARD
- ☐ 88. BOB SKINNER
- ☐ 95. PRESTON WARD
- ☐ 107. CURT ROBERTS
- ☐ 112. NELSON KING
- ☐ 118. BOB PURKEY
- ☐ 126. DICK HALL
- ☐ 127. DALE LONG
- ☐ 135. JOHNNY O'BRIEN
- ☐ 142. JERRY LYNCH
- ☐ 147. LAURIN PEPPER
- ☐ 164. ROBERTO CLEMENTE
- ☐ 205. GENE FREESE

ST. LOUIS CARDINALS

☐ 21. ALEX GRAMMAS
☐ 37. JOE CUNNINGHAM
☐ 43. HARVEY HADDIX
☐ 55. RIP REPULSKI
☐ 67. WALLY MOON
☐ 78. GORDON JONES
☐ 89. JOE FRAZIER
☐ 98. JOHNNY RIDDLE(C)
☐ 125. KEN BOYER
☐ 137. HARRY ELLIOTT
☐ 143. DICK SCHOFIELD
☐ 183. TONY JACOBS
☐ 191. ED STANKY(M)
☐ 204. FRANK SMITH

WASHINGTON SENATORS

☐ 16. ROY SIEVERS
☐ 34. WAYNE TERWILLIGER
☐ 41. CHUCK STOBBS
☐ 60. DEAN STONE
☐ 84. CAMILO PASCUAL
☐ 97. CARLOS PAULA
☐ 124. HARMON KILLEBREW
☐ 136. BUNKY STEWART
☐ 141. TOM WRIGHT
☐ 159. JOHNNY SCHMITZ
☐ 169. BOB OLDIS
☐ 173. BOB KLINE

1956 TOPPS (340)
2 5/8" X 3 3/4"

BALTIMORE ORIOLES

☐ 19. CHUCK DIERING
☐ 23. FRED MARSH
☐ 43. RAY MOORE
☐ 62. HAL W. SMITH
☐ 80. GUS TRIANDOS
☐ 100. TEAM CARD
☐ 103. WILLIE MIRANDA
☐ 154. DAVE POPE
☐ 167. HARRY DORISH
☐ 169. BOB NELSON
☐ 171. JIM WILSON
☐ 206. ERV PALICA
☐ 222. DAVE PHILLEY
☐ 229. HARRY BRECHEEN(C)
☐ 231. BOB HALE
☐ 266. DON FERRARESE
☐ 276. GEORGE ZUVERINK
☐ 286. BILL WIGHT
☐ 287. BOBBY ADAMS
☐ 303. JIM DYCK

BOSTON RED SOX

☐ 5. TED WILLIAMS
☐ 26. GRADY HATTON
☐ 34. TOM BREWER
☐ 71. FRAMK SULLIVAN
☐ 89. NORM ZAUCHIN
☐ 93. GEORGE SUSCE
☐ 111. TEAM CARD
☐ 115. JACKIE JENSEN
☐ 122. WILLARD NIXON
☐ 143. JIM PIERSALL
☐ 168. SAMMY WHITE
☐ 217. BILLY KLAUS
☐ 228. MICKEY VERNON
☐ 245. BILLY GOODMAN
☐ 248. BOB PORTERFIELD
☐ 256. TOM HURD
☐ 284. IKE DELOCK
☐ 298. JOHNNY SCHMITZ
☐ 304. FRANK MALZONE
☐ 313. GENE STEPHENS
☐ 315. MILT BOLLING

BROOKLYN DODGERS

☐ 8. WALTER ALSTON(M)
☐ 30. JACKIE ROBINSON
☐ 42. SANDY AMOROS
☐ 58. ED ROEBUCK
☐ 63. ROGER CRAIG
☐ 79. SANDY KOUFAX
☐ 83. KARL SPOONER
☐ 99. DON ZIMMER
☐ 101. ROY CAMPANELLA
☐ 145. GIL HODGES
☐ 150. DUKE SNIDER
☐ 166. TEAM CARD
☐ 173. JOHNNY PODRES
☐ 184. DON BESSENT
☐ 190. CARL FURILLO
☐ 223. RANDY JACKSON
☐ 233. CARL ERSKINE
☐ 235. DON NEWCOMBE
☐ 260. PEE WEE REESE
☐ 270. BILLY LOES
☐ 280. JIM GILLIAM
☐ 295. CLEM LABINE
☐ 299. CHARLEY NEAL
☐ 333. RUBE WALKER

CHICAGO CUBS

☐ 11. TEAM CARD
☐ 15. ERNIE BANKS
☐ 41. HANK SAUER
☐ 66. BOB SPEAKE
☐ 74. JIM KING
☐ 96. BILL TREMEL
☐ 102. JIM DAVIS
☐ 112. DEE FONDY
☐ 124. DON KAISER
☐ 142. GENE BAKER
☐ 179. HARRY CHITI
☐ 182. PAUL MINNER
☐ 194. MONTE IRVIN
☐ 214. BOB RUSH
☐ 227. RUSS MEYER
☐ 259. SAM JONES
☐ 282. WARREN HACKER
☐ 285. EDDIE MIKSIS
☐ 291. FRANK KELLERT
☐ 314. HOBIE LANDRITH
☐ 335. DON HOAK

CHICAGO WHITE SOX

☐ 18. DICK DONOVAN
☐ 29. JACK HARSHMAN
☐ 38. BOB KENNEDY
☐ 54. BOB KEEGAN
☐ 70. JIM RIVERA
☐ 118. NELLIE FOX
☐ 125. MINNIE MINOSO
☐ 144. BOB POWELL
☐ 149. DIXIE HOWELL
☐ 160. BILLY PIERCE
☐ 186. RON JACKSON
☐ 188. TEAM CARD
☐ 195. GEORGE KELL
☐ 238. WALT DROPO
☐ 243. SHERM LOLLAR
☐ 250. LARRY DOBY
☐ 262. HOWIE POLLET
☐ 265. SANDY CONSUEGRA
☐ 267. BOB NIEMAN
☐ 292. LUIS APARICIO
☐ 326. CONNIE JOHNSON

CINCINNATI REDS

☐ 25. TED KLUSZEWSKI
☐ 36. RUDY MINARCIN
☐ 47. ART FOWLER
☐ 86. RAY JABLONSKI
☐ 90. TEAM CARD
☐ 123. ROY MCMILLAN
☐ 137. AL SILVERA
☐ 158. WALLY POST
☐ 162. GUS BELL
☐ 178. JOE BLACK
☐ 192. SMOKY BURGESS
☐ 212. JOHNNY TEMPLE
☐ 218. JOE NUXHALL
☐ 224. BUD PODBIELAN
☐ 242. HERSHELL FREEMAN
☐ 249. JOHNNY KLIPPSTEIN
☐ 289. HAL JEFFCOAT
☐ 305. BROOKS LAWRENCE
☐ 308. CHUCK HARMON
☐ 324. ROCKY BRIDGES

CLEVELAND INDIANS

☐ 35. AL ROSEN
☐ 39. DON MOSSI
☐ 48. JIM HEGAN
☐ 59. JOSE SANTIAGO
☐ 85. TEAM CARD
☐ 105. AL SMITH
☐ 132. BOBBY AVILA
☐ 133. RAY NARLESKI
☐ 140. HERB SCORE
☐ 163. GENE WOODLING
☐ 187. EARLY WYNN
☐ 200. BOB FELLER
☐ 210. MIKE GARCIA
☐ 230. CHICO CARRASQUEL
☐ 255. BOB LEMON
☐ 268. DALE MITCHELL
☐ 281. ART HOUTTEMAN
☐ 300. VIC WERTZ
☐ 311. HAL NARAGON
☐ 330. JIM BUSBY

DETROIT TIGERS

☐ 6. RAY BOONE
☐ 20. AL KALINE
☐ 32. FRANK HOUSE
☐ 57. DUKE MAAS
☐ 84. BABE BIRRER
☐ 92. RED WILSON
☐ 117. VIRGIL TRUCKS
☐ 126. JIM BRADY
☐ 147. EARL TORGESON
☐ 152. BILLY HOEFT
☐ 155. HARVEY KUENN
☐ 189. NED GARVER
☐ 191. FRANK LARY
☐ 203. BILL TUTTLE
☐ 207. JIM SMALL
☐ 213. TEAM CARD
☐ 263. BOB G. MILLER
☐ 310. STEVE GROMEK
☐ 317. AL ABER
☐ 318. FRED HATFIELD
☐ 338. JIM DELSING

KANSAS CITY ATHLETICS

☐ 3. ELMER VALO
☐ 16. HECTOR LOPEZ
☐ 22. JIM FINIGAN
☐ 45. GUS ZERNIAL
☐ 53. ARNOLD PORTOCARRERO
☐ 67. VIC POWER
☐ 82. BILL RENNA
☐ 106. JOE ASTROTH
☐ 109. ENOS SLAUGHTER
☐ 151. SPOOK JACOBS
☐ 161. JOE DEMAESTRI
☐ 176. ALEX KELLNER
☐ 236. TEAM CARD
☐ 239. HARRY SIMPSON
☐ 246. TOM GORMAN
☐ 258. ART DITMAR
☐ 261. BOBBY SHANTZ
☐ 279. JOHNNY GROTH
☐ 319. JACK CRIMIAN
☐ 339. RANCE PLESS

MILWAUKEE BRAVES

- ☐ 10. WARREN SPAHN
- ☐ 17. GENE CONLEY
- ☐ 31. HANK AARON
- ☐ 69. CHUCK TANNER
- ☐ 76. RAY CRONE
- ☐ 95. TEAM CARD
- ☐ 107. ED MATHEWS
- ☐ 131. BOB ROSELLI
- ☐ 136. JOHNNY LOGAN
- ☐ 172. FRANK TORRE
- ☐ 175. DEL CRANDALL
- ☐ 185. BILL BRUTON
- ☐ 219. LEW BURDETTE
- ☐ 244. BOB BUHL
- ☐ 254. GEORGE CROWE
- ☐ 257. BOBBY THOMSON
- ☐ 272. DANNY O'CONNELL
- ☐ 278. CHET NICHOLS
- ☐ 294. ERNIE JOHNSON
- ☐ 312. ANDY PAFKO
- ☐ 320. JOE ADCOCK

NEW YORK GIANTS

- ☐ 9. RUBEN GOMEZ
- ☐ 28. BOBBY HOFMAN
- ☐ 44. WINDY MCCALL
- ☐ 50. DUSTY RHODES
- ☐ 73. WAYNE TERWILLIGER
- ☐ 91. GAIL HARRIS
- ☐ 104. BOB LENNON
- ☐ 130. WILLIE MAYS
- ☐ 138. JOHNNY ANTONELLI
- ☐ 148. ALVIN DARK
- ☐ 156. WES WESTRUM
- ☐ 199. HANK THOMPSON
- ☐ 202. JIM HEARN
- ☐ 205. WHITEY LOCKMAN
- ☐ 226. TEAM CARD
- ☐ 241. DON MUELLER
- ☐ 264. RAY MONZANT
- ☐ 271. FOSTER CASTLEMAN
- ☐ 277. DARYL SPENCER
- ☐ 301. MARV GRISSOM
- ☐ 307. HOYT WILHELM
- ☐ 325. DON LIDDLE

NEW YORK YANKEES

- ☐ 12. ANDY CAREY
- ☐ 21. JOE COLLINS
- ☐ 40. BOB TURLEY
- ☐ 52. BOB GRIM
- ☐ 61. BILL SKOWRON
- ☐ 88. JOHNNY KUCKS
- ☐ 110. YOGI BERRA
- ☐ 113. PHIL RIZZUTO
- ☐ 135. MICKEY MANTLE
- ☐ 139. TOMMY CARROLL
- ☐ 177. HANK BAUER
- ☐ 181. BILLY MARTIN
- ☐ 208. ELSTON HOWARD
- ☐ 215. TOMMY BYRNE
- ☐ 225. GIL MCDOUGALD
- ☐ 240. WHITEY FORD
- ☐ 251. TEAM CARD
- ☐ 253. IRV NOREN
- ☐ 288. BOB CERV
- ☐ 302. EDDIE ROBINSON
- ☐ 316. JERRY COLEMAN
- ☐ 321. JIM KONSTANTY
- ☐ 332. DON LARSEN
- ☐ 340. MICKEY MCDERMOTT

PHILADELPHIA PHILLIES

- ☐ 7. RON NEGRAY
- ☐ 60. MAYO SMITH(M)
- ☐ 72. TEAM CARD
- ☐ 78. HERM WEHMEIER
- ☐ 81. WALLY WESTLAKE
- ☐ 114. JIM OWENS
- ☐ 120. RICHIE ASHBURN
- ☐ 127. WILLIE JONES
- ☐ 174. GLEN GORBOUS
- ☐ 180. ROBIN ROBERTS
- ☐ 183. STAN LOPATA
- ☐ 197. GRANNY HAMNER
- ☐ 211. MURRY DICKSON
- ☐ 220. DEL ENNIS
- ☐ 269. JACK MEYER
- ☐ 274. FRANK BAUMHOLTZ
- ☐ 275. JIM GREENGRASS
- ☐ 290. CURT SIMMONS
- ☐ 296. ANDY SEMINICK
- ☐ 334. BOB J. MILLER
- ☐ 337. BOBBY MORGAN

PITTSBURGH PIRATES

- ☐ 13. ROY FACE
- ☐ 24. DICK GROAT
- ☐ 33. ROBERTO CLEMENTE
- ☐ 46. GENE FREESE
- ☐ 56. DALE LONG
- ☐ 65. JOHNNY O'BRIEN
- ☐ 94. RON KLINE
- ☐ 97. JERRY LYNCH
- ☐ 108. LAURIN PEPPER
- ☐ 116. EDDIE O'BRIEN
- ☐ 121. TEAM CARD
- ☐ 129. JAKE MARTIN
- ☐ 153. FRANK THOMAS
- ☐ 204. ART SWANSON
- ☐ 209. MAX SURKONT
- ☐ 221. BOB FRIEND
- ☐ 232. TOBY ATWELL
- ☐ 252. VERNON LAW
- ☐ 297. BOB SKINNER
- ☐ 306. CURT ROBERTS
- ☐ 328. PRESTON WARD
- ☐ 331. DICK HALL

ST. LOUIS CARDINALS

- ☐ 14. KEN BOYER
- ☐ 27. NELSON BURBRINK
- ☐ 37. ALEX GRAMMAS
- ☐ 55. WALLY MOON
- ☐ 64. LUIS ARROYO
- ☐ 77. HARVEY HADDIX
- ☐ 119. LARRY JACKSON
- ☐ 134. TEAM CARD
- ☐ 141. JOE FRAZIER
- ☐ 165. RED SCHOENDIENST
- ☐ 170. BILL VIRDON
- ☐ 193. WILMER MIZELL
- ☐ 196. TOM POHOLSKY
- ☐ 201. RIP REPULSKI
- ☐ 247. BILL SARNI
- ☐ 273. WALKER COOPER
- ☐ 283. HAL R. SMITH
- ☐ 293. STU MILLER
- ☐ 309. DON BLASINGAME
- ☐ 323. WILLARD SCHMIDT.
- ☐ 336. ELLIS KINDER

WASHINGTON SENATORS

- ☐ 4. CARLOS PAULA
- ☐ 49. PEDRO RAMOS
- ☐ 51. ERNIE ORAVETZ
- ☐ 68. CHUCK STOBBS
- ☐ 75. ROY SIEVERS
- ☐ 87. DEAN STONE
- ☐ 98. CAMILO PASCUAL
- ☐ 128. EDDIE YOST
- ☐ 146. TEAM CARD
- ☐ 157. DICK BRODOWSKI
- ☐ 159. CLINT COURTNEY
- ☐ 164. HARMON KILLEBREW
- ☐ 198. ED FITZ GERALD
- ☐ 216. JERRY SCHOONMAKER
- ☐ 234. PETE RUNNELS
- ☐ 237. JOSE VALDIVIELSO
- ☐ 322. KARL OLSON
- ☐ 327. BOB WIESLER
- ☐ 329. LOU BERBERET

1957 TOPPS (407)
2 1/2" X 3 1/2"

BALTIMORE ORIOLES

- ☐ 11. GEORGE ZUVERINK
- ☐ 14. BOB NIEMAN
- ☐ 17. BILLY GARDNER
- ☐ 26. BOB BOYD
- ☐ 43. CONNIE JOHNSON
- ☐ 59. DICK WILLIAMS
- ☐ 106. RAY MOORE
- ☐ 116. MIKE FORNIELES
- ☐ 146. DON FERRARESE
- ☐ 151. WILLIE MIRANDA
- ☐ 156. GUS TRIANDOS
- ☐ 184. TITO FRANCONA
- ☐ 194. HAL BROWN
- ☐ 230. GEORGE KELL
- ☐ 236. JOE GINSBERG
- ☐ 244. BILLY LOES
- ☐ 251. TEAM CARD
- ☐ 276. JIM PYBURN
- ☐ 311. AL PILARCIK
- ☐ 316. BILLY O' DELL
- ☐ 328. BROOKS ROBINSON
- ☐ 340. BILL WIGHT
- ☐ 382. JIM BRIDEWESER
- ☐ 406. BOB HALE

BOSTON RED SOX

- ☐ 1. TED WILLIAMS
- ☐ 21. FRANK SULLIVAN
- ☐ 56. DAVE SISLER
- ☐ 63. IKE DELOCK
- ☐ 75. JIM PIERSALL
- ☐ 92. MICKEY VERNON
- ☐ 112. TOM BREWER
- ☐ 118. BOB PORTERFIELD
- ☐ 131. MILT BOLLING
- ☐ 163. SAMMY WHITE
- ☐ 171. TEAM CARD
- ☐ 189. WILLARD NIXON
- ☐ 202. DICK GERNERT
- ☐ 217. GENE STEPHENS
- ☐ 220. JACKIE JENSEN
- ☐ 229. GEORGE SUSCE
- ☐ 288. TED LEPCIO
- ☐ 292. BILLY KLAUS
- ☐ 303. BILLY GOODMAN
- ☐ 313. MEL PARNELL
- ☐ 336. HAYWOOD SULLIVAN
- ☐ 342. GENE MAUCH
- ☐ 355. FRANK MALZONE
- ☐ 372. NORM ZAUCHIN
- ☐ 381. DEAN STONE
- ☐ 388. PETE DALEY
- ☐ 399. BILLY CONSOLO

BROOKLYN DODGERS

- ☐ 5. SAL MAGLIE
- ☐ 18. DON DRYSDALE
- ☐ 30. PEE WEE REESE
- ☐ 45. CARL FURILLO
- ☐ 53. CLEM LABINE
- ☐ 80. GIL HODGES
- ☐ 115. JIM GILLIAM
- ☐ 130. DON NEWCOMBE
- ☐ 147. AL WALKER
- ☐ 170. DUKE SNIDER
- ☐ 173. ROGER CRAIG
- ☐ 178. DON BESSENT
- ☐ 190. RANDY JACKSON

- □ 201. SANDY AMOROS
- □ 210. ROY CAMPANELLA
- □ 242. CHARLEY NEAL
- □ 252. CARL ERSKINE
- □ 277. JOHNNY PODRES
- □ 284. DON ZIMMER
- □ 302. SANDY KOUFAX
- □ 319. GINO CIMOLI
- □ 324. TEAM CARD
- □ 337. RENE VALDES
- □ 366. KEN LEHMAN
- □ 376. DON ELSTON

CHICAGO CUBS

- □ 16. WALT MORYN
- □ 42. DEE FONDY
- □ 55. ERNIE BANKS
- □ 74. VITO VALENTINETTI
- □ 84. MOE DRABOWSKY
- □ 134. DON KAISER
- □ 137. BOB RUSH
- □ 155. JIM BROSNAN
- □ 159. SOLLY DRAKE
- □ 176. GENE BAKER
- □ 183. TEAM CARD
- □ 186. JIM KING
- □ 218. RAY JABLONSKI
- □ 235. TOM POHOLSKY
- □ 247. TURK LOWN
- □ 255. CHARLIE SILVERA
- □ 268. JACKIE COLLUM
- □ 289. JIM BOLGER
- □ 339. BOB SPEAKE
- □ 346. DICK LITTLEFIELD
- □ 351. DAVE HILLMAN
- □ 353. CAL NEEMAN
- □ 371. BOB LENNON
- □ 378. ELMER SINGLETON
- □ 396. CASEY WISE

CHICAGO WHITE SOX

- □ 7. LUIS APARICIO
- □ 23. SHERM LOLLAR
- □ 31. RON NORTHEY
- □ 38. NELLIE FOX
- □ 85. LARRY DOBY
- □ 99. BOB KEEGAN
- □ 107. JIM RIVERA
- □ 124. DAVE PHILLEY
- □ 138. MINNIE MINOSO
- □ 152. JACK HARSHMAN
- □ 160. BILL PIERCE
- □ 181. DICK DONOVAN
- □ 213. LES MOSS
- □ 221. DIXIE HOWELL
- □ 227. JERRY STALEY
- □ 257. WALT DROPO
- □ 278. FRED HATFIELD
- □ 301. SAM ESPOSITO
- □ 329. TEAM CARD
- □ 330. JIM WILSON
- □ 344. PAUL LAPALME
- □ 352. ELLIS KINDER
- □ 375. JIM LANDIS
- □ 395. BUBBA PHILLIPS
- □ 401. EARL BATTEY

CINCINNATI REDS

- □ 9. JOHNNY TEMPLE
- □ 32. HERSH FREEMAN
- □ 35. FRANK ROBINSON
- □ 66. BROOKS LAWRENCE
- □ 69. ROY MCMILLAN
- □ 73. GEORGE CROWE
- □ 93. HAL JEFFCOAT
- □ 103. JOE NUXHALL
- □ 128. ED BAILEY
- □ 157. WALLY POST
- □ 165. TED KLUSZEWSKI
- □ 180. GUS BELL
- □ 219. TOM ACKER
- □ 222. ALEX GRAMMAS
- □ 228. SMOKY BURGESS
- □ 233. ART FOWLER
- □ 274. DON HOAK
- □ 279. BOB THURMAN
- □ 294. ROCKY BRIDGES
- □ 296. JOHNNY KLIPPSTEIN
- □ 322. TEAM CARD
- □ 341. DON GROSS
- □ 358. JERRY LYNCH
- □ 370. WARREN HACKER
- □ 373. PETE WHISENANT
- □ 393. RAUL SANCHEZ

CLEVELAND INDIANS

- □ 8. DON MOSSI
- □ 40. EARLY WYNN
- □ 50. HERB SCORE
- □ 67. CHICO CARRASQUEL
- □ 78. VIC WERTZ
- □ 96. HANK AGUIRRE
- □ 120. BOB LEMON
- □ 136. JIM HEGAN
- □ 144. RAY NARLESKI
- □ 145. AL SMITH
- □ 172. GENE WOODLING
- □ 195. BOBBY AVILA
- □ 212. ROCKY COLAVITO
- □ 226. PRESTON WARD
- □ 249. DAVE POPE
- □ 263. GEORGE STRICKLAND
- □ 266. KEN KUHN
- □ 275. TEAM CARD
- □ 300. MIKE GARCIA
- □ 309. JIM BUSBY
- □ 347. HAL NARAGON
- □ 364. CAL MCLISH
- □ 385. ART HOUTTEMAN

DETROIT TIGERS

- □ 19. BOB WILSON
- □ 33. JIM SMALL
- □ 60. BILLY HOEFT
- □ 72. BILL TUTTLE
- □ 77. PAUL FOYTACK
- □ 88. HARVEY KUENN
- □ 102. RAY BOONE
- □ 125. AL KALINE
- □ 141. AL ABER
- □ 149. BOB KENNEDY
- □ 168. FRANK LARY
- □ 198. TEAM CARD
- □ 205. CHARLEY MAXWELL
- □ 223. FRANK HOUSE
- □ 238. EDDIE ROBINSON
- □ 248. JIM FINIGAN
- □ 258. STEVE GROMEK
- □ 282. JACK DITTMER
- □ 297. JACK CRIMIAN
- □ 307. JACK PHILLIPS
- □ 325. FRANK BOLLING
- □ 338. JIM BUNNING
- □ 357. EARL TORGESON
- □ 379. DON LEE
- □ 390. RENO BERTOIA
- □ 405. DUKE MAAS

KANSAS CITY ATHLETICS

- □ 6. HECTOR LOPEZ
- □ 13. WALLY BURNETTE
- □ 41. HAL W. SMITH
- □ 44. JOE DEMAESTRI
- □ 83. LOU SKIZAS
- □ 87. TOM GORMAN
- □ 121. CLETE BOYER
- □ 139. LOU KRETLOW
- □ 142. CHARLEY THOMPSON
- □ 167. VIC POWER
- □ 187. VIRGIL TRUCKS
- □ 204. TEAM CARD
- □ 207. BILLY HUNTER
- □ 225. HARRY SIMPSON
- □ 239. TOM MORGAN
- □ 253. GUS ZERNIAL
- □ 269. BOB CERV
- □ 280. ALEX KELLNER
- □ 285. NED GARVER
- □ 298. IRV NOREN
- □ 318. MICKEY MCDERMOTT
- □ 354. RIP COLEMAN
- □ 360. JOHNNY GROTH
- □ 369. MILT GRAFF
- □ 402. JIM PISONI

MILWAUKEE BRAVES

- □ 4. JOHNNY LOGAN
- □ 20. HANK AARON
- □ 28. GENE CONLEY
- □ 37. FRANK TORRE
- □ 48. BILL BRUTON
- □ 68. RAY CRONE
- □ 90. WARREN SPAHN
- □ 114. TEAM CARD
- □ 117. JOE ADCOCK
- □ 127. BOB BUHL
- □ 133. DEL CRANDALL
- □ 143. ANDY PAFKO
- □ 188. FELIX MANTILLA
- □ 193. DEL RICE
- □ 208. LEW BURDETTE
- □ 250. ED METHEWS
- □ 262. BOBBY THOMSON
- □ 271. DANNY O'CONNELL
- □ 283. WES COVINGTON
- □ 321. RED MURFF
- □ 333. ERNIE JOHNSON
- □ 343. TAYLOR PHILLIPS
- □ 383. JUAN PIZARRO
- □ 389. DAVE JOLLY
- □ 392. CHUCK TANNER

NEW YORK GIANTS

- □ 10. WILLIE MAYS
- □ 39. AL WORTHINGTON
- □ 49. DARYL SPENCER
- □ 58. RUBEN GOMEZ
- □ 61. DUSTY RHODES
- □ 86. BILL SARNI
- □ 105. JOHNNY ANTONELLI
- □ 109. HANK THOMPSON
- □ 123. STEVE RIDZIK
- □ 148. DON MUELLER
- □ 154. RED SCHOENDIENST
- □ 191. JOE MARGONERI
- □ 197. HANK SAUER
- □ 216. MARV GRISSOM
- □ 232. WHITEY LOCKMAN
- □ 237. FOSTER CASTLEMAN
- □ 281. GAIL HARRIS
- □ 291. WINDY MCCALL
- □ 310. MAX SURKONT
- □ 317. TEAM CARD
- □ 323. WES WESTRUM
- □ 331. RAY KATT
- □ 361. CURT BARCLAY
- □ 365. OSSIE VIRGIL
- □ 377. ANDRE RODGERS

NEW YORK YANKEES

- □ 2. YOGI BERRA
- □ 25. WHITEY FORD
- □ 34. TOM STURDIVANT
- □ 36. BOB GRIM
- □ 62. BILLY MARTIN
- □ 82. ELSTON HOWARD
- □ 95. MICKEY MANTLE
- □ 97. TEAM CARD
- □ 108. TOMMY BYRNE
- □ 132. ART DITMAR
- □ 135. BILL SKOWRON
- □ 164. TOMMY CARROLL
- □ 175. DON LARSEN
- □ 185. JOHNNY KUCKS
- □ 192. JERRY COLEMAN

1957 Topps

□ 200. GIL MCDOUGALD
□ 215. ENOS SLAUGHTER
□ 240. HANK BAUER
□ 264. BOB TURLEY
□ 272. BOBBY SHANTZ
□ 286. BOBBY RICHARDSON
□ 290. ANDY CAREY
□ 295. JOE COLLINS
□ 306. DARRELL JOHNSON
□ 312. TONY KUBEK
□ 391. RALPH TERRY
□ 398. AL CICOTTE

PHILADELPHIA PHILLIES

□ 15. ROBIN ROBERTS
□ 27. TED KAZANSKI
□ 46. BOB J. MILLER
□ 54. ELMER VALO
□ 70. RICHIE ASHBURN
□ 91. MACK BURK
□ 119. STAN LOPATA
□ 129. SAUL ROGOVIN
□ 158. CURT SIMMONS
□ 162. JACK MEYER
□ 174. WILLIE JONES
□ 214. TEAM CARD
□ 224. MARV BLAYLOCK
□ 231. SOLLY HEMUS
□ 241. JOE LONNETT
□ 245. RIP REPULSKI
□ 254. RON NEGRAY
□ 265. HARVEY HADDIX
□ 305. CHICO FERNADEZ
□ 314. ED BOUCHEE
□ 332. BOB BOWMAN
□ 335. GRANNY HAMNER
□ 348. JIM HEARN
□ 374. DON CARDWELL
□ 387. JACK SANFORD
□ 397. ROY SMALLEY
□ 404. HARRY ANDERSON

PITTSBURGH PIRATES

□ 3. DALE LONG
□ 12. DICK GROAT
□ 24. BILL MAZEROSKI
□ 52. LEE WALLS
□ 76. BOB CLEMENTE
□ 104. HANK FOILES
□ 110. BILL VIRDON
□ 140. FRANK THOMAS
□ 150. BOB FRIEND
□ 161. TEAM CARD
□ 166. ROY FACE
□ 199. VERNON LAW
□ 209. BOB SKINNER
□ 234. DICK COLE
□ 256. RON KLINE
□ 259. EDDIE O'BRIEN
□ 267. DANNY KRAVITZ
□ 308. DICK HALL
□ 327. JIM PENDLETON
□ 345. PAUL SMITH
□ 349. NELSON KING
□ 362. ROMAN MEJIAS
□ 368. BOB PURKEY
□ 394. LUIS ARROYO

ST. LOUIS CARDINALS

□ 47. DON BLASINGAME
□ 65. WALLY MOON
□ 71. MURRY DICKSON
□ 79. LINDY MCDANIEL
□ 81. HERM WEHMEIER
□ 94. BOBBY DEL GRECO
□ 98. AL DARK
□ 111. HAL R. SMITH
□ 113. WILMER MIZELL
□ 122. KEN BOYER
□ 182. HOBIE LANDRITH
□ 196. LARRY JACKSON
□ 203. HOYT WILHELM
□ 206. WILLARD SCHMIDT
□ 243. TEAM CARD
□ 260. DEL ENNIS
□ 273. JIM DAVIS
□ 287. SAM JONES
□ 299. CHUCK HARMON
□ 304. JOE CUNNINGHAM
□ 350. EDDIE MIKSIS
□ 359. TOM CHENEY
□ 363. EDDIE KASKO
□ 380. WALKER COOPER
□ 384. BOBBY GENE SMITH

WASHINGTON SENATORS

□ 22. JERRY SNYDER
□ 29. WHITEY HERZOG
□ 51. CLINT COURTNEY
□ 57. JIM LEMON
□ 64. PETE RUNNELS
□ 89. ROY SIEVERS
□ 101. CHUCK STOBBS
□ 126. BOB WIESLER
□ 153. KARL OLSON
□ 169. HERB PLEWS
□ 177. EDDIE YOST
□ 179. ERNIE ORAVETZ
□ 211. CAMILO PASCUAL
□ 246. JOSE VALDIVIELSO
□ 261. BOB CHAKALES
□ 270. TEAM CARD
□ 293. TED ABERNATHY
□ 315. LOU BERBERET
□ 320. NEIL CHRISLEY
□ 326. PEDRO RAMOS
□ 334. JERRY SCHOONMAKER
□ 356. FAYE THRONEBERRY
□ 367. ED FITZ GERALD
□ 386. LYLE LUTTRELL
□ 403. DICK HYDE

1958 TOPPS (494)
2 1/2" X 3 1/2"

BALTIMORE ORIOLES

□ 6. GEORGE ZUVERINK
□ 28. JIM BUSBY
□ 40. GEORGE KELL
□ 67. JOE GINSBERG
□ 84. BILLY O'DELL
□ 96. JOE DURHAM
□ 105. BILLY GARDNER
□ 113. JERRY WALKER
□ 121. EDDIE MIKSIS
□ 141. KEN LEHMAN
□ 165. BOB NIEMAN
□ 179. WILLIE MIRANDA
□ 191. ART CECCARELLI
□ 217. JACK HARSHMAN
□ 229. FRANK ZUPO
□ 259. AL PILARCIK
□ 266. CONNIE JOHNSON
□ 279. BOB BOYD
□ 307. BROOKS ROBINSON
□ 336. BERT HAMRIC
□ 359. BILLY LOES
□ 381. HAL BROWN
□ 398. GENE WOODLING
□ 408. TEAM CARD
□ 416. FOSTER CASTLEMAN
□ 429. GUS TRIANDOS
□ 441. JIM MARSHALL
□ 457. MILT PAPPAS
□ 465. ARNIE PORTOCARRERO
□ 471. LENNY GREEN

BOSTON RED SOX

□ 1. TED WILLIAMS
□ 18. FRANK SULLIVAN
□ 29. TED LEPCIO
□ 38. DICK GERNERT
□ 59. DAVE SISLER
□ 73. PETE DALEY
□ 89. BILLY KLAUS
□ 130. JACKIE JENSEN
□ 148. BILLY CONSOLO
□ 167. FRANK BAUMANN
□ 189. GEORGE SUSCE
□ 197. HAYWOOD SULLIVAN
□ 204. LEO KIELY
□ 220. TOM BREWER
□ 227. GENE STEPHENS
□ 260. FRANK MALZONE
□ 265. PETE RUNNELS
□ 280. JIM PIERSALL
□ 297. DON BUDDIN
□ 312. TEAM CARD
□ 328. IKE DELOCK
□ 344. BOB PORTERFIELD
□ 361. MIKE FORNIELES
□ 371. MARTY KEOUGH
□ 383. LOU BERBERET
□ 395. WILLARD NIXON
□ 410. MURRAY WALL
□ 414. SAMMY WHITE
□ 445. BOB W. SMITH
□ 473. BILL RENNA

CHICAGO CUBS

□ 7. DALE LONG
□ 33. CAL NEEMAN
□ 41. DAVE HILLMAN
□ 66. LEE WALLS
□ 80. DICK DROTT
□ 91. CHUCK TANNER
□ 99. BOBBY ADAMS
□ 122. WALT MORYN
□ 135. MOE BRABOWSKY
□ 144. BOBBY MORGAN
□ 159. TAYLOR PHILLIPS
□ 184. ELVIN TAPPE
□ 201. JIM BOLGER
□ 209. BOB ANDERSON
□ 221. JERRY KINDALL
□ 241. DICK LITTLEFIELD
□ 261. TURK LOWN
□ 281. SAM TAYLOR
□ 310. ERNIE BANKS
□ 327. TEAM CARD
□ 342. JIM BROSNAN
□ 363. DON ELSTON
□ 384. JOHN GORYL
□ 411. TONY TAYLOR
□ 430. BOBBY THOMSON
□ 449. GENE FODGE
□ 461. ED MAYER
□ 467. GLEN HOBBIE

CHICAGO WHITE SOX

□ 11. JIM RIVERA
□ 26. RON JACKSON
□ 50. BILLY PIERCE
□ 56. BILL FISCHER
□ 85. LUIS APARICIO
□ 100. EARLY WYNN
□ 108. JIM LANDIS
□ 129. JIM DERRINGTON
□ 138. EARL TORGESON
□ 153. LES MOSS
□ 163. JIM WILSON
□ 177. AL SMITH
□ 200. BOB KEEGAN
□ 212. BUBBA PHILLIPS
□ 225. BILLY GOODMAN
□ 249. RAY MOORE
□ 256. TEAM CARD
□ 267. SHERM LOLLAR
□ 290. DICK DONOVAN
□ 316. TITO FRANCONA
□ 338. WALT DROPO
□ 347. DON RUDOLPH
□ 364. EARL BATTEY
□ 400. NELLIE FOX
□ 412. JERRY STALEY
□ 421. DIXIE HOWELL
□ 425. SAM ESPOSITO
□ 453. TOM QUALTERS

CINCINNATI REDS

□ 12. GEORGE CROWE
□ 27. BUD FREEMAN
□ 34. BOB THURMAN
□ 49. SMOKY BURGESS
□ 63. JOE NUXHALL
□ 75. GUS BELL
□ 103. JERRY LYNCH
□ 118. HARVEY HADDIX
□ 126. STAN PALYS
□ 131. BOB HENRICH
□ 149. TOM ACKER
□ 157. DEE FONDY
□ 160. DON HOAK
□ 205. JOHNNY TEMPLE
□ 214. WILLARD SCHMIDT

□ 237. BILL WIGHT
□ 242. JOHNNY KLIPPSTEIN
□ 254. ALEX GRAMMAS
□ 285. FRANK ROBINSON
□ 294. HAL JEFFCOAT
□ 311. BOB PURKEY
□ 330. ED BAILEY
□ 346. STEVE BILKO
□ 360. ROY MCMILLAN
□ 374. BROOKS LAWRENCE
□ 376. CHARLEY RABE
□ 396. DUTCH DOTTERER
□ 420. VADA PINSON
□ 428. TEAM CARD
□ 466. PETE WHISENANT

CLEVELAND INDIANS

□ 2. BOB LEMON
□ 22. HAL NARAGON
□ 35. DON MOSSI
□ 47. ROGER MARIS
□ 55. CHICO CARRASQUEL
□ 79. DICK WILLIAMS
□ 102. GEORGE STRICKLAND
□ 123. DICK TOMANEK
□ 133. RUSS NIXON
□ 158. TEAM CARD
□ 170. VIC WERTZ
□ 182. JOE CAFFIE
□ 196. MIKE GARCIA
□ 208. CAL MCLISH
□ 222. BUD DALEY
□ 233. MICKEY VERNON
□ 243. LARRY RAINES
□ 276. BOBBY AVILA
□ 295. MINNIE MINOSO
□ 324. HOYT WILHELM
□ 339. FRED HATFIELD
□ 352. HERB SCORE
□ 368. ROCKY COLAVITO
□ 388. BILLY MORAN
□ 394. JIM GRANT
□ 424. LARRY DOBY
□ 439. RAY NARLESKI
□ 443. BILLY HARRELL
□ 446. CARROLL HARDY
□ 456. DICK BROWN
□ 462. GARY GEIGER
□ 469. DON FERRARESE

DETROIT TIGERS

□ 13. BILLY HOEFT
□ 32. J.W. PORTER
□ 46. LOU SLEATER
□ 57. TIM THOMPSON
□ 70. AL KALINE
□ 81. STEVE BOROS
□ 95. FRANK BOLLING
□ 112. GUS ZERNIAL
□ 115. JIM BUNNING
□ 154. HARRY BYRD
□ 185. RAY BOONE
□ 206. BOB SHAW
□ 213. RED WILSON
□ 232. RENO BERTOIA
□ 245. FRANK LARY
□ 262. JOHNNY GROTH
□ 271. BILLY MARTIN
□ 282. PAUL FOYTACK
□ 309. GAIL HARRIS
□ 319. LOU SKIZAS
□ 337. HANK AGUIRRE
□ 345. JIM HEGAN
□ 365. TOM MORGAN
□ 380. CHARLEY MAXWELL
□ 389. BILL TAYLOR
□ 397. TEAM CARD
□ 434. HARVEY KUENN
□ 448. CHARLIE LAU
□ 463. VITO VALENTINETTI

KANSAS CITY ATHLETICS

□ 3. ALEX KELLNER
□ 23. BILL TUTTLE
□ 39. BOB MARTYN
□ 62. JOE DEMAESTRI
□ 69. WALLY BURNETTE
□ 98. BILLY HUNTER
□ 119. HARRY CHITI
□ 139. GEORGE BRUNET
□ 155. HECTOR LOPEZ
□ 169. RALPH TERRY
□ 174. TEAM CARD
□ 192. MILT GRAFF
□ 202. WOODY HELD
□ 228. DUKE MAAS
□ 235. TOM GORMAN

□ 257. HAL W. SMITH
□ 277. VIRGIL TRUCKS
□ 292. NED GARVER
□ 302. MIKE BAXES
□ 318. FRANK HOUSE
□ 329. BOB CERV
□ 349. MURRY DICKSON
□ 367. JACK URBAN
□ 379. RAY HERBERT
□ 391. DAVE MELTON
□ 406. VIC POWER
□ 450. PRESTON WARD

LOS ANGELES DODGERS

□ 16. CHARLEY NEAL
□ 25. DON DRYSDALE
□ 42. JOHN ROSEBORO
□ 71. TEAM CARD
□ 77. DON ZIMMER
□ 88. DUKE SNIDER
□ 93. SANDY AMOROS
□ 120. JOHNNY PODRES
□ 146. DICK GRAY
□ 162. GIL HODGES
□ 187. SANDY KOUFAX
□ 194. ROGER CRAIG
□ 203. AL WALKER
□ 215. JIM GILLIAM
□ 244. DON DEMETER
□ 258. CARL ERSKINE
□ 286. GINO CIMOLI
□ 301. RANDY JACKSON
□ 305. CLEM LABINE
□ 323. ELMER VALO
□ 340. DON NEWCOMBE
□ 357. DANNY MCDEVITT
□ 373. JOE PIGNATANO
□ 375. PEE WEE REESE
□ 401. DON BESSENT
□ 417. CARL FURILLO
□ 435. ED ROEBUCK

MILWAUKEE BRAVES

□ 10. LEW BURDETTE
□ 17. FELIX MANTILLA
□ 30. HANK AARON
□ 51. DEL RICE
□ 78. ERNIE JOHNSON
□ 83. BOB HAZLE
□ 110. JOHNNY LOGAN
□ 117. FRANK TORRE
□ 140. WES COVINGTON

□ 147. DON MCMAHON
□ 164. BOB TAYLOR
□ 176. BOB BUHL
□ 190. RED SCHOENDIENST
□ 223. ANDY PAFKO
□ 234. CARL SAWATSKI
□ 247. CASEY WISE
□ 252. BOB TROWBRIDGE
□ 270. WARREN SPAHN
□ 283. RAY SHEARER
□ 313. BOB RUSH
□ 325. JOE ADCOCK
□ 355. BILL BRUTON
□ 377. TEAM CARD
□ 390. DEL CRANDALL
□ 407. CARLTON WILLEY
□ 431. GENE CONLEY
□ 440. ED MATHEWS
□ 454. HARRY HANEBRINK
□ 472. JOE JAY

NEW YORK YANKEES

□ 9. HANK BAUER
□ 20. GIL MCDOUGALD
□ 43. SAL MAGLIE
□ 54. NORM SIEBERN
□ 61. DARRELL JOHNSON
□ 87. JOHNNY KUCKS
□ 101. BOBBY RICHARDSON
□ 127. TOM STURDIVANT
□ 142. ENOS SLAUGHTER
□ 150. MICKEY MANTLE
□ 161. DON LARSEN
□ 175. MARV THRONEBERRY
□ 193. JERRY LUMPE
□ 224. BOB GRIM
□ 240. BILL SKOWRON
□ 246. TEAM CARD
□ 255. BOB TURLEY
□ 275. ELSTON HOWARD
□ 296. RYNE DUREN
□ 299. HARRY SIMPSON
□ 320. WHITEY FORD
□ 333. ANDY CAREY
□ 354. ART DITMAR
□ 370. YOGI BERRA
□ 382. AL CICOTTE
□ 393. TONY KUBEK
□ 419. BOBBY SHANTZ

PHILADELPHIA PHILLIES

□ 14. RIP REPULSKI
□ 36. TED KAZANSKI
□ 48. CHUCK HARMON
□ 64. JOE LONNETT
□ 76. DICK FARRELL
□ 90. ROBIN ROBERTS
□ 116. DAVE PHILLEY
□ 134. TEAM CARD
□ 171. HARRY ANDERSON
□ 181. WILLIE JONES
□ 186. JACK MEYER
□ 207. SOLLY HEMUS
□ 230. RICHIE ASHBURN
□ 251. WARREN HACKER
□ 264. JACK SANFORD
□ 268. GRANNY HAMNER
□ 278. MACK BURK
□ 291. DON LANDRUM
□ 298. JIM HEARN
□ 326. BOB J. MILLER
□ 348. CHICO FERNANDEZ
□ 353. STAN LOPATA
□ 372. DON CARDWELL
□ 387. WALLY POST
□ 404. CURT SIMMONS
□ 415. BOB BOWMAN
□ 433. PANCHO HERRERA
□ 460. CHUCK ESSEGIAN
□ 474. ROMAN SEMPROCH

PITTSBURGH PIRATES

□ 4. HANK FOILES
□ 45. DICK GROAT
□ 52. BOB CLEMENTE
□ 74. ROY FACE
□ 82. RON KLINE
□ 94. BOB SKINNER
□ 104. JIM PENDLETON
□ 132. VERN LAW
□ 151. BUDDY PRITCHARD
□ 172. DON GROSS
□ 178. TED KLUSZEWSKI
□ 198. BILL VIRDON
□ 218. DICK RAND
□ 226. BOB G. SMITH
□ 238. BILL MAZEROSKI

☐ 269. PAUL SMITH
☐ 293. GENE FREESE
☐ 306. WHAMMY DOUGLAS
☐ 315. BOB FRIEND
☐ 322. HARDING PETERSON
☐ 341. TEAM CARD
☐ 358. GENE BAKER
☐ 392. BENNIE DANIELS
☐ 409. FRANK THOMAS
☐ 426. JOHNNY O'BRIEN
☐ 432. JOHN POWERS
☐ 444. DANNY KRAVITZ
☐ 452. ROMAN MEJIAS
☐ 459. RON BLACKBURN
☐ 470. R.C. STEVENS

ST. LOUIS CARDINALS

☐ 8. EDDIE KASKO
☐ 24. HOBIE LANDRITH
☐ 53. MORRIE MARTIN
☐ 60. DEL ENNIS
☐ 65. VON MCDANIEL
☐ 97. LARRY JACKSON
☐ 106. DICK SCHOFIELD
☐ 114. IRV NOREN
☐ 125. AL DARK
☐ 143. BILLY MUFFETT
☐ 168. JOE CUNNINGHAM
☐ 180. LINDY MCDANIEL
☐ 199. DON BLASINGAME
☐ 210. WALLY MOON
☐ 216. TEAM CARD
☐ 231. LLOYD MERRITT
☐ 248. HERM WEHMEIER
☐ 273. HAL R. SMITH
☐ 287. SAM JONES
☐ 350. KEN BOYER
☐ 366. GENE GREEN
☐ 385. WILMER MIZELL
☐ 402. BOBBY GENE SMITH
☐ 423. PHIL CLARK
☐ 442. PHIL PAINE
☐ 451. JOE TAYLOR
☐ 464. CURT FLOOD

SAN FRANCISCO GIANTS

☐ 5. WILLIE MAYS
☐ 19. TEAM CARD
☐ 21. CURT BARCLAY
☐ 37. MIKE MCCORMICK
☐ 68. DARYL SPENCER
☐ 86. VALMY THOMAS
☐ 107. OSSIE VIRGIL
☐ 111. STU MILLER
☐ 128. WILLIE KIRKLAND
☐ 136. JIM FINIGAN
☐ 152. JOHNNY ANTONELLI
☐ 166. DANNY O'CONNELL
☐ 183. DAVE JOLLY
☐ 195. WHITEY LOCKMAN
☐ 211. PETE BURNSIDE
☐ 253. DON MUELLER
☐ 263. EDDIE BRESSOUD
☐ 272. RAY CRONE
☐ 284. RAY KATT
☐ 308. PAUL GIEL
☐ 332. JIM KING
☐ 335. RUBEN GOMEZ
☐ 343. ORLANDO CEPEDA
☐ 362. RAY JABLONSKI
☐ 378. HANK SAUER
☐ 399. MARV GRISSOM
☐ 413. JIM DAVENPORT
☐ 427. AL WORTHINGTON
☐ 437. BOB SPEAKE
☐ 447. RAY MONZANT
☐ 468. BOB SCHMIDT

WASHINGTON SENATORS

☐ 15. JIM LEMON
☐ 31. TEX CLEVENGER
☐ 44. TEAM CARD
☐ 58. ART SCHULT
☐ 72. BUD BYERLY
☐ 92. CLINT COURTNEY
☐ 109. HERB PLEWS
☐ 124. BOBBY USHER
☐ 137. RUSS KEMMERER
☐ 156. DICK HYDE
☐ 173. EDDIE YOST
☐ 188. MILT BOLLING
☐ 219. CAMILO PASCUAL
☐ 236. ED FITZ GERALD
☐ 239. CHUCK STOBBS
☐ 250. ROY SIEVERS
☐ 274. ROCKY BRIDGES
☐ 288. HARMON KILLEBREW
☐ 303. NEIL CHRISLEY
☐ 317. ALBIE PEARSON
☐ 331. PEDRO RAMOS
☐ 356. BOB MALKMUS
☐ 369. RALPH LUMENTI
☐ 403. STEVE KORCHECK
☐ 405. KEN ASPROMONTE
☐ 422. NORM ZAUCHIN
☐ 438. WHITEY HERZOG
☐ 455. HAL GRIGGS
☐ 458. JULIO BECQUER

1959 TOPPS (572)
2 1/2" X 3 1/2"

BALTIMORE ORIOLES

☐ 7. AL PILARCIK
☐ 21. CONNIE JOHNSON
☐ 47. JIM FINIGAN
☐ 48. TEAM CARD
☐ 66. JOE GINSBERG
☐ 82. BOB BOYD
☐ 89. BILLY GARDNER
☐ 98. ARNIE PORTOCARRERO
☐ 143. WILLIE TASBY
☐ 144. JERRY WALKER
☐ 170. GENE WOODLING
☐ 192. CHARLEY BEAMON
☐ 209. LENNY GREEN
☐ 219. GEORGE ZUVERINK
☐ 250. BILLY O'DELL
☐ 264. CHICO CARRASQUEL
☐ 279. ERNIE JOHNSON
☐ 299. BILLY KLAUS
☐ 330. GUS TRIANDOS
☐ 336. BILLY LOES
☐ 349. HOYT WILHELM
☐ 363. BOBBY AVILA
☐ 375. BOB NIEMAN
☐ 391. MILT PAPPAS
☐ 411. WHITEY LOCKMAN
☐ 439. BROOKS ROBINSON
☐ 444. RON HANSEN
☐ 475. JACK HARSHMAN
☐ 487. HAL BROWN
☐ 507. BOB HALE
☐ 529. GEORGE BAMBERGER
☐ 540. WILLY MIRANDA

BOSTON RED SOX

☐ 13. DICK GERNERT
☐ 32. DON BUDDING
☐ 42. MURRAY WALL
☐ 55. TOM BREWER
☐ 72. BILL RENNA
☐ 91. HERB MOFORD
☐ 112. BILLY CONSOLO
☐ 139. ED SADOWSKI
☐ 146. JERRY ZIMMERMAN
☐ 161. FRANK BAUMANN
☐ 173. BILL MONBOUQUETTE
☐ 185. JIM BUSBY
☐ 199. LEO KIELY
☐ 220. FRANK MALZONE
☐ 236. TED BOWSFIELD
☐ 248. TEAM CARD
☐ 261. GENE STEPHENS
☐ 276. PETE DALEY
☐ 286. DEAN STONE
☐ 303. MARTY KEOUGH
☐ 323. FRANK SULLIVAN
☐ 348. TED LEPCIO
☐ 361. WILLARD NIXON
☐ 370. PETE RUNNELS
☐ 384. DAVE SISLER
☐ 400. JACKIE JENSEN
☐ 416. HAYWOOD SULLIVAN
☐ 437. IKE DELOCK
☐ 456. JERRY CASALE
☐ 473. MIKE FORNIELES
☐ 486. SAMMY WHITE
☐ 500. VIC WERTZ
☐ 521. GARY GEIGER

CHICAGO CUBS

☐ 15. DICK DROTT
☐ 29. JIM BOLGER
☐ 46. BILL R. HENRY
☐ 62. TONY TAYLOR
☐ 77. JOHN GORYL
☐ 105. LEE WALLS
☐ 113. TAYLOR PHILLIPS
☐ 118. JOHN BUZHARDT
☐ 130. LOU JACKSON
☐ 153. JIM MARSHALL
☐ 177. JOHNNY BRIGGS
☐ 193. SAMMY TAYLOR
☐ 214. MARCELINO SOLIA
☐ 226. ART CECCARELLI
☐ 234. CHUCK TANNER
☐ 249. BOBBY ADAMS
☐ 274. JERRY KINDALL
☐ 301. EARL AVERILL
☐ 304. TEAM CARD
☐ 319. DAVE HILLMAN
☐ 334. GLEN HOBBIE
☐ 350. ERNIE BANKS
☐ 362. DOLAN NICHOLS
☐ 367. CAL NEEMAN
☐ 388. BOB WILL
☐ 407. MOE DRABOWSKY
☐ 414. DALE LONG
☐ 429. BOBBY THOMSON
☐ 447. BOB ANDERSON
☐ 474. MOE THACKER
☐ 488. WALT MORYN
☐ 502. AL DARK
☐ 512. GEORGE ALTMAN
☐ 520. DON ELSTON
☐ 538. CHICK KING
☐ 548. ELMER SINGLETON

CHICAGO WHITE SOX

☐ 5. DICK DONOVAN
☐ 22. AL SMITH
☐ 30. NELLIE FOX
☐ 73. RON JACKSON
☐ 86. BOB KEEGAN
☐ 94. TEAM CARD
☐ 103. BILLY GOODMAN
☐ 114. EARL BATTEY
☐ 119. JOHN CALLISON
☐ 138. JOHN ROMANO
☐ 159. BOB SHAW
☐ 179. DON RUDOLPH
☐ 187. BUBBA PHILLIPS
☐ 213. JIM RIVERA
☐ 252. RAY BOONE
☐ 260. EARLY WYNN
☐ 277. TURK LOWN
☐ 293. RAY MOORE
☐ 310. LUIS APARICIO
☐ 328. LOU SKIZAS
☐ 341. TOM QUALTERS
☐ 351. EARL TORGESON
☐ 368. DON MUELLER
☐ 385. SHERM LOLLAR
☐ 410. BILLY PIERCE
☐ 426. JERRY STALEY
☐ 438. SAM ESPOSITO
☐ 453. LES MOSS
☐ 477. BARRY LATMAN
☐ 493. JIM LANDIS
☐ 509. NORM CASH
☐ 537. RODOLFO ARIAS

CINCINNATI REDS

☐ 14. PETE WHISENANT
☐ 25. DON HOAK
☐ 58. EDDIE MIKSIS
☐ 67. BROOKS LAWRENCE
☐ 81. HAL JEFFCOAT
☐ 97. JERRY LYNCH
☐ 111. TEAM CARD
☐ 120. CHUCK COLES
☐ 136. JIM O'TOOLE
☐ 158. WALT DROPO
☐ 171. WILLARD SCHMIDT
☐ 184. HARVEY HADDIX
☐ 201. TOM ACKER
☐ 210. ED BAILEY
☐ 224. CLAUDE OSTEEN
☐ 232. EDDIE KASKO
☐ 255. DEL ENNIS

□ 271. ORLANDO PENA
□ 288. DUTCH DOTTERER
□ 312. DON NEWCOMBE
□ 335. JOHNNY TEMPLE
□ 356. BOB MABE
□ 365. GUS BELL
□ 389. JOE NUXHALL
□ 405. ROY MCMILLAN
□ 431. WHAMMY DOUGLAS
□ 435. FRANK ROBINSON
□ 448. VADA PINSON
□ 489. JOHN POWERS
□ 490. FRANK THOMAS
□ 494. DON PAVLETICH
□ 506. BOB PURKEY
□ 518. MIKE CUELLER
□ 541. BOB THURMAN

CLEVELAND INDIANS

□ 11. BILLY HUNTER
□ 38. MORRIE MARTIN
□ 57. AL CICOTTE
□ 61. DICK BROWN
□ 80. MINNIE MINOSO
□ 88. HERB SCORE
□ 106. HAL WOODESHICK
□ 115. MICKEY VERNON
□ 123. DON DILLARD
□ 142. DICK STIGMAN
□ 168. CARROLL HARDY
□ 186. JIM GRANT
□ 196. BILLY MORAN
□ 207. GEORGE STRICKLAND
□ 229. VIC POWER
□ 247. DON FERRARESE
□ 266. WOODY HELD
□ 283. RUSS HEMAN
□ 295. BILLY MARTIN
□ 327. GARY BELL
□ 344. RUSS NIXON
□ 355. JIM PIERSALL
□ 371. DICK BRODOWSKI
□ 376. HAL NARAGON
□ 394. RANDY JACKSON
□ 420. HECTOR LOPEZ
□ 445. CAL MCLISH
□ 476. TEAM CARD
□ 501. BOBBY TIEFENAUER
□ 516. MIKE GARCIA
□ 531. RAY WEBSTER
□ 542. JIM PERRY

DETROIT TIGERS

□ 2. EDDIE YOST
□ 24. RED WILSON
□ 36. HANK AGUIRRE
□ 52. COOT VEAL
□ 70. HARVEY KUENN
□ 96. LOU BERBERET
□ 132. DON LEE
□ 149. JIM BUNNING
□ 164. JOHNNY GROTH
□ 189. NEIL CHRISLEY
□ 203. OSSIE VIRGIL
□ 233. PAUL FOYTACK
□ 256. JERRY DAVIE
□ 268. TITO FRANCONA
□ 280. FRANK BOLLING
□ 302. DON MOSSIE
□ 318. ROCKY BRIDGES
□ 329. TEAM CARD
□ 331. STEVE BOROS
□ 343. BILLY HOEFT
□ 354. PETE BURNSIDE
□ 360. AL KALINE
□ 378. GAIL HARRIS
□ 393. FRANK LARY
□ 409. GUS ZERNIAL
□ 421. HERM WEHMEIER
□ 442. RAY NARLESKI
□ 455. LARRY DOBY
□ 481. CHARLEY MAXWELL
□ 504. OSSIE ALVAREZ
□ 511. GEORGE SUSCE
□ 524. LARRY OSBORNE
□ 545. TOM MORGAN

KANSAS CITY ATHLETICS

□ 18. JACK URBAN
□ 41. BOB MARTYN
□ 51. RIP COLEMAN
□ 64. JOE DEMAESTRI
□ 79. HARRY CHITI
□ 100. BOB CERV
□ 127. KENT HADLEY
□ 140. CHARLIE SECREST
□ 154. RAY HERBERT
□ 172. TEAM CARD
□ 176. PRESTON WARD
□ 182. MILT GRAFF
□ 202. ROGER MARIS
□ 227. HAL W. SMITH
□ 245. NED GARVER
□ 254. ZEKE BELLA
□ 263. BUDDY DALEY
□ 281. WALT CRADDOCK
□ 292. DICK WILLIAMS
□ 313. FRANK HOUSE
□ 333. HARRY SIMPSON
□ 358. RALPH TERRY
□ 369. DICK TOMANEK
□ 381. MIKE BAXES
□ 392. WHITEY HERZOG
□ 402. HECTOR LOPEZ
□ 423. BOB GRIM
□ 449. TOM GORMAN
□ 459. BILL TUTTLE
□ 482. RUSS MEYER
□ 496. WAYNE TERWILLIGER
□ 513. TOM CARROLL
□ 532. MARK FREEMAN

LOS ANGELES DODGERS

□ 16. JOE PIGNATANO
□ 20. DUKE SNIDER
□ 43. STEVE BILKO
□ 53. STAN WILLIAMS
□ 71. DON BESSENT
□ 107. NORM LARKER
□ 125. RON FAIRLY
□ 133. BOB LILLIS
□ 152. JOHNNY KLIPPSTEIN
□ 163. SANDY KOUFAX
□ 195. RIP REPULSKI
□ 206. CARL FURILLO
□ 217. CARL ERSKINE
□ 244. DICK GRAY
□ 258. FRED KIPP
□ 270. GIL HODGES
□ 287. DON ZIMMER
□ 306. JIM GILLIAM
□ 321. BOB GIALLOMBARDO
□ 324. DON DEMETER
□ 364. DANNY MCDEVITT
□ 387. DON DRYSDALE
□ 403. CLEM LABINE
□ 406. SOLLY DRAKE
□ 427. CHARLIE NEAL
□ 441. JOHN ROSEBORO
□ 457. TEAM CARD
□ 495. JOHNNY PODRES
□ 508. ART FOWLER
□ 522. GENE SNYDER
□ 530. WALLY MOON
□ 547. JIM BAXES

MILWAUKEE BRAVES

□ 3. DON MCMAHON
□ 27. ANDY PAFKO
□ 40. WARREN SPAHN
□ 54. MEL ROACH
□ 65. FRANK TORRE
□ 95. CARL WILLEY
□ 104. DEL RICE
□ 126. EDDIE HAAS
□ 128. BOB HARTMAN
□ 157. FELIX MANTILLA
□ 165. BILL BRUTON
□ 188. JUAN PIZARRO
□ 204. CASEY WISE
□ 225. JOHNNY LOGAN
□ 239. BOB TROWBRIDGE
□ 259. JIM PISONI
□ 273. JOE JAY
□ 290. WES COVINGTON
□ 315. JOE ADCOCK
□ 322. HARRY HANEBRINK
□ 347. BOB BUHL
□ 366. HUMBERTO ROBINSON
□ 380. HANK AARON
□ 396. BOB RUSH
□ 419. TEAM CARD
□ 425. DEL CRANDALL
□ 440. LOU BURDETTE
□ 450. ED MATHEWS
□ 480. RED SCHOENDIENST
□ 499. JOHNNY O'BRIEN

NEW YORK YANKEES

□ 10. MICKEY MANTLE
□ 23. MURRY DICKSON
□ 45. ANDY CAREY
□ 60. BOB TURLEY
□ 76. BOBBY RICHARDSON
□ 90. BILL SKOWRON
□ 108. ZACK MONROE
□ 117. JOHN BLANCHARD
□ 131. DERON JOHNSON
□ 155. ENOS SLAUGHTER
□ 167. DUKE MAAS
□ 180. YOGI BERRA
□ 205. DON LARSEN
□ 222. BOBBY SHANTZ
□ 240. HANK BAUER
□ 251. CLETIS BOYER
□ 272. JERRY LUMPE
□ 289. JOHNNY KUCKS
□ 308. NORM SIEBERN
□ 326. MARV THRONEBERRY
□ 345. GIL MCDOUGALD
□ 374. ART DITMAR
□ 395. ELSTON HOWARD
□ 417. VIRGIL TRUCKS
□ 430. WHITEY FORD
□ 471. TOM STURDIVANT
□ 485. RYNE DUREN
□ 505. TONY KUBEK
□ 510. TEAM CARD
□ 525. JIM COATES
□ 533. DARRELL JOHNSON

PHILIADELPHIA PHILLIES

□ 8. TEAM CARD
□ 31. KEN LEHMAN
□ 39. ED BOUCHEE
□ 56. CARL SAWATSKI
□ 63. JIM HEARN
□ 85. HARRY ANDERSON
□ 92. DAVE PHILLEY
□ 99. TED KAZANSKI
□ 121. BOB CONLEY
□ 129. FRANK HERRERA
□ 175. DICK FARRELL
□ 178. RUBEN AMARO
□ 197. RAY SEMPROCH
□ 208. WILLIE JONES
□ 221. BOB BOWMAN
□ 235. VALMY THOMAS
□ 253. SETH MOREHEAD
□ 269. JACK MEYER
□ 300. RICHIE ASHBURN
□ 314. DON CARDWELL
□ 338. SPARKY ANDERSON
□ 352. ROBIN ROBERTS
□ 372. JIM HEGAN
□ 382. CURT SIMMONS
□ 398. WALLY POST
□ 412. STAN LOPATA
□ 436. GRANNY HAMNER
□ 452. CHICO FERNANDEZ
□ 472. GENE FREESE
□ 492. GENE CONLEY
□ 503. JIM OWENS
□ 517. JOE KOPPE
□ 535. RUBEN GOMEZ
□ 546. AL SCHROLL

PITTSBURGH PIRATES

□ 12. VERN LAW
□ 35. TED KLUSZEWSKI
□ 49. BILL HALL
□ 68. DICK SCHOFIELD
□ 83. BOB G. SMITH
□ 110. GEORGE WITT
□ 122. BENNIE DANIELS
□ 134. JIM MCDANIEL
□ 160. DICK GROAT
□ 174. JIM PENDLETON

☐ 181. BOB PORTERFIELD
☐ 190. BILL VIRDON
☐ 218. ROMAN MEJIAS
☐ 228. DON GROSS
☐ 238. GENE BAKER
☐ 265. RON KLINE
☐ 282. R.C. STEVENS
☐ 294. HANK FOILES
☐ 305. CURT RAYDON
☐ 320. BOB SKINNER
☐ 339. ROY FACE
☐ 357. DICK STUART
☐ 401. RON BLACKBURN
☐ 415. BILL MAZEROSKI
☐ 432. SMOKY BURGESS
☐ 446. ROCKY NELSON
☐ 460. BOB FRIEND
☐ 478. BOB CLEMENTE
☐ 523. HARRY BRIGHT
☐ 528. TEAM CARD
☐ 536. DAN KRAVITZ

ST. LOUIS CARDINALS

☐ 6. ALEX GRAMMAS
☐ 26. CHUCK STOBBS
☐ 37. GENE GREEN
☐ 59. IRV NOREN
☐ 75. SAM JONES
☐ 101. ALEX KELLNER
☐ 135. GENE OLIVER
☐ 137. DICK RICKETTS
☐ 150. STAN MUSIAL
☐ 162. BOBBY GENE SMITH
☐ 194. JIM BROSNAN
☐ 211. BOB BLAYLOCK
☐ 223. TEAM CARD
☐ 231. ELLIS BURTON
☐ 243. MARV GRISSOM
☐ 278. CHUCK ESSEGIAN
☐ 285. JOE CUNNINGHAM
☐ 296. ERNIE BROGLIO
☐ 309. SAL MAGLIE
☐ 325. KEN BOYER
☐ 337. GEORGE CROWE
☐ 353. CURT FLOOD
☐ 379. BOB J. MILLER
☐ 399. LARRY JACKSON
☐ 418. GINO CIMOLI
☐ 433. BILLY HARRELL
☐ 454. PHIL CLARK
☐ 479. LINDY MCDANIEL
☐ 491. DON BLASINGAME
☐ 497. HAL R. SMITH
☐ 514. BOB GIBSON
☐ 527. SOLLY HEMUS(M)
☐ 539. GARY BLAYLOCK
☐ 544. LEE TATE
☐ 549. HOWIE NUNN

SAN FRANCISCO GIANTS

☐ 9. PAUL GIEL
☐ 19. ED BRESSOUD
☐ 28. RED WORTHINGTON
☐ 50. WILLIE MAYS
☐ 69. TEAM CARD
☐ 87. DANNY O'CONNELL
☐ 102. FELIPE ALOU
☐ 109. BOB SCHMIDT
☐ 141. JOE SHIPLEY
☐ 145. DOM ZANNI
☐ 148. MIKE MCCORMICK
☐ 183. STU MILLER
☐ 198. JIM DAVENPORT
☐ 216. ANDRE RODGERS
☐ 241. BILLY MUFFETT

☐ 257. LEON WAGNER
☐ 275. JACK SANFORD
☐ 297. JACKIE BRANDT
☐ 307. CURT BARCLAY
☐ 332. RAY MONZANT
☐ 342. RAY JABLONSKI
☐ 359. BILL WHITE
☐ 377. JOHNNY ANTONELLI
☐ 390. ORLANDO CEPEDA
☐ 404. HANK SAUER
☐ 422. HOBIE LANDRITH
☐ 443. DARYL SPENCER
☐ 458. GORDON JONES
☐ 484. WILLIE KIRKLAND
☐ 526. BOB SPEAKE

WASHINGTON SENATORS

☐ 4. ALBIE PEARSON
☐ 33. ED FITZ GERALD
☐ 44. VITO VALENTINETTI
☐ 78. PEDRO RAMOS
☐ 84. RENO BERTOIA
☐ 93. JULIO BECQUER
☐ 116. BOB ALLISON
☐ 124. DAN DOBBEK
☐ 151. BOB MALKMUS
☐ 169. TED ABERNATHY
☐ 191. RUSS KEMMERER
☐ 215. JIM LEMON
☐ 230. BILL FISCHER
☐ 242. RON SAMFORD
☐ 246. J.W. PORTER
☐ 267. JOHN ROMONOSKY
☐ 284. STEVE KORCHECK
☐ 298. TEX CLEVENGER
☐ 311. NORM ZAUCHIN
☐ 316. RALPH LUMENTI
☐ 340. ROY SIEVERS
☐ 373. HERB PLEWS
☐ 386. JIM DELSING
☐ 397. TEAM CARD
☐ 413. CAMILO PASCUAL
☐ 424. KEN ASPROMONTE
☐ 434. HAL GRIGGS
☐ 451. JIMMY CONSTABLE
☐ 483. CLINT COURTNEY
☐ 498. DICK HYDE
☐ 515. HARMON KILLEBREW
☐ 534. FAYE THRONEBERRY

1960 TOPPS (572)
2 1/2" X 3 1/2"

BALTIMORE ORIOLES

☐ 12. MILT PAPPAS
☐ 28. BROOKS ROBINSON
☐ 46. JACK FISHER
☐ 53. JACKIE BRANDT
☐ 60. GUS TRIANDOS
☐ 79. WALT DROPO
☐ 89. HAL BROWN
☐ 98. GORDON JONES
☐ 106. BILLY GARDNER
☐ 126. CHUCK ESTRADA
☐ 127. RON HANSEN
☐ 179. RIP COLEMAN
☐ 190. GENE WOODLING
☐ 207. BOB BOYD
☐ 224. PAUL RICHARDS(M)
☐ 241. ALBIE PEARSON
☐ 254. ARNIE PORTOCARRERO
☐ 269. GENE GREEN
☐ 288. BOB MABE
☐ 304. JOE GINSBERG
☐ 322. WILLIE TASBY
☐ 348. BARRY SHETRONE
☐ 369. BILLY HOEFT
☐ 395. HOYT WILHELM
☐ 406. BILLY KLAUS
☐ 422. JOHNNY POWERS

☐ 448. JIM GENTILE
☐ 455. COACHES CARD
☐ 481. WES STOCK
☐ 494. TEAM CARD
☐ 498. AL PILARCIK
☐ 514. STEVE BARBER
☐ 525. MARV BREEDING
☐ 540. JERRY WALKER

BOSTON RED SOX

☐ 15. PETE RUNNELS
☐ 38. JERRY CASALE
☐ 54. MIKE FORNIELES
☐ 68. DAVE HILLMAN
☐ 71. MARTY KEOUGH
☐ 94. LEO KIELY
☐ 111. VIC WERTZ
☐ 117. TOM BORLAND
☐ 148. CARL YASTRZEMSKI
☐ 153. BOBBY THOMSON
☐ 184. GARY GEIGER
☐ 203. SAMMY WHITE
☐ 220. BILLY JURGES(M)
☐ 232. JIM BUSBY
☐ 249. EARL WILSON
☐ 267. JIM MARSHALL
☐ 280. FRANK SULLIVAN
☐ 296. NELSON CHITTUM
☐ 310. FRANK MALZONE
☐ 317. PUMPSIE GREEN
☐ 336. IKE DELOCK
☐ 363. GENE STEPHENS
☐ 382. TED BOWSFIELD
☐ 403. ED SADOWSKI
☐ 426. RON JACKSON
☐ 439. TOM BREWER
☐ 452. RAY WEBSTER
☐ 456. COACHES CARD
☐ 474. HAYWOOD SULLIVAN
☐ 487. TOM STURDIVANT
☐ 520. DON BUDDIN
☐ 533. LU CLINTON
☐ 537. TEAM CARD
☐ 544. BILL MONBOUQUETTE

CHICAGO CUBS

☐ 10. ERNIE BANKS
☐ 27. DICK DROTT
☐ 39. EARL AVERILL
☐ 74. WALT MORYN
☐ 86. DICK GERNERT
☐ 93. ART SCHULT
☐ 95. FRANK THOMAS
☐ 125. DICK ELLSWORTH
☐ 147. BOB WILL
☐ 156. ART CECCARELLI
☐ 162. SAMMY TAYLOR
☐ 182. GLEN HOBBIE
☐ 217. CHARLEY GRIMM(M)
☐ 233. DON ELSTON
☐ 248. DEL RICE
☐ 259. GEORGE ALTMAN
☐ 277. HARRY BRIGHT
☐ 294. TONY TAYLOR
☐ 305. RICHIE ASHBURN
☐ 337. CAL NEEMAN
☐ 349. MOE DRABOWSKY
☐ 357. AL SCHROLL
☐ 375. DALE LONG
☐ 412. BOB ANDERSON
☐ 433. IRV NOREN
☐ 444. JERRY KINDALL
☐ 457. COACHES CARD
☐ 476. LOU JOHNSON
☐ 489. STEVE RIDZIK
☐ 504. SETH MOREHEAD
☐ 513. TEAM CARD
☐ 528. BEN JOHNSON

CHICAGO WHITE SOX

☐ 1. EARLY WYNN
☐ 31. SAMMY ESPOSITO
☐ 41. BARRY LATMAN
☐ 69. BILLY GOODMAN
☐ 100. NELLIE FOX
☐ 116. JIM RIVERA
☐ 121. CAMILO CARREON
☐ 131. ED HOBAUGH
☐ 150. BILLY PIERCE
☐ 169. JAKE STRIKER
☐ 180. HARRY SIMPSON
☐ 199. DICK DONOVAN
☐ 208. TEAM CARD
☐ 222. AL LOPEZ(M)
☐ 240. LUIS APARICIO
☐ 256. DICK BROWN
☐ 276. KEN MCBRIDE

- □ 299. EARL TORGESON
- □ 306. FRANK BAUMANN
- □ 313. TURK LOWN
- □ 328. EARL BATTEY
- □ 346. J.C. MARTIN
- □ 365. MINNIE MINOSO
- □ 380. BOB SHAW
- □ 407. GARY PETERS
- □ 428. AL SMITH
- □ 435. GENE FREESE
- □ 447. RAY MOORE
- □ 458. COACHES CARD
- □ 477. DON FERRARESE
- □ 495. SHERM LOLLAR
- □ 505. TED KLUSZEWSKI
- □ 510. JERRY STALEY
- □ 532. MIKE GARCIA
- □ 538. FRANK BARNES
- □ 550. JIM LANDIS

CINCINNATI REDS

- □ 4. BOB PURKEY
- □ 21. DUTCH DOTTERER
- □ 45. ROY MCMILLAN
- □ 61. EDDIE KASKO
- □ 110. CAL MCLISH
- □ 119. CHICO CARDENAS
- □ 146. TED WIEAND
- □ 164. TEAM CARD
- □ 173. BILLY MARTIN
- □ 176. VADA PINSON
- □ 187. JAY HOOK
- □ 198. JERRY LYNCH
- □ 206. CLAUDE OSTEEN
- □ 219. FRED HUTCHINSON(M)
- □ 235. GUS BELL
- □ 257. GORDY COLEMAN
- □ 282. JOE NUXHALL
- □ 289. WILLIE JONES
- □ 311. RAUL SANCHEZ
- □ 325. JIM O'TOOLE
- □ 345. DON NEWCOMBE
- □ 359. BUDDY GILBERT
- □ 372. FRANK HOUSE
- □ 398. MIKE CUELLAR
- □ 411. ED BAILEY
- □ 424. PETE WHISENANT
- □ 434. BROOKS LAWRENCE
- □ 449. JIM BROSNAN
- □ 459. COACHES CARD
- □ 490. FRANK ROBINSON
- □ 506. LEE WALLS
- □ 518. TONY GONZALEZ
- □ 524. BILL R. HENRY
- □ 535. WHITEY LOCKMAN
- □ 543. ELIO CHACON

CLEVELAND INDIANS

- □ 14. JIM GRANT
- □ 30. TITO FRANCONA
- □ 36. RUSS NIXON
- □ 44. BOBBY LOCKE
- □ 63. GEORGE STRICKLAND
- □ 75. VIC POWER
- □ 112. JACK HARSHMAN
- □ 122. DON DILLARD
- □ 139. CARL MATHIAS
- □ 159. JIM PIERSALL
- □ 174. TEAM CARD
- □ 178. WOODY HELD
- □ 216. JOE GORDON
- □ 228. ERNIE JOHNSON
- □ 243. BUBBA PHILLIPS
- □ 279. CHUCK TANNER
- □ 309. BOB HALE
- □ 318. JIM BAXES
- □ 323. JOHNNY ROMANO
- □ 324. JIM PERRY
- □ 341. CARROLL HARDY
- □ 360. HERBY SCORE
- □ 376. JOHNNY BRIGGS
- □ 400. ROCKY COLAVITO
- □ 423. ED FITZ GERALD
- □ 441. GARY BELL
- □ 460. COACHES CARD
- □ 473. AL CICOTTE
- □ 500. JOHNNY TEMPLE
- □ 507. DICK STIGMAN
- □ 521. MIKE LEE
- □ 536. WYNN HAWKINS
- □ 552. WALT BOND

DETROIT TIGERS

- □ 6. LOU BERBERET
- □ 22. ROCKY BRIDGES
- □ 33. TOM MORGAN
- □ 50. AL KALINE
- □ 72. TEAM CARD
- □ 85. FRANK LARY
- □ 118. BOB BRUCE
- □ 141. JIM PROCTOR
- □ 152. GAIL HARRIS
- □ 161. RAY NARLESKI
- □ 171. JOHNNY GROTH
- □ 186. DAVE SISLER
- □ 201. LARRY OSBORNE
- □ 214. JIMMIE DYKES(M)
- □ 245. EDDIE YOST
- □ 261. PETE BURNSIDE
- □ 273. NEIL CHRISLEY
- □ 286. RAY SEMPROCH
- □ 301. JERRY DAVIE
- □ 314. CHICO FERNADEZ
- □ 330. HARVEY KUENN
- □ 342. CASEY WISE
- □ 364. PAUL FOYTACK
- □ 379. RED WILSON
- □ 396. STEVE BILKO
- □ 418. DON MOSSI
- □ 443. CHARLIE MAXWELL
- □ 461. COACHES CARD
- □ 482. FRANK BOLLING
- □ 488. NORM CASH
- □ 502. JIM BUNNING
- □ 531. SANDY AMOROS
- □ 546. HANK AGUIRRE

KANSAS CITY ATHLETICS

- □ 8. BUD DALEY
- □ 11. NORM SIEBERN
- □ 26. WAYNE TERWILLIGER
- □ 66. BOB TROWBRIDGE
- □ 77. HANK FOILES
- □ 78. BOB GRIM
- □ 81. RUSS SNYDER
- □ 92. WHITEY HERZOG
- □ 108. PETE DALEY
- □ 135. KEN JOHNSON
- □ 137. LOU KLIMCHOCK
- □ 177. JOHNNY KUCKS
- □ 188. DICK WILLIAMS
- □ 215. BOB ELLIOTT(M)
- □ 229. JOE MORGAN
- □ 252. RAY HERBERT
- □ 262. HANK BAUER
- □ 274. TOM ACKER
- □ 290. JERRY LUMPE
- □ 308. DICK HALL
- □ 339. HARRY CHITI
- □ 353. DON LARSEN
- □ 367. BILL TUTTLE
- □ 413. TEAM CARD
- □ 415. BOB CERV
- □ 427. AL GRUNWALD
- □ 436. MARV THRONEBERRY
- □ 462. COACHES CARD
- □ 471. NED GARVER
- □ 497. JOHN TSITOURIS
- □ 516. MARTY KUTYNA
- □ 542. KEN HAMLIN

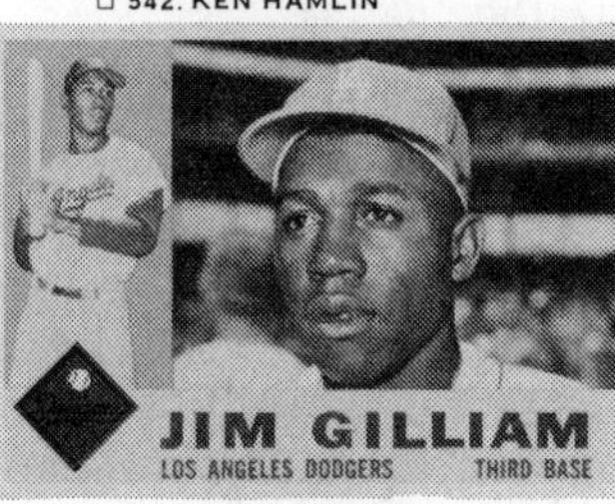

LOS ANGELES DODGERS

- □ 5. WALLY MOON
- □ 18. TEAM CARD
- □ 29. CLEM LABINE
- □ 47. DON ZIMMER
- □ 62. ROGER CRAIG
- □ 88. JOHN ROSEBORO
- □ 105. LARRY SHERRY
- □ 128. BILL HARRIS
- □ 132. FRANK HOWARD
- □ 155. CHARLIE NEAL
- □ 166. CHUCK ESSEGIAN
- □ 191. JOHNNY KLIPPSTEIN
- □ 202. FRED KIPP
- □ 212. WALT ALSTON(M)
- □ 234. DON DEMETER
- □ 255. JIM GILLIAM
- □ 265. RIP REPULSKI
- □ 278. STAN WILLIAMS
- □ 295. GIL HODGES
- □ 321. RON FAIRLY
- □ 333. DANNY MCDEVITT
- □ 343. SANDY KOUFAX
- □ 354. BOB LILLIS
- □ 394. NORM LARKER
- □ 408. CARL FURILLO
- □ 425. JOHNNY PODRES
- □ 442. JOE PIGNATANO
- □ 463. COACHES CARD
- □ 475. DON DRYSDALE
- □ 493. DUKE SNIDER
- □ 509. TOMMY DAVIS
- □ 519. ED ROEBUCK
- □ 529. NORM SHERRY
- □ 547. BOB ASPROMONTE
- □ 551. ED RAKOW

MILWAUKEE BRAVES

- □ 3. JOE ADCOCK
- □ 19. FELIX MANTILLA
- □ 37. BILL BRUTON
- □ 59. JUAN PIZARRO
- □ 70. LOU BURDETTE
- □ 90. BOBBY AVILA
- □ 107. CARL WILLEY
- □ 129. BOB HARTMAN
- □ 143. AL SPANGLER
- □ 158. WES COVINGTON
- □ 170. DEL CRANDALL
- □ 189. DON MCMAHON
- □ 205. JOHNNY LOGAN
- □ 213. CHUCK DRESSEN(M)
- □ 246. LEE MAYE
- □ 266. JOE JAY
- □ 281. RAY BOONE
- □ 300. HANK AARON
- □ 312. CHARLIE LAU
- □ 335. RED SCHOENDIENST
- □ 351. DON NOTTEBART
- □ 374. BOB BUHL
- □ 381. TEAM CARD
- □ 404. BOB RUSH
- □ 417. CHUCK COTTIER
- □ 420. ED MATHEWS
- □ 445. WARREN SPAHN
- □ 464. COACHES CARD
- □ 478. FRANK TORRE
- □ 491. MEL ROACH
- □ 515. STAN LOPATA
- □ 534. KEN MACKENZIE

NEW YORK YANKEES

- □ 35. WHITEY FORD
- □ 51. JIM COATES
- □ 65. ELSTON HOWARD
- □ 83. TONY KUBEK
- □ 96. RALPH TERRY
- □ 102. KENT HADLEY
- □ 109. CLETIS BOYER
- □ 134. DERON JOHNSON
- □ 142. BILL SHORT
- □ 163. HECTOR LOPEZ
- □ 183. ELI GRBA
- □ 196. ANDY CAREY
- □ 204. RYNE DUREN
- □ 227. CASEY STENGEL(M)
- □ 237. ELMER VALO
- □ 247. GIL MCDOUGALD
- □ 270. BOB TURLEY
- □ 283. JOHN BLANCHARD
- □ 315. BOBBY SHANTZ
- □ 329. ZACK MONROE
- □ 332. TEAM CARD
- □ 350. MICKEY MANTLE
- □ 358. JOE DEMAESTRI
- □ 370. BILL SKOWRON
- □ 377. ROGER MARIS
- □ 405. BOBBY RICHARDSON
- □ 421. DUKE MAAS
- □ 430. ART DITMAR
- □ 465. COACHES CARD
- □ 480. YOGI BERRA
- □ 499. JOHNNY JAMES
- □ 522. KEN L. HUNT

PHILADELPHIA PHILLIES

- □ 13. WALLY POST
- □ 17. JOHNNY CALLISON
- □ 34. SPARKY ANDERSON
- □ 52. DAVE PHILLEY
- □ 64. JACK MEYER
- □ 82. RUBEN GOMEZ
- □ 97. TED LEPCIO
- □ 103. DICK FARRELL
- □ 130. FRANK HERRERA
- □ 138. ART MAHAFFEY
- □ 167. VALMY THOMAS
- □ 185. JIM OWENS
- □ 194. BOBBY GENE SMITH
- □ 211. TAYLOR PHILLIPS
- □ 226. EDDIE SAWYER(M)
- □ 251. BOBBY MALKMUS
- □ 264. ROBIN ROBERTS
- □ 285. HARRY ANDERSON
- □ 293. GENE CONLEY
- □ 302. TEAM CARD
- □ 319. JOE KOPPE
- □ 331. HENRY MASON
- □ 347. ED BOUCHEE
- □ 366. DALLAS GREEN
- □ 384. DON CARDWELL
- □ 416. HUMBERTO ROBINSON
- □ 438. JIM COKER
- □ 451. CURT SIMMONS
- □ 466. COACHES CARD
- □ 472. AL DARK
- □ 486. BOBBY DEL GRECO
- □ 511. KEN WALTERS
- □ 523. CLAY DALRYMPLE
- □ 541. TONY CURRY
- □ 549. JOHN BUZHARDT

PITTSBURGH PIRATES

- □ 2. ROMAN MEJIAS
- □ 20. ROY FACE
- □ 48. HAL W. SMITH
- □ 49. CURT RAYDON
- □ 55. BILL MAZEROSKI
- □ 58. GINO CIMOLI

☐ 91. BENNIE DANIELS
☐ 104. DICK SCHOFIELD
☐ 113. BOB SKINNER
☐ 133. JULIAN JAVIER
☐ 145. JIM UMBRICHT
☐ 157. ROCKY NELSON
☐ 209. RON BLACKBURN
☐ 223. DANNY MURTAUGH(M)
☐ 238. DANNY KRAVITZ
☐ 258. DICK GROAT
☐ 272. FRED GREEN
☐ 284. DON GROSS
☐ 298. GEORGE WITT
☐ 326. BOB CLEMENTE
☐ 340. HARVEY HADDIX
☐ 361. BOB OLDIS
☐ 373. DON HOAK
☐ 393. SMOKY BURGESS
☐ 402. DICK STUART
☐ 414. DON WILLIAMS
☐ 437. BOB FRIEND
☐ 453. VERN LAW
☐ 467. COACHES CARD
☐ 484. TEAM CARD
☐ 496. BILL VIRDON
☐ 512. JOE GIBBON
☐ 526. PAUL GIEL
☐ 539. GENE BAKER

ST. LOUIS CARDINALS

☐ 16. ERNIE BROGLIO
☐ 24. DICK GRAY
☐ 40. JOE CUNNINGHAM
☐ 73. BOB GIBSON
☐ 84. HAL R. SMITH
☐ 101. BOB L. MILLER
☐ 120. DUKE CARMEL
☐ 124. JIM DONOHUE
☐ 149. BOB NIEMAN
☐ 168. ALEX GRAMMAS
☐ 195. LINDY MCDANIEL
☐ 197. RON KLINE
☐ 218. SOLLY HEMUS(M)
☐ 236. DICK RICKETTS
☐ 242. TEAM CARD
☐ 250. STAN MUSIAL
☐ 263. DARRELL JOHNSON
☐ 275. CURT FLOOD
☐ 291. BOB KEEGAN
☐ 307. GENE OLIVER
☐ 327. RAY SADECKI
☐ 355. BILL WHITE
☐ 368. DARYL SPENCER
☐ 383. LEON WAGNER
☐ 401. BOB DULIBA
☐ 419. GEORGE CROWE
☐ 446. ELLIS BURTON
☐ 468. COACHES CARD
☐ 485. KEN BOYER
☐ 492. LARRY JACKSON
☐ 517. CHARLEY JAMES
☐ 545. CARL SAWATSKI

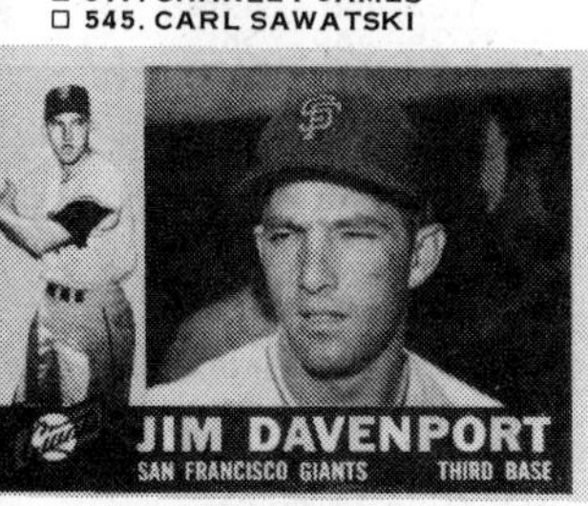

SAN FRANCISCO GIANTS

☐ 23. EDDIE FISHER
☐ 42. HOBIE LANDRITH
☐ 67. JOSE PAGAN
☐ 80. JOHNNY ANTONELLI
☐ 140. JULIO NAVARRO
☐ 144. AL STIEGLITZ
☐ 151. TEAM CARD
☐ 154. JIM DAVENPORT
☐ 165. JACK SANFORD
☐ 172. WILLIE KIRKLAND
☐ 181. BILLY LOES
☐ 192. DANNY O'CONNELL
☐ 200. WILLIE MAYS
☐ 225. BILL RIGNEY(M)
☐ 239. JOE SHIPLEY
☐ 253. EDDIE BRESSOUD
☐ 268. AL WORTHINGTON
☐ 287. FELIPE ALOU
☐ 303. BILLY O'DELL
☐ 316. WILLIE MCCOVEY
☐ 338. RAY MONZANT
☐ 356. JOE AMALFITANO
☐ 371. BUD BYERLY
☐ 378. STU MILLER
☐ 397. DON BLASINGAME
☐ 410. SAM JONES
☐ 431. ANDRE RODGERS
☐ 450. ORLANDO CEPEDA
☐ 469. COACHES CARD
☐ 479. GEORGES MARANDA
☐ 501. BOB SCHMIDT
☐ 530. MIKE MCCORMICK

WASHINGTON SENATORS

☐ 9. FAYE THRONEBERRY
☐ 25. ROY SIEVERS
☐ 43. TEAM CARD
☐ 56. STEVE KORCHECK
☐ 76. BILL FISCHER
☐ 87. JOHN ROMONOSKY
☐ 99. LENNY GREEN
☐ 114. KEN ASPROMONTE
☐ 123. DAN DOBBEK
☐ 136. JIM KAAT
☐ 175. PEDRO RAMOS
☐ 193. DICK HYDE
☐ 210. HARMON KILLEBREW
☐ 221. COOKIE LAVAGETTO(M)
☐ 231. HAL NARAGON
☐ 244. HAL GRIGGS
☐ 271. JULIO BECQUER
☐ 297. RENO BERTOILA
☐ 320. BOB ALLISON
☐ 334. TED ABERNATHY
☐ 344. CLINT COURTNEY
☐ 362. RUSS KEMMERER
☐ 392. TEX CLEVENGER
☐ 409. RON SAMFORD
☐ 432. CHUCK STOBBS
☐ 440. JIM LEMON
☐ 454. HAL WOODESHICK
☐ 470. COACHES CARD
☐ 483. CAMILO PASCUAL
☐ 503. DON LEE
☐ 508. BILLY CONSOLO
☐ 527. JOSE VALDIVIELSO
☐ 548. DON MINCHER

1961 TOPPS (587)
2 1/2" X 3 1/2"

BALTIMORE ORIOLES

☐ 10. BROOKS ROBINSON
☐ 26. WES STOCK
☐ 62. AL PILARCIK
☐ 71. JERRY ADAIR
☐ 85. JERRY WALKER
☐ 102. GENE STEPHENS
☐ 125. STEVE BARBER
☐ 131. PAUL RICHARDS
☐ 140. GUS TRIANDOS
☐ 143. RUSS SNYDER(B)
☐ 159. TEAM CARD
☐ 182. DAVE NICHOLSON
☐ 218. HAL BROWN
☐ 240. RON HANSEN
☐ 256. BILLY HOEFT
☐ 277. HANK FOILES
☐ 295. MILT PAPPAS
☐ 321. MARV BREEDING
☐ 343. EARL ROBINSON
☐ 369. DAVE PHILLEY
☐ 395. CHUCK ESTRADA
☐ 428. RAY BARKER
☐ 442. GORDON JONES
☐ 463. JACK FISHER
☐ 489. WALT DROPO
☐ 515. JACKIE BRANDT
☐ 545. HOYT WILHELM
☐ 559. JIM GENTILE

BOSTON RED SOX

☐ 16. BILLY MUFFETT
☐ 33. GARY GEIGER
☐ 53. RUSS NIXON
☐ 69. EARL WILSON
☐ 81. TRACY STALLARD
☐ 99. DON BUDDIN
☐ 113. MIKE FORNIELES
☐ 128. RIP REPULSKI
☐ 193. GENE CONLEY
☐ 210. PETE RUNNELS
☐ 221. MIKE HIGGINS(M)
☐ 236. DON GILE
☐ 257. CARROLL HARDY
☐ 268. IKE DELOCK
☐ 287. CARL YASTRZEMSKI
☐ 301. CHET NICHOLS
☐ 326. DAVE HILLMAN
☐ 340. VIC WERTZ
☐ 354. BILLY HARRELL
☐ 373. TEAM CARD
☐ 419. TOM BORLAND
☐ 434. TOM BREWER
☐ 445. FRANK MALZONE
☐ 454. PUMPSIE GREEN
☐ 499. CHUCK SCHILLING
☐ 519. JIM PAGLIARONI
☐ 540. JACKIE JENSEN
☐ 548. TED WILLS
☐ 562. BILL MONBOUQUETTE

CHICAGO CUBS

☐ 12. MOE THACKER
☐ 27. JERRY KINDALL
☐ 35. RON SANTO
☐ 58. JOE SCHAFFERNOTH
☐ 88. RICHIE ASHBURN
☐ 107. SETH MOREHEAD
☐ 122. TEAM CARD
☐ 141. BILLY WILLIAMS
☐ 169. DON ELSTON
☐ 196. ED BOUCHEE
☐ 214. DANNY MURPHY
☐ 231. DICK DROTT
☐ 253. SAMMY TAYLOR
☐ 264. GLEN HOBBIE
☐ 283. BOB ANDERSON
☐ 302. AL HEIST
☐ 317. JIM BREWER
☐ 350. ERNIE BANKS
☐ 364. MOE DRABOWSKY
☐ 382. FRANK THOMAS
☐ 427. DICK ELLSWORTH
☐ 441. DICK BERTELL
☐ 493. DON ZIMMER
☐ 512. BOB WILL
☐ 533. JACK CURTIS
☐ 551. GEORGE ALTMAN
☐ 564. DON CARDWELL

CHICAGO WHITE SOX

☐ 7. TEAM CARD
☐ 30. NELLIE FOX
☐ 56. RUSS KEMMERER
☐ 79. JOE GINSBERG
☐ 90. JERRY STALEY
☐ 124. J.C. MARTIN
☐ 132. AL LOPEZ(M)
☐ 152. EARL TORGESON
☐ 157. CAL MCLISH
☐ 170. AL SMITH
☐ 185. HERB SCORE
☐ 205. BILL PIERCE
☐ 227. JUAN PIZARRO
☐ 247. BILLY GOODMAN
☐ 271. JIM LANDIS
☐ 285. SHERM LOLLAR
☐ 303. GARY PETERS
☐ 323. SAMMY ESPOSITO
☐ 352. BOB SHAW
☐ 367. JIM RIVERA
☐ 380. MINNIE MINOSO
☐ 391. WINSTON BROWN
☐ 424. TURK LOWN
☐ 440. LUIS APARICIO
☐ 455. EARLY WYNN

□ 470. ROY SIEVERS
□ 509. CAMILO CARREON
□ 529. BOB ROSELLI
□ 550. FRANK BAUMANN

CINCINNATI REDS

□ 9. BOB PURKEY
□ 66. BILL R. HENRY
□ 76. HARRY ANDERSON
□ 97. JERRY LYNCH
□ 110. VADA PINSON
□ 135. FRED HUTCHINSON(M)
□ 162. JAY HOOK
□ 166. DANNY KRAVITZ
□ 175. GENE FREESE
□ 194. GORDY COLEMAN
□ 215. GUS BELL
□ 233. JOE JAY
□ 244. CHICO CARDENAS
□ 249. TEAM CARD
□ 276. RAY RIPPELMEYER
□ 292. JIM BAUMER
□ 328. JIM O'TOOLE
□ 346. HOWIE NUNN
□ 360. FRANK ROBINSON
□ 378. WALLY POST
□ 399. CLIFF COOK
□ 418. ED BAILEY
□ 436. JIM MALONEY
□ 456. HAL BEVAN
□ 497. WILLIE JONES
□ 513. JIM BROSNAN
□ 534. EDDIE KASKO
□ 556. KEN R. HUNT

CLEVELAND INDIANS

□ 5. JOHN ROMANO
□ 15. WILLIE KIRKLAND
□ 18. JIM GRANT
□ 34. WYNN HAWKINS
□ 60. WOODIE HELD
□ 77. DICK STIGMAN
□ 101. BUBBA PHILLIPS
□ 115. JOHNNY ANTONELLI
□ 155. JOHNNY TEMPLE
□ 172. DON DILLARD
□ 191. MIKE DE LA HOZ
□ 222. JIMMIE DYKES(M)
□ 255. VIC POWER
□ 274. GARY BELL
□ 319. VALMY THOMAS
□ 334. WALT BOND
□ 345. JIM PIERSALL
□ 362. FRANK FUNK
□ 385. JIM PERRY
□ 421. TY CLINE
□ 452. BOB ALLEN
□ 467. TEAM CARD
□ 503. TITO FRANCONA
□ 511. JOE MORGAN
□ 532. BOB HALE
□ 537. BOBBY LOCKE
□ 560. BARRY LATMAN

DETROIT TIGERS

□ 13. CHUCK COTTIER
□ 14. DON MOSSI
□ 37. CHARLIE MAXWELL
□ 51. TEAM CARD
□ 67. OSSIE VIRGIL
□ 83. BOB BRUCE
□ 95. NORM CASH
□ 112. CHICO FERNANDEZ
□ 151. JIM DONOHUE
□ 171. PAUL FOYTACK
□ 192. DICK BROWN
□ 208. LARRY OSBORNE
□ 223. BOB SCHEFFING(M)
□ 239. DAVE SISLER(B)
□ 243. FRANK LARY
□ 251. BILL BRUTON
□ 269. HARRY CHITI
□ 284. DICK GERNERT
□ 324. HANK AGUIRRE
□ 330. ROCKY COLAVITO
□ 348. STEVE BOROS
□ 376. MIKE ROARKE
□ 429. AL KALINE
□ 439. PHIL REGAN
□ 459. TERRY FOX
□ 490. JIM BUNNING
□ 514. JAKE WOOD
□ 544. GEORGE THOMAS
□ 553. BILL FISCHER

KANSAS CITY ATHLETICS

□ 8. DICK WILLIAMS
□ 24. KEN JOHNSON
□ 39. LEO POSADA
□ 57. MARV THRONEBERRY
□ 94. JOHNNY KUCKS
□ 106. WHITEY HERZOG
□ 143. RUSS SNYDER(F)
□ 177. DON LARSEN
□ 197. DICK HALL
□ 199. BOB BOYD
□ 212. HAYWOOD SULLIVAN
□ 224. JOE GORDON(M)
□ 248. ED KEEGAN
□ 267. NORM SIEBERN
□ 297. TEAM CARD
□ 322. BILL KUNKEL
□ 342. CLINT COURTNEY
□ 365. JERRY LUMPE
□ 381. DAVE WICKERSHAM
□ 384. CHUCK ESSEGIAN
□ 398. HANK BAUER
□ 416. DICK HOWSER
□ 422. BUD DALEY
□ 444. JOE NUXHALL
□ 462. LOU KLIMCHOCK
□ 498. RAY HERBERT
□ 518. ANDY CAREY
□ 536. BILL TUTTLE(F)
□ 552. JIM ARCHER

LOS ANGELES ANGELS

□ 65. TED KLUSZEWSKI
□ 121. ELI GRBA
□ 156. KEN L. HUNT
□ 163. ED SADOWSKI
□ 176. KEN ASPROMONTE
□ 184. STEVE BILKO
□ 195. JERRY CASALE
□ 209. KEN MCBRIDE
□ 216. TED BOWSFIELD
□ 225. BILL RIGNEY(M)
□ 246. BOB DAVIS
□ 263. KEN HAMLIN
□ 272. TOM MORGAN
□ 282. FAYE THRONEBERRY
□ 288. ALBIE PEARSON
□ 291. TEX CLEVENGER
□ 329. JULIO BECQUER
□ 331. NED GARVER
□ 358. EARL AVERILL
□ 413. EDDIE YOST
□ 448. DEL RICE
□ 457. JOHNNY JAMES
□ 464. LEROY THOMAS
□ 466. RON MOELLER
□ 508. ROCKY BRIDGES
□ 527. GENE LEEK
□ 547. LEON WAGNER

LOS ANGELES DODGERS

□ 6. ED ROEBUCK
□ 23. DON DEMETER
□ 38. BOB LILLIS
□ 74. JOE PIGNATANO
□ 86. TEAM CARD
□ 109. JOHNNY PODRES
□ 130. NORM LARKER
□ 136. WALT ALSTON(M)
□ 147. ED RAKOW
□ 168. TOMMY DAVIS
□ 190. STAN WILLIAMS
□ 238. JIM GILLIAM
□ 260. DON DRYSDALE
□ 280. FRANK HOWARD
□ 298. JIM GOLDEN
□ 325. WALLY MOON
□ 344. SANDY KOUFAX
□ 363. JOHN ROSEBORO
□ 396. BOB ASPROMONTE
□ 412. LARRY SHERRY
□ 423. CHARLIE NEAL
□ 443. DUKE SNIDER
□ 460. GIL HODGES
□ 492. RON FAIRLY
□ 506. WILLIE DAVIS
□ 522. DICK FARRELL
□ 525. RON PERRANOSKI
□ 543. ROGER CRAIG

MILWAUKEE BRAVES

□ 29. DON NOTTEBART
□ 61. RON PICHE
□ 73. AL SPANGLER
□ 84. LEE MAYE
□ 89. BILLY MARTIN
□ 105. CARL WILLEY
□ 120. ED MATHEWS
□ 137. CHUCK DRESSEN(M)
□ 145. BOB BUHL
□ 164. FELIX MANTILLA
□ 183. ANDRE RODGERS
□ 200. WARREN SPAHN
□ 217. MEL ROACH
□ 245. JOE ADCOCK
□ 261. CHARLIE LAU
□ 278. DON MCMAHON
□ 296. WES COVINGTON
□ 320. LOU BURDETTE
□ 335. FRANK BOLLING
□ 353. HOWIE BEDELL
□ 372. BOB HENDLEY
□ 390. DEL CRANDALL
□ 415. HANK AARON
□ 446. BOB TAYLOR
□ 463. TEAM CARD
□ 465. ROY MCMILLAN
□ 496. KEN MACKENZIE
□ 501. JOHN DEMERIT
□ 524. JOHNNY LOGAN

MINNESOTA TWINS

□ 4. LENNY GREEN
□ 21. ZORRO VERSALLES
□ 36. JACK KRALICK
□ 63. JIM KAAT
□ 80. HARMON KILLEBREW
□ 92. HAL NARAGON
□ 108. DAN DOBBEK
□ 123. BILLY GARDNER
□ 153. DON LEE
□ 186. ELMER VALO
□ 201. PETE WHISENANT
□ 226. COOKIE LAVAGETTO(M)
□ 235. CAMILO PASCUAL
□ 254. TED SADOWSKI
□ 289. RAY MOORE
□ 315. EARL BATTEY
□ 336. DON MINCHER
□ 355. BOB ALLISON
□ 374. PAUL GIEL
□ 392. RENO BERTOIA
□ 431. CHUCK STOBBS
□ 450. JIM LEMON
□ 469. RALPH LUMENTI
□ 504. BILLY CONSOLO
□ 528. PEDRO RAMOS
□ 536. BILL TUTTLE(B)
□ 542. TEAM CARD
□ 557. JOSE VALDIVIELSO

NEW YORK YANKEES

□ 2. ROGER MARIS
□ 19. CLETIS BOYER
□ 28. HECTOR LOPEZ
□ 40. BOB TURLEY
□ 68. DERON JOHNSON
□ 104. JOHN BLANCHARD
□ 116. JOE DEMAESTRI
□ 133. RALPH HOUK(M)
□ 142. LUIS ARROYO
□ 160. WHITEY FORD
□ 180. BOBBY RICHARDSON
□ 213. BILL STAFFORD
□ 228. TEAM CARD
□ 252. BILL SHORT
□ 265. TONY KUBEK
□ 300. MICKEY MANTLE
□ 333. FRITZ BRICKELL
□ 349. DANNY MCDEVITT
□ 356. RYNE DUREN

- ☐ 371. BILL SKOWRON
- ☐ 387. DUKE MAAS
- ☐ 389. RALPH TERRY
- ☐ 425. YOGI BERRA
- ☐ 495. ELSTON HOWARD
- ☐ 510. ART DITMAR
- ☐ 531. JIM COATES
- ☐ 541. ROLAND SHELDON
- ☐ 563. BOB CERV

PHILADELPHIA PHILLIES

- ☐ 3. JOHN BUZHARDT
- ☐ 20. ROBIN ROBERTS
- ☐ 59. JIM WOODS
- ☐ 78. LEE WALLS
- ☐ 93. TONY GONZALEX
- ☐ 103. RUBEN AMARO
- ☐ 111. JACK MEYER
- ☐ 144. JIM COKER
- ☐ 154. BOBBY DEL GRECO
- ☐ 179. JOE KOPPE
- ☐ 202. AL NEIGER
- ☐ 219. GENE MAUCH(M)
- ☐ 234. TED LEPCIO
- ☐ 262. TONY CURRY
- ☐ 281. FRANK SULLIVAN
- ☐ 299. CLAY DALRYMPLE
- ☐ 316. BOBBY GENE SMITH
- ☐ 341. JIM OWENS
- ☐ 359. DALLAS GREEN
- ☐ 377. RUBEN GOMEZ
- ☐ 394. KEN WALTERS
- ☐ 411. TONY TAYLOR
- ☐ 433. ART MAHAFFEY
- ☐ 468. JOHNNY CALLISON
- ☐ 491. TEAM CARD
- ☐ 502. CLARENCE COLEMAN
- ☐ 530. BOBBY MALKMUS
- ☐ 558. DON FERRARESE

PITTSBURGH PIRATES

- ☐ 1. DICK GROAT
- ☐ 22. CLEM LABINE
- ☐ 54. EARL FRANCIS
- ☐ 70. BILL VIRDON
- ☐ 82. JOE CHRISTOPHER
- ☐ 100. HARVEY HADDIX
- ☐ 126. DICK STUART
- ☐ 138. DANNY MURTAUGH(M)
- ☐ 149. BOB OLDIS
- ☐ 165. GINO CIMOLI
- ☐ 181. FRED GREEN
- ☐ 204. BOB SKINNER
- ☐ 230. DON HOAK
- ☐ 242. HAL W. SMITH
- ☐ 270. BOB FRIEND
- ☐ 286. GEORGE WITT
- ☐ 304. ROCKY NELSON
- ☐ 339. GENE BAKER
- ☐ 370. ROY FACE
- ☐ 379. BOBBY SHANTZ
- ☐ 388. BOB CLEMENTE
- ☐ 400. VERN LAW
- ☐ 430. BILL MAZEROSKI
- ☐ 453. DICK SCHOFIELD
- ☐ 461. SMOKY BURGESS
- ☐ 494. TOM CHENEY
- ☐ 523. JOE GIBBON
- ☐ 554. TEAM CARD

ST. LOUIS CARDINALS

- ☐ 11. CURT SIMMONS
- ☐ 32. RAY SADECKI
- ☐ 52. GEORGE CROWE
- ☐ 64. ALEX GRAMMAS
- ☐ 91. WALT MORYN
- ☐ 118. CHRIS CANNIZZARO
- ☐ 127. RON KLINE
- ☐ 139. SOLLY HEMUS(M)
- ☐ 148. JULIAN JAVIER
- ☐ 178. BOB NIEMAN
- ☐ 198. CARL SAWATSKI
- ☐ 211. BOB GIBSON
- ☐ 232. BILL WHITE
- ☐ 241. AL CICOTTE
- ☐ 266. LINDY MCDANIEL
- ☐ 290. STAN MUSIAL
- ☐ 314. BOB L. MILLER
- ☐ 338. DON LANDRUM
- ☐ 347. TEAM CARD
- ☐ 357. DARYL SPENCER
- ☐ 375. KEN BOYER
- ☐ 420. ERNIE BROGLIO
- ☐ 438. CURT FLOOD
- ☐ 487. GENE OLIVER
- ☐ 505. RED SCHOENDIENST
- ☐ 520. JOE CUNNINGHAM
- ☐ 535. LARRY JACKSON
- ☐ 549. HAL R. SMITH
- ☐ 561. CHARLEY JAMES

SAN FRANCISCO GIANTS

- ☐ 31. BOB SCHMIDT
- ☐ 55. JIM DAVENPORT
- ☐ 72. STU MILLER
- ☐ 87. JOE AMALFITANO
- ☐ 96. BILLY O'DELL
- ☐ 114. HOBIE LANDRITH
- ☐ 150. WILLIE MAYS
- ☐ 161. SHERMAN JONES
- ☐ 167. TEAM CARD
- ☐ 188. JIM MARSHALL
- ☐ 203. EDDIE BRESSOUD
- ☐ 220. AL DARK(M)
- ☐ 237. BILLY LOES
- ☐ 258. JACK SANFORD
- ☐ 279. JOSE PAGAN
- ☐ 294. DON BLASINGAME
- ☐ 305. MIKE MCCORMICK
- ☐ 327. MATTY ALOU
- ☐ 366. EDDIE FISHER
- ☐ 417. JUAN MARICHAL
- ☐ 435. ORLANDO CEPEDA
- ☐ 449. BOBBY BOLIN
- ☐ 500. HARVEY KUEEN
- ☐ 517. WILLIE MCCOVEY
- ☐ 538. CHUCK HILLER
- ☐ 555. SAM JONES
- ☐ 565. FELIPE ALOU

WASHINGTON SENATORS

- ☐ 117. DALE LONG
- ☐ 129. ED HOBAUGH
- ☐ 134. MICKEY VERNON(M)
- ☐ 146. MARTY KEOUGH
- ☐ 158. PETE DALEY
- ☐ 174. RAY SEMPROCH
- ☐ 187. BILLY KLAUS
- ☐ 206. GENE GREEN
- ☐ 229. RUDY HERNANDEX
- ☐ 239. DAVE SISLER(F)
- ☐ 259. JOHN SCHAIVE
- ☐ 275. GENE WOODLING
- ☐ 293. TOM STURDIVANT
- ☐ 318. DANNY O'CONNELL
- ☐ 332. DUTCH DOTTERER
- ☐ 351. JIM KING
- ☐ 368. BENNIE DANIELS
- ☐ 386. JOE HICKS
- ☐ 397. HAL WOODESHICK
- ☐ 414. DICK DONOVAN
- ☐ 432. COOT VEAL
- ☐ 447. HARRY BRIGHT
- ☐ 458. WILLIE TASBY
- ☐ 488. JOE MCCLAIN
- ☐ 507. PETE BURNSIDE
- ☐ 526. R.C. STEVENS
- ☐ 539. JOHNNY KLIPPSTEIN
- ☐ 546. MARTY KUTYNA

1962 TOPPS (598)
2 1/2" X 3 1/2"

BALTIMORE ORIOLES

- ☐ 6. MARV BREEDING
- ☐ 34. JOHNNY TEMPLE
- ☐ 45. BROOKS ROBINSON
- ☐ 64. RUSS SNYDER
- ☐ 75. MILT PAPPAS
- ☐ 99. BOOG POWELL
- ☐ 112. HANK FOILES
- ☐ 121. BILLY HITCHCOCK(M)
- ☐ 134. BILLY HOEFT
- ☐ 165. JACKIE BRANDT
- ☐ 189. DICK HALL
- ☐ 203. JACK FISHER
- ☐ 221. BILL SHORT
- ☐ 245. RON HANSEN
- ☐ 272. EARL ROBINSON
- ☐ 290. JIM GENTILE
- ☐ 327. OSSIE VIRGIL
- ☐ 355. STEVE BARBER
- ☐ 382. DICK WILLIAMS
- ☐ 420. GUS TRIANDOS
- ☐ 442. WES STOCK
- ☐ 449. JERRY ADAIR
- ☐ 476. TEAM CARD
- ☐ 488. HAL BROWN
- ☐ 513. WHITEY HERZOG
- ☐ 533. CHARLEY LAU
- ☐ 545. HOYT WILHELM
- ☐ 560. CHUCK ESTRADA
- ☐ 577. DAVE NICHOLSON
- ☐ 591. ART QUIRK(R)

BOSTON RED SOX

- ☐ 3. PETE RUNNELS
- ☐ 35. DON SCHWALL
- ☐ 81. JIM PAGLIARONI
- ☐ 101. CARROLL HARDY
- ☐ 117. GARY GEIGER
- ☐ 153. PUMPSIE GREEN
- ☐ 187. GENE CONLEY
- ☐ 201. IKE DELOCK
- ☐ 225. FRANK MALZONE
- ☐ 244. DON GILE
- ☐ 276. HAL KOLSTAD
- ☐ 301. GALEN CISCO
- ☐ 334. TEAM CARD
- ☐ 336. BILLY MUFFETT
- ☐ 345. CHUCK SCHILLING
- ☐ 368. BOB TILLMAN
- ☐ 403. CHET NICHOLS
- ☐ 425. CARL YASTRZEMSKI
- ☐ 444. TED WILLS
- ☐ 457. LOU CLINTON
- ☐ 504. EDDIE BRESSOUD
- ☐ 512. MIKE FORNIELES
- ☐ 523. RUSS NIXON
- ☐ 542. DAVE PHILLEY
- ☐ 559. MIKE HIGGINS(M)
- ☐ 567. TRACY STALLARD
- ☐ 580. BILL MONBOUQUETTE
- ☐ 591. DICK RADATZ(R)

CHICAGO CUBS

- ☐ 25. ERNIE BANKS
- ☐ 47. BOB WILL
- ☐ 66. CUNO BARRAGON
- ☐ 89. BARNEY SCHULTZ
- ☐ 119. DANNY MURPHY

- □ 170. RON SANTO
- □ 191. JIM BREWER
- □ 240. GEORGE ALTMAN
- □ 264. DICK ELLSWORTH
- □ 274. SAMMY TAYLOR
- □ 288. BILLY WILLIAMS
- □ 309. MOE MORHARDT
- □ 359. BOBBY LOCKE
- □ 372. JACK CURTIS
- □ 387. LOU BROCK
- □ 446. DON ELSTON
- □ 458. BOB BUHL
- □ 461. KEN HUBBS
- □ 477. ANDRE RODGERS
- □ 495. DON CARDWELL
- □ 546. MOE THACKER
- □ 552. TEAM CARD
- □ 557. BOB ANDERSON
- □ 585. GLEN HOBBIE
- □ 597. JIM MCKNIGHT(R)

CHICAGO WHITE SOX

- □ 8. RAY HERBERT
- □ 73. NELLIE FOX
- □ 91. J.C. MARTIN
- □ 113. TEAM CARD
- □ 116. HERB SCORE
- □ 161. FRANK BAUMANN
- □ 178. CAMILO CARREON
- □ 195. JOE CUNNINGHAM
- □ 214. DOM ZANNI
- □ 255. JUAN PIZARRO
- □ 283. CHARLIE SMITH
- □ 286. AL LOPEZ(M)
- □ 325. LUIS APARICIO
- □ 341. MIKE HERSHBERGER
- □ 363. BOB ROSELLI
- □ 385. EARLY WYNN
- □ 410. AL SMITH
- □ 426. BOB FARLEY
- □ 454. FLOYD ROBINSON
- □ 479. JOEL HORLEN
- □ 514. SHERM LOLLAR
- □ 528. TURK LOWN
- □ 540. JIM LANDIS
- □ 555. JOHN BUZHARDT
- □ 576. RUSS KEMMERER
- □ 586. SAMMY ESPOSITO
- □ 595. BOB FRANK SADOWSKI(R)

CINCINNATI REDS

- □ 2. JIM BROSNAN
- □ 16. DARRELL JOHNSON
- □ 41. CLIFF COOK
- □ 80. VADA PINSON
- □ 103. DON BLASINGAME
- □ 120. BOB PURKEY
- □ 148. WALLY POST
- □ 151. JOHNNY KLIPPSTEIN
- □ 171. DAVE SISLER
- □ 172. FRED HUTCHINSON(M)
- □ 193. EDDIE KASKO
- □ 205. GENE FREESE
- □ 258. MARTY KEOUGH
- □ 267. DAN DOBBEK
- □ 282. DAVE HILLMAN
- □ 302. JOHN EDWARDS
- □ 331. MOE DRABOWSKY
- □ 350. FRANK ROBINSON
- □ 364. KEN R. HUNT
- □ 381. CHICO CARDENAS
- □ 414. JOE GAINES
- □ 440. JOE JAY
- □ 450. JIM O'TOOLE
- □ 465. TEAM CARD
- □ 478. DON ZIMMER
- □ 487. JERRY LYNCH
- □ 508. GORDY COLEMAN
- □ 524. HOWIE NUNN
- □ 562. BILL R. HENRY
- □ 594. DON PAVLETICH(R)

CLEVELAND INDIANS

- □ 15. DICK DONOVAN
- □ 49. HAL JONES
- □ 78. GENE GREEN
- □ 97. TITO FRANCONA
- □ 123. MIKE DE LA HOZ
- □ 145. BARRY LATMAN
- □ 182. BOB NIEMAN
- □ 215. WOODY HELD
- □ 224. DON RUDOLPH
- □ 242. MEL MCGAHA(M)
- □ 253. HARRY CHITI
- □ 273. GARY BELL
- □ 292. JERRY KINDALL
- □ 307. JIM GRANT
- □ 330. JOHNNY ROMANO
- □ 362. TY CLINE
- □ 379. CHUCK ESSEGIAN
- □ 405. JIM PERRY
- □ 447. WILLIE KIRKLAND
- □ 462. WILLIE TASBY
- □ 485. PEDRO RAMOS
- □ 511. BUBBA PHILLIPS
- □ 537. TEAM CARD
- □ 543. BOB ALLEN
- □ 563. KEN ASPROMONTE
- □ 587. FRANK FUNK
- □ 591. SAM MCDOWELL(R)
- □ 591. RON TAYLOR(R)
- □ 594. DOC EDWARDS(R)
- □ 598. AL LUPLOW(R)

DETROIT TIGERS

- □ 20. ROCKY COLAVITO
- □ 24. TEAM CARD
- □ 62. STEVE BOROS
- □ 87. MIKE ROARKE
- □ 92. SAM JONES
- □ 105. DON MOSSI
- □ 114. HOWIE KOPLITZ
- □ 150. AL KALINE
- □ 173. CHICO FERNANDEZ
- □ 196. TERRY FOX
- □ 216. RON KLINE
- □ 250. NORM CASH
- □ 261. GEORGE ALUSIK
- □ 299. DON WERT
- □ 335. BILL BRUTON
- □ 349. PAUL FOYTACK
- □ 366. PHIL REGAN
- □ 407. HANK AGUIRRE
- □ 416. BOB SCHEFFING(M)
- □ 427. JAKE WOOD
- □ 438. DICK BROWN
- □ 460. JIM BUNNING
- □ 481. VIC WERTZ
- □ 506. CHARLIE MAXWELL
- □ 527. DICK MCAULIFFE
- □ 554. BUBBA MORTON
- □ 583. LARRY OSBORNE
- □ 591. RON NISCHWITZ(R)

HOUSTON COLT .45'S

- □ 12. HARRY CRAFT(M)
- □ 23. NORM LARKER
- □ 44. DON TAUSSIG
- □ 74. BOB LILLIS
- □ 126. AL CICOTTE
- □ 156. MERRITT RANEW
- □ 177. BOBBY SHANTZ
- □ 204. JOHNNY WEEKLY
- □ 227. BOBBY TIEFENAUER
- □ 248. BOB ASPROMONTE
- □ 278. KEN JOHNSON
- □ 304. DICK FARRELL
- □ 332. DON BUDDIN
- □ 354. ROMAN MEJIAS
- □ 373. AL HEIST
- □ 419. BOB BRUCE
- □ 432. JIM PENDLETON
- □ 456. JOE AMALFITANO
- □ 483. DON MCMAHON(B)
- □ 492. HAL W. SMITH
- □ 509. DAVE GIUSTI
- □ 526. HAL WOODESHICK
- □ 536. DICK GERNERT
- □ 556. AL SPANGLER
- □ 568. JIM GOLDEN
- □ 574. DEAN STONE
- □ 598. ED OLIVARES(R)

KANSAS CITY ATHLETICS

- □ 13. DICK HOWSER
- □ 38. GENE STEPHENS
- □ 82. DERON JOHNSON
- □ 122. NORM BASS
- □ 147. BILL KUNKEL
- □ 168. LEO POSADA
- □ 184. HAYWOOD SULLIVAN
- □ 246. ART DITMAR
- □ 254. GORDON WINDHORN
- □ 275. NORM SIEBERN
- □ 305. JERRY LUMPE
- □ 333. FRANK CIPRIANI
- □ 342. ED RAKOW
- □ 357. JERRY WALKER
- □ 384. TEAM CARD
- □ 402. GINO CIMOLI
- □ 417. JOE AZCUE
- □ 433. JIM ARCHER
- □ 451. JOSE TARTABULL
- □ 463. HANK BAUER(M)
- □ 493. DANNY MCDEVITT
- □ 496. WAYNE CAUSEY
- □ 517. DAVE WICKERSHAM
- □ 548. BOBBY DEL GRECO
- □ 564. BOB GRIM
- □ 592. DAN PFISTER(R)
- □ 595. MARLAN COUGHTRY(R)
- □ 598. MANNY JIMENEZ(R)

LOS ANGELES ANGELS

- □ 11. TOM MORGAN
- □ 39. JOE KOPPE
- □ 68. KEN L. HUNT
- □ 96. ELI GRBA
- □ 128. ART FOWLER
- □ 132. TEAM CARD
- □ 154. LEE THOMAS
- □ 176. EDDIE YOST
- □ 194. DEAN CHANCE
- □ 209. JIM FREGOSI
- □ 257. JACK SPRING
- □ 268. KEN MCBRIDE
- □ 287. GEORGE WITT
- □ 343. ALBIE PEARSON
- □ 369. TED BOWSFIELD
- □ 388. RYNE DUREN
- □ 422. STEVE BILKO
- □ 431. BOB RODGERS
- □ 452. EARL AVERILL
- □ 491. LEON WAGNER
- □ 498. JIM DONOHUE
- □ 525. GEORGE THOMAS
- □ 539. BILLY MORAN
- □ 549. BILL RIGNEY(M)
- □ 569. ED SADOWSKI
- □ 592. BO BELINSKY(R)
- □ 595. FELIX TORRES(R)

LOS ANGELES DODGERS

- □ 5. SANDY KOUFAX
- □ 32. JOHN ROSEBORO
- □ 43. TEAM CARD
- □ 69. PHIL ORTEGA
- □ 108. WILLIE DAVIS
- □ 129. LEE WALLS
- □ 131. PETE RICHERT
- □ 175. FRANK HOWARD
- □ 190. WALLY MOON
- □ 197. DARYL SPENCER
- □ 217. WALT ALSTON(M)
- □ 238. NORM SHERRY
- □ 280. JOHNNY PODRES
- □ 297. RON PERRANOSKI
- □ 340. DON DRYSDALE
- □ 348. LARRY BURRIGHT
- □ 358. TOMMY DAVIS
- □ 375. RON FAIRLY
- □ 404. TIM HARKNESS
- □ 418. ANDY CAREY
- □ 435. LARRY SHERRY
- □ 486. JIM GILLIAM
- □ 500. DUKE SNIDER
- □ 515. STAN WILLIAMS
- □ 535. ED ROEBUCK
- □ 594. DOUG CAMILLI(R)

MILWAUKEE BRAVES

- □ 30. ED MATHEWS
- □ 63. TONY CLONINGER
- □ 76. HOWIE BEDELL
- □ 100. WARREN SPAHN
- □ 109. BOB SHAW
- □ 130. FRANK BOLLING
- □ 158. TEAM CARD
- □ 174. CARL WILLEY

☐ 186. MACK JONES
☐ 218. JOE TORRE
☐ 239. CECIL BUTLER
☐ 259. LOU KLIMCHOCK
☐ 265. JOE ADCOCK
☐ 289. MIKE KRSNICH
☐ 320. HANK AARON
☐ 361. BOB HENDLEY
☐ 380. LOU BURDETTE
☐ 406. BOB TAYLOR
☐ 443. DEL CRANDALL
☐ 483. DON MCMAHON(F)
☐ 518. LEE MAVE
☐ 541. DON NOTTEBART
☐ 582. RON PICHE
☐ 588. BIRDIE TEBBETTS(M)
☐ 594. BOB UECKER(R)
☐ 597. DENIS MENKE(R)
☐ 597. AMADO SAMUEL(R)

MINNESOTA TWINS

☐ 21. JIM KAAT
☐ 70. HARMON KILLEBREW
☐ 84. LENNY GREEN
☐ 102. AL SCHROLL
☐ 124. BILL PLEIS
☐ 164. HAL NARAGON
☐ 166. DON LEE
☐ 180. BOB ALLISON
☐ 208. BILLY MARTIN
☐ 222. JERRY ZIMMERMAN
☐ 230. CAMILO PASCUAL
☐ 298. BILL TUTTLE
☐ 321. LEE STANGE
☐ 339. JOSE VALDIVIELSO
☐ 346. JACK KRALICK
☐ 371. EARL BATTEY
☐ 386. DON MINCHER
☐ 437. RAY MOORE
☐ 445. VIC POWER
☐ 482. SAM MELE(M)
☐ 499. ZOILO VERSALLES
☐ 510. JIM LEMON
☐ 532. DICK STIGMAN
☐ 558. JOHN GORYL
☐ 584. TEAM CARD
☐ 592. JOE BONIKOWSKI(R)
☐ 596. BERNIE ALLEN(R)
☐ 596. RICH ROLLINS(R)

NEW YORK METS

☐ 4. JOHN DEMERIT
☐ 7. FRANK THOMAS
☐ 26. CHRIS CANNIZZARO
☐ 29. CASEY STENGEL(M)
☐ 85. GIL HODGES
☐ 94. JAY HOOK
☐ 162. SAMMY DRAKE
☐ 183. ROGER CRAIG
☐ 213. RICHIE ASHBURN
☐ 256. ELIO CHACON
☐ 279. HOBIE LANDRITH
☐ 293. BOB L. MILLER
☐ 308. NEIL CHRISLEY
☐ 337. JIM MARSHALL
☐ 365. CHARLEY NEAL
☐ 408. GUS BELL
☐ 421. KEN MACKENZIE
☐ 436. FELIX MANTILLA
☐ 464. AL JACKSON
☐ 497. ED BOUCHEE
☐ 572. BOB G. MILLER
☐ 593. CRAIG ANDERSON(R)
☐ 593. BOB MOORHEAD(R)
☐ 597. ROD KANEHL(R)
☐ 598. JIM HICKMAN(R)

NEW YORK YANKEES

☐ 1. ROGER MARIS
☐ 31. TOM TRESH
☐ 48. RALPH TERRY
☐ 65. BOBBY RICHARDSON
☐ 88. RALPH HOUK(M)
☐ 93. JOHN BLANCHARD
☐ 110. BILL SKOWRON
☐ 159. HAL RENIFF
☐ 169. BOB CERV
☐ 185. ROLAND SHELDON
☐ 200. MICKEY MANTLE
☐ 219. AL DOWNING
☐ 243. ROBIN ROBERTS
☐ 251. TEAM CARD
☐ 281. JAKE GIBBS
☐ 291. HAL STOWE
☐ 310. WHITEY FORD
☐ 338. BILLY GARDNER
☐ 360. YOGI BERRA
☐ 376. BUD DALEY
☐ 400. ELSTON HOWARD
☐ 430. TONY KUBEK
☐ 455. LUIS ARROYO
☐ 490. CLETE BOYER
☐ 502. HECTOR LOPEZ
☐ 553. JIM COATES
☐ 570. BILL STAFFORD
☐ 589. BOB TURLEY
☐ 592. JIM BOUTON(R)
☐ 596. PHIL LINZ(R)
☐ 596. JOE PEPITONE(R)

PHILADELPHIA PHILLIES

☐ 17. JOHN CALLISON
☐ 46. JACK BALDSCHUN
☐ 77. TONY TAYLOR
☐ 104. TED SAVAGE
☐ 111. DALLAS GREEN
☐ 146. DON DEMETER
☐ 157. WES COVINGTON
☐ 181. PAUL BROWN
☐ 212. JIM OWENS
☐ 220. ROY SIEVERS
☐ 249. ED KEEGAN
☐ 269. BOB OLDIS
☐ 284. RUBEN AMARO
☐ 294. TEAM CARD
☐ 303. FRANK TORRE
☐ 328. KEN WALTERS
☐ 352. FRANK SULLIVAN
☐ 374. GENE MAUCH(M)
☐ 434. CLAY DALRYMPLE
☐ 453. CAL MCLISH
☐ 494. SAMMY WHITE
☐ 521. JACKIE DAVIS
☐ 534. TONY GONZALEZ
☐ 550. ART MAHAFFEY
☐ 571. BILLY KLAUS
☐ 581. MEL ROACH
☐ 593. JACK HAMILTON(R)

PITTSBURGH PIRATES

☐ 10. ROBERTO CLEMENTE
☐ 36. DON LEPPERT
☐ 67. HARVEY HADDIX
☐ 86. DONN CLENDENON
☐ 95. DON HOAK
☐ 115. BOB SKINNER
☐ 160. DICK STUART
☐ 179. TOM STURDIVANT
☐ 210. ROY FACE
☐ 229. JESUS MCFARLANE
☐ 252. EARL FRANCIS
☐ 270. DICK GROAT
☐ 295. VERN LAW
☐ 326. TOM PARSONS
☐ 353. BILL MAZEROSKI
☐ 389. SMOKY BURGESS
☐ 409. TEAM CARD
☐ 415. BILL VIRDON
☐ 424. AL MCBEAN
☐ 448. JOE GIBBON
☐ 484. DICK SCHOFIELD
☐ 503. DANNY MURTAUGH(M)
☐ 520. BOB FRIEND
☐ 573. JOHNNY LOGAN
☐ 593. JACK LAMABE(R)
☐ 593. BOB VEALE(R)
☐ 598. HOWIE GOSS(R)

ST. LOUIS CARDINALS

☐ 14. BILL WHITE
☐ 19. RAY WASHBURN
☐ 28. MINNIE MINOSO
☐ 50. STAN MUSIAL
☐ 61. TEAM CARD
☐ 83. LARRY JACKSON
☐ 106. CARL SAWATSKI
☐ 118. JULIAN JAVIER
☐ 149. BOB DULIBA
☐ 167. TIM MCCARVER
☐ 198. JOHNNY KEANE(M)
☐ 202. CARL WARWICK
☐ 223. ALEX GRAMMAS
☐ 241. JOHNNY KUCKS
☐ 266. JOHN ANDERSON
☐ 285. CURT SIMMONS
☐ 323. DON LANDRUM
☐ 344. ED BAUTA
☐ 370. KEN BOYER
☐ 383. RAY SADECKI
☐ 412. CHARLIE JAMES
☐ 439. JERRY BUCHEK
☐ 489. JULIO GOTAY
☐ 507. ERNIE BROGLIO
☐ 522. LINDY MCDANIEL
☐ 530. BOB GIBSON
☐ 531. BOBBY GENE SMITH
☐ 547. DON FERRARESE
☐ 561. GENE OLIVER
☐ 575. RED SCHOENDIENST
☐ 579. JIM SCHAFFER
☐ 590. CURT FLOOD

SAN FRANCISCO GIANTS

☐ 9. JIM DAVENPORT
☐ 33. DON LARSEN
☐ 40. ORLANDO CEPEDA
☐ 71. DICK LEMAY
☐ 107. MIKE MCCORMICK
☐ 133. FELIPE ALOU
☐ 155. STU MILLER
☐ 188. CHUCK HILLER
☐ 199. GAYLORD PERRY
☐ 226. TEAM CARD
☐ 231. ERNIE BOWMAN
☐ 247. JOE PIGNATANO
☐ 260. BILL PIERCE
☐ 300. WILLIE MAYS
☐ 322. AL DARK(M)
☐ 329. BOB BOLIN
☐ 356. TOM HALLER
☐ 377. JOHNNY ORSINO
☐ 413. MATTY ALOU
☐ 429. BILLY O'DELL
☐ 459. ED BAILEY
☐ 480. HARVEY KUENN
☐ 505. JUAN MARICHAL
☐ 538. JACK SANFORD
☐ 544. WILLIE MCCOVEY
☐ 565. JOSE PAGAN
☐ 578. JIM DUFFALO

WASHINGTON SENATORS

☐ 27. CHUCK COTTIER
☐ 42. JIM KING
☐ 79. ED HOBAUGH
☐ 90. JIM PIERSALL
☐ 125. GENE WOODLING
☐ 152. MICKEY VERNON(M)
☐ 206. TEAM CARD
☐ 207. PETE BURNSIDE
☐ 228. DALE LONG
☐ 262. BOB SCHMIDT
☐ 271. RAY RIPPELMEYER
☐ 296. KEN HAMLIN
☐ 324. JOE MCCLAIN
☐ 347. CHUCK HINTON
☐ 378. BENNIE DANIELS
☐ 411. DANNY O'CONNELL
☐ 428. JOE HICKS
☐ 501. CLAUDE OSTEEN
☐ 519. BOB W. JOHNSON
☐ 529. JOHN SCHAIVE
☐ 551. HARRY BRIGHT
☐ 566. MARTY KUTYNA
☐ 592. DAVE STENHOUSE(R)
☐ 594. KEN RETZER(R)

1963 TOPPS (576)
2 1/2" X 3 1/2"

BALTIMORE ORIOLES

□ 12. STEVE BARBER
□ 19. PETE BURNSIDE
□ 41. CHARLIE LAU
□ 65. JACKIE BRANDT
□ 88. RON HANSEN
□ 108. HOYT WILHELM
□ 112. DICK BROWN
□ 125. ROBIN ROBERTS
□ 158. BOB SAVERINE(R)
□ 205. LUIS APARICIO
□ 208. JOHN MILLER(R)
□ 209. HOBIE LANDRITH
□ 213. BILLY HITCHCOCK(M)
□ 260. JIM GENTILE
□ 286. STU MILLER
□ 319. JOE GAINES
□ 345. BROOKS ROBINSON
□ 358. MILT PAPPAS
□ 377. TEAM CARD
□ 398. BOOG POWELL
□ 418. JOHNNY ORSINO
□ 438. WES STOCK
□ 465. CHUCK ESTRADA
□ 488. JERRY ADAIR
□ 496. STEVE DALKOWSKI(R)
□ 504. BOB W. JOHNSON
□ 526. DICK HALL
□ 543. RUSS SNYDER
□ 562. DAVE MCNALLY(R)
□ 563. MIKE MCCORMICK

BOSTON RED SOX

□ 28. MIKE FORNIELES
□ 52. CHUCK SCHILLING
□ 76. EARL WILSON
□ 96. LOU CLINTON
□ 115. CARL YASTRZEMSKI
□ 136. IKE DELOCK
□ 168. RUSS NIXON
□ 188. EDDIE BRESSOUD
□ 202. TEAM CARD
□ 216. GENE CONLEY
□ 232. FRANK MALZONE
□ 251. JACK LAMABE
□ 253. PETE JERNIGAN(R)
□ 285. DICK STUART
□ 299. DAVE MOREHEAD(R)
□ 307. CHET NICHOLS
□ 328. DICK WILLIAMS
□ 343. JOHNNY PESKY(M)
□ 363. DICK RADATZ
□ 384. BOB TILLMAN
□ 408. BILLY GARDNER
□ 432. ROMAN MEJIAS
□ 447. FELIX MANTILLA
□ 480. BILL MONBOUQUETTE
□ 513. GARY GEIGER
□ 553. JIM GOSGER(R)
□ 574. HAL KOLSTAD

CHICAGO CUBS

□ 15. KEN HUBBS
□ 31. CAL KOONCE
□ 54. NELSON MATHEWS(R)
□ 58. BOB WILL
□ 81. JIMMIE SCHAFFER
□ 95. LARRY JACKSON
□ 113. DON LANDRUM
□ 175. BOB BUHL
□ 193. ANDRE RODGERS
□ 212. GLEN HOBBIE
□ 222. TEAM CARD
□ 252. RON SANTO
□ 272. DANNY MURPHY
□ 287. DICK BERTELL
□ 309. JIM BREWER
□ 329. LINDY MCDANIEL
□ 353. BILLY WILLIAMS
□ 380. ERNIE BANKS
□ 399. DICK ELLSWORTH
□ 416. ALEX GRAMMAS
□ 452. BARNEY SCHULTZ
□ 459. DICK LEMAY
□ 464. KEN ASPROMONTE
□ 472. LOU BROCK
□ 489. PAUL TOTH
□ 515. DON ELSTON
□ 532. STEVE BOROS
□ 557. CUNO BARRAGAN

CHICAGO WHITE SOX

□ 16. AL SMITH
□ 35. JOHN BUZHARDT
□ 54. DAVE DEBUSSCHERE(R)
□ 66. MIKE JOYCE
□ 86. CHARLEY MAXWELL
□ 100. JOE CUNNINGHAM
□ 118. SHERM LOLLAR
□ 160. JUAN PIZARRO
□ 181. SAMMY ESPOSITO
□ 223. EDDIE FISHER
□ 234. DAVE NICHOLSON
□ 253. DEACON JONES(R)
□ 254. MIKE HERSHBERGER
□ 271. DEAN STONE
□ 288. TEAM CARD
□ 308. CAMILO CARREON
□ 324. PETE WARD(R)
□ 332. JOEL HORLEN
□ 354. DOM ZANNI
□ 381. FRANK BAUMANN
□ 405. FLOYD ROBINSON
□ 424. CHARLEY SMITH
□ 458. AL LOPEZ(M)
□ 485. JIM LANDIS
□ 499. J.C. MARTIN
□ 522. GARY PETERS(R)
□ 525. NELLIE FOX
□ 537. AL WEIS(R)
□ 560. RAY HERBERT

CINCINNATI REDS

□ 21. MARTY KEOUGH
□ 29. SAMMY ELLIS(R)
□ 29. JESSE GONDER(R)
□ 37. JERRY LYNCH
□ 63. TEAM CARD
□ 70. JIM O'TOOLE
□ 90. GORDY COLEMAN
□ 116. JIM BROSNAN
□ 133. GENE FREESE
□ 158. TOMMY HARPER(R)
□ 178. JOHNNY EDWARDS
□ 194. JOE NUXHALL
□ 203. CHICO CARDENAS
□ 225. JOE JAY
□ 244. JOHN TSITOURIS
□ 265. VADA PINSON
□ 284. DAVE SISLER
□ 304. HARRY BRIGHT
□ 326. HANK FOILES
□ 350. BOB PURKEY
□ 378. BILL R. HENRY
□ 400. FRANK ROBINSON
□ 407. CHICO RUIZ(R)
□ 422. FRED HUTCHINSON(M)
□ 444. JIM MALONEY
□ 462. WALLY POST
□ 483. JIM OWENS
□ 498. EDDIE KASKO
□ 518. DON BLASINGAME
□ 534. KEN WALTERS
□ 537. PETE ROSE(R)
□ 556. AL WORTHINGTON

CLEVELAND INDIANS

□ 14. PEDRO RAMOS
□ 36. JERRY KINDALL
□ 48. BIRDIE TEBBETTS(M)
□ 72. JOHNNY ROMANO
□ 103. CHUCK ESSEGIAN
□ 129. GARY BELL
□ 152. RON NISCHWITZ
□ 170. JOE ADCOCK
□ 187. WILLIE KIRKLAND
□ 211. FRED WHITFIELD
□ 227. JIM GRANT
□ 228. MAX ALVIS(R)
□ 248. TITO FRANCONA
□ 266. BOB ALLEN
□ 296. DOC EDWARDS
□ 317. SAM MCDOWELL
□ 324. VIC DAVALILLO(R)
□ 351. AL LUPLOW
□ 370. DICK DONOVAN
□ 391. BILL DAILEY
□ 413. JERRY WALKER
□ 426. BARRY LATMAN
□ 435. WOODY HELD
□ 451. TEAM CARD
□ 463. JOE SCHAFFERNOTH
□ 466. TONY MARTINEZ(R)
□ 493. WALT BOND
□ 506. GENE GREEN
□ 558. BOB LIPSKI(R)
□ 561. MIKE DE LA HOZ

DETROIT TIGERS

□ 25. AL KALINE
□ 44. TERRY FOX
□ 64. DICK MCAULIFFE
□ 84. RON KLINE
□ 134. BOB SCHEFFING(M)
□ 140. FRANK LARY
□ 164. BUBBA MORTON
□ 169. DICK EGAN(R)
□ 177. BUBBA PHILLIPS
□ 224. MIKE ROARKE
□ 240. ROCKY COLAVITO
□ 257. HANK AGUIRRE
□ 278. CHICO FERNANDEZ
□ 299. BOB DUSTAL(R)
□ 302. WHITEY HERZOG
□ 327. PAUL FOYTACK
□ 348. VIC WERTZ
□ 365. JIM BUNNING
□ 379. BOB ANDERSON
□ 406. HOWIE KOPLITZ
□ 407. FRANK KOSTRO(R)
□ 437. BILL BRUTON
□ 445. NORM CASH
□ 453. JAKE WOOD
□ 466. BILL FREEHAN(R)
□ 475. GUS TRIANDOS
□ 494. PHIL REGAN
□ 516. PURNAL GOLDY
□ 530. DON MOSSI
□ 552. TEAM CARD
□ 558. BILL FAUL(R)
□ 573. COOT VEAL

HOUSTON COLT .45'S

□ 24. BOB BRUCE
□ 45. BOB ASPROMONTE
□ 77. AL SPANGLER
□ 99. JIM UMBRICHT
□ 119. BOB LILLIS
□ 141. MANNY MOTA
□ 153. HAL W. SMITH
□ 158. DAVE L. ROBERTS(R)
□ 189. DAVE GIUSTI
□ 204. DON NOTTEBART
□ 208. WALLY WOLF(R)
□ 230. PETE RUNNELS
□ 262. ELLIS BURON
□ 277. DICK FARRELL

- ☐ 297. JIM GOLDEN
- ☐ 312. TEAM CARD
- ☐ 324. GEORGE WILLIAMS(R)
- ☐ 333. CARL WARWICK
- ☐ 338. RUSS KEMMERER
- ☐ 352. KEN JOHNSON
- ☐ 373. JIM CAMPBELL
- ☐ 386. JOHN BATEMAN(R)
- ☐ 395. DON MCMAHON
- ☐ 442. J.C. HARTMAN
- ☐ 468. CARROLL HARDY
- ☐ 491. HARRY CRAFT(M)
- ☐ 517. HAL WOODESHICK
- ☐ 538. GEORGE BRUNET
- ☐ 544. RUSTY STAUB(R)
- ☐ 553. BROCK DAVIS(R)
- ☐ 562. RANDY CARDINAL(R)
- ☐ 576. JOHNNY TEMPLE

KANSAS CITY ATHLETICS

- ☐ 23. ED LOPAT(M)
- ☐ 51. GEORGE ALUSIK
- ☐ 67. ED CHARLES
- ☐ 82. ED RAKOW
- ☐ 104. LEW KRAUSSE
- ☐ 124. DICK HOWSER
- ☐ 157. DIEGO SEGUI
- ☐ 195. MANNY JIMENEZ
- ☐ 214. ORLANDO PENA
- ☐ 236. BILL BRYAN
- ☐ 253. JOHN WOJCIK(R)
- ☐ 256. JERRY LUMPE
- ☐ 282. BOB DEL GRECO
- ☐ 301. BILL FISCHER
- ☐ 321. GINO CIMOLI
- ☐ 339. TED BOWSFIELD
- ☐ 359. HAYWOOD SULLIVAN
- ☐ 376. JOHNNIE WYATT
- ☐ 397. TEAM CARD
- ☐ 430. NORM SIEBERN
- ☐ 449. JOSE TARTABULL
- ☐ 461. NORM BASS
- ☐ 492. DAVE WICKERSHAM
- ☐ 501. JOE AZCUE
- ☐ 521. DAN PFISTER
- ☐ 539. WAYNE CAUSEY
- ☐ 549. PETE LOVRICH(R)

LOS ANGELES ANGELS

- ☐ 17. RYNE DUREN
- ☐ 33. BO BELINSKY
- ☐ 39. TEAM CARD
- ☐ 57. BILLY MORAN
- ☐ 98. GEORGE THOMAS
- ☐ 114. DAN OSINSKI
- ☐ 117. JACKE DAVIS
- ☐ 167. JIM FREGOSI
- ☐ 169. JULIO NAVARRO(R)
- ☐ 182. ALBIE PEARSON
- ☐ 207. KEN L. HUNT
- ☐ 231. ELI GRBA
- ☐ 249. LEO BURKE
- ☐ 280. BOB RODGERS
- ☐ 294. BILL RIGNEY(M)
- ☐ 322. BOB TURLEY
- ☐ 335. LEON WAGNER
- ☐ 355. DEAN CHANCE
- ☐ 372. DON LEE
- ☐ 386. ED KIRKPATRICK(R)
- ☐ 396. JOE KOPPE
- ☐ 407. DICK SIMPSON(R)
- ☐ 421. TOM MORGAN
- ☐ 441. LEE THOMAS
- ☐ 454. ART FOWLER
- ☐ 482. FELIX TORRES
- ☐ 496. FRED NEWMAN(R)
- ☐ 510. KEN MCBRIDE
- ☐ 522. MEL NELSON(R)
- ☐ 527. ED SADOWSKI
- ☐ 541. RON MOELLER
- ☐ 548. TOM SATRIANO
- ☐ 568. BOB FRANK SADOWSKI
- ☐ 572. JACK SPRING

LOS ANGELES DODGERS

- ☐ 11. LEE WALLS
- ☐ 53. JOE MOELLER
- ☐ 80. JIM GILLIAM
- ☐ 105. RON FAIRLY
- ☐ 123. FRANK HOWARD
- ☐ 150. JOHNNY PODRES
- ☐ 154. WALTER ALSTON(M)
- ☐ 180. BILL SKOWRON
- ☐ 196. DOUG CAMILLI
- ☐ 210. SANDY KOUFAX
- ☐ 229. WILLIE DAVIS
- ☐ 261. BOB L. MILLER
- ☐ 279. WALLY MOON
- ☐ 295. ED ROEBUCK
- ☐ 310. TOMMY DAVIS
- ☐ 337. TEAM CARD
- ☐ 360. DON DRYSDALE
- ☐ 383. PETE RICHERT
- ☐ 403. RON PERRANOSKI
- ☐ 439. DON ZIMMER
- ☐ 466. NATE OLIVER(R)
- ☐ 467. PHIL ORTEGA
- ☐ 487. JOHN ROSEBORO
- ☐ 496. JACK SMITH(R)
- ☐ 502. DARYL SPENCER
- ☐ 537. KEN MCMULLEN(R)
- ☐ 544. BILL HAAS(R)
- ☐ 562. KEN ROWE(R)
- ☐ 565. LARRY SHERRY

MILWAUKEE BRAVES

- ☐ 46. TOMMIE AARON
- ☐ 62. BOB HENDLEY
- ☐ 73. BOBBY BRAGAN(M)
- ☐ 74. DENVER LEMASTER
- ☐ 109. LEE MAYE
- ☐ 126. BOB UECKER
- ☐ 137. MACK JONES
- ☐ 156. ROY MCMILLAN
- ☐ 179. RON PICHE
- ☐ 201. CECIL BUTLER
- ☐ 238. LOU JOHNSON
- ☐ 253. LEN GABRIELSON(R)
- ☐ 255. BOB SHAW
- ☐ 275. ED MATHEWS
- ☐ 298. DON DILLARD
- ☐ 299. DAN SCHNEIDER(R)
- ☐ 320. WARREN SPAHN
- ☐ 324. PHILL ROOF(R)
- ☐ 347. JOE TORRE
- ☐ 367. TONY CLONINGER
- ☐ 390. HANK AARON
- ☐ 411. JIM CONSTABLE
- ☐ 414. TY CLINE
- ☐ 429. LOU BURDETTE
- ☐ 433. DENIS MENKE
- ☐ 460. DEL CRANDALL
- ☐ 476. FRANK FUNK
- ☐ 481. BOB TAYLOR
- ☐ 503. TEAM CARD
- ☐ 519. CLAUDE RAYMOND
- ☐ 536. NORM LARKER
- ☐ 547. GUS BELL
- ☐ 554. HANK FISCHER
- ☐ 570. FRANK BOLLING

MINNESOTA TWINS

- ☐ 26. RAY MOORE
- ☐ 40. VIC POWER
- ☐ 75. BOB ALLISON
- ☐ 89. DICK STIGMAN
- ☐ 110. RICH ROLLINS
- ☐ 127. BILL TUTTLE
- ☐ 162. TEAM CARD
- ☐ 165. JIM KAAT
- ☐ 186. JERRY ZIMMERMAN
- ☐ 198. LENNY GREEN
- ☐ 220. CAMILO PASCUAL
- ☐ 228. TONY OLIVA(R)
- ☐ 246. LEE STANGE
- ☐ 269. DON MINCHER
- ☐ 293. BILL PLEIS
- ☐ 314. JOHN GORYL
- ☐ 349. ZOILO VERSALLES
- ☐ 369. JIM LEMON
- ☐ 386. GARRY ROGGENBURK(R)
- ☐ 389. FRANK SULLIVAN
- ☐ 410. EARL BATTEY
- ☐ 427. BERNIE ALLEN
- ☐ 448. JACK KRALICK
- ☐ 500. HARMON KILLEBREW
- ☐ 522. JIM ROLAND(R)
- ☐ 531. SAM MELE(M)
- ☐ 535. JIM PERRY
- ☐ 549. PAUL RATLIFF(R)
- ☐ 564. GEORGE BANKS

NEW YORK METS

- ☐ 27. CHOO CHOO COLEMAN
- ☐ 59. CRAIG ANDERSON
- ☐ 78. MARV THRONEBERRY
- ☐ 93. GALEN CISCO
- ☐ 107. JIM HICKMAN
- ☐ 111. AL JACKSON
- ☐ 135. RICHIE ASHBURN
- ☐ 174. LARRY BURRIGHT
- ☐ 197. ROGER CRAIG
- ☐ 217. JOE CHRISTOPHER
- ☐ 228. ED KRANEPOOL(R)
- ☐ 233. CASEY STENGEL(M)
- ☐ 245. GIL HODGES
- ☐ 273. SAMMY TAYLOR
- ☐ 292. PUMPSIE GREEN
- ☐ 316. NORM SHERRY
- ☐ 334. WYNN HAWKINS
- ☐ 342. GENE WOODLING
- ☐ 371. ROD KANEHL
- ☐ 386. LARRY BEARNARTH(R)
- ☐ 393. KEN MACKENZIE
- ☐ 419. TRACY STALLARD
- ☐ 436. TIM HARKNESS
- ☐ 469. JAY HOOK
- ☐ 473. TEAM CARD
- ☐ 495. FRANK THOMAS
- ☐ 511. CHARLIE NEAL
- ☐ 528. CARL WILLEY
- ☐ 550. DUKE SNIDER
- ☐ 558. AL MORAN(R)
- ☐ 558. RON HUNT(R)
- ☐ 562. DON ROWE(R)
- ☐ 566. CLIFF COOK

NEW YORK YANKEES

- ☐ 20. TONY KUBEK
- ☐ 38. BUD DALEY
- ☐ 42. STAN WILLIAMS
- ☐ 54. JACK CULLEN(R)
- ☐ 60. ELSTON HOWARD
- ☐ 92. HECTOR LOPEZ
- ☐ 120. ROGER MARIS
- ☐ 155. BILL STAFFORD
- ☐ 183. JOE PEPITONE
- ☐ 200. MICKEY MANTLE
- ☐ 237. JIM COATES
- ☐ 247. TEAM CARD
- ☐ 264. PHIL LINZ
- ☐ 289. HAL BROWN
- ☐ 315. RALPH TERRY
- ☐ 340. YOGI BERRA
- ☐ 361. CLETE BOYER
- ☐ 382. RALPH HOUK(M)
- ☐ 401. JIM BOUTON
- ☐ 420. BOBBY RICHARDSON
- ☐ 446. WHITEY FORD
- ☐ 457. TEX CLEVENGER
- ☐ 470. TOM TRESH
- ☐ 484. DALE LONG
- ☐ 507. ROLAND SHELDON

□ 523. BILL KUNKEL
□ 537. PEDRO GONZALEZ(R)
□ 546. HAL RENIFF
□ 555. JOHN BLANCHARD
□ 569. LUIS ARROYO

PHILADELPHIA PHILLIES

□ 13. TEAM CARD
□ 29. JOHN BOOZER(R)
□ 29. RAY CULP(R)
□ 32. TONY GONZALEZ
□ 56. DENNIS BENNETT
□ 71. BOBBY WINE
□ 91. DALLAS GREEN
□ 132. JACK HAMILTON
□ 139. EARL AVERILL
□ 161. FRANK TORRE
□ 192. CLAY DALRYMPLE
□ 221. COOKIE ROJAS
□ 241. BILLY SMITH
□ 268. DON DEMETER
□ 283. ROY SIEVERS
□ 305. DON HOAK
□ 318. GENE MAUCH(M)
□ 341. JACK BALDSCHUN
□ 366. TONY TAYLOR
□ 385. ART MAHAFFEY
□ 404. BOB OLDIS
□ 434. JOHNNY CALLISON
□ 455. RUBEN AMARO
□ 478. PAUL BROWN
□ 512. CAL MCLISH
□ 529. WES COVINGTON
□ 549. MARCELINO LOPEZ(R)
□ 551. BILLY KLAUS
□ 553. JOHN HERNSTEIN(R)
□ 571. JOHNNY KLIPPSTEIN

PITTSBURGH PIRATES

□ 34. DICK SCHOFIELD
□ 55. BILL VIRDON
□ 87. BOB VEALE
□ 101. JOE GIBBON
□ 122. JULIO GOTAY
□ 151. TEAM CARD
□ 159. JIM PAGLIARONI
□ 169. TOMMIE SISK(R)
□ 184. VERNON LAW
□ 215. BOB SKINNER
□ 228. BOB BAILEY(R)
□ 239. HARVEY HADDIX
□ 259. JOHNNY LOGAN
□ 281. TOM STURDIVANT
□ 299. TOM BUTTERS(R)
□ 303. EARL FRANCIS
□ 323. BILL MAZEROSKI
□ 344. DON SCHWALL
□ 364. HOWIE GOSS
□ 387. AL MCBEAN
□ 407. LARRY ELLIOT(R)
□ 409. ROY FACE
□ 425. SMOKY BURGESS
□ 450. BOB FRIEND
□ 477. DONN CLENDENON
□ 508. TED SAVAGE
□ 540. BOB CLEMENTE
□ 549. ELMO PLASKETT(R)
□ 553. WILLIE STARGELL(R)
□ 559. DANNY MURTAUGH(M)
□ 575. DON CARDWELL

ST. LOUIS CARDINALS

□ 22. CURT SIMMONS
□ 49. DAL MAXVILL
□ 54. HARRY FANOK(R)
□ 83. CHARLEY JAMES
□ 97. BOB DULIBA
□ 130. DICK GROAT
□ 166. JOHNNY KEANE(M)
□ 172. GENE OLIVER
□ 190. MINNIE MINOSO
□ 206. RAY WASHBURN
□ 208. RON TAYLOR(R)
□ 226. JULIAN JAVIER
□ 250. STAN MUSIAL
□ 267. CARL SAWATSKI
□ 290. BILL WHITE
□ 313. ERNIE BROGLIO
□ 336. ED BAUTA
□ 357. GEORGE ALTMAN
□ 375. KEN BOYER
□ 394. TIM MCCARVER
□ 415. BOB GIBSON
□ 486. RAY SADECKI
□ 505. CURT FLOOD
□ 524. TEAM CARD
□ 533. BOBBY SHANTZ
□ 544. DUKE CARMEL(R)

SAN FRANCISCO GIANTS

□ 30. HARVEY KUEEN
□ 50. BILL PIERCE
□ 61. ERNIE BOWMAN
□ 85. TOM HALLER
□ 106. BOB BOLIN
□ 128. MATTY ALOU
□ 163. DON LARSEN
□ 169. GAYLORD PERRY(R)
□ 185. CHUCK HILLER
□ 199. JOE AMALFITANO
□ 208. RON HERBEL(R)
□ 235. BILLY O'DELL
□ 258. ALVIN DARK(M)
□ 270. FELIPE ALOU
□ 300. WILLIE MAYS
□ 325. JACK SANFORD
□ 346. BILLY HOEFT
□ 368. ED BAILEY
□ 388. JIM DAVENPORT
□ 417. TEAM CARD
□ 428. CARL BOLES
□ 440. JUAN MARICHAL
□ 456. JIM COKER
□ 466. JERRY ROBINSON(R)
□ 474. JACK FISHER
□ 490. WILLIE MCCOVEY
□ 520. ORLANDO CEPEDA
□ 545. JOSE PAGAN
□ 567. JIM DUFFALO

WASHINGTON SENATORS

□ 47. DON LOCK
□ 69. BUD ZIPFEL
□ 94. BOB SCHMIDT
□ 121. JIM HANNAN
□ 131. TEAM CARD
□ 149. MARV BREEDING
□ 158. ROGELIO ALVAREZ(R)
□ 171. STEVE HAMILTON
□ 176. JIM KING
□ 219. CHUCK COTTIER
□ 243. DON LEPPERT
□ 263. DAVE STENHOUSE
□ 276. BARRY SHETRONE
□ 291. DON RUDOLPH
□ 311. JOE MCCLAIN
□ 330. CHUCK HINTON
□ 356. JOHN SCHAIVE
□ 374. CLAUDE OSTEEN
□ 402. MICKEY VERNON(M)
□ 423. ED HOBAUGH
□ 443. JIM PIERSALL
□ 471. KEN RETZER
□ 479. ED BRINKMAN
□ 496. CARL BOULDIN(R)
□ 497. BENNIE DANIELS
□ 514. LARRY OSBORNE
□ 522. ART QUIRK(R)
□ 542. LOU KLIMCHOCK
□ 544. DICK PHILLIPS(R)

1964 TOPPS (587)
2 1/2" X 3 1/2"

BALTIMORE ORIOLES

□ 17. WILLIE KIRKLAND
□ 22. JERRY ADAIR
□ 45. MILT PAPPAS
□ 63. JOHNNY ORSINO
□ 89. BOOG POWELL
□ 126. RUSS SNYDER
□ 145. NORM SIEBERN
□ 161. DAVE MCNALLY
□ 178. HANK BAUER(M)
□ 201. SAM BOWENS(R)
□ 201. WALLY BUNKER(R)
□ 221. BOB SAVERINE
□ 230. BROOKS ROBINSON
□ 239. HERM STARRETTE
□ 263. CHUCK ESTRADA
□ 285. ROBIN ROBERTS
□ 304. BOB W. JOHNSON
□ 322. GEORGE BRUNET
□ 364. JOE GAINES
□ 382. WES STOCK
□ 399. JACKIE BRANDT
□ 418. DAROLD KNOWLES(R)
□ 418. LES NARUM(R)
□ 439. HARVEY HADDIX
□ 450. STEVE BARBER
□ 473. TEAM CARD
□ 487. MIKE MCCORMICK
□ 511. LOU JACKSON
□ 540. LUIS APARICIO
□ 565. STU MILLER

BOSTON RED SOX

□ 25. BILL MONBOUQUETTE
□ 60. FRANK MALZONE
□ 79. BOB HEFFNER
□ 93. GARY GEIGER
□ 112. BOB TILLMAN
□ 153. DICK WILLIAMS
□ 170. DICK RADATZ
□ 186. ROMAN MEJIAS
□ 210. CARL YASTRZEMSKI
□ 228. FELIX MANTILLA
□ 248. JOHNNY PESKY(M)
□ 267. WILBUR WOOD
□ 287. TONY CONIGLIARO(R)
□ 287. BILL SPANSWICK(R)
□ 305. JACK LAMABE
□ 329. RUSS NIXON
□ 352. ED BRESSOUD
□ 376. DAVE MOREHEAD
□ 410. DICK STUART
□ 428. ARCHIE SKEEN(R)
□ 428. PETE SMITH(R)
□ 459. PETE CHARTON(R)
□ 459. DALTON JONES(R)
□ 481. CHUCK SCHILLING
□ 503. EARL WILSON
□ 526. LOU CLINTON
□ 572. DAVE GRAY(R)
□ 579. TEAM CARD

CHICAGO CUBS

- ☐ 29. LOU BROCK
- ☐ 55. ERNIE BANKS
- ☐ 78. MERRITT RANEW
- ☐ 96. BOB BUHL
- ☐ 111. DON ELSTON
- ☐ 131. STEVE BOROS
- ☐ 175. BILLY WILLIAMS
- ☐ 192. JOHN BOCCABELLA(R)
- ☐ 192. BILLY COWAN(R)
- ☐ 220. DICK ELLSWORTH
- ☐ 237. TEAM CARD
- ☐ 252. KEN ASPROMONTE
- ☐ 269. ELLIS BURTON
- ☐ 286. DON LANDRUM
- ☐ 309. PAUL TOTH
- ☐ 336. ANDRE RODGERS
- ☐ 359. JIM SCHAFFER
- ☐ 375. RON SANTO
- ☐ 408. JIM STEWART(R)
- ☐ 408. FRED BURDETTE(R)
- ☐ 424. DICK BERTELL
- ☐ 444. LARRY JACKSON
- ☐ 451. JOE AMALFITANO
- ☐ 469. FRED NORMAN(R)
- ☐ 469. STERLING SLAUGHTER(R)
- ☐ 486. BOB KENNEDY(HC)
- ☐ 510. LINDY MCDANIEL
- ☐ 548. WAYNE SCHURR(R)
- ☐ 557. LEO BURKE
- ☐ 578. GLEN HOBBIE

CHICAGO WHITE SOX

- ☐ 13. HOYT WILHELM
- ☐ 31. DAVE NICHOLSON
- ☐ 66. EDDIE FISHER
- ☐ 85. PETE WARD
- ☐ 107. BRUCE HOWARD
- ☐ 107. FRANK KREUTZER(R)
- ☐ 130. GARY PETERS
- ☐ 148. J.C. MARTIN
- ☐ 168. AL WEIS
- ☐ 195. FLOYD ROBINSON
- ☐ 215. RAY HERBERT
- ☐ 232. AL LOPEZ(M)
- ☐ 247. DAVE DEBUSSCHERE
- ☐ 264. JIM LANDIS
- ☐ 283. TOMMY MCCRAW
- ☐ 308. GENE STEPHENS
- ☐ 323. JOHN BUZHARDT
- ☐ 340. JOE CUNNINGHAM
- ☐ 368. FRITZ ACKLEY(R)
- ☐ 368. DON BUFORD(R)
- ☐ 384. RON HANSEN
- ☐ 401. CHARLIE MAXWELL
- ☐ 421. CAMILO CARREON
- ☐ 430. JUAN PIZARRO
- ☐ 453. FRANK BAUMANN
- ☐ 465. MIKE HERSHBERGER
- ☐ 496. TEAM CARD
- ☐ 538. MINNIE MINOSO
- ☐ 564. JERRY MCNERTNEY(R)
- ☐ 584. JOEL HORLEN

CINCINNATI REDS

- ☐ 33. SAMMY ELLIS(R)
- ☐ 33. MEL QUEEN(R)
- ☐ 49. BILL R. HENRY
- ☐ 72. CHICO CARDENAS
- ☐ 80. VADA PINSON
- ☐ 106. JOE NUXHALL
- ☐ 125. PETE ROSE
- ☐ 144. AL WORTHINGTON
- ☐ 166. MARTY KEOUGH
- ☐ 185. JIM O'TOOLE
- ☐ 207. FRED HUTCHINSON(M)
- ☐ 233. HAL W. SMITH
- ☐ 260. FRANK ROBINSON
- ☐ 275. JOHN TSITOURIS
- ☐ 303. JIM CAMPBELL
- ☐ 330. TOMMY HARPER
- ☐ 346. JOE JAY
- ☐ 356. BILL MCCOOL(R)
- ☐ 356. CHICO RUIZ(R)
- ☐ 377. BOB SKINNER
- ☐ 403. TEAM CARD
- ☐ 420. JIM MALONEY
- ☐ 436. CHARLIE NEAL
- ☐ 449. DERON JOHNSON
- ☐ 480. BOB PURKEY
- ☐ 507. JOHN EDWARDS
- ☐ 524. JIM DICKSON(R)
- ☐ 524. BOBBY KLAUS(R)
- ☐ 577. GORDY COLEMAN

CLEVELAND INDIANS

- ☐ 64. TED ABERNATHY
- ☐ 77. JERRY WALKER
- ☐ 105. WOODY HELD
- ☐ 122. DON MCMAHON
- ☐ 133. JIM GRANT
- ☐ 146. TOMMY JOHN(R)
- ☐ 146. BOB CHANCE(R)
- ☐ 172. TEAM CARD
- ☐ 184. AL LUPLOW
- ☐ 199. JOSE AZCUE
- ☐ 216. MIKE DE LA HOZ
- ☐ 234. GARY BELL
- ☐ 253. WALLY POST
- ☐ 301. LARRY BROWN
- ☐ 317. AL SMITH
- ☐ 338. JACK KRALICK
- ☐ 367. FRED WHITFIELD
- ☐ 391. SAM MCDOWELL
- ☐ 404. TONY MARTINEZ
- ☐ 435. VIC DAVALILLO
- ☐ 462. BIRDIE TEBBETTS(M)
- ☐ 478. DICK HOWSER
- ☐ 499. CHICO SALMON(R)
- ☐ 499. GORDON SEYFRIED(R)
- ☐ 515. JOHN ROMANO
- ☐ 530. LEON WAGNER
- ☐ 545. MAX ALVIS
- ☐ 552. TOM KELLEY(R)
- ☐ 552. SONNY SIEBERT(R)
- ☐ 562. PEDRO RAMOS
- ☐ 571. GENE CONLEY
- ☐ 583. TITO FRANCONA

DETROIT TIGERS

- ☐ 19. DON WERT
- ☐ 39. HANK AGUIRRE
- ☐ 58. DON DEMETER
- ☐ 67. TEAM CARD
- ☐ 98. BILL BRUTON
- ☐ 128. MICKEY LOLICH
- ☐ 143. BUBBA PHILLIPS
- ☐ 165. JERRY LUMPE
- ☐ 181. DAVE WICKERSHAM
- ☐ 197. FRANK LARY
- ☐ 236. BILL FAUL
- ☐ 250. AL KALINE
- ☐ 272. JAKE WOOD
- ☐ 292. MIKE ROARKE
- ☐ 312. FRITZ FISHER(R)
- ☐ 312. FRED GLADDING(R)
- ☐ 335. DON MOSSI
- ☐ 363. DICK MCAULIFFE
- ☐ 387. TERRY FOX
- ☐ 407. BILL FREEHAN
- ☐ 425. NORM CASH
- ☐ 443. CHARLIE DRESSEN(M)
- ☐ 461. GEORGE THOMAS
- ☐ 471. GATES BROWN
- ☐ 474. LARRY SHERRY
- ☐ 489. JULIO NAVARRO
- ☐ 491. ED RAKOW
- ☐ 512. WILLIE HORTON(R)
- ☐ 512. JOE SPARMA(R)
- ☐ 535. PHIL REGAN
- ☐ 572. DICK EGAN(R)

HOUSTON COLT .45'S

- ☐ 23. CHRIS ZACHARY
- ☐ 38. JIM WYNN
- ☐ 56. HAL BROWN
- ☐ 109. RUSTY STAUB
- ☐ 121. PETE RUNNELS
- ☐ 142. JOHN BATEMAN
- ☐ 158. KEN JOHNSON
- ☐ 179. CARL WARWICK
- ☐ 205. NELLIE FOX
- ☐ 226. JERRY GROTE(R)
- ☐ 226. LARRY YELLEN(R)
- ☐ 241. JIM OWENS
- ☐ 256. JOHNNY WEEKLY
- ☐ 282. BOB BRUCE
- ☐ 298. HARRY CRAFT(M)
- ☐ 321. BOB LILLIS
- ☐ 339. WALT BOND
- ☐ 354. DAVE GIUSTI
- ☐ 370. HAL WOODESHICK
- ☐ 389. JIM UMBRICHT
- ☐ 406. AL SPANGLER
- ☐ 434. DON NOTTEBART
- ☐ 467. BOB ASPROMONTE
- ☐ 492. JIM BEAUCHAMP(R)
- ☐ 492. MIKE WHITE(R)
- ☐ 504. CLAUDE RAYMOND
- ☐ 544. STEVE HERTZ(R)
- ☐ 544. JOE HOERNER(R)
- ☐ 560. DICK FARRELL

KANSAS CITY ATHLETICS

- ☐ 26. GINO CIMOLI
- ☐ 42. MOE DRABOWSKY
- ☐ 75. WAYNE CAUSEY
- ☐ 108. JOHN WYATT
- ☐ 124. ORLANDO PENA
- ☐ 151. TEAM CARD
- ☐ 174. DOC EDWARDS
- ☐ 196. JIM GENTILE
- ☐ 212. PETE LOVRICH
- ☐ 229. CHARLEY LAU
- ☐ 244. TONY LARUSSA
- ☐ 276. JOSE TARTABULL
- ☐ 302. DAN PFISTER
- ☐ 320. ROCKY COLAVITO
- ☐ 334. LEW KRAUSSE
- ☐ 348. ED LOPAT(M)
- ☐ 366. NELSON MATHEWS
- ☐ 388. JOHN O'DONOGHUE(R)
- ☐ 388. GEORGE WILLIAMS(R)
- ☐ 402. TOM STURDIVANT
- ☐ 419. KEN HARRELSON
- ☐ 431. GEORGE ALUSIK
- ☐ 447. TED BOWSFIELD
- ☐ 466. DICK GREEN(R)
- ☐ 466. AURELIO MONTEAGUDO(R)
- ☐ 475. ED CHARLES
- ☐ 508. DIEGO SEGUI
- ☐ 528. DAVE DUNCAN(R)
- ☐ 528. TOM REYNOLDS(R)
- ☐ 574. MANNY JIMENEZ

LOS ANGELES ANGELS

- ☐ 32. DEAN CHANCE
- ☐ 48. BOB PERRY
- ☐ 71. JACK SPRING
- ☐ 97. JIM FREGOSI
- ☐ 110. ALBIE PEARSON
- ☐ 127. AUBREY GATEWOOD(R)
- ☐ 127. DICK SIMPSON(R)
- ☐ 149. PAUL FOYTACK
- ☐ 159. CHARLIE DEES
- ☐ 213. TEAM CARD
- ☐ 227. BARRY LATMAN
- ☐ 255. LEE THOMAS
- ☐ 273. MEL NELSON

☐ 279. JOE KOPPE
☐ 296. ED KIRKPATRICK
☐ 315. BO BELINSKY
☐ 333. BILLY MORAN
☐ 349. ART FOWLER
☐ 383. BILL RIGNEY
☐ 405. KEN MCBRIDE
☐ 426. BOB RODGERS
☐ 441. BOB DULIBA
☐ 493. DON LEE
☐ 502. BOBBY KNOOP(R)
☐ 502. BOB LEE(R)
☐ 521. TOM SATRIANO
☐ 537. DAN OSINSKI
☐ 554. HANK FOILES
☐ 569. FRED NEWMAN
☐ 586. JIM PIERSALL

LOS ANGELES DODGERS

☐ 14. DICK NEN(R)
☐ 14. NICK WILLHITE(R)
☐ 30. RON PERRANOSKI
☐ 51. PETE RICHERT
☐ 68. WILLIE DAVIS
☐ 88. JOHN ROSEBORO
☐ 101. WALT ALSTON(M)
☐ 120. DON DRYSDALE
☐ 154. DICK TRACEWSKI
☐ 180. TOMMY DAVIS
☐ 200. SANDY KOUFAX
☐ 214. KEN MCMULLEN
☐ 231. DICK CALMUS
☐ 249. DOUG CAMILLI
☐ 291. PHIL ORTEGA
☐ 310. JIM GILLIAM
☐ 337. AL FERRARA(R)
☐ 337. JEFF TORBORG(R)
☐ 353. WALLY MOON
☐ 371. FRANK HOWARD
☐ 394. BOB L. MILLER
☐ 411. LEE WALLS
☐ 456. WES PARKER(R)
☐ 456. JOHN WERHAS(R)
☐ 490. RON FAIRLY
☐ 531. TEAM CARD
☐ 548. PAUL SPECKENBACH(R)
☐ 549. JOE MOELLER
☐ 553. JIM BREWER
☐ 580. JOHNNY PODRES

MILWAUKEE BRAVES

☐ 35. ED MATHEWS
☐ 53. DENIS MENKE
☐ 65. FELIPE ALOU
☐ 70. JOE TORRE
☐ 94. JIM BRITTON(R)
☐ 94. LARRY MAXIE(R)
☐ 115. FRANK BOLLING
☐ 132. TEAM CARD
☐ 152. DENVER LEMASTER
☐ 171. TY CLINE
☐ 198. LEN GABRIELSON
☐ 218. HANK FISCHER
☐ 238. ROY MCMILLAN
☐ 271. BOB SADOWSKI
☐ 289. FRANK FUNK
☐ 300. HANK AARON
☐ 316. GENE OLIVER
☐ 351. DAN SCHNEIDER
☐ 378. WOODY WOODWARD(R)
☐ 378. JACK SMITH(R)
☐ 400. WARREN SPAHN
☐ 416. LEE MAYE
☐ 437. ED BAILEY
☐ 454. TOMMIE AARON
☐ 476. RICO CARTY(R)
☐ 476. DICK KELLEY(R)
☐ 506. BOBBY BRAGAN(M)
☐ 522. BOB TIEFENAUER
☐ 534. GUS BELL
☐ 541. PHIL ROOF(R)
☐ 541. PHIL NIEKRO(R)
☐ 551. BILLY HOEFT
☐ 575. TONY CLONINGER

MINNESOTA TWINS

☐ 15. ZOILO VERSALLES
☐ 34. JIM PERRY
☐ 54. SAM MELE(M)
☐ 73. JIMMIE HALL
☐ 90. EARL BATTEY
☐ 116. JAY WARD(R)
☐ 116. TONY OLIVA(R)
☐ 156. BILL DAILEY
☐ 177. HARMON KILLEBREW
☐ 194. JOHN GORYL
☐ 223. GEORGE BANKS
☐ 245. DICK STIGMAN
☐ 258. GARRY ROGGENBURK
☐ 270. RICH ROLLINS
☐ 290. BOB ALLISON
☐ 318. TEAM CARD
☐ 341. JIM ROLAND
☐ 355. VIC POWER
☐ 369. JERRY ZIMMERMAN
☐ 386. LENNY GREEN
☐ 409. BILL FISCHER
☐ 455. BERNIE ALLEN
☐ 484. BILL PLEIS
☐ 500. CAMILO PASCUAL
☐ 516. JERRY ARRIGO(R)
☐ 516. DWIGHT SIEBLER(R)
☐ 532. BUD BLOOMFIELD(R)
☐ 532. JOE NOSSEK(R)
☐ 542. DON MINCHER
☐ 555. LEE STANGE
☐ 564. JOE MCCABE(R)
☐ 567. JIM KAAT

NEW YORK METS

☐ 27. TEAM CARD
☐ 44. DUKE CARMEL
☐ 57. TIM HARKNESS
☐ 84. CARL WILLEY
☐ 95. GEORGE ALTMAN
☐ 113. GROVER POWELL
☐ 129. AMADO SAMUEL
☐ 155. DUKE SNIDER
☐ 176. TRACY STALLARD
☐ 202. GALEN CISCO
☐ 235. RON HUNT
☐ 251. CHOO CHOO COLEMAN
☐ 288. AL MORAN
☐ 324. CASEY STENGEL(M)
☐ 345. FRANK THOMAS
☐ 361. JAY HOOK
☐ 381. BOB TAYLOR
☐ 398. BILL HAAS(R)
☐ 398. DICK SMITH(R)
☐ 422. JACK FISHER
☐ 442. PUMPSIE GREEN
☐ 457. JESSE GONDER
☐ 477. MIKE JOYCE
☐ 494. AL JACKSON
☐ 514. JIM HICKMAN
☐ 519. CHARLIE SMITH
☐ 527. LARRY BEARNARTH
☐ 536. LARRY ELLIOT(R)
☐ 536. JOHN STEPHENSON(R)
☐ 546. JOE CHRISTOPHER
☐ 556. STEVE DILLON(R)
☐ 556. RON LOCKE(R)
☐ 566. ED KRANEPOOL
☐ 576. JERRY HINSLEY(R)
☐ 576. BILL WAKEFIELD
☐ 582. ROD KANEHL

NEW YORK YANKEES

☐ 21. YOGI BERRA(M)
☐ 36. HAL RENIFF
☐ 50. MICKEY MANTLE
☐ 69. CLETE BOYER
☐ 86. AL DOWNING
☐ 100. ELSTON HOWARD
☐ 118. JOHN BLANCHARD
☐ 164. BUD DALEY
☐ 190. BOBBY RICHARDSON
☐ 206. STEVE HAMILTON
☐ 225. ROGER MARIS
☐ 259. HARRY BRIGHT
☐ 281. JAKE GIBBS(R)
☐ 281. TOM METCALF(R)
☐ 299. BILL STAFFORD
☐ 325. HECTOR LOPEZ
☐ 344. PHIL LINZ
☐ 360. JOE PEPITONE
☐ 380. WHITEY FORD
☐ 395. TOM TRESH
☐ 415. TONY KUBEK
☐ 433. TEAM CARD
☐ 458. RALPH TERRY
☐ 470. JIM BOUTON
☐ 488. PETE MIKKELSEN(R)
☐ 488. BOB MEYER(R)
☐ 505. STAN WILLIAMS
☐ 581. PEDRO GONZALEZ(R)
☐ 581. ARCHIE MOORE(R)

PHILADELPHIA PHILLIES

☐ 16. JOHN BOOZER
☐ 43. ROY SIEVERS
☐ 83. GUS TRIANDOS
☐ 104. ART MAHAFFEY
☐ 135. JOHNNY CALLISON
☐ 157. GENE MAUCH(M)
☐ 173. RYNE DUREN
☐ 191. CLAY DALRYMPLE
☐ 208. WES COVINGTON
☐ 243. RICHIE ALLEN
☐ 243. JOHN HERRNSTEIN(R)
☐ 254. DON HOAK
☐ 265. JIM BUNNING
☐ 293. TEAM CARD
☐ 319. PAUL BROWN
☐ 347. BOBBY WINE
☐ 365. CAL MCLISH
☐ 379. TONY GONZALEZ
☐ 396. DENNIS BENNETT
☐ 412. RAY CULP
☐ 432. RUBEN AMARO
☐ 448. COOKIE ROJAS
☐ 464. DALLAS GREEN
☐ 482. JOHN BRIGGS(R)
☐ 482. DANNY CARTER(R)
☐ 520. JACK BALDSCHUN
☐ 533. JOHNNY KLIPPSTEIN
☐ 561. DAVE BENNETT(R)
☐ 561. RICK WISE(R)
☐ 585. TONY TAYLOR

PITTSBURGH PIRATES

☐ 20. BOB FRIEND
☐ 37. SMOKY BURGESS
☐ 62. TED SAVAGE
☐ 74. BOB PRIDDY(R)
☐ 74. TOM BUTTERS(R)
☐ 91. BOB BAILEY
☐ 117. EARL FRANCIS
☐ 141. DANNY MURTAUGH(M)
☐ 163. DONN CLENDENON
☐ 193. JERRY LYNCH
☐ 209. BOB ALLEN
☐ 224. TOMMIE SISK
☐ 246. MANNY MOTA
☐ 266. GENE FREESE
☐ 284. DICK SCHOFIELD
☐ 307. JOE GIBBON
☐ 326. RON BRAND
☐ 342. WILLIE STARGELL
☐ 373. TEAM CARD
☐ 392. JIM PAGLIARONI
☐ 417. DON CARDWELL
☐ 440. BOB CLEMENTE
☐ 472. VERNON LAW
☐ 495. BILL VIRDON
☐ 501. BOB VEALE
☐ 509. GENE ALLEY(R)
☐ 509. ORLANDO MCFARLANE(R)
☐ 525. AL MCBEAN
☐ 539. ROY FACE
☐ 558. DON SCHWALL
☐ 570. BILL MAZEROSKI

ST. LOUIS CARDINALS

☐ 24. CARL SAWATSKI
☐ 40. DICK GROAT
☐ 59. ERNIE BROGLIO
☐ 87. TEAM CARD
☐ 103. CURT FLOOD

☐ 119. GARY KOLB
☐ 147. RAY SADECKI
☐ 160. KEN BOYER
☐ 183. RON TAYLOR
☐ 211. JIM COKER
☐ 240. BILL WHITE
☐ 262. MIKE SHANNON(R)
☐ 262. HARRY FANOK(R)
☐ 278. BOBBY SHANTZ
☐ 295. ROGER CRAIG
☐ 314. JERRY BUCHEK
☐ 332. RAY WASHBURN
☐ 357. CHARLIE JAMES
☐ 385. CURT SIMMONS
☐ 413. JOHNNY KEANE(M)
☐ 429. TIM MCCARVER
☐ 446. JULIAN JAVIER
☐ 460. BOB GIBSON
☐ 479. DAVE BAKENHASTER(R)
☐ 479. JOHNNY LEWIS(R)
☐ 497. JEOFF LONG
☐ 523. LOU BURDETTE
☐ 543. BOB UECKER
☐ 563. DAL MAXVILL
☐ 568. PHIL GAGLIANO(R)

SAN FRANCISCO GIANTS

☐ 18. BILLY O'DELL
☐ 47. JESUS ALOU(R)
☐ 47. RON HERBEL(R)
☐ 82. JIM DAVENPORT
☐ 99. AL STANEK
☐ 123. JOSE PAGAN
☐ 150. WILLIE MAYS
☐ 169. DEL CRANDALL
☐ 189. BOB HENDLEY
☐ 204. MATTY ALOU
☐ 222. BILL PIERCE
☐ 242. HARVEY KUENN
☐ 257. TEAM CARD
☐ 280. JUAN MARICHAL
☐ 297. KEN MACKENZIE
☐ 313. CHUCK HILLER
☐ 328. BOB SHAW
☐ 350. WILLIE MCCOVEY
☐ 374. BOBBY BOLIN
☐ 390. ORLANDO CEPEDA
☐ 414. JACK SANFORD
☐ 452. GIL GARRIDO(R)
☐ 452. JIM HART(R)
☐ 468. GAYLOR PERRY
☐ 485. TOM HALLER
☐ 513. DON LARSEN
☐ 529. AL DARK(M)
☐ 568. CAP PETERSON(R)
☐ 573. JIM DUFFALO

WASHINGTON SENATORS

☐ 28. CLAUDE OSTEEN
☐ 46. ED BRINKMAN
☐ 52. CHUCK HINTON
☐ 92. STEVE RIDZIK
☐ 114. DON LOCK
☐ 134. DON ZIMMER
☐ 167. MIKE BRUMLEY(R)
☐ 167. LOU PINIELLA(R)
☐ 187. ED ROEBUCK
☐ 203. JOHN KENNEDY
☐ 217. JIM KING
☐ 261. JIM HANNAN
☐ 277. KEN RETZER
☐ 294. KEN L. HUNT
☐ 311. TOM BROWN
☐ 327. DON BLASINGAME
☐ 343. TEAM CARD
☐ 358. RON KLINE
☐ 372. HOWIE KOPLITZ
☐ 397. CHUCK COTTIER
☐ 427. DON RUDOLPH
☐ 445. BILL SKOWRON
☐ 463. DON LEPPERT
☐ 483. FRED VALENTINE
☐ 498. DAVE STENHOUSE
☐ 518. CARL BOULDIN
☐ 547. GIL HODGES(M)
☐ 559. DICK PHILLIPS
☐ 587. BENNIE DANIELS

1965 TOPPS (598)
2 1/2" X 3 1/2"

BALTIMORE ORIOLES

☐ 15. ROBIN ROBERTS
☐ 33. JACKIE BRANDT
☐ 49. CURT BLEFARY(R)
☐ 49. JOHN MILLER()R
☐ 67. HARVEY HADDIX
☐ 94. CHARLIE LAU
☐ 113. STEVE BARBER
☐ 150. BROOKS ROBINSON
☐ 169. DAVE VINEYARD
☐ 188. SAM BOWENS
☐ 204. RUSS SNYDER
☐ 231. JERRY ADAIR
☐ 249. DAVE MCNALLY
☐ 270. MILT PAPPAS
☐ 290. WALLY BUNKER
☐ 303. JOHNNY ORSINO
☐ 323. HANK BAUER
☐ 343. MIKE MCCORMICK
☐ 363. BOB W. JOHNSON
☐ 378. CHUCK ESTRADA
☐ 396. FRANK BERTAINA
☐ 410. LUIS APARICIO
☐ 427. BOB SAVERINE
☐ 455. NORM SIEBERN
☐ 473. PAUL BLAIR(R)
☐ 473. DAVE A. JOHNSON(R)
☐ 499. STU MILLER
☐ 518. KEN ROWE
☐ 539. HERM STARRETTE
☐ 560. BOOG POWELL
☐ 572. TEAM CARD
☐ 577. DAROLD KNOWLES(R)

BOSTON RED SOX

☐ 29. FELIX MANTILLA
☐ 42. EARL WILSON
☐ 55. TONY CONIGLIARO
☐ 74. RICO PETROCELLI(R)
☐ 74. JERRY STEPHENSON(R)
☐ 88. JACK LAMABE
☐ 111. LEE THOMAS
☐ 142. BILL MONBOUQUETTE
☐ 147. DENNIS BENNETT
☐ 162. RUSS NIXON
☐ 178. DALTON JONES
☐ 199. BOB HEFFNER
☐ 222. BOB TILLMAN
☐ 251. BILLY HERMAN(M)
☐ 272. CHUCK SCHILLING
☐ 295. DICK RADATZ
☐ 315. FRANK MALZONE
☐ 356. BILL SPANSWICK
☐ 385. CARL YASTRZEMSKI
☐ 403. TEAM CARD
☐ 434. DAVE MOREHEAD
☐ 452. GARY GEIGER
☐ 494. JAY RITCHIE
☐ 509. BOB GUINDON(R)
☐ 509. GERRY VEZENDY(R)
☐ 525. ED BRESSOUD
☐ 543. ED CONNOLLY
☐ 573. JIM LONBORG(R)
☐ 573. GERRY MOSES(R)
☐ 573. MIKE RYAN(R)
☐ 573. BILL SCHLESINGER(R)
☐ 588. LENNY GREEN

CALIFORNIA ANGELS*

☐ 26. BOBBY KNOOP
☐ 46. BOB LEE
☐ 66. BILL RIGNEY(M)
☐ 85. WILLIE SMITH
☐ 101. FRED NEWMAN
☐ 124. TOM SATRIANO
☐ 140. DEAN CHANCE
☐ 172. JIM PIERSALL
☐ 194. BILL KELSO(R)
☐ 194. RICK REICHARDT(R)
☐ 210. JIM FREGOSI
☐ 229. LOU CLINTON
☐ 242. GEORGE BRUNET
☐ 268. KEN MCBRIDE
☐ 293. TEAM CARD
☐ 307. BARRY LATMAN
☐ 324. BOBBY LOCKE
☐ 342. BOB RODGERS
☐ 358. ALBIE PEARSON
☐ 374. JOSE CARDENAL(R)
☐ 374. DICK SIMPSON
☐ 393. ED KIRKPATRICK
☐ 422. AUBREY GATEWOOD
☐ 442. VIC POWER
☐ 464. RON PICHE
☐ 486. TOM EGAN(R)
☐ 486. PAT ROGAN(R)
☐ 517. PAUL SCHAAL(R)
☐ 517. JACKIE J. WARNER(R)
☐ 537. MARCELINO LOPEZ(R)
☐ 537. RUDY MAY(R)
☐ 537. PHIL ROOF(R)
☐ 552. JULIO GOTAY
☐ 569. GINO CIMOLI
☐ 595. DON LEE

CHICAGO CUBS

☐ 14. LEN GABRIELSON
☐ 27. DICK BERTELL
☐ 34. CAL KOONCE
☐ 64. LOU BURDETTE
☐ 91. TEAM CARD
☐ 110. RON SANTO
☐ 149. WAYNE SCHURR
☐ 161. FRANK BAUMANN
☐ 165. DICK ELLSWORTH
☐ 186. BILLY COWAN
☐ 202. LEO BURKE
☐ 220. BILLY WILLIAMS
☐ 244. LINDY MCDANIEL
☐ 264. BOB BUHL
☐ 298. JIM STEWART
☐ 314. STERLING SLAUGHTER
☐ 334. VIC ROZNOVSKY
☐ 354. BILLY OTT(R)
☐ 354. JACK D. WARNER(R)
☐ 386. PAUL JAECKEL(R)
☐ 386. FRED NORMAN(R)
☐ 402. JOE AMALFITANO
☐ 420. LARRY JACKSON
☐ 436. DON ELSTON
☐ 457. BOB KENNEDY(HC)

* All of the cards appear as Los Angeles Angels.

- □ 510. ERNIE BANKS
- □ 528. GEORGE ALTMAN
- □ 549. ROBERTA PENA(R)
- □ 549. GLENN BECKERT(R)
- □ 565. ERNIE BROGLIO
- □ 584. HARRY BRIGHT
- □ 596. DON LANDRUM

CHICAGO WHITE SOX

- □ 41. BRUCE HOWARD(R)
- □ 41. MARV STAEHLE(R)
- □ 58. FRED TALBOT
- □ 70. BILL SKOWRON
- □ 81. DON BUFORD
- □ 89. MIKE HERSHBERGER
- □ 125. JUAN PIZARRO
- □ 146. RON HANSEN
- □ 183. DAVE NICHOLSON
- □ 198. SMOKY BURGESS
- □ 208. TOMMY JOHN
- □ 215. PETE WARD
- □ 234. TEAM CARD
- □ 253. DANNY CATER
- □ 276. HOYT WILHELM
- □ 297. DAVE DEBUSSCHERE
- □ 313. JIMMIE SCHAFFTER
- □ 328. EDDIE FISHER
- □ 345. FLOYD ROBINSON
- □ 368. KEN BERRY
- □ 368. JOEL GIBSON(R)
- □ 382. J.C. MARTIN
- □ 414. AL LOPEZ(M)
- □ 430. GARY PETERS
- □ 458. JOHN BUZHARDT
- □ 480. JOEL HORLEN
- □ 498. GENE STEPHENS
- □ 516. AL WEIS
- □ 541. GREG BOLLO(R)
- □ 541. BOB LOCKER(R)
- □ 586. TOMMY MCCRAW

CINCINNATI REDS

- □ 18. BILL MCCOOL
- □ 47. TOMMY HARPER
- □ 60. JIM O'TOOLE
- □ 75. DERON JOHNSON
- □ 102. STEVE BOROS
- □ 120. FRANK ROBINSON
- □ 141. CHARLIE JAMES
- □ 158. DICK SISLER(M)
- □ 174. JOE JAY
- □ 192. JIM COKER
- □ 207. PETE ROSE
- □ 221. JOHN TSITOURIS
- □ 243. TED DAVIDSON(R)
- □ 243. TOMMY HELMS(R)
- □ 263. MARTY KEOUGH
- □ 289. GORDY COLEMAN
- □ 312. JOE NUXHALL
- □ 316. TEAM CARD
- □ 339. RYNE DUREN
- □ 355. VADA PINSON
- □ 398. DAN NEVILLE(R)
- □ 398. ART SHAMSKY(R)
- □ 411. ROGER CRAIG
- □ 418. JOHNNY EDWARDS
- □ 437. CHICO CARDENAS
- □ 456. BILL R. HENRY
- □ 472. DON PAVLETICH
- □ 488. TED WILLS
- □ 507. SAMMY ELLIS
- □ 530. JIM MALONEY
- □ 554. CHICO RUIZ
- □ 581. TONY PEREZ(R)

CLEVELAND INDIANS

- □ 17. JOHNNY ROMANO
- □ 76. SAM MCDOWELL
- □ 92. DICK HOWSER
- □ 96. SONNY SIEBERT
- □ 105. CHICO SALMON
- □ 128. VIC DAVALILLO
- □ 145. LUIS TIANT
- □ 166. GEORGE CULVER(R)
- □ 166. TOMMIE AGEE
- □ 185. MAX ALVIS
- □ 235. CHUCK HINTON
- □ 262. BUD DALEY
- □ 283. FRED WHITFIELD
- □ 301. BIRDIE TEBBETTS(M)
- □ 317. DON MCMAHON
- □ 332. TED ABERNATHY
- □ 348. GEORGE BANKS
- □ 367. LEON WAGNER
- □ 380. ROCKY COLAVITO
- □ 404. STAN WILLIAMS
- □ 406. RALPH TERRY
- □ 424. GARY BELL
- □ 448. LEE STANGE
- □ 468. LARRY BROWN
- □ 481. TEAM CARD
- □ 501. RALPH GAGLIANO(R)
- □ 501. JIM RITTWAGE(R)
- □ 514. JOE AZCUE
- □ 535. JACK KRALICK
- □ 546. BILL DAVIS(R)
- □ 546. MIKE HEDLUND(R)
- □ 546. FLOYD WEAVER(R)
- □ 546. RAY BARKER(R)
- □ 562. BILLY MORAN
- □ 577. RICHIE SCHEINBLUM(R)
- □ 578. CAMILO CARREON

DETROIT TIGERS

- □ 19. GATES BROWN
- □ 37. FRED GLADDING
- □ 53. DICK MCAULIFFE
- □ 83. GEORGE THOMAS
- □ 130. AL KALINE
- □ 153. NORM CASH
- □ 173. TEAM CARD
- □ 191. PHIL REGAN
- □ 206. WILLIE HORTON
- □ 236. DENNIS MCLAIN
- □ 259. JIM NORTHRUP(R)
- □ 259. RAY OYLER(R)
- □ 271. DON WERT
- □ 288. JACK HAMILTON
- □ 306. BUBBA PHILLIPS
- □ 335. MICKEY LOLICH
- □ 353. JERRY LUMPE
- □ 375. DAVE WICKERSHAM
- □ 390. BILL FREEHAN
- □ 408. LARRY SHERRY
- □ 429. DON DEMETER
- □ 454. ED RAKOW
- □ 471. BILLY HOEFT
- □ 483. GEORGE SMITH
- □ 493. BILL ROMAN(R)
- □ 493. BRUCE BRUBAKER(R)
- □ 522. HANK AGUIRRE
- □ 538. CHUCK DRESSEN(M)
- □ 547. JAKE WOOD
- □ 563. JULIO NAVARRO
- □ 576. TERRY FOX
- □ 587. JOE SPARMA
- □ 593. JACKIE MOORE(R)
- □ 593. JOHN SULLIVAN(R)

HOUSTON ASTROS

- □ 16. JOE MORGAN(R)
- □ 16. SONNY JACKSON(R)
- □ 31. MIKE WHITE
- □ 48. CLAUDE RAYMOND
- □ 80. TURK FARRELL
- □ 109. WALT BOND
- □ 164. AL SPANGLER
- □ 175. BOB ASPROMONTE
- □ 179. HAL WOODESHICK
- □ 212. RON BRAND
- □ 240. BOB BRUCE
- □ 257. JIM WYNN
- □ 274. LUM HARRIS(M)
- □ 292. LARRY YELLEN
- □ 321. RUSTY STAUB
- □ 359. KEN JOHNSON
- □ 389. DON LARSEN
- □ 409. JIM BEAUCHAMP(R)
- □ 409. LARRY DIERKER(R)
- □ 433. JOHN BATEMAN
- □ 451. JIM OWENS
- □ 469. DON NOTTEBART
- □ 485. NELLIE FOX
- □ 504. JERRY GROTE
- □ 524. DAVE GIUSTI
- □ 553. DAN COOMBS(R)
- □ 553. JACK MCCLURE(R)
- □ 553. GENE RATLIFF(R)
- □ 594. JOE GAINES

KANSAS CITY ATHLETICS

- □ 35. ED CHARLES
- □ 51. BILLY BRYAN
- □ 71. JOHN O'DONOGHUE
- □ 87. NELSON MATHEWS
- □ 117. WES STOCK
- □ 151. TEAM CARD
- □ 168. DICK GREEN
- □ 197. DIEGO SEGUI
- □ 219. BOB MEYER
- □ 239. DOC EDWARDS
- □ 266. BERT CAMPANERIS
- □ 286. JIM DICKSON
- □ 286. AURELIO MONTEAGUDO(R)
- □ 311. ORLANDO PENA
- □ 333. TOMMIE REYNOLDS
- □ 365. JIM GENTILE
- □ 376. JIM LANDIS
- □ 391. MEL MCGAHA(M)
- □ 425. WAYNE CAUSEY
- □ 439. MOE DRABOWSKY
- □ 462. LEW KRAUSSE
- □ 479. KEN HARRELSON
- □ 526. RENE LACHEMANN(R)
- □ 526. JOHN ODOM(R)
- □ 526. SKIP LOCKWOOD(R)
- □ 526. JIM HUNTER(R)
- □ 557. JOSE SANTIAGO
- □ 577. DON BUSCHHORN(R)
- □ 590. JOHN WYATT

LOS ANGELES DODGERS

- □ 40. FRANK HOWARD
- □ 59. NATE OLIVER
- □ 77. DOUG CAMILLI
- □ 98. BOB L. MILLER
- □ 112. DERRELL GRIFFITH
- □ 119. JOHN KENNEDY
- □ 126. TEAM CARD
- □ 196. RON FAIRLY
- □ 217. WALT ALSTON(M)
- □ 238. JOE MOELLER
- □ 247. WALLY MOON
- □ 260. DON DRYSDALE
- □ 279. DICK TRACEWSKI
- □ 300. SANDY KOUFAX
- □ 331. AL FERRARA(R)
- □ 331. JOHN PURDIN(R)
- □ 344. WES PARKER
- □ 370. TOMMY DAVIS
- □ 387. JOHNNY PODRES
- □ 405. JOHN ROSEBORO
- □ 416. JIM BREWER
- □ 435. WILLIE DAVIS
- □ 453. WILLIE CRAWFORD(R)
- □ 453. JOHN WERHAS(R)
- □ 484. RON PERRANOSKI
- □ 527. JEFF TORBORG
- □ 544. HOWIE REED
- □ 561. DENNIS DABOLL(R)
- □ 561. MIKE KEKICH(R)

- ☐ 561. JIM LEFEBVRE(R)
- ☐ 561. HECTOR VALLE(R)
- ☐ 570. CLAUDE OSTEEN
- ☐ 579. DICK SMITH

MILWAUKEE BRAVES

- ☐ 23. BOB TIEFENAUER
- ☐ 44. WADE BLASINGAME
- ☐ 63. TY CLINE
- ☐ 82. SANDY ALOMAR(R)
- ☐ 82. JOHN BRAUN(R)
- ☐ 106. GENE OLIVER
- ☐ 127. FRANK LARY
- ☐ 156. BOB SADOWSKI
- ☐ 170. HANK AARON
- ☐ 182. MIKE DE LA HOZ
- ☐ 200. JOE TORRE
- ☐ 223. DAN OSINSKI
- ☐ 241. MACK JONES
- ☐ 269. FRANK BOLLING
- ☐ 287. GARY KOLB
- ☐ 305. RICO CARTY
- ☐ 327. DENIS MENKE
- ☐ 346. BOBBY BRAGAN(M)
- ☐ 366. DAN SCHNEIDER
- ☐ 383. FELIPE ALOU
- ☐ 407. LEE MAYE
- ☐ 426. TEAM CARD
- ☐ 441. DENNY LEMASTER
- ☐ 461. CLAY CARROLL(R)
- ☐ 461. PHIL NIEKRO(R)
- ☐ 476. BILLY O'DELL
- ☐ 487. WOODY WOODWARD
- ☐ 500. EDDIE MATHEWS
- ☐ 520. TONY CLONINGER
- ☐ 542. LOU KLIMCHOCK
- ☐ 567. TOMMIE AARON
- ☐ 585. HANK FISCHER

MINNESOTA TWINS

- ☐ 24. TEAM CARD
- ☐ 39. GERRY ARRIGO
- ☐ 62. JIM KAAT
- ☐ 90. RICH ROLLINS
- ☐ 108. DON MINCHER
- ☐ 122. BILL PLEIS
- ☐ 157. ZOILO VERSALLES
- ☐ 171. JIM ROLAND
- ☐ 180. BOB ALLISON
- ☐ 201. SANDY VALDESPINO(R)
- ☐ 201. CESAR TOVAR(R)
- ☐ 216. AL WORTHINGTON
- ☐ 237. BERNIE ALLEN
- ☐ 255. CAMILO PASCUAL
- ☐ 278. KEN RETZER
- ☐ 299. JERRY ZIMMERMAN
- ☐ 326. DWIGHT SIEBLER
- ☐ 340. TONY OLIVA
- ☐ 351. JIM PERRY
- ☐ 384. JOHNNY KLIPPSTEIN
- ☐ 400. HARMON KILLEBREW
- ☐ 421. GARY DOTTER(R)
- ☐ 421. JAY WARD(R)
- ☐ 432. JIM GRANT
- ☐ 459. FRANK KOSTRO
- ☐ 490. EARL BATTEY
- ☐ 506. SAM MELE(M)
- ☐ 529. JERRY FOSNOW
- ☐ 548. DICK STIGMAN
- ☐ 564. MEL NELSON
- ☐ 580. JIMMIE HALL
- ☐ 597. JOE NOSSEK(R)
- ☐ 597. RICH REESE(R)
- ☐ 597. JOHN SEVCIK(R)

NEW YORK METS

- ☐ 22. CHARLIE SMITH
- ☐ 45. ROY MCMILLAN
- ☐ 61. CHRIS CANNIZZARO
- ☐ 73. DENNIS RIBANT
- ☐ 93. JACK FISHER
- ☐ 114. JIM HICKMAN
- ☐ 144. ED KRANEPOOL
- ☐ 167. BILLY WAKEFIELD
- ☐ 187. CASEY STENGEL(M)
- ☐ 205. WARREN SPAHN
- ☐ 227. BOBBY KLAUS
- ☐ 258. LARRY BEARNARTH
- ☐ 277. JOHNNY LEWIS
- ☐ 285. RON HUNT
- ☐ 308. CLEON JONES(R)
- ☐ 308. TOM PARSONS(R)
- ☐ 329. HAWK TAYLOR
- ☐ 349. LARRY MILLER
- ☐ 364. GALEN CISCO
- ☐ 381. AL JACKSON
- ☐ 401. CARL WILLEY
- ☐ 423. JESSE GONDER
- ☐ 449. JERRY HINSLEY(R)
- ☐ 449. GARY KROLL(R)
- ☐ 470. YOGI BERRA
- ☐ 495. JOE CHRISTOPHER
- ☐ 511. RON LOCKE
- ☐ 533. DAN NAPOLEON(R)
- ☐ 533. RON SWOBODA(R)
- ☐ 533. JIM BETHKE(R)
- ☐ 533. TUG MCGRAW(R)
- ☐ 551. TEAM CARD
- ☐ 581. KEVIN COLLINS(R)

NEW YORK YANKEES

- ☐ 13. PEDRO RAMOS
- ☐ 30. JIM BOUTON
- ☐ 65. TONY KUBEK
- ☐ 97. PEDRO GONZALEZ
- ☐ 115. BOBBY RICHARDSON
- ☐ 131. JOHNNY KEANE(M)
- ☐ 155. ROGER MARIS
- ☐ 177. PETE MIKKELSEN
- ☐ 226. ELVIO JIMENEZ(R)
- ☐ 226. JAKE GIBBS(R)
- ☐ 245. JOE PEPITONE
- ☐ 254. ROLAND SHELDON
- ☐ 261. DUKE CARMEL
- ☐ 281. BILL STAFFORD
- ☐ 309. STEVE HAMILTON
- ☐ 330. WHITEY FORD
- ☐ 350. MICKEY MANTLE
- ☐ 369. PHIL LINZ
- ☐ 388. JOHN BLANCHARD
- ☐ 413. HAL RENIFF
- ☐ 440. TOM TRESH
- ☐ 450. ELSTON HOWARD
- ☐ 475. CLETE BOYER
- ☐ 513. TEAM CARD
- ☐ 532. HECTOR LOPEZ
- ☐ 550. MEL STOTTLEMYRE
- ☐ 566. GIL BLANCO(R)
- ☐ 566. ART LOPEZ(R)
- ☐ 566. ROSS MOSCHITTO(R)
- ☐ 582. BOB SCHMIDT
- ☐ 598. AL DOWNING

PHILADELPHIA PHILLIES

- ☐ 20. JIM BUNNING
- ☐ 36. BOBBY WINE
- ☐ 52. ED ROEBUCK
- ☐ 72. TONY GONZALEZ
- ☐ 107. PAT CORRALES(R)
- ☐ 107. COSTEN SHOCKLEY(R)
- ☐ 123. FRANK THOMAS
- ☐ 163. JOHN BRIGGS
- ☐ 184. JOHN BOOZER
- ☐ 203. DALLAS GREEN
- ☐ 225. BOB BELINSKY
- ☐ 248. GUS TRIANDOS
- ☐ 280. DICK STUART
- ☐ 296. TONY TAYLOR
- ☐ 310. JOHNNY CALLISON
- ☐ 322. RICK WISE
- ☐ 338. TEAM CARD
- ☐ 352. ALEX JOHNSON
- ☐ 372. CLAY DALRYMPLE
- ☐ 399. RAY HERBERT
- ☐ 419. RUBEN AMARO
- ☐ 446. ART MAHAFFEY
- ☐ 460. RICHIE ALLEN
- ☐ 474. COOKIE ROJAS
- ☐ 489. GENE MAUCH(M)
- ☐ 505. RAY CULP
- ☐ 521. DAVE BENNETT(R)
- ☐ 521. MORRIE STEEVENS(R)
- ☐ 534. JOHN HERRNSTEIN
- ☐ 555. JACK BALDSCHUN
- ☐ 583. WES COVINGTON

PITTSBURGH PIRATES

- ☐ 25. AL MCBEAN
- ☐ 54. JOE GIBBON
- ☐ 69. BILL VIRDON
- ☐ 95. BILL MAZEROSKI
- ☐ 121. GENE ALLEY
- ☐ 143. JOHN GELNAR(R)
- ☐ 143. JERRY MAY(R)
- ☐ 160. BOB CLEMENTE
- ☐ 195. BOB VEALE
- ☐ 209. TEAM CARD
- ☐ 218. DICK SCHOFIELD
- ☐ 232. STEVE BLASS
- ☐ 246. TOM BUTTERS
- ☐ 265. JIM PAGLIARONI
- ☐ 291. JERRY LYNCH
- ☐ 325. DONN CLENDENON
- ☐ 347. ROY FACE
- ☐ 362. DON SCHWALL
- ☐ 377. WILLIE STARGELL
- ☐ 392. BOB FRIEND
- ☐ 412. BOB BAILEY
- ☐ 438. HARRY WALKER(M)
- ☐ 463. MANNY MOTA
- ☐ 478. WILBUR WOOD
- ☐ 492. GENE FREESE
- ☐ 502. DON CARDWELL
- ☐ 515. VERN LAW
- ☐ 536. ANDRE RODGERS
- ☐ 558. TOMMIE SISK
- ☐ 571. OSSIE VIRGIL
- ☐ 592. FRANK BORK

ST. LOUIS CARDINALS

- ☐ 28. BARNEY SCHULTZ
- ☐ 43. MIKE SHANNON
- ☐ 57. TEAM CARD
- ☐ 78. DAL MAXVILL
- ☐ 100. KEN BOYER
- ☐ 116. DAVE DOWLING(R)
- ☐ 116. BOB TOLAN(R)
- ☐ 154. BOB HUMPHREYS
- ☐ 190. BILL WHITE
- ☐ 214. BOB PURKEY
- ☐ 230. RAY SADECKI
- ☐ 256. TITO FRANCONA
- ☐ 275. DICK GROAT
- ☐ 294. TIM MCCARVER
- ☐ 320. BOB GIBSON
- ☐ 337. MIKE CUELLAR
- ☐ 357. CARL WARWICK
- ☐ 373. CURT SIMMONS
- ☐ 397. JERRY BUCHEK
- ☐ 415. CURT FLOOD
- ☐ 431. NELSON BRILES(R)
- ☐ 431. ED SPIEZIO(R)
- ☐ 447. JULIAN JAVIER
- ☐ 467. RAY WASHBURN
- ☐ 477. FRITZ ACKLEY(R)
- ☐ 477. STEVE CARLTON(R)
- ☐ 491. TRACY STALLARD
- ☐ 503. PHIL GAGLIANO
- ☐ 519. BOB UECKER
- ☐ 540. LOU BROCK
- ☐ 556. RED SCHOENDIENST(M)
- ☐ 568. RON TAYLOR
- ☐ 581. DAVE RICKETTS(R)
- ☐ 591. BOB SKINNER

SAN FRANCISCO GIANTS

- ☐ 32. HERMAN FRANKS(M)
- ☐ 50. JUAN MARICHAL
- ☐ 68. DEL CRANDALL
- ☐ 84. RON HERBEL
- ☐ 103. HARVEY KUENN
- ☐ 118. HAL LANIER
- ☐ 159. JIM DUFFALO
- ☐ 176. WILLIE MCCOVEY
- ☐ 193. GAYLORD PERRY
- ☐ 213. JIM DAVENPORT
- ☐ 228. JACK SANFORD
- ☐ 250. WILLIE MAYS
- ☐ 282. DICK ESTELLE(R)
- ☐ 282. MASANORI MURAKAMI(R)
- ☐ 302. AL STANEK
- ☐ 318. MATTY ALOU
- ☐ 341. BOBBY BOLIN

- □ 360. ORLANDO CEPEDA
- □ 379. TEAM CARD
- □ 395. JIM HART
- □ 428. BOB SHAW
- □ 444. BOB HENDLEY
- □ 465. TOM HALLER
- □ 482. BOB PRIDDY
- □ 497. KEN HENDERSON(R)
- □ 497. JACK HIATT(R)
- □ 512. CAP PETERSON
- □ 531. CHUCK HILLER
- □ 545. JESUS ALOU
- □ 559. ED BAILEY
- □ 575. JOSE PAGAN
- □ 589. FRANK LINZY(R)
- □ 589. BOB SCHRODER(R)

WASHINGTON SENATORS

- □ 21. DON BLASINGAME
- □ 38. JIM KING
- □ 56. RON KLINE
- □ 86. LES NARUM
- □ 99. GIL HODGES(M)
- □ 129. BENNIE DANIELS
- □ 148. WILLIE KIRKLAND
- □ 152. PHIL ORTEGA
- □ 181. DON LOUN(R)
- □ 181. JOE MCCABE(R)
- □ 211. STEVE RIDZIK
- □ 224. BOB CHANCE
- □ 233. DON ZIMMER
- □ 252. PETE RICHERT
- □ 267. TEAM CARD
- □ 284. NICK WILLHITE
- □ 304. DAVE STENHOUSE
- □ 319. KEN MCMULLEN
- □ 336. WOODY HELD
- □ 371. FRANK KREUTZER
- □ 394. JIM HANNAN
- □ 417. ED BRINKMAN
- □ 445. DON LOCK
- □ 466. PETE CRAIG(R)
- □ 466. DICK NEN(R)
- □ 496. JOE CUNNINGHAM
- □ 523. MIKE BRUMLEY
- □ 574. ROY SIEVERS

1966 TOPPS (598)
2 1/2" X 3 1/2"

ATLANTA BRAVES

- □ 10. TONY CLONINGER
- □ 28. PHIL NIEKRO
- □ 49. WOODY WOODWARD
- □ 84. JIM BEAUCHAMP(R)
- □ 84. DICK KELLEY(R)
- □ 96. FELIPE ALOU
- □ 130. JOE TORRE
- □ 153. RICO CARTY
- □ 168. DAN OSINSKI
- □ 184. DENIS MENKE
- □ 200. EDDIE MATHEWS
- □ 237. BILLY O'DELL
- □ 252. DENVER LEMASTER
- □ 268. JOHN BLANCHARD
- □ 286. GARY GEIGER
- □ 307. CLAY CARROLL
- □ 326. TEAM CARD
- □ 346. MIKE DE LA HOZ
- □ 355. WADE BLASINGAME
- □ 381. HANK FISCHER
- □ 408. LEE THOMAS
- □ 428. SANDY ALOMAR
- □ 446. MACK JONES
- □ 466. KEN JOHNSON
- □ 476. BOBBY BRAGAN(M)
- □ 497. CHRIS CANNIZZARO
- □ 500. HANK AARON
- □ 518. HERB HIPPAUF(R)
- □ 518. ARNIE UMBACH(R)
- □ 541. GENE OLIVER
- □ 553. PAT GARRETT(R)
- □ 578. CHI CHI OLIVO

BALTIMORE ORIOLES

- □ 14. NORM SIEBERN
- □ 27. DAROLD KNOWLES(R)
- □ 27. ANDY ETCHEBARREN(R)
- □ 48. PAUL BLAIR
- □ 90. LUIS APARICIO
- □ 105. MILT PAPPAS
- □ 126. JIM PALMER
- □ 136. WOODY HELD
- □ 148. BOB W. JOHNSON
- □ 167. BOOG POWELL
- □ 193. DAVE MCNALLY
- □ 229. HANK BAUER(M)
- □ 247. CARL WARWICK
- □ 265. STU MILLER
- □ 291. MOE DRABOWSKY
- □ 310. FRANK ROBINSON
- □ 348. TEAM CARD
- □ 368. CHARLIE LAU
- □ 390. BROOKS ROBINSON
- □ 412. SAM BOWENS
- □ 427. JOHN MILLER
- □ 442. EDDIE BARNOWSKI(R)
- □ 442. EDDIE WATT(R)
- □ 460. CURT BLEFARY
- □ 467. VIC ROZNOVSKY
- □ 477. STEVE BARBER
- □ 499. WALLY BUNKER

- □ 513. CAMILO CARREON
- □ 533. JERRY ADAIR
- □ 562. RUSS SNYDER
- □ 579. FRANK BERTAINA(R)
- □ 579. GENE BRABENDER(R)
- □ 579. DAVE A. JOHNSON

BOSTON RED SOX

- □ 6. CHUCK SCHILLING
- □ 37. BILLY HERMAN(M)
- □ 53. BOB DULIBA
- □ 70. CARL YASTRZEMSKI
- □ 93. JIM LONBORG
- □ 114. JIM GOSGER
- □ 135. DAVE MOREHEAD
- □ 178. BOB TILLMAN
- □ 203. JOSE SANTIAGO
- □ 227. RUSS NIXON
- □ 259. TEAM CARD
- □ 277. GEORGE THOMAS
- □ 298. RICO PETROCELLI
- □ 317. DALTON JONES
- □ 329. PETE CHARTON
- □ 343. JOE CHRISTOPHER
- □ 356. OWEN JOHNSON(R)
- □ 356. KEN SANDERS(R)
- □ 380. TONY CONIGLIARO
- □ 396. JERRY STEPHENSON
- □ 419. MIKE RYAN
- □ 456. DARRELL BRANDON(R)
- □ 456. JOE FOY(R)
- □ 475. DICK RADATZ
- □ 491. DENNIS BENNETT
- □ 502. LENNY GREEN
- □ 512. DICK STIGMAN(F)
- □ 523. BOB SADOWSKI
- □ 542. GEORGE SMITH
- □ 558. GUIDO GRILLI(R)
- □ 558. PETE MAGRINI(R)
- □ 558. GEORGE SCOTT(R)
- □ 575. EARL WILSON

CALIFORNIA ANGELS

- □ 5. JIM FREGOSI
- □ 23. JACK SANFORD
- □ 42. AUBREY GATEWOOD
- □ 62. MERRITT RANEW
- □ 83. ALBIE PEARSON
- □ 102. ED KIRKPATRICK
- □ 131. TEAM CARD
- □ 152. FRANK MALZONE
- □ 155. MARCELINO LOPEZ
- □ 173. AL SPANGLER
- □ 192. VIC POWER
- □ 213. FRED NEWMAN
- □ 249. BILL RIGNEY(M)
- □ 263. TOM EGAN
- □ 280. BOBBY KNOOP
- □ 299. LOU BURDETTE
- □ 321. RICK REICHARDT
- □ 340. DEAN CHANCE
- □ 361. TOM SATRIANO
- □ 376. PAUL SCHAAL
- □ 393. GEORGE BRUNET
- □ 417. ED SUKLA(R)
- □ 417. JIM MCGLOTHLIN(R)
- □ 438. WILLIE SMITH
- □ 462. BOB RODGERS
- □ 481. BOB LEE
- □ 505. JOSE CARDENAL
- □ 536. DICK EGAN
- □ 553. JACKIE J. WARNER(R)
- □ 565. JIMMY PIERSALL

CHICAGO CUBS

- □ 2. TED ABERNATHY
- □ 24. DON KESSINGER
- □ 43. DON LANDRUM
- □ 63. JIM STEWART
- □ 82. BOB HENDLEY
- □ 110. ERNIE BANKS
- □ 139. BYRON BROWNE(R)
- □ 139. DON YOUNG(R)
- □ 146. GEORGE ALTMAN
- □ 166. CHRIS KRUG
- □ 185. BUB BUHL

- □ 204. TEAM CARD
- □ 232. GLENN BECKERT
- □ 246. ED BAILEY
- □ 278. CALVIN KOONCE
- □ 290. RON SANTO
- □ 306. TY CLINE
- □ 322. BILL FAUL
- □ 342. BOB HUMPHREYS
- □ 372. HARVEY KUENN
- □ 392. BILL HANDS(R)
- □ 392. RANDY HUNDLEY(R)
- □ 409. BILLY HOEFT
- □ 423. ERNIE BROGLIO
- □ 447. DICK ELLSWORTH
- □ 482. JOHN BOCCABELLA(R)
- □ 482. DAVE DOWLING(R)
- □ 484. WES COVINGTON
- □ 559. ROBERTO PENA
- □ 580. BILLY WILLIAMS

CHICAGO WHITE SOX

- □ 8. FLOYD ROBINSON
- □ 25. PETE WARD
- □ 47. J.C. MARTIN
- □ 66. AL WEIS
- □ 85. EDDIE FISHER
- □ 111. GARY PETERS
- □ 127. KEN BERRY
- □ 141. TOM MCCRAW
- □ 164. TOMMY AGEE(R)
- □ 164. MARV STAEHLE(R)
- □ 245. JOHN BUZHARDT
- □ 261. RON HANSEN
- □ 281. BRUCE HOWARD
- □ 301. GREG BOLLO
- □ 319. GENE FREESE
- □ 335. JUAN PIZARRO
- □ 354. SMOKY BURGESS
- □ 374. BOB LOCKER
- □ 398. DANNY CATER
- □ 413. JOHN ROMANO
- □ 426. TEAM CARD
- □ 448. EDDIE STANKY(M)
- □ 465. DON BUFORD
- □ 486. TOMMY JOHN
- □ 510. HOYT WILHELM
- □ 529. LEE ELIA
- □ 529. DENNIS HIGGINS(R)
- □ 529. BILL VOSS(R)
- □ 560. JOEL HORLEN
- □ 577. JACK LAMABE
- □ 590. BILL SKOWRON

CINCINNATI REDS

- □ 12. JOHN TSITOURIS
- □ 30. PETE ROSE
- □ 59. TEAM CARD
- □ 72. TONY PEREZ
- □ 89. TED DAVIDSON
- □ 119. ART SHAMSKY
- □ 140. JIM MALONEY
- □ 159. CHICO RUIZ
- □ 180. VADA PINSON
- □ 196. DON PAVLETICH
- □ 214. TOMMY HARPER
- □ 233. DOM ZANNI
- □ 250. SAM ELLIS
- □ 269. DON HEFFNER(M)
- □ 272. JACK BALDSCHUN
- □ 292. JIM COKER
- □ 311. TOMMY HELMS(R)
- □ 311. DICK SIMPSON(R)
- □ 334. MARTY KEOUGH
- □ 357. GERRY ARRIGO
- □ 370. LEO CARDENAS
- □ 389. JIM O'TOOLE
- □ 406. JOE JAY
- □ 424. LEE MAY(R)
- □ 424. DARRELL OSTEEN(R)
- □ 440. DERON JOHNSON
- □ 459. BILL MCCOOL
- □ 483. JOE NUXHALL
- □ 494. GORDY COLEMAN
- □ 507. JOHN EDWARDS
- □ 556. MEL QUEEN

CLEVELAND INDIANS

- □ 16. LARRY BROWN
- □ 44. BILL DAVIS(R)
- □ 44. TOM KELLEY(R)
- □ 65. LEON WAGNER
- □ 88. FRED WHITFIELD
- □ 109. RALPH TERRY
- □ 128. JIM LANDIS
- □ 129. JACK KRALICK
- □ 133. DON MCMAHON
- □ 150. ROCKY COLAVITO
- □ 169. DUKE SIMS
- □ 197. SONNY SIEBERT
- □ 231. FLOYD WEAVER
- □ 266. PEDRO GONZALES
- □ 285. LUIS TIANT
- □ 303. TEAM CARD
- □ 325. VIC DAVALILLO
- □ 339. DEL CRANDALL
- □ 371. LEE STANGE
- □ 391. CHUCK HINTON
- □ 415. MAX ALVIS
- □ 432. BOB HEFFNER
- □ 452. JOE AZCUE
- □ 470. SAM MCDOWELL
- □ 488. GEORGE BANKS
- □ 501. JOHN O'DONOGHUE
- □ 508. STEVE HARGAN
- □ 525. GARY BELL
- □ 538. BOB ALLEN
- □ 552. BIRDIE TEBBETTS
- □ 567. DICK HOWSER
- □ 581. TONY MARTINEZ
- □ 594. CHICO SALMON

DETROIT TIGERS

- □ 20. WILLIE HORTON
- □ 38. RON NISCHWITZ
- □ 58. DAVE WICKERSHAM
- □ 81. RAY OYLER
- □ 98. DON DEMETER
- □ 113. HANK AGUIRRE
- □ 145. BILL FREEHAN
- □ 161. JERRY LUMPE
- □ 187. CHUCK DRESSEN(M)
- □ 198. MICKEY STANLEY
- □ 209. FRITZ FISHER(R)
- □ 209. JOHN HILLER(R)
- □ 239. ORLANDO PENA
- □ 253. DON WERT
- □ 267. JOE SPARMA
- □ 289. LARRY SHERRY
- □ 315. NORM CASH
- □ 337. FRED GLADDING
- □ 362. GATES BROWN
- □ 378. DICK TRACEWSKI
- □ 410. AL KALINE
- □ 429. BILL MONBOUQUETTE
- □ 455. MICKEY LOLICH
- □ 472. TERRY FOX
- □ 495. DICK MCAULIFFE
- □ 509. JAKE WOOD
- □ 527. JULIO NAVARRO
- □ 540. DENNY MCLAIN
- □ 554. JIM NORTHRUP
- □ 569. ORLANDO MCFARLANE
- □ 583. TEAM CARD
- □ 597. JOHN SULLIVAN

HOUSTON ASTROS

- □ 21. DON NOTTEBART
- □ 45. JIM GENTILE
- □ 64. BOB BRUCE
- □ 86. JOHN BATEMAN
- □ 106. RUSTY STAUB
- □ 122. JOE GAINES
- □ 147. LUM HARRIS(M)
- □ 162. LEE MAYE
- □ 174. RON TAYLOR
- □ 195. JOE MORGAN
- □ 228. LARRY DIERKER
- □ 244. CHUCK HARRISON(R)
- □ 244. SONNY JACKSON(R)
- □ 258. DAVE GIUSTI
- □ 297. JIM OWENS
- □ 313. CHRIS ZACHARY
- □ 352. BOB ASPROMONTE
- □ 377. TURK FARRELL
- □ 394. RON BRAND
- □ 414. DAN COOMBS
- □ 431. WALT BOND
- □ 451. BARRY LATMAN
- □ 504. GRADY HATTON(M)
- □ 520. JIM WYNN
- □ 530. ROBIN ROBERTS
- □ 539. BILL HEATH(R)
- □ 539. CARROLL SEMBERA(R)
- □ 548. GARY KROLL
- □ 557. FELIX MANTILLA
- □ 566. MIKE CUELLAR
- □ 576. DAVE NICHOLSON
- □ 586. CLAUDE RAYMOND
- □ 596. NATE COLBERT(R)
- □ 596. GREG SIMS(R)

KANSAS CITY ATHLETICS

- □ 18. ROLAND SHELDON
- □ 36. JIM HUNTER
- □ 55. KEN HARRELSON
- □ 74. DON MOSSI
- □ 107. LARRY STAHL(R)
- □ 107. RON TOMPKINS(R)
- □ 143. JOSE TARTABULL
- □ 157. RENE LACHEMANN
- □ 175. BERT CAMPANERIS
- □ 201. JIM DICKSON
- □ 236. MIKE HERSHBERGER
- □ 256. LEW KRAUSSE
- □ 287. JACK AKER
- □ 309. DIEGO SEGUI
- □ 332. BILLY BRYAN
- □ 366. WAYNE CAUSEY
- □ 382. PHIL ROOF
- □ 403. FRED TALBOT
- □ 422. ED CHARLES
- □ 433. ALVIN DARK(M)
- □ 458. MANNY JIMENEZ
- □ 492. TEAM CARD
- □ 521. JOHN WYATT
- □ 532. AURELIO MONTEAGUDO
- □ 545. DICK GREEN
- □ 568. PAUL LINDBLAD(R)
- □ 568. RON STONE(R)
- □ 588. CHUCK DOBSON(R)
- □ 588. KEN SUAREZ(R)

LOS ANGELES DODGERS

- □ 13. LOU JOHNSON
- □ 41. DON LE JOHN
- □ 57. JIM LEFEBVRE
- □ 75. TOMMY DAVIS
- □ 100. SANDY KOUFAX
- □ 116. WALTER ALSTON(M)
- □ 134. WES PARKER
- □ 158. JIM BREWER
- □ 171. NICK WILLHITE
- □ 189. JOHN ROSEBORO
- □ 208. BOB L. MILLER
- □ 238. TEAM CARD
- □ 257. JEFF TORBORG
- □ 270. CLAUDE OSTEEN
- □ 288. BILL SINGER(R)

☐ 288. DON SUTTON(R)
☐ 314. HECTOR VALLE
☐ 330. RON FAIRLY
☐ 347. PHIL REGAN
☐ 364. NATE OLIVER
☐ 387. HOWIE REED
☐ 407. JOHN KENNEDY
☐ 430. DON DRYSDALE
☐ 449. JOE MOELLER
☐ 468. JOHNNY PODRES
☐ 487. AL FERRARA
☐ 535. WILLIE DAVIS
☐ 555. RON PERRANOSKI
☐ 573. DERRELL GRIFFITH
☐ 591. BART SHIRLEY(R)

MINNESOTA TWINS

☐ 3. SAM MELE(M)
☐ 22. JOE NOSSEK
☐ 40. JIM GRANT
☐ 56. SANDY VALDESPINO
☐ 73. JERRY ZIMMERMAN
☐ 97. JIM MERRITT
☐ 120. HARMON KILLEBREW
☐ 181. AL WORTHINGTON
☐ 190. JIMMIE HALL
☐ 207. FRANK QUILICI
☐ 240. EARL BATTEY
☐ 264. ANDY KOSCO(R)
☐ 264. TED UHLAENDER(R)
☐ 283. JIM PERRY
☐ 305. CAMILO PASCUAL
☐ 327. BERNIE ALLEN
☐ 345. BOB ALLISON
☐ 367. MEL NELSON
☐ 388. DON MINCHER
☐ 400. ZOILO VERSALLES
☐ 445. JIM KAAT
☐ 450. TONY OLIVA
☐ 473. RICH ROLLINS
☐ 493. JOHN KLIPPSTEIN
☐ 512. DICK STIGMAN(B)
☐ 526. TEAM CARD
☐ 546. DWIGHT SIEBLER
☐ 563. PETE CIMINO(R)
☐ 563. CESAR TOVAR(R)
☐ 582. GARRY ROGGENBURK

NEW YORK METS

☐ 17. JOHN STEPHENSON
☐ 35. RON SWOBODA
☐ 51. GORDON RICHARDSON
☐ 67. CLEON JONES(R)
☐ 67. DICK SELMA(R)
☐ 87. DAN NAPOLEON
☐ 108. BOBBY KLAUS
☐ 124. TUG MCGRAW
☐ 154. CHUCK HILLER
☐ 172. TEAM CARD
☐ 188. AL LUPLOW
☐ 191. DARRELL SUTHERLAND
☐ 212. ED KRANEPOOL
☐ 241. DENNIS RIBANT
☐ 262. JACK HAMILTON
☐ 282. JOHNNY LEWIS
☐ 302. ERNIE BOWMAN
☐ 316. JACK FISHER
☐ 328. JERRY GROTE
☐ 341. WES WESTRUM(M)
☐ 360. RON HUNT
☐ 385. KEN BOYER
☐ 402. JIM HICKMAN
☐ 421. ROY MCMILLAN
☐ 443. BILL WAKEFIELD
☐ 464. LARRY BEARNARTH
☐ 480. DICK STUART
☐ 516. EDDIE BRESSOUD
☐ 534. DAVE EILERS(R)
☐ 534. ROB GARDNER(R)
☐ 561. CHOO CHOO COLEMAN
☐ 574. BILL HELPER(R)
☐ 574. BILL MURPHY(R)
☐ 589. LOU KLIMCHOCK

NEW YORK YANKEES

☐ 9. CLETE BOYER
☐ 31. JACK CULLEN
☐ 50. MICKEY MANTLE
☐ 68. HAL RENIFF
☐ 79. JOE PEPITONE
☐ 92. TEAM CARD
☐ 117. JAKE GIBBS
☐ 138. ROGER REPOZ
☐ 160. WHITEY FORD
☐ 177. HECTOR LOPEZ
☐ 186. RUBEN AMARO
☐ 205. TOM TRESH
☐ 234. RICH BECK(R)
☐ 234. ROY WHITE(R)
☐ 276. JIM BOUTON
☐ 296. JOHNNY KEANE(M)
☐ 323. RAY BARKER
☐ 350. MEL STOTTLEMYRE
☐ 365. ROGER MARIS
☐ 384. AL DOWNING
☐ 405. ELSTON HOWARD
☐ 439. PEDRO RAMOS
☐ 469. BOBBY MURCER(R)
☐ 469. DOOLEY WOMACK(R)
☐ 490. BOBBY RICHARDSON
☐ 503. STEVE HAMILTON
☐ 519. BOB FRIEND
☐ 547. HORACE CLARKE
☐ 584. FRANK FERNANDEZ(R)
☐ 584. FRITZ PETERSON(R)

PHILADELPHIA PHILLIES

☐ 4. RAY CULP
☐ 32. ADOLFO PHILLIPS
☐ 80. RICHIE ALLEN
☐ 104. ALEX JOHNSON
☐ 121. RAY HERBERT
☐ 151. GARY WAGNER
☐ 170. COOKIE ROJAS
☐ 202. CLAY DALRYMPLE
☐ 230. JOHNNY CALLISON
☐ 254. FERGUSON JENKINS(R)
☐ 254. BILL SORRELL(R)
☐ 284. BOBBY WINE
☐ 304. JOHN HERRNSTEIN
☐ 324. JOHN BOOZER
☐ 359. JOHN BRIGGS
☐ 383. JACKIE BRANDT
☐ 397. BILL WHITE
☐ 411. GENE MAUCH(M)
☐ 435. JIM BUNNING
☐ 463. TEAM CARD
☐ 478. TONY GONZALEZ
☐ 506. BO BELINSKY
☐ 522. PHIL LINZ
☐ 543. ROGER CRAIG
☐ 585. TONY TAYLOR
☐ 591. GRANT JACKSON(R)
☐ 595. LARRY JACKSON

PITTSBURGH PIRATES

☐ 15. VERN LAW
☐ 33. JIM PAGLIARONI
☐ 54. JOSE PAGAN
☐ 71. FRANK CARPIN
☐ 112. MANNY MOTA
☐ 123. FRANK BORK(R)
☐ 123. JERRY MAY(R)
☐ 144. DON SCHWALL
☐ 182. JERRY LYNCH
☐ 210. BILL MAZEROSKI
☐ 235. DON CARDWELL
☐ 248. PETE MIKKELSEN
☐ 255. WILLIE STARGELL
☐ 300. BOB CLEMENTE
☐ 318. HARRY WALKER(M)
☐ 336. GENE ALLEY
☐ 344. STEVE BLASS
☐ 353. AL MCBEAN
☐ 375. DONN CLENDENON
☐ 404. TEAM CARD
☐ 425. BOB VEALE
☐ 441. TOMMIE SISK
☐ 461. ROY FACE
☐ 485. BOB BAILEY

☐ 498. LUKE WALKER(R)
☐ 498. WOODY FRYMAN(R)
☐ 528. JESSE GONDER
☐ 551. BOB PURKEY
☐ 571. DAVE L. ROBERTS
☐ 592. ANDRE RODGERS

ST. LOUIS CARDINALS

☐ 7. TRACY STALLARD
☐ 26. RAY SADECKI
☐ 60. CURT FLOOD
☐ 76. RED SCHOENDIENST(M)
☐ 91. BOB UECKER
☐ 103. DICK GROAT
☐ 125. LOU BROCK
☐ 137. PAT CORRALES
☐ 142. DON DENNIS
☐ 163. TITO FRANCONA
☐ 179. DENNIS AUST(R)
☐ 179. BOB TOLAN
☐ 206. ALVIN JACKSON
☐ 243. NELSON BRILES
☐ 275. TIM MCCARVER
☐ 293. MIKE SHANNON
☐ 320. BOB GIBSON
☐ 338. DAL MAXVILL
☐ 358. CHARLIE SMITH
☐ 379. TEAM CARD
☐ 399. RAY WASHBURN
☐ 418. PHIL GAGLIANO
☐ 436. JULIAN JAVIER
☐ 454. JERRY BUCHEK
☐ 471. BOB SKINNER
☐ 489. CURT SIMMONS
☐ 514. HAL WOODESHICK
☐ 544. JOE HOERNER(R)
☐ 544. GEORGE KERNEK(R)
☐ 544. JIMMY WILLIAMS(R)
☐ 570. ART MAHAFFEY

SAN FRANCISCO GIANTS

☐ 1. WILLIE MAYS
☐ 19. TEAM CARD
☐ 39. KEN HENDERSON
☐ 61. BOB BOLIN
☐ 78. FRANK LINZY
☐ 94. MATTY ALOU
☐ 115. BILL R. HENRY
☐ 132. ORLANDO CEPEDA
☐ 176. JIM DAVENPORT
☐ 242. JESUS ALOU
☐ 260. BOB SHAW
☐ 271. HAL LANIER
☐ 295. JIM HART
☐ 308. TOM HALLER
☐ 331. RON HERBEL
☐ 349. CAP PETERSON
☐ 373. JACK HIATT(R)
☐ 373. DICK ESTELLE(R)
☐ 395. LEN GABRIELSON
☐ 420. JUAN MARICHAL
☐ 437. AL STANEK
☐ 457. JOE GIBBON
☐ 474. DICK SCHOFIELD
☐ 496. LINDY MCDANIEL
☐ 511. BOB BARTON(R)
☐ 511. TITO FUENTES(R)
☐ 524. OLLIE BROWN(R)
☐ 524. DON MASON(R)
☐ 537. HERMAN FRANKS(M)
☐ 550. WILLIE MCCOVEY
☐ 572. BOB PRIDDY
☐ 587. DICK BERTELL
☐ 598. GAYLORD PERRY

WASHINGTON SENATORS

☐ 11. BRANT ALYEA(R)
☐ 11. PETE CRAIG(R)
☐ 29. MIKE BRUMLEY
☐ 46. HOWIE KOPLITZ
☐ 69. KEN HAMLIN
☐ 77. JOHNNY ORSINO
☐ 95. PETE RICHERT
☐ 118. MIKE MCCORMICK
☐ 149. DICK NEN
☐ 165. DON LOCK

☐ 194. TEAM CARD
☐ 211. FRANK KREUTZER
☐ 251. ED BRINKMAN
☐ 274. BUSTER NARUM
☐ 294. STEVE RIDZIK
☐ 312. BOB SAVERINE
☐ 333. JOE COLEMAN
☐ 333. JIM FRENCH(R)
☐ 351. FRED VALENTINE
☐ 369. JIM KING
☐ 386. GIL HODGES(M)
☐ 401. KEN MCMULLEN
☐ 416. PHIL ORTEGA
☐ 434. WILLIE KIRKLAND
☐ 453. RON KLINE
☐ 479. JIM HANNAN
☐ 515. FRANK HOWARD
☐ 531. JOE CUNNINGHAM
☐ 549. AL CLOSTER(R)
☐ 549. CASEY COX(R)
☐ 564. BOB CHANCE
☐ 593. DOUG CAMILLI

1967 TOPPS (609)
2 1/2" X 3 1/2"

ATLANTA BRAVES

☐ 18. GENE OLIVER
☐ 35. RICO CARTY
☐ 57. PAT JARVIS
☐ 89. FELIX MILLAN
☐ 101. KEN JOHNSON
☐ 113. DAVE NICHOLSON
☐ 119. WADE BLASINGAME
☐ 138. DICK KELLEY
☐ 179. CHARLEY VAUGHN(R)
☐ 179. CECIL UPSHAW(R)
☐ 199. BILLY HITCHCOCK(M)
☐ 219. CLAY CARROLL
☐ 250. HANK AARON
☐ 267. DON SCHWALL
☐ 288. DENVER LEMASTER
☐ 307. JIM BEAUCHAMP
☐ 328. CLETE BOYER
☐ 350. JOE TORRE
☐ 372. MIKE DE LA HOZ
☐ 417. BOB BRUCE
☐ 435. MACK JONES
☐ 456. PHIL NIEKRO
☐ 477. TEAM CARD
☐ 490. TONY CLONINGER
☐ 504. ORLANDO MARTINEZ
☐ 518. DENIS MENKE
☐ 530. FELIPE ALOU
☐ 546. WOODY WOODWARD
☐ 566. GARY GEIGER
☐ 576. RAMON HERNANDEZ(R)
☐ 591. TY CLINE

BALTIMORE ORIOLES

☐ 22. GENE BRABENDER
☐ 38. BOB W. JOHNSON
☐ 60. LUIS APARICIO
☐ 82. STEVE BARBER
☐ 100. FRANK ROBINSON
☐ 125. MOE DRABOWSKY
☐ 141. JOHN MILLER
☐ 163. VIC ROZNOVSKY
☐ 180. CURT BLEFARY
☐ 204. MIKE EPSTEIN(R)
☐ 204. TOM PHOEBUS(R)
☐ 230. BOOG POWELL
☐ 251. WOODY HELD
☐ 271. EDDIE WATT
☐ 302. TEAM CARD
☐ 319. PAUL BLAIR
☐ 329. CHARLEY LAU
☐ 345. STU MILLER
☐ 363. DAVE A. JOHNSON
☐ 382. DAVE MCNALLY
☐ 405. RUSS SNYDER
☐ 434. EDDIE FISHER
☐ 457. ANDY ETCHEBARREN
☐ 475. JIM PALMER
☐ 491. SAM BOWENS
☐ 507. ED BARNOWSKI(R)
☐ 507. LARRY HANEY(R)
☐ 534. HANK BAUER(M)
☐ 558. MARK BELANGER(R)
☐ 558. BILL DILLMAN(R)
☐ 585. WALLY BUNKER
☐ 600. BROOKS ROBINSON

BOSTON RED SOX

☐ 7. DON MCMAHON
☐ 36. BOB TILLMAN
☐ 56. JOSE TARTABULL
☐ 75. GEORGE SCOTT
☐ 99. LEE STANGE
☐ 117. DARRELL BRANDON
☐ 139. DALTON JONES
☐ 161. DICK WILLIAMS(M)
☐ 184. GEORGE THOMAS
☐ 206. DENNIS BENNETT
☐ 223. MIKE RYAN
☐ 261. JOHN WYATT
☐ 280. TONY CONIGLIARO
☐ 297. DAVE MOREHEAD
☐ 314. MIKE ANDREWS(R)
☐ 314. REGGIE SMITH(R)
☐ 331. JOE FOY
☐ 342. HANK FISCHER
☐ 355. CARL YASTRZEMSKI
☐ 371. JIM LONBORG
☐ 429. GARRY ROGGENBURK
☐ 444. GEORGE SMITH
☐ 473. JOSE SANTIAGO
☐ 528. RICO PETROCELLI
☐ 547. RUSS GIBSON(R)
☐ 547. BILL ROHR(R)
☐ 572. DON DEMETER
☐ 594. DAN OSINSKI
☐ 596. GALEN CISCO
☐ 604. TEAM CARD

CALIFORNIA ANGELS

☐ 19. JIM MCGLOTHLIN
☐ 34. PETE CIMINO
☐ 40. RICK REICHARDT
☐ 58. PAUL SCHAAL
☐ 79. BUBBA MORTON
☐ 104. MINNIE ROJAS
☐ 122. GEORGE BRUNET
☐ 147. TOM EGAN
☐ 175. BOBBY KNOOP
☐ 193. JOSE CARDENAL
☐ 213. JAY JOHNSTONE
☐ 249. NICK WILLHITE
☐ 265. LOU BURDETTE
☐ 281. BOB RODGERS
☐ 293. ED KIRKPATRICK
☐ 312. DON MINCHER
☐ 327. TEAM CARD
☐ 343. TOM SATRIANO
☐ 367. BILL KELSO(R)
☐ 367. DON WALLACE(R)
☐ 385. JIM FREGOSI
☐ 401. JIM COATES
☐ 432. JIMMIE HALL
☐ 451. FRED NEWMAN
☐ 469. LEN GABRIELSON
☐ 494. BILL RIGNEY(M)
☐ 496. ORLANDO MCFARLANE
☐ 513. MARCELINO LOPEZ
☐ 549. JACK SANFORD
☐ 584. JIM PIERSALL

CHICAGO CUBS

☐ 16. BILL HANDS
☐ 39. CURT SIMMONS
☐ 70. RON SANTO
☐ 87. GEORGE ALTMAN
☐ 106. RANDY HUNDLEY
☐ 124. JIM STEWART
☐ 148. ADOLFO PHILLIPS
☐ 168. RAY CULP
☐ 171. CAL KOONCE
☐ 185. KEN HOLTZMAN
☐ 215. ERNIE BANKS
☐ 256. BOB HENDLEY
☐ 272. BILL CONNORS(R)
☐ 272. DAVE DOWLING(R)
☐ 296. GLENN BECKERT
☐ 315. BILLY WILLIAMS
☐ 333. FERGUSON JENKINS
☐ 354. TEAM CARD
☐ 388. ARNOLD EARLEY
☐ 419. DON KESSINGER
☐ 439. BYRON BROWNE
☐ 458. LEE THOMAS
☐ 481. LEO DUROCHER(M)
☐ 497. RON CAMPBELL
☐ 524. FELIX MANTILLA
☐ 536. JOE NIEKRO(R)
☐ 536. PAUL POPOVICH(R)
☐ 552. TED SAVAGE
☐ 576. NORM GIGON(R)
☐ 578. JOHN BOCCABELLA
☐ 608. RICH NYE(R)
☐ 608. JOHN UPHAM(R)

CHICAGO WHITE SOX

☐ 9. RON HANSEN
☐ 29. TOMMY MCCRAW
☐ 52. DENNIS HIGGINS
☐ 67. KEN BERRY
☐ 81. EDDIE STANKY(M)
☐ 107. JOEL HORLEN
☐ 159. BRUCE HOWARD
☐ 178. JOHN BUZHARDT.
☐ 208. JACK LAMABE
☐ 232. DON BUFORD
☐ 259. DON DENNIS
☐ 286. WAYNE CAUSEY
☐ 310. GARY PETERS
☐ 338. BOB LOCKER
☐ 357. BILL SKOWRON
☐ 373. DUANE JOSEPHSON(R)
☐ 373. FRED KLAGES(R)
☐ 391. WILBUR WOOD
☐ 406. LEE ELIA
☐ 422. HOYT WILHELM
☐ 436. PETE WARD
☐ 455. TOMMIE AGEE
☐ 467. JIM O'TOOLE
☐ 484. JERRY ADAIR
☐ 506. SMOKY BURGESS
☐ 532. JIM HICKS
☐ 538. J.C. MARTIN

- ☐ 556. AL WEIS
- ☐ 573. TEAM CARD
- ☐ 598. WALT WILLIAMS(R)
- ☐ 598. ED STROUD(R)
- ☐ 609. TOMMY JOHN

CINCINNATI REDS

- ☐ 6. DICK SIMPSON
- ☐ 21. DAVE BRISTOL(M)
- ☐ 44. JOE NUXHALL
- ☐ 61. GORDY COLEMAN
- ☐ 80. JIM MALONEY
- ☐ 96. ART SHAMSKY
- ☐ 114. JACK BALDSCHUN
- ☐ 120. FLOYD ROBINSON
- ☐ 135. DERON JOHNSON
- ☐ 158. JIMMIE COKER
- ☐ 176. SAMMY ELLIS
- ☐ 202. JOHNNY EDWARDS
- ☐ 222. DARRELL OSTEEN(R)
- ☐ 222. LEE MAY(R)
- ☐ 254. MILT PAPPAS
- ☐ 269. DON NOTTEBART
- ☐ 292. DON PAVLETICH
- ☐ 325. CHICO CARDENAS
- ☐ 339. CHICO RUIZ
- ☐ 353. BILL MCCOOL
- ☐ 374. MEL QUEEN
- ☐ 392. TOMMY HARPER
- ☐ 407. TEAM CARD
- ☐ 430. PETE ROSE
- ☐ 453. AURELIO MONTEAGUDO
- ☐ 476. TONY PEREZ
- ☐ 488. GERRY ARRIGO
- ☐ 505. TOMMY HELMS
- ☐ 519. TED DAVIDSON
- ☐ 550. VADA PINSON
- ☐ 597. TED ABERNATHY

CLEVELAND INDIANS

- ☐ 3. DUKE SIMS
- ☐ 24. BOB ALLEN
- ☐ 43. CHICO SALMON
- ☐ 69. VIC DAVALILLO
- ☐ 95. SONNY SIEBERT
- ☐ 127. JOHN O'DONOGHUE
- ☐ 145. LARRY BROWN
- ☐ 174. DICK RADATZ
- ☐ 189. CHUCK HINTON
- ☐ 214. TOM KELLEY
- ☐ 253. BILL DAVIS(R)
- ☐ 253. GUS GIL(R)
- ☐ 258. LEE MAYE
- ☐ 275. FRED WHITFIELD
- ☐ 295. SAM MCDOWELL
- ☐ 316. JACK KRALICK
- ☐ 336. JOE AZCUE
- ☐ 360. LEON WAGNER
- ☐ 377. LUIS TIANT
- ☐ 397. WILLIE SMITH
- ☐ 424. PEDRO GONZALEZ
- ☐ 440. STEVE HARGAN
- ☐ 479. GARY BELL
- ☐ 499. GEORGE CULVER(R)
- ☐ 499. JOSE VIDAL(R)
- ☐ 520. MAX ALVIS
- ☐ 544. TEAM CARD
- ☐ 563. JOE ADCOCK
- ☐ 580. ROCKY COLAVITO

DETROIT TIGERS

- ☐ 13. JOE SPARMA
- ☐ 30. AL KALINE
- ☐ 48. BILL FREEHAN
- ☐ 72. GEORGE KORINCE(R)
- ☐ 72. JOHN MATCHICK(R)
- ☐ 88. MICKEY LOLICH
- ☐ 112. DAVE WICKERHAM
- ☐ 134. GATES BROWN
- ☐ 170. DICK MCAULIFFE
- ☐ 192. FRED GLADDING
- ☐ 247. JERRY LUMPE
- ☐ 263. HANK AGUIRRE
- ☐ 284. JOHNNY PODRES
- ☐ 305. EARL WILSON
- ☐ 321. MAYO SMITH(M)
- ☐ 352. RAY OYLER
- ☐ 378. TEAM CARD
- ☐ 394. JAKE WOOD
- ☐ 408. JIM NORTHRUP
- ☐ 420. DENNIS MCLAIN
- ☐ 449. ORLANDO PENA
- ☐ 465. WILLIE HORTON
- ☐ 482. BILL MONBOUQUETTE
- ☐ 511. DON WERT
- ☐ 526. PAT DOBSON(R)
- ☐ 526. GEORGE KORINCE(R)
- ☐ 540. NORM CASH
- ☐ 559. DICK TRACEWSKI
- ☐ 571. LARRY SHERRY
- ☐ 588. JOHNNY KLIPPSTEIN
- ☐ 607. MICKEY STANLEY

HOUSTON ASTROS

- ☐ 8. CHUCK HARRISON
- ☐ 28. BARRY LATMAN
- ☐ 51. DAVE ADLESH(R)
- ☐ 51. WES BALES(R)
- ☐ 73. RUSTY STAUB
- ☐ 97. MIKE CUELLAR
- ☐ 136. CARROLL SEMBERA
- ☐ 166. ED MATHEWS
- ☐ 172. BILL HEATH
- ☐ 190. TURK FARRELL
- ☐ 212. CHRIS ZACHARY
- ☐ 231. JOHN BATEMAN
- ☐ 274. BOB ASPROMONTE
- ☐ 298. RON DAVIS
- ☐ 318. DAVE GUISTI
- ☐ 337. JOE MORGAN
- ☐ 347. GRADY HATTON(M)
- ☐ 364. CLAUDE RAYMOND
- ☐ 390. JIM WYNN
- ☐ 412. NORM MILLER(R)
- ☐ 412. DOUG RADER(R)
- ☐ 415. SONNY JACKSON
- ☐ 447. BOB BELINSKY
- ☐ 464. DAN COOMBS
- ☐ 483. JIM LANDIS
- ☐ 498. LARRY DIERKER
- ☐ 502. DERRELL GRIFFITH
- ☐ 543. DAN SCHNEIDER
- ☐ 564. ALONZO HARRIS(R)
- ☐ 564. AARON POINTER(R)
- ☐ 582. JIM OWENS

KANSAS CITY ATHLETICS

- ☐ 17. JIM GOSGER
- ☐ 33. SAL BANDO(R)
- ☐ 33. RANDY SCHWARTZ(R)
- ☐ 54. DICK GREEN
- ☐ 74. WES STOCK
- ☐ 90. JIM NASH
- ☐ 110. JACK AKER
- ☐ 129. PHIL ROOF
- ☐ 157. DANNY CATER
- ☐ 182. ED CHARLES
- ☐ 209. JOE NOSSEK
- ☐ 227. PAUL LINDBLAD
- ☐ 262. TEAM CARD
- ☐ 282. JOHNNY ODOM
- ☐ 303. GIL BLANCO
- ☐ 323. MIKE HERSHBERGER
- ☐ 344. OSSIE CHAVARRIA
- ☐ 369. JIM HUNTER
- ☐ 389. AL DARK(M)
- ☐ 416. ROGER REPOZ
- ☐ 438. CHUCK DOBSON
- ☐ 471. RENE LACHEMANN
- ☐ 515. BERT CAMPANERIS
- ☐ 542. RICK MONDAY(R)
- ☐ 542. TONY PIERCE(R)
- ☐ 565. LEW KRAUSSE
- ☐ 599. BOB DULIBA
- ☐ 603. TIM TALTON(R)
- ☐ 603. RAMON WEBSTER(R)

LOS ANGELES DODGERS

- ☐ 12. JIMMY CAMPANIS(R)
- ☐ 12. BILL SINGER(R)
- ☐ 31. JIM BREWER
- ☐ 32. BOB BAILEY
- ☐ 55. DON DRYSDALE
- ☐ 76. JIM BARBIERI
- ☐ 94. RON FAIRLY
- ☐ 111. JOHN KENNEDY
- ☐ 130. PHIL REGAN
- ☐ 149. JOE MOELLER
- ☐ 160. WILLIE DAVIS
- ☐ 197. RON PERRANOSKI
- ☐ 218. WES PARKER
- ☐ 260. JIM LEFEBVRE
- ☐ 276. BRUCE BRUBAKER
- ☐ 294. WALT ALSTON(M)
- ☐ 313. BOB LEE
- ☐ 330. CLAUDE OSTEEN
- ☐ 346. JIM HICKMAN
- ☐ 365. JOHN ROSEBORO
- ☐ 381. DICK SCHOFIELD
- ☐ 398. JEFF TORBORG
- ☐ 410. LOU JOHNSON
- ☐ 428. TOM HUTTON(R)
- ☐ 428. GENE MICHAEL(R)
- ☐ 445. DON SUTTON
- ☐ 461. BOB L. MILLER
- ☐ 503. TEAM CARD
- ☐ 514. JOHN WERHAS
- ☐ 525. RON HUNT
- ☐ 539. DICK EGAN
- ☐ 557. AL FERRARA

MINNESOTA TWINS

- ☐ 15. EARL BATTEY
- ☐ 50. TONY OLIVA
- ☐ 98. RICH ROLLINS
- ☐ 133. RON KLINE
- ☐ 137. RON CLARK(R)
- ☐ 137. JIM OLLOM(R)
- ☐ 164. DWIGHT SIEBLER
- ☐ 194. BOB ALLISON
- ☐ 211. TEAM CARD
- ☐ 224. WALT BOND
- ☐ 246. JIM PERRY
- ☐ 270. ZOILO VERSALLES
- ☐ 300. JIM KAAT
- ☐ 317. CESAR TOVAR
- ☐ 366. ANDY KOSCO
- ☐ 380. DEAN CHANCE
- ☐ 399. AL WORTHINGTON
- ☐ 418. SAM MELE(M)
- ☐ 431. TEN UHLAENDER
- ☐ 446. RUSS NIXON
- ☐ 460. HARMON KILLEBREW
- ☐ 486. RICH REESE(R)
- ☐ 486. BILL WHITBY(R)
- ☐ 501. JERRY ZIMMERMAN
- ☐ 523. JIM MERRITT
- ☐ 545. JIM GRANT
- ☐ 569. ROD CAREW(R)
- ☐ 575. DAVE BOSWELL

NEW YORK METS

- ☐ 2. JACK HAMILTON
- ☐ 23. LARRY ELLIOT
- ☐ 42. TEAM CARD
- ☐ 59. RALPH TERRY
- ☐ 91. JOHNNY LEWIS
- ☐ 105. KEN BOYER

- □ 121. ED BRESSOUD
- □ 144. BILL HEPLER
- □ 165. CLEON JONES
- □ 198. CHUCK HILLER
- □ 217. ROB GARDNER
- □ 264. RON SWOBODA
- □ 287. GREG GOOSSEN(R)
- □ 287. BART SHIRLEY(R)
- □ 306. BUD HARRELSON
- □ 348. TUG MCGRAW
- □ 370. TOMMY DAVIS
- □ 386. DICK SELMA
- □ 413. JERRY GROTE
- □ 433. AL LUPLOW
- □ 452. ED KRANEPOOL
- □ 470. BOB SHAW
- □ 487. TOMMIE REYNOLDS
- □ 522. JOHN STEPHENSON
- □ 533. JACK FISHER
- □ 537. CHUCK ESTRADA
- □ 555. DON CARDWELL
- □ 561. SANDY ALOMAR
- □ 568. JACKIE SULLIVAN
- □ 574. JERRY BUCHEK
- □ 581. BILL DENEHY(R)
- □ 581. TOM SEAVER(R)
- □ 587. DON SHAW(R)
- □ 593. WES WESTRUM(M)
- □ 606. RON TAYLOR

NEW YORK YANKEES

- □ 5. WHITEY FORD
- □ 25. ELSTON HOWARD
- □ 77. DOOLEY WOMACK
- □ 93. STAN BAHNSEN(R)
- □ 93. BOBBY MURCER(R)
- □ 131. TEAM CARD
- □ 150. MICKEY MANTLE
- □ 169. HORACE CLARKE
- □ 201. HAL RENIFF
- □ 225. MEL STOTTLEMYRE
- □ 257. CHARLEY SMITH
- □ 277. STEVE WHITAKER
- □ 289. TOM TRESH
- □ 308. AL DOWNING
- □ 340. JOE PEPITONE
- □ 358. RUBEN AMARO
- □ 375. JAKE GIBBS
- □ 393. JIM BOUTON
- □ 411. DICK HOWSER
- □ 426. LOU CLINTON
- □ 442. BILL ROBINSON(R)
- □ 442. JOE VERBANIC(R)
- □ 468. RALPH HOUK(M)
- □ 495. FRITZ PETERSON
- □ 517. FRED TALBOT
- □ 553. MIKE HEGAN(R)
- □ 553. THAD TILLOTSON(R)
- □ 567. STEVE HAMILTON
- □ 583. RAY BARKER
- □ 601. BILL BRYAN

PHILADELPHIA PHILLIES

- □ 14. PHIL LINZ
- □ 37. RICK WISE
- □ 53. CLAY DALRYMPLE
- □ 68. BOB BUHL
- □ 85. JOHNNY CALLISON
- □ 102. TEAM CARD
- □ 126. TONY TAYLOR
- □ 142. JACKIE BRANDT
- □ 181. TERRY FOX
- □ 187. PEDRO RAMOS
- □ 205. DICK GROAT
- □ 229. LARRY JACKSON
- □ 248. GENE MAUCH(M)
- □ 268. JOHN BRIGGS
- □ 290. BILL WHITE
- □ 326. BOB UECKER
- □ 359. DICK ELLSWORTH
- □ 376. DON LOCK
- □ 395. CHRIS SHORT
- □ 402. GRANT JACKSON(R)
- □ 402. BILLY WILSON(R)
- □ 427. RUBEN GOMEZ
- □ 443. TITO FRANCONA
- □ 450. RICHIE ALLEN
- □ 466. BOBBY WINE
- □ 489. DOUG CLEMENS
- □ 508. DICK HALL
- □ 529. GARY WAGNER
- □ 548. TONY GONZALEZ
- □ 560. JIM BUNNING
- □ 587. GARY SUTHERLAND(R)
- □ 595. COOKIE ROJAS

PITTSBURGH PIRATES

- □ 10. MATTY ALOU
- □ 49. ROY FACE
- □ 66. MANNY MOTA
- □ 84. TOMMIE SISK
- □ 123. JIMMIE PRICE(R)
- □ 123. LUKE WALKER(R)
- □ 140. WILLIE STARGELL
- □ 162. BILLY O'DELL
- □ 183. JIM PAGLIARONI
- □ 203. AL MCBEAN
- □ 221. WOODY FRYMAN
- □ 283. GENE ALLEY
- □ 301. JESSE GONDER
- □ 322. JOSE PAGAN
- □ 335. BOB VEALE
- □ 351. VERN LAW
- □ 379. JERRY MAY
- □ 400. BOB CLEMENTE
- □ 425. PETE MIKKELSON
- □ 448. HARRY WALKER(M)
- □ 472. JOHN GELNAR(R)
- □ 472. GEORGE SPRIGGS(R)
- □ 492. TEAM CARD
- □ 510. BILL MAZEROSKI
- □ 527. DENNIS RIBANT
- □ 535. DONN CLENDENON
- □ 554. ANDRE RODGERS
- □ 562. STEVE BLASS
- □ 570. MAURY WILLS
- □ 577. BILL SHORT
- □ 586. MANNY JIMENEZ
- □ 592. JIM SHELLENBACK(R)
- □ 602. JUAN PIZARRO

ST. LOUIS CARDINALS

- □ 20. ORLANDO CEPEDA
- □ 41. JOE HOERNER
- □ 45. ROGER MARIS
- □ 78. PAT CORRALES
- □ 92. RAY WASHBURN
- □ 108. ALEX JOHNSON
- □ 128. ED SPIEZIO
- □ 146. STEVE CARLTON
- □ 173. TEAM CARD
- □ 195. AL JACKSON
- □ 196. JOHN ROMANO
- □ 210. BOB GIBSON
- □ 226. JULIAN JAVIER
- □ 245. CURT FLOOD
- □ 285. LOU BROCK
- □ 304. PHIL GAGLIANO
- □ 324. HAL WOODESHICK
- □ 356. LARRY JASTER
- □ 384. JIM COSMAN(R)
- □ 384. DICK HUGHES(R)
- □ 404. NELSON BRILES
- □ 421. DAL MAXVILL
- □ 474. BOB TOLAN
- □ 485. TIM MCCARVER
- □ 512. RED SCHOENDIENST(M)
- □ 589. DAVE RICKETTS
- □ 592. RON WILLIS(R)
- □ 605. MIKE SHANNON

SAN FRANCISCO GIANTS

- □ 4. HAL LANIER
- □ 26. BOB PRIDDY(R)
- □ 46. LINDY MCDANIEL
- □ 65. TOM HALLER
- □ 83. OLLIE BROWN
- □ 86. MIKE MCCORMICK(B)
- □ 116. HERMAN FRANKS(M)
- □ 132. OSSIE VIRGIL
- □ 156. RON HERBEL
- □ 177. TITO FUENTES
- □ 200. WILLIE MAYS
- □ 220. JIM HART
- □ 252. BOB BOLIN
- □ 279. FRANK LINZY
- □ 299. NORM SIEBERN
- □ 320. GAYLORD PERRY
- □ 332. JESUS ALOU
- □ 341. DICK DIETZ(R)
- □ 341. BILL SORRELL(R)
- □ 368. JACK HIATT
- □ 383. KEN HENDERSON
- □ 409. RAY SADECKI
- □ 441. JIM DAVENPORT
- □ 462. BOB BARTON
- □ 480. WILLIE MCCOVEY
- □ 500. JUAN MARICHAL
- □ 516. TEAM CARD
- □ 541. JOE GIBBON
- □ 579. BILL R. HENRY

WASHINGTON SENATORS

- □ 11. BARRY MOORE
- □ 26. BOB PRIDDY
- □ 27. BOB SAVERINE
- □ 47. KEN MCMULLEN
- □ 64. FRED VALENTINE
- □ 71. CAMILO PASCUAL
- □ 86. MIKE MCCORMICK(R)
- □ 115. PAUL CASANOVA
- □ 118. BERNIE ALLEN
- □ 167. JOE COLEMAN
- □ 167. TIM CULLEN(R)
- □ 188. KEN HARRELSON
- □ 207. JOHN ORSINO
- □ 228. GIL HODGES(M)
- □ 255. FRANK HOWARD
- □ 273. DICK LINES
- □ 291. JIM HANNAN
- □ 311. ED BRINKMAN
- □ 349. BOB CHANCE
- □ 362. DAROLD KNOWLES
- □ 387. CAP PETERSTON
- □ 403. DICK NEN
- □ 414. CASEY COX
- □ 437. TEAM CARD
- □ 459. DICK BOSMAN(R)
- □ 459. PETE CRAIG(R)
- □ 478. BOB HUMPHREYS
- □ 493. PHIL ORTEGA
- □ 509. JIM KING
- □ 551. DOUG CAMILLI
- □ 569. HANK ALLEN(R)
- □ 590. PETE RICHERT

1968 TOPPS (598)
2 1/2" X 3 1/2"

ATLANTA BRAVES

- ☐ 30. JOE TORRE
- ☐ 55. FELIPE ALOU
- ☐ 76. JIM BRITTON(R)
- ☐ 76. RON REED(R)
- ☐ 93. TONY CLONINGER
- ☐ 110. HANK AARON
- ☐ 134. PAT JARVIS
- ☐ 166. CLAUDE RAYMOND
- ☐ 174. BOB TILLMAN
- ☐ 187. SONNY JACKSON
- ☐ 203. DICK KELLEY
- ☐ 221. TEAM CARD
- ☐ 241. FELIX MILLAN
- ☐ 257. PHIL NIEKRO
- ☐ 286. CECIL UPSHAW
- ☐ 304. SANDY VALDESPINO
- ☐ 323. DERON JOHNSON
- ☐ 342. KEN JOHNSON
- ☐ 394. TOMMIE AARON
- ☐ 412. CLAY CARROLL
- ☐ 439. LUMAN HARRIS(M)
- ☐ 455. RICO CARTY
- ☐ 476. WOODY WOODWARY
- ☐ 527. TITO FRANCONA
- ☐ 550. CLETE BOYER
- ☐ 578. ORLANDO MARTINEZ
- ☐ 579. MIKE LUM(R)

BALTIMORE ORIOLES

- ☐ 20. BROOKS ROBINSON
- ☐ 42. LARRY HANEY
- ☐ 56. DAVE LEONHARD(R)
- ☐ 56. DAVE MAY(R)
- ☐ 82. SAM BOWENS
- ☐ 97. TOM PHOEBUS
- ☐ 118. MARK BELANGER
- ☐ 135. PAUL BLAIR
- ☐ 163. GENE BRABENDER
- ☐ 186. EDDIE WATT
- ☐ 194. DON BUFORD
- ☐ 204. ANDY ETCHEBARREN
- ☐ 222. JIM HARDIN
- ☐ 242. MOE DRABOWSKY
- ☐ 273. DAVE A. JOHNSON
- ☐ 293. BRUCE HOWARD
- ☐ 312. CURT BLEFARY
- ☐ 334. TEAM CARD
- ☐ 354. PETE RICHERT
- ☐ 381. BOOG POWELL
- ☐ 409. FRANK PETERS(R)
- ☐ 409. RON STONE(R)
- ☐ 428. VIC ROZNOVSKY
- ☐ 456. JOHN O'DONOGHUE
- ☐ 466. BILL DILLMAN
- ☐ 478. DAVE MCNALLY
- ☐ 489. WALLY BUNKER
- ☐ 500. FRANK ROBINSON
- ☐ 513. HANK BAUER(M)
- ☐ 549. CURT MOTTON(R)
- ☐ 549. ROGER NELSON(R)
- ☐ 575. JIM PALMER

BOSTON RED SOX

- ☐ 26. DARRELL BRANDON
- ☐ 43. GARY BELL
- ☐ 61. REGGIE SMITH
- ☐ 87. DICK WILLIAMS(M)
- ☐ 106. DALTON JONES
- ☐ 123. JOSE SANTIAGO
- ☐ 140. TONY CONIGLIARO
- ☐ 167. ELSTON HOWARD
- ☐ 189. BILL LANDIS
- ☐ 212. DAVE MOREHEAD
- ☐ 233. GEORGE SCOTT
- ☐ 250. CARL YASTRZEMSKI
- ☐ 272. RAY CULP
- ☐ 297. RUSS GIBSON
- ☐ 314. BILL ROHR(R)
- ☐ 314. GEORGE SPRIGGS(R)
- ☐ 331. DAN OSINSKI
- ☐ 346. JERRY ADAIR
- ☐ 387. JOE FOY
- ☐ 406. DICK ELLSWORTH
- ☐ 430. RICO PETROCELLI
- ☐ 449. GENE OLIVER
- ☐ 460. JIM LONBORG
- ☐ 481. JOHN WYATT
- ☐ 502. MIKE ANDREWS
- ☐ 519. JERRY STEPHENSON
- ☐ 537. NORM SIEBERN
- ☐ 555. JOSE TARTABULL
- ☐ 566. KEN HARRELSON
- ☐ 581. GARRY ROGGENBURK
- ☐ 593. LEE STANGE

CALIFORNIA ANGELS

- ☐ 24. BOBBY LOCKE
- ☐ 52. HAWK TAYLOR
- ☐ 75. DON MINCHER
- ☐ 102. JOSE CARDENAL
- ☐ 121. JIMMIE HALL
- ☐ 143. PETE CIMINO
- ☐ 170. JIM FREGOSI
- ☐ 193. JACK HAMILTON
- ☐ 216. BUBBA MORTON
- ☐ 238. TOM SATRIANO
- ☐ 252. TEAM CARD
- ☐ 271. BOBBY KNOOP
- ☐ 289. WOODY HELD
- ☐ 305. MINNIE ROJAS
- ☐ 328. CHUCK VINSON(R)
- ☐ 328. JIM WEAVER(R)
- ☐ 347. GEORGE BRUNET
- ☐ 389. JAY JOHNSTONE
- ☐ 416. BILL RIGNEY(M)
- ☐ 433. BOB RODGERS
- ☐ 453. SAMMY ELLIS
- ☐ 474. PAUL SCHAAL
- ☐ 493. JIM MCGLOTHLIN
- ☐ 531. CHUCK HINTON
- ☐ 552. ED KIRKPATRICK
- ☐ 570. RICK REICHARDT
- ☐ 587. ROGER REPOZ

CHICAGO CUBS

- ☐ 13. CHUCK HARTENSTEIN
- ☐ 37. BILLY WILLIAMS
- ☐ 60. KEN HOLTZMAN
- ☐ 83. JOHN STEPHENSON
- ☐ 101. GLENN BECKERT
- ☐ 119. TED SAVAGE
- ☐ 136. RANDY HUNDLEY
- ☐ 159. DON KESSINGER
- ☐ 179. BILL STONEMAN
- ☐ 184. LOU JOHNSON
- ☐ 202. ADOLFO PHILLIPS
- ☐ 219. ROB GARDNER
- ☐ 235. RON SANTO
- ☐ 258. JOSE ARCIA(R)
- ☐ 258. BILL SCHLESINGER(R)
- ☐ 279. BILL HANDS
- ☐ 296. BYRON BROWNE
- ☐ 321. LEO DUROCHER(M)
- ☐ 339. RICH NYE
- ☐ 355. ERNIE BANKS
- ☐ 382. RAMON HERNANDEZ
- ☐ 410. FERGUSON JENKINS
- ☐ 427. DICK CALMUS
- ☐ 451. AL SPANGLER
- ☐ 475. JOE NIEKRO
- ☐ 506. CLARENCE JONES
- ☐ 516. PETE MIKKELSON
- ☐ 542. JOHN BOCCABELLA
- ☐ 561. LEE ELIA
- ☐ 591. DICK NEN

CHICAGO WHITE SOX

- ☐ 14. JERRY MCNERTNEY
- ☐ 33. PETE WARD
- ☐ 51. BOB LOCKER
- ☐ 72. TOMMY JOHN
- ☐ 99. ROCKY COLAVITO
- ☐ 125. JOE HORLEN
- ☐ 142. BUDDY BRADFORD(R)
- ☐ 142. BILL VOSS(R)
- ☐ 172. WALT WILLIAMS
- ☐ 210. GARY PETERS
- ☐ 229. FRED KLAGES
- ☐ 259. KEN BOYER
- ☐ 265. TOMMY DAVIS
- ☐ 287. MICKEY ABARBANEL(R)
- ☐ 287. CISCO CARLOS(R)
- ☐ 310. LUIS APARICIO
- ☐ 329. DUANE JOSEPHSON
- ☐ 350. HOYT WILHELM
- ☐ 391. BOB PRIDDY
- ☐ 413. TOMMY MCCRAW
- ☐ 424. TEAM CARD
- ☐ 444. JACK FISHER
- ☐ 464. DON MCMAHON
- ☐ 485. KEN BERRY
- ☐ 504. RUSS SNYDER
- ☐ 522. WAYNE CAUSEY
- ☐ 541. SANDY ALOMAR
- ☐ 564. EDDIE STANKY(M)
- ☐ 585. WILBUR WOOD

CINCINNATI REDS

- ☐ 23. CHICO CARDENAS
- ☐ 48. TED DAVIDSON
- ☐ 74. MILT PAPPAS
- ☐ 90. VADA PINSON
- ☐ 108. DON PAVLETICH
- ☐ 130. TONY PEREZ
- ☐ 133. FRED WHITFIELD
- ☐ 148. DAVE BRISTOL(M)
- ☐ 171. DON NOTTEBART
- ☐ 196. GARY NOLAN
- ☐ 213. CHICO RUIZ
- ☐ 230. PETE ROSE
- ☐ 247. JOHNNY BENCH(R)
- ☐ 247. RON TOMPKINS(R)
- ☐ 264. TED ABERNATHY
- ☐ 283. MEL QUEEN
- ☐ 302. GERRY ARRIGO
- ☐ 319. GEORGE CULVER
- ☐ 338. BOB W. JOHNSON
- ☐ 353. MACK JONES
- ☐ 384. BILL F. HENRY(R)
- ☐ 384. HAL MCRAE(R)
- ☐ 405. TOMMY HELMS
- ☐ 425. JIM MALONEY
- ☐ 441. ALEX JOHNSON
- ☐ 463. JIMMIE SCHAFFER
- ☐ 487. LEE MAY
- ☐ 511. BILL KELSO
- ☐ 523. JOHN TSITOURIS

□ 543. BOB LEE
□ 574. TEAM CARD
□ 597. BILL MCCOOL

CLEVELAND INDIANS

□ 16. LOU PINIELLA(R)
□ 16. RICHIE SCHEINBLUM(R)
□ 35. STEVE HARGAN
□ 54. STAN WILLIAMS
□ 71. VERN FULLER
□ 94. LEE MAYE
□ 115. SAM MCDOWELL
□ 176. BOB ALLEN
□ 197. LARRY BROWN
□ 218. KEN SUAREZ
□ 237. ALVIN DARK(M)
□ 269. BOB TIEFENAUER
□ 295. SONNY SIEBERT
□ 318. CHICO SALMON
□ 340. MAX ALVIS
□ 397. VIC DAVALILLO
□ 418. EDDIE FISHER
□ 432. BILL DAVIS(R)
□ 432. JOSE VIDAL(R)
□ 443. JOE AZCUE
□ 471. ORLANDO PENA
□ 495. LEON WAGNER
□ 508. DUKE SIMS
□ 532. LUIS TIANT
□ 551. DARRELL SUTHERLAND
□ 568. WILLIE SMITH
□ 590. TOMMY HARPER

DETROIT TIGERS

□ 22. PAT DOBSON
□ 40. DENNY MCLAIN
□ 58. ED MATHEWS
□ 78. JIM NORTHRUP
□ 113. TOM MATCHICK(R)
□ 113. DARYL PATTERSON(R)
□ 129. MICKEY STANLEY
□ 160. EARL WILSON
□ 178. DON WERT
□ 201. MIKE MARSHALL
□ 226. JIMMIE PRICE
□ 240. AL KALINE
□ 256. NORM CASH
□ 285. DICK MCAULIFFE
□ 307. JOHN HILLER
□ 326. DENNIS RIBANT
□ 360. WILLIE HORTON
□ 399. RAY OYLER
□ 414. MICKEY LOLICH
□ 447. GEORGE KORINCE(R)
□ 447. FRED LASHER(R)
□ 470. BILL FREEHAN
□ 488. DICK TRACEWSKI
□ 505. JOE SPARMA
□ 528. TEAM CARD
□ 544. MAYO SMITH(M)
□ 583. GATES BROWN

HOUSTON ASTROS

□ 21. RON DAVIS
□ 41. JULIO GOTAY
□ 57. DAN SCHNEIDER
□ 77. DON WILSON
□ 95. BOB ASPROMONTE
□ 128. TOM DUKES(R)
□ 128. ALONZO HARRIS(R)
□ 144. JOE MORGAN
□ 161. NORM MILLER
□ 182. DAVE GIUSTI
□ 207. CARROLL SEMBERA
□ 232. DENIS MENKE
□ 260. JIM WYNN
□ 274. MIKE CUELLAR
□ 300. RUSTY STAUB
□ 317. RON BRAND
□ 332. DOUG RADER
□ 359. JOE MOELLER
□ 392. GRADY HATTON(M)
□ 403. JOHN BUZHARDT
□ 423. FRED GLADDING
□ 438. LEE THOMAS
□ 468. LARRY SHERRY

□ 491. DENNY LEMASTER
□ 507. WADE BLASINGAME
□ 529. BRUCE VON HOFF
□ 539. JIM RAY(R)
□ 547. DAN COOMBS
□ 565. LARRY DIERKER
□ 569. IVAN MURRELL(R)
□ 576. DAVE ADLESH
□ 592. JOHN BATEMAN

LOS ANGELES DODGERS

□ 15. RON HUNT
□ 34. AL FERRARA
□ 65. JOHN ROSEBORO
□ 88. PHIL REGAN
□ 103. DON SUTTON
□ 124. NATE OLIVER
□ 145. DON DRYSDALE
□ 168. TEAM CARD
□ 208. WILLIE DAVIS
□ 228. JACK BILLINGHAM(R)
□ 228. JIM FAIREY(R)
□ 249. BILL SINGER
□ 266. PAUL POPOVICH
□ 281. JIM CAMPANIS
□ 298. JIM BREWER
□ 315. ZOILO VERSALLES
□ 336. JOHN PURDIN
□ 357. LEN GABRIELSON
□ 398. JIM GRANT
□ 417. WILLIE CRAWFORD
□ 440. CLAUDE OSTEEN
□ 457. JIM LEFEBVRE
□ 472. WALT ALSTON(M)
□ 492. JEFF TORBORG
□ 510. RON FAIRLY
□ 533. WES PARKER
□ 553. HANK AGUIRRE
□ 580. BOB BAILEY

MINNESOTA TWINS

□ 28. TED UHLAENDER
□ 44. FRANK KOSTRO
□ 64. JIM MERRITT
□ 80. ROD CAREW
□ 91. JIM OLLOM
□ 111. RICH REESE
□ 137. TEAM CARD
□ 165. TONY OLIVA
□ 181. JERRY ZIMMERMAN
□ 206. CAL ERMER(M)
□ 220. HARMON KILLEBREW
□ 243. RICH ROLLINS
□ 255. DEAN CHANCE
□ 276. JIM ROLAND
□ 301. GEORGE MITTERWALD(R)
□ 301. RICH RENICK(R)
□ 322. DAVE BOSWELL
□ 335. BOB ALLISON
□ 352. JACKIE HERNANDEZ
□ 393. JIM PERRY
□ 420. CESAR TOVAR
□ 435. RON PERRANOSKI
□ 450. JIM KAAT
□ 473. AL WORTHINGTON
□ 515. RUSS NIXON

□ 534. BOB L. MILLER
□ 557. FRANK QUILICI
□ 589. RON CLARK(R)
□ 589. MOE OGIER(R)

NEW YORK METS

□ 27. GIL HODGES(M)
□ 45. TOM SEAVER
□ 63. DICK KENWORTHY
□ 92. ED KRANEPOOL
□ 114. RON SWOBODA
□ 132. BUD HARRELSON
□ 177. JERRY KOOSMAN(R)
□ 177. NOLAN RYAN(R)
□ 191. DAN FRISELLA
□ 211. J.C. MARTIN
□ 236. TUG MCGRAW
□ 254. CLEON JONES
□ 277. JERRY BUCHEK
□ 292. ART SHAMSKY
□ 313. AL WEIS
□ 345. BOB HENDLEY
□ 386. GREG GOOSSEN
□ 401. TEAM CARD
□ 421. RON TAYLOR
□ 437. DON CARDWELL
□ 465. TOMMIE AGEE
□ 486. CAL KOONCE
□ 503. AL JACKSON
□ 521. DON SHAW
□ 536. BILL SHORT
□ 556. DICK SELMA
□ 563. ED CHARLES
□ 569. LESS ROHR(R)
□ 572. DON BOSCH
□ 582. JERRY GROTE
□ 594. PHIL LINZ

NEW YORK YANKEES

□ 29. JOE VERBANIC
□ 47. RALPH HOUK(M)
□ 69. TOM TRESH
□ 89. JAKE GIBBS
□ 105. AL DOWNING
□ 120. MEL STOTTLEMYRE
□ 138. RUBEN AMARO
□ 195. JOE PEPITONE
□ 214. STAN BAHNSEN(R)
□ 214. FRANK FERNANDEZ(R)
□ 234. BILL MONBOUQUETTE
□ 246. FRITZ PETERSON
□ 263. HORACE CLARKE
□ 280. MICKEY MANTLE
□ 299. GENE MICHAEL
□ 316. STEVE BARBER
□ 337. BILL ROBINSON
□ 383. STEVE WHITAKER
□ 402. MIKE HEGAN
□ 431. DOOLEY WOMACK
□ 467. DICK HOWSER
□ 496. STEVE HAMILTON
□ 524. ANDY KOSCO
□ 539. MIKE FERRARO(R)
□ 546. ROY WHITE
□ 562. JIM BOUTON
□ 577. FRED TALBOT
□ 596. CHARLIE SMITH

OAKLAND A'S

□ 18. MIKE HERSHBERGER
□ 38. TONY PIERCE
□ 62. CHUCK DOBSON
□ 79. TED KUBIAK
□ 109. BERT CAMPANERIS
□ 127. PAUL LINDBLAD
□ 146. SAL BANDO
□ 164. RAMON WEBSTER
□ 183. BOB KENNEDY(M)
□ 199. ROBERTO RODRIQUEZ(R)
□ 199. DARRELL OSTEEN(R)
□ 224. JACK AKER
□ 244. JOHN DONALDSON
□ 261. DAVE DUNCAN
□ 282. RICK MONDAY
□ 303. DICK GREEN
□ 324. JIM NASH

☐ 343. JIM GOSGER
☐ 385. JIM HUNTER
☐ 404. FLOYD ROBINSON
☐ 422. RENE LACHEMANN
☐ 458. LEW KRAUSSE
☐ 484. PHIL ROOF
☐ 501. JOHN ODOM
☐ 517. DIEGO SEGUI
☐ 535. DANNY CATER
☐ 554. TEAM CARD
☐ 571. TONY LARUSSA
☐ 586. JIM PAGLIARONI

PHILADELPHIA PHILLIES

☐ 17. DICK HALL
☐ 39. COOKIE ROJAS
☐ 59. DON LOCK
☐ 81. LARRY JACKSON
☐ 98. GARY SUTHERLAND
☐ 112. WOODY FRYMAN
☐ 122. GENE MAUCH(M)
☐ 139. CHRIS SHORT
☐ 173. JOHN BOOZER
☐ 190. BILL WHITE
☐ 217. TURK FARRELL
☐ 225. RICHIE ALLEN
☐ 245. TONY GONZALEZ
☐ 262. RICK WISE
☐ 284. JOHN BRIGGS
☐ 306. MIKE RYAN
☐ 327. TONY TAYLOR
☐ 348. LARRY COLTON(R)
☐ 348. DICK THOENEN(R)
☐ 396. BOBBY WINE
☐ 415. JOHNNY CALLISON
☐ 434. RICK JOSEPH
☐ 448. GARY WAGNER
☐ 477. TEAM CARD
☐ 512. GRANT JACKSON
☐ 567. CLAY DALRYMPLE
☐ 579. LARRY HISLE(R)

PITTSBURGH PIRATES

☐ 19. JUAN PIZARRO
☐ 36. BOB MOOSE(R)
☐ 36. BOB ROBERTSON(R)
☐ 53. GENE ALLEY
☐ 70. BOB VEALE
☐ 86. WILLIE STARGELL
☐ 150. BOB CLEMENTE
☐ 175. MAURY WILLS
☐ 198. ROY FACE
☐ 215. JIM BUNNING
☐ 251. MANNY SANGUILLEN
☐ 270. MATTY ALOU
☐ 288. DAVE WICKERSHAM
☐ 308. TEAM CARD
☐ 325. MANNY MOTA
☐ 344. DONN CLENDENON
☐ 390. BILL MAZEROSKI
☐ 407. GARY KOLB
☐ 429. TOMMIE SISK
☐ 446. RON KLINE
☐ 461. CHUCK HILLER
☐ 482. JOSE PAGAN
☐ 499. STEVE BLASS
☐ 514. AL MCBEAN
☐ 538. MANNY JIMENEZ
☐ 559. CARL TAYLOR(R)
☐ 559. LUKE WALKER(R)
☐ 584. LARRY SHEPARD(M)
☐ 598. JERRY MAY

ST. LOUIS CARDINALS

☐ 25. JULIAN JAVIER
☐ 46. DAVE RICKETTS
☐ 68. RON WILLIS
☐ 84. BOB TOLAN
☐ 100. BOB GIBSON
☐ 117. LARRY JASTER
☐ 141. DAL MAXVILL
☐ 162. HAL GILSON(R)
☐ 162. MIKE TORREZ(R)
☐ 180. CURT FLOOD
☐ 200. ORLANDO CEPEDA
☐ 227. JOE HOERNER
☐ 253. DICK HUGHES
☐ 275. TIM MCCARVER
☐ 294. RED SCHOENDIENST(M)
☐ 311. JACK LAMABE
☐ 330. ROGER MARIS
☐ 349. ED SPIEZIO
☐ 388. RAY WASHBURN
☐ 408. STEVE CARLTON
☐ 445. MIKE SHANNON
☐ 459. DICK SIMPSON
☐ 479. PHIL GAGLIANO
☐ 497. TEAM CARD
☐ 520. LOU BROCK
☐ 540. NELSON BRILES
☐ 558. JOHN EDWARDS
☐ 588. DICK SCHOFIELD

SAN FRANCISCO GIANTS

☐ 32. JOE GIBBON
☐ 50. WILLIE MAYS
☐ 73. JIM HART
☐ 85. GAYLORD PERRY
☐ 104. DICK DIETZ
☐ 126. BOBBY ETHERIDGE
☐ 147. FRANK LINZY
☐ 169. BOB BOLIN
☐ 185. TOM HALLER
☐ 205. JUAN MARICAHL
☐ 223. OLLIE BROWN
☐ 239. BILL R. HENRY
☐ 267. HERMAN FRANKS(M)
☐ 290. WILLIE MCCOVEY
☐ 309. KEN HENDERSON
☐ 333. RON HERBEL
☐ 351. BOB BARTON
☐ 400. MIKE MCCORMICK
☐ 419. JACK HIATT
☐ 436. HAL LANIER
☐ 452. JESUS ALOU
☐ 469. TY CLINE
☐ 494. RAY SADECKI
☐ 525. JIM DAVENPORT
☐ 545. LINDY MCDANIEL

WASHINGTON SENATORS

☐ 31. ED STROUD
☐ 49. ED BRINKMAN
☐ 66. CASEY COX
☐ 96. FRANK COGGINS(R)
☐ 96. DICK NOLD(R)
☐ 116. KEN MCMULLEN
☐ 131. FRANK BERTAINA
☐ 149. BOB SAVERINE
☐ 188. CAP PETERSON
☐ 209. TIM CULLEN
☐ 231. DAVE BALDWIN
☐ 248. FRED VALENTINE
☐ 268. BOB HUMPHREYS
☐ 291. DICK LINES
☐ 320. FRANK HOWARD
☐ 341. JIM LEMON(M)
☐ 358. MIKE EPSTEIN
☐ 395. CAMILO PASCUAL
☐ 411. RON HANSEN
☐ 426. HANK ALLEN
☐ 442. DICK BOSMAN
☐ 462. BARRY MOORE
☐ 483. DAROLD KNOWLES
☐ 498. BILL BRYAN
☐ 509. DENNIS HIGGINS
☐ 526. BILL DENEHY
☐ 548. BERNIE ALLEN
☐ 560. PAUL CASANOVA
☐ 573. JOE COLEMAN
☐ 595. PHIL ORTEGA

1969 TOPPS (664)
2 1/2" X 3 1/2"

ATLANTA BRAVES

☐ 33. WAYNE CAUSEY
☐ 53. SONNY JACKSON
☐ 79. MILT PAPPAS
☐ 100. HANK AARON
☐ 128. TOMMIE AARON
☐ 154. JIM BRITTON
☐ 177. RON REED
☐ 196. LUM HARRIS(M)
☐ 210. FELIX MILLAN
☐ 238. KEN JOHNSON
☐ 261. BOB W. JOHNSON
☐ 282. PAT JARVIS
☐ 300. FELIPE ALOU
☐ 331. GIL GARRIDO(R)
☐ 331. TOM HOUSF(R)
☐ 355. PHIL NIEKRO
☐ 374. BOB TILLMAN
☐ 385. ORLANDO CEPEDA
☐ 398. TITO FRANCONA
☐ 446. CLAUDE RAYMOND
☐ 489. CLETE BOYER
☐ 514. MIKE LUM
☐ 542. BOB ASPROMONTE
☐ 568. CECIL UPSHAW
☐ 590. RICO CARTY
☐ 611. BOB DIDIER(R)
☐ 611. WALT HRINIAK(R)
☐ 611. GARY NEIBAUER(R)
☐ 627. GEORGE STONE

BALTIMORE ORIOLES

☐ 15. BOOG POWELL
☐ 37. CURT MOTTON
☐ 66. MIKE ADAMSON(R)
☐ 66. MERV RETTENMUND(R)
☐ 86. PETE RICHERT
☐ 113. DAVE MAY
☐ 141. BILL DILLMAN
☐ 151. CLAY DALRYMPLE
☐ 185. TOM PHOEBUS
☐ 203. DAVE A. JOHNSON
☐ 228. DAVE LEONHARD
☐ 250. FRANK ROBINSON
☐ 277. ELROD HENDRICKS
☐ 299. MARK BELANGER
☐ 323. LARRY MILLER
☐ 340. DAVE MCNALLY
☐ 368. VIC ROZNOVSKY
☐ 393. GENE BRABENDER
☐ 453. MIKE CUELLAR
☐ 478. DON BUFORD
☐ 506. PAUL BLAIR
☐ 516. EARL WEAVER(M)
☐ 550. BROOKS ROBINSON
☐ 573. JIM PALMER
☐ 597. BOBBY FLOYD(R)
☐ 610. JIM HARDIN
☐ 634. ANDY ETCHEBARREN
☐ 652. EDDIE WATT

BOSTON RED SOX

- ☐ 21. JOSE SANTIAGO
- ☐ 52. MIKE ANDREWS
- ☐ 89. RUSS GIBSON
- ☐ 109. JIM LONBORG
- ☐ 130. CARL YASTRZEMSKI
- ☐ 148. LEE STANGE
- ☐ 172. JERRY STEPHENSON
- ☐ 189. JOE LAHOUD(R)
- ☐ 189. JOHN THIBDEAU(R)
- ☐ 215. RICO PETROCELLI
- ☐ 240. KEN HARRELSON
- ☐ 264. BILL LANDIS
- ☐ 287. JOSE TARTABULL
- ☐ 311. SPARKY LYLE
- ☐ 330. TONY CONIGLIARO
- ☐ 349. DICK WILLIAMS(M)
- ☐ 391. RAY CULP
- ☐ 457. DALTON JONES
- ☐ 476. KEN BRETT(R)
- ☐ 476. GERRY MOSES(R)
- ☐ 498. JUAN PIZARRO
- ☐ 521. GEORGE THOMAS
- ☐ 543. FRED NEWMAN
- ☐ 574. GEORGE SCOTT
- ☐ 628. BILL CONIGLIARO(R)
- ☐ 628. SYD O'BRIEN(R)
- ☐ 628. FRED WENZ(R)
- ☐ 660. REGGIE SMITH

CALIFORNIA ANGELS

- ☐ 32. SAMMY ELLIS
- ☐ 59. JAY JOHNSTONE
- ☐ 78. TOM SATRIANO
- ☐ 103. ROGER REPOZ
- ☐ 134. JIM WEAVER
- ☐ 157. BOB RODGERS
- ☐ 182. BILL RIGNEY(M)
- ☐ 205. RICK REICHARDT.
- ☐ 224. BILL HARRELSON(R)
- ☐ 224. STEVE KEALEY(R)
- ☐ 252. CHUCK COTTIER
- ☐ 275. VIC DAVALILLO
- ☐ 296. ANDY MESSERSMITH
- ☐ 315. EDDIE FISHER
- ☐ 342. BUBBA MORTON
- ☐ 365. JIM FREGOSI
- ☐ 386. JIM MCGLOTHLIN
- ☐ 407. TOM EGAN
- ☐ 445. BOBBY KNOOP
- ☐ 474. TOM MURPHY
- ☐ 502. MINNIE ROJAS
- ☐ 523. BOB CHANCE
- ☐ 565. HOYT WILHELM
- ☐ 583. CLYDE WRIGHT
- ☐ 598. RUBEN AMARO
- ☐ 621. BILL VOSS
- ☐ 645. GEORGE BRUNET
- ☐ 653. AURELIO RODRIGUEZ

CHICAGO CUBS

- ☐ 20. ERNIE BANKS
- ☐ 43. JOE NIEKRO
- ☐ 63. JIM HICKMAN
- ☐ 88. RICH NYE
- ☐ 115. BILL HANDS
- ☐ 147. LEO DUROCHER(M)
- ☐ 171. GLENN BECKERT
- ☐ 198. WILLIE SMITH
- ☐ 225. DON KESSINGER
- ☐ 247. GENE OLIVER
- ☐ 268. AL SPANGLER
- ☐ 288. KEN HOLTZMAN
- ☐ 312. LEE ELIA
- ☐ 347. RANDY HUNDLEY
- ☐ 372. ADOLFO PHILLIPS
- ☐ 404. VIC LAROSE(R)
- ☐ 404. GARY ROSS(R)
- ☐ 450. BILLY WILLIAMS
- ☐ 483. TED ABERNATHY
- ☐ 535. PHIL REGAN
- ☐ 538. CHARLIE SMITH
- ☐ 570. RON SANTO
- ☐ 593. DON NOTTEBART
- ☐ 602. ALEC DISTASO(R)
- ☐ 602. DON YOUNG(R)
- ☐ 602. JIM QUALLS(R)
- ☐ 640. FERGIE JENKINS

CHICAGO WHITE SOX

- ☐ 34. GARY PETERS
- ☐ 54. CISCO CARLOS
- ☐ 75. LUIS APARICIO
- ☐ 97. BUDDY BRADFORD
- ☐ 123. WILBUR WOOD
- ☐ 155. PETE WARD
- ☐ 173. BOB CHRISTIAN(R)
- ☐ 173. GERRY NYMAN(R)
- ☐ 179. DON PAVLETICH
- ☐ 222. DUANE JOSEPHSON
- ☐ 248. BOB PRIDDY
- ☐ 283. SANDY ALOMAR
- ☐ 309. WALT WILLIAMS
- ☐ 328. JOE HORLEN
- ☐ 363. RUSS NIXON
- ☐ 388. TOM MCCRAW
- ☐ 439. ED HERRMANN(R)
- ☐ 439. DAN LAZAR(R)
- ☐ 465. TOMMY JOHN
- ☐ 481. BILL MELTON
- ☐ 494. KEN BERRY
- ☐ 527. AL LOPEZ(M)
- ☐ 548. BOB LOCKER
- ☐ 566. RON HANSEN
- ☐ 622. DAN OSINSKI
- ☐ 636. WOODIE HELD
- ☐ 654. CARLOS MAY(R)
- ☐ 654. DON SECRIST(R)
- ☐ 654. RICH MORALES(R)

CINCINNATI REDS

- ☐ 26. CLAY CARROLL
- ☐ 70. TOMMY HELMS
- ☐ 81. MEL QUEEN
- ☐ 95. JOHNNY BENCH
- ☐ 120. PETE ROSE
- ☐ 142. WOODY WOODWARD
- ☐ 187. LEON WAGNER
- ☐ 213. GERRY ARRIGO
- ☐ 234. DAVE BRISTOL(M)
- ☐ 259. BILL SHORT
- ☐ 280. ALEX JOHNSON
- ☐ 295. TONY PEREZ
- ☐ 318. JACK FISHER
- ☐ 339. STEVE MINGORI(R)
- ☐ 339. JOE PENA(R)
- ☐ 362. JIM MALONEY
- ☐ 382. PAT CORRALES
- ☐ 405. LEE MAY
- ☐ 448. BOB TOLAN
- ☐ 469. CHICO RUIZ
- ☐ 492. TONY CLONINGER
- ☐ 518. FRED WHITFIELD
- ☐ 551. WAYNE GRANGER
- ☐ 581. GARY NOLAN
- ☐ 613. JIM BEAUCHAMP
- ☐ 624. DARREL CHANEY(R)
- ☐ 635. GEORGE CULVER
- ☐ 661. JIM MERRITT

CLEVELAND INDIANS

- ☐ 19. KEN SUAREZ
- ☐ 61. JIMMIE HALL
- ☐ 91. ALVIN DARK(M)
- ☐ 118. STAN WILLIAMS
- ☐ 145. MAX ALVIS
- ☐ 176. JOE AZCUE
- ☐ 201. RUSS SNYDER
- ☐ 220. SAM MCDOWELL
- ☐ 244. RAY FOSSE(R)
- ☐ 244. GEORGE WOODSON(R)
- ☐ 267. VICENTE ROMO
- ☐ 291. VERN FULLER
- ☐ 325. JOSE CARDENAL
- ☐ 348. STEVE HARGAN
- ☐ 367. LOU JOHNSON
- ☐ 414. DUKE SIMS
- ☐ 455. SONNY SIEBERT
- ☐ 479. RICHIE SCHEINBLUM
- ☐ 503. LARRY BROWN
- ☐ 537. MIKE PAUL
- ☐ 560. LUIS TIANT
- ☐ 571. CAP PETERSON
- ☐ 579. DAVE NELSON
- ☐ 595. LEE MAYE
- ☐ 597. LARRY BURCHART(R)
- ☐ 605. DICK ELLSWORTH
- ☐ 629. JACK HAMILTON
- ☐ 644. CHUCK HINTON

DETROIT TIGERS

- ☐ 13. MICKEY STANLEY
- ☐ 40. MAYO SMITH(M)
- ☐ 80. NORM CASH
- ☐ 101. DARYL PATTERSON
- ☐ 126. DICK TRACEWSKI
- ☐ 150. DENNY MCLAIN
- ☐ 180. WILLIE HORTON
- ☐ 207. ROY FACE
- ☐ 231. PAT DOBSON
- ☐ 256. GATES BROWN
- ☐ 270. MICKEY LOLICH
- ☐ 305. DICK MCAULIFFE
- ☐ 324. LES CAIN(R)
- ☐ 324. DAVE CAMPBELL(R)
- ☐ 344. TOM MATCHICK
- ☐ 373. FRED LASHER
- ☐ 390. BILL FREEHAN
- ☐ 410. AL KALINE
- ☐ 443. DON WERT
- ☐ 472. JIM PRICE
- ☐ 488. JOE SPARMA
- ☐ 525. EARL WILSON
- ☐ 544. MIKE KILKENNEY(R)
- ☐ 544. RON WOODS(R)
- ☐ 580. JIM NORTHRUP
- ☐ 616. DON MCMAHON
- ☐ 642. JOHN HILLER
- ☐ 663. DICK RADATZ

HOUSTON ASTROS

- ☐ 35. JOE MORGAN
- ☐ 58. FRED GLADDING
- ☐ 76. NORM MILLER
- ☐ 96. DENVER LEMASTER
- ☐ 119. DOUG RADER
- ☐ 156. HAL GILSON(R)
- ☐ 156. LEON MCFADDEN(R)
- ☐ 186. JOHN EDWARDS
- ☐ 202. DON WILSON
- ☐ 208. DONN CLENDENON
- ☐ 257. JIM RAY
- ☐ 278. GARY GEIGER
- ☐ 308. WADE BLASINGAME
- ☐ 337. MARTY MARTINEZ
- ☐ 360. JIM WYNN
- ☐ 389. DAN COOMBS
- ☐ 411. LARRY DIERKER
- ☐ 458. CURT BLEFARY
- ☐ 487. DENIS MENKE
- ☐ 499. DON BRYANT(R)
- ☐ 499. STEVE SHEA(R)
- ☐ 526. HECTOR TORRES
- ☐ 562. BOB WATSON
- ☐ 594. DOOLEY WOMACK
- ☐ 614. TOM GRIFFIN(R)
- ☐ 614. SKIP GUINN(R)
- ☐ 633. HARRY WALKER(M)
- ☐ 656. DAN SCHNEIDER

KANSAS CITY ROYALS

- ☐ 29. DAVE MOREHEAD
- ☐ 49. STEVE JONES
- ☐ 49. ELLIE RODRIGUEZ(R)
- ☐ 71. STEVE WHITAKER
- ☐ 93. JOE FOY
- ☐ 116. CHUCK HARRISON
- ☐ 137. WALLY BUNKER
- ☐ 159. JERRY ADAIR
- ☐ 211. GALEN CISCO
- ☐ 239. BOB TAYLOR
- ☐ 258. JACKIE HERNANDEZ
- ☐ 279. ROGER NELSON
- ☐ 298. DAVE NICHOLSON
- ☐ 352. PAUL SCHAAL
- ☐ 376. MIKE FIORE(R)
- ☐ 376. JIM ROOKER(R)
- ☐ 396. JIM CAMPANIS
- ☐ 437. LUIS ALCARAZ
- ☐ 463. DENNIS RIBANT
- ☐ 484. JOE GORDON(M)
- ☐ 508. MOE DRABOWSKY
- ☐ 529. ED KIRKPATRICK

- ☐ 558. TOM BURGMEIER
- ☐ 569. BILLY HARRIS
- ☐ 591. MIKE HEDLUND
- ☐ 603. JOE KEOUGH
- ☐ 619. BILL BUTLER(R)
- ☐ 619. H. PAT KELLY(R)
- ☐ 619. JUAN RIOS(R)
- ☐ 632. JON WARDEN
- ☐ 647. DAVE WICKERSHAM
- ☐ 662. DICK DRAGO(R)
- ☐ 662. GEORGE SPRIGGS(R)
- ☐ 662. BOB OLIVER(R)

LOS ANGELES DODGERS

- ☐ 24. WALTER ALSTON(M)
- ☐ 47. PAUL POPOVICH
- ☐ 65. WILLIE DAVIS
- ☐ 94. HANK AGUIRRE
- ☐ 122. RON FAIRLY
- ☐ 139. ANDY KOSCO
- ☐ 140. JIM LEFEBVRE
- ☐ 161. JOHN PURDIN
- ☐ 216. DON SUTTON
- ☐ 241. JIM BREWER
- ☐ 266. TOM HUTTON(R)
- ☐ 266. ALAN FOSTER(R)
- ☐ 289. BART SHIRLEY
- ☐ 310. TOM HALLER
- ☐ 327. WILLIE CRAWFORD
- ☐ 353. JEFF TORBORG
- ☐ 379. KEN BOYER
- ☐ 400. DON DRYSDALE
- ☐ 444. JOE MOELLER
- ☐ 471. TED SAVAGE
- ☐ 493. WES PARKER
- ☐ 528. CLAUDE OSTEEN
- ☐ 552. TED SIZEMORE(R)
- ☐ 552. BILL SUDAKIS(R)
- ☐ 575. BILL SINGER
- ☐ 615. LEN GABRIELSON
- ☐ 641. BOBBY DARWIN(R)
- ☐ 641. JOHN MILLER(R)

MINNESOTA TWINS

- ☐ 30. BOB ALLISON
- ☐ 56. RICH REESE
- ☐ 77. RON PERRANOSKI
- ☐ 99. DANNY MORRIS(R)
- ☐ 99. GRAIG NETTLES(R)
- ☐ 121. JOE GRZENDA
- ☐ 146. JIM PERRY
- ☐ 194. TED UHLAENDER
- ☐ 218. JOHN ROSEBORO
- ☐ 242. FRANK KOSTRO
- ☐ 265. CHICO CARDENAS
- ☐ 290. JIM KAAT
- ☐ 317. BRUCE LOOK
- ☐ 336. JIM ROLAND
- ☐ 356. FRANK QUILICI
- ☐ 375. HARMON KILLEBREW
- ☐ 403. BOB L. MILLER
- ☐ 459. DAVE BOSWELL
- ☐ 491. JERRY CRIDER(R)
- ☐ 491. GEORGE MITTERWALD(R)
- ☐ 510. ROD CAREW
- ☐ 530. CESAR TOVAR
- ☐ 547. BILLY MARTIN(M)
- ☐ 561. RON CLARK
- ☐ 600. TONY OLIVA
- ☐ 620. DEAN CHANCE
- ☐ 658. TOM HALL(R)

MONTREAL EXPOS

- ☐ 22. JESUS ALOU
- ☐ 45. MAURY WILLS
- ☐ 67. BILL STONEMAN
- ☐ 92. JACK BILLINGHAM
- ☐ 117. JIM FAIREY
- ☐ 138. JOHN BATEMAN
- ☐ 183. DON SHAW
- ☐ 230. RUSTY STAUB
- ☐ 236. MANNY MOTA
- ☐ 284. JERRY ROBERTSON(R)
- ☐ 284. MIKE WEGENER(R)
- ☐ 306. JIM GRANT
- ☐ 326. GARY SUTHERLAND
- ☐ 351. CARROLL SEMBERA
- ☐ 378. JOSE HERRERA
- ☐ 399. BOB BAILEY
- ☐ 442. TY CLINE
- ☐ 466. JOHN BOCCABELLA
- ☐ 496. LARRY JASTER
- ☐ 524. JOSE LABOY(R)
- ☐ 524. FLOYD WICKER(R)
- ☐ 549. RON BRAND
- ☐ 578. DON BOSCH
- ☐ 606. GENE MAUCH(M)
- ☐ 625. MACK JONES
- ☐ 646. DAN MCGINN(R)
- ☐ 646. CARL MORTON(R)
- ☐ 648. BOBBY WINE

NEW YORK METS

- ☐ 31. GARY GENTRY(R)
- ☐ 31. AMOS OTIS(R)
- ☐ 55. JERRY GROTE
- ☐ 72. RON TAYLOR
- ☐ 90. JERRY KOOSMAN
- ☐ 112. J.C. MARTIN
- ☐ 127. KEVIN COLLINS
- ☐ 144. BOB HENDLEY
- ☐ 193. DON CARDWELL
- ☐ 221. ART SHAMSKY
- ☐ 245. ED CHARLES
- ☐ 269. AL WEIS
- ☐ 303. CAL KOONCE
- ☐ 321. JIM MCANDREW
- ☐ 343. DAN FRISELLA
- ☐ 364. TOMMIE AGEE
- ☐ 381. ED KRANEPOOL
- ☐ 402. KEN BOSWELL
- ☐ 456. BUD HARRELSON
- ☐ 480. TOM SEAVER
- ☐ 512. CLEON JONES
- ☐ 533. NOLAN RYAN
- ☐ 564. GIL HODGES(M)
- ☐ 585. RON SWOBODA
- ☐ 601. TUG MCGRAW
- ☐ 624. DUFFY DYER(R)
- ☐ 649. AL JACKSON

NEW YORK YANKEES

- ☐ 25. ROY WHITE
- ☐ 46. FRITZ PETERSON
- ☐ 69. STEVE HAMILTON
- ☐ 87. HORACE CLARKE
- ☐ 114. ALAN CLOSTER(R)
- ☐ 114. JOHN CUMBERLAND(R)
- ☐ 191. LINDY MCDANIEL
- ☐ 212. TOM TRESH
- ☐ 237. BOBBY COX
- ☐ 262. MIKE KEKICH
- ☐ 292. AL DOWNING
- ☐ 313. BILL ROBINSON
- ☐ 332. FRED TALBOT
- ☐ 354. NATE OLIVER
- ☐ 380. STAN BAHNSEN
- ☐ 401. JAKE GIBBS
- ☐ 447. RALPH HOUK(M)
- ☐ 470. MEL STOTTLEMYRE
- ☐ 500. MICKEY MANTLE
- ☐ 519. GERRY KENNEY(R)
- ☐ 519. LEN BOEHMER(R)
- ☐ 541. JOE VERBANIC
- ☐ 557. FRANK FERNANDEZ
- ☐ 589. JOE PEPITONE
- ☐ 608. DICK SIMPSON
- ☐ 626. GENE MICHAEL
- ☐ 643. BILLY COWAN
- ☐ 657. BOBBY MURCER
- ☐ 658. BILL BURBACH(R)

OAKLAND A'S

- ☐ 23. LEW KRAUSSE
- ☐ 44. DANNY CATER
- ☐ 68. DAVE DUNCAN
- ☐ 105. RICK MONDAY
- ☐ 124. HANK BAUER(M)
- ☐ 143. JOE NOSSEK
- ☐ 195. JOHN ODOM
- ☐ 217. JOHN DONALDSON
- ☐ 235. JIM HUNTER
- ☐ 260. REGGIE JACKSON
- ☐ 281. TED KUBIAK
- ☐ 302. JIM PAGLIARONI
- ☐ 334. PHIL ROOF
- ☐ 358. GEORGE LAUZERIQUE(R)
- ☐ 358. ROBERTO RODRIQUEZ(R)
- ☐ 371. SAL BANDO
- ☐ 397. CHUCK DOBSON
- ☐ 449. PAUL LINDBLAD
- ☐ 467. TOM REYNOLDS
- ☐ 495. BERT CAMPANERIS
- ☐ 515. DICK GREEN
- ☐ 546. JIM NASH
- ☐ 587. JOE RUDI
- ☐ 597. ROLLIE FINGERS(R)
- ☐ 618. RAMON WEBSTER
- ☐ 638. ED SPRAGUE
- ☐ 655. MIKE HERSHBERGER

PHILADELPHIA PHILLIES

- ☐ 28. MIKE RYAN
- ☐ 51. WOODY FRYMAN
- ☐ 73. JOHNNY BRIGGS
- ☐ 108. TONY TAYLOR
- ☐ 133. JOHNNY CALLISON
- ☐ 174. GRANT JACKSON
- ☐ 188. RICK WISE
- ☐ 206. LARRY HISLE(R)
- ☐ 206. BARRY LERSCH(R)
- ☐ 229. DON LOCK
- ☐ 253. JERRY JOHNSON
- ☐ 276. GARY WAGNER
- ☐ 297. DERON JOHNSON
- ☐ 329. RICK JOSEPH
- ☐ 350. RICHIE ALLEN
- ☐ 369. BOB SKINNER
- ☐ 395. CHRIS SHORT
- ☐ 454. LARRY COLTON(R)
- ☐ 454. DON MONEY(R)
- ☐ 477. JEFF JAMES
- ☐ 507. COOKIE ROJAS
- ☐ 531. DICK FARRELL
- ☐ 576. RON STONE(R)
- ☐ 576. BILL WILSON(R)
- ☐ 599. JOHN BOOZER
- ☐ 624. TERRY HARMON(R)

PITTSBURGH PIRATES

- ☐ 36. LUKE WALKER
- ☐ 50. BOB CLEMENTE
- ☐ 82. RICH HEBNER(R)
- ☐ 82. AL OLIVER(R)
- ☐ 104. STEVE BLASS
- ☐ 131. CHRIS CANNIZZARO
- ☐ 152. TOMMIE SISK
- ☐ 175. JIM BUNNING
- ☐ 192. JOSE PAGAN
- ☐ 219. FREDDIE PATEK
- ☐ 243. RON KLINE
- ☐ 263. JERRY MAY
- ☐ 286. DOCK ELLIS
- ☐ 307. GARY KOLB
- ☐ 335. BILL MAZEROSKI
- ☐ 357. CARL TAYLOR
- ☐ 384. LARRY SHEPARD(M)
- ☐ 409. BOB MOOSE
- ☐ 436. GENE ALLEY
- ☐ 468. BRUCE DAL CANTON(R)
- ☐ 468. BOB ROBERTSON(R)
- ☐ 490. MATTY ALOU
- ☐ 509. MANNY SANGUILLEN
- ☐ 520. BOB VEALE
- ☐ 545. WILLIE STARGELL
- ☐ 553. RON DAVIS
- ☐ 567. ELVIO JIMENEZ(R)
- ☐ 567. JIM SHELLENBACK(R)
- ☐ 596. CHUCK HARTENSTEIN

ST. LOUIS CARDINALS

- ☐ 18. DICK SCHOFIELD
- ☐ 39. DICK HUGHES
- ☐ 60. NELSON BRILES
- ☐ 85. LOU BROCK
- ☐ 110. MIKE SHANNON
- ☐ 136. STEVE HUNTZ(R)
- ☐ 136. MIKE TORREZ(R)
- ☐ 160. VADA PINSON

1969 Topps

- □ 181. MEL NELSON
- □ 200. BOB GIBSON
- □ 232. DAVE RICKETTS
- □ 255. STEVE CARLTON
- □ 273. RON WILLIS
- □ 320. DAL MAXVILL
- □ 341. DAVE ADLESH
- □ 366. BO BELINSKY
- □ 415. RAY WASHBURN
- □ 438. GARY WASLEWSKI
- □ 460. JOE TORRE
- □ 462. RED SCHOENDIENST(M)
- □ 475. TIM MCCARVER
- □ 497. JULIAN JAVIER
- □ 522. JOE HOERNER
- □ 540. CURT FLOOD
- □ 559. JOE HAGUE(R)
- □ 559. JIM HICKS(R)
- □ 588. BILL WHITE
- □ 609. PHIL GAGLIANO

SAN DIEGO PADRES

- □ 14. AL MCBEAN
- □ 38. ZOILO VERSALLES
- □ 74. PRESTON GOMEZ(M)
- □ 98. DAVE GIUSTI
- □ 129. BILL MCCOOL
- □ 149. OLLIE BROWN
- □ 184. ROBERTO PENA
- □ 197. DICK SELMA
- □ 223. TOM DUKES
- □ 249. ED SPIEZIO
- □ 271. LARRY STAHL
- □ 304. BILL DAVIS(R)
- □ 304. CLARENCE GASTON(R)
- □ 333. IVAN MURRELL
- □ 359. DICK KELLEY
- □ 387. BOBBY KLAUS
- □ 408. NATE COLBERT
- □ 452. AL FERRARA
- □ 473. JOSE ARCIA
- □ 501. TONY GONZALEZ
- □ 536. DANNY BREEDEN(R)
- □ 536. DAVE A. ROBERTS(R)
- □ 592. RAFAEL ROBLES(R)
- □ 592. AL SANTORINI(R)
- □ 617. JESSE GONDER
- □ 637. JERRY DAVANON(R)
- □ 637. FRANK REBERGER(R)
- □ 637. CLAY KIRBY(R)
- □ 641. TOMMY DEAN(R)
- □ 659. JOHNNY PODRES

SAN FRANCISCO GIANTS

- □ 16. CESAR GUTIERREZ(R)
- □ 16. RICH ROBERTSON(R)
- □ 41. BOB BARTON
- □ 64. BILL MONBOUQUETTE
- □ 102. JIM DAVENPORT
- □ 125. RAY SADECKI
- □ 158. JOE GIBBON
- □ 190. WILLIE MAYS
- □ 204. JACK HIATT
- □ 227. FRANK JOHNSON
- □ 251. RON HERBEL
- □ 274. CLYDE KING(M)
- □ 293. DICK DIETZ
- □ 316. HAL LANIER
- □ 345. FRANK LINZY
- □ 370. JUAN MARICHAL
- □ 392. BOB BURDA
- □ 440. WILLIE MCCOVEY
- □ 464. DAVE MARSHALL
- □ 485. GAYLOR PERRY
- □ 505. BOBBY BOLIN
- □ 517. MIKE MCCORMICK
- □ 555. JIM HART
- □ 584. DON MASON
- □ 604. BOBBY ETHERIDGE
- □ 630. BOBBY BONDS
- □ 664. RON HUNT

SEATTLE PILOTS

- □ 17. MIKE MARSHALL
- □ 42. TOMMY HARPER
- □ 62. CHICO SALMON
- □ 83. MIKE FERRARO
- □ 111. JOHNNY MORRIS
- □ 135. TOMMY DAVIS
- □ 178. RAY OYLER
- □ 209. LARRY HANEY
- □ 233. STEVE BARBER
- □ 254. JOE SCHULTZ(M)
- □ 285. DON MINCHER
- □ 301. DARRELL BRANDON
- □ 322. JOSE VIDAL
- □ 346. WAYNE COMER
- □ 377. GARY BELL
- □ 394. LOU PINIELLA(R)
- □ 394. MARV STAEHLE(R)
- □ 413. ROLAND SHELDON
- □ 451. RICH ROLLINS
- □ 482. JIM GOSGER
- □ 511. DIEGO SEGUI
- □ 534. JERRY MCNERTNEY
- □ 563. MARTY PATTIN
- □ 577. MIKE HEGAN
- □ 612. JACK AKER
- □ 631. JOHN KENNEDY
- □ 651. GUS GIL

WASHINGTON SENATORS

- □ 27. BERNIE ALLEN
- □ 48. BRANT ALYEA
- □ 84. BOB HUMPHREYS
- □ 106. JIM HANNAN
- □ 132. DAVE BALDWIN
- □ 153. ED BRINKMAN
- □ 170. FRANK HOWARD
- □ 199. JIM FRENCH
- □ 226. BRUCE HOWARD
- □ 246. JOE COLEMAN
- □ 272. ED STROUD
- □ 294. JIM LEMON(M)
- □ 319. KEN MCMULLEN
- □ 338. DEL UNSER
- □ 361. GARY HOLMAN
- □ 383. CASEY COX
- □ 406. PHIL ORTEGA
- □ 441. DENNIS HIGGINS
- □ 461. MIKE EPSTEIN
- □ 486. PAUL CASANOVA
- □ 513. CAMILO PASCUAL
- □ 554. FRANK BERTAINA
- □ 586. TIM CULLEN
- □ 607. DICK BOSMAN
- □ 623. HANK ALLEN
- □ 639. BARRY MOORE
- □ 650. TED WILLIAMS(M)
- □ 658. JIM MILES(R)

1970 TOPPS (720)
2 1/2" X 3 1/2"

ATLANTA BRAVES

- □ 17. HOYT WILHELM
- □ 48. GIL GARRIDO
- □ 86. LUM HARRIS(M)
- □ 105. TONY GONZALEZ
- □ 122. GEORGE STONE
- □ 145. RICO CARTY
- □ 160. PHIL NIEKRO
- □ 171. JIM NASH
- □ 172. GARRY HILL(R)
- □ 172. RALPH GARR(R)
- □ 206. CLETE BOYER
- □ 232. BOB DIDIER
- □ 278. TOMMIE AARON
- □ 295. CECIL UPSHAW
- □ 327. HAL KING
- □ 367. MIKE LUM
- □ 384. GARY NEIBAUER
- □ 413. SONNY JACKSON
- □ 438. PAT JARVIS
- □ 472. TEAM CARD
- □ 500. HANK AARON
- □ 529. BOB ASPROMONTE
- □ 546. RON REED
- □ 555. ORLANDO CEPEDA
- □ 576. MILT PAPPAS
- □ 621. MIKE MCQUEEN(R)
- □ 621. DARRELL EVANS(R)
- □ 621. RICK KESTER(R)
- □ 668. BOB TILLMAN
- □ 687. BOB PRIDDY
- □ 710. FELIX MILLAN

BALTIMORE ORIOLES

- □ 20. DAVE MCNALLY
- □ 45. DAVE A. JOHNSON
- □ 81. DAVE MAY
- □ 101. BOBBY FLOYD
- □ 121. FRED BEENE(R)
- □ 121. TERRY CROWLEY(R)
- □ 148. EARL WEAVER(M)
- □ 182. DICK HALL
- □ 213. ANDY ETCHEBARREN
- □ 230. BROOKS ROBINSON
- □ 261. CURT MOTTON
- □ 285. PAUL BLAIR
- □ 301. CHICO SALMON
- □ 319. CLAYTON DALRYMPLE
- □ 344. MARCELINO LOPEZ

☐ 363. TOMY SHOPAY
☐ 387. TEAM CARD
☐ 410. BOOG POWELL
☐ 428. DON BUFORD
☐ 449. JIM PALMER
☐ 477. AL SEVERINSEN(R)
☐ 477. ROGER FREED(R)
☐ 497. EDDIE WATT
☐ 528. ELROD HENDRICKS
☐ 590. MIKE CUELLAR
☐ 601. PETE RICHERT
☐ 615. MARK BELANGER
☐ 629. MERV RETTENMUND
☐ 638. FRANK BERTAINA
☐ 656. JIM HARDIN
☐ 674. DAVE LEONHARD
☐ 700. FRANK ROBINSON
☐ 717. TOM PHOEBUS

BOSTON RED SOX

☐ 10. CARL YASTRZEMSKI
☐ 39. MIKE NAGY
☐ 78. JOE LAHOUD
☐ 104. GERRY MOSES
☐ 116. SPARKY LYLE
☐ 144. RAY CULP
☐ 163. SYD O'BRIEN
☐ 191. VICENTE ROMO
☐ 215. REGGIE SMITH
☐ 237. RUSS GIBSON
☐ 251. DICK SCHOFIELD
☐ 279. BILL LEE
☐ 317. BILL CONIGLIARO(R)
☐ 317. LUIS ALVARADO(R)
☐ 340. TONY CONIGLIARO
☐ 361. RAY JARVIS
☐ 385. GEORGE SCOTT
☐ 406. MIKE ANDREWS
☐ 447. LEE STANGE
☐ 489. EDDIE KASKO(M)
☐ 504. DON PAVLETICH
☐ 540. GARY PETERS
☐ 563. TEAM CARD
☐ 581. TOM SATRIANO
☐ 597. SONNY SIEBERT
☐ 627. GARY WAGNER
☐ 647. TOM MATCHICK
☐ 665. JIM LONBORG
☐ 680. RICO PETROCELLI
☐ 708. JOSE SANTIAGO

CALIFORNIA ANGELS

☐ 4. TOM EGAN
☐ 29. SANDY ALOMAR
☐ 74. GREG WASHBURN(R)
☐ 74. WALLY WOLF(R)
☐ 132. JIM MCGLOTHLIN
☐ 156. EDDIE FISHER
☐ 173. JIM HICKS
☐ 203. RUDY MAY
☐ 228. AURELIO RODRIGUEZ
☐ 255. JIM SPENCER
☐ 277. PAUL DOYLE
☐ 294. JOSE AZCUE
☐ 326. BILL VOSS
☐ 351. TOM MURPHY
☐ 376. LEFTY PHILLIPS(M)
☐ 397. ROGER REPOZ
☐ 430. ANDY MESSERSMITH
☐ 485. JAY JOHNSTONE
☐ 522. TEAM CARD
☐ 543. CLYDE WRITHT
☐ 570. JIM FREGOSI
☐ 586. RICKEY CLARK
☐ 606. CHICO RUIZ
☐ 642. GREG GARRETT(R)
☐ 642. GORDON LUND(R)
☐ 642. JARVIS TATUM(R)
☐ 658. KEN TATUM
☐ 684. JACK FISHER
☐ 720. RICK REICHARDT

CHICAGO CUBS

☐ 46. KEN RUDOLPH
☐ 80. DON KESSINGER
☐ 117. DON YOUNG
☐ 170. BILLY WILLIAMS
☐ 192. JIM QUALLS
☐ 223. NATE OLIVER
☐ 240. FERGIE JENKINS
☐ 258. PAUL POPOVICH
☐ 265. RANDY HUNDLEY
☐ 291. LEO DUROCHER(M)
☐ 318. WILLIE SMITH
☐ 334. PHIL REGAN
☐ 375. JOHNNY CALLISON
☐ 405. BILL HANDS
☐ 429. RANDY BOBB(R)
☐ 429. JIM COSMAN(R)
☐ 480. GLENN BECKERT
☐ 505. KEN HOLTZMAN
☐ 541. BILL HEATH
☐ 562. TED ABERNATHY
☐ 593. TEAM CARD
☐ 612. JIM HICKMAN
☐ 630. ERNIE BANKS
☐ 649. JIMMIE HALL
☐ 654. BOOTS DAY(R)
☐ 670. RON SANTO
☐ 699. HANK AGUIRRE
☐ 714. AL SPANGLER

CHICAGO WHITE SOX

☐ 18. CARLOS MAY
☐ 35. JOE HORLEN
☐ 51. BOB CHRISTIAN
☐ 91. RICH MORALES
☐ 123. DON GUTTERIDGE(M)
☐ 146. DANNY MURPHY
☐ 180. TOMMY JOHN
☐ 217. RON HANSEN
☐ 239. KEN BERRY
☐ 263. DUANE JOSEPHSON
☐ 274. GERRY ARRIGO
☐ 299. BUDDY BRADFORD
☐ 315. LUIS APARICIO
☐ 342. WILBUR WOOD
☐ 368. ED HERRMANN
☐ 395. WALT WILLIAMS
☐ 414. PAUL EDMONDSON
☐ 444. BILLY FARMER(R)
☐ 444. JOHN MATIAS(R)
☐ 483. GAIL HOPKINS
☐ 501. TEAM CARD
☐ 518. BILL MELTON
☐ 561. TOM MCCRAW
☐ 618. BILLY WYNNE
☐ 669. BART JOHNSON(R)
☐ 669. DAN LAZAR(R)
☐ 669. MICKEY SCOTT(R)
☐ 695. BOBBY KNOOP

CINCINNATI REDS

☐ 3. DARRELL CHANEY
☐ 22. RAY WASHBURN
☐ 36. DANNY BREEDEN(R)
☐ 36. BERNIE CARBO(R)
☐ 73. WAYNE GRANGER
☐ 115. ALEX JOHNSON
☐ 133. CLAY CARROLL
☐ 159. TOMMY HELMS
☐ 181. SPARKY ANDERSON(M)
☐ 225. LEE RAY
☐ 254. CAMILO PASCUAL
☐ 283. ANGEL BRAVO
☐ 296. WOOODY WOODWARD
☐ 320. JIM MALONEY
☐ 358. PEDRO BORBON
☐ 380. TONY PEREZ
☐ 409. BOB TOLAN
☐ 443. AL JACKSON
☐ 484. GARY NOLAN
☐ 507. PAT CORRALES
☐ 544. TEAM CARD
☐ 580. PETE ROSE
☐ 602. TED SAVAGE
☐ 616. JIM MERRITT
☐ 636. JIM STEWART
☐ 660. JOHNNY BENCH
☐ 683. VERN GEISHERT(R)
☐ 683. HAL MCRAE(R)
☐ 683. WAYNE SIMPSON(R)
☐ 705. TONY CLONINGER

CLEVELAND INDIANS

☐ 7. GARY BOYD(R)
☐ 7. RUSS NAGELSON(R)
☐ 27. CHUCK HINTON
☐ 59. DICK ELLSWORTH
☐ 85. MAX ALVIS
☐ 112. DAVE NELSON
☐ 136. STEVE HARGAN
☐ 161. RICHIE SCHEINBLUM
☐ 184. RAY FOSSE
☐ 209. KEN SUAREZ
☐ 247. LOU KLIMCHOCK
☐ 257. DENNIS HIGGINS
☐ 275. DUKE SIMS
☐ 292. EDDIE LEON
☐ 347. RUSS SNYDER
☐ 366. BARRY MOORE
☐ 391. LARRY BROWN
☐ 412. LARRY BURCHART
☐ 445. VADA PINSON
☐ 491. GRAIG NETTLES
☐ 524. ALVIN DARK(M)
☐ 545. KEN HARRELSON
☐ 558. VERN FULLER
☐ 582. MIKE PAUL
☐ 625. DEAN CHANCE
☐ 637. TEAM CARD
☐ 650. SAM MCDOWELL
☐ 673. TED UHLAENDER
☐ 704. FRANK BAKER

DETROIT TIGERS

☐ 12. JOHN HILLER
☐ 33. DON WERT
☐ 95. EARL WILSON
☐ 98. GATES BROWN
☐ 129. JIMMIE PRICE
☐ 152. IKE BROWN
☐ 177. JIM NORTHRUP
☐ 207. NORMAN MCRAE(R)
☐ 207. BOB REED(R)
☐ 269. CESAR GUTIERREZ
☐ 313. MAYO SMITH(M)
☐ 335. BILL FREEHAN
☐ 356. FRED LASHER
☐ 383. MICKEY STANLEY
☐ 400. DENNY MCLAIN
☐ 424. MIKE KILKENNY
☐ 475. DICK MCAULIFFE
☐ 508. JOE NIEKRO
☐ 520. WILLIE HORTON
☐ 554. TOM TIMMERMANN
☐ 579. TEAM CARD
☐ 592. DARYL PATTERSON
☐ 611. NORM CASH
☐ 640. AL KALINE
☐ 661. JERRY ROBERTSON
☐ 682. DALTON JONES
☐ 698. TOM TRESH
☐ 715. MICKEY LOLICH

HOUSTON ASTROS

☐ 15. LARRY DIERKER
☐ 32. HARRY WALKER(M)
☐ 60. JIM WYNN
☐ 113. JIM RAY
☐ 126. MARTY MARTINEZ
☐ 155. DENIS MENKE
☐ 178. DENNY LEMASTER
☐ 208. FRED GLADDING
☐ 227. JOHN MAYBERRY(R)
☐ 227. BOB WATKINS(R)
☐ 248. JESUS ALOU
☐ 272. HECTOR TORRES
☐ 316. SKIP GUINN
☐ 339. JOHNNY EDWARDS
☐ 355. DOUG RADER
☐ 382. JACK DILAURO
☐ 407. BOB WATSON
☐ 448. TEAM CARD
☐ 492. KEITH LAMPARD(R)
☐ 492. SCIPIO SPINKS(R)
☐ 515. DON WILSON
☐ 537. JOE MORGAN
☐ 559. TOMMY DAVIS
☐ 578. TOM GRIFFIN
☐ 598. JOE PEPITONE
☐ 619. NORM MILLER
☐ 672. LEON MCFADDEN
☐ 701. JACK BILLINGHAM

KANSAS CITY ROYALS

- ☐ 16. CHARLIE METRO(M)
- ☐ 37. DICK DRAGO
- ☐ 57. H. PAT KELLY
- ☐ 89. JUAN RIOS
- ☐ 108. TOM BURGMEIER
- ☐ 165. ED KIRKPATRICK
- ☐ 187. MIKE HEDLUND
- ☐ 222. JIM ROOKER
- ☐ 241. AL FITZMORRIS(R)
- ☐ 241. SCOTT NORTHEY(R)
- ☐ 266. WALLY BUNKER
- ☐ 321. LOU PINIELLA
- ☐ 338. PAUL SCHAAL
- ☐ 354. AMOS OTIS
- ☐ 377. BILL BUTLER
- ☐ 402. ELLIE RODRIGUEZ
- ☐ 422. TEAM CARD
- ☐ 471. CHRIS ZACHARY
- ☐ 495. DAVE MOREHEAD
- ☐ 512. BILLY HARRIS
- ☐ 525. JERRY ADAIR
- ☐ 552. DON O'RILEY(R)
- ☐ 552. DENNIS PAEPKE(R)
- ☐ 552. FRED RICO(R)
- ☐ 567. BOB OLIVER
- ☐ 589. JOE KEOUGH
- ☐ 609. BUCK MARTINEZ
- ☐ 633. ROGER NELSON
- ☐ 653. MOE DRABOWSKY
- ☐ 671. JIM CAMPANIS
- ☐ 686. JACKIE HERNANDEZ
- ☐ 702. BOB D. JOHNSON(R)
- ☐ 709. MIKE FIORE

LOS ANGELES DODGERS

- ☐ 5. WES PARKER
- ☐ 34. WILLIE CRAWFORD
- ☐ 54. JEFF TORBORG
- ☐ 97. JOE MOELLER
- ☐ 131. RAY LAMB(R)
- ☐ 131. BOB STINSON(R)
- ☐ 157. MANNY MOTA
- ☐ 174. TED SIZEMORE
- ☐ 204. LEN GABRIELSON
- ☐ 242. WALTER ALSTON(M)
- ☐ 260. CLAUDE OSTEEN
- ☐ 286. JACK JENKINS(R)
- ☐ 286. BILL BUCKNER(R)
- ☐ 304. BILL RUSSELL
- ☐ 341. BILL SUDAKIS
- ☐ 369. ALAN FOSTER
- ☐ 390. WILLIE DAVIS
- ☐ 411. TEAM CARD
- ☐ 427. FRED NORMAN
- ☐ 446. BILL GRABARKEWITZ
- ☐ 490. BILL SINGER
- ☐ 523. JOSE PENA
- ☐ 535. ANDY KOSCO
- ☐ 553. JIM LEFEBVRE
- ☐ 571. JIM BREWER
- ☐ 595. MAURY WILLS
- ☐ 622. DON SUTTON
- ☐ 641. AL MCBEAN
- ☐ 685. TOM HALLER

MILWAUKEE BREWERS*

- ☐ 2. DIEGO SEGUI
- ☐ 31. MARTY PATTIN
- ☐ 53. JOHN KENNEDY
- ☐ 88. MIGUEL FUENTES(R)
- ☐ 88. DICK BANEY(R)
- ☐ 111. MIKE HEGAN
- ☐ 134. DANNY WALTON
- ☐ 158. JERRY MCNERTNEY
- ☐ 185. DON MINCHER
- ☐ 224. STEVE BARBER
- ☐ 249. BOB LOCKER
- ☐ 271. GREG GOOSSEN
- ☐ 289. GENE BRABENDER
- ☐ 323. WAYNE COMER
- ☐ 359. PHIL ROOF
- ☐ 370. TOMMY HARPER
- ☐ 393. JOHN GELNAR
- ☐ 418. JOHN DONALDSON
- ☐ 441. JOHN O'DONOGHUE
- ☐ 473. DON BRYANT
- ☐ 499. SKIP LOCKWOOD
- ☐ 514. STEVE HOVLEY
- ☐ 533. BUZZ STEPHEN
- ☐ 556. DAVE BRISTOL(M)
- ☐ 574. BOBBY BOLIN
- ☐ 596. MIKE HERSHBERGER
- ☐ 613. DAVE BALDWIN
- ☐ 652. RICH ROLLINS
- ☐ 667. BOB MEYER
- ☐ 688. TED KUBIAK
- ☐ 713. TEAM CARD

MINNESOTA TWINS

- ☐ 25. CESAR TOVAR
- ☐ 47. BOB L. MILLER
- ☐ 75. JIM KAAT
- ☐ 93. RICK RENICK
- ☐ 118. GEORGE MITTERWALD
- ☐ 150. HARMON KILLEBREW
- ☐ 169. TOM HALL
- ☐ 194. CHUCK MANUEL
- ☐ 226. RON PERRANOSKI
- ☐ 231. LUIS TIANT
- ☐ 245. LEO CARDENAS
- ☐ 267. HERMAN HILL(R)
- ☐ 267. PAUL RATLIFF(R)
- ☐ 290. ROD CAREW
- ☐ 325. DAVE BOSWELL
- ☐ 353. STAN WILLIAMS
- ☐ 379. TOM TISCHINSKI
- ☐ 404. RICH REESE
- ☐ 426. BILL RIGNEY(M)
- ☐ 479. DICK WOODSON
- ☐ 510. TONY OLIVA
- ☐ 534. TEAM CARD
- ☐ 572. FRANK QUILICI
- ☐ 620. JIM PERRY
- ☐ 635. BOB ALLISON
- ☐ 702. BILL ZEPP(R)

MONTREAL EXPOS

- ☐ 19. JOHN BOCCABELLA
- ☐ 38. MACK JONES
- ☐ 87. STEVE RENKO
- ☐ 109. GARRY JESTADT(R)
- ☐ 109. CARL MORTON(R)
- ☐ 124. LARRY JASTER
- ☐ 147. ANGEL HERMOSO
- ☐ 164. TY CLINE
- ☐ 193. MIKE WEGENER
- ☐ 221. RON BRAND
- ☐ 238. JOSE LABOY
- ☐ 243. JOE SPARMA
- ☐ 268. CLAUDE RAYMOND
- ☐ 293. BOB BAILEY
- ☐ 332. BOBBY WINE
- ☐ 364. DAN MCGINN
- ☐ 398. BILL STONEMAN
- ☐ 417. JOHN BATEMAN
- ☐ 442. GENE MAUCH(M)
- ☐ 476. DON SHAW
- ☐ 509. TEAM CARD
- ☐ 527. DON BOSCH
- ☐ 548. HOWIE REED
- ☐ 585. RUSTY STAUB
- ☐ 607. GARY WASLEWSKI
- ☐ 632. GARY SUTHERLAND
- ☐ 646. JIM BRITTON
- ☐ 666. ADOLFO PHILLIPS
- ☐ 690. RON FAIRLY
- ☐ 707. KEVIN COLLINS

NEW YORK METS

- ☐ 1. TEAM CARD
- ☐ 26. TUG MCGRAW
- ☐ 50. TOMMIE AGEE
- ☐ 83. DON CARDWELL
- ☐ 99. BOBBY PFEIL
- ☐ 137. ART SHAMSKY
- ☐ 138. JOE FOY
- ☐ 153. GARY GENTRY
- ☐ 183. JERRY GROTE
- ☐ 214. KEN BOSWELL
- ☐ 246. JIM MCANDREW
- ☐ 280. DONN CLENDENON
- ☐ 300. TOM SEAVER
- ☐ 348. MIKE JORGENSEN(R)
- ☐ 348. JESSE HUDSON(R)
- ☐ 371. ROD GASPAR
- ☐ 394. GIL HODGES(M)
- ☐ 419. RON TAYLOR
- ☐ 431. RON SWOBODA
- ☐ 488. J.C. MARTIN
- ☐ 498. AL WEIS
- ☐ 521. CAL KOONCE
- ☐ 557. ED KRANEPOOL
- ☐ 575. CLEON JONES
- ☐ 610. JERRY KOOSMAN
- ☐ 628. WAYNE GARRETT
- ☐ 634. BUD HARRELSON
- ☐ 679. RAY SADECKI
- ☐ 692. DUFFY DYER
- ☐ 712. NOLAN RYAN

NEW YORK YANKEES

- ☐ 23. BILL ROBINSON
- ☐ 43. JACK AKER
- ☐ 82. FRANK FERNANDEZ
- ☐ 100. MEL STOTTLEMYRE
- ☐ 114. GENE MICHAEL
- ☐ 142. FRITZ PETERSON
- ☐ 167. BILL BURBACH
- ☐ 189. THURMAN MUNSON(R)
- ☐ 189. DAVE MCDONALD(R)
- ☐ 219. JERRY KENNEY
- ☐ 253. RON WOODS
- ☐ 273. RALPH HOUK(M)
- ☐ 297. CURT BLEFARY
- ☐ 333. BOBBY MURCER
- ☐ 349. STEVE HAMILTON
- ☐ 373. ROY WHITE
- ☐ 399. TEAM CARD
- ☐ 416. JOE VERBANIC
- ☐ 437. DANNY CATER
- ☐ 493. LINDY MCDANIEL
- ☐ 516. JOHN ELLIS(R)
- ☐ 516. JIM LYTTLE(R)
- ☐ 536. MIKE KEKICH
- ☐ 568. STAN BAHNSEN
- ☐ 594. JAKE GIBBS
- ☐ 623. HORACE CLARKE
- ☐ 659. PETE WARD
- ☐ 689. FRANK TEPEDINO
- ☐ 702. RON KLIMKOWSKI(R)

* All cards appear as Seattle Pilots.

OAKLAND A'S

- ☐ 21. VIDA BLUE(R)
- ☐ 21. GENE TENACE(R)
- ☐ 41. GEORGE LAUZERIQUE
- ☐ 55. JOHN ODOM
- ☐ 102. JOE RUDI
- ☐ 120. SAL BANDO
- ☐ 140. REGGIE JACKSON
- ☐ 205. BERT CAMPENERIS
- ☐ 233. LEW KRAUSSE
- ☐ 259. TOMMIE REYNOLDS
- ☐ 287. FRED TALBOT
- ☐ 311. DICK GREEN
- ☐ 331. CHUCK DOBSON
- ☐ 381. BOBBY BROOKS(R)
- ☐ 381. MIKE OLIVO(R)
- ☐ 408. PAUL LINDBLAD
- ☐ 434. FELIPE ALOU
- ☐ 481. JOSE TARTABULL
- ☐ 502. ROLLIE FINGERS
- ☐ 531. RON CLARK
- ☐ 547. RICK MONDAY
- ☐ 565. JIM HUNTER
- ☐ 584. AL DOWNING
- ☐ 603. RAY OYLER
- ☐ 631. TEAM CARD
- ☐ 648. LARRY HANEY
- ☐ 663. TITO FRANCONA
- ☐ 678. DAVE DUNCAN
- ☐ 693. BOB W. JOHNSON
- ☐ 706. JOHN MCNAMARA(M)
- ☐ 719. JIM ROLAND

PHILADELPHIA PHILLIES

- ☐ 6. GRANT JACKSON
- ☐ 24. DICK SELMA
- ☐ 28. BILLY WILSON
- ☐ 56. JOE LIS(R)
- ☐ 56. SCOTT REID(R)
- ☐ 90. TIM MCCARVER
- ☐ 125. DERON JOHNSON
- ☐ 149. BILLY CHAMPION
- ☐ 168. DAVE WATKINS
- ☐ 186. RICK JOSEPH
- ☐ 218. RON STONE
- ☐ 252. LOWELL PALMER
- ☐ 270. CHRIS SHORT
- ☐ 288. LARRY HISLE
- ☐ 302. JEFF JAMES
- ☐ 324. TONY TAYLOR
- ☐ 360. CURT FLOOD
- ☐ 388. BYRON BROWNE
- ☐ 403. JIM BUNNING
- ☐ 436. TEAM CARD
- ☐ 486. TERRY HARMON
- ☐ 511. JOE HOERNER
- ☐ 539. DENNY DOYLE(R)
- ☐ 539. LARRY BOWA(R)
- ☐ 564. JOHNNY BRIGGS
- ☐ 591. MIKE RYAN
- ☐ 605. RICK WISE
- ☐ 645. DON MONEY
- ☐ 654. OSCAR GAMBLE(R)
- ☐ 662. FRANK LUCCHESI(M)
- ☐ 677. WOODIE FRYMAN

PITTSBURGH PIRATES

- ☐ 8. JOSE MARTINEZ
- ☐ 30. MATTY ALOU
- ☐ 52. BRUCE DAL CANTON
- ☐ 94. FRED PATEK
- ☐ 110. BOB MOOSE
- ☐ 141. DAVE CASH(R)
- ☐ 141. JOHNNY JETER(R)
- ☐ 166. AL OLIVER
- ☐ 188. MANNY SANGUILLEN
- ☐ 216. CHUCK HARTENSTEIN
- ☐ 236. BOB VEALE
- ☐ 264. RICH HEBNER
- ☐ 322. LUKE WALKER
- ☐ 350. ROBERTO CLEMENTE
- ☐ 372. DAVE GIUSTI
- ☐ 396. STEVE BLASS
- ☐ 423. JERRY MAY
- ☐ 440. BILL MAZEROSKI
- ☐ 470. WILLIE STARGELL
- ☐ 517. JOE GIBBON
- ☐ 532. DANNY MURTAUGH(M)
- ☐ 551. DOCK ELLIS
- ☐ 566. GENE ALLEY
- ☐ 608. TEAM CARD
- ☐ 626. DAVE RICKETTS
- ☐ 643. JOSE PAGAN
- ☐ 654. ANGEL MANGUAL(R)
- ☐ 664. BOB ROBERTSON
- ☐ 703. LOU MARONE

ST. LOUIS CARDINALS

- ☐ 40. RICH ALLEN
- ☐ 76. CARL TAYLOR
- ☐ 92. GEORGE CULVER
- ☐ 96. LERON LEE(R)
- ☐ 96. JERRY REUSS(R)
- ☐ 119. CHUCK TAYLOR
- ☐ 139. RICH NYE
- ☐ 143. PHIL GAGLIANO
- ☐ 162. JERRY JOHNSON
- ☐ 190. JOE TORRE
- ☐ 220. STEVE CARLTON
- ☐ 256. VIC DAVALILLO
- ☐ 282. STEVE HUNTZ
- ☐ 312. MIKE TORREZ
- ☐ 330. LOU BROCK
- ☐ 346. RED SCHOENDIENST(M)
- ☐ 362. JOE HAGUE
- ☐ 386. BILL DILLMAN
- ☐ 415. JULIAN JAVIER
- ☐ 435. NELSON BRILES
- ☐ 482. TOM HILGENDORF
- ☐ 503. DAL MAXVILL
- ☐ 530. BOB GIBSON
- ☐ 549. TEAM CARD
- ☐ 569. COOKIE ROJAS
- ☐ 614. MIKE SHANNON
- ☐ 675. JOSE CARDENAL
- ☐ 716. SAL CAMPISI(R)
- ☐ 716. REGGIE CLEVELAND(R)
- ☐ 716. SANTIAGO GUZMAN(R)

SAN DIEGO PADRES

- ☐ 11. NATE COLBERT
- ☐ 44. ROBERTO PENA
- ☐ 79. CLAY KIRBY
- ☐ 103. FRANK REBERGER
- ☐ 130. OLLIE BROWN
- ☐ 151. DAVE A. ROBERTS
- ☐ 179. IVAN MURRELL
- ☐ 212. AL SANTORINI
- ☐ 234. TOMMY DEAN
- ☐ 262. JERRY MORALES(R)
- ☐ 262. JIM WILLIAMS(R)
- ☐ 284. JACK BALDSCHUN
- ☐ 314. BILL MCCOOL
- ☐ 329. CHRIS CANNIZZARO
- ☐ 345. AL FERRARA
- ☐ 352. BOB BARTON
- ☐ 374. TOMMIE SISK
- ☐ 392. WALT HRINIAK
- ☐ 421. PAT DOBSON
- ☐ 474. DICK KELLEY
- ☐ 494. LARRY STAHL
- ☐ 513. PRESTON GOMEZ(M)
- ☐ 526. RON HERBEL
- ☐ 573. MIKE CORKINS(R)
- ☐ 573. RAFAEL ROBLES(R)
- ☐ 573. RON SLOCUM(R)
- ☐ 587. JOSE ARCIA
- ☐ 604. CLARENCE GASTON
- ☐ 639. DAVE CAMPBELL
- ☐ 644. GERRY NYMAN
- ☐ 657. TEAM CARD
- ☐ 694. GARY ROSS
- ☐ 718. ED SPIEZIO

SAN FRANCISCO GIANTS

- ☐ 13. JACK HIATT
- ☐ 42. TITO FUENTES
- ☐ 58. DAVE MARSHALL
- ☐ 77. FRANK LINZY
- ☐ 107. BOBBY ETHERIDGE
- ☐ 135. DICK DIETZ
- ☐ 176. JIM HART
- ☐ 210. JUAN MARICHAL
- ☐ 229. RICH ROBERTSON
- ☐ 250. WILLIE MCCOVEY
- ☐ 276. RON HUNT
- ☐ 298. KEN HENDERSON
- ☐ 337. MIKE MCCORMICK
- ☐ 357. BOB BURDA
- ☐ 378. JIM DAVENPORT
- ☐ 401. JOHN HARRELL(R)
- ☐ 401. BERNIE WILLIAMS(R)
- ☐ 425. BOBBY BONDS
- ☐ 433. RON BRYANT
- ☐ 478. BOB HEISE
- ☐ 496. STEVE WHITAKER
- ☐ 519. DON MCMAHON
- ☐ 560. GAYLORD PERRY
- ☐ 583. HAL LANIER
- ☐ 600. WILLIE MAYS
- ☐ 624. CLYDE KING(M)
- ☐ 651. JIM GOSGER
- ☐ 681. BOB GARIBALDI
- ☐ 696. TEAM CARD

WASHINGTON SENATORS

- ☐ 14. HANK ALLEN
- ☐ 49. TIM CULLEN
- ☐ 84. PAUL CASANOVA
- ☐ 106. DAROLD KNOWLES
- ☐ 127. JOE COLEMAN
- ☐ 154. JIM MILES(R)
- ☐ 154. JAN DUKES(R)
- ☐ 175. DICK BOSMAN
- ☐ 211. TED WILLIAMS(M)
- ☐ 235. MIKE EPSTEIN
- ☐ 281. CASEY COX
- ☐ 303. BRANT ALYEA
- ☐ 328. GEORGE BRUNET
- ☐ 336. DEL UNSER
- ☐ 365. ZOILO VERSALLES
- ☐ 389. JIM SHELLENBACK
- ☐ 420. KEN MCMULLEN
- ☐ 439. LEE MAYE
- ☐ 487. CISCO CARLOS
- ☐ 506. ED STROUD
- ☐ 538. BOB HUMPHREYS
- ☐ 550. FRANK HOWARD
- ☐ 577. BERNIE ALLEN
- ☐ 599. DICK STELMASZEK(R)
- ☐ 599. GENE MARTIN(R)
- ☐ 599. DICK SUCH(R)
- ☐ 617. JIM FRENCH
- ☐ 655. JOHN ROSEBORO
- ☐ 676. TEAM CARD
- ☐ 691. JOE GRZENDA
- ☐ 697. JIM HANNAN
- ☐ 711. ED BRINKMAN

1971 TOPPS (752) 2 1/2" X 3 1/2"

ATLANTA BRAVES

- ☐ 8. MIKE MCQUEEN
- ☐ 30. PHIL NIEKRO
- ☐ 52. OSCAR BROWN(R)
- ☐ 52. EARL WILLIAMS(R)
- ☐ 81. FELIX MILLAN
- ☐ 88. HAL KING

☐ 147. BOB PRIDDY
☐ 173. GIL GARRIDO
☐ 194. MIKE LUM
☐ 223. CECIL UPSHAL
☐ 244. BOB TILLMAN
☐ 270. RICO CARTY
☐ 306. JIM NASH
☐ 346. LUM HARRIS(M)
☐ 359. RON REED
☐ 374. CLETE BOYER
☐ 387. RON HERBEL
☐ 400. HANK AARON
☐ 432. BOB DIDIER
☐ 463. TOM KELLEY
☐ 494. RALPH GARR(R)
☐ 494. RICK KESTER(R)
☐ 507. GEORGE STONE
☐ 529. MARTY PEREZ(R)
☐ 587. SONNY JACKSON
☐ 605. ORLANDO CEPEDA
☐ 623. PAT JARVIS
☐ 652. TEAM CARD
☐ 663. MARV STAEHLE
☐ 668. GARY NEIBAUER
☐ 709. DUSTY BAKER(R)
☐ 717. TOMMIE AARON

BALTIMORE ORIOLES

☐ 1. TEAM CARD
☐ 29. DON BUFORD
☐ 53. PAUL BLAIR
☐ 99. MARK BELANGER
☐ 122. EDDIE WATT
☐ 137. MARCELINO LOPEZ
☐ 170. MIKE CUELLAR
☐ 193. BOB GRICH
☐ 219. ELROD HENDRICKS
☐ 249. CHICO SALMON
☐ 273. PETE RICHERT
☐ 300. BROOKS ROBINSON
☐ 320. DAVE MCNALLY
☐ 362. MIKE ADAMSON(R)
☐ 362. ROGER FREED(R)
☐ 392. GRANT JACKSON
☐ 393. MERV RETTENMUND
☐ 417. DICK HALL
☐ 453. TERRY CROWLEY
☐ 477. EARL WEAVER(M)
☐ 491. JIM HARDIN
☐ 501. ANDY ETCHEBARREN
☐ 547. PAT DOBSON
☐ 570. JIM PALMER
☐ 595. DAVE A. JOHNSON
☐ 617. CLAY DALRYMPLE
☐ 640. FRANK ROBINSON
☐ 684. CURT MOTTON
☐ 700. BOOG POWELL
☐ 709. DON BAYLOR(R)
☐ 716. DAVE LEONHARD

BOSTON RED SOX

☐ 9. GEORGE SCOTT
☐ 31. EDDIE KASKO(M)
☐ 58. BILL LEE
☐ 89. KEN BRETT
☐ 114. BILLY CONIGLIARO
☐ 159. JARVIS TATUM
☐ 176. BOB MONTGOMERY(R)
☐ 176. DOUG GRIFFIN(R)
☐ 191. MIKE ANDREWS
☐ 225. GARY PETERS
☐ 254. CAL KOONCE
☐ 287. MIKE FIORE
☐ 302. PHIL GAGLIANO
☐ 305. REGGIE SMITH
☐ 340. RICO PETROCELLI
☐ 363. MIKE NAGY
☐ 386. TEAM CARD
☐ 409. DON PAVLETICH
☐ 446. BOBBY BOLIN
☐ 473. GARY WAGNER
☐ 498. JOHN KENNEDY
☐ 512. DICK MILLS(R)
☐ 512. MIKE GARMAN(R)
☐ 530. CARL YASTRZEMSKI
☐ 557. TOM SATRIANO
☐ 577. JIM LONBORG
☐ 601. KEN TATUM
☐ 622. JOE LAHOUD
☐ 649. SPARKY LYLE
☐ 660. RAY CULP
☐ 678. GEORGE THOMAS
☐ 692. ROGELIO MORET(R)
☐ 710. SONNY SIEBERT
☐ 740. LUIS APARICIO

CALIFORNIA ANGELS

☐ 15. ANDY MESSERSMITH
☐ 43. STEVE KEALEY
☐ 78. JIM SPENCER
☐ 105. TONY CONIGLIARO
☐ 152. LLOYD ALLEN(R)
☐ 152. WINSTON LLENAS(R)
☐ 174. DAVE LAROCHE
☐ 205. GERRY MOSES
☐ 240. CLYDE WRITHT
☐ 256. TONY GONZALEZ
☐ 279. LEFTY PHILLIPS(M)
☐ 318. RUDY MAY
☐ 360. JIM FREGOSI
☐ 401. TOM MURPHY
☐ 421. JOHN STEPHENSON
☐ 442. TEAM CARD
☐ 466. KEN BERRY
☐ 485. KEN MCMULLEN
☐ 508. ROGER REPOZ
☐ 526. RAY JARVIS
☐ 559. TERRY COX(R)
☐ 561. SYD O'BRIEN
☐ 590. ALEX JOHNSON
☐ 614. BILLY COWAN
☐ 631. EDDIE FISHER
☐ 645. JIM MALONEY
☐ 657. JOSE AZCUE
☐ 664. ARCHIE REYNOLDS(R)
☐ 666. GENE BRABENDER
☐ 676. TOMMIE REYNOLDS
☐ 686. CHICO RUIZ
☐ 697. RICKEY CLARK
☐ 707. FRED LASHER
☐ 718. BILLY WYNNE
☐ 736. MEL QUEEN
☐ 745. SANDY ALOMAR

CHICAGO CUBS

☐ 12. JOHNNY CALLISON
☐ 38. JIM COLBORN
☐ 90. JOE PEPITONE
☐ 98. JOE DECKER
☐ 121. JIM DUNEGAN(R)
☐ 121. ROE SKIDMORE(R)
☐ 151. TOMMY DAVIS
☐ 175. JIM HICKMAN
☐ 203. LARRY GURA
☐ 220. RON SANTO
☐ 248. HOYT WILHELM
☐ 280. FERGIE JENKINS
☐ 350. BILLY WILLIAMS
☐ 390. GLENN BECKERT
☐ 410. KEN HOLTZMAN
☐ 424. ROBERTO RODRIQUEZ
☐ 441. MILT PAPPAS
☐ 455. DON KESSINGER
☐ 472. KEN RUDOLPH
☐ 502. TEAM CARD
☐ 525. ERNIE BANKS
☐ 542. BOB L. MILLER
☐ 558. HECTOR TORRES
☐ 576. ADRIAN GARRETT(R)
☐ 576. BROCK DAVIS(R)
☐ 576. GARRY JESTADT(R)
☐ 592. RANDY HUNDLEY
☐ 609. LEO DUROCHER(M)
☐ 634. PHIL REGAN
☐ 647. JUAN PIZARRO
☐ 670. BILL HANDS
☐ 704. J.C. MARTIN
☐ 726. PAUL POPOVICH

CHICAGO WHITE SOX

☐ 13. CHARLIE BRINKMAN(R)
☐ 13. DICK MOLONEY(R)
☐ 37. RICH MCKINNEY
☐ 56. DUANE JOSEPHSON
☐ 80. BILL MELTON
☐ 113. JERRY CRIDER
☐ 156. BART JOHNSON
☐ 169. ED HERRMAN
☐ 186. BOB SPENCE
☐ 227. FLOYD WEAVER
☐ 243. CARLOS MAY
☐ 267. RICH MORALES
☐ 289. TEAM CARD
☐ 292. JAY JOHNSTONE
☐ 311. LEE STANGE
☐ 345. JOE HORLEN
☐ 373. TOM MCCRAW
☐ 413. H. PAT KELLY
☐ 436. WILBUR WOOD
☐ 458. RON LOLICH(R)
☐ 458. DAVE LEMONDS(R)
☐ 489. LUIS ALVARADO
☐ 506. BOBBY KNOOP
☐ 520. TOMMY JOHN
☐ 537. TOM EGAN
☐ 555. WALT WILLIAMS
☐ 588. TOM BRADLEY
☐ 627. STEVE HAMILTON
☐ 643. RICK REICHARDT
☐ 661. CHUCK TANNER(M)
☐ 679. DON O'RILEY
☐ 723. VICENTE ROMO
☐ 733. LEE MAYE
☐ 748. JOHN PURDIN

CINCINNATI REDS

☐ 14. DAVE CONCEPCION
☐ 40. LEE MAY
☐ 75. GARY NOLAN
☐ 100. PETE ROSE
☐ 124. DON GULLETT
☐ 164. FRANK DUFFY(R)
☐ 164. MILT WILCOX(R)
☐ 177. HAL MCRAE
☐ 190. BOB TOLAN
☐ 218. TONY CLONINGER
☐ 250. JOHNNY BENCH
☐ 272. TOMMY HELMS
☐ 293. PAT CORRALES
☐ 319. TY CLINE
☐ 339. WAYNE SIMPSON
☐ 357. TEAM CARD
☐ 377. GREG GARRETT
☐ 379. WAYNE GRANGER
☐ 394. CLAY CARROLL
☐ 420. JIM MERRITT
☐ 457. WILLIE SMITH
☐ 478. BERNIE CARBO
☐ 496. WOODY WOODWARD
☐ 538. ANGEL BRAVO
☐ 556. JIM MCGLOTHLIN
☐ 580. TONY PEREZ
☐ 613. PEDRO BORBON
☐ 632. DARREL CHANEY
☐ 644. JIM STEWART
☐ 688. SPARKY ANDERSON(M)
☐ 731. JIM QUALLS

CLEVELAND INDIANS

☐ 24. RICH HAND
☐ 41. RICK AUSTIN
☐ 87. JACK HEIDEMANN
☐ 107. ROY FOSTER
☐ 125. RAY FOSSE
☐ 150. SAM MCDOWELL
☐ 172. DUKE SIMS
☐ 211. PHIL HENNIGAN
☐ 231. VINCE COLBERT(R)
☐ 231. JOHN LOWENSTEIN(R)
☐ 252. EDDIE LEON
☐ 275. VADA PINSON
☐ 294. STEVE DUNNING
☐ 324. GRAIG NETTLES
☐ 347. TED UHLAENDER
☐ 375. STEVE HARGAN
☐ 397. ALVIN DARK(M)
☐ 429. CHUCK HINTON
☐ 454. MIKE PAUL
☐ 479. DENNIS HIGGINS
☐ 510. KEN HARRELSON
☐ 539. LARRY BROWN
☐ 552. BUDDY BRADFORD

□ 584. TEAM CARD
□ 597. KEN SUAREZ
□ 612. LOU CAMILLI(R)
□ 612. TED FORD(R)
□ 612. STEVE MINGORI(R)
□ 689. FRANK BAKER
□ 727. RAY LAMB

DETROIT TIGERS

□ 3. DICK MCAULIFFE
□ 39. LERRIN LAGROW(R)
□ 39. GENE LAMONT(R)
□ 86. MIKE KILKENNY
□ 101. LES CAIN
□ 120. WILLIE HORTON
□ 133. MICKEY LOLICH
□ 154. CESAR GUTIERREZ
□ 180. AL KALINE
□ 208. BILLY MARTIN
□ 229. JIM HANNAN
□ 265. JIM NORTHRUP
□ 296. TOM TIMMERMANN
□ 316. FRED SCHERMAN
□ 336. TEAM CARD
□ 367. DALTON JONES
□ 389. ED BRINKMAN
□ 403. JOE COLEMAN
□ 423. DENNIS SAUNDERS(R)
□ 423. TIM MARTING(R)
□ 444. JIMMIE PRICE
□ 464. AURELIO RODRIGUEZ
□ 481. DARYL PATTERSON
□ 503. GATES BROWN
□ 524. MICKEY STANLEY
□ 553. KEVIN COLLINS
□ 575. BILL FREEHAN
□ 599. NORM CASH
□ 629. JOHN HILLER
□ 669. IKE BROWN
□ 695. JOE NIEKRO
□ 708. RUSS NAGELSON
□ 732. BOB REED
□ 749. KEN SZOTKIEWICZ

HOUSTON ASTROS

□ 18. NORM MILLER
□ 44. JOHNNY EDWARDS
□ 79. WADE BLASINGAME
□ 102. KEN FORSCH(R)
□ 102. LARRY HOWARD(R)
□ 130. DENIS MENKE
□ 148. JOHN MAYBERRY
□ 162. JACK BILLINGHAM
□ 222. BOB WATSON
□ 237. CESAR CEDENO
□ 242. JIM RAY
□ 264. JOE MORGAN
□ 291. GEORGE CULVER
□ 312. HARRY WALKER(M)
□ 337. JESUS ALOU
□ 371. JACK HIATT
□ 381. FRED GLADDING
□ 404. BUDDY HARRIS(R)
□ 404. ROGER METZGER(R)
□ 425. DOUG RADER
□ 447. CESAR GERONIMO
□ 471. TOM GRIFFIN
□ 484. DON WILSON
□ 540. LARRY DIERKER
□ 565. JIM WYNN
□ 583. RON COOK
□ 602. MARTY MARTINEZ
□ 636. DENNY LEMASTER
□ 677. JACK DILAURO
□ 722. TEAM CARD
□ 728. KEITH LAMPARD(R)
□ 741. SKIP GUINN
□ 747. SCIPIO SPINKS(R)

KANSAS CITY ROYALS

□ 17. BILLY SORRELL
□ 35. LOU PINIELLA
□ 91. BOB LEMON(M)
□ 103. RICH SEVERSON
□ 118. COOKIE ROJAS
□ 129. AURELIO MONTEAGUDO
□ 144. JACKIE HERNANDEZ
□ 163. BUCK MARTINEZ
□ 187. TED ABERNATHY
□ 221. DAVE MOREHEAD
□ 247. JERRY CRAM(R)
□ 247. PAUL SPLITTORFF(R)
□ 269. GAIL HOPKINS
□ 299. ED KIRKPATRICK
□ 321. TOM MATCHICK
□ 344. ELLIE RODRIGUEZ
□ 411. GEORGE SPRIGGS
□ 431. TOM BURGMEIER
□ 451. JOE KEOUGH
□ 470. BOB OLIVER
□ 487. PAUL SCHAAL
□ 504. KEN WRIGHT
□ 528. WALLY BUNKER
□ 546. JOHN MATIAS
□ 564. AL FITZMORRIS
□ 581. ROGER NELSON
□ 610. AMOS OTIS
□ 626. FREEDIE PATEK
□ 633. SCOTT NORTHEY(R)
□ 646. BOBBY FLOYD
□ 662. MIKE HEDLUND
□ 681. BILL BUTLER
□ 701. BOB GARIBALDI
□ 719. JERRY MAY
□ 730. JIM ROOKER
□ 742. TEAM CARD
□ 752. DICK DRAGO

LOS ANGELES DODGERS

□ 10. CLAUDE OSTEEN
□ 34. SANDY VANCE
□ 57. VON JOSHUA
□ 85. BILLY GRABARKEWITZ
□ 112. MANNY MOTA
□ 145. BILL SINGER
□ 188. BOB VALENTINE(R)
□ 188. MIKE STRAHLER(R)
□ 207. ALAN FOSTER
□ 226. BILL RUSSELL
□ 253. BILL SUDAKIS
□ 288. JOE MOELLER
□ 314. JEFF TORBORG
□ 341. STEVE GARVEY
□ 361. DON SUTTON
□ 385. MAURY WILLS
□ 402. TEAM CARD
□ 430. WES PARKER
□ 459. JIM LEFEBVRE
□ 488. JERRY STEPHENSON
□ 519. WILLIE CRAWFORD
□ 529. BILL BUCKNER(R)
□ 549. JIM BREWER
□ 567. WALT ALSTON(M)
□ 585. WILLIE DAVIS
□ 639. TOM HALLER
□ 650. RICH ALLEN
□ 693. JOSE PENA
□ 709. TOM PACIOREK(R)

MILWAUKEE BREWERS

□ 22. PHIL ROOF
□ 48. DAVE BALDWIN
□ 76. TED SAVAGE
□ 97. FLOYD WICKER
□ 116. KEN SANDERS
□ 149. MIKE HERSHBERGER
□ 182. AL DOWNING
□ 204. BERNIE SMITH(R)
□ 204. GEORGE KOPACZ(R)
□ 236. BOB HUMPHREYS
□ 260. TOMMY HARPER
□ 281. DANNY WALTON
□ 309. DICK ELLSWORTH
□ 334. ROBERTO PENA
□ 353. CARL TAYLOR
□ 372. LEW KRAUSSE
□ 415. MIKE HEGAN
□ 433. SKIP LOCKWOOD
□ 456. BOB MEYER
□ 493. DAVE MAY
□ 516. TED KUBIAK
□ 579. MARTY PATTIN
□ 604. JOHN GELNAR
□ 633. PETE KOEGEL(R)
□ 637. DAVE BRISTOL(M)
□ 653. RUSS SNYDER
□ 671. BILL VOSS
□ 692. WAYNE TWITCHELL(R)
□ 698. TEAM CARD
□ 721. JOHN MORRIS
□ 746. ANDY KOSCO

MINNESOTA TWINS

□ 7. JIM HOLT
□ 26. BERT BLYLEVEN
□ 74. PETE HAMM(R)
□ 74. JIM NETTLES(R)
□ 95. LUIS TIANT
□ 127. DANNY THOMPSON
□ 141. FRANK QUILICI
□ 165. CESAR TOVAR
□ 189. GEORGE MITTERWALD
□ 210. ROD CAREW
□ 245. JIM KATT
□ 271. BILL ZEPP
□ 290. TONY OLIVA
□ 313. TOM HALL
□ 349. RICH REESE
□ 391. STEVE BRYE(R)
□ 391. COTTON NASH(R)
□ 405. LEO CARDENAS
□ 449. BRANT ALYEA
□ 475. RON PERRANOSKI
□ 500. JIM PERRY
□ 522. TEAM CARD
□ 532. BILL RIGNEY(M)
□ 550. HARMON KILLEBREW
□ 568. SAL CAMPISI
□ 586. DICK WOODSON
□ 607. PAUL RATLIFF
□ 638. STAN WILLIAMS
□ 675. DAVE BOSWELL
□ 692. HAL HAYDEL(R)
□ 694. RICK RENICK
□ 724. TOM TISCHINSKI
□ 744. CHUCK MANUEL

MONTREAL EXPOS

□ 21. DAN MCGINN
□ 42. BOOTS DAY
□ 59. GENE MAUCH(M)
□ 94. DON HAHN
□ 132. JOSE LABOY
□ 142. MACK JONES
□ 157. BOB BAILEY
□ 171. BOBBY WINE
□ 209. STEVE RENKO
□ 232. JOHN STROHMAYER
□ 266. BILL STONEMAN
□ 284. JIM GOSGER
□ 304. RON BRAND
□ 315. RON FAIRLY
□ 376. CLYDE MASHORE(R)
□ 376. ERNIE MCANALLY(R)
□ 398. HOWIE REED
□ 418. ADOLFO PHILLIPS
□ 434. GARY SUTHERLAND
□ 452. JOHN BOCCABELLA
□ 474. JIM FAIREY
□ 515. CARL MORTON
□ 536. CLAUDE RAYMOND

□ 560. RUSTY STAUB
□ 578. RON HUNT
□ 608. MIKE WEGENER
□ 628. JOHN BATEMAN
□ 664. BOB REYNOLDS(R)
□ 665. RON SWOBODA
□ 674. TEAM CARD
□ 699. JIM BRITTON
□ 713. MIKE MARSHALL
□ 743. JOHN O'DONOGHUE
□ 747. BALOR MOORE(R)

NEW YORK METS

□ 16. KEN SINGLETON
□ 36. DEAN CHANCE
□ 83. TIM FOLI(R)
□ 83. RANDY BOBB(R)
□ 104. DAN FRISELLA
□ 115. DONN CLENDENON
□ 136. DUFFY DYER
□ 160. TOM SEAVER
□ 183. GIL HODGES(M)
□ 228. WAYNE GARRETT
□ 259. DAVE MARSHALL
□ 278. JERRY GROTE
□ 310. TOMMIE AGEE
□ 335. JERRY KOOSMAN
□ 355. BUD HARRELSON
□ 406. RAY SADECKI
□ 428. JIM MCANDREW
□ 445. ART SHAMSKY
□ 469. BOB ASPROMONTE
□ 492. KEN BOSWELL
□ 513. NOLAN RYAN
□ 527. CLEON JONES
□ 573. ED KRANEPOOL
□ 596. MIKE JORGENSEN
□ 618. TUG MCGRAW
□ 641. TEAM CARD
□ 648. RICH FOLKERS(R)
□ 648. TED MARTINEZ(R)
□ 648. JON MATLACK(R)
□ 651. JERRY ROBERTSON
□ 687. RON TAYLOR
□ 725. GARY GENTRY
□ 751. AL WEIS

NEW YORK YANKEES

□ 5. THURMAN MUNSON
□ 28. RON KLIMKOWSKI
□ 51. STEVE KLINE
□ 111. LOYD COLSON(R)
□ 111. BOBBY MITCHELL(R)
□ 131. CURT BLEFARY
□ 146. RALPH HOUK(M)
□ 184. STAN BAHNSEN
□ 213. FRANK W. BAKER
□ 234. JIM LYTTLE
□ 263. JOHN ELLIS
□ 277. GARY WASLEWSKI
□ 303. LINDY MCDANIEL
□ 342. FRANK TEPEDINO
□ 358. DANNY CATER
□ 382. JAKE GIBBS
□ 395. ROY WHITE
□ 419. RON HANSEN
□ 438. MIKE MCCORMICK
□ 460. FRITZ PETERSON
□ 483. GENE MICHAEL
□ 514. RON WOODS
□ 543. TEAM CARD
□ 559. GARY JONES(R)
□ 572. JERRY KENNEY
□ 593. JACK AKER
□ 615. MEL STOTTLEMYRE
□ 635. BOBBY MURCER
□ 667. PETE WARD
□ 683. BILL BURBACH
□ 703. MIKE KEKICH
□ 715. HORACE CLARKE
□ 734. ROB GARDNER

OAKLAND A'S

□ 20. REGGIE JACKSON
□ 45. JIM HUNTER
□ 84. MARCEL LACHEMANN
□ 109. STEVE HOVLEY
□ 135. RICK MONDAY
□ 178. DAVE DUNCAN
□ 215. DIEGO SEGUI
□ 238. CHUCK DOBSON
□ 258. DICK GREEN
□ 285. SAL BANDO
□ 317. JIM DRISCOLL(R)
□ 317. ANGEL MANGUAL(R)
□ 338. GENE TENACE
□ 356. BOB LOCKER
□ 384. ROLLIE FINGERS
□ 407. JOE RUDI
□ 440. BERT CAMPANERIS
□ 468. FRANK FERNANDEZ
□ 495. FELIPE ALOU
□ 523. JOHN ODOM
□ 544. VIDA BLUE
□ 624. TEAM CARD
□ 633. BOBBY BROOKS(R)
□ 642. JIM ROLAND
□ 658. PAUL LINDBLAD
□ 680. DON MINCHER
□ 714. DICK WILLIAMS(M)

PHILADELPHIA PHILLIES

□ 23. OSCAR GAMBLE
□ 49. DON MONEY
□ 77. MIKE COMPTON
□ 92. FRED WENZ
□ 119. FRANK LUCCHESI(M)
□ 138. JOE LIS(R)
□ 138. WILLIE MONTANEZ(R)
□ 166. JOE HOERNER
□ 192. BILLY WILSON
□ 233. LARRY BOWA
□ 246. TONY TAYLOR
□ 268. TEAM CARD
□ 297. JOHNNY BRIGGS
□ 323. BILLY CHAMPION
□ 352. DENNY DOYLE
□ 366. RON STONE
□ 414. WOODIE FRYMAN
□ 439. GREG LUZINSKI(R)
□ 439. SCOTT REID(R)
□ 465. TIM MCCARVER
□ 490. DERON JOHNSON
□ 511. CHRIS SHORT
□ 533. MIKE RYAN
□ 554. LOWELL PALMER
□ 574. JIM BUNNING
□ 598. RICK WISE
□ 616. LARRY HISLE
□ 659. BYRON BROWNE
□ 664. KEN REYNOLDS(R)
□ 682. TERRY HARMON
□ 705. DICK SELMA
□ 728. WAYNE REDMOND(R)
□ 739. BARRY LERSCH

PITTSBURGH PIRATES

□ 2. DOCK ELLIS
□ 27. FRED CAMBRIA(R)
□ 27. GENE CLINES(R)
□ 47. JOHNNY JETER
□ 73. GEORGE BRUNET
□ 110. BILL MAZEROSKI
□ 143. STEVE BLASS
□ 168. BRUCE DAL CANTON
□ 212. RICH HEBNER
□ 230. WILLIE STARGELL
□ 255. BOB ROBERTSON
□ 282. JOSE PAGAN
□ 298. JIM NELSON
□ 343. ED ACOSTA(R)
□ 343. MILT MAY(R)
□ 365. BOB D. JOHNSON
□ 368. BOB VEALE
□ 388. AL OLIVER
□ 416. GENE ALLEY
□ 437. DANNY MURTAUGH(M)
□ 480. MANNY SANGUILLEN
□ 509. JIM GRANT
□ 534. LUKE WALKER
□ 562. DAVE GIUSTI
□ 582. DAVE CASH
□ 603. TEAM CARD
□ 630. ROBERTO CLEMENTE
□ 690. BOB MOOSE
□ 712. JOSE MARTINEZ

ST. LOUIS CARDINALS

□ 4. VIC DAVALILLO
□ 32. JERRY DAVANON
□ 55. STEVE CARLTON
□ 96. JOE HAGUE
□ 117. TED SIMMONS
□ 158. JERRY REUSS
□ 185. JULIAN JAVIER
□ 216. REGGIE CLEVELAND(R)
□ 216. LUIS MELENDEZ(R)
□ 239. RED SCHOENDIENST(M)
□ 257. NELSON BRILES
□ 286. JERRY MCNERTNEY
□ 308. TEAM CARD
□ 322. JIM BEAUCHAMP
□ 348. FRED NORMAN
□ 370. JOE TORRE
□ 396. DICK SCHOFIELD
□ 422. FRANK BERTAINA
□ 435. JOSE CARDENAL
□ 450. BOB GIBSON
□ 476. DAL MAXVILL
□ 521. LERON LEE
□ 531. MIKE TORREZ
□ 541. BOB BURDA
□ 551. FRANK LINZY
□ 571. TED SIZEMORE
□ 594. BOB CHLUPSA(R)
□ 594. BOB STINSON(R)
□ 594. AL HRABOSKY(R)
□ 606. CHUCK TAYLOR
□ 625. LOU BROCK
□ 654. DON SHAW
□ 672. ED CROSBY
□ 685. MOE DRABOWSKY
□ 702. MILT RAMIREZ
□ 720. MATTY ALOU
□ 735. MIKE SHANNON

SAN DIEGO PADRES

□ 6. ED SPIEZIO
□ 25. CLARENCE GASTON
□ 46. DAVE CAMPBELL
□ 106. TOM DUKES
□ 126. DANNY COOMBS
□ 134. JOSE ARCIA
□ 153. GARY ROSS
□ 179. MIKE CORKINS
□ 214. AL FERRARA
□ 235. NATE COLBERT
□ 262. JIM WILLIAMS(R)
□ 262. DAVE ROBINSON(R)
□ 274. RON SLOCUM
□ 301. EARL WILSON
□ 333. CLAY KIRBY
□ 364. TOMMY DEAN
□ 383. ROD GASPAR
□ 408. RAFAEL ROBLES
□ 426. CHRIS CANNIZZARO
□ 448. DAVE A. ROBERTS
□ 467. AL SANTORINI
□ 482. TEAM CARD
□ 505. OLLIE BROWN
□ 529. ENZO HERNANDEZ(R)
□ 548. DON MASON
□ 569. IVAN MURRELL
□ 589. BOB BARTON
□ 611. TOM PHOEBUS

□ 656. GERRY NYMAN
□ 696. JERRY MORALES
□ 711. LARRY STAHL
□ 737. PRESTON GOMEZ(M)
□ 747. AL SEVERINSEN(R)

SAN FRANCISCO GIANTS

□ 19. SKIP PITLOCK
□ 50. WILLIE MCCOVEY
□ 108. JOHN CUMBERLAND
□ 128. FRANK JOHNSON
□ 140. GAYLORD PERRY
□ 155. KEN HENDERSON
□ 181. HAL LANIER
□ 224. ALAN GALLAGHER
□ 251. FRANK REBERGER
□ 276. MIKE DAVISON(R)
□ 276. GEORGE FOSTER(R)
□ 295. BOBBY BONDS
□ 325. JUAN MARICHAL
□ 354. DON MCMAHON
□ 378. TITO FUENTES
□ 412. JERRY JOHNSON
□ 443. RICH ROBERTSON
□ 461. JIM HART
□ 486. STEVE HUNTZ
□ 517. CHARLIE FOX(M)
□ 545. DICK DIETZ
□ 563. TEAM CARD
□ 600. WILLIE MAYS
□ 621. RON BRYANT
□ 691. BOB HEISE
□ 728. BERNIE WILLIAMS(R)
□ 738. RUSS GIBSON

WASHINGTON SENATORS

□ 11. ELLIOTT MADDOX
□ 33. DEL UNSER
□ 60. DICK BOSMAN
□ 82. CASEY COX
□ 93. NORM MCRAE(R)
□ 93. DENNY RIDDLEBERGER(R)
□ 139. PAUL CASANOVA
□ 167. TOM GRIEVE
□ 217. ED STROUD
□ 241. DAVE NELSON
□ 261. DAROLD KNOWLES
□ 283. DICK SUCH
□ 307. DON WERT
□ 326. RICHIE SCHEINBLUM
□ 351. JIM SHELLENBACK
□ 380. TED WILLIAMS(M)
□ 399. JIM FRENCH
□ 427. BERNIE ALLEN
□ 462. TEAM CARD
□ 497. HORACIO PINA
□ 518. JOE GRZENDA
□ 535. CURT FLOOD
□ 559. BILL GOGOLEWSKI
□ 566. TIM CULLEN
□ 591. JACKIE BROWN
□ 620. FRANK HOWARD
□ 655. MIKE EPSTEIN
□ 673. GERRY JANESKI
□ 706. JOE FOY
□ 729. DICK BILLINGS
□ 750. DENNY MCLAIN

1972 TOPPS (787)
2 1/2" X 3 1/2"

ATLANTA BRAVES

□ 21. TEAM CARD
□ 74. CECIL UPSHAW
□ 97. TOM KELLEY
□ 119. MARTY PEREZ
□ 149. GARY NEIBAUER
□ 171. DARRELL EVANS
□ 195. ORLANDO CEPEDA
□ 214. MIKE MCQUEEN
□ 260. RALPH GARR
□ 299. HANK AARON
□ 318. SONNY JACKSON
□ 333. STEVE BARBER
□ 351. TOM HOUSE(R)
□ 351. RICK KESTER(R)
□ 351. JIMMY BRITTON(R)
□ 380. EARL WILLIAMS
□ 401. JIM NASH
□ 451. TONY LARUSSA
□ 469. RON HERBEL
□ 484. LUM HARRIS(M)
□ 516. OSCAR BROWN
□ 540. FELIX MILLAN
□ 591. PAUL CASANOVA
□ 601. GEORGE STONE
□ 620. PHIL NIEKOR
□ 641. MIKE LUM
□ 675. PAT JARVIS
□ 740. RICO CARTY
□ 758. GIL GARRIDO
□ 764. DUSTY BAKER
□ 787. RON REED

BALTIMORE ORIOLES

□ 26. ANDY ETCHEBARREN
□ 70. MIKE CUELLAR
□ 100. FRANK ROBINSON
□ 128. EDDIE WATT
□ 140. PAT DOBSON
□ 212. GRANT JACKSON
□ 235. MERV RETTENMUND
□ 250. BOOG POWELL
□ 270. JIM PALMER
□ 323. EARL WEAVER(M)
□ 338. BOB GRICH
□ 370. DON BUFORD
□ 418. TOM SHOPAY
□ 456. MARK BELANGER
□ 474. DON BAYLOR(R)
□ 474. RORIC HARRISON(R)
□ 474. JOHNNY OATES(R)
□ 490. DAVE MCNALLY
□ 508. ELLIE HENDRICKS
□ 527. DAVE LEONHARD
□ 550. BROOKS ROBINSON
□ 579. DOYLE ALEXANDER
□ 628. TERRY CROWLEY
□ 646. CHICO SALMON
□ 660. PAUL BLAIR
□ 680. DAVE A. JOHNSON
□ 724. MICKEY SCOTT(R)
□ 731. TEAM CARD

BOSTON RED SOX

□ 2. RAY CULP
□ 30. RICO PETROCELLI
□ 37. CARL YASTRZEMSKI
□ 79. MIKE GARMAN(R)
□ 79. CECIL COOPER(R)
□ 79. CARLTON FISK(R)
□ 113. ROGELIO MORET
□ 144. MARTY PATTIN
□ 199. MIKE FIORE
□ 218. EDDIE KASKO(M)
□ 259. SPARKY LYLE
□ 266. BOBBY BOLIN
□ 290. SONNY SIEBERT
□ 313. LUIS APARICIO
□ 328. TEAM CARD
□ 411. BOB MONTGOMERY
□ 455. TOMMY HARPER
□ 472. PHIL GAGLIANO
□ 488. MIKE NAGY
□ 503. GARY PETERS
□ 543. DUANE JOSEPHSON
□ 565. REGGIE SMITH
□ 592. LEW KRAUSSE
□ 636. BILL LEE
□ 674. JOHN KENNEDY
□ 676. DANNY CATER
□ 681. BOBBY PFEIL
□ 703. DOUG GRIFFIN
□ 724. JOHN CURTIS(R)
□ 734. BOB BURDA
□ 741. RICK MILLER(R)
□ 761. BEN OGLIVIE(R)
□ 772. KEN TATUM

CALIFORNIA ANGELS

□ 19. BILLY COWAN
□ 55. CLYDE WRIGHT
□ 71. TEAM CARD
□ 102. LLOYD ALLEN
□ 115. JIM FREGOSI
□ 135. VADA PINSON
□ 160. ANDY MESSERSMITH
□ 196. MEL QUEEN
□ 213. BILL PARKER(R)
□ 213. ART KUSNYER(R)
□ 213. TOM SILVERIO(R)
□ 253. SANDY ALOMAR
□ 272. MICKEY RIVERS
□ 289. SYD O'BRIEN
□ 354. TOM MURPHY
□ 379. KEN BERRY
□ 404. JEFF TORBORG
□ 419. JIM SPENCER
□ 462. RICKEY CLARK
□ 521. ALAN FOSTER
□ 541. ROGER REPOZ
□ 561. LEO CARDENAS
□ 595. NOLAN RYAN
□ 629. PAUL DOYLE
□ 656. RUDY MAY
□ 672. ARCHIE REYNOLDS
□ 689. EDDIE FISHER
□ 718. DEL RICE(M)
□ 765. KEN MCMULLEN

CHICAGO CUBS

□ 18. JUAN PIZARRO
□ 29. BILL BONHAM
□ 45. GLENN BECKERT
□ 61. BURT HOOTON(R)
□ 61. GENE HISER(R)
□ 61. EARL STEPHENSON(R)
□ 117. CLEO JAMES
□ 145. DON KESSINGER
□ 192. TEAM CARD
□ 208. MILT PAPPAS
□ 258. RANDY HUNDLEY
□ 271. KEN RUDOLPH
□ 303. JOE PEPITONE
□ 335. BILL HANDS
□ 364. JOHNNY CALLISON
□ 410. FERGIE JENKINS
□ 439. BILLY WILLIAMS
□ 485. PHIL REGAN
□ 512. PAUL POPOVICH

□ 534. JIM HICKMAN
□ 555. RON SANTO
□ 576. LEO DUROCHER(M)
□ 612. JOE DECKER
□ 639. J.C. MARTIN
□ 666. HECTOR TORRES
□ 667. RAY NEWMAN
□ 684. HAL BREEDEN
□ 730. RICK MONDAY
□ 766. STEVE HAMILTON

CHICAGO WHITE SOX

□ 15. WALT WILLIAMS
□ 73. STEVE HUNTZ
□ 98. CHUCK TANNER(M)
□ 126. BART JOHNSON
□ 146. STEVE KEALEY
□ 183. BILL MELTON
□ 207. TOM EGAN
□ 233. JAY JOHNSTONE
□ 240. RICH ALLEN
□ 248. TOM BRADLEY
□ 326. H. PAT KELLY
□ 361. MIKE ANDREWS
□ 381. TEAM CARD
□ 413. DON EDDY(R)
□ 413. DAVE LEMONDS(R)
□ 452. ED HERRMANN
□ 476. LEE RICHARD
□ 499. VICENTE ROMO
□ 525. CARLOS MAY
□ 539. TERRY FORSTER
□ 553. WILBUR WOOD
□ 593. RICH MORALES
□ 618. RICH ROBERTSON
□ 648. JIM LYTTLE
□ 662. STAN BAHNSEN
□ 685. JOE HORLEN
□ 746. LOWELL PALMER
□ 774. LUIS ALVARADO
□ 786. CHUCK BRINKMAN

CINCINNATI REDS

□ 3. BOB TOLAN
□ 80. TONY PEREZ
□ 99. ROSS GRIMSLEY
□ 121. ED SPRAGUE
□ 136. DARREL CHANEY
□ 157. DON GULLETT
□ 236. JIM MCGLOTHLIN
□ 256. GEORGE FOSTER
□ 267. DAVE CONCEPCION
□ 291. HAL MCRAE
□ 311. CLAY CARROLL
□ 358. SPARKY ANDERSON(M)
□ 382. JOE GIBBON
□ 417. TOM HALL
□ 433. JOHNNY BENCH
□ 463. BERNIE CARBO
□ 475. GARY NOLAN
□ 524. ED ARMBRISTER(R)
□ 524. MEL BEHNEY(R)
□ 542. JACK BILLINGHAM
□ 559. PETE ROSE
□ 586. DENIS MENKE
□ 614. TED UHLAENDER
□ 651. TEAM CARD
□ 659. BOB ASPROMONTE
□ 705. PAT CORRALES
□ 719. CESAR GERONIMO
□ 738. JIM MERRITT
□ 745. JULIAN JAVIER
□ 762. WAYNE SIMPSON

CLEVELAND INDIANS

□ 24. TED FORD
□ 59. FRED STANLEY
□ 84. VINCE COLBERT
□ 116. ED FARMER
□ 142. CHRIS CHAMBLISS
□ 193. KURT BEVACQUA
□ 215. ALEX JOHNSON
□ 261. STEVE MINGORI
□ 285. GAYLORD PERRY
□ 356. GERRY MOSES
□ 374. JACK HEIDEMANN
□ 399. MILT WILCOX
□ 422. RAY LAMB
□ 470. RAY FOSSE
□ 486. JOHN LOWENSTEIN
□ 506. TERRY LEY(R)
□ 506. JIM MOYER(R)
□ 506. DICK TIDROW(R)
□ 547. TEAM CARD
□ 590. GRAIG NETTLES
□ 607. FRANK DUFFY
□ 615. STEVE HARGAN
□ 642. DENNY RIDDLEBERGER
□ 658. STEVE DUNNING
□ 687. DEL UNSER
□ 721. EDDIE LEON
□ 748. PHIL HENNIGAN
□ 784. KEN ASPROMONTE(M)

DETROIT TIGERS

□ 6. FRED SCHERMAN
□ 33. BILLY MARTIN(M)
□ 83. DALTON JONES
□ 120. BILL FREEHAN
□ 150. NORM CASH
□ 175. TOM HALLER
□ 187. GATES BROWN
□ 216. JOE NIEKRO
□ 239. TOM TIMMERMANN
□ 257. JIM FOOR(R)
□ 257. TIM HOSLEY(R)
□ 257. PAUL JATA(R)
□ 284. IKE BROWN
□ 319. AURELIO RODRIGUEZ
□ 337. MIKE KILKENNY
□ 367. RON PERRANOSKI
□ 385. MICKEY STANLEY
□ 408. JIM NORTHRUP
□ 450. MICKEY LOLICH
□ 487. TEAM CARD
□ 511. TONY TAYLOR
□ 535. ED BRINKMAN
□ 600. AL KALINE
□ 640. JOE COLEMAN
□ 725. DICK MCAULIFFE
□ 750. WILLIE HORTON
□ 783. LES CAIN

HOUSTON ASTROS

□ 20. DON WILSON
□ 56. RICH CHILES
□ 65. CESAR CEDENO
□ 101. BILL GREIF(R)
□ 101. J.R. RICHARD(R)
□ 101. RAY BUSSE(R)
□ 132. JOE MORGAN
□ 155. LARRY DIERKER
□ 202. SCIPIO SPINKS
□ 204. TOMMY HELMS
□ 217. ROGER METZGER
□ 249. HARRY WALKER(M)
□ 282. TEAM CARD
□ 339. RON COOK
□ 355. BOB WATSON
□ 360. DAVE A. ROBERTS
□ 394. KEN FORSCH
□ 416. JOHNNY EDWARDS
□ 466. NORM MILLER
□ 480. LEE MAY
□ 507. FRED GLADDING
□ 536. DOUG RADER
□ 581. WADE BLASINGAME
□ 603. JIM RAY
□ 633. JACK HIATT
□ 679. BOB FENWICK(R)
□ 679. BOB STINSON(R)
□ 716. JESUS ALOU
□ 732. GEORGE CULVER
□ 747. JIM STEWART
□ 770. JIM WYNN

KANSAS CITY ROYALS

□ 10. AMOS OTIS
□ 57. BOB OLIVER
□ 68. JIM YORK
□ 81. MIKE HEDLUND
□ 109. JERRY MAY
□ 133. JOE KEOUGH
□ 177. PAUL SCHAAL
□ 205. DICK DRAGO
□ 246. TOM BURGMEIER
□ 273. BOBBY FLOYD
□ 315. PAUL SPLITTORFF
□ 332. BUCK MARTINEZ
□ 349. AL FITZMORRIS
□ 372. LANCE CLEMONS(R)
□ 372. MONTY MONTGOMERY(R)
□ 373. JOHN MAYBERRY
□ 415. COOKIE ROJAS
□ 449. BOB LEMON(M)
□ 468. RICHIE SCHEINBLUM
□ 519. TED ABERNATHY
□ 531. FREDDIE PATEK
□ 569. ED KIRKPATRICK
□ 580. LOU PINIELLA
□ 617. TEAM CARD
□ 638. KEN WRIGHT
□ 664. BOBBY KNOOP
□ 683. STEVE HOVLEY
□ 717. BRUCE DAL CANTON
□ 728. GAIL HOPKINS
□ 742. JIM ROOKER
□ 763. RON HANSEN

LOS ANGELES DODGERS

□ 11. BOBBY VALENTINE
□ 25. BILL SINGER
□ 63. DUKE SIMS
□ 114. BILL BUCKNER
□ 151. JIM BREWER
□ 198. CHARLIE HOUGH(R)
□ 198. BOB O'BRIEN(R)
□ 198. MIKE STRAHLER(R)
□ 264. TOMMY JOHN
□ 265. WES PARKER
□ 297. CLAUDE OSTEEN
□ 322. JOSE PENA
□ 369. JIM LEFEBVRE
□ 390. WILLIE DAVIS
□ 398. LARRY HISLE
□ 437. MAURY WILLS
□ 460. AL DOWNING
□ 522. TEAM CARD
□ 530. DON SUTTON
□ 578. BILLY GRABARKEWITZ
□ 596. MANNY MOTA
□ 616. JOE FERGUSON
□ 649. PETE RICHERT
□ 669. WILLIE CRAWFORD
□ 686. STEVE GARVEY
□ 736. BILL RUSSELL
□ 749. WALTER ALSTON(M)
□ 759. CHRIS CANNIZZARO
□ 761. RON CEY(R)
□ 777. HOYT WILHELM

MILWAUKEE BREWERS

□ 12. JOSE CARDENAL
□ 77. RON THEOBALD
□ 106. TEAM CARD
□ 118. SKIP LOCKWOOD
□ 153. RICK AUERBACK
□ 161. BROCK DAVIS
□ 162. JERRY BELL(R)
□ 162. DARRELL PORTER(R)
□ 162. BOB REYNOLDS(R)
□ 197. JOHNNY BRIGGS
□ 255. JIM LONBORG
□ 281. BILL PARSONS
□ 321. JOE LAHOUD
□ 359. DON PAVLETICH
□ 376. ANDY KOSCO
□ 386. JIM COLBORN
□ 391. KEN SANDERS
□ 393. CURT MOTTON
□ 402. BOBBY HEISE
□ 421. ELLIE RODRIGUEZ
□ 458. AURELIO MONTEAGUDO
□ 481. BILLY CONIGLIARO
□ 517. KEN BRETT
□ 549. DAVE MAY
□ 585. GEORGE SCOTT
□ 602. DAVE BRISTOL(M)
□ 613. MIKE FERRARO
□ 652. MARCELINO LOPEZ
□ 744. JIM SLATON
□ 776. BILL VOSS

MINNESOTA TWINS

☐ 28. BOB GEBHARD(R)
☐ 28. STEVE BRYE(R)
☐ 28. HAL HAYDEL(R)
☐ 51. HARMON KILLEBREW
☐ 66. RAY CORBIN
☐ 131. JIM NETTLES
☐ 156. TEAM CARD
☐ 201. PHIL ROOF
☐ 220. JIM PERRY
☐ 244. STEVE BRAUN
☐ 275. CESAR TOVAR
☐ 301. GEORGE MITTERWALD
☐ 352. DAVE LAROCHE
☐ 368. DANNY THOMPSON
☐ 389. BILL RIGNEY(M)
☐ 400. TONY OLIVA
☐ 459. RICK RENICK
☐ 501. PETE HAMM
☐ 515. BERT BLYLEVEN
☐ 545. WAYNE GRANGER
☐ 588. JIM HOLT
☐ 611. RICH REESE
☐ 634. DICK WOODSON
☐ 678. STEVE LUEBBER
☐ 695. ROD CAREW
☐ 709. JIM KAAT
☐ 778. VIC ALBURY(R)
☐ 778. RICK DEMPSEY(R)
☐ 778. JIM STRICKLAND(R)

MONTREAL EXPOS

☐ 5. JOHN BATEMAN
☐ 58. ERNIE MCANALLY
☐ 82. RON WOODS
☐ 110. RON HUNT
☐ 134. CARL MORTON
☐ 159. JOHN BOCCABELLA
☐ 211. GARY SUTHERLAND
☐ 234. RON TAYLOR
☐ 254. BOOTS DAY
☐ 276. GENE MAUCH(M)
☐ 307. STEVE RENKO
☐ 331. STAN SWANSON
☐ 371. DENNY LEMASTER
☐ 405. RON FAIRLY
☐ 473. DAN MCGINN
☐ 489. TERRY HUMPHREY(R)
☐ 489. KEITH LAMPARD(R)
☐ 505. MIKE MARSHALL
☐ 526. BOB BAILEY
☐ 582. TEAM CARD
☐ 610. BILL STONEMAN
☐ 631. JOHN STROHMAYER
☐ 653. JIM FAIREY
☐ 657. BOBBY WINE
☐ 727. JOSE LABOY
☐ 743. CESAR GUTIERREZ
☐ 773. RON BRAND

NEW YORK METS

☐ 16. MIKE JORGENSEN
☐ 31. CLEON JONES
☐ 53. BUD HARRELSON
☐ 105. GARY GENTRY
☐ 127. DUFFY DYER
☐ 141. BUZZ CAPRA(R)
☐ 141. LEROY STANTON(R)
☐ 141. JON MATLACK(R)
☐ 163. TUG MCGRAW
☐ 181. ED KRANEPOOL
☐ 245. TOMMIE AGEE
☐ 269. DON HAHN
☐ 293. DANNY FRISELLA
☐ 305. KEN BOSWELL
☐ 362. TEAM CARD
☐ 388. CHARLIE WILLIAMS
☐ 407. CHUCK TAYLOR
☐ 425. KEN SINGLETON
☐ 445. TOM SEAVER
☐ 465. GIL HODGES(M)
☐ 518. WAYNE GARRETT
☐ 544. TED MARTINEZ
☐ 563. RAY SADECKI
☐ 594. JIM BEAUCHAMP
☐ 655. JERRY GROTE
☐ 673. DAVE MARSHALL
☐ 697. JERRY KOOSMAN
☐ 707. TIM FOLI
☐ 722. BILL SUDAKIS
☐ 741. JOHN MILNER(R)
☐ 781. JIM MCANDREW

NEW YORK YANKEES

☐ 8. RON SWOBODA
☐ 22. ROB GARDNER
☐ 47. JOHN ELLIS
☐ 108. GARY WASLEWSKI
☐ 124. ALAN CLOSTER(R)
☐ 124. RUSTY TORRES(R)
☐ 124. ROGER HAMBRIGHT(R)
☐ 138. MIKE KEKICH
☐ 158. JERRY KENNEY
☐ 203. RON BLOMBERG
☐ 237. TEAM CARD
☐ 263. FELIPE ALOU
☐ 287. JIM HARDIN
☐ 325. MEL STOTTLEMYRE
☐ 340. ROY WHITE
☐ 387. HORACE CLARKE
☐ 409. FRANK W. BAKER
☐ 441. THURMAN MUNSON
☐ 467. STEVE KLINE
☐ 513. LINDY MCDANIEL
☐ 533. RALPH HOUK(M)
☐ 573. FRITZ PETERSON
☐ 589. HAL LANIER
☐ 597. JIM MAGNUSON
☐ 619. RICH MCKINNEY
☐ 644. BERNIE ALLEN
☐ 699. BOBBY MURCER
☐ 713. GENE MICHAEL
☐ 724. RICH HINTON(R)
☐ 769. JACK AKER

OAKLAND A'S

☐ 17. DAVE DUNCAN
☐ 41. TOMMY DAVIS
☐ 62. ANGEL MANGUAL
☐ 75. BERT CAMPANERIS
☐ 111. JIM GRANT
☐ 137. DICK WILLIAMS(M)
☐ 169. VIDA BLUE
☐ 189. GENE TENACE
☐ 209. JOE RUDI
☐ 241. ROLLIE FINGERS
☐ 268. DWAIN ANDERSON(R)
☐ 268. CHRIS FLOETHE(R)
☐ 279. LARRY BROWN
☐ 330. JIM HUNTER
☐ 363. RON KLIMKOWSKI
☐ 383. BRANT ALYEA
☐ 406. GEORGE HENDRICK
☐ 435. REGGIE JACKSON
☐ 454. TEAM CARD
☐ 464. JIM ROLAND
☐ 523. CHUCK DOBSON
☐ 537. BOB LOCKER
☐ 557. JOHN ODOM
☐ 583. DAROLD KNOWLES
☐ 632. MIKE HEGAN
☐ 650. SAL BANDO
☐ 670. KEN HOLTZMAN
☐ 691. CURT BLEFARY
☐ 715. MIKE EPSTEIN
☐ 735. DIEGO SEGUI
☐ 780. DICK GREEN

PHILADELPHIA PHILLIES

☐ 14. PETE KOEGEL(R)
☐ 14. MIKE ANDERSON(R)
☐ 14. WAYNE TWITCHELL(R)
☐ 43. RICK WISE
☐ 69. ROGER FREED
☐ 112. GREG LUZINSKI
☐ 139. TIM MCCARVER
☐ 167. DERON JOHNSON
☐ 188. FRANK LUCCHESI(M)
☐ 252. KEN REYNOLDS
☐ 283. DARRELL BRANDON
☐ 324. MIKE RYAN
☐ 357. WOODIE FRYMAN
☐ 377. TERRY HARMON
☐ 397. TEAM CARD
☐ 423. OSCAR GAMBLE
☐ 453. BARRY LERSCH
☐ 482. JOE HOERNER
☐ 520. LARRY BOWA
☐ 528. RON STONE
☐ 587. BILLY WILSON
☐ 599. BILLY CHAMPION
☐ 635. DON MONEY
☐ 665. CHRIS SHORT
☐ 690. WILLIE MONTANEZ
☐ 726. DICK SELMA
☐ 741. TOM HUTTON(R)
☐ 768. DENNY DOYLE

PITTSBURGH PIRATES

☐ 1. TEAM CARD
☐ 27. BOB D. JOHNSON
☐ 60. MANNY SANGUILLEN
☐ 72. BRUCE KISON
☐ 125. DAVE CASH
☐ 152. GENE CLINES
☐ 179. DOCK ELLIS
☐ 190. DAVE GIUSTI
☐ 219. RENNIE STENNETT
☐ 247. MILT MAY
☐ 286. GENE ALLEY
☐ 309. ROBERTO CLEMENTE
☐ 320. STEVE BLASS
☐ 392. FRED CAMBRIA(R)
☐ 392. RICHIE ZISK(R)
☐ 414. BOB L. MILLER
☐ 429. BOB ROBERTSON
☐ 447. WILLIE STARGELL
☐ 471. LUKE WALKER
☐ 502. JACKIE HERNANDEZ
☐ 538. CHARLIE SANDS
☐ 575. AL OLIVER
☐ 605. NELSON BRILES
☐ 630. RICH HEBNER
☐ 647. BOB MOOSE
☐ 661. BILL VIRDON(M)
☐ 701. JOSE PAGAN
☐ 729. BOB VEALE
☐ 760. BILL MAZEROSKI
☐ 785. VIC DAVALILLO

ST. LOUIS CARDINALS

☐ 9. STAN WILLIAMS
☐ 13. JOE GRZENDA
☐ 67. RED SCHOENDIENST(M)
☐ 107. JOSE CRUZ
☐ 130. BOB GIBSON
☐ 154. TED SIMMONS
☐ 200. LOU BROCK
☐ 206. DAL MAXVILL
☐ 243. FRANK LINZY
☐ 278. DENNIS HIGGINS
☐ 316. JIM BIBBY(R)
☐ 316. JORGE ROQUE(R)
☐ 316. SANTIAGO GUZMAN(R)
☐ 336. MARTY MARTINEZ
☐ 353. ART SHAMSKY
☐ 375. REGGIE CLEVELAND
☐ 395. MATTY ALOU
☐ 420. STEVE CARLTON
☐ 479. DON SHAW
☐ 500. JOE TORRE
☐ 514. TED SIZEMORE
☐ 546. JOE HAGUE
☐ 584. JERRY MCNERTNEY
☐ 606. LUIS MELENDEZ

- □ 627. MOE DRABOWSKY
- □ 645. JIM MALONEY
- □ 671. DONN CLENDENON
- □ 688. TEAM CARD
- □ 723. AL SANTORINI
- □ 775. JERRY REUSS
- □ 779. TONY CLONINGER

SAN DIEGO PADRES

- □ 7. ENZO HERNANDEZ
- □ 39. BOB BARTON
- □ 78. STEVE ARLIN
- □ 123. ED ACOSTA
- □ 143. GARRY JESTADT
- □ 173. CLAY KIRBY
- □ 194. FRED NORMAN
- □ 238. LERON LEE
- □ 262. TEAM CARD
- □ 274. AL SEVERINSEN
- □ 288. JOHNNY JETER
- □ 384. DAVE CAMPBELL
- □ 412. DICK KELLEY
- □ 431. CLARENCE GASTON
- □ 457. DARCY FAST(R)
- □ 457. DERREL THOMAS(R)
- □ 457. MIKE IVIE(R)
- □ 477. TOM PHOEBUS
- □ 504. ED SPIEZIO
- □ 532. FRED KENDALL
- □ 551. OLLIE BROWN
- □ 571. NATE COLBERT
- □ 608. MIKE CORKINS
- □ 637. PRESTON GOMEZ(M)
- □ 677. IVAN MURRELL
- □ 739. DON MASON
- □ 782. LARRY STAHL

SAN FRANCISCO GIANTS

- □ 35. JERRY JOHNSON
- □ 49. WILLIE MAYS
- □ 76. DON CARRITHERS
- □ 129. CHARLIE FOX(M)
- □ 147. DAVE KINGMAN
- □ 165. CHRIS SPEIER
- □ 185. RON BRYANT
- □ 232. CHRIS ARNOLD(R)
- □ 232. JIM BARR(R)
- □ 232. DAVE RADER(R)
- □ 280. WILLIE MCCOVEY
- □ 295. DICK DIETZ
- □ 327. STEVE STONE
- □ 366. JIMMY ROSARIO
- □ 403. JOHN CUMBERLAND
- □ 427. TITO FUENTES
- □ 443. KEN HENDERSON
- □ 509. DON MCMAHON
- □ 548. FRANK REBERGER
- □ 567. JUAN MARICHAL
- □ 643. RUSS GIBSON
- □ 663. FRAN HEALY
- □ 682. MIKE MCCORMICK
- □ 693. ALAN GALLAGHER
- □ 711. BOBBY BONDS
- □ 720. SAM MCDOWELL
- □ 733. JIM HART
- □ 761. BERNIE WILLIAMS(R)
- □ 771. TEAM CARD

TEXAS RANGERS

- □ 23. TED KUBIAK
- □ 64. PETE BROBERG
- □ 104. TOBY HARRAH
- □ 122. LARRY BIITTNER
- □ 148. DICK BILLINGS
- □ 191. JEFF BURROUGHS
- □ 210. DENNY MCLAIN
- □ 231. CASEY COX
- □ 242. DON MINCHER
- □ 277. ELLIOTT MADDOX
- □ 317. RICH HAND
- □ 329. ROY FOSTER
- □ 334. BILL FAHEY(R)
- □ 334. JIM MASON(R)
- □ 334. TOM RAGLAND(R)
- □ 350. FRANK HOWARD
- □ 365. DICK BOSMAN
- □ 396. PAUL LINDBLAD
- □ 424. BILL GOGOLEWSKI
- □ 461. TIM CULLEN
- □ 483. KEN SUAREZ
- □ 510. TED WILLIAMS(M)
- □ 529. DAVE NELSON
- □ 577. MIKE PAUL
- □ 598. HAL KING
- □ 609. TOM GRIEVE
- □ 654. HORACIO PINA
- □ 668. TEAM CARD
- □ 737. LENNY RANDLE
- □ 767. TOM MCCRAW

1973 TOPPS (660)
2 1/2" X 3 1/2"

ATLANTA BRAVES

- □ 15. RALPH GARR
- □ 33. JIM BREAZEALE
- □ 72. RON REED
- □ 100. HANK AARON
- □ 124. JIM HARDIN
- □ 144. MARTY PEREZ
- □ 169. RON SCHUELER
- □ 192. PAT JARVIS
- □ 215. DUSTY BAKER
- □ 237. MATHEWS(M) & COACHES
- □ 266. MIKE LUM
- □ 288. GARY GENTRY
- □ 312. OSCAR BROWN
- □ 359. CECIL UPSHAW
- □ 374. DARRELL EVANS
- □ 403. SONNY JACKSON
- □ 432. DAN FRISELLA
- □ 452. PAUL CASANOVA
- □ 503. PHIL NIEKRO
- □ 521. TEAM CARD
- □ 550. DAVE A. JOHNSON
- □ 574. BOB DIDIER
- □ 609. LARVELL BLANKS(R)
- □ 610. JIMMY FREEMAN(R)
- □ 630. DENNY MCLAIN
- □ 653. JOE HOERNER

BALTIMORE ORIOLES

- □ 9. JOHNNY OATES
- □ 34. PAT DOBSON
- □ 56. MERV RETTENMUND
- □ 90. BROOKS ROBINSON
- □ 109. DOYLE ALEXANDER
- □ 136. WEAVER(M) & COACHES
- □ 160. JIM PALMER
- □ 183. DON BUFORD
- □ 229. RORIC HARRISON
- □ 253. MARK BELANGER
- □ 278. TEAM CARD
- □ 302. TERRY CROWLEY
- □ 325. BOOG POWELL
- □ 362. EDDIE WATT
- □ 384. DON BAYLOR
- □ 396. GRANT JACKSON
- □ 418. BOBBY GRICH
- □ 470. MIKE CUELLAR
- □ 504. EARL WILLIAMS
- □ 528. PAUL BLAIR
- □ 553. MICKEY SCOTT
- □ 600. DAVE MCNALLY
- □ 601. SERGIO ROBLES(R)
- □ 604. JESSE JEFFERSON(R)
- □ 605. ENOS CABELL(R)
- □ 611. RICH COGGINS(R)
- □ 612. BOB REYNOLDS(R)
- □ 614. AL BUMBRY(R)
- □ 618. ANDY ETCHEBARREN
- □ 631. TOM MATCHICK

BOSTON RED SOX

- □ 14. SONNY SIEBERT
- □ 40. REGGIE SMITH
- □ 69. PHIL GAGLIANO
- □ 96. DOUG GRIFFIN
- □ 114. LYNN MCGLOTHEN
- □ 131. KASKO(M) & COACHES
- □ 143. JOHN CURTIS
- □ 165. LUIS APARICIO
- □ 193. CARLTON FISK
- □ 224. BILL LEE
- □ 245. CARL YASTRZEMSKI
- □ 270. LUIS TIANT
- □ 291. ROGELIO MORET
- □ 317. DANNY CATER
- □ 365. RICO PETROCELLI
- □ 388. BEN OGLIVIE
- □ 415. MARTY PATTIN
- □ 437. JOHN KENNEDY
- □ 463. KEN TATUM
- □ 491. BOB MONTGOMERY
- □ 518. BOB VEALE
- □ 541. BOB BOLIN
- □ 566. LEW KRAUSSE
- □ 596. TEAM CARD
- □ 607. MARIO GUERRERO(R)
- □ 614. DWIGHT EVANS(R)
- □ 616. MIKE GARMAN(R)
- □ 620. TOMMY HARPER

CALIFORNIA ANGELS

- □ 18. LEROY STANTON
- □ 36. STEVE BARBER
- □ 75. VADA PINSON
- □ 102. RUDY MAY
- □ 123. SANDY ALOMAR
- □ 154. JEFF TORBORG
- □ 175. FRANK ROBINSON
- □ 178. DON ROSE
- □ 220. NOLAN RYAN
- □ 243. TEAM CARD
- □ 267. LLOYD ALLEN
- □ 279. MIKE STRAHLER
- □ 289. BOB OLIVER
- □ 301. BILLY GRABARKEWITZ
- □ 319. JIM SPENCER
- □ 354. BILLY PARKER
- □ 373. CLYDE WRIGHT
- □ 402. JACK HIATT
- □ 421. WINKLES(M) & COACHES
- □ 445. KEN BERRY
- □ 502. BOBBY VALENTINE
- □ 522. LEO CARDENAS
- □ 543. ALAN FOSTER
- □ 570. BILL SINGER
- □ 597. MICKEY RIVERS
- □ 636. RICK CLARK

CHICAGO CUBS

- ☐ 21. RANDY HUNDLEY
- ☐ 44. RICK MONDAY
- ☐ 70. MILT PAPPAS
- ☐ 81. LOCKMAN(M) & COACHES
- ☐ 115. RON SANTO
- ☐ 139. CARMEN FANZONE
- ☐ 180. FERGIE JENKINS
- ☐ 200. BILLY WILLIAMS
- ☐ 262. JACK AKER
- ☐ 285. DON KESSINGER
- ☐ 309. PAUL POPOVICH
- ☐ 328. BILL BONHAM
- ☐ 367. BURT HOOTON
- ☐ 393. JOSE CARDENAL
- ☐ 414. KEN RUDOLPH
- ☐ 426. DAVE LAROCHE
- ☐ 440. GLENN BECKERT
- ☐ 464. TEAM CARD
- ☐ 482. RICK REUSCHEL
- ☐ 501. LARRY GURA
- ☐ 527. DAN MCGINN
- ☐ 552. J.C. MARTIN
- ☐ 565. JIM HICKMAN
- ☐ 580. JOE PEPITONE
- ☐ 603. TERRY HUGHES(R)
- ☐ 605. PAT BOURQUE(R)
- ☐ 645. BOB LOCKER

CHICAGO WHITE SOX

- ☐ 20. STAN BAHNSEN
- ☐ 42. MIKE ANDREWS
- ☐ 73. ED HERRMANN
- ☐ 105. CARLOS MAY
- ☐ 129. TERRY FORSTER
- ☐ 150. WILBUR WOOD
- ☐ 174. RICH GOSSAGE
- ☐ 194. JORGE ORTA
- ☐ 238. TONY MUSER
- ☐ 261. H. PAT KELLY
- ☐ 287. EDDIE LEON
- ☐ 310. DICK ALLEN
- ☐ 356. TANNER(M) & COACHES
- ☐ 379. CY ACOSTA
- ☐ 404. CHUCK BRINKMAN
- ☐ 423. JOHNNY JETER
- ☐ 439. EDDIE FISHER
- ☐ 455. BILL MELTON
- ☐ 481. TEAM CARD
- ☐ 494. RICH MORALES
- ☐ 506. BART JOHNSON
- ☐ 534. DAVE LEMONDS
- ☐ 561. JIM GEDDES
- ☐ 581. STEVE KEALEY
- ☐ 604. DENNIS O'TOOLE(R)
- ☐ 627. LUIS ALVARADO
- ☐ 648. TOM EGAN

CINCINNATI REDS

- ☐ 8. TOM HALL
- ☐ 28. HAL MCRAE
- ☐ 52. DENIS MENKE
- ☐ 89. JACK BILLINGHAM
- ☐ 130. PETE ROSE
- ☐ 156. CESAR GERONIMO
- ☐ 177. BILL PLUMMER
- ☐ 195. CLAY CARROLL
- ☐ 230. JOE MORGAN
- ☐ 260. GARY NOLAN
- ☐ 275. TONY PEREZ
- ☐ 296. ANDERSON(M) & COACHES
- ☐ 318. JIM MCGLOTHLIN
- ☐ 335. BOB TOLAN
- ☐ 357. ROSS GRIMSLEY
- ☐ 380. JOHNNY BENCH
- ☐ 399. GEORGE FOSTER
- ☐ 447. JOE HAGUE
- ☐ 492. PEDRO BORBON
- ☐ 507. DARREL CHANEY
- ☐ 533. LARRY STAHL
- ☐ 554. DAVE CONCEPCION
- ☐ 595. DON GULLETT
- ☐ 602. MEL BEHNEY(R)
- ☐ 626. BOB BARTON
- ☐ 641. TEAM CARD

CLEVELAND INDIANS

- ☐ 11. CHRIS CHAMBLISS
- ☐ 31. BUDDY BELL
- ☐ 53. STEVE DUNNING
- ☐ 86. TOM MCCRAW
- ☐ 134. MILT WILCOX
- ☐ 157. DENNY RIDDLEBERGER
- ☐ 181. JACK BROHAMER
- ☐ 226. RAY FOSSE
- ☐ 247. DEL UNSER
- ☐ 272. ED FARMER
- ☐ 297. WALT WILLIAMS
- ☐ 327. JOHN LOWENSTEIN
- ☐ 339. DICK TIDROW
- ☐ 372. OSCAR GAMBLE
- ☐ 376. FRANK DUFFY
- ☐ 400. GAYLORD PERRY
- ☐ 425. ALEX JOHNSON
- ☐ 449. ASPROMONTE(M) & CHS.
- ☐ 496. RAY LAMB
- ☐ 514. JERRY KENNEY
- ☐ 532. STEVE MINGORI
- ☐ 551. MIKE KILKENNY
- ☐ 571. RUSTY TORRES
- ☐ 591. MIKE HEDLUND
- ☐ 601. GEORGE PENA(R)
- ☐ 608. DICK COLPAERT(R)
- ☐ 612. BRENT STROM(R)
- ☐ 614. CHARLIE SPIKES(R)
- ☐ 629. TEAM CARD
- ☐ 644. JACK HEIDEMANN
- ☐ 656. JOHN ELLIS

DETROIT TIGERS

- ☐ 5. ED BRINKMAN
- ☐ 29. TONY TAYLOR
- ☐ 51. CHUCK SEELBACH
- ☐ 88. MICKEY STANLEY
- ☐ 120. JOE COLEMAN
- ☐ 146. WOODIE FRYMAN
- ☐ 168. JIM NORTHRUP
- ☐ 191. TEAM CARD
- ☐ 218. AURELIO RODRIGUEZ
- ☐ 256. CHRIS ZACHARY
- ☐ 280. AL KALINE
- ☐ 304. DUKE SIMS
- ☐ 323. MARTIN(M) & COACHES
- ☐ 349. DICK MCAULIFFE
- ☐ 369. LERRIN LAGROW
- ☐ 390. MICKEY LOLICH
- ☐ 413. TOM TIMMERMANN
- ☐ 433. WILLIE HORTON
- ☐ 448. JOHN HILLER
- ☐ 460. BILL FREEHAN
- ☐ 485. NORM CASH
- ☐ 508. GATES BROWN
- ☐ 537. BILL SLAYBACK
- ☐ 560. FRANK HOWARD
- ☐ 585. JOE NIEKRO
- ☐ 604. BOB STRAMPE(R)
- ☐ 633. IKE BROWN
- ☐ 660. FRED SCHERMAN

HOUSTON ASTROS

- ☐ 17. FRED GLADDING
- ☐ 39. DAVE A. ROBERTS
- ☐ 76. DOUG RADER
- ☐ 93. JESUS ALOU
- ☐ 110. BOB WATSON
- ☐ 135. LEE MAY
- ☐ 158. TEAM CARD
- ☐ 185. JIM WYNN
- ☐ 217. DON WILSON
- ☐ 242. GEORGE CULVER
- ☐ 290. CESAR CEDENO
- ☐ 313. JIM RAY
- ☐ 351. JIMMY STEWART
- ☐ 375. LARRY DIERKER
- ☐ 395. ROGER METZGER
- ☐ 420. TOMMIE AGEE
- ☐ 446. JERRY REUSS
- ☐ 468. TOM GRIFFIN
- ☐ 495. TOMMY HELMS
- ☐ 519. JOHN EDWARDS
- ☐ 546. JIM YORK
- ☐ 572. GARY SUTHERLAND
- ☐ 589. KEN FORSCH
- ☐ 613. SKIP JUTZE(R)
- ☐ 624. DUROCHER(M) & COACHES
- ☐ 637. NORM MILLER

KANSAS CITY ROYALS

- ☐ 22. TED ABERNATHY
- ☐ 48. PAUL SPLITTORFF
- ☐ 78. RICHIE SCHEINBLUM
- ☐ 99. CARL TAYLOR
- ☐ 118. JOHN MAYBERRY
- ☐ 140. LOU PINIELLA
- ☐ 164. MONTY MONTGOMERY
- ☐ 188. COOKIE ROJAS
- ☐ 233. ED KIRKPATRICK
- ☐ 251. ROGER NELSON
- ☐ 282. STEVE HOVLEY
- ☐ 306. TOM BURGMEIER
- ☐ 334. FREDDIE PATEK
- ☐ 347. TEAM CARD
- ☐ 392. DICK DRAGO
- ☐ 416. PAUL SCHAAL
- ☐ 428. WAYNE SIMPSON
- ☐ 441. GAIL HOPKINS
- ☐ 466. JOSE ARCIA
- ☐ 487. BRUCE DAL CANTON
- ☐ 510. AMOS OTIS
- ☐ 539. TOM MURPHY
- ☐ 558. JERRY MAY
- ☐ 578. KEN WRIGHT
- ☐ 593. MCKEON(M) & COACHES
- ☐ 608. STEVE BUSBY(R)
- ☐ 611. JIM WOHLFORD(R)
- ☐ 616. NORM ANGELINI(R)
- ☐ 643. AL FITZMORRIS

LOS ANGELES DODGERS

- ☐ 10. DON SUTTON
- ☐ 35. WILLIE DAVIS
- ☐ 59. STEVE YEAGER
- ☐ 91. TEAM CARD
- ☐ 108. BILL RUSSELL
- ☐ 126. JIM BREWER
- ☐ 151. WES PARKER
- ☐ 196. KEN MCMULLEN
- ☐ 213. STEVE GARVEY
- ☐ 239. PETE RICHERT
- ☐ 258. TOMMY JOHN
- ☐ 324. AL DOWNING
- ☐ 368. BILL BUCKNER
- ☐ 391. LEE LACY
- ☐ 412. MANNY MOTA
- ☐ 442. DICK DIETZ
- ☐ 490. CLAUDE OSTEEN
- ☐ 515. ANDY MESSERSMITH
- ☐ 544. VON JOSHUA
- ☐ 569. ALSTON(M) & COACHES
- ☐ 602. DOUG RAU(R)
- ☐ 606. TOM PACIOREK(R)
- ☐ 609. DAVE LOPES(R)
- ☐ 610. CHARLIE HOUGH(R)
- ☐ 615. RON CEY(R)
- ☐ 621. JOE FERGUSON
- ☐ 639. WILLIE CRAWFORD

MILWAUKEE BREWERS

- ☐ 45. ELLIE RODRIGUEZ
- ☐ 71. JOHNNY BRIGGS
- ☐ 74. BILLY CHAMPION
- ☐ 92. JERRY BELL
- ☐ 127. TEAM CARD
- ☐ 152. DAVE MAY
- ☐ 176. CHUCK TAYLOR
- ☐ 212. JOE LAHOUD
- ☐ 231. BILL PARSONS
- ☐ 263. GEORGE SCOTT
- ☐ 286. FRANK LINZY
- ☐ 308. SKIP LOCKWOOD
- ☐ 332. JOHN FELSKE
- ☐ 366. BROCK DAVIS
- ☐ 386. DON MONEY
- ☐ 408. JIM COLBORN
- ☐ 427. RICK AUERBACH
- ☐ 451. JOHN VUKOVICH
- ☐ 526. OLLIE BROWN
- ☐ 547. BOBBY HEISE
- ☐ 568. RAY NEWMAN
- ☐ 582. DARRELL PORTER
- ☐ 609. PEDRO GARCIA(R)
- ☐ 628. JIM SLATON
- ☐ 646. CRANDALL(M) & COACHES

MINNESOTA TWINS

- □ 16. STEVE BRAUN
- □ 49. QUILICI(M) & COACHES
- □ 80. TONY OLIVA
- □ 98. DICK WOODSON
- □ 122. JIM STRICKLAND
- □ 148. DAVE GOLTZ
- □ 170. HARMON KILLEBREW
- □ 199. BERT BLYLEVEN
- □ 228. BOBBY DARWIN
- □ 259. JIM HOLT
- □ 284. GLENN BORGMANN
- □ 311. JOE DECKER
- □ 330. ROD CAREW
- □ 353. STEVE BRYE
- □ 358. JIM NETTLES
- □ 385. JIM PERRY
- □ 411. RAY CORBIN
- □ 443. DANNY THOMPSON
- □ 469. DAN MONZON
- □ 516. DANNY WALTON
- □ 530. JIM KAAT
- □ 555. BILL HANDS
- □ 577. ERIC SODERHOLM
- □ 598. PHIL ROOF
- □ 622. LARRY HISLE
- □ 638. KEN REYNOLDS
- □ 654. TEAM CARD

MONTREAL EXPOS

- □ 19. TIM FOLI
- □ 41. TOM WALKER
- □ 77. MIKE TORREZ
- □ 106. TERRY HUMPHREY
- □ 125. RON FAIRLY
- □ 149. RON HUNT
- □ 173. HAL BREEDEN
- □ 211. BALOR MOORE
- □ 232. KEN SINGLETON
- □ 254. BILL STONEMAN
- □ 281. MIKE JORGENSEN
- □ 307. BOOTS DAY
- □ 331. CARL MORTON
- □ 355. MIKE MARSHALL
- □ 377. MAUCH(M) & COACHES
- □ 401. CLYDE MASHORE
- □ 429. JIM FAIREY
- □ 457. JOHN STROHMAYER
- □ 484. ERNIE MCANALLY
- □ 505. BOB BAILEY
- □ 531. RON WOODS
- □ 576. TEAM CARD
- □ 592. JOHN BOCCABELLA
- □ 606. JORGE ROQUE(R)
- □ 607. PEPE FRIAS(R)
- □ 623. STEVE RENKO
- □ 642. JOSE LABOY

NEW YORK METS

- □ 4. JOHN MILNER
- □ 30. TUG MCGRAW
- □ 55. JON MATLACK
- □ 87. KEN BOSWELL
- □ 107. PHIL HENNIGAN
- □ 113. JERRY GROTE
- □ 137. JIM BEAUCHAMP
- □ 161. TED MARTINEZ
- □ 184. JERRY KOOSMAN
- □ 223. BUD HARRELSON
- □ 257. BERRA(M) & COACHES
- □ 283. RAY SADECKI
- □ 305. WILLIE MAYS
- □ 329. ED KRANEPOOL
- □ 350. TOM SEAVER
- □ 389. TEAM CARD
- □ 407. FELIX MILLAN
- □ 436. JIM MCANDREW
- □ 493. DUFFY DYER
- □ 525. JIM FREGOSI
- □ 540. CLEON JONES
- □ 562. WAYNE GARRETT
- □ 586. BILL SUDAKIS
- □ 610. HANK WEBB(R)
- □ 617. RICH CHILES
- □ 647. GEORGE STONE

NEW YORK YANKEES

- □ 25. ROY WHITE
- □ 46. LINDY MCDANIEL
- □ 82. FRITZ PETERSON
- □ 103. CELERINO SANCHEZ
- □ 116. HOUK(M) & COACHES
- □ 132. MATTY ALOU
- □ 142. THURMAN MUNSON
- □ 172. STEVE KLINE
- □ 198. HORACE CLARKE
- □ 240. BOBBY MURCER
- □ 265. GENE MICHAEL
- □ 293. BERNIE ALLEN
- □ 314. RON SWOBODA
- □ 371. MIKE KEKICH
- □ 394. SPARKY LYLE
- □ 419. CASEY COX
- □ 431. GERRY MOSES
- □ 462. RON BLOMBERG
- □ 479. HAL LANIER
- □ 498. GRAIG NETTLES
- □ 520. MEL STOTTLEMYRE
- □ 535. JOHN CALLISON
- □ 556. TEAM CARD
- □ 573. FRED BEENE
- □ 608. GEORGE MEDICH(R)
- □ 616. STEVE BLATERIC(R)
- □ 634. ALAN CLOSTER
- □ 650. FELIPE ALOU

OAKLAND A'S

- □ 13. GEORGE HENDRICK
- □ 38. MIKE EPSTEIN
- □ 60. KEN HOLTZMAN
- □ 84. ROLLIE FINGERS
- □ 155. SAL BANDO
- □ 179. WILLIAMS(M) & COACHES
- □ 214. DAVE HAMILTON
- □ 222. ROB GARDNER
- □ 234. BILL NORTH
- □ 235. JIM HUNTER
- □ 255. REGGIE JACKSON
- □ 274. DAROLD KNOWLES
- □ 295. BERT CAMPANERIS
- □ 315. JOHN ODOM
- □ 337. DAVE DUNCAN
- □ 360. JOE RUDI
- □ 382. MIKE HEGAN
- □ 406. PAUL LINDBLAD
- □ 430. VIDA BLUE
- □ 456. DICK GREEN
- □ 483. DAL MAXVILL
- □ 500. TEAM CARD
- □ 524. GENE TENACE
- □ 545. ORLANDO CEPEDA
- □ 563. LARRY HANEY
- □ 587. RICH MCKINNEY
- □ 605. GONZALO MARQUEZ(R)
- □ 625. ANGEL MANGUAL
- □ 652. TED KUBIAK

PHILADELPHIA PHILLIES

- □ 3. JIM LONBORG
- □ 6. MAC SCARCE
- □ 37. BILL ROBINSON
- □ 97. WILLIE MONTANEZ
- □ 119. LARRY BOWA
- □ 147. MIKE ANDERSON
- □ 166. TERRY HARMON
- □ 189. GREG LUZINSKI
- □ 227. WAYNE TWITCHELL
- □ 246. KEN SANDERS
- □ 271. TOM HUTTON
- □ 300. STEVE CARLTON
- □ 326. DARRELL BRANDON
- □ 405. CESAR TOVAR
- □ 424. DENNY DOYLE
- □ 444. KEN BRETT
- □ 454. TOM HALLER
- □ 467. MIKE RYAN
- □ 486. OZARK(M) & COACHES
- □ 509. JIM NASH
- □ 536. TEAM CARD
- □ 559. BARRY LERSCH
- □ 590. DERON JOHNSON
- □ 613. BOB BOONE(R)
- □ 615. MIKE SCHMIDT(R)
- □ 619. BILLY WILSON
- □ 632. DICK SELMA
- □ 659. JOSE PAGAN

PITTSBURGH PIRATES

- □ 2. RICH HEBNER
- □ 26. TEAM CARD
- □ 50. ROBERTO CLEMENTE
- □ 95. STEVE BLASS
- □ 117. RAMON HERNANDEZ
- □ 141. BRUCE KISON
- □ 163. VIC DAVALILLO
- □ 187. LUKE WALKER
- □ 225. AL OLIVER
- □ 250. MANNY SANGUILLEN
- □ 277. BOB L. MILLER
- □ 303. NELSON BRILES
- □ 333. GENE CLINES
- □ 348. RENNIE STENNETT
- □ 363. JACKIE HERNANDEZ
- □ 370. WILLIE STARGELL
- □ 397. DAVE CASH
- □ 422. BOB ROBERTSON
- □ 465. DAVE GIUSTI
- □ 499. BOB MOOSE
- □ 517. VIRDON(M) & COACHES
- □ 529. MILT MAY
- □ 575. DOCK ELLIS
- □ 611. RICHIE ZISK(R)
- □ 635. GENE ALLEY
- □ 657. BOB D. JOHNSON

ST. LOUIS CARDINALS

- □ 24. AL SANTORINI
- □ 47. LUIS MELENDEZ
- □ 85. TED SIMMONS
- □ 104. REGGIE CLEVELAND
- □ 128. TED SIZEMORE
- □ 153. AL HRABOSKY
- □ 171. BERNIE CARBO
- □ 190. BOB GIBSON
- □ 219. TEAM CARD
- □ 241. DWAIN ANDERSON
- □ 269. TIM MCCARVER
- □ 292. JOSE CRUZ
- □ 320. LOU BROCK
- □ 364. RICK WISE
- □ 383. DIEGO SEGUI
- □ 417. SCIPIO SPINKS
- □ 450. JOE TORRE
- □ 497. SCHOENDIENST(M) & CHS.
- □ 523. WAYNE GRANGER
- □ 548. DON DURHAM
- □ 567. BOB FENWICK
- □ 599. ED CROSBY
- □ 603. KEN REITZ(R)
- □ 607. RAY BUSSE(R)
- □ 649. RICH FOLKERS

SAN DIEGO PADRES

- □ 12. ZIMMER(M) & COACHES
- □ 32. FRED NORMAN
- □ 57. DERREL THOMAS
- □ 83. LERON LEE
- □ 112. GARY ROSS
- □ 133. DAVE W. ROBERTS
- □ 159. CLARENCE GASTON

- ☐ 182. MIKE CALDWELL
- ☐ 221. FRED KENDALL
- ☐ 244. ED ACOSTA
- ☐ 268. JERRY MORALES
- ☐ 294. STEVE ARLIN
- ☐ 316. TEAM CARD
- ☐ 340. NATE COLBERT
- ☐ 381. VICENTE ROMO
- ☐ 409. IVAN MURRELL
- ☐ 438. ENZO HERNANDEZ
- ☐ 461. MIKE CORKINS
- ☐ 488. DAVE CAMPBELL
- ☐ 513. DAVE MARSHALL
- ☐ 542. PAT CORRALES
- ☐ 583. BILL GREIF
- ☐ 602. RALPH GARCIA(R)
- ☐ 613. MIKE IVIE(R)
- ☐ 615. JOHN HILTON(R)
- ☐ 655. CLAY KIRBY

SAN FRANCISCO GIANTS

- ☐ 23. DAVE KINGMAN
- ☐ 43. RANDY MOFFITT
- ☐ 79. JIM WILLOUGHBY
- ☐ 101. KEN HENDERSON
- ☐ 121. DAVE RADER
- ☐ 145. BOBBY BONDS
- ☐ 167. STEVE STONE
- ☐ 197. ED GOODSON
- ☐ 236. TITO FUENTES
- ☐ 248. JERRY JOHNSON
- ☐ 252. FOX(M) & COACHES
- ☐ 273. CHRIS SPEIER
- ☐ 298. RON BRYANT
- ☐ 322. GARRY MADDOX
- ☐ 336. TOM BRADLEY
- ☐ 361. FRAN HEALY
- ☐ 387. JIM BARR
- ☐ 410. WILLIE MCCOVEY
- ☐ 434. TEAM CARD
- ☐ 459. JIMMY HOWARTH
- ☐ 480. JUAN MARICHAL
- ☐ 511. SAM MCDOWELL
- ☐ 538. JIM HART
- ☐ 557. BERNIE WILLIAMS
- ☐ 584. CHRIS ARNOLD
- ☐ 606. GARY MATTHEWS(R)
- ☐ 651. DON CARRITHERS

TEXAS RANGERS

- ☐ 7. TEAM CARD
- ☐ 27. BILL GOGOLEWSKI
- ☐ 58. MIKE PAUL
- ☐ 94. DICK BILLINGS
- ☐ 111. DAVE NELSON
- ☐ 138. HORACIO PINA
- ☐ 162. PETE BROBERG
- ☐ 186. BILL FAHEY
- ☐ 216. TOBY HARRAH
- ☐ 249. LARRY BIITTNER
- ☐ 276. JOE LOVITTO
- ☐ 299. TED FORD
- ☐ 321. RICH HINTON
- ☐ 352. DON STANHOUSE
- ☐ 378. LENNY RANDLE
- ☐ 398. RICH HAND
- ☐ 435. RICO CARTY
- ☐ 458. JIM MASON
- ☐ 489. JEFF BURROUGHS
- ☐ 512. DALTON JONES
- ☐ 549. HERZOG(M) & COACHES
- ☐ 564. MIKE THOMPSON
- ☐ 579. TOM GRIEVE
- ☐ 594. VIC HARRIS
- ☐ 601. RICK STELMASZEK(R)
- ☐ 603. BILL MCNULTY(R)
- ☐ 612. STEVE LAWSON(R)
- ☐ 640. DICK BOSMAN
- ☐ 658. ELLIOTT MADDOX

1974 TOPPS (660)
2 1/2" X 3 1/2"

ATLANTA BRAVES

- ☐ 1. HANK AARON
- ☐ 29. PHIL NIEKRO
- ☐ 45. DAVE A. JOHNSON
- ☐ 71. DANNY FRISELLA
- ☐ 93. ROD GILBREATH
- ☐ 140. DARRELL EVANS
- ☐ 164. TOM HOUSE
- ☐ 183. JOHNNY OATES
- ☐ 227. MIKE LUM
- ☐ 244. CARL MORTON
- ☐ 272. PAUL CASANOVA
- ☐ 298. RORIC HARRISON
- ☐ 320. DUSTY BAKER
- ☐ 346. RON REED
- ☐ 374. MARTY PEREZ
- ☐ 415. GARY GENTRY
- ☐ 439. NORM MILLER
- ☐ 457. CHUCK GOGGIN
- ☐ 483. TEAM CARD
- ☐ 504. JOE NIEKRO
- ☐ 526. FRANK TEPEDINO
- ☐ 544. RON SCHUELER
- ☐ 570. RALPH GARR
- ☐ 591. SONNY JACKSON
- ☐ 607. LEO FOSTER(R)
- ☐ 614. ADRIAN DEVINE
- ☐ 634. MATHEWS(M) & COACHES

BALTIMORE ORIOLES

- ☐ 16. TEAM CARD
- ☐ 40. JIM PALMER
- ☐ 68. GRANT JACKSON
- ☐ 92. PAUL BLAIR
- ☐ 109. BOB GRICH
- ☐ 137. AL BUMBRY
- ☐ 160. BROOKS ROBINSON
- ☐ 187. DON BAYLOR
- ☐ 235. DAVE MCNALLY
- ☐ 259. BOB REYNOLDS
- ☐ 282. DOYLE ALEXANDER
- ☐ 306. WEAVER(M) & COACHES
- ☐ 329. MARK BELANGER
- ☐ 353. RICH COGGINS
- ☐ 375. EARL WILLIAMS
- ☐ 396. TOMMY DAVIS
- ☐ 411. FRANK W. BAKER
- ☐ 436. DON HOOD
- ☐ 460. BOOG POWELL
- ☐ 488. ANDY ETCHEBARREN
- ☐ 509. JESSE JEFFERSON
- ☐ 534. EDDIE WATT
- ☐ 560. MIKE CUELLAR
- ☐ 585. MERV RETTENMUND
- ☐ 596. WAYNE GARLAND(R)
- ☐ 603. SERGIO ROBLES(R)
- ☐ 606. JIM FULLER(R)
- ☐ 648. TERRY CROWLEY

BOSTON RED SOX

- ☐ 33. DON NEWHAUSER
- ☐ 61. LUIS APARICIO
- ☐ 83. ORLANDO CEPEDA
- ☐ 84. RICK WISE
- ☐ 105. CARLTON FISK
- ☐ 113. DICK DRAGO
- ☐ 118. BILL LEE
- ☐ 167. LUIS TIANT
- ☐ 192. MARIO GUERRERO
- ☐ 219. DOUG GRIFFIN
- ☐ 247. RICK MILLER
- ☐ 280. CARL YASTRZEMSKI
- ☐ 301. BOB MONTGOMERY
- ☐ 325. TOMMY HARPER
- ☐ 351. DWIGHT EVANS
- ☐ 373. JOHN CURTIS
- ☐ 403. JOHNSON(M) & COACHES
- ☐ 427. BOBBY BOLIN
- ☐ 495. DICK MCAULIFFE
- ☐ 523. CECIL COOPER
- ☐ 543. DANNY CATER
- ☐ 567. TEAM CARD
- ☐ 590. ROGELIO MORET
- ☐ 596. DICK POLE(R)
- ☐ 609. RICO PETROCELLI
- ☐ 621. BERNIE CARBO
- ☐ 647. JUAN BENIQUEZ

CALIFORNIA ANGELS

- ☐ 20. NOLAN RYAN
- ☐ 37. DAVE SELLS
- ☐ 55. FRANK ROBINSON
- ☐ 76. MICKEY RIVERS
- ☐ 101. BOBBY VALENTINE
- ☐ 114. TEAM CARD
- ☐ 139. AURELIO MONTEAGUDO
- ☐ 188. RUDY MEOLI
- ☐ 210. BILL SINGER
- ☐ 243. BOB OLIVER
- ☐ 276. WINKLES(M) & COACHES
- ☐ 302. RUDY MAY
- ☐ 323. RICHIE SCHEINBLUM
- ☐ 347. SANDY ALOMAR
- ☐ 381. CHARLIE SANDS
- ☐ 405. ELLIE RODRIGUEZ
- ☐ 429. DICK LANGE
- ☐ 449. TOM MCCRAW
- ☐ 467. WINSTON LLENAS
- ☐ 490. VADA PINSON
- ☐ 512. JOE LAHOUD
- ☐ 532. SKIP LOCKWOOD
- ☐ 552. DENNY DOYLE
- ☐ 571. RICH HAND
- ☐ 594. LEROY STANTON
- ☐ 597. DAVE CHALK(R)
- ☐ 605. FRANK TANANA(R)
- ☐ 611. RICK STELMASZEK
- ☐ 625. OLLIE BROWN
- ☐ 650. MIKE EPSTEIN

CHICAGO CUBS

- ☐ 14. PAUL POPOVICH
- ☐ 38. DON KESSINGER
- ☐ 62. BOB LOCKER
- ☐ 110. BILLY WILLIAMS
- ☐ 136. RICK REUSCHEL
- ☐ 157. VIC HARRIS
- ☐ 161. RAY BURRIS
- ☐ 185. JOSE CARDENAL
- ☐ 211. TEAM CARD
- ☐ 258. JERRY MORALES
- ☐ 270. RON SANTO
- ☐ 295. RICK MONDAY
- ☐ 319. RANDY HUNDLEY
- ☐ 354. LOCKMAN(M) & COACHES
- ☐ 378. BURT HOOTON
- ☐ 399. MIKE PAUL

- ☐ 422. GONZALO MARQUEZ
- ☐ 452. GENE HISER
- ☐ 484. CARMEN FANZONE
- ☐ 502. DAVE LAROCHE
- ☐ 528. BILL BONHAM
- ☐ 562. JACK AKER
- ☐ 584. KEN RUDOLPH
- ☐ 598. JIM TYRONE(R)
- ☐ 600. BILL MADLOCK(R)
- ☐ 603. TOM LUNDSTEDT(R)
- ☐ 604. ANDY THORNTON(R)
- ☐ 607. DAVE ROSELLO(R)
- ☐ 616. LARRY GURA
- ☐ 640. MILT PAPPAS
- ☐ 656. ADRIAN GARRETT

CHICAGO WHITE SOX

- ☐ 22. CY ACOSTA
- ☐ 46. H. PAT KELLY
- ☐ 70. DICK ALLEN
- ☐ 96. JERRY HAIRSTON
- ☐ 120. WILBUR WOOD
- ☐ 147. BART JOHNSON
- ☐ 170. BILL MELTON
- ☐ 195. CARLOS MAY
- ☐ 221. TANNER(M) & COACHES
- ☐ 254. STAN BAHNSEN
- ☐ 286. TONY MUSER
- ☐ 310. TERRY FORSTER
- ☐ 357. BUDDY BRADFORD
- ☐ 376. JORGE ORTA
- ☐ 394. KEN HENDERSON
- ☐ 416. TEAM CARD
- ☐ 438. ED HERRMANN
- ☐ 440. JIM KAAT
- ☐ 462. LUIS ALVARADO
- ☐ 486. STEVE STONE
- ☐ 501. EDDIE LEON
- ☐ 519. BILL SHARP
- ☐ 542. RICH GOSSAGE
- ☐ 557. JIM MCGLOTHLIN
- ☐ 582. BUCKY DENT
- ☐ 601. BRIAN DOWNING(R)
- ☐ 605. KEN FRAILING(R)
- ☐ 615. JOHNNY JETER
- ☐ 641. CHUCK BRINKMAN

CINCINNATI REDS

- ☐ 10. JOHNNY BENCH
- ☐ 34. ANDY KOSCO
- ☐ 59. ROSS GRIMSLEY
- ☐ 85. JOE MORGAN
- ☐ 111. CLAY CARROLL
- ☐ 134. DENIS MENKE
- ☐ 158. JACK BILLINGHAM
- ☐ 181. CESAR GERONIMO
- ☐ 230. TONY PEREZ
- ☐ 248. TOM HALL
- ☐ 277. GARY NOLAN
- ☐ 287. CLAY KIRBY
- ☐ 300. PETE ROSE
- ☐ 326. ANDERSON(M) & CHS.
- ☐ 341. DAN DRIESSEN
- ☐ 362. HAL KING
- ☐ 385. DON GULLETT
- ☐ 410. PEDRO BORBON
- ☐ 435. DAVE CONCEPCION
- ☐ 459. TEAM CARD
- ☐ 491. ROGER NELSON
- ☐ 507. LARRY STAHL
- ☐ 524. BILL PLUMMER
- ☐ 559. DARREL CHANEY
- ☐ 581. FRED NORMAN
- ☐ 598. KEN GRIFFEY(R)
- ☐ 601. ED ARMBRISTER(R)
- ☐ 608. DICK BANEY(R)
- ☐ 622. PHIL GAGLIANO
- ☐ 646. GEORGE FOSTER

CLEVELAND INDIANS

- ☐ 13. TOM HILGENDORF
- ☐ 35. GAYLORD PERRY
- ☐ 58. CHARLIE SPIKES
- ☐ 81. FRANK DUFFY
- ☐ 128. JOHN ELLIS
- ☐ 152. OSCAR GAMBLE
- ☐ 176. JOHN LOWENSTEIN
- ☐ 199. MIKE KEKICH
- ☐ 231. DICK TIDROW
- ☐ 257. BUDDY BELL
- ☐ 284. DAVE DUNCAN
- ☐ 303. GEORGE HENDRICK
- ☐ 327. TOM TIMMERMANN
- ☐ 359. BRENT STROM
- ☐ 384. CHRIS CHAMBLISS
- ☐ 418. WALT WILLIAMS
- ☐ 441. TOM RAGLAND
- ☐ 465. DICK BOSMAN
- ☐ 499. RUSTY TORRES
- ☐ 521. ASPROMONTE(M) & CHS.
- ☐ 541. TEAM CARD
- ☐ 565. MILT WILCOX
- ☐ 586. JACK BROHAMER
- ☐ 606. TOMMY SMITH(R)
- ☐ 617. TED FORD
- ☐ 638. KEN SANDERS

DETROIT TIGERS

- ☐ 9. MICKEY LOLICH
- ☐ 24. JOHN HILLER
- ☐ 48. DICK SHARON
- ☐ 72. AURELIO RODRIGUEZ
- ☐ 94. TEAM CARD
- ☐ 115. WILLIE HORTON
- ☐ 138. ED BRINKMAN
- ☐ 162. BILL FREEHAN
- ☐ 186. FRED SCHERMAN
- ☐ 215. AL KALINE
- ☐ 240. JOE COLEMAN
- ☐ 256. JIM NORTHRUP
- ☐ 292. CHUCK SEELBACH
- ☐ 316. JIM PERRY
- ☐ 367. NORM CASH
- ☐ 389. GATES BROWN
- ☐ 409. IKE BROWN
- ☐ 433. LERRIN LAGROW
- ☐ 482. BOB DIDIER
- ☐ 506. ED FARMER
- ☐ 530. MICKEY STANLEY
- ☐ 555. WOODIE FRYMAN
- ☐ 578. RALPH HOUK(M)
- ☐ 596. FRED HOLDSWORTH(R)
- ☐ 597. JOHN GAMBLE(R)
- ☐ 600. RON CASH(R)
- ☐ 600. REGGIE SANDERS(R)
- ☐ 604. JOHN KNOX(R)

HOUSTON ASTROS

- ☐ 21. BOB GALLAGHER
- ☐ 31. GOMEZ(M) & COACHES
- ☐ 43. JIM WYNN
- ☐ 67. TOMMY HELMS
- ☐ 91. KEN FORSCH
- ☐ 154. TEAM CARD
- ☐ 177. DAVE A. ROBERTS
- ☐ 200. CESAR CEDENO
- ☐ 224. ROGER METZGER
- ☐ 256. TOM GRIFFIN
- ☐ 279. JIM CRAWFORD
- ☐ 293. MILT MAY
- ☐ 304. DON WILSON
- ☐ 328. SKIP JUTZE
- ☐ 370. BOB WATSON
- ☐ 395. DOUG RADER
- ☐ 428. GARY SUTHERLAND
- ☐ 458. JIM RAY
- ☐ 500. LEE MAY
- ☐ 522. J.R. RICHARD
- ☐ 556. DAVE CAMPBELL
- ☐ 579. CECIL UPSHAW
- ☐ 635. JOHN EDWARDS
- ☐ 660. LARRY DIERKER

KANSAS CITY ROYALS

- ☐ 17. DOUG BIRD
- ☐ 41. BOBBY FLOYD
- ☐ 65. AMOS OTIS
- ☐ 88. FREDDIE PATEK
- ☐ 150. JOHN MAYBERRY
- ☐ 166. MCKEON(M) & COACHES
- ☐ 191. AL FITZMORRIS
- ☐ 225. PAUL SPLITTORFF
- ☐ 238. FRAN HEALY
- ☐ 262. ED KIRKPATRICK
- ☐ 278. COOKIE ROJAS
- ☐ 308. BRUCE DAL CANTON
- ☐ 343. TEAM CARD
- ☐ 365. STEVE BUSBY
- ☐ 390. LOU PINIELLA
- ☐ 407. JIM WOHLFORD
- ☐ 431. GENE GARBER
- ☐ 454. KURT BEVACQUA
- ☐ 493. JOE HOERNER
- ☐ 514. PAUL SCHAAL
- ☐ 537. STEVE MINGORI
- ☐ 563. HAL MCRAE
- ☐ 583. MARTY PATTIN
- ☐ 596. MARK LITTELL(R)
- ☐ 604. FRANK WHITE(R)
- ☐ 627. CARL TAYLOR
- ☐ 652. GAIL HOPKINS

LOS ANGELES DODGERS

- ☐ 42. CLAUDE OSTEEN
- ☐ 64. DOUG RAU
- ☐ 86. JOE FERGUSON
- ☐ 112. DAVE LOPES
- ☐ 127. TOM PACIOREK
- ☐ 144. ALSTON(M) & COACHES
- ☐ 165. WILLIE DAVIS
- ☐ 189. JIM BREWER
- ☐ 220. DON SUTTON
- ☐ 239. BILL RUSSEL
- ☐ 267. ANDY MESSERSMITH
- ☐ 289. RICK AUERBACH
- ☐ 315. RON CEY
- ☐ 348. PETE RICHERT
- ☐ 368. MANNY MOTA
- ☐ 408. CHARLIE HOUGH
- ☐ 434. KEN MCMULLEN
- ☐ 451. TOMMY JOHN
- ☐ 480. WILLIE CRAWFORD
- ☐ 505. BILL BUCKNER
- ☐ 551. VON JOSHUA
- ☐ 575. STEVE GARVEY
- ☐ 593. STEVE YEAGER
- ☐ 599. GREG SHANAHAN(R)
- ☐ 620. AL DOWNING
- ☐ 643. TEAM CARD
- ☐ 658. LEE LACY

MILWAUKEE BREWERS

- ☐ 12. DAVE MAY
- ☐ 27. GEORGE SCOTT
- ☐ 51. BOBBY HEISE
- ☐ 75. JIM COLBORN
- ☐ 99. CRANDALL(M) & COACHES
- ☐ 124. BOB COLUCCIO
- ☐ 142. PEDRO GARCIA
- ☐ 163. KEN BERRY
- ☐ 171. EDUARDO RODRIGUEZ
- ☐ 194. DARRELL PORTER
- ☐ 218. JOHNNY BRIGGS
- ☐ 261. JERRY BELL
- ☐ 288. GORMAN THOMAS
- ☐ 314. TEAM CARD
- ☐ 349. JOHN VUKOVICH
- ☐ 371. JIM SLATON
- ☐ 391. BILLY CHAMPION
- ☐ 413. DON MONEY

☐ 497. BOBBY MITCHELL
☐ 525. CLYDE WRIGHT
☐ 554. TIM JOHNSON
☐ 574. BILL PARSONS
☐ 603. CHARLIE MOORE(R)
☐ 605. KEVIN KOBEL(R)
☐ 606. WILBUR HOWARD(R)
☐ 631. STEVE BARBER

MINNESOTA TWINS

☐ 26. BILL CAMPBELL
☐ 50. ROD CAREW
☐ 74. TEAM CARD
☐ 98. BERT BLYLEVEN
☐ 122. JIM HOLT
☐ 143. DICK WOODSON
☐ 168. DANNY THOMPSON
☐ 190. TONY OLIVA
☐ 232. STEVE BRYE
☐ 249. GEORGE MITTERWALD
☐ 271. BILL HANDS
☐ 296. RAY CORBIN
☐ 321. STEVE BRAUN
☐ 366. LARRY HISLE
☐ 388. PHIL ROOF
☐ 400. HARMON KILLEBREW
☐ 421. DAN FIFE
☐ 447. QUILICI(M) & COACHES
☐ 469. JOE DECKER
☐ 481. JERRY TERRELL
☐ 503. ERIC SODERHOLM
☐ 527. BOBBY DARWIN
☐ 547. GLENN BORGMANN
☐ 573. MIKE ADAMS
☐ 592. ED BANE
☐ 602. DAN VOSSLER(R)
☐ 605. VIC ALBURY(R)
☐ 613. DAN MONZON
☐ 636. DAVE GOLTZ
☐ 659. JOE LIS

MONTREAL EXPOS

☐ 25. KEN SINGLETON
☐ 49. STEVE RENKO
☐ 73. MIKE MARSHALL
☐ 97. BOB BAILEY
☐ 121. LARRY LINTZ
☐ 146. RON FAIRLY
☐ 169. STEVE ROGERS
☐ 193. TOM WALKER
☐ 217. TIM FOLI
☐ 253. JOHN BOCCABELLA
☐ 275. RON HUNT
☐ 297. HAL BREEDEN
☐ 322. ERNIE MCANALLY
☐ 352. BILL STONEMAN
☐ 377. RON WOODS
☐ 412. CHUCK TAYLOR
☐ 437. JIM LYTTLE
☐ 453. BALOR MOORE
☐ 468. PEPE FRIAS
☐ 485. FELIPE ALOU
☐ 508. TEAM CARD
☐ 531. MAUCH(M) & COACHES
☐ 549. MIKE JORGENSEN
☐ 568. MIKE TORREZ
☐ 589. BOOTS DAY
☐ 600. JIM COX(R)
☐ 603. BARRY FOOTE(R)
☐ 653. BOB STINSON

NEW YORK METS

☐ 8. GEORGE THEODORE
☐ 56. TEAM CARD
☐ 80. TOM SEAVER
☐ 106. HARRY PARKER
☐ 132. FELIX MILLAN
☐ 153. JON MATLACK
☐ 179. BERRA(M) & COACHES
☐ 216. RAY SADECKI
☐ 234. JOHN MILNER
☐ 245. CLEON JONES
☐ 265. TUG MCGRAW
☐ 291. DON HAHN
☐ 311. JERRY GROTE
☐ 356. JERRY KOOSMAN
☐ 380. BUD HARRELSON
☐ 397. GEORGE STONE
☐ 424. JIM BEAUCHAMP
☐ 448. RON HODGES
☐ 487. TED MARTINEZ
☐ 510. WAYNE GARRETT
☐ 536. DUFFY DYER
☐ 561. ED KRANEPOOL
☐ 602. CRAIG SWAN(R)
☐ 608. BOB APODACA(R)
☐ 624. BOB L. MILLER
☐ 629. RUSTY STAUB
☐ 645. KEN BOSWELL

NEW YORK YANKEES

☐ 19. GERRY MOSES
☐ 44. MEL STOTTLEMYRE
☐ 66. SPARKY LYLE
☐ 90. BOBBY MURCER
☐ 117. RON BLOMBERG
☐ 135. ROY WHITE
☐ 159. JIM HART
☐ 182. LINDY MCDANIEL
☐ 229. FRITZ PETERSON
☐ 251. GRAIG NETTLES
☐ 274. FRED BEENE
☐ 299. GENE MICHAEL
☐ 324. STEVE KLINE
☐ 340. THURMAN MUNSON
☐ 363. TEAM CARD
☐ 398. DUKE SIMS
☐ 423. FRED STANLEY
☐ 445. GEORGE MEDICH
☐ 463. PAT DOBSON
☐ 517. MIKE HEGAN
☐ 529. HORACE CLARKE
☐ 550. SAM MCDOWELL
☐ 569. RICK DEMPSEY
☐ 588. HAL LANIER
☐ 601. RICH BLADT(R)
☐ 606. OTTO VELEZ(R)
☐ 623. CELERINO SANCHEZ
☐ 644. WAYNE GRANGER

OAKLAND A'S

☐ 7. JIM HUNTER
☐ 57. DAROLD KNOWLES
☐ 79. GENE TENACE
☐ 103. SAL BANDO
☐ 130. REGGIE JACKSON
☐ 141. PAT BOURQUE
☐ 155. BERT CAMPANERIS
☐ 180. KEN HOLTZMAN
☐ 212. ROLLIE FINGERS
☐ 228. TED KUBIAK
☐ 246. TEAM CARD
☐ 264. JOE RUDI
☐ 290. VIDA BLUE
☐ 312. DERON JOHNSON
☐ 345. BILL NORTH
☐ 369. PAUL LINDBLAD
☐ 392. DICK GREEN
☐ 420. RAY FOSSE
☐ 444. VIC DAVALILLO
☐ 461. JOHN ODOM
☐ 516. HORACIO PINA
☐ 545. BILLY CONIGLIARO
☐ 597. MANNY TRILLO(R)
☐ 602. GLENN ABBOTT(R)
☐ 633. DAVE HAMILTON
☐ 654. JESUS ALOU

PHIADELPHIA PHILLIES

☐ 23. CRAIG ROBINSON
☐ 47. DICK RUTHVEN
☐ 69. DEL UNSER
☐ 95. STEVE CARLTON
☐ 119. OZARK(M) & COACHES
☐ 131. BOB BOONE
☐ 149. MAC SCARCE
☐ 174. BILL ROBINSON
☐ 198. DAVE CASH
☐ 214. BILLY GRABARKEWITZ
☐ 255. LARRY BOWA
☐ 283. MIKE SCHMIDT
☐ 313. BARRY LERSCH
☐ 342. JIM LONBORG
☐ 360. GREG LUZINSKI
☐ 383. TEAM CARD
☐ 419. WAYNE TWITCHELL
☐ 443. TOM HUTTON
☐ 492. MIKE ROGODZINSKI
☐ 515. WILLIE MONTANEZ
☐ 538. CESAR TOVAR
☐ 564. MIKE RYAN
☐ 587. LARRY CHRISTENSON
☐ 599. RON DIORIO(R)
☐ 608. MIKE WALLACE(R)
☐ 619. MIKE ANDERSON
☐ 632. GEORGE CULVER
☐ 642. TERRY HARMON

PITTSBURGH PIRATES

☐ 28. MANNY SANGUILLEN
☐ 52. AL OLIVER
☐ 82. DAVE GIUSTI
☐ 100. WILLIE STARGELL
☐ 116. JERRY REUSS
☐ 123. NELSON BRILES
☐ 145. DOCK ELLIS
☐ 172. GENE CLINES
☐ 222. RAMON HERNANDEZ
☐ 237. KEN BRETT
☐ 252. DAVE PARKER
☐ 269. BOB D. JOHNSON
☐ 317. RICHIE ZISK
☐ 358. DAL MAXVILL
☐ 382. BOB MOOSE
☐ 402. JIM ROOKER
☐ 426. RENNIE STENNETT
☐ 450. RICH HEBNER
☐ 489. MURTAUGH(M) & COACHES
☐ 513. JIM CAMPANIS
☐ 540. BOB ROBERTSON
☐ 566. JACKIE HERNANDEZ
☐ 595. STEVE BLASS
☐ 598. DAVE AUGUSTINE(R)
☐ 607. FRANK TAVERAS(R)
☐ 612. LUKE WALKER
☐ 626. TEAM CARD
☐ 649. FERNANDO GONZALEZ

ST. LOUIS CARDINALS

☐ 15. JOE TORRE
☐ 36. TEAM CARD
☐ 60. LOU BROCK
☐ 108. AL HRABOSKY
☐ 151. DIEGO SEGUI
☐ 175. REGGIE CLEVELAND
☐ 209. TED SIZEMORE
☐ 236. SCHOENDIENST(M) & CHS.
☐ 260. TED SIMMONS
☐ 285. REGGIE SMITH
☐ 307. LUIS MELENDEZ
☐ 350. BOB GIBSON
☐ 372. KEN REITZ
☐ 393. ORLANDO PENA
☐ 417. RICH FOLKERS
☐ 442. ALAN FOSTER
☐ 464. JOSE CRUZ
☐ 496. TOM MURPHY
☐ 520. TIM MCCARVER
☐ 548. SONNY SIEBERT
☐ 576. SCIPIO SPINKS
☐ 601. BAKE MCBRIDE(R)
☐ 604. TERRY HUGHES(R)
☐ 607. TOM HEINTZELMAN(R)
☐ 630. TOMMIE AGEE
☐ 655. MIKE TYSON

SAN DIEGO PADRES

☐ 32. JOHN GRUBB*
☐ 53. FRED KENDALL*
☐ 77. RICH TROEDSON*
☐ 102. BILL GREIF*
☐ 125. NATE COLBERT*
☐ 148. DAVE HILTON*
☐ 173. RANDY JONES*
☐ 197. VICENTE ROMO*
☐ 226. TEAM CARD*
☐ 241. GLENN BECKERT*
☐ 250. WILLIE MCCOVEY*
☐ 309. DAVE W. ROBERTS*
☐ 364. CLARENCE GASTON*
☐ 387. RICH MORALES*

* Cards appear with both San Diego Padres and Washington National League Identifications.

- □ 406. STEVE ARLIN
- □ 430. MATTY ALOU
- □ 456. DAVE WINFIELD
- □ 498. PAT CORRALES
- □ 518. DERREL THOMAS
- □ 535. BOB TOLAN
- □ 546. MIKE CORKINS
- □ 572. ENZO HERNANDEZ
- □ 599. DAVE FREISLEBEN(R)*
- □ 628. IVAN MURRELL
- □ 651. LERON LEE

SAN FRANCISCO GIANTS

- □ 18. GARY THOMASSON
- □ 30. BOBBY BONDS
- □ 54. ELIAS SOSA
- □ 78. FOX(M) & COACHES
- □ 104. RON BRYANT
- □ 129. CHRIS SPEIER
- □ 156. RANDY MOFFITT
- □ 178. GARRY MADDOX
- □ 213. DAVE RADER
- □ 233. JIM BARR
- □ 281. TEAM CARD
- □ 305. TITO FUENTES
- □ 330. JUAN MARICHAL
- □ 344. MIKE CALDWELL
- □ 361. DON CARRITHERS
- □ 386. GARY MATTHEWS
- □ 404. JIM HOWARTH
- □ 432. CHRIS ARNOLD
- □ 455. TOM BRADLEY
- □ 494. ED GOODSON
- □ 533. MIKE PHILLIPS
- □ 553. JIM WILLOUGHBY
- □ 577. MIKE SADEK
- □ 598. STEVE ONTIVEROS(R)
- □ 599. FRANK RICELLI(R)
- □ 608. JOHN D'ACQUISTO(R)
- □ 610. DAVE KINGMAN

TEXAS RANGERS

- □ 11. JIM BIBBY
- □ 39. KEN SUAREZ
- □ 63. BILL SUDAKIS
- □ 87. FERGIE JENKINS
- □ 89. JACKIE BROWN
- □ 107. ALEX JOHNSON
- □ 133. DAVID CLYDE
- □ 184. TEAM CARD
- □ 196. JIM FREGOSI
- □ 223. JEFF BURROUGHS
- □ 242. BILL GOGOLEWSKI
- □ 268. TOM GRIEVE
- □ 294. STEVE FOUCAULT
- □ 318. JIM MERRITT
- □ 355. DAVE NELSON
- □ 379. MARTIN(M) & COACHES
- □ 401. ELLIOTT MADDOX
- □ 425. PETE BROBERG
- □ 446. LEN RANDLE
- □ 466. DICK BILLINGS
- □ 511. TOBY HARRAH
- □ 539. LLOYD ALLEN
- □ 558. BILL FAHEY
- □ 580. JIM SPENCER
- □ 597. PETE MACKANIN(R)
- □ 602. RICK HENNINGER(R)
- □ 618. JIM MASON
- □ 639. JOE LOVITTO
- □ 657. JIM SHELLENBACK

1974 TOPPS TRADED (44) 2 1/2" X 3 1/2"

ATLANTA BRAVES

- □ 23T. CRAIG ROBINSON
- □ 313T. BARRY LERSCH

BALTIMORE ORIOLES

- □ 59T. ROSS GRIMSLEY

BOSTON RED SOX

- □ 151T. DIEGO SEGUI
- □ 175T. REGGIE CLEVELAND
- □ 330T. JUAN MARICHAL

CALIFORNIA ANGELS

NO CARDS ISSUED

CHICAGO CUBS

- □ 249T. GEORGE MITTERWALD
- □ 486T. STEVE STONE
- □ 516T. HORACIO PINA

CHICAGO WHITE SOX

- □ 270T. RON SANTO

CINCINNATI REDS

- □ 585T. MERV RETTENMUND

CLEVELAND INDIANS

- □ 269T. BOB JOHNSON
- □ 579T. CECIL UPSHAW

DETROIT TIGERS

- □ 428T. GARY SUTHERLAND
- □ 458T. JIM RAY
- □ 612T. LUKE WALKER

HOUSTON ASTROS

- □ 42T. CLAUDE OSTEEN
- □ 186T. FRED SCHERMAN

KANSAS CITY ROYALS

- □ 123T. NELSON BRILES
- □ 182T. LINDY MCDANIEL
- □ 649T. FERNANDO GONZALEZ

LOS ANGELES DODGERS

- □ 43T. JIM WYNN
- □ 73T. MIKE MARSHALL
- □ 630T. TOMMIE AGEE

MILWAUKEE BREWERS

- □ 485T. FELIPE ALOU
- □ 496T. TOM MURPHY

MINNESOTA TWINS

- □ 319T. RANDY HUNDLEY

MONTREAL EXPOS

- □ 165T. WILLIE DAVIS

NEW YORK METS

NO CARDS ISSUED

NEW YORK YANKEES

- □ 63T. BILL SUDAKIS
- □ 390T. LOU PINIELLA
- □ 618T. JIM MASON

OAKLAND A'S

- □ 62T. BOB LOCKER

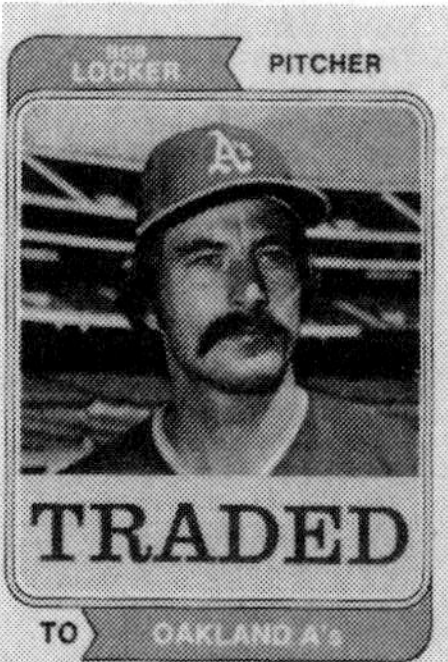

PHILADELPHIA PHILLIES

- □ 139T. AURELIO MONTEAGUDO
- □ 534T. EDDIE WATT
- □ 544T. RON SCHUELER

PITTSBURGH PIRATES

- □ 262T. ED KIRKPATRICK
- □ 454T. KURT BEVACQUA

ST. LOUIS CARDINALS

- □ 51T. BOBBY HEISE
- □ 348T. PETE RICHERT
- □ 373T. JOHN CURTIS

SAN DIEGO PADRES

NO CARDS ISSUED

SAN FRANCISCO GIANTS

NO CARDS ISSUED

TEXAS RANGERS

- □ 538T. CESAR TOVAR
- □ 616T. LARRY GURA
- □ 648T. TERRY CROWLEY

1975 TOPPS (660)
2 1/2" X 3 1/2"

1975 TOPPS MINIS (660)
2 1/4" X 3 1/8"

ATLANTA BRAVES

- □ 9. FRANK TEPEDINO
- □ 33. DUSTY BAKER
- □ 57. DAVE A. JOHNSON
- □ 81. RON REED
- □ 105. BUZZ CAPRA
- □ 130. PHIL NIEKRO
- □ 154. MIKE LUM
- □ 177. VIC CORRELL
- □ 237. CARL MORTON
- □ 262. ROWLAND OFFICE
- □ 287. RORIC HARRISON
- □ 319. JOHNNY OATES
- □ 367. CRAIG ROBINSON
- □ 393. GARY GENTRY
- □ 394. LARVELL BLANKS
- □ 418. LEO FOSTER
- □ 427. CLARENCE GASTON
- □ 431. ROD GILBREATH
- □ 442. MAXIMINO LEON
- □ 475. DARRELL EVANS
- □ 499. MARTY PEREZ
- □ 525. TOM HOUSE
- □ 550. RALPH GARR
- □ 589. TEAM & KING(M)
- □ 595. JOE NIEKRO
- □ 603. LEW KRAUSSE
- □ 618. JAMIE EASTERLY(R)
- □ 633. PAUL CASANOVA
- □ 650. DAVE MAY

BALTIMORE ORIOLES

- □ 26. DAVE MCNALLY
- □ 50. BROOKS ROBINSON
- □ 74. MARK BELANGER
- □ 97. EARL WILLIAMS
- □ 117. TEAM & WEAVER(M)
- □ 142. BOB REYNOLDS
- □ 167. RICH COGGINS
- □ 225. BOB GRICH
- □ 247. ENOS CABELL
- □ 275. PAUL BLAIR
- □ 303. GRANT JACKSON
- □ 335. JIM PALMER
- □ 358. AL BUMBRY
- □ 382. DON BAYLOR
- □ 410. MIKE CUELLER
- □ 458. ROSS GRIMSLEY
- □ 491. DOYLE ALEXANDER
- □ 516. DON HOOD
- □ 539. JESSE JERRERSON
- □ 564. TOMMY DAVIS
- □ 583. ANDY ETCHEBARREN
- □ 594. JIM FULLER
- □ 609. ELLIE HENDRICKS
- □ 614. DYAR MILLER(R)
- □ 617. DOUG DECINCES(R)
- □ 625. BOOG POWELL
- □ 641. JIM NORTHRUP
- □ 657. BOB OLIVER

BOSTON RED SOX

- □ 8. ROGELIO MORET
- □ 32. REGGIE CLEVELAND
- □ 56. RICK WISE
- □ 80. CARLTON FISK
- □ 103. RICK MILLER
- □ 128. BILL LEE
- □ 152. MARIO GUERRERO
- □ 172. TEAM & JOHNSON(M)
- □ 232. DIEGO SEGUI
- □ 255. DWIGHT EVANS
- □ 280. CARL YASTRZEMSKI
- □ 302. RICK BURLESON
- □ 333. DICK DRAGO
- □ 356. RICO PETROCELLI
- □ 379. BERNIE CARBO
- □ 430. LUIS TIANT
- □ 454. DOUG GRIFFIN
- □ 489. CECIL COOPER
- □ 513. DICK POLE
- □ 537. TOMMY HARPER
- □ 559. BOB MONTGOMERY
- □ 586. TIM MCCARVER
- □ 601. JUAN BENIQUEZ
- □ 612. TERRY HUGHES
- □ 616. JIM RICE(R)
- □ 622. FRED LYNN(R)
- □ 645. DANNY CATER

CALIFORNIA ANGELS

- □ 16. FRANK TANANA
- □ 40. BILL SINGER
- □ 64. DAVE CHALK
- □ 88. TOM EGAN
- □ 114. DICK LANGE
- □ 139. HORACIO PINA
- □ 164. MICKEY RIVERS
- □ 187. DENNY DOYLE
- □ 215. BOBBY VALENTINE
- □ 236. TEAM & WILLIAMS(M)
- □ 261. ANDY HASSLER
- □ 285. ELLIE RODRIGUEZ
- □ 317. JOE LAHOUD
- □ 342. LEROY STANTON
- □ 366. KEN SANDERS
- □ 392. BRUCE BOCHTE
- □ 417. SKIP LOCKWOOD
- □ 441. BOBBY HEISE
- □ 476. ED FIGUEROA
- □ 500. NOLAN RYAN
- □ 524. JOHN DOHERTY
- □ 533. RUDY MEOLI
- □ 548. CHARLIE SANDS
- □ 573. ORLANDO PENA
- □ 597. WINSTON LLENAS
- □ 632. MORRIS NETTLES
- □ 635. CHUCK DOBSON

CHICAGO CUBS

- □ 15. JOSE CARDENAL
- □ 39. ANDY THRONTON
- □ 63. STEVE SWISHER
- □ 85. BILL BONHAM
- □ 104. BILL MADLOCK
- □ 129. RICK MONDAY
- □ 153. RICK REUSCHEL
- □ 176. BURT HOOTON
- □ 233. BILLY GRABARKEWITZ
- □ 258. DAVE LAROCHE
- □ 282. JERRY MORALES
- □ 315. DON KESSINGER
- □ 338. RICK STELMASZEK
- □ 352. DAROLD KNOWLES
- □ 363. CARMEN FANZONE
- □ 388. STEVE STONE
- □ 411. GEORGE MITTERWALD
- □ 434. BOB LOCKER
- □ 436. KEN FRAILING
- □ 469. TOM DETTORE
- □ 494. PETE LACOCK
- □ 519. JIM TOOD
- □ 566. RAY BURRIS
- □ 587. CHRIS WARD
- □ 604. OSCAR ZAMORA
- □ 617. MANNY TRILLO(R)
- □ 638. TEAM & MARSHALL(M)
- □ 658. VIC HARRIS

CHICAGO WHITE SOX

- □ 11. BILL MELTON
- □ 35. RON SANTO
- □ 59. KEN HENDERSON
- □ 82. H. PAT KELLY
- □ 110. WILBUR WOOD
- □ 137. TERRY FORSTER
- □ 161. STAN BAHNSEN
- □ 184. JORGE ORTA
- □ 219. ED HERRMANN
- □ 243. JIM KAAT
- □ 276. TEAM & TANNER(M)
- □ 299. BUCKY DENT
- □ 327. JERRY HAIRSTON
- □ 348. TONY MUSER
- □ 373. BILL SHARP
- □ 400. DICK ALLEN
- □ 422. BRIAN DOWNING
- □ 446. BART JOHNSON
- □ 480. CARLOS MAY
- □ 504. BUDDY BRADFORD
- □ 528. EDDIE LEON
- □ 554. RICH GOSSAGE
- □ 572. ROGER NELSON
- □ 579. SKIP PITLOCK
- □ 614. JACK KUCEK(R)
- □ 619. NYLS NYMAN(R)
- □ 624. JIM OTTEN(R)
- □ 634. CY ACOSTA
- □ 653. LEE RICHARD

CINCINNATI REDS

- □ 17. DAVE CONCEPCION
- □ 41. CESAR GERONIMO
- □ 65. DON GULLETT
- □ 87. GEORGE FOSTER
- □ 108. TOM HALL
- □ 133. DAN DRIESSEN
- □ 157. PEDRO BORBON
- □ 180. JOE MORGAN
- □ 235. JACK BILLINGHAM
- □ 260. JOHNNY BENCH
- □ 284. KEN GRIFFEY
- □ 320. PETE ROSE
- □ 345. CLAY CARROLL
- □ 369. MERV RETTENMUND
- □ 396. FRED NORMAN
- □ 423. CLAY KIRBY
- □ 447. TERRY CROWLEY
- □ 481. WILL MCENANEY
- □ 507. TOM CARROLL
- □ 531. TEAM & ANDERSON(M)
- □ 560. TONY PEREZ
- □ 562. GARY NOLAN
- □ 581. DARREL CHANEY
- □ 602. JOHN VUKOVICH
- □ 615. PAT DARCY(R)
- □ 621. RAWLY EASTWICK(R)
- □ 622. ED ARMBRISTER(R)
- □ 656. BILL PLUMMER

CLEVELAND INDIANS

- □ 14. MILT WILCOX
- □ 38. BUDDY BELL
- □ 62. FRITZ PETERSON

□ 86. JOE LIS
□ 109. GEORGE HENDRICK
□ 135. CHARLIE SPIKES
□ 159. STEVE ARLIN
□ 181. FRED BEENE
□ 213. OSCAR GAMBLE
□ 238. DAVE DUNCAN
□ 263. JIM PERRY
□ 288. BRUCE ELLINGSEN
□ 331. TEAM & ROBINSON(M)
□ 354. DICK BOSMAN
□ 377. TOM HILGENDORF
□ 403. TOM BUSKEY
□ 424. JOHN LOWENSTEIN
□ 448. FRANK DUFFY
□ 482. TOM MCCRAW
□ 506. LERON LEE
□ 530. GAYLORD PERRY
□ 552. JACK BROHAMER
□ 580. FRANK ROBINSON
□ 605. JOHN ELLIS
□ 619. TOMMY SMITH(R)
□ 621. JIM KERN(R)
□ 639. STEVE KLINE
□ 655. RICO CARTY

DETROIT TIGERS

□ 18. TEAM & HOUK(M)
□ 42. JOE COLEMAN
□ 66. WILLIE HORTON
□ 89. JIM RAY
□ 116. LERRIN LAGROW
□ 141. MICKEY STANLEY
□ 166. WOODIE FRYMAN
□ 221. AURELIO RODRIGUEZ
□ 245. MICKEY LOLICH
□ 271. JERRY MOSES
□ 293. DICK SHARON
□ 323. FRED HOLDSWORTH
□ 344. BEN OGLIVIE
□ 371. GATES BROWN
□ 397. BILL FREEHAN
□ 415. JOHN HILLER
□ 439. ED BRINKMAN
□ 474. LUKE WALDER
□ 497. JIM NETTLES
□ 522. GARY SUTHERLAND
□ 546. JOHN KNOX
□ 571. DAVE LEMANCZYK
□ 593. GENE LAMONT
□ 599. NATE COLBERT
□ 614. VERN RUHLE(R)
□ 617. REGGIE SANDERS(R)
□ 620. DANNY MEYER(R)
□ 620. LEON ROBERTS(R)
□ 623. TOM VERYZER(R)
□ 628. RON LEFLORE

HOUSTON ASTROS

□ 25. LEE MAY
□ 49. LARRY DIERKER
□ 73. J.R. RICHARD
□ 96. MIKE COSGROVE
□ 119. TOMMY HELMS
□ 143. CLIFF JOHNSON
□ 165. DOUG RADER
□ 188. TOM GRIFFIN
□ 218. JERRY JOHNSON
□ 227. BOB WATSON
□ 252. FRED SCHERMAN
□ 279. MILT MAY
□ 301. DAVE A. ROBERTS
□ 334. GREG GROSS
□ 357. KEN FORSCH
□ 383. JIM YORK
□ 455. DON WILSON
□ 479. KEN BOSWELL
□ 487. TEAM & GOMEZ(M)
□ 512. LARRY MILBOURNE
□ 514. JOSE CRUZ
□ 541. ROGER METZGER
□ 563. WILBUR HOWARD
□ 590. CESAR CEDENO
□ 614. PAUL SIEBERT(R)
□ 624. DOUG KONIECZNY(R)

KANSAS CITY ROYALS

□ 24. AL FITZMORRIS
□ 48. FREDDIE PATEK
□ 72. TEAM & MCKEON(M)
□ 95. JOHN MAYBERRY
□ 120. STEVE BUSBY
□ 144. JIM WOHLFORD
□ 169. COOKIE ROJAS
□ 228. GEORGE BRETT
□ 251. FRAN HEALY
□ 268. HAL MCRAE
□ 295. VADA PINSON
□ 314. BUCK MARTINEZ
□ 340. PAUL SPLITTORFF
□ 364. DOUG BIRD
□ 389. TONY SOLAITA
□ 413. MARTY PATTIN
□ 437. AL COWENS
□ 472. BRUCE DAL CANTON
□ 495. NELSON BRILES
□ 520. AMOS OTIS
□ 544. STEVE MINGORI
□ 569. FRANK WHITE
□ 615. DENNIS LEONARD(R)
□ 622. TOM POQUETTE(R)
□ 629. JOE HOERNER
□ 652. LINDY MCDANIEL

LOS ANGELES DODGERS

□ 23. BILL RUSSELL
□ 47. TOMMY JOHN
□ 71. CHARLIE HOUGH
□ 93. DAVE LOPES
□ 115. JOE FERGUSON
□ 140. STEVE GARVEY
□ 163. JIM BREWER
□ 186. WILLIE CRAWFORD
□ 220. DON SUTTON
□ 244. BILL BUCKNER
□ 269. DOUG RAU
□ 294. GEOFF ZAHN
□ 330. MIKE MARSHALL
□ 361. TEAM ALSTON(M)
□ 376. STEVE YEAGER
□ 390. RON CEY
□ 414. MANNY MOTA
□ 440. ANDY MESSERSMITH
□ 473. KEN MCMULLEN
□ 498. AL DOWNING
□ 523. TOM PACIOREK
□ 547. VON JOSHUA
□ 570. JIM WYNN
□ 588. RICK AUERBACH
□ 618. RICK RHODEN(R)
□ 624. EDDIE SOLOMON(R)
□ 631. LEE LACY

MILWAUKEE BREWERS

□ 28. TOM MURPHY
□ 52. DARRELL PORTER
□ 76. ED SPRAGUE
□ 99. MIKE HEGAN
□ 123. JOHNNY BRIGGS
□ 147. PEDRO GARCIA
□ 175. DON MONEY

□ 223. ROBIN YOUNT
□ 256. BILLY CHAMPION
□ 281. JIM SLATON
□ 305. JIM COLBORN
□ 337. KEVIN KOBEL
□ 360. GEORGE SCOTT
□ 384. TEAM & CRANDALL(M)
□ 408. CLYDE WRIGHT
□ 432. KEN BERRY
□ 456. BOB COLUCCIO
□ 468. BOBBY MITCHELL
□ 488. BILL TRAVERS
□ 508. BOB HANSEN
□ 532. GORMAN THOMAS
□ 556. TIM JOHNSON
□ 582. EDUARDO RODRIGUEZ
□ 623. BOB SHELDON(R)
□ 636. CHARLIE MOORE
□ 660. HANK AARON

MINNESOTA TWINS

□ 30. BERT BLYLEVEN
□ 54. ERIC SODERHOLM
□ 78. RAY CORBIN
□ 102. JOE DECKER
□ 127. GLENN BORGMANN
□ 151. STEVE BRYE
□ 226. BILL CAMPBELL
□ 249. DANNY THOMPSON
□ 273. STEVE BRAUN
□ 297. CRAIG KUSICK
□ 325. TONY OLIVA
□ 346. BOBBY DARWIN
□ 368. VIC ALBURY
□ 419. DAVE GOLTZ
□ 443. TEAM & QUILICI(M)
□ 478. TOM BURGMEIER
□ 526. LARRY HISLE
□ 549. BILL BUTLER
□ 576. PHIL ROOF
□ 600. ROD CAREW
□ 618. TOM JOHNSON(R)
□ 621. JUAN VEINTIDOS(R)
□ 640. HARMON KILLEBREW
□ 654. JERRY TERRELL

MONTREAL EXPOS

□ 10. WILLIE DAVIS
□ 34. STEVE RENKO
□ 58. CHUCK TAYLOR
□ 101. TEAM & MAUCH(M)
□ 125. KEN SINGLETON
□ 149. TIM FOLI
□ 173. STEVE ROGERS
□ 229. BARRY FOOTE
□ 254. MIKE TORREZ
□ 270. RON FAIRLY
□ 286. MIKE JORGENSON
□ 318. ERNIE MCANALLY
□ 341. HAL BREEDEN
□ 365. BOB BAILEY
□ 391. DON DEMOLA
□ 405. JOHN MONTAGUE
□ 416. LARRY LINTZ
□ 438. DON CARRITHERS
□ 471. BOB STINSON
□ 496. PEPE FRIAS
□ 521. DENNIS BLAIR

- ☐ 543. LARRY BIITTNER
- ☐ 568. DALE MURRAY
- ☐ 592. BALOR MOORE
- ☐ 616. PEPE MANGUAL(R)
- ☐ 620. GARY CARTER(R)
- ☐ 627. TOM WALKER

NEW YORK METS

- ☐ 19. JERRY KOOSMAN
- ☐ 43. CLEON JONES
- ☐ 67. TUG MCGRAW
- ☐ 90. RUSTY STAUB
- ☐ 111. WAYNE GARETT
- ☐ 134. RON HODGES
- ☐ 158. JERRY GROTE
- ☐ 182. DON HAHN
- ☐ 214. HARRY PARKER
- ☐ 239. GEORGE STONE
- ☐ 264. JOHN MILNER
- ☐ 290. JON MATLACK
- ☐ 324. ED KRANEPOOL
- ☐ 370. TOM SEAVER
- ☐ 395. BUD HARRELSON
- ☐ 406. BOB GALLAGHER
- ☐ 421. TEAM & BERRA(M)
- ☐ 445. FELIX MILLAN
- ☐ 565. JOE TORRE
- ☐ 575. GENE CLINES
- ☐ 615. HANK WEBB(R)
- ☐ 619. BENNY AYALA(R)
- ☐ 637. TED MARTINEZ
- ☐ 659. BOB APODACA

NEW YORK YANKEES

- ☐ 20. THURMAN MUNSON
- ☐ 44. PAT DOBSON
- ☐ 55. BOBBY BONDS
- ☐ 68. RON BLOMBERG
- ☐ 92. CECIL UPSHAW
- ☐ 113. ELLIOTT MADDOX
- ☐ 136. JIM MASON
- ☐ 160. GRAIG NETTLES
- ☐ 183. MEL STOTTLEMYRE
- ☐ 217. LOU PINIELLA
- ☐ 241. DICK TIDROW
- ☐ 266. SANDY ALOMAR
- ☐ 291. BILL SUDAKIS
- ☐ 321. RUDY MAY
- ☐ 375. ROY WHITE
- ☐ 401. MIKE WALLACE
- ☐ 426. GEORGE MEDICH
- ☐ 451. RICK DEMPSEY
- ☐ 485. SPARKY LYLE
- ☐ 503. FRED STANLEY
- ☐ 534. ALEX JOHNSON
- ☐ 557. LARRY GURA
- ☐ 585. CHRIS CHAMBLISS
- ☐ 608. GENE MICHAEL
- ☐ 611. TEAM & VIRDON(M)
- ☐ 618. SCOTT MCGREGOR(R)
- ☐ 622. TERRY WHITFIELD(R)
- ☐ 648. DAVE PAGAN

OAKLAND A'S

- ☐ 21. ROLLIE FINGERS
- ☐ 45. JOE RUDI
- ☐ 69. JOHNNY ODOM
- ☐ 91. DICK GREEN
- ☐ 121. BILL NORTH
- ☐ 145. KEN HOLTZMAN
- ☐ 170. BERT CAMPANERIS
- ☐ 230. JIM HUNTER
- ☐ 253. JESUS ALOU
- ☐ 278. PAUL LINDBLAD
- ☐ 300. REGGIE JACKSON
- ☐ 329. TED KUBIAK
- ☐ 380. SAL BANDO
- ☐ 407. HERB WASHINGTON
- ☐ 428. DAVE HAMILTON
- ☐ 452. ANGEL MANGUAL
- ☐ 486. RAY FOSSE
- ☐ 502. PAT BOURQUE
- ☐ 510. VIDA BLUE
- ☐ 535. GENE TENACE
- ☐ 545. BILLY WILLIAMS
- ☐ 561. TEAM & DARK(M)
- ☐ 591. GLENN ABBOTT
- ☐ 607. JIM HOLT
- ☐ 613. BILL PARSONS
- ☐ 623. PHIL GARNER(R)
- ☐ 626. LARRY HANEY
- ☐ 647. CLAUDELL WASHINGTON

PHILADELPHIA PHILLIES

- ☐ 22. DAVE CASH
- ☐ 46. TEAM & OZARK(M)
- ☐ 70. MIKE SCHMIDT
- ☐ 94. JIM LONBORG
- ☐ 118. MIKE ANDERSON
- ☐ 138. DEL UNSER
- ☐ 162. WILLIE MONTANEZ
- ☐ 185. STEVE CARLTON
- ☐ 242. JAY JOHNSTONE
- ☐ 267. DICK RUTHVEN
- ☐ 292. RON SCHUELER
- ☐ 326. WAYNE TWITCHELL
- ☐ 351. BOB BOONE
- ☐ 374. EDDIE WATT
- ☐ 399. TERRY HARMON
- ☐ 420. LARRY BOWA
- ☐ 444. GENE GARBER
- ☐ 477. TOM HUTTON
- ☐ 501. BILL ROBINSON
- ☐ 527. MAC SCARCE
- ☐ 551. LARRY CHRISTENSON
- ☐ 574. TONY TAYLOR
- ☐ 596. OLLIE BROWN
- ☐ 615. TOM UNDERWOOD(R)
- ☐ 630. GREG LUZINSKI

PITTSBURGH PIRATES

- ☐ 29. DAVE PARKER
- ☐ 53. DAVE GIUSTI
- ☐ 77. RICHIE ZISK
- ☐ 100. WILLIE STARGELL
- ☐ 124. JERRY REUSS
- ☐ 148. JIM ROOKER
- ☐ 171. ED KIRKPATRICK
- ☐ 224. RAMON HERNANDEZ
- ☐ 250. KEN BRETT
- ☐ 277. FRANK TAVERAS
- ☐ 304. TEAM & MURTAUGH(M)
- ☐ 336. RENNIE STENNETT
- ☐ 359. PAUL POPOVICH
- ☐ 385. DOCK ELLIS
- ☐ 409. BOB ROBERTSON
- ☐ 433. LARRY DEMEREY
- ☐ 457. MARIO MENDOZA
- ☐ 492. RICH HEBNER
- ☐ 515. MANNY SANGUILLEN
- ☐ 536. BOB MOOSE
- ☐ 538. DUFFY DYER
- ☐ 555. AL OLIVER
- ☐ 598. BRUCE KISON
- ☐ 616. DAVE AUGUSTINE(R)
- ☐ 651. JOHN MORLAN

ST. LOUIS CARDINALS

- ☐ 27. KEN REITZ
- ☐ 51. BOB FORSCH
- ☐ 75. TED SIMMONS
- ☐ 98. RICH FOLKERS
- ☐ 122. AL HRABOSKY
- ☐ 150. BOB GIBSON
- ☐ 174. BAKE MCBRIDE
- ☐ 231. MIKE TYSON
- ☐ 246. TEAM & SCHOENDIENST(M)
- ☐ 272. LYNN MCGLOTHEN
- ☐ 289. KEN RUDOLPH
- ☐ 296. ALAN FOSTER
- ☐ 328. SONNY SIEBERT
- ☐ 349. RAY SADECKI
- ☐ 353. LUIS MELENDEZ
- ☐ 381. JOHN CURTIS
- ☐ 398. ELIAS SOSA
- ☐ 404. TED SIZEMORE
- ☐ 429. JIM DWYER
- ☐ 453. CLAUDE OSTEEN
- ☐ 490. REGGIE SMITH
- ☐ 540. LOU BROCK
- ☐ 584. MIKE GARMAN
- ☐ 610. RON HUNT
- ☐ 621. JOHN DENNY(R)
- ☐ 623. KEITH HERNANDEZ(R)
- ☐ 649. JACK HEIDEMANN

SAN DIEGO PADRES

- ☐ 13. GENE LOCKLEAR
- ☐ 37. DAVE FREISLEBEN
- ☐ 61. DAVE WINFIELD
- ☐ 84. ENZO HERNANDEZ
- ☐ 112. LARRY HARDY
- ☐ 146. TEAM & MCNAMARA(M)
- ☐ 168. BILL GREIF
- ☐ 222. DAN SPILLNER
- ☐ 248. RANDY JONES
- ☐ 274. VICENTE ROMO
- ☐ 298. JOHNNY GRUBB
- ☐ 332. FRED KENDALL
- ☐ 343. DANNY FRIESELLA
- ☐ 355. CHRIS CANNIZZARO
- ☐ 378. DERREL THOMAS
- ☐ 402. BOB TOLAN
- ☐ 450. WILLIE MCCOVEY
- ☐ 484. GLENN BECKERT
- ☐ 509. DAVE HILTON
- ☐ 558. DAVE W. ROBERTS
- ☐ 578. DAVE TOMLIN
- ☐ 616. JOHN SCOTT(R)
- ☐ 619. JERRY TURNER(R)
- ☐ 643. BRENT STROM

SAN FRANCISCO GIANTS

- ☐ 31. DAVE RADER
- ☐ 79. GARY MATTHEWS
- ☐ 107. JIM BARR
- ☐ 132. RANDY MOFFITT
- ☐ 156. DAVE KINGMAN
- ☐ 179. TOM BRADLEY
- ☐ 216. TEAM & WESTRUM(M)
- ☐ 240. GARRY MADDOX
- ☐ 265. RON BRYANT
- ☐ 322. ED GOODSON
- ☐ 347. MIKE CALDWELL
- ☐ 350. BOBBY MURCER
- ☐ 372. JOHN D'ACQUISTO
- ☐ 425. TITO FUENTES
- ☐ 449. CHARLIE WILLIAMS
- ☐ 467. ED HALICKI
- ☐ 483. STEVE ONTIVEROS
- ☐ 505. CHRIS SPEIER
- ☐ 529. GARY THOMASSON
- ☐ 553. JOHN BOCCABELLA
- ☐ 577. JOHN MORRIS
- ☐ 606. BRUCE MILLER
- ☐ 620. MARC HILL(R)
- ☐ 624. GARY LAVELLE(R)
- ☐ 642. MIKE PHILLIPS

TEXAS RANGERS

- ☐ 12. DAVID CLYDE
- ☐ 36. JOE LOVITTO
- ☐ 60. FERGIE JENKINS
- ☐ 83. JIM MERRITT
- ☐ 106. MIKE HARGROVE
- ☐ 131. TOBY HARRAH
- ☐ 155. JIM BIBBY
- ☐ 178. CESAR TOVAR
- ☐ 234. TOM GRIEVE
- ☐ 259. LEN RANDLE
- ☐ 283. STEVE FOUCAULT
- ☐ 316. JACKIE BROWN
- ☐ 339. JIM FREGOSI
- ☐ 362. STEVE HARGAN
- ☐ 387. JIM SPENCER
- ☐ 412. BILL HANDS
- ☐ 435. DAVE NELSON
- ☐ 470. JEFF BURROUGHS
- ☐ 493. DON STANHOUSE
- ☐ 511. TEAM & MARTIN(M)
- ☐ 518. LEO CARDENAS
- ☐ 542. PETE BROBERG
- ☐ 567. JIM SUNDBERG
- ☐ 617. MIKE CUBBAGE(R)
- ☐ 644. BILL FAHEY

1976 TOPPS (660)
2 1/2" X 3 1/2"

ATLANTA BRAVES

- □ 28. DUSTY BAKER
- □ 53. MIKE BEARD
- □ 81. DARRELL EVANS
- □ 103. BIFF POCOROBA
- □ 127. LARVELL BLANKS
- □ 153. BUZZ CAPRA
- □ 177. MARTY PEREZ
- □ 208. MIKE LUM
- □ 231. TOM HOUSE
- □ 256. ROWLAND OFFICE
- □ 281. DAVE MAY
- □ 306. ROD GILBREATH
- □ 328. CARL MORTON
- □ 364. ELIAS SOSA
- □ 395. JIM WYNN
- □ 410. RALPH GARR
- □ 435. PHIL NIEKRO
- □ 458. EARL WILLIAMS
- □ 486. BRUCE DAL CANTON
- □ 511. JAMIE EASTERLY
- □ 536. MIKE THOMPSON
- □ 558. CLARENCE GASTON
- □ 576. MAXIMINO LEON
- □ 589. PABLO TORREALBA(R)
- □ 592. JERRY ROYSTER(R)
- □ 597. FRANK LACORTE(R)
- □ 608. VIC CORRELL
- □ 631. TEAM & BRISTOL(M)
- □ 641. TOM PACIOREK
- □ 651. JOHN ODOM

BALTIMORE ORIOLES

- □ 25. MIKE TORREZ
- □ 49. DAVE DUNCAN
- □ 73. TEAM & WEAVER(M)
- □ 95. BROOKS ROBINSON
- □ 125. DON BAYLOR
- □ 149. TOMMY DAVIS
- □ 175. KEN SINGLETON
- □ 210. LEE MAY
- □ 233. GRANT JACKSON
- □ 252. TIM NORDBROOK
- □ 257. ROSS GRIMSLEY
- □ 285. MIKE CUELLAR
- □ 307. AL BUMBRY
- □ 335. BOB GRICH
- □ 371. ELLIE HENDRICKS
- □ 393. PAUL MITCHELL
- □ 414. WAYNE GARLAND
- □ 438. DOUG DECINCES
- □ 450. JIM PALMER
- □ 473. PAUL BLAIR
- □ 505. MARK BELANGER
- □ 537. TONY MUSER
- □ 555. DYAR MILLER
- □ 589. MIKE FLANAGAN(R)
- □ 594. ROYLE STILLMAN(R)
- □ 638. DOYLE ALEXANDER

BOSTON RED SOX

- □ 29. RICK BURLESON
- □ 50. FRED LYNN
- □ 78. CECIL COOPER
- □ 102. JIM WILLOUGHBY
- □ 118. TEAM & JOHNSON(M)
- □ 130. LUIS TIANT
- □ 142. DICK DRAGO
- □ 170. RICK WISE
- □ 230. CARL YASTRZEMSKI
- □ 278. BERNIE CARBO
- □ 302. RICK MILLER
- □ 326. DICK POLE
- □ 340. JIM RICE
- □ 365. CARLTON FISK
- □ 381. DENNY DOYLE
- □ 396. BILL LEE
- □ 419. REGGIE CLEVELAND
- □ 445. RICO PETROCELLI
- □ 471. JIM BURTON
- □ 523. BOB MONTGOMERY
- □ 529. DERON JOHNSON
- □ 575. DWIGHT EVANS
- □ 594. ANDY MERCHANT(R)
- □ 597. DON AASE(R)
- □ 632. ROGELIO MORET
- □ 654. DOUG GRIFFIN

CALIFORNIA ANGELS

- □ 27. ED FIGUEROA
- □ 52. DAVE CHALK
- □ 85. MICKEY RIVERS
- □ 108. DON KIRKWOOD
- □ 129. ANDY ETCHEBARREN
- □ 152. LEROY STANTON
- □ 176. DICK LANGE
- □ 207. ANDY HASSLER
- □ 229. JERRY REMY
- □ 254. RUDY MEOLI(F)
- □ 276. MICKEY SCOTT
- □ 304. TEAM & WILLIAMS(M)
- □ 330. NOLAN RYAN
- □ 363. DAVE COLLINS
- □ 387. MIKE MILEY
- □ 411. BILL SINGER
- □ 434. MORRIS NETTLES
- □ 459. JIM BREWER
- □ 490. FRANK TANANA
- □ 512. ELLIE RODRIGUEZ
- □ 539. JOHN BALEZ
- □ 562. ADRIAN GARRETT
- □ 589. JOE PACTWA(R)
- □ 595. SID MONGE(R)
- □ 612. JOE LAHOUD
- □ 623. BOB ALLIETTA
- □ 637. BRUCE BOCHTE

CHICAGO CUBS

- □ 26. ANDY THORNTON
- □ 34. MIKE GARMAN
- □ 51. RAY BURRIS
- □ 79. JERRY MORALES
- □ 101. PETE LACOCK
- □ 126. TOM DETTORE
- □ 151. BILL BONHAM
- □ 173. STEVE SWISHER
- □ 206. MANNY TRILLO
- □ 227. OSCAR ZAMORA
- □ 251. RICK MONDAY
- □ 277. TEAM & MARSHALL(M)
- □ 299. CHAMP SUMMERS
- □ 323. BOB SPERRING
- □ 359. RICK REUSCHEL
- □ 378. STEVE STONE
- □ 403. GEOFF ZAHN
- □ 430. JOSE CARDENAL
- □ 482. TIM HOSLEY
- □ 506. GEORGE MITTERWALD
- □ 546. DAVE ROSELLO
- □ 593. KEN CROSBY(R)
- □ 598. JOE WALLIS(R)
- □ 617. DAROLD KNOWLES
- □ 640. BILL MADLOCK

CHICAGO WHITE SOX

- □ 23. BRIAN DOWNING
- □ 47. JESSE JEFFERSON
- □ 80. JIM KAAT
- □ 110. CARLOS MAY
- □ 131. BILL STEIN
- □ 154. BUCKY DENT
- □ 180. RICH GOSSAGE
- □ 212. H. PAT KELLY
- □ 237. DAVE HAMILTON
- □ 258. NYLS NYMAN
- □ 282. DAN OSBORN
- □ 309. BILL MELTON
- □ 333. BOB COLUCCIO
- □ 368. WILBUR WOOD
- □ 391. JERRY HAIRSTON
- □ 413. PETE VARNEY
- □ 437. TERRY FORSTER
- □ 464. KEN HENDERSON
- □ 488. CLAUDE OSTEEN
- □ 513. BART JOHNSON
- □ 533. LEE RICHARD
- □ 560. JORGE ORTA
- □ 590. CHET LEMON(R)
- □ 596. LAMAR JOHNSON(R)
- □ 597. JACK KUCEK(R)
- □ 607. RICH HINTON
- □ 656. TEAM & TANNER(M)

CINCINNATI REDS

- □ 24. CESAR GERONIMO
- □ 48. DAVE CONCEPCION
- □ 77. PEDRO BORBON
- □ 104. TEAM & ANDERSON(M)
- □ 128. KEN GRIFFEY
- □ 155. JACK BILLINGHAM
- □ 179. GEORGE FOSTER
- □ 211. CLAY CARROLL
- □ 240. PETE ROSE
- □ 259. DARRELL CHANEY
- □ 283. MERV RETTENMUND
- □ 300. JOHNNY BENCH
- □ 325. TONY PEREZ
- □ 362. WILL MCENANEY
- □ 390. DON GULLETT
- □ 420. JOE MORGAN
- □ 444. GARY NOLAN
- □ 469. RAWLY EASTWICK
- □ 491. TERRY CROWLEY
- □ 514. DAN DRIESSEN
- □ 518. DOUG FLYNN
- □ 538. PAT DARCY
- □ 561. TOM CARROLL
- □ 579. CLAY KIRBY
- □ 589. SANTO ALCALA(R)
- □ 599. PAT ZACHRY(R)
- □ 609. FRED NORMAN
- □ 627. BILL PLUMMER
- □ 652. ED ARMBRISTER

CLEVELAND INDIANS

- □ 21. DAVE LAROCHE
- □ 45. BOOG POWELL
- □ 74. OSCAR GAMBLE
- □ 98. DENNIS ECKERSLEY
- □ 132. DON HOOD
- □ 156. RICO CARTY
- □ 178. TOM BUSKEY
- □ 209. ALAN ASHBY
- □ 232. FRANK DUFFY
- □ 255. FRITZ PETERSON
- □ 275. RICK MANNING
- □ 301. JACKIE BROWN
- □ 324. JIM BIBBY
- □ 358. BUDDY BELL
- □ 383. JOHN ELLIS
- □ 408. CHARLIE SPIKES
- □ 433. RICK WAITS
- □ 457. ED CROSBY
- □ 477. TEAM & ROBINSON(M)
- □ 484. ERIC RAICH
- □ 508. DUANE KUIPER
- □ 547. RORIC HARRISON
- □ 570. GEORGE HENDRICK
- □ 618. JACK BROHAMER
- □ 646. JOHN LOWENSTEIN

DETROIT TIGERS

□ 13. JOHNNY WOCKENFUSS
□ 37. JOHN HILLER
□ 61. RON LEFLORE
□ 89. VERN RUHLE
□ 113. GARY SUTHERLAND
□ 138. LERRIN LAGROW
□ 162. JACK PIERCE
□ 186. TOM WALKER
□ 218. JOHN KNOX
□ 242. DAN MEYER
□ 267. AURELIO RODRIGUEZ
□ 292. LEON ROBERTS
□ 320. WILLIE HORTON
□ 361. TEAM & HOUK(M)
□ 385. MICKEY LOLICH
□ 409. DAVE LEMANCZYK
□ 432. TOM VERYZER
□ 456. JOE COLEMAN
□ 483. MICKEY STANLEY
□ 507. RAY BARE
□ 540. BILL FREEHAN
□ 552. TERRY HUMPHREY
□ 591. STEVE GRILLI(R)
□ 596. JERRY MANUEL(R)
□ 614. FERNANDO ARROYO
□ 659. BEN OGLIVIE

HOUSTON ASTROS

□ 20. BOB WATSON
□ 44. DOUG RADER
□ 75. LARRY DIERKER
□ 97. WILBUR HOWARD
□ 122. MIKE COSGROVE
□ 147. TEAM & VIRDON(M)
□ 171. GREG GROSS
□ 224. JIM YORK
□ 249. CLIFF JOHNSON
□ 273. JOE NIEKRO
□ 297. ROGER METZGER
□ 321. JOSE CRUZ
□ 357. KEN FORSCH
□ 379. KEN BOSWELL
□ 404. ENOS CABELL
□ 428. JIM CRAWFORD
□ 454. TOM GRIFFIN
□ 460. CESAR CEDENO
□ 489. SKIP JUTZE
□ 516. WAYNE GRANGER
□ 532. MILT MAY
□ 551. JERRY DAVANON
□ 568. ROB ANDREWS
□ 583. TOMMY HELMS
□ 591. JOSE SOSA(R)
□ 602. DOUG KONIECZNY
□ 625. J.R. RICHARD
□ 649. DAVE A. ROBERTS

KANSAS CITY ROYALS

□ 19. GEORGE BRETT
□ 43. PAUL SPLITTORFF
□ 72. HAL MCRAE
□ 96. DOUG BIRD
□ 121. TONY SOLAITA
□ 144. AL FITZMORRIS
□ 167. FREDDIE PATEK
□ 236. TEAM & HERZOG(M)
□ 260. STEVE BUSBY
□ 286. JIM WOHLFORD
□ 311. COOKIE ROJAS
□ 334. DENNIS LEONARD
□ 369. FRANK WHITE
□ 394. FRAN HEALY
□ 415. VADA PINSON
□ 440. JOHN MAYBERRY
□ 466. BOB STINSON
□ 492. MARTY PATTIN
□ 510. AMOS OTIS
□ 535. DAVE NELSON
□ 541. STEVE MINGORI
□ 591. GEORGE THROOP(R)
□ 593. MARK LITTELL(R)
□ 598. JAMIE QUIRK(R)
□ 599. BOB MCCLURE(R)
□ 616. BUCK MARTINEZ
□ 648. AL COWENS

LOS ANGELES DODGERS

□ 22. BILL RUSSELL
□ 46. TEAM & ALSTON(M)
□ 76. WILLIE CRAWFORD
□ 99. LEE LACY
□ 124. DOUG RAU
□ 150. STEVE GARVEY
□ 174. CHARLIE HOUGH
□ 228. JOHN HALE
□ 253. BILL BUCKNER
□ 280. BURT HOOTON
□ 305. ANDY MESSERSMITH
□ 329. JOE FERGUSON
□ 370. RON CEY
□ 386. ED GOODSON
□ 416. TOMMY JOHN
□ 439. RICK RHODEN
□ 465. MIKE MARSHALL
□ 487. LERON LEE
□ 515. STEVE YEAGER
□ 530. DON SUTTON
□ 548. MANNY MOTA
□ 566. KEN MCMULLEN
□ 584. STAN WALL
□ 590. HENRY CRUZ(R)
□ 605. AL DOWNING
□ 622. RICK AUERBACH
□ 660. DAVE LOPES

MILWAUKEE BREWERS

□ 15. GEORGE SCOTT
□ 39. PETE BROBERG
□ 63. BOBBY DARWIN
□ 92. EDUARDO RODRIGUEZ
□ 116. CHARLIE MOORE
□ 139. GORMAN THOMAS
□ 163. JIM SLATON
□ 187. PEDRO GARCIA
□ 219. TOM MURPHY
□ 244. BILL SHARP
□ 269. RICK AUSTIN
□ 293. BILL CASTRO
□ 316. ROBIN YOUNT
□ 353. SIXTO LEZCANO
□ 377. MIKE HEGAN
□ 402. DON MONEY
□ 427. KURT BEVACQUA
□ 452. TOM HAUSMAN
□ 479. ROBBY MITCHELL
□ 501. BILLY CHAMPION
□ 521. JIM COLBORN
□ 550. HANK AARON
□ 573. BILL TRAVERS
□ 588. KEVIN KOBEL
□ 593. LARRY ANDERSON(R)
□ 606. TEAM & GRAMMAS(M)
□ 613. TIM JOHNSON
□ 626. BOB SHELDON
□ 645. DARRELL PORTER

MINNESOTA TWINS

□ 11. JIM HUGHES
□ 35. TONY OLIVA
□ 59. LARRY HISLE
□ 87. TOM BURGMEIER
□ 111. DANNY THOMPSON
□ 136. DAVE GOLTZ
□ 159. JERRY TERRELL
□ 183. STEVE BRAUN
□ 214. ERIC SODERHOLM
□ 235. BERT BLYLEVEN
□ 263. LYMAN BOSTOCK
□ 288. BILL CAMBELL
□ 313. DAN FORD
□ 336. VIC ALBURY
□ 373. JOHNNY BRIGGS
□ 400. ROD CAREW
□ 424. PHIL ROOF
□ 448. TOM JOHNSON
□ 474. RAY CORBIN
□ 498. GLENN BORGMANN
□ 519. STEVE BRYE
□ 556. TEAM & MAUCH(M)
□ 592. DAVE MCKAY(R)
□ 597. MIKE PAZIK(R)
□ 619. BILL BUTLER
□ 636. JOE DECKER

MONTREAL EXPOS

□ 18. DALE MURRAY
□ 42. BARRY FOOTE
□ 71. STEVE ROGERS
□ 94. JIM DWYER
□ 117. MIKE JORGENSEN
□ 141. LARRY PARRISH
□ 164. PEPE MANGUAL
□ 188. FRED SCHERMAN
□ 216. TEAM & KUEHL(M)
□ 238. LARRY BIITTNER
□ 264. STEVE RENKO
□ 287. PETE MACKANIN
□ 312. DON CARRITHERS
□ 338. BOB BAILEY
□ 374. DAN WARTHEN
□ 397. TIM FOLI
□ 418. JOSE MORALES
□ 441. GARY CARTER
□ 467. WOODIE FRYMAN
□ 495. NATE COLBERT
□ 544. PEPE FRIAS
□ 571. DON DEMOLA
□ 590. ELLIS VALENTINE(R)
□ 594. JERRY WHITE(R)
□ 642. DENNIS BLAIR

NEW YORK METS

□ 16. BOB APODACA
□ 40. DAVE KINGMAN
□ 64. JERRY KOOSMAN
□ 93. MIKE PHILLIPS
□ 120. RUSTY STAUB
□ 143. JERRY GROTE
□ 166. SKIP LOCKWOOD
□ 190. JON MATLACK
□ 222. WAYNE GARRETT
□ 245. FELIX MILLAN
□ 268. DEL UNSER
□ 291. KEN SANDERS
□ 314. ED KRANEPOOL
□ 337. BUD HARRELSON
□ 372. RICK BALDWIN
□ 417. GENE CLINES
□ 442. HANK WEBB
□ 468. JESUS ALOU
□ 494. CRAIG SWAN
□ 517. JOHN MILNER
□ 531. TEAM & FRAZIER(M)
□ 549. RANDY TATE
□ 567. GEORGE STONE
□ 585. JOE TORRE
□ 592. ROY STAIGER(R)
□ 600. TOM SEAVER
□ 621. TOM HALL
□ 633. JOHN STEARNS
□ 655. MIKE VAIL

NEW YORK YANKEES

□ 17. TEAM & MARTIN(M)
□ 41. TIPPY MARTINEZ
□ 65. CHRIS CHAMBLISS
□ 100. JIM HUNTER
□ 123. WALT WILLIAMS
□ 146. GEORGE MEDICH
□ 169. GRAIG NETTLES
□ 225. ROY WHITE
□ 248. DICK TIDROW
□ 272. RICK DEMPSEY
□ 296. PAT DOBSON
□ 319. LARRY GURA
□ 354. RON BLOMBERG
□ 380. BOBBY BONDS
□ 406. ED HERRMANN
□ 429. FRED STANLEY
□ 453. LOU PINIELLA
□ 481. RUDY MAY
□ 503. ELLIOTT MADDOX
□ 545. SPARKY LYLE
□ 572. RICH COGGINS
□ 590. TERRY WHITFIELD(R)
□ 599. RON GUIDRY(R)
□ 629. SANDY ALOMAR
□ 650. THURMAN MUNSON

OAKLAND A'S

- ☐ 9. PAUL LINDBLAD
- ☐ 33. BILL NORTH
- ☐ 57. PHIL GARNER
- ☐ 90. SAL BANDO
- ☐ 109. LARRY LINTZ
- ☐ 115. KEN HOLTZMAN
- ☐ 140. VIDA BLUE
- ☐ 165. GENE TENACE
- ☐ 189. CLAUDELL WASHINGTON
- ☐ 221. JIM TODD
- ☐ 246. CESAR TOVAR
- ☐ 274. TOMMY HARPER
- ☐ 298. DICK BOSMAN
- ☐ 322. GLENN ABBOTT
- ☐ 356. TED MARTINEZ
- ☐ 382. MATT ALEXANDER
- ☐ 405. ROLLIE FINGERS
- ☐ 421. TEAM CARD
- ☐ 446. LARRY HANEY
- ☐ 475. JOE RUDI
- ☐ 500. REGGIE JACKSON
- ☐ 525. BILLY WILLIAMS
- ☐ 534. STAN BAHNSEN
- ☐ 554. RAY FOSSE
- ☐ 580. BERT CAMPANERIS
- ☐ 591. CRAIG MITCHELL(R)
- ☐ 603. JIM HOLT
- ☐ 653. MIKE NORRIS

PHIALDELPHIA PHILLIES

- ☐ 14. GENE GARBER
- ☐ 38. GARRY MADDOX
- ☐ 62. JOHNNY OATES
- ☐ 91. TOM HUTTON
- ☐ 114. JAY JOHNSTONE
- ☐ 145. LARRY BOWA
- ☐ 168. TOM HILGENDORF
- ☐ 223. OLLIE BROWN
- ☐ 247. TERRY HARMON
- ☐ 271. JIM LONBORG
- ☐ 295. DAVE CASH
- ☐ 318. BOB BOONE
- ☐ 355. STEVE CARLTON
- ☐ 384. TEAM & OZARK(M)
- ☐ 407. TOM UNDERWOOD
- ☐ 431. DICK RUTHVEN
- ☐ 455. DICK ALLEN
- ☐ 480. MIKE SCHMIDT
- ☐ 502. TIM MCCARVER
- ☐ 527. MIKE ANDERSON
- ☐ 543. WAYNE TWITCHELL
- ☐ 565. TUG MCGRAW
- ☐ 586. RON SCHUELER
- ☐ 595. RANDY LERCH(R)
- ☐ 610. GREG LUZINSKI
- ☐ 624. TONY TAYLOR
- ☐ 634. LARRY CHRISTENSON

PITTSBURGH PIRATES

- ☐ 12. RICHIE ZISK
- ☐ 36. FRANK TAVERAS
- ☐ 60. JERRY REUSS
- ☐ 88. DUFFY DYER
- ☐ 112. KENT TEKULVE
- ☐ 137. BILL ROBINSON
- ☐ 161. BRUCE KISON
- ☐ 185. DAVE PARKER
- ☐ 220. MANNY SANGUILLEN
- ☐ 243. JIM ROOKER
- ☐ 270. WILLIE STARGELL
- ☐ 294. ED KIRKPATRICK
- ☐ 317. JOHN CANDELARIA
- ☐ 352. DAVE GIUSTI
- ☐ 376. RICH HEBNER
- ☐ 401. KEN BRETT
- ☐ 425. RENNIE STENNETT
- ☐ 449. BOB ROBERTSON
- ☐ 476. BOB MOOSE
- ☐ 504. TEAM & MURTAUGH(M)
- ☐ 528. DOCK ELLIS
- ☐ 563. LARRY DEMERY
- ☐ 592. WILLIE RANDOLPH(R)
- ☐ 594. ED OTT(R)
- ☐ 596. CRAIG REYNOLDS(R)
- ☐ 620. AL OLIVER
- ☐ 647. RAMON HERNANDEZ

ST. LOUIS CARDINALS

- ☐ 10. LOU BROCK
- ☐ 58. RON REED
- ☐ 86. MIKE TYSON
- ☐ 135. BAKE MCBRIDE
- ☐ 158. KEN REITZ
- ☐ 182. ERIC RASMUSSEN
- ☐ 215. REGGIE SMITH
- ☐ 239. JOHN CURTIS
- ☐ 290. TED SIMMONS
- ☐ 315. AL HRABOSKY
- ☐ 339. JOHN DENNY
- ☐ 375. RON FAIRLY
- ☐ 399. LUIS MELENDEZ
- ☐ 426. BOB FORSCH
- ☐ 451. BUDDY BRADFORD
- ☐ 478. LYNN MCGLOTHEN
- ☐ 499. MARIO GUERRERO
- ☐ 522. TED SIZEMORE
- ☐ 542. KEITH HERNANDEZ
- ☐ 574. DON KESSINGER
- ☐ 581. TEAM & SCHOENDIENST(M)
- ☐ 598. HECTOR CRUZ(R)
- ☐ 601. KEN RUDOLPH

SAN DIEGO PADRES

- ☐ 8. TITO FUENTES
- ☐ 32. DANNY FRISELLA
- ☐ 56. BOB TOLAN
- ☐ 84. BRENT STROM
- ☐ 107. DAVE W. ROBERTS
- ☐ 134. MIKE IVIE
- ☐ 160. DAVE WINFIELD
- ☐ 184. BILL GREIF
- ☐ 217. DAVE FREISLEBEN
- ☐ 241. HECTOR TORRES
- ☐ 254. RUDY MEOLI(B)
- ☐ 265. WILLIE DAVIS
- ☐ 266. ALAN FOSTER
- ☐ 289. ENZO HERNANDEZ
- ☐ 310. RANDY JONES
- ☐ 331. TEAM & MCNAMARA(M)
- ☐ 351. RANDY HUNDLEY
- ☐ 366. BOBBY VALENTINE
- ☐ 398. DAVE TOMLIN
- ☐ 422. JOHNNY GRUBB
- ☐ 447. GENE LOCKLEAR
- ☐ 472. BOB DAVIS
- ☐ 497. JOE MCINTOSH
- ☐ 520. WILLIE MCCOVEY
- ☐ 557. DAN SPILLNER
- ☐ 578. TED KUBIAK
- ☐ 593. BUTCH METZGER(R)
- ☐ 598. JERRY TURNER(R)
- ☐ 611. RICH FOLKERS
- ☐ 639. FRED KENDALL
- ☐ 658. JERRY JOHNSON

SAN FRANCISCO GIANTS

- ☐ 30. JOHN MONTEFUSCO
- ☐ 54. DAVE RADER
- ☐ 82. VON JOSHUA
- ☐ 105. GARY LAVELLE
- ☐ 133. GARY MATTHEWS
- ☐ 157. MIKE CALDWELL
- ☐ 181. WILLIE MONTANEZ
- ☐ 213. DAVE HEAVERLO
- ☐ 234. MIKE SADEK
- ☐ 261. GARY THOMASSON
- ☐ 283. STEVE ONTIVEROS
- ☐ 308. JIM BARR
- ☐ 332. CHARLIE WILLIAMS
- ☐ 367. BRUCE MILLER
- ☐ 389. GLENN ADAMS
- ☐ 423. ED HALICKI
- ☐ 443. TEAM CARD
- ☐ 470. BOBBY MURCER
- ☐ 493. DERREL THOMAS
- ☐ 524. PETE FALCONE
- ☐ 553. RANDY MOFFITT
- ☐ 577. MARC HILL
- ☐ 596. JOHNNIE LEMASTER(R)
- ☐ 599. ROB DRESSLER(R)
- ☐ 628. JOHN D'ACQUISTO
- ☐ 630. CHRIS SPEIER
- ☐ 644. TOM BRADLEY

TEXAS RANGERS

- ☐ 7. JIM UMBARGER
- ☐ 31. LEN RANDLE
- ☐ 55. GAYLORD PERRY
- ☐ 83. JIM SPENCER
- ☐ 106. TOM GRIEVE
- ☐ 148. STAN THOMAS
- ☐ 172. TEAM & LUCCHESI(M)
- ☐ 226. JIM SUNDBERG
- ☐ 250. FERGIE JENKINS
- ☐ 279. ROY HOWELL
- ☐ 303. STEVE FOUCAULT
- ☐ 327. DAVE MOATES
- ☐ 360. JEFF BURROUGHS
- ☐ 388. STAN PERZANOWSKI
- ☐ 412. TOBY HARRAH
- ☐ 436. BILL FAHEY
- ☐ 463. STEVE HARGAN
- ☐ 485. MIKE HARGROVE
- ☐ 496. JUAN BENIQUEZ
- ☐ 509. BILL HANDS
- ☐ 559. CLYDE WRIGHT
- ☐ 569. NELSON BRILES
- ☐ 582. MIKE KEKICH
- ☐ 587. LEO CARDENAS
- ☐ 595. ART DEFILIPPIS(R)
- ☐ 595. STEVE BARR(R)
- ☐ 604. JOE LOVITTO
- ☐ 615. MIKE CUBBAGE
- ☐ 635. JIM FREGOSI
- ☐ 657. ROY SMALLEY

ST. LOUIS CARDINALS

- ☐ 32. GARRY TEMPLETON
- ☐ 58. BOB FORSCH
- ☐ 88. MIKE PHILLIPS
- ☐ 111. MIKE TYSON
- ☐ 143. KEITH HERNANDEZ
- ☐ 170. LOU BROCK
- ☐ 195. LARRY DIERKER
- ☐ 230. AL HRABOSKY
- ☐ 257. HECTOR CRUZ
- ☐ 281. ERIC RASMUSSEN
- ☐ 301. BUDDY SCHULTZ
- ☐ 324. VERN RAPP(M)
- ☐ 352. TONY SCOTT
- ☐ 380. TED SIMMONS
- ☐ 405. RAWLY EASTWICK

1976 TOPPS TRADED (44) 2 1/2" X 3 1/2"

ATLANTA BRAVES

- ☐ 99T. LEE LACY
- ☐ 259T. DARREL CHANEY
- ☐ 464T. KEN HENDERSON
- ☐ 632T. ROGELIO MORET

BALTIMORE ORIOLES

NO CARDS ISSUED

BOSTON RED SOX

- ☐ 231T. TOM HOUSE
- ☐ 250T. FERGIE JENKINS

CALIFORNIA ANGELS

- ☐ 309T. BILL MELTON
- ☐ 380T. BOBBY BONDS

CHICAGO CUBS

NO CARDS ISSUED

CHICAGO WHITE SOX

- ☐ 83T. JIM SPENCER
- ☐ 211T. CLAY CARROLL
- ☐ 410T. RALPH GARR
- ☐ 434T. MORRIS NETTLES
- ☐ 618T. JACK BROHAMER

CINCINNATI REDS

- ☐ 208T. MIKE LUM
- ☐ 338T. BOB BAILEY

CLEVELAND INDIANS

- ☐ 127T. LARVELL BLANKS
- ☐ 296T. PAT DOBSON
- ☐ 554T. RAY FOSSE

DETROIT TIGERS

- ☐ 120T. RUSTY STAUB
- ☐ 428T. JIM CRAWFORD
- ☐ 532T. MILT MAY
- ☐ 649T. DAVE A. ROBERTS

HOUSTON ASTROS

- ☐ 292T. LEON ROBERTS
- ☐ 497T. JOE MCINTOSH

KANSAS CITY ROYALS

NO CARDS ISSUED

LOS ANGELES DODGERS

- ☐ 28T. DUSTY BAKER

MILWAUKEE BREWERS

NO CARDS ISSUED

MINNESOTA TWINS

NO CARDS ISSUED

MONTREAL TWINS

NO CARDS ISSUED

MONTREAL EXPOS

- ☐ 579T. CLAY KIRBY

NEW YORK METS

- ☐ 358T. MICKEY LOLICH

NEW YORK YANKEES

- ☐ 27T. ED FIGUEROA
- ☐ 74T. OSCAR GAMBLE
- ☐ 85T. MICKEY RIVERS
- ☐ 401T. KEN BRETT
- ☐ 528T. DOCK ELLIS
- ☐ 592T. WILLIE RANDOLPH

OAKLAND A'S

NO CARDS ISSUED

PHILADELPHIA PHILLIES

- ☐ 58T. RON REED
- ☐ 80T. JIM KAAT

PITTSBURGH PIRATES

- ☐ 146T. GEORGE MEDICH
- ☐ 583T. TOMMY HELMS

ST. LOUIS CARDINALS

- ☐ 524T. PETE FALCONE
- ☐ 527T. MIKE ANDERSON

SAN DIEGO PADRES

- ☐ 44T. DOUG RADER

SAN FRANCISCO GIANTS

- ☐ 158T. KEN REITZ

TEXAS RANGERS

- ☐ 383T. JOHN ELLIS
- ☐ 411T. BILL SINGER

1977 TOPPS (660) 2 1/2" X 3 1/2"

ATLANTA BRAVES

- ☐ 24. CARL MORTON
- ☐ 48. TOM PACIOREK
- ☐ 80. ANDY MESSERSMITH
- ☐ 114. BRUCE DAL CANTON
- ☐ 126. ROD GILBREATH
- ☐ 165. JIM WYNN
- ☐ 192. CLARENCE GASTON
- ☐ 194. GARY MATTHEWS
- ☐ 213. MAXIMINO LEON
- ☐ 242. KEN HENDERSON
- ☐ 263. MIKE MARSHALL
- ☐ 292. ROGELIO MORET
- ☐ 312. ROB BELLOIR
- ☐ 339. ADRIAN DEVINE
- ☐ 364. VIC CORRELL
- ☐ 384. DARREL CHANEY
- ☐ 410. WILLIE MONTANEZ
- ☐ 432. BUZZ CAPRA
- ☐ 442. TEAM & BRISTOL(M)
- ☐ 475. RICK CAMP(R)
- ☐ 476. DALE MURPHY(R)
- ☐ 479. BRIAN ASSELSTINE(R)
- ☐ 499. PABLO TORREALBA
- ☐ 524. ROWLAND OFFICE
- ☐ 549. JERRY ROYSTER
- ☐ 575. DICK RUTHVEN
- ☐ 594. BIFF POCOROBA
- ☐ 615. PHIL NIEKRO

BALTIMORE ORIOLES

- ☐ 56. RUDY MAY
- ☐ 77. DYAR MILLER
- ☐ 106. MIKE FLANAGAN
- ☐ 135. MARK BELANGER
- ☐ 162. MIKE CUELLAR
- ☐ 189. RICK DEMPSEY
- ☐ 216. DOUG DECINCES
- ☐ 238. TIPPY MARTINEZ
- ☐ 251. TONY MUSER
- ☐ 285. BROOKS ROBINSON
- ☐ 313. PAUL BLAIR
- ☐ 380. LEE MAY
- ☐ 414. TOMMY HARPER
- ☐ 445. KEN SINGLETON
- ☐ 466. FRED HOLDSWORTH
- ☐ 469. H. PAT KELLY
- ☐ 474. KIKO GARCIA(R)
- ☐ 475. SCOTT MCGREGOR(R)
- ☐ 477. RICH DAUER(R)
- ☐ 491. DENNY MARTINEZ(R)

□ 546. TEAM & WEAVER(M)
□ 572. ROSS GRIMSLEY
□ 600. JIM PALMER
□ 626. AL BUMBRY
□ 646. ANDRES MORA

BOSTON RED SOX

□ 25. DWIGHT EVANS
□ 60. JIM RICE
□ 89. BUTCH HOBSON
□ 111. RICO PETROCELLI
□ 142. STEVE DILLARD
□ 166. BILL CAMPBELL
□ 191. DOUG GRIFFIN
□ 210. FRED LYNN
□ 235. CECIL COOPER
□ 258. LUIS TIANT
□ 288. BOB MONTGOMERY
□ 309. TEAM & ZIMMER(M)
□ 336. DENNY DOYLE
□ 358. TOM HOUSE
□ 396. TOM MURPHY
□ 430. FERGIE JENKINS
□ 455. RICK WISE
□ 472. DON AASE(R)
□ 480. CARL YASTRZEMSKI
□ 503. BILL LEE
□ 532. JIM WILLOUGHBY
□ 566. RICK MILLER
□ 585. RICK BURLESON
□ 613. REGGIE CLEVELAND
□ 617. BOBBY DARWIN
□ 640. CARLTON FISK

CALIFORNIA ANGELS

□ 16. BOB JONES
□ 34. TEAM & SHERRY(M)
□ 68. BRUCE BOCHTE
□ 91. JOHN VERHOEVEN
□ 107. BILL MELTON
□ 131. ORLANDO RAMIREZ
□ 153. RON JACKSON
□ 155. JOE RUDI
□ 179. PAUL HARTZELL
□ 200. FRANK TANANA
□ 224. RUSTY TORRES
□ 257. MIKE MILEY
□ 282. SID MONGE
□ 315. DAVE CHALK
□ 342. JERRY REMY
□ 369. TERRY HUMPHREY
□ 401. MICKEY SCOTT
□ 426. DICK DRAGO
□ 454. ANDY ETCHEBARREN
□ 462. DON BAYLOR
□ 482. TONY SOLAITA
□ 489. MIKE OVERY(R)
□ 519. DON KIRKWOOD
□ 521. BOB GRICH
□ 544. GARY ROSS
□ 570. BOBBY BONDS
□ 592. DAN BRIGGS
□ 628. MARIO GUERRERO
□ 650. NOLAN RYAN

CHICAGO CUBS

□ 64. LARRY BIITTNER
□ 92. DAVE ROSELLO
□ 124. GEORGE MITTERWALD
□ 144. BRUCE SUTTER
□ 169. DAROLD KNOWLES
□ 190. RAY BURRIS
□ 219. JOE COLEMAN
□ 250. BILL MADLOCK
□ 279. JOE WALLIS
□ 302. MIKE GARMAN
□ 333. PAUL REUSCHEL
□ 360. RICK MONDAY
□ 395. MANNY TRILLO
□ 419. STEVE SWISHER
□ 446. BILL BONHAM
□ 468. RAMON HERNANDEZ
□ 493. MIKE KRUKOW(R)
□ 502. RANDY HUNDLEY
□ 518. TEAM & FRANKS(M)
□ 530. RICK REUSCHEL

□ 561. PETE LACOCK
□ 586. STEVE RENKO
□ 610. JOSE CARDENAL
□ 639. JERRY MORALES
□ 657. MICK KELLEHER

CHICAGO WHITE SOX

□ 17. STEVE STONE
□ 29. BUCKY DENT
□ 58. CHET LEMON
□ 83. KEVIN BELL
□ 109. JORGE ORTA
□ 133. RALPH GARR
□ 157. KEN BRETT
□ 177. BART JOHNSON
□ 198. WILBUR WOOD
□ 222. FRANCISCO BARRIOS
□ 247. CHRIS KNAPP
□ 271. TERRY FORSTER
□ 273. ERIC SODERHOLM
□ 293. JACK BROHAMER
□ 319. RICH GOSSAGE
□ 338. DAVE DUNCAN
□ 344. BRIAN DOWNING
□ 367. DAVE HAMILTON
□ 389. KEN KRAVEC
□ 418. TEAM & LEMON(M)
□ 443. LAMAR JOHNSON
□ 487. GREG TERLECKY(R)
□ 493. JIM OTTEN(R)
□ 497. CLAY CARROLL
□ 529. JIM ESSIAN
□ 559. ALAN BANNISTER
□ 623. JACK KUCEK
□ 648. JIM SPENCER

CINCINNATI REDS

□ 23. DAN DRIESSEN
□ 45. RAWLY EASTWICK
□ 70. JOHNNY BENCH
□ 86. PAT ZACHRY
□ 100. JOE MORGAN
□ 121. GARY NOLAN
□ 139. FRED NORMAN
□ 160. WILL MCENANEY
□ 186. DOUG FLYNN
□ 203. ED ARMBRISTER
□ 221. BOB BAILEY
□ 239. BILL PLUMMER
□ 287. TEAM & ANDERSON(M)
□ 320. KEN GRIFFEY
□ 347. GEORGE FOSTER
□ 450. PETE ROSE
□ 475. MANNY SARMIENTO(R)
□ 487. JOE HENDERSON(R)
□ 512. JACK BILLINGHAM
□ 535. CESAR GERONIMO
□ 548. JOEL YOUNGBLOOD
□ 560. DAVE CONCEPCION
□ 581. PEDRO BORBON
□ 601. MIKE LUM
□ 636. SANTO ALCALA
□ 655. TONY PEREZ

CLEVELAND INDIANS

□ 18. TEAM & ROBINSON(M)
□ 33. WAYNE GARLAND
□ 41. JIM KERN
□ 62. ERIC RAICH
□ 85. DUANE KUIPER
□ 115. RICK MANNING
□ 147. JACKIE BROWN
□ 168. CHARLIE SPIKES
□ 206. BOOG POWELL
□ 236. TOM BUSKEY
□ 267. RAY FOSSE
□ 296. DON HOOD
□ 306. RICK WAITS
□ 330. GEORGE HENDRICK
□ 385. DAVE LAROCHE
□ 393. JOHN LOWENSTEIN
□ 441. LARVELL BLANKS
□ 449. AL FITZMORRIS
□ 476. RICK CERONE(R)
□ 477. ORLANDO GONZALEZ(R)
□ 501. JIM BIBBY
□ 525. DENNIS ECKERSLEY

□ 542. FRANK DUFFY
□ 590. BUDDY BELL
□ 618. PAT DOBSON
□ 654. RON PRUITT

DETROIT TIGERS

□ 22. BILL FREEHAN
□ 43. RAY BARE
□ 69. JIM CRAWFORD
□ 98. MILT MAY
□ 122. BEN OGLIVIE
□ 145. TOM VERYZER
□ 173. CHUCK SCRIVENER
□ 240. RON LEFLORE
□ 265. MARK FIDRYCH
□ 291. JASON THOMPSON
□ 311. VERN RUHLE
□ 363. DAVE A. ROBERTS
□ 420. RUSTY STAUB
□ 453. PEDRO GARCIA
□ 477. PHIL MANKOWSKI(R)
□ 487. ED GLYNN(R)
□ 490. MARK WAGNER(R)
□ 491. BOB SYKES(R)
□ 492. STEVE KEMP(R)
□ 506. STEVE GRILLI
□ 533. MICKEY STANLEY
□ 554. BRUCE KIMM
□ 574. AURELIO RODRIGUEZ
□ 595. JOHN HILLER
□ 621. TEAM & HOUK(M)
□ 637. ALEX JOHNSON
□ 660. WILLIE HORTON

HOUSTON ASTROS

□ 21. KEN FORSCH
□ 42. JOSE CRUZ
□ 67. JOAQUIN ANDUJAR
□ 90. CESAR CEDENO
□ 116. JOE NIEKRO
□ 143. ED HERRMANN
□ 184. BO MCLAUGHLIN
□ 209. ROB ANDREWS
□ 227. JOE SAMBITO
□ 248. WILBUR HOWARD
□ 260. J.R. RICHARD
□ 283. JERRY DAVANON
□ 308. GENE PENTZ
□ 327. TEAM & VIRDON(M)
□ 350. LARRY DIERKER
□ 429. KEN BOSWELL
□ 456. LEON ROBERTS
□ 474. ALEX TAVERAS(R)
□ 478. MARK LEMONGELLO(R)
□ 481. ROGER METZGER
□ 514. CLIFF JOHNSON
□ 540. BOB WATSON
□ 567. ENOS CABELL
□ 589. MIKE COSGROVE
□ 614. GREG GROSS
□ 641. DAN LARSON

KANSAS CITY ROYALS

□ 46. BUCK MARTINEZ
□ 75. DENNIS LEONARD
□ 93. TOM POQUETTE

□ 117. FRANK WHITE
□ 141. MARK LITTELL
□ 171. KEN SANDERS
□ 193. LARRY GURA
□ 218. JOHN WATHAN
□ 244. JOHN MAYBERRY
□ 262. AL COWENS
□ 290. AMOS OTIS
□ 314. STEVE MINGORI
□ 340. HAL MCRAE
□ 362. TOMMY DAVIS
□ 371. TEAM & HERZOG(M)
□ 422. FREDDIE PATEK
□ 463. JAMIE QUIRK
□ 472. BOB MCCLURE(R)
□ 509. COOKIE ROJAS
□ 534. PAUL SPLITTORFF
□ 556. DOUG BIRD
□ 580. GEORGE BRETT
□ 602. ANDY HASSLER
□ 622. JIM WOHLFORD
□ 658. MARTY PATTIN

LOS ANGELES DODGERS

□ 27. BILL BUCKNER
□ 50. RON CEY
□ 88. STAN WALL
□ 105. STEVE YEAGER
□ 128. TOMMY JOHN
□ 146. DUSTY BAKER
□ 180. DAVE LOPES
□ 245. RICK RHODEN
□ 253. JOHN HALE
□ 272. LEE LACY
□ 298. CHARLIE HOUGH
□ 322. BILL RUSSELL
□ 345. REGGIE SMITH
□ 366. TED SIZEMORE
□ 386. MANNY MOTA
□ 400. STEVE GARVEY
□ 421. DOUG RAU
□ 448. ELLIE RODRIGUEZ
□ 476. KEVIN PASLEY(R)
□ 484. BURT HOOTON
□ 504. TEAM & LASORDA(M)
□ 558. ELIAS SOSA
□ 584. ED GOODSON
□ 620. DON SUTTON

MILWAUKEE BREWERS

□ 26. RAY SADECKI
□ 51. TEAM & GRAMMAS(M)
□ 79. DON MONEY
□ 99. TOM HAUSMAN
□ 125. BILL TRAVERS
□ 159. BERNIE CARBO
□ 185. SIXTO LEZCANO
□ 214. DARRELL PORTER
□ 255. GEORGE SCOTT
□ 278. DANNY FRISELLA
□ 307. GARY SUTHERLAND
□ 331. JIM COLBORN
□ 361. EDUARDO RODRIGUEZ
□ 382. CHARLIE MOORE
□ 406. TIM JOHNSON
□ 439. GORMAN THOMAS
□ 488. DAN THOMAS(R)
□ 494. JIM GANTNER(R)
□ 498. SAL BANDO
□ 507. MIKE HEGAN
□ 528. BILL CASTRO
□ 553. JACK HEIDEMANN
□ 577. JERRY AUGUSTINE
□ 604. JIM SLATON
□ 635. ROBIN YOUNT
□ 651. VON JOSHUA

MINNESOTA TWINS

□ 13. LUIS GOMEZ
□ 38. CRAIG KUSICK
□ 66. ROY SMALLEY
□ 87. GLENN BORGMANN
□ 120. ROD CAREW
□ 149. MIKE CUBBAGE
□ 175. BUTCH WYNEGAR
□ 202. TOM JOHNSON
□ 228. TEAM & MAUCH(M)
□ 249. PETE REDFERN
□ 304. JIM HUGHES
□ 321. DAVE GOLTZ
□ 375. LARRY HISLE
□ 398. TOM BURGMEIER
□ 424. STEVE BRYE
□ 457. STEVE LUEBBER
□ 478. JIM GIDEON(R)
□ 486. ED BANE
□ 513. JERRY TERRELL
□ 531. LYMAN BOSTOCK
□ 536. VIC ALBURY
□ 555. DAN FORD
□ 578. BOB RANDALL
□ 643. MIKE PAZIK

MONTREAL EXPOS

□ 28. WOODIE FRYMAN
□ 52. ELLIS VALENTINE
□ 76. TIM FOLI
□ 102. JOSE MORALES
□ 112. BILL GREIF
□ 132. CHIP LANG
□ 156. PETE MACKANIN
□ 178. BOMBO RIVERA
□ 199. PEPE FRIAS
□ 223. EARL WILLIAMS
□ 252. DALE MURRAY
□ 274. DON STANHOUSE
□ 295. GARY CARTER
□ 316. STEVE ROGERS
□ 341. JOE KERRIGAN
□ 368. MIKE JORGENSEN
□ 391. DAN WARTHEN
□ 417. WAYNE GARRETT
□ 471. DEL UNSER
□ 473. ANDRE DAWSON(R)
□ 479. SAM MEJIAS(R)
□ 526. LARRY PARRISH
□ 557. JERRY WHITE
□ 579. DON CARRITHERS
□ 593. DENNIS BLAIR
□ 612. BARRY FOOTE
□ 647. TEAM & WILLIAMS(M)
□ 649. DAVE CASH

NEW YORK METS

□ 44. BUD HARRELSON
□ 65. SKIP LOCKWOOD
□ 94. CRAIG SWAN
□ 119. JOHN STEARNS
□ 150. TOM SEAVER
□ 172. JOHN MILNER
□ 201. ED KRANEPOOL
□ 225. BOB APODACA
□ 246. MIKE VAIL
□ 259. TEAM & FRAZIER(M)
□ 281. ROY STAIGER
□ 300. JERRY KOOSMAN
□ 329. RON HODGES
□ 352. MIKE PHILLIPS
□ 376. NINO ESPINOSA
□ 399. BRUCE BOISCLAIR
□ 425. JOE TORRE
□ 440. JON MATLACK
□ 458. LEO FOSTER
□ 488. LEE MAZZILLI(R)
□ 500. DAVE KINGMAN
□ 552. PEPE MANGUAL
□ 565. MICKEY LOLICH
□ 587. RICK BALDWIN
□ 605. FELIX MILLAN
□ 627. BOB MYRICK

NEW YORK YANKEES

□ 10. REGGIE JACKSON
□ 15. DON GULLETT
□ 20. GRAIG NETTLES
□ 54. SANDY ALOMAR
□ 71. DOCK ELLIS
□ 96. LOU PINIELLA
□ 123. FRED STANLEY
□ 148. FRAN HEALY
□ 170. THURMAN MUNSON
□ 195. ED FIGUEROA
□ 220. CHRIS CHAMBLISS
□ 280. JIM HUNTER
□ 305. MICKEY RIVERS
□ 332. ELLIOTT MADDOX
□ 359. WILLIE RANDOLPH
□ 387. TEAM & MARTIN(M)
□ 408. CESAR TOVAR
□ 461. DICK TIDROW
□ 472. GIL PATTERSON(R)
□ 485. ROY WHITE
□ 490. MICKEY KLUTTS(R)
□ 505. OSCAR GAMBLE
□ 543. RON BLOMBERG
□ 568. CARLOS MAY
□ 598. SPARKY LYLE
□ 625. KEN HOLTZMAN
□ 656. RON GUIDRY

OAKLAND A'S

□ 12. LARRY HANEY
□ 31. JIM TODD
□ 53. PAUL MITCHELL
□ 61. MANNY SANGUILLEN
□ 74. TEAM & MCKEON(M)
□ 101. DICK BOSMAN
□ 127. RON FAIRLY
□ 181. KEN MCMULLEN
□ 204. JEFF NEWMAN
□ 230. VIDA BLUE
□ 261. PHIL GARNER
□ 284. MIKE NORRIS
□ 323. LARRY LINTZ
□ 349. JIM HOLT
□ 365. MIKE TORREZ
□ 383. STAN BAHNSEN
□ 402. TOMMY HELMS
□ 405. CLAUDELL WASHINGTON
□ 473. DENNY WALLING(R)
□ 475. CHRIS BATTON(R)
□ 479. WAYNE GROSS(R)
□ 491. CRAIG MITCHELL(R)
□ 551. BILL NORTH
□ 583. PAUL LINDBLAD
□ 616. TOMMY SANDT
□ 644. MATT ALEXANDER

PHILADELPHIA PHILLIES

□ 30. GREG LUZINSKI
□ 59. LARRY CHRISTENSON
□ 84. OLLIE BROWN
□ 110. STEVE CARLTON
□ 140. MIKE SCHMIDT
□ 164. TUG MCGRAW
□ 188. BOB TOLAN
□ 217. TOM UNDERWOOD
□ 243. RON REED
□ 264. TOM HUTTON
□ 289. GENE GARBER
□ 310. LARRY BOWA
□ 337. RON SCHUELER
□ 357. TIM MCCARVER
□ 388. TERRY HARMON
□ 415. JAY JOHNSTONE
□ 444. WAYNE TWITCHELL
□ 467. TEAM & OZARK(M)
□ 489. RANDY LERCH(R)
□ 520. GARRY MADDOX
□ 545. BOB BOONE

- □ 569. JIM LONBORG
- □ 596. JERRY MARTIN
- □ 619. JOHNNY OATES
- □ 638. JIM KAAT

PITTSBURGH PIRATES

- □ 35. RENNIE STENNETT
- □ 82. JIM ROOKER
- □ 104. OMAR MORENO
- □ 130. AL OLIVER
- □ 154. DAVE GIUSTI
- □ 167. RICH HEBNER
- □ 176. BOB ROBERTSON
- □ 197. ED OTT
- □ 270. DAVE PARKER
- □ 294. DOC MEDICH
- □ 318. DUFFY DYER
- □ 335. BILL ROBINSON
- □ 354. TEAM & TANNER(M)
- □ 374. KENT TEKULVE
- □ 460. WILLIE STARGELL
- □ 474. CRAIG REYNOLDS(R)
- □ 483. RICHIE ZISK
- □ 492. TONY ARMAS(R)
- □ 510. JOHN CANDELARIA
- □ 538. FRANK TAVERAS
- □ 563. BRUCE KISON
- □ 582. ED KIRKPATRICK
- □ 607. LARRY DEMERY
- □ 645. JERRY REUSS

ST. LOUIS CARDINALS

- □ 19. JOHN D'ACQUISTO
- □ 47. LYNN MCGLOTHEN
- □ 72. MIKE ANDERSON
- □ 95. KEITH HERNANDEZ
- □ 136. JERRY MUMPHREY
- □ 161. GARRY TEMPLETON
- □ 183. TEAM & RAPP(M)
- □ 205. PETE FALCONE
- □ 229. DON KESSINGER
- □ 355. LOU BROCK
- □ 381. BOB FORSCH
- □ 404. ERIC RASMUSSEN
- □ 427. DAVE RADER
- □ 452. MIKE CALDWELL
- □ 470. TED SIMMONS
- □ 495. AL HRABOSKY
- □ 516. BAKE MCBRIDE
- □ 541. JOHN DENNY
- □ 573. JOE FERGUSON
- □ 599. MIKE TYSON
- □ 624. HECTOR CRUZ
- □ 652. TOM WALKER

SAN DIEGO PADRES

- □ 9. DOUG RADER
- □ 39. TOM GRIFFIN
- □ 63. TITO FUENTES
- □ 78. BOB DAVIS
- □ 108. ALAN FOSTER
- □ 134. TEAM & MCNAMARA(M)
- □ 158. TED KUBIAK
- □ 182. DAN SPILLNER
- □ 215. BUTCH METZGER
- □ 241. DAVE TOMLIN
- □ 268. RICK SAWYER
- □ 286. JOHNNY GRUBB
- □ 303. GENE TENACE
- □ 325. MIKE IVIE
- □ 348. BRENT STROM
- □ 372. RICH FOLKERS
- □ 390. DAVE WINFIELD
- □ 407. DAVE FREISLEBEN
- □ 447. JERRY TURNER
- □ 472. DAVE WEHRMEISTER(R)
- □ 473. GENE RICHARDS(R)
- □ 490. BILLY ALMON(R)
- □ 491. MIKE DUPREE(R)
- □ 494. MIKE CHAMPION(R)
- □ 522. ENZO HERNANDEZ
- □ 523. ROLLIE FINGERS
- □ 550. RANDY JONES
- □ 576. FRED KENDALL
- □ 603. WILLIE DAVIS
- □ 629. BOBBY VALENTINE
- □ 659. MERV TETTENMUND

SAN FRANCISCO GIANTS

- □ 11. ROB DRESSLER
- □ 40. BOBBY MURCER
- □ 57. MARC HILL
- □ 73. CHARLIE WILLIAMS
- □ 97. DAVE HEAVERLO
- □ 129. MIKE SADEK
- □ 151. JOHNNIE LEMASTER
- □ 211. TEAM & ALTOBELLI(M)
- □ 266. DERRELL THOMAS
- □ 297. KEN REITZ
- □ 324. JOHN CURTIS
- □ 343. ED HALICKI
- □ 370. JOHN MONTEFUSCO
- □ 397. LARRY HERNDON
- □ 423. GARY LAVELLE
- □ 438. MARTY PEREZ
- □ 464. RANDY MOFFITT
- □ 476. GARY ALEXANDER(R)
- □ 488. JACK CLARK(R)
- □ 489. GREG MINTON(R)
- □ 496. GARY THOMASSON
- □ 515. CHRIS SPEIER
- □ 547. WILLIE MCCOVEY
- □ 571. DARRELL EVANS
- □ 591. CHRIS ARNOLD
- □ 609. JIM BARR
- □ 642. WILLIE CRAWFORD

SEATTLE MARINERS

- □ 14. TOMMY SMITH
- □ 49. GRANT JACKSON
- □ 118. RICK JONES
- □ 138. BOB STINSON
- □ 187. DICK POLE
- □ 207. GLENN ABBOTT
- □ 226. LEROY STANTON
- □ 269. JOE LIS
- □ 317. KURT BEVACQUA
- □ 334. BILL STEIN
- □ 353. STAN THOMAS
- □ 379. LARRY COX
- □ 394. BILL LAXTON
- □ 409. PETE BROBERG
- □ 431. DAVE COLLINS
- □ 478. DAVE C. JOHNSON(R)
- □ 488. RUPPERT JONES(R)
- □ 490. TOMMY MCMILLAN(R)
- □ 492. CARLOS LOPEZ(R)
- □ 493. GARY WHEELOCK(R)
- □ 494. JUAN BERNHARDT(R)
- □ 508. DAVE PAGAN
- □ 527. DAN MEYER
- □ 597. JOHNSON(M) & COACHS
- □ 606. STEVE BRAUN
- □ 653. DIEGO SEGUI

TEXAS RANGERS

- □ 36. JOHN ELLIS
- □ 55. JEFF BURROUGHS
- □ 81. JUAN BENIQUEZ
- □ 103. MIKE BACSIK
- □ 137. JEFF TERPKO
- □ 152. GAYLORD PERRY
- □ 174. NELSON BRILES
- □ 196. LEN RANDLE
- □ 237. GENE CLINES
- □ 254. DOYLE ALEXANDER
- □ 256. JOE HOERNER
- □ 275. MIKE HARGROVE
- □ 301. TOBY HARRAH
- □ 328. TOMMY BOGGS
- □ 351. JIM SUNDBERG
- □ 373. BERT CAMPANERIS
- □ 378. JIM UMBARGER
- □ 403. TOM GRIEVE
- □ 428. TEAM & LUCCHESI(M)
- □ 459. STEVE FOUCAULT
- □ 489. LEN BARKER(R)
- □ 494. BUMP WILLS(R)
- □ 511. BILL FAHEY
- □ 539. MIKE WALLACE
- □ 588. DAVE MOATES
- □ 608. ROY HOWELL
- □ 630. BERT BLYLEVEN

TORONTO BLUE JAYS

- □ 37. STEVE HARGAN
- □ 113. HARTSFIELD(M) & CHS.
- □ 163. DAVE HILTON
- □ 212. JIM MASON
- □ 299. OTTO VELEZ
- □ 326. JESSE JEFFERSON
- □ 346. BILL SINGER
- □ 377. DAVE MCKAY
- □ 392. PHIL ROOF
- □ 416. CHUCK HARTENSTEIN
- □ 465. RICO CARTY
- □ 473. JOHN SCOTT(R)
- □ 474. BOB BAILOR(R)
- □ 477. DOUG AULT(R)
- □ 478. LEON HOOTEN(R)
- □ 479. ALVIS WOODS(R)
- □ 487. LARRY ANDERSON(R)
- □ 492. GARY WOODS(R)
- □ 493. MIKE WILLIS(R)
- □ 517. PETE VUCKOVICH
- □ 537. DAVE W. ROBERTS
- □ 564. ALAN ASHBY
- □ 611. DAVE LEMANCZYK

1978 TOPPS (726)
2 1/2" X 3 1/2"

ATLANTA BRAVES

- □ 10. PHIL NIEKRO
- □ 38. WILLIE MONTANEZ
- □ 75. DICK RUTHVEN
- □ 93. BOBBY COX(M)
- □ 130. JEFF BURROUGHS
- □ 156. ANDY MESSERSMITH
- □ 187. JERRY ROYSTER
- □ 217. ROD GILBREATH
- □ 242. BARRY BONNELL
- □ 264. JAMIE EASTERLY
- □ 296. BIFF POCOROBA
- □ 322. TOM PACIOREK
- □ 349. RICK CAMP
- □ 372. BRIAN ASSELSTINE
- □ 402. DAVE CAMPBELL
- □ 443. DARREL CHANEY
- □ 475. GARY MATTHEWS
- □ 502. PAT ROCKETT
- □ 527. VIC CORRELL
- □ 551. TEAM CARD
- □ 578. BUZZ CAPRA
- □ 598. EDDIE SOLOMON
- □ 617. JOE NOLAN
- □ 632. ROWLAND OFFICE
- □ 681. ROB BELLOIR
- □ 703. MICKEY MAHLER(R)
- □ 708. DALE MURPHY(R)
- □ 716. CLARENCE GASTON

BALTIMORE ORIOLES

- □ 9. DOUG DECINCES
- □ 36. EDDIE MURRAY
- □ 65. KEN SINGLETON
- □ 96. TEAM CARD
- □ 119. DENNY MARTINEZ
- □ 160. JIM PALMER

☐ 188. AL BUMBRY
☐ 211. EARL WEAVER(M)
☐ 237. RICH DAUER
☐ 262. RUDY MAY
☐ 287. KIKO GARCIA
☐ 315. MARK BELANGER
☐ 341. MIKE FLANAGAN
☐ 367. RICK DEMPSEY
☐ 393. TIPPY MARTINEZ
☐ 418. TONY MUSER
☐ 466. DENNIS BLAIR
☐ 491. SCOTT MCGREGOR
☐ 517. ANDRES MORA
☐ 543. LARRY HARLOW
☐ 593. DAVE SKAGGS
☐ 616. H. PAT KELLY
☐ 640. LEE MAY
☐ 666. BILLY SMITH
☐ 691. ROSS GRIMSLEY
☐ 717. NELSON BRILES

BOSTON RED SOX

☐ 12. DON AASE
☐ 40. CARL YASTRZEMSKI
☐ 63. DON ZIMMER(M)
☐ 83. BOB MONTGOMERY
☐ 105. REGGIE CLEVELAND
☐ 125. GEORGE SCOTT
☐ 155. BUTCH HOBSON
☐ 186. BOB STANLEY
☐ 216. MIKE PAXTON
☐ 245. RICK BURLESON
☐ 270. CARLTON FISK
☐ 295. BILL LEE
☐ 320. FRED LYNN
☐ 345. LUIS TIANT
☐ 373. JIM WILLOUGHBY
☐ 416. JACK BROHAMER
☐ 424. TEAM CARD
☐ 457. BOB BAILEY
☐ 482. RICK MILLER
☐ 524. BERNIE CARBO
☐ 545. BILL CAMPBELL
☐ 567. DICK DRAGO
☐ 572. RICK WISE
☐ 597. STEVE DILLARD
☐ 618. TOMMY HELMS
☐ 642. DENNY DOYLE
☐ 645. MIKE TORREZ
☐ 670. JIM RICE
☐ 695. DWIGHT EVANS
☐ 706. TED COX(R)
☐ 708. BO DIAZ(R)
☐ 720. FERGIE JENKINS

CALIFORNIA ANGELS

☐ 18. BOB GRICH
☐ 48. DON BAYLOR
☐ 71. TERRY HUMPHREY
☐ 115. GARY NOLAN
☐ 150. BOBBY BONDS
☐ 178. DAVE CHALK
☐ 214. TEAM CARD
☐ 239. DYAR MILLER
☐ 268. GIL FLORES
☐ 291. GARY ROSS
☐ 313. ANDY ETCHEBARREN
☐ 339. MARIO GUERRERO
☐ 368. BALOR MOORE
☐ 400. NOLAN RYAN
☐ 429. MIKE BARLOW
☐ 454. DAVE LAROCHE
☐ 478. JERRY REMY
☐ 503. IKE HAMPTON
☐ 529. PAUL HARTZELL
☐ 557. TONY SOLAITA
☐ 579. RANCE MULLINIKS
☐ 600. FRANK TANANA
☐ 619. THAD BOSLEY
☐ 635. JOE RUDI
☐ 655. LYMAN BOSTOCK
☐ 656. DAVE GARCIA(M)
☐ 682. KEN BRETT
☐ 718. RON JACKSON

CHICAGO CUBS

☐ 17. MIKE KRUKOW
☐ 50. RICK REUSCHEL
☐ 76. STEVE ONTIVEROS
☐ 99. WILLIE HERNANDEZ
☐ 123. MANNY TRILLO
☐ 152. IVAN DEJESUS
☐ 175. JERRY MORALES
☐ 234. HERMAN FRANKS(M)
☐ 252. STEVE SWISHER
☐ 302. TEAM CARD
☐ 325. BRUCE SUTTER
☐ 346. LARRY BIITTNER
☐ 371. RAY BURRIS
☐ 397. GREG GROSS
☐ 423. DAVE ROSELLO
☐ 473. BILL BUCKNER
☐ 489. RUDY MEOLI
☐ 501. DAVE A. ROBERTS
☐ 523. DONNIE MOORE
☐ 541. LARRY COX
☐ 564. MICK KELLEHER
☐ 570. DAVE KINGMAN
☐ 585. WOODIE FRYMAN
☐ 590. BOBBY MURCER
☐ 614. JOE WALLIS
☐ 639. GENE CLINES
☐ 663. PAUL REUSCHEL
☐ 688. GEORGE MITTERWALD
☐ 711. DENNIS LAMP(R)
☐ 722. PETE BROBERG

CHICAGO WHITE SOX

☐ 14. LERRIN LAGROW
☐ 42. JORGE ORTA
☐ 66. TEAM CARD
☐ 98. JIM ESSIAN
☐ 127. CHET LEMON
☐ 153. STEVE STONE
☐ 182. JIM SPENCER
☐ 213. ALAN BANNISTER
☐ 231. WAYNE NORDHAGEN
☐ 251. DON KIRKWOOD
☐ 272. ROYLE STILLMAN
☐ 288. DAVE HAMILTON
☐ 316. HENRY CRUZ
☐ 329. JOHN VERHOEVEN
☐ 361. CHRIS KNAPP
☐ 395. JIM HUGHES
☐ 409. RON SCHUELER
☐ 421. JUNIOR MOORE
☐ 439. KEN KRAVEC
☐ 463. KEVIN BELL
☐ 493. STEVE RENKO
☐ 506. RON BLOMBERG
☐ 519. BRIAN DOWNING
☐ 552. FRANCISCO BARRIOS
☐ 574. BOB LEMON(M)
☐ 602. ERIC SODERHOLM
☐ 615. CLAY CARROLL
☐ 628. RALPH GARR
☐ 672. DON KESSINGER
☐ 693. LAMAR JOHNSON
☐ 702. BILL NAHORODNY(R)
☐ 726. WILBUR WOOD

CINCINNATI REDS

☐ 20. PETE ROSE
☐ 47. JACK BILLINGHAM
☐ 80. KEN GRIFFEY
☐ 106. BILL PLUMMER
☐ 126. PAUL MOSKAU
☐ 149. DALE MURRAY
☐ 180. DAVE CONCEPCION
☐ 220. PEDRO BORBON
☐ 246. DAN DRIESSEN
☐ 273. FRED NORMAN
☐ 276. BILL BONHAM
☐ 300. JOE MORGAN
☐ 326. MIKE LUM
☐ 354. CESAR GERONIMO
☐ 377. MANNY SARMIENTO
☐ 401. SPARKY ANDERSON(M)
☐ 427. MARIO SOTO
☐ 450. TOM SEAVER
☐ 477. DOUG CAPILLA
☐ 500. GEORGE FOSTER

☐ 526. TEAM CARD
☐ 556. ED ARMBRISTER
☐ 622. CHAMP SUMMERS
☐ 646. RICK AUERBACH
☐ 674. RAY KNIGHT
☐ 700. JOHNNY BENCH
☐ 701. TOM HUME(R)
☐ 702. DON WERNER(R)
☐ 706. DAVE REVERING(R)

CLEVELAND INDIANS

☐ 11. RICK MANNING
☐ 37. RICK WAITS
☐ 61. LARVELL BLANKS
☐ 87. JOHN LOWENSTEIN
☐ 101. SID MONGE
☐ 122. DENNIS ECKERSLEY
☐ 148. ANDRE THORNTON
☐ 174. WAYNE GARLAND
☐ 198. RON PRUITT
☐ 227. AL FITZMORRIS
☐ 253. JIM KERN
☐ 280. BUDDY BELL
☐ 305. RICO CARTY
☐ 332. DUANE KUIPER
☐ 351. JEFF TORBORG(M)
☐ 398. DON HOOD
☐ 426. FRED KENDALL
☐ 459. CHARLIE SPIKES
☐ 484. JIM NORRIS
☐ 511. FRANK DUFFY
☐ 537. BRUCE BOCHTE
☐ 575. PAT DOBSON
☐ 608. JOHNNY GRUBB
☐ 636. JIM BIBBY
☐ 662. PAUL DADE
☐ 689. TEAM CARD
☐ 703. LARRY ANDERSEN(R)
☐ 704. DAVE OLIVER(R)
☐ 706. WAYNE CAGE(R)
☐ 711. CARDELL CAMPER(R)

DETROIT TIGERS

☐ 21. STEVE KEMP
☐ 45. MARK FIDRYCH
☐ 68. STEVE FOUCAULT
☐ 94. CHUCK SCRIVENER
☐ 124. DAVE ROZEMA
☐ 151. MILT WILCOX
☐ 176. MILT MAY
☐ 232. MICKEY STANLEY
☐ 258. JOHN HILLER
☐ 286. BEN OGLIVIE
☐ 342. AURELIO RODRIGUEZ
☐ 370. RUSTY STAUB
☐ 385. TITO FUENTES
☐ 404. TEAM CARD
☐ 456. VERN RUHLE
☐ 480. RON LEFLORE
☐ 515. TIM CORCORAN
☐ 536. RORIC HARRISON
☐ 559. PHIL MANKOWSKI
☐ 607. FERNANDO ARROYO
☐ 633. TOM VERYZER
☐ 660. JASON THOMPSON
☐ 684. RALPH HOUK(M)
☐ 701. BRUCE TAYLOR(R)
☐ 703. JACK MORRIS(R)
☐ 704. LOU WHITAKER(R)
☐ 707. ALAN TRAMMELL(R)
☐ 708. LANCE PARRISH(R)
☐ 723. JOHN WOCKENFUSS

HOUSTON ASTROS

☐ 13. ART HOWE
☐ 39. FLOYD BANNISTER
☐ 64. GENE PENTZ
☐ 91. OSCAR ZAMORA
☐ 112. TEAM CARD
☐ 132. ENOS CABELL
☐ 158. JOAQUIN ANDUJAR
☐ 181. KEN FORSCH
☐ 226. JOE FERGUSON
☐ 263. DANNY WALTON
☐ 279. BILL VIRDON(M)
☐ 306. JOE NIEKRO
☐ 330. BOB WATSON

□ 358. MARK LEMONGELLO
□ 389. JULIO GONZALEZ
□ 437. BO MCLAUGHLIN
□ 470. J.R. RICHARD
□ 498. JOE SAMBITO
□ 514. ROB SPERRING
□ 534. WILBUR HOWARD
□ 553. TERRY PUHL
□ 625. JOSE CRUZ
□ 650. CESAR CEDENO
□ 677. ED HERRMANN
□ 697. ROGER METZGER
□ 705. DAVE BERGMAN(R)
□ 711. ROY THOMAS(R)

KANSAS CITY ROYALS

□ 19. DARRELL PORTER
□ 46. AL COWENS
□ 73. ANDY HASSLER
□ 100. GEORGE BRETT
□ 129. JIM COLBORN
□ 157. PETE LACOCK
□ 183. DOUG BIRD
□ 218. MARTY PATTIN
□ 248. FRANK WHITE
□ 274. FRED PATEK
□ 299. WHITEY HERZOG(M)
□ 331. MARK LITTELL
□ 336. STEVE BUSBY
□ 343. JOHN WATHAN
□ 357. TOM POQUETTE
□ 382. JOE LAHOUD
□ 408. JOE ZDEB
□ 441. LARRY GURA
□ 465. HAL MCRAE
□ 490. AMOS OTIS
□ 525. JERRY TERRELL
□ 550. JOHN MAYBERRY
□ 571. BUCK MARTINEZ
□ 638. PAUL SPLITTORFF
□ 665. DENNIS LEONARD
□ 696. STEVE MINGORI
□ 705. CLINT HURDLE(R)
□ 707. U.L. WASHINGTON(R)
□ 724. TEAM CARD

LOS ANGELES DODGERS

□ 22. CHARLIE HOUGH
□ 41. BURT HOOTON
□ 104. LEE LACY
□ 128. BILL RUSSELL
□ 145. RICK MONDAY
□ 168. REGGIE SMITH
□ 189. TOM LASORDA(M)
□ 228. MANNY MOTA
□ 259. TEAM CARD
□ 285. STEVE YEAGER
□ 310. DON SUTTON
□ 347. TERRY FORSTER
□ 350. STEVE GARVEY
□ 375. TOMMY JOHN
□ 417. MIKE GARMAN
□ 440. DAVE LOPES
□ 464. JERRY GROTE
□ 508. JOHNNY OATES
□ 539. VIC DAVALILLO
□ 546. TED MARTINEZ
□ 562. GLENN BURKE
□ 586. ED GOODSON
□ 605. RICK RHODEN
□ 630. RON CEY
□ 641. DOUG RAU
□ 668. DUSTY BAKER
□ 694. ELIAS SOSA
□ 709. LANCE RAUTZHAN(R)

MILWAUKEE BREWERS

□ 24. DON MONEY
□ 51. CHARLIE MOORE
□ 77. ED KIRKPATRICK
□ 95. JAMIE QUIRK
□ 108. VON JOSHUA
□ 133. JERRY AUGUSTINE
□ 154. CECIL COOPER
□ 173. ROBIN YOUNT
□ 212. MIKE CALDWELL
□ 243. BOB MCCLURE
□ 265. SAL BANDO
□ 303. SAM HINDS
□ 328. TEAM CARD
□ 355. BILL TRAVERS
□ 376. JIM WOHLFORD
□ 391. LARRY HANEY
□ 415. RAY FOSSE
□ 448. BILL CASTRO
□ 474. JIM SLATON
□ 516. GARY BEARE
□ 520. LARRY HISLE
□ 542. TIM JOHNSON
□ 569. LARY SORENSEN
□ 595. SIXTO LEZCANO
□ 623. EDUARDO RODRIGUEZ
□ 649. MOOSE HAAS
□ 673. STEVE BRYE
□ 707. PAUL MOLITOR(R)

DON MONEY

MINNESOTA TWINS

□ 27. GEOFF ZAHN
□ 54. TOM JOHNSON
□ 81. PETE REDFERN
□ 113. DON CARRITHERS
□ 137. CRAIG KUSICK
□ 162. PAUL THORMODSGARD
□ 193. RICH CHILES
□ 219. MIKE CUBBAGE
□ 249. DAVE GOLTZ
□ 275. DAN FORD
□ 307. GLENN BORGMANN
□ 363. BOB RANDALL
□ 386. BOB GORINSKI
□ 432. TERRY BULLING
□ 451. TEAM CARD
□ 471. ROY SMALLEY
□ 497. GLENN ADAMS
□ 555. BUTCH WYNEGAR
□ 580. ROD CAREW
□ 601. GENE MAUCH(M)
□ 627. DAVE C. JOHNSON
□ 657. BOMBO RIVERA
□ 678. TOM BURGMEIER
□ 704. SAM PERLOZZO(R)
□ 705. WILLIE NORWOOD(R)

MONTREAL EXPOS

□ 15. TONY PEREZ
□ 43. BILL ATKINSON
□ 72. ANDRE DAWSON
□ 97. STAN BAHNSEN
□ 120. GARY CARTER
□ 185. ELLIS VALENTINE
□ 221. CHRIS SPEIER
□ 244. TEAM CARD
□ 269. WAYNE TWITCHELL
□ 294. LARRY PARRISH
□ 321. SANTO ALCALA
□ 348. DEL UNSER
□ 374. JOSE MORALES
□ 399. PETE MACKANIN
□ 414. DAROLD KNOWLES
□ 425. STEVE ROGERS
□ 449. TIM BLACKWELL
□ 468. WARREN CROMARTIE
□ 495. DAVE CASH
□ 522. DICK WILLIAMS(M)
□ 549. JOE KERRIGAN
□ 576. SAM MEJIAS
□ 603. WILL MCENANEY
□ 629. DON STANHOUSE
□ 654. PEPE FRIAS
□ 679. WAYNE GARRETT
□ 699. JACKIE BROWN
□ 701. LARRY LANDRETH(R)
□ 709. DAN SCHATZEDER(R)

NEW YORK METS

□ 25. JON MATLACK
□ 49. ED KRANEPOOL
□ 69. MIKE VAIL
□ 109. JOE TORRE
□ 134. STEVE HENDERSON
□ 147. LEE MAZZILLI
□ 171. PAT ZACHRY
□ 197. NINO ESPINOSA
□ 229. LEO FOSTER
□ 277. BRUCE BOISCLAIR
□ 304. JOHN MILNER
□ 334. JOHN STEARNS
□ 356. TEAM CARD
□ 379. SKIP LOCKWOOD
□ 403. BUD HARRELSON
□ 428. JOEL YOUNGBLOOD
□ 442. ELLIOTT MADDOX
□ 453. DOUG FLYNN
□ 481. JACKSON TODD
□ 505. FELIX MILLAN
□ 544. LEN RANDLE
□ 565. JERRY KOOSMAN
□ 592. BOB APODACA
□ 621. CRAIG SWAN
□ 653. RON HODGES
□ 676. BOB MYRICK
□ 712. BOBBY VALENTINE

NEW YORK YANKEES

□ 16. ROY WHITE
□ 35. SPARKY LYLE
□ 60. THURMAN MUNSON
□ 70. RICH GOSSAGE
□ 89. KEN CLAY
□ 114. PAUL BLAIR
□ 135. RON GUIDRY
□ 159. LOU PINIELLA
□ 179. DICK TIDROW
□ 200. REGGIE JACKSON
□ 225. DON GULLETT
□ 250. GRAIG NETTLES
□ 282. TEAM CARD
□ 309. CLIFF JOHNSON
□ 335. BUCKY DENT
□ 365. ED FIGUEROA
□ 387. KEN HOLTZMAN
□ 460. JIM HUNTER
□ 485. CHRIS CHAMBLISS
□ 582. FRAN HEALY
□ 591. GEORGE ZEBER
□ 620. WILLIE RANDOLPH
□ 664. FRED STANLEY
□ 690. MICKEY RIVERS
□ 707. MICKEY KLUTTS(R)
□ 710. DELL ALSTON(R)
□ 721. BILLY MARTIN(M)

OAKLAND A'S

□ 29. BOB LACEY
□ 55. MITCHELL PAGE
□ 78. PABLO TORREALBA
□ 102. MATT ALEXANDER
□ 139. WAYNE GROSS
□ 163. BILL NORTH
□ 191. RODNEY SCOTT
□ 224. JERRY TABB
□ 261. TIM HOSLEY
□ 298. TONY ARMAS
□ 327. RICK LANGFORD
□ 353. DOUG BAIR
□ 378. BOBBY WINKLES(M)
□ 406. MIKE JORGENSEN
□ 434. MIKE NORRIS
□ 458. JEFF NEWMAN
□ 487. JIM TYRONE
□ 507. WILLIE CRAWFORD

- ☐ 528. ROB PICCIOLO
- ☐ 554. JOE COLEMAN
- ☐ 577. TEAM CARD
- ☐ 604. EARL WILLIAMS
- ☐ 613. MARTY PEREZ
- ☐ 647. STEVE DUNNING
- ☐ 658. MANNY SANGUILLEN
- ☐ 680. VIDA BLUE
- ☐ 701. STEVE MCCATTY(R)
- ☐ 709. MATT KEOUGH(R)
- ☐ 711. CRAIG MITCHELL(R)

PHILADELPHIA PHILLIES

- ☐ 26. RICH HEBNER
- ☐ 52. JIM LONBORG
- ☐ 90. LARRY BOWA
- ☐ 118. TERRY HARMON
- ☐ 136. TED SIZEMORE
- ☐ 161. BOB BOONE
- ☐ 177. GENE GARBER
- ☐ 210. JOSE CARDENAL
- ☐ 222. JERRY MARTIN
- ☐ 235. TIM MCCARVER
- ☐ 247. LARRY CHRISTENSON
- ☐ 271. RANDY LERCH
- ☐ 297. WARREN BRUSSTAR
- ☐ 317. DAVE A. JOHNSON
- ☐ 340. BAKE MCBRIDE
- ☐ 360. MIKE SCHMIDT
- ☐ 381. TEAM CARD
- ☐ 420. GREG LUZINSKI
- ☐ 446. TUG MCGRAW
- ☐ 472. RON REED
- ☐ 513. BARRY FOOTE
- ☐ 540. STEVE CARLTON
- ☐ 568. TOM HUTTON
- ☐ 610. GARRY MADDOX
- ☐ 631. DANNY OZARK(M)
- ☐ 675. JAY JOHNSTONE
- ☐ 715. JIM KAAT

PITTSBURGH PIRATES

- ☐ 28. ED OTT
- ☐ 53. PHIL GARNER
- ☐ 84. KENT TEKULVE
- ☐ 138. LARRY DEMERY
- ☐ 165. RENNIE STENNETT
- ☐ 190. JOHN CANDELARIA
- ☐ 223. BRUCE KISON
- ☐ 255. JERRY REUSS
- ☐ 283. OMAR MORENO
- ☐ 308. JIM ROOKER
- ☐ 323. JIM FREGOSI
- ☐ 383. MARIO MENDOZA
- ☐ 407. ODELL JONES
- ☐ 430. AL OLIVER
- ☐ 433. FERNANDO GONZALEZ
- ☐ 455. BILL ROBINSON
- ☐ 483. KEN MACHA
- ☐ 494. CHUCK TANNER(M)
- ☐ 510. WILLIE STARGELL
- ☐ 560. DAVE PARKER
- ☐ 606. TEAM CARD
- ☐ 637. DUFFY DYER
- ☐ 661. GRANT JACKSON
- ☐ 685. FRANK TAVERAS
- ☐ 703. TIM JONES(R)
- ☐ 705. MIGUEL DILONE(R)
- ☐ 710. MIKE EASLER(R)

- ☐ 431. BUTCH METZGER
- ☐ 452. JERRY MUMPHREY
- ☐ 479. TEAM CARD
- ☐ 504. ROGER FREED
- ☐ 531. TOM UNDERWOOD
- ☐ 563. DAVE RADER
- ☐ 587. JOHN URREA
- ☐ 609. JOHN DENNY
- ☐ 644. JIM DWYER
- ☐ 669. PETE FALCONE
- ☐ 692. KEN REITZ
- ☐ 710. RICK BOSETTI(R)
- ☐ 714. MIKE ANDERSON

SAN DIEGO PADRES

- ☐ 30. GEORGE HENDRICK
- ☐ 56. RANDY JONES
- ☐ 86. DAVE TOMLIN
- ☐ 116. TUCKER ASHFORD
- ☐ 140. ROLLIE FINGERS
- ☐ 164. BOB OWCHINKO
- ☐ 192. TEAM CARD
- ☐ 240. GENE TENACE
- ☐ 266. BOB SHIRLEY
- ☐ 292. GENE RICHARDS
- ☐ 318. TOM GRIFFIN
- ☐ 364. JERRY TURNER
- ☐ 390. OSCAR GAMBLE
- ☐ 392. BILLY ALMON
- ☐ 445. MIKE IVIE
- ☐ 467. ALVIN DARK(M)
- ☐ 488. DAN SPILLNER
- ☐ 509. BRENT STROM
- ☐ 530. DAVE WINFIELD
- ☐ 566. MERV RETTENMUND
- ☐ 594. DAVE FREISLEBEN
- ☐ 611. PAT SCANLON
- ☐ 683. MIKE CHAMPION
- ☐ 702. RICK SWEET(R)
- ☐ 713. BOB DAVIS

SAN FRANCISCO GIANTS

- ☐ 8. MIKE SADEK
- ☐ 34. WILLIE MCCOVEY
- ☐ 62. JIM BARR
- ☐ 82. TEAM CARD
- ☐ 107. ED HALICKI
- ☐ 142. JOHN MONTEFUSCO
- ☐ 167. TIM FOLI
- ☐ 194. DERREL THOMAS
- ☐ 215. DARRELL EVANS
- ☐ 236. TERRY WHITFIELD
- ☐ 256. JOE ALTOBELLI(M)
- ☐ 284. RANDY MOFFITT
- ☐ 312. GREG MINTON
- ☐ 338. DAVE HEAVERLO
- ☐ 359. MARC HILL
- ☐ 384. JACK CLARK
- ☐ 410. BILL MADLOCK
- ☐ 436. VIC HARRIS
- ☐ 461. ROB ANDREWS
- ☐ 486. JOHN CURTIS
- ☐ 512. LARRY HERNDON
- ☐ 538. JOHNNIE LEMASTER
- ☐ 561. CHARLIE WILLIAMS
- ☐ 581. LYNN MCGLOTHEN

- ☐ 589. BOB KNEPPER
- ☐ 624. GARY ALEXANDER
- ☐ 648. GARY THOMASSON
- ☐ 671. GARY LAVELLE
- ☐ 719. RANDY ELLIOTT

SEATTLE MARINERS

- ☐ 31. GLENN ABBOTT
- ☐ 57. DAN MEYER
- ☐ 79. DARRELL JOHNSON(M)
- ☐ 117. JOHN MONTAGUE
- ☐ 141. RUPPERT JONES
- ☐ 166. CARLOS LOPEZ
- ☐ 199. CRAIG REYNOLDS
- ☐ 233. DICK POLE
- ☐ 254. DAVE COLLINS
- ☐ 278. ENRIQUE ROMO
- ☐ 311. JOSE BAEZ
- ☐ 333. JIM TODD
- ☐ 366. LARRY MILBOURNE
- ☐ 396. BOB STINSON
- ☐ 422. STEVE BRAUN
- ☐ 447. LEROY STANTON
- ☐ 476. BILL STEIN
- ☐ 499. TEAM CARD
- ☐ 532. SKIP JUTZE
- ☐ 558. PAUL MITCHELL
- ☐ 584. JOHN HALE
- ☐ 596. GARY WHEELOCK
- ☐ 643. TOM HOUSE
- ☐ 687. JULIO CRUZ
- ☐ 698. JUAN BERNHARDT
- ☐ 702. KEVIN PASLEY(R)
- ☐ 709. STEVE BURKE(R)

TEXAS RANGERS

- ☐ 23. BUMP WILLS
- ☐ 44. TOBY HARRAH
- ☐ 67. CLAUDELL WASHINGTON
- ☐ 92. ADRIAN DEVINE
- ☐ 110. RICHIE ZISK
- ☐ 131. BERT BLYLEVEN
- ☐ 146. DOYLE ALEXANDER
- ☐ 172. MIKE HARGROVE
- ☐ 209. DOCK ELLIS
- ☐ 238. JUAN BENIQUEZ
- ☐ 260. BERT CAMPANERIS
- ☐ 290. WILLIE HORTON
- ☐ 314. PAUL LINDBLAD
- ☐ 337. TOM GRIEVE
- ☐ 362. DAVE MAY
- ☐ 388. BILL FAHEY
- ☐ 438. JOHN ELLIS
- ☐ 462. ROGELIO MORET
- ☐ 492. JIM SUNDBERG
- ☐ 518. TOMMY BOGGS
- ☐ 533. SANDY ALOMAR
- ☐ 548. BILLY HUNTER(M)
- ☐ 583. DOC MEDICH
- ☐ 588. JIM MASON
- ☐ 612. KEN HENDERSON
- ☐ 634. LEN BARKER
- ☐ 659. TEAM CARD
- ☐ 686. GAYLORD PERRY
- ☐ 706. PAT PUTNAM(R)
- ☐ 710. KEITH SMITH(R)
- ☐ 725. KURT BEVACQUA

TORONTO BLUE JAYS

- ☐ 33. DAVE LEMANCZYK
- ☐ 59. OTTO VELEZ
- ☐ 85. RON FAIRLY
- ☐ 103. TOM MURPHY
- ☐ 121. ALVIS WOODS
- ☐ 144. JESSE JEFFERSON
- ☐ 169. JERRY JOHNSON
- ☐ 196. BOB BAILOR
- ☐ 241. PETE VUCKOVICH
- ☐ 267. DOUG AULT
- ☐ 293. MIKE WILLIS
- ☐ 319. ALAN ASHBY
- ☐ 344. SAM EWING
- ☐ 369. TIM NORDBROOK
- ☐ 394. ROY HOWELL
- ☐ 419. JERRY GARVIN
- ☐ 444. ROY HARTSFIELD(M)
- ☐ 469. RICK CERONE

☐ 496. JIM CLANCY
☐ 521. STEVE STAGGS
☐ 547. JOHN SCOTT
☐ 573. LUIS GOMEZ
☐ 599. GARY WOODS
☐ 626. TEAM CARD
☐ 651. DOUG RADER
☐ 667. JEFF BYRD
☐ 704. GARTH IORG(R)
☐ 708. ERNIE WHITT(R)

1979 TOPPS (726)
2 1/2" X 3 1/2"

ATLANTA BRAVES

☐ 9. DAVE CAMPBELL
☐ 39. DALE MURPHY
☐ 85. GARY MATTHEWS
☐ 105. RICK CAMP
☐ 132. ROWLAND OFFICE
☐ 156. BUDDY SOLOMON
☐ 184. DARREL CHANEY
☐ 222. BOB BEALL
☐ 245. JEFF BURROUGHS
☐ 257. ADRIAN DEVINE
☐ 296. PRESTON HANNA
☐ 302. TEAM & COX(M)
☐ 331. MICKEY MAHLER
☐ 344. JERRY ROYSTER
☐ 363. CRAIG SKOK
☐ 384. TOMMY BOGGS
☐ 464. JOE NOLAN
☐ 496. BARRY BONNELL
☐ 504. LARRY MCWILLIAMS
☐ 529. BRIAN ASSELSTINE
☐ 555. BIFF POCOROBA
☐ 572. ROD GILBREATH
☐ 586. BOB HORNER
☐ 595. PHIL NIEKRO
☐ 629. GENE GARBER
☐ 684. JAMIE EASTERLY
☐ 715. BRUCE BENEDICT(P)
☐ 715. GLENN HUBBARD(P)
☐ 715. LARRY WHISENTON(P)

BALTIMORE ORIOLES

☐ 10. LEE MAY
☐ 37. JOE KERRIGAN
☐ 65. MARK BELANGER
☐ 91. TERRY CROWLEY
☐ 102. MIKE ANDERSON
☐ 119. DON STANHOUSE
☐ 160. MIKE FLANAGAN
☐ 188. H. PAT KELLY
☐ 211. DENNY MARTINEZ
☐ 237. BILLY SMITH
☐ 262. NELSON BRILES
☐ 287. ANDRES MORA
☐ 314. LARRY HARLOW
☐ 340. JIM PALMER
☐ 367. DAVE SKAGGS
☐ 393. SCOTT MCGREGOR
☐ 421. DOUG DECINCES
☐ 491. TIPPY MARTINEZ
☐ 517. AL BUMBRY
☐ 543. KIKO GARCIA
☐ 568. CARLOS LOPEZ
☐ 593. RICK DEMPSEY
☐ 615. KEN SINGLETON
☐ 640. EDDIE MURRAY
☐ 666. RICH DAUER
☐ 689. TEAM & WEAVER(M)
☐ 701. MARK COREY(P)
☐ 701. JOHN FLINN(P)
☐ 701. SAMMY STEWART(P)

BOSTON RED SOX

☐ 12. DICK DRAGO
☐ 40. DENNIS ECKERSLEY
☐ 63. JACK BROHAMER
☐ 83. FRED KENDALL
☐ 106. FRANK DUFFY
☐ 125. RICK BURLESON
☐ 155. DWIGHT EVANS
☐ 185. MIKE TORREZ
☐ 214. TEAM & ZIMMER(M)
☐ 270. BUTCH HOBSON
☐ 320. CARL YASTRZEMSKI
☐ 349. JIM C. WRIGHT
☐ 375. BILL CAMPBELL
☐ 400. JIM RICE
☐ 423. BOB MONTGOMERY
☐ 455. BILL LEE
☐ 480. FRED LYNN
☐ 524. TOM BURGMEIER
☐ 549. BOB BAILEY
☐ 575. LUIS TIANT
☐ 597. BOB STANLEY
☐ 618. JERRY REMY
☐ 645. GEORGE SCOTT
☐ 680. CARLTON FISK
☐ 696. ANDY HASSLER
☐ 702. JOEL FINCH(P)
☐ 702. GARRY HANCOCK(P)
☐ 702. ALLEN RIPLEY(P)

CALIFORNIA ANGELS

☐ 18. TONY SOLAITA
☐ 48. MERV RETTENMUND
☐ 71. BRIAN DOWNING
☐ 115. NOLAN RYAN
☐ 212. CARNEY LANSFORD
☐ 267. JOE RUDI
☐ 291. TOM GRIFFIN
☐ 313. DYAR MILLER
☐ 322. DANNY GOODWIN
☐ 339. RON JACKSON
☐ 368. DON AASE
☐ 402. PAUL HARTZELL
☐ 424. TEAM & FREGOSI(M)
☐ 453. CHRIS KNAPP
☐ 477. BOB GRICH
☐ 503. TERRY HUMPHREY
☐ 530. FRANK TANANA
☐ 557. KEN BRETT
☐ 580. RON FAIRLY
☐ 601. DAVE LAROCHE
☐ 619. KEN LANDREAUX
☐ 635. DON BAYLOR
☐ 638. AL FITZMORRIS
☐ 654. RICK MILLER
☐ 682. DAVE CHALK
☐ 703. JIM ANDERSON(P)
☐ 703. DAVE FROST(P)
☐ 703. BOB SLATER(P)

CHICAGO CUBS

☐ 17. DONNIE MOORE
☐ 53. MICK KELLEHER
☐ 86. RODNEY SCOTT
☐ 98. RAY BURRIS
☐ 135. BOBBY MURCER
☐ 153. DENNIS LAMP
☐ 171. GENE CLINES
☐ 240. RICK REUSCHEL
☐ 299. STEVE ONTIVEROS
☐ 323. LYNN MCGLOTHEN
☐ 346. BILL BUCKNER
☐ 370. DAVE KINGMAN
☐ 398. IVAN DEJESUS
☐ 433. LARRY BIITTNER
☐ 457. BRUCE SUTTER
☐ 473. DAVE A. ROBERTS
☐ 489. LARRY COX
☐ 494. JERRY WHITE
☐ 513. DAVE A. JOHNSON
☐ 522. KEN HOLTZMAN
☐ 551. TEAM & FRANKS(M)
☐ 579. GREG GROSS
☐ 592. MIKE KRUKOW
☐ 614. WILLIE HERNANDEZ
☐ 639. MANNY TRILLO
☐ 663. MIKE VAIL
☐ 693. DAVE RADER
☐ 716. DAVE GEISEL(P)
☐ 716. KARL PAGEL(P)
☐ 716. SCOT THOMPSON(P)

CHICAGO WHITE SOX

☐ 42. RON BLOMBERG
☐ 88. BOB MOLINARO
☐ 127. THAD BOSLEY
☐ 134. ALAN BANNISTER
☐ 169. BILL NAHORODNY
☐ 186. ERIC SODERHOLM
☐ 216. WILBUR WOOD
☐ 227. STEVE STONE
☐ 242. PABLO TORREALBA
☐ 266. JIM WILLOUGHBY
☐ 275. JUNIOR MOORE
☐ 283. KEN KRAVEC
☐ 309. RALPH GARR
☐ 333. CHET LEMON
☐ 351. WAYNE NORDHAGEN
☐ 372. LAMAR JOHNSON
☐ 386. FRANCISCO BARRIOS
☐ 404. TEAM & KESSINGER(M)
☐ 467. DON KESSINGER
☐ 514. MIKE PROLY
☐ 527. LERRIN LAGROW
☐ 559. GREG PRYOR
☐ 574. CLAUDELL WASHINGTON
☐ 631. JORGE ORTA
☐ 662. KEVIN BELL
☐ 686. RON SCHUELER
☐ 704. ROSS BAUMGARTEN(P)
☐ 704. MIKE COLBERN(P)
☐ 704. MIKE SQUIRES(P)

CINCINNATI REDS

☐ 20. JOE MORGAN
☐ 47. FRED NORMAN
☐ 73. KEN HENDERSON
☐ 100. TOM SEAVER
☐ 126. DOUG BAIR
☐ 149. MANNY SARMIENTO
☐ 174. RICK AUERBACH
☐ 200. JOHNNY BENCH
☐ 220. CESAR GERONIMO
☐ 259. TEAM & ANDERSON(M)
☐ 281. VIC CORRELL
☐ 301. TOM HUME
☐ 326. PEDRO BORBON
☐ 354. BILL BONHAM
☐ 377. PAUL MOSKAU
☐ 401. RAY KNIGHT
☐ 420. KEN GRIFFEY
☐ 450. DAVE CONCEPCION
☐ 475. DAN DRIESSEN
☐ 501. JUNIOR KENNEDY
☐ 516. CHAMP SUMMERS
☐ 556. MIKE LUM
☐ 600. GEORGE FOSTER
☐ 622. DAVE COLLINS
☐ 650. PETE ROSE
☐ 674. DAVE TOMLIN
☐ 717. MIKE LACOSS(P)
☐ 717. RON OESTER(P)
☐ 717. HARRY SPILMAN(P)

CLEVELAND INDIANS

☐ 13. PAUL DADE
☐ 38. BERNIE CARBO
☐ 61. BO DIAZ
☐ 77. DAN BRIGGS
☐ 79. TED COX
☐ 96. TEAM & TORBORG(M)
☐ 122. MIKE PAXTON
☐ 146. DUANE KUIPER

□ 150. WAYNE CAGE
□ 168. DAVE FREISLEBEN
□ 226. RON PRUITT
□ 253. RICK WISE
□ 280. ANDRE THORNTON
□ 307. LARVELL BLANKS
□ 332. GARY ALEXANDER
□ 359. DAN SPILLNER
□ 399. DAVID CLYDE
□ 425. RICK MANNING
□ 438. HORACE SPEED
□ 459. SID MONGE
□ 484. RICK WAITS
□ 511. PAUL REUSCHEL
□ 537. TOM VERYZER
□ 573. JIM KERN
□ 611. JIM NORRIS
□ 636. WAYNE GARLAND
□ 667. DON HOOD
□ 690. BUDDY BELL
□ 705. ALFREDO GRIFFIN(P)
□ 705. TIM NORRID(P)
□ 705. DAVE OLIVER(P)

DETROIT TIGERS

□ 33. DAVE ROZEMA
□ 66. TEAM & MOSS(M)
□ 80. JASON THOMPSON
□ 93. PHIL MANKOWSKI
□ 123. LOU WHITAKER
□ 151. JOHN HILLER
□ 176. AURELIO RODRIGUEZ
□ 196. STEVE KEMP
□ 217. STEVE DILLARD
□ 231. JOHNNY WOCKENFUSS
□ 251. JACK MORRIS
□ 272. TIM CORCORAN
□ 288. MILT WILCOX
□ 316. MILT MAY
□ 343. ED GLYNN
□ 358. ALAN TRAMMELL
□ 388. JACK BILLINGHAM
□ 440. RUSTY STAUB
□ 469. LANCE PARRISH
□ 541. JIM SLATON
□ 569. BOB SYKES
□ 598. MARK WAGNER
□ 625. MARK FIDRYCH
□ 660. RON LEFLORE
□ 692. MICKEY STANLEY
□ 706. DAVE STEGMAN(P)
□ 706. DAVE TOBIK(P)
□ 706. KIP YOUNG(P)

HOUSTON ASTROS

□ 14. RAFAEL LANDESTORY
□ 49. VERN RUHLE
□ 68. JOE NIEKRO
□ 107. JESUS ALOU
□ 130. BOB WATSON
□ 139. LUIS PUJOLS
□ 158. JOE SAMBITO
□ 187. MARK LEMONGELLO
□ 232. JIMMY SEXTON
□ 268. JULIO GONZALEZ
□ 289. JOSE CRUZ
□ 306. FLOYD BANNISTER
□ 327. ART HOWE
□ 361. TOM DIXON
□ 381. TEAM & VIRDON(M)
□ 437. RICK WILLIAMS
□ 471. JOAQUIN ANDUJAR
□ 515. ENOS CABELL
□ 534. KEN FORSCH
□ 553. DENNY WALLING
□ 570. CESAR CEDENO
□ 590. J.R. RICHARD
□ 617. TERRY PUHL
□ 642. WILBUR HOWARD
□ 697. DAVE BERGMAN
□ 718. BRUCE BOCHY(P)
□ 718. MIKE FISCHLIN(P)
□ 718. DON PISKER(P)

KANSAS CITY ROYALS

□ 19. LARRY GURA
□ 26. JAMIE QUIRK
□ 45. AL HRABOSKY
□ 72. STEVE MINGORI
□ 99. JOHN WATHAN
□ 129. MARTY PATTIN
□ 157. U.L. WASHINGTON
□ 183. PAUL SPLITTORFF
□ 218. DENNIS LEONARD
□ 248. PETE LACOCK
□ 273. JERRY TERRELL
□ 298. RICH GALE
□ 330. GEORGE BRETT
□ 360. AMOS OTIS
□ 389. JOE ZDEB
□ 409. WILLIE WILSON
□ 439. FRANK WHITE
□ 451. TEAM & HERZOG(M)
□ 476. TOM POQUETTE
□ 490. AL COWENS
□ 502. STEVE BRAUN
□ 525. FREDDIE PATEK
□ 547. CLINT HURDLE
□ 571. DARRELL PORTER
□ 585. HAL MCRAE
□ 664. DOUG BIRD
□ 707. RANDY BASS(P)
□ 707. JIM GAUDET(P)
□ 707. RANDY MCGILBERRY(P)

LOS ANGELES DODGERS

□ 23. TERRY FORSTER
□ 50. STEVE GARVEY
□ 75. STEVE YEAGER
□ 104. JOHNNY OATES
□ 128. TED MARTINEZ
□ 145. RICK RHODEN
□ 170. DON SUTTON
□ 190. RON CEY
□ 228. VIC DAVALILLO
□ 255. TOMMY JOHN
□ 279. JERRY GROTE
□ 290. DAVE LOPES
□ 318. BOB WELCH
□ 347. DOUG RAU
□ 373. LANCE RAUTZHAN
□ 441. LEE LACY
□ 465. REGGIE SMITH
□ 508. CHARLIE HOUGH
□ 526. TEAM & LASORDA(M)
□ 546. BILL RUSSELL
□ 562. DUSTY BAKER
□ 605. RICK MONDAY
□ 641. BOBBY CASTILLO
□ 644. MANNY MOTA
□ 668. BILL NORTH
□ 671. JOE FERGUSON
□ 694. BURT HOOTON
□ 719. PEDRO GUERRERO(P)
□ 719. RUDY LAW(P)
□ 719. JOE SIMPSON(P)

MILWAUKEE BREWERS

□ 24. PAUL MOLITOR
□ 51. RAY FOSSE
□ 95. ROBIN YOUNT
□ 108. EDUARDO RODRIGUEZ
□ 133. BILL CASTRO
□ 154. JIM GANTNER
□ 180. LARRY HISLE
□ 213. BILL TRAVERS
□ 243. BUCK MARTINEZ
□ 265. DON MONEY
□ 303. LARY SORENSEN
□ 325. CECIL COOPER
□ 357. JERRY AUGUSTINE
□ 376. GORMAN THOMAS
□ 394. RANDY STEIN
□ 408. CHARLIE MOORE
□ 427. ANDY REPLOGLE
□ 448. MOOSE HAAS
□ 474. DICK DAVIS
□ 519. BEN OGLIVIE
□ 550. SAL BANDO
□ 577. TEAM & BAMBERGER(M)
□ 596. JIM WOHLFORD
□ 623. BOB MCCLURE
□ 651. MIKE CALDWELL
□ 685. SIXTO LEZCANO
□ 708. KEVIN BASS(P)
□ 708. EDDIE ROMERO(P)
□ 708. NED YOST(P)

MINNESOTA TWINS

□ 27. DAVE GOLTZ
□ 41. TEAM & MAUCH(M)
□ 58. BOB RANDALL
□ 81. ROGER ERICKSON
□ 113. PETE REDFERN
□ 137. LARRY WOLFE
□ 162. TOM JOHNSON
□ 193. GLENN ADAMS
□ 219. ROY SMALLEY
□ 246. DARRELL JACKSON
□ 249. PAUL THORMODSGARD
□ 274. WILLIE NORWOOD
□ 300. ROD CAREW
□ 362. MIKE CUBBAGE
□ 371. JEFF HOLLY
□ 385. DAN FORD
□ 405. BUTCH WYNEGAR
□ 431. GLENN BORGMANN
□ 449. BOMBO RIVERA
□ 472. CRAIG KUSICK
□ 498. RICH CHILES
□ 552. JOSE MORALES
□ 627. GARY SERUM
□ 633. ROB WILFONG
□ 656. HOSKEN POWELL
□ 676. JOHNNY SUTTON
□ 678. GEOFF ZAHN
□ 709. SAM PERLOZZO(P)
□ 709. RICK SOFIELD(P)
□ 709. KEVIN STANFIELD(P)

MONTREAL EXPOS

□ 15. ROSS GRIMSLEY
□ 43. WAYNE TWITCHELL
□ 76. WARREN CROMARTIE
□ 97. SAM MEJIAS
□ 124. DAN SCHATZEDER
□ 181. MIKE GARMAN
□ 235. STEVE ROGERS
□ 269. WOODIE FRYMAN
□ 294. PEPE FRIAS
□ 348. ANDRE DAWSON
□ 374. ED HERRMANN
□ 395. DAVE CASH
□ 426. CHRIS SPEIER
□ 468. STAN BAHNSEN
□ 495. TONY PEREZ
□ 520. GARY CARTER
□ 535. ELLIS VALENTINE
□ 581. DAROLD KNOWLES
□ 603. RUDY MAY
□ 606. TEAM & WILLIAMS(M)
□ 628. DEL UNSER
□ 652. STAN PAPI
□ 673. TOM HUTTON
□ 677. LARRY PARRISH
□ 699. HAL DUES
□ 720. JERRY FRY(P)
□ 720. JERRY PIRTLE(P)
□ 720. SCOTT SANDERSON(P)

NEW YORK METS

□ 21. KEVIN KOBEL
□ 46. RON HODGES
□ 69. ELLIOTT MADDOX
□ 82. TEAM & TORRE(M)
□ 109. JOEL YOUNGBLOOD
□ 148. BRUCE BOISCLAIR
□ 172. MIKE BRUHERT
□ 197. BOB APODACA
□ 229. DOUG FLYNN
□ 277. TOM GRIEVE

☐ 305. WILLIE MONTANEZ
☐ 334. CRAIG SWAN
☐ 355. LEE MAZZILLI
☐ 379. DALE MURRAY
☐ 397. SERGIO FERRER
☐ 403. TIM FOLI
☐ 428. BOBBY VALENTINE
☐ 445. STEVE HENDERSON
☐ 454. LEN RANDLE
☐ 481. SKIP LOCKWOOD
☐ 505. ED KRANEPOOL
☐ 545. JOHN STEARNS
☐ 566. NINO ESPINOSA
☐ 621. PAT ZACHRY
☐ 643. TOM HAUSMAN
☐ 655. JERRY KOOSMAN
☐ 721. JUAN BERENGUER(P)
☐ 721. DWIGHT BERNARD(P)
☐ 721. DAN NORMAN(P)

NEW YORK YANKEES

☐ 16. FRED STANLEY
☐ 35. ED FIGUEROA
☐ 60. MICKEY RIVERS
☐ 89. DICK TIDROW
☐ 114. CLIFF JOHNSON
☐ 140. DON GULLETT
☐ 159. ROY WHITE
☐ 179. JIM BEATTIE
☐ 225. RICH GOSSAGE
☐ 250. WILLIE RANDOLPH
☐ 278. ANDY MESSERSMITH
☐ 310. THURMAN MUNSON
☐ 335. CHRIS CHAMBLISS
☐ 365. SPARKY LYLE
☐ 387. GARY THOMASSON
☐ 434. KEN CLAY
☐ 460. GRAIG NETTLES
☐ 485. BUCKY DENT
☐ 500. RON GUIDRY
☐ 558. JAY JOHNSTONE
☐ 582. PAUL BLAIR
☐ 599. JIM SPENCER
☐ 626. TEAM & LEMON(M)
☐ 634. PAUL LINDBLAD
☐ 648. LOU PINIELLA
☐ 670. JIM HUNTER
☐ 700. REGGIE JACKSON
☐ 710. BRIAN DOYLE(P)
☐ 710. MIKE HEATH(P)
☐ 710. DAVE RAJSICH(P)

OAKLAND A'S

☐ 29. RICK LANGFORD
☐ 54. DELL ALSTON
☐ 78. ELIAS SOSA
☐ 163. GLENN BURKE
☐ 191. MIKE NORRIS
☐ 224. DAVE REVERING
☐ 261. MARIO GUERRERO
☐ 295. MITCHELL PAGE
☐ 328. TEAM & MCKEON(M)
☐ 352. STEVE RENKO
☐ 378. ROB PICCIOLO
☐ 406. JOE WALLIS
☐ 432. DAVE HEAVERLO
☐ 458. JIM ESSIAN
☐ 487. MIGUEL DILONE
☐ 507. TONY ARMAS
☐ 528. WAYNE GROSS
☐ 554. MATT KEOUGH
☐ 565. RICO CARTY
☐ 578. PETE BROBERG
☐ 604. JEFF NEWMAN
☐ 613. MIKE EDWARDS
☐ 647. BOB LACEY
☐ 658. TAYLOR DUNCAN
☐ 681. JOHN HENRY JOHNSON
☐ 711. DWAYNE MURPHY(P)
☐ 711. BRUCE ROBINSON(P)
☐ 711. ALAN WIRTH(P)

PHILADELPHIA PHILLIES

☐ 25. STEVE CARLTON
☐ 52. RANDY LERCH
☐ 90. BOB BOONE
☐ 112. TEAM & OZARK(M)
☐ 118. BUD HARRELSON
☐ 136. JIM KAAT
☐ 161. BARRY FOOTE
☐ 177. RON REED
☐ 210. LARRY BOWA
☐ 271. RAWLY EASTWICK
☐ 297. TED SIZEMORE
☐ 317. JOSE CARDENAL
☐ 345. TUG MCGRAW
☐ 382. JERRY MARTIN
☐ 419. DICK RUTHVEN
☐ 446. JIM LONBORG
☐ 470. GARRY MADDOX
☐ 493. LARRY CHRISTENSON
☐ 540. GREG LUZINSKI
☐ 567. RICH HEBNER
☐ 610. MIKE SCHMIDT
☐ 630. BAKE MCBRIDE
☐ 653. WARREN BRUSSTAR
☐ 675. TIM MCCARVER
☐ 722. JIM MORRISON(P)
☐ 722. LONNIE SMITH(P)
☐ 722. JIM L. WRIGHT(P)

PITTSBURGH PIRATES

☐ 28. STEVE BRYE
☐ 55. WILLIE STARGELL
☐ 70. JOHN CANDELARIA
☐ 92. JIM BIBBY
☐ 117. GRANT JACKSON
☐ 147. DAVE HAMILTON
☐ 165. FRANK TAVERAS
☐ 189. EDDIE WHITSON
☐ 208. CLARENCE GASTON
☐ 223. KENT TEKULVE
☐ 244. TEAM & TANNER(M)
☐ 264. DON ROBINSON
☐ 286. DUFFY DYER
☐ 308. BERT BLYLEVEN
☐ 383. PHIL GARNER
☐ 430. DAVE PARKER
☐ 447. MANNY SANGUILLEN
☐ 509. MARIO MENDOZA
☐ 523. JOHN MILNER
☐ 536. JERRY REUSS
☐ 561. ED OTT
☐ 584. JIM ROOKER
☐ 607. OMAR MORENO
☐ 637. BILL ROBINSON
☐ 661. BRUCE KISON
☐ 687. RENNIE STENNETT
☐ 723. DALE BERRA(P)
☐ 723. EUGENIO COTES(P)
☐ 723. BEN WILTBANK(P)

ST. LOUIS CARDINALS

☐ 32. JERRY MUMPHREY
☐ 59. JOHN DENNY
☐ 87. PETE FALCONE
☐ 111. ROGER FREED
☐ 143. TONY SCOTT
☐ 175. GEORGE HENDRICK
☐ 192. TEAM & BOYER(M)
☐ 230. BOB FORSCH
☐ 258. MIKE PHILLIPS
☐ 304. STEVE SWISHER
☐ 319. WAYNE GARRETT
☐ 324. MIKE TYSON
☐ 350. GARRY TEMPLETON
☐ 407. PETE VUCKOVICH
☐ 429. JOHN URREA
☐ 444. AURELIO LOPEZ
☐ 452. JERRY MORALES
☐ 466. MARK LITTELL
☐ 510. TED SIMMONS
☐ 532. BUDDY SCHULTZ
☐ 563. ROY THOMAS
☐ 587. KEN REITZ
☐ 609. SILVIO MARTINEZ
☐ 665. LOU BROCK
☐ 695. KEITH HERNANDEZ
☐ 724. TOM BRUNO(P)
☐ 724. GEORGE FRAZIER(P)
☐ 724. TERRY KENNEDY(P)

SAN DIEGO PADRES

☐ 30. DAVE WINFIELD
☐ 57. ERIC RASMUSSEN
☐ 116. OZZIE SMITH
☐ 138. MARK LEE
☐ 164. MICKEY LOLICH
☐ 194. RANDY JONES
☐ 247. TUCKER ASHFORD
☐ 263. OSCAR GAMBLE
☐ 292. DON REYNOLDS
☐ 321. GAYLORD PERRY
☐ 342. DAVE W. ROBERTS
☐ 364. GENE RICHARDS
☐ 390. ROLLIE FINGERS
☐ 435. GENE TENACE
☐ 456. CHUCK BAKER
☐ 479. TEAM & CRAIG(M)
☐ 488. BOB OWCHINKO
☐ 506. JOHN D'ACQUISTO
☐ 531. FERNANDO GONZALEZ
☐ 564. JERRY TURNER
☐ 594. BOB SHIRLEY
☐ 616. BILLY ALMON
☐ 646. RICK SWEET
☐ 679. DERREL THOMAS
☐ 725. JIM BESWICK(P)
☐ 725. STEVE MURA(P)
☐ 725. BRODERICK PERKINS(P)

SAN FRANCISCO GIANTS

☐ 11. MARC HILL
☐ 34. ROB ANDREWS
☐ 62. RANDY MOFFITT
☐ 84. GREG MINTON
☐ 110. VIDA BLUE
☐ 142. CHARLIE WILLIAMS
☐ 167. ROGER METZGER
☐ 195. BILL MADLOCK
☐ 215. WILLIE MCCOVEY
☐ 236. JIM DWYER
☐ 256. MIKE SADEK
☐ 284. JOHNNIE LEMASTER
☐ 311. GARY LAVELLE
☐ 338. VIC HARRIS
☐ 356. TEAM & ALTOBELLI(M)
☐ 410. DARRELL EVANS
☐ 436. HECTOR CRUZ
☐ 461. JIM BARR
☐ 486. BOB KNEPPER
☐ 512. JACK CLARK
☐ 538. MIKE IVIE
☐ 560. JOHN MONTEFUSCO
☐ 589. TERRY WHITFIELD
☐ 624. LARRY HERNDON
☐ 649. JOHN CURTIS
☐ 672. ED HALICKI
☐ 726. GREG JOHNSTON(P)
☐ 726. JOE STRAIN(P)
☐ 726. JOHN TAMARGO(P)

SEATTLE MARINERS

☐ 31. TOM HOUSE
☐ 56. JOHN HALE
☐ 74. SHANE RAWLEY
☐ 103. JIM TODD
☐ 141. TOM PACIOREK
☐ 166. LEON ROBERTS
☐ 199. LARRY MILBOURNE
☐ 233. PAUL MITCHELL
☐ 252. BOB STINSON
☐ 276. JIM COLBORN
☐ 312. BOB ROBERTSON
☐ 337. JOHN MONTAGUE
☐ 366. JUAN BERNHARDT
☐ 396. BILL PLUMMER
☐ 422. RUPPERT JONES
☐ 443. BRUCE BOCHTE
☐ 482. CRAIG REYNOLDS
☐ 497. GLENN ABBOTT
☐ 533. LEROY STANTON
☐ 548. ENRIQUE ROMO
☐ 576. MIKE PARROTT
☐ 583. JULIO CRUZ
☐ 612. RICK HONEYCUTT
☐ 659. TEAM & JOHNSON(M)
☐ 683. DAN MEYER
☐ 698. BILL STEIN
☐ 712. BUD ANDERSON(P)
☐ 712. GREG BIERCEVICZ(P)
☐ 712. BYRON MCLAUGHLIN(P)

TEXAS RANGERS

- ☐ 22. MIKE JORGENSEN
- ☐ 44. KURT BEVACQUA
- ☐ 67. JIM MASON
- ☐ 94. LEN BARKER
- ☐ 120. JIM SUNDBERG
- ☐ 144. SANDY ALOMAR
- ☐ 173. JOHN LOWENSTEIN
- ☐ 198. JOHNNY GRUBB
- ☐ 209. REGGIE CLEVELAND
- ☐ 234. TOBY HARRAH
- ☐ 260. RICHIE ZISK
- ☐ 285. BOBBY BONDS
- ☐ 315. JON MATLACK
- ☐ 336. BOBBY THOMPSON
- ☐ 369. BUMP WILLS
- ☐ 391. AL OLIVER
- ☐ 442. DOYLE ALEXANDER
- ☐ 463. STEVE COMER
- ☐ 478. JUAN BENIQUEZ
- ☐ 499. TEAM & CORRALES(M)
- ☐ 518. JIM UMBARGER
- ☐ 539. JOHN ELLIS
- ☐ 544. FERGIE JENKINS
- ☐ 591. MIKE HARGROVE
- ☐ 620. BERT CAMPANERIS
- ☐ 657. GEORGE MEDICH
- ☐ 691. DOCK ELLIS
- ☐ 713. DANNY DARWIN(P)
- ☐ 713. PAT PUTNAM(P)
- ☐ 713. BILLY SAMPLE(P)

TORONTO BLUE JAYS

- ☐ 36. ALAN ASHBY
- ☐ 64. TOM UNDERWOOD
- ☐ 101. ROY HOWELL
- ☐ 131. JIM CLANCY
- ☐ 152. RICK CERONE
- ☐ 178. ALVIS WOODS
- ☐ 182. TIM JOHNSON
- ☐ 207. DAVE LEMANCZYK
- ☐ 221. JESSE JEFFERSON
- ☐ 238. BALOR MOORE
- ☐ 239. WILLIE HORTON
- ☐ 254. LUIS GOMEZ
- ☐ 282. TEAM & HARTSFIELD(M)
- ☐ 293. JERRY GARVIN
- ☐ 329. JOE COLEMAN
- ☐ 341. WILLIE UPSHAW
- ☐ 380. JOHN MAYBERRY
- ☐ 392. DOUG AULT
- ☐ 462. OTTO VELEZ
- ☐ 492. BOB BAILOR
- ☐ 521. SAM EWING
- ☐ 542. RICK BOSETTI
- ☐ 588. TOM MURPHY
- ☐ 608. DAVE MCKAY
- ☐ 632. DON KIRKWOOD
- ☐ 688. MIKE WILLIS
- ☐ 714. VICTOR CRUZ(P)
- ☐ 714. D. PAT KELLY(P)
- ☐ 714. ERNIE WHITT(P)

1980 TOPPS (726)
2 1/2" X 3 1/2"

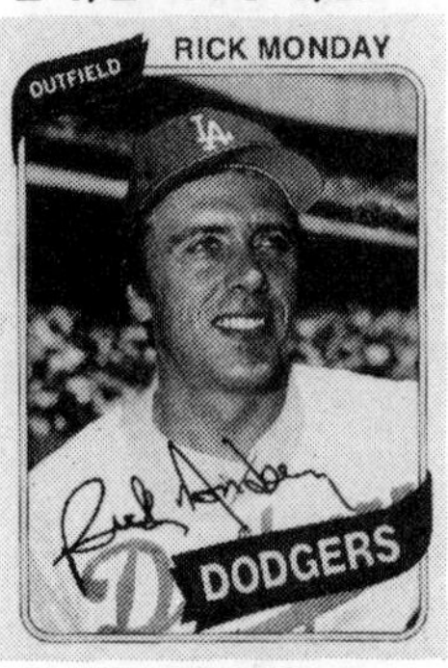

ATLANTA BRAVES

- ☐ 7. MIKE LUM
- ☐ 39. ROWLAND OFFICE
- ☐ 64. JOE NOLAN
- ☐ 87. PEPE FRIAS
- ☐ 108. BOB HORNER
- ☐ 132. BIFF POCOROBA
- ☐ 156. TONY BRIZZOLARA
- ☐ 192. TEAM & COX(M)
- ☐ 245. PHIL NIEKRO
- ☐ 274. DALE MURPHY
- ☐ 294. CHARLIE SPIKES
- ☐ 309. LARRY MCWILLIAMS
- ☐ 326. BO MCLAUGHLIN
- ☐ 346. BUDDY SOLOMON
- ☐ 355. GARY MATTHEWS
- ☐ 384. JOEY MCLAUGHLIN
- ☐ 463. JERRY ROYSTER
- ☐ 489. PRESTON HANNA
- ☐ 504. GENE GARBER
- ☐ 528. ADRIAN DEVINE
- ☐ 545. JEFF BURROUGHS
- ☐ 596. RICK MATULA
- ☐ 632. BARRY BONNELL
- ☐ 675. BRUCE BENEDICT(FS)
- ☐ 675. LARRY BRADFORD(FS)
- ☐ 675. EDDIE MILLER(FS)

BALTIMORE ORIOLES

- ☐ 10. DENNY MARTINEZ
- ☐ 37. KIKO GARCIA
- ☐ 65. AL BUMBRY
- ☐ 91. RICK DEMPSEY
- ☐ 102. RICH DAUER
- ☐ 119. SAMMY STEWART
- ☐ 160. EDDIE MURRAY
- ☐ 188. TERRY CROWLEY
- ☐ 211. DAVE SKAGGS
- ☐ 237. SCOTT MCGREGOR
- ☐ 262. BENNY AYALA
- ☐ 287. JOHN LOWENSTEIN
- ☐ 314. TIM STODDARD
- ☐ 340. KEN SINGLETON
- ☐ 367. BILLY SMITH
- ☐ 404. TEAM & WEAVER(M)
- ☐ 425. MARK BELANGER
- ☐ 490. LEE MAY
- ☐ 517. DON STANHOUSE
- ☐ 543. H. PAT KELLY
- ☐ 568. GARY ROENICKE
- ☐ 590. JIM PALMER
- ☐ 615. DOUG DECINCES
- ☐ 640. MIKE FLANAGAN
- ☐ 661. MARK COREY(FS)
- ☐ 661. DAVE FORD(FS)
- ☐ 661. WAYNE KRENCHICKI(FS)
- ☐ 688. STEVE STONE
- ☐ 706. TIPPY MARTINEZ

BOSTON RED SOX

- ☐ 15. BILL CAMPBELL
- ☐ 40. CARLTON FISK
- ☐ 63. BOB STANLEY
- ☐ 81. TED SIZEMORE
- ☐ 110. FRED LYNN
- ☐ 128. TOM BURGMEIER
- ☐ 155. JERRY REMY
- ☐ 184. STEVE RENKO
- ☐ 200. JIM RICE
- ☐ 271. DICK DRAGO
- ☐ 320. DENNIS ECKERSLEY
- ☐ 349. JACK BROHAMER
- ☐ 376. GARY ALLENSON
- ☐ 405. DWIGHT EVANS
- ☐ 413. ALLEN RIPLEY
- ☐ 420. BUTCH HOBSON
- ☐ 455. MIKE TORREZ
- ☐ 480. BOB WATSON
- ☐ 524. JIM C. WRIGHT
- ☐ 549. LARRY WOLFE
- ☐ 576. JIM DWYER
- ☐ 597. TOM POQUETTE
- ☐ 618. BOB MONTGOMERY
- ☐ 645. RICK BURLESON
- ☐ 662. JOEL FINCH(FS)
- ☐ 662. MIKE O'BERRY(FS)
- ☐ 662. CHUCK RAINEY(FS)
- ☐ 689. TEAM & ZIMMER(M)
- ☐ 720. CARL YASTRZEMSKI

CALIFORNIA ANGELS

- ☐ 20. DAN FORD
- ☐ 48. RICK MILLER
- ☐ 68. LARRY HARLOW
- ☐ 105. FRANK TANANA
- ☐ 183. JIM ANDERSON
- ☐ 214. TEAM & FREGOSI(M)
- ☐ 239. DON AASE
- ☐ 253. JOHN MONTAGUE
- ☐ 263. DAVE LAROCHE
- ☐ 285. DON BAYLOR
- ☐ 312. MIKE BARLOW
- ☐ 337. CARNEY LANSFORD
- ☐ 368. WILLIE AIKENS
- ☐ 402. MERV RETTENMUND
- ☐ 423. DAVE FROST
- ☐ 454. TOM DONOHUE
- ☐ 505. BERT CAMPANERIS
- ☐ 529. JIM BARR
- ☐ 556. JOE RUDI
- ☐ 580. NOLAN RYAN
- ☐ 602. BRIAN DOWNING
- ☐ 621. BOB GRICH
- ☐ 638. MARK CLEAR
- ☐ 658. CHRIS KNAPP
- ☐ 663. RALPH BOTTING(FS)
- ☐ 663. BOB CLARK(FS)
- ☐ 663. DICKIE THON(FS)
- ☐ 700. ROD CAREW

CHICAGO CUBS

- ☐ 17. BRUCE SUTTER
- ☐ 54. DENNIS LAMP
- ☐ 103. BILL CAUDILL
- ☐ 135. BILL BUCKNER
- ☐ 153. TIM BLACKWELL
- ☐ 175. RICK REUSCHEL
- ☐ 240. DAVE KINGMAN
- ☐ 298. KEN HOLTZMAN
- ☐ 232. MICK KELLEHER
- ☐ 343. MIKE VAIL
- ☐ 381. TEAM & GOMEZ(M)
- ☐ 398. BARRY FOOTE
- ☐ 431. MIKE KRUKOW
- ☐ 452. STEVE DILLARD
- ☐ 472. WILLIE HERNANDEZ
- ☐ 493. JERRY MARTIN
- ☐ 514. STEVE ONTIVEROS
- ☐ 523. KEN HENDERSON
- ☐ 541. MIGUEL DILONE
- ☐ 574. SCOT THOMPSON
- ☐ 594. DICK TIDROW
- ☐ 628. DOUG CAPILLA
- ☐ 639. LARRY BIITTNER
- ☐ 676. DAVE GEISEL(FS)
- ☐ 676. STEVE MACKO(FS)
- ☐ 676. KARL PAGEL(FS)
- ☐ 691. IVAN DEJESUS
- ☐ 716. LYNN MCGLOTHEN

CHICAGO WHITE SOX

- ☐ 36. RUSTY TORRES
- ☐ 72. FRED HOWARD
- ☐ 83. STEVE TROUT
- ☐ 107. FRANCISCO BARRIOS
- ☐ 112. TEAM & LARUSSA(M)
- ☐ 138. ROSS BAUMGARTEN
- ☐ 164. GREG PRYOR
- ☐ 186. JUNIOR MOORE
- ☐ 242. LAMAR JOHNSON
- ☐ 272. RALPH GARR
- ☐ 291. RANDY SCARBERY
- ☐ 322. CLAUDELL WASHINGTON
- ☐ 347. HARRY CHAPPAS
- ☐ 379. KEVIN BELL
- ☐ 399. MIKE PROLY
- ☐ 412. THAD BOSLEY
- ☐ 442. JORGE ORTA
- ☐ 466. MIKE SQUIRES
- ☐ 487. WAYNE NORDHAGEN
- ☐ 502. RICH WORTHAM
- ☐ 522. JIM MORRISON
- ☐ 552. BILL NAHORODNY
- ☐ 575. KEN KRAVEC
- ☐ 589. CHET LEMON
- ☐ 608. ALAN BANNISTER
- ☐ 647. MILT MAY
- ☐ 664. MIKE COLBERN(FS)
- ☐ 664. GUY HOFFMAN(FS)
- ☐ 664. DEWEY ROBINSON(FS)
- ☐ 702. ED FARMER

CINCINNATI REDS

- ☐ 21. MANNY SARMIENTO
- ☐ 47. BILL BONHAM
- ☐ 73. DAVE COLLINS
- ☐ 100. JOHNNY BENCH
- ☐ 126. DAVE TOMLIN
- ☐ 149. TOM HUME
- ☐ 174. RAY KNIGHT
- ☐ 199. MIKE LACOSS
- ☐ 220. DAVE CONCEPCION
- ☐ 258. PAUL MOSKAU
- ☐ 281. PAUL BLAIR
- ☐ 325. DAN DRIESSEN
- ☐ 354. RICK AUERBACH
- ☐ 377. JUNIOR KENNEDY
- ☐ 400. GEORGE FOSTER
- ☐ 419. VIC CORRELL
- ☐ 449. DOUG BAIR
- ☐ 475. CESAR GERONIMO
- ☐ 500. TOM SEAVER
- ☐ 516. HECTOR CRUZ
- ☐ 550. KEN GRIFFEY
- ☐ 606. TEAM & MCNAMARA(M)
- ☐ 622. MARIO SOTO
- ☐ 650. JOE MORGAN
- ☐ 677. ART DEFREITES(FS)
- ☐ 677. FRANK PASTORE(FS)
- ☐ 677. HARRY SPILMAN(FS)
- ☐ 714. FRED NORMAN

CLEVELAND INDIANS

- ☐ 13. RON PRUITT
- ☐ 38. DAN SPILLNER
- ☐ 74. SID MONGE
- ☐ 99. VICTOR CRUZ
- ☐ 122. DAVE ROSELLO
- ☐ 141. GARY ALEXANDER
- ☐ 168. RICK WAITS
- ☐ 198. DELL ALSTON
- ☐ 208. WAYNE CAGE
- ☐ 222. RON HASSEY
- ☐ 227. LEN BARKER
- ☐ 252. TED COX
- ☐ 276. TOM VERYZER
- ☐ 308. MIKE HARGROVE
- ☐ 333. JIM NORRIS
- ☐ 361. WAYNE GARLAND
- ☐ 388. MIKE PAXTON
- ☐ 410. BOBBY BONDS
- ☐ 429. DUANE KUIPER
- ☐ 451. TEAM & GARCIA(M)
- ☐ 483. BO DIAZ
- ☐ 511. ERIC WILKINS
- ☐ 534. ANDRE THORNTON
- ☐ 564. RICK MANNING
- ☐ 612. CLIFF JOHNSON
- ☐ 636. TOBY HARRAH
- ☐ 665. LARRY ANDERSEN(FS)
- ☐ 665. BOBBY CUELLAR(FS)
- ☐ 665. SANDY WIHTOL(FS)
- ☐ 697. DAVID CLYDE
- ☐ 725. RICK WISE

DETROIT TIGERS

- ☐ 29. MARK WAGNER
- ☐ 59. EDDY PUTMAN
- ☐ 80. RON LEFLORE
- ☐ 101. AURELIO LOPEZ
- ☐ 123. LYNN JONES
- ☐ 150. JASON THOMPSON
- ☐ 176. CHAMP SUMMER
- ☐ 196. LANCE PARRISH
- ☐ 216. PHIL MANKOWSKI
- ☐ 232. ALAN TRAMMELL
- ☐ 251. KIP YOUNG
- ☐ 269. DAVE TOBIK
- ☐ 288. DAVE ROZEMA
- ☐ 315. STEVE KEMP
- ☐ 338. JOHNNY WOCKENFUSS
- ☐ 358. LOU WHITAKER
- ☐ 371. JACK MORRIS
- ☐ 373. DAN PETRY
- ☐ 392. MILT WILCOX
- ☐ 416. TOM BROOKENS
- ☐ 445. MARK FIDRYCH
- ☐ 468. AURELIO RODRIGUEZ
- ☐ 572. JERRY MORALES
- ☐ 603. JACK BILLINGHAM
- ☐ 614. JOHN HILLER
- ☐ 626. TEAM & ANDERSON(M)
- ☐ 666. MIKE CHRIS(FS)
- ☐ 666. AL GREENE(FS)
- ☐ 666. BRUCE ROBBINS(FS)
- ☐ 709. PAT UNDERWOOD

HOUSTON ASTROS

- ☐ 11. JIMMY SEXTON
- ☐ 50. J.R. RICHARD
- ☐ 69. RICK WILLIAMS
- ☐ 82. TEAM & VIRDON(M)
- ☐ 106. JEFF LEONARD
- ☐ 129. CRAIG REYNOLDS
- ☐ 147. TERRY PUHL
- ☐ 187. ALAN ASHBY
- ☐ 234. VERN RUHLE
- ☐ 247. FRANK RICCELLI
- ☐ 268. RAFAEL LANDESTOY
- ☐ 289. BRUCE BOCHY
- ☐ 306. DENNY WALLING
- ☐ 329. BERT ROBERGE
- ☐ 370. CESAR CEDENO
- ☐ 385. ENOS CABELL
- ☐ 411. FRANK LACORTE
- ☐ 437. JOE NIEKRO
- ☐ 469. RANDY NIEMANN
- ☐ 513. TOM DIXON
- ☐ 554. ART HOWE
- ☐ 571. JOE SAMBITO
- ☐ 593. JESUS ALOU
- ☐ 617. JOAQUIN ANDUJAR
- ☐ 642. KEN FORSCH
- ☐ 678. REGGIE BALDWIN(FS)
- ☐ 678. ALAN KNICELY(FS)
- ☐ 678. PETE LADD(FS)
- ☐ 696. JULIO GONZALEZ
- ☐ 722. JOSE CRUZ

KANSAS CITY ROYALS

- ☐ 9. STEVE BRAUN
- ☐ 26. MARTY PATTIN
- ☐ 45. FRANK WHITE
- ☐ 66. TEAM CARD
- ☐ 98. JERRY TERRELL
- ☐ 130. AMOS OTIS
- ☐ 157. WILLIE WILSON
- ☐ 185. HAL MCRAE
- ☐ 219. STEVE MINGORI
- ☐ 248. JAMIE QUIRK
- ☐ 273. EDUARDO RODRIGUEZ
- ☐ 295. LARRY GURA
- ☐ 330. AL COWENS
- ☐ 360. DARRELL PORTER
- ☐ 389. PETE LACOCK
- ☐ 409. PAUL SPLITTORFF
- ☐ 417. CRAIG CHAMBERLAIN
- ☐ 433. RICH GALE
- ☐ 450. GEORGE BRETT
- ☐ 474. STEVE BUSBY
- ☐ 492. TODD CRUZ
- ☐ 508. U.L. WASHINGTON
- ☐ 525. CLINT HURDLE
- ☐ 547. JOHN WATHAN
- ☐ 565. DENNIS LEONARD
- ☐ 585. AL HRABOSKY
- ☐ 667. RENIE MARTIN(FS)
- ☐ 667. BILL PASCHALL(FS)
- ☐ 667. DAN QUISENBERRY(FS)
- ☐ 705. FREDDIE PATEK

LOS ANGELES DODGERS

- ☐ 23. DERREL THOMAS
- ☐ 51. JOE FERGUSON
- ☐ 75. BILL RUSSELL
- ☐ 104. MANNY MOTA
- ☐ 127. GARY THOMASSON
- ☐ 146. BOB WELCH
- ☐ 170. BURT HOOTON
- ☐ 191. TED MARTINEZ
- ☐ 209. VON JOSHUA
- ☐ 228. JOHNNY OATES
- ☐ 255. DUSTY BAKER
- ☐ 290. STEVE GARVEY
- ☐ 302. TEAM & LASORDA(M)
- ☐ 318. JERRY REUSS
- ☐ 440. DON SUTTON
- ☐ 465. RICK MONDAY
- ☐ 510. RON CEY
- ☐ 521. KEN BRETT
- ☐ 527. DOUG RAU
- ☐ 544. RICK SUTCLIFFE
- ☐ 560. DAVE LOPES
- ☐ 605. TERRY FORSTER
- ☐ 624. LERRIN LAGROW
- ☐ 644. CHARLIE HOUGH
- ☐ 679. JOE BECKWITH(FS)
- ☐ 679. MICKEY HATCHER(FS)
- ☐ 679. DAVE PATTERSON(FS)
- ☐ 695. REGGIE SMITH
- ☐ 726. STEVE YEAGER

MILWAUKEE BREWERS

- ☐ 24. JIM SLATON
- ☐ 53. BEN OGLIVIE
- ☐ 95. CECIL COOPER
- ☐ 109. BILL TRAVERS
- ☐ 131. PAUL MITCHELL
- ☐ 154. LARY SORENSEN
- ☐ 181. MOOSE HAAS
- ☐ 215. SIXTO LEZCANO
- ☐ 243. JERRY AUGUSTINE
- ☐ 265. ROBIN YOUNT
- ☐ 303. BILL CASTRO
- ☐ 327. RAY FOSSE
- ☐ 357. BOB MCCLURE
- ☐ 374. JIM GANTNER
- ☐ 394. REGGIE CLEVELAND
- ☐ 406. PAUL MOLITOR
- ☐ 430. LARRY HISLE
- ☐ 448. JIM WOHLFORD
- ☐ 477. BUCK MARTINEZ
- ☐ 515. MIKE CALDWELL
- ☐ 553. DICK DAVIS
- ☐ 579. CHARLIE MOORE
- ☐ 595. DON MONEY
- ☐ 623. GORMAN THOMAS
- ☐ 659. TEAM & BAMBERGER(M)
- ☐ 668. DANNY BOITANO(FS)
- ☐ 668. WILLIE MUELLER(FS)
- ☐ 668. LENN SAKATA(FS)
- ☐ 711. BOB GALASSO
- ☐ 715. SAL BANDO

MINNESOTA TWINS

- ☐ 18. RON JACKSON
- ☐ 43. BOMBO RIVERA
- ☐ 61. GARY SERUM
- ☐ 88. KEN LANDREAUX
- ☐ 113. GEOFF ZAHN
- ☐ 137. JOHN CASTINO
- ☐ 162. BOB RANDALL
- ☐ 193. DAVE GOLTZ

- ☐ 218. JOSE MORALES
- ☐ 238. ROB WILFONG
- ☐ 256. ROGER ERICKSON
- ☐ 275. JERRY KOOSMAN
- ☐ 304. BUTCH WYNEGAR
- ☐ 328. TEAM & MAUCH(M)
- ☐ 362. DANNY GOODWIN
- ☐ 386. DARRELL JACKSON
- ☐ 403. PETE REDFERN
- ☐ 432. WILLIE NORWOOD
- ☐ 453. MIKE BACSIK
- ☐ 471. HOSKEN POWELL
- ☐ 503. MIKE CUBBAGE
- ☐ 570. ROY SMALLEY
- ☐ 604. GLENN ADAMS
- ☐ 634. GLENN BORGMANN
- ☐ 657. DAVE EDWARDS
- ☐ 669. DAN GRAHAM(FS)
- ☐ 669. RICK SOFIELD(FS)
- ☐ 669. GARY WARD(FS)
- ☐ 721. PAUL HARTZELL

MONTREAL EXPOS

- ☐ 14. DAVE CASH
- ☐ 42. DAVE PALMER
- ☐ 70. GARY CARTER
- ☐ 97. BILL LEE
- ☐ 125. TONY PEREZ
- ☐ 180. WARREN CROMARTIE
- ☐ 235. ANDRE DAWSON
- ☐ 267. DAN SCHATZEDER
- ☐ 293. ELIAS SOSA
- ☐ 319. CHRIS SPEIER
- ☐ 345. LARRY PARRISH
- ☐ 375. ROSS GRIMSLEY
- ☐ 395. ELLIS VALENTINE
- ☐ 415. BILL ATKINSON
- ☐ 427. TOM HUTTON
- ☐ 446. DUFFY DYER
- ☐ 479. TEAM & WILLIAMS(M)
- ☐ 497. JIM MASON
- ☐ 520. STEVE ROGERS
- ☐ 539. RUDY MAY
- ☐ 559. DALE MURRAY
- ☐ 578. SCOTT SANDERSON
- ☐ 607. WOODIE FRYMAN
- ☐ 653. STAN BAHNSEN
- ☐ 660. RUSTY STAUB
- ☐ 680. TONY BERNAZARD(FS)
- ☐ 680. RANDY MILLER(FS)
- ☐ 680. JOHN TAMARGO(FS)
- ☐ 712. RODNEY SCOTT
- ☐ 724. JERRY WHITE

NEW YORK METS

- ☐ 8. CRAIG SWAN
- ☐ 25. LEE MAZZILLI
- ☐ 58. DOUG FLYNN
- ☐ 76. JOHN STEARNS
- ☐ 94. NEIL ALLEN
- ☐ 117. DOCK ELLIS
- ☐ 151. TOM HAUSMAN
- ☐ 172. RON HODGES
- ☐ 189. KEVIN KOBEL
- ☐ 259. TEAM & TORRE(M)
- ☐ 299. STEVE HENDERSON
- ☐ 331. RICH HEBNER
- ☐ 353. ANDY HASSLER
- ☐ 364. RAY BURRIS
- ☐ 372. JOEL YOUNGBLOOD
- ☐ 401. PETE FALCONE
- ☐ 428. PAT ZACHRY
- ☐ 456. FRANK TAVERAS
- ☐ 478. GIL FLORES
- ☐ 509. ED GLYNN
- ☐ 512. JOSE CARDENAL
- ☐ 537. ALEX TREVINO
- ☐ 567. SKIP LOCKWOOD
- ☐ 619. SERGIO FERRER
- ☐ 633. BOB APODACA
- ☐ 641. ED KRANEPOOL
- ☐ 654. BRUCE BOISCLAIR
- ☐ 681. DAN NORMAN(FS)
- ☐ 681. JESSE OROSCO(FS)
- ☐ 681. MIKE SCOTT(FS)
- ☐ 707. ELLIOTT MADDOX

NEW YORK YANKEES

- ☐ 16. JERRY NARRON
- ☐ 35. LUIS TIANT
- ☐ 60. BUCKY DENT
- ☐ 89. DON HOOD
- ☐ 114. JUAN BENIQUEZ
- ☐ 140. RICH GOSSAGE
- ☐ 159. KEN CLAY
- ☐ 179. RON DAVIS
- ☐ 225. LOU PINIELLA
- ☐ 250. JIM KAAT
- ☐ 278. JIM SPENCER
- ☐ 300. RON GUIDRY
- ☐ 334. JIM BEATTIE
- ☐ 365. BOBBY MURCER
- ☐ 387. FRED STANLEY
- ☐ 414. GEORGE SCOTT
- ☐ 424. TEAM & HOWSER(M)
- ☐ 435. DON GULLETT
- ☐ 460. WILLIE RANDOLPH
- ☐ 555. ED FIGUEROA
- ☐ 582. BRAIN DOYLE
- ☐ 600. REGGIE JACKSON
- ☐ 625. CHRIS CHAMBLISS
- ☐ 648. ROY WHITE
- ☐ 670. BOBBY BROWN(FS)
- ☐ 670. BRAD GULDEN(FS)
- ☐ 670. DARRYL JONES(FS)
- ☐ 690. TOMMY JOHN
- ☐ 698. OSCAR GAMBLE
- ☐ 710. GRAIG NETTLES

OAKLAND A'S

- ☐ 34. JEFF NEWMAN
- ☐ 49. MARIO GUERRERO
- ☐ 86. DAVE HAMILTON
- ☐ 96. TEAM & MARSHALL(M)
- ☐ 134. MATT KEOUGH
- ☐ 158. ROB PICCIOLO
- ☐ 177. DAVE HEAVERLO
- ☐ 231. STEVE MCCATTY
- ☐ 261. DAVE CHALK
- ☐ 284. LARRY MURRAY
- ☐ 301. MIKE EDWARDS
- ☐ 316. BOB LACEY
- ☐ 341. JIM ESSIAN
- ☐ 363. WAYNE GROSS
- ☐ 391. TONY ARMAS
- ☐ 438. DAVE REVERING
- ☐ 461. DWAYNE MURPHY
- ☐ 482. RICKEY HENDERSON
- ☐ 494. CRAIG MINETTO
- ☐ 546. RICK LANGFORD
- ☐ 562. JOE WALLIS
- ☐ 586. MITCHELL PAGE
- ☐ 599. MIKE NORRIS
- ☐ 629. JIM TODD
- ☐ 671. DEREK BRYANT(FS)
- ☐ 671. BRIAN KINGMAN(FS)
- ☐ 671. MIKE MORGAN(FS)
- ☐ 687. MIKE HEATH
- ☐ 717. MICKEY KLUTTS

PHILADELPHIA PHILLIES

- ☐ 27. DEL UNSER
- ☐ 52. WARREN BRUSSTAR
- ☐ 90. MANNY TRILLO
- ☐ 120. GREG LUZINSKI
- ☐ 136. DICK RUTHVEN
- ☐ 161. LARRY CHRISTENSON
- ☐ 178. TIM MCCARVER
- ☐ 210. STEVE CARLTON
- ☐ 270. MIKE SCHMIDT
- ☐ 296. DAVE RADER
- ☐ 317. MIKE ANDERSON
- ☐ 344. RANDY LERCH
- ☐ 380. GARRY MADDOX
- ☐ 421. DOUG BIRD
- ☐ 447. NINO ESPINOSA
- ☐ 470. BOB BOONE
- ☐ 495. BAKE MCBRIDE
- ☐ 526. TEAM & GREEN(M)
- ☐ 540. PETE ROSE
- ☐ 566. BUD HARRELSON
- ☐ 609. RON REED
- ☐ 630. LARRY BOWA
- ☐ 655. TUG MCGRAW
- ☐ 682. RAMON AVILES(FS)
- ☐ 682. DICKIE NOLES(FS)
- ☐ 682. KEVIN SAUCIER(FS)
- ☐ 692. RAWLY EASTWICK
- ☐ 718. GREG GROSS

PITTSBURGH PIRATES

- ☐ 28. BRUCE KISON
- ☐ 55. BILL MADLOCK
- ☐ 71. JOHN MILNER
- ☐ 92. RICK RHODEN
- ☐ 118. PHIL GARNER
- ☐ 148. MANNY SANGUILLEN
- ☐ 165. OMAR MORENO
- ☐ 194. MIKE EASLER
- ☐ 212. DAVE A. ROBERTS
- ☐ 229. JIM BIBBY
- ☐ 246. TIM FOLI
- ☐ 264. BILL ROBINSON
- ☐ 292. DALE BERRA
- ☐ 310. DAVE PARKER
- ☐ 332. ENRIQUE ROMO
- ☐ 383. ED OTT
- ☐ 426. GRANT JACKSON
- ☐ 457. BERT BLYLEVEN
- ☐ 501. RENNIE STENNETT
- ☐ 519. STEVE NICOSIA
- ☐ 536. LEE LACY
- ☐ 542. JOE COLEMAN
- ☐ 551. TEAM & TANNER(M)
- ☐ 573. KENT TEKULVE
- ☐ 610. WILLIE STARGELL
- ☐ 635. JOHN CANDELARIA
- ☐ 683. DORIAN BOYLAND(FS)
- ☐ 683. ALBERTO LOIS(FS)
- ☐ 683. HERRY SAFERIGHT(FS)
- ☐ 694. JIM ROOKER
- ☐ 719. DON ROBINSON

ST. LOUIS CARDINALS

- ☐ 33. TONY SCOTT
- ☐ 57. PETE VUCKOVICH
- ☐ 85. TED SIMMONS
- ☐ 139. DANE IORG
- ☐ 152. JOHN FULGHAM
- ☐ 163. STEVE SWISHER
- ☐ 182. KEN REITZ
- ☐ 223. BOB SYKES
- ☐ 244. TEAM & BOYER(M)
- ☐ 266. BERNIE CARBO
- ☐ 286. DAROLD KNOWLES
- ☐ 321. KEITH HERNANDEZ
- ☐ 350. GEORGE HENDRICK
- ☐ 378. JERRY MUMPHREY
- ☐ 397. ROY THOMAS
- ☐ 418. ROGER FREED
- ☐ 439. MIKE PHILLIPS
- ☐ 464. JOHN DENNY
- ☐ 486. MIKE TYSON
- ☐ 496. SILVIO MARTINEZ
- ☐ 535. BOB FORSCH
- ☐ 563. WILL MCEANEY
- ☐ 569. TERRY KENNEDY
- ☐ 587. GARRY TEMPLETON
- ☐ 601. BUDDY SCHULTZ
- ☐ 631. MARK LITTELL
- ☐ 684. GEORGE FRAZIER(FS)
- ☐ 684. TOM HERR(FS)
- ☐ 684. DAN O'BRIEN(FS)
- ☐ 701. KEN OBERKFELL

SAN DIEGO PADRES

- ☐ 31. JAY JOHNSTONE
- ☐ 44. BILL FAHEY
- ☐ 79. BOB OWCHINKO
- ☐ 133. JERRY TURNER
- ☐ 171. FERNANDO GONZALEZ
- ☐ 230. DAVE WINFIELD
- ☐ 254. PAUL DADE
- ☐ 280. GAYLORD PERRY
- ☐ 305. RANDY JONES
- ☐ 339. JOHN D'ACQUISTO
- ☐ 352. DAN BRIGGS
- ☐ 356. TEAM & COLEMAN(M)
- ☐ 393. OZZIE SMITH
- ☐ 436. BILLY ALMON
- ☐ 459. MICKEY LOLICH
- ☐ 476. BOB SHIRLEY
- ☐ 491. STEVE MURA
- ☐ 531. ERIC RASMUSSEN
- ☐ 557. MARK LEE
- ☐ 584. KURT BEVACQUA
- ☐ 598. FRED KENDALL
- ☐ 616. GENE RICHARDS
- ☐ 651. ROLLIE FINGERS
- ☐ 685. TIM FLANNERY(FS)
- ☐ 685. BRIAN GREER(FS)
- ☐ 685. JIM WILHELM(FS)
- ☐ 704. GENE TENACE
- ☐ 708. BOB TOLAN

SAN FRANCISCO GIANTS

- ☐ 12. JOHN CURTIS
- ☐ 30. VIDA BLUE
- ☐ 62. MIKE IVIE
- ☐ 84. GARY LAVELLE
- ☐ 111. BOB KNEPPER
- ☐ 145. DARRELL EVANS
- ☐ 167. JACK CLARK
- ☐ 195. JOHN MONTEFUSCO
- ☐ 217. ED HALICKI
- ☐ 236. MARC HILL
- ☐ 257. LARRY HERNDON
- ☐ 279. ROB ANDREWS
- ☐ 311. ROGER METZGER
- ☐ 335. WILLIE MCCOVEY
- ☐ 359. RANDY MOFFITT
- ☐ 408. BILL NORTH
- ☐ 434. JOHNNIE LEMASTER
- ☐ 462. MIKE SADEK
- ☐ 499. TEAM & BRISTOL(M)
- ☐ 538. JOE STRAIN
- ☐ 561. EDDIE WHITSON
- ☐ 588. GREG MINTON
- ☐ 627. PEDRO BORBON
- ☐ 649. TOM GRIFFIN
- ☐ 686. GREG JOHNSTON(FS)
- ☐ 686. DENNIS LITTLEJOHN(FS)
- ☐ 686. PHIL NASTU(FS)
- ☐ 713. TERRY WHITFIELD

SEATTLE MARINERS

- ☐ 32. JULIO CRUZ
- ☐ 56. BOBBY VALENTINE
- ☐ 78. RUPPERT JONES
- ☐ 116. LARRY COX
- ☐ 143. BRUCE BOCHTE
- ☐ 166. GLENN ABBOTT
- ☐ 197. BYRON MCLAUGHLIN
- ☐ 226. BILL STEIN
- ☐ 282. TEAM & JOHNSON(M)
- ☐ 307. RICK HONEYCUTT
- ☐ 342. ODELL JONES
- ☐ 366. ROB DRESSLER
- ☐ 396. DAN MEYER
- ☐ 422. LARRY MILBOURNE
- ☐ 443. MIKE PARROTT
- ☐ 481. TOM PACIOREK
- ☐ 507. LEON ROBERTS
- ☐ 532. WILLIE HORTON
- ☐ 583. BOB STINSON
- ☐ 613. RANDY STEIN
- ☐ 637. JOE SIMPSON
- ☐ 652. MARIO MENDOZA
- ☐ 672. CHARLIE BEAMON(FS)
- ☐ 672. RODNEY CRAIG(FS)
- ☐ 672. RAFAEL VASQUEZ(FS)
- ☐ 699. FLOYD BANNISTER
- ☐ 723. SHANE RAWLEY

TEXAS RANGERS

- ☐ 22. PAT PUTNAM
- ☐ 41. TEAM & CORRALES(M)
- ☐ 67. DOYLE ALEXANDER
- ☐ 93. DAVE W. ROBERTS
- ☐ 115. SPARKY LYLE
- ☐ 144. STEVE COMER
- ☐ 173. JOHN HENRY JOHNSON
- ☐ 190. BUDDY BELL
- ☐ 213. MIKE JORGENSEN
- ☐ 224. WILLIE MONTANEZ
- ☐ 233. LARUE WASHINGTON
- ☐ 260. AL OLIVER
- ☐ 283. JOHN ELLIS
- ☐ 313. JOHNNY GRUBB
- ☐ 336. GEORGE MEDICH
- ☐ 369. JIM KERN
- ☐ 390. FERGIE JENKINS
- ☐ 441. ERIC SODERHOLM
- ☐ 458. BILLY SAMPLE
- ☐ 473. BUMP WILLS
- ☐ 485. MICKEY RIVERS
- ☐ 498. DANNY DARWIN
- ☐ 518. NELSON NORMAN
- ☐ 530. JIM SUNDBERG
- ☐ 548. DAVE RAJSICH
- ☐ 592. JON MATLACK
- ☐ 620. RICHIE ZISK
- ☐ 656. LARVELL BLANKS
- ☐ 673. BRIAN ALLARD(FS)
- ☐ 673. JERRY DON GLEATON(FS)
- ☐ 673. GREG MAHLBERG(FS)

TORONTO BLUE JAYS

- ☐ 19. BALOR MOORE
- ☐ 46. RICO CARTY
- ☐ 77. DAVE STIEB
- ☐ 124. DAVE LEMANCZYK
- ☐ 142. PHIL HUFFMAN
- ☐ 169. LUIS GOMEZ
- ☐ 221. JOE CANNON
- ☐ 249. JIM CLANCY
- ☐ 277. RICK BOSETTI
- ☐ 297. TIM JOHNSON
- ☐ 324. TOM UNDERWOOD
- ☐ 351. BOB DAVIS
- ☐ 382. DAVE FREISLEBEN
- ☐ 407. TONY SOLAITA
- ☐ 444. ALVIS WOODS
- ☐ 467. JESSE JEFFERSON
- ☐ 488. ROY HOWELL
- ☐ 506. TOM BUSKEY
- ☐ 558. ALFREDO GRIFFIN
- ☐ 577. TEAM CARD
- ☐ 581. BOB BAILOR
- ☐ 591. RICK CERONE
- ☐ 611. JERRY GARVIN
- ☐ 643. JOHN MAYBERRY
- ☐ 674. BUTCH EDGE(FS)
- ☐ 674. D. PAT KELLY(FS)
- ☐ 674. TED WILBORN(FS)
- ☐ 693. CRAIG KUSICK
- ☐ 703. OTTO VELEZ

1981 TOPPS (726)
2 1/2" X 3 1/2"

ATLANTA BRAVES

- ☐ 20. JEFF BURROUGHS
- ☐ 44. LARRY MCWILLIAMS
- ☐ 64. BRIAN ASSELSTINE
- ☐ 87. RICK CAMP
- ☐ 108. BRUCE BENEDICT
- ☐ 132. TOMMY BOGGS
- ☐ 155. CHRIS CHAMBLISS
- ☐ 192. TERRY HARPER(FS)
- ☐ 192. ED MILLER(FS)
- ☐ 192. RAFAEL RAMIREZ(FS)
- ☐ 247. GLENN HUBBARD
- ☐ 268. JERRY ROYSTER
- ☐ 296. BILL NAHORODNY
- ☐ 307. GENE GARBER
- ☐ 326. BIFF POCOROBA
- ☐ 355. BOB HORNER
- ☐ 387. PHIL NIEKRO
- ☐ 457. MIKE LUM
- ☐ 477. LUIS GOMEZ
- ☐ 504. DALE MURPHY
- ☐ 528. GARY MATTHEWS
- ☐ 542. LARRY BRADFORD
- ☐ 594. PRESTON HANNA
- ☐ 611. RICK MATULA
- ☐ 636. AL HRABOSKY
- ☐ 675. TEAM & COX(M)
- ☐ 708. DOYLE ALEXANDER

BALTIMORE ORIOLES

- ☐ 10. MIKE FLANAGAN
- ☐ 37. GARY ROENICKE
- ☐ 65. SCOTT MCGREGOR
- ☐ 91. TIM STODDARD
- ☐ 101. BENNY AYALA
- ☐ 119. TIPPY MARTINEZ
- ☐ 161. DAN GRAHAM
- ☐ 188. DOUG DECINCES
- ☐ 210. JIM PALMER
- ☐ 262. SAMMY STEWART
- ☐ 287. LENN SAKATA
- ☐ 314. RICH DAUER
- ☐ 367. DENNY MARTINEZ
- ☐ 399. MIKE BODDICKER(FS)
- ☐ 399. MARK COREY(FS)
- ☐ 399. FLOYD RAYFORD(FS)
- ☐ 425. AL BUMBRY
- ☐ 490. EDDIE MURRAY
- ☐ 520. STEVE STONE
- ☐ 543. TERRY CROWLEY
- ☐ 570. KEN SINGLETON
- ☐ 591. JOHN LOWENSTEIN
- ☐ 615. RICK DEMPSEY
- ☐ 641. MARK BELANGER
- ☐ 661. TEAM & WEAVER(M)
- ☐ 688. KIKO GARCIA
- ☐ 706. DAVE FORD

BOSTON RED SOX

- ☐ 14. JOHN TUDOR
- ☐ 38. WIN REMMERSWAAL
- ☐ 63. STEVE RENKO
- ☐ 81. DAVE STAPLETON

☐ 110. CARL YASTRZEMSKI
☐ 128. GARY ALLENSON
☐ 153. TOM POQUETTE
☐ 184. JIM DWYER
☐ 199. CHUCK RAINEY
☐ 233. SKIP LOCKWOOD
☐ 275. DWIGHT EVANS
☐ 320. TOM BURGMEIER
☐ 349. GLENN HOFFMAN
☐ 378. DAVE RADER
☐ 396. BILL CAMPBELL
☐ 421. BOB STANLEY
☐ 455. RICK BURLESON
☐ 480. CARLTON FISK
☐ 500. JIM RICE
☐ 525. MIKE TORREZ
☐ 549. JERRY REMY
☐ 575. TONY PEREZ
☐ 595. BUTCH HOBSON
☐ 620. DENNIS ECKERSLEY
☐ 647. DICK DRAGO
☐ 662. TEAM & HOUK(M)
☐ 689. BRUCE HURST(FS)
☐ 689. KEITH MACWHORTER(FS)
☐ 689. REID NICHOLS(FS)
☐ 720. FRED LYNN

CALIFORNIA ANGELS

☐ 12. MARK CLEAR
☐ 48. DAVE SKAGGS
☐ 69. ED HALICKI
☐ 100. ROD CAREW
☐ 121. LARRY HARLOW
☐ 182. BOB GRICH
☐ 209. DICKIE THON
☐ 214. RALPH BOTTING(FS)
☐ 214. JIM DORSEY(FS)
☐ 214. JOHN HARRIS(FS)
☐ 227. FRED MARTINEZ
☐ 239. RICK MILLER
☐ 263. BRIAN DOWNING
☐ 286. DAVE FROST
☐ 288. BOB CLARK
☐ 311. FREDDIE PATEK
☐ 340. BRUCE KISON
☐ 369. FRANK TANANA
☐ 391. DAVE LEMANCZYK
☐ 410. BERT CAMPANERIS
☐ 422. DAN FORD
☐ 454. ANDY HASSLER
☐ 505. JASON THOMPSON
☐ 529. DAVE LAROCHE
☐ 557. CHRIS KNAPP
☐ 580. DON BAYLOR
☐ 601. DON AASE
☐ 621. TOM DONOHUE
☐ 639. CARNEY LANSFORD
☐ 652. JOHN MONTAGUE
☐ 663. TEAM & FREGOSI(M)
☐ 701. JOE RUDI
☐ 717. JIM BARR

CHICAGO CUBS

☐ 17. CLIFF JOHNSON
☐ 54. IVAN DEJESUS
☐ 78. STEVE DILLARD
☐ 103. JERRY MARTIN
☐ 136. DOUG CAPILLA
☐ 176. MIKE KRUKOW
☐ 238. WILLIE HERNANDEZ
☐ 294. MIKE TYSON
☐ 331. DENNIS LAMP
☐ 352. DICK TIDROW
☐ 381. CARLOS LEZCANO(FS)
☐ 381. STEVE MACKO(FS)
☐ 381. RANDY MARTZ(FS)
☐ 395. SCOT THOMPSON
☐ 429. MICK KELLEHER
☐ 450. DAVE KINGMAN
☐ 471. MIKE VAIL
☐ 492. BARRY FOOTE
☐ 514. GEORGE RILEY
☐ 533. JESUS FIGUEROA
☐ 553. TIM BLACKWELL
☐ 574. BILL CAUDILL
☐ 590. BRUCE SUTTER
☐ 609. LYNN MCGLOTHEN
☐ 625. BILL BUCKNER
☐ 645. RICK REUSCHEL
☐ 676. TEAM & AMALFITANO(M)
☐ 692. LENNY RANDLE
☐ 718. LARRY BIITTNER

CHICAGO WHITE SOX

☐ 36. ED FARMER
☐ 67. KEN KRAVEC
☐ 83. MIKE PROLY
☐ 107. RICH WORTHAM
☐ 112. RUSTY KUNTZ(FS)
☐ 112. FRAN MULLINS(FS)
☐ 112. LEO SUTHERLAND(FS)
☐ 138. RICH DOTSON
☐ 164. LAMARR HOYT
☐ 186. WAYNE NORDHAGEN
☐ 242. CHET LEMON
☐ 272. BRUCE KIMM
☐ 292. MIKE SQUIRES
☐ 323. JIM MORRISON
☐ 347. HAROLD BAINES
☐ 398. ROSS BAUMGARTEN
☐ 412. BRITT BURNS
☐ 442. RON PRUITT
☐ 466. BOB MOLINARO
☐ 487. DEWEY ROBINSON
☐ 522. MIKE COLBERN
☐ 552. STEVE TROUT
☐ 571. TODD CRUZ
☐ 589. LAMAR JOHNSON
☐ 608. GREG PRYOR
☐ 646. MARVIS FOLEY
☐ 664. TEAM & LARUSSA(M)
☐ 716. GLENN BORGMANN

CINCINNATI REDS

☐ 21. RON OESTER
☐ 52. HECTOR CRUZ
☐ 73. DOUG BAIR
☐ 94. HARRY SPILMAN
☐ 126. CHARLIE LEIBRANDT
☐ 149. JOE NOLAN
☐ 175. DAVE COLLINS
☐ 200. GEORGE FOSTER
☐ 220. TOM SEAVER
☐ 258. JOE PRICE
☐ 280. KEN GRIFFEY
☐ 325. RAY KNIGHT
☐ 354. MARIO SOTO
☐ 375. DAVE CONCEPCION
☐ 390. CESAR GERONIMO
☐ 419. TOM HUME
☐ 447. JUNIOR KENNEDY
☐ 474. MIKE LACOSS
☐ 499. FRANK PASTORE
☐ 521. SAM MEJIAS
☐ 546. PAUL MOSKAU
☐ 600. JOHNNY BENCH
☐ 606. BRUCE BERENYI(FS)
☐ 606. GEOFF COMBE(FS)
☐ 606. PAUL HOUSEHOLDER(FS)
☐ 628. VIC CORRELL
☐ 655. DAN DRIESSEN
☐ 677. TEAM & MCNAMARA(M)
☐ 712. BILL BONHAM

CLEVELAND INDIANS

☐ 13. JOE CHARBONEAU
☐ 39. TOM VERYZER
☐ 74. MIKE HARGROVE
☐ 99. ERIC WILKINS
☐ 122. JOHN DENNY
☐ 141. MIGUEL DILONE
☐ 170. ROSS GRIMSLEY
☐ 198. JERRY DYBZINSKI
☐ 222. JORGE ORTA
☐ 252. VICTOR CRUZ
☐ 276. DAN SPILLNER
☐ 308. RICK MANNING
☐ 333. SID MONGE
☐ 362. BO DIAZ
☐ 388. ANDRE THORNTON
☐ 416. GARY ALEXANDER
☐ 432. LEN BARKER
☐ 451. CHRIS BANDO(FS)
☐ 451. TOM BRENNAN(FS)
☐ 451. SANDY WIHTOL(FS)
☐ 462. JACK BROHAMER
☐ 511. WAYNE GARLAND
☐ 536. BOB OWCHINKO
☐ 564. RON HASSEY
☐ 612. DUANE KUIPER
☐ 632. ALAN BANNISTER
☐ 665. TEAM & GARCIA(M)
☐ 697. RICK WAITS
☐ 721. TOBY HARRAH

DETROIT TIGERS

☐ 27. CHAMP SUMMERS
☐ 59. DAN PETRY
☐ 79. BRUCE ROBBINS
☐ 102. DAVE TOBIK
☐ 123. AL COWENS
☐ 150. MARK FIDRYCH
☐ 177. RICK PETERS
☐ 196. DUFFY DYER
☐ 217. RICH HEBNER
☐ 234. LOU WHITAKER
☐ 251. TOM BROOKENS
☐ 273. STAN PAPI
☐ 291. AURELIO LOPEZ
☐ 315. KIRK GIBSON
☐ 337. LYNN JONES
☐ 358. MARK WAGNER
☐ 373. PAT UNDERWOOD
☐ 392. LANCE PARRISH
☐ 417. DAN SCHATZEDER
☐ 448. TIM CORCORAN
☐ 468. JOHNNY WOCKENFUSS
☐ 572. JACK MORRIS
☐ 593. STEVE KEMP
☐ 614. DAVE ROZEMA
☐ 626. DAVE STEFFEN(FS)
☐ 626. JERRY UJDUR(FS)
☐ 626. ROGER WEAVER(FS)
☐ 658. MILT WILCOX
☐ 666. TEAM & ANDERSON(M)
☐ 709. ALAN TRAMMELL

HOUSTON ASTROS

☐ 45. ENOS CABELL
☐ 82. DANNY HEEP(FS)
☐ 82. ALAN KNICELY(FS)
☐ 82. BOBBY SPROWL(FS)
☐ 105. JOSE CRUZ
☐ 129. ART HOWE
☐ 148. RANDY NIEMANN
☐ 172. GARY WOODS
☐ 190. CESAR CEDENO
☐ 240. NOLAN RYAN
☐ 253. DAVE BERGMAN
☐ 269. KEN FORSCH
☐ 313. LUIS PUJOLS
☐ 329. JOAQUIN ANDUJAR
☐ 350. J.R. RICHARD
☐ 385. JOE SAMBITO
☐ 411. TERRY PUHL
☐ 439. DENNY WALLING
☐ 469. JEFF LEONARD
☐ 491. GORDY PLADSON
☐ 513. FRANK LACORTE
☐ 534. DAVE SMITH
☐ 560. JOE MORGAN
☐ 597. RAFAEL LANDESTOY
☐ 617. CRAIG REYNOLDS
☐ 642. VERN RUHLE
☐ 678. TEAM & VIRDON(M)
☐ 696. ALAN ASHBY
☐ 722. JOE NIEKRO

KANSAS CITY ROYALS

- ☐ 9. PETE LACOCK
- ☐ 26. U.L. WASHINGTON
- ☐ 47. KEN BRETT
- ☐ 66. MANNY CASTILLO(FS)
- ☐ 66. TIM IRELAND(FS)
- ☐ 66. MIKE JONES(FS)
- ☐ 98. CLINT HURDLE
- ☐ 130. LARRY GURA
- ☐ 157. JOHN WATHAN
- ☐ 185. DENNIS LEONARD
- ☐ 218. PAUL SPLITTORFF
- ☐ 274. CRAIG CHAMBERLAIN
- ☐ 295. HAL MCRAE
- ☐ 330. FRANK WHITE
- ☐ 360. WILLIE WILSON
- ☐ 389. MARTY PATTIN
- ☐ 433. RANCE MULLINIKS
- ☐ 452. RENIE MARTIN
- ☐ 473. JOSE CARDENAL
- ☐ 493. DAN QUISENBERRY
- ☐ 507. JAMIE QUIRK
- ☐ 524. WILLIE AIKENS
- ☐ 544. RICH GALE
- ☐ 585. AMOS OTIS
- ☐ 610. DARRELL PORTER
- ☐ 667. TEAM & FREY(M)
- ☐ 700. GEORGE BRETT

LOS ANGELES DODGERS

- ☐ 24. DON STANHOUSE
- ☐ 50. DAVE LOPES
- ☐ 75. REGGIE SMITH
- ☐ 104. TERRY FORSTER
- ☐ 127. RUDY LAW
- ☐ 146. BOBBY CASTILLO
- ☐ 174. DOUG RAU
- ☐ 191. RICK SUTCLIFFE
- ☐ 211. DERREL THOMAS
- ☐ 231. JOE BECKWITH
- ☐ 260. RON CEY
- ☐ 289. MICKEY HATCHER
- ☐ 302. JACK PERCONTE(FS)
- ☐ 302. MIKE SCIOSCIA(FS)
- ☐ 302. FERNANDO VALENZUELA(FS)
- ☐ 318. STEVE YEAGER
- ☐ 372. JAY JOHNSTONE
- ☐ 440. JERRY REUSS
- ☐ 465. BILL RUSSELL
- ☐ 495. DUSTY BAKER
- ☐ 512. GARY THOMASSON
- ☐ 530. STEVE GARVEY
- ☐ 548. DAVE GOLTZ
- ☐ 565. BURT HOOTON
- ☐ 605. DON SUTTON
- ☐ 624. BOB WELCH
- ☐ 651. PEDRO GUERRERO
- ☐ 679. TEAM & LA SORDA(M)
- ☐ 693. STEVE HOWE
- ☐ 711. JOE FERGUSON
- ☐ 726. RICK MONDAY

MILWAUKEE BREWERS

- ☐ 25. SIXTO LEZCANO
- ☐ 56. BUCK MARTINEZ
- ☐ 85. MIKE CALDWELL
- ☐ 106. DON MONEY
- ☐ 135. GORMAN THOMAS
- ☐ 156. BOB MCCLURE
- ☐ 183. DICK DAVIS
- ☐ 215. LARRY HISLE
- ☐ 237. CHARLIE MOORE
- ☐ 271. BILL CASTRO
- ☐ 300. PAUL MOLITOR
- ☐ 327. MOOSE HAAS
- ☐ 357. JIM SLATON
- ☐ 379. LARY SORENSEN
- ☐ 415. BEN OGLIVIE
- ☐ 449. PAUL MITCHELL
- ☐ 482. JIM GANTNER
- ☐ 515. ROBIN YOUNT
- ☐ 555. CECIL COOPER
- ☐ 576. REGGIE CLEVELAND
- ☐ 596. JERRY AUGUSTINE
- ☐ 623. SAL BANDO
- ☐ 659. JOHN FLINN(FS)
- ☐ 659. ED ROMERO(FS)
- ☐ 659. NED YOST(FS)
- ☐ 668. TEAM & RODGERS(M)
- ☐ 704. BILL TRAVERS

MINNESOTA TWINS

- ☐ 18. GLENN ADAMS
- ☐ 43. JOSE MORALES
- ☐ 61. BUTCH WYNEGAR
- ☐ 89. DARRELL JACKSON
- ☐ 115. ROY SMALLEY
- ☐ 137. HOSKEN POWELL
- ☐ 162. DOUG CORBETT
- ☐ 219. KEN LANDREAUX
- ☐ 243. SAL BUTERA
- ☐ 256. BOMBO RIVERA
- ☐ 278. RICK SOFIELD
- ☐ 304. JOHN CASTINO
- ☐ 328. DAVE ENGLE(FS)
- ☐ 328. GREG JOHNSTON(FS)
- ☐ 328. GARY WARD(FS)
- ☐ 363. GEOFF ZAHN
- ☐ 386. DAVE EDWARDS
- ☐ 408. FERNANDO ARROYO
- ☐ 434. ROGER ERICKSON
- ☐ 453. ROB WILFONG
- ☐ 476. JERRY KOOSMAN
- ☐ 509. PETE MACKANIN
- ☐ 527. DANNY GOODWIN
- ☐ 569. AL WILLIAMS
- ☐ 603. JOHN VERHOEVEN
- ☐ 631. RON JACKSON
- ☐ 657. MIKE CUBBAGE
- ☐ 669. TEAM & GORYL(M)
- ☐ 714. PETE REDFERN

MONTREAL EXPOS

- ☐ 15. LARRY PARRISH
- ☐ 42. JERRY WHITE
- ☐ 71. HAL DUES
- ☐ 97. CHRIS SPEIER
- ☐ 125. ANDRE DAWSON
- ☐ 181. ELIAS SOSA
- ☐ 235. SCOTT SANDERSON
- ☐ 267. STAN BAHNSEN
- ☐ 293. CHARLIE LEA
- ☐ 319. ROWLAND OFFICE
- ☐ 345. WARREN CROMARTIE
- ☐ 374. TOM HUTTON
- ☐ 394. WOODIE FRYMAN
- ☐ 413. TONY BERNAZARD
- ☐ 427. JOHN D'ACQUISTO
- ☐ 445. ELLIS VALENTINE
- ☐ 479. BOBBY PATE(FS)
- ☐ 479. TIM RAINES(FS)
- ☐ 479. ROBERTO RAMOS(FS)
- ☐ 497. FRED NORMAN
- ☐ 519. JOHN TAMARGO
- ☐ 539. RODNEY SCOTT
- ☐ 559. WILLIE MONTANEZ
- ☐ 578. BILL GULLICKSON
- ☐ 607. DAVE PALMER
- ☐ 633. BILL LEE
- ☐ 660. GARY CARTER
- ☐ 680. TEAM & WILLIAMS(M)
- ☐ 710. RON LEFLORE
- ☐ 725. STEVE ROGERS

NEW YORK METS

- ☐ 23. ALEX TREVINO
- ☐ 58. JOEL YOUNGBLOOD
- ☐ 93. ED GLYNN
- ☐ 109. MIKE SCOTT
- ☐ 117. PETE FALCONE
- ☐ 151. CLAUDELL WASHINGTON
- ☐ 163. BILLY ALMON
- ☐ 189. CRAIG SWAN
- ☐ 223. ROY LEE JACKSON
- ☐ 224. PAT ZACHRY
- ☐ 259. JUAN BERENGUER(FS)
- ☐ 259. HUBIE BROOKS(FS)
- ☐ 259. MOOKIE WILSON(FS)
- ☐ 299. ELLIOTT MADDOX
- ☐ 322. NEIL ALLEN
- ☐ 343. FRANK TAVERAS
- ☐ 359. TOM HAUSMAN
- ☐ 377. JERRY MORALES
- ☐ 414. JOHN PACELLA
- ☐ 428. JOHN STEARNS
- ☐ 456. JEFF REARDON
- ☐ 472. DYAR MILLER
- ☐ 510. LEE MAZZILLI
- ☐ 537. ROD HODGES
- ☐ 567. MARK BOMBACK
- ☐ 619. STEVE HENDERSON
- ☐ 634. DOUG FLYNN
- ☐ 654. RAY BURRIS
- ☐ 681. TEAM & TORRE(M)
- ☐ 698. MIKE JORGENSEN

NEW YORK YANKEES

- ☐ 16. RON DAVIS
- ☐ 34. AURELIO RODRIGUEZ
- ☐ 60. WILLIE RANDOLPH
- ☐ 88. JOE LEFEBVRE
- ☐ 114. TOM UNDERWOOD
- ☐ 139. OSCAR GAMBLE
- ☐ 159. BRIAN DOYLE
- ☐ 179. RUDY MAY
- ☐ 225. RUPPERT JONES
- ☐ 250. RON GUIDRY
- ☐ 281. FRED STANLEY
- ☐ 303. JOHNNY OATES
- ☐ 335. RICK CERONE
- ☐ 365. GRAIG NETTLES
- ☐ 383. ERIC SODERHOLM
- ☐ 400. REGGIE JACKSON
- ☐ 418. BOBBY BROWN
- ☐ 424. TIM LOLLAR(FS)
- ☐ 424. BRUCE ROBINSON(FS)
- ☐ 424. DENNIS WERTH(FS)
- ☐ 435. JIM SPENCER
- ☐ 460. RICH GOSSAGE
- ☐ 483. MIKE GRIFFIN
- ☐ 516. DOUG BIRD
- ☐ 550. TOMMY JOHN
- ☐ 582. GAYLORD PERRY
- ☐ 602. BOBBY MURCER
- ☐ 627. LUIS TIANT
- ☐ 650. BUCKY DENT
- ☐ 670. TEAM & MICHAEL(M)
- ☐ 690. BOB WATSON
- ☐ 724. LOU PINIELLA

OAKLAND A'S

- ☐ 35. MITCHELL PAGE
- ☐ 55. MIKE NORRIS
- ☐ 86. WAYNE GROSS
- ☐ 96. DAVE BEARD(FS)
- ☐ 96. ERNIE CAMACHO(FS)
- ☐ 96. PAT DEMPSEY(FS)
- ☐ 133. JEFF COX
- ☐ 154. RICK LANGFORD
- ☐ 178. JIM ESSIAN
- ☐ 232. MICKEY KLUTTS
- ☐ 261. RICKEY HENDERSON
- ☐ 284. BRIAN KINGMAN
- ☐ 301. MATT KEOUGH
- ☐ 316. CRAIG MINETTO
- ☐ 341. DWAYNE MURPHY
- ☐ 364. MIKE DAVIS
- ☐ 437. MIKE HEATH
- ☐ 461. DAVE MCKAY
- ☐ 481. BOB LACEY
- ☐ 503. STEVE MCCATTY
- ☐ 547. MARIO GUERRERO
- ☐ 568. DAVE REVERING
- ☐ 587. JEFF NEWMAN
- ☐ 604. ROB PICCIOLO
- ☐ 629. TONY ARMAS
- ☐ 671. TEAM & MARTIN(M)
- ☐ 687. JEFF JONES

PHILADELPHIA PHILLIES

- ☐ 40. TUG MCGRAW
- ☐ 53. KEVIN SAUCIER
- ☐ 90. BAKE MCBRIDE
- ☐ 120. LARRY BOWA
- ☐ 131. KEITH MORELAND
- ☐ 160. GARRY MADDOX
- ☐ 180. PETE ROSE
- ☐ 270. GREG LUZINSKI
- ☐ 290. BOB BOONE
- ☐ 317. LONNIE SMITH
- ☐ 346. LARRY CHRISTENSON
- ☐ 376. RON REED

- ☐ 405. NINO ESPINOSA
- ☐ 406. DICKIE NOLES
- ☐ 426. WARREN BRUSSTAR
- ☐ 459. GREG GROSS
- ☐ 470. MANNY TRILLO
- ☐ 494. BOB WALK
- ☐ 526. MARTY BYSTROM(FS)
- ☐ 526. JAY LOVIGLIO(FS)
- ☐ 526. JIM L. WRGHT(FS)
- ☐ 540. MIKE SCHMIDT
- ☐ 566. DEL UNSER
- ☐ 584. RANDY LERCH
- ☐ 598. GEORGE VUKOVICH
- ☐ 630. STEVE CARLTON
- ☐ 644. RAMON AVILES
- ☐ 682. TEAM & GREEN(M)
- ☐ 691. DICK RUGHVEN
- ☐ 719. SPARKY LYLE

PITTSBURGH PIRATES

- ☐ 28. ENRIQUE ROMO
- ☐ 51. BILL ROBINSON
- ☐ 68. MATT ALEXANDER
- ☐ 92. MIKE EASLER
- ☐ 118. KURT BEVACQUA
- ☐ 147. DALE BERRA
- ☐ 168. DON ROBINSON
- ☐ 194. ROD SCURRY
- ☐ 212. STEVE NICOSIA
- ☐ 226. MANNY SANGUILLEN
- ☐ 246. ED OTT
- ☐ 265. JOHN CANDELARIA
- ☐ 298. BUDDY SOLOMON
- ☐ 312. RICK RHODEN
- ☐ 332. LEE LACY
- ☐ 380. WILLIE STARGELL
- ☐ 430. JIM BIBBY
- ☐ 501. TIM FOLI
- ☐ 518. GRANT JACKSON
- ☐ 535. OMAR MORENO
- ☐ 551. VANCE LAW(FS)
- ☐ 551. TONY PENA(FS)
- ☐ 551. PASCUAL PEREZ(FS)
- ☐ 554. BERT BLYLEVEN
- ☐ 573. PHIL GARNER
- ☐ 618. JOHN MILNER
- ☐ 640. DAVE PARKER
- ☐ 683. TEAM & TANNER(M)
- ☐ 695. KENT TEKULVE
- ☐ 715. BILL MADLOCK

ST. LOUIS CARDINALS

- ☐ 32. KEN OBERKFELL
- ☐ 113. MIKE PHILLIPS
- ☐ 140. BOB FORSCH
- ☐ 152. JOHN URREA
- ☐ 165. TONY SCOTT
- ☐ 193. PETE VUCKOVICH
- ☐ 230. GEORGE HENDRICK
- ☐ 244. TITO LANDRUM(FS)
- ☐ 244. AL OLMSTED(FS)
- ☐ 244. ANDY RINCON(FS)
- ☐ 255. MARK LITTELL
- ☐ 266. TOM HERR
- ☐ 321. LEON DURHAM
- ☐ 334. DANE IORG
- ☐ 348. BOB SYKES
- ☐ 353. TERRY KENNEDY
- ☐ 366. MIKE RAMSEY
- ☐ 420. KEITH HERNANDEZ
- ☐ 441. KEN REITZ
- ☐ 485. GARRY TEMPLETON
- ☐ 489. JOHN LITTLEFIELD
- ☐ 523. JOHN FULGHAM
- ☐ 541. STEVE SWISHER
- ☐ 563. JIM KAAT
- ☐ 586. SILVIO MARTINEZ
- ☐ 635. BOBBY BONDS
- ☐ 684. TEAM & HERZOG(M)
- ☐ 705. TED SIMMONS

SAN DIEGO PADRES

- ☐ 29. GENE TENACE
- ☐ 49. BOB SHIRLEY
- ☐ 72. BARRY EVANS
- ☐ 134. STEVE MURA
- ☐ 171. GENE RICHARDS
- ☐ 229. ROLLIE FINGERS
- ☐ 254. OZZIE SMITH
- ☐ 285. JERRY TURNER
- ☐ 309. LUIS SALAZAR
- ☐ 342. ERIC RASMUSSEN
- ☐ 356. GEORGE STABLEIN(FS)
- ☐ 356. CRAIG STIMAC(FS)
- ☐ 356. TOM TELLMAN(FS)
- ☐ 370. DAVE WINFIELD
- ☐ 393. BRODERICK PERKINS
- ☐ 436. GARY LUCAS
- ☐ 458. RANDY JONES
- ☐ 478. JUAN EICHELBERGER
- ☐ 496. PAUL DADE
- ☐ 531. JOHN CURTIS
- ☐ 556. JERRY MUMPHREY
- ☐ 579. TIM FLANNERY
- ☐ 579. DENNIS KINNEY
- ☐ 616. RICK WISE
- ☐ 653. BILL FAHEY
- ☐ 685. TEAM & HOWARD(M)
- ☐ 707. DAVE CASH

SAN FRANCISCO GIANTS

- ☐ 11. JIM WOHLFORD
- ☐ 30. JACK CLARK
- ☐ 62. JOE PETTINI
- ☐ 84. JOHNNIE LEMASTER
- ☐ 111. GREG MINTON
- ☐ 144. ALLEN RIPLEY
- ☐ 167. TERRY WHITFIELD
- ☐ 195. RICH MURRAY
- ☐ 213. AL HOLLAND
- ☐ 236. MIKE IVIE
- ☐ 257. RENNIE STENNETT
- ☐ 279. BOB KNEPPER
- ☐ 310. VIDA BLUE
- ☐ 336. EDDIE WHITSON
- ☐ 361. JOE STRAIN
- ☐ 384. MIKE SADEK
- ☐ 409. LARRY HERNDON
- ☐ 438. JOHN MONTEFUSCO
- ☐ 463. MILT MAY
- ☐ 484. MAX VENABLE
- ☐ 502. CHRIS BOURJOS(FS)
- ☐ 502. AL HARGESHEIMER(FS)
- ☐ 502. MIKE ROWLAND(FS)
- ☐ 538. TOM GRIFFIN
- ☐ 561. DENNIS LITTLEJOHN
- ☐ 588. GARY LAVELLE
- ☐ 622. RANDY MOFFITT
- ☐ 648. DARRELL EVANS
- ☐ 686. TEAM & BRISTOL(M)
- ☐ 713. BILL NORTH

SEATTLE MARINERS

- ☐ 33. RICK HONEYCUTT
- ☐ 57. DAVE A. ROBERTS
- ☐ 76. MARIO MENDOZA
- ☐ 116. JOE SIMPSON
- ☐ 143. DAN MEYER
- ☐ 166. FLOYD BANNISTER
- ☐ 187. MIKE PARROTT
- ☐ 228. TOM PACIOREK
- ☐ 249. LARRY COX
- ☐ 282. RICK ANDERSON(FS)
- ☐ 282. GREG BIERCEVICZ(FS)
- ☐ 282. RODNEY CRAIG(FS)
- ☐ 306. JUAN BENIQUEZ
- ☐ 344. BYRON MCLAUGHLIN
- ☐ 368. LEON ROBERTS
- ☐ 397. JULIO CRUZ
- ☐ 423. SHANE RAWLEY
- ☐ 443. JIM BEATTIE
- ☐ 486. MARC HILL
- ☐ 508. ROB DRESSLER
- ☐ 532. BILL STEIN
- ☐ 583. LARRY MILBOURNE
- ☐ 613. JIM ANDERSON
- ☐ 637. JERRY NARRON
- ☐ 649. MANNY SARMIENTO
- ☐ 672. TEAM & WILLS(M)
- ☐ 699. GLENN ABBOTT
- ☐ 723. BRUCE BOCHTE

TEXAS RANGERS

- ☐ 22. DANNY DARWIN
- ☐ 41. BOB BABCOCK(FS)
- ☐ 41. JOHN BUTCHER(FS)
- ☐ 41. JERRY DON GLEATON(FS)
- ☐ 70. AL OLIVER
- ☐ 80. RUSTY STAUB
- ☐ 95. JIM SUNDBERG
- ☐ 145. MICKEY RIVERS
- ☐ 158. FERGIE JENKINS
- ☐ 173. BUMP WILLS
- ☐ 197. JIM KERN
- ☐ 216. JOHN HENRY JOHNSON
- ☐ 245. ED FIGUEROA
- ☐ 264. JIM NORRIS
- ☐ 283. BILLY SAMPLE
- ☐ 305. KEN CLAY
- ☐ 339. JOHN ELLIS
- ☐ 371. CHARLIE HOUGH
- ☐ 431. DAVE W. ROBERTS
- ☐ 464. ADRIAN DEVINE
- ☐ 475. BUDDY BELL
- ☐ 498. PAT PUTNAM
- ☐ 517. RICHIE ZISK
- ☐ 545. JOHNNY GRUBB
- ☐ 592. STEVE COMER
- ☐ 656. JON MATLACK
- ☐ 673. TEAM & ZIMMER(M)
- ☐ 694. BUD HARRELSON
- ☐ 702. GEORGE MEDICH

TORONTO BLUE JAYS

- ☐ 19. JIM CLANCY
- ☐ 46. RICK BOSETTI
- ☐ 77. MIKE BARLOW
- ☐ 124. JERRY GARVIN
- ☐ 142. JACKSON TODD
- ☐ 169. JOHN MAYBERRY
- ☐ 221. BOB DAVIS
- ☐ 248. JOEY MCLAUGHLIN
- ☐ 277. ALFREDO GRIFFIN
- ☐ 297. BOB BAILOR
- ☐ 324. MIKE WILLIS
- ☐ 351. OTTO VELEZ
- ☐ 382. PAUL MIRABELLA
- ☐ 407. ERNIE WHITT
- ☐ 444. GARTH IORG
- ☐ 467. DAVE STIEB
- ☐ 488. DAMASO GARCIA
- ☐ 506. PHIL HUFFMAN
- ☐ 558. BARRY BONNELL
- ☐ 577. LUIS LEAL(FS)
- ☐ 577. BRIAN MILNER(FS)
- ☐ 577. KEN SCHROM(FS)
- ☐ 581. ROY HOWELL
- ☐ 643. LLOYD MOSEBY
- ☐ 674. TEAM & MATTICK(M)
- ☐ 703. ALVIS WOODS

1981 TOPPS TRADED (132) 2 1/2" X 3 1/2"

ATLANTA BRAVES

- □ 804. JOHN MONTEFUSCO
- □ 812. GAYLORD PERRY
- □ 853. BOB WALK
- □ 854. CLAUDELL WASHINGTON

BALTIMORE ORIOLES

- □ 757. JIM DWYER
- □ 806. JOSE MORALES

BOSTON RED SOX

- □ 748. MARK CLEAR
- □ 788. CARNEY LANSFORD
- □ 803. RICK MILLER
- □ 826. JOE RUDI
- □ 841. FRANK TANANA

CALIFORNIA ANGELS

- □ 733. JUAN BENIQUEZ
- □ 743. RICK BURLESON
- □ 764. KEN FORSCH
- □ 771. BUTCH HOBSON
- □ 797. FRED LYNN
- □ 810. ED OTT
- □ 818. DOUG RAU
- □ 821. STEVE RENKO
- □ 845. BILL TRAVERS
- □ 856. GEOFF ZAHN

CHICAGO CUBS

- □ 737. DOUG BIRD
- □ 740. BOBBY BONDS
- □ 750. HECTOR CRUZ
- □ 756. LEON DURHAM
- □ 769. STEVE HENDERSON
- □ 783. KEN KRAVEC
- □ 795. MIKE LUM
- □ 805. JERRY MORALES
- □ 820. KEN REITZ
- □ 837. JOE STRAIN

CHICAGO WHITE SOX

- □ 730. BILLY ALMON
- □ 735. TONY BERNAZARD
- □ 759. JOM ESSIAN
- □ 762. CARLTON FISK
- □ 770. MARC HILL
- □ 785. DENNIS LAMP
- □ 791. RON LEFLORE
- □ 796. GREG LUZINSKI

CINCINNATI REDS

- □ 736. LARRY BIITTNER
- □ 786. RAFAEL LANDESTOY
- □ 848. MIKE VAIL

CLEVELAND INDIANS

- □ 738. BERT BLYLEVEN
- □ 784. BOB LACEY

DETROIT TIGERS

- □ 760. BILL FAHEY
- □ 779. MICK KELLEHER
- □ 827. KEVIN SAUCIER

HOUSTON ASTROS

- □ 765. KIKO GARCIA
- □ 774. MIKE IVIE
- □ 782. BOB KNEPPER
- □ 824. DAVE W. ROBERTS
- □ 828. TONY SCOTT
- □ 833. HARRY SPILMAN
- □ 839. DON SUTTON
- □ 844. DICKIE THON

KANSAS CITY ROYALS

- □ 766. CESAR GERONIMO

LOS ANGELES DODGERS

- □ 787. KEN LANDREAUX
- □ 850. FERNANDO VALENZUELA

MILWAUKEE BREWERS

- □ 761. ROLLIE FINGERS
- □ 773. ROY HOWELL
- □ 792. RANDY LERCH
- □ 830. TED SIMMONS
- □ 851. PETE VUCKOVICH

MINNESOTA TWINS

- □ 768. MICKEY HATCHER

MONTREAL EXPOS

- □ 744. RAY BURRIS
- □ 813. MIKE PHILLIPS
- □ 816. TIM RAINES
- □ 819. JEFF REARDON

NEW YORK METS

- □ 732. BOB BAILOR
- □ 742. HUBIE BROOKS
- □ 752. MIKE CUBBAGE
- □ 777. RANDY JONES
- □ 781. DAVE KINGMAN
- □ 835. RUSTY STAUB
- □ 849. ELLIS VALENTINE

NEW YORK YANKEES

- □ 763. BARRY FOOTE
- □ 789. DAVE LAROCHE
- □ 802. LARRY MILBOURNE
- □ 808. JERRY MUMPHREY
- □ 809. GENE NELSON
- □ 822. RICK REUSCHEL
- □ 823. DAVE REVERING
- □ 855. DAVE WINFIELD

OAKLAND A'S

- □ 741. RICK BOSETTI
- □ 754. BRIAN DOYLE
- □ 776. CLIFF JOHNSON
- □ 811. BOB OWCHINKO
- □ 832. JIM SPENCER
- □ 834. FRED STANLEY
- □ 846. TOM UNDERWOOD

PHILADELPHIA PHILLIES

- □ 753. DICK DAVIS
- □ 800. GARY MATTHEWS
- □ 815. MIKE PROLY

PITTSBURGH PIRATES

- □ 729. GARY ALEXANDER
- □ 751. VICTOR CRUZ
- □ 843. JASON THOMPSON

ST. LOUIS CARDINALS

- □ 731. JOAQUIN ANDUJAR
- □ 793. SIXTO LEZCANO
- □ 814. DARRELL PORTER
- □ 829. BOB SHIRLEY
- □ 831. LARY SORENSEN
- □ 838. BRUCE SUTTER
- □ 842. GENE TENACE

SAN DIEGO PADRES

- □ 758. DAVE EDWARDS
- □ 778. RUPPERT JONES
- □ 780. TERRY KENNEDY
- □ 790. JOE LEFEVRE
- □ 794. JOHN LITTLEFIELD
- □ 840. STEVE SWISHER
- □ 847. JOHN URREA

SAN FRANCISCO GIANTS

- □ 728. DOYLE ALEXANDER
- □ 734. DAVE BERGMAN
- □ 746. ENOS CABELL
- □ 798. JERRY MARTIN
- □ 807. JOE MORGAN

SEATTLE MARINERS

- □ 745. JEFF BURROUGHS
- □ 747. KEN CLAY
- □ 755. DICK DRAGO
- □ 767. GARY GRAY
- □ 817. LENNY RANDLE
- □ 857. RICHIE ZISK

TEXAS RANGERS

- □ 749. LARRY COX
- □ 772. RICK HONEYCUTT
- □ 801. MARIO MENDOZA
- □ 825. LEON ROBERTS
- □ 836. BILL STEIN
- □ 852. MARK WAGNER

TORONTO BLUE JAYS

- □ 727. DANNY AINGE
- □ 739. MARK BOMBACK
- □ 775. ROY LEE JACKSON
- □ 799. BUCK MARTINEZ

1982 TOPPS (792)
2 1/2" X 3 1/2"

ATLANTA BRAVES

□ 32. GENE GARBER
□ 61. TOMMY BOGGS
□ 88. BIFF POCOROBA
□ 115. GAYLORD PERRY
□ 126. TEAM LEADER CARD
□ 145. BOB HORNER
□ 185. PHIL NIEKRO
□ 214. BRIAN ASSELSTINE
□ 244. RUFINO LINARES
□ 271. LARRY BRADFORD
□ 296. BOB WALK
□ 320. CHRIS CHAMBLISS
□ 372. LUIS GOMEZ
□ 393. AL HRABOSKY
□ 424. BRUCE BENEDICT
□ 451. ED MILLIER
□ 482. GLENN HUBBARD
□ 502. STEVE BEDROSIAN(FS)
□ 502. BRETT BUTLER(FS)
□ 502. LARRY OWEN(FS)
□ 507. TERRY HARPER
□ 536. RAFAEL RAMIREZ
□ 579. RICK MAHLER
□ 608. JERRY ROYSTER
□ 637. RICK CAMP
□ 668. DALE MURPHY
□ 697. JOHN MONTEFUSCO
□ 733. LARRY MCWILLIAMS
□ 758. CLAUDELL WASHINGTON

BALTIMORE ORIOLES

□ 8. RICH DAUER
□ 21. BOB BONNER(FS)
□ 21. CAL RIPKEN(FS)
□ 21. JEFF SCHNEIDER(FS)
□ 37. DAN GRAHAM
□ 80. JIM PALMER
□ 107. WAYNE KRENCHICKI
□ 136. LENN SAKATA
□ 174. DAVE FORD
□ 204. GARY ROENICKE
□ 232. TERRY CROWLEY
□ 265. AL BUMBRY
□ 290. KEN SINGLETON
□ 331. BENNY AYALA
□ 359. JIM DWYER
□ 390. EDDIE MURRAY
□ 419. STEVE STONE
□ 426. TEAM LEADER CARD
□ 457. TIM STODDARD
□ 489. RICK DEMPSEY
□ 520. MIKE FLANAGAN
□ 564. DOUG DECINCES
□ 583. TIPPY MARTINEZ
□ 617. SCOTT MCGREGOR
□ 648. JOSE MORALES
□ 679. SAMMY STEWART
□ 712. DENNY MARTINEZ
□ 747. JOHN LOWENSTEIN
□ 776. MARK BELANGER

BOSTON RED SOX

□ 25. JERRY REMY
□ 59. RICH GEDMAN
□ 91. CARNEY LANSFORD
□ 124. REID NICHOLS
□ 157. STEVE CRAWFORD
□ 189. GLENN HOFFMAN
□ 225. MIKE TORREZ
□ 255. TONY PEREZ
□ 274. BOB OJEDA
□ 289. BOB STANLEY
□ 322. GARRY HANCOCK
□ 355. DWIGHT EVANS
□ 381. BRUCE HURST(FS)
□ 381. DAVE F. SCHMIDT(FS)
□ 381. JULIO VALDEZ(FS)
□ 388. JOE RUDI
□ 421. MARK CLEAR
□ 455. TOM BURGMEIER
□ 490. DENNIS ECKERSLEY
□ 522. CHUCK RAINEY
□ 558. JOHN TUDOR
□ 589. DAVE STAPLETON
□ 619. BILL CAMPBELL
□ 650. CARL YASTRZEMSKI
□ 686. GARY ALLENSON
□ 717. RICK MILLER
□ 750. JIM RICE
□ 786. TEAM LEADER CARD
□ 792. FRANK TANANA

CALIFORNIA ANGELS

□ 24. DAVE FROST
□ 55. RICK BURLESON
□ 58. JOHN D'ACQUISTO
□ 74. BOB CLARK
□ 94. ANDY HASSLER
□ 134. DAN FORD
□ 158. BRIAN DOWNING
□ 199. DON AASE
□ 229. GEOFF ZAHN
□ 251. FRED LYNN
□ 257. LARRY HARLOW
□ 276. TEAM LEADER CARD
□ 284. BOB GRICH
□ 313. JOHN HARRIS
□ 357. BUTCH HOBSON
□ 385. KEN FORSCH
□ 415. DON BAYLOR
□ 442. BRUCE KISON
□ 469. ED OTT
□ 500. ROD CAREW
□ 514. JOE FERGUSON
□ 572. JUAN BENIQUEZ
□ 602. FREDDIE PATEK
□ 628. BILL TRAVERS
□ 653. TOM BRUNANSKY(FS)
□ 653. LUIS SANCHEZ(FS)
□ 653. DARYL SCONIERS(FS)
□ 659. FRED MARTINEZ
□ 682. JESSE JEFFERSON
□ 702. STEVE RENKO
□ 744. MIKE WITT
□ 772. BERT CAMPANERIS

CHICAGO CUBS

□ 23. WILLIE HERNANDEZ
□ 33. JERRY MORALES
□ 51. JAY HOWELL(FS)
□ 51. CARLOS LEZCANO(FS)
□ 51. TY WALLER(FS)
□ 62. MIKE TYSON
□ 89. STEVE HENDERSON
□ 117. RAWLY EASTWICK
□ 146. MIKE GRIFFIN
□ 188. RANDY MARTZ
□ 215. MIKE KRUKOW
□ 245. KEN REITZ
□ 273. DOUG GIRD
□ 303. BILL CAUDILL
□ 324. STEVE DILLARD
□ 374. TIM BLACKWELL
□ 403. JIM TRACY
□ 436. JOE STRAIN
□ 452. LEE SMITH
□ 456. TEAM LEADER CARD
□ 484. IVAN DEJESUS
□ 508. JODY DAVIS
□ 537. DOUG CAPILLA
□ 580. BOBBY BONDS
□ 607. LEON DURHAM
□ 639. KEN DRAVEC
□ 663. HECTOR CRUZ
□ 699. DICK TIDROW
□ 732. MIKE LUM
□ 760. BILL BUCKNER

CHICAGO WHITE SOX

□ 13. LAMAR JOHNSON
□ 44. BRITT BURNS
□ 76. GREG PRYOR
□ 85. LYNN MCGLOTHEN
□ 110. CARLTON FISK
□ 140. RON LEFLORE
□ 176. DEWEY ROBINSON
□ 206. TONY BERNAZARD
□ 216. TEAM LEADER CARD
□ 237. RUSTY KUNTZ
□ 269. JIM ESSIAN
□ 299. STEVE TROUT
□ 328. ED FARMER
□ 363. BOB MOLINARO
□ 398. MIKE SQUIRES
□ 428. LAMARR HOYT
□ 461. RICH DOTSON
□ 493. CHET LEMON
□ 521. BILLY ALMON
□ 563. ROSS BAUMGARTEN
□ 597. WAYNE NORDHAGEN
□ 599. JAY LOVIGLIO(FS)
□ 599. REGGIE PATTERSON(FS)
□ 599. LEO SUTHERLAND(FS)
□ 622. DENNIS LAMP
□ 654. JIM MORRISON
□ 684. HAROLD BAINES
□ 714. JERRY KOOSMAN
□ 720. GREG LUZINSKI
□ 736. JERRY TURNER
□ 748. MARC HILL
□ 778. KEVIN HICKEY

CINCINNATI REDS

□ 30. TOM SEAVER
□ 63. MARIO SOTO
□ 97. PAUL MOSKAU
□ 128. FRANK PASTORE
□ 159. LARRY BIITTNER
□ 169. CHARLIE LEIBRANDT
□ 194. MIKE VAIL
□ 228. SAM MEJIAS
□ 294. MIKE LACOSS
□ 327. JOE NOLAN
□ 351. SCOTT BROWN(FS)
□ 351. GEOFF COMBE(FS)
□ 351. PAUL HOUSEHOLDER(FS)
□ 361. RAFAEL LANDESTOY
□ 400. JOHNNY BENCH
□ 427. RON OESTER
□ 459. BRUCE BERENYI
□ 492. JOE PRICE
□ 525. RAY KNIGHT
□ 562. MIKE O'BERRY
□ 595. DAVE COLLINS
□ 620. KEN GRIFFEY
□ 660. DAVE CONCEPCION
□ 700. GEORGE FOSTER
□ 723. JUNIOR KENNEDY
□ 756. TEAM LEADER CARD
□ 763. TOME HUME
□ 785. DAN DRIESSEN

CLEVELAND INDIANS

□ 26. JORGE ORTA
□ 54. RON HASSEY
□ 77. MIGUEL DILONE
□ 141. CHRIS BANDO(FS)
□ 141. TOM BRENNAN(FS)
□ 141. VON HAYES(FS)
□ 202. RICK MANNING
□ 233. DUANE KUIPER
□ 258. BO DIAZ
□ 287. ALAN BANNISTER
□ 310. MIKE HARGROVE
□ 356. DENNY LEWALLYN
□ 360. LEN BARKER
□ 387. TOM VERYZER

- ☐ 417. H. PAT KELLY
- ☐ 446. WAYNE GARLAND
- ☐ 473. MIKE STANTON
- ☐ 512. JERRY DYBZINSKI
- ☐ 532. TOBY HARRAH
- ☐ 559. TEAM LEADER CARD
- ☐ 573. RICK WAITS
- ☐ 601. SID MONGE
- ☐ 630. JOE CHARBONEAU
- ☐ 664. DAN SPILLNER
- ☐ 685. BERT BLYLEVEN
- ☐ 724. DAVE ROSELLO
- ☐ 746. ANDRE THORNTON
- ☐ 773. JOHN DENNY

DETROIT TIGERS

- ☐ 39. LOU WHITAKER
- ☐ 64. LYNN JONES
- ☐ 105. KIRK GIBSON
- ☐ 133. PAT UNDERWOOD
- ☐ 137. GEORGE CAPPUZZELLO
- ☐ 184. MICK KELLEHER
- ☐ 211. DAN PETRY
- ☐ 238. KEVIN SAUCIER
- ☐ 261. HOWARD BAILEY(FS)
- ☐ 261. MARTY CASTILLO(FS)
- ☐ 261. DAVE RUCKER(FS)
- ☐ 266. RICK LEACH
- ☐ 286. BILL FAHEY
- ☐ 319. DAVE ROZEMA
- ☐ 369. CHAMP SUMMERS
- ☐ 391. DAVE TOBIK
- ☐ 423. STAN PAPI
- ☐ 450. JACK MORRIS
- ☐ 475. ALAN TRAMMELL
- ☐ 488. RON JACKSON
- ☐ 504. RICK PETERS
- ☐ 535. LANCE PARRISH
- ☐ 575. AL COWENS
- ☐ 603. RICH HEBNER
- ☐ 629. JOHNNY WOCKENFUSS
- ☐ 666. TEAM LEADER CARD
- ☐ 670. STEVE KEMP
- ☐ 691. DAN SCHATZEDER
- ☐ 728. AURELIO LOPEZ
- ☐ 753. TOM BROOKENS
- ☐ 784. MILT WILCOX

HOUSTON ASTROS

- ☐ 34. JOE SAMBITO
- ☐ 57. CRAIG REYNOLDS
- ☐ 66. TEAM LEADER CARD
- ☐ 90. NOLAN RYAN
- ☐ 119. JOE PITTMAN
- ☐ 147. DANNY WALLING
- ☐ 190. J. R. RICHARD
- ☐ 218. DAVE W. ROBERTS
- ☐ 248. FRANK LACORTE
- ☐ 277. TERRY PUHL
- ☐ 305. DON SUTTON
- ☐ 325. JOSE CRUZ
- ☐ 377. KIKO GARCIA
- ☐ 404. DICKIE THON
- ☐ 433. ALAN ASHBY
- ☐ 441. DANNY HEEP(FS)
- ☐ 441. BILLY L. SMITH(FS)
- ☐ 441. BOBBY SPROWL(FS)
- ☐ 453. ART HOWE
- ☐ 483. GARY WOODS
- ☐ 509. HARRY SPILMAN
- ☐ 539. VERN RUHLE
- ☐ 582. LUIS PUJOLS
- ☐ 611. JOE NIEKRO
- ☐ 640. CESAR CEDENO
- ☐ 672. BOB KNEPPER
- ☐ 683. PHIL GARNER
- ☐ 698. TONY SCOTT
- ☐ 734. MIKE IVIE
- ☐ 761. DAVE SMITH

KANSAS CITY ROYALS

- ☐ 35. WILLIE AIKENS
- ☐ 67. RICH GALE
- ☐ 96. TEAM LEADER CARD
- ☐ 104. RANCE MULLINIKS
- ☐ 132. LEE MAY
- ☐ 173. JAMIE QUIRK
- ☐ 200. GEORGE BRETT
- ☐ 230. WILLIE WILSON
- ☐ 264. DAN QUISENBERRY
- ☐ 297. CLINT HURDLE
- ☐ 329. U.L. WASHINGTON
- ☐ 362. JIM L. WRIGHT
- ☐ 397. KEN BRETT
- ☐ 429. JOHN WATHAN
- ☐ 462. DAVE CHALK
- ☐ 471. ATLEE HAMMAKER(FS)
- ☐ 471. MIKE JONES(FS)
- ☐ 471. DARRYL MOTLEY(FS)
- ☐ 495. DENNIS LEONARD
- ☐ 594. RENIE MARTIN
- ☐ 625. HAL MCRAE
- ☐ 645. FRANK WHITE
- ☐ 693. CESAR GERONIMO
- ☐ 725. AMOS OTIS
- ☐ 759. PAUL SPLITTORFF
- ☐ 790. LARRY GURA

LOS ANGELES DODGERS

- ☐ 14. STEVE HOWE
- ☐ 48. BOBBY CASTILLO
- ☐ 82. BOB WELCH
- ☐ 114. KEN LANDREAUX
- ☐ 179. STEVE GARVEY
- ☐ 213. DAVE STEWART
- ☐ 247. PEDRO GUERRERO
- ☐ 279. BILL RUSSELL
- ☐ 311. TEAM LEADER CARD
- ☐ 315. BURT HOOTON
- ☐ 348. DERREL THOMAS
- ☐ 375. DUSTY BAKER
- ☐ 410. RON CEY
- ☐ 444. TERRY FORSTER
- ☐ 477. STEVE YEAGER
- ☐ 510. FERNANDO VALENZUELA
- ☐ 545. REGGIE SMITH
- ☐ 577. RICK MONDAY
- ☐ 609. RICK SUTCLIFFE
- ☐ 642. MIKE SCIOSCIA
- ☐ 674. DAVE GOLTZ
- ☐ 681. MIKE A. MARSHALL(FS)
- ☐ 681. RON ROENICKE(FS)
- ☐ 681. STEVE SAX(FS)
- ☐ 710. JERRY REUSS
- ☐ 740. DAVE LOPES
- ☐ 774. JAY JOHNSTONE

MILWAUKEE BREWERS

- ☐ 12. MOOSE HAAS
- ☐ 46. JERRY AUGUSTINE
- ☐ 68. ROY HOWELL
- ☐ 93. LARRY HISLE
- ☐ 122. JAMIE EASTERLY
- ☐ 150. TED SIMMONS
- ☐ 195. PAUL MOLITOR
- ☐ 221. JIM SLATON
- ☐ 268. RICKEY KEETON
- ☐ 280. BEN OGLIVIE
- ☐ 308. CHARLIE MOORE
- ☐ 333. FRANK DIPINO(FS)
- ☐ 333. MARSHALL EDWARDS(FS)
- ☐ 333. CHUCK PORTER(FS)
- ☐ 350. THAD BOSLEY
- ☐ 378. MIKE CALDWELL
- ☐ 408. ED ROMERO
- ☐ 435. ROBIN YOUNT
- ☐ 466. RANDY LERCH
- ☐ 487. BOB MCCLURE
- ☐ 517. MARK BROUHARD
- ☐ 542. NED YOST
- ☐ 585. ROLLIE FINGERS
- ☐ 613. JIM GANTNER
- ☐ 643. PETE VUCKOVICH
- ☐ 675. CECIL COOPER
- ☐ 703. TEAM LEADER CARD
- ☐ 709. DON MONEY
- ☐ 737. REGGIE CLEVELAND
- ☐ 765. GORMAN THOMAS

MINNESOTA TWINS

- ☐ 18. FERNANDO ARROYO
- ☐ 42. RICK SOFIELD
- ☐ 69. AL WILLIAMS
- ☐ 92. BRAD HAVENS
- ☐ 123. DANNY GOODWIN
- ☐ 153. ROGER ERICKSON
- ☐ 193. DARRELL JACKSON
- ☐ 222. BUTCH WYNEGAR
- ☐ 253. CHUCK BAKER
- ☐ 281. JOHN VERHOEVEN
- ☐ 309. PETE REDFERN
- ☐ 353. JACK O'CONNOR
- ☐ 379. ROB WILFONG
- ☐ 396. TEAM LEADER CARD
- ☐ 409. DON COOPER
- ☐ 438. PETE MACKANIN
- ☐ 467. MICKEY HATCHER
- ☐ 519. GLENN ADAMS
- ☐ 560. DOUG CORBETT
- ☐ 584. HOSKEN POWELL
- ☐ 612. GARY WARD
- ☐ 644. JOHN CASTINO
- ☐ 676. SAL BUTERA
- ☐ 738. DAVE ENGLE
- ☐ 766. LENNY FAEDO(FS)
- ☐ 766. KENT HRBEK(FS)
- ☐ 766. TIM LAUDNER(FS)
- ☐ 767. ROY SMALLEY

MONTREAL EXPOS

- ☐ 7. SCOTT SANDERSON
- ☐ 38. CHARLIE LEA
- ☐ 70. TIM RAINES
- ☐ 102. DAN BRIGGS
- ☐ 118. TERRY FRANCONA(FS)
- ☐ 118. BRAD MILLS(FS)
- ☐ 118. BRYN SMITH(FS)
- ☐ 131. STAN BAHNSEN
- ☐ 172. BILL GULLICKSON
- ☐ 191. TIM WALLACH
- ☐ 198. CHRIS SPEIER
- ☐ 227. RAY BURRIS
- ☐ 259. RODNEY SCOTT
- ☐ 292. DAVE PALMER
- ☐ 323. BILL LEE
- ☐ 354. ROBERTO RAMOS
- ☐ 386. JERRY WHITE
- ☐ 414. ELIAS SOSA
- ☐ 445. LARRY PARRISH
- ☐ 479. ROWLAND OFFICE
- ☐ 526. TEAM LEADER CARD
- ☐ 540. ANDRE DAWSON
- ☐ 605. STEVE ROGERS
- ☐ 638. JOHN MILNER

- ☐ 667. JEFF REARDON
- ☐ 695. WARREN CROMARTIE
- ☐ 730. GARY CARTER
- ☐ 762. MIKE PHILLIPS
- ☐ 779. GRANT JACKSON
- ☐ 788. WOODIE FRYMAN

NEW YORK METS

- ☐ 15. ELLIS VALENTINE
- ☐ 43. MIKE CUBBAGE
- ☐ 79. BOB BAILOR
- ☐ 121. ED LYNCH
- ☐ 143. MOOKIE WILSON
- ☐ 178. DYAR MILLER
- ☐ 205. NEIL ALLEN
- ☐ 234. RON HODGES
- ☐ 246. TEAM LEADER CARD
- ☐ 270. RUSTY STAUB
- ☐ 302. DOUG FLYNN
- ☐ 326. PETE FALCONE
- ☐ 368. ALEX TREVINO
- ☐ 399. PAT ZACHRY
- ☐ 432. MIKE SCOTT
- ☐ 465. LEE MAZZILLI
- ☐ 478. RAY SEARAGE
- ☐ 494. HUBIE BROOKS
- ☐ 524. TOM HAUSMAN
- ☐ 566. MIKE JORGENSEN
- ☐ 592. CRAIG SWAN
- ☐ 623. RON GARDENHIRE(FS)
- ☐ 623. TERRY LEACH(FS)
- ☐ 623. TIM LEARY(FS)
- ☐ 626. RANDY JONES
- ☐ 655. JOEL YOUNGBLOOD
- ☐ 690. DAVE KINGMAN
- ☐ 743. JOHN STEARNS
- ☐ 782. FRANK TAVERAS
- ☐ 783. GREG HARRIS

NEW YORK YANKEES

- ☐ 9. RON GUIDRY
- ☐ 45. RICK CERONE
- ☐ 75. TOMMY JOHN
- ☐ 83. STEVE BALBONI(FS)
- ☐ 83. ANDY MCGAFFIGAN(FS)
- ☐ 83. ANDRE ROBERTSON(FS)
- ☐ 109. DAVE REVERING
- ☐ 142. DAVE LAROCHE
- ☐ 154. DENNIS WERTH
- ☐ 175. JERRY MUMPHREY
- ☐ 208. BOBBY MURCER
- ☐ 240. BUCKY DENT
- ☐ 275. BOB WATSON
- ☐ 300. REGGIE JACKSON
- ☐ 334. AURELIO RODRIGUEZ
- ☐ 349. GEORGE FRAZIER
- ☐ 373. GENE NELSON
- ☐ 405. RICK REUSCHEL
- ☐ 439. DAVE RIGHETTI
- ☐ 472. OSCAR GAMBLE
- ☐ 486. TEAM LEADER CARD
- ☐ 505. GRAIG NETTLES
- ☐ 538. LOU PINIELLA
- ☐ 569. WILLIE RANDOLPH
- ☐ 600. DAVE WINFIELD
- ☐ 635. RON DAVIS
- ☐ 669. LARRY MILBOURNE
- ☐ 694. DAVE WEHRMEISTER
- ☐ 706. BARRY FOOTE
- ☐ 735. RUDY MAY
- ☐ 770. RICH GOSSAGE
- ☐ 791. BOBBY BROWN

OAKLAND A'S

- ☐ 29. DWAYNE MURPHY
- ☐ 60. TONY ARMAS
- ☐ 87. MATT KEOUGH
- ☐ 113. STEVE MCCATTY
- ☐ 139. JEFF JONES
- ☐ 148. MICKEY KLUTTS
- ☐ 156. TEAM LEADER CARD
- ☐ 187. JEFF NEWMAN
- ☐ 217. BO MCLAUGHLIN
- ☐ 243. BOB OWCHINKO
- ☐ 293. ROB PICCIOLO
- ☐ 318. MIKE HEATH
- ☐ 370. MIKE NORRIS
- ☐ 392. RICK BOSETTI
- ☐ 422. CLIFF JOHNSON
- ☐ 454. RICK LANGFORD
- ☐ 476. BRIAN KINGMAN
- ☐ 531. RICH BORDI(FS)
- ☐ 531. MARK BUDASKA(FS)
- ☐ 531. KELVIN MOORE(FS)
- ☐ 534. DAVE MCKAY
- ☐ 578. SHOOTY BABITT
- ☐ 610. RICKEY HENDERSON
- ☐ 633. MITCHELL PAGE
- ☐ 671. MIKE DAVIS
- ☐ 673. KEITH DRUMRIGHT
- ☐ 692. WAYNE GROSS
- ☐ 729. JIM SPENCER
- ☐ 757. TOM UNDERWOOD
- ☐ 787. FRED STANLEY

PHILADELPHIA PHILLIES

- ☐ 20. GARRY MADDOX
- ☐ 53. GREG GROSS
- ☐ 100. MIKE SCHMIDT
- ☐ 127. LONNIE SMITH
- ☐ 152. RAMON AVILES
- ☐ 183. MIKE PROLY
- ☐ 220. MANNY TRILLO
- ☐ 231. MARK DAVIS(FS)
- ☐ 231. BOB DERNIER(FS)
- ☐ 231. OZZIE VIRGIL(FS)
- ☐ 250. TUG MCGRAW
- ☐ 285. SPARKY LYLE
- ☐ 317. DICK RUTHVEN
- ☐ 352. DICK DAVIS
- ☐ 384. KEITH MORELAND
- ☐ 389. GEORGE VUKOVICH
- ☐ 416. MARTY BYSTROM
- ☐ 449. LUIS AGUAYO
- ☐ 480. STEVE CARLTON
- ☐ 515. LARRY BOWA
- ☐ 530. DICKIE NOLES
- ☐ 544. LARRY CHRISTENSON
- ☐ 581. RON REED
- ☐ 615. BOB BOONE
- ☐ 636. TEAM LEADER CARD
- ☐ 647. WARREN BRUSSTAR
- ☐ 680. GARY MATTHEWS
- ☐ 713. DEL UNSER
- ☐ 745. BAKE MCBRIDE
- ☐ 780. PETE ROSE

PITTSBURGH PIRATES

- ☐ 11. GARY ALEXANDER
- ☐ 40. DAVE PARKER
- ☐ 73. BUDDY SOLOMON
- ☐ 106. ENRIQUE ROMO
- ☐ 138. TONY PENA
- ☐ 160. LUIS TIANT
- ☐ 170. JIM BIBBY
- ☐ 207. ROD SCURRY
- ☐ 235. MIKE EASLER
- ☐ 263. VICTOR CRUZ
- ☐ 267. KURT BEVACQUA
- ☐ 291. VANCE LAW(FS)
- ☐ 291. BOB LONG(FS)
- ☐ 291. JOHNNY RAY(FS)
- ☐ 295. JASON THOMPSON
- ☐ 332. DON ROBINSON
- ☐ 365. BILL MADLOCK
- ☐ 383. PASCUAL PEREZ
- ☐ 395. OMAR MORENO
- ☐ 425. JOHN CANDELARIA
- ☐ 458. WILLIE MONTANEZ
- ☐ 485. KENT TEKULVE
- ☐ 513. RICK RHODEN
- ☐ 528. MATT ALEXANDER
- ☐ 543. BILL ROBINSON
- ☐ 588. DALE BERRA
- ☐ 618. TIM FOLI
- ☐ 652. STEVE NICOSIA
- ☐ 696. TEAM LEADER CARD
- ☐ 715. WILLIE STARGELL
- ☐ 752. LEE LACY

ST. LOUIS CARDINALS

- ☐ 27. TOM HERR
- ☐ 56. MARK LITTELL
- ☐ 86. DANE IORG
- ☐ 108. BOB SYKES
- ☐ 135. ANDY RINCON
- ☐ 181. SILVIO MARTINEZ
- ☐ 186. TEAM LEADER CARD
- ☐ 210. KEITH HERNANDEZ
- ☐ 236. JOHN MARTIN
- ☐ 260. BRUCE SUTTER
- ☐ 262. DOUG BAIR
- ☐ 288. GARRY TEMPLETON
- ☐ 316. STEVE BRAUN
- ☐ 367. JIM KAAT
- ☐ 420. GEORGE HENDRICK
- ☐ 447. DARRELL PORTER
- ☐ 474. KEN OBERKFELL
- ☐ 503. JULIO GONZALEZ
- ☐ 533. JOAQUIN ANDUJAR
- ☐ 561. GLENN BRUMMER(FS)
- ☐ 561. LUIS DELEON(FS)
- ☐ 561. GENE ROOF(FS)
- ☐ 574. MIKE RAMSEY
- ☐ 604. ORLANDO SANCHEZ
- ☐ 631. GENE TENACE
- ☐ 658. TITO LANDRUM
- ☐ 689. LARY SORENSEN
- ☐ 727. SIXTO LEZCANO
- ☐ 749. BOB SHIRLEY
- ☐ 775. BOB FORSCH

SAN DIEGO PADRES

- ☐ 28. JOHN URREA
- ☐ 65. TERRY KENNEDY
- ☐ 95. OZZIE SMITH
- ☐ 120. GARY LUCAS
- ☐ 151. DAVE EDWARDS
- ☐ 192. BRODERICK PERKINS
- ☐ 219. JOHN CURTIS
- ☐ 249. TIM FLANNERY
- ☐ 278. JOHN LITTLEFIELD
- ☐ 307. RANDY BASS
- ☐ 330. RICK WISE
- ☐ 366. TEAM LEADER CARD
- ☐ 376. CHRIS WELSH
- ☐ 407. DANNY BOONE
- ☐ 434. JOE LEFEBVRE
- ☐ 464. JUAN BONILLA
- ☐ 511. RUPPERT JONES
- ☐ 541. BARRY EVANS
- ☐ 587. TIM LOLLAR
- ☐ 614. JUAN EICHELBERGER
- ☐ 641. STEVE MURA
- ☐ 662. LUIS SALAZAR
- ☐ 708. GENE RICHARDS
- ☐ 731. MIKE ARMSTRONG(FS)
- ☐ 731. DOUG GWOSDZ(FS)
- ☐ 731. FRED KUHAULUA(FS)
- ☐ 764. STEVE SWISHER

SAN FRANCISCO GIANTS

- ☐ 17. DARRELL EVANS
- ☐ 47. JEFF LEONARD
- ☐ 84. RENNIE STENNETT
- ☐ 116. JIM WOHLFORD
- ☐ 144. FRED BREINING
- ☐ 171. BOB BRENLY(FS)
- ☐ 171. CHILI DAVIS(FS)
- ☐ 171. BOB TUFTS(FS)
- ☐ 182. LARRY HERNDON
- ☐ 209. GARY LAVELLE
- ☐ 242. MILT MAY
- ☐ 304. JOHNNIE LEMASTER
- ☐ 364. DOYLE ALEXANDER
- ☐ 406. AL HOLLAND
- ☐ 430. VIDA BLUE
- ☐ 460. JACK CLARK
- ☐ 498. DAVE BERGMAN
- ☐ 529. ALLEN RIPLEY
- ☐ 568. JOE PETTINI
- ☐ 576. TEAM LEADER CARD
- ☐ 593. BILLY E. SMITH
- ☐ 627. ENOS CABELL
- ☐ 656. EDDIE WHITSON
- ☐ 687. GREG MINTON
- ☐ 722. JERRY MARTIN
- ☐ 754. JOE MORGAN
- ☐ 777. TOM GRIFFIN

SEATTLE MARINERS

- ☐ 22. JIM BEATTIE
- ☐ 52. LARRY ANDERSON
- ☐ 72. RICK AUERBACH
- ☐ 98. TERRY BULLING

□ 130. JULIO CRUZ
□ 197. SHANE RAWLEY
□ 224. BRUCE BOCHTE
□ 283. BRIAN ALLARD
□ 312. LENNY RANDLE
□ 336. TEAM LEADER CARD
□ 358. MIKE PARROTT
□ 371. JERRY DON GLEATON
□ 382. JOE SIMPSON
□ 413. DAN MEYER
□ 440. JEFF BURROUGHS
□ 468. FLOYD BANNISTER
□ 497. JIM ANDERSON
□ 523. GARY GRAY
□ 571. GLENN ABBOTT
□ 598. BOB GALASSO
□ 632. BRYAN CLARK
□ 649. KEN CLAY
□ 678. TOM PACIOREK
□ 711. DAVE EDLER(FS)
□ 711. DAVE HENDERSON(FS)
□ 711. REGGIE WALTON(FS)
□ 719. JERRY NARRON
□ 742. DICK DRAGO
□ 769. RICHIE ZISK

TEXAS RANGERS

□ 16. STEVE COMER
□ 36. TEAM LEADER CARD
□ 50. BUDDY BELL
□ 78. GEORGE MEDICH
□ 103. BOB LACEY
□ 112. BILLY SAMPLE
□ 149. PAT PUTNAM
□ 177. JOHN ELLIS
□ 212. MARIO MENDOZA
□ 239. JON MATLACK
□ 272. BUMP WILLS
□ 298. DANNY DARWIN
□ 335. JIM SUNDBERG
□ 402. BILL STEIN
□ 418. JOHN BUTCHER(FS)
□ 418. BOBBY JOHNSON(FS)
□ 418. DAVE J. SCHMIDT(FS)
□ 443. MARK WAGNER
□ 463. JIM KERN
□ 496. JOHNNY GRUBB
□ 527. JOHN HERNY JOHNSON
□ 567. BOB BABCOCK
□ 590. AL OLIVER
□ 624. FERGIE JENKINS
□ 657. TOM POQUETTE
□ 688. LEON ROBERTS
□ 704. MICKEY RIVERS
□ 718. CHARLIE HOUGH
□ 751. RICK HONEYCUTT

TORONTO BLUE JAYS

□ 19. ERNIE WHITT
□ 49. ALVIS WOODS
□ 71. ROY LEE JACKSON
□ 99. BARRY BONNELL
□ 125. DANNY AINGE
□ 155. OTTO VELEZ
□ 196. WILLIE UPSHAW
□ 203. JESSE BARFIELD(FS)
□ 203. BRIAN MILNER(FS)
□ 203. BOOMER WELLS(FS)
□ 223. LLOYD MOSEBY
□ 254. JORGE BELL
□ 282. KEN MACHA
□ 314. BUCK MARTINEZ
□ 380. DAVE STIEB
□ 412. LUIS LEAL
□ 437. JUAN BERENGUER
□ 470. JOHN MAYBERRY
□ 499. PAUL MIRABELLA
□ 518. GARTH IORG
□ 565. JACKSON TODD
□ 596. DAMASO GARCIA
□ 606. TEAM LEADER CARD
□ 665. JIM CLANCY
□ 677. ALFREDO GRIFFIN
□ 707. MARK BOMBACK
□ 739. JOEY MCLAUGHLIN
□ 768. JERRY GARVIN

1982 TOPPS TRADED (132) 2 1/2" X 3 1/2"

ATLANTA BRAVES

□ 4T. STEVE BEDROSIAN
□ 125T. BOB WATSON

BALTIMORE ORIOLES

□ 35T. DAN FORD
□ 81T. JOE NOLAN
□ 98T. CAL RIPKEN

BOSTON RED SOX

NO CARDS ISSUED

CALIFORNIA ANGELS

□ 9T. BOB BOONE
□ 21T. DOUG CORBETT
□ 26T. DOUG DECINCES
□ 34T. TIM FOLI
□ 47T. REGGIE JACKSON
□ 48T. RON JACKSON
□ 53T. MICK KELLEHER
□ 128T. ROB WILFONG

CHICAGO CUBS

□ 10T. LARRY BOWA
□ 11T. DAN BRIGGS
□ 16T. BILL CAMPBELL
□ 49T. FERGIE JENKINS
□ 52T. JAY JOHNSTONE
□ 55T. JUNIOR KENNEDY
□ 76T. KEITH MORELAND
□ 82T. DICKIE NOLES
□ 92T. MIKE PROLY
□ 99T. ALLEN RIPLEY
□ 129T. BUMP WILLS
□ 130T. GARY WOODS

CHICAGO WHITE SOX

□ 54T. STEVE KEMP
□ 85T. TOM PACIOREK
□ 101T. AURELIO RODRIGUEZ

CINCINNATI REDS

□ 19T. CESAR CEDENO
□ 41T. GREG HARRIS
□ 56T. JIM KERN
□ 58T. WAYNE KRENCHICKI
□ 72T. EDDIE MILNER
□ 105T. BOB SHIRLEY
□ 120T. ALEX TREVINO

CLEVELAND INDIANS

□ 42T. VON HAYES
□ 69T. BAKE MCBRIDE
□ 71T. LARRY MILBOURNE
□ 87T. JACK PERCONTE
□ 111T. LARY SORENSEN
□ 116T. RICK SUTCLIFFE
□ 127T. EDDIE WHITSON

DETROIT TIGERS

□ 15T. ENOS CABELL
□ 43T. LARRY HERNDON
□ 45T. MIKE IVIE
□ 62T. CHET LEMON
□ 112T. ELIAS SOSA
□ 121T. JERRY TURNER

HOUSTON ASTROS

□ 57T. RAY KNIGHT
□ 61T. MIKE LACOSS

KANSAS CITY ROYALS

□ 8T. VIDA BLUE
□ 37T. DAVE FROST
□ 46T. GRANT JACKSON
□ 65T. JERRY MARTIN
□ 93T. GREG PRYOR
□ 126T. DENNIS WERTH

LOS ANGELES DODGERS

□ 5T. MARK BELANGER
□ 75T. JOSE MORALES
□ 84T. JORGE ORTA
□ 103T. STEVE SAX

MILWAUKEE BREWERS

□ 89T. ROB PICIOLO

MINNESOTA TWINS

□ 13T. TOM BRUNANSKY
□ 17T. BOBBY CASTILLO
□ 25T. RON DAVIS
□ 44T. KENT HRBEK
□ 51T. RANDY JOHNSON
□ 124T. RON WASHINGTON

MONTREAL EXPOS

□ 7T. TIM BLACKWELL
□ 83T. AL OLIVER
□ 104T. DAN SCHATZEDER
□ 118T. FRANK TAVERAS

NEW YORK METS

□ 36T. GEORGE FOSTER
□ 39T. RON GARDERHIRE
□ 94T. CHARLIE PULEO
□ 123T. TOM VERYZER

NEW YORK YANKEES

□ 1T. DOYLE ALEXANDER
□ 20T. DAVE COLLINS
□ 30T. ROGER ERICKSON
□ 40T. KEN GRIFFEY
□ 67T. JOHN MAYBERRY
□ 95T. SHANE RAWLEY
□ 107T. ROY SMALLEY
□ 131T. BUTCH WYNEGAR

OAKLAND A'S

□ 14T. JEFF BURROUGHS
□ 64T. DAVE LOPES
□ 70T. DAN MEYER
□ 102T. JOE RUDI

PHILADELPHIA PHILLIES

□ 27T. IVAN DEJESUS
□ 28T. BOB DERNIER
□ 29T. BO DIAZ
□ 32T. ED FARMER
□ 59T. MIKE KRUKOW
□ 73T. SID MONGE
□ 100T. BILL ROBINSON

PITTSBURGH PIRATES

□ 3T. ROSS BAUGARTEN
□ 24T. DICK DAVIS
□ 77T. JIM MORRISON
□ 96T. JOHNNY RAY

ST. LOUIS CARDINALS

□ 79T. STEVE MURA
□ 108T. LONNIE SMITH
□ 109T. OZZIE SMITH

SAN DIEGO PADRES

□ 6T. KURT BEVACQUA
□ 63T. SIXTO LEZCANO
□ 74T. JOHN MONTEFUSCO
□ 90T. JOE PITTMAN
□ 106T. ERIC SHOW
□ 119T. GARRY TEMPLETON

SAN FRANCISCO GIANTS

□ 23T. CHILI DAVIS
□ 38T. RICH GALE
□ 60T. DUANE KUIPER
□ 66T. RENIE MARTIN
□ 110T. REGGIE SMITH
□ 115T. CHAMP SUMMERS

SEATTLE MARINERS

□ 12T. BOBBY BROWN
□ 18T. BILL CAUDILL
□ 22T. AL COWENS
□ 31T. JIM ESSIAN
□ 80T. GENE NELSON
□ 88T. GAYLORD PERRY
□ 113T. MIKE STANTON
□ 114T. STEVE STROUGHTER
□ 122T. ED VANDEBERG

TEXAS RANGERS

□ 33T. DOUG FLYNN
□ 50T. LAMAR JOHNSON
□ 68T. LEE MAZZILLI
□ 86T. LARRY PARRISH
□ 117T. FRANK TANANA

TORONTO BLUE JAYS

□ 2T. JESSE BARFIELD
□ 78T. RANCE MULLINIKS
□ 91T. HOSKEN POWELL
□ 97T. DAVE REVERING

1983 TOPPS (792)
2 1/2" X 3 1/2"

ATLANTA BRAVES

□ 26. JERRY ROYSTER
□ 50. BOB HORNER
□ 76. RICK MAHLER
□ 104. BOB WALK
□ 126. JOE TORRE(M)
□ 157. STEVE BEDROSIAN
□ 207. RICK CAMP
□ 235. CLAUDELL WASHINGTON
□ 255. GENE GARBER
□ 288. JOE COWLEY
□ 314. KEN DAYLEY
□ 339. TERRY HARPER
□ 364. BREET BUTLER
□ 410. PHIL NIEKRO
□ 417. TOM HAUSMAN
□ 439. RAFAEL RAMIREZ
□ 467. RUFINO LINARES
□ 502. TEAM LEADER CARD
□ 521. BRUCE BENEDICT
□ 544. LARRY WHISENTON
□ 572. BOB WATSON
□ 596. RANDY JOHNSON
□ 624. GLENN HUBBARD
□ 649. TOMMY BOGGS
□ 676. BIFF POCOROBA
□ 760. DALE MURPHY
□ 792. CHRIS CHAMBLISS

BALTIMORE ORIOLES

□ 21. TEAM LEADER CARD
□ 59. BENNY AYALA
□ 85. KEN SINGLETON
□ 138. RICK DEMPSEY
□ 163. CAL RIPKEN
□ 192. FLOYD RAYFORD
□ 217. TIM STODDARD
□ 242. JOE NOLAN
□ 268. STORM DAVIS
□ 293. GLENN GULLIVER
□ 319. LENN SAKATA
□ 347. SAMMY STEWART
□ 372. TERRY CROWLEY
□ 426. EARL WEAVER(M)
□ 445. MIKE FLANAGAN
□ 473. JOHN LOWENSTEIN
□ 490. JIM PALMER
□ 530. EDDIE MURRAY
□ 553. DENNY MARTINEZ
□ 579. RICH DAUER
□ 605. GARY ROENICKE
□ 631. TIPPY MARTINEZ
□ 655. AL BUMBRY
□ 683. DAN FORD
□ 718. JIM DWYER
□ 745. SCOTT MCGREGOR

BOSTON RED SOX

□ 30. JIM RICE
□ 56. CHUCK RAINEY
□ 82. BRUCE HURST
□ 108. GLENN HOFFMAN
□ 135. DWIGHT EVANS
□ 162. MARK CLEAR
□ 188. RICK MILLER
□ 213. TOM BURGMEIER
□ 239. DAVE STAPLETON
□ 270. DENNIS ECKERSLEY
□ 295. JERRY REMY
□ 318. JOHN TUDOR
□ 344. ROGER LAFRANCOIS
□ 381. TEAM LEADER CARD
□ 419. STEVE CRAWFORD
□ 446. REID NICHOLS
□ 472. GARY ALLENSON
□ 498. WADE BOGGS
□ 523. CARNEY LANSFORD
□ 550. CARL YASTRZEMSKI
□ 577. LUIS APONTE
□ 602. RICH GEDMAN
□ 628. JULIO VALDEZ
□ 654. BOB OJEDA
□ 682. BOB STANLEY
□ 715. TONY PEREZ
□ 743. MIKE TORREZ
□ 786. RALPH HOUK(M)

CALIFORNIA ANGELS

□ 27. DOUG CORBETT
□ 53. MIKE WITT
□ 79. MICK KELLEHER
□ 105. DON BAYLOR
□ 131. ED OTT
□ 158. ROB WILFONG
□ 178. LUIS TIANT
□ 184. BOB CLARK
□ 200. ROD CAREW
□ 236. STEVE RENKO
□ 262. RON JACKSON
□ 276. GENE MAUCH(M)
□ 315. RICK BURLESON
□ 341. DOUG DECINCES
□ 416. JOE FERGUSON
□ 442. BRIAN DOWNING
□ 468. DAVE GOLTZ
□ 500. REGGIE JACKSON
□ 520. FRED LYNN
□ 547. GEOFF ZAHN
□ 573. ANDY HASSLER
□ 599. DON AASE
□ 623. LUIS SANCHEZ
□ 625. KEN FORSCH
□ 651. TEAM LEADER CARD
□ 678. JUAN BENIQUEZ
□ 712. BRUCE KISON
□ 735. TOMMY JOHN
□ 738. TIM FOLI
□ 765. BOB BOONE
□ 777. JOHN CURTIS
□ 790. BOB GRICH

CHICAGO CUBS

□ 22. RANDY MARTZ
□ 51. TEAM LEADER CARD
□ 73. ALLEN RIPLEY
□ 83. RYNE SANDBERG
□ 99. DICKIE NOLES
□ 125. LEON DURHAM
□ 152. JAY JOHNSTONE
□ 204. JUNIOR KENNEDY
□ 230. FERGIE JENKINS
□ 250. BILL BUCKNER
□ 305. LARRY BOWA
□ 335. STEVE HENDERSON
□ 356. GARY WOODS
□ 436. BILL CAMPBELL
□ 456. LEE ELIA(M)
□ 481. SCOT THOMPSON
□ 508. TOM FILER
□ 542. JODY DAVIS
□ 568. WILLIE HERNANDEZ
□ 597. MIKE PROLY
□ 619. KEITH MORELAND
□ 643. BUMP WILLS
□ 699. LEE SMITH
□ 729. JERRY MORALES
□ 759. DOUG BIRD
□ 787. DICK TIDROW

CHICAGO WHITE SOX

□ 20. CARLTON FISK
□ 46. RICHARD DOTSON
□ 72. TOM PACIOREK

- ☐ 98. VANCE LAW
- ☐ 124. MARC HILL
- ☐ 153. JERRY KOOSMAN
- ☐ 177. HAROLD BAINES
- ☐ 216. TONY LARUSSA(M)
- ☐ 260. STEVE KEMP
- ☐ 278. KEVIN HICKEY
- ☐ 310. GREG LUZINSKI
- ☐ 362. BILL ALMON
- ☐ 409. MARVIS FOLEY
- ☐ 434. DENNIS LAMP
- ☐ 461. STEVE TROUT
- ☐ 487. JERRY HAIRSTON
- ☐ 514. RUDY LAW
- ☐ 541. BRITT BURNS
- ☐ 560. RON LEFLORE
- ☐ 591. TEAM LEADER CARD
- ☐ 618. LAMARR LOYT
- ☐ 669. MIKE SQUIRES
- ☐ 693. SPARKY LYLE
- ☐ 698. TONY BERNAZARD
- ☐ 758. AURELIO RODRIGUEZ
- ☐ 772. JIM KERN

CINCINNATI REDS

- ☐ 34. PAUL HOUSEHOLDER
- ☐ 60. JOHNNY BENCH
- ☐ 86. TOM HUME
- ☐ 112. BOB SHIRLEY
- ☐ 139. BRUCE BERENYI
- ☐ 165. DAN DRIESSEN
- ☐ 191. JOE PRICE
- ☐ 215. MARIO SOTO
- ☐ 243. DUANE WALKER
- ☐ 269. RON OESTER
- ☐ 296. GREG HARRIS
- ☐ 322. DAVE VAN GORDER
- ☐ 351. TEAM LEADER CARD
- ☐ 374. WAYNE KRENCHICKI
- ☐ 423. TOM LAWLESS
- ☐ 449. EDDIE MILNER
- ☐ 475. CESAR CEDENO
- ☐ 527. LARRY BIITTNER
- ☐ 554. MIKE VAIL
- ☐ 580. TOM SEAVER
- ☐ 607. CHARLIE LEIBRANDT
- ☐ 632. ALEX TREVINO
- ☐ 658. FRANK PASTORE
- ☐ 684. RAFAEL LANDESTOY
- ☐ 720. DAVE CONCEPION
- ☐ 756. RUSS NIXON(M)

CLEVELAND INDIANS

- ☐ 48. LARY SORENSEN
- ☐ 91. LARRY MILBOURNE
- ☐ 120. LEN BARKER
- ☐ 141. TEAM LEADER CARD
- ☐ 182. MIKE FISCHLIN
- ☐ 227. CHRIS BANDO
- ☐ 248. BAKE MCBRIDE
- ☐ 280. BERT BLYLEVEN
- ☐ 289. JERRY DYBZINSKI
- ☐ 303. MIGUEL DILONE
- ☐ 325. VON HAYES
- ☐ 348. ALAN BANNISTER
- ☐ 367. BUD ANDERSON
- ☐ 429. EDDIE WHITSON
- ☐ 480. TOBY HARRAH
- ☐ 497. RICK SUTCLIFFE
- ☐ 524. TOM BRENNAN
- ☐ 546. DAVE GARCIA(M)
- ☐ 569. JACK PERCONTE
- ☐ 614. ED GLYNN
- ☐ 616. BILL NAHORODNY
- ☐ 640. ANDRE THORNTON
- ☐ 660. MIKE HARGROVE
- ☐ 689. RON HASSEY
- ☐ 725. DAN SPILLNER
- ☐ 757. RICK MANNING
- ☐ 779. RICK WAITS

DETROIT TIGERS

- ☐ 13. LARRY HERNDON
- ☐ 41. JERRY TURNER
- ☐ 65. JACK MORRIS
- ☐ 95. ALAN TRAMMELL
- ☐ 119. TOM BROOKENS
- ☐ 147. RICK LEACH
- ☐ 174. JERRY UJDUR
- ☐ 196. BILL FAHEY
- ☐ 225. ENOS CABELL
- ☐ 261. TEAM LEADER CARD
- ☐ 285. LANCE PARRISH
- ☐ 304. DAVE RUCKER
- ☐ 332. GLENN WILSON
- ☐ 373. KEVIN SAUCIER
- ☐ 430. KIRK GIBSON
- ☐ 457. MILT WILCOX
- ☐ 483. LYNN JONES
- ☐ 509. LOU WHITAKER
- ☐ 536. JOHNNY WOCKENFUSS
- ☐ 562. DAVE ROZEMA
- ☐ 588. PAT UNDERWOOD
- ☐ 613. MIKE IVIE
- ☐ 638. DAN PETRY
- ☐ 666. SPARKY ANDERSON(M)
- ☐ 691. DAVE TOBIK
- ☐ 727. CHET LEMON
- ☐ 753. ELIAS SOSA

HOUSTON ASTROS

- ☐ 14. FRANK LACORTE
- ☐ 39. TERRY PUHL
- ☐ 66. BOB LILLIS(M)
- ☐ 92. MIKE LACOSS
- ☐ 117. ALAN KNICELY
- ☐ 172. VERN RUHLE
- ☐ 193. HARRY SPILMAN
- ☐ 198. KIKO GARCIA
- ☐ 221. JOE NIEKRO
- ☐ 247. DAVE SMITH
- ☐ 275. RAY KNIGHT
- ☐ 328. CRAIG REYNOLDS
- ☐ 360. NOLAN RYAN
- ☐ 382. BOB KNEPPER
- ☐ 422. GEORGE CAPPUZZELLO
- ☐ 441. TEAM LEADER CARD
- ☐ 478. PHIL GARNER
- ☐ 507. TONY SCOTT
- ☐ 538. DANNY HEEP
- ☐ 558. DICKIE THON
- ☐ 585. JOSE CRUZ
- ☐ 611. BERT ROBERGE
- ☐ 639. ART HOWE
- ☐ 662. JOE SAMBITO
- ☐ 692. DENNY WALLING
- ☐ 723. RANDY MOFFITT
- ☐ 774. ALAN ASHBY
- ☐ 752. LUIS PUJOLS

KANSAS CITY ROYALS

- ☐ 25. HAL MCRAE
- ☐ 52. ONIX CONCEPCION
- ☐ 75. AMOS OTIS
- ☐ 96. DICK HOWSER (M)
- ☐ 136. WILLIE AIKENS
- ☐ 155. DAN QUISENBERRY
- ☐ 194. CESAR GERONIMO
- ☐ 219. MIKE ARMSTRONG
- ☐ 238. BUD BLACK
- ☐ 264. JAMIE QUIRK
- ☐ 316. PAUL SPLITTORFF
- ☐ 340. LARRY GURA
- ☐ 377. LEE MAY
- ☐ 418. GREG PRYOR
- ☐ 443. DON HOOD
- ☐ 471. TEAM LEADER CARD
- ☐ 525. FRANK WHITE
- ☐ 570. VIDA BLUE
- ☐ 600. GEORGE BRETT
- ☐ 626. JERRY MARTIN
- ☐ 656. DAVE FROST
- ☐ 687. U. L. WASHINGTON
- ☐ 710. WILLIE WILSON
- ☐ 746. JOHN WATHAN
- ☐ 785. DENNIS LEONARD

LOS ANGELES DODGERS

- ☐ 15. RON CEY
- ☐ 40. FERNANDO VALENZUELA
- ☐ 63. RICK MONDAY
- ☐ 90. JERRY REUSS
- ☐ 113. RON ROENICKE
- ☐ 170. STEVE HOWE
- ☐ 220. DUSTY BAKER
- ☐ 245. STEVE SAX
- ☐ 273. MARK BELANGER
- ☐ 306. TOM LASORDA(M)
- ☐ 324. MIKE MARSHALL
- ☐ 352. MIKE SCIOSCIA
- ☐ 376. KEN LANDREAUX
- ☐ 425. PEDRO GUERRERO
- ☐ 454. BOB WELCH
- ☐ 477. TOM NIEDENFUER
- ☐ 532. DAVE STEWART
- ☐ 555. STEVE YEAGER
- ☐ 583. TERRY FORSTER
- ☐ 610. STEVE GARVEY
- ☐ 633. VICENTE ROMO
- ☐ 661. BILL RUSSELL
- ☐ 681. TEAM LEADER CARD
- ☐ 722. JORGE ORTA
- ☐ 748. DERREL THOMAS
- ☐ 775. BURT HOOTON

MILWAUKEE BREWERS

- ☐ 10. GORMAN THOMAS
- ☐ 35. ROLLIE FINGERS
- ☐ 62. BOB MCCLURE
- ☐ 88. JIM GANTNER
- ☐ 114. JIM SLATON
- ☐ 142. MIKE CALDWELL
- ☐ 145. DON SUTTON
- ☐ 167. MARK BROUHARD
- ☐ 190. CECIL COOPER
- ☐ 218. ROY HOWELL
- ☐ 244. DWIGHT BERNARD
- ☐ 271. ED ROMERO
- ☐ 297. NED YOST
- ☐ 321. TEAM LEADER CARD
- ☐ 350. ROBIN YOUNT
- ☐ 375. PETE VUCKOVICH
- ☐ 424. JERRY AUGUSTINE
- ☐ 450. TED SIMMONS
- ☐ 476. ROB PICCIOLO
- ☐ 503. MOOSE HAAS
- ☐ 528. JAMIE EASTERLY
- ☐ 582. MARSHALL EDWARDS
- ☐ 608. DON MONEY
- ☐ 630. PAUL MOLITOR
- ☐ 659. CHARLIE MOORE
- ☐ 726. HARVEY KUENN(M)
- ☐ 750. BEN OGLIVIE
- ☐ 773. LARRY HISLE

MINNESOTA TWINS

- ☐ 11. BILLY GARDNER(M)
- ☐ 33. JACK O'CONNOR
- ☐ 67. SAL BUTERA
- ☐ 93. JOHN CASTINO
- ☐ 121. MICKEY HATCHER
- ☐ 166. JOHN PACELLA
- ☐ 181. TERRY FELTON
- ☐ 197. JIM EISENREICH
- ☐ 232. TOM BRUNANSKY
- ☐ 266. PAUL BORIS
- ☐ 294. DAVE ENGLE
- ☐ 308. JESUS VEGA
- ☐ 327. BOBBY CASTILLO
- ☐ 354. RANDY JOHNSON
- ☐ 380. RON DAVIS
- ☐ 431. GARY GAETTI
- ☐ 458. RON WASHINGTON
- ☐ 499. JEFF LITTLE
- ☐ 517. GARY WARD
- ☐ 529. TIM LAUDNER
- ☐ 559. PETE REDFERN
- ☐ 586. FRANK VIOLA
- ☐ 647. BOBBY MITCHELL
- ☐ 671. LENNY FAEDO
- ☐ 690. KENT HRBEK
- ☐ 731. AL WILLIAMS
- ☐ 751. BRAD HAVENS
- ☐ 771. TEAM LEADER CARD

MONTREAL EXPOS

- ☐ 31. BILL GULLICKSON
- ☐ 57. TIM BLACKWELL
- ☐ 111. TEAM LEADER CARD
- ☐ 137. WOODIE FRYMAN
- ☐ 164. DAVE PALMER
- ☐ 169. DOUG FLYNN

- □ 189. DAN SCHATZEDER
- □ 214. JERRY WHITE
- □ 237. DAN NORMAN
- □ 265. JOEL YOUNGBLOOD
- □ 267. TERRY FRANCONA
- □ 290. JEFF REARDON
- □ 320. STEVE ROGERS
- □ 370. GARY CARTER
- □ 420. AL OLIVER
- □ 447. BRYN SMITH
- □ 474. RAY BURRIS
- □ 495. WARREN CROMARTIE
- □ 516. BILL VIRDON(M)
- □ 552. TIM WALLACH
- □ 595. TIM RAINES
- □ 629. CHARLIE LEA
- □ 657. MIKE GATES
- □ 680. ANDRE DAWSON
- □ 686. RANDY LERCH
- □ 717. SCOTT SANDERSON
- □ 744. BRAD MILLS
- □ 768. CHRIS SPEIER

NEW YORK METS

- □ 29. RANDY JONES
- □ 55. MOOKIE WILSON
- □ 80. GEROGE FOSTER
- □ 107. MIKE JORGENSEN
- □ 134. HUBIE BROOKS
- □ 160. DAVE KINGMAN
- □ 187. TERRY LEACH
- □ 212. JOHN STEARNS
- □ 246. GEORGE BAMBERGER(M)
- □ 292. CRAIG SWAN
- □ 317. GARY RAJSICH
- □ 343. BOB BAILOR
- □ 369. JESSE OROSCO
- □ 444. WALLY BACKMAN
- □ 469. RON GARDENHIRE
- □ 496. TOM VERYZER
- □ 522. PAT ZACHRY
- □ 548. BRIAN GILES
- □ 549. CHARLIE PULEO
- □ 575. NEIL ALLEN
- □ 601. ED LYNCH
- □ 621. TEAM LEADER CARD
- □ 653. ELLIS VALENTINE
- □ 679. MIKE SCOTT
- □ 713. RON HODGES
- □ 739. RICK OWNBEY
- □ 740. RUSTY STAUB
- □ 764. PETE FALCONE

NEW YORK YANKEES

- □ 8. STEVE BALBONI
- □ 19. OSCAR GAMBLE
- □ 45. JOHN MAYBERRY
- □ 81. TEAM LEADER CARD
- □ 110. KEN GRIFFEY
- □ 123. GEORGE FRAZIER
- □ 140. WILLIE RANDOLPH
- □ 176. DAVE RIGHETTI
- □ 203. MIKE MORGAN
- □ 240. RICH GOSSAGE
- □ 254. RICK CERONE
- □ 281. ANDRE ROBERTSON
- □ 307. LOU PINIELLA
- □ 333. DAVE LAROCHE
- □ 359. DAVE COLLINS
- □ 408. RUDY MAY
- □ 440. RON GUIDRY
- □ 460. ROY SMALLEY
- □ 486. CLYDE KING(M)
- □ 512. DOYLE ALEXANDER
- □ 539. ROGER ERICKSON
- □ 592. SHANE RAWLEY
- □ 617. BUTCH WYNEGAR
- □ 635. GRAIG NETTLES
- □ 652. BUTCH HOBSON
- □ 670. JERRY MUMPHREY
- □ 685. LEE MAZZILLI
- □ 697. BARRY FOOTE
- □ 770. DAVE WINFIELD
- □ 782. BOBBY MURCER

OAKLAND A'S

- □ 23. MIKE HEATH
- □ 47. DAVE MCKAY
- □ 87. JOE RUDI
- □ 102. DAVE BEARD
- □ 127. PRESTON HANNA
- □ 156. BILLY MARTIN(M)
- □ 180. RICKEY HENDERSON
- □ 208. DAN MEYER
- □ 233. WAYNE GROSS
- □ 259. JEFF JONES
- □ 286. RICK LANDFORD
- □ 312. BRIAN KINGMAN
- □ 338. BOB OWCHINKO
- □ 365. DAVE LOPES
- □ 413. MATT KEOUGH
- □ 435. TONY ARMAS
- □ 466. TOM UNDERWOOD
- □ 493. STEVE MCCATTY
- □ 513. FRED STANLEY
- □ 531. TEAM LEADER CARD
- □ 571. MICKEY KLUTTS
- □ 598. DWAYNE MURPHY
- □ 620. MIKE NORRIS
- □ 648. JEFF BURROUGHS
- □ 709. JIMMY SEXTON
- □ 737. MITCHELL PAGE
- □ 762. CLIFF JOHNSON
- □ 784. JEFF NEWMAN

PHILADELPHIA PHILLIES

- □ 16. GEORGE VUKOVICH
- □ 43. BOB DERNIER
- □ 70. STEVE CARLTON
- □ 100. PETE ROSE
- □ 148. DAVE W. ROBERTS
- □ 175. BO DIAZ
- □ 199. MARTY BYSTROM
- □ 211. JOHN DENNY
- □ 229. TEAM LEADER CARD
- □ 252. LUIS AGUAYO
- □ 279. GREG GROSS
- □ 300. MIKE SCHMIDT
- □ 331. MIKE KRUKOW
- □ 357. LEN MATUSZEK
- □ 383. OZZIE VIRGIL
- □ 432. PORFIRIO ALTAMIRANO
- □ 459. ED FARMER
- □ 484. DICK RUTHVEN
- □ 510. TUG MCGRAW
- □ 535. MANNY TRILLO
- □ 564. SID MONGE
- □ 587. IVAN DEJESUS
- □ 615. GARRY MADDOX
- □ 637. PAT CORRALES(M)
- □ 664. BOB MOLINARO
- □ 668. LARRY CHRISTENSON
- □ 728. RON REED
- □ 754. BILL ROBINSON
- □ 780. GARY MATTHEWS

PITTSBURGH PIRATES

- □ 17. KENT TEKULVE
- □ 44. DON ROBINSON
- □ 69. LEE LACY
- □ 97. ROSS BAUMGARTEN
- □ 122. JIMMY SMITH
- □ 149. JOHNNY RAY
- □ 173. JIM MORRISON
- □ 205. DAVE PARKER
- □ 226. ENRIQUE ROMO
- □ 253. LARRY MCWILLIAMS
- □ 291. TEAM LEADER CARD
- □ 329. RANDY NIEMANN
- □ 355. JIM BIBBY
- □ 385. MIKE EASLER
- □ 433. DALE BERRA
- □ 462. STEVE NICOSIA
- □ 485. OMAR MORENO
- □ 537. ROD SCURRY
- □ 566. MANNY SARMIENTO
- □ 590. TONY PENA
- □ 645. BILL MADLOCK
- □ 667. DICK DAVIS
- □ 696. CHUCK TANNER(M)
- □ 730. JASON THOMPSON
- □ 755. JOHN CANDELARIA
- □ 778. RICH HEBNER
- □ 781. RICK RHODEN

ST. LOUIS CARDINALS

- □ 24. STEVE MURA
- □ 49. WILLIE MCGEE
- □ 74. JULIO GONZALEZ
- □ 103. DARRELL PORTER
- □ 128. MIKE RAMSEY
- □ 150. BRUCE SUTTER
- □ 186. WHITEY HERZOG(M)
- □ 206. KEN OBERKFELL
- □ 228. JOAQUIN ANDUJAR
- □ 284. JEFF LAHTI
- □ 311. GLENN BRUMMER
- □ 337. TITO LANDRUM
- □ 363. JOHN STUPER
- □ 415. BOB FORSCH
- □ 438. DAVE LAPOINT
- □ 465. LONNIE SMITH
- □ 489. TOM HERR
- □ 515. GENE TENACE
- □ 540. OZZIE SMITH
- □ 561. TEAM LEADER CARD
- □ 578. DAVID GREEN
- □ 594. ERIC RASMUSSEN
- □ 627. DOUG BAIR
- □ 650. GEORGE HENDRICK
- □ 672. JIM KAAT
- □ 700. KEITH HERNANDEZ
- □ 721. JOHN MARTIN
- □ 734. STEVE BRAUN
- □ 788. DANE IORG

SAN DIEGO PADRES

- □ 7. GENE RICHARDS
- □ 38. TIM FLANNERY
- □ 68. ERIC SHOW
- □ 94. DAVE EDWARDS
- □ 118. CHRIS WELSH
- □ 168. JUAN EICHELBERGER
- □ 185. TIM LOLLAR
- □ 223. JOHN MONTEFUSCO
- □ 251. ALAN WIGGINS
- □ 274. TERRY KENNEDY
- □ 298. FLOYD CHIFFER
- □ 323. LUIS DELEON
- □ 346. JOE PITTMAN
- □ 366. DICK WILLIAMS(M)
- □ 384. DAVE DRAVECKY
- □ 455. SIXTO LEZCANO
- □ 482. TONY GWYNN
- □ 505. GARRY TEMPLETON
- □ 533. LUIS SALAZAR
- □ 563. JUAN BONILLA
- □ 593. BRODERICK PERKINS
- □ 612. STEVE SWISHER
- □ 644. JOE LEFEBVRE
- □ 674. KURT BEVACQUA
- □ 695. RUPPERT JONES
- □ 742. TEAM LEADER CARD
- □ 761. GARY LUCAS

SAN FRANCISCO GIANTS

- □ 32. DAVE BERGMAN
- □ 58. AL HOLLAND
- □ 84. MILT MAY
- □ 115. CHILI DAVIS
- □ 133. JIM BARR
- □ 143. JOE PETTINI

- □ 154. JOHNNIE LEMASTER
- □ 171. TEAM LEADER CARD
- □ 210. JACK CLARK
- □ 263. RENIE MARTIN
- □ 282. REGGIE SMITH
- □ 309. JEFF LEONARD
- □ 342. ATLEE HAMMAKER
- □ 379. GUY SULARZ
- □ 428. CHAMP SUMMERS
- □ 448. DARRELL EVANS
- □ 470. GREG MINTON
- □ 494. BOB BRENLY
- □ 518. BILL LASKEY
- □ 543. ALAN FOWLKES
- □ 576. FRANK ROBINSON(M)
- □ 603. JOE MORGAN
- □ 634. MAX VENABLE
- □ 663. TOM O'MALLEY
- □ 688. JIM WOHLFORD
- □ 719. RICH GALE
- □ 747. FRED BREINING
- □ 767. DUANE KUIPER
- □ 791. GARY LAVELLE

SEATTLE MARINERS

- □ 28. BRUCE BOCHTE
- □ 54. JIM MALER
- □ 78. BILL CAUDILL
- □ 106. GENE NELSON
- □ 132. TODD CRUZ
- □ 159. MIKE STANTON
- □ 183. ED VANDE BERG
- □ 195. BOB STODDARD
- □ 209. MIKE MOORE
- □ 234. LARRY ANDERSEN
- □ 258. MANNY CASTILLO
- □ 287. BOBBY BROWN
- □ 313. GARY GRAY
- □ 336. RENE LACHEMANN(M)
- □ 368. RICHIE ZISK
- □ 414. JULIO CRUZ
- □ 437. RICK SWEET
- □ 463. GAYLORD PERRY
- □ 492. PAUL SERNA
- □ 519. TERRY BULLING
- □ 545. FLOYD BANNISTER
- □ 567. JOE SIMPSON
- □ 622. DAVE EDLER
- □ 646. JIM ESSIAN
- □ 675. JIM BEATTIE
- □ 677. DAVE REVERING
- □ 711. TEAM LEADER CARD
- □ 732. DAVE HENDERSON
- □ 763. AL COWENS
- □ 789. BRYAN CLARK

TEXAS RANGERS

- □ 12. PAUL MIRABELLA
- □ 37. DARRELL JOHNSON(M)
- □ 64. BILL STEIN
- □ 116. DAVE J. SCHMIDT
- □ 144. MARK WAGNER
- □ 224. MICKEY RIVERS
- □ 272. FRANK TANANA
- □ 299. GEORGE WRIGHT
- □ 330. BUDDY BELL
- □ 353. STEVE COMER
- □ 371. MIKE RICHARDT
- □ 412. TEAM LEADER CARD
- □ 453. LAMAR JOHNSON
- □ 479. CHARLIE HOUGH
- □ 504. DON WERNER
- □ 534. JOHN BUTCHER
- □ 557. RICK HONEYCUTT
- □ 565. BUCKY DENT
- □ 584. DAVE HOSTETLER
- □ 609. DANNY DARWIN
- □ 641. BILLY SAMPLE
- □ 665. JIM SUNDBERG
- □ 724. JOHNNY GRUBB
- □ 749. JON MATLACK
- □ 776. LARRY PARRISH

TORONTO BLUE JAYS

- □ 9. JOE MCLAUGHLIN
- □ 42. DALE MURRAY
- □ 77. HOSKEN POWELL
- □ 89. LEON ROBERTS
- □ 109. LUIS LEAL
- □ 130. DAVE STIEB
- □ 202. TEAM LEADER CARD
- □ 222. DAMASO GARCIA
- □ 257. JESSE BARFIELD
- □ 277. RANCE MULLINIKS
- □ 302. ERNIE WHITT
- □ 326. GARTH IORG
- □ 345. JIM CLANCY
- □ 358. JERRY GARVIN
- □ 427. ROY LEE JACKSON
- □ 452. LLOYD MOSEBY
- □ 488. ALFREDO GRIFFIN
- □ 506. JIM GOTT
- □ 556. WILLIE UPSHAW
- □ 574. GLENN ADAMS
- □ 589. ALVIS WOODS
- □ 606. BOBBY COX(M)
- □ 714. WAYNE NORDHAGEN
- □ 733. BUCK MARTINEZ
- □ 766. BARRY BONNELL

1983 TOPPS TRADED (132) 2 1/2" X 3 1/2"

ATLANTA BRAVES

- □ 31T. PETE FALCONE
- □ 33T. TERRY FORSTER
- □ 51T. MIKE JORGENSEN
- □ 69T. CRAIG MCMURTRY
- □ 84T. PASCUAL PEREZ

BALTIMORE ORIOLES

- □ 3T. JOE ALTOBELLI(M)
- □ 44T. LEO HERNANDEZ
- □ 97T. AURELIO RODRIGUEZ
- □ 102T. JOHN SHELBY

BOSTON RED SOX

- □ 4T. TONY ARMAS
- □ 12T. DOUB BIRD
- □ 15T. MIKE BROWN
- □ 80T. JEFF NEWMAN

CALIFORNIA ANGELS

- □ 70T. JOHN MCNAMARA(M)
- □ 99T. DARYL SCONIERS
- □ 120T. ELLIS VALENTINE

CHICAGO CUBS

- □ 19T. RON CEY
- □ 39T. MEL HALL
- □ 92T. CHUCK RAINEY
- □ 98T. DICK RUTHVEN
- □ 117T. STEVE TROUT
- □ 121T. TOM VERYZER

CHICAGO WHITE SOX

- □ 7T. FLOYD BANNISTER
- □ 23T. JULIO CRUZ
- □ 27T. JERRY DYBZINSKI
- □ 55T. RON KITTLE
- □ 112T. DICK TIDROW
- □ 124T. GREG WALKER

CINCINNATI REDS

- □ 11T. DANN BILARDELLO
- □ 35T. RICH GALE
- □ 57T. ALAN KNICELY
- □ 88T. CHARLIE PULEO
- □ 84T. GARY REDUS

CLEVELAND INDIANS

- □ 28T. JAMIE EASTERLY
- □ 29T. JUAN EICHELBERGER
- □ 30T. JIM ESSIAN
- □ 32T. MIKE FERRARO(M)
- □ 34T. JULIO FRANCO
- □ 86T. BRODERICK PERKINS
- □ 111T. GORMAN THOMAS
- □ 116T. MANNY TRILLO
- □ 122T. GEORGE VUKOVICH

DETRIOT TIGERS

- □ 5T. DOUG BAIR
- □ 38T. JOHNNY GRUBB
- □ 63T. AURELIO LOPEZ

HOUSTON ASTROS

- □ 25T. FRANK DIPINO
- □ 26T. BILL DORAN
- □ 64T. MIKE MADDEN
- □ 76T. OMAR MORENO
- □ 100T. MIKE SCOTT

KANSAS CITY ROYALS

- □ 95T. STEVE RENKO
- □ 96T. LEON ROBERTS
- □ 104T. JOE SIMPSON

LOS ANGELES DODGERS

- □ 14T. GREG BROCK
- □ 59T. RAFAEL LANDESTOY
- □ 75T. JOSE MORALES
- □ 83T. ALEJANDRO PENA
- □ 131T. PAT ZACHRY

1983 Topps Traded

MILWAUKEE BREWERS

- ☐ 65T. RICK MANNING
- ☐ 109T. TOM TELLMANN
- ☐ 123T. RICK WAITS

MINNESOTA TWINS

- ☐ 17T. RANDY BUSH
- ☐ 126T. LEN WHITEHOUSE

MONTREAL EXPOS

- ☐ 22T. TERRY CROWLEY
- ☐ 62T. BRYAN LITTLE
- ☐ 93T. BOBBY RAMOS
- ☐ 119T. MIKE VAIL
- ☐ 125T. CHRIS WELSH
- ☐ 128T. JIM WOHLFORD

NEW YORK METS

- ☐ 41T. DANNY HEEP
- ☐ 43T. KEITH HERNANDEZ
- ☐ 47T. FRANK HOWARD(M)
- ☐ 101T. TOM SEAVER
- ☐ 105T. DOUG SISK
- ☐ 108T. DARRYL STRAWBERRY
- ☐ 115T. MIKE TORREZ

NEW YORK YANKEES

- ☐ 8T. DON BAYLOR
- ☐ 18T. BERT CAMPANERIS
- ☐ 53T. STEVE KEMP
- ☐ 54T. MATT KEOUGH
- ☐ 66T. BILLY MARTIN(M)
- ☐ 79T. DALE MURRAY
- ☐ 103T. BOB SHIRLEY

OAKLAND A'S

- ☐ 2T. BILL ALMON
- ☐ 6T. STEVE BAKER
- ☐ 13T. STEVE BOROS(M)
- ☐ 16T. TOM BURGMEIER
- ☐ 20T. CHRIS CODIROLI
- ☐ 24T. MIKE DAVIS
- ☐ 52T. BOB KEARNEY
- ☐ 60T. CARNEY LANSFORD
- ☐ 87T. TONY PHILLIPS

PHILADELPHIA PHILLIES

- ☐ 36T. KIKO GARCIA
- ☐ 40T. VON HAYES
- ☐ 45T. WILLIE HERNANDEZ
- ☐ 46T. AL HOLLAND
- ☐ 61T. JOE LEFEBVRE
- ☐ 72T. LARRY MILBOURNE
- ☐ 77T. JOE MORGAN
- ☐ 85T. TONY PEREZ

PITTSBURGH PIRATES

- ☐ 67T. LEE MAZZILLI
- ☐ 110T. GENE TENACE
- ☐ 118T. LEE TUNNELL

ST. LOUIS CARDINALS

- ☐ 1T. NEIL ALLEN
- ☐ 90T. JAMIE QUIRK

SAN DIEGO PADRES

- ☐ 37T. STEVE GARVEY
- ☐ 74T. SID MONGE
- ☐ 107T. ELIAS SOSA
- ☐ 127T. ED WHITSON

SAN FRANCISCO GIANTS

- ☐ 58T. MIKE KRUKOW
- ☐ 68T. ANDY MCGAFFIGAN
- ☐ 130T. JOEL YOUNGBLOOD

SEATTLE MARINERS

- ☐ 9T. TONY BERNAZARD
- ☐ 42T. STEVE HENDERSON
- ☐ 71T. ORLANDO MERCADO
- ☐ 89T. PAT PUTNAM
- ☐ 129T. MATT YOUNG

TEXAS RANGERS

- ☐ 10T. LARRY BITTNER
- ☐ 48T. BOBBY JOHNSON
- ☐ 50T. ODELL JONES
- ☐ 81T. PETE O'BRIEN
- ☐ 91T. DOUG RADER(M)
- ☐ 106T. MIKE SMITHSON
- ☐ 113T. DAVE TOBIK
- ☐ 114T. WAYNE TOLLESON

TORONTO BLUE JAYS

- ☐ 21T. DAVE COLLINS
- ☐ 49T. CLIFF JOHNSON
- ☐ 56T. MICKEY KLUTTS
- ☐ 73T. RANDY MOFFITT
- ☐ 78T. MIKE MORGAN
- ☐ 82T. JORGE ORTA

1984 TOPPS (792)
2 1/2" X 3 1/2"

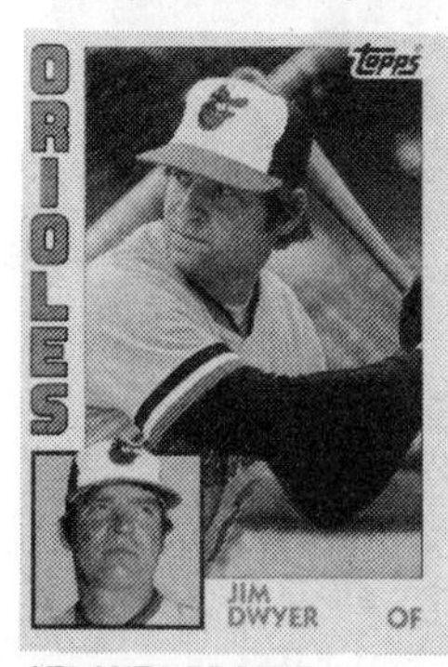

ATLANTA BRAVES

- ☐ 25. GLENN HUBBARD
- ☐ 50. CHRIS CHAMBLISS
- ☐ 77. BRETT BUTLER
- ☐ 104. KEN DAYLEY
- ☐ 126. TEAM LEADER CARD
- ☐ 150. DALE MURPHY
- ☐ 207. DONNIE MOORE
- ☐ 234. RAFAEL RAMIREZ
- ☐ 255. BRUCE BENEDICT
- ☐ 289. RANDY JOHNSON
- ☐ 313. MIKE JORGENSEN
- ☐ 365. STEVE BEDROSIAN
- ☐ 410. CLAUDELL WASHINGTON
- ☐ 438. BIFF POCORBA
- ☐ 466. GENE GARBER
- ☐ 502. JOE TORRE(M)
- ☐ 521. PETE FALCONE
- ☐ 543. CRAIG MCMURTRY
- ☐ 572. JERRY ROYSTER
- ☐ 597. RICK CAMP
- ☐ 614. LEN BARKER
- ☐ 624. TERRY HARPER
- ☐ 650. PHIL NIEKRO
- ☐ 675. PASCUAL PEREZ
- ☐ 739. BOB WATSON
- ☐ 760. BOB HORNER
- ☐ 791. TERRY FORSTER

BALTIMORE ORIOLES

- ☐ 21. JOE ALTOBELLI(M)
- ☐ 59. SAMMY STEWART
- ☐ 71. LEO HERNANDEZ
- ☐ 86. JOHN SHELBY
- ☐ 106. TIM STODDARD
- ☐ 140. STORM DAVIS
- ☐ 165. KEN SINGLETON
- ☐ 191. MIKE BODDICKER
- ☐ 215. TIPPY MARTINEZ
- ☐ 240. EDDIE MURRAY
- ☐ 260. SCOTT MCGREGOR
- ☐ 272. RICK DEMPSEY
- ☐ 295. MIKE FLANAGAN
- ☐ 319. AL BUMBRY
- ☐ 347. ALLAN RAMIREZ
- ☐ 372. GARY ROENICKE
- ☐ 426. TEAM CARD LEADER
- ☐ 443. BENNY AYALA
- ☐ 473. JIM DWYER
- ☐ 490. CAL RIPKEN
- ☐ 530. DAN FORD
- ☐ 553. JOE NOLAN
- ☐ 578. LENN SAKATA
- ☐ 604. JOHN LOWENSTEIN
- ☐ 631. DENNY MARTINEZ
- ☐ 682. DAN MOROGIELLO
- ☐ 723. RICH DAUER
- ☐ 750. JIM PALMER
- ☐ 773. TODD CRUZ

BOSTON RED SOX

- ☐ 30. WADE BOGGS
- ☐ 56. GARY ALLENSON
- ☐ 82. DOUG BIRD
- ☐ 105. TONY ARMAS
- ☐ 162. BOB OJEDA
- ☐ 187. LUIS APONTE
- ☐ 213. BRUCE HURST
- ☐ 238. REID NICHOLS
- ☐ 296. JEFF NEWMAN
- ☐ 320. BOB STANLEY
- ☐ 344. RICK MILLER
- ☐ 381. RALPH HOUK(M)
- ☐ 419. JOHN HENRY JOHNSON
- ☐ 445. JERRY REMY
- ☐ 472. MIKE BROWN
- ☐ 498. RICH GEDMAN
- ☐ 523. GLENN HOFFMAN
- ☐ 550. JIM RICE
- ☐ 577. MARK CLEAR
- ☐ 601. JOHN TUDOR
- ☐ 628. ED JURAK
- ☐ 653. DAVE STAPLETON
- ☐ 683. MARTY BARRETT
- ☐ 720. DWIGHT EVANS
- ☐ 745. DENNIS ECKERSLEY
- ☐ 786. TEAM LEADER CARD

CALIFORNIA ANGELS

- ☐ 27. DARYL SCONIERS
- ☐ 53. JUAN BENIQUEZ
- ☐ 79. ROB WILFONG
- ☐ 100. REGGIE JACKSON
- ☐ 158. JOHN CURTIS
- ☐ 184. MIKE O'BERRY
- ☐ 201. BRUCE KISON
- ☐ 236. ELLIS VALENTINE
- ☐ 258. LUIS SANCHEZ
- ☐ 266. STEVE LUBRATICH
- ☐ 276. TEAM LEADER CARD
- ☐ 315. BOB GRICH
- ☐ 342. TIM FOLI
- ☐ 414. TOMMY JOHN
- ☐ 442. BYRON MCLAUGHLIN
- ☐ 468. GEOFF ZAHN

- ☐ 487. RICKY ADAMS
- ☐ 499. MIKE WITT
- ☐ 520. BOB BOONE
- ☐ 548. RON JACKSON
- ☐ 574. BRIAN DOWNING
- ☐ 600. ROD CAREW
- ☐ 626. BOB CLARK
- ☐ 643. MIKE BROWN
- ☐ 651. JOHN MCNAMARA(M)
- ☐ 680. FRED LYNN
- ☐ 719. ANDY HASSLER
- ☐ 735. RICK BURLESON
- ☐ 765. KEN FORSCH
- ☐ 790. DOUG DECINCES

CHICAGO CUBS

- ☐ 23. KEITH MORELAND
- ☐ 51. JIM FREY(M)
- ☐ 73. JODY DAVIS
- ☐ 99. CRAIG LEFFERTS
- ☐ 117. TOM VERYZER
- ☐ 151. STEVE TROUT
- ☐ 176. LEE SMITH
- ☐ 231. GARY WOODS
- ☐ 249. JAY JOHNSTONE
- ☐ 267. CARMELO MARTINEZ
- ☐ 304. WARREN BRUSSTAR
- ☐ 334. CHUCK RAINEY
- ☐ 357. RON CEY
- ☐ 437. MIKE PROLY
- ☐ 456. TEAM LEADER CARD
- ☐ 483. FERGIE JENKINS
- ☐ 508. MEL HALL
- ☐ 545. BILL BUCKNER
- ☐ 565. LEON DURHAM
- ☐ 596. RYNE SANDBERG
- ☐ 618. DICKIE NOLES
- ☐ 657. THAD BOSLEY
- ☐ 691. STEVE LAKE
- ☐ 736. DICK RUTHVEN
- ☐ 757. LARRY BOWA
- ☐ 787. BILL CAMPBELL

CHICAGO WHITE SOX

- ☐ 20. GREG LUZINSKI
- ☐ 47. RUDY LAW
- ☐ 72. MIKE SQUIRES
- ☐ 97. LAMARR HOYT
- ☐ 125. BRITT BURNS
- ☐ 153. DICK TIDROW
- ☐ 163. LORENZO GRAY
- ☐ 177. JERRY HAIRSTON
- ☐ 216. TEAM LEADER CARD
- ☐ 257. JULIO CRUZ
- ☐ 269. AURELIO RODRIGUEZ
- ☐ 280. FLOYD BANNISTER
- ☐ 311. JERRY KOOSMAN
- ☐ 364. SCOTT FLETCHER
- ☐ 382. CHRIS NYMAN
- ☐ 409. JUAN AGOSTO
- ☐ 434. HAROLD BAINES
- ☐ 459. KEVIN HICKEY
- ☐ 480. RON KITTLE
- ☐ 518. GREG WALKER
- ☐ 541. DENNIS LAMP
- ☐ 560. CARLTON FISK
- ☐ 591. TONY LARUSSA(M)
- ☐ 619. JERRY DYBZINSKI
- ☐ 664. DAVE STEGMAN
- ☐ 667. VANCE LAW
- ☐ 698. MARC HILL
- ☐ 759. RICHARD DOTSON
- ☐ 777. TOM PACIOREK

CINCINNATI REDS

- ☐ 34. EDDIE MILNER
- ☐ 55. DAVE CONCEPCION
- ☐ 87. FRANK PASTORE
- ☐ 113. KELLY PARIS
- ☐ 142. RICH GALE
- ☐ 160. MARIO SOTO
- ☐ 192. NICK ESASKY
- ☐ 214. PAUL HOUSEHOLDER
- ☐ 242. ALEX TREVINO
- ☐ 270. JEFF RUSSELL
- ☐ 273. CHARLIE PULEO
- ☐ 297. BRUCE BERENYI
- ☐ 323. ALAN KNICELY
- ☐ 351. RUSS NIXON(M)
- ☐ 373. BILL SCHERRER
- ☐ 424. DANN BILARDELLO
- ☐ 448. BEN HAYES
- ☐ 475. GARY REDUS
- ☐ 526. RON OESTER
- ☐ 554. TED POWER
- ☐ 585. DAN DRIESSEN
- ☐ 607. TOM HUME
- ☐ 632. TOM FOLEY
- ☐ 659. DUANE WALKER
- ☐ 686. JOE PRICE
- ☐ 725. CESAR CEDENO
- ☐ 756. TEAM LEADER CARD

CLEVELAND INDIANS

- ☐ 48. JULIO FRANCO
- ☐ 91. DAN SPILLNER
- ☐ 115. ANDRE THORNTON
- ☐ 141. PAT CORRALES(M)
- ☐ 212. BRODERICK PERKINS
- ☐ 226. JUAN EICHELBERGER
- ☐ 245. RICK SUTCLIFFE
- ☐ 286. LARY SORENSEN
- ☐ 308. RON HASSEY
- ☐ 329. PAT TABLER
- ☐ 348. TOBY HARRAH
- ☐ 367. JAMIE EASTERLY
- ☐ 431. CHRIS BANDO
- ☐ 478. ALAN BANNISTER
- ☐ 497. BUD ANDERSON
- ☐ 515. GORMAN THOMAS
- ☐ 546. TEAM LEADER CARD
- ☐ 569. BAKE MCBRIDE
- ☐ 638. GEORGE VUKOVICH
- ☐ 662. TOM BRENNAN
- ☐ 689. MIKE FISCHLIN
- ☐ 737. JIM ESSIAN
- ☐ 764. MIKE HARGROVE
- ☐ 789. BERT BLYLEVEN

DETROIT TIGERS

- ☐ 14. TOM BROOKENS
- ☐ 24. JOHN MARTIN
- ☐ 42. JOHNNY GRUBB
- ☐ 65. KIRK GIBSON
- ☐ 95. AURELIO LOPEZ
- ☐ 119. JOHNNY WOCKENFUSS
- ☐ 147. DAN PETRY
- ☐ 174. JUAN BERENGUER
- ☐ 195. JACK MORRIS
- ☐ 223. WAYNE KRENCHICKI
- ☐ 259. SPARKY ANDERSON(M)
- ☐ 284. HOWARD BAILEY
- ☐ 303. MARTY CASTILLO
- ☐ 333. LARRY HERDON
- ☐ 356. GLENN ABBOTT
- ☐ 371. DAVE GUMPERT
- ☐ 427. RICK LEACH
- ☐ 457. DAVE ROZEMA
- ☐ 482. ENOS CABELL
- ☐ 510. ALAN TRAMMELL
- ☐ 536. DOUG BAIR
- ☐ 563. GLENN WILSON
- ☐ 588. MILT WILCOX
- ☐ 611. CHET LEMON
- ☐ 640. LANCE PARRISH
- ☐ 666. TEAM LEADER CARD
- ☐ 695. LOU WHITKER
- ☐ 731. LYNN JONES

HOUSTON ASTROS

- ☐ 36. DENNY WALLING
- ☐ 45. JERRY MUMPHREY
- ☐ 66. TEAM LEADER CARD
- ☐ 93. BOB KNEPPER
- ☐ 116. GEORGE BJORKMAN
- ☐ 127. MIKE MADDEN
- ☐ 172. FRANK DIPINO
- ☐ 198. BILL DORAN
- ☐ 217. ALAN ASHBY
- ☐ 248. BILL DAWLEY
- ☐ 292. TONY SCOTT
- ☐ 301. FRANK LACORTE
- ☐ 328. VERN RUHLE
- ☐ 361. DAVE SMITH
- ☐ 383. TERRY PUHL
- ☐ 422. JOSE CRUZ
- ☐ 441. BOB LILLIS(M)
- ☐ 446. LUIS PUJOLS
- ☐ 470. NOLAN RYAN
- ☐ 507. MIKE LACOSS
- ☐ 438. KEVIN BASS
- ☐ 559. MIKE SCOTT
- ☐ 586. JOE NIEKRO
- ☐ 612. HARRY SPILMAN
- ☐ 660. RAY KNIGHT
- ☐ 679. ART HOWE
- ☐ 692. DICKIE THON
- ☐ 752. PHIL GARNER
- ☐ 776. CRAIG REYNOLDS

KANSAS CITY ROYALS

- ☐ 26. BUD BLACK
- ☐ 52. PAUL SPLITTORFF
- ☐ 74. JERRY MARTIN
- ☐ 96. TEAM LEADER CARD
- ☐ 121. PAT SHERIDAN
- ☐ 155. FRANK WHITE
- ☐ 196. DON SLAUGHT
- ☐ 219. JOE SIMPSON
- ☐ 247. ONIX CONCEPCION
- ☐ 294. U.L. WASHINGTON
- ☐ 317. GREG PRYOR
- ☐ 340. HAL MCRAE
- ☐ 375. DENNIS LEONARD
- ☐ 417. MIKE ARMSTRONG
- ☐ 444. STEVE RENKO
- ☐ 471. DICK HOWSER(M)
- ☐ 500. GEORGE BRETT
- ☐ 525. WILLIE WILSON
- ☐ 544. CESAR GERONIMO
- ☐ 570. DAN QUISENBERRY
- ☐ 602. JOHN WATHAN
- ☐ 625. LARRY GURA
- ☐ 655. AMOS OTIS
- ☐ 685. WILLIE AIKENS
- ☐ 724. ERIC RASMUSSEN
- ☐ 743. DON HOOD
- ☐ 784. LEON ROBERTS

LOS ANGELES DODGERS

- ☐ 15. BURT HOOTON
- ☐ 40. DUSTY BAKER
- ☐ 64. MIKE SCIOSCIA
- ☐ 90. PEDRO GUERRERO
- ☐ 112. TOM NIEDENFUER
- ☐ 142. JOSE MORALES
- ☐ 170. JERRY REUSS
- ☐ 220. FERANDO VALENZUELA
- ☐ 222. RICK HONEYCUTT
- ☐ 244. CANDY MALDONADO
- ☐ 263. JACK FIMPLE
- ☐ 274. RICK MONDAY
- ☐ 306. TEAM LEADER CARD
- ☐ 324. ALEJANDRO PENA
- ☐ 376. DAVE ANDERSON
- ☐ 425. STEVE HOWE
- ☐ 454. JOE BECKWITH
- ☐ 477. RAFAEL LANDESTOY
- ☐ 533. KEN LANDREAUX
- ☐ 555. GREG BROCK
- ☐ 583. DERREL THOMAS
- ☐ 610. STEVE SAX

- ☐ 634. MIKE MARSHALL
- ☐ 661. STEVE YEAGER
- ☐ 681. TOM LASORDA(M)
- ☐ 722. BOB WELCH
- ☐ 747. PAT ZACHRY
- ☐ 792. BILL RUSSELL

MILWAUKEE BREWERS

- ☐ 10. ROBIN YOUNT
- ☐ 35. DON SUTTON
- ☐ 60. PAUL MOLITOR
- ☐ 88. ROB PICCIOLO
- ☐ 107. NED YOST
- ☐ 128. RICK MANNING
- ☐ 146. ED ROMERO
- ☐ 167. MARSHALL EDWARDS
- ☐ 190. BEN OGLIVIE
- ☐ 218. RICK WAITS
- ☐ 243. PETE LADD
- ☐ 262. TOM CANDIOTTI
- ☐ 271. MOOSE HAAS
- ☐ 298. JIM GANTNER
- ☐ 321. HARVEY KUENN(M)
- ☐ 349. BOB GIBSON
- ☐ 374. DON MONEY
- ☐ 420. CECIL COOPER
- ☐ 452. CHUCK PORTER
- ☐ 476. TOM TELLMANN
- ☐ 495. ROLLIE FINGERS
- ☐ 505. PETE VUCKOVICH
- ☐ 528. MARK BROUHARD
- ☐ 582. BOB MCCLURE
- ☐ 605. MIKE CALDWELL
- ☐ 630. TED SIMMONS
- ☐ 658. JERRY AUGUSTINE
- ☐ 687. ROY HOWELL
- ☐ 726. TEAM LEADER CARD
- ☐ 738. BILL SCHROEDER
- ☐ 751. CHARLIE MOORE
- ☐ 772. JIM SLATON

MINNESOTA TWINS

- ☐ 11. TEAM CARD LEADER CARD
- ☐ 28. FRANK VIOLA
- ☐ 46. RAY SMITH
- ☐ 67. GARY WARD
- ☐ 84. LENNY FAEDO
- ☐ 157. GARY GAETTI
- ☐ 183. AL WILLIAMS
- ☐ 193. DARRELL BROWN
- ☐ 237. JOHN CASTINO
- ☐ 268. JACK O'CONNOR
- ☐ 307. BOBBY MITCHELL
- ☐ 322. KEN SCHROM
- ☐ 345. KENT HRBEK
- ☐ 363. TIM LAUDNER
- ☐ 411. HOUSTON JIMENEZ
- ☐ 429. RANDY BUSH
- ☐ 447. TOM BRUNANSKY
- ☐ 463. DAVE ENGLE
- ☐ 491. BOBBY CASTILLO
- ☐ 509. BRAD HAVENS
- ☐ 519. RON DAVIS
- ☐ 551. SCOTT ULLGER
- ☐ 568. PETE FILSON
- ☐ 598. RUSTY KUNTZ
- ☐ 623. RON WASHINGTON
- ☐ 639. RICK LYSANDER
- ☐ 648. LEN WHITEHOUSE
- ☐ 673. MIKE WALTERS
- ☐ 746. MICKEY HATCHER
- ☐ 771. BILLY GARDNER(M)

MONTREAL EXPOS

- ☐ 32. BOBBY RAMOS
- ☐ 57. DAN SCHATZEDER
- ☐ 80. STEVE ROGERS
- ☐ 111. BILL VIRDON(M)
- ☐ 164. SCOTT SANDERSON
- ☐ 180. MANNY TRILLO
- ☐ 188. BRYAN LITTLE
- ☐ 200. ANDRE DAWSON
- ☐ 232. TIM WALLACH
- ☐ 253. JIM WOHLFORD
- ☐ 287. WARREN CROMARTIE
- ☐ 318. BILL GULLICKSON
- ☐ 370. TIM RAINES
- ☐ 421. CHARLIE LEA
- ☐ 450. GARY CARTER
- ☐ 474. GREG BARGAR
- ☐ 496. TERRY FRANCONA
- ☐ 516. TEAM LEADER CARD
- ☐ 552. RAY BURRIS
- ☐ 579. BOB JAMES
- ☐ 595. JEFF REARDON
- ☐ 620. AL OLIVER
- ☐ 656. BRYN SMITH
- ☐ 678. CHRIS SPEIER
- ☐ 732. TERRY CROWLEY
- ☐ 749. DOUG FLYNN
- ☐ 766. MIKE VAIL

NEW YORK METS

- ☐ 13. SCOTT HOLMAN
- ☐ 29. DANNY HEEP
- ☐ 54. JESSE OROSCO
- ☐ 78. MIKE TORREZ
- ☐ 120. KEITH HERNANDEZ
- ☐ 161. JUNIOR ORTIZ
- ☐ 182. DARRYL STRAWBERRY
- ☐ 208. JOSE OQUENDO
- ☐ 246. TEAM LEADER CARD
- ☐ 293. ED LYNCH
- ☐ 316. MARK BARDLEY
- ☐ 350. GEORGE FOSTER
- ☐ 368. HUBIE BROOKS
- ☐ 418. RON HODGES
- ☐ 430. RUSTY STAUB
- ☐ 465. MOOKIE WILSON
- ☐ 492. TUCKER ASHFORD
- ☐ 524. CARLOS DIAZ
- ☐ 549. WALT TERRELL
- ☐ 573. DAVE KINGMAN
- ☐ 599. DOUG SISK
- ☐ 621. FRANK HOWARD(M)
- ☐ 654. BOB BAILOR
- ☐ 676. BRIAN GILES
- ☐ 740. TOM SEAVER
- ☐ 763. CRAIG SWAN
- ☐ 774. TOM GORMAN

NEW YORK YANKEES

- ☐ 8. DON MATTINGLY
- ☐ 16. OMAR MORENO
- ☐ 19. RAY FONTENOT
- ☐ 81. BILLY MARTIN(M)
- ☐ 110. RON GUIDRY
- ☐ 123. BUTCH WYNEGAR
- ☐ 139. BERT CAMPANERIS
- ☐ 175. GRAIG NETTLES
- ☐ 203. MATT KEOUGH
- ☐ 204. BOBBY MEACHAM
- ☐ 239. JAY HOWELL
- ☐ 254. SHANE RAWLEY
- ☐ 281. LARRY MILBOURNE
- ☐ 305. ROY SMALLEY
- ☐ 335. DON BAYLOR
- ☐ 360. WILLIE RANDOLPH
- ☐ 408. LOU PINIELLA
- ☐ 440. STEVE KEMP
- ☐ 460. DAVE WINFIELD
- ☐ 486. TEAM LEADER CARD
- ☐ 512. OSCAR GAMBLE
- ☐ 539. GEORGE FRAZIER
- ☐ 592. ANDRE ROBERTSON
- ☐ 617. RICK CERONE
- ☐ 635. DAVE RIGHETTI
- ☐ 652. RUDY MAY
- ☐ 670. RICH GOSSAGE
- ☐ 684. BOB SHIRLEY
- ☐ 697. DALE MURRAY
- ☐ 761. JOHN MONTEFUSCO
- ☐ 770. KEN GRIFFEY
- ☐ 782. STEVE BALBONI

OAKLAND A'S

- ☐ 33. TOM BURGMEIER
- ☐ 61. CHRIS CODIROLI
- ☐ 103. DWAYNE MURPHY
- ☐ 156. TEAM LEADER CARD
- ☐ 159. DARRYL CIAS
- ☐ 178. BILL KRUEGER
- ☐ 189. TIM CONROY
- ☐ 197. GARRY HANCOCK
- ☐ 230. RICKEY HENDERSON
- ☐ 241. BILL ALMON
- ☐ 265. DONNIE HILL
- ☐ 309. TONY PHILLIPS
- ☐ 326. BOB KEARNEY
- ☐ 338. MIKE WARREN
- ☐ 354. JEFF BURROUGHS
- ☐ 369. STEVE MCCATTY
- ☐ 414. MITCHELL PAGE
- ☐ 436. RICK PETERS
- ☐ 464. JEFF JONES
- ☐ 493. MIKE NORRIS
- ☐ 513. DAVE BEARD
- ☐ 529. KEITH ATHERTON
- ☐ 521. STEVE BOROS(M)
- ☐ 558. MIKE DAVIS
- ☐ 567. MIKE HEATH
- ☐ 609. DAN MEYER
- ☐ 629. RICK LANGFORD
- ☐ 642. TOM UNDERWOOD
- ☐ 669. DAVE LOPES
- ☐ 741. WAYNE GROSS
- ☐ 767. CARNEY LANSFORD

PHILADELPHIA PHILLIES

- ☐ 17. JOHN DENNY
- ☐ 43. RON REED
- ☐ 70. GARY MATTHEWS
- ☐ 101. PORFIRIO ALTAMIRANO
- ☐ 158. JOE LEFEBVRE
- ☐ 185. SIXTO LEZCANO
- ☐ 199. WILLIE HERNANDEZ
- ☐ 210. JOE MORGAN
- ☐ 229. PAUL OWENS(M)
- ☐ 252. LARRY CHRISTENSON
- ☐ 275. LEN MATUSZEK
- ☐ 279. IVAN DEJESUS
- ☐ 300. PETE ROSE
- ☐ 332. KEVIN GROSS
- ☐ 358. BOB DERNIER
- ☐ 385. TONY PEREZ
- ☐ 432. CHARLIE HUDSON
- ☐ 458. KIKO GARCIA
- ☐ 484. OZZIE VIRGIL
- ☐ 511. MARTY BYSTROM
- ☐ 535. BO DIAZ
- ☐ 564. AL HOLLAND
- ☐ 587. VON HAYES
- ☐ 613. GREG GROSS
- ☐ 637. TEAM LEADER CARD
- ☐ 700. MIKE SCHMIDT
- ☐ 728. TUG MCGRAY
- ☐ 755. GARRY MADDOX
- ☐ 780. STEVE CARLTON

PITTSBURGH PIRATES

- ☐ 18. DALE BERRA
- ☐ 44. JIM MORRISON
- ☐ 69. ROD SCURRY
- ☐ 122. CECILIO GUANTE
- ☐ 144. BRIAN HARPER
- ☐ 173. MARVELL WYNNE
- ☐ 209. MANNY SARMIENTO
- ☐ 225. LEE MAZZILLI
- ☐ 250. BILL MADLOCK
- ☐ 264. DOUG FROBEL
- ☐ 291. CHUCK TANNER(M)
- ☐ 330. JOHN CANDELARIA
- ☐ 355. JASON THOMPSON
- ☐ 384. LEE TUNNELL
- ☐ 433. RICH HEBNER
- ☐ 462. LEE LACY
- ☐ 485. RICK RHODEN
- ☐ 537. JOHNNY RAY
- ☐ 566. JIM BIBBY
- ☐ 581. JOSE DELEON
- ☐ 589. MIKE EASLER
- ☐ 616. DON ROBINSON
- ☐ 645. TONY PENA
- ☐ 668. LARRY MCWILLIAMS
- ☐ 696. TEAM LEADER CARD
- ☐ 729. GENE TENACE
- ☐ 754. KENT TEKULVE
- ☐ 775. DAVE PARKER
- ☐ 788. MILT MAY

ST. LOUIS CARDINALS

□ 49. JOHN STUPER
□ 75. BOB FORSCH
□ 102. KEN OBERKFELL
□ 130. OZZIE SMITH
□ 152. GLENN BRUMMER
□ 186. TEAM LEADER CARD
□ 206. ANDY VAN SLYKE
□ 227. STEVE BRAUN
□ 285. DARRELL PORTER
□ 310. WILLIE MCGEE
□ 337. KEVIN HAGEN
□ 362. DAVID GREEN
□ 416. DANE IORG
□ 435. NEIL ALLEN
□ 467. MIKE RAMSEY
□ 489. DAVE VON OHLEN
□ 514. FLOYD RAYFORD
□ 540. GEORGE HENDRICK
□ 561. WHITEY HERZOG(M)
□ 580. LONNIE SMITH
□ 593. JEFF LAHTI
□ 627. DAVE LAPOINT
□ 649. TOM HERR
□ 671. JAMIE QUIRK
□ 699. DAVE RUCKER
□ 730. BRUCE SUTTER
□ 785. JOAQUIN ANDUJAR

SAN DIEGO PADRES

□ 7. GARY LUCAS
□ 38. LUIS DELEON
□ 68. LUIS SALAZAR
□ 94. MARIO RAMIREZ
□ 168. JUAN BONILLA
□ 224. SID MONGE
□ 251. TONY GWYNN
□ 261. BOBBY BROWN
□ 277. EDDIE WHITSON
□ 290. DAVE DRAVECKY
□ 327. RUPPERT JONES
□ 346. KURT BEVACQUA
□ 366. TEAM LEADER CARD
□ 380. STEVE GARVEY
□ 455. TERRY KENNEDY
□ 481. MARK THURMOND
□ 503. ELIAS SOSA
□ 532. ERIC SHOW
□ 571. BRUCE BOCHY
□ 594. GENE RICHARDS
□ 615. GARRY TEMPLETON
□ 644. TIM LOLLAR
□ 674. TIM FLANNERY
□ 693. ALAN WIGGINS
□ 742. DICK WILLIAMS(M)
□ 753. DOUG GWOSDZ
□ 778. ANDY HAWKINS

SAN FRANCISCO GIANTS

□ 31. ANDY MCGAFFIGAN
□ 58. MAX VENABLE
□ 85. ATLEE HAMMAKER
□ 98. STEVE NICOSIA
□ 109. BRAD WELLMAN
□ 129. BILL LASKEY
□ 145. GARY LAVELLE
□ 171. FRANK ROBINSON(M)
□ 205. GREG MINTON
□ 228. JOHN RABB
□ 282. JIM BARR
□ 325. DARRELL EVANS
□ 343. MARK DAVIS
□ 378. BOB BRENLY
□ 428. FRED BREINING
□ 449. JOE PETTINI
□ 469. TOM O'MALLEY
□ 494. CHILI DAVIS
□ 522. DAVE BERGMAN
□ 542. DUANE KUIPER
□ 576. TEAM LEADER CARD
□ 603. RENIE MARTIN
□ 633. MIKE KRUKOW
□ 663. JOHNNIE LEMASTER
□ 690. JACK CLARK
□ 727. JOEL YOUNGBLOOD
□ 748. JEFF LEONARD
□ 768. CHAMP SUMMERS

SEATTLE MARINERS

□ 22. BRYAN CLARK
□ 41. TONY BERNAZARD
□ 63. ED VANDE BERG
□ 83. RICHIE ZISK
□ 154. DAVE HENDERSON
□ 166. JAMIE NELSON
□ 181. ROY THOMAS
□ 194. DOMINGO RAMOS
□ 211. RICK SWEET
□ 235. MATT YOUNG
□ 288. JIM BEATTIE
□ 314. ORLANDO MERCADO
□ 336. TEAM LEADER CARD
□ 413. SPIKE OWEN
□ 439. BOB STODDARD
□ 461. JIM MALER
□ 501. STEVE HENDERSON
□ 517. JOHN MOSES
□ 547. MIKE MOORE
□ 562. MANNY CASTILLO
□ 622. AL COWENS
□ 636. PAT PUTNAM
□ 647. RON ROENICKE
□ 672. RICKY NELSON
□ 694. MIKE STANTON
□ 721. DEL CRANDALL(M)
□ 744. JAMIE ALLEN
□ 769. BILL CAUDILL

TEXAS RANGERS

□ 12. BILLY SAMPLE
□ 37. TEAM LEADER CARD
□ 62. DAVE HOSTETLER
□ 89. MIKE SMITHSON
□ 118. CHARLIE HOUGH
□ 149. JON MATLACK
□ 169. LARRY PARRISH
□ 283. LARRY BITTNER
□ 299. JOHN BUTCHER
□ 331. BUCKY DENT
□ 341. DAVE TOBIK
□ 352. DAVE STEWART
□ 353. JIM ANDERSON
□ 377. DANNY DARWIN
□ 412. DOUG RADER(M)
□ 451. BOB JONES
□ 479. FRANK TANANA
□ 504. MICKEY RIVERS
□ 534. PETE O'BRIEN
□ 557. WAYNE TOLLESON
□ 584. DAVE SCHMIDT
□ 608. BOBBY JOHNSON
□ 641. MIKE RICHARDT
□ 665. BUDDY BELL
□ 688. GEORGE WRIGHT
□ 734. ODELL JONES
□ 758. BILL STEIN
□ 779. JIM SUNDBERG

TORONTO BLUE JAYS

□ 9. JIM GOTT
□ 39. GARTH IORG
□ 76. ALFREDO GRIFFIN
□ 92. LLOYD MOSEBY
□ 108. RANDY MOFFITT
□ 124. DAMASO GARCIA
□ 179. BUCK MARTINEZ
□ 202. BOBBY COX(M)
□ 221. CLIFF JOHNSON
□ 256. DAVE GEISEL
□ 278. JORGE BELL
□ 302. BARRY BONNELL
□ 312. JORGE ORTA
□ 339. ROY LEE JACKSON
□ 359. JIM ACKER
□ 423. MIKE MORGAN
□ 453. WILLIE UPSHAW
□ 488. JESSE BARFIELD
□ 506. ERNIE WHITT
□ 556. JOEY MCLAUGHLIN
□ 575. JIM CLANCY
□ 590. DAVE STIEB
□ 606. TEAM LEADER CARD
□ 677. DOYLE ALEXANDER
□ 733. DAVE COLLINS
□ 762. RANCE MULLINKS
□ 783. LUIS LEAL

1984 TOPPS TRADED (132) 2 1/2" X 3 1/2"

ATLANTA BRAVES

□ 30T. JEFF DEDMON
□ 85T. KEN OBERKFELL
□ 92T. GERALD PERRY
□ 120T. ALEX TREVINO

BALTIMORE ORIOLES

□ 44T. WAYNE GROSS
□ 96T. FLOYD RAYFORD
□ 123T. TOM UNDERWOOD

BOSTON RED SOX

□ 17T. BILL BUCKNER
□ 33T. MIKE EASLER
□ 40T. RICH GALE
□ 46T. JACKIE GUTIERREZ

CALIFORNIA ANGELS

□ 68T. FRANK LACORTE
□ 93T. GARY PETTIS
□ 94T. ROB PICCIOLO
□ 102T. RON ROMANICK
□ 107T. DICK SCHOFIELD
□ 109T. JIM SLATON
□ 116T. CRAIG SWAN

CHICAGO CUBS

□ 31T. BOB DERNIER
□ 34T. DENNIS ECKERSLEY
□ 39T. GEORGE FRAZIER
□ 49T. RON HASSEY
□ 50T. RICH HEBNER
□ 77T. GARY MATTHEWS
□ 106T. SCOTT SANDERSON
□ 112T. TIM STODDARD
□ 115T. RICK SUTCLIFFE

1984 Topps Traded

CHICAGO WHITE SOX

- ☐ 98T. RON REED
- ☐ 108T. TOM SEAVER

CINCINNATI REDS

- ☐ 65T. WAYNE KRENCHICKI
- ☐ 90T. DAVE PARKER
- ☐ 91T. TONY PEREZ
- ☐ 95T. VERN RAPP(M)

CLEVELAND INDIANS

- ☐ 2T. LUIS APONTE
- ☐ 12T. TONY BERNAZARD
- ☐ 20T. BRETT BUTLER
- ☐ 47T. MEL HALL
- ☐ 55T. BROOK JACOBY
- ☐ 56T. MIKE JEFFCOAT
- ☐ 125T. TOM WADDELL

DETROIT TIGERS

- ☐ 11T. DAVE BERGMAN
- ☐ 36T. DARRELL EVANS
- ☐ 41T. BARBARO GARBEY
- ☐ 51T. WILLIE HERNANDEZ
- ☐ 59T. RUPPERT JONES
- ☐ 66T. RUSTY KUNTZ
- ☐ 80T. SID MONGE

HOUSTON ASTROS

- ☐ 21T. ENOS CABELL

KANSAS CITY ROYALS

- ☐ 6T. STEVE BALBONI
- ☐ 9T. JOE BECKWITH
- ☐ 45T. MARK GUBICZA
- ☐ 54T. DANE IORG
- ☐ 57T. LYNN JONES
- ☐ 88T. JORGE ORTA
- ☐ 104T. BRET SABERHAGEN

LOS ANGELES DODGERS

- ☐ 4T. BOB BAILOR
- ☐ 32T. CARLOS DIAZ
- ☐ 124T. MIKE VAIL

MILWAUKEE BREWERS

- ☐ 24T. BOB CLARK
- ☐ 26T. JAIME COCANOWER
- ☐ 67T. RENE LACHEMANN(M)
- ☐ 97T. RANDY READY
- ☐ 114T. JIM SUNDBERG

MINNESOTA TWINS

- ☐ 19T. JOHN BUTCHER
- ☐ 110T. MIKE SMITHSON
- ☐ 117T. TIM TEUFEL

MONTREAL EXPOS

- ☐ 16T. FRED BREINING
- ☐ 73T. GARY LUCAS
- ☐ 78T. ANDY MCGAFFIGAN
- ☐ 103T. PETE ROSE
- ☐ 118T. DERREL THOMAS

NEW YORK METS

- ☐ 10T. BRUCE BERENYI
- ☐ 27T. RON DARLING
- ☐ 37T. MIKE FITZGERALD
- ☐ 42T. DWIGHT GOODEN
- ☐ 57T. DAVE JOHNSON(M)
- ☐ 74T. JERRY MARTIN

NEW YORK YANKEES

- ☐ 3T. MIKE ARMSTRONG
- ☐ 13T. YOGI BERRA(M)
- ☐ 38T. TIM FOLI
- ☐ 48T. TOBY HARRAH
- ☐ 84T. PHIL NIEKRO
- ☐ 86T. MIKE O'BERRY
- ☐ 100T. JOSE RIJO

OAKLAND A'S

- ☐ 18T. RAY BURRIS
- ☐ 23T. BILL CAUDILL
- ☐ 35T. JIM ESSIAN
- ☐ 63T. DAVE KINGMAN
- ☐ 81T. JACKIE MOORE(M)
- ☐ 82T. JOE MORGAN
- ☐ 111T. LARY SORENSEN

PHIADELPHIA PHILLIES

- ☐ 22T. BILL CAMPBELL
- ☐ 64T. JERRY KOOSMAN
- ☐ 105T. JUAN SAMUEL
- ☐ 129T. GLENN WILSON
- ☐ 130T. JOHNNY WOCKENFUSS

PITTSBURGH PIRATES

- ☐ 89T. AMOS OTIS
- ☐ 122T. JOHN TUDOR

ST. LOUIS CARDINALS

- ☐ 29T. KEN DAYLEY
- ☐ 52T. RICKY HORTON
- ☐ 53T. ART HOWE
- ☐ 60T. MIKE JORGENSEN

SAN DIEGO PADRES

- ☐ 43T. RICH GOSSAGE
- ☐ 72T. CRAIG LEFFERTS
- ☐ 75T. CARMELO MARTINEZ
- ☐ 83T. GRAIG NETTLES
- ☐ 113T. CHAMP SUMMERS

SAN FRANCISCO GIANTS

- ☐ 5T. DUSTY BAKER
- ☐ 87T. AL OLIVER
- ☐ 99T. GENE RICHARDS
- ☐ 101T. JEFF ROBINSON
- ☐ 121T. MANNY TRILLO
- ☐ 128T. FRANK WILLIAMS

SEATTLE MARINERS

- ☐ 8T. DAVE BEARD
- ☐ 14T. BARRY BONNELL
- ☐ 15T. PHIL BRADLEY
- ☐ 28T. ALVIN DAVIS
- ☐ 61T. BOB KEARNEY
- ☐ 70T. MARK LANGSTON
- ☐ 79T. LARRY MILBOURNE
- ☐ 119T. GORMAN THOMAS

TEXAS RANGERS

- ☐ 7T. ALAN BANNISTER
- ☐ 76T. MIKE MASON
- ☐ 126T. GARY WARD
- ☐ 127T. CURT WILDERSON
- ☐ 131. NED YOST

TORONTO BLUE JAYS

- ☐ 1T. WILLIE AIKENS
- ☐ 25T. BRYAN CLARK
- ☐ 62T. JIMMY KEY
- ☐ 69T. DENNIS LAMP
- ☐ 71T. RICK LEACH

1985 TOPPS (792) 2 1/2" X 3 1/2"

ATLANTA BRAVES

- ☐ 25. STEVE BEDROSIAN
- ☐ 51. BOB WATSON
- ☐ 79. RICK MAHLER
- ☐ 106. PASCUAL PEREZ
- ☐ 129. GENE GARBER
- ☐ 167. RUFINO LINARES
- ☐ 195. GLENN HUBBARD
- ☐ 219. GERALD PERRY
- ☐ 248. TERRY FORSTER
- ☐ 292. BRAD KOMMINSK
- ☐ 320. DALE MURPHY
- ☐ 335. BRUCE BENEDICT
- ☐ 362. CRAIG MCMURTRY
- ☐ 410. BOB HORNER
- ☐ 438. JOE TORRE(M)
- ☐ 458. RANDY JOHNSON
- ☐ 491. RICK CAMP
- ☐ 518. CHRIS CHAMBLISS
- ☐ 540. CLAUDELL WASHINGTON
- ☐ 557. LEN BARKER
- ☐ 569. KEN OBERKFELL
- ☐ 602. JEFF DEDMON
- ☐ 618. PETE FALCONE
- ☐ 647. RAFAEL RAMIREZ
- ☐ 676. ALBERT HALL
- ☐ 699. DONNIE MOORE
- ☐ 747. ALEX TREVINO
- ☐ 776. JERRY ROYSTER

BALTIMORE ORIOLES

- □ 30. CAL RIPKEN
- □ 56. JIM DWYER
- □ 81. LENN SAKATA
- □ 109. GARY ROENICKE
- □ 147. BILL SWAGGERTY
- □ 173. MIKE YOUNG
- □ 199. DENNY MARTINEZ
- □ 225. MIKE BODDICKER
- □ 252. DAN FORD
- □ 289. TOM UNDERWOOD
- □ 316. JOHN LOWENSTEIN
- □ 341. FLOYD RAYFORD
- □ 366. TODD CRUZ
- □ 416. WAYNE GROSS
- □ 445. TIPPY MARTINEZ
- □ 469. SAMMY STEWART
- □ 494. RICH DAUER
- □ 508. JOHN SHELBY
- □ 521. RICK DEMPSEY
- □ 550. SCOTT MCGREGOR
- □ 574. JOE ALTOBELLI(M)
- □ 599. STORM DAVIS
- □ 624. BENNY AYALA
- □ 652. JOE NOLAN
- □ 700. EDDIE MURRAY
- □ 726. AL BUMBRY
- □ 755. KEN SINGLETON
- □ 780. MIKE FLANAGAN

BOSTON RED SOX

- □ 11. RALPH HOUK(M)
- □ 37. REID NICHOLS
- □ 65. BILL BUCKNER
- □ 89. JACKIE GUTIERREZ
- □ 116. DENNIS BOYD
- □ 150. JIM RICE
- □ 181. ROGER CLEMENS
- □ 207. MARK CLEAR
- □ 233. ED JURAK
- □ 259. GARY ALLENSON
- □ 298. MARTY BARRETT
- □ 322. DAVE STAPLETON
- □ 350. WADE BOGGS
- □ 376. JEFF NEWMAN
- □ 424. AL NIPPER
- □ 451. BRUCE HURST
- □ 477. BOB OJEDA
- □ 502. RICK MILLER
- □ 529. RICH GEDMAN
- □ 555. BOB STANLEY
- □ 580. DWIGHT EVANS
- □ 606. RICH GALE
- □ 633. GLENN HOFFMAN
- □ 661. STEVE CRAWFORD
- □ 686. MIKE EASLER
- □ 734. JOHN HENRY JOHNSON
- □ 761. JERRY REMY
- □ 785. TONY ARMAS

CALIFORNIA ANGELS

- □ 42. LUIS SANCHEZ
- □ 61. CURT KAUFMAN
- □ 86. DON AASE
- □ 111. DOUG DECINCES
- □ 153. FRANK LACORTE
- □ 179. TOMMY JOHN
- □ 200. REGGIE JACKSON
- □ 220. FRED LYNN
- □ 226. JUAN BENIQUEZ
- □ 234. JERRY NARRON
- □ 258. MIKE BROWN
- □ 300. ROD CAREW
- □ 309. MIKE WITT
- □ 348. BOB BOONE
- □ 374. BRIAN DOWNING
- □ 442. KEN FORSCH
- □ 465. BOB GRICH
- □ 497. GARY PETTIS
- □ 524. ROB WILFONG
- □ 544. BRUCE KISON
- □ 579. RON ROMANICK
- □ 604. DARYL SCONIERS
- □ 629. DICK SCHOFIELD
- □ 657. JIM SLATON
- □ 682. DOUG CORBETT
- □ 732. JOHN MCNAMARA(M)
- □ 756. ROB PICCIOLO
- □ 771. GEOFF ZAHN

CHICAGO CUBS

- □ 19. GEORGE FRAZIER
- □ 46. GARY WOODS
- □ 72. RICK SUTCLIFFE
- □ 98. STEVE LAKE
- □ 124. RICH HEBNER
- □ 163. DENNIS ECKERSLEY
- □ 189. WARREN BRUSSTAR
- □ 210. GARY MATTHEWS
- □ 241. JIM FREY(M)
- □ 267. HENRY COTTO
- □ 306. RICK REUSCHEL
- □ 330. LEON DURHAM
- □ 357. RICH BORDI
- □ 384. JODY DAVIS
- □ 405. TOM VERYZER
- □ 432. THAD BOSLEY
- □ 460. RYNE SANDBERG
- □ 484. LARRY BOWA
- □ 511. LEE SMITH
- □ 538. KEITH MORELAND
- □ 563. DICK RUTHVEN
- □ 589. BOB DERNIER
- □ 616. SCOTT SANDERSON
- □ 642. DAVE OWEN
- □ 668. STEVE TROUT
- □ 693. TIM STODDARD
- □ 742. RON HASSEY
- □ 768. RON CEY

CHICAGO WHITE SOX

- □ 26. ROY SMALLEY
- □ 52. JERRY DYBZINSKI
- □ 78. SCOTT FLETCHER
- □ 105. RON KITTLE
- □ 169. DAN SPILLNER
- □ 194. DAVE STEGMAN
- □ 216. JERRY DON GLEATON
- □ 221. RON REED
- □ 249. HAROLD BAINES
- □ 286. RUDY LAW
- □ 312. MARC HILL
- □ 338. BRITT BURNS
- □ 351. JUAN AGOSTO
- □ 364. RICHARD DOTSON
- □ 388. BERT ROBERGE
- □ 413. VANCE LAW
- □ 437. AL JONES
- □ 466. TONY LARUSSA(M)
- □ 488. JOEL SKINNER
- □ 520. LAMARR HOYT
- □ 543. MIKE SQUIRES
- □ 572. TOM PACIOREK
- □ 596. JERRY HAIRSTON
- □ 623. GREG WALKER
- □ 650. GREG LUZINSKI
- □ 670. TOM SEAVER
- □ 725. FLOYD BANNISTER
- □ 749. JULIO CRUZ
- □ 770. CARLTON FISK

CINCINNATI REDS

- □ 28. DANN BILARDELLO
- □ 54. CESAR CEDEON
- □ 82. JOE PRICE
- □ 107. TOM FOLEY
- □ 146. GARY REDUS
- □ 175. DAVE PARKER
- □ 198. EDDIE MILNER
- □ 223. TOM HUME
- □ 251. BRAD GULDEN
- □ 314. RON OESTER
- □ 323. ANDY MCGAFFIGAN
- □ 342. TED POWER
- □ 367. KEEFE CATO
- □ 417. JOHN FRANCO
- □ 441. DUANE WALKER
- □ 468. WAYNE KRENCHICKI
- □ 495. MARIO SOTO
- □ 515. DAVE CONCEPCION
- □ 547. PETE ROSE(M)
- □ 573. JAY TIBBS
- □ 597. BRAD LESLEY
- □ 600. PETE ROSE
- □ 627. ERIC DAVIS
- □ 651. JEFF RUSSELL
- □ 675. TONY PEREZ
- □ 727. FRANK PASTORE
- □ 752. BOB OWCHINKO
- □ 779. NICK ESASKY

CLEVELAND INDIANS

- □ 14. CHRIS BANDO
- □ 41. MIKE FISCHLIN
- □ 93. DON SCHULZE
- □ 119. PAT CORRALES(M)
- □ 158. PAT TABLER
- □ 184. CARMEN CASTILLO
- □ 212. GEORGE VUKOVICH
- □ 237. JULIO FRANCO
- □ 263. MEL HALL
- □ 303. MIKE JEFFCOAT
- □ 327. BROOK JACOBY
- □ 355. BERT BLYLEVEN
- □ 381. ROY SMITH
- □ 425. MIKE HARGROVE
- □ 453. TOM WADDELL
- □ 475. ANDRE THORNTON
- □ 504. JERRY WILLARD
- □ 533. TONY BERNAZARD
- □ 609. BRODERICK PERKINS
- □ 637. BRETT BUTLER
- □ 664. STEVE FARR
- □ 694. JOE CARTER
- □ 739. ERNIE CAMACHO
- □ 764. JAMIE EASTERLY
- □ 788. STEVE COMER

DETROIT TIGERS

- □ 20. CHET LEMON
- □ 47. DAVE ROZEMA
- □ 73. RUSTY KUNTZ
- □ 99. MILT WILCOX
- □ 126. RUPPERT JONES
- □ 160. LANCE PARRISH
- □ 192. HOWARD JOHNSON
- □ 243. BARBARO GARBEY
- □ 269. DOUG BAKER
- □ 307. SPARKY ANDERSON(M)
- □ 333. WILLIE HERNANDEZ
- □ 368. DAVE BERGMAN
- □ 408. SID MONGE
- □ 435. DAN PETRY
- □ 461. MARTY CASTILLO
- □ 480. LOU WHITAKER
- □ 512. TOM BROOKENS
- □ 539. AURELIO LOPEZ
- □ 565. KIRK GIBSON
- □ 586. BILL SCHERRER
- □ 591. LARRY HERNDON
- □ 610. JACK MORRIS
- □ 643. JOHNNY GRUBB
- □ 672. JUAN BERENGUER
- □ 690. ALAN TRAMMELL
- □ 744. DOUG BAIR
- □ 792. DARRELL EVANS

HOUSTON ASTROS

- □ 17. MIKE SCOTT
- □ 44. DICKIE THON
- □ 64. MARK BAILEY
- □ 95. JOSE CRUZ

- □ 123. DAVE SMITH
- □ 156. CRAIG REYNOLDS
- □ 186. BOB LILLIS(M)
- □ 206. PHIL GARNER
- □ 264. JOE SAMBITO
- □ 295. JOE NIEKRO
- □ 326. KEVIN BASS
- □ 353. JULIO SOLANO
- □ 382. DENNY WALLING
- □ 426. VERN RUHLE
- □ 455. BOB KNEPPER
- □ 479. MIKE MADDEN
- □ 482. HARRY SPILMAN
- □ 532. FRANK DIPINO
- □ 564. ALAN ASHBY
- □ 613. TERRY PUHL
- □ 634. BILL DAWLEY
- □ 666. MIKE LACOSS
- □ 684. BILL DORAN
- □ 736. JERRY MUMPHREY
- □ 760. NOLAN RYAN
- □ 786. ENOS CABELL

KANSAS CITY ROYALS

- □ 23. BRET SABERHAGEN
- □ 49. BUTCH DAVIS
- □ 77. JOE BECKWITH
- □ 100. GEORGE BRETT
- □ 127. MARK GUBICZA
- □ 164. JORGE ORTA
- □ 188. GREG PRYOR
- □ 217. LEON ROBERTS
- □ 244. MIKE JONES
- □ 270. DAN QUISENBERRY
- □ 308. JOHN WATHAN
- □ 334. DICK HOWSER(M)
- □ 359. PAT SHERIDAN
- □ 387. BUDDY BIANCALANA
- □ 412. BUD BLACK
- □ 431. U.L. WASHINGTON
- □ 459. CHARLIE LEIBRANDT
- □ 486. STEVE BALBONI
- □ 513. LYNN JONES
- □ 542. DON SLAUGHT
- □ 561. DARRYL MOTLEY
- □ 595. LARRY GURA
- □ 617. WILLIE WILSON
- □ 644. MARK HUISMANN
- □ 671. DANE IORG
- □ 697. ONIX CONCEPCION
- □ 743. FRANK WHITE
- □ 773. HAL MCRAE

LOS ANGELES DODGERS

- □ 31. TERRY WHITFIELD
- □ 57. PAT ZACHRY
- □ 85. MIKE MARSHALL
- □ 110. ALEJANDRO PENA
- □ 148. STEVE YEAGER
- □ 159. CARLOS DIAZ
- □ 174. RICK HONEYCUTT
- □ 201. BURT HOOTON
- □ 253. SID BREAM
- □ 291. BOB WELCH
- □ 343. BILL RUSSELL
- □ 369. R.J. REYNOLDS
- □ 418. KEN LANDREAUX
- □ 440. FERNANDO VALENZUELA
- □ 470. STEVE SAX
- □ 493. OREL HERSHISER
- □ 506. FRANKLIN STUBBS
- □ 523. CANDY MALDONADO
- □ 549. MIKE SCIOSCIA
- □ 575. PEDRO GUERRERO
- □ 601. TOM LASORDA(M)
- □ 626. GERMAN RIVERA
- □ 654. DAVE ANDERSON
- □ 680. JERRY REUSS
- □ 728. BOB BAILOR
- □ 753. GREG BROCK
- □ 782. TOM NIEDENFUER

MILWAUKEE BREWERS

- □ 32. CHUCK PORTER
- □ 59. RICK WAITS
- □ 83. CHARLIE MOORE
- □ 112. TOM TELLMANN
- □ 151. MOOSE HAAS
- □ 176. BILL SCHROEDER
- □ 203. BOB MCCLURE
- □ 228. DION JAMES
- □ 254. PETE VUCKOVICH
- □ 290. CECIL COOPER
- □ 317. JACK LAZORKO
- □ 318. TED SIMMONS
- □ 340. ROBIN YOUNT
- □ 372. ROY HOWELL
- □ 419. MIKE CALDWELL
- □ 446. JIM SUNDBERG
- □ 471. PETE LADD
- □ 498. ED ROMERO
- □ 522. PAUL MOLITOR
- □ 553. BOB CLARK
- □ 576. JAIME COCANOWER
- □ 603. RICK MANNING
- □ 628. RENE LACHEMANN(M)
- □ 653. MARK BROUHARD
- □ 681. BEN OGLIVIE
- □ 729. DON SUTTON
- □ 750. ROLLIE FINGERS
- □ 781. JIM GANTNER

MINNESOTA TWINS

- □ 18. MICKEY HATCHER
- □ 43. ANDRE DAVID
- □ 71. TIM LAUDNER
- □ 97. PETE FILSON
- □ 122. TOM BRUNANSKY
- □ 161. KEN SCHROM
- □ 187. MIKE WALTERS
- □ 213. BILLY GARDNER(M)
- □ 239. TIM TEUFEL
- □ 266. FRANK VIOLA
- □ 304. GARY GAETTI
- □ 329. RON WASHINGTON
- □ 356. DAVE MEIER
- □ 383. RICK LYSANDER
- □ 406. LEN WHITEHOUSE
- □ 430. RON DAVIS
- □ 452. JOHN CASTINO
- □ 483. MIKE SMITHSON
- □ 510. KENT HRBEK
- □ 535. PAT PUTNAM
- □ 536. KIRBY PUCKETT
- □ 562. HOUSTON JIMENEZ
- □ 577. CHRIS SPEIER
- □ 588. BOBBY CASTILLO
- □ 614. AL WILLIAMS
- □ 639. ED HODGE
- □ 667. DAVE ENGLE
- □ 692. RANDY BUSH
- □ 741. JOHN BUTCHER
- □ 767. DARRELL BROWN

MONTREAL EXPOS

- □ 36. FRED BREINING
- □ 62. MIKE RAMSEY
- □ 88. BRYN SMITH
- □ 114. BOB JAMES
- □ 154. ARGENIS SALAZAR
- □ 178. MIGUEL DILONE
- □ 205. STEVE ROGERS
- □ 230. GARY CARTER
- □ 257. BRYAN LITTLE
- □ 285. DAN DRIESSEN
- □ 297. GARY LUCAS
- □ 345. CHARLIE LEA
- □ 375. JEFF REARDON
- □ 407. BOBBY RAMOS
- □ 420. ANDRE DAWSON
- □ 448. DERREL THOMAS
- □ 473. TIM WALLACH
- □ 501. DAN SCHATZEDER
- □ 526. DAVE PALMER
- □ 554. DOUG FLYNN
- □ 578. TERRY FRANCONA
- □ 630. TIM RAINES
- □ 658. MIKE STENHOUSE
- □ 687. BILL GULLICKSON
- □ 733. TONY SCOTT
- □ 759. JIM FANNING(M)
- □ 787. JIM WOHLFORD

NEW YORK METS

- □ 27. BRUCE BERENYI
- □ 53. TOM GORMAN
- □ 67. RAFAEL SANTANA
- □ 80. KEITH HERNANDEZ
- □ 104. MIKE FITZGERALD
- □ 144. RON GARDENHIRE
- □ 170. GEORGE FOSTER
- □ 190. RUSTY STAUB
- □ 222. HUBIE BROOKS
- □ 250. JESSE OROSCO
- □ 287. WALT TERRRELL
- □ 315. DOUG SISK
- □ 339. DANNY HEEP
- □ 363. RON HODGES
- □ 415. RON DARLING
- □ 439. JUNIOR ORTIZ
- □ 467. ED LYNCH
- □ 492. DAVE JOHNSON(M)
- □ 517. JERRY MARTIN
- □ 546. BRENT GAFF
- □ 570. DARRYL STRAWBERRY
- □ 590. RAY KNIGHT
- □ 598. JOSE EQUENDO
- □ 620. DWIGHT GOODEN
- □ 649. SID FERNANDEZ
- □ 677. WALLY BACKMAN
- □ 751. KELVIN CHAPMAN
- □ 775. MOOKIE WILSON

NEW YORK YANKEES

- □ 16. BOBBY MEACHAM
- □ 40. PHIL NIEKRO
- □ 70. DON BAYLOR
- □ 94. TOBY HARRAH
- □ 120. STEVE KEMP
- □ 155. YOGI BERRA(M)
- □ 180. DAVE WINFIELD
- □ 211. CLAY CHRISTIANSEN
- □ 238. JOSE RIJO
- □ 260. DAVE RIGHETTI
- □ 284. MARTY BYSTROM
- □ 301. JOHN MONTEFUSCO
- □ 328. BOB SHIRLEY
- □ 354. ANDRE ROBERTSON
- □ 380. KEN GRIFFEY
- □ 429. RICK CERONE
- □ 456. TIM FOLI
- □ 481. DALE MURRAY
- □ 507. RAY FONTENOT
- □ 534. BRIAN DAYETT
- □ 559. JAY HOWELL
- □ 585. BUTCH WYNEGAR
- □ 612. MIKE ARMSTRONG
- □ 638. MIKE PAGLIARULO
- □ 665. DON MITTINGLY
- □ 691. DENNIS RASMUSSEN
- □ 724. OSCAR GAMBLE
- □ 738. OMAR MORENO
- □ 765. WILLIE RANDOLPH
- □ 769. JOE COWLEY
- □ 790. RON GUIDRY

OAKLAND A'S

- □ 12. DAVE LOPES
- □ 38. JACKIE MOORE(M)
- □ 63. STEVE MCCATTY
- □ 91. JEFF BURROUGHS
- □ 115. RICKEY HENDERSON

- □ 166. KEITH ATHERON
- □ 197. MIKE WARREN
- □ 231. DWAYNE MURPHY
- □ 246. MIKE NORRIS
- □ 293. CURT YOUNG
- □ 319. JEFF JONES
- □ 347. RICK LANGFORD
- □ 352. JOE MORGAN
- □ 422. CARNEY LANSFORD
- □ 444. TONY PHILLIPS
- □ 472. JIM ESSIAN
- □ 503. TIM CONROY
- □ 528. BILL KRUEGER
- □ 552. CHRIS CODIROLI
- □ 581. MARK WAGNER
- □ 607. BILL ALMON
- □ 632. BRUCE BOCHTE
- □ 662. MIKE HEATH
- □ 685. BILL CAUDILL
- □ 730. DAVE KINGMAN
- □ 758. RAY BURRIS
- □ 778. MIKE DAVIS

PHILADEPHIA PHILLIES

- □ 15. JERRY KOOSMAN
- □ 39. JOHNNY WOCKENFUSS
- □ 68. VON HAYES
- □ 92. PAUL OWENS(M)
- □ 117. GREG GROSS
- □ 130. AL OLVIER
- □ 157. TUG MCGRAW
- □ 185. AL HOLLAND
- □ 209. BILL CAMPBELL
- □ 235. GARRY MADDOX
- □ 265. JUAN SAMUEL
- □ 302. TIM CORCORAN
- □ 325. JOHN DENNY
- □ 360. STEVE CARLTON
- □ 379. CHARLES HUDSON
- □ 428. LARRY ANDERSEN
- □ 454. GLENN WILSON
- □ 476. JEFF STONE
- □ 500. MIKE SCHMIDT
- □ 531. JOE LEFEBVRE
- □ 556. SIXTON LEZCANO
- □ 584. KEVIN GROSS
- □ 611. OZZIE VIRGIL
- □ 636. SHANE RAWLEY
- □ 663. LUIS AGUAYO
- □ 688. LEN MATUSZEK
- □ 737. BO DIAZ
- □ 763. KIKO GARCIA
- □ 791. IVAN DEJESUS

PITTSBURGH PIRATES

- □ 21. LEE TUNNELL
- □ 50. JOHN CANDELARIA
- □ 69. JIM WINN
- □ 96. JOHNNY RAY
- □ 125. KENT TEKULVE
- □ 162. BENNY DISTEFANO
- □ 183. LARRY MCWILLIAMS
- □ 214. JOHN TUDOR
- □ 268. CHUCK TANNER(M)
- □ 305. DALE BERRA
- □ 332. BRIAN HARPER
- □ 358. TONY PENA
- □ 385. JOSE DELEON
- □ 433. JIM MORRISON
- □ 457. CECILIO GUANTE
- □ 490. JASON THOMPSON
- □ 509. MILT MAY
- □ 537. DON ROBINSON
- □ 560. BILL MADLOCK
- □ 587. DOUG FROBEL
- □ 615. MARVELL WYNNE
- □ 641. ROD SCURRY
- □ 669. LEE LACY
- □ 695. RICK RHODEN
- □ 748. LEE MAZZILLI

ST. LOUIS CARDINALS

- □ 33. TITO LANDRUM
- □ 60. GEORGE HENDRICK
- □ 87. DAVID GREEN
- □ 113. TOM HERR
- □ 152. STEVE BRAUN
- □ 177. DAVE VON OHLEN
- □ 204. ART HOWE
- □ 229. DAVE LAPOINT
- □ 255. LONNIE SMITH
- □ 294. TOM JIETO
- □ 321. RICKY HORTON
- □ 346. TERRY PENDLETON
- □ 370. BRUCE SUTTER
- □ 421. DAVE RUCKER
- □ 447. JEFF LAHTI
- □ 474. KURT KEPSHIRE
- □ 499. DANNY COX
- □ 525. DARRELL PORTER
- □ 551. ANDY VAN SLYKE
- □ 605. OZZIE SMITH
- □ 631. BOB FORSCH
- □ 655. JOAQUIN ANDUJAR
- □ 683. WHITE HERZOG(M)
- □ 731. NEIL ALLEN
- □ 757. WILLIE MCGEE
- □ 783. MIKE JORGENSEN

SAN DIEGO PADRES

- □ 13. TIM LOLLAR
- □ 35. GRAIG NETTLES
- □ 66. DICK WILLIAMS(M)
- □ 90. RICH GOSSAGE
- □ 118. ERIC SHOW
- □ 182. TIM FLANNERY
- □ 208. CHAMP SUMMERS
- □ 236. MARK THURMOND
- □ 242. GREG HARRIS
- □ 262. GREG BOOKER
- □ 299. ANDY HAWKINS
- □ 324. BRUCE BOCHY
- □ 378. ALAN WIGGINS
- □ 427. MARIO RAMIREZ
- □ 450. STEVE GARVEY
- □ 478. KURT BEVACQUA
- □ 530. DAVE DRAVECKY
- □ 558. CARMELO MARTINEZ
- □ 583. BOBBY BROWN
- □ 608. CRAIG LEFFERTS
- □ 635. TERRY KENNEDY
- □ 660. TONY GWYNN
- □ 689. LUIS DELEON
- □ 735. GARRY TEMPLETON
- □ 762. EDDIE WHITSON
- □ 789. LUIS SALAZAR

SAN FRANCISCO GIANTS

- □ 22. DUANE KUIPER
- □ 45. GREG MINTON
- □ 74. MIKE KRUKOW
- □ 103. RANDY LERCH
- □ 165. DUSTY BAKER
- □ 191. STEVE NICOSIA
- □ 215. BOB BRENLY
- □ 245. CHILI DAVIS
- □ 283. FRAN MULLINS
- □ 310. MANNY TRILLO
- □ 331. BILL LASKEY
- □ 365. DANNY OZARK(M)
- □ 386. DAN GLADDEN
- □ 409. BRAD WELLMAN
- □ 434. GENE RICHARDS
- □ 462. GARY LAVELLE
- □ 487. FRANK WILLIAMS
- □ 514. JEFF CORNELL
- □ 541. MARK DAVIS
- □ 567. JOEL YOUNGBLOOD
- □ 592. JEFF ROBINSON
- □ 619. JEFF LEONARD
- □ 646. SCOT THOMPSON
- □ 674. ATLEE HAMMAKER
- □ 696. JOHN RABB
- □ 740. JACK CLARK
- □ 772. JOHNNIE LEMASTER

SEATTLE MARINERS

- □ 34. ED NUNEZ
- □ 58. ORLANDO MERCADO
- □ 84. SPIKE OWEN
- □ 108. DARNELL COLES
- □ 145. ALVIN DAVIS
- □ 172. JACK PERCONTE
- □ 202. GORMAN THOMAS
- □ 224. AL COWENS
- □ 232. DAVE BEARD
- □ 256. MIKE STANTON
- □ 296. RICKY NELSON
- □ 344. DAVE HENDERSON
- □ 349. DOMINGO RAMOS
- □ 373. MIKE MOORE
- □ 423. BARRY BONNELL
- □ 449. PHIL BRADLEY
- □ 485. MATT YOUNG
- □ 505. JIM BEATTIE
- □ 566. ED VAND BERG
- □ 582. KEN PHELPS
- □ 625. MARK LANGSTON
- □ 640. STEVE HENDERSON
- □ 656. CHUCK COTTIER(M)
- □ 679. BOB KEARNEY
- □ 754. LARRY MILBOURNE
- □ 766. PAUL MIRABRELLA

TEXAS RANGERS

- □ 29. ODELL JONES
- □ 55. FRANK TANANA
- □ 76. ALAN BANNISTER
- □ 102. TOMMY DUNBAR
- □ 149. DICKIE NOLES
- □ 171. BILL STEIN
- □ 196. PETE O'BRIEN
- □ 227. DANNY DARWIN
- □ 247. WAYNE TOLLESON
- □ 288. JEFF KUNKEL
- □ 313. DAVE SCHMIDT
- □ 337. BILLY SAMPLE
- □ 371. MICKEY RIVERS
- □ 414. GARY WARD
- □ 443. GEORGE WRIGHT
- □ 464. MIKE MASON
- □ 496. DONNIE SCOTT
- □ 519. DOUG RADER(M)
- □ 548. LARRY PARRISH
- □ 571. CHARLIE HOUGH
- □ 594. CURT WILKERSON
- □ 621. MARVIS FOLEY
- □ 648. BOB JONES
- □ 678. JOEY MCLAUGHLIN
- □ 723. DAVE STEWART
- □ 745. BUDDY BELL
- □ 777. NED YOST

TORONTO BLUE JAYS

- □ 24. JESSE BARFIELD
- □ 48. TONY FERNANDEZ
- □ 75. WILLIE UPSHAW
- □ 101. JIM ACKER
- □ 128. ERNIE WHITT
- □ 168. GARTH IORG
- □ 193. JIMMY KEY
- □ 218. DOYLE ALEXANDER
- □ 240. DAVE STIEB
- □ 311. JIM GOTT
- □ 336. RANCE MULLINIKS
- □ 361. ALFREDO GRIFFIN
- □ 411. BOBBY COX(M)
- □ 436. WILLIE AIKENS
- □ 463. DAVE COLLINS
- □ 489. BRYAN CLARK
- □ 516. ROY LEE JACKSON
- □ 545. LLOYD MOSEBY
- □ 568. CLIFF JOHNSON
- □ 593. RICK LEACH
- □ 622. LUIS LEAD
- □ 645. DAMASCO GARCIA
- □ 673. BUCK MARTINEZ
- □ 698. JORGE BELL
- □ 746. JIM CLANCY
- □ 774. DENNIS LAMP

U. S. OLYMPIC TEAM

- □ 389. ROD DEDEAUX (HC)
- □ 390. SID AKINS
- □ 391. FLAVIO ALFARO
- □ 392. DON AUGUST
- □ 393. SCOTT BANKHEAD
- □ 394. BOB CAFFREY
- □ 395. MIKE DUNNE
- □ 396. GARY GREEN
- □ 397. JOHN HOOVER
- □ 398. SHANE MACK
- □ 399. JOHN MARZANO
- □ 400. ODDIBE MCDOWELL
- □ 401. MARK MCGWIRE
- □ 402. PAT PACILLO
- □ 403. CORY SNYDER
- □ 404. BILLY SWIFT

1985 TOPPS TRADED (132) 2 1/2 X 3 1/2

ATLANTA BRAVES

- □ 20T. RICK CERONE
- □ 44T. EDDIE HAAS(M)
- □ 45T. TERRY HARPER
- □ 100T. PAUL RUNGE
- □ 115T. BRUCE SUTTER

BALTIMORE ORIOLES

- □ 1T. DON AASE
- □ 31T. KEN DIXON
- □ 70T. LEE LACY
- □ 77T. FRED LYNN
- □ 106T. LARRY SHEETS
- □ 110T. NATE SNELL
- □ 129T. EARL WEAVER(M)

BOSTON RED SOX

- □ 67T. BRUCE KISON
- □ 84T. JOHN MCNAMARA(M)

CALIFORNIA ANGELS

- □ 23T. PAT CLEMENTS
- □ 65T. RUPPERT JONES
- □ 81T. GENE MAUCH(M)
- □ 85T. DONNIE MOORE

CHICAGO CUBS

- □ 29T. BRIAN DAYETT
- □ 35T. RAY FONTENOT
- □ 111T. CHRIS SPEIER

CHICAGO WHITE SOX

- □ 8T. DARYL BOSTON
- □ 37T. OSCAR GAMBLE
- □ 43T. OZZIE GUILLEN
- □ 60T. TIM HULETT
- □ 61T. BOB JAMES
- □ 76T. TIM LOLLAR
- □ 86T. GENE NELSON
- □ 102T. LUIS SALAZAR

CINCINNATI REDS

- □ 11T. TOM BROWNING
- □ 68T. ALAN KNICELY

CLEVELAND INDIANS

- □ 3T. BENNY AYALA
- □ 21T. BRYAN CLARK
- □ 99T. VERN RUHLE
- □ 122T. RICH THOMPSON
- □ 127T. DAVE VON OHLEN

DETROIT TIGERS

- □ 91T. CHRIS PITTARO
- □ 119T. WALT TERRELL

HOUSTON ASTROS

- □ 79T. RON MATHIS

KANSAS CITY ROYALS

- □ 69T. MIKE LACOSS
- □ 109T. LONNIE SMITH
- □ 114T. JIM SUNDBERG

LOS ANGELES DODGERS

- □ 18T. BOBBY CASTILLO
- □ 32T. MARIANO DUNCAN
- □ 58T. KEN HOWELL
- □ 88T. AL OLIVER

MILWAUKEE BREWERS

- □ 5T. GEORGE BAMBERGER(M)
- □ 13T. RAY BURRIS
- □ 26T. DANNY DARWIN
- □ 39T. BOB GIBSON
- □ 53T. TEDDY HIGUERA

MINNESOTA TWINS

- □ 36T. GREG GAGNE
- □ 101T. MARK SALAS
- □ 108T. ROY SMALLEY
- □ 112T. MIKE STENHOUSE

MONTREAL EXPOS

- □ 9T. HUBIE BROOKS
- □ 34T. MIKE FITZGERALD
- □ 52T. JOE HESKETH
- □ 73T. VANCE LAW
- □ 87T. STEVE NICOSIA
- □ 94T. BERT ROBERGE
- □ 95T. BOB RODGERS(M)
- □ 128T. U.L. WASHINGTON
- □ 131T. HERM WINNINGHAM

NEW YORK METS

- □ 17T. GARY CARTER
- □ 64T. HOWARD JOHNSON
- □ 83T. ROGER MCDOWELL
- □ 103T. JOE SAMBITO

NEW YORK YANKEES

- □ 6T. DALE BERRA
- □ 7T. RICH BORDI
- □ 48T. RON HASSEY
- □ 49T. RICKEY HENDERSON
- □ 78T. BILLY MARTIN(M)
- □ 130T. EDDIE WHITSON

OAKLAND A'S

- □ 4T. DUSTY BAKER
- □ 25T. DAVE COLLINS
- □ 42T. ALFREDO GRIFFIN
- □ 50T. STEVE HENDERSON
- □ 54T. DONNIE HILL
- □ 57T. JAY HOWELL
- □ 90T. ROB PICCIOLO
- □ 116T. DON SUTTON
- □ 118T. TOM TELLMANN
- □ 120T. MICKEY TETTLETON

PHILADELPHIA PHILLIES

- □ 16T. DON CARMAN
- □ 33T. JOHN FELSKE(M)
- □ 62T. STEVE JELTZ
- □ 98T. DAVE RUCKER
- □ 104T. RICK SCHU
- □ 117T. KENT TEKULVE
- □ 121T. DERREL THOMAS

PITTSBURGH PIRATES

- □ 2T. BILL ALMON
- □ 51T. GEORGE HENDRICK
- □ 55T. AL HOLLAND
- □ 66T. STEVE KEMP
- □ 74T. JOHNNIE LEMASTER
- □ 75T. SIXTO LEZCANO
- □ 89T. JOE ORSULAK
- □ 93T. RICK REUSCHEL

ST. LOUIS CARDINALS

- □ 15T. BILL CAMPBELL
- □ 22T. JACK CLARK
- □ 24T. VINCE COLEMAN
- □ 30T. IVAN DEJESUS
- □ 124T. JOHN TUDOR

SAN DIEGO PADRES

- □ 12T. AL BUMBRY
- □ 28T. JERRY DAVIS
- □ 59T. LAMARR HOYT
- □ 96T. JERRY ROYSTER
- □ 113T. TIM STODDARD

SAN FRANCISCO GIANTS

- □ 10T. CHRIS BROWN
- □ 27T. JIM DAVENPORT(M)
- □ 38T. SCOTT GARRELTS
- □ 40T. JIM GOTT
- □ 41T. DAVID GREEN
- □ 71T. DAVE LAPOINT
- □ 123T. ALEX TREVINO
- □ 125T. JOSE URIBE

SEATTLE MARINERS

- □ 92T. JIM PRESLEY
- □ 105T. DONNIE SCOTT

TEXAS RANGERS

- □ 46T. TOBY HARRAH
- □ 47T. GREG HARRIS
- □ 56T. BURT HOOTON
- □ 63T. CLIFF JOHNSON
- □ 82T. ODDIBE MCDOWELL
- □ 97T. DAVE ROZEMA
- □ 107T. DON SLAUGHT
- □ 126T. BOBBY VALENTINE(M)

TORONTO BLUE JAYS

- □ 14T. JEFF BURROUGHS
- □ 19T. BILL CAUDILL
- □ 72T. GARY LAVELLE
- □ 80T. LEN MATUSZEK

1986 TOPPS (792)
2 1/2 X 3 1/2

ATLANTA BRAVES

- ☐ 24. LEN BARKER
- ☐ 57. BOBBY WINE(M)
- ☐ 78. BRUCE BENEDICT
- ☐ 107. RAFAEL RAMIREZ
- ☐ 129. JEFF DEDMON
- ☐ 167. ZANE SMITH
- ☐ 194. CRAIG MCMURTRY
- ☐ 220. BOB HORNER
- ☐ 247. TERRY HARPER
- ☐ 293. CHRIS CHAMBLISS
- ☐ 319. RICK CAMP
- ☐ 334. KEN OBERKFELL
- ☐ 363. TERRY FORSTER
- ☐ 409. PAUL RUNGE
- ☐ 437. RICK MAHLER
- ☐ 456. TEAM LEADER CARD
- ☐ 491. PASCUAL PEREZ
- ☐ 517. MILT THOMPSON
- ☐ 539. GLENN HUBBARD
- ☐ 557. GERALD PERRY
- ☐ 572. PAUL ZUVELLA
- ☐ 600. DALE MURPHY
- ☐ 620. BRUCE SUTTER
- ☐ 648. STEVE BEDROSIAN
- ☐ 675. CLAUDELL WASHINGTON
- ☐ 698. BRAD KOMMINSK
- ☐ 747. RICK CERONE
- ☐ 776. GENE GARBER

BALTIMORE ORIOLES

- ☐ 30. EDDIE MURRARY
- ☐ 55. FRED LYNN
- ☐ 82. TIPPY MARTINEZ
- ☐ 110. SCOTT MCGREGOR
- ☐ 147. LARRY SHEETS
- ☐ 173. WAYNE GROSS
- ☐ 198. KEN DIXON
- ☐ 226. LEE LACY
- ☐ 251. RICH DAUER
- ☐ 279. AL PARDO
- ☐ 288. DON AASE
- ☐ 309. JOHN SHELBY
- ☐ 321. EARL WEAVER(M)
- ☐ 340. CAL RIPKEN
- ☐ 358. RICK DEMPSEY
- ☐ 365. MIKE FLANAGAN
- ☐ 416. DENNY MARTINEZ
- ☐ 446. LENN SAKATA
- ☐ 469. STORM DAVIS
- ☐ 494. GARY ROENICKE
- ☐ 508. ALAN WIGGINS
- ☐ 521. NATE SNELL
- ☐ 548. MIKE YOUNG
- ☐ 575. MIKE BODDICKER
- ☐ 597. SAMMY STEWART
- ☐ 623. FLOYD RAYFORD
- ☐ 653. JIM DWYER
- ☐ 726. TEAM LEADER CARD
- ☐ 753. DAN FORD
- ☐ 781. JOE NOLAN

BOSTON RED SOX

- ☐ 11. BOB OJEDA
- ☐ 38. GLENN HOFFMAN
- ☐ 60. DWIGHT EVANS
- ☐ 91. STEVE CRAWFORD
- ☐ 117. BRUCE KISON
- ☐ 151. DAVE STAPLETON
- ☐ 181. AL NIPPER
- ☐ 233. STEVE LYONS
- ☐ 255. TONY ARMAS
- ☐ 297. TIM LOLLAR
- ☐ 307. DAVE SAX
- ☐ 320. JIM RICE
- ☐ 349. MARK CLEAR
- ☐ 375. RICH GEDMAN
- ☐ 396. TEAM LEADER CARD
- ☐ 424. RICK MILLER
- ☐ 443. BILL BUCKNER
- ☐ 477. MIKE EASLER
- ☐ 510. WADE BOGGS
- ☐ 529. MARC SULLIVAN
- ☐ 581. BRUCE HURST
- ☐ 605. DENNIS BOYD
- ☐ 633. JACKIE GUTIERREZ
- ☐ 661. ROGER CLEMENS
- ☐ 687. MIKE TRUJILLO
- ☐ 734. MARTY BARRETT
- ☐ 749. ED JURAK
- ☐ 771. JOHN MCNAMARA(M)
- ☐ 785. BOB STANLEY

CALIFORNIA ANGELS

- ☐ 42. GEOFF ZAHN
- ☐ 62. BOB BOONE
- ☐ 81. GENE MAUCH(M)
- ☐ 124. LUIS SANCHEZ
- ☐ 127. JACK HOWELL
- ☐ 140. JOHN CANDELARIA
- ☐ 155. BOB GRICH
- ☐ 179. STU CLIBURN
- ☐ 190. GEORGE HENDRICK
- ☐ 193. DARYL SCONIERS
- ☐ 222. CRAIG GERBER
- ☐ 234. DOUG CORBETT
- ☐ 257. DOUG DECINCES
- ☐ 311. DICK SCHOFIELD
- ☐ 325. JUAN BENIQUEZ
- ☐ 335. DON SUTTON
- ☐ 345. DONNIE MOORE
- ☐ 369. AL HOLLAND
- ☐ 373. URBANO LUGO
- ☐ 400. ROD CAREW
- ☐ 464. RUPPERT JONES
- ☐ 486. TEAM LEADER CARD
- ☐ 524. DARRELL MILLER
- ☐ 543. JERRY NARRON
- ☐ 579. JIM SLATON
- ☐ 604. GARY PETTIS
- ☐ 628. KIRK MCCASKILL
- ☐ 658. ROB WILFONG
- ☐ 700. REGGIE JACKSON
- ☐ 733. RON ROMANICK
- ☐ 772. BRIAN DOWNING

CHICAGO CUBS

- ☐ 19. RICH HEBNER
- ☐ 46. BILLY HATCHER
- ☐ 72. SHAWON DUNSTON
- ☐ 98. DICK RUTHVEN
- ☐ 125. DAVE LOPES
- ☐ 188. BOB DERNIER
- ☐ 212. CHRIS SPEIER
- ☐ 231. JIM FREY(M)
- ☐ 266. KEITH MORELAND
- ☐ 284. BRIAN DAYETT
- ☐ 308. RAY FONTENOT
- ☐ 330. RICK SUTCLIFFE
- ☐ 355. LEE SMITH
- ☐ 384. STEVE TROUT
- ☐ 406. SCOTT SANDERSON
- ☐ 431. GOERGE FRAZIER
- ☐ 460. LEON DURHAM
- ☐ 485. GARY MATTHEWS
- ☐ 512. THAD BOSLEY
- ☐ 538. DENNIS ECKERSLEY
- ☐ 564. WARREN BRUSSTAR
- ☐ 588. STEVE LAKE
- ☐ 611. GARY WOODS
- ☐ 636. TEAM LEADER CARD
- ☐ 669. RON CEY
- ☐ 690. RYNE SANDBERG
- ☐ 744. LARY SORENSEN
- ☐ 767. JODY DAVIS

CHICAGO WHITE SOX

- ☐ 14. JULIO CRUZ
- ☐ 64. FLOYD BANNISTER
- ☐ 103. LUIS SALAZAR
- ☐ 123. GREG WALKER
- ☐ 139. DARYL BOSTON
- ☐ 156. TEAM LEADER CARD
- ☐ 187. SCOTT FLETCHER
- ☐ 227. AL JONES
- ☐ 239. JOEL SKINNER
- ☐ 254. OZZIE GUILLEN
- ☐ 290. CARLTON FISK
- ☐ 313. JOE DESA
- ☐ 346. BRYAN LITTLE
- ☐ 364. REID NICHOLS
- ☐ 390. TOM SEAVER
- ☐ 423. DAN SPILLNER
- ☐ 447. JERRY DON GLEATON
- ☐ 467. BOB JAMES
- ☐ 493. GENE NELSON
- ☐ 531. TONY LARUSSA(M)
- ☐ 552. MARC HILL
- ☐ 574. RON KITTLE
- ☐ 612. RICHARD DOTSON
- ☐ 637. RUDY LAW
- ☐ 657. JUAN AGOSTO
- ☐ 679. BRITT BURNS
- ☐ 724. TIM HULETT
- ☐ 755. HAROLD BAINES
- ☐ 778. JERRY HAIRSTON

CINCINNATI REDS

- ☐ 1. PETE ROSE
- ☐ 28. ERIC DAVIS
- ☐ 54. JOHN FRANCO
- ☐ 85. TONY PEREZ
- ☐ 108. TED POWER
- ☐ 133. ANDY MCGAFFIGAN
- ☐ 143. DAVE VAN GORDER
- ☐ 176. JAY TIBBS
- ☐ 195. DAVE CONCEPCION
- ☐ 253. DANN BILARDELLO
- ☐ 285. BUDDY BELL
- ☐ 314. FRANK PASTORE
- ☐ 342. GARY REDUS
- ☐ 366. TEAM LEADER CARD
- ☐ 428. MAX VENABLE
- ☐ 442. RON ROBINSON
- ☐ 497. JOHN STUPER
- ☐ 523. JOE PRICE
- ☐ 544. EDDIE MILNER
- ☐ 573. TOM HUME
- ☐ 595. DAVE PARKER
- ☐ 627. RON OESTER
- ☐ 639. BO DIAZ
- ☐ 652. TOM BROWNING
- ☐ 677. NICK ESASKY
- ☐ 725. MARIO SOTO
- ☐ 741. PETE ROSE(M)
- ☐ 777. WAYNE KRENCHICKI

CLEVELAND INDIANS

- ☐ 9. ROY SMITH
- ☐ 31. JAMIE EASTERLY
- ☐ 59. ANDRE THORNTON
- ☐ 86. TOM WADDELL
- ☐ 116. BROOK JACOBY
- ☐ 136. MIKE HARGROVE
- ☐ 149. BRETT BUTLER
- ☐ 172. JERRY REED
- ☐ 208. RAMON ROMERO
- ☐ 242. RICH THOMPSON
- ☐ 273. JERRY WILLARD
- ☐ 283. MIKE FISCHLIN
- ☐ 303. CURT WARDLE
- ☐ 336. TEAM LEADER CARD
- ☐ 354. TONY BERNAZARD
- ☐ 377. JOE CARTER
- ☐ 391. JULIO FRANCO
- ☐ 483. GEORGE VUKOVICH
- ☐ 509. ERNIE CAMACHO
- ☐ 542. DON SCHULZE

☐ 567. JEFF BARKLEY
☐ 594. CHRIS BANDO
☐ 632. DAVE VON OHLEN
☐ 647. MEL HALL
☐ 674. PAT TABLER
☐ 699. PAT CORRALES(M)
☐ 768. VERN RUHLE

DETROIT TIGERS

☐ 20. LOU WHITAKER
☐ 36. TEAM LEADER CARD
☐ 47. JUAN BERENGUER
☐ 73. RANDY O NEAL
☐ 101. DAVE BERGMAN
☐ 121. NELSON SIMMONS
☐ 130. ALAN TRAMMELL
☐ 160. CHET LEMON
☐ 192. MILT WILCOX
☐ 217. BILL SCHERRER
☐ 243. JOHNNY GRUBB
☐ 270. JACK MORRIS
☐ 295. KIRK GIVSON
☐ 367. AURELIO LOPEZ
☐ 393. CHRIS PITTARO
☐ 411. SPARKY ANDERSON(M)
☐ 436. DOUG FLYNN
☐ 461. WALT TERRELL
☐ 479. BOB MELVIN
☐ 515. DARRELL EVANS
☐ 540. DAN PETRY
☐ 563. ALEJANDRO SANCHEZ
☐ 592. FRANK TANANA
☐ 609. BARBARO GARBEY
☐ 643. TOM BROOKENS
☐ 670. WILLIE HERNANDEZ
☐ 688. LARRY HERNDON
☐ 740. LANCE PARRISH
☐ 788. MARTY CASTILLO

HOUSTON ASTROS

☐ 26. FRANK DIPINO
☐ 57. BILL DORAN
☐ 83. PHIL GARNER
☐ 100. NOLAN RYAN
☐ 166. DICKIE THON
☐ 186. TEAM LEADER CARD
☐ 268. MIKE SCOTT
☐ 272. TIM TOLMAN
☐ 282. JERRY MUMPHREY
☐ 298. CRAIG REYNOLDS
☐ 331. ALAN ASHBY
☐ 352. HARRY SPILMAN
☐ 376. BILL DAWLEY
☐ 389. GLENN DAVIS
☐ 408. DAVE SMITH
☐ 432. MARK BAILEY
☐ 458. KEVIN BASS
☐ 476. RON MATHIS
☐ 504. DENNY WALLING
☐ 534. JEFF CALHOUN
☐ 561. BOB LILLIS(M)
☐ 590. BOB KNEPPER
☐ 618. JIM PANKOVITS
☐ 640. JOSE CRUZ
☐ 691. MIKE MADDEN
☐ 763. TERRY PUHL

KANSAS CITY ROYALS

☐ 25. WILLIE WILSON
☐ 50. DAN QUISENBERRY
☐ 77. CHARLIE LEIBRANDT
☐ 99. BUDDY BIANCALANA
☐ 128. JOHN WATHAN
☐ 164. STEVE BALBONI
☐ 199. DICK HOWSER(M)
☐ 215. FRANK WHITE
☐ 245. JIM SUNDBERG
☐ 269. DANE IORG
☐ 300. GEORGE BRETT
☐ 332. DARRYL MOTLEY
☐ 359. MIKE LACOSS
☐ 415. HAL MCRAE
☐ 487. BRET SABERHAGEN
☐ 514. MIKE JONES
☐ 541. JORGE ORTA
☐ 562. JOE BECKWITH
☐ 596. ONIX CONCEPCION
☐ 606. TEAM LEADER CARD

☐ 617. LONNIE SMITH
☐ 644. MARK GUBICZA
☐ 671. LYNN JONES
☐ 697. BUD BLACK
☐ 743. PAT SHERIDAN
☐ 773. GREG PRYOR

LOS ANGELES DODGERS

☐ 32. STEVE YEAGER
☐ 56. TOM NIEDENFUER
☐ 87. CANDY MALDONADO
☐ 109. LEN MATUSZEK
☐ 145. PEDRO GUERRERO
☐ 159. OREL HERSHISER
☐ 175. STEVE SAX
☐ 197. ENOS CABELL
☐ 252. BOBBY CASTILLO
☐ 291. TOM LASORDA(M)
☐ 318. TERRY WHITFIELD
☐ 343. CARLOS DIAZ
☐ 368. GREG BROCK
☐ 439. RICK HONEYCUTT
☐ 468. MIKE SCIOSCIA
☐ 470. BILL MADLOCK
☐ 496. JAY JOHNSTONE
☐ 506. BILL RUSSELL
☐ 522. BOB BAILOR
☐ 549. BOB WELCH
☐ 577. JERRY REUSS
☐ 602. MARIANO DUNCAN
☐ 630. FERNANDO VALENZUELA
☐ 654. KEN HOWELL
☐ 665. ALEJANDRO PENA
☐ 696. TEAM LEADER CARD
☐ 728. MIKE MARSHALL
☐ 758. DAVE ANDERSON
☐ 782. KEN LANDREAUX

MILWAUKEE BREWERS

☐ 21. GEORGE BAMBERGER(M)
☐ 49. RICK MANNING
☐ 76. DION JAMES
☐ 106. RAY BURRIS
☐ 137. CHARLIE MOORE
☐ 163. PETE LADD
☐ 185. ROLLIE FINGERS
☐ 209. RANDY READY
☐ 237. TED SIMMONS
☐ 267. PAUL MOLITOR
☐ 277. JAIME COCANOWER
☐ 292. CHUCK PORTER
☐ 317. ED ROMERO
☐ 347. TEDDY HIGUERA
☐ 372. BEN OGLIVIE
☐ 385. CECIL COOPER
☐ 398. EARNIE RILES
☐ 426. TEAM LEADER CARD
☐ 452. BOB CLARK
☐ 473. MARK BROUHARD
☐ 499. BOB GIBSON
☐ 519. DANNY DARWIN
☐ 554. PAUL HOUSEHOLDER
☐ 582. JIM GANTNER
☐ 614. RICK WAITS
☐ 642. RAY SEARAGE
☐ 662. BILL SCHROEDER
☐ 684. BOB MCCLURE
☐ 737. PETE VUCKOVICH
☐ 759. MOOSE HAAS
☐ 780. ROBIN YOUNT

MINNESOTA TWINS

☐ 17. MIKE STENHOUSE
☐ 43. DAVE ENGLE
☐ 71. KEN SCHROM
☐ 97. GARY GAETTI
☐ 122. PETE FILSON
☐ 162. GREG GAGNE
☐ 184. TIM LAUDNER
☐ 214. RANDY BUSH
☐ 236. FRANK EUFEMIA
☐ 265. RON DAVIS
☐ 329. KIRBY PUCKETT
☐ 356. MICKEY HATCHER
☐ 381. RAY MILLER(M)
☐ 430. KENT HRBEK
☐ 445. BERT BLYLEVEN

☐ 451. MARK BROWN
☐ 482. RICK LYSANDER
☐ 513. RON WASHINGTON
☐ 537. MARK SALAS
☐ 565. TOM BRUNANSKY
☐ 613. ROY SMALLEY
☐ 638. JOHN BUTCHER
☐ 667. TIM TEUFEL
☐ 695. MIKE SMITHSON
☐ 742. FRANK VIOLA
☐ 786. TEAM LEADER CARD

MONTREAL EXPOS

☐ 35. JEFF REARDON
☐ 89. RANDY ST. CLAIRE
☐ 93. SCOT THOMPSON
☐ 113. U.L. WASHINGTON
☐ 132. RAZOR SHINES
☐ 154. BERT ROBERGE
☐ 141. BOB RODGERS(M)
☐ 229. BILL GULLICKSON
☐ 258. TIM BURKE
☐ 280. TIM RAINES
☐ 299. BRYN SMITH
☐ 324. DAN SCHATZEDER
☐ 344. JIM WOHLFORD
☐ 374. TERRY FRANCONA
☐ 407. SAL BUTERA
☐ 421. DAVE PALMER
☐ 448. HERM WINNINGHAM
☐ 472. JOE HESKETH
☐ 503. MIKE FITZGERALD
☐ 526. CHARLIE LEA
☐ 555. HUBIE BROOKS
☐ 576. TEAM LEADER CARD
☐ 601. GARY LUCAS
☐ 603. BILL LASKEY
☐ 629. MITCH WEBSTER
☐ 685. TIM WALLACH
☐ 732. FLOYD YOUMANS
☐ 760. ANDRE DAWSON
☐ 787. VANCE LAW

NEW YORK METS

☐ 18. BRENT GAFF
☐ 27. RAY KNIGHT
☐ 53. LEN DYKSTRA
☐ 68. ED LYNCH
☐ 80. DARRYL STRAWBERRY
☐ 104. SID FERNANDEZ
☐ 126. TEAM LEADER CARD
☐ 144. DOUG SISK
☐ 170. GARY CARTER
☐ 191. WALLY BACKMAN
☐ 210. CALVIN SCHIRALDI
☐ 225. RON DARLING
☐ 250. DWIGHT GOODEN
☐ 274. RON GARDENHIRE
☐ 287. JOHN CHRISTENSEN
☐ 315. MOOKIE WILSON
☐ 339. BRUCE BERENYI
☐ 362. TOM PACIOREK
☐ 414. TOM GORMAN
☐ 438. CLINT HURDLE
☐ 465. JESSE OROSCO
☐ 492. KELVIN CHAPMAN
☐ 501. DAVE JOHNSON(M)
☐ 520. KEITH HERNANDEZ
☐ 547. ROGER MCDOWELL

☐ 570. RUSTY STAUB
☐ 587. RAFAEL SANTANA
☐ 599. RICK AGUILERA
☐ 619. DANNY HEEP
☐ 649. RONN REYNOLDS
☐ 680. GEORGE FOSTER
☐ 751. HOWARD JOHNSON
☐ 774. TERRY LEACH

NEW YORK YANKEES

☐ 15. EDDIE WHITSON
☐ 40. KEN GRIFFEY
☐ 70. DAVE WINFIELD
☐ 94. RICH BORDI
☐ 135. JOE NIEKRO
☐ 157. RON HASSEY
☐ 180. DON MATTINGLY
☐ 213. BOB SHIRLEY
☐ 235. BUTCH WYNEGAR
☐ 259. DAN PASQUA
☐ 276. TEAM LEADER CARD
☐ 301. DENNIS RASMUSSEN
☐ 327. MIKE PAGLIARULO
☐ 379. BOBBY MEACHAM
☐ 427. JOE COWLEY
☐ 449. ROD SCURRY
☐ 455. WILLIE RANDOLPH
☐ 481. SCOTT BRADLEY
☐ 500. RICKEY HENDERSON
☐ 533. BILLY SAMPLE
☐ 560. DAVE RIGHETTI
☐ 584. BRIAN FISHER
☐ 610. RON GUIDRY
☐ 651. BILLY MARTIN(M)
☐ 663. NEIL ALLEN
☐ 692. DALE BERRA
☐ 723. MARTY BYSTROM
☐ 738. ANDRE ROBERTSON
☐ 765. DON BAYLOR
☐ 790. PHIL NIEKRO

OAKLAND A'S

☐ 8. DWAYNE MURPHY
☐ 29. TONY PHILLIPS
☐ 58. BILL KRUEGER
☐ 84. CURT YOUNG
☐ 115. JAY HOWELL
☐ 134. CARNEY LANSFORD
☐ 148. MIKE HEATH
☐ 165. MIKE DAVIS
☐ 216. TEAM LEADER CARD
☐ 240. TOMMY JOHN
☐ 271. DAVE COLLINS
☐ 281. STEVE MURA
☐ 304. MIKE GALLEGO
☐ 353. KEITH ATHERTON
☐ 378. BRUCE BOCHTE
☐ 410. DAVE KINGMAN
☐ 433. CHRIS CODIROLI
☐ 457. MICKEY TETTLETON
☐ 484. DONNIE HILL
☐ 507. STEVE ONTIVEROS
☐ 536. JOE RIJO
☐ 566. ALFREDO GRIFFIN
☐ 591. JACKIE MOORE
☐ 624. STEVE MCCATTY
☐ 645. DUSTY BAKER
☐ 672. ROB PICCIOLO
☐ 693. TOM TELLMAN
☐ 748. STEVE HENDERSON
☐ 766. RICK LANGFORD

PHILADELPHIA PHILLIES

☐ 16. RICK SCHU
☐ 39. DAVE RUCKER
☐ 69. LUIS AGUAYO
☐ 95. OZZIE VIRGIL
☐ 120. STEVE CARLTON
☐ 158. DERREL THOMAS
☐ 183. LARRY ANDERSEN
☐ 200. MIKE SCHMIDT
☐ 246. TEAM LEADER CARD
☐ 264. DARREN DAULTON
☐ 302. GREG GROSS
☐ 326. KENT TEKULVE
☐ 361. SHANE RAWLEY
☐ 392. JOHN RUSSELL
☐ 418. ALAN KNICELY
☐ 420. VON HAYES
☐ 453. STEVE JELTZ
☐ 466. TOM FOLEY
☐ 475. JUAN SAMUEL
☐ 505. JERRY KOOSMAN
☐ 532. DON CARMAN
☐ 556. JOHN DENNY
☐ 585. GARRY MADDOX
☐ 621. JOHN FELSKE(M)
☐ 664. TIM CORCORAN
☐ 686. JEFF STONE
☐ 689. DAVE STEWART
☐ 736. GLENN WILSON
☐ 764. KEVIN GROSS
☐ 792. CHARLES HUDSON

PITTSBURGH PIRATES

☐ 48. BILL ALMON
☐ 75. JOSE DELEON
☐ 102. JOE ORSULAK
☐ 114. MIKE BROWN
☐ 161. LEE TUNNELL
☐ 232. RICK RHODEN
☐ 260. TONY PENA
☐ 278. SIXTO LEZCANO
☐ 289. JOHNNIE LEMASTER
☐ 316. SAMMY KHALIFA
☐ 351. CHUCK TANNER(M)
☐ 387. STEVE KEMP
☐ 417. R.J. REYNOLDS
☐ 425. LARRY MCWILLIAMS
☐ 489. JIM WINN
☐ 525. MARVELL WYNNE
☐ 553. JIM MORRISON
☐ 578. LEE MAZZILLI
☐ 589. SID BREAM
☐ 615. JOHNNY RAY
☐ 635. JASON THOMPSON
☐ 668. CECILIO GUANTE
☐ 682. JUNIOR ORTIZ
☐ 731. DON ROBINSON
☐ 746. DENNY GONZALEZ
☐ 754. PAT CLEMENTS
☐ 756. TEAM LEADER CARD
☐ 779. RICK REUSCHEL

ST. LOUIS CARDINALS

☐ 33. JEFF LAHTI
☐ 66. TEAM LEADER CARD
☐ 88. TOM NIETO
☐ 112. BILL CAMPBELL
☐ 150. JOAQUIN ANDUJAR
☐ 178. IVAN DEJESUS
☐ 218. RANDY HUNT
☐ 224. CESAR CEDENO
☐ 228. TOM LAWLESS
☐ 256. KURT KEPSHIRE
☐ 294. DANNY COX
☐ 322. BOB FORSCH
☐ 350. JACK CLARK
☐ 370. VINCE COLEMAN
☐ 422. MIKE JORGENSEN
☐ 441. WHITEY HERZOG(M)
☐ 474. JOHN TUDOR
☐ 498. TITO LANDRUM
☐ 528. TERRY PENDLETON
☐ 550. TOM HERR
☐ 580. WILLIE MCGEE
☐ 607. KEN DAYLEY
☐ 631. STEVE BRAUN
☐ 656. BRIAN HARPER
☐ 683. ANDY VAN SLYKE
☐ 730. OZZIE SMITH
☐ 757. DARRELL PORTER
☐ 783. RICKY HORTON

SAN DIEGO PADRES

☐ 10. TONY GWYNN
☐ 37. MARK THURMOND
☐ 44. LANCE MCCULLERS
☐ 67. CARMELO MARTINEZ
☐ 90. GARRY TEMPLETON
☐ 118. JERRY ROYSTER
☐ 182. BOBBY BROWN
☐ 211. ED WOJNA
☐ 230. TERRY KENNEDY
☐ 244. CRAIG LEFFERTS
☐ 262. MARIO RAMIREZ
☐ 286. LUIS DELEON
☐ 306. TEAM LEADER CARD
☐ 323. JERRY DAVIS
☐ 380. LAMARR HOYT
☐ 413. TIM FLANNERY
☐ 429. GREG BOOKER
☐ 450. GRAIG NETTLES
☐ 478. ANDY HAWKINS
☐ 530. RICH GOSSAGE
☐ 558. TIM STODDARD
☐ 583. AL BUMBRY
☐ 608. BRUCE BOCHY
☐ 634. ROY LEE JACKSON
☐ 660. STEVE GARVEY
☐ 681. DICK WILLIAMS(M)
☐ 735. DAVE DRAVECKY
☐ 762. ERIC SHOW
☐ 789. KURT BEVACQUA

SAN FRANCISCO GIANTS

☐ 12. JOSE URIBE
☐ 41. BRAD WELLMAN
☐ 63. RON ROENICKE
☐ 65. DAN DRIESSEN
☐ 111. ROGER CRAIG(M)
☐ 138. MARK DAVIS
☐ 153. RICKY ADAMS
☐ 177. JOEL YOUNGBLOOD
☐ 223. ATLEE HAMMAKER
☐ 249. ROB DEER
☐ 310. GREG MINTON
☐ 341. FRANK WILLIAMS
☐ 383. CHRIS BROWN
☐ 395. SCOTT GARRELTS
☐ 444. ALEX TREVINO
☐ 463. JIM GOTT
☐ 490. JEFF LEONARD
☐ 516. TEAM LEADER CARD
☐ 551. DAVE LAPOINT
☐ 571. MIKE JEFFCOAT
☐ 625. BOB BRENLY
☐ 655. MANNY TRILLO
☐ 678. DAN GLADDEN
☐ 727. DAVID GREEN
☐ 752. MIKE KRUKOW
☐ 770. VIDA BLUE

SEATTLE MARINERS

☐ 13. BOB KEARNEY
☐ 34. KEN PHELPS
☐ 61. KARL BEST
☐ 92. AL COWENS
☐ 119. BARRY BONNELL
☐ 141. CHUCK COTTIER(M)
☐ 146. JACK PERCONTE
☐ 152. MIKE MORGAN
☐ 174. BRIAN SNYDER
☐ 221. DAVE HENDERSON
☐ 248. SPIKE OWEN
☐ 305. PHIL BRADLEY
☐ 337. DARNELL COLES
☐ 357. ED VANDEBERG
☐ 382. IVAN CALDERON
☐ 399. BILL SWIFT
☐ 419. FRANK WILLS
☐ 440. ALVIN DAVIS
☐ 462. DOMINGO RAMOS
☐ 495. MARK LANGSTON

- ☐ 511. ED NUNEZ
- ☐ 546. TEAM LEADER CARD
- ☐ 568. DONNIE SCOTT
- ☐ 598. JIM PRESLEY
- ☐ 626. ROY THOMAS
- ☐ 646. MIKE MOORE
- ☐ 676. MATT YOUNG
- ☐ 729. JIM BEATTIE
- ☐ 750. GORMAN THOMAS
- ☐ 769. HAROLD REYNOLDS

TEXAS RANGERS

- ☐ 22. DUANE WALKER
- ☐ 52. CHRIS WELSH
- ☐ 79. DAVE SCHMIDT
- ☐ 105. GARY WARD
- ☐ 142. BOB JONES
- ☐ 169. GEORGE WRIGHT
- ☐ 189. MIKE MASON
- ☐ 238. LARRY PARRISH
- ☐ 261. BOBBY VALENTINE(M)
- ☐ 275. CHARLIE HOUGH
- ☐ 296. GENO PETRALLI
- ☐ 328. PETE O'BRIAN
- ☐ 371. BILL STEIN
- ☐ 388. DICKIE NOLES
- ☐ 397. STEVE BUECHELE
- ☐ 434. CURT WILKERSON
- ☐ 454. BURT HOOTON
- ☐ 480. ODDIBE MCDOWELL
- ☐ 502. GLEN COOK
- ☐ 535. TOBY HARRAH
- ☐ 559. TOMMY DUNBAR
- ☐ 586. GREG HARRIS
- ☐ 616. GLENN BRUMMER
- ☐ 641. WAYNE TOLLESON
- ☐ 666. TEAM LEADER CARD
- ☐ 739. DAVE ROZEMA
- ☐ 761. DON SLAUGHT
- ☐ 784. ALAN BANNISTER

TORONTO BLUE JAYS

- ☐ 23. MANNY LEE
- ☐ 45. DAMASO GARCIA
- ☐ 74. RANCE MULLINIKS
- ☐ 96. TEAM LEADER CARD
- ☐ 168. JEFF BURROUGHS
- ☐ 196. DOYLE ALEXANDER
- ☐ 219. DENNIS LAMP
- ☐ 241. TONY FERNANDEZ
- ☐ 312. TOM FILER
- ☐ 333. TOM HENKE
- ☐ 338. JORGE BELL
- ☐ 348. CLIFF JOHNSON
- ☐ 360. LLOYD MOSEBY
- ☐ 386. CECIL FIELDER
- ☐ 412. JIM CLANCY
- ☐ 435. BILL CAUDILL
- ☐ 459. LUIS LEAL
- ☐ 471. BOBBY COX(M)
- ☐ 488. LOU THORNTON
- ☐ 518. BUCK MARTINEZ
- ☐ 545. JIMMY KEY
- ☐ 569. JIM ACKER
- ☐ 593. JESSE BARFIELD
- ☐ 622. GARY LAVELLE
- ☐ 650. DAVE STIEB
- ☐ 673. ERNIE WHITT
- ☐ 694. GARTH IORG
- ☐ 745. WILLIE UPSHAW
- ☐ 775. AL OLIVER

1986 TOPPS TRADED (132) 2 1/2 X 3 1/2

ATLANTA BRAVES

- ☐ 4T. PAUL ASSENMACHER
- ☐ 41T. KEN GRIFFEY
- ☐ 75T. OMAR MORENO
- ☐ 84T. DAVE PALMER
- ☐ 98T. BILLY SAMPLE
- ☐ 102T. TED SIMMONS
- ☐ 107T. CHUCK TANNER(M)
- ☐ 111T. ANDRES THOMAS
- ☐ 119T. OZZIE VIRGIL

BALTIMORE ORIOLES

- ☐ 8T. JUAN BENIQUEZ
- ☐ 13T. JUAN BONILLA
- ☐ 14T. RICH BORDI

BOSTON RED SOX

- ☐ 6T. DON BAYLOR
- ☐ 89T. REY QUINONES
- ☐ 95T. ED ROMERO
- ☐ 97T. JOE SAMBITO
- ☐ 101T. TOM SEAVER
- ☐ 103T. SAMMY STEWART

CALIFORNIA ANGELS

- ☐ 16T. RICK BURLESON
- ☐ 37T. TERRY FORSTER
- ☐ 51T. WALLY JOYNER

CHICAGO CUBS

- ☐ 38T. TERRY FRANCONA
- ☐ 73T. GENE MICHAEL(M)
- ☐ 76T. JERRY MUMPHREY
- ☐ 117T. MANNY TRILLO

CHICAGO WHITE SOX

- ☐ 2T. NEIL ALLEN
- ☐ 12T. BOBBY BONILLA
- ☐ 19T. JOHN CANGELOSI
- ☐ 29T. JOE COWLEY
- ☐ 30T. JOEL DAVIS
- ☐ 39T. JIM FREGOSI(M)
- ☐ 67T. STEVE LYONS
- ☐ 99T. DAVE SCHMIDT
- ☐ 115T. WAYNE TOLLESON

CINCINNATI REDS

- ☐ 32T. JOHN DENNY
- ☐ 42T. BILL GULLICKSON
- ☐ 104T. KURT STILLWELL

CLEVELAND INDIANS

- ☐ 1T. ANDY ALLANSON
- ☐ 5T. SCOTT BAILES
- ☐ 18T. TOM CANDIOTTI
- ☐ 21T. CARMEN CASTILLO
- ☐ 77T. PHIL NIEKRO
- ☐ 80T. OTIS NIXON
- ☐ 100T. KEN SCHROM

DETROIT TIGERS

- ☐ 17T. BILL CAMBELL
- ☐ 26T. DARNELL COLES
- ☐ 27T. DAVE COLLINS
- ☐ 53T. ERIC KING
- ☐ 59T. MIKE LAGA
- ☐ 61T. DAVE LAPOINT

HOUSTON ASTROS

- ☐ 45T. BILLY HATCHER
- ☐ 52T. CHARLIE KERFELD
- ☐ 60T. HAL LANIER(M)

KANSAS CITY ROYALS

- ☐ 35T. STEVE FARR
- ☐ 50T. BO JACKSON
- ☐ 62T. RUDY LAW
- ☐ 65T. DENNIS LEONARD
- ☐ 96T. ARGENIS SALAZAR

LOS ANGELES DODGERS

- ☐ 105T. FRANKLIN STUBBS
- ☐ 116T. ALEX TREVINO
- ☐ 118T. ED VANDEBERG

MILWAUKEE BREWERS

- ☐ 22T. RICK CERONE
- ☐ 25T. MARK CLEAR
- ☐ 31T. ROB DEER
- ☐ 64T. TIM LEARY
- ☐ 79T. JUAN NIEVES
- ☐ 87T. DAN PLESAC
- ☐ 92T. BILL JO ROBIDOUX
- ☐ 106T. DALE SVEUM
- ☐ 123T. BILL WEGMAN

MINNESOTA TWINS

- ☐ 85T. FRANK PASTORE

MONTREAL EXPOS

- ☐ 40T. ANDRES GALARRAGA
- ☐ 55T. WAYNE KRENCHICKI
- ☐ 71T. BOB MCCLURE
- ☐ 72T. ANDY MCGAFFIGAN
- ☐ 114T. JAY TIBBS
- ☐ 128T. GEORGE WRIGHT

NEW YORK METS

- ☐ 74T. KEVIN MITCHELL
- ☐ 78T. RANDY NIEMANN
- ☐ 81T. BOB OJEDA
- ☐ 109T. TIM TEUFEL

NEW YORK YANKEES

- ☐ 33T. MIKE EASLER
- ☐ 86T. LOU PINIELLA
- ☐ 94T. GARY ROENICKE
- ☐ 110T. BOB TEWKSBURY
- ☐ 131T. PAUL ZUVELLA
- ☐ 122T. CLAUDELL WASHINGTON

OAKLAND A'S

- □ 3T. JOAQUIN ANDUJAR
- □ 20T. JOSE CANSECO
- □ 44T. MOOSE HAAS

PHILADELPHIA PHILLIES

- □ 7T. STEVE BEDROSIAN
- □ 47T. TOM HUME
- □ 90T. GARY REDUS
- □ 112T. MILT THOMPSON

PITTSBURGH PIRATES

- □ 10T. MIKE BIELECKI
- □ 11T. BARRY BONDS
- □ 54T. BOB KNIPPER
- □ 66T. JIM LEYLAND(M)
- □ 120T. BOB WALK

ST. LOUIS CARDINALS

- □ 28T. TIM CONROY
- □ 46T. MIKE HEATH
- □ 82T. JOSE OQUENDO
- □ 127T. TODD WORRELL

SAN DIEGO PADRES

- □ 15T. STEVE BOROS(M)
- □ 49T. DANE IORG
- □ 56T. JOHN KRUK
- □ 91T. BIP ROBERTS
- □ 121T. GENE WALTERS

SAN FRANCISCO GIANTS

- □ 9T. JUAN BERENGUER
- □ 24T. WILL CLARK
- □ 57T. MIKE LACOSS
- □ 69T. CANDY MALDONADO
- □ 70T. ROGER MASON
- □ 93T. JEFF ROBINSON
- □ 113T. ROBBY THOMPSON

SEATTLE MARINERS

- □ 58T. PETE LADD
- □ 108T. DANNY TARTABULL
- □ 124T. DICK WILLIAMS(M)
- □ 130T. STEVE YEAGER

TEXAS RANGERS

- □ 36T. SCOTT FLETCHER
- □ 43T. JOSE GUZMAN
- □ 48T. PETE INCAVIGLIA
- □ 68T. MICKEY MAHLER
- □ 83T. TOM PACIOREK
- □ 88T. DARRELL PORTER
- □ 125T. MITCH WILLIAMS
- □ 126T. BOBBY WITT
- □ 129T. RICKY WRIGHT

TORONTO BLUE JAYS

- □ 23T. JOHN CERUTTI
- □ 34T. MARK EICHHORN
- □ 63T. RICK LEACH

1987 TOPPS (792)
2 1/2 X 3 1/2

ATLANTA BRAVES

- □ 31. TEAM LEADER CARD
- □ 49. TERRY HARPER
- □ 76. RAFAEL RAMIREZ
- □ 104. BILLY SAMPLE
- □ 132. PAUL ASSENMACHER
- □ 159. ED OLWINE
- □ 186. BRUCE BENEDICT
- □ 214. OMAR MORENO
- □ 242. RICH MAHLER
- □ 269. CLIFF SPECK
- □ 296. ANDRES THOMAS
- □ 324. DAVE PALMER
- □ 351. GENE GARBER
- □ 373. JEFF DEDMON
- □ 407. JIM ACKER
- □ 435. BRUCE SUTTER
- □ 461. CRAIG MCMURTRY
- □ 490. DALE MURPHY
- □ 516. TED SIMMONS
- □ 544. ZANE SMITH
- □ 571. OZZIE VIRGIL
- □ 593. CHUCK TANNER(M)
- □ 627. KEN OBERKFELL
- □ 639. GERALD PERRY
- □ 660. BOB HORNER
- □ 686. DOYLE ALEXANDER
- □ 711. KEN GRIFFEY
- □ 745. GLENN HUBBARD
- □ 777. CHRIS CHAMBLISS

BALTIMORE ORIOLES

- □ 28. RICK DEMPSEY
- □ 86. NATE SNELL
- □ 120. EDDIE MURRAY
- □ 154. TOM O'MALLEY
- □ 182. LEE LACY
- □ 208. JOHN SHELBY
- □ 246. JIM DWYER
- □ 276. JACKIE GUTIERREZ
- □ 309. MIKE YOUNG
- □ 349. STORM DAVIS
- □ 370. FRED LYNN
- □ 398. BRAD HAVENS
- □ 426. FLOYD RAYFORD
- □ 455. MIKE BODDICKER
- □ 484. JIM TRABER
- □ 506. TEAM LEADER CARD
- □ 528. KEN DIXON
- □ 552. LARRY SHEETS
- □ 563. JOHN STEFERO
- □ 568. EARL WEAVER(M)
- □ 638. RICH BORDI
- □ 668. JUAN BONILLA
- □ 688. JUAN BENIQUEZ
- □ 708. SCOTT MCGREGOR
- □ 728. TIPPY MARTINEZ
- □ 748. MIKE FLANAGAN
- □ 766. DON AASE
- □ 784. CAL RIPKEN

BOSTON RED SOX

- □ 12. JEFF SELLERS
- □ 39. MARTY BARRETT
- □ 66. MARC SULLIVAN
- □ 94. CALVIN SCHIRALDI
- □ 121. KEVIN ROMINE
- □ 150. WADE BOGGS
- □ 175. BOB STANLEY
- □ 204. SAMMY STEWART
- □ 230. DON BAYLOR
- □ 259. MIKE GREENWELL
- □ 285. DENNIS BOYD
- □ 306. TEAM LEADER CARD
- □ 340. ROGER CLEMENS
- □ 368. JOHN MCNAMARA(M)
- □ 374. GLENN HOFFMAN
- □ 396. TIM LOLLAR
- □ 425. TOM SEAVER
- □ 449. PAT DODSON
- □ 451. JOE SAMBITO
- □ 452. DAVE HENDERSON
- □ 480. JIM RICE
- □ 507. DAVE STAPLETON
- □ 535. TONY ARMAS
- □ 589. STEVE CRAWFORD
- □ 591. SPIKE OWEN
- □ 617. AL NIPPER
- □ 632. ROB WOODWARD
- □ 645. DWIGHT EVANS
- □ 675. ED ROMERO
- □ 705. BRUCE HURST
- □ 740. RICH GEDMAN
- □ 764. BILL BUCKNER

CALIFORNIA ANGELS

- □ 22. DOUG DECINCES
- □ 53. RUPPERT JONES
- □ 80. WALLY JOYNER
- □ 92. URBANO LUGO
- □ 115. DONNIE MOORE
- □ 136. RON ROMANICK
- □ 139. DEVON WHITE
- □ 166. BOB BOONE
- □ 194. KIRK MCCASKILL
- □ 221. VERN RUHLE
- □ 251. ROB WILFONG
- □ 278. GARY PETTIS
- □ 300. REGGIE JACKSON
- □ 337. DARRELL MILLER
- □ 359. DOUG CORBETT
- □ 387. T.R. BRYDEN
- □ 422. JACK HOWELL
- □ 446. CHUCK FINLEY
- □ 474. JERRY NARRON
- □ 502. DICK SCHOFIELD
- □ 518. GENE MAUCH(M)
- □ 556. TEAM LEADER CARD
- □ 579. RICK BURLESON
- □ 630. JOHN CANDELARIA
- □ 652. TERRY FORSTER
- □ 673. DON SUTTON
- □ 677. BOB GRICH
- □ 696. GARY LUCAS
- □ 725. GEORGE HENDRICK
- □ 760. MIKE WITT
- □ 782. BRIAN DOWNING

CHICAGO CUBS

- □ 23. LEE SMITH
- □ 43. GENE MICHAEL(M)
- □ 58. THAD BOSLEY
- □ 142. RICK SUTCLIFFE
- □ 177. KEITH MORELAND
- □ 227. JAMIE MOYER
- □ 270. JODY DAVIS
- □ 290. LEON DURHAM
- □ 346. SHAWON DUNSTON
- □ 369. BRIAN DAYETT
- □ 372. JERRY MUMPHREY
- □ 383. RON DAVIS
- □ 390. GARY MATTHEWS
- □ 424. CHRIS SPEIER
- □ 459. DENNIS ECKERSLEY
- □ 487. DAVE GUMPERT
- □ 534. SCOTT SANDERSON
- □ 581. TEAM LEADER CARD
- □ 634. RAFAEL PALMEIRO
- □ 662. FRANK DIPINO
- □ 680. RYNE SANDBERG
- □ 695. CHICO WALKER
- □ 697. ED LYNCH
- □ 715. BOB DERNIER
- □ 732. MANNY TRILLO
- □ 750. STEVE TROUT
- □ 767. RON CEY
- □ 785. TERRY FRANCONA

CHICAGO WHITE SOX

- □ 27. JOE COWLEY
- □ 54. BILL DAWLEY
- □ 61. BOBBY THIGPEN
- □ 89. OZZIE GUILLEN
- □ 113. NEIL ALLEN
- □ 149. RAY SEARAGE
- □ 201. JOHN CANGELOSI
- □ 233. RUSS MORMAN
- □ 273. GENE NELSON
- □ 299. JOEL DAVIS
- □ 318. JIM FREGOSI(M)
- □ 342. BOB JAMES
- □ 356. TEAM LEADER CARD
- □ 397. GREG WALKER
- □ 421. JOSE DELEON
- □ 454. LUIS SALAZAR
- □ 482. DARYL BOSTON
- □ 491. RON KARKOVICE
- □ 511. STEVE LYONS
- □ 539. REID NICHOLS
- □ 566. TIM HULETT
- □ 667. RON HASSEY
- □ 685. JERRY HAIRSTON
- □ 703. DAVE SCHMIDT
- □ 718. STEVE CARLTON
- □ 720. RICHARD DOTSON
- □ 737. FLOYD BANNISTER
- □ 756. CARLTON FISK
- □ 772. HAROLD BAINES
- □ 790. JULIO CRUZ

CINCINNATI REDS

- □ 13. NICK ESASKY
- □ 41. BO DIAZ
- □ 65. TOM BROWNING
- □ 82. ROB MURPHY
- □ 101. CARL WILLIS
- □ 119. RON ROBINSON
- □ 146. TRACY JONES
- □ 172. RON OESTER
- □ 200. PETE ROSE
- □ 226. MAX VENABLE
- □ 253. EDDIE MILNER
- □ 281. TEAM LEADER CARD
- □ 305. JOHN FRANCO
- □ 332. JOE PRICE
- □ 358. SAL BUTERA
- □ 393. PETE ROSE(M)
- □ 412. ERIC DAVIS
- □ 437. TED POWER
- □ 453. SCOTT TERRY
- □ 466. KAL DANIELS
- □ 489. BILL GULLICKSON
- □ 517. MARIO SOTO
- □ 545. BUDDY BELL
- □ 569. WADE ROWDON
- □ 592. CHRIS WELSH
- □ 623. KURT STILLWELL
- □ 644. JOHN DENNY
- □ 648. BARRY LARKIN
- □ 691. DAVE PARKER
- □ 731. DAVE CONCEPCION

CLEVELAND INDIANS

- □ 11. TEAM LEADER CARD
- □ 51. MEL HALL
- □ 77. BRYAN OELKERS
- □ 107. JOHN BUTCHER
- □ 134. RICH YETT
- □ 160. JULIO FRANCO
- □ 192. CORY SNYDER
- □ 220. JOE CARTER
- □ 244. DICKIE NOLES
- □ 268. PAT CORRALES(M)
- □ 297. DON SCHULZE
- □ 319. GREG SWINDELL
- □ 322. CHRIS BANDO
- □ 353. ERNIE CAMACHO
- □ 405. BROOK JACOBY
- □ 436. ANDY ALLANSON
- □ 463. TOM CANDIOTTI
- □ 486. OTIS NIXON
- □ 513. CARMEN CASTILLO
- □ 551. FRANK WILLS
- □ 575. PAT TABLER
- □ 585. SCOTT BAILES
- □ 635. KEN SCHROM
- □ 657. TOM WADDELL
- □ 694. PHIL NIEKRO
- □ 723. BRETT BUTLER
- □ 758. TONY BERNAZARD
- □ 780. ANDRE THORNTON

DETROIT TIGERS

- □ 36. ERIC KING
- □ 72. WALT TERRELL
- □ 98. BILL SCHERRER
- □ 148. DAVE COLLINS
- □ 171. CHUCK CARY
- □ 196. RANDY O'NEAL
- □ 218. SPARKY ANDERSON(M)
- □ 234. PAT SHERIDAN
- □ 265. DARRELL EVANS
- □ 298. LARRY HERNDON
- □ 361. MARK THURMOND
- □ 384. JOHNNY GRUBB
- □ 411. DARNELL COLES
- □ 432. JIM SLATON
- □ 483. DWIGHT LOWRY
- □ 492. MIKE HEATH
- □ 515. WILLIE HERNANDEZ
- □ 631. TEAM LEADER CARD
- □ 661. LOU WHITAKER
- □ 674. BILL CAMPBELL
- □ 687. ALAN TRAMMELL
- □ 700. DAVE BERGMAN
- □ 713. TOM BROOKENS
- □ 726. FRANK TANANA
- □ 739. CHET LEMON
- □ 752. DAN PETRY
- □ 765. KIRK GIBSON
- □ 778. JACK MORRIS
- □ 791. LANCE PARRISH

HOUSTON ASTROS

- □ 24. TONY WALKER
- □ 50. DAVE SMITH
- □ 85. KEVIN BASS
- □ 112. ALAN ASHBY
- □ 145. CHARLIE KERFELD
- □ 157. DANNY DARWIN
- □ 167. JIM DESHAIES
- □ 197. MARK BAILEY
- □ 222. DENNY WALLING
- □ 249. JIM PANKOVITS
- □ 282. JEFF CALHOUN
- □ 304. PHIL GARNER
- □ 330. MIKE SCOTT
- □ 343. HAL LANIER(M)
- □ 386. DICKIE THON
- □ 408. JOHN MIZEROCK
- □ 445. DAVE LOPES
- □ 472. BILL DORAN
- □ 503. LARRY ANDERSON
- □ 531. TEAM LEADER CARD
- □ 560. GLENN DAVIS
- □ 578. BILLY HATCHER
- □ 659. AURELIO LOPEZ
- □ 670. JOSE CRUZ
- □ 693. TERRY PUHL
- □ 722. BOB KNEPPER
- □ 757. NOLAN RYAN
- □ 779. CRAIG REYNOLDS

KANSAS CITY ROYALS

- □ 18. DICK HOWSER(M)
- □ 38. DENNIS LEONARD
- □ 69. LONNIE SMITH
- □ 99. DARRYL MOTLEY
- □ 140. BRET SABERHAGEN
- □ 170. BO JACKSON
- □ 190. JIM SUNDBERG
- □ 203. MIKE KINGERY
- □ 223. CHARLIE LEIBRANDT
- □ 240. STEVE BALBONI
- □ 256. TEAM LEADER CARD
- □ 326. MARK GUBICZA
- □ 354. JAMIE QUIRK
- □ 382. RUDY LAW
- □ 400. GEORGE BRETT
- □ 473. STEVE FARR
- □ 508. SCOTT BANKHEAD
- □ 533. ARGENIS SALAZAR
- □ 554. BUDDY BIANCALANA
- □ 573. HAL MCRAE
- □ 669. BUD BLACK
- □ 692. FRANK WHITE
- □ 714. DAN QUISENBERRY
- □ 738. JORGE ORTA
- □ 761. GREG PRYOR
- □ 783. WILLIE WILSON

LOS ANGELES DODGERS

- □ 26. GREG BROCK
- □ 47. DENNIS POWELL
- □ 73. DAVE ANDERSON
- □ 116. BIL RUSSELL
- □ 144. MIKE SCIOSCIA
- □ 173. ALEX TREVINO
- □ 199. MARIANO DUNCAN
- □ 232. REGGIE WILLIAMS
- □ 266. JEFF HAMILTON
- □ 292. FRANKLIN STUBBS
- □ 328. BOB WELCH
- □ 360. PEDRO GUERRERO
- □ 385. OREL HERSHISER
- □ 410. FERNANDO VALENZUELA
- □ 431. TEAM LEADER CARD
- □ 457. LEN MATUSZEK
- □ 477. KEN HOWELL
- □ 493. TOM LASORDA(M)
- □ 509. ENOS CABELL
- □ 538. TOM NIEDENFUER
- □ 664. MIKE MARSHALL
- □ 682. JERRY REUSS
- □ 699. KEN LANDREAUX
- □ 717. ED VANDEBERG
- □ 734. BILL MADLOCK
- □ 753. RICK HONEYCUTT
- □ 769. STEVE SAX
- □ 787. ALEJANDRO PENA

MILWAUKEE BREWERS

- ☐ 10. CECIL COOPER
- ☐ 32. TIM LEARY
- ☐ 56. TEAM LEADER CARD
- ☐ 79. JUAN NIEVES
- ☐ 108. JIM GANTNER
- ☐ 129. RICK CERONE
- ☐ 179. BILL WEGMAN
- ☐ 216. B.J. SURHOFF
- ☐ 229. MIKE BIRKBECK
- ☐ 250. TEDDY HIGUERA
- ☐ 279. DAN PLESAC
- ☐ 302. BILL SCHROEDER
- ☐ 327. DALE SVEUM
- ☐ 352. MIKE FELDER
- ☐ 377. JOHN HENRY JOHNSON
- ☐ 401. BILL JO ROBIDOUX
- ☐ 423. JAIME COCANOWER
- ☐ 448. CHRIS BOSIO
- ☐ 468. GEORGE BAMBERGER(M)
- ☐ 495. GORMAN THOMAS
- ☐ 523. EARNIE RILES
- ☐ 547. ROB DEER
- ☐ 562. BRYAN CLUTTERBUCK
- ☐ 586. BEN OGLIVIE
- ☐ 622. GLENN BRAGGS
- ☐ 640. MARK CLEAR
- ☐ 676. CHARLIE MOORE
- ☐ 706. RICK MANNING
- ☐ 741. PAUL MOLITOR
- ☐ 773. ROBIN YOUNT

MINNESOTA TWINS

- ☐ 25. BERT BLYLEVEN
- ☐ 52. KEITH ATHERTON
- ☐ 87. MARK SALAS
- ☐ 114. BILLY BEANE
- ☐ 124. RAY FONTENOT
- ☐ 138. ROY LEE JACKSON
- ☐ 169. RON WASHINGTON
- ☐ 206. TEAM LEADER CARD
- ☐ 207. GEORGE FRAZIER
- ☐ 225. MIKE SMITHSON
- ☐ 247. JEFF REED
- ☐ 277. JUAN AGOSTO
- ☐ 310. FRANK VIOLA
- ☐ 336. ALLAN ANDERSON
- ☐ 364. RANDY BUSH
- ☐ 419. MARK PORTUGAL
- ☐ 450. KIRBY PUCKETT
- ☐ 478. TIM LAUDNER
- ☐ 504. MICKEY HATCHER
- ☐ 529. ALVARO ESPINOZA
- ☐ 558. GREG GAGNE
- ☐ 576. FRANK PASTORE
- ☐ 618. TOM KELLY(M)
- ☐ 679. KENT HRBEK
- ☐ 710. GARY GAETTI
- ☐ 744. ROY SMALLEY
- ☐ 776. TOM BRUNANSKY

MONTREAL EXPOS

- ☐ 9. JAY TIBBS
- ☐ 30. TIM RAINES
- ☐ 55. TIM WALLACH
- ☐ 78. TIM FOLEY
- ☐ 105. FLOYD YOUMANS
- ☐ 127. VANCE LAW
- ☐ 141. HERM WINNINGHAM
- ☐ 165. JEFF REARDON
- ☐ 189. JOE HESKETH
- ☐ 212. MIKE FITZGERALD
- ☐ 252. DENNY MARTINEZ
- ☐ 272. ANDRES GALARRAGA
- ☐ 293. BOB RODGERS(M)
- ☐ 323. AL NEWMAN
- ☐ 345. ANDRE DAWSON
- ☐ 381. TEAM LEADER CARD
- ☐ 416. TOM NIETO
- ☐ 442. MITCH WEBSTER
- ☐ 467. RANDY ST. CLAIRE
- ☐ 479. BOB SEBRA
- ☐ 505. BRYN SMITH
- ☐ 527. JIM WOHLFORD
- ☐ 577. DANN BILARDELLO
- ☐ 588. WALLACE JOHNSON
- ☐ 624. TIM BURKE
- ☐ 650. HUBIE BROOKS
- ☐ 707. BOB MCCLURE
- ☐ 742. ANDY MCGAFFIGAN
- ☐ 774. WAYNE KRENCHICKI

NEW YORK METS

- ☐ 20. GARY CARTER
- ☐ 48. WALLY BACKMAN
- ☐ 75. RON DARLING
- ☐ 103. RICK AGUILERA
- ☐ 130. DWIGHT GOODEN
- ☐ 147. RANDY NIEMANN
- ☐ 158. TIM TEUFEL
- ☐ 185. ROGER MCDOWELL
- ☐ 198. LEE MAZZILLI
- ☐ 213. RANDY MYERS
- ☐ 241. DANNY HEEP
- ☐ 267. HOWARD JOHNSON
- ☐ 295. LEN DYKSTRA
- ☐ 331. TEAM LEADER CARD
- ☐ 350. KEITH HERNANDEZ
- ☐ 378. RAFAEL SANTANA
- ☐ 404. DOUG SISK
- ☐ 433. ED HEARN
- ☐ 460. DARRYL STRAWBERRY
- ☐ 488. RAY KNIGHT
- ☐ 512. DAVE MAGADAN
- ☐ 543. DAVE JOHNSON(M)
- ☐ 570. SID FERNANDEZ
- ☐ 582. BRUCE BERENYI
- ☐ 594. RICK ANDERSON
- ☐ 625. MOOKIE WILSON
- ☐ 653. KEVIN MITCHELL
- ☐ 704. JESSE OROSCO
- ☐ 746. BOB OJEDA

NEW YORK YANKEES

- ☐ 15. CLAUDELL WASHINGTON
- ☐ 40. DAVE RIGHETTI
- ☐ 57. SCOTT NIELSEN
- ☐ 62. BOBBY MEACHAM
- ☐ 74. DAN PASQUA
- ☐ 102. PAUL ZUVELLA
- ☐ 135. MIKE EASLER
- ☐ 168. LOU PINIELLA(M)
- ☐ 174. HENRY COTTO
- ☐ 195. MIKE PAGLIARULO
- ☐ 224. WAYNE TOLLESON
- ☐ 236. TOMMY JOHN
- ☐ 239. JUAN ESPINO
- ☐ 254. BOB TEWKSBURY
- ☐ 283. DOUG DRABEK
- ☐ 316. BRIAN FISHER
- ☐ 344. JOE NIEKRO
- ☐ 375. RON GUIDRY
- ☐ 406. TEAM LEADER CARD
- ☐ 434. MIKE FISCHLIN
- ☐ 464. BUTCH WYNEGAR
- ☐ 500. DON MATTINGLY
- ☐ 524. BOB SHIRLEY
- ☐ 555. DENNIS RASMUSSEN
- ☐ 584. RON KITTLE
- ☐ 626. JOEL SKINNER
- ☐ 642. AL PULIDO
- ☐ 665. ROD SCURRY
- ☐ 683. GARY ROENICKE
- ☐ 701. WILLIE RANDOLPH
- ☐ 735. RICKEY HENDERSON
- ☐ 770. DAVE WINFIELD
- ☐ 788. TIM STODDARD

OAKLAND A'S

- ☐ 14. DAVE STEWART
- ☐ 34. JOSE RIJO
- ☐ 68. TONY LARUSSA(M)
- ☐ 83. MIKE DAVIS
- ☐ 111. ALFREDO GRIFFIN
- ☐ 137. JERRY WILLARD
- ☐ 161. STEVE ONTIVEROS
- ☐ 188. TONY PHILLIPS
- ☐ 217. CHRIS CODIROLI
- ☐ 238. BILL KRUEGER
- ☐ 263. STAN JAVIER
- ☐ 287. DAVE VON OHLEN
- ☐ 339. DONNIE HILL
- ☐ 366. MARK MCGWIRE
- ☐ 391. JAY HOWELL
- ☐ 413. MOOSE HAAS
- ☐ 441. DAVE LEIPER
- ☐ 456. TEAM LEADER CARD
- ☐ 496. BRUCE BOCHTE
- ☐ 519. CURT YOUNG
- ☐ 548. BILL MOONEYHAM
- ☐ 565. DUSTY BAKER
- ☐ 587. ERIC PLUNK
- ☐ 620. JOSE CANSECO
- ☐ 649. MICKEY TETTLETON
- ☐ 678. CARNEY LANSFORD
- ☐ 709. DAVE KINGMAN
- ☐ 743. DWAYNE MURPHY
- ☐ 775. JOAQUIN ANDUJAR

PHILADELPHIA PHILLIES

- ☐ 42. GARY REDUS
- ☐ 63. FRED TOLIVER
- ☐ 97. GLENN WILSON
- ☐ 163. KEVIN GROSS
- ☐ 191. CHARLES HUDSON
- ☐ 209. RICK SCHU
- ☐ 255. JUAN SAMUEL
- ☐ 294. STEVE JELTZ
- ☐ 329. RON ROENICKE
- ☐ 355. DON CARMAN
- ☐ 379. JOHN RUSSELL
- ☐ 409. MILT THOMPSON
- ☐ 430. MIKE SCHMIDT
- ☐ 443. JOHN FELSKE(M)
- ☐ 471. RONN REYNOLDS
- ☐ 481. TEAM LEADER CARD
- ☐ 499. BRUCE RUFFIN
- ☐ 532. JEFF STONE
- ☐ 553. MIKE MADDUX
- ☐ 636. DARREN DAULTON
- ☐ 666. VON HAYES
- ☐ 684. KENT TEKULVE
- ☐ 702. GREG GROSS
- ☐ 719. TOM HUME
- ☐ 736. STEVE BEDROSIAN
- ☐ 755. LUIS AGUAYO
- ☐ 771. SHANE RAWLEY
- ☐ 789. DAN SCHATZEDER

PITTSBURGH PIRATES

- ☐ 16. PAT CLEMENTS
- ☐ 35. SID BREAM
- ☐ 60. TONY PENA
- ☐ 93. JIM LEYLAND(M)
- ☐ 109. R.J. REYNOLDS
- ☐ 131. TEAM LEADER CARD
- ☐ 164. SAMMY KHALIFA
- ☐ 184. BOBBY BONILLA
- ☐ 219. CECILIO GUANTE
- ☐ 237. JIM MORRISON
- ☐ 262. JIM WINN
- ☐ 289. BOB KIPPER
- ☐ 320. BARRY BONDS
- ☐ 341. MIKE BROWN
- ☐ 365. RICK RHODEN
- ☐ 394. MIKE BIELECKI
- ☐ 414. JOE ORSULAK
- ☐ 447. BILL ALMON
- ☐ 469. MIKE DIAZ
- ☐ 494. BARY JONES
- ☐ 521. RICK REUSCHEL
- ☐ 541. RAFAEL BELLIARD
- ☐ 564. LARRY MCWILLIAMS
- ☐ 583. JUNIOR ORTIZ
- ☐ 628. BOB WALK
- ☐ 651. BENNY DISTEFANO
- ☐ 712. DON ROBINSON
- ☐ 747. JOHNNY RAY

ST. LOUIS CARDINALS

- ☐ 8. TERRY PENDLETON
- ☐ 33. ANDY VAN SLYKE
- ☐ 59. KEN DAYLEY
- ☐ 84. STEVE LAKE
- ☐ 110. JOHN TUDOR
- ☐ 133. JOSE OQUENDO
- ☐ 162. MIKE LAVALLIERE
- ☐ 181. TEAM LEADER CARD
- ☐ 211. JOHN MORRIS
- ☐ 243. WHITEY HERZOG(M)
- ☐ 257. BOB FORSCH
- ☐ 288. TITO LANDRUM
- ☐ 317. CLINT HURDLE

☐ 321. MIKE LAGA
☐ 338. TIM CONROY
☐ 367. JEFF LAHTI
☐ 399. CURT FORD
☐ 417. PAT PERRY
☐ 440. WILLIE MCGEE
☐ 465. TODD WORRELL
☐ 520. JACK CLARK
☐ 542. RICKY HORTON
☐ 567. GREG MATHEWS
☐ 590. VINCE COLEMAN
☐ 621. DANNY COX
☐ 647. TOM LAWLESS
☐ 671. RAY SOFF
☐ 721. TOM HERR
☐ 749. OZZIE SMITH

SAN DIEGO PADRES

☐ 37. MARVELL WYNNE
☐ 81. TEAM LEADER CARD
☐ 88. ED WOJNA
☐ 100. STEVE GARVEY
☐ 123. JOHN KRUK
☐ 143. STEVE BOROS(M)
☐ 155. EDDIE WHITSON
☐ 183. ANDY HAWKINS
☐ 205. GRAIG NETTLES
☐ 248. GENE WALTER
☐ 275. LAMARR HOYT
☐ 325. GARRY TEMPLETON
☐ 348. CARMELO MARTINEZ
☐ 380. RICH GOSSAGE
☐ 403. JERRY ROYSTER
☐ 428. BRUCE BOCHY
☐ 429. TIM PYZNARSKI
☐ 470. DAVE DRAVECKY
☐ 501. CRAIG LEFFERTS
☐ 530. TONY GWYNN
☐ 540. TERRY KENNEDY
☐ 559. LANCE MCCULLERS
☐ 637. BIP ROBERTS
☐ 690. DANE IORG
☐ 730. ERIC SHOW
☐ 754. DAVE LAPOINT
☐ 763. TIM FLANNERY

SAN FRANCISCO GIANTS

☐ 21. MARK DAVIS
☐ 46. DANNY GLADDEN
☐ 64. HARRY SPILMAN
☐ 71. MIKE ALDRETE
☐ 96. FRANK WILLIAMS
☐ 125. BOB BRENLY
☐ 151. MIKE LACOSS
☐ 180. CHRIS BROWN
☐ 193. ROGER CRAIG(M)
☐ 231. TEAM LEADER CARD
☐ 260. VIDA BLUE
☐ 280. JEFFREY LEONARD
☐ 286. MIKE WOODARD
☐ 303. JUAN BERENGUER
☐ 335. CANDY MALDONADO
☐ 362. LUIS QUINONES
☐ 389. JEFF ROBINSON
☐ 420. WILL CLARK
☐ 438. KELLY DOWNS
☐ 475. SCOTT GARRELTS
☐ 526 ROGER MASON
☐ 536. TERRY MULHOLLAND
☐ 549. BOB MELVIN
☐ 580. MIKE KRUKOW
☐ 633. JOSE URIBE
☐ 658. ROBBY THOMPSON
☐ 672. CHILI DAVIS
☐ 724. GREG MINTON
☐ 759. JOEL YOUNGBLOOD
☐ 781. ATLEE HAMMAKER

SEATTLE MARINERS

☐ 19. MATT YOUNG
☐ 45. JIM PRESLEY
☐ 67. BILL SWIFT
☐ 91. HAROLD REYNOLDS
☐ 117. JIM BEATTIE
☐ 156. TEAM LEADER CARD
☐ 187. MARK HUISMANN
☐ 215. MARK LANGSTON
☐ 235. ALVIN DAVIS
☐ 258. STEVE YEAGER
☐ 271. MIKE BROWN
☐ 284. JOHN MOSES
☐ 307. LEE GUETTERMAN
☐ 333. KEN PHELPS
☐ 347. MICKEY BRANTLEY
☐ 357. STEVE FIREOVID
☐ 376. SCOTT BRADLEY
☐ 402. MIKE TRUJILLO
☐ 418. DICK WILLIAMS(M)
☐ 427. ED NUNEZ
☐ 439. KARL BEST
☐ 476. DANNY TARTABULL
☐ 498. BOB KEARNEY
☐ 525. PHIL BRADLEY
☐ 546. MIKE MORGAN
☐ 561. REY QUINONES
☐ 572. PETE LADD
☐ 619. JERRY REED
☐ 641. DOMINGO RAMOS
☐ 727. MIKE MOORE

TEXAS RANGERS

☐ 17. PETE O'BRIEN
☐ 44. GREG HARRIS
☐ 70. CHARLIE HOUGH
☐ 95. ODDIBE MCDOWELL
☐ 118. BOBBY VALENTINE(M)
☐ 126. MIKE LOYND
☐ 152. TOBY HARRAH
☐ 176. STEVE BUECHELE
☐ 202. RICKY WRIGHT
☐ 228. CURT WILKERSON
☐ 261. RUBEN SIERRA
☐ 291. MITCH WILLIAMS
☐ 308. DON SLAUGHT
☐ 334. ED CORREA
☐ 363. JOSE GUZMAN
☐ 388. GENO PETRALLI
☐ 415. BOBBY WITT
☐ 444. JEFF RUSSELL
☐ 462. SCOTT FLETCHER
☐ 497. DALE MOHORCIC
☐ 514. ORLANDO MERCADO
☐ 550. PETE INCAVIGLIA
☐ 629. LARRY PARRISH
☐ 646. MIKE MASON
☐ 656. TEAM LEADER CARD
☐ 689. DARRELL PORTER
☐ 729. TOM PACIOREK
☐ 762. GARY WARD

TORONTO BLUE JAYS

☐ 29. JIMMY KEY
☐ 90. DAVE STIEB
☐ 106. TEAM LEADER CARD
☐ 122. JIM CLANCY
☐ 153. DUANE WARD
☐ 178. CECIL FIELDER
☐ 210. LLOYD MOSEBY
☐ 245. WILLIE UPSHAW
☐ 274. JEFF HEARRON
☐ 301. LUIS AQUINO
☐ 371. MARK EICHHORN
☐ 395. DAMASO GARCIA
☐ 458. KELLY GRUBER
☐ 485. TONY FERNANDEZ
☐ 510. TOM HENKE
☐ 537. RANCE MULLINIKS
☐ 557. JOHN CERUTTI
☐ 574. MANNY LEE
☐ 643. RON SHEPHERD
☐ 655. JESSE BARFIELD
☐ 663. CLIFF JOHNSON
☐ 681. GEORGE BELL
☐ 698. ERNIE WHITT
☐ 716. RICK LEACH
☐ 733. BILL CAUDILL
☐ 751. GARTH IORG
☐ 768. DENNIS LAMP
☐ 786. JIMY WILLIAMS(M)

1987 TOPPS TRADED (132) 2 1/2 X 3 1/2

ATLANTA BRAVES

☐ 41T. ALBERT HALL
☐ 54T. DION JAMES
☐ 85T. GRAIG NETTLES
☐ 105T. GARY ROENICKE

BALTIMORE ORIOLES

☐ 3T. ERIC BELL
☐ 37T. KEN GERHART
☐ 57T. TERRY KENNEDY
☐ 59T. RAY KNIGHT
☐ 88T. TOM NIEDENFUER
☐ 102T. CAL RIPKEN (M)
☐ 110T. DAVE SCHMIDT
☐ 126T. ALAN WIGGINS

BOSTON RED SOX

☐ 14T. ELLIS BURKS

CALIFORNIA ANGELS

☐ 13T. DEWAYNE BUICE
☐ 35T. WILLIE FRASER
☐ 62T. JACK LAZORKO
☐ 75T. MARK MCLEMORE
☐ 79T. GREG MINTON

CHICAGO CUBS

☐ 27T. ANDRE DAWSON
☐ 70T. GREG MADDUX
☐ 73T. DAVE MARTINEZ
☐ 92T. DICKIE NOLES
☐ 119T. JIM SUNDBERG

CHICAGO WHITE SOX

☐ 15T. IVAN CALDERON
☐ 47T. DONNIE HILL
☐ 67T. BILL LONG
☐ 99T. GARY REDUS
☐ 106T. JERRY RYOSTER
☐ 130T. JIM WINN

CINCINNATI REDS

☐ 34T. TERRY FRANCONA
☐ 48T. GUY HOFFMAN
☐ 93T. PAT PACILLO
☐ 128T. FRANK WILLIAMS

CLEVELAND INDIANS

☐ 19T. STEVE CARLTON
☐ 28T. RICK DEMPSEY
☐ 128T. ED VANDEBERG

DETROIT TIGERS

☐ 46T. MIKE HENNEMAN
☐ 71T. BILL MADLOCK
☐ 91T. MATT NOKES
☐ 104T. JEFF ROBINSON

HOUSTON ASTROS

- ☐ 77T. DAVE MEADS

KANSAS CITY ROYALS

- ☐ 4T. JUAN BENIQUEZ
- ☐ 7T. THAD BOSLEY
- ☐ 36T. BILLY GARDNER (M)
- ☐ 51T. DANNY JACKSON
- ☐ 111T. KEVIN SEITZER
- ☐ 120T. DANNY TARTABULL

LOS ANGLES DODGERS

- ☐ 12T. RALPH BRYANT
- ☐ 43T. MICKEY HATCHER
- ☐ 44T. BRAD HAVENS
- ☐ 49T. BRIAN HOLTON
- ☐ 64T. TIM LEARY
- ☐ 112T. JOHN SHELBY
- ☐ 131T. MATT YOUNG

MILWAUKEE BREWERS

- ☐ 9T. GREG BROCK
- ☐ 20T. JUAN CASTILLO
- ☐ 25T. CHUCK CRIM
- ☐ 121T. TOM TREBELHORN (M)

MINNESOTA TWINS

- ☐ 5T. JUAN BERENGUER
- ☐ 38T. DANNY GLADDEN
- ☐ 60T. GENE LARKIN
- ☐ 66T. STEVE LOMBARDOZZI
- ☐ 86T. AL NEWMAN
- ☐ 89T. JOE NIEKRO
- ☐ 90T. TOM NIETO
- ☐ 98T. JEFF REARDON
- ☐ 118T. LES STRAKER

MONTREAL EXPOS

- ☐ 17T. CASEY CANDAELE
- ☐ 45T. NEAL HEATON
- ☐ 87T. REID NICHOLS
- ☐ 100T. JEFF REED

NEW YORK METS

- ☐ 1T. BILL ALMON
- ☐ 24T. DAVE CONE
- ☐ 63T. TERRY LEACH
- ☐ 68T. BARRY LYONS
- ☐ 76T. KEVIN MCREYNOLDS
- ☐ 80T. JOHN MITCHELL

NEW YORK YANKEES

- ☐ 21T. RICK CERONE
- ☐ 40T. CECILIO GUANTE
- ☐ 50T. CHARLES HUDSON
- ☐ 101T. RICK RHODEN
- ☐ 107T. MARK SALAS
- ☐ 125T. GARY WARD

OAKLAND A'S

- ☐ 22T. RON CEY
- ☐ 31T. DENNIS ECKERSLEY
- ☐ 52T. REGGIE JACKSON
- ☐ 84T. GENE NELSON
- ☐ 96T. LUIS POLONIA
- ☐ 117T. TERRY STIENBACH

PHILADELPHIA PHILLIES

- ☐ 16T. JEFF CALHOUN
- ☐ 32T. LEE ELIA (M)
- ☐ 53T. CHRIS JAMES
- ☐ 94T. LANCE PARRISH
- ☐ 103T. WALLY RITCHIE

PITTSBURGH PIRATES

- ☐ 18T. JOHN CANGELOSI
- ☐ 29T. DOUG DRABEK
- ☐ 30T. MIKE DUNNE
- ☐ 33T. BRIAN FISHER
- ☐ 42T TERRY HARPER
- ☐ 61T. MIKE LAVALLIERE
- ☐ 114T. JOHN SMILEY
- ☐ 124T. ANDY VAN SLYKE

ST. LOUIS CARDINALS

- ☐ 65T. JIM LINDEMAN
- ☐ 72T. JOE MAGRANE
- ☐ 95T. TONY PENA

SAN DIEGO PADRES

- ☐ 6T. GREG BOOKER
- ☐ 8T. LARRY BOWA (M)
- ☐ 26T. STORM DAVIS
- ☐ 55T. STAN JEFFERSON
- ☐ 69T. SHANE MACK
- ☐ 97T. RANDY READY
- ☐ 108T. LUIS SALAZAR
- ☐ 109T. BENNY SANTIAGO

SAN FRANCISCO GIANTS

- ☐ 39T. JIM GOTT
- ☐ 78T. EDDIE MILNER
- ☐ 81T. KEVIN MITCHELL
- ☐ 115T. CHRIS SPEIER
- ☐ 129T. MATT WILLIAMS

SEATTLE MARINERS

- ☐ 2T. SCOTT BANKHEAD
- ☐ 23T. JOHN CHRISTENSEN
- ☐ 58T. MIKE KINGERY
- ☐ 113T. STEVE SHIELDS
- ☐ 122T. DAVE VALLE
- ☐ 127T. BILL WILKINSON

TEXAS RANGERS

- ☐ 10T. BOB BROWER
- ☐ 11T. JERRY BROWNE
- ☐ 116T. MIKE STANLEY

TORONTO BLUE JAYS

- ☐ 56T. JOE JOHNSON
- ☐ 74T. FRED MCGRIFF
- ☐ 82T. CHARLIE MOORE
- ☐ 83T. JEFF MUSSELMAN

1988 TOPPS (792)
2 1/2 X 3 1/2

ATLANTA BRAVES

- ☐ 13. ANDRES THOMAS
- ☐ 39. GERALD PERRY
- ☐ 67. KEN OBERKFELL
- ☐ 90. DALE MURPHY
- ☐ 134. CHUCK TANNER (M)
- ☐ 155. BRUCE SUTTER
- ☐ 179. CHARLIE PULEO
- ☐ 213. ALBERT HALL
- ☐ 241. DAMASO GARCIA
- ☐ 266. PAUL ASSENMACHER
- ☐ 297. ZANE SMITH
- ☐ 325. GLENN HUBBARD
- ☐ 353. ED OLWINE
- ☐ 379. RAFAEL RAMIREZ
- ☐ 408. DION JAMES
- ☐ 443. KEN GRIFFEY
- ☐ 469. JEFF DEDMON
- ☐ 523. GARY ROENICKE
- ☐ 549. TEAM LEADER CARD
- ☐ 574. GRAIG NETTLES
- ☐ 627. JOE BOEVER
- ☐ 652. BRUCE BENEDICT
- ☐ 678. JIM ACKER
- ☐ 706. RICK MAHLER
- ☐ 732. DAVE PALMER
- ☐ 755. OZZIE VIRGIL
- ☐ 779. TOM GLAVINE
- ☐ 791. TED SIMMONS

BALTIMORE ORIOLES

- ☐ 11. MIKE YOUNG
- ☐ 51. TEAM LEADER CARD
- ☐ 69. MIKE HART
- ☐ 98. RENE GONZALES
- ☐ 124. RAY KNIGHT
- ☐ 153. JOHN HABYAN
- ☐ 180. TERRY KENNEDY
- ☐ 214. DAVE SCHMIDT
- ☐ 242. TOM NIEDENFUER
- ☐ 271. KEN GERHART
- ☐ 296. FLOYD RAYFORD
- ☐ 327. LARRY SHEETS
- ☐ 352. BILLY RIPKEN
- ☐ 383. ERIC BELL
- ☐ 419. SCOTT MCGREGOR
- ☐ 444. CAL RIPKEN (M)
- ☐ 467. DON AASE
- ☐ 495. EDDIE MURRAY
- ☐ 521. JIM DWYER
- ☐ 544. JIM TRABER
- ☐ 571. MARK WILLIAMSON
- ☐ 598. LEE LACY
- ☐ 650. CAL RIPKEN
- ☐ 676. KEN DIXON
- ☐ 707. FRED LYNN
- ☐ 725. MIKE BODDICKER
- ☐ 782. JEFF BALLARD

BOSTON RED SOX

- ☐ 21. TEAM LEADER CARD
- ☐ 37. ED ROMERO
- ☐ 70. ROGER CLEMENS
- ☐ 96. TODD BENZINGER

- ☐ 125. BRUCE HURST
- ☐ 152. JODY REED
- ☐ 189. WES GARDNER
- ☐ 200. WADE BOGGS
- ☐ 245. RICH GEDMAN
- ☐ 269. ELLIS BURKS
- ☐ 299. STEVE CRAWFORD
- ☐ 326. AL NIPPER
- ☐ 354. MARC SULLIVAN
- ☐ 377. SAM HORN
- ☐ 414. JOHN MCNAMARA (M)
- ☐ 442. TOM BOLTON
- ☐ 470. DWIGHT EVANS
- ☐ 493. MIKE GREENWELL
- ☐ 525. MARTY BARRETT
- ☐ 573. BOB STANLEY
- ☐ 599. CALVIN SCHIRALDI
- ☐ 653. JEFF SELLERS
- ☐ 675. JIM RICE
- ☐ 704. DENNIS BOYD
- ☐ 733. SPIKE OWEN
- ☐ 757. JOHN MARZANO
- ☐ 784. JOE SAMBITO

CALIFORNIA ANGELS

- ☐ 16. KIRK MCCASKILL
- ☐ 43. DICK SCHOEFIELD
- ☐ 71. GARY PETTIS
- ☐ 99. CHUCK FINLEY
- ☐ 115. JOHNNY RAY
- ☐ 129. GREG MINTON
- ☐ 147. BILL BUCKNER
- ☐ 162. MARK LCLEMORE
- ☐ 192. DEVON WHITE
- ☐ 216. JERRY REUSS
- ☐ 243. MARK RYAL
- ☐ 270. MIKE WITT
- ☐ 304. GEORGE HENDRICK
- ☐ 331. BRIAN DOWNING
- ☐ 363. WILLIE FRASER
- ☐ 381. TEAM LEADER CARD
- ☐ 420. WALLY JOYNER
- ☐ 446. DOUG DECINCES
- ☐ 471. DONNIE MOORE
- ☐ 498. BOB BOONE
- ☐ 524. GARY LUCAS
- ☐ 575. DON SUTTON
- ☐ 601. JACK LAZORKO
- ☐ 631. JACK HOWELL
- ☐ 649. DEWAYNE BUICE
- ☐ 679. DARRELL MILLER
- ☐ 708. GUS POLIDOR
- ☐ 737. BUTCH WYNEGAR
- ☐ 761. TONY ARMAS
- ☐ 774. GENE MAUCH (M)

CHICAGO CUBS

- ☐ 10. RYNE SANDBERG
- ☐ 36. JAMIE MOYER
- ☐ 65. LEON DURHAM
- ☐ 87. MIKE MASON
- ☐ 112. LES LANCASTER
- ☐ 136. BRIAN DAYETT
- ☐ 171. TEAM LEADER CARD
- ☐ 186. RAFAEL PALMEIRO
- ☐ 211. FRANK DIPINO
- ☐ 240. LEE SMITH
- ☐ 262. DREW HALL
- ☐ 287. MANNY TRILLO
- ☐ 311. SCOTT SANDERSON
- ☐ 336. ED LYNCH
- ☐ 361. GREG MADDUX
- ☐ 416. KEITH MORELAND
- ☐ 439. DAVE MARTINEZ
- ☐ 466. JERRY MUMPHREY
- ☐ 500. ANDRE DAWSON
- ☐ 516. JIM SUNDBERG
- ☐ 542. PAUL NOCE
- ☐ 564. FRANK LUCCHESI (M)
- ☐ 593. BOB TEWKSBURY
- ☐ 615. JODY DAVIS
- ☐ 642. BOB DERNIER
- ☐ 667. LUIS QUINONES
- ☐ 695. SHAWON DUNSTON
- ☐ 717. JAY BALLER
- ☐ 740. RICK SUTCLIFFE
- ☐ 768. DICKIE NOLES

CHICAGO WHITE SOX

- ☐ 35. HAROLD BAINES
- ☐ 86. RON KARKOVICE
- ☐ 108. STEVE LYONS
- ☐ 132. DONNIE HILL
- ☐ 158. TIM HULETT
- ☐ 184. IVAN CALDERON
- ☐ 209. RICHARD DOTSON
- ☐ 232. BOB JAMES
- ☐ 281. JERRY HAIRSTON
- ☐ 309. BILL LONG
- ☐ 321. TEAM LEADER CARD
- ☐ 334. DAVE LAPOINT
- ☐ 357. FLOYD BANNISTER
- ☐ 385. CARLTON FISK
- ☐ 409. JOEL MCKEON
- ☐ 437. FRED MANRIQUE
- ☐ 458. RON HASSEY
- ☐ 486. PAT KEEDY
- ☐ 511. JOEL DAVIS
- ☐ 559. KEN WILLIAMS
- ☐ 585. OZZIE GUILLEN
- ☐ 613. BOBBY THIGPEN
- ☐ 634. JOSE DELEON
- ☐ 657. JIM WINN
- ☐ 714. JIM FREGOSI (M)
- ☐ 739. DARYL BOSTON
- ☐ 764. GREG WALKER
- ☐ 788. RAY SEARAGE

CINCINNATI REDS

- ☐ 17. RON OESTER
- ☐ 42. BILL LANDRUM
- ☐ 81. TEAM LEADER CARD
- ☐ 102. BARRY LARKIN
- ☐ 130. BUDDY BELL
- ☐ 135. DENNIS RASMUSSEN
- ☐ 150. ERIC DAVIS
- ☐ 172. LLOYD MCCLENDON
- ☐ 204. PAUL O'NEILL
- ☐ 236. TED POWER
- ☐ 265. BO DIAZ
- ☐ 282. PAT PERRY
- ☐ 288. PAT PACILLO
- ☐ 315. DAVE PARKER
- ☐ 339. KURT STILLWELL
- ☐ 364. NICK ESASKY
- ☐ 422 DAVE CONCEPCION
- ☐ 477. JEFF MONTGOMERY
- ☐ 475. PETE ROSE (M)
- ☐ 496. GUY HOFFMAN
- ☐ 517. RON ROBINSON
- ☐ 553. TRACY JONES
- ☐ 577. TOM BROWNING
- ☐ 603. ROB MURPHY
- ☐ 622. KAL DANIELS
- ☐ 644. TERRY MCGRIFF
- ☐ 666. MARIO SOTO
- ☐ 686. TERRY FRANCONA
- ☐ 730. JOHN FRANCO
- ☐ 773. FRANK WILLIAMS

CLEVELAND INDIANS

- ☐ 22. GREG SWINDELL
- ☐ 49. DAVE CLARK
- ☐ 75. JOE CARTER
- ☐ 82. DARREL AKERFELDS
- ☐ 107. SCOTT BAILES
- ☐ 123. TOM CANDIOTTI
- ☐ 144. DON GORDON
- ☐ 230. PAT TABLER
- ☐ 256. KEN SCHROM
- ☐ 293. DOUG JONES
- ☐ 318. MEL HALL
- ☐ 341. CARMEN CASTILLO
- ☐ 374. DOC EDWARDS (M)
- ☐ 421. ED VANDEBERG
- ☐ 479. BRETT BUTLER
- ☐ 503. JUNIOR NOBOA
- ☐ 531. RICH YETT
- ☐ 533. JOHN FARRELL
- ☐ 555. BROOK JACOBY
- ☐ 576. TOMMY HINZO
- ☐ 604. CHRIS BANDO
- ☐ 620. CORY SNYDER
- ☐ 637. JAY BELL
- ☐ 683. JULIO FRANCO
- ☐ 701. SAMMY STEWART
- ☐ 728. ANDY ALLANSON
- ☐ 758. EDDIE WILLIAMS
- ☐ 789. TEAM LEADER CARD

DETROIT TIGERS

- ☐ 14. SPARKY ANDERSON (M)
- ☐ 78. DAN PETRY
- ☐ 106. JIM WALEWANDER
- ☐ 128 JOHNNY GRUBB
- ☐ 145. BILL MADLOCK
- ☐ 177. FRANK TANANA
- ☐ 237. MIKE HEATH
- ☐ 267. BILLY BEAN
- ☐ 289. DAVE BERGMAN
- ☐ 320. ALAN TRAMMELL
- ☐ 340. JACK MORRIS
- ☐ 366. CHET LEMON
- ☐ 429. TEAM LEADER CARD
- ☐ 449. JEFF ROBINSON
- ☐ 474. TOM BROOKENS
- ☐ 492. DOYLE ALEXANDER
- ☐ 499. ERIC KING
- ☐ 514. PAT SHERIDAN
- ☐ 552. MARK THURMOND
- ☐ 582. MIKE HENNEMAN
- ☐ 605. KIRK GIBSON
- ☐ 630. DARRELL EVANS
- ☐ 645. MATT NOKES
- ☐ 668. WALT TERRELL
- ☐ 713. WILLIE HERNANDEZ
- ☐ 743. LARRY HERNDON
- ☐ 751. JIM MORRISON
- ☐ 770. LOU WHITAKER

HOUSTON ASTROS

- ☐ 24. JIM DESHAIES
- ☐ 48. ALAN ASHBY
- ☐ 64. KEN CAMINITI
- ☐ 94. CHUCK JACKSON
- ☐ 119. ROBBIE WINE
- ☐ 151. BOB KNEPPER
- ☐ 175. KEVIN BASS
- ☐ 199. DAVE MEADS
- ☐ 226. DAVE LOPES
- ☐ 250. NOLAN RYAN
- ☐ 278. JOSE CRUZ
- ☐ 291. TEAM LEADER CARD
- ☐ 306. BILLY HATCHER
- ☐ 342. LARRY ANDERSON
- ☐ 368. GERALD YOUNG
- ☐ 430. GLENN DAVIS
- ☐ 461. DANNY DARWIN
- ☐ 487. JIM PANKOVITS
- ☐ 520. DAVE SMITH
- ☐ 557. CRAIG REYNOLDS
- ☐ 587. TERRY PUHL
- ☐ 608. CHARLIE KERFELD
- ☐ 643. ROCKY CHILDRESS
- ☐ 684. HAL LANIER (M)
- ☐ 719. DENNY WALLING
- ☐ 745. BILL DORAN
- ☐ 760. MIKE SCOTT

KANSAS CITY ROYALS

- ☐ 29. ARGENIS SALAZAR
- ☐ 56. ED HEARN
- ☐ 89. GARY THURMAN
- ☐ 116. JERRY DON GLEATON
- ☐ 141. TEAM LEADER CARD
- ☐ 169. ROSS JONES
- ☐ 195. DAN QUISENBERRY

- ☐ 222. STEVE FARR
- ☐ 247. THAD BOSLEY
- ☐ 275. KEVIN SEITZER
- ☐ 301. BUD BLACK
- ☐ 324. DANNY JACKSON
- ☐ 348. JIM EISENREICH
- ☐ 433. BILL PECOTA
- ☐ 452. WILLIE WILSON
- ☐ 477. JAMIE QUIRK
- ☐ 507. MARK GUBICZA
- ☐ 534. JOHN WATHAN (M)
- ☐ 540. BRET SABERHAGEN
- ☐ 569. CHARLIE LEIBRANDT
- ☐ 595. FRANK WHITE
- ☐ 597. GENE GARBER
- ☐ 638. STEVE BALBONI
- ☐ 672. JOHN DAVIS
- ☐ 700. GEORGE BRETT
- ☐ 724. DANNY TARTABULL
- ☐ 750. BO JACKSON
- ☐ 777. LONNIE SMITH

LOS ANGELES DODGERS

- ☐ 23. KEN LANDREAUX
- ☐ 40. OREL HERSHISER
- ☐ 57. TIM CREWS
- ☐ 62. JEFF HAMILTON
- ☐ 74. TOM LASORDA (M)
- ☐ 92. LEN MATUSZEK
- ☐ 118. BOB WELCH
- ☐ 149. KEN HOWELL
- ☐ 174. PHIL GARNER
- ☐ 198. FRANKLIN STUBBS
- ☐ 202. GLENN HOFFMAN
- ☐ 225. MIKE SCIOSCIA
- ☐ 249. MIKE MARSHALL
- ☐ 277. ALEJANDRO PENA
- ☐ 305. STEVE SAX
- ☐ 338. BRIAN HOLTON
- ☐ 367. TIM LEARY
- ☐ 428. JOHN SHELBY
- ☐ 455. SHAWN HILLEGAS
- ☐ 456. DAVE ANERSON
- ☐ 481. MARIANO DUNCAN
- ☐ 489. TEAM LEADER CARD
- ☐ 512. ALEX TREVINO
- ☐ 550. PEDRO GUERRERO
- ☐ 581. TITO LANDRUM
- ☐ 607. MICKEY HATCHER
- ☐ 698. BARD HAVENS
- ☐ 736. MATT YOUNG
- ☐ 753. DANNY HEEP
- ☐ 780. FERNANDO VALENZUELA

MILWAUKEE BREWERS

- ☐ 12. BILL SCHROEDER
- ☐ 33. ROB DEER
- ☐ 61. MARK KNUDSON
- ☐ 88. EARNIE RILES
- ☐ 110. TEDDY HIGUERA
- ☐ 137. CHRIS BOSIO
- ☐ 165. ROBIN YOUNT
- ☐ 187. STEVE KIEFER
- ☐ 212. GREG BROCK
- ☐ 224. TOM TREBELHORN (M)
- ☐ 263. GLENN BRAGGS
- ☐ 286. CHUCK CRIM
- ☐ 312. JOEY MEYER
- ☐ 337. JIM GANTNER
- ☐ 362. JUAN CASTILLO
- ☐ 417. MARK CIARDI
- ☐ 441. RICK MANNING
- ☐ 465. PAUL MOLITOR
- ☐ 491. B.J. SURHOFF
- ☐ 515. JUAN NIEVES
- ☐ 538. BILL WEGMAN
- ☐ 566. CHARLIE O'BRIEN
- ☐ 592. DALE SVEUM
- ☐ 616. JAY ALDRICH
- ☐ 639. TEAM LEADER CARD
- ☐ 670. DAN PLESAC
- ☐ 692. MIKE BIRKBECK
- ☐ 718. MIKE FELDER
- ☐ 742. MARK CLEAR
- ☐ 769. CECIL COOPER

MINNESOTA TWINS

- ☐ 19. MARK DAVIDSON
- ☐ 45. KENT HRBEK
- ☐ 73. RANDY BUSH
- ☐ 101. ALLAN ANDERSON
- ☐ 120. KIRBY PUCKETT
- ☐ 194. TOM KELLY (M)
- ☐ 218. DAN SCHATZEDER
- ☐ 239. ROY SMALLEY
- ☐ 264. LES STRAKER
- ☐ 295. BERT BLYLEVEN
- ☐ 317. TOM NIETO
- ☐ 343. GREG GAGNE
- ☐ 375. TOM BRUNANSKY
- ☐ 425. JEFF REARDON
- ☐ 451. KEITH ATHERTON
- ☐ 473. JOE NIEKRO
- ☐ 502. DANNY GLADDEN
- ☐ 526. JUAN BERENGUER
- ☐ 545. DON BAYLOR
- ☐ 554. MIKE SMITHSON
- ☐ 578. GARY GAETTI
- ☐ 609. TEAM LADER CARD
- ☐ 625. FRANK VIOLA
- ☐ 648. AL NEWMAN
- ☐ 671. TIM LAUDNER
- ☐ 697. STEVE LOMBARDOZZI
- ☐ 709. GEORGE FRAZIER
- ☐ 772. SAL BUTERA

MONTREAL EXPOS

- ☐ 25. ANDRES GALARRAGA
- ☐ 50. HUBIE BROOKS
- ☐ 76. DENNY MARTINEZ
- ☐ 93. BOB SEBRA
- ☐ 111. TEAM LEADER CARD
- ☐ 138. MITCH WEBSTER
- ☐ 161. BRYN SMITH
- ☐ 176. JEFF REED
- ☐ 196. DAVE ENGLE
- ☐ 228. WALLACE JOHNSON
- ☐ 251. TOM FOLEY
- ☐ 279. RANDY ST. CLAIRE
- ☐ 313. BOB MCCLURE
- ☐ 346. VANCE LAW
- ☐ 365. FLOYD YOUMANS
- ☐ 371. JOE HESKETH
- ☐ 431. CASEY CANDAELE
- ☐ 464. JAY TIBBS
- ☐ 488. ANDY MCGAFFIGAN
- ☐ 504. BOB RODGERS (M)
- ☐ 529. TIM BURKE
- ☐ 560. TIM WALLACH
- ☐ 588. JEFF PARRETT
- ☐ 614. HERM WINNINGHAM
- ☐ 647. PASCUAL PEREZ
- ☐ 674. MIKE FITZGERALD
- ☐ 720. TIM RAINES
- ☐ 748. REID NICHOLS
- ☐ 765. NEAL HEATON

NEW YORK METS

- ☐ 8. KEVIN ELSTER
- ☐ 30. SID FERNANDEZ
- ☐ 58. DAVE MAGADEN
- ☐ 85. HOWARD JOHNSON
- ☐ 105. JESSE OROSCO
- ☐ 131. DON SCHULZE
- ☐ 164. DAVE JOHNSON (M)
- ☐ 181. DAVE CONE
- ☐ 207. JOHN MITCHELL
- ☐ 233. RAFAEL SANTANA
- ☐ 255. MOOKIE WILSON
- ☐ 308. LEE MAZZILLI
- ☐ 333. WALLY BACKMAN
- ☐ 355. ROGER MCDOWELL
- ☐ 382. KEITH MILLER
- ☐ 412. RANDY MYERS
- ☐ 434. RICK AGUILERA
- ☐ 457. TERRY LEACH
- ☐ 480. DWIGHT GOODEN
- ☐ 508. TIM TEUFEL
- ☐ 530. GARY CARTER
- ☐ 546. JOHN CANDELARIA
- ☐ 558. BOB OJEDA
- ☐ 579. TEAM LEADER CARD
- ☐ 610. KEITH HERNANDEZ
- ☐ 633. BARRY LYONS
- ☐ 655. LEN DYKSTRA
- ☐ 685. RON DARLING
- ☐ 710. DARRYL STRAWBERRY
- ☐ 735. KEVIN MCREYNOLDS
- ☐ 746. BOB OJEDA
- ☐ 763. DOUG SISK
- ☐ 787. BILL ALMON

NEW YORK YANKEES

- ☐ 18. AL LEITER
- ☐ 44. LOU PINIELLA (M)
- ☐ 60. RICKEY HENDERSON
- ☐ 84. CECILIO GUANTE
- ☐ 109. JOEL SKINNER
- ☐ 159. BRAD ARNSBERG
- ☐ 185. RICK RHODEN
- ☐ 210. WILLIE RANDOLPH
- ☐ 235. GARY WARD
- ☐ 257. JERRY ROYSTER
- ☐ 259. RON KITTLE
- ☐ 283. PHIL LOMBARDI
- ☐ 300. DON MATTINGLY
- ☐ 335. CLAUDELL WASHINGTON
- ☐ 359. TIM STODDARD
- ☐ 384. NEIL ALLEN
- ☐ 411. WAYNE TOLLESON
- ☐ 435. MIKE PAGLIARULO
- ☐ 459. TEAM LEADER CARD
- ☐ 484. PAT CLEMENTS
- ☐ 510. DAVE WINFIELD
- ☐ 535. RON GUIDRY
- ☐ 561. RICK CERONE
- ☐ 584. STEVE TROUT
- ☐ 611. TOMMY JOHN
- ☐ 636. CHARLES HUDSON
- ☐ 659. BOBBY MEACHAM
- ☐ 691. DAN PASQUA
- ☐ 711. BILL GULLICKSON
- ☐ 716. LENN SAKATA
- ☐ 741. MIKE EASLER
- ☐ 766. HENRY COTTO
- ☐ 790. DAVE RIGHETTI

OAKLAND A'S

- ☐ 47. JOAQUIN ANDUJAR
- ☐ 72. DENNIS ECKERSLEY
- ☐ 103. CURT YOUNG
- ☐ 122. TONY BERNAZARD
- ☐ 143. MICKEY TETTLETON
- ☐ 166. RICK RODRIGUEZ
- ☐ 173. ERIC PLUNK
- ☐ 238. LUIS POLONIA
- ☐ 248. STORM DAVIS
- ☐ 272. STEVE ONTIVEROS
- ☐ 292. CARNEY LANSFORD
- ☐ 316. JOSE RIJO
- ☐ 328. GREG CADARET
- ☐ 344. TONY LARUSSA (M)
- ☐ 370. JOSE CANSECO
- ☐ 424. DWAYNE MURPHY
- ☐ 448. MIKE DAVIS
- ☐ 476. DAVE STEWART
- ☐ 501. TIM BIRTSAS
- ☐ 527. STEVE HENDERSON
- ☐ 551. TERRY STEINBACH
- ☐ 580. MARK MCGWIRE
- ☐ 606. MOOSE HAAS
- ☐ 621. GENE NELSON
- ☐ 641. RICK HONEYCUTT
- ☐ 673. TONY PHILLIPS
- ☐ 690. JAY HOWELL
- ☐ 702. MIKE GALLEGO
- ☐ 726. ALFREDO GRIFFIN
- ☐ 759. TEAM LEADER CARD

PHILADELPHIA PHILLIES

- ☐ 20. KEVIN GROSS
- ☐ 38. JEFF CALHOUN
- ☐ 66. SHANE RAWLEY
- ☐ 95. LANCE PARRISH
- ☐ 126. STEVE JELTZ
- ☐ 154. JEFF STONE
- ☐ 188. JOHN RUSSELL
- ☐ 203. FRED TOLIVER
- ☐ 215. VON HAYES
- ☐ 254. LEE ELIA (M)
- ☐ 268. BRUCE RUFFIN
- ☐ 298. MILT THOMPSON

- ☐ 356. LUIS AGUAYO
- ☐ 378. TODD FROHWIRTH
- ☐ 415. DON CARMAN
- ☐ 440. STEVE BEDROSIAN
- ☐ 468. DARREN DAULTON
- ☐ 494. WALLY RITCHIE
- ☐ 518. GREG GROSS
- ☐ 543. KENT TEKULVE
- ☐ 572. CHRIS JAMES
- ☐ 600. MIKE SCHMIDT
- ☐ 626. GLENN WILSON
- ☐ 651. MIKE JACKSON
- ☐ 669. TEAM LEADER CARD
- ☐ 705. JUAN SAMUEL
- ☐ 731. RICK SCHU
- ☐ 756. MIKE MADDUX
- ☐ 781. KEITH HUGHES
- ☐ 783. RON ROENICKE

PITTSBURGH PIRATES

- ☐ 27. R.J. REYNOLDS
- ☐ 46. DARNELL COLES
- ☐ 127. JIM GOTT
- ☐ 142. ANDY VAN SLYKE
- ☐ 168. BARRY JONES
- ☐ 193. BRIAN FISHER
- ☐ 221. RAFAEL BELLIARD
- ☐ 231. TEAM LEADER CARD
- ☐ 244. JEFF ROBINSON
- ☐ 274. JUNIOR ORTIZ
- ☐ 294. AL PEDRIQUE
- ☐ 322. VICENTE PALACIOS
- ☐ 349. BOB WALK
- ☐ 423. JOHN SMILEY
- ☐ 436. MIKE BIELECKI
- ☐ 450. BARRY BONDS
- ☐ 478. SID BREAM
- ☐ 506. JOHN CANGELOSI
- ☐ 522. BOB PATTERSON
- ☐ 539. MIKE LAVALLIERE
- ☐ 547. FELIX FERMIN
- ☐ 567. MIKE DIAZ
- ☐ 591. DOUG DRABEK
- ☐ 619. MIKE DUNNE
- ☐ 624. JIM LEYLAND (M)
- ☐ 681. BOBBY BONILLA
- ☐ 723. BOB KIPPER
- ☐ 767. JOSE LIND

ST. LOUIS CARDINALS

- ☐ 34. RICKY HORTON
- ☐ 59. DANNY COX
- ☐ 83. JOSE OQUENDO
- ☐ 100. JACK CLARK
- ☐ 133. GREG MATHEWS
- ☐ 160. WILLIE MCGEE
- ☐ 183. TOM LAWLESS
- ☐ 208. STEVE LAKE
- ☐ 234. KEN DAYLEY
- ☐ 260. VINCE COLEMAN
- ☐ 310. TOM HERR
- ☐ 351. TEAM LEADER CARD
- ☐ 380. JOE MAGRANE
- ☐ 410. TONY PENA
- ☐ 460. OZZIE SMITH
- ☐ 483. ROD BOOKER
- ☐ 509. BILL DAWLEY
- ☐ 536. JOHN MORRIS
- ☐ 562. JIM LINDEMAN
- ☐ 586. BOB FORSCH
- ☐ 612. CURT FORD
- ☐ 635. TERRY PENDLETON
- ☐ 658. TIM CONROY
- ☐ 689. TOM PAGNOZZI
- ☐ 715. TODD WORRELL
- ☐ 744. WHITEY HERZOG (M)
- ☐ 792. JOHN TUDOR

SAN DIEGO PADRES

- ☐ 9. ANDY HAWKINS
- ☐ 31. BRUCE BOCHY
- ☐ 63. JIMMY JONES
- ☐ 91. JOEY CORA
- ☐ 117. JAMES STEELS
- ☐ 148. CARMELO MARTINEZ
- ☐ 170. RICH GOSSAGE
- ☐ 197. LANCE MCCULLERS
- ☐ 223. STAN JEFFERSON
- ☐ 276. LUIS SALAZAR
- ☐ 284. LARRY BOWA (M)
- ☐ 303. ERIC SHOW
- ☐ 330. EDDIE WHITSON
- ☐ 360. TONY GWYNN
- ☐ 426. RANDY READY
- ☐ 454. MARVELL WYNNE
- ☐ 482. MARK DAVIS
- ☐ 513. TIM FLANNERY
- ☐ 548. SHANE MACK
- ☐ 568. CHRIS BROWN
- ☐ 596. JOHN KRUK
- ☐ 640. GARY TEMPLETON
- ☐ 693. BENNY SANTIAGO
- ☐ 694. ERIC NOLTE
- ☐ 699. TEAM LEADER CARD
- ☐ 727. GREG BOOKER
- ☐ 752. MARK GRANT
- ☐ 778. KEITH COMSTOCK

SAN FRANCISCO GIANTS

- ☐ 15. CHILI DAVIS
- ☐ 41. BOB MELVIN
- ☐ 52. DON ROBINSON
- ☐ 68. DAVE DRAVECKY
- ☐ 97. SCOTT GARRELTS
- ☐ 157. ATLEE HAMMAKER
- ☐ 190. CANDY MALDONADO
- ☐ 217. HARRY SPILMAN
- ☐ 261. TEAM LEADER CARD
- ☐ 302. JOSE URIBE
- ☐ 329. CHRIS SPEIER
- ☐ 350. WILL CLARK
- ☐ 372. MATT WILLIAMS
- ☐ 418. JOEL YOUNGBLOOD
- ☐ 445. MIKE KRUKOW
- ☐ 472. ROBBY THOMPSON
- ☐ 497. KEVIN MITCHELL
- ☐ 570. JEFFREY LEONARD
- ☐ 602. MIKE ALDRETE
- ☐ 628. DAVE HENDERSON
- ☐ 629. KELLY DOWNS
- ☐ 654. ROGER CRAIG (M)
- ☐ 660. RICK REUSCHEL
- ☐ 677. EDDIE MILNER
- ☐ 703. BOB BRENLY
- ☐ 734. CRAIG LEFFERTS
- ☐ 754. MIKE LACOSS
- ☐ 786. JOE PRICE

SEATTLE MARINERS

- ☐ 32. MIKE MORGAN
- ☐ 55. PHIL BRADLEY
- ☐ 80. MARK LANGSTON
- ☐ 104. DICK WILLIAMS (M)
- ☐ 146. DONELL NIXON
- ☐ 156. GARY MATTHEWS
- ☐ 182. KEN PHELPS
- ☐ 206. DOMINGO RAMOS
- ☐ 246. MIKE CAMPBELL
- ☐ 258. ED NUNEZ
- ☐ 285. JIM PRESLEY
- ☐ 307. MIKE TRUJILLO
- ☐ 332. JERRY REED
- ☐ 358. REY QUINONES
- ☐ 376. BIL WILKINSON
- ☐ 413. JOHN CHRISTENSEN
- ☐ 432. MIKE MOORE
- ☐ 453. DENNIS POWELL
- ☐ 485. HAROLD REYNOLDS
- ☐ 519. TEAM LEADER CARD
- ☐ 532. MIKE KINGERY
- ☐ 556. STAN CLARKE
- ☐ 583. DAVE VALLE
- ☐ 632. STEVE SHIELDS
- ☐ 656. LEE GUETTERMAN
- ☐ 687. MIKEY BRANTLEY
- ☐ 712. JOHN MOSES
- ☐ 738. SCOTT BANKHEAD
- ☐ 762. SCOTT BRADLEY
- ☐ 785. ALVIN DAVIS

TEXAS RANGERS

- ☐ 26. MITCH WILLIAMS
- ☐ 53. CURT WILKERSON
- ☐ 77. TOM O'MALLEY
- ☐ 114. JEFF RUSSELL
- ☐ 139. JERRY BROWNE
- ☐ 163. DALE MOHORCIC
- ☐ 178. DWAYNE HENRY
- ☐ 201. TEAM LEADER CARD
- ☐ 219. MIKE STANLEY
- ☐ 227. ED CORREA
- ☐ 252. BOB BROWER
- ☐ 280. PETE INCAVIGLIA
- ☐ 319. MIKE LOYND
- ☐ 345. SCOTT FLETCHER
- ☐ 369. GREG HARRIS
- ☐ 427. PAUL KILGUS
- ☐ 462. DON SLAUGHT
- ☐ 490. LARRY PARRISH
- ☐ 537. STEVE BUECHELE
- ☐ 563. JOSE GUZMAN
- ☐ 589. GENO PETRALLI
- ☐ 594. BOBBY BALENTINE (M)
- ☐ 617. ODDIBE MCDOWELL
- ☐ 680. CHARLIE HOUGH
- ☐ 721. PETE O'BRIEN
- ☐ 747. BOBBY WITT
- ☐ 771. RUBEN SIERRA

TORONTO BLUE JAYS

- ☐ 28. JOSE NUNEZ
- ☐ 54. JIM CLANCY
- ☐ 79. ERNIE WHITT
- ☐ 113. KELLY GRUBER
- ☐ 140. JESSE BARFIELD
- ☐ 167. RANCE MULLINIKS
- ☐ 191. JOHN CERUTTI
- ☐ 205. NELSON LIRIANO
- ☐ 220. TOM HENKE
- ☐ 229. JEFF MUSSELMAN
- ☐ 273. GARTH IORG
- ☐ 290. TONY FERNANDEZ
- ☐ 314. JIMY WILLIAMS (M)
- ☐ 323. RICK LEACH
- ☐ 347. JOE JOHNSON
- ☐ 438. ROB DUCEY
- ☐ 463. FRED MCGRIFF
- ☐ 505. WILLIE UPSHAW
- ☐ 541. JUAN BENIQUEZ
- ☐ 565. LLOYD MOSEBY
- ☐ 590. GEORGE BELL
- ☐ 618. CECIL FIELDER
- ☐ 623. MIKE FLANAGAN
- ☐ 682. JIMMY KEY
- ☐ 696. DUANE WARD
- ☐ 722. MANNY LEE
- ☐ 729. TEAM LEADER CARD
- ☐ 749. MARK EICHHORN
- ☐ 775. DAVE STIEB

1988 TOPPS TRADED (132) 2 1/2 X 3 1/2

ATLANTA BRAVES

- ☐ 29T. KEVIN COFFMAN
- ☐ 39T. RON GANT
- ☐ 76T. RUSS NIXON (M)
- ☐ 111T. PETE SMITH

BALTIMORE ORIOLES

- ☐ 10T. JOSE BAUTISTA
- ☐ 73T. MIKE MORGAN
- ☐ 78T. JOE ORSULAK
- ☐ 96T. FRANK ROBINSON (M)
- ☐ 114T. PETE STANICEK
- ☐ 120T. MICKEY TETTLETON

BOSTON RED SOX

- ☐ 5T. BRADY ANDERSON
- ☐ 27T. RICK CERONE
- ☐ 110T. LEE SMITH

CALIFORNIA ANGELS

- ☐ 32T. CHILI DAVIS
- ☐ 45T. BRYAN HARVEY
- ☐ 85T. DAN PETRY
- ☐ 97T. COOKIE ROJAS (M)

CHICAGO CUBS

- ☐ 15T. DAMON BERRYHILL
- ☐ 41T. RICH GOSSAGE
- ☐ 42T. MARK GRACE
- ☐ 56T. DARRIN JACKSON
- ☐ 60T. VANCE LAW
- ☐ 75T. AL NIPPER
- ☐ 87T. JEFF PICO
- ☐ 104T. CALVIN SCHIRALDI
- ☐ 131T. DON ZIMMER (M)

CHICAGO WHITE SOX

- ☐ 51T. RICKY HORTON
- ☐ 68T. JACK MCDOWELL
- ☐ 82T. DAN PASQUA
- ☐ 83T. MELIDO PEREZ
- ☐ 99T. MARK SALAS

CINCINNATI REDS

- ☐ 6T. JACK ARMSTRONG
- ☐ 55T. DANNY JACKSON
- ☐ 92T. JOSE RIJO
- ☐ 98T. CHRIS SABO
- ☐ 122T. JEFF TREADWAY

CLEVELAND INDIANS

- ☐ 16T. BUD BLACK
- ☐ 58T. RON KITTLE
- ☐ 123T. WILLIE UPSHAW
- ☐ 125T. RON WASHINGTON

DETROIT TIGERS

- ☐ 59T. RAY KNIGHT
- ☐ 86T. GARY PETTIS
- ☐ 100T. LUIS SALAZAR

HOUSTON ASTROS

- ☐ 2T. JUAN AGOSTO
- ☐ 13T. BUDDY BELL
- ☐ 90T. RAFAEL RAMIREZ

KANSAS CITY ROYALS

- ☐ 8T. FLOYD BANNISTER
- ☐ 62T. MIKE MACFARLANE
- ☐ 63T. SCOTTI MADISON
- ☐ 89T. TED POWER
- ☐ 115T. KURT STILLWELL
- ☐ 118T. PAT TABLER

LOS ANGELES DODGERS

- ☐ 12T. TIM BELCHER
- ☐ 33T. MIKE DAVIS
- ☐ 40T. KIRK GIBSON
- ☐ 43T. ALFREDO GIRFFIN
- ☐ 52T. JAY HOWELL
- ☐ 77T. JESSE OROSCO

MILWAUKEE BREWERS

- ☐ 7T. DON AUGUST
- ☐ 37T. TOM FILER
- ☐ 61T. JEFFREY LEONARD

MINNESOTA TWINS

- ☐ 49T. TOM HERR

MONTREAL EXPOS

- ☐ 94T. LUIS RIVERA
- ☐ 102T. NELSON SANTOVENIA

NEW YORK METS

- ☐ 54T. JEFF INNIS
- ☐ 103T. MACKEY SASSER

NEW YORK YANKEES

- ☐ 21T. JAY BUHNER
- ☐ 25T. JOHN CANDELARIA
- ☐ 28T. JACK CLARK
- ☐ 35T. RICHARD DOTSON
- ☐ 57T. ROBERTO KELLY
- ☐ 101T. RAFAEL SANTANA
- ☐ 108T. DON SLAUGHT

OAKLAND A'S

- ☐ 11T. DON BAYLOR
- ☐ 46T. RON HASSEY
- ☐ 48T. DAVE HENDERSON
- ☐ 53T. GLENN HUBBARD
- ☐ 81T. DAVE PARKER
- ☐ 126T. WALT WEISS
- ☐ 127T. BOB WELCH

PHILADELPHIA PHILLIES

- ☐ 18T. PHIL BRADLEY
- ☐ 79T. DAVE PALMER

PITTSBURGH PIRATES

NO CARDS ISSUED

ST. LOUIS CARDINALS

- ☐ 3T. LUIS ALICEA
- ☐ 20T. TOM BRUNANSKY
- ☐ 34T. JOSE DELEON
- ☐ 50T. BOB HORNER
- ☐ 70T. LARRY MCWILLIAMS
- ☐ 84T. STEVE PETERS
- ☐ 119T. SCOTT TERRY

SAN DIEGO PADRES

- ☐ 4T. ROBERTO ALOMAR
- ☐ 69T. JACK MCKEON (M)
- ☐ 72T. KEITH MORELAND
- ☐ 80T. MARK PARENT
- ☐ 91T. DENNIS RASMUSSEN
- ☐ 121T. DICKIE THON

SAN FRANCISCO GIANTS

- ☐ 22T. BRETT BUTLER
- ☐ 64T. KIRT MANWARING
- ☐ 93T. EARNIE RILES

SEATTLE MARINERS

- ☐ 31T. HENRY COTTO
- ☐ 105T. MIKE SCHOOLER
- ☐ 112T. JIM SNYDER (M)
- ☐ 117T. BILL SWIFT
- ☐ 129T. GLENN WILSON

TEXAS RANGERS

- ☐ 26T. JOSE CECENA
- ☐ 36T. CECIL ESPY
- ☐ 47T. RAY HAYWARD

TORONTO BLUE JAYS

- ☐ 17T. PAT BORDERS
- ☐ 24T. SIL CAMPUSANO
- ☐ 116T. TODD STOTTLEMYRE
- ☐ 128T. DAVID WELLS

U. S. OLYMPIC TEAM

- ☐ 1T. JIM ABBOTT
- ☐ 9T. BRET BARBERIE
- ☐ 14T. ANDY BENES
- ☐ 19T. JEFF BARNSON
- ☐ 23T. JIM CAMPANIS
- ☐ 30T. PAT COMBS
- ☐ 38T. MIKE FIORE
- ☐ 44T. TY GRIFFIN
- ☐ 65T. MARK MARQUESS (HC)
- ☐ 66T. TINO MARTINEZ
- ☐ 67T. BILLY MASSE
- ☐ 71T. MICKEY MORANDINI
- ☐ 74T. CHARLES NAGY

- ☐ 88T. JIM POOLE
- ☐ 95T. DOUG ROBBINS
- ☐ 106T. SCOTT SERVAIS
- ☐ 107T. DAVE SILVESTRI
- ☐ 109T. JOE SLUSARSKI
- ☐ 113T. ED SPRAGUE
- ☐ 124T. ROBIN VENTURA
- ☐ 130T. TED WOOD

1989 TOPPS (792)
2 1/2 X 3 1/2

ATLANTA BRAVES

- ☐ 11. BRUCE SUTTER
- ☐ 38. PAUL RUNGE
- ☐ 76. TERRY BLOCKER
- ☐ 83. JEFF BLAUSER
- ☐ 130. GERALD PERRY
- ☐ 157. TOM GLAVINE
- ☐ 171. TEAM LEADER CARD
- ☐ 179. OZZIE VIRGIL
- ☐ 210. DALE MURPHY
- ☐ 244. JIM ACKER
- ☐ 253. JOSE ALVAREZ
- ☐ 296. RON GANT
- ☐ 327. MARK LEMKE
- ☐ 382. JOHN SMOLTZ
- ☐ 433. ALBERT HALL
- ☐ 454. PAUL ASSENMACHER
- ☐ 488. KEVIN COFFMAN
- ☐ 523. ANDRES THOMAS
- ☐ 537. PETE SMITH
- ☐ 564. RUSS NIXON (M)
- ☐ 569. GERMAN JIMENEZ
- ☐ 586. JOE BOEVER
- ☐ 621. RICK MAHLER
- ☐ 678. DION JAMES
- ☐ 688. ZANE SMITH
- ☐ 728. CHARLIE PULEO
- ☐ 778. BRUCE BENEDICT
- ☐ 784. STEVE AVERY

BALTIMORE ORIOLES

- ☐ 13. DOUG SISK
- ☐ 69. JEFF BALLARD
- ☐ 98. LARRY SHEETS
- ☐ 124. JIM TRABER
- ☐ 152. MARK THURMOND
- ☐ 161. GREGG OLSON
- ☐ 181. CRAIG WORTHINGTON
- ☐ 213. RENE GONZALES
- ☐ 250. CAL RIPKEN
- ☐ 271. JAY TIBBS
- ☐ 297. OSWALD PERAZA
- ☐ 324. BOB MILACKI
- ☐ 352. RICK SCHU
- ☐ 381. TEAM LEADER CARD
- ☐ 469. JOSE BAUTISTA
- ☐ 497. PETE STANICEK
- ☐ 521. MICKEY TETTLETON
- ☐ 546. MARK WILLIAMSON
- ☐ 571. BILLY RIPKEN
- ☐ 598. KEN GERHART
- ☐ 625. EDDIE MURRAY
- ☐ 651. TOM NIEDENFUER
- ☐ 677. DAVE SCHMIDT
- ☐ 705. TERRY KENNEDY
- ☐ 727. JOE ORSULAK
- ☐ 757. BRADY ANDERSON
- ☐ 774. FRANK ROBINSON (M)
- ☐ 788. MIKE MORGAN

BOSTON RED SOX

- ☐ 37. BOB STANLEY
- ☐ 71. MIKE BODDICKER
- ☐ 96. RICK CERONE
- ☐ 123. SPIKE OWEN
- ☐ 155. MARTY BARRETT
- ☐ 188. DENNIS LAMP
- ☐ 205. DWIGHT EVANS
- ☐ 245. JIM RICE
- ☐ 269. TOM BOLTON
- ☐ 299. STEVE ELLSWORTH
- ☐ 321. TEAM LEADER CARD
- ☐ 326. DENNIS BOYD
- ☐ 354. LARRY PARRISH
- ☐ 377. MIKE SMITHSON
- ☐ 450. ROGER CLEMENS
- ☐ 471. STEVE CURRY
- ☐ 493. TODD BENZINGER
- ☐ 526. WES GARDNER
- ☐ 544. JEFF SELLERS
- ☐ 600. WADE BOGGS
- ☐ 630. MIKE GREENWELL
- ☐ 652. RICH GEDMAN
- ☐ 675. BRUCE HURST
- ☐ 704. CARLOS QUINTANA
- ☐ 714. JOE MORGAN (M)
- ☐ 734. JODY REED
- ☐ 760. LEE SMITH
- ☐ 785. ELLIS BURKS

CALIFORNIA ANGELS

- ☐ 17. BRIAN DOWNING
- ☐ 42. JIM EPPARD
- ☐ 51. TEAM LEADER CARD
- ☐ 68. DARRELL MILLER
- ☐ 99. SHERMAN CORBETT
- ☐ 129. TERRY CLARK
- ☐ 147. DEWAYNE BUICE
- ☐ 190. MIKE WITT
- ☐ 216. JACK HOWELL
- ☐ 243. BOB BOONE
- ☐ 270. WALLY JOYNER
- ☐ 332. TONY ARMAS
- ☐ 362. JACK LAZORKO
- ☐ 421. KIRK MCCASKILL
- ☐ 444. MOOSE STUBING (M)
- ☐ 455. JOHNNY RAY
- ☐ 477. DICK SCHOFIELD
- ☐ 525. CHILI DAVIS
- ☐ 547. MARK MCLEMORE
- ☐ 573. JIM ABBOTT
- ☐ 576. GREG MINTON
- ☐ 602. DEVON WHITE
- ☐ 632. BRYAN HARVEY
- ☐ 649. STEWART CLIBURN
- ☐ 679. WILLIE FRASER
- ☐ 708. CHUCK FINLEY
- ☐ 761. DANTE BICHETTE

CHICAGO CUBS

- ☐ 10. ANDRE DAWSON
- ☐ 36. MITCH WEBSTER
- ☐ 66. MANNY TRILLO
- ☐ 86. AL NIPPER
- ☐ 115. JODY DAVIS
- ☐ 134. DON ZIMMER (M)
- ☐ 140. SHAWON DUNSTON
- ☐ 149. DOUG DASCENZO
- ☐ 186. PAT PERRY
- ☐ 212. SCOTT SANDERSON
- ☐ 240. GREG MADDUX
- ☐ 262. JEFF PICO
- ☐ 286. DARRIN JACKSON
- ☐ 310. RAFAEL PALMEIRO
- ☐ 337. CALVIN SCHIRALDI
- ☐ 360. RYNE SANDBERG
- ☐ 415. RICH GOSSAGE
- ☐ 439. FRANK DIPINO
- ☐ 465. MARK GRACE
- ☐ 501. VANCE LAW
- ☐ 520. RICK SUTCLIFFE
- ☐ 543. DAMON BERRYHILL
- ☐ 549. TEAM LEADER CARD
- ☐ 593. DREW HALL
- ☐ 613. GARY VARSHO
- ☐ 642. ARGENIS SALAZAR
- ☐ 668. MIKE BIELECKI
- ☐ 694. LES LANCASTER
- ☐ 713. TY GRIFFIN
- ☐ 717. JAMIE MOYER
- ☐ 742. MIKE HARKEY
- ☐ 767. MIKE CAPEL

CHICAGO WHITE SOX

- ☐ 21. TEAM LEADER CARD
- ☐ 34. KEN WILLIAMS
- ☐ 108. FRED MANRIQUE
- ☐ 122. LANCE JOHNSON
- ☐ 133. BILL LONG
- ☐ 142. MIKE DIAZ
- ☐ 156. DAVE GALLAGHER
- ☐ 162. JOHN DAVIS
- ☐ 195. OZZIE GUILLEN
- ☐ 209. JEFF BITTIGER
- ☐ 247. SHAWN HILLEGAS
- ☐ 308. RON KARKOVICE
- ☐ 334. STEVE LYONS
- ☐ 357. JERRY REUSS
- ☐ 384. MARK SALAS
- ☐ 408. GREG WALKER
- ☐ 414. JIM FREGOSI (M)
- ☐ 434. KEN PATTERSON
- ☐ 458. DONN PALL
- ☐ 486. JACK MCDOWELL
- ☐ 512. DONNIE HILL
- ☐ 539. BARRY JONES
- ☐ 558. DAN PASQUA
- ☐ 585. HAROLD BAINES
- ☐ 616. STEVE ROSENBERG
- ☐ 633. DARYL BOSTON
- ☐ 656. IVAN CALDERON
- ☐ 695. CARLTON FISK
- ☐ 762. BOBBY THIGPEN
- ☐ 764. ROBIN VENTURA
- ☐ 786. MELIDO PEREZ

CINCINNATTI REDS

- ☐ 16. RON ROBINSON
- ☐ 45. KAL DANIELS
- ☐ 103. TIM BIRTSAS
- ☐ 111. TEAM LEADER CARD
- ☐ 135. JOSE RIJO
- ☐ 151. TERRY MCGRIFF
- ☐ 172. FRANK WILLIAMS
- ☐ 234. TOM BROWNING
- ☐ 264. ROB DIBBLE
- ☐ 290. JOHN FRANCO
- ☐ 317. JACK ARMSTRONG
- ☐ 330. ERIC DAVIS
- ☐ 366. HERM WINNINGHAM
- ☐ 422. BO DIAZ
- ☐ 446. ROB MURPHY
- ☐ 490. CHRIS SABO
- ☐ 505. PETE ROSE (M)
- ☐ 515. BARRY LARKIN
- ☐ 554. NICK ESASKY
- ☐ 604. PAUL O'NEILL
- ☐ 626. JEFF REED
- ☐ 644. LLOYD MCCLENDON
- ☐ 666. RANDY ST. CLAIRE
- ☐ 685. JEFF TREADWAY
- ☐ 711. CANDY SIERRA
- ☐ 730. DANNY JACKSON
- ☐ 737. NORM CHARLTON
- ☐ 772. RON OESTER

CLEVELAND INDIANS

- ☐ 31. TERRY FRANCONA
- ☐ 55. JULIO FRANCO
- ☐ 80. CORY SNYDER
- ☐ 106. WILLIE UPSHAW
- ☐ 141. TEAM LEADER CARD
- ☐ 144. JAY BELL
- ☐ 173. MEL HALL
- ☐ 204. BRAD HAVENS
- ☐ 222. MARK LEWIS
- ☐ 227. JOHN FARRELL
- ☐ 283. ANDY ALLANSON
- ☐ 315. GREG SWINDELL
- ☐ 339. SCOTT BAILES
- ☐ 363. RICH YETT
- ☐ 420. JOE CARTER
- ☐ 443. ROD NICHOLS
- ☐ 476. JON PERLMAN
- ☐ 509. BUD BLACK

- □ 528. LUIS MEDINA
- □ 534. DOC EDWARDS (M)
- □ 574. DAVE CLARK
- □ 599. TOM CANDIOTTI
- □ 637. CARMEN CASTILLO
- □ 690. DOUG JONES
- □ 721. RON TINGLEY
- □ 739. BROOK JACOBY
- □ 771. RON KITTLE

DETROIT TIGERS

- □ 43. WILLIE HERNANDEZ
- □ 77. DOYLE ALEXANDER
- □ 127. WALT TERRELL
- □ 146. GARY PETTIS
- □ 167. STEVE SEARCY
- □ 193. SPARKY ANDERSON (M)
- □ 238. ERIC KING
- □ 267. JEFF ROBINSON
- □ 288. PAT SHERIDAN
- □ 320. LOU WHITAKER
- □ 342. TOM BOOKENS
- □ 365. MIKE HENNEMAN
- □ 416. FRED LYNN
- □ 445. MATT NOKES
- □ 467. JIM WALEWANDER
- □ 487. SCOTT LUSADER
- □ 499. DON HEINKEL
- □ 514. CHET LEMON
- □ 553. LUIS SALAZAR
- □ 583. PAUL GIBSON
- □ 603. FRANK TANANA
- □ 609. TEAM LEADER CARD
- □ 631. DAVE BERGMAN
- □ 645. JACK MORRIS
- □ 667. DWAYNE MURPHY
- □ 743. MIKE HEATH
- □ 770. ALAN TRAMMELL
- □ 777. TED POWER

HOUSTON ASTROS

- □ 24. LARRY ANDERSEN
- □ 49. CRAIG BIGGIO
- □ 64. ALEX TREVINE
- □ 95. GERALD YOUNG
- □ 119. TERRY PUHL
- □ 153. JIM PANKOVITS
- □ 163. BOB FORSCH
- □ 164. HAL LANIER (M)
- □ 180. MIKE SCOTT
- □ 226. BILL DORAN
- □ 252. BILLY HATCHER
- □ 280. BOB KNEPPER
- □ 305. DAVE SMITH
- □ 341. JIM DESHAIES
- □ 369. KEN CAMINITI
- □ 428. CRAIG REYNOLDS
- □ 461. BUDDY BELL
- □ 492. ALAN ASHBY
- □ 530. NOLAN RYAN
- □ 559. JUAN AGOSTO
- □ 579. TEAM LEADER CARD
- □ 589. DAVE MEADS
- □ 607. WILLIE ANSLEY
- □ 643. LOUIE MEADOWS
- □ 646. KEVIN BASS
- □ 719. DANNY DARWIN
- □ 749. RAFAEL RAMIREZ
- □ 765. GLENN DAVIS

KANSAS CITY ROYALS

- □ 25. FRANK WHITE
- □ 56. PAT TABLER
- □ 87. LARRY OWEN
- □ 116. JEFF MONTGOMERY
- □ 148. BILL PECOTA
- □ 168. WILLIE WILSON
- □ 200. GEORGE BRETT
- □ 266. LUIS AQUINO
- □ 275. DANNY TARTABULL
- □ 301. CHARLIE LEIBRANDT
- □ 323. GARY THURMAN
- □ 348. ED HEARN
- □ 374. JOHN WATHAN (M)
- □ 430. MARK GUBICZA
- □ 452. ISRAEL SANCHEZ
- □ 479. MIKE MACFARLANE
- □ 507. STEVE FARR
- □ 540. BO JACKSON
- □ 596. KURT STILLWELL
- □ 638. FLOYD BANNISTER
- □ 670. KEVIN SEITZER
- □ 702. JAMIE QUIRK
- □ 724. JERRY DON GLEATON
- □ 750. BRET SABERHAGER
- □ 789. TEAM LEADER CARD

LOS ANGELES DODGERS

- □ 22. TIM CREWS
- □ 35. JOHN TUDOR
- □ 40. STEVE SAX
- □ 57. ALEJANDRO PENA
- □ 62. ALFREDO GRIFFIN
- □ 84. BILL BENE
- □ 93. KEN HOWELL
- □ 117. DAVE ANDERSON
- □ 150. FERNANDO VALENZUELA
- □ 175. JOHN SHELBY
- □ 198. DANNY HEEP
- □ 225. RAMON MARTINEZ
- □ 232. RICKY HORTON
- □ 249. TIM LEARY
- □ 254. TOM LASORDA (M)
- □ 277. MIKE DAVIS
- □ 306. TRACY WOODSON
- □ 340. KIRK GIBSON
- □ 368. BRIAN HOLTON
- □ 425. JAY HOWELL
- □ 456. TIM BELCHER
- □ 483. MICKEY HATCHER
- □ 513. JESSE OROSCO
- □ 550. OREL HERSHISER
- □ 582. MIKE MARSHALL
- □ 606. RICK DEMPSEY
- □ 669. TEAM LEADER CARD
- □ 697. FRANKLIN STUBBS
- □ 736. JEFF HAMILTON
- □ 755. MIKE SCIOSCIA

MILWAUKEE BREWERS

- □ 12. DALE SVEUM
- □ 33. B. J. SURHOFF
- □ 63. MARK CLEAR
- □ 88. DARRYL HAMILTON
- □ 110. PAUL MOLITOR
- □ 136. JOEY MEYER
- □ 160. JEFFREY LEONARD
- □ 192. PAUL MIRABELLA
- □ 214. CHARLIE O'BRIEN
- □ 263. MIKE FELDER
- □ 287. JUAN NIEVES
- □ 311. CHRIS BOSIO
- □ 338. JIM ADDUCI
- □ 343. GARY SHEFFIELD
- □ 344. TOM TREBELHORN (M)
- □ 364. ROB DEER
- □ 419. TOM FILER
- □ 466. CHUCK CRIM
- □ 491. MIKE BIRKBECK
- □ 517. GREG BROCK
- □ 538. JUAN CASTILLO
- □ 563. BILL SCHROEDER
- □ 595. TEDDY HIGUERA
- □ 615. ROBIN YOUNT
- □ 671. JIM GANTNER
- □ 696. DON AUGUST
- □ 718. GLENN BRAGGS
- □ 731. MIKE YOUNG
- □ 740. DAN PLESAC
- □ 759. TEAM LEADER CARD
- □ 768. BILL WEGMAN

MINNESOTA TWINS

- □ 14. TOM KELLY (M)
- □ 19. GREG GAGNE
- □ 46. MARK PORTUGAL
- □ 72. JOHN MOSES
- □ 101. LES STRAKER
- □ 120. FRANK VIOLA
- □ 220. GARY GAETTI
- □ 239. TIM LAUDNER
- □ 265. KENT HRBEK
- □ 294. JUAN BERENGUER
- □ 318. GENE LARKIN
- □ 376. STEVE LOMBARDOZZI
- □ 426. DANNY GLADDEN
- □ 429. TEAM LEADER CARD
- □ 451. MARK DAVIDSON
- □ 472. BRIAN HARPER
- □ 503. AL NEWMAN
- □ 555. BERT BLYLEVEN
- □ 577. RANDY BUSH
- □ 623. FRED TOLIVER
- □ 650. KIRBY PUCKETT
- □ 672. ALLAN ANDERSON
- □ 698. KEITH ATHERTON
- □ 709. TOM HERR
- □ 746. GERMAN GONZALEZ
- □ 775. JEFF REARDON

MONTREAL EXPOS

- □ 23. MIKE FITZGERALD
- □ 48. TIM BURKE
- □ 73. PASCUAL PEREZ
- □ 81. TEAM LEADER CARD
- □ 91. FLOYD YOUMANS
- □ 138. WALLACE JOHNSON
- □ 176. JEFF PARRETT
- □ 197. NEAL HEATON
- □ 228. NELSON SANTOVENIA
- □ 251. JOHN DOPSON
- □ 278. ANDY MCGAFFIGAN
- □ 313. DENNY MARTINEZ
- □ 346. REX HUDLER
- □ 367. JOHNNY PAREDES
- □ 373. TRACY JONES
- □ 431. LUIS RIVERA
- □ 464. BRYN SMITH
- □ 474. BOB RODGERS (M)
- □ 485. HUBIE BROOKS
- □ 529. TOM FOLEY
- □ 560. TIM RAINES
- □ 590. ANDRES GALARRAGA
- □ 614. JOE HESKETH
- □ 647. RANDY JOHNSON
- □ 674. OTIS NIXON
- □ 720. TIM WALLACH
- □ 747. WIL TEJADA
- □ 763. DAVE MARTINEZ

NEW YORK METS

- □ 9. TIM TEUFEL
- □ 30. DWIGHT GOODEN
- □ 58. LEE MAZZILLI
- □ 85. KEVIN MCREYNOLDS
- □ 105. RON DARLING
- □ 182. BOB MCCLURE
- □ 207. TERRY LEACH
- □ 233. GREGG JEFFERIES
- □ 257. RICK AGUILERA
- □ 291. TEAM LEADER CARD
- □ 300. DARRYL STRAWBERRY
- □ 333. BOB OJEDA
- □ 356. KEVIN ELSTER
- □ 383. HOWARD JOHNSON
- □ 412. BARRY LYONS
- □ 435. LEN DYKSTRA
- □ 457. MACKEY SASSER
- □ 480. KEITH HERNANDEZ
- □ 508. WALLY BACKMAN
- □ 545. MOOKIE WILSON
- □ 557. KEITH MILLER
- □ 610. RANDY MYERS
- □ 655. DAVE MAGADAN
- □ 680. GARY CARTER
- □ 684. DAVE JOHNSON (M)
- □ 710. DAVE CONE
- □ 735. ROGER MCDOWELL
- □ 787. DAVE WEST
- □ 790. SID FERNANDEZ

NEW YORK YANKEES

- ☐ 8. DAVE EILAND
- ☐ 18. RICK RHODEN
- ☐ 26. DALE MOHORÇIC
- ☐ 61. NEIL ALLEN
- ☐ 104. DALLAS GREEN (M)
- ☐ 109. HIPOLITO PENA
- ☐ 159. PAT CLEMENTS
- ☐ 185. CLAUDELL WASHINGTON
- ☐ 211. MIKE PAGLIARULO
- ☐ 236. CHARLES HUDSON
- ☐ 255. RON GUIDRY
- ☐ 260. DAVE WINFIELD
- ☐ 285. JOHN CANDELARIA
- ☐ 302. GARY WARD
- ☐ 335. DAVE RIGHETTI
- ☐ 359. TOMMY JOHN
- ☐ 380. RICKEY HENDERSON
- ☐ 410. JACK CLARK
- ☐ 436. BOBBY MEACHAM
- ☐ 484. STEVE SHIELDS
- ☐ 511. RICHARD DOTSON
- ☐ 519. TEAM LEADER CARD
- ☐ 536. JOEL SKINNER
- ☐ 561. LUIS AGUAYO
- ☐ 584. RANDY VELARDE
- ☐ 611. DON SLAUGHT
- ☐ 635. WILLIE RANDOLPH
- ☐ 659. AL LEITER
- ☐ 691. ROBERTO KELLY
- ☐ 700. DON MATTINGLY
- ☐ 716. WAYNE TOLLESON
- ☐ 741. KEN PHELPS
- ☐ 792. RAFAEL SANTANA

OAKLAND A'S

- ☐ 47. CARNEY LANSFORD
- ☐ 70. MARK MCGWIRE
- ☐ 102. MIKE GALLEGO
- ☐ 131. DAVE OTTO
- ☐ 145. DAVE STEWART
- ☐ 166. DOUG JENNINGS
- ☐ 174. TODD BURNS
- ☐ 224. TONY LARUSSA (M)
- ☐ 237. GLENN HUBBARD
- ☐ 248. TONY PHILLIPS
- ☐ 272. RON HASSEY
- ☐ 292. JIM CORSI
- ☐ 316. WALT WEISS
- ☐ 328. RICK HONEYCUTT
- ☐ 370. DENNIS ECKERSLEY
- ☐ 424. LUIS POLONIA
- ☐ 448. ERIC PLUNK
- ☐ 475. DAVE PARKER
- ☐ 500. JOSE CANSECO
- ☐ 527. DAVE HENDERSON
- ☐ 552. GREG CADARET
- ☐ 581. GENE NELSON
- ☐ 605. BOB WELCH
- ☐ 622. STAN JAVIER
- ☐ 639. TEAM LEADER CARD
- ☐ 641. CURT YOUNG
- ☐ 673. DON BAYLOR
- ☐ 692. STEVE ONTIVEROS
- ☐ 701. STORM DAVIS
- ☐ 725. TERRY STEINBACH

PHILADELPHIA PHILLIES

- ☐ 20. STEVE BEDROSIAN
- ☐ 39. MIKE MADDUX
- ☐ 67. DAVE PALMER
- ☐ 74. NICK LEYVA (M)
- ☐ 100. MIKE SCHMIDT
- ☐ 128. MILT THOMPSON
- ☐ 154. DON CARMAN
- ☐ 187. DARREN DAULTON
- ☐ 202. BRAD MOORE
- ☐ 215. KEVIN GROSS
- ☐ 268. KEITH MILLER
- ☐ 298. CHRIS JAMES
- ☐ 349. RON JONES
- ☐ 358. RICKY JORDAN
- ☐ 385. VON HAYES
- ☐ 418. BOB DERNIER
- ☐ 438. GREG GROSS
- ☐ 470. LANCE PARRISH
- ☐ 489. TEAM LEADER CARD
- ☐ 494. SHANE RAWLEY
- ☐ 518. BRUCE RUFFIN
- ☐ 542. TODD FROHWIRTH
- ☐ 575. JUAN SAMUEL
- ☐ 608. PHIL BRADLEY
- ☐ 627. GREG HARRIS
- ☐ 634. MARVIN FREEMAN
- ☐ 653. TOMMY BARRETT
- ☐ 707. STEVE JELTZ

PITTSBURGH PIRATES

- ☐ 27. ORESTES DESTRADE
- ☐ 89. DAVE LAPOINT
- ☐ 114. BOB KIPPER
- ☐ 126. SID BREAM
- ☐ 165. MIKE DUNNE
- ☐ 218. MIKE LAVALLIER
- ☐ 273. JOSE LIND
- ☐ 281. GARY REDUS
- ☐ 284. JIM LEYLAND (M)
- ☐ 293. GLENN WILSON
- ☐ 303. FELIX FERMIN
- ☐ 322. JOHN SMILEY
- ☐ 350. ANDY VAN SLYKE
- ☐ 423. BRIAN FISHER
- ☐ 440. BOBBY BONILLA
- ☐ 453. TOM PRINCE
- ☐ 478. DOUG DRABEK
- ☐ 504. BOB WALK
- ☐ 522. RANDY KRAMER
- ☐ 566. AL PEDRIQUE
- ☐ 592. JOHN CANGELOSI
- ☐ 620. BARRY BONDS
- ☐ 658. R. J. REYNOLDS
- ☐ 681. JEFF ROBINSON
- ☐ 699. TEAM LEADER CARD
- ☐ 723. RAFAEL BELLIARD
- ☐ 751. KEN OBERKFELL
- ☐ 752. JIM GOTT
- ☐ 756. SCOTT MEDVIN
- ☐ 769. JUNIOR ORTIZ

ST. LOUIS CARDINALS

- ☐ 60. TOM BRUNANSKY
- ☐ 90. VINCE COLEMAN
- ☐ 97. GREG MATHEWS
- ☐ 107. JOSE DELEON
- ☐ 132. CURT FORD
- ☐ 184. JOHN COSTELLO
- ☐ 196. DENNY WALLING
- ☐ 208. TOM PAGNOZZI
- ☐ 230. OZZIE SMITH
- ☐ 259. LARRY MCWILLIAMS
- ☐ 261. TEAM LEADER CARD
- ☐ 282. CHRIS CARPENTER
- ☐ 312. TOM LAWLESS
- ☐ 375. TERRY PENDLETON
- ☐ 409. KEN DAYLEY
- ☐ 442. JOSE OQUENDO
- ☐ 463. STEVE LAKE
- ☐ 482. STEVE PETERS
- ☐ 510. BOB HORNER
- ☐ 535. TODD WORRELL
- ☐ 562. DANNY COX
- ☐ 578. JOHN MORRIS
- ☐ 588. LUIS ALICEA
- ☐ 612. DAN QUISENBERRY
- ☐ 640. WILLIE MCGEE
- ☐ 654. WHITEY HERZOG (M)
- ☐ 657. JOE MAGRANE
- ☐ 686. SCOTT TERRY
- ☐ 715. TONY PENA
- ☐ 780. PEDRO GUERRERO
- ☐ 791. JIM LINDEMAN

SAN DIEGO PADRES

- ☐ 32. DENNIS RASMUSSEN
- ☐ 59. MARK DAVIS
- ☐ 82. DAVE LEIPER
- ☐ 121. GARRY TEMPLETON
- ☐ 178. MARK GRANT
- ☐ 194. GREG HARRIS
- ☐ 206. ROBERTO ALOMAR
- ☐ 231. TEAM LEADER CARD
- ☐ 235. JOHN KRUK
- ☐ 256. BENNY SANTIAGO
- ☐ 307. LANCE MCCULLERS
- ☐ 319. GREG BOOKER
- ☐ 353. MARVELL WYNNE
- ☐ 379. TIM FLANNERY
- ☐ 427. ERIC SHOW
- ☐ 437. ANDY BENES
- ☐ 449. CARMELO MARTINEZ
- ☐ 481. CHRIS BROWN
- ☐ 516. EDDIE WHITSON
- ☐ 533. ANDY HAWKINS
- ☐ 551. RANDY READY
- ☐ 570. TONY GWYNN
- ☐ 617. MARK PARENT
- ☐ 624. JACK MCKEON (M)
- ☐ 648. SANDY ALOMAR
- ☐ 689. STAN JEFFERSON
- ☐ 726. DICKIE THON
- ☐ 748. JIMMY JONES
- ☐ 773. KEITH MORELAND

SAN FRANCISCO GIANTS

- ☐ 15. ROBBY THOMPSON
- ☐ 41. TERRY MULHOLLAND
- ☐ 52. BOB BRENLY
- ☐ 65. RICK REUSCHEL
- ☐ 94. CHRIS SPEIER
- ☐ 125. MIKE KRUKOW
- ☐ 158. MIKE ALDRETE
- ☐ 189. KEVIN MITCHELL
- ☐ 217. JOE PRICE
- ☐ 241. BRETT BUTLER
- ☐ 304. JOEL YOUNGBLOOD
- ☐ 329. BOB MELVIN
- ☐ 351. TEAM LEADER CARD
- ☐ 361. KELLY DOWNS
- ☐ 372. CRAIG LEFFERTS
- ☐ 417. MIKE LACROSS
- ☐ 447. DONELL NIXON
- ☐ 473. DON ROBINSON
- ☐ 495. CANDY MALDONADO
- ☐ 506. KIRT MANWARING
- ☐ 572. ATLEE HAMMAKER
- ☐ 601. DAVE DRAVECKY
- ☐ 628. MATT WILLIAMS
- ☐ 660. WILL CLARK
- ☐ 676. ERNIE RILES
- ☐ 703. SCOTT GARRELTS
- ☐ 733. RANDY BOCKUS
- ☐ 744. ROGER CRAIG (M)
- ☐ 753. JOSE URIBE
- ☐ 783. TREVOR WILSON

SEATTLE MARINERS

- ☐ 28. MIKE MOORE
- ☐ 44. JIM SNYDER (M)
- ☐ 54. STEVE TROUT
- ☐ 79. SCOTT BANKHEAD
- ☐ 112. JIM PRESLEY
- ☐ 143. MIKE CAMPBELL
- ☐ 169. MIKE JACKSON
- ☐ 199. MIKE SCHOOLER
- ☐ 223. JAY BUHNER
- ☐ 246. REY QUINONES
- ☐ 279. SCOTT BRADLEY
- ☐ 309. MARIO DIAZ
- ☐ 336. STEVE BALBONI
- ☐ 355. MARK LANGSTON
- ☐ 413. MIKE KINGERY
- ☐ 441. JERRY REED
- ☐ 459. TEAM LEADER CARD
- ☐ 468. HENRY COTTO
- ☐ 498. DAVE VALLE
- ☐ 531. DAVE HENGEL
- ☐ 556. BRUCE FIELDS
- ☐ 568. MICKEY BRANTLEY

□ 580. HAROLD REYNOLDS
□ 597. TERRY TAYLOR
□ 636. BILL WILKINSON
□ 687. ALVIN DAVIS
□ 712. BILL SWIFT
□ 738. DARNELL COLES
□ 758. GENE WALTER
□ 781. GREG BRILEY

TEXAS RANGERS

□ 53. RUBEN SIERRA
□ 78. JIM SUNDBERG
□ 92. JEFF KUNKEL
□ 137. GENO.PETRALLI
□ 177. MONTY FARISS
□ 183. ODDIBE MCDOWELL
□ 221. CECIL ESPY
□ 242. ED VANDEBERG
□ 276. PAUL KILGUS
□ 295. SCOTT FLETCHER
□ 314. BOBBY VALENTINE (M)
□ 331. CURT WILKERSON
□ 345. CHARLIE HOUGH
□ 411. MITCH WILLIAMS
□ 432. CHAD KREUTER
□ 462. JOSE GUZMAN
□ 496. DWAYANE HENRY
□ 532. JERRY BROWNE
□ 548. BOBBY WITT
□ 565. JEFF RUSSELL
□ 587. MIKE STANLEY
□ 629. PETE O'BRIEN
□ 683. JOSE CECENA
□ 706. PETE INCAVIGLIA
□ 729. TEAM LEADER CARD
□ 732. STEVE BUECHELE
□ 754. BOB BROWER
□ 766. CECILIO GUANTE
□ 779. CRAIG MCMURTRY

TORONTO BLUE JAYS

□ 29. KELLY GRUBER
□ 50. GEORGE BELL
□ 75. TOM HENKE
□ 113. LLOYD MOSEBY
□ 139. MIKE FLANAGAN
□ 170. TONY FERNANDEZ
□ 191. SIL CAMPUSANO
□ 201. TEAM LEADER CARD
□ 203. ROB DUCEY
□ 219. JIM CLANCY
□ 229. JIMMY KEY
□ 274. MARK EICHHORN
□ 289. ERNIE WHITT
□ 325. JESSE BARFIELD
□ 347. JOHN CERUTTI
□ 371. MANNY LEE
□ 460. DAVE STIEB
□ 502. DUANE WARD
□ 541. CECIL FIELDER
□ 567. DAVID WELLS
□ 591. JEFF MUSSELMAN
□ 594. JIMY WILLIAMS (M)
□ 618. RANCE MULLINIKS
□ 682. RICK LEACH
□ 693. PAT BORDERS
□ 722. TODD STOTTLEMYRE
□ 745. FRED MCGRIFF
□ 776. NELSON LIRIANO

1989 TOPPS TRADED (132) 2 1/2" X 3 1/2"

ATLANTA BRAVES

□ 10T. GERONIMO BERROA
□ 22T. JODY DAVIS
□ 31T. DARRELL EVANS
□ 39T. TOMMY GREGG
□ 73T. DEREK LILLIQUIST
□ 78T. ODDIBE MCDOWELL
□ 114T. LONNIE SMITH
□ 121T. JEFF TREADWAY

BALTIMORE ORIOLES

□ 13T. PHIL BRADLEY
□ 23T. MIKE DEVEREAUX
□ 52T. BRIAN HOLTON
□ 81T. RANDY MILLIGAN
□ 89T. GREGG OLSON

BOSTON RED SOX

□ 26T. JOHN DOPSON
□ 29T. NICK ESASKY
□ 64T. RANDY KUTCHER
□ 86T. ROB MURPHY
□ 105T. ED ROMERO

CALIFORNIA ANGELS

□ 2T. JIM ABBOTT
□ 3T. KENT ANDERSON
□ 11T. BERT BLYLEVEN
□ 96T. LANCE PARRISH
□ 99T. DOUG RADER (M)
□ 125T. CLAUDELL WASHINGTON

CHICAGO CUBS

□ 60T. PAUL KILGUS
□ 76T. LLOYD MCCLENDON
□ 113T. DWIGHT SMITH
□ 123T. JEROME WALTON
□ 126T. CURT WILKERSON
□ 130T. MITCH WILLIAMS
□ 131T. STEVE WILSON

CHICAGO WHITE SOX

□ 61T. ERIC KING
□ 62T. RON KITTLE
□ 75T. TOM MCCARTHY
□ 120T. JEFF TORBORG (M)
□ 127T. EDDIE WILLIAMS

CINCINNATI REDS

□ 9T. TODD BENZINGER
□ 40T. KEN GRIFFEY
□ 74T. RICK MAHLER
□ 116T. KENT TEKULVE

CLEVELAND INDIANS

□ 4T. KEITH ATHERTON
□ 16T. JERRY BROWNE
□ 33T. FELIX FERMIN
□ 88T. PETE O'BRIEN
□ 91T. JESSE OROSCO

DETROIT TIGERS

□ 83T. KEITH MORELAND
□ 112T. RICK SCHU
□ 124T. GARY WARD
□ 128T. FRANK WILLIAMS
□ 129T. KEN WILLIAMS

HOUSTON ASTROS

□ 19T. JIM CLANCY
□ 53T. ART HOWE (M)

KANSAS CITY ROYALS

□ 12T. BOB BOONE
□ 28T. JIM EISENREICH
□ 38T. TOM GORDON
□ 69T. TERRY LEACH

LOS ANGELES DODGERS

□ 84T. MIKE MORGAN
□ 87T. EDDIE MURRAY
□ 100T. WILLIE RANDOLPH

MILWAUKEE BREWERS

□ 21T. BRYAN CLUTTERBUCK
□ 35T. TERRY FRANCONA
□ 115T. BILLY SPIERS

MINNESOTA TWINS

□ 5T. WALLY BACKMAN
□ 18T. CARMEN CASTILLO
□ 101T. SHANE RAWLEY

MONTREAL EXPOS

□ 42T. KEVIN GROSS
□ 66T. MARK LANGSTON
□ 92T. SPIKE OWEN

NEW YORK METS

□ 1T. DON AASE
□ 108T. JUAN SAMUEL

NEW YORK YANKEES

□ 6T. STEVE BALBONI
□ 7T. JESSE BARFIELD
□ 17T. CHUCK CARY
□ 30T. ALVARO ESPINOZA
□ 37T. BOB GEREN
□ 43T. LEE GUETTERMAN
□ 44T. MEL HALL
□ 47T. ANDY HAWKINS
□ 58T. JIMMY JONES
□ 67T. DAVE LAPOINT
□ 77T. LANCE MCCULLERS
□ 94T. CLAY PARKER
□ 110T. DEION SANDERS
□ 111T. STEVE SAX

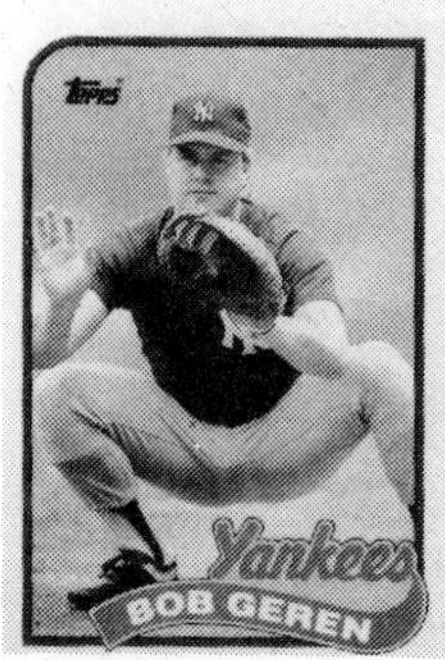

OAKLAND A'S

- ☐ 48T. RICKEY HENDERSON
- ☐ 82T. MIKE MOORE

PHILADELPHIA PHILLIES

- ☐ 27T. LEN DYKSTRA
- ☐ 49T. TOM HERR
- ☐ 54T. KEN HOWELL
- ☐ 63T. JOHN KRUK
- ☐ 65T. STEVE LAKE
- ☐ 79T. ROGER MCDOWELL
- ☐ 80T. LARRY MCWILLIAMS
- ☐ 90T. STEVE ONTIVEROS
- ☐ 95T. JEFF PARRETT
- ☐ 102T. RANDY READY
- ☐ 119T. DICKIE THON

PITTSBURGH PIRATES

- ☐ 25T. BENNY DISTEFANO
- ☐ 98T. REY QUINONES

ST. LOUIS CARDINALS

- ☐ 24T. FRANK DIPINO
- ☐ 50T. KEN HILL
- ☐ 118T. MILT THOMPSON

SAN DIEGO PADRES

- ☐ 20T. JACK CLARK
- ☐ 55T. BRUCE HURST
- ☐ 56T. CHRIS JAMES
- ☐ 103T. BIP ROBERTS
- ☐ 107T. LUIS SALAZAR
- ☐ 117T. WALT TERRELL

SAN FRANCISCO GIANTS

- ☐ 8T. STEVE BEDROSIAN
- ☐ 14T. JEFF BRANTLEY
- ☐ 59T. TERRY KENNEDY

SEATTLE MARINERS

- ☐ 41T. KEN GRIFFEY, JR.
- ☐ 45T. ERIK HANSON
- ☐ 46T. GENE HARRIS
- ☐ 51T. BRIAN HOLMAN
- ☐ 57T. RANDY JOHNSON
- ☐ 70T. JIM LEFEBVRE (M)
- ☐ 72T. JEFFREY LEONARD
- ☐ 97T. DENNIS POWELL
- ☐ 122T. OMAR VIZQUEL

TEXAS RANGERS

- ☐ 15T. KEVIN BROWN
- ☐ 34T. JULIO FRANCO
- ☐ 68T. RICK LEACH
- ☐ 85T. JAMIE MOYER
- ☐ 93T. RAFAEL PALMEIRO
- ☐ 104T. KENNY ROGERS
- ☐ 106T. NOLAN RYAN

TORONTO BLUE JAYS

- ☐ 32T. JUNIOR FELIX
- ☐ 36T. CITO GASTON (M)
- ☐ 71T. AL LEITER
- ☐ 109T. ALEX SANCHEZ

1990 TOPPS (792)
2 1/2" X 3 1/2"

ATLANTA BRAVES

- ☐ 55. DARRELL EVANS
- ☐ 111. ED WHITED
- ☐ 142. JEFF WETHERBY
- ☐ 152. LONNIE SMITH
- ☐ 171. RUSS NIXON (M)
- ☐ 199. SERGIO VALDEZ
- ☐ 223. TOMMY GREGG
- ☐ 251. JEFF BLAUSER
- ☐ 254. FRANCISCO CABRERA
- ☐ 282. DEREK LILLIQUIST
- ☐ 304. MARTY CLARY
- ☐ 329. ODDIBE MCDOWELL
- ☐ 358. ANDRES THOMAS
- ☐ 410. JOE BOEVER
- ☐ 451. MARK LEMKE
- ☐ 453. JODY DAVIS
- ☐ 486. JEFF TREADWAY
- ☐ 506. TOM GLAVINE
- ☐ 513. MARK EICHHORN
- ☐ 535. JOHN SMOLT
- ☐ 564. TYLER HOUSTON
- ☐ 567. RON GANT
- ☐ 583. BRUCE BENEDICT
- ☐ 617. GERONIMO BERROA
- ☐ 620. TONY CASTILLO
- ☐ 694. MIKE STANTON
- ☐ 744. KELLY MANN
- ☐ 750. DALE MURPHY
- ☐ 771. PETE SMITH
- ☐ 782. JOSE ALVAREZ
- ☐ 792. GERALD PERRY

BALTIMORE ORIOLES

- ☐ 13. MARK WILLIAMSON
- ☐ 73. BOB MILACKI
- ☐ 97. CURT SCHILLING
- ☐ 127. MIKE DEVEREAUX
- ☐ 153. RANDY MILLIGAN
- ☐ 163. PHIL BRADLEY
- ☐ 179. BRIAN HOLTON
- ☐ 212. JOE ORSULAK
- ☐ 249. MIKE SMITH
- ☐ 275. MICKEY TETTLETON
- ☐ 296. JEFF BALLARD
- ☐ 324. PETE HARNISCH
- ☐ 349. STEVE FINLEY
- ☐ 377. MICKEY WESTON
- ☐ 381. FRANK ROBINSON (M)
- ☐ 416. DAVE JOHNSON
- ☐ 468. BILLY RIPKEN
- ☐ 497. DAVE SCHMIDT
- ☐ 521. CRAIG WORTHINGTON
- ☐ 546. KEVIN HICKEY
- ☐ 570. CAL RIPKEN
- ☐ 598. BRADY ANDERSON
- ☐ 626. BOB MELVIN
- ☐ 655. GREGG OLSON
- ☐ 677. JAY TIBBS
- ☐ 708. LARRY SHEETS
- ☐ 724. JUAN BELL
- ☐ 758. MARK THURMOND
- ☐ 774. BEN MCDONALD
- ☐ 787. RENE GONZALES

BOSTON RED SOX

- ☐ 18. CARLOS QUINTANA
- ☐ 38. WES GARDNER
- ☐ 70. MIKE GREENWELL
- ☐ 96. JODY REED
- ☐ 123. RICH GEDMAN
- ☐ 155. ELLIS BURKS
- ☐ 188. MIKE SMITHSON
- ☐ 206. NICK ESASKY
- ☐ 245. ROGER CLEMENS
- ☐ 268. ROB MURPHY
- ☐ 303. RICK CERONE
- ☐ 321. JOE MORGAN (M)
- ☐ 338. DENNIS LAMP
- ☐ 355. MARTY BARRETT
- ☐ 375. DWIGHT EVANS
- ☐ 473. JOE PRICE
- ☐ 495. LEE SMITH
- ☐ 529. GREG HARRIS
- ☐ 544. DENNIS BOYD
- ☐ 573. DANNY HEEP
- ☐ 601. LUIS RIVERA
- ☐ 629. ERIC HETZEL
- ☐ 652. MIKE BODDICKER
- ☐ 676. RANDY KUTCHER
- ☐ 733. JOHN DOPSON
- ☐ 760. WADE BOGGS
- ☐ 785. JIM RICE

CALIFORNIA ANGELS

- ☐ 14. MIKE FETTERS
- ☐ 16. KENT ANDERSON
- ☐ 43. DANTE BICHETTE
- ☐ 51. DOUG RADER (M)
- ☐ 65. DEVON WHITE
- ☐ 99. RICH MONTELEONE
- ☐ 130. BERT BLYLEVEN
- ☐ 147. CHUCK FINLEY
- ☐ 189. DICK SCHOFIELD
- ☐ 215. KIRK MCCASKILL
- ☐ 244. BILL SCHROEDER
- ☐ 272. BRYAN HARVEY
- ☐ 334. JOHNNY RAY
- ☐ 363. DAN PETRY
- ☐ 421. GREG MINTON
- ☐ 444. KYLE ABBOTT
- ☐ 458. BOB MCCLURE
- ☐ 477. WILLIE FRASER
- ☐ 525. WALLY JOYNER
- ☐ 547. JACK HOWELL
- ☐ 575. LANCE PARRISH
- ☐ 603. TONY ARMAS
- ☐ 635. BRIAN DOWNING
- ☐ 650. MIKE WITT
- ☐ 675. JIM ABBOTT
- ☐ 705. CLAUDELL WASHINGTON
- ☐ 765. CHILI DAVIS

CHICAGO CUBS

- ☐ 12. JOE GIRARDI
- ☐ 37. DOMINGO RAMOS
- ☐ 67. SCOTT SANDERSON
- ☐ 86. PAUL KILGUS
- ☐ 114. MIKE BIELECKI
- ☐ 134. EARL CUNNINGHAM
- ☐ 140. ANDRE DAWSON
- ☐ 187. RICK WRONA
- ☐ 210. RYNE SANDBERG
- ☐ 240. MARK GRACE
- ☐ 256. MARVELL WYNNE
- ☐ 287. VANCE LAW
- ☐ 311. DWIGHT SMITH
- ☐ 337. LLOYD MCCLENDON
- ☐ 362. DAMON BERRYHILL
- ☐ 378. LUIS SALAZAR
- ☐ 415. SHAWON DUNSTON
- ☐ 437. LES LANCASTER
- ☐ 464. JEROME WALTON
- ☐ 502. MITCH WEBSTER
- ☐ 520. MITCH WILLIAMS
- ☐ 541. PAT PERRY
- ☐ 549. DON ZIMMER (M)
- ☐ 613. JEFF PICO
- ☐ 640. RICK SUTCLIFFE
- ☐ 644. PAUL ASSENMACHER
- ☐ 667. CURT WILKERSON
- ☐ 715. GREG MADDUX
- ☐ 741. STEVE WILSON
- ☐ 762. DOUG DASCENZO

CHICAGO WHITE SOX

- ☐ 21. JEFF TORBORG (M)
- ☐ 33. GREG WALKER
- ☐ 79. RON KITTLE
- ☐ 93. SHAWN HILLEGAS
- ☐ 121. ROBIN VENTURA
- ☐ 156. KEN PATTERSON
- ☐ 169. RICHARD DOTSON
- ☐ 219. DONN PALL
- ☐ 243. BARRY JONES
- ☐ 255. BOBBY THIGPEN
- ☐ 299. ADAM PETERSON
- ☐ 326. TOM MCCARTHY
- ☐ 365. OZZIE GUILLEN
- ☐ 379. STEVE ROSENBERG
- ☐ 414. FRANK THOMAS
- ☐ 420. CARLTON FISK
- ☐ 446. DAN PASQUA
- ☐ 461. CARLOS MARTINEZ
- ☐ 499. BILL LONG
- ☐ 524. DARYL BOSTON
- ☐ 565. SCOTT FLETCHER
- ☐ 569. IVAN CALDERON
- ☐ 587. LANCE JOHNSON
- ☐ 612. DAVE GALLAGHER
- ☐ 621. MELIDO PEREZ
- ☐ 692. SAMMY SOSA
- ☐ 717. RON KARKOVICE
- ☐ 751. STEVE LYONS
- ☐ 769. GREG HIBBARD
- ☐ 786. ERIC KING

CINCINNATI REDS

- ☐ 10. BARRY LARKIN
- ☐ 46. ROB DIBBLE
- ☐ 94. HERM WINNINGHAM
- ☐ 110. TOMMY HELMS (M)
- ☐ 120. JOHN FRANCO
- ☐ 151. RICK MAHLER
- ☐ 176. LUIS QUINONES
- ☐ 203. MIKE ROESLER
- ☐ 234. MARIANO DUNCAN
- ☐ 260. ERIC DAVIS
- ☐ 289. NORM CHARLTON
- ☐ 332. PAUL O'NEILL
- ☐ 364. ROLANDO ROOMES
- ☐ 418. TOM BROWNING
- ☐ 445. DANNY JACKSON
- ☐ 492. RON OESTER
- ☐ 516. TIM LEARY
- ☐ 553. SCOTT SCUDDER
- ☐ 581. KEN GRIFFEY
- ☐ 604. RON ROBINSON
- ☐ 627. JOSE RIJO
- ☐ 642. JACK ARMSTRONG
- ☐ 668. JOE OLIVER
- ☐ 687. TIM BIRTSAS
- ☐ 712. TODD BENZINGER
- ☐ 737. CHRIS SABO
- ☐ 772. JEFF REED

CLEVELAND INDIANS

- ☐ 32. JOHN FARRELL
- ☐ 54. JOEL SKINNER
- ☐ 75. DOUG JONES
- ☐ 108. ROD NICHOLS
- ☐ 141. JOHN HART (M)
- ☐ 144. BUD BLACK
- ☐ 172. TOM LAMPKIN
- ☐ 208. BROOK JACOBY
- ☐ 265. PETE O'BRIEN
- ☐ 283. JOEY BELLE
- ☐ 319. DION JAMES
- ☐ 339. DAVE CLARK
- ☐ 419. BEAU ALLRED
- ☐ 428. STEVE DAVIS
- ☐ 433. STEVE OLIN
- ☐ 442. JERRY BROWNE
- ☐ 476. BRAD KOMMINSK
- ☐ 514. ANDY ALLANSON
- ☐ 528. KEVIN WICKANDER
- ☐ 580. JOE CARTER
- ☐ 595. GREG SWINDELL
- ☐ 636. JESSE OROSCO
- ☐ 689. RICH YETT
- ☐ 722. FELIX FERMIN
- ☐ 743. TOM CANDIOTTI
- ☐ 770. CORY SNYDER
- ☐ 784. SCOTT BAILES

DETROIT TIGERS

- ☐ 11. PAUL GIBSON
- ☐ 42. JEFF ROBINSON
- ☐ 77. DAVE BERGMAN
- ☐ 107. FRED LYNN
- ☐ 131. MATT NOKES
- ☐ 146. ROB RICHIE
- ☐ 177. MIKE HENNEMAN
- ☐ 237. KEVIN RITZ
- ☐ 271. CHET LEMON
- ☐ 280. LOU WHITAKER
- ☐ 327. KEN WILLIAMS
- ☐ 343. FRANK TANANA
- ☐ 366. MIKE HEATH
- ☐ 413. BRIAN DUBOIS
- ☐ 440. ALAN TRAMMELL
- ☐ 471. MIKE BRUMLEY
- ☐ 487. STEVE SEARCY
- ☐ 498. RICK SCHU
- ☐ 512. GARY PETTIS
- ☐ 555. JACK MORRIS
- ☐ 586. ED NUNEZ
- ☐ 599. FRANK WILLIAMS
- ☐ 609. SPARKY ANDERSON (M)
- ☐ 632. SCOTT LUSADER
- ☐ 641. DOUG STRANGE
- ☐ 679. GARY WARD
- ☐ 748. DOYLE ALEXANDER
- ☐ 767. TRACY JONES

HOUSTON ASTROS

- ☐ 50. GLENN DAVIS
- ☐ 64. DANNY DARWIN
- ☐ 112. GLENN WILSON
- ☐ 157. CRAIG BIGGIO
- ☐ 164. JEFF JUDEN
- ☐ 181. JUAN AGOSTO
- ☐ 196. GERALD YOUNG
- ☐ 225. JIM DESHAIES
- ☐ 253. MARK PORTUGAL
- ☐ 267. MARK DAVIDSON
- ☐ 281. KEVIN BASS
- ☐ 309. ERIC YELDING
- ☐ 342. ALEX TREVINO
- ☐ 368. BILL DORAN
- ☐ 460. MIKE SCOTT
- ☐ 494. TERRY PUHL
- ☐ 531. KEN CAMINITI
- ☐ 534. LOUIE MEADOWS
- ☐ 558. RAFAEL RAMIREZ
- ☐ 579. ART HOWE (M)
- ☐ 588. RICK RHODEN
- ☐ 608. ERIC ANTHONY
- ☐ 637. CRAIG REYNOLDS
- ☐ 648. JIM CLANCY
- ☐ 746. DAVE SMITH
- ☐ 766. BRIAN MEYER

KANSAS CITY ROYALS

- ☐ 20. MARK GUBICZA
- ☐ 60. GEORGE BRETT
- ☐ 87. RICK LUECKEN
- ☐ 116. FLOYD BANNISTER
- ☐ 149. STEVE FARR
- ☐ 167. KEVIN APPIER
- ☐ 202. MIKE MACFARLANE
- ☐ 222. KURT STILLWELL
- ☐ 246. JIM EISENREICH
- ☐ 263. MEL STOTTLEMYRE, JR.
- ☐ 276. GARY THURMAN
- ☐ 300. BO JACKSON
- ☐ 323. WILLIE WILSON
- ☐ 350. BRET SABERHAGEN
- ☐ 435. KEVIN SEITZER
- ☐ 452. LUIS DE LOS SANTOS
- ☐ 479. FRANK WHITE
- ☐ 508. TERRY LEACH
- ☐ 540. DANNY TARTABULL
- ☐ 596. JOSE DEJESUS
- ☐ 638. JEFF MONTGOMERY
- ☐ 671. BOB BOONE
- ☐ 707. LUIS AQUINO
- ☐ 727. PAT TABLER
- ☐ 752. TOM GORDON
- ☐ 776. CHARLIE LEIBRANDT
- ☐ 789. JOHN WATHAN (M)

LOS ANGELES DODGERS

- ☐ 25. WILLIE RANDOLPH
- ☐ 40. JAY HOWELL
- ☐ 56. FRANKLIN STUBBS
- ☐ 62. RAMON MARTINEZ
- ☐ 84. RAY SEARAGE
- ☐ 98. JOSE GONZALEZ
- ☐ 117. MIKE SHARPERSON
- ☐ 150. KIRK GIBSON
- ☐ 173. TIM BELCHER
- ☐ 198. MIKE MARSHALL
- ☐ 226. MICKEY HATCHER
- ☐ 248. DAVE ANDERSON
- ☐ 277. LENNY HARRIS
- ☐ 305. EDDIE MURRAY
- ☐ 340. FERNANDO VALENZUELA
- ☐ 367. MIKE MORGAN
- ☐ 426. JEFF HAMILTON
- ☐ 456. CHRIS GWYNN
- ☐ 483. ALEJANDRO PENA
- ☐ 551. TIM CREWS
- ☐ 585. KAL DANIELS
- ☐ 605. MIKE SCIOSCIA
- ☐ 631. JOHN WETTELAND
- ☐ 643. ALFREDO GRIFFIN
- ☐ 669. TOM LASORDA (M)
- ☐ 697. MIKE DAVIS
- ☐ 736. RICK DEMPSEY
- ☐ 780. OREL HERSHISER

MILWAUKEE BREWERS

- ☐ 15. TEDDY HIGUERA
- ☐ 34. TONY FOSSAS
- ☐ 57. GREG VAUGHN
- ☐ 88. GLENN BRAGGS
- ☐ 106. CHARLIE O'BRIEN
- ☐ 139. GREG BROCK
- ☐ 159. MIKE FELDER
- ☐ 192. DON AUGUST
- ☐ 214. TERRY FRANCONA
- ☐ 264. BRYAN CLUTTERBUCK
- ☐ 290. ROBIN YOUNT
- ☐ 313. GUS POLIDOR
- ☐ 333. BILL WEGMAN
- ☐ 344. GEORGE CANALE
- ☐ 360. PAUL MOLITOR
- ☐ 417. JIM GANTNER
- ☐ 424. JERRY REUSS
- ☐ 467. JUAN NIEVES
- ☐ 490. DAN PLESAC
- ☐ 518. BILL KRUEGER
- ☐ 538. BILLY SPIERS
- ☐ 566. MARK KNUDSON
- ☐ 597. CHRIS BOSIO
- ☐ 615. ROB DEER
- ☐ 673. JOEY MEYER
- ☐ 696. B. J. SURHOFF
- ☐ 718. GARY SHEFFIELD
- ☐ 739. DALE SVEUM
- ☐ 759. TOM TREBELHORN (M)
- ☐ 768. CHUCK CRIM

MINNESOTA TWINS

- ☐ 19. AL NEWMAN
- ☐ 47. BRIAN HARPER
- ☐ 71. ALLAN ANDERSON
- ☐ 101. SHANE RAWLEY

□ 125. KENT HRBEK
□ 218. WALLY BACKMAN
□ 227. KEVIN TAPANI
□ 235. JEFF REARDON
□ 266. GERMAN GONZALEZ
□ 298. DANNY GLADDEN
□ 317. MARK GUTHRIE
□ 348. GARY WAYNE
□ 357. DAVE WEST
□ 427. CARMELO CASTILLO
□ 429. TOM KELLY (M)
□ 448. GREG GAGNE
□ 503. RANDY ST. CLAIRE
□ 556. GENE LARKIN
□ 576. MIKE DYER
□ 630. GARY GAETTI
□ 653. JOHN MOSES
□ 672. ROY SMITH
□ 700. KIRBY PUCKETT
□ 704. CHIP HALE
□ 709. JUAN BERENGUER
□ 711. RICK AGUILERA
□ 713. TIM DRUMMOND
□ 747. RANDY BUSH
□ 777. TIM LAUDNER

MONTREAL EXPOS

□ 24. JOE HESKETH
□ 48. ZANE SMITH
□ 72. JEFF HUSON
□ 81. BOB RODGERS (M)
□ 91. STEVE FREY
□ 137. MARTY PEVEY
□ 180. TIM RAINES
□ 195. TIM BURKE
□ 224. DELINO DESHIELDS
□ 228. DAVE MARTINEZ
□ 252. OTIS NIXON
□ 278. PASCUAL PEREZ
□ 284. MARK GARDNER
□ 318. WALLACE JOHNSON
□ 341. TOM FOLEY
□ 352. BRYN SMITH
□ 370. TIM WALLACH
□ 432. DAMASO GARCIA
□ 465. KEVIN GROSS
□ 474. RICH THOMPSON
□ 484. MIKE FITZGERALD
□ 485. JOHN CANDELARIA
□ 530. MARK LANGSTON
□ 559. ANDY MCGAFFIGAN
□ 589. MIKE ALDRETE
□ 614. NELSON SANTOVENIA
□ 647. REX HUDLER
□ 674. SPIKE OWEN
□ 714. MARQUIS GRISSOM
□ 720. ANDRES GALARRAGA
□ 745. HUBIE BROOKS
□ 757. LARRY WALKER
□ 763. DENNY MARTINEZ

NEW YORK METS

□ 30. DAVID CONE
□ 58. KEITH MILLER
□ 85. JUAN SAMUEL
□ 105. RANDY MYERS
□ 135. DAVE MAGADAN
□ 207. BOB OJEDA
□ 230. KEITH HERNANDEZ
□ 258. BARRY LYONS
□ 291. DAVE JOHNSON (M)
□ 301. DON AASE
□ 330. RON DARLING
□ 382. JEFF MUSSELMAN
□ 434. MARK CARREON
□ 457. GREGG JEFFERIES
□ 470. FRANK VIOLA
□ 480. SID FERNANDEZ
□ 504. TOM O'MALLEY
□ 510. DWIGHT GOODEN
□ 545. KEVIN MCREYNOLDS
□ 557. JEFF INNIS
□ 600. DARRYL STRAWBERRY
□ 656. MACKEY SASSER
□ 680. HOWARD JOHNSON
□ 684. JULIO MACHADO
□ 719. WALLY WHITEHURST
□ 734. KEVIN ELSTER
□ 764. TIM TEUFEL
□ 790. GARY CARTER

NEW YORK YANKEES

□ 9. ERIC PLUNK
□ 23. RANDY VELARDE
□ 26. DON SLAUGHT
□ 61. DEION SANDERS
□ 83. HENSLEY MEULENS
□ 109. ROBERTO KELLY
□ 160. DAVE RIGHETTI
□ 186. DAVE LAPOINT
□ 200. DON MATTINGLY
□ 236. HAL MORRIS
□ 259. LANCE MCCULLERS
□ 286. LEE GUETTERMAN
□ 302. MARCUS LAWTON
□ 335. ANDY HAWKINS
□ 359. JIMMY JONES
□ 380. DAVE WINFIELD
□ 436. MEL HALL
□ 511. CLAY PARKER
□ 519. BUCKY DENT (M)
□ 536. BOB GEREN
□ 560. STEVE SAX
□ 611. WALT TERRELL
□ 634. LUIS POLONIA
□ 651. RAFAEL SANTANA
□ 659. GREG CADARET
□ 691. CHUCK CARY
□ 701. BERNIE WILLIAMS
□ 716. STEVE BALBONI
□ 740. JESSE BARFIELD
□ 791. ALVARO ESPINOZA

OAKLAND A'S

□ 45. DAVE PARKER
□ 68. DAVE HENDERSON
□ 102. STAN JAVIER
□ 132. LANCE BLANKENSHIP
□ 145. TERRY STEINBACH
□ 165. WALT WEISS
□ 175. MIKE MOORE
□ 238. FELIX JOSE
□ 250. JOSE CANSECO
□ 270. DAVE STEWART
□ 293. MIKE GALLEGO
□ 316. CARNEY LANSFORD
□ 328. CURT YOUNG
□ 369. TODD BURNS
□ 411. KEN PHELPS
□ 450. RICKEY HENDERSON
□ 475. BOB WELCH
□ 501. MATT YOUNG
□ 527. RON HASSEY
□ 582. RICK HONEYCUTT
□ 606. STORM DAVIS
□ 623. JIM CORSI
□ 639. TONY LARUSSA (M)
□ 670. DENNIS ECKERSLEY
□ 690. MARK MCGWIRE
□ 702. TONY PHILLIPS
□ 726. GENE NELSON

PHILADELPHIA PHILLIES

□ 22. BRUCE RUFFIN
□ 39. CURT FORD
□ 69. TODD FROHWIRTH
□ 74. JEFF JACKSON
□ 103. MARVIN FREEMAN
□ 129. RON JONES
□ 154. MIKE MADDUX
□ 183. STEVE LAKE
□ 204. BOB DERNIER
□ 216. RICKY JORDAN
□ 269. DICKIE THON
□ 297. TOM HERR
□ 356. RANDY READY
□ 384. PAT COMBS
□ 439. JEFF PARRETT
□ 469. JOHN KRUK
□ 489. NICK LEYVA (M)
□ 493. JASON GRIMSLEY
□ 515. LEN DYKSTRA
□ 542. DARREN DAULTON
□ 577. CHARLIE HAYES
□ 607. STEVE JELTZ
□ 625. ROGER MCDOWELL
□ 633. DENNIS COOK
□ 657. TERRY MULHOLLAND
□ 710. VAN HAYES

□ 731. DON CARMAN
□ 756. KEN HOWELL

PITTSBURGH PIRATES

□ 29. JOHN CANGELOSI
□ 119. BILLY HATCHER
□ 126. RANDY KRAMER
□ 143. RAFAEL BELLIARD
□ 168. JOSE LIND
□ 197. DOUG DRABEK
□ 220. BARRY BONDS
□ 273. BOBBY BONILLA
□ 292. JIM GOTT
□ 322. JUNIOR ORTIZ
□ 354. STAN BELINDA
□ 425. BILL LANDRUM
□ 441. BOB KIPPER
□ 454. JEFF KING
□ 478. MIKE LAVALLIERE
□ 482. STEVE CARTER
□ 507. GARY REDUS
□ 523. JAY BELL
□ 539. NEAL HEATON
□ 552. MIKE SMITH
□ 568. JOHN SMILEY
□ 592. R. J. REYNOLDS
□ 622. SID BREAM
□ 666. BRIAN FISHER
□ 682. DANN BILARDELLO
□ 699. JIM LEYLAND (M)
□ 723. JEFF ROBINSON
□ 754. BOB WALK
□ 775. ANDY VAN SLYKE

ST. LOUIS CARDINALS

□ 36. JOHN COSTELLO
□ 59. TED POWER
□ 82. SCOTT TERRY
□ 95. TODD WORRELL
□ 115. TONY PENA
□ 133. RICKY HORTON
□ 162. TODD ZEILE
□ 184. DANNY COX
□ 209. GREG MATHEWS
□ 233. KEN HILL
□ 257. JOSE DELEON
□ 261. WHITEY HERZOG (M)
□ 285. WILLIE MCGEE
□ 312. DAN QUISENBERRY
□ 383. JOHN MORRIS
□ 409. TOM BRUNANSKY
□ 443. CRIS CARPENTER
□ 462. DENNY WALLING
□ 509. TOM PAGNOZZI
□ 533. TIM JONES
□ 561. KEN DAYLEY
□ 578. JOE MAGRANE
□ 590. OZZIE SMITH
□ 610. PEDRO GUERRERO
□ 645. JOSE OQUENDO
□ 654. PAUL COLEMAN
□ 660. VINCE COLEMAN
□ 688. MILT THOMPSON
□ 725. TERRY PENDLETON
□ 788. FRANK DIPINO

SAN DIEGO PADRES

- ☐ 35. BENNY SANTIAGO
- ☐ 63. MIKE PAGLIARULO
- ☐ 90. JACK CLARK
- ☐ 122. SHAWN ABNER
- ☐ 178. CHRIS JAMES
- ☐ 193. ANDY BENES
- ☐ 205. MARK DAVIS
- ☐ 231. JACK MCKEON(M)
- ☐ 239. ERIC SHOW
- ☐ 307. BIP ROBERTS
- ☐ 315. BRUCE HURST
- ☐ 353. SANDY ALOMAR
- ☐ 423. FRED TOLIVER
- ☐ 449. DENNIS RASMUSSEN
- ☐ 481. GARRY TEMPLETON
- ☐ 517. ROBERTO ALOMAR
- ☐ 537. MARK GRANT
- ☐ 548. PAT CLEMENTS
- ☐ 572. GREG HARRIS
- ☐ 584. PHIL STEPHENSON
- ☐ 618. EDDIE WHITSON
- ☐ 624. DARRIN JACKSON
- ☐ 649. DAN MURPHY
- ☐ 686. CARMELO MARTINEZ
- ☐ 693. CALVIN SCHIRALDI
- ☐ 730. TONY GWYNN
- ☐ 749. MARK PARENT
- ☐ 773. DAVE LEIPER

SAN FRANCISCO GIANTS

- ☐ 17. KELLY DOWNS
- ☐ 41. MATT WILLIAMS
- ☐ 53. MIKE LACOSS
- ☐ 66. GREG LITTON
- ☐ 100. WILL CLARK
- ☐ 104. BOB KNEPPER
- ☐ 124. DAVE DRAVECKY
- ☐ 158. CRAIG LEFFERTS
- ☐ 190. RICK REUSCHEL
- ☐ 217. DON ROBINSON
- ☐ 241. MIKE KRUKOW
- ☐ 310. STEVE BEDROSIAN
- ☐ 325. ROBBY THOMPSON
- ☐ 351. ROGER CRAIG(M)
- ☐ 361. RANDY MCCAMENT
- ☐ 372. TERRY KENNEDY
- ☐ 408. TREVOR WILSON
- ☐ 422. PAT SHERIDAN
- ☐ 447. ATLEE HAMMAKER
- ☐ 472. JOSE URIBE
- ☐ 488. KEN OBERKFELL
- ☐ 500. KEVIN MITCHELL
- ☐ 571. BRETT BUTLER
- ☐ 602. SCOTT GARRELTS
- ☐ 628. CANDY MALDONADO
- ☐ 658. DONELL NIXON
- ☐ 678. KIRT MANWARING
- ☐ 703. JEFF BRANTLEY
- ☐ 732. ERNIE RILES
- ☐ 753. CHRIS SPEIER

SEATTLE MARINERS

- ☐ 31. HENRY COTTO
- ☐ 44. ROGER SALKELD
- ☐ 76. DAVE VALLE
- ☐ 89. CLINT ZAVARAS
- ☐ 118. ERIK HANSON
- ☐ 148. EDGAR MARTINEZ
- ☐ 161. HAROLD REYNOLDS
- ☐ 213. SCOTT BANKHEAD
- ☐ 232. DARNELL COLES
- ☐ 247. JERRY REED
- ☐ 288. GREG BRILEY
- ☐ 306. TOM NIEDENFUER
- ☐ 336. KEN GRIFFEY, JR.
- ☐ 346. JIM PRESLEY
- ☐ 373. ALVIN DAVIS
- ☐ 431. RANDY JOHNSON
- ☐ 455. JEFFREY LEONARD
- ☐ 459. JIM LEFEBVRE(M)
- ☐ 491. DAVE COCHRANE
- ☐ 522. MIKE DUNNE
- ☐ 554. JAY BUHNER
- ☐ 574. BILL SWIFT
- ☐ 593. SCOTT BRADLEY
- ☐ 616. BRIAN HOLMAN
- ☐ 681. MIKE SCHOOLER
- ☐ 698. OMAR VIZQUEL
- ☐ 738. GENE HARRIS
- ☐ 761. MIKE JACKSON
- ☐ 781. MARIO DIAZ

TEXAS RANGERS

- ☐ 1. NOLAN RYAN
- ☐ 27. RICK LEACH
- ☐ 52. JACK DAUGHERTY
- ☐ 80. JEFF RUSSELL
- ☐ 92. MIKE STANLEY
- ☐ 136. KEVIN BROWN
- ☐ 166. BOBBY WITT
- ☐ 174. JEFF KUNKEL
- ☐ 185. RUBEN SIERRA
- ☐ 221. GARY MIELKE
- ☐ 242. FRED MANRIQUE
- ☐ 279. STEVE BUECHELE
- ☐ 294. CRAIG MCMURTRY
- ☐ 308. JOSE GUZMAN
- ☐ 314. DONALD HARRIS
- ☐ 331. JUAN GONZALEZ
- ☐ 345. HAROLD BAINES
- ☐ 412. JAMIE MOYER
- ☐ 430. PETE INCAVIGLIA
- ☐ 463. DREW HALL
- ☐ 496. CECIL ESPY
- ☐ 532. CECILIO GUANTE
- ☐ 550. JULIO FRANCO
- ☐ 562. CHAD KREUTER
- ☐ 683. KENNY ROGERS
- ☐ 706. GENO PETRALLI
- ☐ 729. BOBBY VALENTINE(M)
- ☐ 735. CHARLIE HOUGH
- ☐ 755. RAFAEL PALMEIRO
- ☐ 778. MIKE JEFFCOAT

TORONTO BLUE JAYS

- ☐ 28. DUANE WARD
- ☐ 49. TOM LAWLESS
- ☐ 78. MIKE FLANAGAN
- ☐ 113. MANNY LEE
- ☐ 138. AL LEITER
- ☐ 170. GEORGE BELL
- ☐ 182. MOOKIE WILSON
- ☐ 191. PAT BORDERS
- ☐ 194. GLENALLEN HILL
- ☐ 201. CITO GASTON(M)
- ☐ 211. JOHN CERUTTI
- ☐ 229. DAVID WELLS
- ☐ 274. GOOSE GOZZO
- ☐ 295. FRED MCGRIFF
- ☐ 320. DAVE STIEB
- ☐ 347. JUNIOR FELIX
- ☐ 371. JIMMY KEY
- ☐ 374. STEVE CUMMINGS
- ☐ 438. GREG MYERS
- ☐ 466. RANCE MULLINIKS
- ☐ 505. KELLY GRUBER
- ☐ 543. NELSON LIRIANO
- ☐ 563. ALEX SANCHEZ
- ☐ 591. TODD STOTTLEMYRE
- ☐ 594. LUIS SOJO
- ☐ 619. ROB DUCEY
- ☐ 685. TONY FERNANDEZ
- ☐ 695. TOM HENKE
- ☐ 721. LEE MAZZILLI
- ☐ 728. JIM ACKER
- ☐ 742. ERNIE WHITT
- ☐ 779. LLOYD MOSEBY

1990 TOPPS TRADED (132) 2 1/2 X 3 1/2

ATLANTA BRAVES

- ☐ 4T. STEVE AVERY
- ☐ 23T. BOBBY COX(M)
- ☐ 30T. NICK ESASKY
- ☐ 40T. JOE HESKETH
- ☐ 48T. DAVE JUSTICE
- ☐ 60T. CHARLIE LEIBRANDT
- ☐ 84T. GREG OLSON
- ☐ 98T. JIM PRESLEY
- ☐ 128T. ERNIE WHITT

BALTIMORE ORIOLES

- ☐ 42T. SAM HORN
- ☐ 53T. BRAD KOMMINSK
- ☐ 70T. BEN MCDONALD

BOSTON RED SOX

- ☐ 15T. TOM BRUNANSKY
- ☐ 50T. DANA KIECKER
- ☐ 69T. JOHN MARZANO
- ☐ 79T. TIM NAEHRING
- ☐ 90T. TONY PENA
- ☐ 101T. JEFF REARDON
- ☐ 105T. KEVIN ROMINE

CALIFORNIA ANGELS

- ☐ 28T. MARK EICHHORN
- ☐ 54T. MARK LANGSTON
- ☐ 97T. LUIS POLONIA
- ☐ 130T. DAVE WINFIELD

CHICAGO CUBS

- ☐ 10T. SHAWN BOSKIE
- ☐ 36T. MIKE HARKEY
- ☐ 126T. HECTOR VILLANUEVA

CHICAGO WHITE SOX

- ☐ 27T. WAYNE EDWARDS
- ☐ 71T. JACK MCDOWELL
- ☐ 99T. SCOTT RADINSKY

CINCINNATI REDS

- ☐ 13T. GLENN BRAGGS
- ☐ 38T. BILLY HATCHER
- ☐ 55T. TIM LAYANA
- ☐ 76T. HAL MORRIS
- ☐ 78T. RANDY MYERS
- ☐ 96T. LOU PINIELLA(M)

CLEVELAND INDIANS

- ☐ 2T. SANDY ALOMAR

- ☐ 6T. CARLOS BAERGA
- ☐ 39T. KEITH HERNANDEZ
- ☐ 46T. CHRIS JAMES
- ☐ 49T. JEFF KAISER
- ☐ 65T. CANDY MALDONADO
- ☐ 72T. JOHN MCNAMARA(M)
- ☐ 127T. MITCH WEBSTER

DETROIT TIGERS

- ☐ 31T. CECIL FIELDER
- ☐ 33T. TRAVIS FRYMAN
- ☐ 77T. LLOYD MOSEBY
- ☐ 93T. DAN PETRY
- ☐ 95T. TONY PHILLIPS

HOUSTON ASTROS

- ☐ 17T. CASEY CANDAELE
- ☐ 34T. BILL GULLICKSON
- ☐ 120T. FRANKLIN STUBBS

KANSAS CITY ROYALS

- ☐ 24T. MARK DAVIS
- ☐ 25T. STORM DAVIS
- ☐ 92T. GERALD PERRY
- ☐ 114T. TERRY SHUMPERT

LOS ANGELES DODGERS

- ☐ 14T. HUBIE BROOKS
- ☐ 47T. STAN JAVIER
- ☐ 109T. JUAN SAMUEL

MILWAUKEE BREWERS

- ☐ 26T. EDGAR DIAZ
- ☐ 35T. DARRYL HAMILTON
- ☐ 86T. DAVE PARKER
- ☐ 104T. RON ROBINSON
- ☐ 125T. RANDY VERES

MINNESOTA TWINS

- ☐ 18T. JOHN CANDELARIA
- ☐ 29T. SCOTT ERICKSON
- ☐ 57T. TERRY LEACH
- ☐ 64T. SHANE MACK
- ☐ 66T. FRED MANRIQUE
- ☐ 85T. JUNIOR ORTIZ
- ☐ 111T. JACK SAVAGE
- ☐ 119T. PAUL SORRENTO

MONTREAL EXPOS

- ☐ 12T. DENNIS BOYD
- ☐ 80T. JUNIOR NOBOA
- ☐ 108T. BILL SAMPEN
- ☐ 112T. DAVE SCHMIDT

NEW YORK METS

- ☐ 11T. DARYL BOSTON
- ☐ 32T. JOHN FRANCO
- ☐ 37T. BUD HARRELSON(M)
- ☐ 44T. TODD HUNDLEY
- ☐ 67T. MIKE MARSHALL
- ☐ 73T. ORLANDO MERCADO
- ☐ 89T. ALEJANDRO PENA

NEW YORK YANKEES

- ☐ 9T. MIKE BLOWERS
- ☐ 21T. RICK CERONE
- ☐ 58T. TIM LEARY
- ☐ 61T. JIM LEYRITZ
- ☐ 63T. KEVIN MAAS
- ☐ 74T. STUMP MERRILL(M)
- ☐ 75T. ALAN MILLS
- ☐ 81T. MATT NOKES
- ☐ 91T. PASCUAL PEREZ
- ☐ 103T. JEFF ROBINSON
- ☐ 123T. WAYNE TOLLESON

OAKLAND A'S

- ☐ 43T. STEVE HOWARD
- ☐ 51T. JOE KLINK
- ☐ 100T. WILLIE RANDOLPH
- ☐ 110T. SCOTT SANDERSON

PHILADELPHIA PHILLIES

- ☐ 1T. DARREL AKERFELDS
- ☐ 41T. DAVE HOLLINS
- ☐ 68T. CARMELO MARTINEZ

PITTSBURGH PIRATES

- ☐ 5T. WALLY BACKMAN
- ☐ 88T. BOB PATTERSON
- ☐ 106T. SCOTT RUSKIN
- ☐ 116T. DON SLAUGHT

ST. LOUIS CARDINALS

- ☐ 113T. RED SCHOENDIENST(M)
- ☐ 117T. BRYN SMITH
- ☐ 118T. LEE SMITH
- ☐ 122T. BOB TEWKSBURY
- ☐ 124T. JOHN TUDOR

SAN DIEGO PADRES

- ☐ 20T. JOE CARTER
- ☐ 59T. CRAIG LEFFERTS
- ☐ 62T. FRED LYNN
- ☐ 102T. GREG RIDDOCH(M)

SAN FRANCISCO GIANTS

- ☐ 7T. KEVIN BASS
- ☐ 16T. JOHN BURKETT
- ☐ 19T. GARY CARTER
- ☐ 56T. RICK LEACH
- ☐ 87T. RICK PARKER

SEATTLE MARINERS

- ☐ 52T. BRENT KNACKERT
- ☐ 82T. PETE O'BRIEN
- ☐ 115T. MATT SINATRO
- ☐ 121T. RUSS SWAN
- ☐ 131T. MATT YOUNG

TEXAS RANGERS

- ☐ 3T. BRAD ARNSBERG
- ☐ 22T. SCOTT COOLBAUGH
- ☐ 45T. JEFF HUSON
- ☐ 94T. GARY PETTIS
- ☐ 107T. JOHN RUSSELL

TORONTO BLUE JAYS

- ☐ 8T. WILLIE BLAIR
- ☐ 83T. JOHN OLERUD
- ☐ 129T. FRANK WILLS

1991 TOPPS (792)
2 1/2 X 3 1/2

ATLANTA BRAVES

- ☐ 56. JEFF PARRETT
- ☐ 82. TOM GLAVINE
- ☐ 111. ANDRES THOMAS
- ☐ 139. JEFF TREADWAY
- ☐ 157. JOHN SMOLTZ
- ☐ 196. JIM VATCHER
- ☐ 227. STEVE AVERY
- ☐ 251. MARK LEMKE
- ☐ 287. MARK GRANT
- ☐ 306. LONNIE SMITH
- ☐ 329. DAVE JUSTICE
- ☐ 333. CHIPPER JONES
- ☐ 353. TONY CASTILLO
- ☐ 383. PETE SMITH
- ☐ 418. NICK ESASKY
- ☐ 456. CHARLIE LEIBRANDT
- ☐ 492. ERNIE WHITT
- ☐ 514. MIKE STANTON
- ☐ 533. ODDIBE MCDOWELL
- ☐ 567. DWAYNE HENRY
- ☐ 582. MARTY CLARY
- ☐ 623. JEFF BLAUSER
- ☐ 643. JIM PRESLEY
- ☐ 673. GREG OLSON
- ☐ 693. FRANCISCO CABRERA
- ☐ 725. RON GANT
- ☐ 742. TOMMY GREGG
- ☐ 753. PAUL MARAK
- ☐ 759. BOBBY COX(M)
- ☐ 772. KENT MERCKER

BALTIMORE ORIOLES

- ☐ 10. GREGG OLSON
- ☐ 42. CHRIS HOILES
- ☐ 73. CRAIG WORTHINGTON
- ☐ 97. BRADY ANDERSON
- ☐ 127. JOE PRICE
- ☐ 150. CAL RIPKEN
- ☐ 163. DAVE JOHNSON
- ☐ 179. PETE HARNISCH
- ☐ 212. STEVE FINLEY
- ☐ 249. BOB MELVIN
- ☐ 296. MARK WILLIAMSON
- ☐ 319. JEFF MCKNIGHT
- ☐ 324. RON KITTLE
- ☐ 349. DAVE GALLAGHER
- ☐ 377. RENE GONZALES
- ☐ 385. MICKEY TETTLETON
- ☐ 416. RANDY MILLIGAN
- ☐ 468. TIM HULETT
- ☐ 497. BEN MCDONALD
- ☐ 512. JOSE MESA
- ☐ 521. JOE ORSULAK
- ☐ 546. JEFF BALLARD
- ☐ 569. CURT SCHILLING
- ☐ 598. SAM HORN
- ☐ 639. FRANK ROBINSON(M)
- ☐ 653. ANTHONY TELFORD
- ☐ 677. BILLY RIPKEN
- ☐ 708. JOHN MITCHELL
- ☐ 724. DAVID SEGUI

☐ 758. MIKE DEVEREAUX
☐ 788. BOB MILACKI

BOSTON RED SOX

☐ 14. DENNIS LAMP
☐ 21. JOE MORGAN(M)
☐ 37. TOM BOLTON
☐ 70. ELLIS BURKS
☐ 94. JOHN DOPSON
☐ 123. GREG HARRIS
☐ 155. DWIGHT EVANS
☐ 189. DARYL IRVINE
☐ 206. CARLOS QUINTANA
☐ 247. JODY REED
☐ 269. JOE HESKETH
☐ 303. MIKE BODDICKER
☐ 338. LUIS RIVERA
☐ 356. MIKE MARSHALL
☐ 375. TONY PENA
☐ 450. WADE BOGGS
☐ 474. PHIL PLANTIER
☐ 496. MARTY BARRETT
☐ 530. ROGER CLEMENS
☐ 542. ROB MURPHY
☐ 574. JOHN MARZANO
☐ 605. JEFF REARDON
☐ 629. WES GARDNER
☐ 652. KEVIN ROMINE
☐ 675. TOM BRUNANSKY
☐ 702. TIM NAEHRING
☐ 731. JEFF GRAY
☐ 761. LARRY ANDERSEN
☐ 763. DANA KIECKER
☐ 792. MIKE GREENWELL

CALIFORNIA ANGELS

☐ 36. DONNIE HILL
☐ 57. JACK HOWELL
☐ 84. BOB MCCLURE
☐ 107. LUIS POLONIA
☐ 129. MARK EICHHORN
☐ 153. BRYAN HARVEY
☐ 176. JOHN ORTON
☐ 195. WALLY JOYNER
☐ 210. LANCE PARRISH
☐ 231. DOUG RADER(M)
☐ 255. BRIAN DOWNING
☐ 273. JOHNNY RAY
☐ 285. JIM ABBOTT
☐ 355. CHILI DAVIS
☐ 426. JOE GRAHE
☐ 452. BILL SCHROEDER
☐ 477. MIKE FETTERS
☐ 505. CHUCK FINLEY
☐ 532. KIRK MCCASKILL
☐ 564. DANTE BICHETTE
☐ 615. BERT BLYLEVEN
☐ 630. DAVE WINFIELD
☐ 648. LEE STEVENS
☐ 667. KENT ANDERSON
☐ 704. DEVON WHITE
☐ 736. DICK SCHOFIELD
☐ 755. MARK LANGSTON
☐ 784. WILLIE FRASER

CHICAGO CUBS

☐ 12. PAUL ASSENMACHER
☐ 35. GREG MADDUX
☐ 69. STEVE WILSON
☐ 86. LES LANCASTER
☐ 114. LANCE DICKSON
☐ 135. JEROME WALTON
☐ 142. CURT WILKERSON
☐ 188. DAMON BERRYHILL
☐ 214. JOE GIRARDI
☐ 241. DAVE CLARK
☐ 254. SHAWN BOSKIE
☐ 288. DERRICK MAY
☐ 311. JEFF PICO
☐ 335. MITCH WILLIAMS
☐ 362. HECTOR VILLANUEVA
☐ 376. MIKE HARKEY
☐ 415. RICK SUTCLIFFE
☐ 437. DOUG DASCENZO
☐ 463. DWIGHT SMITH
☐ 501. MIKE BIELECKI
☐ 520. MARK GRACE
☐ 541. DOMINGO RAMOS
☐ 560. GREG SMITH
☐ 614. LUIS SALAZAR
☐ 640. ANDRE DAWSON
☐ 668. BILL LONG
☐ 714. MARVELL WYNNE
☐ 729. DON ZIMMER(M)
☐ 740. RYNE SANDBERG
☐ 765. SHAWON DUNSTON

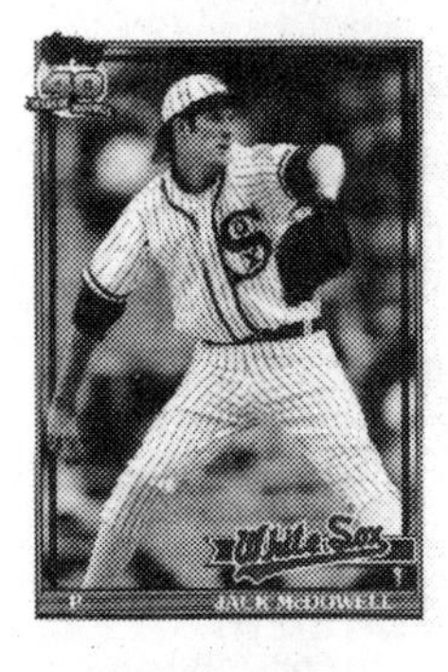

CHICAGO WHITE SOX

☐ 33. BARRY JONES
☐ 79. FRANK THOMAS
☐ 93. IVAN CALDERON
☐ 121. ERIC KING
☐ 156. CARLOS MARTINEZ
☐ 170. CARLTON FISK
☐ 219. JACK MCDOWELL
☐ 243. LANCE JOHNSON
☐ 256. GREG HIBBARD
☐ 278. ALEX FERNANDEZ
☐ 299. SCOTT RADINSKY
☐ 326. KEN PATTERSON
☐ 364. DAN PASQUA
☐ 378. WILSON ALVAREZ
☐ 414. SAMMY SOSA
☐ 420. BOBBY THIGPEN
☐ 446. CRAIG GREBECK
☐ 461. ROBIN VENTURA
☐ 499. MELIDO PEREZ
☐ 523. RODNEY MCCRAY
☐ 559. ADAM PETERSON
☐ 568. RON KARKOVICE
☐ 609. JEFF TORBORG(M)
☐ 612. STEVE LYONS
☐ 620. OZZIE GUILLEN
☐ 717. PHIL BRADLEY
☐ 751. WAYNE EDWARDS
☐ 768. DONN PALL
☐ 785. SCOTT FLETCHER

CINCINNATI REDS

☐ 13. MARIANO DUNCAN
☐ 45. CHRIS SABO
☐ 92. DANNY JACKSON
☐ 122. PAUL O'NEILL
☐ 151. TOM BROWNING
☐ 175. JACK ARMSTRONG
☐ 204. HERM WINNINGHAM
☐ 258. CHRIS HAMMOND
☐ 289. TIM BIRTSAS
☐ 309. NORM CHARLTON
☐ 334. TODD BENZINGER
☐ 363. RICK MAHLER
☐ 419. JEFF REED
☐ 444. GLENN BRAGGS
☐ 493. JOSE RIJO
☐ 517. JOE OLIVER
☐ 550. ERIC DAVIS
☐ 577. BILL DORAN
☐ 581. LUIS QUINONES
☐ 604. BILLY HATCHER
☐ 627. TIM LAYANA
☐ 642. HAL MORRIS
☐ 662. ROB DIBBLE
☐ 669. LOU PINIELLA(M)
☐ 688. ROSARIO RODRIGUEZ
☐ 713. SCOTT SCUDDER
☐ 730. BARRY LARKIN
☐ 767. DAN WILSON
☐ 780. RANDY MYERS

CLEVELAND INDIANS

☐ 31. COLBY WARD
☐ 47. BROOK JACOBY
☐ 76. JERRY BROWNE
☐ 98. SERGIO VALDEZ
☐ 103. TIM COSTO
☐ 117. DION JAMES
☐ 147. CARLOS BAERGA
☐ 165. SANDY ALOMAR
☐ 193. FELIX FERMIN
☐ 246. KEVIN WICKANDER
☐ 268. TOM BROOKENS
☐ 323. CORY SNYDER
☐ 346. JESSE OROSCO
☐ 421. ALEX COLE
☐ 445. GREG SWINDELL
☐ 466. CHARLES NAGY
☐ 488. JEFF MANTO
☐ 494. CHRIS JAMES
☐ 549. JOHN MCNAMARA(M)
☐ 555. TURNER WARD
☐ 576. JEFF KAISER
☐ 593. MIKE WALKER
☐ 624. TOM CANDIOTTI
☐ 664. JOHN FARRELL
☐ 692. EFRAIN VALDEZ
☐ 696. STEVE OLIN
☐ 723. CANDY MALDONADO
☐ 745. DOUG JONES
☐ 762. MITCH WEBSTER
☐ 783. JOEL SKINNER

DETROIT TIGERS

☐ 16. MIKE HEATH
☐ 75. JACK MORRIS
☐ 106. ED NUNEZ
☐ 128. TRAVIS FRYMAN
☐ 145. LOU WHITAKER
☐ 183. CLAY PARKER
☐ 236. FRANK TANANA
☐ 275. ALAN TRAMMELL
☐ 281. LARRY SHEETS
☐ 328. WALT TERRELL
☐ 369. STEVE SEARCY
☐ 412. DAVE BERGMAN
☐ 431. PAUL GIBSON
☐ 469. CHET LEMON
☐ 498. MARK SALAS
☐ 506. DARNELL COLES
☐ 519. SPARKY ANDERSON(M)
☐ 556. GARY WARD
☐ 583. TONY PHILLIPS
☐ 597. JERRY DON GLEATON
☐ 632. LLOYD MOSEBY
☐ 641. MIKE HENNEMAN
☐ 658. SCOTT ALDRED
☐ 684. MILT CUYLER
☐ 720. CECIL FIELDER
☐ 746. JOHN SHELBY
☐ 766. JEFF ROBINSON

HOUSTON ASTROS

☐ 32. MIKE SIMMS
☐ 51. ART HOWE(M)
☐ 59. ERIC YELDING
☐ 119. CARL NICHOLS
☐ 149. AL OSUNA
☐ 174. KEN CAMINITI
☐ 194. XAVIER HERNANDEZ
☐ 215. DAVE SMITH
☐ 240. MIKE SCOTT
☐ 286. KEN OBERKFELL
☐ 331. ERIC ANTHONY
☐ 350. GLENN DAVIS
☐ 423. RAFAEL RAMIREZ
☐ 476. GLENN WILSON
☐ 516. KARL RHODES
☐ 531. DAVE ROHDE
☐ 565. CRAIG BIGGIO
☐ 602. CASEY CANDAELE
☐ 626. GERALD YOUNG
☐ 646. ANDUJAR CEDENO
☐ 647. MARK PORTUGAL
☐ 666. DANNY DARWIN

- ☐ 678. MARK DAVIDSON
- ☐ 703. JUAN AGOSTO
- ☐ 732. FRANKLIN STUBBS
- ☐ 782. JIM DESHAIES

KANSAS CITY ROYALS

- ☐ 22. STORM DAVIS
- ☐ 58. MEL STOTTLEMYRE
- ☐ 90. DANNY TARTABULL
- ☐ 116. MARK DAVIS
- ☐ 148. REY PALACIOS
- ☐ 169. LUIS AQUINO
- ☐ 208. WILLIE WILSON
- ☐ 222. BRIAN MCRAE
- ☐ 248. TOM GORDON
- ☐ 265. MARK GUBICZA
- ☐ 280. BRET SABERHAGEN
- ☐ 291. JOHN WATHAN(M)
- ☐ 301. STEVE FARR
- ☐ 322. TERRY SHUMPERT
- ☐ 352. FRANK WHITE
- ☐ 371. JEFF MONTGOMERY
- ☐ 384. GERALD PERRY
- ☐ 454. KEVIN APPIER
- ☐ 478. KURT STILLWELL
- ☐ 507. STEVE JELTZ
- ☐ 540. GEORGE BRETT
- ☐ 600. BO JACKSON
- ☐ 638. MIKE MACFARLANE
- ☐ 671. ANDY MCGAFFIGAN
- ☐ 695. KEVIN SEITZER
- ☐ 707. JIM EISENREICH
- ☐ 718. STEVE CRAWFORD
- ☐ 754. BILL PECOTA
- ☐ 776. BRENT MAYNE

LOS ANGELES DODGERS

- ☐ 25. TIM BELCHER
- ☐ 39. JIM NEIDLINGER
- ☐ 53. MIKE SHARPERSON
- ☐ 61. STAN JAVIER
- ☐ 80. FERNANDO VALENZUELA
- ☐ 99. CHRIS GWYNN
- ☐ 115. HUBIE BROOKS
- ☐ 152. MICKEY HATCHER
- ☐ 199. MIKE HARTLEY
- ☐ 226. ALFREDO GRIFFIN
- ☐ 245. KAL DANIELS
- ☐ 279. JOSE GONZALEZ
- ☐ 305. MIKE SCIOSCIA
- ☐ 340. RAMON MARTINEZ
- ☐ 367. DAVE WALSH
- ☐ 427. RICK DEMPSEY
- ☐ 453. LENNY HARRIS
- ☐ 467. DENNIS COOK
- ☐ 490. KIRK GIBSON
- ☐ 552. JEFF HAMILTON
- ☐ 587. JOSE OFFERMAN
- ☐ 590. EDDIE MURRAY
- ☐ 596. RONNIE WALDEN
- ☐ 606. JIM GOTT
- ☐ 631. MIKE MORGAN
- ☐ 645. JUAN SAMUEL
- ☐ 690. OREL HERSHISER
- ☐ 737. TIM CREWS
- ☐ 770. JAY HOWELL
- ☐ 789. TOM LASORDA(M)

MILWAUKEE BREWERS

- ☐ 23. JIM GANTNER
- ☐ 44. MIKE FELDER
- ☐ 68. GARY SHEFFIELD
- ☐ 95. PAUL MOLITOR
- ☐ 118. TOM EDENS
- ☐ 146. DAN PLESAC
- ☐ 164. EDGAR DIAZ
- ☐ 192. ROB DEER
- ☐ 217. CHRIS BOSIO
- ☐ 235. DAVE PARKER
- ☐ 267. MARK KNUDSON
- ☐ 284. BILLY SPIERS
- ☐ 313. RON ROBINSON
- ☐ 347. GREG VAUGHN
- ☐ 417. BILL KRUEGER
- ☐ 434. JULIO MACHADO
- ☐ 459. TOM TREBELHORN(M)
- ☐ 475. TEDDY HIGUERA
- ☐ 548. JAIME NAVARRO
- ☐ 561. TIM MCINTOSH
- ☐ 575. ROBIN YOUNT
- ☐ 592. B.J. SURHOFF
- ☐ 617. BILL WEGMAN
- ☐ 644. CHUCK CRIM
- ☐ 663. GREG BROCK
- ☐ 694. RANDY VERES
- ☐ 721. MARK LEE
- ☐ 747. TONY FOSSAS
- ☐ 781. DARRYL HAMILTON

MINNESOTA TWINS

- ☐ 18. NELSON LIRIANO
- ☐ 46. TIM DRUMMOND
- ☐ 72. JUNIOR ORTIZ
- ☐ 102. GENE LARKIN
- ☐ 124. RANDY BUSH
- ☐ 201. TOM KELLY(M)
- ☐ 207. GARY WAYNE
- ☐ 216. GREG GAGNE
- ☐ 223. ALLAN ANDERSON
- ☐ 234. SCOTT ERICKSON
- ☐ 266. CARMELO CASTILLO
- ☐ 300. KIRBY PUCKETT
- ☐ 318. RICK AGUILERA
- ☐ 341. JOHN MOSES
- ☐ 357. JACK SAVAGE
- ☐ 374. LARRY CASIAN
- ☐ 430. GARY GAETTI
- ☐ 449. JUAN BERENGUER
- ☐ 503. ROY SMITH
- ☐ 554. BRIAN HARPER
- ☐ 578. DAVE WEST
- ☐ 594. RICH GARCES
- ☐ 633. KEVIN TAPANI
- ☐ 654. PAUL SORRENTO
- ☐ 672. SHANE MACK
- ☐ 698. MARK GUTHRIE
- ☐ 710. KENT HRBEK
- ☐ 748. AL NEWMAN
- ☐ 778. DANNY GLADDEN

MONTREAL EXPOS

- ☐ 24. DAVE MARTINEZ
- ☐ 48. DENNIS BOYD
- ☐ 74. SHANE ANDREWS
- ☐ 77. DREW HALL
- ☐ 91. GREG COLBRUNN
- ☐ 136. DAVE SCHMIDT
- ☐ 182. JUNIOR NOBOA
- ☐ 197. CHRIS NABHOLZ
- ☐ 211. BRIAN BARNES
- ☐ 220. TIM WALLACH
- ☐ 252. MEL ROJAS
- ☐ 283. MARQUIS GRISSOM
- ☐ 317. MIKE FITZGERALD
- ☐ 321. BOB RODGERS(M)
- ☐ 339. LARRY WALKER
- ☐ 360. TIM RAINES
- ☐ 372. SPIKE OWEN
- ☐ 432. DELINO DESHIELDS
- ☐ 462. STEVE FREY
- ☐ 483. MIKE ALDRETE
- ☐ 526. MOISES ALOU
- ☐ 528. DENNY MARTINEZ
- ☐ 558. OTIS NIXON
- ☐ 589. SCOTT RUSKIN
- ☐ 610. ANDRES GALARRAGA
- ☐ 649. BILL SAMPEN
- ☐ 674. KEVIN GROSS
- ☐ 715. TIM BURKE
- ☐ 744. NELSON SANTOVENIA
- ☐ 757. MARK GARDNER
- ☐ 773. TOM FOLEY

NEW YORK METS

- ☐ 30. GREGG JEFFERIES
- ☐ 60. FRANK VIOLA
- ☐ 64. TOM HERR
- ☐ 83. DARYL BOSTON
- ☐ 105. KEVIN MCREYNOLDS
- ☐ 134. KEVIN ELSTER
- ☐ 200. DARRYL STRAWBERRY
- ☐ 230. SID FERNANDEZ
- ☐ 257. TOM O'MALLEY
- ☐ 261. BUD HARRELSON(M)
- ☐ 302. TIM TEUFEL
- ☐ 330. DWIGHT GOODEN
- ☐ 382. MACKEY SASSER
- ☐ 433. PAT TABLER
- ☐ 442. CHARLIE O'BRIEN
- ☐ 443. JEFF INNIS
- ☐ 457. TODD HUNDLEY
- ☐ 470. HOWARD JOHNSON
- ☐ 480. DAVE MAGADAN
- ☐ 504. JULIO VALERA
- ☐ 510. JOHN FRANCO
- ☐ 544. ALEJANDRO PENA
- ☐ 557. WALLY WHITEHURST
- ☐ 601. BOB OJEDA
- ☐ 680. DAVID CONE
- ☐ 719. KEITH MILLER
- ☐ 735. RON DARLING
- ☐ 764. MARK CARREON

NEW YORK YANKEES

- ☐ 11. ROBERTO KELLY
- ☐ 19. JEFF ROBINSON
- ☐ 28. ALVARO ESPINOZA
- ☐ 62. LEE GUETTERMAN
- ☐ 85. JESSE BARFIELD
- ☐ 100. DON MATTINGLY
- ☐ 113. CARL EVERETT
- ☐ 161. TIM LEARY
- ☐ 187. GREG CADARET
- ☐ 202. JIM LEYRITZ
- ☐ 237. RICK CERONE
- ☐ 259. HENSLEY MEULENS
- ☐ 290. STEVE SAX
- ☐ 336. MATT NOKES
- ☐ 359. CHUCK CARY
- ☐ 379. RANDY VELARDE
- ☐ 410. DAVE RIGHETTI
- ☐ 429. STUMP MERRILL(M)
- ☐ 435. KEVIN MAAS
- ☐ 484. DAVE LAPOINT
- ☐ 511. STEVE BALBONI
- ☐ 536. MIKE WITT
- ☐ 611. DAVE EILAND
- ☐ 635. ANDY HAWKINS
- ☐ 651. ALAN MILLS
- ☐ 659. OSCAR AZOCAR
- ☐ 691. MIKE BLOWERS
- ☐ 701. PASCUAL PEREZ
- ☐ 716. BOB GEREN
- ☐ 738. MEL HALL
- ☐ 786. ERIC PLUNK

OAKLAND A'S

- ☐ 50. BOB WELCH
- ☐ 67. RICK HONEYCUTT
- ☐ 132. JAMIE QUIRK
- ☐ 144. DAVE HENDERSON
- ☐ 162. OZZIE CANSECO
- ☐ 166. HAROLD BAINES
- ☐ 171. TONY LARUSSA(M)
- ☐ 177. REGGIE HARRIS
- ☐ 239. DARREN LEWIS
- ☐ 250. DENNIS ECKERSLEY
- ☐ 270. MARK MCGWIRE
- ☐ 294. MIKE MOORE
- ☐ 316. GENE NELSON
- ☐ 327. RON HASSEY
- ☐ 380. WILLIE MCGEE
- ☐ 411. LANCE BLANKENSHIP
- ☐ 455. WALT WEISS
- ☐ 473. CURT YOUNG
- ☐ 502. CARNEY LANSFORD
- ☐ 525. WILLIE RANDOLPH
- ☐ 553. JOE KLINK
- ☐ 580. DAVE STEWART
- ☐ 608. TODD BURNS
- ☐ 625. TERRY STEINBACH
- ☐ 670. RICKEY HENDERSON
- ☐ 686. MIKE GALLEGO
- ☐ 700. JOSE CANSECO
- ☐ 728. SCOTT SANDERSON

PHILADELPHIA PHILLIES

- ☐ 9. DARRIN FLETCHER
- ☐ 15. VON HAYES
- ☐ 43. ROGER MCDOWELL
- ☐ 89. DARREN DAULTON
- ☐ 137. RANDY READY
- ☐ 141. NICK LEYVA(M)
- ☐ 159. JOE BOEVER

- ☐ 173. JASON GRIMSLEY
- ☐ 186. ROD BOOKER
- ☐ 209. KEN HOWELL
- ☐ 232. JOSE DEJESUS
- ☐ 264. DAVE HOLLINS
- ☐ 282. DON CARMAN
- ☐ 312. CHARLIE HAYES
- ☐ 342. MICKEY MORANDINI
- ☐ 345. LEN DYKSTRA
- ☐ 413. TERRY MULHOLLAND
- ☐ 439. DICKIE THON
- ☐ 471. MIKE LIEBERTHAL
- ☐ 486. TOMMY GREENE
- ☐ 524. DARREL AKERFELDS
- ☐ 545. DALE MURPHY
- ☐ 571. PAT COMBS
- ☐ 603. WES CHAMBERLAIN
- ☐ 618. SIL CAMPUSANO
- ☐ 637. BRUCE RUFFIN
- ☐ 661. STEVE LAKE
- ☐ 689. JOHN KRUK
- ☐ 712. RICKY JORDAN

PITTSBURGH PIRATES

- ☐ 29. BOB WALK
- ☐ 143. JOHN SMILEY
- ☐ 167. RANDY TOMLIN
- ☐ 198. R.J. REYNOLDS
- ☐ 221. DON SLAUGHT
- ☐ 272. JEFF KING
- ☐ 293. JAY BELL
- ☐ 354. SID BREAM
- ☐ 381. JIM LEYLAND(M)
- ☐ 425. ANDY VAN SLYKE
- ☐ 438. VICENTE PALACIOS
- ☐ 441. ZANE SMITH
- ☐ 451. NEAL HEATON
- ☐ 479. BOB PATTERSON
- ☐ 487. RAFAEL BELLIARD
- ☐ 491. KURT MILLER
- ☐ 508. MIKE YORK
- ☐ 522. STAN BELINDA
- ☐ 537. JOSE LIND
- ☐ 551. BOB KIPPER
- ☐ 570. BARRY BONDS
- ☐ 595. BILL LANDRUM
- ☐ 621. TED POWER
- ☐ 665. MIKE LAVALLIERE
- ☐ 685. DOUG DRABEK
- ☐ 722. WALLY BACKMAN
- ☐ 750. BOBBY BONILLA
- ☐ 771. GARY REDUS
- ☐ 779. CARMELO MARTINEZ

ST. LOUIS CARDINALS

- ☐ 20. PEDRO GUERRERO
- ☐ 41. KEN DAYLEY
- ☐ 63. MILT THOMPSON
- ☐ 88. BOB TEWKSBURY
- ☐ 112. FRANK DIPINO
- ☐ 126. BERNARD GILKEY
- ☐ 130. OZZIE SMITH
- ☐ 160. VINCE COLEMAN
- ☐ 185. JOE MAGRANE
- ☐ 205. MIKE PEREZ
- ☐ 228. REX HUDLER
- ☐ 262. TIM JONES
- ☐ 271. OMAR OLIVARES
- ☐ 308. TOM PAGNOZZI
- ☐ 343. JOSE OQUENDO
- ☐ 351. JOE TORRE(M)
- ☐ 368. FELIX JOSE
- ☐ 485. TERRY PENDLETON
- ☐ 518. CRIS CARPENTER
- ☐ 539. SCOTT TERRY
- ☐ 566. CRAIG WILSON
- ☐ 591. KEN HILL
- ☐ 616. TODD ZEILE
- ☐ 636. GERONIMO PENA
- ☐ 660. LEE SMITH
- ☐ 682. RAY LANKFORD
- ☐ 711. JOSE DELEON
- ☐ 743. BRYN SMITH
- ☐ 769. TIM SHERRILL

SAN DIEGO PADRES

- ☐ 34. ATLEE HAMMAKER
- ☐ 65. BRUCE HURST
- ☐ 109. GREG RIDDOCH(M)
- ☐ 120. JOE CARTER
- ☐ 180. TONY GWYNN
- ☐ 238. MIKE DUNNE
- ☐ 253. GARRY TEMPLETON
- ☐ 307. ANDY BENES
- ☐ 315. ROBERTO ALOMAR
- ☐ 358. MARK PARENT
- ☐ 373. DARRIN JACKSON
- ☐ 424. CALVIN SCHIRALDI
- ☐ 448. CRAIG LEFFERTS
- ☐ 481. EDDIE WHITSON
- ☐ 513. JERALD CLARK
- ☐ 538. BIP ROBERTS
- ☐ 547. MIKE PAGLIARULO
- ☐ 573. RICH RODRIGUEZ
- ☐ 586. FRED LYNN
- ☐ 613. ERIC SHOW
- ☐ 650. JACK CLARK
- ☐ 683. DEREK LILLIQUIST
- ☐ 697. SHAWN ABNER
- ☐ 726. PHIL STEPHENSON
- ☐ 749. GREG HARRIS
- ☐ 760. BENNY SANTIAGO
- ☐ 774. DENNIS RASMUSSEN

SAN FRANCISCO GIANTS

- ☐ 17. JEFF BRANTLEY
- ☐ 40. KEVIN MITCHELL
- ☐ 52. FRANCISCO OLIVERAS
- ☐ 66. TERRY KENNEDY
- ☐ 96. TREVOR WILSON
- ☐ 104. DON ROBINSON
- ☐ 125. STEVE BEDROSIAN
- ☐ 158. JOSE URIBE
- ☐ 190. MATT WILLIAMS
- ☐ 218. RICK PARKER
- ☐ 242. MIKE LACOSS
- ☐ 310. GARY CARTER
- ☐ 325. BRETT BUTLER
- ☐ 361. SCOTT GARRELTS
- ☐ 408. ERNIE RILES
- ☐ 422. RICK REUSCHEL
- ☐ 447. JOHN BURKETT
- ☐ 472. KIRT MANWARING
- ☐ 500. WILL CLARK
- ☐ 572. DAVE ANDERSON
- ☐ 579. ROGER CRAIG(M)
- ☐ 628. GREG LITTON
- ☐ 657. MIKE KINGERY
- ☐ 679. BILL BATHE
- ☐ 705. ROBBY THOMPSON
- ☐ 733. KELLY DOWNS
- ☐ 752. KEVIN BASS
- ☐ 791. MIKE BENJAMIN

SEATTLE MARINERS

- ☐ 38. SCOTT BRADLEY
- ☐ 55. JEFFREY LEONARD
- ☐ 87. TRACY JONES
- ☐ 108. MATT YOUNG
- ☐ 133. GREG BRILEY
- ☐ 154. JAY BUHNER
- ☐ 178. DAVE VALLE
- ☐ 203. GENE HARRIS
- ☐ 225. RANDY JOHNSON
- ☐ 260. HAROLD REYNOLDS
- ☐ 276. BILL SWIFT
- ☐ 298. OMAR VIZQUEL
- ☐ 337. KEITH COMSTOCK
- ☐ 365. MIKE SCHOOLER
- ☐ 436. SCOTT BANKHEAD
- ☐ 458. BRIAN HOLMAN
- ☐ 465. KEN GRIFFEY
- ☐ 482. TINO MARTINEZ
- ☐ 515. ALVIN DAVIS
- ☐ 529. MARC NEWFIELD
- ☐ 534. MIKE JACKSON
- ☐ 563. BRENT KNACKERT
- ☐ 585. PETE O'BRIEN
- ☐ 607. EDGAR MARTINEZ
- ☐ 634. HENRY COTTO
- ☐ 655. ERIK HANSON
- ☐ 681. JEFF SCHAEFER
- ☐ 699. JIM LEFEBVRE(M)
- ☐ 709. MATT SINATRO
- ☐ 739. RUSS SWAN
- ☐ 790. KEN GRIFFEY, JR.

TEXAS RANGERS

- ☐ 1. NOLAN RYAN
- ☐ 27. BOBBY WITT
- ☐ 54. GARY MIELKE
- ☐ 78. GENO PETRALLI
- ☐ 138. JAMIE MOYER
- ☐ 172. PETE INCAVIGLIA
- ☐ 184. GARY GREEN
- ☐ 224. JUAN GONZALEZ
- ☐ 244. MIKE JEFFCOAT
- ☐ 277. SCOTT COOLBAUGH
- ☐ 295. RAFAEL PALMEIRO
- ☐ 304. KEVIN REIMER
- ☐ 314. GARY PETTIS
- ☐ 332. KENNY ROGERS
- ☐ 344. JEFF RUSSELL
- ☐ 409. MIKE STANLEY
- ☐ 428. JOHN BARFIELD
- ☐ 464. STEVE BUECHELE
- ☐ 489. BOBBY VALENTINE(M)
- ☐ 495. CHARLIE HOUGH
- ☐ 535. RUBEN SIERRA
- ☐ 562. JEFF KUNKEL
- ☐ 584. KEVIN BROWN
- ☐ 622. JACK DAUGHERTY
- ☐ 676. SCOTT CHIAMPARINO
- ☐ 706. BRAD ARNSBERG
- ☐ 734. JOHN RUSSELL
- ☐ 756. JEFF HUSON
- ☐ 775. JULIO FRANCO

TORONTO BLUE JAYS

- ☐ 26. LUIS SOJO
- ☐ 49. PAT BORDERS
- ☐ 71. JIM ACKER
- ☐ 81. CITO GASTON(M)
- ☐ 101. ROB DUCEY
- ☐ 110. TOM HENKE
- ☐ 140. FRED MCGRIFF
- ☐ 168. JOHN OLERUD
- ☐ 181. DUANE WARD
- ☐ 191. WILLIE BLAIR
- ☐ 213. FRANK WILLS
- ☐ 229. RANCE MULLINIKS
- ☐ 233. AL LEITER
- ☐ 274. KEN WILLIAMS
- ☐ 292. BUD BLACK
- ☐ 297. MANNY LEE
- ☐ 320. TONY FERNANDEZ
- ☐ 348. TODD STOTTLEMYRE
- ☐ 370. KELLY GRUBER
- ☐ 440. GEORGE BELL
- ☐ 460. DAVE STIEB
- ☐ 509. GLENALLEN HILL
- ☐ 543. JUNIOR FELIX
- ☐ 588. MARK WHITEN
- ☐ 599. GREG MYERS
- ☐ 619. DAVID WELLS
- ☐ 687. JOHN CERUTTI
- ☐ 727. MOOKIE WILSON
- ☐ 741. JIMMY KEY
- ☐ 777. JOHN CANDELARIA

1991 TOPPS TRADED (132) 2 1/2 X 3 1/2

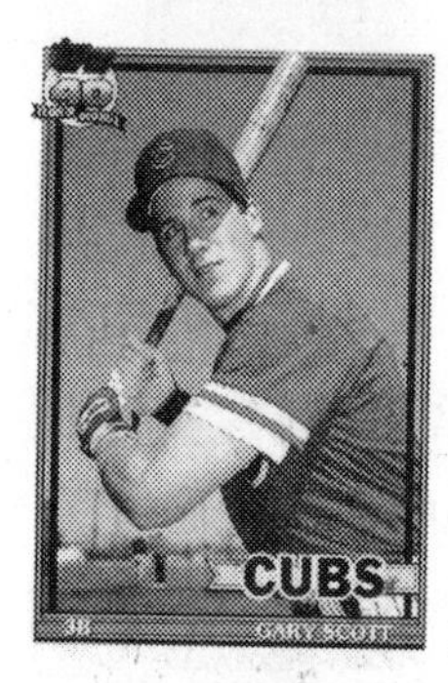

ATLANTA BRAVES

- ☐ 9T. RAFAEL BELLIARD
- ☐ 13T. SID BREAM
- ☐ 84T. OTIS NIXON
- ☐ 90T. TERRY PENDLETON

BALTIMORE ORIOLES

- ☐ 28T. GLENN DAVIS
- ☐ 37T. DWIGHT EVANS
- ☐ 47T. LEO GOMEZ
- ☐ 85T. JOHNNY OATES(M)
- ☐ 100T. JEFF ROBINSON

BOSTON RED SOX

- ☐ 22T. JACK CLARK
- ☐ 26T. DANNY DARWIN
- ☐ 123T. MO VAUGHN

CALIFORNIA ANGELS

- ☐ 40T. JUNIOR FELIX
- ☐ 44T. GARY GAETTI
- ☐ 89T. DAVE PARKER
- ☐ 99T. JEFF ROBINSON
- ☐ 112T. LUIS SOJO

CHICAGO CUBS

- ☐ 8T. GEORGE BELL
- ☐ 36T. JIM ESSIAN(M)
- ☐ 59T. DANNY JACKSON
- ☐ 105T. BOB SCANLAN
- ☐ 107T. GARY SCOTT
- ☐ 110T. DAVE SMITH

CHICAGO WHITE SOX

- ☐ 56T. CHARLIE HOUGH
- ☐ 58T. BO JACKSON
- ☐ 94T. TIM RAINES

CINCINNATI REDS

- ☐ 65T. CHRIS JONES

CLEVELAND INDIANS

- ☐ 52T. MIKE HARGROVE(M)
- ☐ 55T. GLENALLEN HILL
- ☐ 60T. REGGIE JEFFERSON
- ☐ 73T. MARK LEWIS
- ☐ 126T. MARK WHITEN

DETROIT TIGERS

- ☐ 5T. SKEETER BARNES
- ☐ 30T. ROB DEER
- ☐ 57T. PETE INCAVIGLIA
- ☐ 119T. MICKEY TETTLETON

HOUSTON ASTROS

- ☐ 4T. JEFF BAGWELL
- ☐ 42T. STEVE FINLEY
- ☐ 48T. LUIS GONZALEZ
- ☐ 53T. PETE HARNISCH
- ☐ 68T. DARRYL KILE

KANSAS CITY ROYALS

- ☐ 12T. MIKE BODDICKER
- ☐ 46T. KIRK GIBSON
- ☐ 79T. HAL MCRAE(M)

LOS ANGELES DODGERS

- ☐ 15T. BRETT BUTLER
- ☐ 17T. JOHN CANDELARIA
- ☐ 19T. GARY CARTER
- ☐ 86T. BOB OJEDA
- ☐ 114T. DARRYL STRAWBERRY

MILWAUKEE BREWERS

- ☐ 10T. DANTE BICHETTE
- ☐ 74T. CANDY MALDONADO
- ☐ 95T. WILLIE RANDOLPH
- ☐ 115T. FRANKLIN STUBBS

MINNESOTA TWINS

- ☐ 6T. STEVE BEDROSIAN
- ☐ 27T. CHILI DAVIS
- ☐ 69T. CHUCK KNOBLAUCH
- ☐ 71T. SCOTT LEIUS
- ☐ 82T. JACK MORRIS
- ☐ 87T. MIKE PAGLIARULO

MONTREAL EXPOS

- ☐ 16T. IVAN CALDERON
- ☐ 39T. JEFF FASSERO
- ☐ 64T. BARRY JONES
- ☐ 92T. DOUG PIATT
- ☐ 103T. TOM RUNNELLS(M)

NEW YORK METS

- ☐ 14T. HUBIE BROOKS
- ☐ 21T. RICK CERONE
- ☐ 23T. VINCE COLEMAN
- ☐ 106T. PETE SCHOUREK
- ☐ 109T. DOUG SIMONS
- ☐ 118T. GARRY TEMPLETON

NEW YORK YANKEES

- ☐ 38T. STEVE FARR
- ☐ 62T. JEFF JOHNSON
- ☐ 66T. SCOTT KAMIENIECKI
- ☐ 67T. PAT KELLY
- ☐ 104T. SCOTT SANDERSON
- ☐ 117T. WADE TAYLOR

OAKLAND A'S

- ☐ 35T. KIRK DRESSENDORFER
- ☐ 97T. ERNIE RILES
- ☐ 129T. WILLIE WILSON

PHILADELPHIA PHILLIES

- ☐ 3T. WALLY BACKMAN
- ☐ 25T. DANNY COX
- ☐ 43T. JIM FREGOSI(M)
- ☐ 127T. MITCH WILLIAMS

PITTSBURGH PIRATES

- ☐ 81T. ORLANDO MERCED

ST. LOUIS CARDINALS

- ☐ 1T. JUAN AGOSTO

SAN DIEGO PADRES

- ☐ 24T. SCOTT COOLBAUGH
- ☐ 41T. TONY FERNANDEZ
- ☐ 77T. FRED MCGRIFF
- ☐ 120T. TIM TEUFEL

SAN FRANCISCO GIANTS

- ☐ 11T. BUD BLACK
- ☐ 29T. STEVE DECKER
- ☐ 76T. WILLIE MCGEE
- ☐ 96T. DAVE RIGHETTI

SEATTLE MARINERS

- ☐ 31T. RICH DELUCIA
- ☐ 70T. BILL KRUEGER

TEXAS RANGERS

- ☐ 33T. BRIAN DOWNING
- ☐ 88T. DEAN PALMER
- ☐ 101T. IVAN RODRIGUEZ

TORONTO BLUE JAYS

- ☐ 2T. ROBERTO ALOMAR
- ☐ 7T. DEREK BELL
- ☐ 18T. TOM CANDIOTTI
- ☐ 20T. JOE CARTER
- ☐ 111T. CORY SNYDER
- ☐ 121T. MIKE TIMLIN
- ☐ 125T. DEVON WHITE

TEAM U.S.A.

- ☐ 32T. JOHN DETTMER
- ☐ 34T. DARREN DREIFORT
- ☐ 45T. JASON GIAMBI
- ☐ 49T. JEFF GRANGER
- ☐ 50T. TODD GREENE
- ☐ 51T. JEFFREY HAMMONDS
- ☐ 54T. RICK HELLINGS
- ☐ 61T. CHARLES JOHNSON
- ☐ 63T. TODD JOHNSON
- ☐ 72T. DONNIE LESHNOCK
- ☐ 75T. JASON MCDONALD
- ☐ 78T. BILLY MCMILLON
- ☐ 80T. DAN MELENDEZ
- ☐ 83T. PHIL NEVIN
- ☐ 91T. TONY PHILLIPS
- ☐ 93T. RON POLK(HC)

1991 Topps Traded

- ☐ 98T. CHRIS ROBERTS
- ☐ 102T. STEVE RODRIGUEZ
- ☐ 108T. PAUL SHUEY
- ☐ 113T. KENNIE STEENSTRA
- ☐ 116T. TODD TAYLOR
- ☐ 122T. DAVID TUTTLE
- ☐ 124T. JEFF WARE
- ☐ 128T. CRAIG WILSON
- ☐ 130T. CHRIS WIMMER
- ☐ 131T. IVAN ZWEIG

1992 TOPPS (792)
2 1/2" X 3 1/2"

ATLANTA BRAVES

- ☐ 25. RON GANT
- ☐ 26. MIKE BIELECKI
- ☐ 39. GREG OLSON
- ☐ 49. DAMON BERRYHILL
- ☐ 53. TOMMY GREGG
- ☐ 68. MARVIN FREEMAN
- ☐ 80. DAVID JUSTICE
- ☐ 99. JEFF TREADWAY
- ☐ 115. TERRY PENDLETON
- ☐ 126. RYAN KLESKO(P)
- ☐ 152. CHARLIE LEIBRANDT
- ☐ 172. JUAN BERENGUER
- ☐ 199. JEFF BLAUSER
- ☐ 226. PETE SMITH
- ☐ 245. JOHN SMOLTZ
- ☐ 279. JIM CLANCY
- ☐ 305. TOM GLAVINE
- ☐ 337. ALEJANDRO PENA
- ☐ 340. OTIS NIXON
- ☐ 367. RAFAEL BELLIARD
- ☐ 467. LONNIE SMITH
- ☐ 489. BOBBY COX(M)
- ☐ 512. MIKE HEATH
- ☐ 542. KEITH MITCHELL
- ☐ 551. CHIPPER JONES(P)
- ☐ 574. STEVE AVERY
- ☐ 596. KENT MERCKER
- ☐ 611. BRIAN HUNTER
- ☐ 631. ARMANDO REYNOSO
- ☐ 645. DEION SANDERS
- ☐ 689. MARK LEMKE
- ☐ 703. MARK WOHLERS
- ☐ 770. SID BREAM
- ☐ 788. MIKE STANTON

BALTIMORE ORIOLES

- ☐ 17. RANDY MILLIGAN
- ☐ 40. CAL RIPKEN
- ☐ 52. JUAN BELL
- ☐ 58. DOUG ROBBINS(P)
- ☐ 84. LEO GOMEZ
- ☐ 104. JEFF BALLARD
- ☐ 125. CHRIS HOILES
- ☐ 158. TODD FROHWIRTH
- ☐ 190. GLENN DAVIS
- ☐ 218. MIKE FLANAGAN
- ☐ 242. MIKE MUSSINA
- ☐ 268. BRADY ANDERSON
- ☐ 310. JOSE MESA
- ☐ 325. JOE ORSULAK
- ☐ 350. GREGG OLSON
- ☐ 408. BOB MILACKI
- ☐ 422. SAM HORN
- ☐ 447. DAVID SEGUI
- ☐ 479. CHITO MARTINEZ
- ☐ 492. MIKE DEVEREAUX
- ☐ 540. BEN MCDONALD
- ☐ 551. MANNY ALEXANDER(P)
- ☐ 579. JOHNNY OATES(M)
- ☐ 603. LUIS MERCEDES
- ☐ 628. MARK WILLIAMSON
- ☐ 657. DAVE JOHNSON
- ☐ 683. JIM POOLE
- ☐ 705. DWIGHT EVANS
- ☐ 733. BOB MELVIN
- ☐ 752. BILLY RIPKEN
- ☐ 771. ARTHUR RHODES

BOSTON RED SOX

- ☐ 10. WADE BOGGS
- ☐ 59. MO VAUGHN
- ☐ 97. LUIS RIVERA
- ☐ 113. MIKE GREENWELL
- ☐ 127. CARLOS QUINTANA
- ☐ 150. ROGER CLEMENS
- ☐ 163. DANA KIECKER
- ☐ 182. JEFF REARDON
- ☐ 207. JACK CLARK
- ☐ 249. TONY FOSSAS
- ☐ 296. TOM BRUNANSKY
- ☐ 324. DANNY DARWIN
- ☐ 349. STEVE LYONS
- ☐ 377. BOB ZUPCIC
- ☐ 416. ELLIS BURKS
- ☐ 468. GREG HARRIS
- ☐ 488. SCOTT COOPER
- ☐ 504. AARON SELE
- ☐ 521. JOE HESKETH
- ☐ 569. TONY PENA
- ☐ 598. JODY REED
- ☐ 618. JEFF MCNEELY(P)
- ☐ 639. WAYNE HOUSIE
- ☐ 653. DENNIS LAMP
- ☐ 677. JOHN MARZANO
- ☐ 694. MIKE GARDINER
- ☐ 708. TOM BOLTON
- ☐ 724. KEVIN MORTON
- ☐ 734. SCOTT HATTEBERG
- ☐ 758. TIM NAEHRING
- ☐ 782. PHIL PLANTIER

CALIFORNIA ANGELS

- ☐ 21. BUCK RODGERS(M)
- ☐ 37. LUIS POLONIA
- ☐ 70. GARY GAETTI
- ☐ 95. SCOTT BAILES
- ☐ 137. JEFF ROBINSON
- ☐ 165. MARK LANGSTON
- ☐ 189. JUNIOR FELIX
- ☐ 206. LUIS SOJO
- ☐ 230. DICK SCHOFIELD
- ☐ 247. CHUCK FINLEY
- ☐ 269. RUBEN AMARO
- ☐ 301. KIRK MCCASKILL
- ☐ 338. SHAWN ABNER
- ☐ 360. LANCE PARRISH
- ☐ 375. BERT BLYLEVEN
- ☐ 435. MARK EICHHORN
- ☐ 496. JOE GRAHE
- ☐ 530. JIM ABBOTT
- ☐ 552. DAVE GALLAGHER
- ☐ 568. BRYAN HARVEY
- ☐ 602. MIKE FETTERS
- ☐ 629. WALLY JOYNER
- ☐ 652. BOBBY ROSE
- ☐ 702. LEE STEVENS
- ☐ 731. DONNIE HILL
- ☐ 763. KYLE ABBOTT
- ☐ 792. DAVE WINFIELD

CHICAGO CUBS

- ☐ 67. LUIS SALAZAR
- ☐ 81. CED LANDRUM
- ☐ 98. MIKE HARKEY
- ☐ 110. RYNE SANDBERG
- ☐ 140. MARK GRACE
- ☐ 168. DWIGHT SMITH
- ☐ 181. HECTOR VILLANUEVA
- ☐ 196. FRANK CASTILLO
- ☐ 213. LES LANCASTER
- ☐ 229. SHAWN BOSKIE
- ☐ 274. BOB SCANLAN
- ☐ 320. GEORGE BELL
- ☐ 348. RICK WILKINS
- ☐ 370. SHAWON DUNSTON
- ☐ 439. CHICO WALKER
- ☐ 460. ANDRE DAWSON
- ☐ 509. DOUG DASCENZO
- ☐ 529. JOE GIRARDI
- ☐ 543. JEROME WALTON
- ☐ 551. ALEX ARIAS(P)
- ☐ 561. JOSE VIZCAINO
- ☐ 576. HEATHCLIFF SLOCUMB
- ☐ 580. GREG MADDUX
- ☐ 601. DAVE SMITH
- ☐ 619. DANNY JACKSON
- ☐ 676. TURK WENDELL(P)
- ☐ 727. CHUCK MCELROY
- ☐ 753. PAUL ASSENMACHER

CHICAGO WHITE SOX

- ☐ 11. JACK MCDOWELL
- ☐ 36. SCOTT RUFFCORN
- ☐ 57. DONN PALL
- ☐ 94. SAMMY SOSA
- ☐ 107. DAN PASQUA
- ☐ 129. MELIDO PEREZ
- ☐ 153. RON KARKOVICE
- ☐ 176. RAMON GARCIA
- ☐ 179. CESAR BERNHARDT(P)
- ☐ 191. CHARLIE HOUGH
- ☐ 210. OZZIE GUILLEN
- ☐ 231. BRIAN DRAHMAN
- ☐ 255. ROBIN VENTURA
- ☐ 273. CRAIG GREBECK
- ☐ 290. BO JACKSON
- ☐ 302. JOEY CORA
- ☐ 355. WARREN NEWSON
- ☐ 426. TIM RAINES
- ☐ 452. WILSON ALVAREZ
- ☐ 477. GREG HIBBARD
- ☐ 505. BOBBY THIGPEN
- ☐ 532. MIKE HUFF
- ☐ 555. FRANK THOMAS
- ☐ 615. MATT MERULLO
- ☐ 630. CARLTON FISK
- ☐ 648. SCOTT FLETCHER
- ☐ 667. ROBERTO HERNANDEZ
- ☐ 701. SCOTT RADINSKY
- ☐ 736. LANCE JOHNSON
- ☐ 755. ALEX FERNANDEZ
- ☐ 784. KEN PATTERSON

CINCINNATI REDS

- ☐ 24. RANDY MYERS
- ☐ 48. SCOTT SCUDDER
- ☐ 61. PAUL O'NEILL
- ☐ 77. JACK ARMSTRONG
- ☐ 91. JEFF REED
- ☐ 136. BILL DORAN
- ☐ 197. GLENN BRAGGS
- ☐ 220. JOSE RIJO
- ☐ 262. TERRY LEE
- ☐ 283. REGGIE SANDERS
- ☐ 304. JOE OLIVER
- ☐ 321. LOU PINIELLA(M)
- ☐ 332. CHRIS JONES
- ☐ 339. TOM BROWNING
- ☐ 356. LUIS QUINONES
- ☐ 372. KIP GROSS
- ☐ 432. BILLY HATCHER
- ☐ 465. BARRY LARKIN
- ☐ 485. CHRIS SABO
- ☐ 528. STEVE FOSTER
- ☐ 547. HERM WINNINGHAM
- ☐ 589. MARIANO DUNCAN
- ☐ 610. ERIC DAVIS
- ☐ 649. NORM CHARLTON
- ☐ 674. MO SANFORD
- ☐ 714. CALVIN REESE
- ☐ 744. CHRIS HAMMOND
- ☐ 757. ROB DIBBLE
- ☐ 773. HAL MORRIS

CLEVELAND INDIANS

- □ 33. CARLOS BAERGA
- □ 79. JESSE OROSCO
- □ 93. REGGIE JEFFERSON
- □ 156. MANNY RAMIREZ
- □ 170. ALEX COLE
- □ 219. JERRY BROWNE
- □ 256. MIKE ALDRETE
- □ 280. CARLOS MARTINEZ
- □ 299. CHARLES NAGY
- □ 326. ERIC KING
- □ 364. GLENALLEN HILL
- □ 378. JOEL SKINNER
- □ 420. SANDY ALOMAR
- □ 427. EDDIE TAUBENSEE
- □ 446. MARK LEWIS
- □ 461. DOUG JONES
- □ 499. DAVE OTTO
- □ 523. SHAWN HILLEGAS
- □ 559. STEVE OLIN
- □ 586. ROD NICHOLS
- □ 591. ALAN COCKRELL(P)
- □ 609. MIKE HARGROVE(M)
- □ 632. FELIX FERMIN
- □ 656. LEE TINSLEY(P)
- □ 671. MARK WHITEN
- □ 709. CHRIS JAMES
- □ 735. GREG SWINDELL
- □ 768. JIM THOME
- □ 785. ALBERT BELLE

DETROIT TIGERS

- □ 29. MICKEY TETTLETON
- □ 120. ALAN TRAMMELL
- □ 126. RICO BROGNA(P)
- □ 143. PAUL GIBSON
- □ 167. ANDY ALLANSON
- □ 198. SCOTT ALDRED
- □ 221. SKEETER BARNES
- □ 272. JERRY DON GLEATON
- □ 293. MIKE HENNEMAN
- □ 319. TONY PHILLIPS
- □ 354. DAVE BERGMAN
- □ 381. SPARKY ANDERSON(M)
- □ 425. CECIL FIELDER
- □ 441. ROB DEER
- □ 458. FRANK TANANA
- □ 472. RICH ROWLAND
- □ 487. JOHN CERUTTI
- □ 508. BILL GULLICKSON
- □ 522. MILT CUYLER
- □ 537. MARK LEITER
- □ 570. LOU WHITAKER
- □ 621. DAN GAKELER
- □ 656. RUDY PEMBERTON(P)
- □ 665. DAVE HAAS
- □ 679. PETE INCAVIGLIA
- □ 684. TREVER MILLER
- □ 685. SCOTT LIVINGSTONE
- □ 722. WALT TERRELL
- □ 750. TRAVIS FRYMAN

HOUSTON ASTROS

- □ 12. LUIS GONZALEZ
- □ 34. JEFF JUDEN
- □ 69. KENNY LOFTON
- □ 86. STEVE FINLEY
- □ 114. MARK PORTUGAL
- □ 124. SHAWN LIVSEY
- □ 134. DARRYL KILE
- □ 161. CASEY CANDAELE
- □ 184. JIMMY JONES
- □ 214. ANDY MOTA
- □ 241. GERALD YOUNG
- □ 254. RYAN BOWEN
- □ 288. ANDUJAR CEDENO
- □ 316. CURT SCHILLING
- □ 362. JAVIER ORTIZ
- □ 415. JIM DESHAIES
- □ 437. SCOTT SERVAIS
- □ 463. MIKE SIMMS
- □ 501. ROB MALLICOAT
- □ 520. JEFF BAGWELL
- □ 541. JOSE TOLENTINO
- □ 564. JIMMY GONZALEZ
- □ 614. AL OSUNA
- □ 640. XAVIER HERNANDEZ
- □ 668. DWAYNE HENRY
- □ 715. CRAIG BIGGIO
- □ 729. ART HOWE(M)
- □ 740. KEN CAMINITI
- □ 765. PETE HARNISCH

KANSAS CITY ROYALS

- □ 16. JEFF MONTGOMERY
- □ 42. MIKE MACFARLANE
- □ 75. BRET SABERHAGEN
- □ 106. MIKE BODDICKER
- □ 128. KURT STILLWELL
- □ 145. DANNY TARTABULL
- □ 183. BRENT MAYNE
- □ 236. BILL PECOTA
- □ 246. JASON PRUITT
- □ 281. KEVIN APPIER
- □ 328. JOEL JOHNSTON
- □ 342. TIM SPEHR
- □ 412. LUIS AQUINO
- □ 431. TOM GORDON
- □ 469. JIM EISENREICH
- □ 483. TERRY SHUMPERT
- □ 494. GARY THURMAN
- □ 506. TODD BENZINGER
- □ 519. HAL MCRAE(M)
- □ 556. STORM DAVIS
- □ 577. KEVIN SEITZER
- □ 591. JACOB BRUMFIELD(P)
- □ 597. MIKE MAGNANTE
- □ 620. GEORGE BRETT
- □ 641. DAVID HOWARD
- □ 659. BRIAN MCRAE
- □ 687. HARVEY PULLIAM
- □ 720. KIRK GIBSON
- □ 741. MARK GUBICZA
- □ 766. MARK DAVIS

LOS ANGELES DODGERS

- □ 13. MIKE SCIOSCIA
- □ 45. GARY CARTER
- □ 92. LENNY HARRIS
- □ 123. BOB OJEDA
- □ 151. JEFF HAMILTON
- □ 175. OREL HERSHISER
- □ 194. ERIC KARROS
- □ 205. JAY HOWELL
- □ 233. MITCH WEBSTER
- □ 261. TOM LASORDA(M)
- □ 289. MIKE MORGAN
- □ 315. JUAN SAMUEL
- □ 334. KEVIN GROSS
- □ 363. JOHN CANDELARIA
- □ 418. ALFREDO GRIFFIN
- □ 493. JOSE OFFERMAN
- □ 517. JIM GOTT
- □ 550. DARRYL STRAWBERRY
- □ 581. STAN JAVIER
- □ 604. CHRIS GWYNN
- □ 627. MIKE SHARPERSON
- □ 642. TIM CREWS
- □ 655. BRETT BUTLER
- □ 656. HENRY RODRIGUEZ(P)
- □ 688. TIM BELCHER
- □ 713. ROGER MCDOWELL
- □ 730. RAMON MARTINEZ
- □ 751. STEVE WILSON
- □ 767. KAL DANIELS
- □ 780. EDDIE MURRAY

MILWAUKEE BREWERS

- □ 7. JIM OLANDER
- □ 22. BILL WEGMAN
- □ 58. DAVE NILSSON(P)
- □ 90. ROBIN YOUNT
- □ 116. WILLIE RANDOLPH
- □ 126. JOHN JAHA(P)
- □ 169. CHUCK CRIM
- □ 208. JULIO MACHADO
- □ 222. JAIME NAVARRO
- □ 248. JIM GANTNER
- □ 265. TEDDY HIGUERA
- □ 278. DARRYL HAMILTON
- □ 291. PHIL GARNER(M)
- □ 303. DAN PLESAC
- □ 329. FRANKLIN STUBBS
- □ 352. ED NUNEZ
- □ 371. DANTE BICHETTE
- □ 384. MARK LEE
- □ 433. CAL ELDRED
- □ 444. TYRONE HILL
- □ 454. DARREN HOLMES
- □ 478. DALE SVEUM
- □ 572. GREG VAUGHN
- □ 600. PAUL MOLITOR
- □ 638. CHRIS BOSIO
- □ 695. GARY SHEFFIELD
- □ 718. B.J. SURHOFF
- □ 742. BILLY SPIERS
- □ 776. DOUG HENRY

MINNESOTA TWINS

- □ 23. CHUCK KNOBLAUCH
- □ 44. RICK AGUILERA
- □ 66. SCOTT STAHOVIAK
- □ 74. SCOTT LEIUS
- □ 118. CHILI DAVIS
- □ 146. AL NEWMAN
- □ 164. SHANE MACK
- □ 177. DANNY GLADDEN
- □ 217. BRIAN HARPER
- □ 235. JACK MORRIS
- □ 267. STEVE BEDROSIAN
- □ 284. GENE LARKIN
- □ 313. KEVIN TAPANI
- □ 347. KENT HRBEK
- □ 417. ALLAN ANDERSON
- □ 442. DAVE WEST
- □ 459. TOM KELLY(M)
- □ 473. PAUL RUSSO(P)
- □ 476. RANDY BUSH
- □ 546. PAUL SORRENTO
- □ 548. MARK GUTHRIE
- □ 575. KIRBY PUCKETT
- □ 585. LENNY WEBSTER
- □ 592. DENNY NEAGLE
- □ 605. SCOTT ERICKSON
- □ 613. PEDRO MUNOZ
- □ 617. JUNIOR ORTIZ
- □ 644. TERRY LEACH
- □ 663. GREG GAGNE
- □ 676. PAT MAHOMES(P)
- □ 721. MIKE PAGLIARULO
- □ 747. WILLIE BANKS
- □ 781. PAUL ABBOTT

MONTREAL EXPOS

- □ 15. DENNY MARTINEZ
- □ 32. CHRIS NABHOLZ
- □ 51. TOM RUNNELLS(M)
- □ 73. BRIAN BARNES
- □ 119. MARK GARDNER
- □ 174. STEVE FREY
- □ 186. CLIFF FLOYD
- □ 224. BRET BARBERIE
- □ 240. ANDRES GALARRAGA
- □ 286. GILBERTO REYES
- □ 309. DAVE MARTINEZ
- □ 343. JOHN VANDER WAL
- □ 361. BARRY JONES
- □ 385. TIM WALLACH
- □ 423. JEFF FASSERO
- □ 443. SPIKE OWEN
- □ 515. DELINO DESHIELDS
- □ 526. DOUG PIATT

- ☐ 531. LARRY WALKER
- ☐ 551. WIL CORDERO(P)
- ☐ 566. BILL SAMPEN
- ☐ 583. MEL ROJAS
- ☐ 618. CESAR HERNANDEZ(P)
- ☐ 626. CHRIS HANEY
- ☐ 647. MARQUIS GRISSOM
- ☐ 666. TOM FOLEY
- ☐ 692. SCOTT RUSKIN
- ☐ 732. NELSON SANTOVENIA
- ☐ 761. MIKE FITZGERALD
- ☐ 775. IVAN CALDERON

NEW YORK METS

- ☐ 56. CHARLIE O'BRIEN
- ☐ 82. DOUG SIMONS
- ☐ 111. MARK CARREON
- ☐ 139. JEFF INNIS
- ☐ 148. ANTHONY YOUNG
- ☐ 157. KEITH MILLER
- ☐ 195. DAVID CONE
- ☐ 227. DARYL BOSTON
- ☐ 251. KEVIN ELSTER
- ☐ 287. PETE SCHOUREK
- ☐ 306. AL SHIRLEY
- ☐ 322. TIM BURKE
- ☐ 376. CHRIS DONNELS
- ☐ 382. SID FERNANDEZ
- ☐ 419. WALLY WHITEHURST
- ☐ 457. HUBIE BROOKS
- ☐ 500. VINCE COLEMAN
- ☐ 510. FRANK VIOLA
- ☐ 533. MACKEY SASSER
- ☐ 590. HOWARD JOHNSON
- ☐ 591. JEROMY BURNITZ(P)
- ☐ 591. D.J. DOZIER(P)
- ☐ 625. KEVIN MCREYNOLDS
- ☐ 643. RICK CERONE
- ☐ 673. TODD HUNDLEY
- ☐ 690. JOHN FRANCO
- ☐ 707. GREGG JEFFERIES
- ☐ 725. DWIGHT GOODEN
- ☐ 745. DAVE MAGADAN
- ☐ 759. JEFF TORBORG(M)
- ☐ 772. GARRY TEMPLETON

NEW YORK YANKEES

- ☐ 6. BRIEN TAYLOR
- ☐ 18. GREG CADARET
- ☐ 46. STEVE FARR
- ☐ 58. BRAD AUSMUS(P)
- ☐ 102. SCOTT KAMIENIECKI
- ☐ 154. HENSLEY MEULENS
- ☐ 179. BOBBY DE JARDIN(P)
- ☐ 179. ANDY STANKIEWICZ(P)
- ☐ 201. BUCK SHOWALTER(M)
- ☐ 212. RANDY VELARDE
- ☐ 223. MEL HALL
- ☐ 243. ALVARO ESPINOZA
- ☐ 266. ROBERTO KELLY
- ☐ 300. DON MATTINGLY
- ☐ 318. STEVE HOWE
- ☐ 341. BOB GEREN
- ☐ 357. MIKE WITT
- ☐ 374. BERNIE WILLIAMS
- ☐ 430. STEVE SAX
- ☐ 449. JEFF JOHNSON
- ☐ 480. SCOTT SANDERSON
- ☐ 503. PASCUAL PEREZ
- ☐ 562. WADE TAYLOR
- ☐ 578. LEE GUETTERMAN
- ☐ 612. PAT KELLY
- ☐ 650. JESSE BARFIELD
- ☐ 656. GERALD WILLIAMS(P)
- ☐ 672. ERIC PLUNK
- ☐ 676. SAM MILITELLO(P)
- ☐ 698. JOHN HABYAN
- ☐ 710. KEVIN MAAS
- ☐ 748. MATT NOKES
- ☐ 778. TIM LEARY

OAKLAND A'S

- ☐ 19. JAMIE QUIRK
- ☐ 62. GENE NELSON
- ☐ 76. MIKE GALLEGO
- ☐ 100. JOSE CANSECO
- ☐ 132. ERIC SHOW
- ☐ 142. TODD VAN POPPEL
- ☐ 187. ERNIE RILES
- ☐ 202. RICK HONEYCUTT
- ☐ 216. BRENT GATES
- ☐ 234. TERRY STEINBACH
- ☐ 259. RON DARLING
- ☐ 285. BOB WELCH
- ☐ 317. MIKE BORDICK
- ☐ 335. DAVE HENDERSON
- ☐ 359. MIKE MOORE
- ☐ 379. STEVE CHITREN
- ☐ 410. DAVE STEWART
- ☐ 429. TONY LARUSSA(M)
- ☐ 450. MARK MCGWIRE
- ☐ 473. CRAIG PAQUETTE(P)
- ☐ 474. MIKE ROSSITER
- ☐ 495. CARNEY LANSFORD
- ☐ 536. WILLIE WILSON
- ☐ 560. RICKEY HENDERSON
- ☐ 606. BROOK JACOBY
- ☐ 635. HAROLD BAINES
- ☐ 651. JOE SLUSARSKI
- ☐ 678. JOE KLINK
- ☐ 691. WALT WEISS
- ☐ 704. CURT YOUNG
- ☐ 716. KIRK DRESSENDORFER
- ☐ 738. DENNIS ECKERSLEY

PHILADELPHIA PHILLIES

- ☐ 14. WES CHAMBERLAIN
- ☐ 30. JOHN KRUK
- ☐ 63. RANDY READY
- ☐ 83. TOMMY GREENE
- ☐ 103. RICKY JORDAN
- ☐ 135. VON HAYES
- ☐ 159. DARRIN FLETCHER
- ☐ 200. LEN DYKSTRA
- ☐ 244. DARREN DAULTON
- ☐ 258. JIM LINDEMAN
- ☐ 307. BRUCE RUFFIN
- ☐ 331. STEVE LAKE
- ☐ 353. BRAULIO CASTILLO
- ☐ 383. DAVE HOLLINS
- ☐ 434. WALLY BACKMAN
- ☐ 456. PAT COMBS
- ☐ 471. JOSE DEJESUS
- ☐ 484. MIKE HARTLEY
- ☐ 497. ANDY ASHBY
- ☐ 514. KIM BATISTE
- ☐ 544. CLIFF BRANTLEY
- ☐ 557. DICKIE THON
- ☐ 587. MICKEY MORANDINI
- ☐ 599. STEVE SEARCY
- ☐ 633. MITCH WILLIAMS
- ☐ 669. JIM FREGOSI(M)
- ☐ 680. DALE MURPHY
- ☐ 696. JOE BOEVER
- ☐ 719. TERRY MULHOLLAND
- ☐ 754. CHARLIE HAYES
- ☐ 764. TYLER GREEN
- ☐ 791. DANNY COX

PITTSBURGH PIRATES

- ☐ 9. JON FARRELL
- ☐ 43. JOSE LIND
- ☐ 64. BOB KIPPER
- ☐ 89. NEAL HEATON
- ☐ 122. GARY VARSHO
- ☐ 141. JIM LEYLAND(M)
- ☐ 160. BOBBY BONILLA
- ☐ 179. ARMANDO MORENO(P)
- ☐ 209. LLOYD MCCLENDON
- ☐ 232. JOHN SMILEY
- ☐ 263. BOB PATTERSON
- ☐ 282. JOHN WEHNER
- ☐ 312. MIKE LAVALLIERE
- ☐ 345. ZANE SMITH
- ☐ 380. BARRY BONDS
- ☐ 440. DOUG DRABEK
- ☐ 453. GARY REDUS
- ☐ 466. STAN BELINDA
- ☐ 486. BOB WALK
- ☐ 524. DON SLAUGHT
- ☐ 545. ANDY VAN SLYKE
- ☐ 571. RANDY TOMLIN
- ☐ 582. VICENTE PALACIOS
- ☐ 622. STEVE BUECHELE
- ☐ 637. ORLANDO MERCED
- ☐ 661. BILL LANDRUM
- ☐ 693. JEFF KING
- ☐ 712. CURT WILKERSON
- ☐ 779. JAY BELL

ST. LOUIS CARDINALS

- ☐ 31. BRYN SMITH
- ☐ 47. REX HUDLER
- ☐ 85. JOSE DELEON
- ☐ 96. TOM MCKINNON
- ☐ 105. FELIX JOSE
- ☐ 117. SCOTT TERRY
- ☐ 147. CRIS CARPENTER
- ☐ 166. GERONIMO PENA
- ☐ 193. OMAR OLIVARES
- ☐ 275. TODD ZEILE
- ☐ 292. RAY LANKFORD
- ☐ 323. MILT THOMPSON
- ☐ 346. RHEAL CORMIER
- ☐ 421. JUAN AGOSTO
- ☐ 448. TOM PAGNOZZI
- ☐ 470. PEDRO GUERRERO
- ☐ 498. GERALD PERRY
- ☐ 549. JOE TORRE(M)
- ☐ 565. LEE SMITH
- ☐ 594. BRIAN BARBER
- ☐ 623. BOB TEWKSBURY
- ☐ 646. CRAIG WILSON
- ☐ 654. ALLEN WATSON
- ☐ 664. KEN HILL
- ☐ 723. JOSE OQUENDO
- ☐ 746. BERNARD GILKEY
- ☐ 760. OZZIE SMITH
- ☐ 783. JOE MAGRANE

SAN DIEGO PADRES

- ☐ 20. BIP ROBERTS
- ☐ 41. CRAIG LEFFERTS
- ☐ 60. TONY FERNANDEZ
- ☐ 88. DARRIN JACKSON
- ☐ 112. OSCAR AZOCAR
- ☐ 126. DAVE STATON(P)
- ☐ 162. PAUL FARIES
- ☐ 185. BENNY SANTIAGO
- ☐ 211. JEREMY HERNANDEZ
- ☐ 228. EDDIE WHITSON
- ☐ 252. DENNIS RASMUSSEN
- ☐ 270. TONY GWYNN
- ☐ 308. CRAIG SHIPLEY
- ☐ 336. GREG ANTHONY
- ☐ 351. GREG RIDDOCH(M)
- ☐ 413. TIM TEUFEL
- ☐ 438. MIKE MADDUX
- ☐ 462. RICH RODRIGUEZ
- ☐ 473. TOM REDINGTON(P)
- ☐ 518. JOSE MELENDEZ
- ☐ 539. THOMAS HOWARD
- ☐ 595. BRUCE HURST
- ☐ 616. LARRY ANDERSEN
- ☐ 636. GREG HARRIS
- ☐ 660. FRED MCGRIFF
- ☐ 682. ANDY BENES
- ☐ 711. RICKY BONES
- ☐ 749. JERALD CLARK
- ☐ 769. JACK HOWELL

SAN FRANCISCO GIANTS

- ☐ 8. BRYAN HICKERSON
- ☐ 35. DAVE RIGHETTI
- ☐ 65. WILLIE MCGEE
- ☐ 109. ROGER CRAIG(M)
- ☐ 180. KEVIN MITCHELL
- ☐ 204. TREVOR WILSON
- ☐ 238. GREG LITTON
- ☐ 253. TERRY KENNEDY
- ☐ 330. WILL CLARK
- ☐ 358. TED WOOD
- ☐ 369. STEVE WHITAKER
- ☐ 373. DON ROBINSON
- ☐ 424. PAUL MCCLELLAN
- ☐ 445. MATT WILLIAMS
- ☐ 475. ROBBY THOMPSON
- ☐ 491. JEFF BRANTLEY
- ☐ 513. KEVIN BASS
- ☐ 538. JOSE URIBE
- ☐ 558. SCOTT GARRELTS
- ☐ 573. KELLY DOWNS
- ☐ 593. STEVE DECKER
- ☐ 618. STEVE HOSEY(P)
- ☐ 697. MIKE FELDER

- ☐ 726. KIRT MANWARING
- ☐ 743. DARREN LEWIS
- ☐ 762. JOHN BURKETT
- ☐ 774. BUD BLACK
- ☐ 786. ROYCE CLAYTON

SEATTLE MARINERS

- ☐ 28. MIKE SCHOOLER
- ☐ 50. KEN GRIFFEY, JR.
- ☐ 58. JIM CAMPANIS(P)
- ☐ 71. ERIK HANSON
- ☐ 101. OMAR VIZQUEL
- ☐ 130. ALVIN DAVIS
- ☐ 144. BILL SWIFT
- ☐ 155. SCOTT BANKHEAD
- ☐ 171. BILL PLUMMER(M)
- ☐ 192. DAVE FLEMING
- ☐ 239. BRIAN HOLMAN
- ☐ 250. KEN GRIFFEY
- ☐ 271. TRACY JONES
- ☐ 294. DAVE VALLE
- ☐ 295. ALONZO POWELL
- ☐ 311. HENRY COTTO
- ☐ 327. JAY BUHNER
- ☐ 368. BILL KRUEGER
- ☐ 411. MIKE JACKSON
- ☐ 455. PETE O'BRIEN
- ☐ 473. FRANK BOLICK(P)
- ☐ 481. TINO MARTINEZ
- ☐ 502. GREG BRILEY
- ☐ 525. RANDY JOHNSON
- ☐ 553. EDGAR MARTINEZ
- ☐ 588. RUSS SWAN
- ☐ 608. SCOTT BRADLEY
- ☐ 624. SHAWN ESTES
- ☐ 670. HAROLD REYNOLDS
- ☐ 676. ROGER SALKELD(P)
- ☐ 686. RICH DELUCIA
- ☐ 706. ROB MURPHY
- ☐ 728. DAVE BURBA

TEXAS RANGERS

- ☐ 1. NOLAN RYAN
- ☐ 27. JUAN GONZALEZ
- ☐ 55. RAFAEL PALMEIRO
- ☐ 78. IVAN RODRIGUEZ
- ☐ 138. MONTY FARISS
- ☐ 149. BRIAN BOHANON
- ☐ 173. BRIAN DOWNING
- ☐ 188. JOSE GUZMAN
- ☐ 215. RICH GOSSAGE
- ☐ 237. JOSE HERNANDEZ
- ☐ 257. JEFF RUSSELL
- ☐ 277. SCOTT CHIAMPARINO
- ☐ 297. KEVIN BROWN
- ☐ 314. JEFF HUSON
- ☐ 344. JACK DAUGHERTY
- ☐ 409. GENO PETRALLI
- ☐ 428. DENNIS BOYD
- ☐ 464. MIKE JEFFCOAT
- ☐ 490. JULIO FRANCO
- ☐ 511. KENNY ROGERS
- ☐ 534. BENJI GIL
- ☐ 554. DONALD HARRIS
- ☐ 567. DEAN PALMER
- ☐ 584. WAYNE ROSENTHAL
- ☐ 618. DAN PELTIER(P)
- ☐ 675. BOBBY WITT
- ☐ 700. RUBEN SIERRA
- ☐ 737. KEVIN REIMER
- ☐ 756. GARY PETTIS
- ☐ 789. BOBBY VALENTINE(M)

TORONTO BLUE JAYS

- ☐ 38. TOM CANDIOTTI
- ☐ 54. DAVID WELLS
- ☐ 72. EDDIE ZOSKY
- ☐ 87. BOB MACDONALD
- ☐ 108. MIKE TIMLIN
- ☐ 121. DEREK BELL
- ☐ 133. RANCE MULLINIKS
- ☐ 178. JIM ACKER
- ☐ 203. GREG MYERS
- ☐ 225. ROBERTO ALOMAR
- ☐ 260. DEVON WHITE
- ☐ 276. SHAWN GREEN
- ☐ 298. KELLY GRUBER

- ☐ 333. PAT TABLER
- ☐ 365. DUANE WARD
- ☐ 414. JEFF WARE
- ☐ 436. MOOKIE WILSON
- ☐ 451. TOM HENKE
- ☐ 482. JIMMY KEY
- ☐ 507. CANDY MALDONADO
- ☐ 516. ED SPRAGUE
- ☐ 535. DAVE STIEB
- ☐ 563. PAT BORDERS
- ☐ 607. TODD STOTTLEMYRE
- ☐ 634. MANUEL LEE
- ☐ 662. JUAN GUZMAN
- ☐ 681. RENE GONZALES
- ☐ 699. CITO GASTON(M)
- ☐ 717. KEN DAYLEY
- ☐ 739. ROB DUCEY
- ☐ 777. JOHN OLERUD
- ☐ 790. JOE CARTER

1992 TOPPS TRADED (132) 2 1/2" X 3 1/2"

ATLANTA BRAVES

NO CARDS ISSUED

BALTIMORE ORIOLES

- ☐ 113T. RICK SUTCLIFFE
- ☐ 115T. JEFF TACKETT

BOSTON RED SOX

- ☐ 32T. JOHN FLAHERTY
- ☐ 52T. BUTCH HOBSON(M)
- ☐ 125T. FRANK VIOLA
- ☐ 131T. HERM WINNINGHAM

CALIFORNIA ANGELS

- ☐ 15T. HUBIE BROOKS
- ☐ 25T. CHAD CURTIS
- ☐ 28T. GARY DISARCINA
- ☐ 31T. MIKE FITZGERALD
- ☐ 42T. RENE GONZALES
- ☐ 47T. VON HAYES
- ☐ 122T. JULIO VALERA

CHICAGO CUBS

- ☐ 17T. JIM BULLINGER
- ☐ 63T. JIM LEFEBVRE(M)
- ☐ 68T. DERRICK MAY
- ☐ 76T. MIKE MORGAN
- ☐ 98T. REY SANCHEZ
- ☐ 102T. GARY SCOTT
- ☐ 109T. SAMMY SOSA

CHICAGO WHITE SOX

- ☐ 9T. GEORGE BELL
- ☐ 62T. GENE LAMONT(M)
- ☐ 69T. KIRK MCCASKILL
- ☐ 99T. STEVE SAX

CINCINNATI REDS

- ☐ 7T. SCOTT BANKHEAD
- ☐ 8T. TIM BELCHER
- ☐ 10T. FREDDIE BENAVIDES
- ☐ 67T. DAVE MARTINEZ
- ☐ 92T. BIP ROBERTS
- ☐ 96T. SCOTT RUSKIN

CLEVELAND INDIANS

- ☐ 6T. JACK ARMSTRONG
- ☐ 66T. KENNY LOFTON
- ☐ 84T. JUNIOR ORTIZ
- ☐ 108T. PAUL SORRENTO

DETROIT TIGERS

- ☐ 21T. MARK CARREON
- ☐ 24T. PHIL CLARK
- ☐ 41T. DANNY GLADDEN

HOUSTON ASTROS

- ☐ 12T. JOE BOEVER
- ☐ 49T. BUTCH HENRY
- ☐ 54T. PETE INCAVIGLIA
- ☐ 57T. DOUG JONES
- ☐ 117T. EDDIE TAUBENSEE
- ☐ 120T. SCOOTER TUCKER

KANSAS CITY ROYALS

- ☐ 55T. GREGG JEFFERIES
- ☐ 59T. WALLY JOYNER
- ☐ 71T. KEVIN MCREYNOLDS
- ☐ 72T. RUSTY MEACHAM
- ☐ 73T. KEITH MILLER
- ☐ 89T. HIPOLITO PICHARDO

LOS ANGELES DODGERS

- ☐ 11T. TODD BENZINGER
- ☐ 20T. TOM CANDIOTTI
- ☐ 26T. ERIC DAVIS
- ☐ 50T. CARLOS HERNANDEZ

MILWAUKEE BREWERS

- ☐ 13T. RICKY BONES
- ☐ 34T. SCOTT FLETCHER
- ☐ 65T. PAT LISTACH
- ☐ 83T. DAVE NILSSON
- ☐ 95T. BRUCE RUFFIN
- ☐ 103T. KEVIN SEITZER

MINNESOTA TWINS

- ☐ 61T. BILL KRUEGER
- ☐ 106T. JOHN SMILEY

MONTREAL EXPOS

- ☐ 3T. FELIPE ALOU(M)
- ☐ 4T. MOISES ALOU
- ☐ 22T. GARY CARTER
- ☐ 23T. ARCHI CIANFROCCO
- ☐ 33T. DARRIN FLETCHER
- ☐ 51T. KEN HILL
- ☐ 91T. DARREN REED
- ☐ 110T. MATT STAIRS

NEW YORK METS

- ☐ 14T. BOBBY BONILLA
- ☐ 37T. DAVE GALLAGHER
- ☐ 79T. EDDIE MURRAY
- ☐ 86T. BILL PECOTA
- ☐ 90T. WILLIE RANDOLPH
- ☐ 97T. BRET SABERHAGEN
- ☐ 101T. DICK SCHOFIELD

NEW YORK YANKEES

- ☐ 38T. MIKE GALLEGO
- ☐ 46T. CHARLIE HAYES
- ☐ 87T. MELIDO PEREZ
- ☐ 111T. ANDY STANKIEWICZ
- ☐ 116T. DANNY TARTABULL

OAKLAND A'S

- ☐ 16T. JERRY BROWNE
- ☐ 19T. KEVIN CAMPBELL
- ☐ 53T. VINCE HORSMAN

PHILADELPHIA PHILLIES

- ☐ 5T. RUBEN AMARO
- ☐ 30T. MARIANO DUNCAN
- ☐ 100T. CURT SCHILLING

PITTSBURGH PIRATES

- ☐ 81T. DENNY NEAGLE

ST. LOUIS CARDINALS

- ☐ 36T. ANDRES GALARRAGA
- ☐ 58T. BRIAN JORDAN
- ☐ 85T. DONOVAN OSBORNE
- ☐ 88T. MIKE PEREZ

SAN DIEGO PADRES

- ☐ 80T. RANDY MYERS
- ☐ 104T. FRANK SEMINARA
- ☐ 105T. GARY SHEFFIELD
- ☐ 112T. KURT STILLWELL
- ☐ 127T. DAN WALTERS

SAN FRANCISCO GIANTS

- ☐ 18T. DAVE BURBA
- ☐ 107T. CORY SNYDER
- ☐ 114T. BILL SWIFT

SEATTLE MARINERS

- ☐ 74T. KEVIN MITCHELL

TEXAS RANGERS

- ☐ 64T. DANNY LEON
- ☐ 118T. DICKIE THON

TORONTO BLUE JAYS

- ☐ 77T. JACK MORRIS
- ☐ 130T. DAVE WINFIELD

TEAM USA

- ☐ 1T. WILLIE ADAMS
- ☐ 2T. JEFF ALKIRE
- ☐ 27T. TIM DAVIS
- ☐ 29T. DARREN DREIFORT
- ☐ 35T. RON FRASER(HC)
- ☐ 39T. NOMAR GARCIAPARRA
- ☐ 40T. JASON GIAMBI
- ☐ 43T. JEFF GRANGER
- ☐ 44T. RICK GREENE
- ☐ 45T. JEFFREY HAMMONDS
- ☐ 48T. RICK HELLING
- ☐ 56T. CHARLES JOHNSON
- ☐ 60T. DARON KIRKREIT
- ☐ 70T. CHAD MCCONNELL
- ☐ 75T. JASON MOLER
- ☐ 78T. CALVIN MURRAY
- ☐ 82T. PHIL NEVIN
- ☐ 93T. CHRIS ROBERTS
- ☐ 94T. STEVE RODRIGUEZ
- ☐ 119T. MICHAEL TUCKER
- ☐ 121T. MARC VALDES
- ☐ 123T. JASON VARITEK
- ☐ 124T. RON VILLONE
- ☐ 126T. B.J. WALLACE
- ☐ 128T. CRAIG WILSON
- ☐ 129T. CHRIS WIMMER

1993 TOPPS (825)
2 1/2" X 3 1/2"

ATLANTA BRAVES

- ☐ 8. MARK WOHLERS
- ☐ 35. JOHN SMOLTZ
- ☐ 62. RAFAEL BELLIARD
- ☐ 88. MIKE STANTON
- ☐ 102. BRIAN HUNTER
- ☐ 116. MARK LEMKE
- ☐ 144. KENT MERCKER
- ☐ 170. DAVID JUSTICE
- ☐ 198. ALEJANDRO PENA
- ☐ 224. SID BREAM
- ☐ 251. MIKE BIELECKI
- ☐ 280. TOM GLAVINE
- ☐ 306. DAMON BERRYHILL
- ☐ 333. OTIS NIXON
- ☐ 393. RON GANT
- ☐ 413. PETE SMITH
- ☐ 423. RYAN KLESKO(P)
- ☐ 451. RAMON CARABALLO(P)
- ☐ 475. JEFF REARDON
- ☐ 501. BOBBY COX(M)
- ☐ 529. CHIPPER JONES(P)
- ☐ 552. JEFF BLAUSER
- ☐ 559. JAMIE ARNOLD
- ☐ 583. MARVIN FREEMAN
- ☐ 615. STEVE AVERY
- ☐ 650. TERRY PENDLETON
- ☐ 658. MELVIN NIEVES(P)
- ☐ 677. CHARLIE LEIBRANDT
- ☐ 708. GREG OLSON
- ☐ 769. FRANCISCO CABRERA
- ☐ 795. DEION SANDERS
- ☐ 811. JAVY LOPEZ

BALTIMORE ORIOLES

- ☐ 6. JEFF TACKETT
- ☐ 28. JOE ORSULAK
- ☐ 55. MARK MCLEMORE
- ☐ 82. DAVID SEGUI
- ☐ 109. SAM HORN
- ☐ 137. ALAN MILLS
- ☐ 164. LEO GOMEZ
- ☐ 192. BOB MILACKI
- ☐ 218. BEN MCDONALD
- ☐ 246. GREGG OLSON
- ☐ 274. RICK SUTCLIFFE
- ☐ 300. CAL RIPKEN
- ☐ 327. TIM HULETT
- ☐ 355. BRADY ANDERSON
- ☐ 381. MIKE FLANAGAN
- ☐ 415. TODD FROHWIRTH
- ☐ 446. LUIS MERCEDES
- ☐ 485. GLENN DAVIS
- ☐ 501. JOHNNY OATES(M)
- ☐ 524. CHRIS HOILES
- ☐ 554. ARTHUR RHODES
- ☐ 576. DAMON BUFORD(P)
- ☐ 587. MANNY ALEXANDER
- ☐ 617. CRAIG LEFFERTS
- ☐ 647. BRIAN SACKINSKY
- ☐ 678. RANDY MILLIGAN
- ☐ 710. MIKE MUSSINA

- ☐ 741. MIKE DEVEREAUX
- ☐ 772. CHITO MARTINEZ
- ☐ 793. JIM POOLE
- ☐ 797. BRAD PENNINGTON

BOSTON RED SOX

- ☐ 4. ROGER CLEMENS
- ☐ 24. TIM NAEHRING
- ☐ 51. MO VAUGHN
- ☐ 78. GREG HARRIS
- ☐ 103. JODY REED
- ☐ 162. JOE HESKETH
- ☐ 187. JOHN DOPSON
- ☐ 214. DANNY DARWIN
- ☐ 241. MIKE GARDINER
- ☐ 270. FRANK VIOLA
- ☐ 296. LUIS RIVERA
- ☐ 323. MIKE GREENWELL
- ☐ 351. ELLIS BURKS
- ☐ 377. HERM WINNINGHAM
- ☐ 390. WADE BOGGS
- ☐ 424. JOHN VALENTIN
- ☐ 456. SCOTT TAYLOR
- ☐ 502. BUTCH HOBSON(M)
- ☐ 528. PAUL QUANTRILL
- ☐ 532. TOM BRUNANSKY
- ☐ 562. BOB ZUPCIC
- ☐ 592. PHIL PLANTIER
- ☐ 618. TONY PENA
- ☐ 655. SCOTT COOPER
- ☐ 687. TONY SHEFFIELD
- ☐ 725. BILLY HATCHER
- ☐ 781. JACK CLARK
- ☐ 786. KEN RYAN(P)
- ☐ 798. GREG BLOSSER

CALIFORNIA ANGELS

- ☐ 20. TIM SALMON
- ☐ 48. BERT BLYLEVEN
- ☐ 77. JUNOR FELIX
- ☐ 104. MIKE BUTCHER
- ☐ 129. JOE GRAHE
- ☐ 139. GARY GAETTI
- ☐ 157. GARY DISARCINA
- ☐ 184. DAMION EASLEY
- ☐ 210. MARK LANGSTON
- ☐ 266. RENE GONZALES
- ☐ 293. ROB DUCEY
- ☐ 320. TIM FORTUGNO
- ☐ 347. LUIS SOJO
- ☐ 374. JULIO VALERA
- ☐ 467. LEE STEVENS
- ☐ 494. EDUARDO PEREZ(P)
- ☐ 499. CHUCK CRIM
- ☐ 503. BUCK RODGERS(M)
- ☐ 521. KEVIN FLORA
- ☐ 543. REGGIE WILLIAMS
- ☐ 574. DESHAWN WARREN
- ☐ 605. CHUCK FINLEY
- ☐ 633. RUSSIAN ANGELS
- ☐ 637. GREG MYERS
- ☐ 668. SCOTT LEWIS
- ☐ 699. CHAD CURTIS
- ☐ 728. STEVE FREY
- ☐ 760. LUIS POLONIA
- ☐ 780. JIM ABBOTT
- ☐ 799. JIM EDMONDS

CHICAGO CUBS

- ☐ 3. RYNE SANDBERG
- ☐ 21. LUIS SALAZAR
- ☐ 47. BOB SCANLAN
- ☐ 74. STEVE BUECHELE
- ☐ 101. JIM BULLINGER
- ☐ 128. KAL DANIELS
- ☐ 156. SAMMY SOSA
- ☐ 183. GREG MADDUX
- ☐ 211. DOUG DASCENZO
- ☐ 237. JOSE VIZCAINO
- ☐ 265. ANDRE DAWSON
- ☐ 292. REY SANCHEZ
- ☐ 319. PAUL ASSENMACHER
- ☐ 346. CHUCK MCELROY
- ☐ 373. MIKE MORGAN
- ☐ 391. DERRICK MAY
- ☐ 459. DEREK WALLACE
- ☐ 487. JESSIE HOLLINS
- ☐ 502. JIM LEFEBVRE(M)
- ☐ 533. FRANK CASTILLO
- ☐ 563. SHAWN BOSKIE
- ☐ 595. SHAWON DUNSTON
- ☐ 630. MARK GRACE
- ☐ 657. MIKE HARKEY
- ☐ 688. DWIGHT SMITH
- ☐ 721. RICK WILKINS
- ☐ 783. HEATHCLIFF SLOCUMB
- ☐ 786. AARON TAYLOR(P)
- ☐ 812. MATT WALBECK

CHICAGO WHITE SOX

- ☐ 13. ESTEBAN BELTRE
- ☐ 41. ALEX FERNANDEZ
- ☐ 70. ROBERTO HERNANDEZ
- ☐ 94. LANCE JOHNSON
- ☐ 122. JOEY CORA
- ☐ 150. FRANK THOMAS
- ☐ 175. KIRK MCCASKILL
- ☐ 204. DAN PASQUA
- ☐ 230. CARLTON FISK
- ☐ 259. CRAIG GREBECK
- ☐ 286. RON KARKOVICE
- ☐ 313. GREG HIBBARD
- ☐ 344. JACK MCDOWELL
- ☐ 367. STEVE SAX
- ☐ 400. BO JACKSON
- ☐ 443. TERRY LEACH
- ☐ 474. OZZIE GUILLEN
- ☐ 504. GENE LAMONT(M)
- ☐ 550. SCOTT RADINSKY
- ☐ 582. SHAWN ABNER
- ☐ 612. BYRON MATHEWS
- ☐ 645. BOBBY THIGPEN
- ☐ 675. TIM RAINES
- ☐ 707. DONN PALL
- ☐ 737. WILSON ALVAREZ
- ☐ 770. ROBIN VENTURA
- ☐ 790. GEORGE BELL
- ☐ 800. SHAWN JETER

CINCINNATI REDS

- ☐ 29. DWAYNE HENRY
- ☐ 56. CHAD MOTTOLA
- ☐ 57. NORM CHARLTON
- ☐ 83. REGGIE SANDERS
- ☐ 110. BARRY LARKIN
- ☐ 138. JOE OLIVER
- ☐ 165. JOSE RIJO
- ☐ 193. STEVE FOSTER
- ☐ 219. BIP ROBERTS
- ☐ 245. CHRIS SABO
- ☐ 276. PAUL O'NEILL
- ☐ 301. CESAR HERNANDEZ
- ☐ 328. SCOTT RUSKIN
- ☐ 356. FREDDIE BENAVIDES
- ☐ 361. SCOTT BANKHEAD
- ☐ 382. TIM BELCHER
- ☐ 437. CHRIS HAMMOND
- ☐ 470. ROB DIBBLE
- ☐ 503. TONY PEREZ(M)
- ☐ 515. GREG SWINDELL
- ☐ 546. HAL MORRIS
- ☐ 577. TIM COSTO
- ☐ 608. BILL DORAN
- ☐ 642. MILT HILL
- ☐ 671. DAVE MARTINEZ
- ☐ 702. TIM PUGH
- ☐ 733. TOM BROWNING
- ☐ 764. WILLIE GREENE
- ☐ 784. JEFF BRANSON
- ☐ 813. DAN WILSON

CLEVELAND INDIANS

- ☐ 31. DEREK LILLIQUIST
- ☐ 59. CARLOS MARTINEZ
- ☐ 85. SANDY ALOMAR
- ☐ 113. THOMAS HOWARD
- ☐ 141. DENNIS COOK
- ☐ 167. STEVE OLIN
- ☐ 199. JUNIOR ORTIZ
- ☐ 221. CARLOS BAERGA
- ☐ 248. SCOTT SCUDDER
- ☐ 264. PAUL SORRENTO
- ☐ 277. MARK WHITEN
- ☐ 303. BROOK JACOBY
- ☐ 331. KENNY LOFTON
- ☐ 358. KEVIN WICKANDER
- ☐ 372. ROD NICHOLS
- ☐ 434. JACK ARMSTRONG
- ☐ 462. FELIX FERMIN
- ☐ 496. REGGIE JEFFERSON
- ☐ 505. MIKE HARGROVE(M)
- ☐ 571. DAVE MLICKI
- ☐ 603. JIM THOME
- ☐ 616. TRACY SANDERS(P)
- ☐ 635. ALBERT BELLE
- ☐ 666. GLENALLEN HILL
- ☐ 696. JOSE MESA
- ☐ 730. CHARLES NAGY
- ☐ 742. ALAN EMBREE(P)
- ☐ 762. MARK LEWIS
- ☐ 786. MIKE CHRISTOPHER(P)
- ☐ 787. MIKE MATTHEWS
- ☐ 801. JESSE LEVIS

COLORADO ROCKIES

- ☐ 419. MARK THOMPSON
- ☐ 425. JOE GIRARDI
- ☐ 433. TOM SCHMIDT(FS)
- ☐ 433. ROGER BAILEY(FS)
- ☐ 444. DAVID NIED
- ☐ 447. KEITH SHEPHERD
- ☐ 451. QUINTON MCCRACKEN(P)
- ☐ 461. STEVE REED
- ☐ 463. SCOTT ALDRED
- ☐ 476. WILL SCALZITTI(FS)
- ☐ 476. MARK VOISARD(FS)
- ☐ 486. ERIC WEDGE
- ☐ 489. SCOTT FREDRICKSON
- ☐ 504. DON BAYLOR(M)
- ☐ 523. DOUG BOCHTLER
- ☐ 537. RYAN TURNER(FS)
- ☐ 537. JASON HUTCHINS(FS)
- ☐ 541. DENIS BOUCHER
- ☐ 551. ERIC YOUNG
- ☐ 565. JERALD CLARK
- ☐ 579. JASON BATES(FS)
- ☐ 579. NEIL GARRETT(FS)
- ☐ 591. ALEX COLE
- ☐ 593. BRETT MERRIMAN
- ☐ 606. J. OWENS
- ☐ 616. RYAN FREEBURG(P)
- ☐ 621. GREG BOYD(FS)
- ☐ 621. MIKE KOTARSKI(FS)
- ☐ 634. MO SANFORD
- ☐ 644. DANTE BICHETTE
- ☐ 648. RYAN HAWBLITZEL
- ☐ 661. MICHAEL CASE(FS)
- ☐ 661. GARVIN ALSTON(FS)
- ☐ 664. CALVIN JONES
- ☐ 676. RUDY SEANEZ
- ☐ 681. DARREN HOLMES
- ☐ 691. JIM TATUM
- ☐ 704. DANNY FIGUEROA(FS)
- ☐ 704. JON GOODRICH(FS)
- ☐ 719. BUTCH HENRY
- ☐ 732. TRAVIS BUCKLEY
- ☐ 738. LANCE PAINTER
- ☐ 746. LAMARR ROGERS(FS)
- ☐ 746. MARK STRITTMATTER(FS)
- ☐ 759. CHARLIE HAYES
- ☐ 771. KEVIN RITZ
- ☐ 774. CURTIS LESKANIC

- ☐ 794. ANDY ASHBY

DETROIT TIGERS

- ☐ 26. SKEETER BARNES
- ☐ 53. FRANK TANANA
- ☐ 80. CECIL FIELDER
- ☐ 107. JOHN KIELY
- ☐ 135. MICKEY TETTLETON
- ☐ 160. LOU WHITAKER
- ☐ 189. TONY PHILLIPS
- ☐ 216. MARK LEITER
- ☐ 233. RICK GREENE
- ☐ 243. ROB DEER
- ☐ 272. KURT KNUDSEN
- ☐ 298. SCOTT LIVINGSTONE
- ☐ 325. BILL GULLICKSON
- ☐ 353. BUDDY GROOM
- ☐ 379. MIKE MUNOZ
- ☐ 392. TRAVIS FRYMAN
- ☐ 423. IVAN CRUZ(P)
- ☐ 429. MILT CUYLER
- ☐ 491. SHAWN HARE
- ☐ 506. SPARKY ANDERSON(M)
- ☐ 536. DAVE HAAS
- ☐ 567. MARK CARREON
- ☐ 598. RICO BROGNA
- ☐ 626. DANNY GLADDEN
- ☐ 660. ALAN TRAMMELL
- ☐ 692. CHAD KREUTER
- ☐ 713. JOHN DOHERTY
- ☐ 756. MIKE HENNEMAN
- ☐ 802. PHIL CLARK

FLORIDA MARLINS

- ☐ 412. JAMIE MCANDREW
- ☐ 426. NIGEL WILSON
- ☐ 439. BRYAN HARVEY
- ☐ 441. TODD PRIDY(FS)
- ☐ 441. DON LEMON(FS)
- ☐ 454. JOHN JOHNSTONE
- ☐ 483. BRIAN GRIFFITHS
- ☐ 494. LOU LUCCA(P)
- ☐ 497. WILLIE BROWN(FS)
- ☐ 497. MATT PETERSEN(FS)
- ☐ 505. RENE LACHEMANN(M)
- ☐ 516. ALEX ARIAS
- ☐ 520. CHARLIE HOUGH
- ☐ 544. STEVE DECKER
- ☐ 558. MARK SKEELS(FS)
- ☐ 558. RYAN WHITMAN(FS)
- ☐ 572. TREVOR HOFFMAN
- ☐ 586. JEFF TABAKA
- ☐ 599. DANIEL ROBINSON(FS)
- ☐ 599. CLEMENTE NUNEZ(FS)
- ☐ 613. JOEL ADAMSON
- ☐ 627. ANDRES BERUMEN
- ☐ 629. CRIS CARPENTER
- ☐ 641. GAVIN BAUGH(FS)
- ☐ 641. PAT LEAHY(FS)
- ☐ 656. GARY SCOTT
- ☐ 669. KIP YAUGHN
- ☐ 683. EDDIE CHRISTIAN(FS)
- ☐ 683. JERRY STAFFORD(FS)
- ☐ 697. DARRELL WHITMORE
- ☐ 711. SCOTT CHIAMPARINO
- ☐ 722. CHUCK CARR
- ☐ 726. KEN KENDRENA(FS)
- ☐ 726. MIKE VENEZIALE(FS)
- ☐ 739. DAVE WEATHERS
- ☐ 753. JIM CORSI
- ☐ 767. RICH IRELAND
- ☐ 782. DAN ROMAN(FS)
- ☐ 782. REYNOL MENDOZA(FS)
- ☐ 789. JEFF CONINE
- ☐ 791. PAT RAPP

HOUSTON ASTROS

- ☐ 7. PETE INCAVIGLIA
- ☐ 36. SCOTT SERVAIS
- ☐ 63. AL OSUNA
- ☐ 89. ERIC ANTHONY
- ☐ 117. EDDIE TAUBENSEE
- ☐ 148. STEVE FINLEY
- ☐ 171. DOUG JONES
- ☐ 195. PETE HARNISCH
- ☐ 227. JEFF BAGWELL
- ☐ 252. XAVIER HERNANDEZ
- ☐ 281. BUTCH HENRY
- ☐ 308. DARRYL KILE
- ☐ 335. MARK PORTUGAL
- ☐ 362. LUIS GONZALEZ
- ☐ 414. JUAN GUERRERO
- ☐ 448. KEN CAMINITI
- ☐ 477. JIMMY JONES
- ☐ 506. ART HOWE(M)
- ☐ 522. SHANE REYNOLDS
- ☐ 553. ANDUJAR CEDENO
- ☐ 584. CASEY CANDAELE
- ☐ 614. BRIAN WILLIAMS
- ☐ 646. RICH SCHEID
- ☐ 680. CRAIG BIGGIO
- ☐ 709. JEFF JUDEN
- ☐ 743. DAVE LANDAKER
- ☐ 792. JOE BOEVER
- ☐ 814. SCOOTER TUCKER

KANSAS CITY ROYALS

- ☐ 22. JIM EISENREICH
- ☐ 49. BRIAN MCRAE
- ☐ 76. KEVIN APPIER
- ☐ 105. GREGG JEFFERIES
- ☐ 130. JEFF MONTGOMERY
- ☐ 158. KEVIN KOSLOFSKI
- ☐ 186. MIKE MAGNANTE
- ☐ 212. RICK REED
- ☐ 239. MIKE BODDICKER
- ☐ 267. KEITH MILLER
- ☐ 294. BRENT MAYNE
- ☐ 321. RUSTY MEACHAM
- ☐ 349. HIPOLITO PICHARDO
- ☐ 375. WALLY JOYNER
- ☐ 397. GEORGE BRETT
- ☐ 423. LARRY SUTTON(P)
- ☐ 442. KEVIN MCREYNOLDS
- ☐ 472. CHRIS GWYNN
- ☐ 507. HAL MCRAE(M)
- ☐ 519. DAVID HOWARD
- ☐ 581. CHRIS HANEY
- ☐ 611. TOM GORDON
- ☐ 643. LUIS AQUINO
- ☐ 674. MARK GUBICZA
- ☐ 706. SHERARD CLINKSCALES
- ☐ 735. STEVE SHIFFLETT
- ☐ 768. MIKE MACFARLANE
- ☐ 803. ED PIERCE

LOS ANGELES DODGERS

- ☐ 11. ERIC KARROS
- ☐ 39. ROGER MCDOWELL
- ☐ 65. BRETT BUTLER
- ☐ 93. PEDRO ASTACIO
- ☐ 120. RAMON MARTINEZ
- ☐ 133. STEVE WILSON
- ☐ 145. ERIC YOUNG
- ☐ 177. LENNY HARRIS
- ☐ 202. MIKE SCIOSCIA
- ☐ 228. TOM GOODWIN
- ☐ 255. OREL HERSHISER
- ☐ 284. HENRY RODRIGUEZ
- ☐ 311. JAY HOWELL
- ☐ 338. BOB OJEDA
- ☐ 365. TOM CANDIOTTI
- ☐ 418. JIM GOTT
- ☐ 450. DARRYL STRAWBERRY
- ☐ 469. DAVE HANSEN
- ☐ 481. RYAN LUZINSKI
- ☐ 507. TOM LASORDA(M)
- ☐ 526. MIKE SHARPERSON
- ☐ 557. PEDRO MARTINEZ
- ☐ 576. MICHAEL MOORE(P)
- ☐ 589. CARLOS HERNANDEZ
- ☐ 620. TODD BENZINGER
- ☐ 651. RAFAEL BOURNIGAL
- ☐ 682. JOHN CANDELARIA
- ☐ 701. MIKE PIAZZA(P)
- ☐ 714. KEVIN GROSS
- ☐ 745. ERIC DAVIS
- ☐ 776. JOSE OFFERMAN
- ☐ 815. BILLY ASHLEY

MILWAUKEE BREWERS

- ☐ 1. ROBIN YOUNT
- ☐ 16. DAN PLESAC
- ☐ 44. KEVIN SEITZER
- ☐ 71. RICKY BONES
- ☐ 97. SCOTT FLETCHER
- ☐ 124. FRANKLIN STUBBS
- ☐ 153. GREG VAUGHN
- ☐ 181. JOHN JAHA
- ☐ 207. PAUL MOLITOR
- ☐ 234. TIM MCINTOSH
- ☐ 261. BILL WEGMAN
- ☐ 289. JESSE OROSCO
- ☐ 316. DAVE NILSSON
- ☐ 343. DOUG HENRY
- ☐ 369. JAIME NAVARRO
- ☐ 417. B.J. SURHOFF
- ☐ 449. JAMES AUSTIN
- ☐ 480. PAT LISTACH
- ☐ 508. PHIL GARNER(M)
- ☐ 527. MIKE FETTERS
- ☐ 556. DARRYL HAMILTON
- ☐ 590. CAL ELDRED
- ☐ 616. MATT MIESKE(P)
- ☐ 619. BILLY SPIERS
- ☐ 723. KENNY FELDER
- ☐ 744. CHRIS GEORGE
- ☐ 775. CHRIS BOSIO
- ☐ 804. JOSE VALENTIN

MINNESOTA TWINS

- ☐ 9. KENT HRBEK
- ☐ 37. LENNY WEBSTER
- ☐ 61. GENE LARKIN
- ☐ 90. SCOTT ERICKSON
- ☐ 119. PEDRO MUNOZ
- ☐ 146. SCOTT LEIUS
- ☐ 172. JEFF REBOULET
- ☐ 200. KIRBY PUCKETT
- ☐ 226. WILLIE BANKS
- ☐ 250. CHUCK KNOBLAUCH
- ☐ 282. SHANE MACK
- ☐ 307. DAN SERAFINI
- ☐ 309. J.T. BRUETT
- ☐ 336. MIKE PAGLIARULO
- ☐ 363. JOHN SMILEY
- ☐ 389. BRIAN HARPER
- ☐ 420. KEVIN TAPANI
- ☐ 455. CHILI DAVIS
- ☐ 482. DARREN REED
- ☐ 509. TOM KELLY(M)
- ☐ 588. MIKE TROMBLEY
- ☐ 625. RICK AGUILERA
- ☐ 652. DAVE WEST
- ☐ 658. RICH BECKER(P)
- ☐ 684. PAT MAHOMES
- ☐ 715. GREG GAGNE
- ☐ 747. CARL WILLIS
- ☐ 777. MARK GUTHRIE
- ☐ 786. GUS GANDARILLAS(P)
- ☐ 805. TERRY JORGENSEN

MONTREAL EXPOS

- ☐ 15. MARQUIS GRISSOM
- ☐ 33. B.J. WALLACE
- ☐ 42. SPIKE OWEN
- ☐ 69. JOHN VANDER WAL
- ☐ 95. LARRY WALKER
- ☐ 112. BRIAN BARNES
- ☐ 123. MOISES ALOU
- ☐ 151. ARCHI CIANFROCCO

- ☐ 178. JEFF FASSERO
- ☐ 205. GARY CARTER
- ☐ 231. JOHN WETTELAND
- ☐ 256. WIL CORDERO
- ☐ 278. CHRIS NABHOLZ
- ☐ 314. MARK GARDNER
- ☐ 341. MEL ROJAS
- ☐ 368. DELINO DESHIELDS
- ☐ 432. PETE YOUNG
- ☐ 464. GREG COLBRUNN
- ☐ 495. KEN HILL
- ☐ 508. FELIPE ALOU(M)
- ☐ 540. IVAN CALDERON
- ☐ 570. TIM WALLACH
- ☐ 576. CLIFF FLOYD(P)
- ☐ 610. DENNY MARTINEZ
- ☐ 665. DARRIN FLETCHER
- ☐ 695. KENT BOTTENFIELD
- ☐ 727. JONATHAN HURST
- ☐ 758. SEAN BERRY
- ☐ 816. TIM LAKER

NEW YORK METS

- ☐ 25. JOHN FRANCO
- ☐ 52. BOBBY BONILLA
- ☐ 79. DICK SCHOFIELD
- ☐ 106. HOWARD JOHNSON
- ☐ 132. PRESTON WILSON
- ☐ 134. LEE GUETTERMAN
- ☐ 188. SID FERNANDEZ
- ☐ 215. PAT HOWELL
- ☐ 238. CHRIS DONNELS
- ☐ 242. CHARLIE O'BRIEN
- ☐ 271. WALLY WHITEHURST
- ☐ 297. JEFF INNIS
- ☐ 324. WILLIE RANDOLPH
- ☐ 352. PETE SCHOUREK
- ☐ 380. TODD HUNDLEY
- ☐ 399. DARYL BOSTON
- ☐ 430. EDDIE MURRAY
- ☐ 471. DAVE GALLAGHER
- ☐ 509. JEFF TORBORG(M)
- ☐ 517. BILL PECOTA
- ☐ 547. RYAN THOMPSON
- ☐ 578. DAVE MAGADAN
- ☐ 640. DOC GOODEN
- ☐ 658. JEROMY BURNITZ(P)
- ☐ 672. KEVIN BASS
- ☐ 701. BROOK FORDYCE(P)
- ☐ 703. JEFF KENT
- ☐ 734. ANTHONY YOUNG
- ☐ 751. ERIC HILLMAN
- ☐ 765. VINCE COLEMAN
- ☐ 788. MACKEY SASSER
- ☐ 817. BOBBY JONES

NEW YORK YANKEES

- ☐ 32. DON MATTINGLY
- ☐ 60. ROBERTO KELLY
- ☐ 86. JOHN HABYAN
- ☐ 98. DEREK JETER
- ☐ 114. MEL HALL
- ☐ 142. CHARLIE HAYES
- ☐ 168. KEVIN MAAS
- ☐ 174. RANDY VELARDE
- ☐ 196. PAT KELLY
- ☐ 222. BERNIE WILLIAMS
- ☐ 249. TIM BURKE
- ☐ 287. MIKE GALLEGO
- ☐ 304. MELIDO PEREZ
- ☐ 330. DANNY TARTABULL
- ☐ 348. ANDY STANKIEWICZ
- ☐ 359. MIKE STANLEY
- ☐ 385. JIM LEYRITZ
- ☐ 422. J.T. SNOW
- ☐ 452. BOB WICKMAN
- ☐ 478. GREG CADARET
- ☐ 510. BUCK SHOWALTER(M)
- ☐ 525. SCOTT SANDERSON
- ☐ 529. DAVE SILVESTRI(P)
- ☐ 530. STERLING HITCHCOCK
- ☐ 549. HENSLEY MEULENS
- ☐ 561. MATT NOKES
- ☐ 594. JERRY NIELSEN
- ☐ 600. BRET SABERHAGEN
- ☐ 624. SAM MILITELLO
- ☐ 654. GERALD WILLIAMS
- ☐ 686. RUSS SPRINGER
- ☐ 701. DONNIE LESHNOCK(P)
- ☐ 717. STEVE FARR
- ☐ 742. BRIEN TAYLOR(P)
- ☐ 749. SCOTT KAMIENIECKI
- ☐ 779. RICH MONTELEONE
- ☐ 806. MARK HUTTON

OAKLAND A'S

- ☐ 18. TERRY STEINBACH
- ☐ 46. ERIC FOX
- ☐ 73. MIKE MOORE
- ☐ 100. MARK MCGWIRE
- ☐ 127. CARNEY LANSFORD
- ☐ 155. DENNIS ECKERSLEY
- ☐ 182. RON DARLING
- ☐ 209. JEFF PARRETT
- ☐ 236. KEVIN CAMPBELL
- ☐ 263. VINCE HORSMAN
- ☐ 290. DAVE STEWART
- ☐ 318. WILLIE WILSON
- ☐ 345. HAROLD BAINES
- ☐ 383. JERRY BROWNE
- ☐ 398. BOBBY WITT
- ☐ 440. RUBEN SIERRA
- ☐ 451. BRENT GATES(P)
- ☐ 473. DAVE HENDERSON
- ☐ 511. TONY LARUSSA(M)
- ☐ 518. BENJI GRIGSBY
- ☐ 548. LANCE BLANKENSHIP
- ☐ 580. WALT WEISS
- ☐ 602. HENRY MERCEDES
- ☐ 639. MIKE BORDICK
- ☐ 673. TODD VAN POPPEL
- ☐ 705. BOB WELCH
- ☐ 736. JEFF RUSSELL
- ☐ 750. RICKEY HENDERSON
- ☐ 766. TODD REVENIG
- ☐ 796. SCOTT BROSIUS
- ☐ 807. TROY NEEL

PHILADELPHIA PHILLIES

- ☐ 17. DAVE HOLLINS
- ☐ 43. RUBEN AMARO
- ☐ 72. JEFF GROTEWOLD
- ☐ 99. MIKE WILLIAMS
- ☐ 126. BOB AVRAULT
- ☐ 154. WES CHAMBERLAIN
- ☐ 161. CHAD MCCONNELL
- ☐ 180. DARREN DAULTON
- ☐ 208. MIKE HARTLEY
- ☐ 235. MITCH WILLIAMS
- ☐ 262. MICKEY MORANDINI
- ☐ 291. TOMMY GREENE
- ☐ 317. KYLE ABBOTT
- ☐ 340. JOHN KRUK
- ☐ 371. MARIANO DUNCAN
- ☐ 421. CURT SCHILLING
- ☐ 445. DALE MURPHY
- ☐ 479. TODD PRATT
- ☐ 510. JIM FREGOSI(M)
- ☐ 531. JOE MILLETTE
- ☐ 555. TERRY MULHOLLAND
- ☐ 585. RICKY JORDAN
- ☐ 622. BEN RIVERA
- ☐ 649. TOM MARSH
- ☐ 679. KIM BATISTE
- ☐ 712. STAN JAVIER
- ☐ 740. LEN DYKSTRA
- ☐ 773. CLIFF BRANTLEY
- ☐ 818. BRAD BRINK

PITTSBURGH PIRATES

- ☐ 2. BARRY BONDS
- ☐ 27. CARLOS GARCIA
- ☐ 54. MIKE LAVALLIERE
- ☐ 81. LLOYD MCCLENDON
- ☐ 108. JOSE LIND
- ☐ 136. JEFF KING
- ☐ 163. TIM WAKEFIELD
- ☐ 190. DOUG DRABEK
- ☐ 244. DENNY NEAGLE
- ☐ 275. ANDY VAN SLYKE
- ☐ 299. BOB PATTERSON
- ☐ 326. GARY VARSHO
- ☐ 334. JASON KENDALL
- ☐ 354. JAY BELL
- ☐ 378. ORLANDO MERCED
- ☐ 416. RANDY TOMLIN
- ☐ 453. VICTOR COLE
- ☐ 484. JOHN WEHNER
- ☐ 494. KEVIN YOUNG(P)
- ☐ 511. JIM LEYLAND(M)
- ☐ 560. ZANE SMITH
- ☐ 616. MIDRE CUMMINGS(P)
- ☐ 623. AL MARTIN
- ☐ 658. SHON WALKER(P)
- ☐ 685. BOB WALK
- ☐ 716. STEVE COOKE
- ☐ 748. STAN BELINDA
- ☐ 778. DAN SLAUGHT
- ☐ 819. WILLIAM PENNYFEATHER

ST. LOUIS CARDINALS

- ☐ 12. LEE SMITH
- ☐ 40. OZZIE SMITH
- ☐ 67. FELIX JOSE
- ☐ 92. TOM PAGNOZZI
- ☐ 121. TODD WORRELL
- ☐ 149. RHEAL CORMIER
- ☐ 173. ANDRES GALARRAGA
- ☐ 191. SEAN LOWE
- ☐ 203. BERNARD GILKEY
- ☐ 229. MIKE PEREZ
- ☐ 257. LUIS ALICEA
- ☐ 285. BOB TEWKSBURY
- ☐ 312. GERONIMO PENA
- ☐ 339. MARK CLARK
- ☐ 366. CRAIG WILSON
- ☐ 386. RAY LANKFORD
- ☐ 428. TODD ZEILE
- ☐ 457. TRACY WOODSON
- ☐ 490. OMAR OLIVARES
- ☐ 512. JOE TORRE(M)
- ☐ 535. JOSE OQUENDO
- ☐ 566. ROD BREWER
- ☐ 597. GERALD PERRY
- ☐ 662. DONOVAN OSBORNE
- ☐ 690. BIEN FIGUEROA
- ☐ 742. RENE AROCHA(P)
- ☐ 754. BRIAN JORDAN
- ☐ 820. STAN ROYER

SAN DIEGO PADRES

- ☐ 5. TONY GWYNN
- ☐ 30. FRED MCGRIFF
- ☐ 58. JOSE MELENDEZ
- ☐ 84. KURT STILLWELL
- ☐ 111. BRUCE HURST
- ☐ 140. GARY SHEFFIELD
- ☐ 166. TIM SCOTT
- ☐ 194. JERALD CLARK
- ☐ 220. BENNY SANTIAGO
- ☐ 247. FRANK SEMINARA
- ☐ 273. DAN WALTERS
- ☐ 302. RANDY MYERS
- ☐ 329. MIKE MADDUX
- ☐ 357. PHIL STEPHENSON
- ☐ 388. JEREMY HERNANDEZ
- ☐ 436. GREG HARRIS
- ☐ 465. TONY FERNANDEZ
- ☐ 492. TOM LAMPKIN
- ☐ 513. JIM RIGGLEMAN(M)
- ☐ 538. JIMMY BARON
- ☐ 568. ANDY BENES
- ☐ 576. DARRELL SHERMAN(P)
- ☐ 601. CRAIG SHIPLEY
- ☐ 636. TIM TEUFEL
- ☐ 663. JEFF GARDNER
- ☐ 693. RICH RODRIGUEZ
- ☐ 724. GUILLERMO VELASQUEZ
- ☐ 761. DARRIN JACKSON
- ☐ 821. DOUG BROCAIL

SAN FRANCISCO GIANTS

- ☐ 10. WILL CLARK
- ☐ 38. CHRIS JAMES
- ☐ 66. JOHN BURKETT
- ☐ 91. CRAIG COLBERT
- ☐ 115. ROBBY THOMPSON
- ☐ 147. BRYAN HICKERSON
- ☐ 176. DARREN LEWIS
- ☐ 201. JOSE URIBE
- ☐ 225. MATT WILLIAMS
- ☐ 254. CORY SNYDER

- ☐ 283. MIKE JACKSON
- ☐ 310. DAVE RIGHETTI
- ☐ 337. KIRT MANWARING
- ☐ 364. TREVOR WILSON
- ☐ 384. MIKE BENJAMIN
- ☐ 435. WILLIE MCGEE
- ☐ 466. MIKE FELDER
- ☐ 494. ADELL DAVENPORT(P)
- ☐ 498. BUD BLACK
- ☐ 514. DUSTY BAKER(M)
- ☐ 542. ROYCE CLAYTON
- ☐ 573. JOHN PATTERSON
- ☐ 604. ROD BECK
- ☐ 631. JEFF BRANTLEY
- ☐ 653. STEVE HOSEY
- ☐ 667. JIM ROSENBOHM
- ☐ 698. TED WOOD
- ☐ 729. MARK LEONARD
- ☐ 755. BILL SWIFT
- ☐ 822. KEVIN ROGERS

SEATTLE MARINERS

- ☐ 14. GREG BRILEY
- ☐ 45. DAVE FLEMING
- ☐ 68. OMAR VIZQUEL
- ☐ 96. RUSS SWAN
- ☐ 125. PETE O'BRIEN
- ☐ 152. RICH DELUCIA
- ☐ 179. KEN GRIFFEY, JR
- ☐ 206. HENRY COTTO
- ☐ 217. KEVIN MITCHELL
- ☐ 232. TINO MARTINEZ
- ☐ 258. MIKE SCHOOLER
- ☐ 288. DAVE COCHRANE
- ☐ 315. EDGAR MARTINEZ
- ☐ 342. ERIK HANSON
- ☐ 370. DAVE VALLE
- ☐ 423. BUBBA SMITH(P)
- ☐ 431. RICH AMARAL
- ☐ 460. RANDY JOHNSON
- ☐ 493. JEFF NELSON
- ☐ 512. LOU PINIELLA(M)
- ☐ 539. KERRY WOODSON
- ☐ 569. SHAWN BARTON
- ☐ 609. LANCE PARRISH
- ☐ 632. CHRIS WIDGER
- ☐ 694. SHANE TURNER
- ☐ 718. JAY BUHNER
- ☐ 757. HAROLD REYNOLDS
- ☐ 808. BRET BOONE

TEXAS RANGERS

- ☐ 19. ED NUNEZ
- ☐ 34. JUAN GONZALEZ
- ☐ 64. SCOTT CHIAMPARINO
- ☐ 87. KEVIN REIMER
- ☐ 118. DAVID HULSE
- ☐ 143. JEFF HUSON
- ☐ 169. KENNY ROGERS
- ☐ 197. JEFF FRYE
- ☐ 223. ROGER PAVLIK
- ☐ 253. JOSE GUZMAN
- ☐ 279. TODD BURNS
- ☐ 305. RAFAEL PALMEIRO
- ☐ 332. GENO PETRALLI
- ☐ 360. IVAN RODRIGUEZ
- ☐ 438. RITCHIE MOODY
- ☐ 451. JON SHAVE(P)
- ☐ 468. MATT WHITESIDE
- ☐ 500. JOSE CANSECO
- ☐ 513. KEVIN KENNEDY(M)
- ☐ 529. BENJI GIL(P)
- ☐ 545. DEAN PALMER
- ☐ 575. MONTY FARISS
- ☐ 607. DAN SMITH
- ☐ 638. BRIAN BOHANON
- ☐ 670. JULIO FRANCO
- ☐ 700. NOLAN RYAN
- ☐ 731. DONALD HARRIS
- ☐ 763. ROB MAURER
- ☐ 785. KEVIN BROWN
- ☐ 809. CRIS COLON

TORONTO BLUE JAYS

- ☐ 23. TODD STOTTLEMYRE
- ☐ 50. ROBERTO ALOMAR
- ☐ 75. JUAN GUZMAN
- ☐ 131. DAVE WINFIELD
- ☐ 159. DOUG LINTON
- ☐ 185. JACK MORRIS
- ☐ 213. CANDY MALDONADO
- ☐ 240. JOHN OLERUD
- ☐ 260. DUANE WARD
- ☐ 268. DEREK BELL
- ☐ 269. TODD STEVERSON
- ☐ 295. DAVE STIEB
- ☐ 322. PAT BORDERS
- ☐ 350. JOE CARTER
- ☐ 376. TOM HENKE
- ☐ 387. DEVON WHITE
- ☐ 427. BOB MACDONALD
- ☐ 458. DAVID WELLS
- ☐ 488. MANUEL LEE
- ☐ 514. CITO GASTON(M)
- ☐ 529. JEFF PATZKE(P)
- ☐ 534. RANDY KNORR
- ☐ 564. MIKE TIMLIN
- ☐ 596. JIMMY KEY
- ☐ 628. KELLY GRUBER
- ☐ 659. ED SPRAGUE
- ☐ 689. EDDIE ZOSKY
- ☐ 701. CARLOS DELGADO(P)
- ☐ 720. DAVID CONE
- ☐ 742. TIM CRABTREE(P)
- ☐ 752. PAT HENTGEN
- ☐ 810. DOMINGO MARTINEZ

1993 TOPPS TRADED (132) 2 1/2" X 3 1/2"

ATLANTA BRAVES

- ☐ 6T. GREG MCMICHAEL
- ☐ 54T. GREG MADDUX
- ☐ 88T. FRED MCGRIFF

BALTIMORE ORIOLES

- ☐ 23T. SHERMAN OBANDO
- ☐ 27T. JACK VOIGT
- ☐ 63T. DAMON BUFORD

BOSTON RED SOX

- ☐ 3T. AARON SELE
- ☐ 25T. JEFF RUSSELL
- ☐ 81T. JEFF RICHARDSON
- ☐ 92T. ANDRE DAWSON
- ☐ 103T. KEN RYAN

CALIFORNIA ANGELS

- ☐ 62T. J.T. SNOW
- ☐ 87T. HILLY HATHAWAY

CHICAGO CUBS

- ☐ 49T. TURK WENDELL
- ☐ 65T. RANDY MYERS

CHICAGO WHITE SOX

- ☐ 26T. JASON BERE
- ☐ 104T. ELLIS BURKS

CINCINNATI REDS

- ☐ 36T. DAVEY JOHNSON(M)
- ☐ 105T. BOBBY KELLY
- ☐ 112T. KEVIN MITCHELL

CLEVELAND INDIANS

NO CARDS ISSUED

COLORADO ROCKIES

- ☐ 7T. FREDDIE BENAVIDES
- ☐ 10T. JAY GAINER
- ☐ 16T. GARY WAYNE
- ☐ 31T. ANDRES GALARRAGA
- ☐ 33T. VINNY CASTILLA
- ☐ 39T. DANNY SHEAFFER
- ☐ 46T. JEFF PARRETT
- ☐ 53T. NELSON LIRIANO
- ☐ 69T. PEDRO CASTELLANO
- ☐ 96T. WILLIE BLAIR
- ☐ 102T. CHRIS JONES
- ☐ 116T. ARMANDO REYNOSO
- ☐ 126T. DARYL BOSTON

DETROIT TIGERS

- ☐ 8T. KIRK GIBSON
- ☐ 50T. DAVID WELLS

FLORIDA MARLINS

- ☐ 2T. RICH RENTERIA
- ☐ 11T. ORESTES DESTRADE
- ☐ 18T. WALT WEISS
- ☐ 35T. GREG BRILEY
- ☐ 44T. BENNY SANTIAGO
- ☐ 51T. GARY SHEFFIELD
- ☐ 56T. MATT TURNER
- ☐ 61T. MITCH LYDEN
- ☐ 71T. RICH RODRIGUEZ
- ☐ 74T. CARL EVERETT
- ☐ 76T. LUIS AQUINO
- ☐ 80T. JACK ARMSTRONG
- ☐ 86T. CHRIS HAMMOND
- ☐ 90T. RICHIE LEWIS
- ☐ 95T. JOE KLINK
- ☐ 108T. ROB NATAL
- ☐ 111T. MONTY FARISS
- ☐ 113T. SCOTT POSE
- ☐ 117T. GERONIMO BERROA
- ☐ 121T. HENRY COTTO
- ☐ 130T. RYAN BOWEN

HOUSTON ASTROS

- ☐ 32T. GREG SWINDELL
- ☐ 94T. DOUG DRABEK

1993 Topps Traded

KANSAS CITY ROYALS

- ☐ 29T. PHIL HIATT
- ☐ 66T. FELIX JOSE
- ☐125T. DAVID CONE

LOS ANGELES DODGERS

- ☐ 24T. MIKE PIAZZA
- ☐127T. TIM WALLACH

MILWAUKEE BREWERS

- ☐ 59T. TROY O'LEARY
- ☐ 72T. MATT MIESKE

MINNESOTA TWINS

- ☐ 17T. DAVID MCCARTY
- ☐ 83T. DAVE WINFIELD
- ☐ 98T. PAT MEARES

MONTREAL EXPOS

- ☐ 99T. MIKE LANSING

NEW YORK METS

- ☐ 36T. DALLAS GREEN(M)
- ☐ 43T. DOUG SAUNDERS
- ☐ 89T. DAVE TELGHEDER
- ☐110T. JEROMY BURNITZ
- ☐119T. TIM BOGAR

NEW YORK YANKEES

- ☐ 13T. BOBBY MUNOZ
- ☐ 47T. WADE BOGGS
- ☐ 68T. JIMMY KEY
- ☐ 75T. JIM ABBOTT
- ☐ 84T. PAUL O'NEILL

OAKLAND A'S

- ☐ 38T. CRAIG PAQUETTE
- ☐ 91T. BRENT GATES
- ☐100T. MARCOS ARMAS

PHILADELPHIA PHILLIES

- ☐ 37T. TYLER GREEN
- ☐ 73T. PETE INCAVIGLIA

PITTSBURGH PIRATES

- ☐ 52T. KEVIN YOUNG
- ☐ 82T. BLAS MINOR
- ☐109T. PAUL WAGNER

ST. LOUIS CARDINALS

- ☐ 5T. ERIK PAPPAS
- ☐ 20T. MARK WHITEN
- ☐ 77T. RENE AROCHA
- ☐122T. GREGG JEFFERIES

SAN DIEGO PADRES

- ☐ 21T. RICKY GUTIERREZ
- ☐ 42T. PHIL PLANTIER
- ☐ 55T. DEREK BELL
- ☐ 64T. GENE HARRIS

SAN FRANCISCO GIANTS

- ☐ 1T. BARRY BONDS

SEATTLE MARINERS

- ☐ 28T. CHRIS BOSIO
- ☐ 40T. JIM CONVERSE
- ☐ 58T. MIKE HAMPTON
- ☐106T. DAVE MAGADAN
- ☐123T. NORM CHARLTON
- ☐129T. JOHN CUMMINGS

TEXAS RANGERS

- ☐ 14T. TOM HENKE
- ☐ 60T. BENJI GIL
- ☐ 78T. JON SHAVE

TORONTO BLUE JAYS

- ☐ 9T. TONY FERNANDEZ
- ☐ 15T. ROB BUTLER
- ☐ 48T. PAUL MOLITOR
- ☐114T. DAVE STEWART
- ☐118T. WOODY WILLIAMS

TEAM USA

- ☐ 4T. CARLTON LOEWER
- ☐ 12T. A.J. HINCH
- ☐ 19T. TODD HELTON
- ☐ 22T. DUSTIN HERMANSON
- ☐ 30T. MATT BEAUMONT
- ☐ 34T. PAT CLOUGHERTY
- ☐ 41T. TERRY HARVEY
- ☐ 45T. DANTE POWELL
- ☐ 57T. CHARLIE NELSON
- ☐ 67T. TODD DUNN
- ☐ 70T. MARK MERILA
- ☐ 79T. TODD WALKER
- ☐ 85T. STEVE REICH
- ☐ 93T. ANDY BARKETT
- ☐ 97T. DANNY GRAVES
- ☐101T. DARREN GRASS
- ☐107T. PAUL WILSON
- ☐115T. RUSS JOHNSON
- ☐120T. BOB SCAFA
- ☐124T. BRET WAGNER
- ☐128T. MIKE MARTIN
- ☐131T. JOHN POWELL

1994 TOPPS (792)
2 1/2" X 3 1/2"

ATLANTA BRAVES

- ☐ 23. MARK LEMKE
- ☐ 52. OTIS NIXON
- ☐ 81. GREG MCMICHAEL
- ☐ 107. MIKE STANTON
- ☐ 137. STEVE AVERY
- ☐ 166. RON GANT
- ☐ 194. JAVY LOPEZ
- ☐ 232. MARK WOHLERS
- ☐ 261. RAFAEL BELLIARD
- ☐ 289. DAMON BERRYHILL
- ☐ 318. JEFF BLAUSER
- ☐ 318. TERRELL WADE(P)
- ☐ 346. GREG OLSON
- ☐ 374. MARVIN FREEMAN
- ☐ 375. DEION SANDERS
- ☐ 414. BILL PECOTA
- ☐ 442. TONY TARASCO
- ☐ 475. TOM GLAVINE
- ☐ 499. GREG MADDUX
- ☐ 528. SID BREAM
- ☐ 565. FRED MCGRIFF
- ☐ 592. JAY HOWELL
- ☐ 617. STEVE BEDROSIAN
- ☐ 630. DAVID JUSTICE
- ☐ 658. PETE SMITH
- ☐ 687. JOHN SMOLTZ
- ☐ 718. KENT MERCKER
- ☐ 735. TERRY PENDLETON
- ☐ 752. ANDRE KING
- ☐ 777. CHIPPER JONES(CA)
- ☐ 777. RYAN KLESKO(CA)

BALTIMORE ORIOLES

- ☐ 4. PAUL CAREY
- ☐ 32. TIM HULETT
- ☐ 61. DAMON BUFORD
- ☐ 91. RICK SUTCLIFFE
- ☐ 117. JACK VOIGT
- ☐ 145. BRADY ANDERSON
- ☐ 175. FERNANDO VALENZUELA
- ☐ 200. CAL RIPKEN
- ☐ 242. TODD FROHWIRTH
- ☐ 271. BRAD PENNINGTON
- ☐ 295. CHRIS HOILES
- ☐ 324. ALAN MILLS
- ☐ 355. HAROLD REYNOLDS
- ☐ 370. MARK MCLEMORE
- ☐ 420. HAROLD BAINES
- ☐ 449. JIM POOLE
- ☐ 477. ARTHUR RHODES
- ☐ 506. LEO GOMEZ
- ☐ 526. JAMIE MOYER
- ☐ 534. MIKE DEVEREAUX
- ☐ 571. DAVID SEGUI
- ☐ 598. MIKE MUSSINA
- ☐ 636. BEN MCDONALD
- ☐ 664. JEFF TACKETT
- ☐ 723. GREGG OLSON
- ☐ 745. JAY POWELL
- ☐ 763. JOHN O'DONOGHUE(CA)
- ☐ 763. MIKE OQUIST(CA)

BOSTON RED SOX

- ☐ 26. BILLY HATCHER
- ☐ 55. JEFF RUSSELL
- ☐ 85. TONY PENA
- ☐ 112. FRANK RODRIGUEZ
- ☐ 140. FRANK VIOLA
- ☐ 169. SCOTT FLETCHER
- ☐ 197. JOHN FLAHERTY
- ☐ 235. SCOTT COOPER
- ☐ 264. KEN RYAN
- ☐ 292. DANNY DARWIN
- ☐ 321. JOHN DOPSON
- ☐ 349. CARLOS QUINTANA
- ☐ 378. TONY FOSSAS
- ☐ 389. LUIS ORTIZ(P)
- ☐ 417. PAUL QUANTRILL
- ☐ 445. AARON SELE
- ☐ 474. TIM NAEHRING
- ☐ 502. MIKE GREENWELL
- ☐ 531. ROB DEER
- ☐ 568. JOHN VALENTIN
- ☐ 595. ANDRE DAWSON
- ☐ 633. SCOTT BANKHEAD
- ☐ 661. BOB ZUPCIC
- ☐ 690. MO VAUGHN
- ☐ 716. NATE MINCHEY
- ☐ 720. ROGER CLEMENS

- ☐ 738. GREG HARRIS
- ☐ 746. RYAN MCGUIRE
- ☐ 764. CORY BAILEY(CA)
- ☐ 764. SCOTT HATTEBERG(CA)

CALIFORNIA ANGELS

- ☐ 27. JOE MAGRANE
- ☐ 56. CHAD CURTIS
- ☐ 84. GARRET ANDERSON
- ☐ 113. RUSS SPRINGER
- ☐ 141. RENE GONZALES
- ☐ 171. GREG MYERS
- ☐ 198. KURT STILLWELL
- ☐ 236. MIKE BUTCHER
- ☐ 237. MARK SWEENEY(P)
- ☐ 265. CHILI DAVIS
- ☐ 293. J.T. SNOW
- ☐ 322. CHRIS TURNER
- ☐ 351. GARY DISARCINA
- ☐ 381. CHUCK FINLEY
- ☐ 389. GEORGE ARIAS(P)
- ☐ 397. TIM SALMON
- ☐ 404. JIM EDMONDS
- ☐ 418. DAMION EASLEY
- ☐ 446. STAN JAVIER
- ☐ 471. PHIL LEFTWICH
- ☐ 503. STEVE FREY
- ☐ 532. ROD CORREIA
- ☐ 566. LUIS POLONIA
- ☐ 596. HILLY HATHAWAY
- ☐ 634. TOREY LOVULLO
- ☐ 665. MARK LANGSTON
- ☐ 691. JOE GRAHE
- ☐ 713. RON WATSON(P)
- ☐ 721. EDUARDO PEREZ
- ☐ 760. RYAN HANCOCK
- ☐ 765. MARK HOLZEMER(CA)
- ☐ 765. PAUL SWINGLE(CA)

CHICAGO CUBS

- ☐ 6. DERRICK MAY
- ☐ 35. JOSE GUZMAN
- ☐ 63. GLENALLEN HILL
- ☐ 92. JOSE BAUTISTA
- ☐ 119. KEVIN ROBERSON
- ☐ 148. GREG HIBBARD
- ☐ 177. SHAWN BOSKIE
- ☐ 205. BROOKS KIESCHNICK
- ☐ 215. DAN PLESAC
- ☐ 244. RICK WILKINS
- ☐ 272. MIKE HARKEY
- ☐ 300. RYNE SANDBERG
- ☐ 329. MATT WALBECK
- ☐ 360. MARK GRACE
- ☐ 399. FRANK CASTILLO
- ☐ 422. REY SANCHEZ
- ☐ 451. BOB SCANLAN
- ☐ 479. MIKE MORGAN
- ☐ 536. DWIGHT SMITH
- ☐ 575. RANDY MYERS
- ☐ 613. CHUCK MCELROY
- ☐ 616. EDDIE ZAMBRANO(P)
- ☐ 638. JOSE VIZCAINO
- ☐ 657. KARL RHODES
- ☐ 666. STEVE BUECHELE
- ☐ 698. WILLIE WILSON
- ☐ 725. SAMMY SOSA

- ☐ 739. JON RATLIFF
- ☐ 762. KEVIN ORIE
- ☐ 778. STEVE TRACHSEL(CA)
- ☐ 778. TURK WENDELL(CA)

CHICAGO WHITE SOX

- ☐ 5. OZZIE GUILLEN
- ☐ 33. JEFF SCHWARZ
- ☐ 62. TIM BELCHER
- ☐ 79. CRAIG MCCLURE(P)
- ☐ 90. ROBIN VENTURA
- ☐ 118. JASON BERE
- ☐ 147. MIKE LAVALLIERE
- ☐ 158. BRANDON WILSON(P)
- ☐ 176. CRAIG GREBECK
- ☐ 214. GEORGE BELL
- ☐ 243. TIM RAINES
- ☐ 270. FRANK THOMAS
- ☐ 299. WILSON ALVAREZ
- ☐ 356. SCOTT RUFFCORN
- ☐ 421. SCOTT RADINSKY
- ☐ 452. LANCE JOHNSON
- ☐ 478. JOEY CORA
- ☐ 500. BO JACKSON
- ☐ 515. JACK MCDOWELL
- ☐ 527. NORBERTO MARTIN(P)
- ☐ 538. ELLIS BURKS
- ☐ 572. ROBERTO HERNANDEZ
- ☐ 599. ALEX FERNANDEZ
- ☐ 662. STEVE SAX
- ☐ 684. RON KARKOVICE
- ☐ 724. KIRK MCCASKILL
- ☐ 758. GREG NORTON
- ☐ 766. JAMES BALDWIN(CA)
- ☐ 766. ROD BOLTON(CA)

CINCINNATI REDS

- ☐ 12. JOHN SMILEY
- ☐ 41. KEVIN WICKANDER
- ☐ 69. JACOB BRUMFIELD
- ☐ 95. TIM PUGH
- ☐ 126. HAL MORRIS
- ☐ 154. DAN WILSON
- ☐ 183. ROB DIBBLE
- ☐ 221. LARRY LUEBBERS
- ☐ 246. THOMAS HOWARD
- ☐ 250. BARRY LARKIN
- ☐ 278. CALVIN REESE
- ☐ 306. SCOTT SERVICE
- ☐ 335. KEVIN MITCHELL
- ☐ 368. JEFF BRANSON
- ☐ 428. WILLIE GREENE
- ☐ 457. BOBBY KELLY
- ☐ 485. JOE OLIVER
- ☐ 513. TIM COSTO
- ☐ 527. CHRIS SEXTON(P)
- ☐ 542. CHRIS SABO
- ☐ 581. JOHN ROPER
- ☐ 616. CHAD MOTTOLA(P)
- ☐ 619. TOM BROWNING
- ☐ 647. REGGIE SANDERS
- ☐ 673. BOBBY AYALA
- ☐ 686. PAUL BAKO(P)
- ☐ 688. BRIAN DORSETT
- ☐ 705. JOSE RIJO
- ☐ 733. BIP ROBERTS
- ☐ 743. PAT WATKINS
- ☐ 779. JOHNNY RUFFIN(CA)
- ☐ 779. JERRY SPRADLIN(CA)

CLEVELAND INDIANS

- ☐ 7. JOSE MESA
- ☐ 36. FELIX FERMIN
- ☐ 64. BILL WERTZ
- ☐ 93. BOB OJEDA
- ☐ 121. REGGIE JEFFERSON
- ☐ 149. KENNY LOFTON
- ☐ 158. MIKE NEAL(P)
- ☐ 178. ALBIE LOPEZ
- ☐ 216. MANNY RAMIREZ
- ☐ 273. SANDY ALOMAR
- ☐ 301. DEREK LILLIQUIST
- ☐ 318. CHAD OGEA(P)
- ☐ 330. CHARLES NAGY
- ☐ 358. PAUL SORRENTO
- ☐ 389. DAVID BELL(P)
- ☐ 423. JUNIOR ORTIZ

- ☐ 450. CARLOS BAERGA
- ☐ 480. ALBERT BELLE
- ☐ 508. WAYNE KIRBY
- ☐ 537. JEREMY HERNANDEZ
- ☐ 577. ERIC PLUNK
- ☐ 612. JIM THOME
- ☐ 642. TOM KRAMER
- ☐ 667. CANDY MALDONADO
- ☐ 678. MARK LEWIS
- ☐ 696. MARK CLARK
- ☐ 726. ALVARO ESPINOZA
- ☐ 756. CASEY WHITTEN
- ☐ 767. JERRY DIPOTO(CA)
- ☐ 767. JULIAN TAVAREZ(CA)

COLORADO ROCKIES

- ☐ 18. GREG HARRIS
- ☐ 49. ARMANDO REYNOSO
- ☐ 77. JERALD CLARK
- ☐ 106. DARYL BOSTON
- ☐ 135. DAVID NIED
- ☐ 163. VINNY CASTILLA
- ☐ 186. MARCUS MOORE
- ☐ 191. CURTIS LESKANIC
- ☐ 229. LANCE PAINTER
- ☐ 258. ROBERTO MEJIA
- ☐ 286. MARK THOMPSON
- ☐ 314. DANNY SHEAFFER
- ☐ 343. MO SANFORD
- ☐ 372. JOE GIRARDI
- ☐ 407. BRUCE RUFFIN
- ☐ 439. WILLIE BLAIR
- ☐ 468. DANTE BICHETTE
- ☐ 496. CHRIS JONES
- ☐ 525. ANDRES GALARRAGA
- ☐ 553. FREDDIE BENAVIDES
- ☐ 562. DARREN HOLMES
- ☐ 589. KENT BOTTENFIELD
- ☐ 627. STEVE REED
- ☐ 655. CHARLIE HAYES
- ☐ 712. ERIC YOUNG
- ☐ 744. JAMEY WRIGHT
- ☐ 780. JASON BATES(CA)
- ☐ 780. JOHN BURKE(CA)

DETROIT TIGERS

- ☐ 19. SCOTT LIVINGSTONE
- ☐ 48. TONY PHILLIPS
- ☐ 75. ALAN TRAMMELL
- ☐ 105. DAVID WELLS
- ☐ 133. MARK LEITER
- ☐ 162. BOB MACDONALD
- ☐ 190. CECIL FIELDER
- ☐ 228. KIRK GIBSON
- ☐ 257. CHAD KREUTER
- ☐ 285. TRAVIS FRYMAN
- ☐ 313. JUSTIN THOMPSON
- ☐ 342. DANNY GLADDEN
- ☐ 371. JOHN DOHERTY
- ☐ 410. LOU WHITAKER
- ☐ 438. MIKE HENNEMAN
- ☐ 448. SHAWN WOOTEN(P)
- ☐ 467. JOE BOEVER
- ☐ 488. ERIC DAVIS
- ☐ 495. MICKEY TETTLETON
- ☐ 523. MIKE MOORE
- ☐ 552. BILL KRUEGER
- ☐ 561. SKEETER BARNES
- ☐ 588. RICH ROWLAND
- ☐ 626. CHRIS GOMEZ
- ☐ 654. BILL GULLICKSON
- ☐ 682. STORM DAVIS
- ☐ 711. GREG GOHR
- ☐ 757. TONY FUDURIC
- ☐ 768. DANNY BAUTISTA(CA)
- ☐ 768. SEAN BERGMAN(CA)

FLORIDA MARLINS

- ☐ 20. BRYAN HARVEY
- ☐ 47. RICHIE LEWIS
- ☐ 76. LUIS AQUINO
- ☐ 79. TIM CLARK(P)
- ☐ 104. ALEX ARIAS
- ☐ 132. BRET BARBERIE
- ☐ 161. DARRELL WHITMORE
- ☐ 189. CHRIS HAMMOND
- ☐ 227. PAT RAPP

- ☐ 256. WALT WEISS
- ☐ 284. ROBB NEN
- ☐ 312. RICH RODRIGUEZ
- ☐ 341. NIGEL WILSON
- ☐ 370. BENNY SANTIAGO
- ☐ 409. JOE KLINK
- ☐ 437. BOB NATAL
- ☐ 466. JEFF CONINE
- ☐ 494. RYAN BOWEN
- ☐ 522. HENRY COTTO
- ☐ 551. JACK ARMSTONG
- ☐ 560. GARY SHEFFIELD
- ☐ 587. MATT TURNER
- ☐ 625. CHARLIE HOUGH
- ☐ 653. CHUCK CARR
- ☐ 681. RICK RENTERIA
- ☐ 710. ORESTES DESTRADE
- ☐ 750. MARC VALDES
- ☐ 751. DAN EHLER
- ☐ 781. CARL EVERETT(CA)
- ☐ 781. DAVE WEATHERS(CA)

HOUSTON ASTROS

- ☐ 11. ANDUJAR CEDENO
- ☐ 40. JEFF BAGWELL
- ☐ 68. EDDIE TAUBENSEE
- ☐ 97. TODD JONES
- ☐ 125. GREG SWINDELL
- ☐ 153. CHRIS DONNELS
- ☐ 158. ORLANDO MILLER(P)
- ☐ 182. ERIC ANTHONY
- ☐ 209. BILLY WAGNER
- ☐ 220. DOUG DRABEK
- ☐ 249. BRIAN WILLIAMS
- ☐ 277. AL OSUNA
- ☐ 305. CRAIG BIGGIO
- ☐ 334. DOUG JONES
- ☐ 362. KEVIN BASS
- ☐ 427. TOM EDENS
- ☐ 448. ROBERTO PETAGINE(P)
- ☐ 456. PETE HARNISCH
- ☐ 484. LUIS GONZALEZ
- ☐ 512. XAVIER HERNANDEZ
- ☐ 541. JEFF JUDEN
- ☐ 580. STEVE FINLEY
- ☐ 646. KEN CAMINITI
- ☐ 674. SCOTT SERVAIS
- ☐ 703. DARRYL KILE
- ☐ 734. MARK PORTUGAL
- ☐ 782. GARY MOTA(CA)
- ☐ 782. JAMES MOUTON(CA)

KANSAS CITY ROYALS

- ☐ 9. CHRIS HANEY
- ☐ 38. BRENT MAYNE
- ☐ 66. TOM GORDON
- ☐ 94. PHIL HIATT
- ☐ 123. BILLY BREWER
- ☐ 151. GREG GAGNE
- ☐ 180. GEORGE BRETT
- ☐ 204. JEFF GRANGER
- ☐ 218. KEVIN MCREYNOLDS
- ☐ 247. STAN BELINDA
- ☐ 275. WALLY JOYNER
- ☐ 303. GREG CADARET
- ☐ 332. JOSE LIND
- ☐ 357. MARK GUBICZA
- ☐ 403. GARY GAETTI
- ☐ 425. BRIAN MCRAE
- ☐ 454. KEITH MILLER
- ☐ 482. HIPOLITO PICHARDO
- ☐ 510. DAVID CONE
- ☐ 535. JEFF MONTGOMERY
- ☐ 578. MIKE MACFARLANE
- ☐ 614. JOHN HABYAN
- ☐ 672. FELIX JOSE
- ☐ 701. KEVIN APPIER
- ☐ 731. CHRIS GWYNN
- ☐ 769. BOB HAMELIN(CA)
- ☐ 769. JOE VITIELLO(CA)

LOS ANGELES DODGERS

- ☐ 1. MIKE PIAZZA
- ☐ 29. OMAR DAAL
- ☐ 53. BILLY ASHLEY
- ☐ 87. JIM GOTT
- ☐ 115. ERIC KARROS
- ☐ 143. TIM WALLACH
- ☐ 172. BRETT BUTLER
- ☐ 211. TOM CANDIOTTI
- ☐ 237. EDDIE DAVIS(P)
- ☐ 241. JOSE OFFERMAN
- ☐ 268. PEDRO MARTINEZ
- ☐ 276. RICKY TRLICEK
- ☐ 296. ROGER MCDOWELL
- ☐ 325. JODY REED
- ☐ 353. CARLOS HERNANDEZ
- ☐ 382. MITCH WEBSTER
- ☐ 431. PEDRO ASTACIO
- ☐ 460. OREL HERSHISER
- ☐ 516. KEVIN GROSS
- ☐ 545. RAMON MARTINEZ
- ☐ 573. STEVE WILSON
- ☐ 611. TODD WORRELL
- ☐ 640. DARRYL STRAWBERRY
- ☐ 683. CORY SNYDER
- ☐ 697. DAVE HANSEN
- ☐ 713. TODD WILLIAMS(P)
- ☐ 727. HENRY RODRIGUEZ
- ☐ 755. DAX WINSLETT
- ☐ 783. RAUL MONDESI(CA)
- ☐ 783. BEN VAN RYN(CA)

MILWAUKEE BREWERS

- ☐ 16. DOUG HENRY
- ☐ 45. CAL ELDRED
- ☐ 73. BILLY SPIERS
- ☐ 102. B.J. SURHOFF
- ☐ 130. PAT LISTACH
- ☐ 159. MIKE FETTERS
- ☐ 187. GRAEME LLOYD
- ☐ 210. KELLY WUNSCH
- ☐ 225. GREG VAUGHN
- ☐ 251. JOSE VALENTIN
- ☐ 283. JOHN JAHA
- ☐ 310. ROBIN YOUNT
- ☐ 339. MATT MIESKE
- ☐ 367. RICKY BONES
- ☐ 411. KEVIN SEITZER
- ☐ 435. DARRYL HAMILTON
- ☐ 464. BILL WEGMAN
- ☐ 492. JESSE OROSCO
- ☐ 519. ALEX DIAZ
- ☐ 548. DAVE NILSSON
- ☐ 558. TOM LAMPKIN
- ☐ 564. MIKE IGNASIAK
- ☐ 585. KEVIN REIMER
- ☐ 623. RAFAEL NOVOA
- ☐ 651. JUAN BELL
- ☐ 679. JAIME NAVARRO
- ☐ 709. ANGEL MIRANDA
- ☐ 759. JEFF D'AMICO
- ☐ 770. MARK KIEFER(CA)
- ☐ 770. TROY O'LEARY(CA)

MINNESOTA TWINS

- ☐ 14. WILLIE BANKS
- ☐ 43. PAT MAHOMES
- ☐ 71. RICH BECKER
- ☐ 100. KIRBY PUCKETT
- ☐ 128. GEORGE TSAMIS
- ☐ 156. DAVID MCCARTY
- ☐ 185. KEVIN TAPANI
- ☐ 223. PAT MEARES
- ☐ 252. LENNY WEBSTER
- ☐ 280. RICK AGUILERA
- ☐ 308. MIKE TROMBLEY
- ☐ 337. SHANE MACK
- ☐ 365. SCOTT ERICKSON
- ☐ 430. DAVE WINFIELD
- ☐ 459. PEDRO MUNOZ
- ☐ 490. KENT HRBEK
- ☐ 517. SCOTT LEIUS
- ☐ 543. LARRY CASIAN
- ☐ 555. CHUCK KNOBLAUCH
- ☐ 583. CHIP HALE
- ☐ 621. CARL WILLIS
- ☐ 649. DEREK PARKS
- ☐ 677. EDDIE GUARDADO
- ☐ 706. BRIAN HARPER
- ☐ 747. MARC BARCELO
- ☐ 771. DENNY HOCKING(CA)
- ☐ 771. OSCAR MUNOZ(CA)

MONTREAL EXPOS

- ☐ 21. WIL CORDERO
- ☐ 50. MOISES ALOU
- ☐ 78. MEL ROJAS
- ☐ 109. DELINO DESHIELDS
- ☐ 134. GREG COLBRUNN
- ☐ 164. DENIS BOUCHER
- ☐ 192. LOU FRAZIER
- ☐ 230. LARRY WALKER
- ☐ 237. CURTIS PRIDE(P)
- ☐ 259. CLIFF FLOYD
- ☐ 287. MIKE LANSING
- ☐ 315. KEN HILL
- ☐ 344. SEAN BERRY
- ☐ 373. TIM SCOTT
- ☐ 412. DARRIN FLETCHER
- ☐ 440. DENNY MARTINEZ
- ☐ 469. JEFF SHAW
- ☐ 497. JOHN WETTELAND
- ☐ 524. TIM LAKER
- ☐ 554. JEFF FASSERO
- ☐ 563. JOHN VANDER WAL
- ☐ 590. MARQUIS GRISSOM
- ☐ 616. GLENN MURRAY(P)
- ☐ 628. KIRK RUETER
- ☐ 656. CHRIS NABHOLZ
- ☐ 694. BRIAN BARNES
- ☐ 714. TIM SPEHR
- ☐ 741. JOSUE ESTRADA
- ☐ 784. GABE WHITE(CA)
- ☐ 784. RONDELL WHITE(CA)

NEW YORK METS

- ☐ 8. TODD HUNDLEY
- ☐ 37. JEFF INNIS
- ☐ 65. EDDIE MURRAY
- ☐ 98. RYAN THOMPSON
- ☐ 122. JEROMY BURNITZ
- ☐ 150. DOC GOODEN
- ☐ 179. BUTCH HUSKEY
- ☐ 217. MIKE MADDUX
- ☐ 245. BRET SABERHAGEN
- ☐ 274. DAVE GALLAGHER
- ☐ 302. HOWARD JOHNSON
- ☐ 331. JEFF MCKNIGHT
- ☐ 359. ANTHONY YOUNG
- ☐ 402. DAVE TELGHEDER
- ☐ 424. JEFF KENT
- ☐ 453. ERIC HILLMAN
- ☐ 481. JOHN FRANCO
- ☐ 509. TIM BOGAR
- ☐ 539. BOBBY JONES
- ☐ 576. DARRIN JACKSON
- ☐ 615. SID FERNANDEZ
- ☐ 643. JOE ORSULAK
- ☐ 671. CHARLIE O'BRIEN
- ☐ 699. PETE SCHOUREK
- ☐ 713. MIKE WELCH(P)
- ☐ 730. BOBBY BONILLA
- ☐ 740. KIRK PRESLEY
- ☐ 785. BROOK FORDYCE(CA)
- ☐ 785. BILL PULSIPHER(CA)

NEW YORK YANKEES

- ☐ 2. BERNIE WILLIAMS
- ☐ 31. MELIDO PEREZ
- ☐ 59. MATT NOKES
- ☐ 79. BILLY MASSE(P)
- ☐ 88. PAT KELLY
- ☐ 103. STERLING HITCHCOCK
- ☐ 110. LEE SMITH
- ☐ 120. JIMMY KEY
- ☐ 144. BOBBY MUNOZ
- ☐ 158. DEREK JETER(P)
- ☐ 173. BOB WICKMAN
- ☐ 212. DOMINGO JEAN
- ☐ 239. PAUL ASSENMACHER
- ☐ 269. MARK HUTTON
- ☐ 297. SPIKE OWEN
- ☐ 326. RICH MONTELEONE
- ☐ 350. JIM ABBOTT
- ☐ 383. GERALD WILLIAMS
- ☐ 432. MIKE GALLEGO
- ☐ 461. RANDY VELARDE
- ☐ 489. SCOTT KAMIENIECKI
- ☐ 520. WADE BOGGS
- ☐ 546. PAUL O'NEILL

☐ 600. DAN MATTINGLY
☐ 637. STEVE HOWE
☐ 641. STEVE FARR
☐ 670. DANNY TARTABULL
☐ 695. MIKE STANLEY
☐ 728. JIM LEYRITZ
☐ 748. SLOAN SMITH
☐ 772. RUSS DAVIS(CA)
☐ 772. BRIEN TAYLOR(CA)

OAKLAND A'S

☐ 17. LANCE BLANKENSHIP
☐ 46. CRAIG PAQUETTE
☐ 74. SCOTT BROSIUS
☐ 131. STEVE KARSAY
☐ 160. SCOTT LYDY
☐ 188. MIKE BORDICK
☐ 226. SCOTT HEMOND
☐ 255. BOBBY WITT
☐ 282. MIKE MOHLER
☐ 311. MARCOS ARMAS
☐ 318. CHRIS MICHALAK(P)
☐ 340. MARK MCGWIRE
☐ 363. ERIC HELFAND
☐ 389. JASON GIAMBI(P)
☐ 436. VINCE HORSMAN
☐ 465. DENNIS ECKERSLEY
☐ 493. TROY NEEL
☐ 521. BOB WELCH
☐ 549. RON DARLING
☐ 559. TODD VAN POPPEL
☐ 586. BRENT GATES
☐ 610. TERRY STEINBACH
☐ 624. JERRY BROWNE
☐ 652. ROGER SMITHBERG
☐ 680. RUBEN SIERRA
☐ 708. DAVE HENDERSON
☐ 749. JOHN WASDIN
☐ 773. KURT ABBOTT(CA)
☐ 773. MIGUEL JIMENEZ(CA)

PHILADELPHIA PHILLIES

☐ 28. TONY LONGMIRE
☐ 57. KEVIN STOCKER
☐ 86. RICKY JORDAN
☐ 114. MITCH WILLIAMS
☐ 142. CURT SCHILLING
☐ 170. TERRY MULHOLLAND
☐ 199. DANNY JACKSON
☐ 238. KIM BATISTE
☐ 266. DAVE WEST
☐ 294. TYLER GREEN
☐ 323. PETE INCAVIGLIA
☐ 328. DONN PALL
☐ 352. BEN RIVERA
☐ 380. DARREN DAULTON
☐ 401. JOHN KRUK
☐ 419. WES CHAMBERLAIN
☐ 447. MIKE WILLIAMS
☐ 476. DAVE HOLLINS
☐ 504. JIM EISENREICH
☐ 533. ROGER MASON
☐ 570. TOMMY GREENE
☐ 597. TODD PRATT
☐ 635. LEN DYKSTRA
☐ 663. MARIANO DUNCAN
☐ 692. MICKEY MORANDINI
☐ 722. MILT THOMPSON
☐ 742. WAYNE GOMES
☐ 786. KEVIN FOSTER(CA)
☐ 786. GENE SCHALL(CA)

PITTSBURGH PIRATES

☐ 15. JAY BELL
☐ 44. JEFF KING
☐ 72. STEVE COOKE
☐ 79. STANTON CAMERON(P)
☐ 101. MARK DEWEY
☐ 129. DENNY NEAGLE
☐ 157. PAUL WAGNER
☐ 207. CHARLES PETERSON
☐ 208. ANDY RICE
☐ 224. DANNY MICELI
☐ 253. BLAS MINOR
☐ 281. ORLANDO MERCED
☐ 309. CARLOS GARCIA
☐ 338. RANDY TOMLIN
☐ 366. AL MARTIN
☐ 405. DON SLAUGHT
☐ 434. BOB WALK
☐ 463. JERRY GOFF
☐ 491. JOHN HOPE
☐ 518. LLOYD MCCLENDON
☐ 557. JOEL JOHNSTON
☐ 584. SCOTT BULLETT
☐ 616. J. ALLENSWORTH(P)
☐ 622. KEVIN YOUNG
☐ 650. ANDY VAN SLYKE
☐ 669. TIM WAKEFIELD
☐ 686. JASON KENDALL(P)
☐ 707. ZANE SMITH
☐ 787. RICH AUDE(CA)
☐ 787. MIDRE CUMMINGS(CA)

ST. LOUIS CARDINALS

☐ 25. TODD ZEILE
☐ 54. MARK WHITEN
☐ 83. TOM URBANI
☐ 139. TRIPP CROMER
☐ 168. STEVE DIXON
☐ 196. ALLEN WATSON
☐ 202. ALAN BENES
☐ 234. ERIK PAPPAS
☐ 263. GERALD PERRY
☐ 320. OZZIE SMITH
☐ 348. RENE AROCHA
☐ 377. BERNARD GILKEY
☐ 406. JOSE OQUENDO
☐ 416. LUIS ALICEA
☐ 444. GERONIMO PENA
☐ 473. BOB TEWKSBURY
☐ 501. DONOVAN OSBORNE
☐ 530. RAY LANKFORD
☐ 567. MIKE PEREZ
☐ 594. RHEAL CORMIER
☐ 632. BRIAN JORDAN
☐ 660. GREGG JEFFERIES
☐ 689. OMAR OLIVARES
☐ 713. KIRK BULLINGER(P)
☐ 719. TOM PAGNOZZI
☐ 737. PAUL KILGUS
☐ 788. BRIAN BARBER(CA)
☐ 788. R. BATCHELOR(CA)

SAN DIEGO PADRES

☐ 13. PHIL PLANTIER
☐ 42. RICKY GUTIERREZ
☐ 70. ANDY BENES
☐ 99. TIM MAUSER
☐ 127. BRAD AUSMUS
☐ 152. RAY MCDAVID
☐ 184. CRAIG SHIPLEY
☐ 222. TREVOR HOFFMAN
☐ 254. TIM TEUFEL
☐ 279. KEVIN HIGGINS
☐ 307. MELVIN NIEVES
☐ 336. LUIS LOPEZ
☐ 364. DEREK BELL
☐ 408. PHIL CLARK
☐ 458. TIM WORRELL
☐ 486. WALLY WHITEHURST
☐ 507. DAVE STATON
☐ 514. GENE HARRIS
☐ 527. JASON HARDTKE(P)
☐ 544. JEFF GARDNER
☐ 556. GUILLERMO VELASQUEZ
☐ 579. DOUG BROCAIL
☐ 620. TONY GWYNN
☐ 648. ANDY ASHBY
☐ 676. PEDRO MARTINEZ
☐ 704. ARCHI CIANFROCCO
☐ 753. GREG KEAGLE
☐ 789. BRIAN JOHNSON(CA)
☐ 789. SCOTT SANDERS(CA)

SAN FRANCISCO GIANTS

☐ 3. KEVIN ROGERS
☐ 30. KIRT MANWARING
☐ 58. MIKE JACKSON
☐ 89. BUD BLACK
☐ 116. JEFF BRANTLEY
☐ 146. ROD BECK
☐ 174. DAVE MARTINEZ
☐ 213. JOHN BURKETT
☐ 240. WILL CLARK
☐ 267. ROYCE CLAYTON
☐ 291. JEFF REED
☐ 298. SALOMON TORRES
☐ 327. MARK CARREON
☐ 354. DARREN LEWIS
☐ 398. TODD BENZINGER
☐ 429. BRYAN HICKERSON
☐ 433. DAVE BURBA
☐ 462. TREVOR WILSON
☐ 487. MIKE BENJAMIN
☐ 505. ROBBY THOMPSON
☐ 547. STEVE HOSEY
☐ 550. MATT WILLIAMS
☐ 574. WILLIE MCGEE
☐ 639 .BILL SWIFT
☐ 700. BARRY BONDS
☐ 729. STEVE SCARSONE
☐ 754. JASON MYERS
☐ 790. RIKKERT FANEYTE(CA)
☐ 790. J.R. PHILLIPS(CA)

SEATTLE MARINERS

☐ 24. JEFF NELSON
☐ 60. CHRIS BOSIO
☐ 82. BRIAN TURANG
☐ 111. GREG LITTON
☐ 138. BILL HASELMAN
☐ 167. TIM DAVIS
☐ 195. EDGAR MARTINEZ
☐ 233. RICH AMARAL
☐ 262. MARC NEWFIELD
☐ 290. RANDY JOHNSON
☐ 319. TED POWER
☐ 347. DAVE MAGADAN
☐ 376. ROGER SALKELD
☐ 400. KEN GRIFFEY, JR.
☐ 415. DAVE FLEMING
☐ 443. JOHN CUMMINGS
☐ 448. GREG PIRKL(P)
☐ 472. JAY BUHNER
☐ 527. RUBEN SANTANA(P)
☐ 529. ERIK HANSON
☐ 569. MIKE FELDER
☐ 593. OMAR VIZQUEL
☐ 631. BRAD HOLMAN
☐ 659. BRET BOONE
☐ 686. CHRIS HOWARD(P)
☐ 693. TINO MARTINEZ
☐ 717. MIKE BLOWERS
☐ 736. DAVE VALLE
☐ 761. DAVID COOPER
☐ 774. KEVIN KING(CA)
☐ 774. ERIK PLANTENBERG(CA)

TEXAS RANGERS

☐ 22. ROGER PAVLIK
☐ 34. NOLAN RYAN
☐ 51. MANUEL LEE
☐ 80. JOSE CANSECO
☐ 108. GARY REDUS
☐ 136. DEAN PALMER
☐ 165. IVAN RODRIGUEZ
☐ 193. STEVE DREYER
☐ 201. MIKE BELL
☐ 231. BENJI GIL
☐ 260. JULIO FRANCO

- ☐ 288. CRAIG LEFFERTS
- ☐ 317. CRIS CARPENTER
- ☐ 318. DUFF BRUMLEY(P)
- ☐ 345. KEVIN BROWN
- ☐ 413. KENNY ROGERS
- ☐ 441. DAN PELTIER
- ☐ 470. RAFAEL PALMEIRO
- ☐ 498. DAVID HULSE
- ☐ 591. DOUG STRANGE
- ☐ 618. ROB DUCEY
- ☐ 629. MATT WHITESIDE
- ☐ 644. TOM HENKE
- ☐ 685. JUAN GONZALEZ
- ☐ 775. JON SHAVE(CA)
- ☐ 775. DESI WILSON(CA)

TORONTO BLUE JAYS

- ☐ 10. JOHN OLERUD
- ☐ 39. HUCK FLENER
- ☐ 67. ALEX GONZALEZ
- ☐ 96. RANDY KNORR
- ☐ 124. WILLIE CANATE
- ☐ 155. TODD STOTTLEMYRE
- ☐ 181. JUAN GUZMAN
- ☐ 203. MATT FARNER
- ☐ 206. JEREMY LEE
- ☐ 219. PAT BORDERS
- ☐ 237. SHAWN GREEN(P)
- ☐ 248. RICKEY HENDERSON
- ☐ 304. PAT HENTGEN
- ☐ 333. MIKE TIMLIN
- ☐ 361. ROB BUTLER
- ☐ 426. ED SPRAGUE
- ☐ 448. D.J. BOSTON(P)
- ☐ 455. DAVE STEWART
- ☐ 483. DUANE WARD
- ☐ 511. DEVON WHITE
- ☐ 540. PAUL MOLITOR
- ☐ 582. DANNY COX
- ☐ 645. JOE CARTER
- ☐ 668. WOODY WILLIAMS
- ☐ 675. ROBERTO ALOMAR
- ☐ 686. CARLOS DELGADO(P)
- ☐ 702. TONY FERNANDEZ
- ☐ 732. AL LEITER
- ☐ 776. DOMINGO CEDENO(CA)
- ☐ 776. PAUL SPOLJARIC(CA)

1994 TOPPS TRADED (132) 2 1/2" X 3 1/2"

ATLANTA BRAVES

- ☐ 8T. DAVE GALLAGHER
- ☐ 13T. JACOB SHUMATE
- ☐ 35T. MIKE KELLY
- ☐ 56T. JASON SCHMIDT(P)
- ☐ 63T. MIKE MORDECAI
- ☐ 92T. CHARLIE O'BRIEN
- ☐ 98T. COREY POINTER
- ☐ 118T. GREGG OLSON

BALTIMORE ORIOLES

- ☐ 4T. MARK SMITH
- ☐ 28T. SID FERNANDEZ
- ☐ 52T. DWIGHT SMITH
- ☐ 76T. RAFAEL PALMEIRO
- ☐ 100T. LEE SMITH
- ☐ 125T. CHRIS SABO

BOSTON RED SOX

- ☐ 11T. DAMON BERRYHILL
- ☐ 40T. OTIS NIXON
- ☐ 68T. CHRIS HOWARD
- ☐ 96T. GAR FINNVOLD
- ☐ 122T. RICH ROWLAND

CALIFORNIA ANGELS

- ☐ 10T. BRIAN ANDERSON
- ☐ 34T. MARK DALESANDRO
- ☐ 62T. JORGE FABREGAS
- ☐ 90T. BO JACKSON
- ☐ 117T. MARK LEITER

CHICAGO CUBS

- ☐ 15T. WILLIE BANKS
- ☐ 46T. SHAWON DUNSTON
- ☐ 79T. KEVIN FOSTER
- ☐ 110T. ANTHONY YOUNG

CHICAGO WHITE SOX

- ☐ 25T. JULIO FRANCO
- ☐ 61T. JOE HALL
- ☐ 108T. DARRIN JACKSON

CINCINNATI REDS

- ☐ 19T. CHUCK MCELROY
- ☐ 37T. JEFF BRANTLEY
- ☐ 55T. RON GANT
- ☐ 73T. ERIK HANSON
- ☐ 77T. BRET BOONE
- ☐ 91T. HECTOR CARRASCO
- ☐ 109T. C.J. NITKOWSKI
- ☐ 127T. TONY FERNANDEZ

CLEVELAND INDIANS

- ☐ 7T. DENNY MARTINEZ
- ☐ 36T. JACK MORRIS
- ☐ 60T. EDDIE MURRAY
- ☐ 78T. PAUL SHUEY
- ☐ 93T. OMAR VIZQUEL
- ☐ 119T. TONY PENA

COLORADO ROCKIES

- ☐ 18T. ELLIS BURKS
- ☐ 49T. MARVIN FREEMAN
- ☐ 56T. TRENIDAD HUBBARD(P)
- ☐ 82T. HOWARD JOHNSON
- ☐ 85T. DOUG MILLION
- ☐ 113T. WALT WEISS

DETROIT TIGERS

- ☐ 30T. RICCARDO INGRAM
- ☐ 32T. TIM BELCHER
- ☐ 89T. JUNIOR FELIX

FLORIDA MARLINS

- ☐ 16T. JERRY BROWNE
- ☐ 47T. GREG COLBRUNN
- ☐ 80T. DAVE MAGADAN
- ☐ 111T. KURT MILLER

HOUSTON ASTROS

- ☐ 45T. JOHN HUDEK
- ☐ 84T. ROSS POWELL

KANSAS CITY ROYALS

- ☐ 23T. DAVE HENDERSON
- ☐ 56T. LARRY SUTTON(P)
- ☐ 66T. TIM GRIEVE
- ☐ 106T. VINCE COLEMAN
- ☐ 116T. MATT SMITH

LOS ANGELES DODGERS

- ☐ 70T. CHAN HO PARK
- ☐ 112T. PAUL KONERKO

MILWAUKEE BREWERS

- ☐ 21T. BRIAN HARPER
- ☐ 38T. LARRY BARNES
- ☐ 57T. JODY REED
- ☐ 104T. TURNER WARD

MINNESOTA TWINS

- ☐ 12T. ALEX COLE
- ☐ 69T. MATT WALBECK
- ☐ 97T. DAVE STEVENS
- ☐ 123T. JEFF REBOULET

MONTREAL EXPOS

- ☐ 31T. GABE WHITE
- ☐ 74T. MIKE THRUMAN
- ☐ 88T. BUTCH HENRY

NEW YORK METS

- ☐ 1T. PAUL WILSON
- ☐ 9T. JOSIAS MANZANILLO
- ☐ 33T. TERRENCE LONG
- ☐ 94T. DAVID SEGUI
- ☐ 120T. JOSE VIZCAINO

NEW YORK YANKEES

- ☐ 20T. LUIS POLONIA
- ☐ 50T. TERRY MULHOLLAND
- ☐ 83T. XAVIER HERNANDEZ
- ☐ 114T. DARYL BOSTON

OAKLAND A'S

- ☐ 2T. BILL TAYLOR
- ☐ 24T. MARK ACRE
- ☐ 44T. BEN GRIEVE
- ☐ 64T. ED VOSBERG
- ☐ 65T. RICKEY HENDERSON
- ☐ 86T. GERONIMO BERROA
- ☐ 107T. STAN JAVIER
- ☐ 128T. CARLOS REYES

PHILADELPHIA PHILLIES

- ☐ 5T. TOBY BORLAND
- ☐ 43T. HEATHCLIFF SLOCUMB
- ☐ 53T. SHAWN BOSKIE
- ☐ 102T. BOBBY MUNOZ
- ☐ 126T. DOUG JONES

PITTSBURGH PIRATES

- ☐ 6T. DAVE CLARK
- ☐ 39T. BRIAN HUNTER
- ☐ 67T. JON LIEBER
- ☐ 87T. MARK FARRIS
- ☐ 121T. RICK WHITE

ST. LOUIS CARDINALS

- ☐ 41T. BRET WAGNER
- ☐ 71T. BRYAN EVERSGERD

SAN DIEGO PADRES

- ☐ 17T. DONNIE ELLIOTT
- ☐ 48T. JOEY HAMILTON
- ☐ 81T. BIP ROBERTS
- ☐ 95T. DUSTIN HERMANSON

SAN FRANCISCO GIANTS

- ☐ 22T. MARK PORTUGAL
- ☐ 105T. BILL VAN LANDINGHAM

SEATTLE MARINERS

- ☐ 3T. DAN WILSON
- ☐ 27T. ERIC ANTHONY
- ☐ 51T. KEITH MITCHELL
- ☐ 75T. BOBBY AYALA
- ☐ 99T. FELIX FERMIN
- ☐ 124T. GREG HIBBARD

TEXAS RANGERS

- ☐ 14T. ODDIBE MCDOWELL
- ☐ 29T. RUSTY GREER
- ☐ 56T. STEPHEN LARKIN(P)
- ☐ 58T. RICK HELLING
- ☐ 59T. JOHN POWELL
- ☐ 72T. JOHN DETTMER
- ☐ 101T. REID RYAN
- ☐ 115T. WILL CLARK
- ☐ 129T. KEVIN BROWN

TORONTO BLUE JAYS

- ☐ 26T. DARREN HALL
- ☐ 54T. KEVIN WITT

1995 TOPPS SERIES 1 (396) 2 1/2" X 3 1/2"

ATLANTA BRAVES

- ☐ 6. JACOB SHUMATE
- ☐ 32. TONY TARASCO
- ☐ 61. MIKE KELLY
- ☐ 91. BRAD WOODALL
- ☐ 117. RAFAEL BELLIARD
- ☐ 145. JOHN SMOLTZ
- ☐ 175. TOM GLAVINE
- ☐ 202. KENT MERCKER
- ☐ 242. TERRY PENDLETON
- ☐ 271. MIKE STANTON
- ☐ 295. GREG MADDUX
- ☐ 316. TERRELL WADE(P)
- ☐ 324. RYAN KLESKO
- ☐ 355. FRED MCGRIFF
- ☐ 369. BRAD CLONTZ(P)
- ☐ 379. CHARLIE O'BRIEN

BALTIMORE ORIOLES

- ☐ 23. MIKE DEVEREAUX
- ☐ 50. MIKE MUSSINA
- ☐ 80. RAFAEL PALMEIRO
- ☐ 107. JIM POOLE
- ☐ 137. CHRIS SABO
- ☐ 165. BEN MCDONALD
- ☐ 232. HAROLD BAINES
- ☐ 261. DWIGHT SMITH
- ☐ 289. ARTHUR RHODES
- ☐ 318. JAMIE MOYER
- ☐ 346. ARMANDO BENITEZ
- ☐ 375. JEFF TACKETT

BOSTON RED SOX

- ☐ 4. SCOTT COOPER
- ☐ 36. JOHN VALENTIN
- ☐ 63. KEN RYAN
- ☐ 92. GAR FINNVOLD
- ☐ 119. TONY FOSSAS
- ☐ 148. OTIS NIXON
- ☐ 177. CHRIS HOWARD
- ☐ 205. MO VAUGHN
- ☐ 215. MIKE GREENWELL
- ☐ 237. JOSE MALAVE(P)
- ☐ 244. FRANK RODRIGUEZ
- ☐ 272. RICH ROWLAND
- ☐ 301. AARON SELE
- ☐ 329. TIM NAEHRING
- ☐ 360. ROGER CLEMENS

CALIFORNIA ANGELS

- ☐ 12. GARY DISARCINA
- ☐ 41. MARK LEITER
- ☐ 69. HAROLD REYNOLDS
- ☐ 95. MARK LANGSTON
- ☐ 126. EDUARDO PEREZ
- ☐ 154. CHAD CURTIS
- ☐ 183. JIM EDMONDS
- ☐ 200. TIM SALMON
- ☐ 221. ANDREW LORRAINE
- ☐ 278. JOE GRAHE
- ☐ 306. DAMION EASLEY
- ☐ 335. CHILI DAVIS
- ☐ 368. MIKE BUTCHER

CHICAGO CUBS

- ☐ 11. SAMMY SOSA
- ☐ 34. EDDIE ZAMBRANO
- ☐ 42. JOSE BAUTISTA
- ☐ 57. REY SANCHEZ
- ☐ 90. MARK GRACE
- ☐ 121. MIKE MORGAN
- ☐ 149. TURK WENDELL
- ☐ 178. KARL RHODES
- ☐ 214. SHAWON DUNSTON
- ☐ 246. BROOKS KIESCHNICK
- ☐ 273. STEVE TRACHSEL
- ☐ 303. STEVE BUECHELE
- ☐ 330. RANDY MYERS
- ☐ 358. FRANK CASTILLO

CHICAGO WHITE SOX

- ☐ 1. FRANK THOMAS
- ☐ 49. JAMES BALDWIN
- ☐ 77. TIM RAINES
- ☐ 79. HAROLD WILLIAMS(P)
- ☐ 106. DARRIN JACKSON
- ☐ 135. JULIO FRANCO
- ☐ 163. ALEX FERNANDEZ
- ☐ 186. WILSON ALVAREZ
- ☐ 191. ROBERTO HERNANDEZ
- ☐ 229. BOB ZUPCIC
- ☐ 258. NORBERTO MARTIN
- ☐ 314. LANCE JOHNSON
- ☐ 343. CRAIG GREBECK
- ☐ 372. RON KARKOVICE

CINCINNATI REDS

- ☐ 27. HAL MORRIS
- ☐ 56. JOHN SMILEY
- ☐ 79. RAY BROWN(P)
- ☐ 84. C.J. NITKOWSKI
- ☐ 113. BRET BOONE
- ☐ 141. CHUCK MCELROY
- ☐ 171. CALVIN REESE
- ☐ 198. JEFF BRANSON
- ☐ 236. JEFF BRANTLEY
- ☐ 270. JOHNNY RUFFIN
- ☐ 293. EDDIE TAUBENSEE
- ☐ 316. EDDIE PRIEST(P)
- ☐ 322. ERIK HANSON
- ☐ 350. BARRY LARKIN
- ☐ 381. THOMAS HOWARD

CLEVELAND INDIANS

- ☐ 20. DENNY MARTINEZ
- ☐ 47. CHAD OGEA
- ☐ 76. CHARLES NAGY
- ☐ 104. KENNY LOFTON
- ☐ 132. PAUL SORRENTO
- ☐ 158. DAVE WINFIELD
- ☐ 161. JOSE MESA
- ☐ 189. DEREK LILLIQUIST
- ☐ 227. WAYNE KIRBY
- ☐ 256. ERIC PLUNK
- ☐ 284. TONY PENA
- ☐ 312. JIM THOME
- ☐ 370. EDDIE MURRAY

COLORADO ROCKIES

- ☐ 26. DARREN HOLMES
- ☐ 52. MARK THOMPSON
- ☐ 81. CHARLIE HAYES
- ☐ 110. WALT WEISS
- ☐ 140. DANTE BICHETTE
- ☐ 169. ROBERTO MEJIA
- ☐ 206. HOWARD JOHNSON
- ☐ 235. ELLIS BURKS
- ☐ 268. GREG HARRIS
- ☐ 286. DOUG MILLION
- ☐ 292. WILLIE BLAIR
- ☐ 316. JUAN ACEVEDO(P)

☐ 321. STEVE REED
☐ 349. ARMANDO REYNOSO

DETROIT TIGERS

☐ 15. LOU WHITAKER
☐ 40. TRAVIS FRYMAN
☐ 68. JUNIOR FELIX
☐ 97. MIKE GARDINER
☐ 125. JOHN DOHERTY
☐ 153. TONY CLARK
☐ 182. MILT CUYLER
☐ 209. TIM BELCHER
☐ 220. CECIL FIELDER
☐ 249. BILL GULLICKSON
☐ 277. CHRIS GOMEZ
☐ 307. MIKE HENNEMAN
☐ 334. JOHN FLAHERTY
☐ 362. CHAD KREUTER

FLORIDA MARLINS

☐ 18. CHRIS HAMMOND
☐ 44. BRET BARBERIE
☐ 73. DAVE WEATHERS
☐ 96. CHUCK CARR
☐ 130. JEFF CONINE
☐ 160. BENNY SANTIAGO
☐ 192. BOB NATAL
☐ 225. DARRELL WHITMORE
☐ 251. KURT MILLER
☐ 283. DAVE MAGADAN
☐ 311. BRYAN HARVEY
☐ 340. RICK RENTERIA
☐ 373. RICHIE LEWIS

HOUSTON ASTROS

☐ 19. SID BREAM
☐ 48. PETE HARNISCH
☐ 75. DOUG DRABEK
☐ 105. KEN CAMINITI
☐ 133. MIKE HAMPTON
☐ 162. LUIS GONZALEZ
☐ 190. CRAIG BIGGIO
☐ 228. DARRYL KILE
☐ 237. BRIAN HUNTER(P)
☐ 257. SHANE REYNOLDS
☐ 285. GREG SWINDELL
☐ 313. RAMON CASTRO
☐ 342. SCOTT SERVAIS
☐ 371. ORLANDO MILLER

KANSAS CITY ROYALS

☐ 5. DAVID CONE
☐ 29. KEITH MILLER
☐ 53. MATT SMITH
☐ 87. TERRY SHUMPERT
☐ 115. WALLY JOYNER
☐ 143. BOB HAMELIN
☐ 172. HIPOLITO PICHARDO
☐ 210. JEFF MONTGOMERY
☐ 241. JEFF GRANGER
☐ 264. BRENT MAYNE
☐ 276. DAVE HENDERSON
☐ 296. MIKE MACFARLANE
☐ 325. KEVIN APPIER
☐ 353. GARY GAETTI
☐ 382. CHRIS HANEY

LOS ANGELES DODGERS

☐ 9. DELINO DESHIELDS
☐ 38. TIM WALLACH
☐ 66. ISMAEL VALDES
☐ 94. CARLOS HERNANDEZ
☐ 123. KEVIN GROSS
☐ 139. PAUL KONERKO
☐ 152. JOSE OFFERMAN
☐ 180. RAUL MONDESI
☐ 204. TODD WORRELL
☐ 218. DAVE HANSEN
☐ 237. KARIM GARCIA(P)
☐ 247. TODD HOLLANDSWORTH
☐ 275. RAMON MARTINEZ
☐ 305. OREL HERSHISER
☐ 332. JIM GOTT
☐ 357. CHRIS GWYNN

MILWAUKEE BREWERS

☐ 17. DAVE NILSSON
☐ 35. RICKY BONES
☐ 64. MATT MIESKE
☐ 79. SCOTT TALANOA(P)
☐ 93. JAIME NAVARRO
☐ 131. DOUG HENRY
☐ 159. BILL WEGMAN
☐ 188. BILLY SPIERS
☐ 216. ALEX DIAZ
☐ 245. DARRYL HAMILTON
☐ 282. JEFF D'AMICO
☐ 309. KEVIN SEITZER
☐ 339. MIKE FETTERS
☐ 367. B.J. SURHOFF

MINNESOTA TWINS

☐ 8. SHANE MACK
☐ 37. KEVIN TAPANI
☐ 65. RICK AGUILERA
☐ 98. DAVID MCCARTY
☐ 122. DENNY HOCKING
☐ 151. DEREK PARKS
☐ 179. LATROY HAWKINS
☐ 194. TRAVIS MILLER
☐ 217. PAT MAHOMES
☐ 250. CHUCK KNOBLAUCH
☐ 274. PEDRO MUNOZ
☐ 302. CARL WILLIS
☐ 331. ALEX COLE
☐ 359. JEFF REBOULET

MONTREAL EXPOS

☐ 22. JOHN WETTELAND
☐ 46. KEN HILL
☐ 74. MEL ROJAS
☐ 108. WIL CORDERO
☐ 134. TIM SPEHR
☐ 164. FREDDIE BENAVIDES
☐ 196. RONDELL WHITE
☐ 226. RANDY MILLIGAN
☐ 255. DARRIN FLETCHER
☐ 259. MIKE THURMAN
☐ 287. GABE WHITE
☐ 315. MARQUIS GRISSOM
☐ 344. KIRK RUETER
☐ 369. SCOTT GENTILE(P)
☐ 374. LENNY WEBSTER

NEW YORK METS

☐ 14. JOSE VIZCAINO
☐ 43. PETE SMITH
☐ 71. KELLY STINNETT
☐ 101. DAVID SEGUI
☐ 112. TERRENCE LONG
☐ 128. JOE ORSULAK
☐ 156. BILL PULSIPHER
☐ 185. JEFF KENT
☐ 223. TODD HUNDLEY
☐ 252. BOBBY JONES
☐ 280. JOHN FRANCO
☐ 308. JOSIAS MANZANILLO
☐ 337. JASON JACOME
☐ 366. JEROMY BURNITZ

NEW YORK YANKEES

☐ 28. BRIAN BUCHANAN
☐ 60. JIM ABBOTT
☐ 86. GERALD WILLIAMS
☐ 114. DARYL BOSTON
☐ 142. MIKE STANLEY
☐ 170. WADE BOGGS
☐ 199. DEREK JETER
☐ 238. MATT NOKES
☐ 266. STERLING HITCHCOCK
☐ 294. STEVE HOWE
☐ 323. LUIS POLONIA
☐ 352. SCOTT KAMIENIECKI
☐ 380. TERRY MULHOLLAND

OAKLAND A'S

☐ 16. RON DARLING
☐ 45. DENNIS ECKERSLEY
☐ 72. CARLOS REYES
☐ 102. SCOTT BROSIUS
☐ 129. BRENT GATES
☐ 157. TROY NEEL
☐ 187. GERONIMO BERROA
☐ 207. JOHN WASDIN
☐ 212. BEN GRIEVE
☐ 224. MARK ACRE
☐ 253. LANCE BLANKENSHIP
☐ 281. MIKE BORDICK
☐ 310. RUBEN SIERRA
☐ 338. STAN JAVIER
☐ 364. BOB WELCH
☐ 369. STEVE PHOENIX(P)

PHILADELPHIA PHILLIES

☐ 2. MICKEY MORANDINI
☐ 31. DAVE WEST
☐ 59. RICKY BOTTALICO
☐ 79. GENE SCHALL(P)
☐ 88. HEATHCLIFF SLOCUMB
☐ 103. MARIANO DUNCAN
☐ 120. LEN DYKSTRA
☐ 144. TOMMY GREENE
☐ 173. KIM BATISTE
☐ 237. SHANE PULLEN(P)
☐ 239. BEN RIVERA
☐ 269. RICKY JORDAN
☐ 297. CURT SCHILLING
☐ 326. JIM EISENREICH
☐ 351. MIKE WILLIAMS
☐ 383. BILLY HATCHER

PITTSBURGH PIRATES

☐ 21. ORLANDO MERCED
☐ 51. AL MARTIN
☐ 78. MIDRE CUMMINGS
☐ 109. DANNY MICELI
☐ 136. MIK DYER
☐ 166. BLAS MINOR
☐ 197. STEVE COOKE
☐ 230. JAY BELL
☐ 260. ANDY VAN SLYKE
☐ 288. TREY BEAMON
☐ 317. PAUL WAGNER
☐ 345. DON SLAUGHT
☐ 363. MARK FARRIS
☐ 378. MARK DEWEY

ST. LOUIS CARDINALS

☐ 24. RENE AROCHA
☐ 62. BRIAN JORDAN
☐ 82. RAY LANKFORD
☐ 111. TOM PAGNOZZI
☐ 138. RHEAL CORMIER
☐ 167. BRET WAGNER
☐ 195. BOB TEWKSBURY
☐ 233. ALAN BENES
☐ 262. ALLEN WATSON
☐ 291. JOSE OQUENDO
☐ 316. MATT ARRANDALE(P)
☐ 319. TODD ZEILE
☐ 347. OZZIE SMITH
☐ 376. TOM URBANI

SAN DIEGO PADRES

- ☐ 7. TREVOR HOFFMAN
- ☐ 33. SCOTT SANDERS
- ☐ 54. JOEY HAMILTON
- ☐ 85. ANDY ASHBY
- ☐ 118. LUIS LOPEZ
- ☐ 147. RAY MCDAVID
- ☐ 176. PHIL PLANTIER
- ☐ 208. EDDIE WILLIAMS
- ☐ 231. DUSTIN HERMANSON
- ☐ 243. MELVIN NIEVES
- ☐ 265. BIP ROBERTS
- ☐ 298. PHIL CLARK
- ☐ 328. CRAIG SHIPLEY
- ☐ 356. TIM MAUSER

SAN FRANCISCO GIANTS

- ☐ 10. MATT WILLIAMS
- ☐ 39. DARREN LEWIS
- ☐ 67. ROYCE CLAYTON
- ☐ 100. BARRY BONDS
- ☐ 124. TODD BENZINGER
- ☐ 155. MARK PORTUGAL
- ☐ 181. JEFF REED
- ☐ 201. STEVE FREY
- ☐ 211. KIRT MANWARING
- ☐ 219. KEVIN ROGERS
- ☐ 248. JOE ROSSELLI
- ☐ 304. DAVE BURBA
- ☐ 333. MIKE JACKSON
- ☐ 361. MARK CARREON

SEATTLE MARINERS

- ☐ 25. JAY BUHNER
- ☐ 55. EDGAR MARTINEZ
- ☐ 83. TIM DAVIS
- ☐ 168. MAC SUZUKI
- ☐ 193. BOBBY AYALA
- ☐ 203. RANDY JOHNSON
- ☐ 234. FELIX FERMIN
- ☐ 263. DAN WILSON
- ☐ 320. CHRIS BOSIO
- ☐ 348. MIKE BLOWERS
- ☐ 377. TINO MARTINEZ

TEXAS RANGERS

- ☐ 13. KENNY ROGERS
- ☐ 70. JUAN GONZALEZ
- ☐ 99. CRIS CARPENTER
- ☐ 127. DAN SMITH
- ☐ 150. CHRIS JAMES
- ☐ 184. HECTOR FAJARDO
- ☐ 222. JACK ARMSTRONG
- ☐ 254. MATT WHITESIDE
- ☐ 279. RUSTY GREER
- ☐ 300. JOSE CANSECO
- ☐ 336. BENJI GIL
- ☐ 365. DEAN PALMER
- ☐ 369. BUCKY BUCKLES(P)

TORONTO BLUE JAYS

- ☐ 30. PAUL MOLITOR
- ☐ 58. MIKE TIMLIN
- ☐ 89. DOMINGO CEDENO
- ☐ 116. ROB BUTLER
- ☐ 146. ED SPRAGUE
- ☐ 174. DARREN HALL
- ☐ 213. PAT HENTGEN
- ☐ 240. JOE CARTER
- ☐ 267. ALEX GONZALEZ
- ☐ 290. JUAN GUZMAN
- ☐ 299. WOODY WILLIAMS
- ☐ 327. RANDY KNORR
- ☐ 341. KEVIN WITT
- ☐ 354. TODD STOTTLEMYRE

TOPPS-STADIUM CLUB

1991 STADIUM CLUB (600) 2 1/2" X 3 1/2"

ATLANTA BRAVES

- ☐ 26. DAVE JUSTICE
- ☐ 48. STEVE AVERY
- ☐ 97. LONNIE SMITH
- ☐ 203. MARK LEMKE
- ☐ 288. GREG OLSON
- ☐ 327. TERRY PENDLETON
- ☐ 341. KENT MERCKER
- ☐ 365. JOHN SMOLTZ
- ☐ 377. JEFF BLAUSER
- ☐ 393. MIKE HEATH
- ☐ 404. RAFAEL BELLIARD
- ☐ 413. MIKE STANTON
- ☐ 427. SID BREAM
- ☐ 454. RON GANT
- ☐ 460. JUAN BERENGUER
- ☐ 497. JEFF TREADWAY
- ☐ 519. PETE SMITH
- ☐ 527. CHARLIE LEIBRANDT
- ☐ 544. JEFF PARRETT
- ☐ 558. TOM GLAVINE
- ☐ 571. TOMMY GREGG

BALTIMORE ORIOLES

- ☐ 20. MARK WILLIAMSON
- ☐ 50. DAVID SEGUI
- ☐ 80. RANDY MILLIGAN
- ☐ 117. DAVE JOHNSON
- ☐ 156. GREGG OLSON
- ☐ 191. JOE ORSULAK
- ☐ 222. BILLY RIPKEN
- ☐ 264. BEN MCDONALD
- ☐ 283. JEFF BALLARD
- ☐ 312. BOB MELVIN
- ☐ 316. SAM HORN
- ☐ 330. ANTHONY TELFORD
- ☐ 351. DWIGHT EVANS
- ☐ 380. JOSE MESA
- ☐ 391. GLENN DAVIS
- ☐ 410. BRADY ANDERSON
- ☐ 430. CAL RIPKEN
- ☐ 441. JEFF ROBINSON
- ☐ 467. CRAIG WORTHINGTON
- ☐ 489. CHRIS HOILES
- ☐ 517. TIM HULETT
- ☐ 555. MIKE DEVEREAUX

BOSTON RED SOX

- ☐ 12. CARLOS QUINTANA
- ☐ 33. JODY REED
- ☐ 55. LUIS RIVERA
- ☐ 83. TIM NAEHRING
- ☐ 108. ELLIS BURKS
- ☐ 122. DARYL IRVINE
- ☐ 140. DANA KEICKER
- ☐ 170. WADE BOGGS
- ☐ 201. JOHN MARZANO
- ☐ 226. MIKE MARSHALL
- ☐ 253. MIKE GREENWELL
- ☐ 271. JEFF GRAY
- ☐ 297. TOM BRUNANSKY
- ☐ 309. ROGER CLEMENS
- ☐ 324. GREG HARRIS
- ☐ 354. JEFF REARDON
- ☐ 394. DANNY DARWIN
- ☐ 426. MATT YOUNG
- ☐ 459. PHIL PLANTIER
- ☐ 500. JACK CLARK
- ☐ 505. TONY PENA
- ☐ 543. MO VAUGHN
- ☐ 588. TOM BOLTON

CALIFORNIA ANGELS

- ☐ 2. WALLY JOYNER
- ☐ 27. MARK LANGSTON
- ☐ 59. DICK SCHOFIELD
- ☐ 81. CHUCK FINLEY
- ☐ 98. BRYAN HARVEY
- ☐ 124. JIM ABBOTT
- ☐ 144. LUIS POLONIA
- ☐ 166. LANCE PARRISH
- ☐ 175. BERT BLYLEVEN
- ☐ 198. JACK HOWELL
- ☐ 211. DANTE BICHETTE
- ☐ 228. MIKE FETTERS
- ☐ 241. KENT ANDERSON
- ☐ 263. DAVE WINFIELD
- ☐ 293. LEE STEVENS
- ☐ 313. KIRK MCCASKILL
- ☐ 353. GARY GAETTI
- ☐ 457. JUNIOR FELIX
- ☐ 507. LUIS SOJO
- ☐ 542. JEFF ROBINSON
- ☐ 563. DAVE GALLAGHER
- ☐ 591. JOHN ORTON

CHICAGO CUBS

- ☐ 3. SHAWON DUNSTON
- ☐ 28. DAMON BERRYHILL
- ☐ 44. LANCE DICKSON
- ☐ 73. DERRICK MAY
- ☐ 94. LUIS SALAZAR
- ☐ 109. MIKE BIELECKI
- ☐ 126. GREG MADDUX
- ☐ 162. JEROME WALTON
- ☐ 181. DWIGHT SMITH
- ☐ 197. MIKE HARKEY
- ☐ 213. HECTOR VILLANUEVA
- ☐ 230. RYNE SANDBERG
- ☐ 247. JOE GIRARDI
- ☐ 261. MITCH WILLIAMS
- ☐ 290. MARK GRACE
- ☐ 310. ANDRE DAWSON
- ☐ 345. DAVE SMITH
- ☐ 407. CHUCK MCELROY
- ☐ 433. DANNY JACKSON
- ☐ 504. GEORGE BELL
- ☐ 521. SHAWN BOSKIE
- ☐ 586. PAUL ASSENMACHER
- ☐ 596. GARY SCOTT

CHICAGO WHITE SOX

- ☐ 6. SAMMY SOSA
- ☐ 30. SCOTT FLETCHER

☐ 57. FRANK THOMAS
☐ 70. OZZIE GUILLEN
☐ 87. JACK MCDOWELL
☐ 102. RON KARKOVICE
☐ 129. WAYNE EDWARDS
☐ 147. ALEX FERNANDEZ
☐ 180. CARLTON FISK
☐ 199. LANCE JOHNSON
☐ 214. DAN PASQUA
☐ 232. MELIDO PEREZ
☐ 256. BOBBY THIGPEN
☐ 274. ROBIN VENTURA
☐ 311. SCOTT RADINSKY
☐ 382. MATT MERULLO
☐ 488. CORY SNYDER
☐ 523. TIM RAINES
☐ 559. CRAIG GREBECK
☐ 579. CHARLIE HOUGH

CINCINNATI REDS

☐ 11. JOSE RIJO
☐ 37. ERIC DAVIS
☐ 68. JOE OLIVER
☐ 92. BARRY LARKIN
☐ 113. TODD BENZINGER
☐ 131. ROB DIBBLE
☐ 148. BILL DORAN
☐ 165. CHRIS SABO
☐ 187. GLENN BRAGGS
☐ 218. PAUL O'NEILL
☐ 235. TOM BROWNING
☐ 251. MARIANO DUNCAN
☐ 275. RANDY MYERS
☐ 305. NORM CHARLTON
☐ 339. HAL MORRIS
☐ 371. BILLY HATCHER
☐ 396. TIM LAYANA
☐ 510. JACK ARMSTRONG
☐ 534. JEFF REED
☐ 546. HERM WINNINGHAM
☐ 575. CHRIS HAMMOND
☐ 587. DAN WILSON

CLEVELAND INDIANS

☐ 25. JERRY BROWNE
☐ 61. SANDY ALOMAR
☐ 115. CARLOS BAERGA
☐ 145. DOUG JONES
☐ 185. JOHN FARRELL
☐ 238. FELIX FERMIN
☐ 286. BROOK JACOBY
☐ 322. JESSE OROSCO
☐ 328. ERIC KING
☐ 336. STEVE OLIN
☐ 392. ALEX COLE
☐ 405. TOM CANDIOTTI
☐ 422. CHRIS JAMES
☐ 428. GREG SWINDELL
☐ 465. ALBERT BELLE
☐ 472. CHARLES NAGY
☐ 483. EFRAIN VALDEZ
☐ 492. MARK LEWIS
☐ 561. JOEL SKINNER
☐ 572. KEVIN WICKANDER
☐ 582. JEFF MANTO
☐ 593. TURNER WARD

DETROIT TIGERS

☐ 23. CHET LEMON
☐ 41. TONY PHILLIPS
☐ 63. ALAN TRAMMELL
☐ 101. LOU WHITAKER
☐ 158. FRANK TANANA
☐ 186. CECIL FIELDER
☐ 287. MIKE HENNEMAN
☐ 315. WALT TERRELL
☐ 352. STEVE SEARCY
☐ 355. TRAVIS FRYMAN
☐ 364. LLOYD MOSEBY
☐ 386. DAVE BERGMAN
☐ 412. MICKEY TETTLETON
☐ 429. SCOTT ALDRED
☐ 445. JOHN CERUTTI
☐ 456. MARK SALAS
☐ 470. MILT CUYLER
☐ 539. ROB DEER
☐ 574. JERRY DON GLEATON

HOUSTON ASTROS

☐ 16. ERIC YELDING
☐ 52. KARL RHODES
☐ 74. XAVIER HERNANDEZ
☐ 107. RAFAEL RAMIREZ
☐ 137. DAVE ROHDE
☐ 176. CRAIG BIGGIO
☐ 209. MIKE SCOTT
☐ 229. ERIC ANTHONY
☐ 262. JIM DESHAIES
☐ 281. MIKE SIMMS
☐ 320. MARK PORTUGAL
☐ 343. PETE HARNISCH
☐ 376. STEVE FINLEY
☐ 388. JEFF BAGWELL
☐ 414. KEN OBERKFELL
☐ 434. CASEY CANDAELE
☐ 440. CARL NICHOLS
☐ 476. ANDUJAR CEDENO
☐ 494. GERALD YOUNG
☐ 520. KEN CAMINITI
☐ 576. LUIS GONZALEZ
☐ 584. MARK DAVIDSON

KANSAS CITY ROYALS

☐ 15. MIKE MACFARLANE
☐ 38. BRET SABERHAGEN
☐ 67. STORM DAVIS
☐ 88. KEVIN SEITZER
☐ 111. TERRY SHUMPERT
☐ 136. MARK DAVIS
☐ 159. GEORGE BRETT
☐ 189. KURT STILLWELL
☐ 224. BO JACKSON
☐ 240. MARK GUBICZA
☐ 254. TOM GORDON
☐ 272. DANNY TARTABULL
☐ 306. GARY THURMAN
☐ 344. KIRK GIBSON
☐ 369. JEFF MONTGOMERY
☐ 373. JIM EISENREICH
☐ 400. MIKE BODDICKER
☐ 418. BRENT MAYNE
☐ 451. LUIS AQUINO
☐ 478. BRIAN MCRAE
☐ 501. KEVIN APPIER
☐ 578. JEFF CONINE

LOS ANGELES DODGERS

☐ 19. MIKE SCIOSCIA
☐ 39. STAN JAVIER
☐ 65. LENNY HARRIS
☐ 90. FERNANDO VALENZUELA
☐ 116. KAL DANIELS
☐ 152. TIM BELCHER
☐ 177. EDDIE MURRAY
☐ 208. JOSE GONZALEZ
☐ 244. OREL HERSHISER
☐ 278. JAY HOWELL
☐ 301. DARRYL STRAWBERRY
☐ 340. JOSE OFFERMAN
☐ 375. TIM CREWS
☐ 389. BRETT BUTLER
☐ 411. DENNIS COOK
☐ 424. GARY CARTER
☐ 449. BOB OJEDA
☐ 480. CHRIS GWYNN
☐ 495. JUAN SAMUEL
☐ 516. RAMON MARTINEZ
☐ 524. ALFREDO GRIFFIN
☐ 538. JOHN CANDELARIA
☐ 541. MIKE SHARPERSON
☐ 550. JEFF HAMILTON
☐ 554. GREG SMITH
☐ 562. MIKE MORGAN

MILWAUKEE BREWERS

☐ 7. DAN PLESAC
☐ 46. TEDDY HIGUERA
☐ 75. DAVE PARKER
☐ 95. GARY SHEFFIELD
☐ 112. CHUCK CRIM
☐ 135. GREG VAUGHN
☐ 164. CHRIS BOSIO
☐ 183. JIM GANTNER

☐ 206. B.J. SURHOFF
☐ 234. DARRYL HAMILTON
☐ 245. PAUL MOLITOR
☐ 269. GREG BROCK
☐ 296. RON ROBINSON
☐ 321. TIM MCINTOSH
☐ 350. CANDY MALDONADO
☐ 360. BILLY SPIERS
☐ 398. BILL WEGMAN
☐ 436. JAIME NAVARRO
☐ 461. FRANKLIN STUBBS
☐ 509. ROBIN YOUNT
☐ 545. WILLIE RANDOLPH
☐ 553. RICK DEMPSEY
☐ 595. ED NUNEZ

MINNESOTA TWINS

☐ 13. JUNIOR ORTIZ
☐ 34. DAVE WEST
☐ 54. DANNY GLADDEN
☐ 76. RICK AGUILERA
☐ 110. KIRBY PUCKETT
☐ 132. GENE LARKIN
☐ 146. AL NEWMAN
☐ 161. KEVIN TAPANI
☐ 188. ALLAN ANDERSON
☐ 219. MARK GUTHRIE
☐ 248. KENT HRBEK
☐ 259. SHANE MACK
☐ 277. GREG GAGNE
☐ 318. PEDRO MUNOZ
☐ 329. CHILI DAVIS
☐ 338. SCOTT LEIUS
☐ 370. RICH GARCES
☐ 397. TERRY LEACH
☐ 408. PAUL SORRENTO
☐ 447. JACK MORRIS
☐ 491. GARY WAYNE
☐ 522. MIKE PAGLIARULO
☐ 531. STEVE BEDROSIAN
☐ 548. CHUCK KNOBLAUCH
☐ 560. SCOTT ERICKSON
☐ 589. BRIAN HARPER

MONTREAL EXPOS

☐ 8. MARQUIS GRISSOM
☐ 31. MOISES ALOU
☐ 69. ANDRES GALARRAGA
☐ 93. LARRY WALKER
☐ 114. BRIAN BARNES
☐ 128. MIKE FITZGERALD
☐ 142. DENNIS BOYD
☐ 174. OTIS NIXON
☐ 194. DELINO DESHIELDS
☐ 215. GREG COLBRUNN
☐ 236. SPIKE OWEN
☐ 249. BILL SAMPEN
☐ 273. DENNY MARTINEZ
☐ 326. CHRIS NABHOLZ
☐ 346. DAVE MARTINEZ
☐ 383. IVAN CALDERON
☐ 416. NELSON SANTOVENIA
☐ 463. TIM WALLACH
☐ 490. RON HASSEY
☐ 514. TIM BURKE
☐ 551. BARRY JONES

☐ 592. MARK GARDNER

NEW YORK METS

☐ 22. JOHN FRANCO
☐ 35. KEVIN MCREYNOLDS
☐ 43. TIM TEUFEL
☐ 60. RON DARLING
☐ 86. HOWARD JOHNSON
☐ 100. DWIGHT GOODEN
☐ 125. DARYL BOSTON
☐ 149. KEVIN ELSTER
☐ 157. CHARLIE O'BRIEN
☐ 172. MACKEY SASSER
☐ 196. MARK CARREON
☐ 210. DAVE MAGADAN
☐ 225. SID FERNANDEZ
☐ 239. KEITH MILLER
☐ 257. GREGG JEFFERIES
☐ 292. FRANK VIOLA
☐ 325. HUBIE BROOKS
☐ 349. TODD HUNDLEY
☐ 367. DAVID CONE
☐ 458. WALLY WHITEHURST
☐ 498. VINCE COLEMAN
☐ 511. RICK CERONE
☐ 532. TOM HERR
☐ 547. JEFF INNIS
☐ 583. ALEJANDRO PENA

NEW YORK YANKEES

☐ 21. DON MATTINGLY
☐ 40. CHUCK CARY
☐ 64. MATT NOKES
☐ 103. JESSE BARFIELD
☐ 134. STEVE BALBONI
☐ 171. BOB GEREN
☐ 204. STEVE SAX
☐ 242. ALVARO ESPINOZA
☐ 282. KEVIN MAAS
☐ 319. ROBERTO KELLY
☐ 333. MEL HALL
☐ 361. LEE GUETTERMAN
☐ 381. PAT KELLY
☐ 401. STEVE HOWE
☐ 419. STEVE FARR
☐ 423. TIM LEARY
☐ 438. RANDY VELARDE
☐ 442. DEION SANDERS
☐ 466. MIKE WITT
☐ 473. ALAN MILLS
☐ 477. DAVE EILAND
☐ 485. PASCUAL PEREZ
☐ 503. HENSLEY MEULENS
☐ 529. ERIC PLUNK
☐ 536. GREG CADARET
☐ 568. SCOTT KAMIENIECKI
☐ 590. JOHN HABYAN

OAKLAND A'S

☐ 1. DAVE STEWART
☐ 49. WALT WEISS
☐ 79. BOB WELCH
☐ 120. RICKEY HENDERSON
☐ 138. ERIC SHOW
☐ 151. MIKE GALLEGO
☐ 155. JOSE CANSECO
☐ 207. TODD BURNS
☐ 231. CARNEY LANSFORD
☐ 284. DAVE HENDERSON
☐ 303. HAROLD BAINES
☐ 332. DENNIS ECKERSLEY
☐ 359. GENE NELSON
☐ 378. WILLIE WILSON
☐ 399. MARK MCGWIRE
☐ 415. RICK HONEYCUTT
☐ 432. ERNIE RILES
☐ 437. LANCE BLANKENSHIP
☐ 464. MIKE MOORE
☐ 487. ANDY HAWKINS
☐ 518. TERRY STEINBACH
☐ 573. JAMIE QUIRK

PHILADELPHIA PHILLIES

☐ 4. DARREN DAULTON
☐ 36. PAT COMBS
☐ 58. TERRY MULHOLLAND
☐ 71. KEN HOWELL
☐ 89. BRUCE RUFFIN
☐ 104. JOSE DEJESUS
☐ 127. VON HAYES
☐ 150. LEN DYKSTRA
☐ 163. CHARLIE HAYES
☐ 184. DICKIE THON
☐ 192. RICKY JORDAN
☐ 227. JOHN KRUK
☐ 243. DALE MURPHY
☐ 265. RANDY READY
☐ 294. JASON GRIMSLEY
☐ 317. WES CHAMBERLAIN
☐ 368. WALLY BACKMAN
☐ 395. STEVE LAKE
☐ 462. JOE BOEVER
☐ 484. SIL CAMPUSANO
☐ 506. ROGER MCDOWELL
☐ 535. MICKEY MORANDINI
☐ 549. TOMMY GREENE
☐ 581. DARRELL AKERFELDS

PITTSBURGH PIRATES

☐ 14. BOB WALK
☐ 53. NEAL HEATON
☐ 84. JAY BELL
☐ 118. ANDY VAN SLYKE
☐ 139. BOBBY BONILLA
☐ 178. RANDY TOMLIN
☐ 202. DOUG DRABEK
☐ 220. BARRY BONDS
☐ 233. JOSE LIND
☐ 260. ZANE SMITH
☐ 279. MIKE LAVALLIERE
☐ 334. BOB KIPPER
☐ 358. DON SLAUGHT
☐ 385. LLOYD MCCLENDON
☐ 431. BILL LANDRUM
☐ 443. VINCENTE PALACIOS
☐ 448. MITCH WEBSTER
☐ 453. STAN BELINDA
☐ 471. JOHN SMILEY
☐ 486. GARY REDUS
☐ 512. CURT WILKERSON
☐ 528. JEFF KING
☐ 594. BOB PATTERSON

ST. LOUIS CARDINALS

☐ 17. BRYN SMITH
☐ 42. LEE SMITH
☐ 66. MILT THOMPSON
☐ 85. JOE MAGRANE
☐ 121. TIM JONES
☐ 154. OZZIE SMITH
☐ 190. JOSE OQUENDO
☐ 223. TOM PAGNOZZI
☐ 255. TODD ZEILE
☐ 280. REX HUDLER
☐ 314. PEDRO GUERRERO
☐ 366. FELIX JOSE
☐ 379. GERALD PERRY
☐ 402. BERNARD GILKEY
☐ 417. BOB TEWKSBURY
☐ 435. KEN HILL
☐ 439. FRANK DIPINO
☐ 455. JOSE DELEON
☐ 469. SCOTT TERRY
☐ 481. JAMIE MOYER
☐ 499. CRIS CARPENTER
☐ 537. RAY LANKFORD
☐ 566. CRAIG WILSON
☐ 570. JUAN AGOSTO

SAN DIEGO PADRES

☐ 18. BIP ROBERTS
☐ 51. ANDY BENES
☐ 72. GARRY TEMPLETON
☐ 105. BENNY SANTIAGO
☐ 169. DENNIS RASMUSSEN
☐ 205. GREG HARRIS
☐ 246. EDDIE WHITSON
☐ 268. DEREK LILLIQUIST
☐ 291. SHAWN ABNER
☐ 308. TONY GWYNN
☐ 347. ATLEE HAMMAKER
☐ 357. FRED MCGRIFF
☐ 390. LARRY ANDERSEN
☐ 403. THOMAS HOWARD
☐ 420. PHIL STEPHENSON
☐ 450. OSCAR AZOCAR
☐ 468. JERALD CLARK
☐ 475. BRUCE HURST
☐ 493. SCOTT COOLBAUGH
☐ 515. TONY FERNANDEZ
☐ 530. TOM LAMPKIN
☐ 533. CRAIG LEFFERTS
☐ 557. PAUL FARIES
☐ 565. RICH RODRIGUEZ

SAN FRANCISCO GIANTS

☐ 5. WILL CLARK
☐ 29. KEVIN BASS
☐ 45. GREG LITTON
☐ 77. ROBBY THOMPSON
☐ 91. TERRY KENNEDY
☐ 119. JOHN BURKETT
☐ 143. MIKE BENJAMIN
☐ 167. DON ROBINSON
☐ 182. SCOTT GARRELTS
☐ 193. KELLY DOWNS
☐ 212. TREVOR WILSON
☐ 250. KEVIN MITCHELL
☐ 267. JOSE URIBE
☐ 295. MATT WILLIAMS
☐ 302. BUD BLACK
☐ 307. MIKE FELDER
☐ 335. WILLIE MCGEE
☐ 356. DAVE RIGHETTI
☐ 362. DARREN LEWIS
☐ 479. MIKE LACOSS
☐ 567. JEFF BRANTLEY
☐ 569. STEVE DECKER

SEATTLE MARINERS

☐ 9. ERIK HANSON
☐ 32. DAVE VALLE
☐ 47. EDGAR MARTINEZ
☐ 82. ALVIN DAVIS
☐ 106. BRIAN HOLMAN
☐ 130. GREG BRILEY
☐ 153. JAY BUHNER
☐ 179. TINO MARTINEZ
☐ 195. OMAR VIZQUEL
☐ 217. HAROLD REYNOLDS
☐ 252. SCOTT BRADLEY
☐ 270. KEN GRIFFEY, JR.
☐ 285. PETE O'BRIEN
☐ 342. KEN GRIFFEY, SR.
☐ 372. BILL SWIFT
☐ 409. RANDY JOHNSON
☐ 446. TRACY JONES
☐ 508. MIKE SCHOOLER
☐ 525. HENRY COTTO
☐ 556. KEITH COMSTOCK
☐ 577. RUSS SWAN
☐ 597. SCOTT BANKHEAD

TEXAS RANGERS

☐ 10. GENO PETRALLI
☐ 56. KEVIN BROWN
☐ 78. PETE INCAVIGLIA
☐ 96. BOBBY WITT

1991 Stadium Club

- ☐ 123. RUBEN SIERRA
- ☐ 141. GARY PETTIS
- ☐ 160. JEFF HUSON
- ☐ 173. JULIO FRANCO
- ☐ 200. NOLAN RYAN
- ☐ 216. MIKE JEFFCOAT
- ☐ 237. JUAN GONZALEZ
- ☐ 258. KENNY ROGERS
- ☐ 276. JACK DAUGHERTY
- ☐ 323. GARY GREEN
- ☐ 337. STEVE BUECHELE
- ☐ 348. BRIAN DOWNING
- ☐ 384. SCOTT CHIAMPARINO
- ☐ 421. JEFF RUSSELL
- ☐ 474. JOHN RUSSELL
- ☐ 502. RAFAEL PALMEIRO
- ☐ 526. MIKE STANLEY
- ☐ 540. BRAD ARNSBERG
- ☐ 580. JEFF KUNKEL

TORONTO BLUE JAYS

- ☐ 24. TOM HENKE
- ☐ 62. DAVE STEIB
- ☐ 99. MOOKIE WILSON
- ☐ 133. DAVID WELLS
- ☐ 168. MANNY LEE
- ☐ 221. JIMMY KEY
- ☐ 266. PAT BORDERS
- ☐ 289. GREG MYERS
- ☐ 304. ROBERTO ALOMAR
- ☐ 331. KELLY GRUBER
- ☐ 363. DUANE WARD
- ☐ 374. ROB DUCEY
- ☐ 387. ED SPRAGUE
- ☐ 406. RENE GONZALES
- ☐ 425. GLENALLEN HILL
- ☐ 444. DEVON WHITE
- ☐ 452. MARK WHITEN
- ☐ 482. JOHN OLERUD
- ☐ 496. WILLIE FRASER
- ☐ 513. JOE CARTER
- ☐ 552. KEN DAYLEY
- ☐ 564. TODD STOTTLEMYRE
- ☐ 585. BOB MACDONALD

1992 STADIUM CLUB (900) 2 1/2" X 3 1/2"

ATLANTA BRAVES

- ☐ 15. DEION SANDERS
- ☐ 44. JUAN BERENGUER
- ☐ 60. STEVE AVERY
- ☐ 82. JEFF TREADWAY
- ☐ 105. RAFAEL BELLIARD
- ☐ 128. MIKE HEATH
- ☐ 147. KENT MERCKER
- ☐ 168. JEFF BLAUSER
- ☐ 182. DAVID JUSTICE
- ☐ 217. MARK WOHLERS
- ☐ 244. TOMMY GREGG
- ☐ 264. MARVIN FREEMAN
- ☐ 282. LONNIE SMITH
- ☐ 316. MARK LEMKE
- ☐ 344. MIKE STANTON
- ☐ 366. CHARLIE LEIBRANDT
- ☐ 395. TOM GLAVINE
- ☐ 432. BRIAN HUNTER
- ☐ 459. JOHN SMOLTZ
- ☐ 478. SID BREAM
- ☐ 497. NICK ESASKY
- ☐ 510. TERRY PENDLETON
- ☐ 551. KEITH MITCHELL
- ☐ 632. PETE SMITH
- ☐ 656. MIEK BIELECKI
- ☐ 675. GREG OLSON
- ☐ 699. JEFF MANTO
- ☐ 730. RON GANT
- ☐ 763. ARMANDO REYNOSO
- ☐ 797. FRANCISCO CABRERA
- ☐ 833. ALEJANDRO PENA
- ☐ 856. DAMON BERRYHILL
- ☐ 882. OTIS NIXON

BALTIMORE ORIOLES

- ☐ 1. CAL RIPKEN
- ☐ 30. MIKE FLANAGAN
- ☐ 61. FRANCISCO DE LA ROSA
- ☐ 81. CRAIG WORTHINGTON
- ☐ 104. TIM HULETT
- ☐ 135. JOE ORSULAK
- ☐ 161. CHRIS HOILES
- ☐ 177. MARK WILLIAMSON
- ☐ 199. MIKE DEVEREAUX
- ☐ 225. MIKE MUSSINA
- ☐ 242. LUIS MERCEDES
- ☐ 269. SAM HORN
- ☐ 293. GREGG OLSON
- ☐ 303. BRADY ANDERSON
- ☐ 331. BOB MILACKI
- ☐ 358. TODD FROHWIRTH
- ☐ 383. JEFF TACKETT
- ☐ 412. JIM POOLE
- ☐ 438. CHITO MARTINEZ
- ☐ 463. DWIGHT EVANS
- ☐ 490. BEN MCDONALD
- ☐ 533. BILLY RIPKEN
- ☐ 557. ANTHONY TELFORD
- ☐ 587. RANDY MILLIGAN
- ☐ 623. MARK PARENT
- ☐ 641. ARTHUR RHODES
- ☐ 664. LEO GOMEZ
- ☐ 700. RICK SUTCLIFFE
- ☐ 728. STORM DAVIS
- ☐ 749. DENNIS RASMUSSEN
- ☐ 783. DAVID SEGUI
- ☐ 808. GLENN DAVIS
- ☐ 835. JUAN BELL
- ☐ 871. ALAN MILLS
- ☐ 888. JOSE MESA

BOSTON RED SOX

- ☐ 25. CARLOS QUINTANA
- ☐ 49. GREG HARRIS
- ☐ 80. ROGER CLEMENS
- ☐ 115. KEVIN MORTON
- ☐ 144. TONY FOSSAS
- ☐ 186. JACK CLARK
- ☐ 222. JEFF GRAY
- ☐ 255. LUIS RIVERA
- ☐ 287. JOHN DOPSON
- ☐ 325. MO VAUGHN
- ☐ 352. WAYNE HOUSIE
- ☐ 377. SCOTT COOPER
- ☐ 399. ELLIS BURKS
- ☐ 424. JOHN MARZANO
- ☐ 446. MIKE GREENWELL
- ☐ 464. TOM BRUNANSKY
- ☐ 481. JEFF PLYMPTON
- ☐ 504. JOSIAS MANZANILLO
- ☐ 520. WADE BOGGS
- ☐ 539. DANNY DARWIN
- ☐ 561. TOM BOLTON
- ☐ 577. JEFFREY MCNEELY
- ☐ 636. JOE HESKETH
- ☐ 657. JEFF REARDON
- ☐ 682. MATT YOUNG
- ☐ 706. TONY PENA
- ☐ 732. MIKE GARDINER
- ☐ 760. PHIL PLANTIER
- ☐ 785. FRANK VIOLA
- ☐ 816. JODY REED
- ☐ 839. BOB ZUPCIC
- ☐ 854. TIM NAEHRING
- ☐ 883. HERM WINNINGHAM

CALIFORNIA ANGELS

- ☐ 16. DICK SCHOFIELD
- ☐ 43. SCOTT LEWIS
- ☐ 79. BOBBY ROSE
- ☐ 94. LANCE PARRISH
- ☐ 122. WALLY JOYNER
- ☐ 141. JUNIOR FELIX
- ☐ 167. SCOTT BAILES
- ☐ 197. SHAWN ABNER
- ☐ 210. JIM ABBOTT
- ☐ 233. RON TINGLEY
- ☐ 263. JOHN ORTON
- ☐ 281. LEE STEVENS
- ☐ 315. CHUCK FINLEY
- ☐ 373. LUIS SOJO
- ☐ 410. BRYAN HARVEY
- ☐ 436. GARY GAETTI
- ☐ 458. GARY DISARCINA
- ☐ 492. CHRIS BEASLEY
- ☐ 528. LUIS POLONIA
- ☐ 562. CLIFF YOUNG
- ☐ 579. JOE GRAHE
- ☐ 617. ALVIN DAVIS
- ☐ 646. JULIO VALERA
- ☐ 670. MARK LANGSTON
- ☐ 693. JOHN FARRELL
- ☐ 704. RENE GONZALES
- ☐ 729. DON ROBINSON
- ☐ 754. HUBIE BROOKS
- ☐ 774. JOSE GONZALEZ
- ☐ 796. JOHN MORRIS
- ☐ 823. CHUCK CRIM
- ☐ 844. MIKE FITZGERALD
- ☐ 857. MARK EICHHORN
- ☐ 880. VON HAYES

CHICAGO CUBS

- ☐ 21. LUIS SALAZAR
- ☐ 50. RYNE SANDBERG
- ☐ 65. FRANK CASTILLO
- ☐ 88. LES LANCASTER
- ☐ 112. BOB SCANLAN
- ☐ 132. JOE GIRARDI
- ☐ 148. DERRICK MAY
- ☐ 174. MARK GRACE
- ☐ 196. DWIGHT SMITH
- ☐ 219. DAVE SMITH
- ☐ 252. DOUG DASCENZO
- ☐ 284. SHAWN BOSKIE
- ☐ 308. REY SANCHEZ
- ☐ 334. CED LANDRUM
- ☐ 359. JOSE VIZCAINO
- ☐ 382. HEATHCLIFF SLOCUMB
- ☐ 406. DANNY JACKSON
- ☐ 421. JEROME WALTON
- ☐ 442. ERIK PAPPAS
- ☐ 474. CHUCK MCELROY
- ☐ 501. MIKE HARKEY
- ☐ 525. GEORGE BELL
- ☐ 540. SHAWON DUNSTON
- ☐ 564. CHICO WALKER
- ☐ 628. SAMMY SOSA
- ☐ 643. RICK WILKINS

☐ 665. GREG MADDUX
☐ 708. GARY SCOTT
☐ 714. JIM BULLINGER
☐ 731. PAUL ASSENMACHER
☐ 756. JEFF ROBINSON
☐ 787. MIKE MORGAN
☐ 810. ANDRE DAWSON
☐ 836. LANCE DICKSON
☐ 858. HECTOR VILLANUEVA

CHICAGO WHITE SOX

☐ 20. OZZIE GUILLEN
☐ 52. JACK MCDOWELL
☐ 70. ROBIN VENTURA
☐ 116. SCOTT FLETCHER
☐ 145. CRAIG GREBECK
☐ 184. DONN PALL
☐ 224. BOBBY THIGPEN
☐ 257. RON KARKOVICE
☐ 289. KEN PATTERSON
☐ 301. FRANK THOMAS
☐ 329. MIKE HUFF
☐ 356. ROBERTO HERNANDEZ
☐ 381. JEFF CARTER
☐ 404. MATT MERULLO
☐ 426. ROCK RAINES
☐ 444. LANCE JOHNSON
☐ 467. ALEX FERNANDEZ
☐ 480. CARLTON FISK
☐ 512. WARREN NEWSON
☐ 535. JOEY CORA
☐ 554. STEVE WAPNICK
☐ 586. GREG HIBBARD
☐ 611. ESTEBAN BELTRE
☐ 635. STEVE SAX
☐ 654. BO JACKSON
☐ 674. WAYNE EDWARDS
☐ 688. KIRK MCCASKILL
☐ 744. BRIAN DRAHMAN
☐ 761. WILSON ALVAREZ
☐ 778. TERRY LEACH
☐ 794. DAN PASQUA
☐ 840. GEORGE BELL
☐ 866. RAMON GARCIA
☐ 894. CHARLIE HOUGH

CINCINNATI REDS

☐ 13. GLENN BRAGGS
☐ 38. BILL DORAN
☐ 63. HAL MORRIS
☐ 100. BARRY LARKIN
☐ 151. LUIS QUINONES
☐ 175. PAUL O'NEILL
☐ 205. HERM WINNINGHAM
☐ 247. KIP GROSS
☐ 273. CHRIS SABO
☐ 306. JOE OLIVER
☐ 336. MO SANFORD
☐ 363. BILLY HATCHER
☐ 394. FREDDIE BENAVIDES
☐ 419. TIM LAYANA
☐ 452. GINO MINUTELLI
☐ 487. JEFF REED
☐ 530. NORM CHARLTON
☐ 559. GLENN SUTKO
☐ 584. ROB DIBBLE
☐ 613. TROY AFENIR
☐ 624. TOM BROWNING
☐ 645. BIP ROBERTS
☐ 673. GREG SWINDELL
☐ 701. SCOTT BANKHEAD
☐ 716. JEFF BRANSON
☐ 723. DAVE MARTINEZ
☐ 733. MILT HILL
☐ 751. CHRIS HAMMOND
☐ 777. SCOTT RUSKIN
☐ 800. JOSE RIJO
☐ 826. STEVE FOSTER
☐ 842. TIM BELCHER
☐ 865. REGGIE SANDERS
☐ 892. DWAYNE HENRY

CLEVELAND INDIANS

☐ 23. CHRIS JAMES
☐ 51. MARK WHITEN
☐ 76. SHAWN HILLEGAS
☐ 102. FELIX FERMIN
☐ 125. ERIC KING
☐ 143. CARLOS BAERGA
☐ 169. STEVE OLIN
☐ 193. MARK LEWIS
☐ 220. ALBERT BELLE
☐ 251. JERRY BROWNE
☐ 278. JOEL SKINNER
☐ 305. MIKE ALDRETE
☐ 335. REGGIE JEFFERSON
☐ 360. JIM THOME
☐ 389. CHARLES NAGY
☐ 413. GLENALLEN HILL
☐ 437. ALEX COLE
☐ 454. TONY PEREZCHICA
☐ 461. DAVE OTTO
☐ 482. CARLOS MARTINEZ
☐ 503. BRUCE EGLOFF
☐ 534. ROD NICHOLS
☐ 556. LUIS LOPEZ
☐ 612. MIKE CHRISTOPHER
☐ 644. SCOTT SCUDDER
☐ 668. BRAD ARNSBERG
☐ 695. KENNY LOFTON
☐ 707. PAUL SORRENTO
☐ 727. JUNIOR ORTIZ
☐ 740. SANDY ALOMAR
☐ 753. DAVE ROHDE
☐ 773. DENIS BOUCHER
☐ 791. JACK ARMSTRONG
☐ 812. TED POWER
☐ 828. BROOK JACOBY
☐ 843. JEFF SHAW
☐ 864. DEREK LILLIQUIST
☐ 887. DENNIS COOK

DETROIT TIGERS

☐ 5. MILT CUYLER
☐ 34. MIKE HENNEMAN
☐ 59. TRAVIS FRYMAN
☐ 71. JOHN CERUTTI
☐ 92. ROB DEER
☐ 119. BILL GULLICKSON
☐ 139. WALT TERRELL
☐ 171. DAVE BERGMAN
☐ 195. MICKEY TETTLETON
☐ 223. PAUL GIBSON
☐ 238. ANDY ALLANSON
☐ 250. CECIL FIELDER
☐ 276. DAN GAKELER
☐ 317. SCOTT LIVINGSTONE
☐ 337. KEVIN RITZ
☐ 362. DAVE HAAS
☐ 384. JOHN KIELY
☐ 416. FRANK TANANA
☐ 441. MIKE MUNOZ
☐ 465. SHAWN HARE
☐ 488. TONY PHILLIPS
☐ 508. RICH ROWLAND
☐ 526. JEFF KAISER
☐ 550. LOU WHITAKER
☐ 585. SKEETER BARNES
☐ 638. ERIC KING
☐ 678. MARK CARREON
☐ 762. SCOTT ALDRED
☐ 801. DANNY GLADDEN
☐ 850. ALAN TRAMMELL
☐ 889. MARK LEITER

HOUSTON ASTROS

☐ 2. ERIC YELDING
☐ 29. STEVE FINLEY
☐ 53. JIMMY JONES
☐ 68. AL OSUNA
☐ 101. RYAN BOWEN
☐ 126. MARK PORTUGAL
☐ 142. KEN CAMINITI
☐ 166. ANDY MOTA
☐ 178. CASEY CANDAELE
☐ 200. CRAIG BIGGIO
☐ 227. LUIS GONZALEZ
☐ 241. KARL RHODES
☐ 262. MIKE SIMMS
☐ 279. CURT SCHILLING
☐ 310. ANDUJAR CEDENO
☐ 330. JEFF BAGWELL
☐ 355. GERALD YOUNG
☐ 391. PETE HARNISCH
☐ 451. RAFAEL RAMIREZ
☐ 479. JEFF JUDEN
☐ 509. SCOTT SERVAIS
☐ 546. TONY EUSEBIO
☐ 575. ERIC ANTHONY
☐ 616. DOUG JONES
☐ 639. JOE BOEVER
☐ 663. ROB MURPHY
☐ 698. CHRIS JONES
☐ 736. XAVIER HERNANDEZ
☐ 742. BUTCH HENRY
☐ 769. RICK PARKER
☐ 775. JUAN GUERRERO
☐ 790. EDDIE TAUBENSEE
☐ 813. WILLIE BLAIR
☐ 837. DARRYL KILE
☐ 874. PETE INCAVIGLIA

KANSAS CITY ROYALS

☐ 12. JEFF MONTGOMERY
☐ 39. MIKE BODDICKER
☐ 74. MIKE MACFARLANE
☐ 96. TIM SPEHR
☐ 114. SEAN BERRY
☐ 131. GARY THURMAN
☐ 150. GEORGE BRETT
☐ 165. TERRY SHUMPERT
☐ 191. DANNY TARTABULL
☐ 212. MARK DAVIS
☐ 229. BRENT MAYNE
☐ 245. DAVID HOWARD
☐ 270. BRIAN MCRAE
☐ 285. KEVIN SEITZER
☐ 323. HECTOR WAGNER
☐ 345. JOEL JOHNSTON
☐ 365. LUIS AQUINO
☐ 388. TOM GORDON
☐ 409. JIM EISENREICH
☐ 428. HARVEY PULLIAM
☐ 448. MIKE MAGNANTE
☐ 473. ARCHIE CORBIN
☐ 495. KIRK GIBSON
☐ 523. KEVIN APPIER
☐ 542. MARK GUBICZA
☐ 553. STU COLE
☐ 569. CARLOS MALDONADO
☐ 619. KEVIN MCREYNOLDS
☐ 629. RICO ROSSY
☐ 642. BOB MELVIN
☐ 683. JEFF CONINE
☐ 710. WALLY JOYNER
☐ 737. GREGG JEFFERIES
☐ 768. RUSTY MEACHAM
☐ 786. KEITH MILLER
☐ 815. CHRIS GWYNN
☐ 849. CURT WILKERSON
☐ 877. NEAL HEATON

LOS ANGELES DODGERS

☐ 11. JUAN SAMUEL
☐ 36. DAVE HANSEN
☐ 72. KEVIN GROSS
☐ 93. MIKE SHARPERSON
☐ 121. LENNY HARRIS
☐ 140. MIKE SCIOSCIA
☐ 164. JOHN CANDELARIA
☐ 187. STAN JAVIER
☐ 207. RAMON MARTINEZ
☐ 236. ERIC KARROS
☐ 268. HENRY RODRIGUEZ
☐ 292. BRETT BUTLER
☐ 322. TOM GOODWIN
☐ 339. JEFF HAMILTON
☐ 349. TIM CREWS
☐ 378. JOSE OFFERMAN
☐ 403. MITCH WEBSTER
☐ 431. OREL HERSHISER
☐ 457. JAY HOWELL
☐ 483. JIM GOTT
☐ 514. KAL DANIELS
☐ 537. BOB OJEDA
☐ 560. DARRYL STRAWBERRY
☐ 626. STEVE WILSON
☐ 660. ERIC DAVIS
☐ 713. RUDY SEANEZ
☐ 764. TODD BENZINGER
☐ 804. ROGER MCDOWELL
☐ 852. MIKE WALKDEN
☐ 875. TOM CANDIOTTI

MILWAUKEE BREWERS

- ☐ 7. DANTE BICHETTE
- ☐ 32. MARK LEE
- ☐ 87. JAMIE NAVARRO
- ☐ 117. B.J. SURHOFF
- ☐ 123. KEVIN BROWN
- ☐ 155. DARREN HOLMES
- ☐ 189. FRANKLIN STUBBS
- ☐ 208. TEDDY HIGUERA
- ☐ 230. PAUL MOLITOR
- ☐ 253. DARRYL HAMILTON
- ☐ 274. JIM OLANDER
- ☐ 309. GARY SHEFFIELD
- ☐ 327. CAL ELDRED
- ☐ 354. CHRIS GEORGE
- ☐ 379. BILLY SPIERS
- ☐ 411. JIM AUSTIN
- ☐ 450. ROBIN YOUNT
- ☐ 477. TIM MCINTOSH
- ☐ 502. JIM GANTNER
- ☐ 532. DAN PLESAC
- ☐ 578. CHRIS BOSIO
- ☐ 615. DOUG HENRY
- ☐ 666. GREG VAUGHN
- ☐ 696. MIKE FETTERS
- ☐ 739. RON ROBINSON
- ☐ 757. PAT LISTACH
- ☐ 758. BILL WEGMAN
- ☐ 776. ED NUNEZ
- ☐ 792. SCOTT FLETCHER
- ☐ 820. KEVIN SEITZER
- ☐ 838. EFRAIN VALDEZ
- ☐ 867. BRUCE RUFFIN

MINNESOTA TWINS

- ☐ 18. CHILI DAVIS
- ☐ 47. SHANE MACK
- ☐ 66. GENE LARKIN
- ☐ 84. RANDY BUSH
- ☐ 110. SCOTT ERICKSON
- ☐ 152. MIKE PAGLIARULO
- ☐ 183. LENNY WEBSTER
- ☐ 204. ALLAN ANDERSON
- ☐ 235. KENT HRBEK
- ☐ 261. GARY WAYNE
- ☐ 296. BRIAN HARPER
- ☐ 321. WILLIE BANKS
- ☐ 350. SCOTT LEIUS
- ☐ 376. GREG GAGNE
- ☐ 398. DAVE WEST
- ☐ 433. KEVIN TAPANI
- ☐ 456. MARK GUTHRIE
- ☐ 500. KIRBY PUCKETT
- ☐ 515. JARVIS BROWN
- ☐ 541. PEDRO MUNOZ
- ☐ 567. PAUL ABBOTT
- ☐ 625. JOHN SMILEY
- ☐ 662. TOM EDENS
- ☐ 702. DONNIE HILL
- ☐ 726. RICK AGUILERA
- ☐ 752. BOB KIPPER
- ☐ 779. CARL WILLIS
- ☐ 830. CHUCK KNOBLAUCH
- ☐ 861. BILL KRUEGER

MONTREAL EXPOS

- ☐ 19. TOM FOLEY
- ☐ 42. MARK GARDNER
- ☐ 73. IVAN CALDERON
- ☐ 120. MARQUIS GRISSOM
- ☐ 173. GILBERTO REYES
- ☐ 221. SPIKE OWEN
- ☐ 256. LARRY WALKER
- ☐ 277. BILL SAMPEN
- ☐ 318. CHRIS NABHOLZ
- ☐ 340. TIM WALLACH
- ☐ 367. HOWARD FARMER
- ☐ 385. JOHN VANDER WAL
- ☐ 408. DOUG PIATT
- ☐ 427. BRET BARBERIE
- ☐ 449. CHRIS HANEY
- ☐ 469. JEFF FASSERO
- ☐ 489. MEL ROJAS
- ☐ 505. DELINO DESHIELDS
- ☐ 519. MOISES ALOU
- ☐ 549. BRIAN BARNES
- ☐ 572. STEVE FREY
- ☐ 659. ERIC BULLOCK
- ☐ 672. BILL LANDRUM
- ☐ 705. RICK CERONE
- ☐ 735. KEN HILL
- ☐ 759. JOHN WETTELAND
- ☐ 789. SERGIO VALDEZ
- ☐ 802. ARCHI CIANFROCCO
- ☐ 824. DARREN REED
- ☐ 845. GARY CARTER
- ☐ 860. DENNY MARTINEZ
- ☐ 885. DAVE WAINHOUSE

NEW YORK METS

- ☐ 17. DAVID CONE
- ☐ 40. VINCE COLEMAN
- ☐ 85. ANTHONY YOUNG
- ☐ 118. DAVE MAGADAN
- ☐ 154. CHARLIE O'BRIEN
- ☐ 201. KEVIN ELSTER
- ☐ 249. MACKEY SASSER
- ☐ 290. TODD HUNDLEY
- ☐ 304. JULIO VALERA
- ☐ 328. DARYL BOSTON
- ☐ 353. CHRIS DONNELS
- ☐ 392. TIM BURKE
- ☐ 430. HOWARD JOHNSON
- ☐ 455. DOC GOODEN
- ☐ 476. WALLY WHITEHURST
- ☐ 521. PETE SCHOUREK
- ☐ 543. KEVIN BAEZ
- ☐ 565. JOHN FRANCO
- ☐ 633. JEFF MCKNIGHT
- ☐ 655. SID FERNANDEZ
- ☐ 676. BILL PULSIPHER
- ☐ 694. PAUL GIBSON
- ☐ 709. JUNIOR NOBOA
- ☐ 738. DICK SCHOFIELD
- ☐ 755. BRET SABERHAGEN
- ☐ 780. BOBBY BONILLA
- ☐ 795. EDDIE MURRAY
- ☐ 811. BILL PECOTA
- ☐ 817. MARK DEWEY
- ☐ 829. RODNEY MCCRAY
- ☐ 841. DAVE GALLAGHER
- ☐ 847. ERIC HILLMAN
- ☐ 863. JEFF INNIS
- ☐ 878. TERREL HANSEN
- ☐ 890. WILLIE RANDOLPH

NEW YORK YANKEES

- ☐ 9. MEL HALL
- ☐ 35. KEVIN MAAS
- ☐ 64. HENSLEY MEULENS
- ☐ 89. PAT KELLY
- ☐ 111. MATT NOKES
- ☐ 133. DAVE EILAND
- ☐ 157. RICH MONTELEONE
- ☐ 176. GREG CADARET
- ☐ 198. JIM LEYRITZ
- ☐ 214. JESSE BARFIELD
- ☐ 237. RANDY VELARDE
- ☐ 260. BERNIE WILLIAMS
- ☐ 291. TIM LEARY
- ☐ 319. MIKE HUMPHREYS
- ☐ 346. LEE GUETTERMAN
- ☐ 393. ROBERTO KELLY
- ☐ 420. DON MATTINGLY
- ☐ 471. JEFF JOHNSON
- ☐ 496. SCOTT SANDERSON
- ☐ 527. ALVARO ESPINOZA
- ☐ 576. JOHN HABYAN
- ☐ 627. MIKE GALLEGO
- ☐ 649. SCOTT KAMIENIECKI
- ☐ 667. WADE TAYLOR
- ☐ 690. DANNY TARTABULL
- ☐ 711. CHARLIE HAYES
- ☐ 725. ANDY STANKIEWICZ
- ☐ 741. MIKE STANLEY
- ☐ 767. ALLAN ANDERSON
- ☐ 793. STEVE FARR
- ☐ 809. TOREY LOVULLO
- ☐ 827. STEVE HOWE
- ☐ 848. MIKE WITT
- ☐ 869. MELIDO PEREZ
- ☐ 884. DION JAMES

OAKLAND A'S

- ☐ 22. TERRY STEINBACH
- ☐ 45. CARNEY LANSFORD
- ☐ 62. SCOTT HEMOND
- ☐ 83. JAMIE QUIRK
- ☐ 106. MIKE GALLEGO
- ☐ 129. TODD VAN POPPEL
- ☐ 158. REGGIE HARRIS
- ☐ 190. DENNIS ECKERSLEY
- ☐ 218. DAVE HENDERSON
- ☐ 248. WALT WEISS
- ☐ 272. MIKE BORDICK
- ☐ 326. JOE KLINK
- ☐ 343. WILLIE WILSON
- ☐ 370. JOSE CANSECO
- ☐ 390. DAVE STEWART
- ☐ 414. GENE NELSON
- ☐ 435. RON WITMEYER
- ☐ 475. MARK MCGWIRE
- ☐ 498. JOHNNY GUZMAN
- ☐ 518. STEVE CHITREN
- ☐ 536. HAROLD BAINES
- ☐ 563. BRUCE WALTON
- ☐ 581. RICK HONEYCUTT
- ☐ 637. VINCE HORSMAN
- ☐ 647. KEVIN CAMPBELL
- ☐ 651. BOB WELCH
- ☐ 669. MIKE MOORE
- ☐ 681. JOHN BRISCOE
- ☐ 685. RON DARLING
- ☐ 719. RICH GOSSAGE
- ☐ 750. RICKEY HENDERSON
- ☐ 782. JOE SLUSARSKI
- ☐ 806. KIRK DRESSENDORFER
- ☐ 834. JEFF PARRETT
- ☐ 862. MIKE KINGERY
- ☐ 897. LANCE BLANKENSHIP

PHILADELPHIA PHILLIES

- ☐ 4. WALLY BACKMAN
- ☐ 27. TOMMY GREENE
- ☐ 54. STEVE LAKE
- ☐ 98. TERRY MULHOLLAND
- ☐ 124. BRAULIO CASTILLO
- ☐ 156. JOE BOEVER
- ☐ 188. RICKY JORDAN
- ☐ 209. JOHN KRUK
- ☐ 246. DAVE HOLLINS
- ☐ 280. DALE MURPHY
- ☐ 324. WALLY RITCHIE
- ☐ 351. DANNY COX
- ☐ 369. MICKEY MORANDINI
- ☐ 396. WES CHAMBERLAIN
- ☐ 418. JASON GRIMSLEY
- ☐ 443. PAT COMBS
- ☐ 470. LEN DYKSTRA
- ☐ 499. MITCH WILLIAMS
- ☐ 529. DARREN DAULTON
- ☐ 558. TIM MAUSER
- ☐ 583. CLIFF BRANTLEY
- ☐ 614. MARIANO DUNCAN
- ☐ 648. STEVE SEARCY
- ☐ 671. BARRY JONES
- ☐ 687. DALE SVEUM
- ☐ 717. ANDY ASHBY
- ☐ 788. KIM BATISTE
- ☐ 818. KYLE ABBOTT

- ☐ 870. RUBEN AMARO
- ☐ 893. JIM LINDEMAN

PITTSBURGH PIRATES

- ☐ 24. JEFF KING
- ☐ 46. CURT WILKERSON
- ☐ 75. STAN BELINDA
- ☐ 95. CECIL ESPY
- ☐ 134. ORLANDO MERCED
- ☐ 170. DOUG DRABEK
- ☐ 216. MIKE LAVALLIERE
- ☐ 232. ANDY VAN SLYKE
- ☐ 266. ROGER MASON
- ☐ 288. SCOTT BULLETT
- ☐ 302. LLOYD MCCLENDON
- ☐ 332. TOM PRINCE
- ☐ 357. NEAL HEATON
- ☐ 380. JOHN SMILEY
- ☐ 405. STEVE BUECHELE
- ☐ 434. RICK REED
- ☐ 486. VICENTE PALACIOS
- ☐ 507. JAY BELL
- ☐ 524. GARY REDUS
- ☐ 545. DON SLAUGHT
- ☐ 568. GARY VARSHO
- ☐ 620. BARRY BONDS
- ☐ 661. RANDY TOMLIN
- ☐ 697. ROSARIO RODRIGUEZ
- ☐ 724. DENNY NEAGLE
- ☐ 746. BOB WALK
- ☐ 784. KIRK GIBSON
- ☐ 807. ZANE SMITH
- ☐ 831. JOHN WEHNER
- ☐ 859. JOSE LIND
- ☐ 876. BOB PATTERSON

ST. LOUIS CARDINALS

- ☐ 8. RAY LANKFORD
- ☐ 33. WILLIE FRASER
- ☐ 58. RICH GEDMAN
- ☐ 67. JOSE DELEON
- ☐ 103. LUIS ALICEA
- ☐ 138. KEN HILL
- ☐ 162. TOM PAGNOZZI
- ☐ 180. LEE SMITH
- ☐ 206. TIM JONES
- ☐ 234. BERNARD GILKEY
- ☐ 258. BOB TEWKSBURY
- ☐ 286. STAN ROYER
- ☐ 320. PEDRO GUERRERO
- ☐ 338. GERALD PERRY
- ☐ 361. CRAIG WILSON
- ☐ 368. BRYN SMITH
- ☐ 386. OMAR OLIVARES
- ☐ 407. FELIX JOSE
- ☐ 429. CRIS CARPENTER
- ☐ 447. MILT THOMPSON
- ☐ 466. GERONIMO PENA
- ☐ 484. BOB MCCLURE
- ☐ 506. RHEAL CORMIER
- ☐ 522. SCOTT TERRY
- ☐ 544. TODD ZEILE
- ☐ 571. JOSE OQUENDO
- ☐ 622. JOE MAGRANE
- ☐ 652. ANDRES GALARRAGA
- ☐ 680. OZZIE SMITH
- ☐ 703. TODD WORRELL
- ☐ 722. PAUL KILGUS
- ☐ 748. DON PRYBYLINSKI
- ☐ 771. JEFF BALLARD
- ☐ 798. MIKE PEREZ
- ☐ 822. TIM SHERRILL
- ☐ 851. REX HUDLER
- ☐ 886. FRANK DIPINO

SAN DIEGO PADRES

- ☐ 26. MIKE MADDUX
- ☐ 48. BIP ROBERTS
- ☐ 78. JIM VATCHER
- ☐ 91. LARRY ANDERSEN
- ☐ 109. RICKY BONES
- ☐ 130. BENNY SANTIAGO
- ☐ 149. JERALD CLARK
- ☐ 172. EDDIE WHITSON
- ☐ 203. TONY FERNANDEZ
- ☐ 226. DARRIN JACKSON
- ☐ 254. DANN BILARDELLO
- ☐ 275. GREG HARRIS
- ☐ 312. BRUCE HURST
- ☐ 342. JOSE MELENDEZ
- ☐ 374. CRAIG SHIPLEY
- ☐ 401. THOMAS HOWARD
- ☐ 423. ANDY BENES
- ☐ 453. TOM LAMPKIN
- ☐ 485. TIM TEUFEL
- ☐ 513. PAUL FARIES
- ☐ 552. OSCAR AZOCAR
- ☐ 580. FRED MCGRIFF
- ☐ 618. CRAIG LEFFERTS
- ☐ 650. KURT STILLWELL
- ☐ 684. PHIL STEPHENSON
- ☐ 712. RICH RODRIGUEZ
- ☐ 734. JEREMY HERNANDEZ
- ☐ 766. GARY SHEFFIELD
- ☐ 805. RANDY MYERS
- ☐ 825. TONY GWYNN
- ☐ 853. KEVIN WARD
- ☐ 879. DAVE EILAND
- ☐ 881. TIM SCOTT

SAN FRANCISCO GIANTS

- ☐ 6. KEVIN BASS
- ☐ 31. DARREN LEWIS
- ☐ 55. BUD BLACK
- ☐ 86. TREVOR WILSON
- ☐ 107. DAVE RIGHETTI
- ☐ 136. JOHN BURKETT
- ☐ 160. ROBBY THOMPSON
- ☐ 194. MIKE FELDER
- ☐ 215. KEVIN MITCHELL
- ☐ 239. WILLIE MCGEE
- ☐ 271. KIRT MANWARING
- ☐ 294. JEFF BRANTLEY
- ☐ 314. MIKE BENJAMIN
- ☐ 347. FRANCISCO OLIVERAS
- ☐ 371. JOSE URIBE
- ☐ 397. ERIC GUNDERSON
- ☐ 417. STEVE DECKER
- ☐ 439. GREG LITTON
- ☐ 460. WILL CLARK
- ☐ 491. ANDRES SANTANA
- ☐ 517. KELLY DOWNS
- ☐ 538. MARK LEONARD
- ☐ 566. PAUL MCCLELLAN
- ☐ 582. MATT WILLIAMS
- ☐ 630. ROYCE CLAYTON
- ☐ 653. MIKE JACKSON
- ☐ 686. BRYAN HICKERSON
- ☐ 718. DAVE BURBA
- ☐ 747. CHRIS JAMES
- ☐ 772. CORY SNYDER
- ☐ 799. TED WOOD
- ☐ 832. SCOTT GARRELTS
- ☐ 855. BILL SWIFT
- ☐ 891. CRAIG COLBERT
- ☐ 895. GIL HEREDIA

SEATTLE MARINERS

- ☐ 14. HENRY COTTO
- ☐ 37. ERIK HANSON
- ☐ 56. DAVE VALLE
- ☐ 69. DAVE COCHRANE
- ☐ 90. ALVIN DAVIS
- ☐ 108. JEFF SCHAEFER
- ☐ 127. CALVIN JONES
- ☐ 146. SCOTT BRADLEY
- ☐ 163. OMAR VIZQUEL
- ☐ 181. HAROLD REYNOLDS
- ☐ 192. PETE O'BRIEN
- ☐ 213. JAY BUHNER
- ☐ 228. GREG BRILEY
- ☐ 243. BILL SWIFT
- ☐ 267. EDGAR MARTINEZ
- ☐ 295. BRIAN HOLMAN
- ☐ 313. MIKE SCHOOLER
- ☐ 348. DAVE BURBA
- ☐ 375. SCOTT BANKHEAD
- ☐ 400. KEN GRIFFEY, JR.
- ☐ 425. GENE HARRIS
- ☐ 472. RUSS SWAN
- ☐ 511. RICH DELUCIA
- ☐ 547. ALONZO POWELL
- ☐ 573. TINO MARTINEZ
- ☐ 631. CLAY PARKER
- ☐ 679. PATRICK LENNON
- ☐ 689. RICH AMARAL
- ☐ 720. RANDY JOHNSON
- ☐ 765. KEVIN MITCHELL
- ☐ 814. DAVE FLEMING
- ☐ 872. MATT SINATRO

TEXAS RANGERS

- ☐ 3. GENO PETRALLI
- ☐ 28. JEFF RUSSELL
- ☐ 57. KEVIN REIMER
- ☐ 99. DENNIS BOYD
- ☐ 153. JOSE GUZMAN
- ☐ 185. GERALD ALEXANDER
- ☐ 211. DEAN PALMER
- ☐ 240. JUAN GONZALEZ
- ☐ 265. MIKE JEFFCOAT
- ☐ 297. BRIAN BOHANON
- ☐ 311. KENNY ROGERS
- ☐ 341. JEFF HUSON
- ☐ 364. JOHN BARFIELD
- ☐ 387. RUBEN SIERRA
- ☐ 415. IVAN RODRIGUEZ
- ☐ 440. JULIO FRANCO
- ☐ 462. ROB MAURER
- ☐ 494. BRIAN DOWNING
- ☐ 516. RAFAEL PALMEIRO
- ☐ 548. GARY PETTIS
- ☐ 574. BILL HASELMAN
- ☐ 634. JACK DAUGHERTY
- ☐ 658. WAYNE ROSENTHAL
- ☐ 677. BOBBY WITT
- ☐ 691. DONALD HARRIS
- ☐ 692. DOUG DAVIS
- ☐ 715. JEFF ROBINSON
- ☐ 743. FLOYD BANNISTER
- ☐ 770. NOLAN RYAN
- ☐ 803. MONTY FARISS
- ☐ 821. AL NEWMAN
- ☐ 846. JOHN RUSSELL
- ☐ 868. DICKIE THON
- ☐ 896. SCOTT CHIAMPARINO

TORONTO BLUE JAYS

- ☐ 10. JOE CARTER
- ☐ 41. DEVON WHITE
- ☐ 77. PAT BORDERS
- ☐ 97. DAVE STIEB
- ☐ 113. TOM CANDIOTTI
- ☐ 137. KEN DAYLEY
- ☐ 159. ROBERTO ALOMAR
- ☐ 179. CANDY MALDONADO
- ☐ 202. RANCE MULLINIKS
- ☐ 231. AL LEITER
- ☐ 259. JIMMY KEY
- ☐ 283. MANUEL LEE
- ☐ 307. TODD STOTTLEMYRE
- ☐ 333. PAT TABLER
- ☐ 372. BOB MAC DONALD
- ☐ 402. JUAN GUZMAN
- ☐ 422. ROB DUCEY
- ☐ 445. ED SPRAGUE
- ☐ 468. GREG MYERS
- ☐ 493. MIKE TIMLIN
- ☐ 531. JOHN OLERUD
- ☐ 555. DEREK BELL
- ☐ 570. KELLY GRUBER
- ☐ 621. TURNER WARD
- ☐ 640. JACK MORRIS
- ☐ 721. DAVID WELLS
- ☐ 745. DAVE WINFIELD
- ☐ 781. DUANE WARD
- ☐ 819. TOM HENKE
- ☐ 873. EDDIE ZOSKY

1993 STADIUM CLUB (750) 2 1/2" X 3 1/2"

ATLANTA BRAVES

- ☐ 28. RON GANT
- ☐ 38. MIKE STANTON
- ☐ 58. RAFAEL BELLIARD
- ☐ 89. MELVIN NIEVES
- ☐ 111. KENT MERCKER
- ☐ 130. MARK WOHLERS
- ☐ 151. SID BREAM
- ☐ 161. JEFF REARDON
- ☐ 172. MARK LEMKE
- ☐ 205. ALEJANDRO PENA
- ☐ 237. PETE SMITH
- ☐ 261. DAMON BERRYHILL
- ☐ 309. MARVIN FREEMAN
- ☐ 338. TERRY PENDLETON
- ☐ 371. MARK DAVIS
- ☐ 408. DEION SANDERS
- ☐ 436. JEFF BLAUSER
- ☐ 450. GREG OLSON
- ☐ 463. JOHN SMOLTZ
- ☐ 491. BRIAN HUNTER
- ☐ 541. RYAN KLESKO
- ☐ 626. STEVE AVERY
- ☐ 630. JAVY LOPEZ
- ☐ 638. CHIPPER JONES
- ☐ 650. TOM GLAVINE
- ☐ 660. DAVID JUSTICE
- ☐ 665. GREG MADDUX
- ☐ 678. OTIS NIXON
- ☐ 696. TONY TARASCO
- ☐ 708. STEVE BEDROSIAN

BALTIMORE ORIOLES

- ☐ 14. TIM HULETT
- ☐ 40. CAL RIPKEN
- ☐ 56. MIKE DEVEREAUX
- ☐ 77. MIKE MUSSINA
- ☐ 92. JOE ORSULAK
- ☐ 123. MIKE FLANAGAN
- ☐ 158. RANDY MILLIGAN
- ☐ 174. STORM DAVIS
- ☐ 186. JEFF TACKETT
- ☐ 246. RICK SUTCLIFFE
- ☐ 259. BEN MCDONALD
- ☐ 326. GLENN DAVIS
- ☐ 345. CHRIS HOILES
- ☐ 362. CHITO MARTINEZ
- ☐ 391. LUIS MERCEDES
- ☐ 418. GREGG OLSON
- ☐ 445. TODD FROHWIRTH
- ☐ 479. DAVID SEGUI
- ☐ 507. BRADY ANDERSON
- ☐ 536. LEO GOMEZ
- ☐ 560. ARTHUR RHODES
- ☐ 613. MARK WILLIAMSON
- ☐ 643. ALAN MILLS
- ☐ 661. FERNANDO VALENZUELA
- ☐ 666. HAROLD BAINES
- ☐ 668. HAROLD REYNOLDS
- ☐ 715. SHERMAN OBANDO
- ☐ 742. KAMON BUFORD

BOSTON RED SOX

- ☐ 20. JACK CLARK
- ☐ 41. JOHN DOPSON
- ☐ 73. JOHN MARZANO
- ☐ 86. MIKE GREENWELL
- ☐ 107. JOE HESKETH
- ☐ 134. WADE BOGGS
- ☐ 147. FRANK VIOLA
- ☐ 164. TONY PENA
- ☐ 187. ELLIS BURKS
- ☐ 220. ROGER CLEMENS
- ☐ 247. TONY FOSSAS
- ☐ 282. PHIL PLANTIER
- ☐ 315. GREG HARRIS
- ☐ 334. MO VAUGHN
- ☐ 368. SCOTT COOPER
- ☐ 428. MATT YOUNG
- ☐ 484. DANNY DARWIN
- ☐ 508. JOHN VALENTIN
- ☐ 533. LUIS RIVERA
- ☐ 563. BOB ZUPCIC
- ☐ 605. CARLOS QUINTANA
- ☐ 623. SCOTT FLETCHER
- ☐ 635. JEFF RUSSELL
- ☐ 647. IVAN CALDERON
- ☐ 655. ANDRE DAWSON

CALIFORNIA ANGELS

- ☐ 6. DAMION EASLEY
- ☐ 27. LUIS SOJO
- ☐ 69. ROB DUCEY
- ☐ 100. LUIS POLONIA
- ☐ 121. RENE GONZALES
- ☐ 169. RON TINGLEY
- ☐ 196. GARY DISARCINA
- ☐ 219. LEE STEVENS
- ☐ 231. TIM FORTUGNO
- ☐ 249. TIM SALMON
- ☐ 262. JOE GRAHE
- ☐ 301. CHUCK FINLEY
- ☐ 327. CHUCK CRIM
- ☐ 355. MARK LANGSTON
- ☐ 386. JULIO VALERA
- ☐ 407. MIKE BUTCHER
- ☐ 459. JOHN ORTON
- ☐ 490. GREG MYERS
- ☐ 512. GARY GAETTI
- ☐ 543. CHAD CURTIS
- ☐ 611. CHILI DAVIS
- ☐ 679. SCOTT SANDERSON
- ☐ 681. TROY PERCIVAL
- ☐ 719. J.T. SNOW
- ☐ 736. RUSS SPRINGER

CHICAGO CUBS

- ☐ 2. GREG MADDUX
- ☐ 36. REY SANCHEZ
- ☐ 68. JOSE VIZCAINO
- ☐ 109. DERRICK MAY
- ☐ 118. JIM BULLINGER
- ☐ 132. DOUG STRANGE
- ☐ 162. KEN PATTERSON
- ☐ 203. ANDRE DAWSON
- ☐ 228. RICK WILKINS
- ☐ 278. DWIGHT SMITH
- ☐ 285. MIKE MORGAN
- ☐ 332. PAUL ASSENMACHER
- ☐ 346. FRANK CASTILLO
- ☐ 366. RYNE SANDBERG
- ☐ 393. SHAWON DUNSTON
- ☐ 419. MARK GRACE
- ☐ 444. BOB SCANLAN
- ☐ 472. CHUCK MCELROY
- ☐ 494. STEVE BUECHELE
- ☐ 531. SAMMY SOSA
- ☐ 549. LUIS SALAZAR
- ☐ 583. SHAWN BOSKIE
- ☐ 606. GREG HIBBARD
- ☐ 622. WILLIE WILSON
- ☐ 648. JOSE GUZMAN
- ☐ 656. MIKE HARKEY
- ☐ 667. RANDY MYERS
- ☐ 669. CANDY MALDONADO

CHICAGO WHITE SOX

- ☐ 21. ROBERTO HERNANDEZ
- ☐ 43. TIM RAINES
- ☐ 54. JOEY CORA
- ☐ 75. JACK MCDOWELL
- ☐ 94. DAN PASQUA
- ☐ 136. CRAIG GREBECK
- ☐ 166. KIRK MCCASKILL
- ☐ 181. WILSON ALVEREZ
- ☐ 200. FRANK THOMAS
- ☐ 221. CARLTON FISK
- ☐ 240. DONN PALL
- ☐ 275. SCOTT RADINSKY
- ☐ 330. GEORGE BELL
- ☐ 359. LANCE JOHNSON
- ☐ 375. ESTEBAN BELTRE
- ☐ 387. ROBIN VENTURA
- ☐ 403. SHAWN ABNER
- ☐ 427. RON KARKOVICE
- ☐ 453. SHAWN JETER
- ☐ 482. STEVE SAX
- ☐ 495. BO JACKSON
- ☐ 517. OZZIE GUILLEN
- ☐ 552. ALEX FERNANDEZ
- ☐ 575. BOBBY THIGPEN
- ☐ 607. ELLIS BURKS
- ☐ 641. DAVE STIEB

CINCINNATI REDS

- ☐ 9. TIM BELCHER
- ☐ 30. BIP ROBERTS
- ☐ 64. RICK WRONA
- ☐ 96. JOE OLIVER
- ☐ 145. SCOTT BANKHEAD
- ☐ 165. GREG SWINDELL
- ☐ 188. JEFF BRANSON
- ☐ 199. SCOTT RUSKIN
- ☐ 209. CHRIS HAMMOND
- ☐ 233. JOSE RIJO
- ☐ 265. TIM PUGH
- ☐ 286. CHRIS SABO
- ☐ 369. ROB DIBBLE
- ☐ 390. TIM COSTO
- ☐ 415. BARRY LARKIN
- ☐ 471. REGGIE SANDERS
- ☐ 534. HAL MORRIS
- ☐ 577. DWAYNE HENRY
- ☐ 602. JEFF REARDON
- ☐ 632. BOBBY KELLY
- ☐ 662. DAN WILSON
- ☐ 694. KEVIN MITCHELL
- ☐ 704. WILLIE GREENE

CLEVELAND INDIANS

- ☐ 8. JIM THOME
- ☐ 35. WAYNE KIRBY
- ☐ 61. CARLOS BAERGA
- ☐ 82. TED POWER
- ☐ 102. ALBERT BELLE
- ☐ 139. FELIX FERMIN
- ☐ 153. DENNIS COOK
- ☐ 194. PAUL SORRENTO
- ☐ 243. SCOTT SCUDDER
- ☐ 255. CARLOS MARTINEZ
- ☐ 277. KENNY LOFTON
- ☐ 308. MIKE CHRISTOPHER
- ☐ 337. MARK LEWIS

- ☐ 352. MARK WHITEN
- ☐ 379. ALAN EMBREE
- ☐ 400. SANDY ALOMAR
- ☐ 425. REGGIE JEFFERSON
- ☐ 441. DEREK LILLIQUIST
- ☐ 468. JESSE LEVIS
- ☐ 486. ERIC PLUNK
- ☐ 515. THOMAS HOWARD
- ☐ 551. CHARLES NAGY
- ☐ 576. GLENALLEN HILL
- ☐ 721. MIKE BIELECKI

COLORADO ROCKIES

- ☐ 311. BUTCH HENRY
- ☐ 367. BRAD AUSMUS
- ☐ 406. ROBERTO MEJIA
- ☐ 414. JEFF PARRETT
- ☐ 454. ANDRES GALARRAGA
- ☐ 456. FREDDIE BENAVIDES
- ☐ 458. ALEX COLE
- ☐ 498. DARYL BOSTON
- ☐ 506. DARREN HOLMES
- ☐ 513. JOHN BURKE
- ☐ 526. ERIC YOUNG
- ☐ 547. VINNY CASTILLA
- ☐ 573. SCOTT ALDRED
- ☐ 578. CALVIN JONES
- ☐ 616. DANTE BICHETTE
- ☐ 620. JOE GIRARDI
- ☐ 652. ARMANDO REYNOSO
- ☐ 671. JERALD CLARK
- ☐ 674. STEVE REED
- ☐ 700. ANDY ASHBY
- ☐ 718. DAVID NIED
- ☐ 730. JIM TATUM
- ☐ 743. CHARLIE HAYES

DETROIT TIGERS

- ☐ 5. TONY PHILLIPS
- ☐ 31. MICKEY TETTLETON
- ☐ 65. KURT KNUDSEN
- ☐ 116. MARK LEITER
- ☐ 135. LOU WHITAKER
- ☐ 156. MILT CUYLER
- ☐ 191. DANNY GLADDEN
- ☐ 212. JOHN KIELY
- ☐ 223. WALT TERRELL
- ☐ 248. MIKE MUNOZ
- ☐ 267. FRANK TANANA
- ☐ 328. SCOTT LIVINGSTONE
- ☐ 357. ROB DEER
- ☐ 389. SKEETER BARNES
- ☐ 416. ALAN TRAMMELL
- ☐ 448. TRAVIS FRYMAN
- ☐ 480. MIKE HENNEMAN
- ☐ 503. CECIL FIELDER
- ☐ 519. RICH ROWLAND
- ☐ 530. RICO BROGNA
- ☐ 574. BILL GULLICKSON
- ☐ 673. KIRK GIBSON
- ☐ 685. GREG GOHR
- ☐ 693. MIKE MOORE

FLORIDA MARLINS

- ☐ 319. BENNY SANTIAGO
- ☐ 322. RAMON MARTINEZ
- ☐ 340. JEFF CONINE
- ☐ 350. RYAN BOWEN
- ☐ 370. WALT WEISS
- ☐ 437. MIKE MYERS
- ☐ 451. TREVOR HOFFMAN
- ☐ 452. DAVE MAGADAN
- ☐ 457. JUNIOR FELIX
- ☐ 481. BRET BARBERIE
- ☐ 516. DARRELL WHITMORE
- ☐ 535. MONTY FARISS
- ☐ 554. ORESTES DESTRADE
- ☐ 564. CHUCK CARR
- ☐ 567. JACK ARMSTRONG
- ☐ 584. SCOTT POSE
- ☐ 604. BRYAN HARVEY
- ☐ 610. CHARLIE HOUGH
- ☐ 619. RICHIE LEWIS
- ☐ 683. JIM CONVERSE
- ☐ 692. STEVE DECKER
- ☐ 706. CRIS CARPENTER
- ☐ 720. NIGEL WILSON
- ☐ 734. JOHN JOHNSTONE
- ☐ 737. ROB NATAL
- ☐ 741. ALEX ARIAS

HOUSTON ASTROS

- ☐ 16. JUAN GUERRERO
- ☐ 47. PETE INCAVIGLIA
- ☐ 70. CASEY CANDAELE
- ☐ 110. PETE HARNISCH
- ☐ 141. ERIC ANTHONY
- ☐ 183. CRAIG BIGGIO
- ☐ 207. ANDUJAR CEDENO
- ☐ 236. AL OSUNA
- ☐ 250. ROB MURPHY
- ☐ 271. XAVIER HERNANDEZ
- ☐ 302. LUIS GONZALEZ
- ☐ 329. EDDIE TAUBENSEE
- ☐ 363. SCOTT SERVAIS
- ☐ 384. JEFF BAGWELL
- ☐ 411. DOUG JONES
- ☐ 426. MARK PORTUGAL
- ☐ 464. KEN CAMINITI
- ☐ 488. SCOOTER TUCKER
- ☐ 518. DARRYL KILE
- ☐ 556. STEVE FINLEY
- ☐ 608. GREG SWINDELL
- ☐ 672. DOUG DRABEK
- ☐ 698. JEFF JUDEN
- ☐ 714. BRIAN WILLIAMS

KANSAS CITY ROYALS

- ☐ 12. MIKE MAGNANTE
- ☐ 25. BRENT MAYNE
- ☐ 33. BRIAN MCRAE
- ☐ 52. GARY THURMAN
- ☐ 84. STEVE SHIFFLETT
- ☐ 106. RICO ROSSY
- ☐ 125. JEFF MONTGOMERY
- ☐ 177. CURT WILKERSON
- ☐ 192. MIKE BODDICKER
- ☐ 211. HIPOLITO PICHARDO
- ☐ 224. JIM EISENREICH
- ☐ 348. KEVIN MCREYNOLDS
- ☐ 374. KEVIN APPIER
- ☐ 401. KEITH MILLER
- ☐ 424. GEORGE BRETT
- ☐ 439. RUSTY MEACHAM
- ☐ 470. MIKE MACFARLANE
- ☐ 505. KEVIN KOSLOFSKI
- ☐ 523. TOM GORDON
- ☐ 537. WALLY JOYNER
- ☐ 555. MARK GUBICZA
- ☐ 570. JOE VITIELLO
- ☐ 631. GREG GAGNE
- ☐ 653. FELIX JOSE
- ☐ 663. MARK GARDNER
- ☐ 695. PHIL HIATT
- ☐ 703. DAVID CONE
- ☐ 729. JOSE LIND

LOS ANGELES DODGERS

- ☐ 7. KIP GROSS
- ☐ 46. MIKE SCIOSCIA
- ☐ 71. RAMON MARTINEZ
- ☐ 98. LENNY HARRIS
- ☐ 129. JOSE OFFERMAN
- ☐ 149. CARLOS HERNANDEZ
- ☐ 197. RAFAEL BOURNIGAL
- ☐ 216. BRETT BUTLER
- ☐ 226. HENRY RODRIGUEZ
- ☐ 251. ROGER MCDOWELL
- ☐ 263. DAVE HANSEN
- ☐ 307. MIKE SHARPERSON
- ☐ 325. TOM CANDIOTTI
- ☐ 342. BILLY ASHLEY
- ☐ 365. PEDRO MARTINEZ
- ☐ 381. ERIC DAVIS
- ☐ 398. DARRYL STRAWBERRY
- ☐ 446. TOM GOODWIN
- ☐ 473. KEVIN GROSS
- ☐ 487. JIM GOTT
- ☐ 511. PEDRO ASTACIO
- ☐ 528. ERIC KARROS
- ☐ 544. OREL HERSHISER
- ☐ 585. MIKE PIAZZA
- ☐ 612. JODY REED
- ☐ 686. TIM WALLACH
- ☐ 728. TODD WORRELL
- ☐ 735. MITCH WEBSTER

MILWAUKEE BREWERS

- ☐ 24. DAN PLESAC
- ☐ 37. JESSE OROSCO
- ☐ 57. KEVIN SEITZER
- ☐ 79. CHRIS BOSIO
- ☐ 112. SCOTT FLETCHER
- ☐ 122. GREG VAUGHN
- ☐ 168. FRANKLIN STUBBS
- ☐ 173. ROBIN YOUNT
- ☐ 225. RICKY BONES
- ☐ 270. BRUCE RUFFIN
- ☐ 303. DARRYL HAMILTON
- ☐ 324. BILL WEGMAN
- ☐ 377. WILLIAM SUERO
- ☐ 417. MARK KIEFER
- ☐ 432. PAT LISTACH
- ☐ 475. CAL ELDRED
- ☐ 502. TIM MCINTOSH
- ☐ 521. DOUG HENRY
- ☐ 566. BILLY SPIERS
- ☐ 587. JAMES AUSTIN
- ☐ 621. JAIME NAVARRO
- ☐ 625. TOM BRUNANSKY
- ☐ 633. MIKE FETTERS
- ☐ 687. MATT MIESKE
- ☐ 699. KEVIN REIMER
- ☐ 701. JOHN JAHA
- ☐ 709. DAVE NILSSON
- ☐ 711. B.J. SURHOFF

MINNESOTA TWINS

- ☐ 10. GARY WAYNE
- ☐ 42. GENE LARKIN
- ☐ 74. DEREK PARKS
- ☐ 95. BRIAN HARPER
- ☐ 117. PEDRO MUNOZ
- ☐ 146. JEFF REBOULET
- ☐ 170. WILLIE BANKS
- ☐ 182. CARL WILLIS
- ☐ 190. JOHN SMILEY
- ☐ 222. CHILI DAVIS
- ☐ 254. SCOTT LEIUS
- ☐ 283. KIRBY PUCKETT
- ☐ 314. CHUCK KNOBLAUCH
- ☐ 336. MIKE TROMBLEY
- ☐ 354. RICK AGUILERA
- ☐ 380. LENNY WEBSTER
- ☐ 397. J.T. BRUETT
- ☐ 420. SHANE MACK
- ☐ 443. SCOTT ERICKSON
- ☐ 492. KEVIN TAPANI
- ☐ 525. KENT HRBEK
- ☐ 550. MARK GUTHRIE
- ☐ 569. DAVID MCCARTY
- ☐ 609. DAVE WINFIELD
- ☐ 645. RANDY BUSH
- ☐ 740. PAT MAHOMES

MONTREAL EXPOS

- ☐ 18. TIM LAKER
- ☐ 78. DELINO DESHIELDS
- ☐ 101. KENT BOTTENFIELD
- ☐ 119. IVAN CALDERON

- ☐ 140. DENNY MARTINEZ
- ☐ 159. MARK GARDNER
- ☐ 171. SERGIO VALDEZ
- ☐ 184. SEAN BERRY
- ☐ 227. KEN HILL
- ☐ 239. MOISES ALOU
- ☐ 272. DARRIN FLETCHER
- ☐ 306. JONATHAN HURST
- ☐ 320. LARRY WALKER
- ☐ 344. JOHN WETTELAND
- ☐ 361. WIL CORDERO
- ☐ 388. ARCHI CIANFROCCO
- ☐ 442. JOHN VANDER WAL
- ☐ 469. CHRIS NABHOLZ
- ☐ 500. BRIAN BARNES
- ☐ 522. GREG COLBRUNN
- ☐ 529. MARQUIS GRISSOM
- ☐ 553. MEL ROJAS
- ☐ 691. MIKE LANSING
- ☐ 724. FRANK BOLICK

NEW YORK METS

- ☐ 3. DARYL BOSTON
- ☐ 29. PAUL GIBSON
- ☐ 50. EDDIE MURRAY
- ☐ 72. TODD HUNDLEY
- ☐ 114. CHICO WALKER
- ☐ 128. CHARLIE O'BRIEN
- ☐ 148. BILL PECOTA
- ☐ 163. BOBBY BONILLA
- ☐ 195. VINCE COLEMAN
- ☐ 214. LEE GUETTERMAN
- ☐ 238. PETE SCHOUREK
- ☐ 269. JEFF KENT
- ☐ 316. JOHN FRANCO
- ☐ 335. BRET SABERHAGEN
- ☐ 351. SID FERNANDEZ
- ☐ 404. HOWARD JOHNSON
- ☐ 433. JEFF INNIS
- ☐ 476. DAVE GALLAGHER
- ☐ 514. DOC GOODEN
- ☐ 542. RYAN THOMPSON
- ☐ 582. ANTHONY YOUNG
- ☐ 644. TONY FERNANDEZ
- ☐ 702. TIM BOGAR
- ☐ 732. MIKE DRAPER

NEW YORK YANKEES

- ☐ 11. SAM MILITELLO
- ☐ 32. RANDY VELARDE
- ☐ 53. BOB WICKMAN
- ☐ 85. DANNY TARTABULL
- ☐ 105. ANDY STANKIEWICZ
- ☐ 126. MIKE GALLEGO
- ☐ 155. PAT KELLY
- ☐ 176. STEVE FARR
- ☐ 189. MATT NOKES
- ☐ 234. JIM LEYRITZ
- ☐ 266. DION JAMES
- ☐ 323. MIKE STANLEY
- ☐ 364. BERNIE WILLIAMS
- ☐ 383. JOHN HABYAN
- ☐ 395. KEVIN MAAS
- ☐ 410. SCOTT KAMIENIECKI
- ☐ 465. MELIDO PEREZ
- ☐ 493. RICH MONTELEONE
- ☐ 557. DON MATTINGLY
- ☐ 571. GERALD WILLIAMS
- ☐ 601. WADE BOGGS
- ☐ 615. JIM ABBOTT
- ☐ 639. JIMMY KEY
- ☐ 677. SPIKE OWEN
- ☐ 689. BRIEN TAYLOR
- ☐ 717. PAUL O'NEILL
- ☐ 738. STEVE HOWE

OAKLAND A'S

- ☐ 17. RICH GOSSAGE
- ☐ 48. TODD VAN POPPEL
- ☐ 62. SCOTT BROSIUS
- ☐ 80. MIKE BORDICK
- ☐ 99. JEFF PARRETT
- ☐ 131. ERIC FOX
- ☐ 150. BOBBY WITT
- ☐ 208. TERRY STEINBACH
- ☐ 235. KEVIN CAMPBELL
- ☐ 256. VINCE HORSMAN
- ☐ 284. JOHNNY GUZMAN
- ☐ 305. RON DARLING
- ☐ 349. DAVE HENDERSON
- ☐ 376. JOE SLUSARSKI
- ☐ 413. LANCE BLANKENSHIP
- ☐ 429. TROY NEEL
- ☐ 461. DENNIS ECKERSLEY
- ☐ 478. MARK MCGWIRE
- ☐ 509. JERRY BROWNE
- ☐ 546. BOB WELCH
- ☐ 558. RICKEY HENDERSON
- ☐ 580. RUBEN SIERRA
- ☐ 657. KEVIN SEITZER
- ☐ 733. HENRY MERCEDES

PHILADELPHIA PHILLIES

- ☐ 4. BOB AYRAULT
- ☐ 34. WES CHAMBERLAIN
- ☐ 63. JEFF GROTEWOLD
- ☐ 83. JOHN KRUK
- ☐ 124. MIKE HARTLEY
- ☐ 157. JUAN BELL
- ☐ 180. MITCH WILLIAMS
- ☐ 201. KYLE ABBOTT
- ☐ 229. RICKY JORDAN
- ☐ 253. CLIFF BRANTLEY
- ☐ 276. MARIANO DUNCAN
- ☐ 313. DARREN DAULTON
- ☐ 339. DAVE HOLLINS
- ☐ 360. JOE MILLETTE
- ☐ 385. RUBEN AMARO
- ☐ 422. CURT SCHILLING
- ☐ 449. MICKEY MORANDINI
- ☐ 466. TOM MARSH
- ☐ 477. LEN DYKSTRA
- ☐ 539. MIKE WILLIAMS
- ☐ 559. TOMMY GREENE
- ☐ 572. DALE MURPHY
- ☐ 636. PETE INCAVIGLIA
- ☐ 642. MILT THOMPSON
- ☐ 654. BEN RIVERA
- ☐ 682. KEVIN STOCKER
- ☐ 716. TERRY MULHOLLAND

PITTSBURGH PIRATES

- ☐ 13. TIM WAKEFIELD
- ☐ 51. BARRY BONDS
- ☐ 66. LLOYD MCCLENDON
- ☐ 93. JEFF KING
- ☐ 104. RANDY TOMLIN
- ☐ 127. DON SLAUGHT
- ☐ 138. JAY BELL
- ☐ 167. DOUG DRABEK
- ☐ 241. DENNY NEAGLE
- ☐ 268. STAN BELINDA
- ☐ 317. JOHN WEHNER
- ☐ 343. ZANE SMITH
- ☐ 372. ORLANDO MERCED
- ☐ 394. ANDY VAN SLYKE
- ☐ 421. BOB WALK
- ☐ 447. W. PENNYFEATHER
- ☐ 496. MIKE LAVALLIERE
- ☐ 545. CARLOS GARCIA
- ☐ 579. AL MARTIN
- ☐ 658. LONNIE SMITH
- ☐ 710. PAUL WAGNER
- ☐ 722. KEVIN YOUNG
- ☐ 726. STEVE COOKE

ST. LOUIS CARDINALS

- ☐ 15. RHEAL CORMIER
- ☐ 49. RAY LANKFORD
- ☐ 60. MARK CLARK
- ☐ 88. CRAIG WILSON
- ☐ 113. REX HUDLER
- ☐ 152. TODD ZEILE
- ☐ 178. LUIS ALICEA
- ☐ 202. MIKE PEREZ
- ☐ 215. GERONIMO PENA
- ☐ 230. BERNARD GILKEY
- ☐ 280. TIM JONES
- ☐ 304. BIEN FIGUEROA
- ☐ 341. BOB TEWKSBURY
- ☐ 399. TOM PAGNOZZI
- ☐ 435. BRIAN JORDAN
- ☐ 462. LEE SMITH
- ☐ 489. OMAR OLIVARES
- ☐ 527. ROD BREWER
- ☐ 548. OZZIE SMITH
- ☐ 586. DONOVAN OSBORNE
- ☐ 628. GREGG JEFFERIES
- ☐ 634. OZZIE CANSECO
- ☐ 646. JOE MAGRANE
- ☐ 712. RENE AROCHA

SAN DIEGO PADRES

- ☐ 19. DARRIN JACKSON
- ☐ 44. RANDY MYERS
- ☐ 76. TIM SCOTT
- ☐ 87. JOSE MELENDEZ
- ☐ 103. MIKE MADDUX
- ☐ 137. RICH RODRIGUEZ
- ☐ 175. DAN WALTERS
- ☐ 213. TIM TEUFEL
- ☐ 257. OSCAR AZOCAR
- ☐ 258. CRAIG SHIPLEY
- ☐ 274. BENNY SANTIAGO
- ☐ 312. GREG HARRIS
- ☐ 347. BRUCE HURST
- ☐ 392. JEREMY HERNANDEZ
- ☐ 438. FRANK SEMINARA
- ☐ 510. FRED MCGRIFF
- ☐ 538. TONY GWYNN
- ☐ 568. KURT STILLWELL
- ☐ 581. ANDY BENES
- ☐ 614. PHIL PLANTIER
- ☐ 618. GARY SHEFFIELD
- ☐ 676. RICKY GUTIERREZ
- ☐ 739. DARRELL SHERMAN
- ☐ 744. GUILLERMO VELASQUEZ

SAN FRANCISCO GIANTS

- ☐ 39. ROYCE CLAYTON
- ☐ 81. ROD BECK
- ☐ 91. WILLIE MCGEE
- ☐ 143. DARREN LEWIS
- ☐ 185. TREVOR WILSON
- ☐ 204. BILL SWIFT
- ☐ 217. BRYAN HICKERSON
- ☐ 245. DAVE BURBA
- ☐ 260. JEFF BRANTLEY
- ☐ 287. MATT WILLIAMS
- ☐ 333. STEVE HOSEY
- ☐ 373. MIKE JACKSON
- ☐ 405. MIKE BENJAMIN
- ☐ 412. JOHN BURKETT
- ☐ 431. DAVE RIGHETTI
- ☐ 455. TED WOOD
- ☐ 497. MARK LEONARD
- ☐ 562. WILL CLARK
- ☐ 624. BUD BLACK
- ☐ 640. DAVE MARTINEZ
- ☐ 680. MARK CARREON
- ☐ 684. BARRY BONDS
- ☐ 688. ROBBY THOMPSON
- ☐ 690. KIRT MANWARING

SEATTLE MARINERS

- ☐ 23. HAROLD REYNOLDS
- ☐ 45. CLAY PARKER
- ☐ 67. OMAR VIZQUEL
- ☐ 97. SHANE TURNER
- ☐ 108. DENNIS POWELL
- ☐ 144. MIKE BLOWERS
- ☐ 179. RUSS SWAN
- ☐ 198. MIKE SCHOOLER
- ☐ 252. LANCE PARRISH
- ☐ 264. RICH AMARAL
- ☐ 273. TINO MARTINEZ
- ☐ 310. JAY BUHNER
- ☐ 331. EDGAR MARTINEZ
- ☐ 358. DAVE FLEMING
- ☐ 378. PETE O'BRIEN
- ☐ 402. RICH DELUCIA
- ☐ 423. ERIK HANSON
- ☐ 440. GREG BRILEY
- ☐ 467. JEFF NELSON
- ☐ 483. DAVE VALLE
- ☐ 501. RANDY JOHNSON
- ☐ 532. BRET BOONE
- ☐ 565. HENRY COTTO
- ☐ 659. NORM CHARLTON
- ☐ 675. MIKE FELDER
- ☐ 707. KEN GRIFFEY, JR.

☐ 731. MIKE HAMPTON

TEXAS RANGERS

☐ 22. DEAN PALMER
☐ 55. KENNY ROGERS
☐ 115. RAFAEL PALMEIRO
☐ 133. JEFF FRYE
☐ 154. BRIAN BOHANON
☐ 193. ROGER PAVLIK
☐ 210. TODD BURNS
☐ 232. GENO PETRALLI
☐ 242. DAN PELTIER
☐ 281. JEFF HUSON
☐ 318. DONALD HARRIS
☐ 353. NOLAN RYAN
☐ 396. KEVIN BROWN
☐ 430. HECTOR FAJARDO
☐ 474. MATT WHITESIDE
☐ 499. JOSE CANSECO
☐ 524. IVAN RODRIGUEZ
☐ 540. JUAN GONZALEZ
☐ 603. BILLY RIPKEN
☐ 637. TOM HENKE
☐ 651. JULIO FRANCO
☐ 664. DOUG DASCENZO
☐ 697. BENJI GIL
☐ 705. DAVID HULSE
☐ 713. MANUEL LEE
☐ 723. CHARLIE LEIBRANDT
☐ 725. JON SHAVE

TORONTO BLUE JAYS

☐ 1. PAT BORDERS
☐ 26. PAT HENTGEN
☐ 59. DAVID WELLS
☐ 90. ED SPRAGUE
☐ 120. MIKE TIMLIN
☐ 142. ROBERTO ALOMAR
☐ 160. PAT TABLER
☐ 206. DAVE WINFIELD
☐ 218. RICKY TRLICEK
☐ 244. JUAN GUZMAN
☐ 279. JOE CARTER
☐ 321. RANDY KNORR
☐ 356. JACK MORRIS
☐ 382. DUANE WARD
☐ 409. TODD STOTTLEMYRE
☐ 434. BOB MACDONALD
☐ 460. EDDIE ZOSKY
☐ 485. DEVON WHITE
☐ 504. DEREK BELL
☐ 520. CARLOS DELGADO
☐ 561. ALFREDO GRIFFIN
☐ 617. MARK EICHHORN
☐ 627. PAUL MOLITOR
☐ 629. DAVE STEWART
☐ 649. JOHN OLERUD
☐ 670. AL LEITER
☐ 727. DOMINGO MARTINEZ

1994 STADIUM CLUB (720) 2 1/2" X 3 1/2"

ATLANTA BRAVES

☐ 64. STEVE BEDROSIAN
☐ 79. SID BREAM
☐ 94. DAVID JUSTICE
☐ 106. OTIS NIXON
☐ 123. RON GANT
☐ 148. RYAN KLESKO
☐ 229. JEFF BLAUSER
☐ 233. PEDRO BORBON
☐ 241. GREG MCMICHAEL
☐ 254. STEVE AVERY
☐ 272. TONY TARASCO
☐ 313. TERRY PENDLETON
☐ 360. KENT MERCKER
☐ 402. MARK LEMKE
☐ 405. JOHN SMOLTZ
☐ 426. RAFAEL BELLIARD
☐ 471. MIKE STANTON
☐ 472. DEION SANDERS
☐ 486. BILL PECOTA
☐ 522. MARK WOHLERS
☐ 544. GREG MADDUX
☐ 574. TOM GLAVINE
☐ 602. GREGG OLSON
☐ 638. CHIPPER JONES
☐ 665. FRED MCGRIFF
☐ 703. JAVY LOPEZ

BALTIMORE ORIOLES

☐ 16. HAROLD BAINES
☐ 17. BRAD PENNINGTON
☐ 53. BRADY ANDERSON
☐ 69. FERNANDO VALENZUELA
☐ 86. JOHN O'DONOGHUE
☐ 95. DAVID SEGUI
☐ 129. ARTHUR RHODES
☐ 196. GREGG OLSON
☐ 248. TODD FROHWIRTH
☐ 284. JAMIE MOYER
☐ 342. MARK MCLEMORE
☐ 373. CAL RIPKEN
☐ 413. BEN MCDONALD
☐ 424. MIKE DEVEREAUX
☐ 430. TIM HULETT
☐ 451. CHRIS HOILES
☐ 488. MIKE MUSSINA
☐ 491. JACK VOIGT
☐ 543. LONNIE SMITH
☐ 557. RAFAEL PALMEIRO
☐ 579. SID FERNANDEZ
☐ 605. LEE SMITH
☐ 676. CHRIS SABO
☐ 693. ALAN MILLS

BOSTON RED SOX

☐ 26. TONY FOSSAS
☐ 48. JEFFREY MCNEELY
☐ 71. TONY PENA
☐ 131. TIM NAEHRING
☐ 139. ROB DEER
☐ 172. GREG BLOSSER
☐ 179. AARON SELE
☐ 198. SCOTT FLETCHER
☐ 251. DANNY DARWIN
☐ 290. CARLOS QUINTANA
☐ 371. ANDRE DAWSON
☐ 386. MIKE GREENWELL
☐ 396. SCOTT COOPER
☐ 404. KEN RYAN
☐ 407. GREG HARRIS
☐ 440. MO VAUGHN
☐ 455. JOE HESKETH
☐ 483. JOHN VALENTIN
☐ 569. FRANK VIOLA
☐ 597. OTIS NIXON
☐ 650. ROGER CLEMENS
☐ 678. AARON SELE
☐ 710. JEFF RUSSELL

CALIFORNIA ANGELS

☐ 11. LUIS POLONIA
☐ 36. TIM SALMON
☐ 78. MIKE BUTCHER
☐ 92. CHRIS TURNER
☐ 124. DAMION EASLEY
☐ 173. CHILI DAVIS
☐ 189. EDUARDO PEREZ
☐ 211. CHUCK FINLEY
☐ 213. GARY DISARCINA
☐ 295. CHAD CURTIS
☐ 352. ROD CORREIA
☐ 385. HILLY HATHAWAY
☐ 442. MARK LANGSTON
☐ 447. J.T. SNOW
☐ 468. GREG MYERS
☐ 506. TOREY LOVULLO
☐ 509. JOE MAGRANE
☐ 547. BO JACKSON
☐ 571. BRIAN ANDERSON
☐ 603. JIM EDMONDS
☐ 625. HAROLD REYNOLDS
☐ 641. JOHN DOPSON
☐ 663. MARK LEITER
☐ 685. REX HUDLER

CHICAGO CUBS

☐ 2. RICK WILKINS
☐ 41. MIKE HARKEY
☐ 62. STEVE TRACHSEL
☐ 80. SAMMY SOSA
☐ 89. JOSE VIZCAINO
☐ 104. REY SANCHEZ
☐ 162. RANDY MYERS
☐ 204. STEVE BUECHELE
☐ 256. DAN PLESAC
☐ 287. DERRICK MAY
☐ 304. MIKE MORGAN
☐ 311. WILLIE WILSON
☐ 337. FRANK CASTILLO
☐ 383. KEVIN ROBERSON
☐ 397. RYNE SANDBERG
☐ 403. MARK GRACE
☐ 421. JOSE BAUTISTA
☐ 499. TURK WENDELL
☐ 576. SHAWON DUNSTON
☐ 608. KARL RHODES
☐ 615. JOSE GUZMAN
☐ 692. WILLIE BANKS

CHICAGO WHITE SOX

☐ 24. JACK MCDOWELL
☐ 57. RON KARKOVICE
☐ 100. JOEY CORA
☐ 118. MIKE LAVALLIERE
☐ 167. BO JACKSON
☐ 182. ROBERTO HERNANDEZ
☐ 194. LANCE JOHNSON
☐ 212. JASON BERE
☐ 225. CRAIG GREBECK
☐ 255. TIM BELCHER
☐ 285. FRANK THOMAS
☐ 315. ROBIN VENTURA
☐ 350. TIM RAINES
☐ 375. DAN PASQUA
☐ 389. OZZIE GUILLEN
☐ 434. SCOTT RADINSKY

☐ 462. WILSON ALVAREZ
☐ 466. ROD BOLTON
☐ 482. JEFF SCHWARZ
☐ 551. SCOTT SANDERSON
☐ 583. ALEX FERNANDEZ
☐ 646. PAUL ASSENMACHER
☐ 659. DARRIN JACKSON
☐ 680. JULIO FRANCO
☐ 702. JASON BERE

CINCINNATI REDS

☐ 7. JOE OLIVER
☐ 20. JEFF BRANSON
☐ 56. JERRY SPRADLIN
☐ 119. TIM COSTO
☐ 136. REGGIE SANDERS
☐ 166. JACOB BRUMFIELD
☐ 186. BIP ROBERTS
☐ 202. ROB DIBBLE
☐ 243. TIM PUGH
☐ 363. HAL MORRIS
☐ 372. ROBERTO KELLY
☐ 414. BARRY LARKIN
☐ 422. KEVIN MITCHELL
☐ 433. TOM BROWNING
☐ 476. JOHN ROPER
☐ 487. JOHN SMILEY
☐ 496. THOMAS HOWARD
☐ 503. BRIAN KOELLING
☐ 552. HECTOR CARRASCO
☐ 596. JOSE RIJO
☐ 623. ERIK HANSON
☐ 671. BRET BOONE
☐ 709. JEFF BRANTLEY

CLEVELAND INDIANS

☐ 15. JUNIOR ORTIZ
☐ 30. JEFF TREADWAY
☐ 43. WAYNE KIRBY
☐ 81. FELIX FERMIN
☐ 128. JULIAN TAVAREZ
☐ 144. SANDY ALOMAR
☐ 169. CARLOS BAERGA
☐ 207. MARK CLARK
☐ 219. ALBERT BELLE
☐ 257. JIM THOME
☐ 301. KENNY LOFTON
☐ 320. MANNY RAMIREZ
☐ 380. JERRY DIPOTO
☐ 420. JEREMY HERNANDEZ
☐ 461. ALVARO ESPINOZA
☐ 464. CANDY MALDONADO
☐ 478. CHARLES NAGY
☐ 481. BILL WERTZ
☐ 508. DEREK LILLIQUIST
☐ 556. JACK MORRIS
☐ 572. OMAR VIZQUEL
☐ 593. STEVE FARR
☐ 619. CHRIS NABOLZ
☐ 636. PAUL SORRENTO
☐ 674. EDDIE MURRAY
☐ 682. DENNY MARTINEZ

COLORADO ROCKIES

☐ 21. ROBERTO MEJIA
☐ 72. ERIC YOUNG
☐ 77. LANCE PAINTER
☐ 98. JERALD CLARK
☐ 132. FREDDIE BENAVIDES
☐ 153. DAVID NIED
☐ 185. DANNY SHEAFFER
☐ 244. VINNY CASTILLA
☐ 249. CHARLIE HAYES
☐ 323. JOE GIRARDI
☐ 332. ARMANDO REYNOSO
☐ 348. WILLIE BLAIR
☐ 366. DANTE BICHETTE
☐ 454. ANDRES GALARRAGA
☐ 475. STEVE REED
☐ 492. MIKE MUNOZ
☐ 507. CURTIS LESKANIC
☐ 512. JAYHAWK OWENS
☐ 560. GREG HARRIS
☐ 581. WALT WEISS
☐ 622. ELLIS BURKS
☐ 640. HOWARD JOHNSON
☐ 672. DARREN HOLMES

☐ 701. MARVIN FREEMAN

DETROIT TIGERS

☐ 25. CECIL FIELDER
☐ 50. SKEETER BARNES
☐ 73. CHRIS GOMEZ
☐ 99. MIKE MOORE
☐ 155. DANNY BAUTISTA
☐ 184. JOHN DOHERTY
☐ 192. MICKEY TETTLETON
☐ 209. ERIC DAVIS
☐ 309. TRAVIS FRYMAN
☐ 331. ALAN TRAMMELL
☐ 351. SCOTT LIVINGSTONE
☐ 370. BILL GULLICKSON
☐ 401. MIKE HENNEMAN
☐ 411. CHAD KREUTER
☐ 443. LOU WHITAKER
☐ 458. JOE BOEVER
☐ 474. MIKE GARDINER
☐ 553. TONY PHILLIPS
☐ 582. TIM BELCHER
☐ 617. DAVID WELLS
☐ 660. JUNIOR FELIX
☐ 679. JUAN SAMUEL

FLORIDA MARLINS

☐ 4. GARY SHEFFIELD
☐ 29. CHUCK CARR
☐ 45. ROBB NENN
☐ 68. JOE KLINK
☐ 87. RICK RENTERIA
☐ 143. BENNY SANTIAGO
☐ 160. LUIS AQUINO
☐ 230. ALEX ARIAS
☐ 235. MATIAS CARRILLO
☐ 245. CHARLIE HOUGH
☐ 291. BOB NATAL
☐ 319. MATT TURNER
☐ 345. RYAN BOWEN
☐ 365. DAVE MAGADAN
☐ 367. CHRIS HAMMOND
☐ 387. ORESTES DESTRADE
☐ 406. JEFF CONINE
☐ 415. BRET BARBERIE
☐ 427. RICHIE LEWIS
☐ 452. BRYAN HARVEY
☐ 546. MARK GARDNER
☐ 588. KURT ABBOTT
☐ 606. PAT RAPP
☐ 673. DAVE WEATHERS
☐ 683. JERRY BROWNE

HOUSTON ASTROS

☐ 35. LUIS GONZALEZ
☐ 108. JEFF BAGWELL
☐ 113. GREG SWINDELL
☐ 138. ANDUJAR CEDENO
☐ 150. SCOTT SERVAIS
☐ 168. EDDIE TAUBENSEE
☐ 190. PETE HARNISCH
☐ 205. BRIAN WILLIAMS
☐ 226. TODD JONES
☐ 293. AL OSUNA
☐ 308. STEVE FINLEY
☐ 322. KEN CAMINITI
☐ 327. DARRYL KILE
☐ 334. CHRIS DONNELS
☐ 374. CRAIG BIGGIO
☐ 408. DOUG DRABEK
☐ 555. MIKE FELDER
☐ 558. SHANE REYNOLDS
☐ 575. MITCH WILLIAMS
☐ 590. KEVIN BASS
☐ 614. MIKE HAMPTON
☐ 635. ANDY STANKIEWCZ
☐ 655. SID BREAM
☐ 668. JAMES MOUTON
☐ 690. TONY EUSEBIO

KANSAS CITY ROYALS

☐ 5. GEORGE BRETT
☐ 8. STAN BELINDA
☐ 49. JEFF MONTGOMERY
☐ 135. JOSE LIND
☐ 154. CHRIS HANEY
☐ 159. GREG GAGNE
☐ 197. MARK GUBICZA
☐ 223. HIPOLITO PICHARDO
☐ 250. MIKE MACFARLANE
☐ 292. DAVID CONE
☐ 294. BOB HAMELIN
☐ 298. FELIX JOSE
☐ 333. BRENT MAYNE
☐ 340. KEVIN APPIER
☐ 431. WALLY JOYNER
☐ 485. GARY GAETTI
☐ 490. BILLY BREWER
☐ 520. BRIAN MCRAE
☐ 570. VINCE COLEMAN
☐ 607. MIKE MAGNANTE
☐ 610. RUSTY MEACHAM
☐ 647. HUBIE BROOKS
☐ 689. DAVE HENDERSON
☐ 712. JIM PITTSLEY

LOS ANGELES DODGERS

☐ 13. JODY REED
☐ 32. TOM CANDIOTTI
☐ 38. ROGER MCDOWELL
☐ 121. BRETT BUTLER
☐ 140. MIKE PIAZZA
☐ 145. CARLOS HERNANDEZ
☐ 176. HENRY RODRIGUEZ
☐ 217. TIM WALLACH
☐ 240. ERIC KARROS
☐ 276. RAMON MARTINEZ
☐ 281. KEVIN GROSS
☐ 282. JOSE OFFERMAN
☐ 335. DARRYL STRAWBERRY
☐ 343. PEDRO ASTACIO
☐ 390. RAUL MONDESI
☐ 400. OREL HERSHISER
☐ 463. CORY SNYDER
☐ 500. RAFAEL BOURNIGAL
☐ 521. CHAN HO PARK
☐ 549. DELINO DESHIELDS
☐ 587. DAVE HANSEN
☐ 612. TODD WORRELL
☐ 648. GARY WAYNE
☐ 694. JEFF TREADWAY

MILWAUKEE BREWERS

☐ 1. ROBIN YOUNT
☐ 90. KEVIN SEITZER
☐ 105. JOHN JAHA
☐ 126. MATT MIESKE
☐ 147. TOM LAMPKIN
☐ 188. DARRYL HAMILTON
☐ 215. B.J. SURHOFF
☐ 236. JUAN BELL
☐ 273. TEDDY HIGUERA
☐ 329. CAL ELDRED
☐ 347. TROY O'LEARY
☐ 354. PAT LISTACH
☐ 376. DAVE NILSSON
☐ 378. GREG VAUGHN
☐ 398. RICKY BONES
☐ 456. JOSE VALENTIN
☐ 489. MIKE IGNASIAK
☐ 550. TURNER WARD
☐ 564. RICKY BONES

☐ 592. JAIME NAVARRO
☐ 642. JODY REED
☐ 661. TOM BRUNANSKY
☐ 677. BILLY SPIERS
☐ 699. JEFF CIRILLO
☐ 707. BRIAN HARPER

MINNESOTA TWINS

☐ 9. DENNY HOCKING
☐ 22. PEDRO MUNOZ
☐ 51. SCOTT STAHOVIAK
☐ 117. KEVIN TAPANI
☐ 134. DAVID MCCARTY
☐ 183. JEFF REBOULET
☐ 193. LENNY WEBSTER
☐ 210. PAT MEARES
☐ 224. KENT HRBEK
☐ 275. RICK AGUILERA
☐ 288. DAVE WINFIELD
☐ 359. KIRBY PUCKETT
☐ 416. CHUCK KNOBLAUCH
☐ 429. SHANE MACK
☐ 477. MIKE TROMBLEY
☐ 479. LARRY CASIAN
☐ 484. CARL WILLIS
☐ 501. CHIP HALE
☐ 561. MATT WALBECK
☐ 584. ALEX COLE
☐ 624. PAT MEARES
☐ 637. SCOTT ERICKSON
☐ 670. SCOTT LEIUS
☐ 688. PAT MAHOMES

MONTREAL EXPOS

☐ 14. MEL ROJAS
☐ 31. CHRIS NABHOLZ
☐ 42. DARRIN FLETCHER
☐ 67. SEAN BERRY
☐ 127. CLIFF FLOYD
☐ 141. MOISES ALOU
☐ 161. JOHN VANDER WAL
☐ 187. DENNY MARTINEZ
☐ 280. LARRY WALKER
☐ 302. KIRK RUETER
☐ 379. JEFF FASSERO
☐ 393. WIL CORDERO
☐ 435. RONDELL WHITE
☐ 445. KEN HILL
☐ 446. JOHN WETTELAND
☐ 515. TIM SPEHR
☐ 517. LOU FRAZIER
☐ 545. DENIS BOUCHER
☐ 577. MIKE LANSING
☐ 611. PEDRO MARTINEZ
☐ 649. SEAN BERRY
☐ 664. GIL HEREDIA
☐ 706. MARQUIS GRISSOM

NEW YORK METS

☐ 28. ANTHONY YOUNG
☐ 33. MIKE MADDUX
☐ 59. BOBBY BONILLA
☐ 82. TODD HUNDLEY
☐ 157. DARRIN JACKSON
☐ 170. TIM BOGAR
☐ 201. JEROMY BURNITZ
☐ 220. DOC GOODEN
☐ 247. KEVIN BAEZ
☐ 274. RYAN THOMPSON
☐ 324. JEFF MCKNIGHT
☐ 339. JOHN FRANCO
☐ 362. JEFF KENT
☐ 368. BRET SABERHAGEN
☐ 384. JOE ORSULAK
☐ 439. PETE SCHOUREK
☐ 473. TITO NAVARRO
☐ 480. ERIC HILLMAN
☐ 566. KEVIN MCREYNOLDS
☐ 599. KELLY STINNETT
☐ 620. BOBBY JONES
☐ 662. JOSE VIZCAINO
☐ 696. DAVID SEGUI

NEW YORK YANKEES

☐ 23. MATT NOKES
☐ 52. PAT KELLY
☐ 74. PAUL O'NEILL
☐ 101. SCOTT KAMIENIECKI
☐ 133. PAUL ASSENMACHER
☐ 156. RANDY VELARDE
☐ 195. DON MATTINGLY
☐ 246. BOBBY MUNOZ
☐ 271. MIKE STANLEY
☐ 279. MARK HUTTON
☐ 283. JIM LEYRITZ
☐ 349. WADE BOGGS
☐ 388. MIKE GALLEGO
☐ 410. DANNY TARTABULL
☐ 469. JIMMY KEY
☐ 494. BOB WICKMAN
☐ 516. JIM ABBOTT
☐ 554. MELIDO PEREZ
☐ 573. BERNIE WILLIAMS
☐ 595. STEVE HOWE
☐ 616. XAVIER HERNANDEZ
☐ 639. LUIS POLONIA
☐ 658. STERLING HITCHCOCK
☐ 700. TERRY MULHOLLAND

OAKLAND A'S

☐ 12. SCOTT HEMOND
☐ 40. TROY NEEL
☐ 65. BRENT GATES
☐ 91. BOBBY WITT
☐ 125. DENNIS ECKERSLEY
☐ 164. SCOTT BROSIUS
☐ 191. RICH GOSSAGE
☐ 227. MIKE BORDICK
☐ 253. DAVE HENDERSON
☐ 297. BOB WELCH
☐ 307. RUBEN SIERRA
☐ 328. CRAIG PAQUETTE
☐ 341. LANCE BLANKENSHIP
☐ 346. TERRY STEINBACH
☐ 356. MIGUEL JIMENEZ
☐ 358. MARK MCGWIRE
☐ 391. SCOTT LYDY
☐ 428. RON DARLING
☐ 562. TODD VAN POPPEL
☐ 591. GERONIMO BERROA
☐ 613. STAN JAVIER
☐ 654. RICKEY HENDERSON
☐ 708. STEVE KARSAY

PHILADELPHIA PHILLIES

☐ 27. JIM EISENREICH
☐ 54. MARIANO DUNCAN
☐ 84. TODD PRATT
☐ 96. DAVE HOLLINS
☐ 120. MICKEY MORANDINI
☐ 130. DAVE WEST
☐ 165. LEN DYKSTRA
☐ 222. TERRY MULHOLLAND
☐ 252. BEN RIVERA
☐ 289. CURT SCHILLING
☐ 296. DANNY JACKSON
☐ 303. KIM BATISTE
☐ 355. MILT THOMPSON
☐ 361. JOHN KRUK
☐ 394. TONY LONGMIRE
☐ 432. WES CHAMBERLAIN
☐ 444. KEVIN STOCKER
☐ 450. DARREN DAULTON
☐ 559. PETE INCAVIGLIA
☐ 580. DOUG JONES
☐ 609. JEFF JUDEN
☐ 657. RICKY JORDAN
☐ 681. HEATHCLIFF SLOCUMB
☐ 705. TOMMY GREENE

PITTSBURGH PIRATES

☐ 6. AL MARTIN
☐ 18. JAY BELL
☐ 47. STEVE COOKE
☐ 70. ANDY TOMBERLIN
☐ 137. DON SLAUGHT
☐ 142. TOM FOLEY
☐ 152. TIM WAKEFIELD
☐ 206. CARLOS GARCIA
☐ 232. DENNY NEAGLE
☐ 277. ORLANDO MERCED
☐ 310. ZANE SMITH
☐ 316. RANDY TOMLIN
☐ 321. KEVIN YOUNG
☐ 338. JEFF KING
☐ 465. BLAS MINOR
☐ 498. DAVE CLARK
☐ 505. PAUL WAGNER
☐ 511. LLOYD MCCLENDON
☐ 589. RICK WHITE
☐ 651. BRIAN HUNTER
☐ 687. ANDY VAN SLYKE

ST. LOUIS CARDINALS

☐ 37. MARK WHITEN
☐ 63. BRIAN JORDAN
☐ 109. GREGG JEFFERIES
☐ 122. TOM PAGNOZZI
☐ 146. LUIS ALICEA
☐ 175. MIKE PEREZ
☐ 216. LEE GUETTERMAN
☐ 231. BERNARD GILKEY
☐ 306. RENE AROCHA
☐ 344. RICH BATCHELOR
☐ 353. RAY LANKFORD
☐ 392. TOM URBANI
☐ 395. TODD ZEILE
☐ 417. OZZIE SMITH
☐ 425. OMAR OLIVARES
☐ 437. RHEAL CORMIER
☐ 448. ERIK PAPPAS
☐ 523. GERONIMO PENA
☐ 586. BOB TEWKSBURY
☐ 618. JOHN HABYAN
☐ 653. ALLEN WATSON
☐ 691. RICK SUTCLIFFE

SAN DIEGO PADRES

☐ 46. TIM TEUFEL
☐ 58. JEFF GARDNER
☐ 75. RICKY GUTIERREZ
☐ 83. KEVIN HIGGINS
☐ 102. ANDY BENES
☐ 115. PHIL PLANTIER
☐ 151. TONY GWYNN
☐ 200. TIM MAUSER
☐ 221. ARCHI CIANFROCCO
☐ 278. GUILLERMO VELASQUEZ
☐ 286. DEREK BELL
☐ 312. TREVOR HOFFMAN
☐ 325. GENE HARRIS
☐ 399. PHIL CLARK
☐ 412. BRAD AUSMUS
☐ 460. CRAIG SHIPLEY
☐ 497. MARK DAVIS
☐ 519. TIM WORRELL
☐ 524. ANDY ASHBY
☐ 567. MELVIN NIEVES
☐ 601. BRIAN JOHNSON
☐ 652. WALLY WHITEHURST
☐ 669. BILLY BEAN
☐ 684. PEDRO MARTINEZ
☐ 698. BIP ROBERTS

SAN FRANCISCO GIANTS

☐ 3. STEVE SCARSONE
☐ 39. ROYCE CLAYTON
☐ 61. TODD BENZINGER

- ☐ 88. JOHN BURKETT
- ☐ 158. J.R. PHILLIPS
- ☐ 203. WILL CLARK
- ☐ 218. KIRT MANWARING
- ☐ 238. BARRY BONDS
- ☐ 314. SALOMON TORRES
- ☐ 318. MIKE BENJAMIN
- ☐ 330. BILL SWIFT
- ☐ 381. JOHN PATTERSON
- ☐ 419. MATT WILLIAMS
- ☐ 436. ROD BECK
- ☐ 453. DARREN LEWIS
- ☐ 459. KEVIN ROGERS
- ☐ 504. JEFF REED
- ☐ 565. MIKE JACKSON
- ☐ 598. ROBBY THOMPSON
- ☐ 644. MARK PORTUGAL
- ☐ 686. WILLIE MCGEE
- ☐ 711. BRYAN HICKERSON

SEATTLE MARINERS

- ☐ 44. RICH AMARAL
- ☐ 60. TINO MARTINEZ
- ☐ 76. BRAD HOLMAN
- ☐ 85. KEN GRIFFEY, JR.
- ☐ 93. OMAR VIZQUEL
- ☐ 103. CHRIS BOSIO
- ☐ 114. BILL HASELMAN
- ☐ 163. TED POWER
- ☐ 177. BRIAN TURANG
- ☐ 237. MIKE HAMPTON
- ☐ 299. JAY BUHNER
- ☐ 357. MARC NEWFIELD
- ☐ 364. EDGAR MARTINEZ
- ☐ 409. DAVE FLEMING
- ☐ 438. RANDY JOHNSON
- ☐ 493. LEE TINSLEY
- ☐ 495. ROGER SALKELD
- ☐ 510. MACKEY SASSER
- ☐ 518. ERIK PLANTENBERG
- ☐ 548. ERIC ANTHONY
- ☐ 578. GREG PIRKL
- ☐ 604. MIKE BLOWERS
- ☐ 656. DAN WILSON
- ☐ 675. FELIX FERMIN
- ☐ 704. GREG HIBBARD
- ☐ 713. BOBBY AYALA

TEXAS RANGERS

- ☐ 19. TOM HENKE
- ☐ 34. NOLAN RYAN
- ☐ 55. BRIAN BOHANON
- ☐ 97. DOUG STRANGE
- ☐ 116. IVAN RODRIGUEZ
- ☐ 171. JOSE CANSECO
- ☐ 178. ROGER PAVLIK
- ☐ 199. JON SHAVE
- ☐ 208. RAFAEL PALMEIRO
- ☐ 239. CRIS CARPENTER
- ☐ 336. DEAN PALMER
- ☐ 369. BILLY RIPKEN
- ☐ 382. KEVIN BROWN
- ☐ 423. MANUEL LEE
- ☐ 449. DAVID HULSE
- ☐ 457. DAN PELTIER
- ☐ 467. KENNY ROGERS
- ☐ 502. MATT WHITESIDE
- ☐ 514. GARY REDUS
- ☐ 568. JUAN GONZALEZ
- ☐ 594. JACK ARMSTRONG
- ☐ 621. CHRIS JAMES
- ☐ 666. WILL CLARK
- ☐ 697. RICK HELLING

TORONTO BLUE JAYS

- ☐ 10. ROBERTO ALOMAR
- ☐ 66. SHAWN GREEN
- ☐ 107. RICKEY HENDERSON
- ☐ 149. JUAN GUZMAN
- ☐ 174. RANDY KNORR
- ☐ 214. TONY FERNANDEZ
- ☐ 228. JOHN OLERUD
- ☐ 234. DICK SCHOFIELD
- ☐ 242. PAT HENTGEN
- ☐ 300. JOE CARTER
- ☐ 305. PAT BORDERS
- ☐ 317. DAVE STEWART
- ☐ 326. DEVON WHITE
- ☐ 377. DUANE WARD
- ☐ 418. ED SPRAGUE
- ☐ 441. MIKE TIMLIN
- ☐ 470. TONY CASTILLO
- ☐ 513. WOODY WILLIAMS
- ☐ 563. TODD STOTTLEMYRE
- ☐ 585. GREG CADARET
- ☐ 600. CARLOS DELGADO
- ☐ 645. PAUL MOLITOR
- ☐ 667. AL LEITER
- ☐ 695. ALEX GONZALEZ

1995 STADIUM CLUB SERIES 1 (270) 2 1/2" X 3 1/2"

ATLANTA BRAVES

- ☐ 19. RYAN KLESKO
- ☐ 66. TERRY PENDLETON
- ☐ 99. JACOB SHUMATE
- ☐ 128. MARK WOHLERS
- ☐ 136. JEFF BLAUSER
- ☐ 151. STEVE AVERY
- ☐ 183. TOM GLAVINE
- ☐ 200. JAVY LOPEZ
- ☐ 234. RAFAEL BELLIARD
- ☐ 258. CHARLIE O'BRIEN

BALTIMORE ORIOLES

- ☐ 1. CAL RIPKEN
- ☐ 12. LEE SMITH
- ☐ 30. RAFAEL PALMEIRO
- ☐ 84. BEN MCDONALD
- ☐ 135. CHRIS HOILES
- ☐ 168. JEFF TACKETT
- ☐ 188. SID FERNANDEZ
- ☐ 254. ARMANDO BENITEZ
- ☐ 268. BRADY ANDERSON

BOSTON RED SOX

- ☐ 10. ROGER CLEMENS
- ☐ 62. JOHN VALENTIN
- ☐ 81. KEN RYAN
- ☐ 97. NOMAR GARCIAPARRA
- ☐ 121. MIKE GREENWELL
- ☐ 146. ANDRE DAWSON
- ☐ 160. LEE TINSLEY
- ☐ 262. OTIS NIXON

CALIFORNIA ANGELS

- ☐ 2. BO JACKSON
- ☐ 40. JIM EDMONDS
- ☐ 51. REX HUDLER
- ☐ 82. CHRIS TURNER
- ☐ 133. CHILI DAVIS
- ☐ 169. CHAD CURTIS
- ☐ 195. EDUARDO PEREZ
- ☐ 246. MARK LANGSTON

CHICAGO CUBS

- ☐ 21. REY SANCHEZ
- ☐ 29. SHAWON DUNSTON
- ☐ 80. STEVE TRACHSEL
- ☐ 112. JAYSON PETERSON
- ☐ 127. WILLIE BANKS
- ☐ 174. SAMMY SOSA
- ☐ 181. STEVE BUECHELE
- ☐ 235. RANDY MYERS
- ☐ 243. DERRICK MAY

CHICAGO WHITE SOX

- ☐ 33. JOEY CORA
- ☐ 71. DARRIN JACKSON
- ☐ 88. RON KARKOVICE
- ☐ 104. MARK JOHNSON
- ☐ 132. WILSON ALVAREZ
- ☐ 155. JACK MCDOWELL
- ☐ 173. LANCE JOHNSON
- ☐ 206. OZZIE GUILLEN
- ☐ 248. JULIO FRANCO

CINCINNATI REDS

- ☐ 35. BARRY LARKIN
- ☐ 95. ERIK HANSON
- ☐ 114. C.J. NITKOWSKI
- ☐ 122. DEION SANDERS
- ☐ 166. EDDIE TAUBENSEE
- ☐ 221. TONY FERNANDEZ
- ☐ 231. HAL MORRIS
- ☐ 252. BRET BOONE
- ☐ 269. JOHN ROPER

CLEVELAND INDIANS

- ☐ 14. CHARLES NAGY
- ☐ 24. JULIAN TAVAREZ
- ☐ 36. CARLOS BAERGA
- ☐ 54. MARK CLARK
- ☐ 87. SANDY ALOMAR
- ☐ 147. JIM THOME
- ☐ 186. EDDIE MURRAY
- ☐ 220. PAUL SORRENTO
- ☐ 264. MANNY RAMIREZ

COLORADO ROCKIES

- ☐ 5. BRUCE RUFFIN
- ☐ 32. ANDRES GALARRAGA
- ☐ 64. STEVE REED
- ☐ 86. JOHN VANDER WAL
- ☐ 94. WALT WEISS
- ☐ 109. DOUG MILLION
- ☐ 123. CHARLIE HAYES
- ☐ 157. WILLIE BLAIR
- ☐ 184. JOE GIRARDI

DETROIT TIGERS

- ☐ 6. TRAVIS FRYMAN
- ☐ 34. MICKEY TETTLETON
- ☐ 78. DANNY BAUTISTA
- ☐ 105. CADE GASPAR

- ☐ 154. JUNIOR FELIX
- ☐ 182. DAVID WELLS
- ☐ 208. TONY PHILLIPS
- ☐ 250. BILL GULLICKSON

FLORIDA MARLINS

- ☐ 3. BRYAN HARVEY
- ☐ 23. BENNY SANTIAGO
- ☐ 63. ALEX ARIAS
- ☐ 75. DAVE WEATHERS
- ☐ 90. GARY SHEFFIELD
- ☐ 159. ROBB NEN
- ☐ 193. JEFF CONINE
- ☐ 265. BRET BARBERIE

HOUSTON ASTROS

- ☐ 18. STEVE FINLEY
- ☐ 91. KEN CAMINITI
- ☐ 108. SCOTT ELARTON
- ☐ 115. RAMON CASTRO
- ☐ 129. TODD JONES
- ☐ 163. SCOTT SERVAIS
- ☐ 185. CRAIG BIGGIO
- ☐ 224. DOUG DRABEK
- ☐ 257. LUIS GONZALEZ
- ☐ 270. SHANE REYNOLDS

KANSAS CITY ROYALS

- ☐ 9. GARY GAETTI
- ☐ 55. HIPOLITO PICHARDO
- ☐ 68. VINCE COLEMAN
- ☐ 79. BOB HAMELIN
- ☐ 110. MATT SMITH
- ☐ 175. MIKE MACFARLANE
- ☐ 204. DAVID CONE
- ☐ 222. STAN BELINDA
- ☐ 232. JOSE LIND
- ☐ 251. DAVE HENDERSON

LOS ANGELES DODGERS

- ☐ 37. OREL HERSHISER
- ☐ 53. TODD WORRELL
- ☐ 57. RAUL MONDESI
- ☐ 102. PAUL KONERKO
- ☐ 116. RAFAEL BOURNIGAL
- ☐ 149. MIKE PIAZZA
- ☐ 161. ISMAEL VALDES
- ☐ 187. KEVIN GROSS
- ☐ 242. BRETT BUTLER
- ☐ 259. TIM WALLACH

MILWAUKEE BREWERS

- ☐ 20. CAL ELDRED
- ☐ 38. JODY REED
- ☐ 49. BILLY SPIERS
- ☐ 140. DAVE NILSSON
- ☐ 176. DARRYL HAMILTON
- ☐ 199. RICKY BONES
- ☐ 226. MATT MIESKE
- ☐ 244. PAT LISTACH

MINNESOTA TWINS

- ☐ 8. DAVID MCCARTY
- ☐ 52. DENNY HOCKING
- ☐ 76. MATT WALBECK
- ☐ 93. KEVIN TAPANI
- ☐ 137. JEFF REBOULET
- ☐ 177. RICK AGUILERA
- ☐ 207. ALEX COLE
- ☐ 249. CHUCK KNOBLAUCH

MONTREAL EXPOS

- ☐ 15. LOU FRAZIER
- ☐ 22. KEN HILL
- ☐ 117. JEFF FASSERO
- ☐ 139. KIRK RUETER
- ☐ 148. LARRY WALKER
- ☐ 164. CLIFF FLOYD
- ☐ 192. DARRIN FLETCHER
- ☐ 255. WIL CORDERO
- ☐ 266. MEL ROJAS

NEW YORK METS

- ☐ 25. JOSE VIZCAINO
- ☐ 61. JEFF KENT
- ☐ 83. DAVID SEGUI
- ☐ 98. TERRENCE LONG
- ☐ 100. PAUL WILSON
- ☐ 118. BOBBY BONILLA
- ☐ 138. BRET SABERHAGEN
- ☐ 170. RICO BROGNA
- ☐ 189. JOHN FRANCO
- ☐ 205. TODD HUNDLEY

NEW YORK YANKEES

- ☐ 7. JIM ABBOTT
- ☐ 56. BOB WICKMAN
- ☐ 85. WADE BOGGS
- ☐ 111. BRIAN BUCHANAN
- ☐ 124. PAUL O'NEILL
- ☐ 156. DANNY TARTABULL
- ☐ 171. LUIS POLONIA
- ☐ 179. MIKE GALLEGO
- ☐ 223. MIKE STANLEY
- ☐ 247. RANDY VELARDE

OAKLAND A'S

- ☐ 50. STAN JAVIER
- ☐ 72. DENNIS ECKERSLEY
- ☐ 96. RUBEN SIERRA
- ☐ 103. BEN GRIEVE
- ☐ 142. RON DARLING
- ☐ 167. SCOTT HEMOND
- ☐ 201. MIGUEL JIMENEZ
- ☐ 225. TODD VAN POPPEL
- ☐ 245. MIKE BORDICK

PHILADELPHIA PHILLIES

- ☐ 4. CURT SCHILLING
- ☐ 27. MARIANO DUNCAN
- ☐ 89. DOUG JONES
- ☐ 144. DAVE HOLLINS
- ☐ 178. DAVE WEST
- ☐ 203. MIKE LIEBERTHAL
- ☐ 209. JIM EISENREICH
- ☐ 263. DARREN DAULTON

PITTSBURGH PIRATES

- ☐ 11. CARLOS GARCIA
- ☐ 44. ZANE SMITH
- ☐ 58. STEVE COOKE
- ☐ 106. MARK FARRIS
- ☐ 125. JAY BELL
- ☐ 153. ANDY VAN SLYKE
- ☐ 198. ORLANDO MERCED
- ☐ 229. MIDRE CUMMINGS
- ☐ 253. AL MARTIN

ST. LOUIS CARDINALS

- ☐ 16. RENE AROCHA
- ☐ 41. BOB TEWKSBURY
- ☐ 65. OZZIE SMITH
- ☐ 69. TOM PAGNOZZI
- ☐ 113. BRET WAGNER
- ☐ 150. MIKE PEREZ
- ☐ 165. ALLEN WATSON
- ☐ 190. BERNARD GILKEY
- ☐ 202. TERRY MCGRIFF

SAN DIEGO PADRES

- ☐ 26. ANDY BENES
- ☐ 43. RAY MCDAVID
- ☐ 77. BRAD AUSMUS
- ☐ 107. DUSTIN HERMANSON
- ☐ 119. RICKY GUTIERREZ
- ☐ 143. DEREK BELL
- ☐ 196. SCOTT LIVINGSTONE
- ☐ 228. ANDY ASHBY
- ☐ 260. SCOTT SANDERS

SAN FRANCISCO GIANTS

- ☐ 42. JOHN PATTERSON
- ☐ 59. ROD BECK
- ☐ 74. DARREN LEWIS
- ☐ 126. ROYCE CLAYTON
- ☐ 134. DAVE BURBA
- ☐ 158. BILL VAN LANDINGHAM
- ☐ 191. MATT WILLIAMS
- ☐ 267. JOHN BURKETT

SEATTLE MARINERS

- ☐ 13. BOBBY AYALA
- ☐ 60. TIM DAVIS
- ☐ 73. JAY BUHNER
- ☐ 92. CHRIS BOSIO
- ☐ 152. DAN WILSON
- ☐ 180. MARC NEWFIELD
- ☐ 227. TINO MARTINEZ
- ☐ 241. KEN GRIFFEY, JR.

TEXAS RANGERS

- ☐ 31. DEAN PALMER
- ☐ 67. KENNY ROGERS
- ☐ 120. ROGER PAVLIK
- ☐ 131. WILL CLARK
- ☐ 145. JUAN GONZALEZ
- ☐ 197. IVAN RODRIGUEZ
- ☐ 230. JEFF FRYE
- ☐ 261. TOM HENKE

TORONTO BLUE JAYS

- ☐ 17. CARLOS DELGADO
- ☐ 39. PAUL MOLITOR
- ☐ 70. ROBERTO ALOMAR
- ☐ 101. KEVIN WITT
- ☐ 130. TODD STOTTLEMYRE
- ☐ 141. PAT BORDERS
- ☐ 162. JUAN GUZMAN
- ☐ 194. ED SPRAGUE
- ☐ 233. SHAWN GREEN
- ☐ 256. AL LEITER

TOPPS-FINEST

1993 FINEST (199)
2 1/2" X 3 1/2"

ATLANTA BRAVES

- ☐ 1. DAVID JUSTICE
- ☐ 68. RON GANT
- ☐ 85. GREG MADDUX
- ☐ 87. TOM GLAVINE
- ☐ 101. TERRY PENDLETON
- ☐ 141. DEION SANDERS
- ☐ 160. STEVE AVERY
- ☐ 166. JOHN SMOLTZ
- ☐ 176. MIKE STANTON
- ☐ 181. OTIS NIXON

BALTIMORE ORIOLES

- ☐ 41. GLENN DAVIS
- ☐ 50. HAROLD REYNOLDS
- ☐ 65. BEN MCDONALD
- ☐ 71. BRADY ANDERSON
- ☐ 74. MIKE DEVEREAUX
- ☐ 96. CAL RIPKEN
- ☐ 121. GREGG OLSON
- ☐ 153. HAROLD BAINES
- ☐ 157. MIKE MUSSINA

BOSTON RED SOX

- ☐ 7. SCOTT COOPER
- ☐ 33. FRANK VIOLA
- ☐ 55. IVAN CALDERON
- ☐ 84. ANDRE DAWSON
- ☐ 104. ROGER CLEMENS
- ☐ 165. MO VAUGHN
- ☐ 197. MIKE GREENWELL

CALIFORNIA ANGELS

- ☐ 72. CHUCK FINLEY
- ☐ 82. MARK LANGSTON
- ☐ 146. CHAD CURTIS
- ☐ 156. J.T. SNOW
- ☐ 163. TIM SALMON

CHICAGO CUBS

- ☐ 73. MARK GRACE
- ☐ 79. SAMMY SOSA
- ☐ 105. RYNE SANDBERG
- ☐ 145. JOSE GUZMAN
- ☐ 182. RANDY MYERS
- ☐ 188. MIKE MORGAN

CHICAGO WHITE SOX

- ☐ 27. ALEX FERNANDEZ
- ☐ 64. LANCE JOHNSON
- ☐ 91. BO JACKSON
- ☐ 93. ROBIN VENTURA
- ☐ 102. FRANK THOMAS
- ☐ 125. CARLTON FISK
- ☐ 128. OZZIE GUILLEN
- ☐ 172. JACK MCDOWELL
- ☐ 175. GEORGE BELL
- ☐ 183. TIM RAINES

CINCINNATI REDS

- ☐ 14. JOHN SMILEY
- ☐ 15. BIP ROBERTS
- ☐ 20. REGGIE SANDERS
- ☐ 24. JOSE RIJO
- ☐ 39. CHRIS SABO
- ☐ 114. BARRY LARKIN
- ☐ 120. BOBBY KELLY
- ☐ 136. KEVIN MITCHELL
- ☐ 148. WILLIE GREENE
- ☐ 180. ROB DIBBLE

CLEVELAND INDIANS

- ☐ 16. ALBERT BELLE
- ☐ 26. SANDY ALOMAR
- ☐ 43. KENNY LOFTON
- ☐ 57. CARLOS BAERGA
- ☐ 58. CHARLES NAGY
- ☐ 139. REGGIE JEFFERSON

COLORADO ROCKIES

- ☐ 12. ALEX COLE
- ☐ 48. ERIC YOUNG
- ☐ 60. CHARLIE HAYES
- ☐ 130. ANDRES GALARRAGA
- ☐ 198. DAVID NIED

DETROIT TIGERS

- ☐ 2. LOU WHITAKER
- ☐ 18. ALAN TRAMMELL
- ☐ 75. TONY PHILLIPS
- ☐ 80. MICKEY TETTLETON
- ☐ 111. CECIL FIELDER
- ☐ 135. TRAVIS FRYMAN

FLORIDA MARLINS

- ☐ 3. BRYAN HARVEY
- ☐ 54. JEFF CONINE
- ☐ 138. BENNY SANTIAGO
- ☐ 144. ORESTES DESTRADE
- ☐ 169. CHARLIE HOUGH
- ☐ 173. JUNIOR FELIX

HOUSTON ASTROS

- ☐ 9. STEVE FINLEY
- ☐ 11. JEFF BAGWELL
- ☐ 62. PETE HARNISCH
- ☐ 69. DOUG JONES
- ☐ 119. CRAIG BIGGIO
- ☐ 127. DOUG DRABEK
- ☐ 131. KEN CAMINITI
- ☐ 137. GREG SWINDELL
- ☐ 179. ERIC ANTHONY
- ☐ 195. LUIS GONZALEZ

KANSAS CITY ROYALS

- ☐ 42. JEFF MONTGOMERY
- ☐ 59. WALLY JOYNER
- ☐ 63. GEORGE BRETT
- ☐ 78. KEVIN APPIER
- ☐ 81. FELIX JOSE
- ☐ 115. DAVID CONE

LOS ANGELES DODGERS

- ☐ 6. BRETT BUTLER
- ☐ 29. RAMON MARTINEZ
- ☐ 32. ERIC KARROS
- ☐ 89. DARRYL STRAWBERRY
- ☐ 118. TIM WALLACH
- ☐ 126. ERIC DAVIS
- ☐ 132. TOM CANDIOTTI
- ☐ 184. OREL HERSHISER
- ☐ 199. MIKE PIAZZA

MILWAUKEE BREWERS

- ☐ 8. B.J. SURHOFF
- ☐ 45. DARRYL HAMILTON
- ☐ 109. PAT LISTACH
- ☐ 147. CAL ELDRED
- ☐ 152. JOHN JAHA
- ☐ 192. ROBIN YOUNT

MINNESOTA TWINS

- ☐ 22. RICK AGUILERA
- ☐ 51. BRIAN HARPER
- ☐ 61. SHANE MACK
- ☐ 76. CHUCK KNOBLAUCH
- ☐ 112. KIRBY PUCKETT
- ☐ 117. KENT HRBEK
- ☐ 142. SCOTT ERICKSON
- ☐ 162. DAVE WINFIELD

MONTREAL EXPOS

- ☐ 35. KEN HILL
- ☐ 40. MARQUIS GRISSOM
- ☐ 97. LARRY WALKER
- ☐ 123. WIL CORDERO
- ☐ 129. JOHN WETTELAND
- ☐ 168. DELINO DESHIELDS
- ☐ 186. MIKE LANSING
- ☐ 189. MOISES ALOU

NEW YORK METS

- ☐ 5. SID FERNANDEZ
- ☐ 36. TONY FERNANDEZ
- ☐ 53. BRET SABERHAGEN
- ☐ 66. BOBBY BONILLA
- ☐ 113. DOC GOODEN
- ☐ 122. EDDIE MURRAY
- ☐ 143. HOWARD JOHNSON
- ☐ 191. JOHN FRANCO

NEW YORK YANKEES

- ☐ 30. BERNIE WILLIAMS
- ☐ 46. JIM ABBOTT
- ☐ 90. WADE BOGGS
- ☐ 98. DON MATTINGLY
- ☐ 167. DANNY TARTABULL
- ☐ 170. PAUL O'NEILL
- ☐ 174. JIMMY KEY

OAKLAND A'S

- ☐ 67. TERRY STEINBACH
- ☐ 86. RICKEY HENDERSON
- ☐ 92. MARK MCGWIRE
- ☐ 100. DENNIS ECKERSLEY
- ☐ 151. BOB WELCH
- ☐ 158. RUBEN SIERRA

PHILADELPHIA PHILLIES

- ☐ 10. CURT SCHILLING
- ☐ 23. DAVE HOLLINS
- ☐ 38. JOHN KRUK

- ☐ 49. MITCH WILLIAMS
- ☐ 149. TOMMY GREENE
- ☐ 171. DARREN DAULTON
- ☐ 177. LEN DYKSTRA

PITTSBURGH PIRATES

- ☐ 4. CARLOS GARCIA
- ☐ 34. KEVIN YOUNG
- ☐ 37. TIM WAKEFIELD
- ☐ 155. AL MARTIN
- ☐ 185. ANDY VAN SLYKE
- ☐ 194. JAY BELL

ST. LOUIS CARDINALS

- ☐ 21. TODD ZEILE
- ☐ 28. OZZIE SMITH
- ☐ 83. GREGG JEFFERIES
- ☐ 95. LEE SMITH
- ☐ 187. RAY LANKFORD
- ☐ 193. BOB TEWKSBURY

SAN DIEGO PADRES

- ☐ 19. ANDY BENES
- ☐ 31. GARY SHEFFIELD
- ☐ 77. TONY GWYNN
- ☐ 106. FRED MCGRIFF

SAN FRANCISCO GIANTS

- ☐ 25. MATT WILLIAMS
- ☐ 44. JOHN BURKETT
- ☐ 103. BARRY BONDS
- ☐ 108. WILL CLARK

SEATTLE MARINERS

- ☐ 110. KEN GRIFFY, JR.
- ☐ 124. JAY BUHNER
- ☐ 140. CHRIS BOSIO
- ☐ 150. ERIK HANSON
- ☐ 154. RANDY JOHNSON
- ☐ 178. NORM CHARLTON
- ☐ 190. EDGAR MARTINEZ
- ☐ 196. DAVE FLEMING

TEXAS RANGERS

- ☐ 47. IVAN RODRIGUEZ
- ☐ 52. RAFAEL PALMEIRO
- ☐ 99. JOSE CANSECO
- ☐ 107. NOLAN RYAN
- ☐ 116. JUAN GONZALEZ
- ☐ 134. KEVIN BROWN
- ☐ 159. DEAN PALMER
- ☐ 161. JULIO FRANCO
- ☐ 164. TOM HENKE

TORONTO BLUE JAYS

- ☐ 13. JOHN OLERUD
- ☐ 17. DUANE WARD
- ☐ 56. JUAN GUZMAN
- ☐ 70. PAUL MOLITOR
- ☐ 88. ROBERTO ALOMAR
- ☐ 94. JOE CARTER
- ☐ 133. PAT BORDERS

1994 FINEST (440)
2 1/2" X 3 1/2"

ATLANTA BRAVES

- ☐ 3. GREG MCMICHAEL
- ☐ 22. DEION SANDERS
- ☐ 27. JEFF BLAUSER
- ☐ 95. MARK LEMKE
- ☐ 100. JOHN SMOLTZ
- ☐ 118. TERRY PENDLETON
- ☐ 165. RON GANT
- ☐ 209. GREG MADDUX
- ☐ 224. FRED MCGRIFF
- ☐ 233. DAVID JUSTICE
- ☐ 246. GREGG OLSON
- ☐ 267. TOM GLAVINE
- ☐ 329. MIKE KELLY
- ☐ 359. STEVE AVERY
- ☐ 422. TONY TARASCO
- ☐ 425. JAVY LOPEZ
- ☐ 437. RYAN KLESKO

BALTIMORE ORIOLES

- ☐ 66. MIKE MUSSINA
- ☐ 103. DAVID SEGUI
- ☐ 115. MARK MCLEMORE
- ☐ 117. MIEK DEVEREAUX
- ☐ 131. BRADY ANDERSON
- ☐ 141. CHRIS HOILES
- ☐ 161. BEN MCDONALD
- ☐ 227. RAFAEL PALMEIRO
- ☐ 235. CAL RIPKEN
- ☐ 254. HAROLD BAINES
- ☐ 335. ARTHUR RHODES
- ☐ 351. LEE SMITH
- ☐ 379. SID FERNANDEZ
- ☐ 418. CHRIS SABO

BOSTON RED SOX

- ☐ 6. AARON SELE
- ☐ 50. ANDRE DAWSON
- ☐ 58. DANNY DARWIN
- ☐ 90. JEFF RUSSELL
- ☐ 128. JOHN VALENTIN
- ☐ 168. SCOTT COOPER
- ☐ 181. SCOTT FLETCHER
- ☐ 217. ROGER CLEMENS
- ☐ 258. MO VAUGHN
- ☐ 274. OTIS NIXON
- ☐ 303. GREG HARRIS
- ☐ 322. MIKE GREENWELL
- ☐ 378. DAVE VALLE
- ☐ 402. GREG BLOSSER
- ☐ 406. FRANK VIOLA

CALIFORNIA ANGELS

- ☐ 18. TIM SALMON
- ☐ 24. MARK LANGSTON
- ☐ 73. EDUARDO PEREZ
- ☐ 112. CHILI DAVIS
- ☐ 143. CHUCK FINLEY
- ☐ 157. J.T. SNOW
- ☐ 171. GARY DISARCINA
- ☐ 193. JOE GRAHE
- ☐ 241. BO JACKSON
- ☐ 264. SPIKE OWEN
- ☐ 304. BRIAN ANDERSON
- ☐ 332. DAMION EASLEY
- ☐ 358. CHAD CURTIS
- ☐ 370. CHRIS TURNER
- ☐ 391. PHIL LEFTWICH

CHICAGO CUBS

- ☐ 51. STEVE BUECHELE
- ☐ 77. KEVIN ROBERSON
- ☐ 86. RICK WILKINS
- ☐ 93. JOSE GUZMAN
- ☐ 96. MIKE MORGAN
- ☐ 162. DERRICK MAY
- ☐ 175. JOSE BAUTISTA
- ☐ 210. RYNE SANDBERG
- ☐ 236. SAMMY SOSA
- ☐ 249. REY SANCHEZ
- ☐ 286. WILLIE BANKS
- ☐ 296. STEVE TRACHSEL
- ☐ 330. KARL RHODES
- ☐ 357. RANDY MYERS
- ☐ 368. SHAWON DUNSTON
- ☐ 390. MARK GRACE

CHICAGO WHITE SOX

- ☐ 12. JASON BERE
- ☐ 26. ALEX FERNANDEZ
- ☐ 54. LANCE JOHNSON
- ☐ 71. RON KARKOVICE
- ☐ 139. WILSON ALVAREZ
- ☐ 146. JOEY CORA
- ☐ 192. TIM RAINES
- ☐ 202. ROBIN VENTURA
- ☐ 203. FRANK THOMAS
- ☐ 226. JACK MCDOWELL
- ☐ 262. DARRIN JACKSON
- ☐ 278. JULIO FRANCO
- ☐ 376. ROBERTO HERNANDEZ
- ☐ 393. OZZIE GUILLEN
- ☐ 440. SCOTT RUFFCORN

CINCINNATI REDS

- ☐ 37. JOE OLIVER
- ☐ 43. REGGIE SANDERS
- ☐ 67. TIM PUGH
- ☐ 70. HAL MORRIS
- ☐ 88. ROB DIBBLE
- ☐ 163. ROBERTO KELLY
- ☐ 179. JOHN SMILEY
- ☐ 189. JEFF BRANSON
- ☐ 240. BARRY LARKIN
- ☐ 283. JOHNNY RUFFIN
- ☐ 308. JOSE RIJO
- ☐ 316. HECTOR CARRASCO
- ☐ 323. KEVIN MITCHELL
- ☐ 337. TOM BROWNING

☐ 386. BRET BOONE
☐ 395. ERIK HANSON

CLEVELAND INDIANS

☐ 36. WAYNE KIRBY
☐ 91. MARK LEWIS
☐ 102. JIM THOME
☐ 104. CHARLES NAGY
☐ 138. JOSE MESA
☐ 185. PAUL SORRENTO
☐ 208. ALBERT BELLE
☐ 218. KENNY LOFTON
☐ 231. CARLOS BAERGA
☐ 251. SANDY ALOMAR
☐ 285. OMAR VIZQUEL
☐ 317. EDDIE MURRAY
☐ 348. STEVE FARR
☐ 412. DENNY MARTINEZ
☐ 420. CHRIS NABHOLZ
☐ 430. MANNY RAMIREZ

COLORADO ROCKIES

☐ 14. ARMANDO REYNOSO
☐ 32. CHARLIE HAYES
☐ 35. ANDRES GALARRAGA
☐ 59. DANTE BICHETTE
☐ 72. JOE GIRARDI
☐ 153. ROBERTO MEJIA
☐ 186. ERIC YOUNG
☐ 199. BRUCE RUFFIN
☐ 259. MIKE HARKEY
☐ 275. ELLIS BURKS
☐ 282. DAVID NIED
☐ 307. DARREN HOLMES
☐ 327. MARVIN FREEMAN
☐ 372. GREG HARRIS
☐ 374. HOWARD JOHNSON
☐ 401. WALT WEISS

DETROIT TIGERS

☐ 34. MIKE HENNEMAN
☐ 80. ERIC DAVIS
☐ 83. MIKE MOORE
☐ 108. DAVID WELLS
☐ 159. ALAN TRAMMELL
☐ 178. TONY PHILLIPS
☐ 219. CECIL FIELDER
☐ 228. TRAVIS FRYMAN
☐ 277. JOHN DOHERTY
☐ 281. MICKEY TETTLETON
☐ 301. TIM BELCHER
☐ 364. LOU WHITAKER
☐ 388. CHAD KREUTER
☐ 398. BILL GULLICKSON
☐ 435. DANNY BAUTISTA

FLORIDA MARLINS

☐ 4. JEFF CONINE
☐ 8. CHUCK CARR
☐ 30. RYAN BOWEN
☐ 130. DAVE MAGADAN
☐ 147. DARRELL WHITMORE
☐ 164. BRYAN HARVEY
☐ 180. CHARLIE HOUGH
☐ 187. BRET BARBERIE
☐ 225. GARY SHEFFIELD
☐ 272. ORESTES DESTRADE
☐ 355. DAVE WEATHERS
☐ 366. BENNY SANTIAGO
☐ 431. KURT ABBOTT

HOUSTON ASTROS

☐ 31. STEVE FINLEY
☐ 44. BRIAN WILLIAMS
☐ 97. ANDUJAR CEDENO
☐ 99. GREG SWINDELL
☐ 120. PETE HARNISCH
☐ 135. SCOTT SERVAIS
☐ 191. KEN CAMINITI
☐ 212. JEFF BAGWELL
☐ 242. MITCH WILLIAMS
☐ 244. DARRYL KILE
☐ 253. ANDY STANKIEWICZ
☐ 265. TODD JONES
☐ 290. LUIS GONZALEZ
☐ 345. DOUG DRABEK
☐ 382. CRAIG BIGGIO
☐ 407. MIKE HAMPTON
☐ 421. JAMES MOUTON

KANSAS CITY ROYALS

☐ 46. JOSE LIND
☐ 52. DAVID CONE
☐ 56. PHIL HIATT
☐ 62. BRIAN MCRAE
☐ 110. BOB HAMELIN
☐ 174. KEVIN APPIER
☐ 176. WALLY JOYNER
☐ 194. HIPOLITO PICHARDO
☐ 260. DAVE HENDERSON
☐ 276. GREG GAGNE
☐ 300. MIKE MACFARLANE
☐ 306. FELIX JOSE
☐ 326. VINCE COLEMAN
☐ 387. JEFF MONTGOMERY
☐ 394. GARY GAETTI
☐ 397. TOM GORDON

LOS ANGELES DODGERS

☐ 1. MIKE PIAZZA
☐ 23. JOSE OFFERMAN
☐ 49. JIM GOTT
☐ 74. RAUL MONDESI
☐ 87. DARRYL STRAWBERRY
☐ 98. OREL HERSHISER
☐ 107. TOM CANDIOTTI
☐ 270. DELINO DESHIELDS
☐ 343. PEDRO ASTACIO
☐ 356. ERIC KARROS
☐ 361. TIM WALLACH
☐ 367. BRETT BUTLER
☐ 405. RAMON MARTINEZ
☐ 426. CHAN HO PARK

MILWAUKEE BREWERS

☐ 48. GRAEME LLOYD
☐ 79. PAT LISTACH
☐ 89. GREG VAUGHN
☐ 106. JOHN JAHA
☐ 129. JAIME NAVARRO
☐ 142. DARRYL HAMILTON
☐ 145. BILL WEGMAN
☐ 247. BRIAN HARPER
☐ 268. DAVE NILSSON
☐ 288. CAL ELDRED
☐ 293. RICKY BONES
☐ 310. BOB SCANLAN
☐ 314. KEVIN SEITZER
☐ 344. B.J. SURHOFF
☐ 346. JODY REED
☐ 399. MATT MIESKE
☐ 404. DOUG HENRY

MINNESOTA TWINS

☐ 17. DAVID MCCARTY
☐ 21. KEVIN TAPANI
☐ 105. SHANE MACK
☐ 119. PAT MEARES
☐ 166. SCOTT ERICKSON
☐ 190. JIM DESHAIES
☐ 204. KIRBY PUCKETT
☐ 215. DAVE WINFIELD
☐ 261. KENT HRBEK
☐ 280. RICK AGUILERA
☐ 292. ALEX COLE
☐ 324. CHUCK KNOBLAUCH
☐ 338. PEDRO MUNOZ
☐ 377. SCOTT LEIUS
☐ 436. MATT WALBECK

MONTREAL EXPOS

☐ 9. KIRK RUETER
☐ 10. MIKE LANSING
☐ 20. WIL CORDERO
☐ 25. KEN HILL
☐ 121. MOISES ALOU
☐ 133. JOHN WETTELAND
☐ 137. DARRIN FLETCHER
☐ 216. LARRY WALKER
☐ 229. MARQUIS GRISSOM
☐ 250. JEFF FASSERO
☐ 294. DENIS BOUCHER
☐ 342. SEAN BERRY
☐ 362. PEDRO MARTINEZ
☐ 424. RONDELL WHITE
☐ 427. CLIFF FLOYD

NEW YORK METS

☐ 15. JEROMY BURNITZ
☐ 33. JEFF KENT
☐ 39. RYAN THOMPSON
☐ 45. JOE ORSULAK
☐ 82. DOC GOODEN
☐ 109. BOBBY JONES
☐ 167. ANTHONY YOUNG
☐ 170. JOHN FRANCO
☐ 234. BOBBY BONILLA
☐ 312. JOSE VIZCAINO
☐ 319. TODD HUNDLEY
☐ 334. KEVIN MCREYNOLDS
☐ 341. FERNANDO VINA
☐ 350. PETE SMITH
☐ 354. TIM BOGAR
☐ 369. KELLY STINNETT
☐ 419. BRET SABERHAGEN

NEW YORK YANKEES

☐ 41. RANDY VELARDE
☐ 60. SCOTT KAMIENIECKI
☐ 63. PAT KELLY
☐ 69. PAUL O'NEILL
☐ 75. MIKE GALLEGO
☐ 76. MIKE STANLEY
☐ 149. JIM ABBOTT
☐ 173. WADE BOGGS
☐ 263. BOB WICKMAN
☐ 279. BERNIE WILLIAMS
☐ 299. JIMMY KEY
☐ 305. TERRY MULHOLLAND
☐ 325. DANNY TARTABULL
☐ 365. LUIS POLONIA
☐ 373. XAVIER HERNANDEZ
☐ 392. DON MATTINGLY

OAKLAND A'S

☐ 7. BRENT GATES
☐ 13. TROY NEEL
☐ 38. TERRY STEINBACH
☐ 78. MARK MCGWIRE
☐ 81. MIKE BORDICK
☐ 158. BOB WELCH
☐ 182. TODD VAN POPPEL
☐ 206. DENNIS ECKERSLEY
☐ 223. RICKEY HENDERSON
☐ 243. RON DARLING
☐ 245. GERONIMO BERROA
☐ 289. BOBBY WITT
☐ 302. CARLOS REYES
☐ 371. RUBEN SIERRA
☐ 396. SCOTT BROSIUS
☐ 403. STAN JAVIER
☐ 438. STEVE KARSAY

PHILADELPHIA PHILLIES

- ☐ 2. KEVIN STOCKER
- ☐ 47. DAVE HOLLINS
- ☐ 123. WES CHAMBERLAIN
- ☐ 140. PETE INCAVIGLIA
- ☐ 150. CURT SCHILLING
- ☐ 152. TOMMY GREENE
- ☐ 198. MILT THOMPSON
- ☐ 220. DARREN DAULTON
- ☐ 237. LEN DYKSTRA
- ☐ 256. TYLER GREEN
- ☐ 273. MICKEY MORANDINI
- ☐ 297. RICKY JORDAN
- ☐ 320. DANNY JACKSON
- ☐ 352. MARIANO DUNCAN
- ☐ 380. DOUG JONES
- ☐ 414. BOBBY MUNOZ
- ☐ 416. JOHN KRUK

PITTSBURGH PIRATES

- ☐ 11. AL MARTIN
- ☐ 19. STEVE COOKE
- ☐ 57. CARLOS GARCIA
- ☐ 61. ORLANDO MERCED
- ☐ 65. JEFF KING
- ☐ 127. DON SLAUGHT
- ☐ 156. RANDY TOMLIN
- ☐ 195. DENNY NEAGLE
- ☐ 298. MARK DEWEY
- ☐ 309. PAUL WAGNER
- ☐ 321. KEVIN YOUNG
- ☐ 336. BRIAN HUNTER
- ☐ 381. ZANE SMITH
- ☐ 383. RICK WHITE
- ☐ 408. ANDY VAN SLYKE
- ☐ 411. JAY BELL

ST. LOUIS CARDINALS

- ☐ 5. RENE AROCHA
- ☐ 40. LUIS ALICEA
- ☐ 42. BOB TEWKSBURY
- ☐ 92. GREGG JEFFERIES
- ☐ 111. BERNARD GILKEY
- ☐ 116. MARK WHITEN
- ☐ 124. MIKE PEREZ
- ☐ 136. OZZIE SMITH
- ☐ 248. RHEAL CORMIER
- ☐ 269. RICH BATCHELOR
- ☐ 287. ERIK PAPPAS
- ☐ 315. GERONIMO PENA
- ☐ 331. ALLEN WATSON
- ☐ 347. RAY LANKFORD
- ☐ 360. BRIAN JORDAN
- ☐ 384. TOM PAGNOZZI
- ☐ 410. TODD ZEILE

SAN DIEGO PADRES

- ☐ 29. BRAD AUSMUS
- ☐ 53. RICKY GUTIERREZ
- ☐ 84. PHIL PLANTIER
- ☐ 101. PEDRO MARTINEZ
- ☐ 114. DEREK BELL
- ☐ 144. ARCHI CIANFROCCO
- ☐ 196. DAVE STATON
- ☐ 201. TONY GWYNN
- ☐ 255. ANDY ASHBY
- ☐ 328. ANDY BENES
- ☐ 340. GENE HARRIS
- ☐ 363. BIP ROBERTS
- ☐ 417. TREVOR HOFFMAN
- ☐ 428. DAVE STATON
- ☐ 432. MELVIN NIEVES

SAN FRANCISCO GIANTS

- ☐ 28. ROYCE CLAYTON
- ☐ 68. ROBBY THOMPSON
- ☐ 85. DARREN LEWIS
- ☐ 151. BILL SWIFT
- ☐ 169. ROD BECK
- ☐ 184. WILLIE MCGEE
- ☐ 197. MIKE BENJAMIN
- ☐ 214. MATT WILLIAMS
- ☐ 230. BARRY BONDS
- ☐ 295. JOHN BURKETT
- ☐ 311. MIKE JACKSON
- ☐ 413. MARK PORTUGAL
- ☐ 415. KIRT MANWARING
- ☐ 429. J.R. PHILLIPS
- ☐ 439. SALOMON TORRES

SEATTLE MARINERS

- ☐ 16. RICH AMARAL
- ☐ 55. TINO MARTINEZ
- ☐ 122. JAY BUHNER
- ☐ 154. EDGAR MARTINEZ
- ☐ 172. DAVE FLEMING
- ☐ 183. MIKE BLOWERS
- ☐ 200. CHRIS HAMMOND
- ☐ 213. RANDY JOHNSON
- ☐ 232. KEN GRIFFEY, JR.
- ☐ 252. CHRIS BOSIO
- ☐ 271. FELIX FERMIN
- ☐ 284. DAN WILSON
- ☐ 291. GREG PIRKL
- ☐ 318. ROGER SALKELD
- ☐ 333. REGGIE JEFFERSON
- ☐ 349. ERIC ANTHONY
- ☐ 389. GREG HIBBARD
- ☐ 409. BOBBY AYALA

TEXAS RANGERS

- ☐ 64. TOM HENKE
- ☐ 94. KENNY ROGERS
- ☐ 126. IVAN RODRIGUEZ
- ☐ 148. DAVID HULSE
- ☐ 155. ROGER PAVLIK
- ☐ 177. DEAN PALMER
- ☐ 188. MANUEL LEE
- ☐ 211. JUAN GONZALEZ
- ☐ 222. JOSE CANSECO
- ☐ 238. WILL CLARK
- ☐ 257. KEVIN BROWN
- ☐ 339. BILLY RIPKEN
- ☐ 353. DOUG STRANGE
- ☐ 385. CHRIS JAMES
- ☐ 434. RICK HELLING

TORONTO BLUE JAYS

- ☐ 113. TODD STOTTLEMYRE
- ☐ 125. DEVON WHITE
- ☐ 132. JUAN GUZMAN
- ☐ 134. DAVE STEWART
- ☐ 160. ED SPRAGUE
- ☐ 205. ROBERTO ALOMAR
- ☐ 207. JOE CARTER
- ☐ 221. JOHN OLERUD
- ☐ 239. PAUL MOLITOR
- ☐ 266. PAT BORDERS
- ☐ 313. ROB BUTLER
- ☐ 375. DUANE WARD
- ☐ 400. PAT HENTGEN
- ☐ 423. CARLOS DELGADO
- ☐ 433. ALEX GONZALEZ

T205 (208)
1 1/2" X 2 5/8"

BOSTON RED SOX

☐ WILLIAM CARRIGAN
☐ EDWARD V. CICOTTE
☐ CLYDE ENGLE
☐ EDWARD KARGER
☐ JOHN KLEINOW
☐ TRIS SPEAKER
☐ JACOB G. STAHL
☐ CHARLES WAGNER

BOSTON RUSTLERS

☐ EDW'D J. ABBATICCHIO
☐ FREDERICK T. BECK
☐ G.C. FERGUSON
☐ WILBUR GOOD
☐ GEORGE F. GRAHAM
☐ CHARLES L. HERZOG
☐ A.A. MATTERN
☐ BAYARD H. SHARPE
☐ DAVID SHEAN (BOSTON)

BROOKLYN SUPERBAS

☐ EDWARD B. BARGER (FULL B)
☐ EDWARD B. BARGER (PART B)
☐ GEORGE G. BELL
☐ WILLIAM BERGEN
☐ WILLIAM DAHLEN
☐ JACOB DAUBERT
☐ JOHN E. HUMMEL
☐ EDGAR LENNOX
☐ PRYOR MCELVEEN
☐ G.N. RUCKER
☐ W.D. SCANLAN
☐ TONY SMITH
☐ ZACH D. WHEAT
☐ IRVIN K. WILHELM

CHICAGO CUBS

☐ JAMES P. ARCHER
☐ MORDECAI BROWN
☐ FRANK L. CHANCE
☐ JOHN J. EVERS
☐ WILLIAM A. FOXEN
☐ GEORGE F. GRAHAM
☐ JOHN KLING
☐ FLOYD M. KROH
☐ HARRY MCINTIRE
☐ THOMAS J. NEEDHAM
☐ ORVAL OVERALL
☐ JOHN A. PFIESTER
☐ EDWARD M. REULBACH
☐ LEWIS RICHIE
☐ FRANK M. SCHULTE
☐ DAVID SHEAN (CUBS)
☐ JAMES T. SHECKARD
☐ HARRY STEINFELDT
☐ JOSEPH B. TINKER

CHICAGO WHITE SOX

☐ RUSSEL BLACKBURNE
☐ J. DONOHUE
☐ PAT'K H. DOUGHERTY (WHITE STOCKING)
☐ PAT'K H. DOUGHERTY (RED STOCKING)
☐ HUGH DUFFY
☐ FRANK LANG
☐ HARRY D. LORD
☐ AMBROSE MCCONNELL
☐ MATTHEW MCINTYRE
☐ FREDERICK OLMSTEAD
☐ F. PARENT
☐ FRED PAYNE
☐ JAMES SCOTT
☐ LEE FORD TANNEHILL
☐ EDWARD WALSH
☐ G.H. WHITE

CINCINNATI REDS

☐ ROBERT H. BESCHER
☐ THOMAS W. DOWNEY
☐ RICHARD J. EGAN
☐ ARTHUR FROMME
☐ HARRY L. GASPAR
☐ EDWARD L. GRANT
☐ CLARK GRIFFITH
☐ RICHARD HOBLITZELL
☐ JOHN B. MCLEAN
☐ MICHAEL MITCHELL
☐ GEORGE SUGGS

CLEVELAND NAPS

☐ NEAL BALL
☐ JOSEPH BIRMINGHAM
☐ A. JOSS
☐ GEORGE T. STOVALL
☐ TERENCE TURNER
☐ DENTON T. YOUNG

DETROIT TIGERS

☐ TYRUS RAYMOND COBB
☐ JAMES DELAHANTY
☐ HUGH JENNINGS
☐ DAVID JONES
☐ THOMAS JONES
☐ EDWARD KILLIAN
☐ GEORGE MORIARITY
☐ GEORGE J. MULLIN
☐ CHARLES O'LEARY
☐ CHARLES SCHMIDT
☐ GEORGE SIMMONS
☐ OSCAR STANAGE
☐ EDGAR SUMMERS
☐ EDGAR WILLETT

NEW YORK GIANTS

☐ LEON AMES
☐ BEALS BECKER
☐ ALBERT BRIDWELL
☐ OTIS CRANDALL
☐ ARTHUR DEVLIN
☐ JOSHUA DEVORE
☐ W.R. DICKSON
☐ LAWRENCE DOYLE
☐ ARTHUR FLETCHER
☐ W.A. LATHAM
☐ RICHARD MARQUARD
☐ CHRISTY MATHEWSON
☐ JOHN J. MCGRAW
☐ FRED MERKLE
☐ JOHN T. MEYERS
☐ JOHN J. MURRAY
☐ ARTHUR L. RAYMOND
☐ GEOREG H. SCHLEI
☐ FRED C. SNODGRASS
☐ GEORGE WILTSE (BOTH EARS)
☐ GEORGE WILTSE (RIGHT EAR ONLY)

NEW YORK YANKEES

☐ JAMES AUSTIN
☐ HAROLD W. CHASE (CHASE ONLY)
☐ HAROLD W. CHASE (HAL CHASE)
☐ LOUIS CRIGER
☐ RAY FISHER
☐ RUSSELL FORD (DARK CAP)
☐ RUSSELL FORD (LIGHT CAP)
☐ EARL GARDNER
☐ CHARLES HEMPHILL
☐ JACK KNIGHT
☐ JOHN QUINN
☐ EDWARD SWEENEY
☐ JAMES VAUGHN
☐ HARRY WOLTER

PHILADELPHIA ATHLETICS

☐ FRANK BAKER
☐ JOHN J. BARRY
☐ CHARLES A. BENDER
☐ EDWARD T. COLLINS (MOUTH CLOSED)
☐ EDWARD T. COLLINS (MOUTH OPEN)
☐ JAMES H. DYGERT
☐ FREDERICK T. HARTSEL
☐ HARRY KRAUSE
☐ PAT'K J. LIVINGSTON
☐ BRISCOE LORD
☐ DANIEL MURPHY
☐ RUEBEN N. OLDRING
☐ IRA THOMAS

PHILADELPHIA PHILLIES

☐ JOHN W. BATES
☐ WM. E. BRANSFIELD
☐ CHARLES S. DOOIN
☐ MICHAEL DOOLAN
☐ ROBERT EWING
☐ FRED JACKLITSCH
☐ JOHN LOBERT
☐ SHERWOOD R. MAGEE
☐ PATRICK J. MORAN
☐ GEORGE PASKERT
☐ JOHN A. ROWAN
☐ JOHN TITUS

PITTSBURGH PIRATES

☐ ROBERT BYRNE
☐ HOWARD CAMNITZ
☐ FRED CLARKE
☐ JOHN FLYNN
☐ GEORGE GIBSON
☐ THOMAS W. LEACH
☐ SAM LEEVER
☐ ALBERT P. LEIFIELD
☐ NICHOLAS MADDOX
☐ JOHN D. MILLER
☐ CHARLES PHILLIPPE
☐ KIRB WHITE
☐ J. OWEN WILSON

ST. LOUIS BROWNS

☐ WILLIAM BAILEY
☐ DANIEL J. HOFFMAN
☐ FRANK LAPORTE
☐ B. PELTY
☐ GEORGE STONE
☐ RODERICK J. WALLACE (WITH CAP)
☐ RODERICK J. WALLACE (WITHOUT CAP)

ST. LOUIS CARDINALS

☐ ROGER BRESNAHAN (MOUTH CLOSED)
☐ ROGER BRESNAHAN (MOUTH OPEN)
☐ FRANK J. CORRIDON
☐ LOUIS EVANS
☐ ROBERT HARMON (BOTH EARS)
☐ ROBERT HARMON (LEFT EAR ONLY)
☐ ARNOLD J. HAUSER
☐ MILLER HUGGINS
☐ EDWARD KONETCHY
☐ JOHN LUSH
☐ "REBEL" OAKES
☐ EDWARD PHELPS

WASHINGTON SENATORS

☐ NORMAN ELBERFELD
☐ GRAY
☐ ROBERT GROOM
☐ WALTER JOHNSON
☐ GEORGE F. MCBRIDE
☐ J. CLYDE MILAN
☐ HERMAN SCHAEFER
☐ CHARLES E. STREET

BALTIMORE

☐ DR. MERLE T. ADKINS
☐ JOHN DUNN

BUFFALO

☐ GEORGE MERRITT

JERSEY CITY

☐ CHARLES HANFORD

NEWARK

☐ FORREST D. CADY
☐ JAMES FRICK
☐ WYATT LEE
☐ LEWIS MCALLISTER
☐ JOHN NEE

PROVIDENCE

☐ JAMES COLLINS
☐ JAMES PHELAN

ROCHESTER

☐ HENRY BATCH

T206 (523)
1 1/2" X 2 5/8"

BOSTON RED SOX

☐ ARRELANES
☐ CARRIGAN
☐ CICOTTE
☐ KLEINOW
☐ LORD
☐ NILES
☐ SPEAKER
☐ SPENCER
☐ STAHL (PORTRAIT)
☐ STAHL (FIELDING)
☐ WAGNER (BATTING/WAIST)
☐ WAGNER (BATTING/HIPS)

BOSTON RUSTLERS

☐ BATES
☐ BEAUMONT
☐ BECK
☐ BECKER
☐ BOWERMAN
☐ DAHLEN
☐ FERGUSON
☐ GRAHAM
☐ HERZOG
☐ LINDAMAN
☐ MATTERN
☐ RITCHEY
☐ STARR
☐ SWEENEY

BROOKLYN SUPERBAS

☐ ALPERMAN
☐ BELL (PITCHING/HIPS)
☐ BELL (PITCHING/WAIST)
☐ BERGEN (BATTING)
☐ BERGEN (CATCHING)
☐ BURCH (BATTING)
☐ BURCH (FIELDING)
☐ DAHLEN
☐ DUNN
☐ HUMMEL
☐ HUNTER
☐ JORDAN (PORTRAIT)
☐ JORDAN (BATTING)
☐ LENNOX
☐ LUMLEY
☐ MARSHALL
☐ MCELVEEN
☐ MCINTYRE
☐ MCINTRYE (BROOKLYN & CHICAGO)
☐ PASTORIUS
☐ PATTEE
☐ RUCKER (PORTRAIT)
☐ RUCKER (PITCHING)
☐ H. SMITH
☐ WHEAT
☐ WILHELM (BATTING)
☐ WILHELM (PORTRAIT)

CHICAGO CUBS

☐ G. BROWN
☐ M. BROWN (PORTRAIT)
☐ M. BROWN (BLACK COLLAR)
☐ M. BROWN (BLUE COLLAR)
☐ CHANCE (BATTING)
☐ CHANCE (PORTRAIT/RED)
☐ CHANCE (PORTRAIT/YELLOW)
☐ EVERS (PORTRAIT)
☐ EVERS (BATTING/BLUE BACKGROUND)
☐ EVERS (BATTING/YELLOW BACKGROUND)
☐ HOFMAN
☐ HOWARD
☐ KLING
☐ KROH
☐ LUNDGREN
☐ MORAN
☐ NEEDHAM
☐ OVERALL (PORTRAIT)
☐ OVERALL (PITCHING/ARMS SIDE)
☐ OVERALL (PITCHING/ARMS UP)
☐ PFEFFER
☐ PFEISTER (PORTRAIT)
☐ PFEISTER (PITCHING)
☐ REULBACH (PORTRAIT)
☐ REULBACH (PITCHING)
☐ SCHULTE (BATTING/FRONT)
☐ SCHULTE (BATTING/BACK)
☐ SHECKARD (THROWING)
☐ SHECKARD (PORTRAIT)
☐ STEINFELDT (PORTRAIT)
☐ STEINFELDT (BATTING)
☐ TINKER (PORTRAIT)
☐ TINKER (HANDS ON KNEES)
☐ TINKER (BAT ON SHOULDER)
☐ TINKER (BAT OFF SHOULDER)
☐ ZIMMERMAN

CHICAGO WHITE SOX

☐ ATZ
☐ BURNS
☐ G. DAVIS
☐ DONOHUE
☐ DOUGHERTY (PORTRAIT)
☐ DOUGHERTY (FIELDING)
☐ DUFFY
☐ FIENE (PORTRAIT)
☐ FIENE (FIELDING)
☐ GANDIL
☐ HAHN
☐ ISBELL
☐ F. JONES (PORTRAIT/HIPS)
☐ F. JONES (PORTRAIT)
☐ OWEN
☐ PARENT
☐ PAYNE
☐ PURTELL
☐ SCOTT
☐ F. SMITH
☐ SMITH
☐ SMITH (CHICAGO & BOSTON)
☐ SULLIVAN
☐ L. TANNEHILL
☐ TANNEHILL
☐ WALSH
☐ WHITE (PORTRAIT)
☐ WHITE (PITCHING/WAIST)

CINCINNATI REDS

☐ BESCHER (PORTRAIT)
☐ BESCHER (FIELDING)
☐ CAMPBELL
☐ DOWNEY (BATTING)
☐ DOWNEY (FIELDING)
☐ DUBUC
☐ EGAN
☐ EWING
☐ FROMME
☐ GASPAR
☐ GRIFFITH (PORTRAIT)
☐ GRIFFITH (BATTING)
☐ HOBLITZELL
☐ HUGGINS (PORTRAIT)
☐ HUGGINS (PORTRAIT/HITTING)
☐ KARGER
☐ LOBERT
☐ MCLEAN
☐ MITCHELL
☐ MOWREY
☐ OAKES
☐ PASKERT
☐ SPADE

CLEVELAND NAPS

☐ BALL
☐ BERGER
☐ BIRMINGHAM
☐ BRADLEY (PORTRAIT)
☐ BRADLEY (BATTING)
☐ J. J. CLARKE
☐ EASTERLY
☐ FLICK
☐ GOODE
☐ HINCHMAN
☐ JOSS (PORTRAIT)
☐ JOSS (PITCHING)
☐ LAJOIE (PORTRAIT)
☐ LAJOIE (BATTING)
☐ LAJOIE (THROWING)
☐ LIEBHARDT
☐ PERRING
☐ RHOADES (PITCHING/WAIST)
☐ RHOADES (PITCHING/HIPS)
☐ STOVALL (PORTRAIT)
☐ STOVALL (BATTING)
☐ TURNER
☐ YOUNG (PORTRAIT)
☐ YOUNG (PITCHING/SIDE)
☐ YOUNG (PITCHING/FRONT)

DETROIT TIGERS

☐ BUSH
☐ COBB (PORTRAIT/RED)
☐ COBB (PORTRAIT/GREEN)
☐ COBB (BATTING/BLACK CAP)
☐ COBB (BATTING/GRAY CAP)
☐ CRAWFORD (BATTING)
☐ CRAWFORD (THROWING)
☐ DONOVAN (PORTRAIT)
☐ DONOVAN (PITCHING)
☐ JENNINGS (PORTRAIT)
☐ JENNINGS (PORTRAIT/WAIST)
☐ JENNINGS (PORTRAIT/HIPS)
☐ JONES
☐ KILLIAN (PORTRAIT)
☐ KILLIAN (PITCHING)
☐ MCINTYRE
☐ MORIARTY
☐ MULLEN
☐ MULLIN (BATTING)
☐ MULLIN (FIELDING/ HORIZONTAL)
☐ O'LEARY (PORTRAIT)
☐ O'LEARY (HANDS ON KNEES)
☐ ROSSMAN
☐ SCHAEFER
☐ SCHMIDT (PORTRAIT)
☐ SCHMIDT (THROWING)
☐ STANAGE
☐ SUMMERS
☐ WILLETT
☐ WILLETTS

NEW YORK GIANTS

☐ AMES (PORTRAIT)
☐ AMES (PITCHING/WAIST)
☐ AMES (PITCHING/HIPS)
☐ BRIDWELL (PORTRAIT)
☐ BRIDWELL (PORTRAIT/ SWEATER)
☐ CRANDALL(PORTRAIT)
☐ CRANDALL (PORTRAIT/ SWEATER)
☐ DEVLIN
☐ DEVORE
☐ DONLIN (PORTRAIT/KNEES)
☐ DONLIN (PORTRAIT/HANDS ON KNEES)
☐ DONLIN (BATTING)
☐ DOYLE (PORTRAIT/SWEATER)
☐ DOYLE (BATTING)
☐ DOYLE (THROWING)
☐ DURHAM
☐ FLETCHER
☐ HERZOG
☐ LATHAM
☐ MARQUARD (PORTRAIT)
☐ MARQUARD (PORTRAIT/HIPS)
☐ MARQUARD (PITCHING)
☐ MATHEWSON (PORTRAIT)
☐ MATHEWSON (PITCHING/WHITE CAP)
☐ MATHEWSON (PITCHING/BLACK CAP)
☐ MCCORMICK
☐ MCGRAW (PORTRAIT)
☐ MCGRAW (PORTRAIT/SWEATER)
☐ MCGRAW (PORTRAIT/HIPS)
☐ MCGRAW (PORTRAIT/KNEES)
☐ MERKLE (PORTRAIT)
☐ MERKLE (THROWING)
☐ MEYERS
☐ MURRAY (PORTRAIT)
☐ MURRAY (BATTING)
☐ MYERS (CATCHING)
☐ MYERS (BATTING)
☐ O'HARA
☐ RAYMOND
☐ SCHLEI (PORTRAIT/SWEATER)
☐ SCHLEI (BATTING)
☐ SCHLEI (CATCHING)
☐ SEYMOUR (PORTRAIT)
☐ SEYMOUR (BATTING)
☐ SEYMOUR (THROWING)
☐ SNODGRASS (BATTING)
☐ SNODGRASS (CATCHING)
☐ TENNEY
☐ WEIMER
☐ WILTSE (PORTRAIT)
☐ WILTSE (PORTRAIT/SWEATER)
☐ WILTSE (PITCHING)

NEW YORK YANKEES

☐ BALL
☐ CHASE (WITH CUP)
☐ CHASE (PORTRAIT/PINK)
☐ CHASE (PORTRAIT/BLUE)
☐ CHASE (THROWING/BLACK CAP)
☐ CHASE (THROWING/WHITE CAP)
☐ CHESBRO
☐ CREE
☐ DEMMITT
☐ DOYLE
☐ ELBERFELD
☐ ENGLE
☐ FORD
☐ FRILL
☐ HEMPHILL
☐ KEELER (PORTRAIT)
☐ KEELER (BATTING)
☐ KLEINOW (CATCHING)
☐ KLEINOW (BATTING)
☐ KNIGHT (PORTRAIT)
☐ KNIGHT (BATTING)
☐ LAKE
☐ LAPORTE
☐ MANNING (BATTING)
☐ MANNING (PITCHING)
☐ QUINN
☐ SWEENEY
☐ WARHOP

PHILADELPHIA ATHLETICS

☐ BAKER
☐ BARRY
☐ BENDER (PORTRAIT)
☐ BENDER (PITCHING/WITH TREES)
☐ BENDER (PITCHING/NO TREES)
☐ COLLINS
☐ DAVIS
☐ H. DAVIS
☐ DYGERT
☐ HARTSELL
☐ KRAUSE (PORTRAIT)
☐ KRAUSE (PITCHING)
☐ LIVINGSTONE
☐ MURPHY (BATTING)
☐ MURPHY (THROWING)
☐ NICHOLLS
☐ NICHOLS
☐ OLDRING (BATTING)
☐ OLDRING (FIELDING)
☐ PLANK
☐ POWERS
☐ THOMAS

PHILADELPHIA PHILLIES

☐ BRANSFIELD
☐ COVALESKI
☐ DOOIN
☐ DOOLAN (BATTING)
☐ DOOLAN (FIELDING)
☐ DOOLIN
☐ JACKLITSCH
☐ KNABE
☐ MAGEE (PORTRAIT)
☐ MAGIE (NAME MISSPELLED)
☐ MAGEE (BATTING)
☐ MCQUILLAN (BATTING)
☐ MCQUILLAN (PITCHING)
☐ TITUS

PITTSBURGH PIRATES

☐ ABBATICCHIO (BATTING/HIPS)
☐ ABBATICCHIO (BATTING/KNEES)
☐ ABSTEIN
☐ CAMNITZ (PORTRAIT)
☐ CAMNITZ (PITCHING/FRONT)
☐ CAMNITZ (PITCHING/SIDE)
☐ CLARKE
☐ F. CLARKE
☐ GIBSON
☐ LEACH (PORTRAIT)
☐ LEACH (FIELDING)
☐ LEIFIELD (PITCHING)
☐ LEIFIELD (BATTING)
☐ MADDOX
☐ MILLER
☐ PHILLIPPE
☐ WAGNER
☐ WILLIS
☐ WILSON

ST. LOUIS BROWNS

☐ CRIGER
☐ CRISS
☐ DEMMITT
☐ DINEEN
☐ FERRIS
☐ GRAHAM
☐ HOFFMAN
☐ HOWELL (PORTRAIT)
☐ HOWELL (PORTRAIT/HIPS)
☐ JONES
☐ LAKE (PITCHING)
☐ LAKE (HANDS ABOVE HEAD)
☐ MCALEESE
☐ PELTY (PITCHING)
☐ PELTY (HORIZONTAL)
☐ POWELL
☐ STEPHENS
☐ STONE
☐ WADDELL (PORTRAIT)
☐ WADDELL (PITCHING)
☐ WALLACE
☐ WILLIAMS

ST. LOUIS CARDINALS

☐ BARBEAU
☐ BLISS
☐ BRESNAHAN (PORTRAIT)
☐ BRESNAHAN (BATTING)
☐ BYRNE
☐ CHARLES
☐ EVANS
☐ GEYER
☐ GILBERT

- ☐ HULSWITT
- ☐ KONETCHY (FIELDING/HIGH BALL)
- ☐ KONETCHY (FIELDING/LOW BALL)
- ☐ O'HARA
- ☐ PHELPS
- ☐ RHODES
- ☐ SHAW
- ☐ WILLIS (BATTING)
- ☐ WILLIS (FIELDING)

WASHINGTON SENATORS

- ☐ G. BROWN
- ☐ CONROY (BATTING)
- ☐ CONROY (FIELDING)
- ☐ DELEHANTY
- ☐ ELBERFELD (PORTRAIT)
- ☐ ELBERFELD (FIELDING)
- ☐ GANLEY
- ☐ GRAY
- ☐ GROOM
- ☐ JOHNSON (PORTRAIT)
- ☐ JOHNSON (PITCHING)
- ☐ MCBRIDE
- ☐ MILAN
- ☐ SCHAEFER
- ☐ SHIPKE
- ☐ STREET (PORTRAIT)
- ☐ STREET (CATCHING)
- ☐ TANNEHILL
- ☐ UNGLAUB

AMERICAN ASSOCIATION

COLUMBUS

- ☐ CLARK
- ☐ CLYMER
- ☐ CONGALTON
- ☐ KRUGER
- ☐ SCHRECK

INDIANAPOLIS

- ☐ BURKE
- ☐ CARR
- ☐ CROSS
- ☐ DAVIDSON
- ☐ HAYDEN

KANSAS CITY

- ☐ BECKLEY
- ☐ BRASHEAR
- ☐ DORNER
- ☐ HALLMAN
- ☐ LUNGREN
- ☐ RITTER
- ☐ SHANNON

LOUISVILLE

- ☐ DELAHANTY
- ☐ PUTTMAN
- ☐ THIELMAN

MILWAUKEE

- ☐ BARRY
- ☐ MCGANN
- ☐ MCGLYNN
- ☐ RANDALL

MINNEAPOLIS

- ☐ COLLINS
- ☐ CRAVATH
- ☐ DOWNS
- ☐ OBERLIN
- ☐ O'NEIL
- ☐ PICKERING
- ☐ QUILLEN
- ☐ YOUNG

ST. PAUL

- ☐ ARMBRUSTER
- ☐ O'BRIEN

TOLEDO

- ☐ ABBOTT
- ☐ FREEMAN
- ☐ HINCHMAN
- ☐ LATTIMORE
- ☐ WRIGHT

EASTERN LEAGUE

BALTIMORE

- ☐ ADKINS
- ☐ CASSIDY
- ☐ DESSAU
- ☐ DUNN
- ☐ HALL
- ☐ JACKSON
- ☐ POLAND
- ☐ SLAGLE
- ☐ STRANG

BUFFALO

- ☐ BRAIN
- ☐ BURCHELL
- ☐ CLANCY
- ☐ FLANAGAN
- ☐ KISINGER
- ☐ MALARKEY
- ☐ NATTRESS
- ☐ SCHIRM
- ☐ SMITH
- ☐ TAYLOR
- ☐ WHITE

JERSEY CITY

- ☐ HANNIFAN
- ☐ MERRITT
- ☐ MILLIGAN
- ☐ MOELLER

MONTREAL

- ☐ CASEY

NEWARK

- ☐ MCGINNITY
- ☐ SCHLAFLY
- ☐ SHARPE

PROVIDENCE

- ☐ ANDERSON
- ☐ ARNDT
- ☐ BLACKBURNE
- ☐ HOFFMAN
- ☐ LAVENDER
- ☐ MORAN
- ☐ PHELAN
- ☐ SHAW

ROCHESTER

- ☐ BARGER
- ☐ BATCH
- ☐ BUTLER
- ☐ CHAPPELLE
- ☐ GANZEL
- ☐ MALONEY

TORONTO

- ☐ GRINSHAW
- ☐ KELLEY
- ☐ MCGINLEY
- ☐ MITCHELL
- ☐ RUDOLPH

SOUTH ATLANTIC LEAGUE

AUGUSTA

- ☐ COLES

CHARLESTON

- ☐ FOSTER
- ☐ PAIGE

COLUMBIA

- ☐ KIERNAN
- ☐ MANION

COLUMBUS

- ☐ HELM

JACKSONVILLE

- ☐ MULLANEY
- ☐ VIOLAT

MACON

- ☐ LAFITTE

SAVANNAH

- ☐ HOWARD

SOUTHERN LEAGUE

ATLANTA

- ☐ JORDAN
- ☐ SMITH

BIRMINGHAM

- ☐ MOLESWORTH

LITTLE ROCK

- ☐ HART
- ☐ LENTZ

MEMPHIS

- ☐ CAREY
- ☐ CRANSTON

MOBILE

- ☐ HICKMAN
- ☐ THORNTON

MONTGOMERY

- ☐ GREMINGER
- ☐ HART
- ☐ PERSONS
- ☐ ROCKENFELD

NASHVILLE

- ☐ BAY
- ☐ BERNHARD
- ☐ ELLAM
- ☐ PERDUE

NEW ORLEANS

- ☐ BREITENSTEIN
- ☐ FRITZ
- ☐ REGAN

TEXAS LEAGUE

DALLAS

□ MILLER

HOUSTON

□ WHITE

SAN ANTONIO

□ BASTIAN
□ STARK

SHREVEPORT

□ SMITH
□ THEBO

VIRGINIA LEAGUE

DANVILLE

□ KING
□ WESTLAKE

LYNCHBURG

□ HOOKER
□ ORTH

NORFOLK

□ OTEY
□ SEITZ

PORTSMOUTH

□ GUIHEEN
□ MCCAULEY

RICHMOND

□ LIPE
□ REVELLE

ROANOKE

□ RYAN
□ SHAUGHNESSY

T207 (207)
BROWN BACKGROUND
1 1/2" X 2 5/8"

BRESNAHAM ST. LOUIS - NAT.

BOSTON RED SOX

□ BRADLEY
□ BUSHELMAN
□ CARRIGAN/CORRECT BACK
□ CARRIGAN/ WAGNER BACK
□ CICOTTTE
□ ENGLE
□ GARDNER
□ HAGEMAN
□ HALL
□ HENRIKSEN
□ HOOPER
□ LEWIS
□ NUNAMAKER
□ O'BRIEN
□ SPEAKER
□ THOMAS
□ WAGNER/CORRECT BACK
□ WAGNER/CARRIGAN BACK
□ WOOD
□ YERKES

BOSTON RUSTLERS

□ DEVLIN
□ DONNELLY
□ GOWDY
□ HOUSER
□ KIRKE
□ KLING
□ LEWIS
□ MCDONALD
□ MILLER
□ PERDUE
□ SPRATT
□ SWEENEY
□ TYLER

BROOKLYN SUPERBAS

□ BARGER
□ COULSON
□ DAUBERT
□ ERWIN
□ KNETZER
□ MILLER
□ NORTHEN
□ RAGAN
□ RUCKER
□ SCHARDT
□ STACK
□ TOOLEY
□ WHEAT

DAUBERT BROOKLYN - NAT.

CHICAGO CUBS

□ CHANCE
□ COLE
□ LENNOX
□ MCINTIRE
□ MILLER
□ NEEDHAM
□ REULBACH
□ SAIER
□ SCHULTE
□ TINKER

CHICAGO WHITE SOX

□ BENZ
□ BLACKBURNE
□ BLOCK
□ BODIE
□ CALLAHAN
□ COLLINS
□ FOURNIER
□ KUHN
□ LANGE
□ LORD
□ MCINTYRE
□ MOGRIDGE
□ PETERS
□ RATH
□ SCOTT
□ SULLIVAN
□ TANNEHILL
□ WEAVER
□ WHITE
□ ZEIDER

CINCINNATI REDS

□ ALMEIDA
□ BESCHER
□ CLARKE
□ FROMME
□ MARSANS
□ MCLEAN
□ MITCHELL
□ PHELAN
□ SEVEROLD
□ SMITH

CLEVELAND NAPS

□ ADAMS
□ BALL
□ BIRMINGHAM
□ BLANDING
□ BUTCHER
□ DAVIS
□ EASTERLY
□ GEORGE
□ GRANEY
□ GREGG
□ KALER
□ LIVINGSTON/"A" SHIRT
□ LIVINGSTON/"C" SHIRT
□ LIVINGSTON/SMALL "C" SHIRT
□ MITCHELL
□ OLSON
□ RYAN
□ TURNER

DETROIT TIGERS

□ BAUMAN
□ COVINGTON
□ DELAHANTY
□ DRAKE
□ GAINOR
□ LIVELY
□ MORIARITY
□ MULLINS WITH "D" ON CAP
□ MULLINS WITHOUT "D" ON CAP
□ STANAGE
□ WORKS

NEW YORK GIANTS

□ BECKER
□ CRANDALL
□ DEVORE
□ DOYLE
□ FLETCHER
□ HARTLEY
□ HERZOG
□ HIGGINS
□ LATHAM
□ MARQUARD
□ MCGRAW
□ SNODGRASS
□ WILSON
□ WILTSE

NEW YORK YANKEES

□ DANIELS
□ FISHER WITH WHITE LETTERS ON CAP
□ FISHER WITH BLUE LETTERS ON CAP
□ HOFF
□ QUINN
□ STREET
□ VAUGHN
□ WARHOP
□ WILLIAMS
□ WOLVERTON

PHILADELPHIA ATHLETICS

□ BARRY
□ BENDER
□ DANFORTH
□ DERRICK
□ KRAUSE
□ LAPP

- ☐ LORD
- ☐ MORGAN
- ☐ OLDRING
- ☐ STRUNK

PHILADELPHIA PHILLIES

- ☐ CHALMERS
- ☐ DOOIN
- ☐ DOWNEY
- ☐ GRAHAM
- ☐ KNABE
- ☐ MOORE
- ☐ MORAN
- ☐ PASKART
- ☐ RASMUSSEN
- ☐ SCANLON

PITTSBURGH PIRATES

- ☐ BYRNE
- ☐ CAMNITZ
- ☐ CAREY
- ☐ DONLIN
- ☐ FERRY
- ☐ HYATT
- ☐ KELLY
- ☐ LEACH
- ☐ LEIFIELD
- ☐ MCCARTHY
- ☐ MCKECHNIE
- ☐ MILLER
- ☐ O'TOOLE
- ☐ SIMON
- ☐ WILSON

ST. LOUIS BROWNS

- ☐ AUSTIN WITH STL ON SHIRT
- ☐ AUSTIN WITHOUT STL ON SHIRT
- ☐ HALLINAN
- ☐ E. HAMILTON
- ☐ HOGAN
- ☐ KUTINA
- ☐ NELSON
- ☐ PELTY
- ☐ STOVALL
- ☐ WALLACE

ST. LOUIS CARDINALS

- ☐ BRESNAHAN
- ☐ ELLIS
- ☐ EVANS
- ☐ GOLDEN
- ☐ HARMON
- ☐ KONETCHY
- ☐ LOUDERMILK
- ☐ OAKES
- ☐ SMITH
- ☐ STEELE
- ☐ STEINFELDT
- ☐ WILIE
- ☐ WINGO
- ☐ WOODBURN

WASHINGTON SENATORS

- ☐ AINSMITH
- ☐ CUNNINGHAM
- ☐ HENRY
- ☐ JOHNSON
- ☐ MCBRIDE
- ☐ MILAN
- ☐ MORGAN
- ☐ SCHAEFER
- ☐ WALKER

1989 UPPER DECK (800)
2 1/2" X 3 1/2"

ATLANTA BRAVES

- ☐ 17. JOHN SMOLTZ
- ☐ 19. MARK LEMKE
- ☐ 52. JIM ACKER
- ☐ 55. PAUL RUNGE
- ☐ 71. ZANE SMITH
- ☐ 74. RICK MAHLER
- ☐ 93. ALBERT HALL
- ☐ 104. OZZIE VIRGIL
- ☐ 113. GERMAN JIMENEZ
- ☐ 121. BRUCE BENEDICT
- ☐ 132. JEFF BLAUSER
- ☐ 144. ANDRES THOMAS
- ☐ 357. DALE MURPHY
- ☐ 360. TOM GLAVINE
- ☐ 378. RON GANT
- ☐ 396. CHUCK CARY
- ☐ 399. TERRY BLOCKER
- ☐ 412. PETE SMITH
- ☐ 414. BRUCE SUTTER
- ☐ 431. GERALD PERRY
- ☐ 433. JERRY ROYSTER
- ☐ 435. ED OLWINE
- ☐ 566. PAUL ASSENMACHER
- ☐ 568. JIM MORRISON
- ☐ 570. TED SIMMONS
- ☐ 587. DION JAMES
- ☐ 589. CHARLIE PULEO
- ☐ 672. TEAM CHECKLIST
- ☐ 731. LONNIE SMITH
- ☐ 734. JOSE ALVAREZ
- ☐ 751. TOMMY GREGG
- ☐ 753. DEREK LILLIQUIST
- ☐ 795. JODY DAVIS

BALTIMORE ORIOLES

- ☐ 254. LARRY SHEETS
- ☐ 261. DOUG SISK
- ☐ 275. EDDIE MURRAY
- ☐ 283. BILLY RIPKEN
- ☐ 294. JIM TRABER
- ☐ 408. BRADY ANDERSON
- ☐ 426. KEN GERHART
- ☐ 429. JOE ORSULAK
- ☐ 447. DAVE SCHMIDT
- ☐ 450. DON AASE
- ☐ 467. CAL RIPKEN
- ☐ 469. TERRY KENNEDY
- ☐ 486. JEFF STONE
- ☐ 488. TOM NIEDENFUER
- ☐ 490. RICK SCHU
- ☐ 553. MICKEY TETTLETON
- ☐ 571. MARK THURMOND
- ☐ 574. JOSE BAUTISTA
- ☐ 592. PETE STANICEK
- ☐ 595. JEFF BALLARD
- ☐ 651. OSWALD PERAZA
- ☐ 653. MIKE MORGAN
- ☐ 655. JAY TIBBS
- ☐ 682. TEAM CHECKLIST
- ☐ 723. GREGG OLSON
- ☐ 725. CRAIG WORTHINGTON
- ☐ 735. BOB MILACKI
- ☐ 740. RANDY MILLIGAN
- ☐ 742. STEVE FINLEY
- ☐ 744. PETE HARNISCH
- ☐ 747. JUAN BELL
- ☐ 749. PHIL BRADLEY

BOSTON RED SOX

- ☐ 26. CARLOS QUINTANA
- ☐ 36. LARRY PARRISH
- ☐ 38. MIKE SMITHSON
- ☐ 40. ED ROMERO
- ☐ 152. RICK CERONE
- ☐ 161. SPIKE OWEN
- ☐ 173. MARTY BARRETT
- ☐ 184. TODD BENZINGER
- ☐ 195. ROGER CLEMENS
- ☐ 366. DWIGHT EVANS
- ☐ 368. RICH GEDMAN
- ☐ 370. JODY REED
- ☐ 387. BRUCE HURST
- ☐ 389. WADE BOGGS
- ☐ 411. BOB STANLEY
- ☐ 413. JIM RICE
- ☐ 415. OIL CAN BOYD
- ☐ 432. MIKE GREENWELL
- ☐ 434. ELLIS BURKS
- ☐ 503. DENNIS LAMP
- ☐ 521. LEE SMITH
- ☐ 524. KEVIN ROMINE
- ☐ 542. MIKE BODDICKER
- ☐ 545. TOM BOLTON
- ☐ 687. TEAM CHECKLIST
- ☐ 757. NICK ESASKY
- ☐ 759. ROB MURPHY

CALIFORNIA ANGELS

- ☐ 24. DANTE BICHETTE
- ☐ 110. DEVON WHITE
- ☐ 119. BOB BOONE
- ☐ 126. CHILI DAVIS
- ☐ 138. JACK HOWELL
- ☐ 147. DEWAYNE BUICE
- ☐ 201. DICK SCHOFIELD
- ☐ 212. TONY ARMAS
- ☐ 223. KIRK MCCASKILL
- ☐ 234. TERRY CLARK
- ☐ 245. MARK MCLEMORE
- ☐ 462. DARRELL MILLER
- ☐ 464. SHERMAN CORBETT
- ☐ 481. JOHNNY RAY
- ☐ 483. STU CLIBURN
- ☐ 485. BRIAN DOWNING
- ☐ 552. DAN PETRY
- ☐ 555. MIKE WITT
- ☐ 573. WALLY JOYNER
- ☐ 591. THAD BOSLEY
- ☐ 594. BRYAN HARVEY
- ☐ 613. WILLIE FRASER
- ☐ 614. JIM EPPARD
- ☐ 632. CHUCK FINLEY
- ☐ 635. GREG MINTON
- ☐ 668. TEAM CHECKLIST
- ☐ 712. BERT BLYLEVEN
- ☐ 755. JIM ABBOTT
- ☐ 775. LANCE PARRISH
- ☐ 794. CLAUDELL WASHINGTON

CHICAGO CUBS

- ☐ 6. ROLANDO ROOMES
- ☐ 10. DOUG DASCENZO
- ☐ 14. MIKE HARKEY
- ☐ 61. FRANK DIPINO
- ☐ 63. JAMIE MOYER
- ☐ 65. MITCH WELSTER
- ☐ 82. CALVIN SCHIRALDI
- ☐ 84. LES LANCASTER
- ☐ 107. SHAWON DUNSTON
- ☐ 120. RYNE SANDBERG
- ☐ 127. MANNY TRILLO
- ☐ 140. MARK GRACE
- ☐ 148. JODY DAVIS
- ☐ 205. ANDRE DAWSON
- ☐ 214. DARRIN JACKSON
- ☐ 222. ANGEL SALAZAR
- ☐ 235. RAFAEL PALMEIRO
- ☐ 241. GREG MADDUX
- ☐ 303. RICK SUTCLIFFE
- ☐ 321. GARY VARSHO
- ☐ 324. DREW HALL
- ☐ 342. SCOTT SANDERSON
- ☐ 345. PAT PERRY

□ 452. GOOSE GOSSAGE
□ 455. DAMON BERRYHILL
□ 473. VANCE LAW
□ 491. JEFF PICO
□ 494. AL NIPPER
□ 675. TEAM CHECKLIST
□ 762. KEVIN BLANKENSHIP
□ 765. JEROME WALTON
□ 776. JOE GIRARDI
□ 778. MITCH WILLIAMS
□ 780. DWIGHT SMITH
□ 797. PAUL KILGUS
□ 799. STEVE WILSON

CHICAGO WHITE SOX

□ 151. JERRY REUSS
□ 164. DAVE GALLAGHER
□ 175. OZZIE GUILLEN
□ 183. RON KARKOVICE
□ 192. KELLY PARIS
□ 204. DAN PASQUA
□ 211. HAROLD BAINES
□ 224. STEVE LYONS
□ 231. GREG WALKER
□ 243. MELIDO PEREZ
□ 457. BARRY JONES
□ 460. MARK SALAS
□ 478. SHAWN HILLEGAS
□ 496. DARYL BOSTON
□ 499. BILL LONG
□ 506. KEN WILLIAMS
□ 509. JEFF BITTIGER
□ 527. DONNIE HILL
□ 530. JACK MCDOWELL
□ 548. JOHN DAVIS
□ 606. MIKE DIAZ
□ 609. CARLTON FISK
□ 628. FRED MANRIQUE
□ 647. BOBBY THIGPEN
□ 650. IVAN CALDERON
□ 692. TEAM CHECKLIST
□ 711. RON KITTLE
□ 715. STEVE ROSENBERG
□ 790. EDDIE WILLIAMS

CINCINNATI REDS

□ 23. VAN SNIDER
□ 29. RANDY ST. CLAIRE
□ 160. KAL DANIELS
□ 169. BO DIAZ
□ 180. CHRIS SABO
□ 187. RON ROBINSON
□ 196. DAVE CONCEPCION
□ 257. JACK ARMSTRONG
□ 270. BARRY LARKIN
□ 276. JEFF REED
□ 287. RON OESTER
□ 299. NICK ESASKY
□ 351. DAVE COLLINS
□ 354. LEON DURHAM
□ 372. ROB MURPHY
□ 375. ROB DIBBLE
□ 393. JEFF TREADWAY
□ 407. JOHN FRANCO
□ 410. ERIC DAVIS
□ 428. PAUL O'NEILL
□ 446. LLOYD MCCLENDON
□ 449. FRANK WILLiAMS
□ 617. TOM BROWNING
□ 619. JOSE RIJO
□ 636. HERM WINNINGHAM
□ 638. TIM BIRTSAS
□ 640. DANNY JACKSON
□ 688. TEAM CHECKLIST
□ 760. RICK MAHLER
□ 781. LENNY HARRIS
□ 783. NORM CHARLTON
□ 785. TODD BENZINGER

CLEVELAND INDIANS

□ 2. LUIS MEDINA
□ 32. DAN FIROVA
□ 34. TOMMY HINZO
□ 157. WILLIE UPSHAW
□ 170. CORY SNYDER
□ 186. JULIO FRANCO
□ 190. JOE CARTER
□ 198. BROOK JACOBY
□ 209. SCOTT BAILES
□ 217. ANDY ALLANSON
□ 228. RON KITTLE
□ 236. PAUL ZUVELLA
□ 250. GREG SWINDELL
□ 466. BUD BLACK
□ 468. JOHN FARRELL
□ 470. TOM CANDIOTTI
□ 487. CARMEN CASTILLO
□ 489. JAY BELL
□ 517. DAVE CLARK
□ 519. RON WASHINGTON
□ 536. TERRY FRANCONA
□ 538. MEL HALL
□ 540. DOUG JONES
□ 679. TEAM CHECKLIST
□ 716. JOE SKALSKI
□ 728. RICK YETT
□ 796. ODDIBE MCDOWELL
□ 800. PETE O'BRIEN

DETROIT TIGERS

□ 47. PAUL GIBSON
□ 49. LARRY HERNDON
□ 106. TOM BROOKENS
□ 117. GARY PETTIS
□ 128. CHET LEMON
□ 136. LUIS SALAZAR
□ 150. MATT NOKES
□ 259. RAY KNIGHT
□ 266. DAVE BERGMAN
□ 279. GUILLERMO HERNANDEZ
□ 290. ALAN TRAMMELL
□ 298. DOYLE ALEXANDER
□ 352. JACK MORRIS
□ 355. IVAN DEJESUS
□ 373. MIKE HENNEMAN
□ 391. FRANK TANANA
□ 394. DARRELL EVANS
□ 451. LOU WHITAKER
□ 454. JIM WALEWANDER
□ 472. JEFF ROBINSON
□ 475. WALT TERRELL
□ 493. ERIC KING
□ 652. PAT SHERIDAN
□ 654. MIKE HEATH
□ 690. TEAM CHECKLIST
□ 714. KEN WILLIAMS
□ 761. FRED LYNN
□ 764. STEVE SEARCY
□ 782. TORY LOVULLO
□ 784. CHRIS BROWN

HOUSTON ASTROS

□ 58. CASEY CANDAELE
□ 76. JIM DESHAIES
□ 79. JOAQUIN ANDUJAR
□ 97. DANNY DARWIN
□ 100. JIM PANKOVITS
□ 101. BILL DORAN
□ 112. BUDDY BELL
□ 135. GERALD YOUNG
□ 141. KEN CAMINITI
□ 145. NOLAN RYAN
□ 251. JUAN AGOSTO
□ 262. ALEX TREVINO
□ 273. CRAIG BIGGIO
□ 284. CRAIG REYNOLDS
□ 295. MIKE SCOTT
□ 302. DAVE SMITH
□ 305. ALAN ASHBY
□ 323. CHUCK JACKSON
□ 341. RAFAEL RAMIREZ
□ 344. BILLY HATCHER
□ 401. LOUIE MEADOWNS
□ 404. LARRY ANDERSEN
□ 422. BOB KNEPPER
□ 425. KEVIN BASS
□ 443. GLENN DAVIS
□ 669. TEAM CHECKLIST

KANSAS CITY ROYALS

□ 12. LUIS DE LOS SANTOS
□ 21. REY PALACIOS
□ 37. BRET SABERHAGEN
□ 42. ED HEARN
□ 44. JIM EISENREICH
□ 202. MARK GUBICZA
□ 215. GEORGE BRETT
□ 221. BO JACKSON
□ 233. PAT TABLER
□ 244. WILLIE WILSON
□ 308. STEVE FARR
□ 326. ISRAEL SANCHEZ
□ 329. DANNY TARTABULL
□ 347. GARY THURMAN
□ 350. FRANK WHITE
□ 507. BILL PECOTA
□ 510. KEVIN SEITZER
□ 528. LARRY OWEN
□ 546. MIKE MACFARLANE
□ 549. FLOYD BANNISTER
□ 616. KURT STILLWELL
□ 618. JEFF MONTGOMERY
□ 620. JAMIE QUIRK
□ 637. CHARLIE LEIBRANDT
□ 639. BILL BUCKNER
□ 689. TEAM CHECKLIST
□ 736. TOM GORDON
□ 767. BOB BOONE
□ 769. JOSE DEJESUS

LOS ANGELES DODGERS

□ 16. WILLIAM BRENNAN
□ 18. RAMON MARTINEZ
□ 20. JUAN BELL
□ 53. STEVE SAX
□ 66. JOHN TUDOR
□ 68. MIKE DEVEREAUX
□ 70. MIKE MARSHALL
□ 72. BRIAN HOLTON
□ 75. JOHN SHELBY
□ 87. JESSE OROSCO
□ 89. DAVE ANDERSON
□ 91. FRANKLIN STUBBS
□ 94. TIM LEARY
□ 108. TRACY WOODSON
□ 116. MIKE SCIOSCIA
□ 130. OREL HERSHISER
□ 137. ALEJANDRO PENA
□ 146. MIKE DAVIS
□ 607. CHRIS GWYNN
□ 610. JAY HOWELL
□ 611. TIM CREWS
□ 615. JEFF HAMILTON
□ 626. JOSE GONZALEZ
□ 629. RICKY HORTON
□ 631. ALFREDO GRIFFIN
□ 633. KIRK GIBSON
□ 648. TIM BELCHER
□ 656. FERNANDO VALENZUELA
□ 676. TEAM CHECKLIST
□ 709. MICKEY HATCHER
□ 713. RICK DEMPSEY
□ 763. EDDIE MURRAY
□ 777. WILLIE RANDOLPH

MILWAUKEE BREWERS

□ 13. GARY SHEFFIELD
□ 252. MIKE FELDER
□ 263. JEFFREY LEONARD
□ 274. JIM GANTNER
□ 285. ROBIN YOUNT
□ 292. CHRIS BOSIO
□ 301. DARRYL HAMILTON
□ 304. DAVE STAPLETON
□ 322. PAUL MIRABELLA
□ 325. DON AUGUST
□ 343. B. J. SURHOFF
□ 403. JOEY MEYER
□ 421. DALE SVEUM
□ 424. TED HIGUERA
□ 442. ROB DEER
□ 445. BILL WEGMAN
□ 501. CHUCK CRIM
□ 504. GLENN BRAGGS
□ 522. JUAN CASTILLO
□ 525. PAUL MOLITOR
□ 543. GREG BROCK
□ 608. ODELL JONES
□ 627. BILL SCHROEDER
□ 630. DAN PLESAC
□ 646. JUAN NIEVES
□ 649. MIKE YOUNG
□ 673. TEAM CHECKLIST
□ 745. BILL SPIERS
□ 788. LAVEL FREEMAN

Ted Higuera

MINNESOTA TWINS

- □ 62. TIM LAUDNER
- □ 64. FRED TOLIVER
- □ 81. CHARLIE LEA
- □ 83. LES STRAKER
- □ 85. ALLAN ANDERSON
- □ 158. RANDY BUSH
- □ 166. GREG GAGNE
- □ 177. KELVIN TORVE
- □ 179. STEVE LOMBARDOZZI
- □ 197. AL NEWMAN
- □ 203. GARY GAETTI
- □ 213. KENT HRBECK
- □ 225. BERY BLYLEVEN
- □ 232. JUAN BERENGUER
- □ 242. JOHN MOSES
- □ 358. MARK PORTUGAL
- □ 376. KIRBY PUCKETT
- □ 379. BRIAN HARPER
- □ 397. FRANK VIOLA
- □ 400. DAN GLADDEN
- □ 558. TOMMY HERR
- □ 577. MARK DAVIDSON
- □ 580. GENE LARKIN
- □ 596. JEFF REARDON
- □ 599. KEITH ATHERTON
- □ 691. TEAM CHECKLIST
- □ 732. WALLY BACKMAN
- □ 786. SHANE RAWLEY

MONTREAL EXPOS

- □ 25. RANDY JOHNSON
- □ 57. JOHN DOPSON
- □ 60. JOE HESKETH
- □ 78. BRYN SMITH
- □ 96. TRACY JONES
- □ 99. NEAL HEATON
- □ 102. TIM WALLACH
- □ 115. ANDRES GALARRAGA
- □ 122. HUBIE BROOKS
- □ 124. WALLACE JOHNSON
- □ 133. MIKE FRITZGERALD
- □ 356. BRIAN HOLMAN
- □ 359. ANDY MCGAFFIGAN
- □ 377. DENNIS MARTINEZ
- □ 380. NELSON SANTOVENIA
- □ 398. JEFF PARRETT
- □ 402. TIM RAINES
- □ 405. REX HUDLER
- □ 423. LUIS RIVERA
- □ 441. TOM FOLEY
- □ 444. DAVE MARTINEZ
- □ 456. TIM BURKE
- □ 459. FLOYD YOUMANS
- □ 477. JOHNNY PAREDES
- □ 480. OTIS NIXON
- □ 498. PASCUAL PEREZ
- □ 677. TEAM CHECKLIST
- □ 717. SPIKE OWEN
- □ 719. KEVIN GROSS
- □ 738. MIKE ALDRETE

NEW YORK METS

- □ 7. DAVID WEST
- □ 9. GREGG JEFFERIES
- □ 159. RON DARLING
- □ 168. SID FERNANDEZ
- □ 176. BARRY LYONS
- □ 188. WALLY BACKMAN
- □ 199. MOOKIE WILSON
- □ 260. DARRYL STRAWBERRY
- □ 269. KEVIN ELSTER
- □ 277. TIM TEUFEL
- □ 288. TERRY LEACH
- □ 296. ROGER MCDOWELL
- □ 367. KEVIN MCREYNOLDS
- □ 369. LEN DYKSTRA
- □ 386. BOB OJEDA
- □ 388. DAVE MAGADAN
- □ 390. GARY CARTER
- □ 561. MACKEY SASSER
- □ 563. RICK AGUILERA
- □ 565. DWIGHT GOODEN
- □ 582. HOWARD JOHNSON
- □ 584. DAVID CONE
- □ 612. KEITH HERNANDEZ
- □ 634. RANDY MYERS
- □ 657. LEE MAZZILLI
- □ 681. TEAM CHECKLIST
- □ 737. WALLY WHITEHURST
- □ 739. KEITH MILLER

NEW YORK YANKEES

- □ 56. RICK RHODEN
- □ 59. DAVE RIGHETTI
- □ 77. BOBBY MEACHAM
- □ 80. RICHARD DOTSON
- □ 98. GARY WARD
- □ 156. LUIS AGUAYO
- □ 167. KEN PHELPS
- □ 178. DON SLAUGHT
- □ 189. RANDY VELARDE
- □ 200. DON MATTINGLY
- □ 210. RICKEY HENDERSON
- □ 216. RAFAEL SANTANA
- □ 230. TOMMY JOHN
- □ 237. WILLIE RANDOLPH
- □ 248. JOHN CANDELARIA
- □ 307. RON GUIDRY
- □ 310. CLAUDELL WASHINGTON
- □ 328. JOEL SKINNER
- □ 346. JACK CLARK
- □ 349. DAVE WINFIELD
- □ 567. NEIL ALLEN
- □ 569. MIKE PAGLIARULO
- □ 586. CHARLES HUDSON
- □ 588. AL LEITER
- □ 590. ROBERTO KELLY
- □ 693. TEAM CHECKLIST
- □ 702. JESSE BARFIELD
- □ 706. DAVE LAPOINT
- □ 708. ANDY HAWKINS
- □ 710. LANCE MCCULLERS
- □ 727. DALE MOHORCIC
- □ 729. MEL HALL
- □ 746. HENSLEY MEULENS
- □ 748. STEVE SAX

OAKLAND A'S

- □ 4. DAVID OTTO
- □ 15. LANCE BLANKENSHIP
- □ 22. FELIX JOSE
- □ 153. STORM DAVIS
- □ 162. LUIS POLONIA
- □ 174. DAVE HENDERSON
- □ 185. DAVE STEWART
- □ 191. BOB WELCH
- □ 256. TERRY STEINBACH
- □ 267. TONY PHILLIPS
- □ 278. RICK HONEYCUTT
- □ 289. DENNIS ECKERSLEY
- □ 300. MARK MCGWIRE
- □ 353. ERIC PLUNK
- □ 371. JOSE CANSECO
- □ 374. WALT WEISS
- □ 392. CURT YOUNG
- □ 395. GLENN HUBBARD
- □ 562. CARNEY LANSFORD
- □ 564. RON HASSEY
- □ 581. STAN JAVIER
- □ 583. MIKE GALLEGO
- □ 585. DOUG JENNINGS
- □ 601. DON BAYLOR
- □ 605. DAVE PARKER
- □ 624. ORLANDO MERCADO
- □ 643. GENE NELSON
- □ 670. TEAM CHECKLIST
- □ 718. TODD BURNS
- □ 756. OZZIE CANSECO
- □ 758. MIKE MOORE

PHILADELPHIA PHILLIES

- □ 11. RON JONES
- □ 31. KEVIN GROSS
- □ 33. JEFF CALHOUN
- □ 35. RICKY JORDAN
- □ 207. KENT TEKULVE
- □ 219. STEVE JELTZ
- □ 229. PHIL BRADLEY
- □ 240. LANCE PARRISH
- □ 246. VON HAYES
- □ 317. MILT THOMPSON
- □ 319. BRUCE RUFFIN
- □ 336. JUAN SAMUEL
- □ 338. MIKE MADDUX
- □ 340. BOB DERNIER
- □ 406. MIKE SCHMIDT
- □ 409. DON CARMAN
- □ 427. SHANE RAWLEY
- □ 430. JACKIE GUTIERREZ
- □ 448. DARREN DAULTON
- □ 511. STEVE BEDROSIAN
- □ 513. CHRIS JAMES
- □ 515. DAVID PALMER
- □ 532. JOHN RUSSELL
- □ 534. GREG GROSS
- □ 684. TEAM CHECKLIST
- □ 704. DICKIE THON
- □ 720. TOMMY HERR
- □ 730. FLOYD YOUMANS
- □ 741. JEFF PARRETT

PITTSBURGH PIRATES

- □ 3. TONY CHANCE
- □ 67. JOHN CANGELOSI
- □ 69. BRIAN FISHER
- □ 86. JUNIOR ORTIZ
- □ 88. FLEX FERMIN
- □ 90. RAFAEL BELLIARD
- □ 311. TOM PRINCE
- □ 313. KEN OBERKFELL
- □ 315. R. J. REYNOLDS
- □ 332. JEFF ROBINSON
- □ 334. JOSE LIND
- □ 417. MIKE LAVALLIERE
- □ 419. GARY REDUS
- □ 436. DAVE RUCKER
- □ 438. BOB WALK
- □ 440. BARRY BONDS
- □ 516. JOHN SMILEY
- □ 518. MIKE DUNNE
- □ 520. BOB KIPPER
- □ 537. ANDY VAN SLYKE
- □ 539. JIM GOTT
- □ 556. SID BREAM
- □ 559. RANDY MILLIGAN
- □ 578. BOBBY BONILLA
- □ 597. DOUG DRABECK
- □ 600. DAVE LAPOINT
- □ 685. TEAM CHECKLIST
- □ 750. REY QUINONES

ST. LOUIS CARDINALS

- □ 8. CRIS CARPENTER
- □ 103. JOE MAGRANE
- □ 114. KEN DAYLEY
- □ 125. BOB HORNER
- □ 131. TERRY PENDLETON
- □ 143. LARRY MCWILLIAMS
- □ 253. VINCE COLEMAN
- □ 265. OZZIE SMITH
- □ 272. TOM BRUNANSKY
- □ 281. LUIS ALICEA
- □ 293. JOSE DELEON
- □ 306. PEDRO GUERRERO
- □ 309. CURT FORD
- □ 327. DENNY WALLING
- □ 330. TONY PENA
- □ 348. TIMMY JONES
- □ 512. TODD WORRELL
- □ 514. JOSE OQUENDO
- □ 531. GREG MATHEWS
- □ 533. DAN QUISENBERRY
- □ 535. DANNY COX

- 602. TOM PAGNOZZI
- 621. WILLIE MCGEE
- 625. JOHN COSTELLO
- 644. ROD BOOKER
- 674. TEAM CHECKLIST
- 754. TODD ZEILE
- 771. STEVE PETERS

SAN DIEGO PADRES

- 5. SANDY ALOMAR
- 30. JERALD CLARK
- 154. MARVELL WYNNE
- 165. BENITO SANTIAGO
- 171. ERIC SHOW
- 182. SHANE MACK
- 193. CHRIS BROWN
- 258. DICKIE THON
- 268. MARK DAVIS
- 280. JOHN KRUK
- 286. JIMMY JONES
- 297. GARRY TEMPLETON
- 361. KEITH MORELAND
- 363. DAVE LEIPER
- 365. CARMELO MARTINEZ
- 382. LANCE MCCULLERS
- 384. TONY GWYNN
- 453. ED WHITSON
- 471. ROBERTO ALOMAR
- 474. RANDY READY
- 492. MARK PARENT
- 495. ANDY HAWKINS
- 603. TIM FLANNERY
- 622. MARK GRANT
- 641. GREG BOOKER
- 645. DENNIS RASMUSSEN
- 683. TEAM CHECKLIST
- 703. WALT TERRELL
- 722. GARY GREEN
- 724. GREG HARRIS
- 726. TOM HOWARD
- 773. JACK CLARK
- 792. BRUCE HURST

SAN FRANCISCO GIANTS

- 39. DAVE DRAVECKY
- 46. MIKE KRUKOW
- 48. MIKE LACOSS
- 50. SCOTT GARRELTS
- 155. WILL CLARK
- 163. KEVIN MITCHELL
- 172. ROB THOMPSON
- 181. JOSE URIBE
- 194. RICK REUSCHEL
- 206. CHRIS SPEIER
- 218. BRETT BUTLER
- 227. BOB MELVIN
- 239. MIKE ALDRETE
- 247. MATT WILLIAMS
- 458. JOEL YOUNGBLOOD
- 476. KELLY DOWNS
- 479. BOB BRENLY
- 497. ERNIE RILES
- 500. KIRT MANWARING
- 502. CANDY MALDONADO
- 505. JOE PRICE
- 523. DON ROBINSON
- 541. CRAIG LEFFERTS
- 544. ATLEE HAMMAKER
- 678. TEAM CHECKLIST
- 707. CHARLIE HAYES
- 733. TREVOR WILSON
- 779. DENNIS COOK
- 798. TRACY JONES

SEATTLE MARINERS

- 1. KEN GRIFFEY, JR.
- 28. MIKE SCHOOLER
- 105. ALVIN DAVIS
- 111. STEVE BALBONI
- 123. MIKE MOORE
- 134. HENRY COTTO
- 142. MIKE JACKSON
- 208. ROD SCURRY
- 220. JAY BUHNER
- 226. SCOTT BRADLEY
- 238. BRUCE FIELDS
- 249. HAROLD REYNOLDS
- 316. SCOTT BANKHEAD
- 318. MARIO DIAZ
- 320. DAVE VALLE
- 337. MIKE CAMPBELL
- 339. DARNELL COLES
- 508. REY QUINONES
- 526. MARK LANGSTON
- 529. JERRY REED
- 547. RICH RENTERIA
- 550. MICKEY BRANTLEY
- 604. GENE WALTER
- 623. BILL SWIFT
- 642. JIM PRESLEY
- 680. TEAM CHECKLIST
- 766. ERIK HANSON
- 768. EDGAR MARTINEZ
- 770. GREG BRILEY
- 787. OMAR VIZQUEL
- 789. JEFFREY LEONARD

TEXAS RANGERS

- 51. DWAYNE HENRY
- 54. PETE O'BRIEN
- 73. JOSE GUZMAN
- 92. CECIL ESPY
- 95. MITCH WILLIAMS
- 312. CHAD KREUTER
- 314. JERRY BROWNE
- 331. JIM SUNDBERG
- 333. ODDIBE MCDOWELL
- 335. PAUL KILGUS
- 416. RUBEN SIERRA
- 418. STEVE BUECHELE
- 420. SCOTT FLETCHER
- 437. CHARLIE HOUGH
- 439. BOB BROWER
- 461. JEFF RUSSELL
- 463. JEFF KUNKEL
- 465. CURTIS WILKERSON
- 482. GENO PETRALLI
- 484. PETE INCAVIGLIA
- 557. BOBBY WITT
- 560. JOSE CECENA
- 576. CECILIO GUANTE
- 579. MIKE STANLEY
- 598. EDWIN CORREA
- 686. TEAM CHECKLIST
- 752. KEVIN BROWN
- 772. RAFAEL PALMEIRO
- 774. NOLAN RYAN
- 791. JAMIE MOYER
- 793. JULIO FRANCO

TORONTO BLUE JAYS

- 41. JEFF MUSSELMAN
- 43. RANCE MULLINIKS
- 45. SIL CAMPUSANO
- 109. NELSON LIRIANO
- 118. ERNIE WHITT
- 129. JOHN CERUTTI
- 139. TONY FERNANDEZ
- 149. JESSE BARFIELD
- 255. GEORGE BELL
- 264. TOM HENKE
- 271. MANNY LEE
- 282. JIM CLANCY
- 291. JIMMY KEY
- 362. TODD STOTTLEMYRE
- 364. CECIL FIELDER
- 381. LLOYD MOSEBY
- 383. DAVE STIEB
- 385. MIKE FLANAGAN
- 551. DUANE WARD
- 554. RICK LEACH
- 572. FRED MCGRIFF
- 575. KELLY GRUBER
- 593. PAT BORDERS
- 671. TEAM CHECKLIST
- 705. AL LEITER
- 721. ROB DUCEY
- 743. JUNIOR FELIX

1990 UPPER DECK
(800)
2 1/2 X 3 1/2

Dave Justice

ATLANTA BRAVES

- 33. KELLY MANN
- 49. TOMMY GREENE
- 61. MIKE STANTON
- 63. KENT MERCKER
- 64. FRANCISCO CABRERA
- 65. STEVE AVERY
- 84. TEAM CHECKLIST
- 101. GERALD PERRY
- 121. TOMMY GREGG
- 141. JEFF TREADWAY
- 143. DARRELL EVANS
- 145. ODIBBE MCDOWELL
- 212. ANDRES THOMAS
- 215. LONNIE SMITH
- 232. RON GANT
- 234. DEREK LILLIQUIST
- 406. JEFF BLAUSER
- 408. JOE BOEVER
- 429. JODY DAVIS
- 447. ED WHITED
- 531. GERONIMO BERROA
- 533. DALE MURPHY
- 535. JOHN SMOLTZ
- 551. TONY CASTILLO
- 571. TOM GLAVINE
- 611. JEFF WETHERBY
- 613. PETE SMITH
- 634. JOSE ALVAREZ
- 665. MARK LEMKE
- 711. DAVE JUSTICE
- 758. NICK ESASKY
- 760. JIM PRESLEY
- 779. MARTY CLARY

BALTIMORE ORIOLES

- 8. JOSE BAUTISTA
- 54. BEN MCDONALD
- 60. TEAM CHECKLIST
- 173. MARK WILLIAMSON
- 175. BRIAN HOLTON
- 184. BILLY RIPKEN
- 194. PHIL BRADLEY
- 259. JEFF BALLARD
- 266. CAL RIPKEN
- 268. JIM TRABER
- 270. JOE ORSULAK
- 287. LARRY SHEETS
- 290. BRADY ANDERSON
- 297. MICKEY TETTLETON
- 299. KEVIN HICKEY
- 401. KEITH MORELAND
- 425. DAVE JOHNSON
- 444. CRAIG WORTHINGTON
- 602. STEVE FINLEY
- 604. GREGG OLSON
- 623. PETE HARNISCH
- 635. BOB MILACKI
- 641. DAVE SCHMIDT
- 644. BOB MELVIN

- ☐ 663. RANDY MILLIGAN
- ☐ 681. MIKE DEVEREAUX
- ☐ 683. MICKEY WESTON
- ☐ 773. DAVID SEGUI
- ☐ 796. SAM HORN

Roger Clemens

BOSTON RED SOX

- ☐ 57. TEAM CHECKLIST
- ☐ 112. DWIGHT EVANS
- ☐ 133. MARTY BARRETT
- ☐ 321. JODY REED
- ☐ 323. ROGER CLEMENS
- ☐ 343. ELLIS BURKS
- ☐ 351. TOM BOLTON
- ☐ 354. MIKE GREENWELL
- ☐ 373. JIM RICE
- ☐ 393. LEE SMITH
- ☐ 402. RICH GEDMAN
- ☐ 405. RICK CERONE
- ☐ 441. KEVIN ROMINE
- ☐ 461. ROB MURPHY
- ☐ 463. NICK ESASKY
- ☐ 465. CARLOS QUINTANA
- ☐ 482. LUIS RIVERA
- ☐ 484. OIL CAN BOYD
- ☐ 555. WADE BOGGS
- ☐ 610. MIKE SMITHSON
- ☐ 652. MIKE BODDICKER
- ☐ 654. BOB STANLEY
- ☐ 671. JOHN DOPSON
- ☐ 673. ERIC HETZEL
- ☐ 694. MIKE ROCHFORD
- ☐ 708. TOM BRUNANSKY
- ☐ 729. JEFF REARDON
- ☐ 748. TONY PENA
- ☐ 764. MICKEY PINA
- ☐ 782. BILLY JO ROBIDOUX

CALIFORNIA ANGELS

- ☐ 5. TEAM CHECKLIST
- ☐ 19. JACK HOWELL
- ☐ 38. CHILI DAVIS
- ☐ 58. TONY ARMAS
- ☐ 77. BOBBY ROSE
- ☐ 81. BOB MCCLURE
- ☐ 83. GREG MINTON
- ☐ 85. WILLIE FRASER
- ☐ 129. DEVON WHITE
- ☐ 146. BRIAN DOWNING
- ☐ 149. BILL SCHROEDER
- ☐ 395. CLAUDELL WASHINGTON
- ☐ 506. KIRK MCCASKILL
- ☐ 509. JOHNNY RAY
- ☐ 527. BERT BLYLEVEN
- ☐ 548. MIKE WITT
- ☐ 645. JIM ABBOTT
- ☐ 667. CHUCK FINLEY
- ☐ 669. DICK SCHOFIELD
- ☐ 672. JOHN ORTON
- ☐ 674. LANCE PARRISH
- ☐ 686. BRYAN HARVEY
- ☐ 688. DANTE BICHETTE
- ☐ 690. DAN PETRY
- ☐ 691. KENT ANDERSON
- ☐ 693. WALLY JOYNER
- ☐ 742. MIKE FETTERS
- ☐ 745. DAVE WINFIELD
- ☐ 761. GARY DISARCINA
- ☐ 783. MARK LANGSTON

CHICAGO CUBS

- ☐ 6. LUIS SALAZAR
- ☐ 14. MARVELL WYNNE
- ☐ 39. SCOTT SANDERSON
- ☐ 47. KEVIN BLANKENSHIP
- ☐ 73. TEAM CHECKLIST
- ☐ 107. MIKE HARKEY
- ☐ 109. RICK SUTCLIFFE
- ☐ 128. MARK GRACE
- ☐ 147. CURTIS WILKERSON
- ☐ 150. DOMINGO RAMOS
- ☐ 153. MITCH WEBSTER
- ☐ 155. PAUL KILGUS
- ☐ 174. MITCH WILLIAMS
- ☐ 211. DOUG DASCENZO
- ☐ 213. GREG MADDUX
- ☐ 231. SHAWON DUNSTON
- ☐ 304. JOE GIRARDI
- ☐ 322. DAMON BERRYHILL
- ☐ 324. RYNE SANDBERG
- ☐ 341. STEVE WILSON
- ☐ 345. JEROME WALTON
- ☐ 357. ANDRE DAWSON
- ☐ 359. MIKE BIELECKI
- ☐ 376. DWIGHT SMITH
- ☐ 380. VANCE LAW
- ☐ 398. LLOYD MCCLENDON
- ☐ 582. RICK WRONA
- ☐ 584. LES LANCASTER
- ☐ 660. PAUL ASSENMACHER
- ☐ 716. JOSE NUNEZ
- ☐ 722. SHAWN BOSKIE
- ☐ 736. DERRICK MAY
- ☐ 738. GREG SMITH
- ☐ 740. JOE KRAEMER
- ☐ 741. HECTOR VILLANUEVA

CHICAGO WHITE SOX

- ☐ 3. TOM DREES
- ☐ 17. SAMMY SOSA
- ☐ 21. ROBIN VENTURA
- ☐ 67. MATT MERULLO
- ☐ 69. RON KARKOVICE
- ☐ 79. TEAM CHECKLIST
- ☐ 90. LANCE JOHNSON
- ☐ 267. OZZIE GUILLEN
- ☐ 269. BOBBY THIGPEN
- ☐ 286. DAN PASQUA
- ☐ 289. EDDIE WILLIAMS
- ☐ 310. SCOTT FLETCHER
- ☐ 328. DAVE GALLAGHER
- ☐ 347. CAROLOS MARTINEZ
- ☐ 350. GREG WALKER
- ☐ 367. CARLTON FISK
- ☐ 386. DONN PALL
- ☐ 390. STEVE LYONS
- ☐ 503. IVAN CALDERON
- ☐ 522. STEVE ROSENBERG
- ☐ 525. MELIDO PEREZ
- ☐ 529. DARYL BOSTON
- ☐ 541. SHAWN HILLEGAS
- ☐ 543. GREG HIBBARD
- ☐ 625. JACK MCDOWELL
- ☐ 651. ERIC KING
- ☐ 721. CRAIG GREBECK
- ☐ 725. SCOTT RADINSKY
- ☐ 762. WAYNE EDWARDS
- ☐ 765. WILSON ALVAREZ
- ☐ 790. RON KITTLE

CINCINNATI REDS

- ☐ 52. CHRIS HAMMOND
- ☐ 99. TEAM CHECKLIST
- ☐ 116. ERIC DAVIS
- ☐ 118. RON OESTER
- ☐ 120. DANNY JACKSON
- ☐ 137. TIM BIRTSAS
- ☐ 139. JOHN FRANCO
- ☐ 161. PAUL O'NEILL
- ☐ 164. SCOTT SCUDDER
- ☐ 165. JEFF REED
- ☐ 167. BARRY LARKIN
- ☐ 170. ROLANDO ROOMES
- ☐ 181. CHRIS SABO
- ☐ 186. TODD BENZINGER
- ☐ 189. TOM BROWNING
- ☐ 216. JOSE RIJO
- ☐ 220. RICK MAHLER
- ☐ 430. MARIANO DUNCAN
- ☐ 566. NORM CHARLTON
- ☐ 568. JOE OLIVER
- ☐ 586. ROB DIBBLE
- ☐ 589. HERM WINNINGHAM
- ☐ 593. LUIS QUINONES
- ☐ 662. TIM LEARY
- ☐ 664. BO DIAZ
- ☐ 682. KEN GRIFFEY
- ☐ 684. JACK ARMSTRONG
- ☐ 714. GLENN BRAGGS
- ☐ 717. TIM LAYANA
- ☐ 778. BILLY HATCHER
- ☐ 797. RANDY MYERS

CLEVELAND INDIANS

- ☐ 53. TEAM CHECKLIST
- ☐ 110. PETE O'BRIEN
- ☐ 126. CORY SNYDER
- ☐ 369. JOEL SKINNER
- ☐ 375. JOE CARTER
- ☐ 388. TOM CANDIOTTI
- ☐ 409. FELIX FERMIN
- ☐ 426. JERRY BROWNE
- ☐ 428. BRAD KOMMINSK
- ☐ 446. JOEY BELLE
- ☐ 449. DAVE CLARK
- ☐ 459. BROOK JACOBY
- ☐ 498. BUD BLACK
- ☐ 553. STEVE OLIN
- ☐ 570. JOHN FARRELL
- ☐ 572. ROD NICHOLS
- ☐ 574. GREG SWINDELL
- ☐ 588. JESSE OROSCO
- ☐ 590. ANDY ALLANSON
- ☐ 591. DION JAMES
- ☐ 595. RICH YETT
- ☐ 632. DOUG JONES
- ☐ 715. KEVIN BEARSE
- ☐ 730. MITCH WEBSTER
- ☐ 737. CARLOS BAERGA
- ☐ 756. SANDY ALOMAR
- ☐ 777. KEITH HERNANDEZ
- ☐ 780. CANDY MALDONADO
- ☐ 798. CHRIS JAMES

DETROIT TIGERS

- ☐ 2. RANDY NOSEK
- ☐ 41. TEAM CHECKLIST
- ☐ 76. ROB RICHIE
- ☐ 78. BRIAN DUBOIS
- ☐ 98. KEVIN RITZ
- ☐ 226. MATT NOKES
- ☐ 247. FRED LYNN
- ☐ 249. KENNY WILLIAMS
- ☐ 306. MIKE HEATH
- ☐ 309. TRACY JONES
- ☐ 312. MIKE BRUMLEY
- ☐ 327. LOU WHITAKER
- ☐ 330. DOYLE ALEXANDER
- ☐ 332. TOREY LOVULLO
- ☐ 348. CHET LEMON
- ☐ 381. DAVE BERGMAN
- ☐ 385. GARY PETTIS
- ☐ 496. PAUL GIBSON
- ☐ 516. FRANK TANANA
- ☐ 518. GUILLERMO HERNANDEZ
- ☐ 520. CHARLES HUDSON
- ☐ 537. MIKE HENNEMAN
- ☐ 539. FRANK WILLIAMS
- ☐ 552. JEFF ROBINSON
- ☐ 554. ALAN TRAMMELL
- ☐ 573. JACK MORRIS
- ☐ 575. STEVE SEARCY
- ☐ 768. TONY PHILLIPS
- ☐ 786. CECIL FIELDER
- ☐ 789. LLOYD MOSEBY

HOUSTON ASTROS

- ☐ 22. BRIAN MEYER
- ☐ 28. ERIC ANTHONY
- ☐ 43. JOSE CANO
- ☐ 88. TEAM CHECKLIST
- ☐ 104. CRAIG BIGGIO
- ☐ 122. KEN CAMINITI

- ☐ 125. MIKE SCOTT
- ☐ 144. RAFAEL RAMIREZ
- ☐ 160. LOUIE MEADOWS
- ☐ 196. GERALD YOUNG
- ☐ 198. BILL DORAN
- ☐ 201. TERRY PUHL
- ☐ 203. JIM CLANCY
- ☐ 205. ALEX TREVINO
- ☐ 221. JIM DESHAIES
- ☐ 245. GLENN DAVIS
- ☐ 302. KEVIN BASS
- ☐ 305. DANNY DARWIN
- ☐ 407. LARRY ANDERSEN
- ☐ 410. GLENN WILSON
- ☐ 427. ERIC YELDING
- ☐ 448. DAVE SMITH
- ☐ 450. JUAN AGOSTO
- ☐ 502. MARK PORTUGAL
- ☐ 504. RICK RHODEN
- ☐ 799. BILL GULLICKSON

KANSAS CITY ROYALS

- ☐ 32. TEAM CHECKLIST
- ☐ 45. BOB HAMELIN
- ☐ 102. KEVIN APPIER
- ☐ 105. BO JACKSON
- ☐ 124. GEORGE BRETT
- ☐ 142. PAT TABLER
- ☐ 252. BILL BUCKNER
- ☐ 255. JOSE DEJESUS
- ☐ 271. BOB BOONE
- ☐ 274. LUIS AQUINO
- ☐ 294. JIM EISENREICH
- ☐ 307. MIKE MACFARLANE
- ☐ 326. BRET SABERHAGEN
- ☐ 349. WILLIE WILSON
- ☐ 361. KURT STILLWELL
- ☐ 363. KEVIN SEITZER
- ☐ 365. TOM GORDON
- ☐ 382. FRANK WHITE
- ☐ 384. ISRAEL SANCHEZ
- ☐ 524. MATT WINTERS
- ☐ 621. RICK LUECKEN
- ☐ 642. TERRY LEACH
- ☐ 656. DANNY TARTABULL
- ☐ 658. CHARLIE LEIBRANDT
- ☐ 676. MARK GUBICZA
- ☐ 680. STEVE FARR
- ☐ 695. FLOYD BANNISTER
- ☐ 698. JEFF MONTGOMERY
- ☐ 707. GERALD PERRY
- ☐ 710. MARK DAVIS
- ☐ 712. STORM DAVIS
- ☐ 733. TERRY SHUMPERT

LOS ANGELES DODGERS

- ☐ 10. TEAM CHECKLIST
- ☐ 44. JOSE VIZCAINO
- ☐ 46. JOSE OFFERMAN
- ☐ 183. WILLIE RANDOLPH
- ☐ 256. OREL HERSHISER
- ☐ 258. MIKE DAVIS
- ☐ 262. MIKE MARSHALL
- ☐ 264. KIRK GIBSON
- ☐ 277. EDDIE MURRAY
- ☐ 279. ALEJANDRO PENA
- ☐ 283. MICKEY HATCHER
- ☐ 296. JEFF HAMILTON
- ☐ 298. MIKE SCIOSCIA
- ☐ 317. MIKE MORGAN
- ☐ 338. ALFREDO GRIFFIN
- ☐ 377. JOHN WETTELAND
- ☐ 396. JOHN TUDOR
- ☐ 423. LENNY HARRIS
- ☐ 445. FERNANDO VALENZUELA
- ☐ 508. JAY HOWELL
- ☐ 510. DAVE ANDERSON
- ☐ 526. CHRIS GWYNN
- ☐ 547. TIM BELCHER
- ☐ 550. FRANKLIN STUBBS
- ☐ 603. KAL DANIELS
- ☐ 666. JOSE GONZALEZ
- ☐ 670. TIM CREWS
- ☐ 675. RAMON MARTINEZ
- ☐ 701. JIM GOTT
- ☐ 791. HUBIE BROOKS
- ☐ 795. JUAN SAMUEL

MILWAUKEE BREWERS

- ☐ 25. GREG VAUGHN
- ☐ 59. GEORGE CANALE
- ☐ 91. TEAM CHECKLIST
- ☐ 96. JERRY REUSS
- ☐ 157. GARY SHEFFIELD
- ☐ 159. B.J. SURHOFF
- ☐ 176. ROB DEER
- ☐ 178. MIKE FELDER
- ☐ 180. TERRY FRANCONA
- ☐ 218. JIM GANTNER
- ☐ 237. BILL SPIERS
- ☐ 239. BRYAN CLUTTERBUCK
- ☐ 254. PAUL MOLITOR
- ☐ 293. CHRIS BOSIO
- ☐ 295. DON AUGUST
- ☐ 456. GLENN BRAGGS
- ☐ 477. DAN PLESAC
- ☐ 480. GUS POLIDOR
- ☐ 499. DALE SVEUM
- ☐ 511. CHUCK CRIM
- ☐ 514. GREG BROCK
- ☐ 567. ROBIN YOUNT
- ☐ 627. TED HIGUERA
- ☐ 629. BILL WEGMAN
- ☐ 646. JAIME NAVARRO
- ☐ 648. JUAN NIEVES
- ☐ 650. CHARLIE O'BRIEN
- ☐ 766. DAVE PARKER

MINNESOTA TWINS

- ☐ 11. RICK AGUILERA
- ☐ 15. DAVID WEST
- ☐ 48. TEAM CHECKLIST
- ☐ 87. KEVIN TAPANI
- ☐ 158. WALLY BACKMAN
- ☐ 199. AL NEWMAN
- ☐ 217. GREG GAGNE
- ☐ 219. ALLAN ANDERSON
- ☐ 236. KIRBY PUCKETT
- ☐ 238. DAN GLADDEN
- ☐ 240. JOHN MOSES
- ☐ 281. CARMEN CASTILLO
- ☐ 284. ROY SMITH
- ☐ 352. GERMAN GONZALEZ
- ☐ 372. GARY WAYNE
- ☐ 374. MIKE DYER
- ☐ 391. BRIAN HARPER
- ☐ 417. JEFF REARDON
- ☐ 419. TIM LAUDNER
- ☐ 436. MARK GUTHRIE
- ☐ 438. SHANE RAWLEY
- ☐ 440. JUAN BERENGUER
- ☐ 452. KENT HRBEK
- ☐ 454. GARY GAETTI
- ☐ 471. GENE LARKIN
- ☐ 475. CHIP HALE
- ☐ 493. RANDY BUSH
- ☐ 720. JOHN CANDELARIA
- ☐ 728. LENNY WEBSTER
- ☐ 784. PAUL SORRENTO

MONTREAL EXPOS

- ☐ 9. MARQUIS GRISSOM
- ☐ 29. TEAM CHECKLIST
- ☐ 177. TIM RAINES
- ☐ 197. HUBIE BROOKS
- ☐ 273. TIM WALLACH
- ☐ 291. SPIKE OWEN
- ☐ 356. ANDRES GALARRAGA
- ☐ 379. OTIS NIXON
- ☐ 411. REX HUDLER
- ☐ 413. DENNIS MARTINEZ
- ☐ 415. MIKE ALDRETE
- ☐ 432. NELSON SANTOVENIA
- ☐ 434. JEFF HUSON
- ☐ 466. LARRY WALKER
- ☐ 468. KEVIN GROSS
- ☐ 470. DAVE MARTINEZ
- ☐ 487. PASCUAL PEREZ
- ☐ 489. TOM FOLEY
- ☐ 512. JOE HESKETH
- ☐ 515. TIM BURKE
- ☐ 558. MIKE FITZGERALD
- ☐ 579. BRYN SMITH
- ☐ 597. ANDY MCGAFFIGAN
- ☐ 607. ZANE SMITH
- ☐ 628. MARTY PEVEY
- ☐ 647. MARK LANGSTON
- ☐ 649. DAMASO GARCIA
- ☐ 724. BILL SAMPEN
- ☐ 743. MARK GARDNER
- ☐ 746. DELINO DESHIELDS
- ☐ 749. OIL CAN BOYD
- ☐ 753. HOWARD FARMER
- ☐ 772. MEL ROJAS

Gary Carter

NEW YORK METS

- ☐ 23. BLAINE BEATTY
- ☐ 62. TEAM CHECKLIST
- ☐ 93. JULIO MACHADO
- ☐ 114. DWIGHT GOODEN
- ☐ 131. DON AASE
- ☐ 135. MARK CARREON
- ☐ 162. JEFF MCKNIGHT
- ☐ 166. GREGG JEFFERIES
- ☐ 168. GARY CARTER
- ☐ 182. DARRYL STRAWBERRY
- ☐ 185. MACKEY SASSER
- ☐ 187. KEVIN ELSTER
- ☐ 190. KEITH MILLER
- ☐ 204. BOB OJEDA
- ☐ 222. KEITH HERNANDEZ
- ☐ 224. DAVID CONE
- ☐ 241. RON DARLING
- ☐ 243. DAVE MAGADAN
- ☐ 261. SID FERNANDEZ
- ☐ 263. HOWARD JOHNSON
- ☐ 265. KEVIN MCREYNOLDS
- ☐ 473. BARRY LYONS
- ☐ 492. TIM TEUFEL
- ☐ 562. JEFF INNIS
- ☐ 564. WALLY WHITEHURST
- ☐ 581. RANDY MYERS
- ☐ 583. JUAN SAMUEL
- ☐ 585. JEFF MUSSELMAN
- ☐ 626. FRANK VIOLA
- ☐ 703. ALEJANDRO PENA
- ☐ 709. JOHN FRANCO
- ☐ 726. TODD HUNDLEY
- ☐ 781. MIKE MARSHALL

NEW YORK YANKEES

- ☐ 13. DEION SANDERS
- ☐ 18. TEAM CHECKLIST
- ☐ 31. HAL MORRIS
- ☐ 70. KEVIN MAAS
- ☐ 138. TOM BROOKENS
- ☐ 152. DON SLAUGHT
- ☐ 163. ALVARO ESPINOZA
- ☐ 172. STEVE SAX
- ☐ 191. DON MATTINGLY
- ☐ 193. ROBERTO KELLY
- ☐ 316. LUIS POLONIA
- ☐ 318. LEE GUETTERMAN
- ☐ 320. WAYNE TOLLESON
- ☐ 337. DAVE WINFIELD
- ☐ 339. ANDY HAWKINS
- ☐ 458. MEL HALL
- ☐ 476. JESSE BARFIELD
- ☐ 479. DAVE RIGHETTI
- ☐ 497. STEVE BALBONI
- ☐ 507. DAVE LAPOINT
- ☐ 528. CHUCK CARY
- ☐ 530. DALE MOHORCIC

- ☐ 546. HENSLEY MEULENS
- ☐ 549. GREG CADARET
- ☐ 608. BOB GEREN
- ☐ 615. LANCE MCCULLERS
- ☐ 630. ERIC PLUNK
- ☐ 661. WALT TERRELL
- ☐ 705. TIM LEARY
- ☐ 723. JIM LEYRITZ
- ☐ 744. MATT NOKES
- ☐ 767. MIKE BLOWERS
- ☐ 769. PASCUAL PEREZ

OAKLAND A'S

- ☐ 4. CURT YOUNG
- ☐ 36. TEAM CHECKLIST
- ☐ 66. JOSE CANSECO
- ☐ 80. GENE NELSON
- ☐ 151. RICK HONEYCUTT
- ☐ 154. TONY PHILLIPS
- ☐ 171. MARK MCGWIRE
- ☐ 192. DAVE PARKER
- ☐ 195. RON HASSEY
- ☐ 206. DAVE HENDERSON
- ☐ 209. STAN JAVIER
- ☐ 228. FELIX JOSE
- ☐ 230. MIKE GALLEGO
- ☐ 246. TERRY STEINBACH
- ☐ 251. BOB WELCH
- ☐ 253. CARNEY LANSFORD
- ☐ 272. DAVE STEWART
- ☐ 275. MIKE MOORE
- ☐ 292. STORM DAVIS
- ☐ 334. RICKEY HENDERSON
- ☐ 513. DENNIS ECKERSLEY
- ☐ 521. JIM CORSI
- ☐ 542. WALT WEISS
- ☐ 687. LANCE BLANKENSHIP
- ☐ 689. TODD BURNS
- ☐ 704. WILLIE RANDOLPH
- ☐ 727. SCOTT HEMOND
- ☐ 739. SCOTT SANDERSON
- ☐ 747. DANN HOWITT

PHILADELPHIA PHILLIES

- ☐ 7. TEAM CHECKLIST
- ☐ 27. JASON GRIMSLEY
- ☐ 35. SCOTT SERVICE
- ☐ 71. DENNIS COOK
- ☐ 92. JEFF PARRETT
- ☐ 94. RON JONES
- ☐ 404. RANDY READY
- ☐ 416. ROGER MCDOWELL
- ☐ 418. DARREN DAULTON
- ☐ 420. DON CARMAN
- ☐ 437. CHARLIE HAYES
- ☐ 439. DICKIE THON
- ☐ 443. TODD FROHWIRTH
- ☐ 453. VON HAYES
- ☐ 472. LEN DYKSTRA
- ☐ 474. TERRY MULHOLLAND
- ☐ 488. TOMMY HERR
- ☐ 490. CURT FORD
- ☐ 491. STEVE LAKE
- ☐ 495. STEVE JELTZ
- ☐ 559. KEN HOWELL
- ☐ 576. RICKY JORDAN
- ☐ 580. BRUCE RUFFIN
- ☐ 668. JOHN KRUK
- ☐ 706. CHUCK MCELROY
- ☐ 763. PAT COMBS
- ☐ 785. DAVE HOLLINS

PITTSBURGH PIRATES

- ☐ 16. TEAM CHECKLIST
- ☐ 86. NEAL HEATON
- ☐ 89. JIM GOTT
- ☐ 97. BRIAN FISHER
- ☐ 208. RAFAEL BELLIARD
- ☐ 227. BARRY BONDS
- ☐ 248. GARY REDUS
- ☐ 250. SID BREAM
- ☐ 366. BOBBY BONILLA
- ☐ 368. STEVE CARTER
- ☐ 370. JOHN CANGELOSI
- ☐ 387. JOHN SMILEY
- ☐ 389. JUNIOR ORTIZ
- ☐ 403. JEFF ROBINSON
- ☐ 422. DOUG DRABEK
- ☐ 424. JOSE LIND
- ☐ 442. BILL LANDRUM
- ☐ 517. JAY BELL
- ☐ 519. RANDY KRAMER
- ☐ 536. ANDY VAN SLYKE
- ☐ 538. MIGUEL GARCIA
- ☐ 540. R.J. REYNOLDS
- ☐ 557. JEFF KING
- ☐ 560. BOB KIPPER
- ☐ 578. MIKE LAVALLIERE
- ☐ 596. BOB WALK
- ☐ 598. BILLY HATCHER
- ☐ 713. SCOTT RUSKIN
- ☐ 759. STAN BELINDA

ST. LOUIS CARDINALS

- ☐ 68. TEAM CHECKLIST
- ☐ 202. FRANK DIPINO
- ☐ 223. VINCE COLEMAN
- ☐ 225. OZZIE SMITH
- ☐ 242. JOE MAGRANE
- ☐ 244. PEDRO GUERERRO
- ☐ 257. TOM BRUNANSKY
- ☐ 260. SCOTT TERRY
- ☐ 276. TONY PENA
- ☐ 278. MILT THOMPSON
- ☐ 280. KEN DAYLEY
- ☐ 319. JOSE OQUENDO
- ☐ 336. KEN HILL
- ☐ 340. TED POWER
- ☐ 467. TODD WORRELL
- ☐ 469. TERRY PENDLETON
- ☐ 486. JOHN COSTELLO
- ☐ 501. TIMMY JONES
- ☐ 505. WILLIE MCGEE
- ☐ 523. CRIS CARPENTER
- ☐ 545. TODD ZEILE
- ☐ 659. DAN QUISENBERRY
- ☐ 678. GREG MATHEWS
- ☐ 697. JOSE DELEON
- ☐ 755. RAY LANKFORD
- ☐ 794. BRYN SMITH

SAN DIEGO PADRES

- ☐ 12. TEAM CHECKLIST
- ☐ 51. ROB NELSON
- ☐ 55. ANDY BENES
- ☐ 288. GARRY TEMPLETON
- ☐ 301. SHAWN ABNER
- ☐ 303. BIP ROBERTS
- ☐ 308. ED WHITSON
- ☐ 325. BENITO SANTAGO
- ☐ 329. MIKE PAGLIARULO
- ☐ 342. JACK CLARK
- ☐ 344. TONY GWYNN
- ☐ 346. ROBERTO ALOMAR
- ☐ 412. MARK GRANT
- ☐ 414. DARRIN JACKSON
- ☐ 431. MARK DAVIS
- ☐ 433. BRUCE HURST
- ☐ 435. CHRIS JAMES
- ☐ 569. MARK PARENT
- ☐ 587. ERIC SHOW
- ☐ 592. CARMELO MARTINEZ
- ☐ 594. DENNIS RASMUSSEN
- ☐ 601. JOEY CORA
- ☐ 622. GREG HARRIS
- ☐ 624. JERALD CLARK
- ☐ 643. CALVIN SCHIRALDI
- ☐ 655. SANDY ALOMAR
- ☐ 751. ALEX COLE
- ☐ 754. JOE CARTER
- ☐ 771. FRED LYNN
- ☐ 775. RAFAEL VALDEZ
- ☐ 792. CRAIG LEFFERTS

SAN FRANCISCO GIANTS

- ☐ 40. TEAM CHECKLIST
- ☐ 117. KEVIN MITCHELL
- ☐ 119. BRETT BUTLER
- ☐ 136. CANDY MALDONADO
- ☐ 140. MIKE LACOSS
- ☐ 169. ROBBY THOMPSON
- ☐ 188. JOSE URIBE
- ☐ 358. JEFF BRANTLEY
- ☐ 360. KEN OBERKFELL
- ☐ 378. ERNIE RILES
- ☐ 397. TERRY KENNEDY
- ☐ 399. CRAIG LEFFERTS
- ☐ 457. KIRT MANWARING
- ☐ 460. PAT SHERIDAN
- ☐ 478. SCOTT GARRELTS
- ☐ 556. WILL CLARK
- ☐ 577. MATT WILLIAMS
- ☐ 599. BOB KNEPPER
- ☐ 616. DON ROBINSON
- ☐ 618. STEVE BEDROSIAN
- ☐ 620. ATLEE HAMMAKER
- ☐ 637. TREVOR WILSON
- ☐ 639. MIKE KRUKOW
- ☐ 657. RANDY MCCAMENT
- ☐ 677. GREG LITTON
- ☐ 679. DAVE DRAVECKY
- ☐ 696. RICK REUSCHEL
- ☐ 699. KELLY DOWNS
- ☐ 732. RICK PARKER
- ☐ 735. JOHN BURKETT
- ☐ 750. MIKE BENJAMIN
- ☐ 752. ERIC GUNDERSON
- ☐ 774. GARY CARTER
- ☐ 793. KEVIN BASS

SEATTLE MARINERS

- ☐ 24. TEAM CHECKLIST
- ☐ 37. TINO MARTINEZ
- ☐ 156. KEN GRIFFEY JR.
- ☐ 179. HAROLD REYNOLDS
- ☐ 207. HENRY COTTO
- ☐ 210. JERRY REED
- ☐ 214. MIKE SCHOOLER
- ☐ 229. DENNIS POWELL
- ☐ 233. OMAR VIZQUEL
- ☐ 235. ERIK HANSON
- ☐ 311. DARNELL COLES
- ☐ 313. BILL SWIFT
- ☐ 315. JIM PRESLEY
- ☐ 331. JEFFREY LEONARD
- ☐ 362. BRIAN HOLMAN
- ☐ 364. ALVIN DAVIS
- ☐ 383. SCOTT BRADLEY
- ☐ 451. DAVE VALLE
- ☐ 455. GREG BRILEY
- ☐ 494. MIKE JACKSON
- ☐ 532. EDGAR MARTINEZ
- ☐ 534. JAY BUHNER
- ☐ 561. SCOTT BANKHEAD
- ☐ 563. RANDY JOHNSON
- ☐ 565. GENE HARRIS
- ☐ 719. PETE O'BRIEN
- ☐ 787. MATT YOUNG

TEXAS RANGERS

- ☐ 42. SCOTT COOLBAUGH
- ☐ 72. JUAN GONZALEZ
- ☐ 74. DEAN PALMER
- ☐ 82. TEAM CHECKLIST
- ☐ 103. JULIO FRANCO
- ☐ 123. KEVIN BROWN
- ☐ 314. CHARLIE HOUGH
- ☐ 333. PETE INCAVIGLIA
- ☐ 335. RAFAEL PALMEIRO
- ☐ 353. HAROLD BAINES
- ☐ 355. RUBEN SIERRA
- ☐ 371. CECIL ESPY
- ☐ 392. FRED MANRIQUE
- ☐ 394. JEFF KUNKEL
- ☐ 544. NOLAN RYAN
- ☐ 606. KENNY ROGERS
- ☐ 609. CHAD KREUTER
- ☐ 612. GARY MIELKE
- ☐ 614. JACK DAUGHERTY
- ☐ 617. JOSE GUZMAN
- ☐ 619. JAMIE MOYER
- ☐ 631. DREW HALL
- ☐ 633. GENO PETRALLI
- ☐ 636. BOBBY WITT
- ☐ 638. JEFF RUSSELL
- ☐ 640. RICK LEACH
- ☐ 685. STEVE BUECHELE
- ☐ 731. BRIAN BOHANON
- ☐ 770. GARY PETTIS
- ☐ 788. JEFF HUSON

TORONTO BLUE JAYS

- ☐ 26. XAVIER HERNANDEZ
- ☐ 30. DAVID WELLS

1990 Upper Deck

- ☐ 56. JOHN OLERUD
- ☐ 95. TEAM CHECKLIST
- ☐ 106. JUNIOR FELIX
- ☐ 108. FRED MCGRIFF
- ☐ 111. KELLY GRUBER
- ☐ 113. PAT BORDERS
- ☐ 115. KEVIN BATISTE
- ☐ 127. GEORGE BELL
- ☐ 130. TONY FERNANDEZ
- ☐ 132. RANCE MULLINIKS
- ☐ 134. NELSON LIRIANO
- ☐ 148. ERNIE WHITT
- ☐ 282. TOM HENKE
- ☐ 285. MANNY LEE
- ☐ 421. LLOYD MOSEBY
- ☐ 462. JIMMY KEY
- ☐ 464. ROB DUCEY
- ☐ 481. MOOKIE WILSON
- ☐ 483. MIKE FLANAGAN
- ☐ 485. JOHN CERUTTI
- ☐ 605. DAVE STIEB
- ☐ 653. DUANE WARD
- ☐ 692. TODD STOTTLEMYRE
- ☐ 718. GREG MYERS
- ☐ 757. ALEX SANCHEZ
- ☐ 776. GLENALLEN HILL

1991 UPPER DECK (800) 2 1/2 X 3 1/2

ATLANTA BRAVES

- ☐ 55. CHIPPER JONES
- ☐ 82. TEAM CHECKLIST
- ☐ 262. JIMMY KREMERS
- ☐ 264. JOHN SMOLTZ
- ☐ 282. JIM PRESLEY
- ☐ 301. MARK GRANT
- ☐ 303. GREG OLSON
- ☐ 305. LONNIE SMITH
- ☐ 361. RON GANT
- ☐ 363. DAVE JUSTICE
- ☐ 365. STEVE AVERY
- ☐ 382. JEFF BLAUSER
- ☐ 384. ANDRES THOMAS
- ☐ 417. JEFF PARRETT
- ☐ 419. MARK LEMKE
- ☐ 439. FRANCISCO CABRERA
- ☐ 458. TONY CASTILLO
- ☐ 460. CHARLIE LEIBRANDT
- ☐ 478. MARTY CLARY
- ☐ 480. TOM GLAVINE
- ☐ 497. ODDIBE MCDOWELL
- ☐ 499. JEFF TREADWAY
- ☐ 604. JIM VATCHER
- ☐ 622. PETE SMITH
- ☐ 642. KENT MERCKER
- ☐ 644. MIKE BELL
- ☐ 701. MIKE HEATH
- ☐ 706. RAFAEL BELLIARD
- ☐ 708. TERRY PENDLETON
- ☐ 710. SID BREAM
- ☐ 743. DEION SANDERS
- ☐ 749. MIKE STANTON

BALTIMORE ORIOLES

- ☐ 6. LEO GOMEZ
- ☐ 47. TEAM CHECKLIST
- ☐ 65. MIKE MUSSINA
- ☐ 141. CRAIG WORTHINGTON
- ☐ 260. JEFF BALLARD
- ☐ 296. MICKEY TETTLETON
- ☐ 299. DAVE JOHNSON
- ☐ 302. PETE HARNISCH
- ☐ 304. ANTHONY TELFORD
- ☐ 306. CHRIS HOILES
- ☐ 308. MIKE DEVEREAUX
- ☐ 310. BOB MELVIN
- ☐ 326. GREGG OLSON
- ☐ 328. BOB MILACKI
- ☐ 330. STEVE FINLEY
- ☐ 342. DAVID SEGUI
- ☐ 347. CAL RIPKEN
- ☐ 349. BRADY ANDERSON
- ☐ 446. BEN MCDONALD
- ☐ 506. JOE ORSULAK
- ☐ 508. DAVE GALLAGHER
- ☐ 510. MARK WILLIAMSON
- ☐ 528. CURT SCHILLING
- ☐ 530. SAM HORN
- ☐ 548. RANDY MILLIGAN
- ☐ 550. BILLY RIPKEN
- ☐ 703. JOSE MESA
- ☐ 745. LUIS MERCEDES
- ☐ 757. GLENN DAVIS
- ☐ 776. DWIGHT EVANS
- ☐ 796. JEFF ROBINSON

BOSTON RED SOX

- ☐ 2. PHIL PLANTIER
- ☐ 5. MO VAUGHN
- ☐ 22. SCOTT COOPER
- ☐ 41. LARRY ANDERSEN
- ☐ 43. TEAM CHECKLIST
- ☐ 70. GREG BLOSSER
- ☐ 86. TOM BOLTON
- ☐ 88. JOHN DOPSON
- ☐ 90. MARTY BARRETT
- ☐ 163. TOM BRUNANSKY
- ☐ 165. MIKE GREENWELL
- ☐ 182. LUIS RIVERA
- ☐ 184. JODY REED
- ☐ 214. WES GARDNER
- ☐ 232. CARLOS QUINTANA
- ☐ 418. JEFF REARDON
- ☐ 436. ELLIS BURKS
- ☐ 438. MIKE BODDICKER
- ☐ 507. DANA KIECKER
- ☐ 509. GREG HARRIS
- ☐ 527. TIM NAEHRING
- ☐ 546. WADE BOGGS
- ☐ 549. DWIGHT EVANS
- ☐ 652. TONY PENA
- ☐ 655. ROGER CLEMENS
- ☐ 681. MIKE MARSHALL
- ☐ 683. ROB MURPHY
- ☐ 685. JEFF GRAY
- ☐ 705. DANNY DARWIN
- ☐ 735. JACK CLARK
- ☐ 740. MATT YOUNG

CALIFORNIA ANGELS

- ☐ 31. TEAM CHECKLIST
- ☐ 51. KYLE ABBOTT
- ☐ 169. DICK SCHOFIELD
- ☐ 187. LUIS POLONIA
- ☐ 190. SCOTT BAILES
- ☐ 211. DONNIE HILL
- ☐ 213. JACK HOWELL
- ☐ 231. BRIAN DOWNING
- ☐ 234. MARK LANGSTON
- ☐ 317. DANTE BICHETTE
- ☐ 337. DAVE WINFIELD
- ☐ 339. CHILI DAVIS
- ☐ 437. CHUCK FINLEY
- ☐ 517. DEVON WHITE
- ☐ 519. MARK EICHHORN
- ☐ 539. KIRK MCCASKILL
- ☐ 552. LANCE PARRISH
- ☐ 554. JIM ABBOTT
- ☐ 571. BERT BLYLEVEN
- ☐ 573. LEE STEVENS
- ☐ 575. WALLY JOYNER
- ☐ 592. BRYAN HARVEY
- ☐ 594. SCOTT LEWIS
- ☐ 657. JOE GRAHE
- ☐ 678. JOHNNY RAY
- ☐ 696. MIKE FETTERS
- ☐ 699. WILLIE FRASER
- ☐ 711. JUNIOR FELIX
- ☐ 714. LUIS SOJO
- ☐ 731. GARY GAETTI
- ☐ 733. DAVE PARKER

CHICAGO CUBS

- ☐ 9. LANCE DICKSON
- ☐ 58. GARY SCOTT
- ☐ 85. DOMINGO RAMOS
- ☐ 99. TEAM CHECKLIST
- ☐ 111. SHAWON DUNSTON
- ☐ 113. JOE GIRARDI
- ☐ 115. GREG MADDUX
- ☐ 132. RYNE SANDBERG
- ☐ 134. MARK GRACE
- ☐ 171. HECTOR VILLANUEVA
- ☐ 173. MITCH WILLIAMS
- ☐ 311. LUIS SALAZAR
- ☐ 314. DAVE CLARK
- ☐ 319. DAMON BERRYHILL
- ☐ 332. JEROME WALTON
- ☐ 334. DERRICK MAY
- ☐ 452. DWIGHT SMITH
- ☐ 454. ANDRE DAWSON
- ☐ 471. SHAWN BOSKIE
- ☐ 473. RICK SUTCLIFFE
- ☐ 475. MIKE HARKEY
- ☐ 491. PAUL ASSENMACHER
- ☐ 493. STEVE WILSON
- ☐ 495. BILL LONG
- ☐ 597. MIKE BIELECKI
- ☐ 704. DAVE SMITH
- ☐ 723. DANNY JACKSON
- ☐ 742. GEORGE BELL
- ☐ 767. HEATHCLIFF SLOCUMB

CHICAGO WHITE SOX

- ☐ 29. TEAM CHECKLIST
- ☐ 39. BARRY JONES
- ☐ 75. LEN BRUTCHER
- ☐ 209. RON KARKOVICE
- ☐ 246. FRANK THOMAS
- ☐ 248. LANCE JOHNSON
- ☐ 261. BOBBY THIGPEN
- ☐ 263. ROBIN VENTURA
- ☐ 265. SAMMY SOSA
- ☐ 281. ERIC KING
- ☐ 283. KEN PATTERSON
- ☐ 285. IVAN CALDERON
- ☐ 321. SCOTT FLETCHER
- ☐ 323. JACK MCDOWELL
- ☐ 325. OZZIE GUILLEN
- ☐ 601. STEVE LYONS
- ☐ 603. DONN PALL
- ☐ 605. DAN PASQUA
- ☐ 621. SCOTT RADINSKY
- ☐ 623. MELIDO PEREZ
- ☐ 625. CARLOS MARTINEZ
- ☐ 641. PHIL BRADLEY
- ☐ 643. CARLTON FISK
- ☐ 645. ALEX FERNANDEZ
- ☐ 679. GREG HIBBARD
- ☐ 697. WAYNE EDWARDS
- ☐ 724. CORY SNYDER
- ☐ 744. BO JACKSON
- ☐ 773. TIM RAINES
- ☐ 792. CHARLIE HOUGH

CINCINNATI REDS

- ☐ 37. TERRY LEE
- ☐ 71. REGGIE SANDERS
- ☐ 77. TEAM CHECKLIST
- ☐ 112. MARIANO DUNCAN
- ☐ 114. BILLY HATCHER
- ☐ 133. PAUL O'NEILL
- ☐ 135. CHRIS SABO
- ☐ 279. JOE OLIVER
- ☐ 280. TODD BENZINGER
- ☐ 298. JOSE RIJO
- ☐ 351. HAL MORRIS
- ☐ 353. BARRY LARKIN
- ☐ 355. ERIC DAVIS

□ 371. RANDY MYERS
□ 373. JACK ARMSTRONG
□ 394. NORM CHARLTON
□ 396. TIM LAYANA
□ 398. BILL DORAN
□ 414. DANNY JACKSON
□ 611. RON OESTER
□ 613. RICK MAHLER
□ 615. SCOTT SCUDDER
□ 631. GLENN BRAGGS
□ 633. TOM BROWNING
□ 635. ROB DIBBLE
□ 746. REGGIE JEFFERSON
□ 748. CHRIS HAMMOND

CLEVELAND INDIANS

□ 17. MARK LEWIS
□ 19. CHARLES NAGY
□ 46. TEAM CHECKLIST
□ 62. TIM COSTO
□ 102. TOM BROOKENS
□ 104. FELIX FERMIN
□ 116. JERRY BROWNE
□ 118. STEVE OLIN
□ 120. MITCH WEBSTER
□ 121. JOEL SKINNER
□ 123. CORY SNYDER
□ 125. CARLOS BAERGA
□ 137. BROOK JACOBY
□ 138. CANDY MALDONADO
□ 140. CHRIS JAMES
□ 144. SANDY ALOMAR
□ 216. DOUG JONES
□ 218. TOM CANDIOTTI
□ 236. GREG SWINDELL
□ 238. JEFF MANTO
□ 240. JESSE OROSCO
□ 358. RUDY SEANEZ
□ 399. DION JAMES
□ 654. ALEX COLE
□ 692. JOHN FARRELL
□ 694. MIKE WALKER
□ 762. TURNER WARD
□ 764. ALBERT BELLE
□ 782. ERIC KING
□ 784. BEAU ALLRED

DETROIT TIGERS

□ 7. SCOTT ALDRED
□ 45. TEAM CHECKLIST
□ 73. RICO BROGNA
□ 131. TONY PHILLIPS
□ 201. JOHN SHELBY
□ 203. LANCE MCCULLERS
□ 205. MARK SALAS
□ 223. ALAN TRAMMELL
□ 225. TRAVIS FRYMAN
□ 241. SCOTT LUSADER
□ 244. CECIL FIELDER
□ 316. DAN PETRY
□ 318. MIKE HEATH
□ 320. WALT TERRELL
□ 336. JACK MORRIS
□ 338. STEVE SEARCY
□ 340. LARRY SHEETS
□ 367. LOU WHITAKER
□ 369. FRANK TANANA
□ 386. MIKE HENNEMAN
□ 389. CHET LEMON
□ 412. GARY WARD
□ 556. MILT CUYLER
□ 559. LLOYD MOSEBY
□ 579. PAUL GIBSON
□ 599. DAVE BERGMAN
□ 676. JEFF ROBINSON
□ 726. ROB DEER
□ 729. MICKEY TETTLETON
□ 747. PETE INCAVIGLIA

HOUSTON ASTROS

□ 23. ANDUJAR CEDENO
□ 52. JEFF JUDEN
□ 81. TEAM CHECKLIST
□ 158. CRAIG BIGGIO
□ 168. FRANKLIN STUBBS
□ 180. KEN CAMINITI
□ 197. ERIC YELDING
□ 208. JIM DESHAIES
□ 210. RAFAEL RAMIREZ
□ 250. MARK PORTUGAL
□ 466. KARL RHODES
□ 511. CASEY CANDAELE
□ 513. DAVE SMITH
□ 515. GLENN WILSON
□ 531. MIKE SCOTT
□ 533. ERIC ANTHONY
□ 535. GLENN DAVIS
□ 567. LUIS GONZALEZ
□ 569. JUAN AGOSTO
□ 586. DANNY DARWIN
□ 588. RICH GEDMAN
□ 590. BILL GULLICKSON
□ 662. DAVE ROHDE
□ 664. MIKE SIMMS
□ 682. JIM CLANCY
□ 752. AL OSUNA
□ 755. JEFF BAGWELL
□ 772. PETE HARNISCH
□ 774. DARRYL KILE
□ 794. STEVE FINLEY

KANSAS CITY ROYALS

□ 10. SEAN BERRY
□ 27. JEFF CONINE
□ 33. TEAM CHECKLIST
□ 72. BRENT MAYNE
□ 219. GERALD PERRY
□ 431. TOM GORDON
□ 433. KEVIN SEITZER
□ 435. BRET SABERHAGEN
□ 502. BOB BOONE
□ 504. LUIS AQUINO
□ 521. TERRY SHUMPERT
□ 523. DANNY TARTABULL
□ 525. GEORGE BRETT
□ 541. MARK GUBICZA
□ 543. BRIAN MCRAE
□ 545. BO JACKSON
□ 566. KEVIN APPIER
□ 568. FRANK WHITE
□ 570. MIKE MACFARLANE
□ 587. KURT STILLWELL
□ 589. MARK DAVIS
□ 607. JEFF SCHULZ
□ 609. WILLIE WILSON
□ 637. JEFF MONTGOMERY
□ 639. STORM DAVIS
□ 658. JIM EISENREICH
□ 660. STEVE FARR
□ 719. MIKE BODDICKER
□ 737. KIRK GIBSON

LOS ANGELES DODGERS

□ 4. DAVE HANSEN
□ 21. HENRY RODRIGUEZ
□ 24. ERIC KARROS
□ 59. KIKI JONES
□ 78. TEAM CHECKLIST
□ 117. JUAN SAMUEL
□ 119. ALFREDO GRIFFIN
□ 136. RAMON MARTINEZ
□ 139. MIKE SCIOSCIA
□ 166. KAL DANIELS
□ 175. FERNANDO VALENZUELA
□ 217. HUBIE BROOKS
□ 237. EDDIE MURRAY
□ 239. LENNY HARRIS
□ 245. DARRYL STRAWBERRY
□ 356. JOSE OFFERMAN
□ 524. OREL HERSHISER
□ 558. JAY HOWELL
□ 560. CHRIS GWYNN
□ 576. TIM BELCHER
□ 578. MIKE MORGAN
□ 580. JOSE VIZCAINO
□ 596. TIM CREWS
□ 598. MIKE SHARPERSON
□ 612. DENNIS COOK
□ 632. JIM NEIDLINGER
□ 634. KIRK GIBSON
□ 666. MICKEY HATCHER
□ 668. JOHN WETTELAND
□ 686. MIKE HARTLEY
□ 688. STAN JAVIER
□ 690. JIM GOTT
□ 713. KEVIN GROSS
□ 715. BOB OJEDA
□ 732. BRETT BUTLER
□ 758. GARY CARTER
□ 779. JEFF HAMILTON

MILWAUKEE BREWERS

□ 13. NARCISO ELVIRA
□ 42. DARRYL HAMILTON
□ 48. TEAM CHECKLIST
□ 56. CHRIS JOHNSON
□ 254. B.J. SURHOFF
□ 266. GARY SHEFFIELD
□ 268. BILL SPIERS
□ 272. ROB DEER
□ 274. DAVE PARKER
□ 286. EDGAR DIAZ
□ 289. GREG BROCK
□ 292. BILL WEGMAN
□ 322. DAN PLESAC
□ 324. PAUL MOLITOR
□ 341. TED HIGUERA
□ 344. ROBIN YOUNT
□ 391. CHUCK CRIM
□ 393. MARK KNUDSON
□ 395. MIKE FELDER
□ 476. JAIME NAVARRO
□ 526. GREG VAUGHN
□ 529. CHRIS BOSIO
□ 547. TIM MCINTOSH
□ 616. TOM EDENS
□ 618. JIM GANTNER
□ 620. RON ROBINSON
□ 712. DANTE BICHETTE
□ 716. JULIO MACHADO
□ 718. FRANKLIN STUBBS
□ 720. WILLIE RANDOLPH
□ 739. CANDY MALDONADO

MINNESOTA TWINS

□ 34. TEAM CHECKLIST
□ 35. SCOTT LEIUS
□ 40. CHUCK KNOBLAUCH
□ 74. WILLIE BANKS
□ 167. KENT HRBEK
□ 170. JUNIOR ORTIZ
□ 188. SHANE MACK
□ 212. BRIAN HARPER
□ 233. GARY GAETTI
□ 360. NELSON LIRIANO
□ 377. DAVE WEST
□ 411. JUAN BERENGUER
□ 413. AL NEWMAN
□ 415. GREG GAGNE
□ 432. PEDRO MUNOZ
□ 434. KEVIN TAPANI
□ 487. PAUL ABBOTT
□ 490. ROY SMITH
□ 501. GENE LARKIN
□ 503. ALLAN ANDERSON
□ 505. MARK GUTHRIE
□ 522. SCOTT ERICKSON
□ 542. RICK AGUILERA
□ 544. KIRBY PUCKETT
□ 659. DAN GLADDEN
□ 680. PAUL SORRENTO
□ 698. TIM DRUMMOND
□ 709. MIKE PAGLIARULO
□ 722. CHILI DAVIS

- ☐ 736. JACK MORRIS
- ☐ 738. STEVE BEDROSIAN
- ☐ 741. RICH GARCES

MONTREAL EXPOS

- ☐ 12. BRIAN BARNES
- ☐ 15. GREG COLBRUNN
- ☐ 60. WILFREDO CORDERO
- ☐ 96. TEAM CHECKLIST
- ☐ 143. TIM RAINES
- ☐ 186. DAVE MARTINEZ
- ☐ 189. SPIKE OWEN
- ☐ 215. TIM BURKE
- ☐ 235. TIM WALLACH
- ☐ 357. MEL ROJAS
- ☐ 359. OIL CAN BOYD
- ☐ 362. HOWARD FARMER
- ☐ 364. DELINO DESHIELDS
- ☐ 380. KEVIN GROSS
- ☐ 381. TOM FOLEY
- ☐ 383. SCOTT RUSKIN
- ☐ 385. DENNIS MARTINEZ
- ☐ 397. STEVE FREY
- ☐ 456. ANDRES GALARRAGA
- ☐ 477. MARQUIS GRISSOM
- ☐ 516. MIKE FITZGERALD
- ☐ 520. OTIS NIXON
- ☐ 536. LARRY WALKER
- ☐ 538. CHRIS NABHOLZ
- ☐ 661. BILL SAMPEN
- ☐ 663. MARK GARDNER
- ☐ 665. MOISES ALOU
- ☐ 684. DAVE SCHMIDT
- ☐ 786. IVAN CALDERON
- ☐ 789. BARRY JONES

NEW YORK METS

- ☐ 3. D.J. DOZIER
- ☐ 64. BROOK FORDYCE
- ☐ 95. TEAM CHECKLIST
- ☐ 101. KEVIN ELSTER
- ☐ 103. MACKEY SASSER
- ☐ 105. KEVIN MCREYNOLDS
- ☐ 122. FRANK VIOLA
- ☐ 124. HOWARD JOHNSON
- ☐ 156. GREGG JEFFERIES
- ☐ 159. DARYL BOSTON
- ☐ 177. DAVE MAGADAN
- ☐ 179. BOB OJEDA
- ☐ 196. KEITH MILLER
- ☐ 198. RON DARLING
- ☐ 221. WALLY WHITEHURST
- ☐ 224. DWIGHT GOODEN
- ☐ 242. SID FERNANDEZ
- ☐ 290. JOHN FRANCO
- ☐ 366. DAVID CONE
- ☐ 370. TIM TEUFEL
- ☐ 388. ALEJANDRO PENA
- ☐ 416. TOM HERR
- ☐ 420. CHARLIE O'BRIEN
- ☐ 440. TODD HUNDLEY
- ☐ 514. CHUCK CARR
- ☐ 534. JULIO VALERA
- ☐ 766. PETE SCHOUREK
- ☐ 768. VINCE COLEMAN
- ☐ 787. HUBIE BROOKS

NEW YORK YANKEES

- ☐ 11. BERNIE WILLIAMS
- ☐ 49. TEAM CHECKLIST
- ☐ 76. PAT KELLY
- ☐ 202. BOB GEREN
- ☐ 204. ALVARO ESPINOZA
- ☐ 222. ALAN MILLS
- ☐ 243. JIM LEYRITZ
- ☐ 333. ANDY HAWKINS
- ☐ 343. GREG CADARET
- ☐ 352. DEION SANDERS
- ☐ 354. DON MATTINGLY
- ☐ 372. ROBERTO KELLY
- ☐ 375. KEVIN MAAS
- ☐ 392. MEL HALL
- ☐ 409. CHUCK CARY
- ☐ 429. MIKE WITT
- ☐ 448. DAVE RIGHETTI
- ☐ 462. STEVE SAX
- ☐ 464. OSCAR AZOCAR
- ☐ 481. LEE GUETTERMAN
- ☐ 483. DAVE LAPOINT
- ☐ 485. JESSE BARFIELD
- ☐ 671. PASCUAL PEREZ
- ☐ 673. MATT NOKES
- ☐ 675. HENSLEY MEULENS
- ☐ 693. TIM LEARY
- ☐ 695. ERIC PLUNK
- ☐ 717. STEVE FARR
- ☐ 730. MIKE BLOWERS
- ☐ 750. SCOTT SANDERSON

OAKLAND A'S

- ☐ 28. TEAM CHECKLIST
- ☐ 53. TODD VAN POPPEL
- ☐ 108. DAVE HENDERSON
- ☐ 127. DAVE STEWART
- ☐ 146. OZZIE CANSECO
- ☐ 151. MIKE GALLEGO
- ☐ 153. TERRY STEINBACH
- ☐ 155. JOSE CANSECO
- ☐ 172. DENNIS ECKERSLEY
- ☐ 174. MARK MCGWIRE
- ☐ 192. WALT WEISS
- ☐ 194. CARNEY LANSFORD
- ☐ 277. STEVE HOWARD
- ☐ 379. RICK HONEYCUTT
- ☐ 401. RON HASSEY
- ☐ 403. GENE NELSON
- ☐ 405. TODD BURNS
- ☐ 421. WILLIE RANDOLPH
- ☐ 423. MIKE MOORE
- ☐ 425. BOB WELCH
- ☐ 442. DANN HOWITT
- ☐ 444. RICKEY HENDERSON
- ☐ 468. JOE KLINK
- ☐ 562. HAROLD BAINES
- ☐ 564. DARREN LEWIS
- ☐ 582. SCOTT SANDERSON
- ☐ 584. WILLIE MCGEE
- ☐ 672. REGGIE HARRIS
- ☐ 753. STEVE CHITREN
- ☐ 756. KIRK DRESSENDORFER
- ☐ 760. VANCE LAW
- ☐ 771. DANA ALLISON
- ☐ 777. JOE SLUSARSKI
- ☐ 780. ERNEST RILES
- ☐ 798. ERIC SHOW

PHILADELPHIA PHILLIES

- ☐ 18. MICKEY MORANDINI
- ☐ 67. MIKE LIEBERTHAL
- ☐ 97. TEAM CHECKLIST
- ☐ 160. RICKY JORDAN
- ☐ 199. JOHN KRUK
- ☐ 267. LENNY DYKSTRA
- ☐ 269. CHARLIE HAYES
- ☐ 288. DON CARMAN
- ☐ 368. VON HAYES
- ☐ 406. ROGER MCDOWELL
- ☐ 408. DARREN DAULTON
- ☐ 410. BRUCE RUFFIN
- ☐ 426. TERRY MULHOLLAND
- ☐ 428. DARRIN FLETCHER
- ☐ 430. JOE BOEVER
- ☐ 447. DALE MURPHY
- ☐ 449. DICKIE THON
- ☐ 469. SIL CAMPUSANO
- ☐ 486. JOSE DEJESUS
- ☐ 488. KEN HOWELL
- ☐ 518. DAVE HOLLINS
- ☐ 537. PAT COMBS
- ☐ 540. RANDY READY
- ☐ 619. DARREL AKERFELDS
- ☐ 626. WES CHAMBERLAIN
- ☐ 649. CHUCK MALONE
- ☐ 769. MITCH WILLIAMS
- ☐ 790. WALLY BACKMAN

PITTSBURGH PIRATES

- ☐ 36. NEAL HEATON
- ☐ 38. GARY REDUS
- ☐ 68. KURT MILLER
- ☐ 84. ORLANDO MERCED
- ☐ 92. CARMELO MARTINEZ
- ☐ 94. TEAM CHECKLIST
- ☐ 109. SID BREAM
- ☐ 129. MIKE LAVALLIERE
- ☐ 150. R.J. REYNOLDS
- ☐ 152. BOBBY BONILLA
- ☐ 154. BARRY BONDS
- ☐ 161. STAN BELINDA
- ☐ 181. DON SLAUGHT
- ☐ 183. JAY BELL
- ☐ 185. WALLY BACKMAN
- ☐ 256. ANDY VAN SLYKE
- ☐ 258. JOSE LIND
- ☐ 278. DOUG DRABEK
- ☐ 407. BOB KIPPER
- ☐ 450. TED POWER
- ☐ 614. BILL LANDRUM
- ☐ 669. JOHN SMILEY
- ☐ 687. JEFF KING
- ☐ 689. BOB WALK
- ☐ 759. ZANE SMITH

ST. LOUIS CARDINALS

- ☐ 16. BERNARD GILKEY
- ☐ 20. GERONIMO PENA
- ☐ 57. JOHN ERICKS
- ☐ 91. TOM PAGNOZZI
- ☐ 98. TEAM CHECKLIST
- ☐ 162. OZZIE SMITH
- ☐ 164. TODD ZEILE
- ☐ 193. JOSE OQUENDO
- ☐ 220. JOSE DELEON
- ☐ 307. BRYN SMITH
- ☐ 309. MILT THOMPSON
- ☐ 327. PEDRO GUERRERO
- ☐ 329. JOHN TUDOR
- ☐ 346. RAY LANKFORD
- ☐ 348. LEE SMITH
- ☐ 350. FRANK DIPINO
- ☐ 387. FELIX JOSE
- ☐ 390. CRAIG WILSON
- ☐ 461. VINCE COLEMAN
- ☐ 463. OMAR OLIVARES
- ☐ 465. JOE MAGRANE
- ☐ 482. REX HUDLER
- ☐ 484. TERRY PENDLETON
- ☐ 628. KEN DAYLEY
- ☐ 630. BOB TEWKSBURY
- ☐ 647. KEN HILL
- ☐ 728. MIKE PEREZ
- ☐ 788. JUAN AGOSTO

SAN DIEGO PADRES

- ☐ 66. DAVE STATON
- ☐ 80. TEAM CHECKLIST
- ☐ 206. MIKE PAGLIARULO
- ☐ 226. JOE CARTER
- ☐ 228. CRAIG LEFFERTS
- ☐ 230. DENNIS RASMUSSEN
- ☐ 251. DEREK LILLIQUIST
- ☐ 253. RAFAEL VALDEZ
- ☐ 255. TONY GWYNN
- ☐ 271. BIP ROBERTS
- ☐ 273. FRED LYNN
- ☐ 275. ANDY BENES
- ☐ 291. JOEY CORA
- ☐ 293. ERIC SHOW
- ☐ 295. GARRY TEMPLETON
- ☐ 312. ED WHITSON
- ☐ 331. JACK CLARK
- ☐ 335. ROBERTO ALOMAR
- ☐ 467. BENITO SANTIAGO
- ☐ 470. MARK PARENT
- ☐ 489. GREG HARRIS
- ☐ 602. BRUCE HURST
- ☐ 624. JERALD CLARK
- ☐ 640. RICH RODRIGUEZ
- ☐ 751. PAUL FARIES
- ☐ 754. TONY FERNANDEZ
- ☐ 775. FRED MCGRIFF
- ☐ 791. JIM PRESLEY
- ☐ 793. LARRY ANDERSEN
- ☐ 795. SHAWN ABNER

SAN FRANCISCO GIANTS

- ☐ 25. STEVE DECKER
- ☐ 61. ROYCE CLAYTON
- ☐ 79. TEAM CHECKLIST
- ☐ 87. ANDRES SANTANA
- ☐ 157. MATT WILLIAMS
- ☐ 176. GARY CARTER
- ☐ 178. ROBBY THOMPSON
- ☐ 207. JOSE URIBE

- ☐ 247. KEVIN MITCHELL
- ☐ 249. RICK REUSCHEL
- ☐ 270. BRETT BUTLER
- ☐ 287. KEVIN BASS
- ☐ 315. ERIC GUNDERSON
- ☐ 402. DON ROBINSON
- ☐ 404. TERRY KENNEDY
- ☐ 422. STEVE BEDROSIAN
- ☐ 424. JEFF BRANTLEY
- ☐ 441. KELLY DOWNS
- ☐ 443. SCOTT GARRELTS
- ☐ 445. WILL CLARK
- ☐ 557. MARK LEONARD
- ☐ 577. JOHN BURKETT
- ☐ 651. MIKE BENJAMIN
- ☐ 653. TREVOR WILSON
- ☐ 674. RAFAEL NOVOA
- ☐ 691. MIKE LACOSS
- ☐ 721. WILLIE MCGEE
- ☐ 778. DAVE RIGHETTI
- ☐ 799. BUD BLACK

SEATTLE MARINERS

- ☐ 14. MIKE GARDINER
- ☐ 32. TEAM CHECKLIST
- ☐ 63. ROGER SALKELD
- ☐ 107. JEFFREY LEONARD
- ☐ 110. HENRY COTTO
- ☐ 128. JAY BUHNER
- ☐ 130. SCOTT BRADLEY
- ☐ 148. HAROLD REYNOLDS
- ☐ 252. BRIAN HOLMAN
- ☐ 294. SCOTT BANKHEAD
- ☐ 376. RANDY JOHNSON
- ☐ 378. BRENT KNACKERT
- ☐ 457. ALVIN DAVIS
- ☐ 459. PETE O'BRIEN
- ☐ 479. GREG BRILEY
- ☐ 496. MIKE JACKSON
- ☐ 498. BILL SWIFT
- ☐ 551. ERIK HANSON
- ☐ 553. TINO MARTINEZ
- ☐ 555. KEN GRIFFEY JR.
- ☐ 572. KEN GRIFFEY
- ☐ 574. EDGAR MARTINEZ
- ☐ 591. MATT YOUNG
- ☐ 593. OMAR VIZQUEL
- ☐ 595. DAVE VALLE
- ☐ 638. MIKE SCHOOLER
- ☐ 707. ROB MURPHY
- ☐ 727. RICH DELUCIA

TEXAS RANGERS

- ☐ 8. SCOTT CHIAMPARINO
- ☐ 26. KEVIN BELCHER
- ☐ 30. TEAM CHECKLIST
- ☐ 69. DAN PELTIER
- ☐ 191. JOHN RUSSELL
- ☐ 195. JEFF HUSON
- ☐ 227. JULIO FRANCO
- ☐ 229. GARY PETTIS
- ☐ 284. JACK DAUGHERTY
- ☐ 313. CHARLIE HOUGH
- ☐ 345. NOLAN RYAN
- ☐ 451. SCOTT COOLBAUGH
- ☐ 453. PETE INCAVIGLIA
- ☐ 455. RUBEN SIERRA
- ☐ 472. KEVIN BROWN
- ☐ 474. RAFAEL PALMEIRO
- ☐ 492. GENO PETRALLI
- ☐ 494. KEVIN REIMER
- ☐ 606. KENNY ROGERS
- ☐ 608. BRAD ARNSBERG
- ☐ 610. JAMIE MOYER
- ☐ 627. BOBBY WITT
- ☐ 629. JOHN BARFIELD
- ☐ 646. JUAN GONZALEZ
- ☐ 648. JEFF RUSSELL
- ☐ 650. STEVE BUECHELE
- ☐ 770. BRIAN DOWNING
- ☐ 797. JOE BITKER

TORONTO BLUE JAYS

- ☐ 44. TEAM CHECKLIST
- ☐ 54. STEVE KARSAY
- ☐ 89. KENNY WILLIAMS
- ☐ 106. DAVE STIEB
- ☐ 126. TONY FERNANDEZ
- ☐ 142. MANNY LEE
- ☐ 145. JOHN OLERUD
- ☐ 147. PAT BORDERS
- ☐ 149. TOM HENKE
- ☐ 257. TODD STOTTLEMYRE
- ☐ 259. GREG MYERS
- ☐ 276. GLENALLEN HILL
- ☐ 297. LUIS SOJO
- ☐ 374. KELLY GRUBER
- ☐ 427. WILLIE BLAIR
- ☐ 512. MOOKIE WILSON
- ☐ 532. GEORGE BELL
- ☐ 561. MARK WHITEN
- ☐ 563. JUNIOR FELIX
- ☐ 565. FRED MCGRIFF
- ☐ 581. DUANE WARD
- ☐ 583. DAVID WELLS
- ☐ 585. JOHN CERUTTI
- ☐ 667. JIMMY KEY
- ☐ 670. JIM ACKER
- ☐ 734. EDDIE ZOSKY
- ☐ 761. DENIS BOUCHER
- ☐ 763. ROBERTO ALOMAR
- ☐ 765. JOE CARTER
- ☐ 781. KEN DAYLEY
- ☐ 783. DEVON WHITE
- ☐ 785. MIKE TIMLIN

1991 UPPER DECK FINAL EDITION (100) 2 1/2 X 3 1/2

ATLANTA BRAVES

- ☐ 8F. RYAN KLESKO
- ☐ 54F. BRIAN HUNTER
- ☐ 56F. KEITH MITCHELL
- ☐ 58F. OTIS NIXON
- ☐ 77F. MARK WOHLERS
- ☐ 90F. TOM GLAVINE

BALTIMORE ORIOLES

- ☐ 13F. ARTHUR RHODES
- ☐ 30F. CHITO MARTINEZ
- ☐ 59F. JUAN BELL
- ☐ 85F. CAL RIPKEN

BOSTON RED SOX

- ☐ 20F. JEFF MCNEELY
- ☐ 21F. FRANKIE RODRIGUEZ
- ☐ 66F. KEVIN MORTON
- ☐ 84F. WADE BOGGS

CALIFORNIA ANGELS

NO CARDS ISSUED

CHICAGO CUBS

- ☐ 3F. LANCE DICKSON
- ☐ 27F. FRANK CASTILLO
- ☐ 29F. CHUCK MCELROY
- ☐ 46F. RICK WILKINS
- ☐ 48F. BOB SCANLAN
- ☐ 93F. RYNE SANDBERG
- ☐ 98F. ANDRE DAWSON

CHICAGO WHITE SOX

- ☐ 42F. WILSON ALVAREZ

CINCINNATI REDS

- ☐ 5F. SCOTT BRYANT
- ☐ 6F. DAN WILSON
- ☐ 11F. REGGIE SANDERS
- ☐ 32F. FREDDIE BENAVIDES
- ☐ 94F. CHRIS SABO

CLEVELAND INDIANS

- ☐ 17F. JIM THOME
- ☐ 52F. GLENALLEN HILL
- ☐ 73F. REGGIE JEFFERSON
- ☐ 75F. MARK WHITEN
- ☐ 81F. SANDY ALOMAR

DETROIT TIGERS

- ☐ 44F. RUSTY MEACHAM
- ☐ 53F. SCOTT LIVINGSTONE
- ☐ 82F. CECIL FIELDER

HOUSTON ASTROS

- ☐ 22F. ANDY MOTA
- ☐ 24F. KENNY LOFTON
- ☐ 45F. RYAN BOWEN
- ☐ 68F. SCOTT SERVAIS

KANSAS CITY ROYALS

- ☐ 19F. KERWIN MOORE
- ☐ 41F. TODD BENZINGER
- ☐ 89F. DANNY TARTABULL

LOS ANGELES DODGERS

- ☐ 2F. PEDRO MARTINEZ
- ☐ 9F. TOM GOODWIN
- ☐ 40F. JOHN CANDELARIA
- ☐ 57F. ROGER MCDOWELL

MILWAUKEE BREWERS

- ☐ 25F. DAVE NILSSON

MINNESOTA TWINS

- ☐ 34F. DENNY NEAGLE
- ☐ 80F. JACK MORRIS

MONTREAL EXPOS

- ☐ 10F. RONDELL WHITE

- ☐ 23F. CHRIS HANEY
- ☐ 67F. BRET BARBERIE
- ☐ 96F. IVAN CALDERON

NEW YORK METS

- ☐ 61F. CHRIS DONNELS
- ☐ 63F. DOUG SIMONS
- ☐ 65F. ANTHONY YOUNG
- ☐ 70F. TIM BURKE

NEW YORK YANKEES

- ☐ 15F. GERALD WILLIAMS
- ☐ 16F. ROBERT EENHOORN
- ☐ 31F. STEVE HOWE
- ☐ 33F. SCOTT KAMIENIECKI
- ☐ 35F. MIKE HUMPHREYS

Ron Darling

OAKLAND A'S

- ☐ 12F. TODD VAN POPPEL
- ☐ 69F. RON DARLING
- ☐ 78F. BROOK JACOBY
- ☐ 86F. RICKEY HENDERSON
- ☐ 88F. DAVE HENDERSON

PHILADELPHIA PHILLIES

- ☐ 62F. TOMMY GREENE
- ☐ 64F. ANDY ASHBY

PITTSBURGH PIRATES

- ☐ 71F. VICENTE PALACIOS
- ☐ 76F. RANDY TOMLIN
- ☐ 99F. BOBBY BONILLA

ST. LOUIS CARDINALS

- ☐ 7F. DMITRI YOUNG
- ☐ 95F. OZZIE SMITH

SAN DIEGO PADRES

- ☐ 37F. SCOTT COOLBAUGH
- ☐ 39F. THOMAS HOWARD
- ☐ 91F. BENITO SANTIAGO
- ☐ 97F. TONY GWYNN

SAN FRANCISCO GIANTS

- ☐ 4F. ROYCE CLAYTON
- ☐ 36F. MIKE REMLINGER
- ☐ 38F. DARREN LEWIS
- ☐ 92F. WILL CLARK

SEATTLE MARINERS

- ☐ 18F. MARC NEWFIELD
- ☐ 43F. PATRICK LENNON
- ☐ 60F. BILL KRUEGER
- ☐ 87F. KEN GRIFFEY JR.

TEXAS RANGERS

- ☐ 51F. OIL CAN BOYD
- ☐ 55F. IVAN RODRIGUEZ
- ☐ 72F. GERALD ALEXANDER
- ☐ 74F. DEAN PALMER

Derek Bell

TORONTO BLUE JAYS

- ☐ 14F. EDDIE ZOSKY
- ☐ 26F. DEREK BELL
- ☐ 28F. CANDY MALDONADO
- ☐ 47F. ED SPRAGUE
- ☐ 49F. TOM CANDIOTTI
- ☐ 83F. ROBERTO ALOMAR

NOTE: Due to page limitations, from this point on each set will be represented by only one photo.

1992 UPPER DECK (800) 2 1/2" X 3 1/2"

ATLANTA BRAVES

- ☐ 24. RYAN KLESKO
- ☐ 29. TEAM CHECKLIST
- ☐ 47. MARK LEMKE
- ☐ 56. MARK WOHLERS
- ☐ 170. CHARLIE LEIBRANDT
- ☐ 189. GREG OLSON
- ☐ 229. TERRY PENDLETON
- ☐ 247. DEION SANDERS
- ☐ 301. LONNIE SMITH
- ☐ 304. MIKE HEATH
- ☐ 322. JOHN SMOLTZ
- ☐ 342. TOM GLAVINE
- ☐ 345. RON GANT
- ☐ 366. BRIAN HUNTER
- ☐ 370. JEFF BLAUSER
- ☐ 389. JEFF TREADWAY
- ☐ 451. OTIS NIXON
- ☐ 454. KEITH MITCHELL
- ☐ 472. KENT MERCKER
- ☐ 475. STEVE AVERY
- ☐ 491. MARVIN FREEMAN
- ☐ 493. JUAN BERENGUER
- ☐ 495. SID BREAM
- ☐ 510. RAFAEL BELLIARD
- ☐ 546. DAVID JUSTICE
- ☐ 653. MIKE STANTON
- ☐ 674. ARMANDO REYNOSO
- ☐ 694. ALEJANDRO PENA
- ☐ 706. DAMON BERRYHILL
- ☐ 730. MIKE BIELECKI
- ☐ 794. MIKE KELLY

BALTIMORE ORIOLES

- ☐ 17. ARTHUR RHODES
- ☐ 66. MARK SMITH
- ☐ 93. TEAM CHECKLIST
- ☐ 161. LEO GOMEZ
- ☐ 163. BEN MCDONALD
- ☐ 165. CAL RIPKEN
- ☐ 181. RANDY MILLIGAN
- ☐ 183. CHRIS HOILES
- ☐ 185. BRADY ANDERSON
- ☐ 207. JOE ORSULAK
- ☐ 209. MIKE DEVEREAUX
- ☐ 227. GREGG OLSON
- ☐ 248. DWIGHT EVANS
- ☐ 250. BILLY RIPKEN
- ☐ 316. DAVID SEGUI
- ☐ 318. TODD FROHWIRTH
- ☐ 320. JEFF ROBINSON
- ☐ 338. SAM HORN
- ☐ 380. MIKE FLANAGAN
- ☐ 480. BOB MILACKI
- ☐ 609. MARK WILLIAMSON
- ☐ 652. LUIS MERCEDES
- ☐ 654. GLENN DAVIS
- ☐ 672. CHITO MARTINEZ
- ☐ 675. MIKE MUSSINA
- ☐ 692. BOB MELVIN
- ☐ 708. RICK SUTCLIFFE

BOSTON RED SOX

- ☐ 71. JEFF PLYMPTON
- ☐ 94. TEAM CHECKLIST
- ☐ 110. TOM BOLTON
- ☐ 252. TONY PENA
- ☐ 275. MIKE GREENWELL
- ☐ 308. LUIS RIVERA
- ☐ 404. JODY REED
- ☐ 421. CARLOS QUINTANA
- ☐ 425. PHILL PLANTIER
- ☐ 443. WADE BOGGS
- ☐ 445. MO VAUGHN
- ☐ 501. JEFF REARDON
- ☐ 503. TONY FOSSAS
- ☐ 505. MATT YOUNG
- ☐ 521. JACK CLARK
- ☐ 523. TIM NAEHRING
- ☐ 525. ELLIS BURKS
- ☐ 541. SCOTT COOPER
- ☐ 543. TOM BRUNANSKY
- ☐ 545. ROGER CLEMENS
- ☐ 570. JOE HESKETH
- ☐ 588. MIKE GARDINER
- ☐ 658. GREG HARRIS
- ☐ 664. WAYNE HOUSIE
- ☐ 676. KEVIN MORTON
- ☐ 678. DANNY DARWIN
- ☐ 733. FRANK VIOLA

CALIFORNIA ANGELS

- ☐ 8. KYLE ABBOTT
- ☐ 52. EDUARDO PEREZ
- ☐ 86. TEAM CHECKLIST
- ☐ 128. KIRK MCCASKILL
- ☐ 147. LUIS POLONIA
- ☐ 149. LUIS SOJO
- ☐ 222. DAVE WINFIELD
- ☐ 244. CHUCK FINLEY
- ☐ 269. DICK SCHOFIELD
- ☐ 287. MARK EICHHORN
- ☐ 289. DAVE GALLAGHER
- ☐ 303. JUNIOR FELIX
- ☐ 305. MARK LANGSTON
- ☐ 321. GARY GAETTI
- ☐ 325. JIM ABBOTT
- ☐ 343. WALLY JOYNER

□ 413. DONNIE HILL
□ 431. LANCE PARRISH
□ 434. BRYAN HARVEY
□ 502. SHAWN ABNER
□ 542. JOE GRAHE
□ 611. BOBBY ROSE
□ 614. CHRIS BEASLEY
□ 634. LEE STEVENS
□ 707. VON HAYES
□ 709. HUBIE BROOKS
□ 726. GARY DISARCINA
□ 729. RENE GONZALES
□ 747. JULIO VALERA
□ 774. CHAD CURTIS

CHICAGO CUBS

□ 35. TEAM CHECKLIST
□ 50. CED LANDRUM
□ 59. RYAN HAWBLITZEL
□ 102. HECTOR VILLANUEVA
□ 104. DANNY JACKSON
□ 122. SHAWON DUNSTON
□ 124. ANDRE DAWSON
□ 143. MARK GRACE
□ 145. RYNE SANDBERG
□ 218. MIKE HARKEY
□ 220. CHUCK MCELROY
□ 236. GEORGE BELL
□ 239. DOUG DASCENZO
□ 351. JOE GIRARDI
□ 353. GREG MADDUX
□ 373. RICK WILKINS
□ 463. JEROME WALTON
□ 481. LES LANCASTER
□ 526. FRANK CASTILLO
□ 529. RICK SUTCLIFFE
□ 549. DAVE SMITH
□ 562. REY SANCHEZ
□ 569. HEATHCLIFF SLOCUMB
□ 590. PAUL ASSENMACHER
□ 617. CHICO WALKER
□ 638. LUIS SALAZAR
□ 703. MIKE MORGAN
□ 723. SAMMY SOSA
□ 780. TURK WENDELL

CHICAGO WHITE SOX

□ 7. ROBERTO HERNANDEZ
□ 76. BOB WICKMAN
□ 87. TEAM CHECKLIST
□ 166. FRANK THOMAS
□ 169. RON KARKOVICE
□ 186. SCOTT FLETCHER
□ 188. LANCE JOHNSON
□ 190. MELIDO PEREZ
□ 263. ROBIN VENTURA
□ 281. DAN PASQUA
□ 285. BOBBY THIGPEN
□ 359. JOEY CORA
□ 418. CHARLIE HOUGH
□ 420. GREG HIBBARD
□ 436. OZZIE GUILLEN
□ 438. SAMMY SOSA
□ 440. KEN PATTERSON
□ 551. ALEX FERNANDEZ
□ 553. JACK MCDOWELL
□ 555. BO JACKSON
□ 571. CARLTON FISK
□ 573. WILSON ALVAREZ
□ 575. TIM RAINES
□ 592. DONN PALL
□ 594. SCOTT RADINSKY
□ 603. CRAIG GREBECK
□ 621. WARREN NEWSON
□ 722. KIRK MCCASKILL
□ 724. GEORGE BELL
□ 743. STEVE SAX

CINCINNATI REDS

□ 27. REGGIE SANDERS
□ 30. TEAM CHECKLIST
□ 45. MO SANFORD
□ 72. DAN WILSON
□ 101. JOE OLIVER
□ 105. CHRIS HAMMOND
□ 121. HAL MORRIS
□ 123. CHRIS SABO
□ 125. ERIC DAVIS
□ 142. ROB DIBBLE
□ 144. BARRY LARKIN
□ 258. JOSE RIJO
□ 278. RANDY MYERS
□ 280. BILL DORAN
□ 296. JACK ARMSTRONG
□ 299. JEFF REED
□ 341. GLENN BRAGGS
□ 461. TOM BROWNING
□ 464. PAUL O'NEILL
□ 485. SCOTT SCUDDER
□ 659. MARIANO DUNCAN
□ 677. NORM CHARLTON
□ 680. TED POWER
□ 696. CARMELO MARTINEZ
□ 699. BILLY HATCHER
□ 761. TIM BELCHER
□ 763. BIP ROBERTS
□ 765. GREG SWINDELL
□ 784. DAVE MARTINEZ

CLEVELAND INDIANS

□ 5. JIM THOME
□ 63. MANNY RAMIREZ
□ 95. TEAM CHECKLIST
□ 137. ALBERT BELLE
□ 156. SANDY ALOMAR
□ 160. FELIX FERMIN
□ 178. CHARLES NAGY
□ 197. ALEX COLE
□ 199. JOEL SKINNER
□ 212. ROD NICHOLS
□ 215. STEVE OLIN
□ 231. CARLOS BAERGA
□ 235. MARK LEWIS
□ 336. GREG SWINDELL
□ 340. JERRY BROWNE
□ 524. MARK WHITEN
□ 558. GLENALLEN HILL
□ 560. CHRIS JAMES
□ 580. JESSE OROSCO
□ 598. CARLOS MARTINEZ
□ 656. REGGIE JEFFERSON
□ 660. JEFF SHAW
□ 679. ERIC KING
□ 698. DAVE OTTO
□ 766. KENNY LOFTON
□ 787. SCOTT SCUDDER
□ 789. JACK ARMSTRONG

COLORADO ROCKIES

□ 710. RYAN TURNER

DETROIT TIGERS

□ 74. RICO BROGNA
□ 96. TEAM CHECKLIST
□ 184. TONY PHILLIPS
□ 251. MICKEY TETTLETON
□ 255. CECIL FIELDER
□ 271. PETE INCAVIGLIA
□ 273. ALAN TRAMMELL
□ 294. ROB DEER
□ 317. BILL GULLICKSON
□ 319. MARK LEITER
□ 339. MIKE HENNEMAN
□ 453. RUSTY MEACHAM
□ 466. TRAVIS FRYMAN
□ 468. LLOYD MOSEBY
□ 470. SKEETER BARNES
□ 487. JOHN CERUTTI
□ 489. PAUL GIBSON
□ 516. LOU WHITAKER
□ 520. WALT TERRELL
□ 536. MILT CUYLER
□ 538. SCOTT LIVINGSTONE
□ 601. JERRY DON GLEATON
□ 605. FRANK TANANA
□ 737. DAN GLADDEN
□ 739. MARK CARREON

FLORIDA MARLINS

□ 701. CLEMENTE NUNEZ

HOUSTON ASTROS

□ 6. JEFF JUDEN
□ 23. BRIAN WILLIAMS
□ 25. KENNY LOFTON
□ 31. TEAM CHECKLIST
□ 53. TOM NEVERS
□ 162. CRAIG BIGGIO
□ 257. ANDUJAR CEDENO
□ 259. AL OSUNA
□ 276. JEFF BAGWELL
□ 279. KEN CAMINITI
□ 297. JIM DESHAIES
□ 354. RYAN BOWEN
□ 368. STEVE FINLEY
□ 372. LUIS GONZALEZ
□ 374. DARRYL KILE
□ 387. CASEY CANDAELE
□ 392. JIMMY JONES
□ 394. ERIC YELDING
□ 430. DWAYNE HENRY
□ 448. MARK PORTUGAL
□ 561. SCOTT SERVAIS
□ 564. ANDY MOTA
□ 582. RAFAEL RAMIREZ
□ 584. MIKE SIMMS
□ 635. PETE HARNISCH
□ 657. JAVIER ORTIZ
□ 757. EDDIE TAUBENSEE
□ 759. PETE INCAVIGLIA
□ 796. BUTCH HENRY
□ 798. DOUG JONES

KANSAS CITY ROYALS

□ 73. JOE VITIELLO
□ 88. TEAM CHECKLIST
□ 157. BRIAN MCRAE
□ 159. KEVIN APPIER
□ 180. KIRK GIBSON
□ 213. MIKE BODDICKER
□ 216. DAVID HOWARD
□ 219. LUIS AQUINO
□ 233. BRET SABERHAGEN
□ 237. DANNY TARTABULL
□ 240. BILL PECOTA
□ 327. KEVIN SEITZER
□ 329. KURT STILLWELL
□ 348. TERRY SHUMPERT
□ 444. GEORGE BRETT
□ 457. HARVEY PULLIAM
□ 459. MARK GUBICZA
□ 476. TOM GORDON
□ 497. MIKE MACFARLANE
□ 499. STORM DAVIS
□ 518. TODD BENZINGER
□ 539. JIM EISENREICH
□ 607. MARK DAVIS
□ 627. JEFF MONTGOMERY
□ 629. GARY THURMAN
□ 704. KEITH MILLER
□ 725. GREGG JEFFERIES
□ 742. KEVIN MCREYNOLDS
□ 744. WALLY JOYNER

LOS ANGELES DODGERS

□ 18. PEDRO MARTINEZ
□ 20. TOM GOODWIN
□ 32. TEAM CHECKLIST
□ 60. RAUL MONDESI
□ 152. MIKE SCIOSCIA
□ 174. DARRYL STRAWBERRY
□ 191. LENNY HARRIS
□ 195. JUAN SAMUEL
□ 261. OREL HERSHISER
□ 265. EDDIE MURRAY
□ 267. GARY CARTER
□ 282. ALFREDO GRIFFIN
□ 284. KAL DANIELS
□ 307. BRETT BUTLER
□ 346. RAMON MARTINEZ
□ 482. JOHN CANDELARIA
□ 484. ROGER MCDOWELL
□ 511. JAY HOWELL
□ 513. MIKE MORGAN
□ 515. KEVIN GROSS
□ 532. JOSE OFFERMAN
□ 534. ERIC KARROS
□ 666. BOB OJEDA
□ 668. TIM BELCHER

- ☐ 687. TIM CREWS
- ☐ 689. CHRIS GWYNN
- ☐ 756. ERIC DAVIS
- ☐ 760. TOM CANDIOTTI
- ☐ 797. CARLOS HERNANDEZ

MILWAUKEE BREWERS

- ☐ 9. CHRIS GEORGE
- ☐ 43. DOUG HENRY
- ☐ 57. DAVE NILSSON
- ☐ 97. TEAM CHECKLIST
- ☐ 120. B.J. SURHOFF
- ☐ 138. TEDDY HIGUERA
- ☐ 198. RON ROBINSON
- ☐ 211. WILLIE RANDOLPH
- ☐ 214. BILL SPIERS
- ☐ 232. GREG VAUGHN
- ☐ 234. GARY SHEFFIELD
- ☐ 360. JIM GANTNER
- ☐ 378. DANTE BICHETTE
- ☐ 396. FRANKLIN STUBBS
- ☐ 423. PAUL MOLITOR
- ☐ 456. ROBIN YOUNT
- ☐ 460. DARRYL HAMILTON
- ☐ 477. CAL ELDRED
- ☐ 479. JULIO MACHADO
- ☐ 496. CHUCK CRIM
- ☐ 498. DALE SVEUM
- ☐ 507. MARK LEE
- ☐ 550. DAN PLESAC
- ☐ 612. BILL WEGMAN
- ☐ 615. CHRIS BOSIO
- ☐ 633. JAIME NAVARRO
- ☐ 762. RICKY BONES
- ☐ 775. PAT LISTACH
- ☐ 783. KEVIN SEITZER

MINNESOTA TWINS

- ☐ 14. WILLIE BANKS
- ☐ 75. DAVID MCCARTY
- ☐ 89. TEAM CHECKLIST
- ☐ 109. JUNIOR ORTIZ
- ☐ 126. CHILI DAVIS
- ☐ 130. RICK AGUILERA
- ☐ 146. SCOTT ERICKSON
- ☐ 168. GREG GAGNE
- ☐ 187. GENE LARKIN
- ☐ 254. KIRBY PUCKETT
- ☐ 293. AL NEWMAN
- ☐ 311. TERRY LEACH
- ☐ 313. SCOTT LEIUS
- ☐ 315. JACK MORRIS
- ☐ 332. DAN GLADDEN
- ☐ 334. KENT HRBEK
- ☐ 426. DENNY NEAGLE
- ☐ 428. SHANE MACK
- ☐ 446. CHUCK KNOBLAUCH
- ☐ 506. ALLAN ANDERSON
- ☐ 509. MIKE PAGLIARULO
- ☐ 527. BRIAN HARPER
- ☐ 548. DAVID WEST
- ☐ 604. MARK GUTHRIE
- ☐ 622. STEVE BEDROSIAN
- ☐ 624. KEVIN TAPANI
- ☐ 764. PEDRO MUNOZ
- ☐ 776. PAT MAHOMES
- ☐ 781. BILL KRUEGER
- ☐ 785. JOHN SMILEY

MONTREAL EXPOS

- ☐ 16. WILFREDO CORDERO
- ☐ 36. TEAM CHECKLIST
- ☐ 61. RONDELL WHITE
- ☐ 167. DELINO DESHIELDS
- ☐ 206. SPIKE OWEN
- ☐ 210. MIKE FITZGERALD
- ☐ 226. IVAN CALDERON
- ☐ 228. TIM WALLACH
- ☐ 230. GILBERTO REYES
- ☐ 249. LARRY WALKER
- ☐ 361. BRIAN BARNES
- ☐ 363. BRET BARBERIE
- ☐ 365. DENNIS MARTINEZ
- ☐ 382. DAVE MARTINEZ
- ☐ 384. SCOTT RUSKIN
- ☐ 455. MARQUIS GRISSOM
- ☐ 474. ANDRES GALARRAGA
- ☐ 492. TOM FOLEY
- ☐ 557. MARK GARDNER
- ☐ 579. CHRIS NABHOLZ
- ☐ 662. CHRIS HANEY
- ☐ 681. BARRY JONES
- ☐ 683. MEL ROJAS
- ☐ 685. JEFF FASSERO
- ☐ 767. GARY CARTER
- ☐ 772. ARCHI CIANFROCCO
- ☐ 786. MATT STAIRS
- ☐ 788. JOHN WETTELAND
- ☐ 790. KEN HILL

NEW YORK METS

- ☐ 37. TEAM CHECKLIST
- ☐ 44. CHRIS DONNELS
- ☐ 65. JEROMY BURNITZ
- ☐ 112. DAVE MAGADAN
- ☐ 114. HUBIE BROOKS
- ☐ 131. VINCE COLEMAN
- ☐ 133. GREGG JEFFERIES
- ☐ 135. DWIGHT GOODEN
- ☐ 256. HOWARD JOHNSON
- ☐ 260. TODD HUNDLEY
- ☐ 277. FRANK VIOLA
- ☐ 298. JEFF INNIS
- ☐ 362. KEVIN MCREYNOLDS
- ☐ 364. DAVID CONE
- ☐ 381. CHARLIE O'BRIEN
- ☐ 383. KEITH MILLER
- ☐ 385. KEVIN ELSTER
- ☐ 398. MARK CARREON
- ☐ 411. GARRY TEMPLETON
- ☐ 414. WALLY WHITEHURST
- ☐ 433. TIM BURKE
- ☐ 514. JOHN FRANCO
- ☐ 531. TERRY BROSS
- ☐ 535. ANTHONY YOUNG
- ☐ 671. SID FERNANDEZ
- ☐ 673. PETE SCHOUREK
- ☐ 751. BRET SABERHAGEN
- ☐ 753. EDDIE MURRAY
- ☐ 755. BOBBY BONILLA
- ☐ 791. DICK SCHOFIELD
- ☐ 793. BILL PECOTA
- ☐ 795. WILLIE RANDOLPH

NEW YORK YANKEES

- ☐ 46. SCOTT KAMIENIECKI
- ☐ 48. STEVE FARR
- ☐ 77. CARLOS RODRIGUEZ
- ☐ 98. TEAM CHECKLIST
- ☐ 117. JIM LEYRITZ
- ☐ 119. ALVARO ESPINOZA
- ☐ 139. JESSE BARFIELD
- ☐ 291. MEL HALL
- ☐ 295. MATT NOKES
- ☐ 356. DON MATTINGLY
- ☐ 358. STEVE SAX
- ☐ 377. KEVIN MAAS
- ☐ 399. RANDY VELARDE
- ☐ 412. GREG CADARET
- ☐ 415. SCOTT SANDERSON
- ☐ 432. MIKE HUMPHREYS
- ☐ 435. PAT KELLY
- ☐ 556. BERNIE WILLIAMS
- ☐ 577. ROBERTO KELLY
- ☐ 606. HENSLEY MEULENS
- ☐ 608. ERIC PLUNK
- ☐ 610. LEE GUETTERMAN
- ☐ 626. JEFF JOHNSON
- ☐ 630. STEVE HOWE
- ☐ 746. DANNY TARTABULL
- ☐ 750. MIKE GALLEGO
- ☐ 768. CHARLIE HAYES
- ☐ 779. ANDY STANKIEWICZ
- ☐ 799. MELIDO PEREZ

OAKLAND A'S

- ☐ 22. TODD VAN POPPEL
- ☐ 54. DAVID ZANCANARO
- ☐ 90. TEAM CHECKLIST
- ☐ 151. WALT WEISS
- ☐ 153. MARK MCGWIRE
- ☐ 155. RICKEY HENDERSON
- ☐ 158. HAROLD BAINES
- ☐ 172. DAVE HENDERSON
- ☐ 193. MIKE GALLEGO
- ☐ 238. WILLIE WILSON
- ☐ 312. SCOTT BROSIUS
- ☐ 331. DENNIS ECKERSLEY
- ☐ 333. JOSE CANSECO
- ☐ 452. BOB WELCH
- ☐ 471. STEVE CHITREN
- ☐ 473. TERRY STEINBACH
- ☐ 494. ERNEST RILES
- ☐ 508. GENE NELSON
- ☐ 528. BROOK JACOBY
- ☐ 530. JOE KLINK
- ☐ 547. DAVE STEWART
- ☐ 632. KIRK DRESSENDORFER
- ☐ 661. MIKE MOORE
- ☐ 663. JOE SLUSARSKI
- ☐ 669. RON DARLING
- ☐ 682. CARNEY LANSFORD
- ☐ 684. RICK HONEYCUTT
- ☐ 727. MIKE BORDICK
- ☐ 749. LANCE BLANKENSHIP

PHILADELPHIA PHILLIES

- ☐ 19. ANDY ASHBY
- ☐ 21. BRAULIO CASTILLO
- ☐ 38. TEAM CHECKLIST
- ☐ 68. TYLER GREEN
- ☐ 106. RICKY JORDAN
- ☐ 108. DARRIN FLETCHER
- ☐ 127. DALE MURPHY
- ☐ 129. TERRY MULHOLLAND
- ☐ 150. DICKIE THON
- ☐ 208. CHARLIE HAYES
- ☐ 246. LENNY DYKSTRA
- ☐ 309. BRUCE RUFFIN
- ☐ 326. JOHN KRUK
- ☐ 347. WES CHAMBERLAIN
- ☐ 350. WALLY BACKMAN
- ☐ 402. JOE BOEVER
- ☐ 406. JASON GRIMSLEY
- ☐ 408. RANDY READY
- ☐ 410. MITCH WILLIAMS
- ☐ 422. KIM BATISTE
- ☐ 427. VON HAYES
- ☐ 429. DARREN DAULTON
- ☐ 442. PAT COMBS
- ☐ 449. MICKEY MORANDINI
- ☐ 567. TOMMY GREENE
- ☐ 586. DAVE HOLLINS
- ☐ 613. MIKE HARTLEY
- ☐ 631. JOSE DEJESUS
- ☐ 752. RUBEN AMARO, JR.
- ☐ 754. KYLE ABBOTT
- ☐ 792. MARIANO DUNCAN

PITTSBURGH PIRATES

- ☐ 39. TEAM CHECKLIST
- ☐ 69. JON FARRELL
- ☐ 111. JEFF KING
- ☐ 113. MIKE LAVALLIERE
- ☐ 115. JAY BELL
- ☐ 132. ANDY VAN SLYKE
- ☐ 134. BARRY BONDS
- ☐ 202. STAN BELINDA
- ☐ 205. JOSE LIND
- ☐ 217. GARY VARSHO
- ☐ 221. DOUG DRABEK
- ☐ 225. BOBBY BONILLA
- ☐ 417. NEAL HEATON
- ☐ 467. JOHN SMILEY
- ☐ 469. JOHN WEHNER
- ☐ 486. ZANE SMITH
- ☐ 488. STEVE BUECHELE
- ☐ 490. CURTIS WILKERSON
- ☐ 517. ORLANDO MERCED
- ☐ 519. GARY REDUS
- ☐ 537. RANDY TOMLIN
- ☐ 540. DON SLAUGHT
- ☐ 619. BOB WALK
- ☐ 636. BILL LANDRUM
- ☐ 665. CARLOS GARCIA
- ☐ 748. DENNY NEAGLE

ST. LOUIS CARDINALS

- ☐ 3. BRIAN JORDAN
- ☐ 40. TEAM CHECKLIST
- ☐ 58. DMITRI YOUNG

- ☐ 177. OZZIE SMITH
- ☐ 262. RAY LANKFORD
- ☐ 264. FELIX JOSE
- ☐ 283. JOSE OQUENDO
- ☐ 357. PEDRO GUERRERO
- ☐ 376. LEE SMITH
- ☐ 379. TOM PAGNOZZI
- ☐ 397. MILT THOMPSON
- ☐ 458. JOSE DELEON
- ☐ 478. OMAR OLIVARES
- ☐ 512. BOB TEWSBURY
- ☐ 533. TODD ZEILE
- ☐ 552. BERNARD GILKEY
- ☐ 574. RHEAL CORMIER
- ☐ 591. BRYN SMITH
- ☐ 596. GERONIMO PENA
- ☐ 628. KEN HILL
- ☐ 670. REX HUDLER
- ☐ 686. CRIS CARPENTER
- ☐ 688. SCOTT TERRY
- ☐ 690. GERALD PERRY
- ☐ 693. JUAN AGOSTO
- ☐ 758. ANDRES GALARRAGA
- ☐ 773. MARK CLARK
- ☐ 777. DONOVAN OSBORNE

SAN DIEGO PADRES

- ☐ 33. TEAM CHECKLIST
- ☐ 42. JEREMY HERNANDEZ
- ☐ 67. JOEY HAMILTON
- ☐ 103. ED WHITSON
- ☐ 141. BIP ROBERTS
- ☐ 253. BENITO SANTIAGO
- ☐ 272. TONY FERNANDEZ
- ☐ 274. TONY GWYNN
- ☐ 292. JERALD CLARK
- ☐ 306. GREG HARRIS
- ☐ 310. PAUL FARIES
- ☐ 323. ANDY BENES
- ☐ 328. DARRIN JACKSON
- ☐ 330. MIKE MADDUX
- ☐ 344. FRED MCGRIFF
- ☐ 349. TIM TEUFEL
- ☐ 416. THOMAS HOWARD
- ☐ 419. JACK HOWELL
- ☐ 437. BRUCE HURST
- ☐ 439. DENNIS RASMUSSEN
- ☐ 566. JOSE MELENDEZ
- ☐ 568. RICH RODRIGUEZ
- ☐ 587. LARRY ANDERSEN
- ☐ 589. CRAIG LEFFERTS
- ☐ 602. ADAM PETERSON
- ☐ 623. RICKY BONES
- ☐ 705. KURT STILLWELL
- ☐ 741. RANDY MYERS
- ☐ 745. GARY SHEFFIELD

SAN FRANCISCO GIANTS

- ☐ 2. ROYCE CLAYTON
- ☐ 12. TED WOOD
- ☐ 34. TEAM CHECKLIST
- ☐ 49. FRANCISCO OLIVERAS
- ☐ 62. STEVE HOSEY
- ☐ 107. KEVIN BASS
- ☐ 148. JOHN BURKETT
- ☐ 154. MATT WILLIAMS
- ☐ 171. DAVE RIGHETTI
- ☐ 173. STEVE DECKER
- ☐ 175. WILL CLARK
- ☐ 192. TERRY KENNEDY
- ☐ 194. WILLIE MCGEE
- ☐ 266. KEVIN MITCHELL
- ☐ 268. MIKE BENJAMIN
- ☐ 270. JOSE URIBE
- ☐ 286. ROBBY THOMPSON
- ☐ 288. MIKE FELDER
- ☐ 290. DAVE ANDERSON
- ☐ 337. TREVOR WILSON
- ☐ 563. PAUL MCCLELLAN
- ☐ 565. DARREN LEWIS
- ☐ 581. JEFF BRANTLEY
- ☐ 583. KELLY DOWNS
- ☐ 585. MIKE REMLINGER
- ☐ 667. BRYAN HICKERSON
- ☐ 697. BUD BLACK
- ☐ 736. BILL SWIFT
- ☐ 738. MIKE JACKSON
- ☐ 740. KIRT MANWARING
- ☐ 778. JOHN PATTERSON

SEATTLE MARINERS

- ☐ 4. DAVE FLEMING
- ☐ 13. PATRICK LENNON
- ☐ 15. ROGER SALKELD
- ☐ 64. MARC NEWFIELD
- ☐ 91. TEAM CHECKLIST
- ☐ 164. RANDY JOHNSON
- ☐ 182. DAVE VALLE
- ☐ 314. HAROLD REYNOLDS
- ☐ 335. KEN GRIFFEY
- ☐ 367. EDGAR MARTINEZ
- ☐ 369. GREG BRILEY
- ☐ 386. ALVIN DAVIS
- ☐ 388. PETE O'BRIEN
- ☐ 390. SCOTT BRADLEY
- ☐ 401. OMAR VIZQUEL
- ☐ 403. BILL KRUEGER
- ☐ 405. MIKE SCHOOLER
- ☐ 424. KEN GRIFFEY JR.
- ☐ 441. JAY BUHNER
- ☐ 554. TINO MARTINEZ
- ☐ 572. ERIK HANSON
- ☐ 593. MIKE JACKSON
- ☐ 595. BRIAN HOLMAN
- ☐ 616. HENRY COTTO
- ☐ 618. RUSS SWAN
- ☐ 620. BILL SWIFT
- ☐ 637. RICH DELUCIA
- ☐ 639. ROB MURPHY
- ☐ 731. CALVIN JONES
- ☐ 735. KEVIN MITCHELL
- ☐ 771. BRET BOONE

TEXAS RANGERS

- ☐ 10. ROB MAURER
- ☐ 11. DONALD HARRIS
- ☐ 70. KURT MILLER
- ☐ 92. TEAM CHECKLIST
- ☐ 176. RUBEN SIERRA
- ☐ 179. GARY PETTIS
- ☐ 196. JEFF HUSON
- ☐ 201. KEVIN REIMER
- ☐ 204. JOSE GUZMAN
- ☐ 223. RAFAEL PALMEIRO
- ☐ 241. JULIO FRANCO
- ☐ 243. JUAN GONZALEZ
- ☐ 245. IVAN RODRIGUEZ
- ☐ 462. MONTY FARISS
- ☐ 465. DEAN PALMER
- ☐ 483. BRIAN DOWNING
- ☐ 559. OIL CAN BOYD
- ☐ 576. BOBBY WITT
- ☐ 578. KEVIN BROWN
- ☐ 597. MIKE JEFFCOAT
- ☐ 599. GENO PETRALLI
- ☐ 651. KENNY ROGERS
- ☐ 655. NOLAN RYAN
- ☐ 691. JOHN BARFIELD
- ☐ 695. JEFF RUSSELL
- ☐ 769. DICKIE THON

TORONTO BLUE JAYS

- ☐ 26. DEREK BELL
- ☐ 55. SHAWN GREEN
- ☐ 99. TEAM CHECKLIST
- ☐ 116. DAVID WELLS
- ☐ 118. MANUEL LEE
- ☐ 136. DAVE STIEB
- ☐ 140. PAT BORDERS
- ☐ 203. PAT TABLER
- ☐ 224. JOE CARTER
- ☐ 242. ED SPRAGUE
- ☐ 302. JIMMY KEY
- ☐ 324. KELLY GRUBER
- ☐ 352. DEVON WHITE
- ☐ 355. ROBERTO ALOMAR
- ☐ 371. TODD STOTTLEMYRE
- ☐ 375. JOHN OLERUD
- ☐ 391. MOOKIE WILSON
- ☐ 393. CANDY MALDONADO
- ☐ 395. TOM HENKE
- ☐ 407. GREG MYERS
- ☐ 409. MIKE TIMLIN
- ☐ 447. TOM CANDIOTTI
- ☐ 450. DUANE WARD
- ☐ 504. CORY SNYDER
- ☐ 522. DAVE PARKER
- ☐ 544. EDDIE ZOSKY
- ☐ 625. JUAN GUZMAN
- ☐ 732. JACK MORRIS
- ☐ 734. DAVE WINFIELD

1993 UPPER DECK (840) 2 1/2" X 3 1/2"

ATLANTA BRAVES

- ☐ 21. MELVIN NIEVES
- ☐ 24. CHIPPER JONES
- ☐ 29. JAVY LOPEZ
- ☐ 75. TOM GLAVINE
- ☐ 90. MIKE STANTON
- ☐ 91. RAFAEL BELLIARD
- ☐ 104. SID BREAM
- ☐ 109. MARK LEMKE
- ☐ 163. TERRY PENDLETON
- ☐ 166. DEION SANDERS
- ☐ 187. GREG OLSON
- ☐ 246. STEVER AVERY
- ☐ 264. RON GANT
- ☐ 292. OTIS NIXON
- ☐ 363. JOHN SMOLTZ
- ☐ 366. DAVID JUSTICE
- ☐ 376. RYAN KLESKO
- ☐ 393. KENT MERCKER
- ☐ 426. JOSE OLIVA
- ☐ 519. MARVIN FREEMAN
- ☐ 535. GREG MADDUX
- ☐ 582. BRIAN HUNTER
- ☐ 589. PETE SMITH
- ☐ 591. JEFF BLAUSER
- ☐ 606. DAMON BERRYHILL
- ☐ 611. FRANCISCO CABRERA
- ☐ 623. TONY TARASCO
- ☐ 652. GREG MCMICHAEL
- ☐ 701. STEVE BEDROSIAN
- ☐ 731. JAY HOWELL
- ☐ 756. MIKE KELLY
- ☐ 816. TEAM CHECKLIST

BALTIMORE ORIOLES

- ☐ 5. MANNY ALEXANDER
- ☐ 80. RICK SUTCLIFFE
- ☐ 111. BRADY ANDERSON
- ☐ 132. LEO GOMEZ
- ☐ 167. MIKE DEVEREAUX
- ☐ 181. BILLY RIPKEN
- ☐ 191. TODD FROHWIRTH
- ☐ 228. RANDY MILLIGAN
- ☐ 233. MIKE MUSSINA
- ☐ 260. JOE ORSULAK
- ☐ 276. BEN MCDONALD
- ☐ 312. ALAN MILLS
- ☐ 353. GLENN DAVIS
- ☐ 384. ARTHUR RHODES
- ☐ 402. CHRIS HOILES
- ☐ 437. BRAD PENNINGTON
- ☐ 514. CHITO MARTINEZ
- ☐ 517. JEFF TACKETT
- ☐ 550. FERNANDO VALENZUELA
- ☐ 585. CAL RIPKEN, JR.

- ☐ 674. GREGG OLSON
- ☐ 691. DAMON BUFORD
- ☐ 722. MARK WILLIAMSON
- ☐ 765. HAROLD BAINES
- ☐ 792. DAVID SEGUI
- ☐ 801. MARK MCLEMORE
- ☐ 803. HAROLD REYNOLDS
- ☐ 827. TEAM CHECKLIST

BOSTON RED SOX

- ☐ 57. SCOTT COOPER
- ☐ 96. JODY REED
- ☐ 131. FRANK VIOLA
- ☐ 135. ROGER CLEMENS
- ☐ 154. MIKE GREENWELL
- ☐ 185. TONY PENA
- ☐ 220. DANNY DARWIN
- ☐ 265. ELLIS BURKS
- ☐ 274. PHIL PLANTIER
- ☐ 277. BOB ZUPCIC
- ☐ 387. JOHN VALENTIN
- ☐ 396. MO VAUGHN
- ☐ 409. JOHN DOPSON
- ☐ 414. GREG A. HARRIS
- ☐ 442. FRANK RODRIGUEZ
- ☐ 523. SCOTT FLETCHER
- ☐ 583. TIM NAEHRING
- ☐ 602. LUIS RIVERA
- ☐ 618. BILLY HATCHER
- ☐ 620. JOE HESKETH
- ☐ 702. JEFF RUSSELL
- ☐ 747. CARLOS QUINTANA
- ☐ 751. IVAN CALDERON
- ☐ 760. SCOTT BANKHEAD
- ☐ 772. KEN RYAN
- ☐ 777. ANDRE DAWSON
- ☐ 832. TEAM CHECKLIST

CALIFORNIA ANGELS

- ☐ 23. J.T. SNOW
- ☐ 25. TIM SALMON
- ☐ 77. CHUCK FINLEY
- ☐ 94. LUIS SOJO
- ☐ 128. MARK LANGSTON
- ☐ 157. JUNIOR FELIX
- ☐ 178. LUIS POLONIA
- ☐ 188. RENE GONZALES
- ☐ 230. GARY DISARCINA
- ☐ 235. CHAD CURTIS
- ☐ 290. JOE GRAHE
- ☐ 317. JOH ORTON
- ☐ 343. JULIO VALERA
- ☐ 370. GARY GAETTI
- ☐ 377. DAMION EASLEY
- ☐ 422. PETE JANICKI
- ☐ 507. TROY PERCIVAL
- ☐ 689. JOHN FARRELL
- ☐ 730. STAN JAVIER
- ☐ 734. SCOTT SANDERSON
- ☐ 750. STEVE FREY
- ☐ 785. J.T. SNOW
- ☐ 789. GREG MYERS
- ☐ 794. CHILI DAVIS
- ☐ 807. KELLY GRUBER
- ☐ 812. TEAM CHECKLIST

CHICAGO CUBS

- ☐ 18. JESSIE HOLLINS
- ☐ 64. DOUG DASCENZO
- ☐ 101. SHAWON DUNSTON
- ☐ 106. MIKE MORGAN
- ☐ 127. SAMMY SOSA
- ☐ 130. CHUCK MCELROY
- ☐ 159. STEVE BUECHELE
- ☐ 175. RYNE SANDBERG
- ☐ 211. JOSE VIZCAINO
- ☐ 248. DERRICK MAY
- ☐ 308. ANDRE DAWSON
- ☐ 320. PAUL ASSENMACHER
- ☐ 379. JIM BULLINGER
- ☐ 382. FERNANDO RAMSEY
- ☐ 408. FRANK CASTILLO
- ☐ 429. DEREK WALLACE
- ☐ 509. MATT WALBECK
- ☐ 515. JOSE GUZMAN
- ☐ 539. GREG HIBBARD
- ☐ 573. MARK GRACE
- ☐ 598. RICK WILKINS
- ☐ 610. MIKE HARKEY
- ☐ 612. REY SANCHEZ
- ☐ 617. BOB SCANLAN
- ☐ 625. WILLIE WILSON
- ☐ 667. RANDY MYERS
- ☐ 741. CANDY MALDONADO
- ☐ 804. DAN PLESAC
- ☐ 819. TEAM CHECKLIST

CHICAGO WHITE SOX

- ☐ 139. OZZIE GUILLEN
- ☐ 199. RON KARKOVICE
- ☐ 207. CHARLIE HOUGH
- ☐ 263. ROBIN VENTURA
- ☐ 272. CARLTON FISK
- ☐ 280. LANCE JOHNSON
- ☐ 298. SCOTT RADINSKY
- ☐ 345. GEORGE BELL
- ☐ 350. WILSON ALVAREZ
- ☐ 352. ROBERTO HERNANDEZ
- ☐ 357. JACK MCDOWELL
- ☐ 362. ALEX FERNANDEZ
- ☐ 369. STEVE SAX
- ☐ 418. TERRY LEACH
- ☐ 448. MIKE ROBERTSON
- ☐ 502. ROD BOLTON
- ☐ 526. ELLIS BURKS
- ☐ 555. FRANK THOMAS
- ☐ 597. TIM RAINES
- ☐ 608. KIRK MCCASKILL
- ☐ 649. DAN PASQUA
- ☐ 671. BOBBY THIGPEN
- ☐ 738. CRAIG GREBECK
- ☐ 742. JOEY CORA
- ☐ 775. BO JACKSON
- ☐ 805. DAVE STIEB
- ☐ 838. TEAM CHECKLIST

CINCINNATI REDS

- ☐ 4. WILLIE GREENE
- ☐ 6. DAN WILSON
- ☐ 11. TIM COSTA
- ☐ 26. TIM PUGH
- ☐ 107. BILL DORAN
- ☐ 112. BIP ROBERTS
- ☐ 121. HAL MORRIS
- ☐ 147. CHRIS SABO
- ☐ 216. CHRIS HAMMOND
- ☐ 226. JOSE RIJO
- ☐ 234. JOE OLIVER
- ☐ 245. BARRY LARKIN
- ☐ 270. TOM BROWNING
- ☐ 329. SCOTT BANKHEAD
- ☐ 354. REGGIE SANDERS
- ☐ 368. TIM BELCHER
- ☐ 400. DAVE MARTINEZ
- ☐ 443. CHAD MOTTOLA
- ☐ 527. JUAN SAMUEL
- ☐ 541. JEFF REARDON
- ☐ 622. RANDY MILLIGAN
- ☐ 642. JEFF BRANSON
- ☐ 646. KEVIN MITCHELL
- ☐ 655. ROBERTO KELLY
- ☐ 675. ROB DIBBLE
- ☐ 694. JOHN SMILEY
- ☐ 833. TEAM CHECKLIST

CLEVELAND INDIANS

- ☐ 12. ALAN EMBRES
- ☐ 17. DAVE MLICKI
- ☐ 70. DEREK LILLIQUIST
- ☐ 88. MARK LEWIS
- ☐ 174. CARLOS BAERGA
- ☐ 196. PAUL SORRENTO
- ☐ 200. BROOK JACOBY
- ☐ 202. DENNIS COOK
- ☐ 206. STEVE OLIN
- ☐ 208. SCOTT SCUDDER
- ☐ 227. MARK WHITEN
- ☐ 243. CHARLES NAGY
- ☐ 255. SANDY ALOMAR, JR.
- ☐ 262. KENNY LOFTON
- ☐ 299. THOMAS HOWARD
- ☐ 433. MANNY RAMIREZ
- ☐ 520. CARLOS MARTINEZ
- ☐ 544. REGGIE JEFFERSON
- ☐ 584. GLENALLEN HILL
- ☐ 586. ALBERT BELLE
- ☐ 603. JUNIOR ORTIZ
- ☐ 615. FELIX FERMIN
- ☐ 629. MARK CLARK
- ☐ 659. MIKE BIELECKI
- ☐ 713. ERIC PLUNK
- ☐ 798. JOSE MESA
- ☐ 808. BOB OJEDA
- ☐ 823. TEAM CHECKLIST

COLORADO ROCKIES

- ☐ 27. DAVE NIED
- ☐ 444. JOHN BURKE
- ☐ 521. ERIC YOUNG
- ☐ 529. JEFF PARRET
- ☐ 538. ALEX COLE
- ☐ 560. VINNY CASTILLA
- ☐ 571. JOE GIRARDI
- ☐ 593. ANDRES GALARRAGA
- ☐ 647. CHARLIE HAYES
- ☐ 653. ERIC WEDGE
- ☐ 668. DARREN HOLMES
- ☐ 670. BRUCE RUFFIN
- ☐ 683. DANTE BICHETTE
- ☐ 706. DALE MURPHY
- ☐ 720. WILLIE BLAIR
- ☐ 723. BRYN SMITH
- ☐ 732. FREDDIE BENAVIDES
- ☐ 737. DARYL BOSTON
- ☐ 740. GERALD YOUNG
- ☐ 752. STEVE REED
- ☐ 761. JIM TATUM
- ☐ 763. ANDY ASHBY
- ☐ 770. BUTCH HENRY
- ☐ 793. ARMANDO REYNOSO
- ☐ 797. JERALD CLARK
- ☐ 834. TEAM CHECKLIST

DETROIT TIGERS

- ☐ 63. SCOTT LIVINGSTONE
- ☐ 68. FRANK TANANA
- ☐ 86. MICKEY TETTLETON
- ☐ 95. MARK LEITER
- ☐ 162. MILT CUYLER
- ☐ 195. TONY PHILLIPS
- ☐ 217. ROB DEER
- ☐ 251. DAN GLADDEN
- ☐ 273. LOU WHITAKER
- ☐ 364. TRAVIS FRYMAN
- ☐ 378. JOHN KIELY
- ☐ 386. RICO BROGNA
- ☐ 398. BILL GULLICKSON
- ☐ 403. MIKE HENNEMAN
- ☐ 446. RICK GREENE
- ☐ 512. MIKE MOORE
- ☐ 530. BILL KRUEGER
- ☐ 532. ALAN TRAMMELL
- ☐ 564. CECIL FIELDER
- ☐ 601. MIKE MUNOZ
- ☐ 633. TOM BOLTON
- ☐ 685. GREG GOHR
- ☐ 699. DAVID WELLS
- ☐ 757. JOHN DOHERTY
- ☐ 766. KIRK GIBSON
- ☐ 836. TEAM CHECKLIST

FLORIDA MARLINS

- ☐ 9. NIGEL WILSON
- ☐ 20. KURT MILLER
- ☐ 435. CHARLES JOHNSON
- ☐ 506. JOSE MARTINEZ
- ☐ 518. CHARLIE HOUGH
- ☐ 524. ORESTES DESTRADE
- ☐ 528. DAVE MAGADAN
- ☐ 533. WALT WEISS
- ☐ 552. BRET BARBERIE
- ☐ 590. CHUCK CARR
- ☐ 631. ALEX ARIAS
- ☐ 634. GREG BRILEY
- ☐ 661. CHRIS HAMMOND
- ☐ 684. BRYAN HARVEY
- ☐ 711. LUIS AQUINO
- ☐ 715. JOE KLINK
- ☐ 717. MONTY FARISS
- ☐ 726. CRIS CARPENTER
- ☐ 744. STEVE DECKER

- ☐ 754. JEFF CONINE
- ☐ 758. JACK ARMSTONG
- ☐ 762. SCOTT POSE
- ☐ 771. JUNIOR FELIX
- ☐ 773. TREVOR HOFFMAN
- ☐ 776. BENITO SANTIAGO
- ☐ 780. RYAN BOWEN
- ☐ 825. TEAM CHECKLIST

HOUSTON ASTROS

- ☐ 97. PETE HARNISCH
- ☐ 99. MARK PORTUGAL
- ☐ 114. CRAIG BIGGIO
- ☐ 171. DOUG JONES
- ☐ 183. ERIC ANTHONY
- ☐ 231. STEVE FINLEY
- ☐ 256. JEFF BAGWELL
- ☐ 286. BRIAN WILLIAMS
- ☐ 294. CASEY CANDAELE
- ☐ 296. EDDIE TAUBENSEE
- ☐ 305. KEN CAMINITI
- ☐ 310. JOE BOEVER
- ☐ 314. DARRYL KILE
- ☐ 319. XAVIER HERNANDEZ
- ☐ 423. TODD JONES
- ☐ 562. ANDUJAR CEDENO
- ☐ 572. LUIS GONZALEZ
- ☐ 613. SCOTT SERVAIS
- ☐ 664. DOUG DRABEK
- ☐ 679. KEVIN BASS
- ☐ 695. GREG SWINDELL
- ☐ 729. JOSE URIBE
- ☐ 813. TEAM CHECKLIST

KANSAS CITY ROYALS

- ☐ 56. GEORGE BRETT
- ☐ 59. RUSTY MEACHAM
- ☐ 62. JEFF MONTGOMERY
- ☐ 72. HIPOLITO PICHARDO
- ☐ 85. MARK GUBICZA
- ☐ 89. KEVIN APPIER
- ☐ 176. GREGG JEFFERIES
- ☐ 180. MIKE MAGNANTE
- ☐ 221. TOM GORDON
- ☐ 238. BRIAN MCRAE
- ☐ 252. WALLY JOYNER
- ☐ 302. KEITH MILLER
- ☐ 327. MIKE MACFARLANE
- ☐ 351. KEVIN KOSLOFSKI
- ☐ 445. MICHAEL TUCKER
- ☐ 513. JOSE LIND
- ☐ 534. DAVID CONE
- ☐ 592. KEVIN MCREYNOLDS
- ☐ 604. BRENT MAYNE
- ☐ 632. CHRIS GWYNN
- ☐ 641. MARK GARDNER
- ☐ 645. PHIL HIATT
- ☐ 680. HUBIE BROOKS
- ☐ 708. GREG GAGNE
- ☐ 835. TEAM CHECKLIST
- ☐ 542. FELIX JOSE

LOS ANGELES DODGERS

- ☐ 2. MIKE PIAZZA
- ☐ 22. BILLY ASHLEY
- ☐ 98. TOM CANDIOTTI
- ☐ 133. RAMON MARTINEZ
- ☐ 148. CARLOS HERNANDEZ
- ☐ 169. OREL HERSHISER
- ☐ 184. LENNY HARRIS
- ☐ 198. KEVIN GROSS
- ☐ 225. JOSE OFFERMAN
- ☐ 250. ROGER MCDOWELL
- ☐ 259. BRETT BUTLER
- ☐ 316. MIKE SHARPERSON
- ☐ 324. PEDRO MARTINEZ
- ☐ 367. PEDRO ASTACIO
- ☐ 385. ERIC KARROS
- ☐ 391. HENRY RODRIGUEZ
- ☐ 430. MICHAEL MOORE
- ☐ 537. DAVE HANSEN
- ☐ 547. TIM WALLACH
- ☐ 568. JODY REED
- ☐ 575. DARRYL STRAWBERRY
- ☐ 595. ERIC DAVIS
- ☐ 666. JIM GOTT
- ☐ 692. TODD WORRELL
- ☐ 791. CORY SNYDER
- ☐ 820. TEAM CHECKLIST

MILWAUKEE BREWERS

- ☐ 13. JIM TETUM
- ☐ 102. B.J. SURHOFF
- ☐ 177. JOHN JAHA
- ☐ 192. DARRYL HAMILTON
- ☐ 193. MIKE FETTERS
- ☐ 237. JAIME NAVARRO
- ☐ 253. PAT LISTACH
- ☐ 269. FRANKLIN STUBBS
- ☐ 295. KEVIN SEITZER
- ☐ 325. BILL SPIERS
- ☐ 328. RICKY BONES
- ☐ 333. PAUL MOLITOR
- ☐ 375. CAL ELDRED
- ☐ 395. DOUG HENRY
- ☐ 416. BILL WEGMAN
- ☐ 427. TYRONE HILL
- ☐ 563. GREG VAUGHN
- ☐ 578. KEVIN REIMER
- ☐ 587. ROBIN YOUNT
- ☐ 704. MATT MIESKE
- ☐ 725. GRAEME LLOYD
- ☐ 769. DICKIE THON
- ☐ 782. JOE KMAK
- ☐ 787. JIM AUSTIN
- ☐ 795. DAVE NILSSON
- ☐ 806. TOM BRUNANSKY
- ☐ 817. TEAM CHECKLIST

MINNESOTA TWINS

- ☐ 28. MIKE TROMBLEY
- ☐ 74. KENT HRBEK
- ☐ 110. BRIAN HARPER
- ☐ 212. SCOTT LEIUS
- ☐ 236. SHANE MACK
- ☐ 239. CHILI DAVIS
- ☐ 254. CHUCK KNOBLAUCH
- ☐ 268. JOHN SMILEY
- ☐ 303. RICK AGUILERA
- ☐ 306. MIKE PAGLIARULO
- ☐ 313. KEVIN TAPANI
- ☐ 337. PAT MAHOMES
- ☐ 341. PEDRO MUNOZ
- ☐ 397. SCOTT ERICKSON
- ☐ 399. MARK GUTHRIE
- ☐ 447. RICH BECKER
- ☐ 540. GENE LARKIN
- ☐ 565. KIRBY PUCKETT
- ☐ 628. LENNY WEBSTER
- ☐ 648. JIM DESHAIES
- ☐ 686. WILLIE BANKS
- ☐ 697. TERRY JORGENSEN
- ☐ 733. JEFF REBOULET
- ☐ 786. DAVE WINFIELD
- ☐ 837. TEAM CHECKLIST

MONTREAL EXPOS

- ☐ 60. WILFREDO CORDERO
- ☐ 138. KEN HILL
- ☐ 142. DELINO DESHIELDS
- ☐ 144. LARRY WALKER
- ☐ 190. MEL ROJAS
- ☐ 214. BRIAN BARNES
- ☐ 219. GARY CARTER
- ☐ 232. DENNIS MARTINEZ
- ☐ 297. MOISES ALOU
- ☐ 342. GREG COLBRUNN
- ☐ 348. MARK GARDNER
- ☐ 356. MARQUIS GRISSOM
- ☐ 392. JOHN WETTELAND
- ☐ 404. CHRIS NABHOLZ
- ☐ 431. CLIFF FLOYD
- ☐ 501. TAVO ALVAREZ
- ☐ 510. RONDELL WHITE
- ☐ 531. FRANK BOLICK
- ☐ 609. JEFF FASSERO
- ☐ 614. DARRIN FLETCHER
- ☐ 619. JOHN VANDER WAL
- ☐ 635. KENT BOTTENFIELD
- ☐ 640. MIKE GARDINER
- ☐ 644. SEAN BERRY
- ☐ 669. TIM SPEHR
- ☐ 677. MIKE LANSING
- ☐ 698. JIMMY JONES
- ☐ 736. ARCHI CIANFROCCO
- ☐ 821. TEAM CHECKLIST

NEW YORK METS

- ☐ 10. JOE VITKO
- ☐ 19. BOBBY JONES
- ☐ 71. ANTHONY YOUNG
- ☐ 115. EDDIE MURRAY
- ☐ 119. JEFF INNIS
- ☐ 161. PAT HOWELL
- ☐ 203. DARYL BOSTON
- ☐ 209. CHARLIE O'BRIEN
- ☐ 275. BOBBY BONILLA
- ☐ 282. BRET SABERHAGEN
- ☐ 293. TODD HUNDLEY
- ☐ 321. JOHN FRANCO
- ☐ 361. SID FERNANDEZ
- ☐ 373. RYAN THOMPSON
- ☐ 401. JEFF KENT
- ☐ 419. WILLIE RANDOLPH
- ☐ 436. BUTCH HUSKEY
- ☐ 626. FRANK TANANA
- ☐ 650. MIKE MADDUX
- ☐ 658. PETE SCHOUREK
- ☐ 665. DWIGHT GOODEN
- ☐ 672. TONY FERNANDEZ
- ☐ 676. HOWARD JOHNSON
- ☐ 712. JOE ORSULAK
- ☐ 727. CHICO WALKER
- ☐ 748. VINCE COLEMAN
- ☐ 826. TEAM CHECKLIST

NEW YORK YANKEES

- ☐ 16. STERLING HITCHCOCK
- ☐ 93. RANDY VELARDE
- ☐ 116. MATT NOKES
- ☐ 134. DON MATTINGLY
- ☐ 215. PAT KELLY
- ☐ 242. DANNY TARTABULL
- ☐ 257. ANDY STANKIEWICZ
- ☐ 291. MEL HALL
- ☐ 326. MELIDO PEREZ
- ☐ 332. BERNIE WILLIAMS
- ☐ 360. GERALD WILLIAMS
- ☐ 372. BOB WICKMAN
- ☐ 383. SAM MILITELLO
- ☐ 410. STEVE FARR
- ☐ 449. DEREK JETER
- ☐ 543. JIMMY KEY
- ☐ 548. SPIKE OWEN
- ☐ 554. JIM ABBOTT
- ☐ 556. WADE BOGGS
- ☐ 594. KEVIN MAAS
- ☐ 600. MIKE GALLEGO
- ☐ 707. STEVE HOWE
- ☐ 719. JOHN HABYAN
- ☐ 796. PAUL O'NEILL
- ☐ 839. TEAM CHECKLIST

OAKLAND A'S

- ☐ 81. HAROLD BAINES
- ☐ 87. BOBBY WITT
- ☐ 108. LANCE BLANKENSHIP
- ☐ 122. WALT WEISS
- ☐ 129. JERRY BROWNE
- ☐ 136. RICKEY HENERSON
- ☐ 145. RUBEN SIERRA
- ☐ 168. RON DARLING
- ☐ 182. MIKE MOORE
- ☐ 189. MIKE BORDICK
- ☐ 271. DENNIS ECKERSLEY
- ☐ 278. TERRY STEINBACH
- ☐ 311. JEFF PARRETT
- ☐ 407. BOB WELCH
- ☐ 417. WILLIE WILSON
- ☐ 424. MIKE NEILL
- ☐ 504. BRENT GATES
- ☐ 566. MARK MCGWIRE
- ☐ 607. DAVE HENDERSON
- ☐ 616. KEVIN SEITZER
- ☐ 636. KELLY DOWNS
- ☐ 681. SCOTT BROSIUS
- ☐ 746. STORM DAVIS
- ☐ 767. TROY NEEL
- ☐ 781. ERIC FOX
- ☐ 810. JOE BOEVER
- ☐ 814. TEAM CHECKLIST

PHILADELPHIA PHILLIES

☐ 67. CURT SCHILLING
☐ 69. LENNY DYKSTRA
☐ 113. MITCH WILLIAMS
☐ 137. DARREN DAULTON
☐ 153. DAVE HOLLINS
☐ 201. MARIANO DUNCAN
☐ 247. JOHN KRUK
☐ 249. STAN JAVIER
☐ 267. WES CHAMBERLAIN
☐ 279. TERRY MULHOLLAND
☐ 285. MICKEY MORANDINI
☐ 300. KYLE ABBOTT
☐ 389. BEN RIVERA
☐ 505. TYLER GREEN
☐ 508. KEVIN STOCKER
☐ 516. KIM BATISTE
☐ 522. PETE INCAVIGLIA
☐ 549. TOMMY GREENE
☐ 558. MILT THOMPSON
☐ 561. RICKY JORDAN
☐ 580. JUAN BELL
☐ 710. DAVID WEST
☐ 753. DANNY JACKSON
☐ 800. JIM EISENREICH
☐ 829. TEAM CHECKLIST
☐ 439. CHAD MCCONNELL

PITTSBURGH PIRATES

☐ 66. TIM WAKEFIELD
☐ 78. BOB WALK
☐ 103. JAY BELL
☐ 120. MIKE LAVALLIERE
☐ 124. ANDY VAN SLYKE
☐ 150. ORLANDO MERCED
☐ 240. JEFF KING
☐ 284. RANDY TOMLIN
☐ 309. JOSE LIND
☐ 334. CARLOS GARCIA
☐ 340. AL MARTIN
☐ 349. ZANE SMITH
☐ 359. STAN BELINDA
☐ 412. BOB PATTERSON
☐ 415. DENNY NEAGLE
☐ 440. MIDRE CUMMINGS
☐ 536. KEVIN YOUNG
☐ 559. LLOYD MCCLENDON
☐ 599. STEVE COOKE
☐ 643. PAUL WAGNER
☐ 690. JOHN CANDELARIA
☐ 716. LONNIE SMITH
☐ 743. DON SLAUGHT
☐ 745. BLAS MNOR
☐ 759. JOHN WEHNER
☐ 779. DENNIS MOELLER
☐ 830. TEAM CHECKLIST

ST. LOUIS CARDINALS

☐ 3. RENE AROCHA
☐ 79. RHEAL CORMIER
☐ 82. LEE SMITH
☐ 84. JOSE OQUENDO
☐ 146. OZZIE SMITH
☐ 156. FELIX JOSE
☐ 194. OMAR OLIVARES
☐ 204. MIKE PEREZ
☐ 244. RAY LANKFORD
☐ 318. BOB TEWKSBURY
☐ 331. GERONIMO PENA
☐ 347. DONOVAN OSBORNE
☐ 381. ROD BREWER
☐ 394. BERNARD GILKEY
☐ 405. TOM PAGNOZZI
☐ 428. DMITRI YOUNG
☐ 545. GREGG JEFFERIES
☐ 569. TODD ZEILE
☐ 596. BRIAN JORDAN
☐ 605. LUIS ALICEA
☐ 621. HECTOR VILLANUEVA
☐ 654. MARK WHITEN
☐ 703. JOE MAGRANE
☐ 728. TRACY WOODSON
☐ 818. TEAM CHECKLIST

SAN DIEGO PADRES

☐ 58. MIKE MADDUX
☐ 61. TIM TEUFEL
☐ 140. JERALD CLARK
☐ 152. KURT STILLWELL
☐ 165. TONY GWYNN
☐ 172. DAN WALTERS
☐ 222. GARY SHEFFIELD
☐ 258. DARRIN JACKSON
☐ 261. ANDY BENES
☐ 283. RANDY MYERS
☐ 288. JOSE MELENDEZ
☐ 304. BRUCE HURST
☐ 307. FRANK SEMINARA
☐ 330. RICH RODRIGUEZ
☐ 438. RAY MCDAVID
☐ 577. FRED MCGRIFF
☐ 639. JEFF GARDNER
☐ 657. GENE HARRIS
☐ 660. RICKY GUTIERREZ
☐ 662. TIM SCOTT
☐ 688. MIKE SCIOSCIA
☐ 696. DEREK BELL
☐ 709. DAVE EILAND
☐ 724. GREG W. HARRIS
☐ 774. PHIL PLANTIER
☐ 784. DARRELL SHERMAN
☐ 788. CRAIG SHIPLEY
☐ 811. JEREMY HERNANDEZ
☐ 828. TEAM CHECKLIST

SAN FRANCISCO GIANTS

☐ 8. KEVIN ROGERS
☐ 15. STEVE HOSEY
☐ 73. ROD BECK
☐ 118. BILL SWIFT
☐ 126. ROBBY THOMPSON
☐ 143. MATT WILLIAMS
☐ 151. ROYCE CLAYTON
☐ 160. JOHN BURKETT
☐ 170. MIKE JACKSON
☐ 173. DARREN LEWIS
☐ 179. KIRT MANWARING
☐ 186. MIKE FELDER
☐ 197. TREVOR WILSON
☐ 218. CORY SNYDER
☐ 229. BUD BLACK
☐ 281. WILLIE MCGEE
☐ 432. CALVIN MURRAY
☐ 567. BARRY BONDS
☐ 570. MARK CARREON
☐ 576. WILL CLARK
☐ 579. DAVE RIGHETTI
☐ 581. JEFF BRANTLEY
☐ 700. DAVE MARTINEZ
☐ 778. BRYAN HICKERSON
☐ 790. TODD BENZINGER
☐ 809. DAVE BURBA
☐ 822. TEAM CHECKLIST

SEATTLE MARINERS

☐ 65. BRET BOONE
☐ 100. DAVE VALLE
☐ 117. LANCE PARRISH
☐ 141. DAVE FLEMING
☐ 213. KEVIN MITCHELL
☐ 224. JAY BUHNER
☐ 287. TINO MARTINEZ
☐ 301. OMAR VIZQUEL
☐ 336. RANDY JOHNSON
☐ 338. ERIK HANSON
☐ 355. KEN GRIFFEY, JR.
☐ 388. KERRY WOODSON
☐ 411. HENRY COTTO
☐ 434. MARC NEWFIELD
☐ 503. JOHN CUMMINGS
☐ 551. RICH AMARAL
☐ 553. EDGAR MARTINEZ
☐ 588. CHRIS BOSIO
☐ 624. RUSS SWAN
☐ 627. PETE O'BRIEN
☐ 663. NORM CHARLTON
☐ 714. MIKE FELDER
☐ 783. MIKE HAMPTON
☐ 799. BRIAN HOLMAN
☐ 824. TEAM CHECKLIST

TEXAS RANGERS

☐ 7. DAN SMITH
☐ 14. CRIS COLON
☐ 76. KEVIN BROWN
☐ 83. GENO PETRALLI
☐ 92. KENNY ROGERS
☐ 123. IVAN RODRIGUEZ
☐ 155. NOLAN RYAN
☐ 241. DEAN PALMER
☐ 289. JEFF HUSON
☐ 323. JOSE GUZMAN
☐ 365. JOSE CANSECO
☐ 371. JEFF FRYE
☐ 374. DAVID HULSE
☐ 380. BRIAN BOHANON
☐ 390. MATT WHITESIDE
☐ 441. BENJI GIL
☐ 511. BILLY RIPKEN
☐ 557. TOM HENKE
☐ 574. RAFAEL PALMEIRO
☐ 637. MANUEL LEE
☐ 656. JULIO FRANCO
☐ 678. CHARLIE LEIBRANDT
☐ 687. ROBB NEN
☐ 718. CRAIG LEFFERTS
☐ 739. DOUG DASCENZO
☐ 749. TODD BURNS
☐ 755. JUAN GONZALEZ
☐ 831. TEAM CHECKLIST

TORONTO BLUE JAYS

☐ 125. ROBERTO ALOMAR
☐ 149. PAT BORDERS
☐ 158. DEREK BELL
☐ 164. JACK MORRIS
☐ 205. MANUEL LEE
☐ 223. JOE CARTER
☐ 266. JUAN GUZMAN
☐ 322. MIKE TIMLIN
☐ 335. DAVID CONE
☐ 339. DUANE WARD
☐ 344. JOHN OLERUD
☐ 346. DEVON WHITE
☐ 358. JIMMY KEY
☐ 406. KELLY GRUBER
☐ 413. TODD STOTTLEMYRE
☐ 425. CARLOS DELGADO
☐ 546. DAVE STEWART
☐ 638. AL LEITER
☐ 651. DOMNGO MARTINEZ
☐ 673. DARRIN JACKSON
☐ 682. RANDY KNORR
☐ 693. PAT HENTGEN
☐ 705. PAUL MOLITOR
☐ 721. DARNELL COLES
☐ 764. ED SPRAGUE
☐ 768. DICK SCHOFIELD
☐ 802. LUIS SOJO
☐ 815. TEAM CHECKLIST

1994 UPPER DECK (550) 2 1/2" X 3 1/2"

ATLANTA BRAVES

☐ 64. RYAN KLESKO

- ☐ 85. DEION SANDERS
- ☐ 87. JOHN SMOLTZ
- ☐ 95. TERRY PENDLETON
- ☐ 144. TOM GLAVINE
- ☐ 185. CHIPPER JONES
- ☐ 206. TONY TARASCO
- ☐ 225. FRED MCGRIFF
- ☐ 255. JAVIER LOPEZ
- ☐ 320. GREG MADDUX
- ☐ 324. JEFF BLAUSER
- ☐ 338. MIKE KELLY
- ☐ 375. DAVID JUSTICE
- ☐ 393. GREGG OLSON
- ☐ 407. GREG MCMICHAEL
- ☐ 420. STEVE AVERY
- ☐ 442. KENT MERCKER
- ☐ 489. MARK LEMKE
- ☐ 527. TERRELL WADE

BALTIMORE ORIOLES

- ☐ 63. BRADY ANDERSON
- ☐ 77. CHRIS HOILES
- ☐ 102. MIKE MUSSINA
- ☐ 147. JAMIE MOYER
- ☐ 188. HAROLD BAINES
- ☐ 210. JEFFREY HAMMONDS
- ☐ 227. BRAD PENNINGTON
- ☐ 248. MARK MCLEMORE
- ☐ 340. RAFAEL PALMEIRO
- ☐ 347. CHRIS SABO
- ☐ 356. MIKE DEVEREAUX
- ☐ 425. CAL RIPKEN, JR.
- ☐ 433. SID FERNANDEZ
- ☐ 456. BEN MCDONALD
- ☐ 505. LEE SMITH
- ☐ 538. ALEX OCHOA

BOSTON RED SOX

- ☐ 5. GREG BLOSSER
- ☐ 21. JEFF MCNEELY
- ☐ 71. MO VAUGHN
- ☐ 80. AARON SELE
- ☐ 96. ANDRE DAWSON
- ☐ 109. LUIS ORTIZ
- ☐ 123. DANNY DARWIN
- ☐ 127. FRANK VIOLA
- ☐ 175. BILLY HALL
- ☐ 187. MIKE GREENWELL
- ☐ 213. JEFF RUSSELL
- ☐ 333. DAVE VALLE
- ☐ 337. TIM NAEHRING
- ☐ 373. JOHN VALENTIN
- ☐ 450. ROGER CLEMENS
- ☐ 461. BILLY HATCHER
- ☐ 497. OTIS NIXON
- ☐ 502. SCOTT COOPER
- ☐ 543. TROT NIXON

CALIFORNIA ANGELS

- ☐ 1. BRIAN ANDERSON
- ☐ 29. CHRIS TURNER
- ☐ 66. DAMION EASLEY
- ☐ 74. CHILI DAVIS
- ☐ 82. CHAD CURTIS
- ☐ 111. TIM SALMON
- ☐ 117. BO JACKSON
- ☐ 124. EDUARDO PEREZ
- ☐ 139. PHIL LEFTWICH
- ☐ 159. JOE MAGRANE
- ☐ 165. GARY DISARCINA
- ☐ 314. CHUCK FINLEY
- ☐ 334. GREG MYERS
- ☐ 401. JOE GRAHE
- ☐ 423. HAROLD REYNOLDS
- ☐ 485. MARK LANGSTON
- ☐ 515. JORGE FABREGAS
- ☐ 523. RYAN HANCOCK

CHICAGO CUBS

- ☐ 28. STEVE TRASCHEL
- ☐ 92. RYNE SANDBERG
- ☐ 108. JOSE BAUTISTA
- ☐ 122. JOSE VIZCAINO
- ☐ 136. STEVE BUECHELE
- ☐ 149. GLENALLEN HILL
- ☐ 154. RICK WILKINS
- ☐ 196. JOSE GUZMAN
- ☐ 199. KEVIN ROBERSON
- ☐ 257. RANDY MYERS
- ☐ 328. DERRICK MAY
- ☐ 434. WILLIE BANKS
- ☐ 440. MARK GRACE
- ☐ 443. ANTHONY YOUNG
- ☐ 451. MIKE MORGAN
- ☐ 464. FRANK CASTILLO
- ☐ 477. SHAWON DUNSTON
- ☐ 492. KARL RHODES
- ☐ 510. SAMMY SOSA
- ☐ 530. BROOKS KLESCHNICK

CHICAGO WHITE SOX

- ☐ 3. JAMES BALDWIN
- ☐ 25. SCOTT RUFFCORN
- ☐ 57. JULIO FRANCO
- ☐ 118. LANCE JOHNSON
- ☐ 121. RON KARKOVICE
- ☐ 146. JASON BERE
- ☐ 156. OZZIE GUILLEN
- ☐ 204. WILSON ALVAREZ
- ☐ 231. ALEX FERNANDEZ
- ☐ 254. TIM RAINES
- ☐ 263. ROBIN VENTURA
- ☐ 300. FRANK THOMAS
- ☐ 371. JOEY CORA
- ☐ 395. JACK MCDOWELL
- ☐ 411. DARRIN JACKSON
- ☐ 468. ROBERTO HERNANDEZ
- ☐ 549. EDDIE PEARSON

CINCINNATI REDS

- ☐ 58. KEVIN MITCHELL
- ☐ 68. JOHN ROPER
- ☐ 134. JOE OLIVER
- ☐ 143. JOSE RIJO
- ☐ 168. TIM COSTO
- ☐ 170. JOHNNY RUFFIN
- ☐ 217. BRIAN KOELLING
- ☐ 222. REGGIE SANDERS
- ☐ 230. WILLIE GREENE
- ☐ 308. ROB DIBBLE
- ☐ 327. JOHN SMILEY
- ☐ 385. BARRY LARKIN
- ☐ 387. ROBERTO KELLY
- ☐ 437. TONY FERNANDEZ
- ☐ 448. BRET BOONE
- ☐ 481. TIM PUGH
- ☐ 494. HAL MORRIS
- ☐ 508. ERIK HANSON
- ☐ 511. HECTOR CARASCO
- ☐ 544. CALVIN REESE

CLEVELAND INDIANS

- ☐ 23. MANNY RAMIREZ
- ☐ 115. CARLOS BAERGA
- ☐ 131. ALBERT BELLE
- ☐ 215. KENNY LOFTON
- ☐ 331. JACK MORRIS
- ☐ 341. EDDIE MURRAY
- ☐ 352. JIM THOME
- ☐ 358. DENNIS MARTINEZ
- ☐ 363. PAUL SORRENTO
- ☐ 381. MARK LEWIS
- ☐ 394. CHARLES NAGY
- ☐ 415. SANDY ALOMAR, JR.
- ☐ 467. STEVE FARR
- ☐ 486. OMAR VIZQUEL
- ☐ 519. HERBERT PERRY
- ☐ 522. PAUL SHUEY
- ☐ 534. DARON KIRKREIT

COLORADO ROCKIES

- ☐ 70. DAVID NIED
- ☐ 76. JOE GIRARDI
- ☐ 105. ROBERTO MEJIA
- ☐ 128. DARREN HOLMES
- ☐ 167. CHARLIE HAYES
- ☐ 194. GREG W. HARRIS
- ☐ 234. MARCUS MOORE
- ☐ 252. ERIC YOUNG
- ☐ 315. ANDRES GALARRAGA
- ☐ 348. ARMANDO REYNOSO
- ☐ 372. MIKE HARKEY
- ☐ 438. WALT WEISS
- ☐ 454. DANTE BICHETTE
- ☐ 462. HOWARD JOHNSON
- ☐ 483. ELLIS BURKS
- ☐ 545. NEIFI PEREZ

DETROIT TIGERS

- ☐ 56. TONY PHILLIPS
- ☐ 93. CHRIS GOMEZ
- ☐ 179. DAVID WELLS
- ☐ 201. ALAN TRAMMELL
- ☐ 220. CECIL FIELDER
- ☐ 247. JOHN DOHERTY
- ☐ 261. ERIC DAVIS
- ☐ 301. MICKEY TETTLETON
- ☐ 316. MIKE MOORE
- ☐ 321. MIKE HENNEMAN
- ☐ 345. TRAVIS FRYMAN
- ☐ 364. TIM BELCHER
- ☐ 392. CHAD KREUTER
- ☐ 414. LOU WHITAKER
- ☐ 458. BILL GULLICKSON
- ☐ 547. MATT BRUNSON

FLORIDA MARLINS

- ☐ 11. CARL EVERETT
- ☐ 73. DAVE MAGADAN
- ☐ 78. RYAN BOWEN
- ☐ 103. NIGEL WILSON
- ☐ 151. BRET BARBERIE
- ☐ 162. JEFF CONINE
- ☐ 202. CHUCK CARR
- ☐ 209. CHRIS HAMMOND
- ☐ 233. DARRELL WHITMORE
- ☐ 304. ORESTES DESTRADE
- ☐ 307. KURT MILLER
- ☐ 313. KURT ABBOTT
- ☐ 397. BENITO SANTIAGO
- ☐ 405. BRYAN HARVEY
- ☐ 447. DAVID WEATHERS
- ☐ 449. CHARLIE HOUGH
- ☐ 475. GARY SHEFFIELD
- ☐ 536. CHARLES JOHNSON

HOUSTON ASTROS

- ☐ 16. BRIAN HUNTER
- ☐ 312. CRAIG BIGGIO
- ☐ 346. STEVE FINLEY
- ☐ 354. ANDUJAR CEDENO
- ☐ 379. PETE HARNISCH
- ☐ 396. LUIS GONZALEZ
- ☐ 404. SCOTT SERVAIS
- ☐ 409. KEN CAMINITI
- ☐ 435. DARRYL KILE
- ☐ 452. DOUG DRABEK
- ☐ 480. JEFF BAGWELL
- ☐ 484. GREG SWINDELL
- ☐ 499. MITCH WILLIAMS
- ☐ 517. JOHN HUDEK
- ☐ 518. JAMES MOUTON
- ☐ 524. BILLY WAGNER

KANSAS CITY ROYALS

- ☐ 14. JEFF GRANGER
- ☐ 79. GREG GAGNE
- ☐ 107. MIKE MACFARLANE
- ☐ 133. KEVIN APPIER
- ☐ 161. JOSE LIND
- ☐ 169. WALLY JOYNER
- ☐ 226. FELIX JOSE
- ☐ 249. BOB HAMELIN
- ☐ 253. BRIAN MCRAE
- ☐ 339. JEFF MONTGOMERY
- ☐ 376. VINCE COLEMAN
- ☐ 413. DAVID CONE
- ☐ 466. GARY GAETTI
- ☐ 474. TOM GORDON
- ☐ 507. DAVE HENDERSON
- ☐ 546. JOHNNY DAMON

LOS ANGELES DODGERS

- ☐ 59. RAUL MONDESI
- ☐ 158. PEDRO ASTACIO
- ☐ 166. KEVIN GROSS
- ☐ 183. BRETT BUTLER

- ☐ 208. ERIC KARROS
- ☐ 236. JOSE OFFERMAN
- ☐ 260. TOM CANDIOTTI
- ☐ 266. CORY SNYDER
- ☐ 336. JIM GOTT
- ☐ 349. RAMON MARTINEZ
- ☐ 355. OREL HERSHISER
- ☐ 408. TIM WALLACH
- ☐ 436. HENRY RODRIGUEZ
- ☐ 465. DELINO DESHIELDS
- ☐ 500. MIKE PIAZZA
- ☐ 520. CHAN HO PARK
- ☐ 531. T. HOLLANDSWORTH

MILWAUKEE BREWERS

- ☐ 303. JOSE VALENTIN
- ☐ 305. PAT LISTACH
- ☐ 326. DARRYL HAMILTON
- ☐ 332. GRAEME LLOYD
- ☐ 359. DAVE NILSSON
- ☐ 369. B.J. SURHOFF
- ☐ 378. KEVIN SEITZER
- ☐ 416. BILL WEGMAN
- ☐ 426. JAIME NAVARRO
- ☐ 431. CAL ELDRED
- ☐ 441. BRIAN HARPER
- ☐ 445. GREG VAUGHN
- ☐ 473. JODY REED
- ☐ 476. JOHN JAHA
- ☐ 528. TODD DUNN

MINNESOTA TWINS

- ☐ 4. RICH BECKER
- ☐ 81. DAVE WINFIELD
- ☐ 98. KENT HRBEK
- ☐ 114. DENNY HOCKING
- ☐ 130. MATT WALBECK
- ☐ 141. RICK AGUILERA
- ☐ 152. CHUCK KNOBLAUCH
- ☐ 197. SHANE MACK
- ☐ 200. DAVID MCCARTY
- ☐ 302. PEDRO MUNOZ
- ☐ 322. SCOTT LEIUS
- ☐ 325. KIRBY PUCKETT
- ☐ 439. KEVIN TAPANI
- ☐ 501. PAT MEARES
- ☐ 503. SCOTT ERICKSON
- ☐ 548. LATROY HAWKINS

MONTREAL EXPOS

- ☐ 2. SHANE ANDREWS
- ☐ 10. JOEY EISCHEN
- ☐ 12. CLIFF FLOYD
- ☐ 30. GABE WHITE
- ☐ 97. WIL CORDERO
- ☐ 125. BRIAN LOONEY
- ☐ 171. KIRK RUETER
- ☐ 173. KEN HILL
- ☐ 192. JEFF FASSERO
- ☐ 237. RONDELL WHITE
- ☐ 244. MIKE LANSING
- ☐ 250. CURTIS PRIDE
- ☐ 318. PEDRO J. MARTINEZ
- ☐ 335. JOHN WETTELAND
- ☐ 351. MOISES ALOU
- ☐ 366. MEL ROJAS
- ☐ 370. LARRY WALKER
- ☐ 390. MARQUIS GRISSOM
- ☐ 427. SEAN BERRY
- ☐ 459. DARRIN FLETCHER
- ☐ 532. BRAD FULLMER

NEW YORK METS

- ☐ 17. BUTCH HUSKEY
- ☐ 69. DAVE TELGHEDER
- ☐ 101. TIM BOGAR
- ☐ 119. BOBBY JONES
- ☐ 160. RYAN THOMPSON
- ☐ 178. JEFF KENT
- ☐ 190. JEROMY BURNITZ
- ☐ 205. DWIGHT GOODEN
- ☐ 242. TODD HUNDLEY
- ☐ 319. KEVIN MCREYNOLDS
- ☐ 323. JOHN FRANCO
- ☐ 329. JOSE VIZCAINO
- ☐ 344. BOBBY BONILLA
- ☐ 419. PETE SMITH
- ☐ 421. DAVID SEGUI
- ☐ 428. BRET SABERHAGEN
- ☐ 537. PRESTON WILSON

NEW YORK YANKEES

- ☐ 18. MARK HUTTON
- ☐ 86. BERNIE WILLIAMS
- ☐ 90. DON MATTINGLY
- ☐ 112. WADE BOGGS
- ☐ 138. STERLING HITCHCOCK
- ☐ 186. PAUL O'NEILL
- ☐ 212. DANNY TARTABULL
- ☐ 229. MIKE STANLEY
- ☐ 259. JIMMY KEY
- ☐ 264. PAT KELLY
- ☐ 310. JIM ABBOTT
- ☐ 342. XAVIER HERNANDEZ
- ☐ 399. TERRY MULHOLLAND
- ☐ 412. MIKE GALLEGO
- ☐ 471. MELIDO PEREZ
- ☐ 496. LUIS POLONIA
- ☐ 509. BOB WICKMAN
- ☐ 514. ROBERT EENHOOM
- ☐ 550. DEREK JETER

OAKLAND A'S

- ☐ 19. MICHAEL JORDAN
- ☐ 20. STEVE KARSAY
- ☐ 60. RICKEY HENDERSON
- ☐ 67. MARK MCGWIRE
- ☐ 110. BRENT GATES
- ☐ 120. BOBBY WITT
- ☐ 174. MIKE BORDICK
- ☐ 195. TODD VAN POPPEL
- ☐ 218. SCOTT LYDY
- ☐ 262. CRAIG PAQUETTE
- ☐ 306. SCOTT BROSIUS
- ☐ 365. DENNIS ECKERSLEY
- ☐ 380. RUBEN SIERRA
- ☐ 384. STAN JAVIER
- ☐ 391. TROY NEEL
- ☐ 429. BOB WELCH
- ☐ 488. TERRY STEINBACH
- ☐ 498. RON DARLING
- ☐ 525. JASON GIAMBI

PHILADELPHIA PHILLIES

- ☐ 6. RICKY BOTTALICO
- ☐ 65. DARREN DAULTON
- ☐ 72. TYLER GREEN
- ☐ 84. KEVIN STOCKER
- ☐ 148. WES CHAMBERLAIN
- ☐ 157. JIM EISENREICH
- ☐ 172. LENNY DYKSTRA
- ☐ 181. MARIANO DUNCAN
- ☐ 184. MILT THOMPSON
- ☐ 203. TOMMY GREENE
- ☐ 343. BOBBY MUNOZ
- ☐ 374. DOUG JONES
- ☐ 410. JOHN KRUK
- ☐ 432. DAVID HOLLINS
- ☐ 453. DANNY JACKSON
- ☐ 460. CURT SCHILLING
- ☐ 463. MICKEY MORANDINI
- ☐ 491. PETE INCAVIGLIA
- ☐ 504. JEFF JUDEN
- ☐ 540. WAYNE GOMES

PITTSBURGH PIRATES

- ☐ 7. MIDRE CUMMINGS
- ☐ 83. ANDY VAN SLYKE
- ☐ 132. STEVE COOKE
- ☐ 177. JAY BELL
- ☐ 182. ORLANDO MERCED
- ☐ 198. CARLOS GARCIA
- ☐ 238. JEFF KING
- ☐ 243. AL MARTIN
- ☐ 251. ZANE SMITH
- ☐ 368. RANDY TOMLIN
- ☐ 383. PAUL WAGNER
- ☐ 479. DON SLAUGHT
- ☐ 482. KEVIN YOUNG
- ☐ 541. J. ALLENSWORTH

ST. LOUIS CARDINALS

- ☐ 106. TOM PAGNOZZI
- ☐ 113. TRIPP CROMER
- ☐ 150. MARK WHITEN
- ☐ 191. RENE AROCHA
- ☐ 223. BRIAN JORDAN
- ☐ 235. ALLEN WATSON
- ☐ 239. LUIS ALICEA
- ☐ 265. GREGG JEFFERIES
- ☐ 353. BOB TEWKSBURY
- ☐ 357. MIKE PEREZ
- ☐ 360. OZZIE SMITH
- ☐ 406. BERNARD GILKEY
- ☐ 422. RHEAL CORMIER
- ☐ 444. TODD ZEILE
- ☐ 446. RAY LANKFORD
- ☐ 529. ALAN BENES

SAN DIEGO PADRES

- ☐ 75. ARCHI CIANFROCCO
- ☐ 104. RICKY GUTIERREZ
- ☐ 129. WALLY WHITEHURST
- ☐ 145. PHIL PLANTIER
- ☐ 153. TREVOR HOFFMAN
- ☐ 214. DAVE STATON
- ☐ 219. TONYT GWYNN
- ☐ 232. BRAD AUSMUS
- ☐ 256. MELVIN NIEVES
- ☐ 362. SCOTT SANDERS
- ☐ 382. BIP ROBERTS
- ☐ 388. ANDY BENES
- ☐ 495. DEREK BELL
- ☐ 513. JOEY HAMILTON
- ☐ 516. TIM HYERS
- ☐ 539. DERREK LEE

SAN FRANCISCO GIANTS

- ☐ 27. SALOMON TORRES
- ☐ 62. BILL SWIFT
- ☐ 100. KIRT MANWARING
- ☐ 116. J.R. PHILLIPS
- ☐ 142. ROD BECK
- ☐ 163. TODD BENZINGER
- ☐ 193. ROBBY THOMPSON
- ☐ 207. DARREN LEWIS
- ☐ 221. ROYCE CLAYTON
- ☐ 258. WILLIE MCGEE
- ☐ 311. MIKE JACKSON
- ☐ 386. MIKE PORTUGAL
- ☐ 400. BARRY BONDS
- ☐ 403. JOHN BURKETT
- ☐ 490. MATT WILLIAMS
- ☐ 521. BILL VAN LANDINGHAM
- ☐ 533. STEVE SODERSTROM

SEATTLE MARINERS

- ☐ 22. MARC NEWFIELD
- ☐ 24. ALEX RODRIGUEZ
- ☐ 61. JAY BUHNER
- ☐ 88. RUBEN SANTANA
- ☐ 94. TINO MARTINEZ
- ☐ 164. ROGER SALKELD
- ☐ 211. RICH AMARAL
- ☐ 224. KEN GRIFFEY, JR.
- ☐ 228. CHRIS BOSIO
- ☐ 240. DAN WILSON
- ☐ 246. DAVE FLEMING
- ☐ 309. MIKE BLOWERS
- ☐ 330. RANDY JOHNSON
- ☐ 361. ERIC ANTHONY
- ☐ 389. FELIX FERMIN
- ☐ 424. EDGAR MARTINEZ
- ☐ 472. GREG HIBBARD
- ☐ 478. REGGIE JEFFERSON
- ☐ 506. BOBBY AYALA
- ☐ 512. TIM DAVIS
- ☐ 535. ARQUIMEDEZ POZO

TEXAS RANGERS

- ☐ 9. STEVE DREYER
- ☐ 135. BENJI GIL
- ☐ 140. JOSE CANSECO
- ☐ 155. JUAN GONZALEZ
- ☐ 180. DEAN PALMER

- ☐ 216. MANUEL LEE
- ☐ 245. IVAN RODRIGUEZ
- ☐ 317. DOUG STRANGE
- ☐ 350. WILL CLARK
- ☐ 367. TOM HENKE
- ☐ 377. DAVID HULSE
- ☐ 398. CHRIS JAMES
- ☐ 418. ROGER PAVLIK
- ☐ 457. KENNY ROGERS
- ☐ 469. JACK ARMSTRONG
- ☐ 487. KEVIN BROWN
- ☐ 542. MIKE BELL

TORONTO BLUE JAYS

- ☐ 8. CARLOS DELGADO
- ☐ 13. ALEX GONZALEZ
- ☐ 15. SHAWN GREEN
- ☐ 26. PAUL SPOLJARIC
- ☐ 89. DAVE STEWART
- ☐ 91. JOE CARTER
- ☐ 99. JOHN OLERUD
- ☐ 126. PAT HENTGEN
- ☐ 137. DEVON WHITE
- ☐ 176. ROB BUTLER
- ☐ 189. TODD STOTTLEMYRE
- ☐ 241. ED SPRAGUE
- ☐ 402. DUANE WARD
- ☐ 417. PAT BOARDERS
- ☐ 430. JUAN GUZMAN
- ☐ 455. ROBERTO ALOMAR
- ☐ 470. PAUL MOLITOR
- ☐ 493. SHAWN GREEN
- ☐ 526. JOSE SILVA

1995 UPPER DECK SERIES 1 (225) 2 1/2" X 3 1/2"

ATLANTA BRAVES

- ☐ 5. DAMON HOLLINS
- ☐ 7. GLENN WILLIAMS
- ☐ 43. ROBERTO KELLY
- ☐ 44. JEFF BLAUSER
- ☐ 45. FRED MCGRIFF
- ☐ 46. TOM GLAVINE
- ☐ 47. MIKE KELLY
- ☐ 48. JAVIER LOPEZ
- ☐ 49. GREG MADDUX
- ☐ 213. TERRELL WADE
- ☐ 214. JOSE OLIVA

BALTIMORE ORIOLES

- ☐ 4. CURTIS GOODWIN
- ☐ 126. BRET BARBERIE
- ☐ 127. BEN MCDONALD
- ☐ 128. HAROLD BAINES
- ☐ 129. JEFFREY HAMMONDS
- ☐ 130. MIKE MUSSINA
- ☐ 131. CHRIS HOILES
- ☐ 132. BRADY ANDERSON
- ☐ 218. ARMANDO BENITEZ

BOSTON RED SOX

- ☐ 10. NOMAR GARCIAPARRA
- ☐ 155. OTIS NIXON
- ☐ 159. ROGER CLEMENS
- ☐ 160. ANDRE DAWSON
- ☐ 161. MO VAUGHN
- ☐ 162. AARON SELE
- ☐ 163. JOHN VALENTIN

CALIFORNIA ANGELS

- ☐ 6. TODD GREENE
- ☐ 16. LEE SMITH
- ☐ 17. CHILI DAVIS
- ☐ 18. BRIAN ANDERSON
- ☐ 19. GARY DISARCINA
- ☐ 20. BO JACKSON
- ☐ 21. CHUCK FINLEY
- ☐ 216. GARRET ANDERSON

CHICAGO CUBS

- ☐ 63. REY SANCHEZ
- ☐ 64. WILLIE BANKS
- ☐ 65. MARK GRACE
- ☐ 66. RANDY MYERS
- ☐ 67. STEVE TRACHSEL
- ☐ 68. DERRICK MAY

CHICAGO WHITE SOX

- ☐ 196. OZZIE GUILLEN
- ☐ 197. WILSON ALVAREZ
- ☐ 198. TIM RAINES
- ☐ 199. SCOTT RUFFCORN
- ☐ 200. MICHAEL JORDAN
- ☐ 201. ROBIN VENTURA
- ☐ 202. JASON BERE
- ☐ 203. DARRIN JACKSON

CINCINNATI REDS

- ☐ 164. BRIAN R. HUNTER
- ☐ 165. BRET BOONE
- ☐ 166. HECTOR CARRASCO
- ☐ 167. PETE SOHOUREK
- ☐ 168. WILLIE GREENE
- ☐ 169. KEVIN MITCHELL
- ☐ 170. DEION SANDERS
- ☐ 171. JOHN ROPER

CLEVELAND INDIANS

- ☐ 90. KENNY LOFTON
- ☐ 91. CHARLES NAGY
- ☐ 92. SANDY ALOMAR, JR.
- ☐ 93. MARK CLARK
- ☐ 94. DENNIS MARTINEZ
- ☐ 95. DAVE WINFIELD
- ☐ 96. JIM THOME
- ☐ 97. MANNY RAMIREZ
- ☐ 221. JULIAN TAVAREZ

COLORADO ROCKIES

- ☐ 172. CHARLIE HAYES
- ☐ 173. DAVID NIED
- ☐ 174. ELLIS BURKS
- ☐ 175. DANTE BICHETTE
- ☐ 176. MARVIN FREEMAN
- ☐ 177. ERIC YOUNG

DETROIT TIGERS

- ☐ 184. CHRIS GOMEZ
- ☐ 185. TRAVIS FRYMAN
- ☐ 186. KIRK GIBSON
- ☐ 187. MIKE MOORE
- ☐ 188. LOU WHITAKER
- ☐ 189. SEAN BERGMAN

FLORIDA MARLINS

- ☐ 114. ROBB NEN
- ☐ 115. JEFF CONINE
- ☐ 116. KURT ABBOTT
- ☐ 117. CHARLIE HOUGH
- ☐ 118. DAVE WEATHERS
- ☐ 220. CHARLES JOHNSON

HOUSTON ASTROS

- ☐ 22. DARRYL KILE
- ☐ 23. SHANE REYNOLDS
- ☐ 24. TONY EUSEBLO
- ☐ 25. CRAIG BIGGIO
- ☐ 26. DOUG DRABEK
- ☐ 27. BRIAN L. HUNTER
- ☐ 28. JAMES MOUTON
- ☐ 211. ORLANDO MILLER

KANSAS CITY ROYALS

- ☐ 12. MATT SMITH
- ☐ 178. DAVID CONE
- ☐ 179. GREG GAGNE
- ☐ 180. BOB HAMELIN
- ☐ 181. WALLY JOYNER
- ☐ 182. JEFF MONTGOMERY
- ☐ 183. JOSE LIND

LOS ANGELES DODGERS

- ☐ 9. KARIM GARCIA
- ☐ 69. BRETT BUTLER
- ☐ 70. ERIC KARROS
- ☐ 71. TIM WALLACH
- ☐ 72. DELINO DESHIELDS
- ☐ 73. DARREN DREIFORT
- ☐ 74. OREL HERSHISER
- ☐ 75. BILLY ASHLEY
- ☐ 224. T. HOLLANDSWORTH

MILWAUKEE BREWERS

- ☐ 50. MATT MIESKE
- ☐ 51. TROY O'LEARY
- ☐ 52. JEFF CIRILLO
- ☐ 53. CAL ELDRED
- ☐ 54. PAT LISTACH
- ☐ 55. JOSE VALENTIN

MINNESOTA TWINS

- ☐ 190. SHANE MACK
- ☐ 191. RICK AGUILERA
- ☐ 192. DENNY HOCKING
- ☐ 193. CHUCK KNOBLAUCH
- ☐ 194. KEVIN TAPANI
- ☐ 195. KENT HRBEK
- ☐ 223. LATROY HAWKINS

MONTREAL EXPOS

- ☐ 76. SEAN BERRY
- ☐ 77. KEN HILL
- ☐ 78. JOHN WETTELAND
- ☐ 79. MOISES ALOU
- ☐ 80. CLIFF FLOYD
- ☐ 81. MARQUIS GRISSOM
- ☐ 82. LARRY WALKER
- ☐ 83. RONDELL WHITE

NEW YORK METS

- ☐ 2. BILL PULSIPHER
- ☐ 13. PAUL WILSON
- ☐ 14. JASON ISRINGHAUSEN
- ☐ 119. JUAN CASTILLO
- ☐ 120. BRET SABERHAGEN
- ☐ 121. RICO BROGNA
- ☐ 122. JOHN FRANCO
- ☐ 123. TODD HUNDLEY
- ☐ 124. JASON JACOME
- ☐ 125. BOBBY JONES

NEW YORK YANKEES

- ☐ 1. RUBEN RIVERA
- ☐ 204. RUSS DAVIS
- ☐ 205. JIMMY KEY
- ☐ 206. JACK MCDOWELL
- ☐ 207. JIM ABBOTT
- ☐ 208. PAUL O'NEILL
- ☐ 209. BERNIE WILLIAMS

☐ 210. DON MATTINGLY
☐ 225. DEREK JETER

OAKLAND A'S

☐ 3. BEN GRIEVE
☐ 29. GERONIMO BERROA
☐ 30. RICKEY HENDERSON
☐ 31. STEVE KARSAY
☐ 32. STEVE ONTIVEROS
☐ 33. ERNIE YOUNG
☐ 34. DENNIS ECKERSLEY
☐ 35. MARK MCGWIRE
☐ 222. JASON GIAMBI

PHILADELPHIA PHILLIES

☐ 140. LENNY DYKSTRA
☐ 141. MARIANO DUNCAN
☐ 142. FERNANDO VALENZUELA
☐ 143. BOBBY MUNOZ
☐ 144. KEVIN STOCKER
☐ 145. JOHN KRUK

PITTSBURGH PIRATES

☐ 146. JON LIEBER
☐ 147. ZANE SMITH
☐ 148. STEVE COOKE
☐ 149. ANDY VAN SLYKE
☐ 150. JAY BELL
☐ 151. CARLOS GARCIA

ST. LOUIS CARDINALS

☐ 8. BRET WAGNER
☐ 56. JOHN MABRY
☐ 57. BOB TEWKSBURY
☐ 58. BRIAN JORDAN
☐ 59. GREGG JEFFERIES
☐ 60. OZZIE SMITH
☐ 61. GERONIMO PENA
☐ 62. MARK WHITEN
☐ 217. ALAN BENES

SAN DIEGO PADRES

☐ 11. RAUL CASANOVA
☐ 133. EDDIE WILLIAMS
☐ 134. ANDY BENES
☐ 135. TONY GWYNN
☐ 136. BIP ROBERTS
☐ 137. JOEY HAMILTON
☐ 138. LUIS LOPEZ
☐ 139. RAY MCDAVID
☐ 219. DUSTON HERMANSON

SAN FRANCISCO GIANTS

☐ 84. BILL VAN LANDINGHAM
☐ 85. MATT WILLIAMS
☐ 86. ROD BECK
☐ 87. DARREN LEWIS
☐ 88. ROBBY THOMPSON
☐ 89. DARRYL STRAWBERRY

SEATTLE MARINERS

☐ 98. RICH GOSSAGE
☐ 99. TINO MARTINEZ
☐ 100. KEN GRIFFEY, JR.
☐ 111. REGGIE JEFFERSON
☐ 112. RANDY JOHNSON
☐ 113. MARC NEWFIELD
☐ 215. ALEX RODRIGUEZ

TEXAS RANGERS

☐ 15. REID RYAN
☐ 152. JOHN DETTMER
☐ 153. DARREN OLIVER
☐ 154. DEAN PALMER
☐ 156. RUSTY GREER
☐ 157. RICK HELLING
☐ 158. JOSE CANSECO

TORONTO BLUE JAYS

☐ 36. DAVE STEWART
☐ 37. PAT HENTGEN
☐ 38. CARLOS DELGADO
☐ 39. JOE CARTER
☐ 40. .ROBERTO ALOMAR
☐ 41. JOHN OLERUD
☐ 42. DEVON WHITE
☐ 212. ALEX GONZALEZ

UPPER DECK-COLLECTOR'S CHOICE

1994 COLLECTOR'S CHOICE (670) 2 1/2" X 3 1/2"

ATLANTA BRAVES

☐ 44. STEVE AVERY
☐ 53. JEFF BLAUSER
☐ 152. CHIPPER JONES
☐ 156. DAVID JUSTICE
☐ 165. RYAN KLESKO
☐ 178. JAVY LOPEZ
☐ 183. GREG MADDUX
☐ 197. FRED MCGRIFF
☐ 199. GREG MCMICHAEL
☐ 221. GREG OLSON
☐ 273. TONY TARASCO
☐ 332. TEAM CHECKLIST
☐ 368. GREGG OLSON
☐ 372. TERRY PENDLETON
☐ 420. JOHN SMOLTZ
☐ 430. TOM GLAVINE
☐ 441. MIKE STANTON
☐ 446. KENT MERCKER
☐ 501. MARK LEMKE
☐ 575. DEION SANDERS
☐ 649. TERRELL WADE
☐ 663. MIKE KELLY

BALTIMORE ORIOLES

☐ 123. JEFFREY HAMMONDS
☐ 140. CHRIS HOILES
☐ 195. BEN MC DONALD
☐ 198. MARK MC LEMORE
☐ 213. JAMIE MOYER
☐ 217. JOHN O'DONOGHUE
☐ 224. MIKE PAGLIARULO
☐ 227. BRAD PENNINGTON
☐ 240. CAL RIPKEN, JR.
☐ 254. DAVID SEGUI
☐ 343. TEAM CHECKLIST
☐ 373. ARTHUR RHODES
☐ 405. BRADY ANDERSON
☐ 475. MIKE MUSSINA
☐ 478. HAROLD BAINES
☐ 485. CHRIS SABO
☐ 502. MIKE DEVEREAUX
☐ 511. SID FERNANDEZ
☐ 556. LEE SMITH
☐ 605. RAFAEL PALMEIRO
☐ 608. ALAN MILLS
☐ 615. LEO GOMEZ
☐ 646. ALEX OCHOA

BOSTON RED SOX

☐ 2. GREG BLOSSER
☐ 15. LUIS ORTIZ
☐ 25. TROT NIXON
☐ 84. SCOTT COOPER
☐ 89. DANNY DARWIN
☐ 90. ROB DEER
☐ 103. SCOTT FLETCHER
☐ 128. BILLY HATCHER
☐ 200. JEFF MC NEELY
☐ 248. KEN RYAN
☐ 255. AARON SELE
☐ 278. JOHN VALENTIN
☐ 281. MO VAUGHN
☐ 283. FRANK VIOLA
☐ 348. TEAM CHECKLIST
☐ 412. ANDRE DAWSON
☐ 440. MIKE GREENWELL
☐ 452. TIM NAEHRING
☐ 506. GREG A. HARRIS
☐ 550. ROGER CLEMENS
☐ 579. OTIS NIXON
☐ 583. JEFF RUSSELL
☐ 602. DAMON BERRYHILL
☐ 627. DAVE VALLE

CALIFORNIA ANGELS

☐ 21. BRIAN ANDERSON
☐ 87. CHAD CURTIS
☐ 94. GARY DI SARCINA
☐ 129. HILLY HATHAWAY
☐ 169. MARK LANGSTON
☐ 173. PHIL LEFTWICH
☐ 179. TOREY LOVULLO
☐ 185. JOE MAGRANE
☐ 228. EDUARDO PEREZ
☐ 251. TIM SALMON
☐ 277. CHRIS TURNER
☐ 328. TEAM CHECKLIST
☐ 356. BO JACKSON
☐ 384. HAROLD REYNOLDS
☐ 436. MIKE BUTCHER
☐ 443. JOHN DOPSON
☐ 461. GREG MYERS
☐ 467. JOE GRAHE
☐ 491. CHILI DAVIS
☐ 505. DAMION EASLEY
☐ 515. CHUCK FINLEY
☐ 517. JIM EDMONDS
☐ 582. DWIGHT SMITH
☐ 591. SPIKE OWEN

CHICAGO CUBS

☐ 28. BROOKS KIESCHNICK
☐ 66. STEVE BUECHELE
☐ 114. MARK GRACE
☐ 137. GLENALLEN HILL
☐ 193. DERRICK MAY
☐ 212. MIKE MORGAN
☐ 241. KEVIN ROBERSON
☐ 263. SAMMY SOSA
☐ 284. JOSE VIZCAINO
☐ 290. TURK WENDELL
☐ 297. RICK WILKINS
☐ 335. TEAM CHECKLIST
☐ 363. SHAWON DUNSTON
☐ 427. ANTHONY YOUNG
☐ 454. FRANK CASTILLO
☐ 460. RANDY MYERS
☐ 463. JOSE GUZMAN
☐ 489. KARL RHODES
☐ 522. WILLIE BANKS
☐ 555. RYNE SANDBERG
☐ 558. REY SANCHEZ
☐ 623. JOSE BAUTISTA

CHICAGO WHITE SOX

- ☐ 36. WILSON ALVAREZ
- ☐ 50. JASON BERE
- ☐ 85. JOEY CORA
- ☐ 99. ALEX FERNANDEZ
- ☐ 134. ROBERTO HERNANDEZ
- ☐ 150. LANCE JOHNSON
- ☐ 157. RON KARKOVICE
- ☐ 235. SCOTT RADINSKY
- ☐ 247. SCOTT RUFFCORN
- ☐ 282. ROBIN VENTURA
- ☐ 354. TEAM CHECKLIST
- ☐ 370. DARRIN JACKSON
- ☐ 385. TIM RAINES
- ☐ 415. JULIO FRANCO
- ☐ 435. OZZIE GUILLEN
- ☐ 445. JACK MC DOWELL
- ☐ 500. FRANK THOMAS
- ☐ 617. DAN PASQUA
- ☐ 652. JAMES BALDWIN
- ☐ 661. MICHAEL JORDAN

CINCINNATI REDS

- ☐ 17. JOHNNY RUFFIN
- ☐ 64. JEFF BRANSON
- ☐ 86. TIM COSTO
- ☐ 93. ROB DIBBLE
- ☐ 116. WILLIE GREENE
- ☐ 171. BARRY LARKIN
- ☐ 220. JOE OLIVER
- ☐ 234. TIM PUGH
- ☐ 239. JOSE RIJO
- ☐ 245. JOHN ROPER
- ☐ 252. REGGIE SANDERS
- ☐ 349. TEAM CHECKLIST
- ☐ 439. TOM BROWNING
- ☐ 470. KEVIN MITCHELL
- ☐ 473. JOHN SMILEY
- ☐ 482. HAL MORRIS
- ☐ 484. ROBERTO KELLY
- ☐ 503. CHUCK MCELROY
- ☐ 544. BRET BOONE
- ☐ 597. ERIK HANSON
- ☐ 607. JEFF BRANTLEY
- ☐ 619. TONY FERNANDEZ
- ☐ 666. POKEY REESE

CLEVELAND INDIANS

- ☐ 16. MANNY RAMIREZ
- ☐ 34. SANDY ALOMAR, JR.
- ☐ 149. REGGIE JEFFERSON
- ☐ 164. WAYNE KIRBY
- ☐ 175. DEREK LILLIQUIST
- ☐ 177. ALBIE LOPEZ
- ☐ 205. JOSE MESA
- ☐ 262. PAUL SORRENTO
- ☐ 274. JULIAN TAVAREZ
- ☐ 339. TEAM CHECKLIST
- ☐ 444. CARLOS BAERGA
- ☐ 514. STEVE FARR
- ☐ 527. CHRIS NABHOLZ
- ☐ 533. MARK LEWIS
- ☐ 538. MARK CLARK
- ☐ 542. JACK MORRIS
- ☐ 546. DENNIS MARTINEZ
- ☐ 565. KENNY LOFTON
- ☐ 578. CHARLES NAGY
- ☐ 595. EDDIE MURRAY
- ☐ 620. ALBERT BELLE
- ☐ 624. JIM THOME
- ☐ 629. OMAR VIZQUEL

COLORADO ROCKIES

- ☐ 52. DANTE BICHETTE
- ☐ 62. DARYL BOSTON
- ☐ 74. VINNY CASTILLA
- ☐ 79. JERALD CLARK
- ☐ 126. GREG W. HARRIS
- ☐ 130. CHARLIE HAYES
- ☐ 203. ROBERTO MEJIA
- ☐ 223. JAYHAWK OWENS
- ☐ 238. ARMANDO REYNOSO
- ☐ 304. ERIC YOUNG
- ☐ 350. TEAM CHECKLIST
- ☐ 360. ANDRES GALARRAGA
- ☐ 396. JOE GIRARDI
- ☐ 407. BRUCE RUFFIN
- ☐ 417. MIKE HARKEY
- ☐ 422. DARREN HOLMES
- ☐ 488. WALT WEISS
- ☐ 530. HOWARD JOHNSON
- ☐ 536. MARCUS MOORE
- ☐ 554. ELLIS BURKS
- ☐ 576. DAVE NIED
- ☐ 618. MARVIN FREEMAN

DETROIT TIGERS

- ☐ 27. MATT BRUNSON
- ☐ 56. TOM BOLTON
- ☐ 100. CECIL FIELDER
- ☐ 110. CHRIS GOMEZ
- ☐ 118. BILL GULLICKSON
- ☐ 132. MIKE HENNEMAN
- ☐ 167. CHAD KREUTER
- ☐ 230. TONY PHILLIPS
- ☐ 275. MICKEY TETTLETON
- ☐ 291. LOU WHITAKER
- ☐ 352. TEAM CHECKLIST
- ☐ 364. JUNIOR FELIX
- ☐ 375. TRAVIS FRYMAN
- ☐ 403. KIRK GIBSON
- ☐ 421. SCOTT LIVINGSTONE
- ☐ 442. JOHN DOHERTY
- ☐ 459. MIKE MOORE
- ☐ 474. ALAN TRAMMELL
- ☐ 499. DAVID WELLS
- ☐ 557. DANNY BAUTISTA
- ☐ 561. TIM BELCHER
- ☐ 563. ERIC DAVIS

FLORIDA MARLINS

- ☐ 6. CARL EVERETT
- ☐ 39. LUIS AQUINO
- ☐ 40. JACK ARMSTRONG
- ☐ 47. BRET BARBERIE
- ☐ 63. RYAN BOWEN
- ☐ 82. JEFF CONINE
- ☐ 127. BRYAN HARVEY
- ☐ 236. PAT RAPP
- ☐ 257. GARY SHEFFIELD
- ☐ 295. DARRELL WHITMORE
- ☐ 301. NIGEL WILSON
- ☐ 341. TEAM CHECKLIST
- ☐ 359. CHARLIE HOUGH
- ☐ 362. CHRIS HAMMOND
- ☐ 367. DAVE MAGADAN
- ☐ 374. BENITO SANTIAGO
- ☐ 389. KURT ABBOTT
- ☐ 397. ORESTES DESTRADE
- ☐ 401. ALEX ARIAS
- ☐ 404. CHUCK CARR
- ☐ 448. JERRY BROWNE
- ☐ 604. ROBB NEN
- ☐ 660. CHARLES JOHNSON

HOUSTON ASTROS

- ☐ 29. BILLY WAGNER
- ☐ 38. ERIC ANTHONY
- ☐ 72. KEN CAMINITI
- ☐ 75. ANDUJAR CEDENO
- ☐ 95. DOUG DRABEK
- ☐ 111. LUIS GONZALEZ
- ☐ 153. TODD JONES
- ☐ 162. DARRYL KILE
- ☐ 256. SCOTT SERVAIS
- ☐ 329. TEAM CHECKLIST
- ☐ 361. MIKE FELDER
- ☐ 456. CRAIG BIGGIO
- ☐ 521. KEVIN BASS
- ☐ 523. STEVE FINLEY
- ☐ 526. GREG SWINDELL
- ☐ 534. PETE HARNISCH
- ☐ 581. ROBERTO PETAGINE
- ☐ 590. JEFF BAGWELL
- ☐ 594. BRIAN WILLIAMS
- ☐ 599. MITCH WILLIAMS
- ☐ 621. EDDIE TAUBENSEE
- ☐ 659. BRIAN HUNTER
- ☐ 664. JAMES MOUTON

KANSAS CITY ROYALS

- ☐ 23. JEFF GRANGER
- ☐ 65. GEORGE BRETT
- ☐ 81. DAVID CONE
- ☐ 112. TOM GORDON
- ☐ 121. CHRIS GWYNN
- ☐ 136. PHIL HIATT
- ☐ 155. WALLY JOYNER
- ☐ 176. JOSE LIND
- ☐ 181. MIKE MACFARLANE
- ☐ 201. BRIAN MC RAE
- ☐ 210. JEFF MONTGOMERY
- ☐ 231. HIPOLITO PICHARDO
- ☐ 351. TEAM CHECKLIST
- ☐ 377. STAN BELINDA
- ☐ 390. KEVIN APPIER
- ☐ 393. BOB HAMELIN
- ☐ 398. CHRIS HANEY
- ☐ 406. GREG GAGNE
- ☐ 409. KEITH MILLER
- ☐ 431. DAVE HENDERSON
- ☐ 493. FELIX JOSE
- ☐ 566. GARY GAETTI
- ☐ 601. VINCE COLEMAN
- ☐ 642. JOHNNY DAMON

LOS ANGELES DODGERS

- ☐ 70. BRETT BUTLER
- ☐ 113. JIM GOTT
- ☐ 135. OREL HERSHISER
- ☐ 158. ERIC KARROS
- ☐ 189. PEDRO J. MARTINEZ
- ☐ 190. RAMON MARTINEZ
- ☐ 196. ROGER MC DOWELL
- ☐ 209. RAUL MONDESI
- ☐ 219. JOSE OFFERMAN
- ☐ 261. CORY SNYDER
- ☐ 336. TEAM CHECKLIST
- ☐ 366. DARRYL STRAWBERRY
- ☐ 394. KEVIN GROSS
- ☐ 400. MIKE PIAZZA
- ☐ 402. TOM CANDIOTTI
- ☐ 416. DAVE HANSEN
- ☐ 466. TIM WALLACH
- ☐ 496. PEDRO ASTACIO
- ☐ 524. DELINO DE SHIELDS
- ☐ 567. TODD WORRELL
- ☐ 596. HENRY RODRIGUEZ
- ☐ 658. T. HOLLANDSWORTH

MILWAUKEE BREWERS

- ☐ 57. RICKY BONES
- ☐ 146. JOHN JAHA
- ☐ 161. MARK KIEFER
- ☐ 207. ANGEL MIRANDA
- ☐ 216. DAVE NILSSON
- ☐ 237. KEVIN REIMER
- ☐ 264. BILL SPIERS
- ☐ 289. BILL WEGMAN
- ☐ 333. TEAM CHECKLIST
- ☐ 379. KEVIN SEITZER
- ☐ 386. DARRYL HAMILTON
- ☐ 413. DOUG HENRY
- ☐ 451. TEDDY HIGUERA
- ☐ 469. B.J. SURHOFF
- ☐ 477. JOSE VALENTIN
- ☐ 492. BRIAN HARPER
- ☐ 518. GRAEME LLOYD
- ☐ 520. PAT LISTACH
- ☐ 531. JAIME NAVARRO
- ☐ 564. JODY REED
- ☐ 585. GREG VAUGHN
- ☐ 603. TOM BRUNANSKY
- ☐ 606. CAL ELDRED
- ☐ 616. JESSE OROSCO

MINNESOTA TWINS

- ☐ 1. RICH BECKER
- ☐ 18. SCOTT STAHOVIAK
- ☐ 46. WILLIE BANKS
- ☐ 96. SCOTT ERICKSON
- ☐ 166. CHUCK KNOBLAUCH
- ☐ 182. SHANE MACK
- ☐ 194. DAVID MC CARTY
- ☐ 202. PAT MEARES
- ☐ 272. KEVIN TAPANI
- ☐ 302. DAVE WINFIELD
- ☐ 353. TEAM CHECKLIST
- ☐ 378. DEREK PARKS
- ☐ 382. SCOTT LEIUS

- ☐ 425. KIRBY PUCKETT
- ☐ 437. JIM DESHAIES
- ☐ 476. RICK AGUILERA
- ☐ 486. KENT HRBEK
- ☐ 543. PEDRO MUNOZ
- ☐ 573. CHIP HALE
- ☐ 577. PAT MAHOMES
- ☐ 611. CARLOS PULIDO
- ☐ 670. MATT WALBECK

MONTREAL EXPOS

- ☐ 7. CLIFF FLOYD
- ☐ 20. GABE WHITE
- ☐ 35. MOISES ALOU
- ☐ 51. SEAN BERRY
- ☐ 92. DELINO DESHIELDS
- ☐ 98. JEFF FASSERO
- ☐ 102. DARRIN FLETCHER
- ☐ 138. KEN HILL
- ☐ 170. MIKE LANSING
- ☐ 233. CURTIS PRIDE
- ☐ 244. MEL ROJAS
- ☐ 246. KIRK RUETER
- ☐ 286. LARRY WALKER
- ☐ 293. RONDELL WHITE
- ☐ 337. TEAM CHECKLIST
- ☐ 395. WIL CORDERO
- ☐ 410. JOHN WETTELAND
- ☐ 465. MARQUIS GRISSOM
- ☐ 541. DENIS BOUCHER
- ☐ 588. PEDRO J. MARTINEZ
- ☐ 643. BRAD FULLMER
- ☐ 651. SHANE ANDREWS
- ☐ 654. TAVO ALVAREZ
- ☐ 656. JOEY EISCHEN

NEW YORK METS

- ☐ 10. BUTCH HUSKEY
- ☐ 26. KIRK PRESLEY
- ☐ 55. TIM BOGAR
- ☐ 58. BOBBY BONILLA
- ☐ 69. JEROMY BURNITZ
- ☐ 139. ERIC HILLMAN
- ☐ 143. TODD HUNDLEY
- ☐ 151. BOBBY JONES
- ☐ 159. JEFF KENT
- ☐ 250. BRET SABERHAGEN
- ☐ 276. RYAN THOMPSON
- ☐ 303. ANTHONY YOUNG
- ☐ 342. TEAM CHECKLIST
- ☐ 414. JOHN FRANCO
- ☐ 419. JOE ORSULAK
- ☐ 449. FERNANDO VINA
- ☐ 509. PETE SMITH
- ☐ 519. DWIGHT GOODEN
- ☐ 529. DAVID SEGUI
- ☐ 532. JOSE VIZCAINO
- ☐ 549. KEVIN MCREYNOLDS
- ☐ 650. PRESTON WILSON

NEW YORK YANKEES

- ☐ 11. MARK HUTTON
- ☐ 30. MATT DREWS
- ☐ 104. MIKE GALLEGO
- ☐ 147. DOMINGO JEAN
- ☐ 160. JIMMY KEY
- ☐ 192. DON MATTINGLY
- ☐ 214. BOBBY MUNOZ
- ☐ 218. PAUL O'NEILL
- ☐ 260. LEE SMITH
- ☐ 265. MIKE STANLEY
- ☐ 296. BOB WICKMAN
- ☐ 298. BERNIE WILLIAMS
- ☐ 355. TEAM CHECKLIST
- ☐ 380. WADE BOGGS
- ☐ 383. DANNY TARTABULL
- ☐ 399. XAVIER HERNANDEZ
- ☐ 432. MELIDO PEREZ
- ☐ 450. JIM ABBOTT
- ☐ 453. JIM LEYRITZ
- ☐ 483. PAT KELLY
- ☐ 487. SCOTT KAMIENIECKI
- ☐ 498. RANDY VELARDE
- ☐ 504. LUIS POLONIA
- ☐ 508. TERRY MULHOLLAND
- ☐ 539. STERLING HITCHCOCK
- ☐ 592. JEFF REARDON
- ☐ 613. STEVE HOWE
- ☐ 644. DEREK JETER

OAKLAND A'S

- ☐ 12. MIGUEL JIMENEZ
- ☐ 13. STEVE KARSAY
- ☐ 31. KURT ABBOTT
- ☐ 61. MIKE BORDICK
- ☐ 88. RON DARLING
- ☐ 107. BRENT GATES
- ☐ 180. SCOTT LYDY
- ☐ 215. TROY NEEL
- ☐ 225. CRAIG PAQUETTE
- ☐ 258. RUBEN SIERRA
- ☐ 267. TERRY STEINBACH
- ☐ 279. TODD VAN POPPEL
- ☐ 330. TEAM CHECKLIST
- ☐ 376. SCOTT BROSIUS
- ☐ 408. SCOTT HEMOND
- ☐ 471. BOBBY WITT
- ☐ 495. DENNIS ECKERSLEY
- ☐ 510. RICKEY HENDERSON
- ☐ 525. MARK MC GWIRE
- ☐ 574. BOB WELCH
- ☐ 598. STAN JAVIER
- ☐ 657. JASON GIAMBI

PHILADELPHIA PHILLIES

- ☐ 22. WAYNE GOMES
- ☐ 48. KIM BATISTE
- ☐ 76. WES CHAMBERLAIN
- ☐ 115. TOMMY GREENE
- ☐ 141. DAVE HOLLINS
- ☐ 144. PETE INCAVIGLIA
- ☐ 145. DANNY JACKSON
- ☐ 168. JOHN KRUK
- ☐ 211. MICKEY MORANDINI
- ☐ 253. CURT SCHILLING
- ☐ 268. KEVIN STOCKER
- ☐ 345. TEAM CHECKLIST
- ☐ 358. DARREN DAULTON
- ☐ 369. LENNY DYKSTRA
- ☐ 388. JIM EISENREICH
- ☐ 429. MARIANO DUNCAN
- ☐ 447. RICKY JORDAN
- ☐ 472. MILT THOMPSON
- ☐ 513. DOUG JONES
- ☐ 553. BOBBY MUNOZ
- ☐ 559. NORM CHARLTON
- ☐ 626. BEN RIVERA
- ☐ 653. RICKY BOTTALICO
- ☐ 662. JEFF JUDEN

PITTSBURGH PIRATES

- ☐ 3. MIDRE CUMMINGS
- ☐ 42. RICH AUDE
- ☐ 78. DAVE CLARK
- ☐ 83. STEVE COOKE
- ☐ 105. CARLOS GARCIA
- ☐ 163. JEFF KING
- ☐ 187. AL MARTIN
- ☐ 204. ORLANDO MERCED
- ☐ 206. BLAS MINOR
- ☐ 259. DON SLAUGHT
- ☐ 280. ANDY VAN SLYKE
- ☐ 346. TEAM CHECKLIST
- ☐ 392. RANDY TOMLIN
- ☐ 433. PAUL WAGNER
- ☐ 438. KEVIN YOUNG
- ☐ 458. ALEJANDRO PENA
- ☐ 497. JAY BELL
- ☐ 562. DENNY NEAGLE
- ☐ 571. ZANE SMITH
- ☐ 584. MARK DEWEY
- ☐ 586. BRIAN HUNTER

ST. LOUIS CARDINALS

- ☐ 32. LUIS ALICEA
- ☐ 41. RENE AROCHA
- ☐ 109. BERNARD GILKEY
- ☐ 148. GREGG JEFFERIES
- ☐ 154. BRIAN JORDAN
- ☐ 222. DONOVAN OSBORNE
- ☐ 229. MIKE PEREZ
- ☐ 288. ALLEN WATSON
- ☐ 294. MARK WHITEN
- ☐ 305. TODD ZEILE
- ☐ 334. TEAM CHECKLIST
- ☐ 365. RAY LANKFORD
- ☐ 457. GERONIMO PENA
- ☐ 464. TOM PAGNOZZI
- ☐ 468. BOB TEWKSBURY
- ☐ 481. RHEAL CORMIER
- ☐ 545. OZZIE SMITH
- ☐ 548. RICK SUTCLIFFE
- ☐ 593. ERIK PAPPAS
- ☐ 641. ALAN BENES

SAN DIEGO PADRES

- ☐ 43. BRAD AUSMUS
- ☐ 77. ARCHI CIANFROCCO
- ☐ 106. JEFF GARDNER
- ☐ 119. RICKY GUTIERREZ
- ☐ 122. TONY GWYNN
- ☐ 125. GENE HARRIS
- ☐ 188. PEDRO A. MARTINEZ
- ☐ 232. PHIL PLANTIER
- ☐ 266. DAVE STATON
- ☐ 344. TEAM CHECKLIST
- ☐ 381. WALLY WHITEHURST
- ☐ 426. PHIL CLARK
- ☐ 434. TIM WORRELL
- ☐ 479. BIP ROBERTS
- ☐ 490. DEREK BELL
- ☐ 494. TREVOR HOFFMAN
- ☐ 528. SCOTT SANDERS
- ☐ 570. ANDY BENES
- ☐ 612. TIM HYERS
- ☐ 645. DERREK LEE
- ☐ 655. DONNIE ELLIOTT
- ☐ 665. RAY HOLBERT
- ☐ 669. LUIS LOPEZ

SAN FRANCISCO GIANTS

- ☐ 19. SALOMON TORRES
- ☐ 24. STEVE SODERSTROM
- ☐ 49. ROD BECK
- ☐ 67. DAVE BURBA
- ☐ 68. JOHN BURKETT
- ☐ 80. ROYCE CLAYTON
- ☐ 91. JIM DESHAIES
- ☐ 97. RIKKERT FANEYTE
- ☐ 174. DARREN LEWIS
- ☐ 186. KIRT MANWARING
- ☐ 243. KEVIN ROGERS
- ☐ 271. BILL SWIFT
- ☐ 299. MATT WILLIAMS
- ☐ 338. TEAM CHECKLIST
- ☐ 535. ROBBY THOMPSON
- ☐ 551. TODD BENZINGER
- ☐ 568. MARK PORTUGAL
- ☐ 587. WILLIE MCGEE
- ☐ 610. BARRY BONDS
- ☐ 622. MIKE JACKSON

SEATTLE MARINERS

- ☐ 14. MARC NEWFIELD
- ☐ 37. RICH AMARAL
- ☐ 45. BOB AYRAULT
- ☐ 54. MIKE BLOWERS
- ☐ 59. BRET BOONE
- ☐ 101. DAVE FLEMING
- ☐ 117. KEN GRIFFEY, JR.
- ☐ 124. ERIK HANSON
- ☐ 184. DAVE MAGADAN
- ☐ 191. TINO MARTINEZ
- ☐ 285. OMAR VIZQUEL
- ☐ 340. TEAM CHECKLIST
- ☐ 357. RANDY JOHNSON
- ☐ 387. FELIX FERMIN
- ☐ 391. CHRIS BOSIO
- ☐ 411. ERIC ANTHONY
- ☐ 424. JAY BUHNER
- ☐ 428. REGGIE JEFFERSON
- ☐ 462. GREG HIBBARD
- ☐ 480. EDGAR MARTINEZ
- ☐ 516. BOBBY THIGPEN
- ☐ 547. DAN WILSON
- ☐ 552. BILL HASELMAN
- ☐ 572. BOBBY AYALA
- ☐ 589. ROGER SALKELD
- ☐ 609. JEFF NELSON
- ☐ 614. BRIAN TURANG
- ☐ 647. ALEX RODRIGUEZ
- ☐ 667. RUBEN SANTANA

TEXAS RANGERS

- ☐ 5. STEVE DREYER
- ☐ 73. CRIS CARPENTER
- ☐ 108. BENJI GIL
- ☐ 142. DAVID HULSE
- ☐ 172. MANNY LEE
- ☐ 226. ROGER PAVLIK
- ☐ 242. KENNY ROGERS
- ☐ 249. NOLAN RYAN
- ☐ 270. DOUG STRANGE
- ☐ 347. TEAM CHECKLIST
- ☐ 418. JACK ARMSTRONG
- ☐ 507. CHRIS JAMES
- ☐ 537. KEVIN BROWN
- ☐ 540. WILL CLARK
- ☐ 560. JOSE CANSECO
- ☐ 580. DEAN PALMER
- ☐ 625. IVAN RODRIGUEZ
- ☐ 628. TOM HENKE
- ☐ 630. JUAN GONZALEZ

TORONTO BLUE JAYS

☐ 4. CARLOS DELGADO
☐ 8. ALEX GONZALEZ
☐ 9. SHAWN GREEN
☐ 33. ROBERTO ALOMAR
☐ 60. PAT BORDERS
☐ 71. ROB BUTLER
☐ 120. JUAN GUZMAN
☐ 131. RICKEY HENDERSON
☐ 133. PAT HENTGEN
☐ 208. PAUL MOLITOR
☐ 269. TODD STOTTLEMYRE
☐ 287. DUANE WARD
☐ 292. DEVON WHITE
☐ 300. WOODY WILLIAMS
☐ 331. TEAM CHECKLIST
☐ 371. DAVE STEWART
☐ 423. ED SPRAGUE
☐ 455. JOE CARTER
☐ 512. AL LEITER
☐ 569. DICK SCHOFIELD
☐ 600. JOHN OLERUD
☐ 648. JOSE SILVA
☐ 668. PAUL SPOLJARIC

1995 COLLECTOR'S CHOICE (530) 2 1/2" X 3 1/2"

ATLANTA BRAVES

☐ 67. GREG MADDUX
☐ 69. FRED MCGRIFF
☐ 154. CHIPPER JONES
☐ 155. RYAN KLESKO
☐ 156. DAVID JUSTICE
☐ 157. MIKE KELLY
☐ 158. ROBERTO KELLY
☐ 159. TONY TARASCO
☐ 160. JAVIER LOPEZ
☐ 161. STEVE AVERY
☐ 162. GREG MCMICHAEL
☐ 163. KENT MERCKER
☐ 164. MARK LEMKE
☐ 165. TOM GLAVINE
☐ 166. JOSE OLIVA
☐ 167. JOHN SMOLTZ
☐ 168. JEFF BLAUSER

BALTIMORE ORIOLES

☐ 4. ARMANDO BENITEZ
☐ 37. CURTIS GOODWIN
☐ 85. CAL RIPKEN, JR.
☐ 330. RAFEAL PALMEIRO
☐ 331. CHRIS HOILES
☐ 332. LEO GOMEZ
☐ 333. CHRIS SABO
☐ 334. BRADY ANDERSON
☐ 335. JEFFREY HAMMONDS
☐ 336. DWIGHT SMITH
☐ 337. JACK VOIGT
☐ 338. HAROLD BAINES
☐ 339. BEN MCDONALD
☐ 340. MIKE MUSSINA
☐ 341. BRET BARBERIE
☐ 342. JAMIE MOYER
☐ 343. MIKE OQUIST
☐ 344. SID FERNANDEZ

BOSTON RED SOX

☐ 29. NOMAR GARCIAPARRA
☐ 406. AARON SELE
☐ 407. CARLOS RODRIGUEZ
☐ 408. SCOTT COOPER
☐ 409. JOHN VALENTIN
☐ 410. ROGER CLEMENS
☐ 411. MIKE GREENWELL
☐ 412. TIM VANEGMOND
☐ 413. TOM BRUNANSKY
☐ 414. STEVE FARR
☐ 415. JOSE CANSECO
☐ 416. JOE HESKETH
☐ 417. KEN RYAN
☐ 418. TIM NAEHRING
☐ 419. FRANK VIOLA
☐ 420. ANDRE DAWSON
☐ 421. MO VAUGHN

CALIFORNIA ANGELS

☐ 13. ANDREW LORRAINE
☐ 23. GARRET ANDERSON
☐ 34. TODD GREENE
☐ 91. JORGE FABREGAS
☐ 92. J.T. SNOW
☐ 93. SPIKE OWEN
☐ 94. EDUARDO PEREZ
☐ 95. BO JACKSON
☐ 96. DAMIAN EASLEY
☐ 97. GARY DISARCINA
☐ 98. JIM EDMONDS
☐ 99. CHAD CURTIS
☐ 100. TIM SALMON
☐ 101. CHILI DAVIS
☐ 102. CHUCK FINLEY
☐ 103. MARK LANGSTON
☐ 104. BRIAN ANDERSON
☐ 105. LEE SMITH
☐ 106. PHIL LEFTWICH

CHICAGO CUBS

☐ 201. ANTHONY YOUNG
☐ 202. REY SANCHEZ
☐ 203. STEVE BUECHELE
☐ 204. SHAWON DUNSTON
☐ 205. MARK GRACE
☐ 206. GLENALLEN HILL
☐ 207. EDDIE ZAMBRANO
☐ 208. RICK WILKINS
☐ 209. DERRICK MARY
☐ 210. SAMMY SOSA
☐ 211. KEVIN ROBERSON
☐ 212. STEVE TRACHSEL
☐ 213. WILLIE BANKS
☐ 214. KEVIN FOSTER
☐ 215. RANDY MYERS
☐ 216. MIKE MORGAN

CHICAGO WHITE SOX

☐ 2. SCOTT RUFFCORN
☐ 3. RAY DURHAM
☐ 75. FRANK THOMAS
☐ 494. OZZIE GUILLEN
☐ 495. TIM RAINES
☐ 496. KIRT MCCASKILL
☐ 497. OLMEDO SAENZ
☐ 498. SCOTT SANDERSON
☐ 499. LANCE JOHNSON
☐ 500. MICHAEL JORDAN
☐ 501. WARREN NEWSON
☐ 502. RON KARKOVICE
☐ 503. WILSON ALVAREZ
☐ 504. JASON BERE
☐ 505. ROBIN VENTURA
☐ 506. ALEX FERNANDEZ
☐ 507. ROBERTO HERNANDEZ
☐ 508. NORBERTO MARTIN

CINCINNATI REDS

☐ 43. C.J. NITKOWSKI
☐ 422. JEFF BRANTLEY
☐ 423. PETE SCHOUREK
☐ 424. HAL MORRIS
☐ 425. DEION SANDERS
☐ 426. BRIAN R. HUNTER
☐ 427. BRET BOONE
☐ 428. WILLIE GREENE
☐ 429. RON GANT
☐ 430. BARRY LARKIN
☐ 431. REGGIE SANDERS
☐ 432. EDDIE TAUBENSEE
☐ 433. JACK MORRIS
☐ 434. JOSE RIJO
☐ 435. JOHNNY RUFFIN
☐ 436. JOHN SMILEY
☐ 437. JOHN ROPER

CLEVELAND INDIANS

☐ 6. JULIAN TAVAREZ
☐ 7. CHAD OGEA
☐ 26. PAUL SHUEY
☐ 81. KENNY LOFTON
☐ 83. ALBERT BELLE
☐ 265. EDDIE MURRAY
☐ 266. MARK CLARK
☐ 267. PAUL SORRENTO
☐ 268. JIM THOME
☐ 269. OMAR VIZQUEL
☐ 270. CARLOS BAERGA
☐ 271. JEFF RUSSELL
☐ 272. HERBERT PERRY
☐ 273. SANDY ALOMAR JR.
☐ 274. DENNIS MARTINEZ
☐ 275. MANNY RAMIREZ
☐ 276. WAYNE KIRBY
☐ 277. CHARLES NAGY
☐ 278. ALBIE LOPEZ
☐ 279. JEROMY BURNITZ
☐ 280. DAVE WINFIELD

COLORADO ROCKIES

☐ 11. MARK THOMPSON
☐ 38. DOUG MILLION
☐ 42. JUAN ACEVEDO
☐ 438. DAVID NIED
☐ 439. ROBERTO MEJIA
☐ 440. ANDRES GALARRAGA
☐ 441. MIKE KINGERY
☐ 442. CURT LESKANIC
☐ 443. WALT WEISS
☐ 444. MARVIN FREEMAN
☐ 445. CHARLIE HAYES
☐ 446. ERIC YOUNG
☐ 447. ELLIS BURKS
☐ 448. JOE GIRARDI
☐ 449. LANCE PAINTER
☐ 450. DANTE BICHETTE
☐ 451. BRUCE RUFFIN

DETROIT TIGERS

☐ 16. TONY CLARK
☐ 465. TRAVIS FRYMAN
☐ 466. DANNY BAUTISTA
☐ 467. SEAN BERGMAN
☐ 468. MIKE HENNEMAN
☐ 469. MIKE MOORE
☐ 470. CECIL FIELDER
☐ 471. ALAN TRAMMELL
☐ 472. KIRK GIBSON
☐ 473. TONY PHILLIPS
☐ 474. MICKEY TETTLETON
☐ 475. LOU WHITAKER
☐ 476. CHRIS GOMEZ
☐ 477. JOHN DOHERTY
☐ 478. GREG GOHR
☐ 479. BILL GULLICKSON

FLORIDA MARLINS

☐ 1. CHARLES JOHNSON
☐ 8. QUILVIO VERAS
☐ 297. YORKIS PEREZ
☐ 298. KURT MILLER
☐ 299. CHUCK CARR
☐ 300. GARY SHEFFIELD
☐ 301. JERRY BROWNE
☐ 302. DAVE MAGADAN
☐ 303. KURT ABBOTT
☐ 304. PAT RAPP
☐ 305. JEFF CONINE
☐ 306. BENITO SANTIAGO
☐ 307. DAVE WEATHERS
☐ 308. ROBB NEN
☐ 309. CHRIS HAMMOND
☐ 310. BRYAN HARVEY
☐ 311. CHARLIE HOUGH
☐ 312. GREG COLBRUNN

HOUSTON ASTROS

☐ 9. PHIL NEVIN
☐ 19. ORLANDO MILLER
☐ 32. SCOTT ELARTON

- ☐ 76. JEFF BAGWELL
- ☐ 107. CHRIS DONNELS
- ☐ 108. JOHN HUDEK
- ☐ 109. CRAIG BIGGIO
- ☐ 110. LUIS GONZALEZ
- ☐ 111. BRIAN L. HUNTER
- ☐ 112. JAMES MOUTON
- ☐ 113. SCOTT SERVAIS
- ☐ 114. TONY EUSEBIO
- ☐ 115. DEREK BELL
- ☐ 116. DOUG DRABEK
- ☐ 117. SHANE REYNOLDS
- ☐ 118. DARRYL KILE
- ☐ 119. GREG SWINDELL
- ☐ 120. PHIL PLANTIER
- ☐ 121. TODD JONES

KANSAS CITY ROYALS

- ☐ 10. MICHAEL TUCKER
- ☐ 14. JOE RANDA
- ☐ 31. JIM PITTSLEY
- ☐ 66. DAVID CONE
- ☐ 78. BOB HAMELIN
- ☐ 452. JEFF GRANGER
- ☐ 453. WALLY JOYNER
- ☐ 454. JOSE LIND
- ☐ 455. JEFF MONTGOMERY
- ☐ 456. GARY GAETTI
- ☐ 457. GREG GAGNE
- ☐ 458. VINCE COLEMAN
- ☐ 459. MIKE MACFARLANE
- ☐ 460. BRIAN MCRAE
- ☐ 461. TOM GORDON
- ☐ 462. KEVIN APPIER
- ☐ 463. BILLY BREWER
- ☐ 464. MARK GUBICZA

LOS ANGELES DODGERS

- ☐ 22. GAREY INGRAM
- ☐ 39. KARIM GARCIA
- ☐ 79. RAUL MONDESI
- ☐ 80. MIKE PIAZZA
- ☐ 217. RAFAEL BOURNIGAL
- ☐ 218. DELINO DESHIELDS
- ☐ 219. TIM WALLACH
- ☐ 220. ERIC KARROS
- ☐ 221. JOSE OFFERMAN
- ☐ 222. TOM CANDIOTTI
- ☐ 223. ISMAEL VALDES
- ☐ 224. HENRY RODRIGUEZ
- ☐ 225. BILLY ASHLEY
- ☐ 226. DARREN DREIFORT
- ☐ 227. RAMON MARTINEZ
- ☐ 228. PEDRO ASTACIO
- ☐ 229. OREL HERSHISER
- ☐ 230. BRETT BUTLER
- ☐ 231. T. HOLLANDSWORTH
- ☐ 232. CHAN HO PARK

MILWAUKEE BREWERS

- ☐ 169. TROY O'LEARY
- ☐ 170. GREG VAUGHN
- ☐ 171. JODY REED
- ☐ 172. KEVIN SEITZER
- ☐ 173. JEFF CIRILLO
- ☐ 174. B.J. SURHOFF
- ☐ 175. CAL ELDRED
- ☐ 176. JOSE VALENTIN
- ☐ 177. TURNER WARD
- ☐ 178. DARRYL HAMILTON
- ☐ 179. PAT LISTACH
- ☐ 180. MATT MIESKE
- ☐ 181. BRIAN HARPER
- ☐ 182. DAVE NILSSON
- ☐ 183. MIKE FETTERS
- ☐ 184. JOHN JAHA
- ☐ 185. RICKY BONES

MINNESOTA TWINS

- ☐ 24. DAVE STEVENS
- ☐ 44. TRAVIS MILLER
- ☐ 77. KIRBY PUCKETT
- ☐ 480. RICK AGUILERA
- ☐ 481. MATT WALBECK
- ☐ 482. KEVIN TAPANI
- ☐ 483. SCOTT ERICKSON
- ☐ 484. STEVE DUNN
- ☐ 485. DAVID MCCARTY
- ☐ 486. SCOTT LEIUS
- ☐ 487. PAT MEARES
- ☐ 488. JEFF REBOULET
- ☐ 489. PEDRO MUNOZ
- ☐ 490. CHUCK KNOBLAUCH
- ☐ 491. RICH BECKER
- ☐ 492. ALEX COLE
- ☐ 493. PAT MAHOMES

MONTREAL EXPOS

- ☐ 12. ROD HENDERSON
- ☐ 233. MIKE LANSING
- ☐ 234. SEAN BERRY
- ☐ 235. RONDELL WHITE
- ☐ 236. KEN HILL
- ☐ 237. MARQUIS GRISSOM
- ☐ 238. LARRY WALKER
- ☐ 239. JOHN WETTELAND
- ☐ 240. CLIFF FLOYD
- ☐ 241. JOEY EISCHEN
- ☐ 242. LOU FRAZIER
- ☐ 243. DARRIN FLETCHER
- ☐ 244. PEDRO J. MARTINEZ
- ☐ 245. WIL CORDERO
- ☐ 246. JEFF FASSERO
- ☐ 247. BUTCH HENRY
- ☐ 248. MEL ROJAS
- ☐ 249. KIRK RUETER
- ☐ 250. MOISES ALOU

NEW YORK METS

- ☐ 17. JUAN CASTILLO
- ☐ 20. PAUL WILSON
- ☐ 35. BILL PULSIPHER
- ☐ 313. DAVID SEGUI
- ☐ 314. RICO BROGNA
- ☐ 315. JEFF KENT
- ☐ 316. JOSE VIZCAINO
- ☐ 317. JIM LINDEMAN
- ☐ 318. CARL EVERETT
- ☐ 319. RYAN THOMPSON
- ☐ 320. BOBBY BONILLA
- ☐ 321. JOE ORSULAK
- ☐ 322. PETE HARNISCH
- ☐ 323. DOUG LINTON
- ☐ 324. TODD HUNDLEY
- ☐ 325. BRET SABERHAGEN
- ☐ 326. KELLY STINNETT
- ☐ 327. JASON JACOME
- ☐ 328. BOBBY JONES
- ☐ 329. JOHN FRANCO

NEW YORK YANKEES

- ☐ 15. DEREK JETER
- ☐ 28. RUBEN RIVERA
- ☐ 68. JIMMY KEY
- ☐ 72. PAUL O'NEILL
- ☐ 509. BOB WICKMAN
- ☐ 510. DON MATTINGLY
- ☐ 511. MELIDO PEREZ
- ☐ 512. PAT KELLY
- ☐ 513. RANDY VELARDE
- ☐ 514. TONY FERNANDEZ
- ☐ 515. JACK MCDOWELL
- ☐ 516. LUIS POLONIA
- ☐ 517. BERNIE WILLIAMS
- ☐ 518. DANNY TARTABULL
- ☐ 519. MIKE STANLEY
- ☐ 520. WADE BOGGS
- ☐ 521. JIM LEYRITZ
- ☐ 522. STEVE HOWE
- ☐ 523. SCOTT KAMIENIECKI
- ☐ 524. RUSS DAVIS
- ☐ 525. JIM ABBOTT

OAKLAND A'S

- ☐ 18. MARK ACRE
- ☐ 30. JOHN WASDIN
- ☐ 40. BEN GRIEVE
- ☐ 122. STEVE ONTIVEROS
- ☐ 123. BOBBY WITT
- ☐ 124. BRENT GATES
- ☐ 125. RICKEY HENDERSON
- ☐ 126. SCOTT BROSIUS
- ☐ 127. MIKE BORDICK
- ☐ 128. FAUSTO CRUZ
- ☐ 129. STAN JAVIER
- ☐ 130. MARK MCGWIRE
- ☐ 131. GERONIMO BERROA
- ☐ 132. TERRY STEINBACH
- ☐ 133. STEVE KARSAY
- ☐ 134. DENNIS ECKERSLEY
- ☐ 135. RUBEN SIERRA
- ☐ 136. RON DARLING
- ☐ 137. TODD VAN POPPEL

PHILADELPHIA PHILLIES

- ☐ 360. GREGG JEFFERIES
- ☐ 361. MARIANO DUNCAN
- ☐ 362. DAVE HOLLINS
- ☐ 363. KEVIN STOCKER
- ☐ 364. FERNANDO VALENZUELA
- ☐ 365. LENNY DYKSTRA
- ☐ 366. JIM EISENREICH
- ☐ 367. RICKY BOTTALICO
- ☐ 368. DOUG JONES
- ☐ 369. RICKY JORDAN
- ☐ 370. DARREN DAULTON
- ☐ 371. MIKE LIEBERTHAL
- ☐ 372. BOBBY MUNOZ
- ☐ 373. JOHN KRUK
- ☐ 374. CURT SCHILLING

PITTSBURGH PIRATES

- ☐ 36. TREY BEAMON
- ☐ 41. MARK FARRIS
- ☐ 375. ORLANDO MERCED
- ☐ 376. CARLOS GARCIA
- ☐ 377. LANCE PARRISH
- ☐ 378. STEVE COOKE
- ☐ 379. JEFF KING
- ☐ 380. JAY BELL
- ☐ 381. AL MARTIN
- ☐ 382. PAUL WAGNER
- ☐ 383. RICK WHITE
- ☐ 384. MIDRE CUMMINGS
- ☐ 385. JON LIEBER
- ☐ 386. DAVE CLARK
- ☐ 387. DON SLAUGHT
- ☐ 388. DENNY NEAGLE
- ☐ 389. ZANE SMITH
- ☐ 390. ANDY VAN SLYKE

ST. LOUIS CARDINALS

- ☐ 21. JOHN MABRY
- ☐ 186. GERONIMO PENA
- ☐ 187. BOB TEWKSBURY
- ☐ 188. TODD ZEILE
- ☐ 189. DANNY JACKSON
- ☐ 190. RAY LANKFORD
- ☐ 191. BERNARD GILKEY
- ☐ 192. BRIAN JORDAN
- ☐ 193. TOM PAGNOZZI
- ☐ 194. RICK SUTCLIFFE
- ☐ 195. MARK WHITEN
- ☐ 196. TOM HENKE
- ☐ 197. RENE AROCHA
- ☐ 198. ALLEN WATSON
- ☐ 199. MIKE PEREZ
- ☐ 200. OZZIE SMITH

SAN DIEGO PADRES

- ☐ 25. DUSTIN HERMANSON
- ☐ 33. RAUL CASANOVA
- ☐ 73. TONY GWYNN
- ☐ 345. EDDIE WILLIAMS
- ☐ 346. JOE HAMILTON
- ☐ 347. BRIAN WILLIAMS
- ☐ 348. LUIS LOPEZ
- ☐ 349. STEVE FINLEY
- ☐ 350. ANDY BENES
- ☐ 351. ANDUJAR CEDENO
- ☐ 352. BIP ROBERTS
- ☐ 353. RAY MCDAVID
- ☐ 354. KEN CAMINITI
- ☐ 355. TREVOR HOFFMAN
- ☐ 356. MELVIN NEIVES
- ☐ 357. BRAD AUSMUS
- ☐ 358. ANDY ASHBY
- ☐ 359. SCOTT SANDERS

SAN FRANCISCO GIANTS

- ☐ 27. J.R. PHILLIPS
- ☐ 71. MATT WILLIAMS
- ☐ 82. BARRY BONDS
- ☐ 251. ROD BECK
- ☐ 252. JOHN PATTERSON
- ☐ 253. ROBBY THOMPSON
- ☐ 254. ROYCE CLAYTON
- ☐ 255. BILL VAN LANDINGHAM
- ☐ 256. DARREN LEWIS
- ☐ 257. KIRT MANWARING
- ☐ 258. MARK PORTUGAL
- ☐ 259. BILLY SWIFT
- ☐ 260. RIKKERT FANEYTE
- ☐ 261. MIKE JACKSON
- ☐ 262. TODD BENZINGER
- ☐ 263. BUD BLACK
- ☐ 264. SALOMON TORRES

SEATTLE MARINERS

☐ 5. ALEX RODRIGUEZ
☐ 70. KEN GRIFFEY, JR.
☐ 74. RANDY JOHNSON
☐ 281. TIM DAVIS
☐ 282. MARC NEWFIELD
☐ 283. TINO MARTINEZ
☐ 284. MIKE BLOWERS
☐ 285. RICH GOSSAGE
☐ 286. LUIS SOJO
☐ 287. EDGAR MARTINEZ
☐ 288. RICH AMARAL
☐ 289. FELIX FERMIN
☐ 290. JAY BUYNER
☐ 291. DAN WILSON
☐ 292. BOBBY AYALA
☐ 293. DAVE FLEMING
☐ 294. GREG PIRKL
☐ 295. REGGIE JEFFERSON
☐ 296. GREG HIBBARD

TEXAS RANGERS

☐ 45. REID RYAN
☐ 84. JUAN GONZALEZ
☐ 391. IVAN RODRIGUEZ
☐ 392. DAVID HULSE
☐ 393. JOHN BURKETT
☐ 394. KEVIN BROWN
☐ 395. DEAN PALMER
☐ 396. OTIS NIXON
☐ 397. RICK HELLING
☐ 398. KENNY ROGERS
☐ 399. DARREN OLIVER
☐ 400. WILL CLARK
☐ 401. JEFF FRYE
☐ 402. KEVIN GROSS
☐ 403. JOHN DETTMER
☐ 404. MANUEL LEE
☐ 405. RUSTY GREER

TORONTO BLUE JAYS

☐ 138. ALEX GONZALEZ
☐ 139. JOHN OLERUD
☐ 140. ROBERTO ALOMAR
☐ 141. DARREN HALL
☐ 142. ED SPRAGUE
☐ 143. DEVON WHITE
☐ 144. SHAWN GREEN
☐ 145. PAUL MOLITOR
☐ 146. PAT BORDERS
☐ 147. CARLOS DELGADO
☐ 148. JUAN GUZMAN
☐ 149. PAT HENTGEN
☐ 150. JOE CARTER
☐ 151. DAVE STEWART
☐ 152. TODD STOTTLEMYRE
☐ 153. DICK SCHOFIELD

1995 COLLECTOR'S CHOICE SPECIAL EDITION (265) 2 1/2" X 3 1/2"

ATLANTA BRAVES

☐ 5. TERRELL WADE
☐ 59. TOM GLAVINE
☐ 60. GREG MADDUX
☐ 61. ROBERTO KELLY
☐ 62. RYAN KLESKO
☐ 63. JAVIER LOPEZ
☐ 64. JOSE OLIVA
☐ 65. FRED MCGRIFF
☐ 66. STEVE AVERY
☐ 67. DAVID JUSTICE

BALTIMORE ORIOLES

☐ 8. ALEX OCHOA
☐ 13. ARMANDO BENITEZ
☐ 152. LEE SMITH
☐ 153. RAFEAL PALMEIRO
☐ 154. BRADY ANDERSON
☐ 155. CAL RIPKEN, JR.
☐ 156. JEFFREY HAMMONDS
☐ 157. MIKE MUSSINA
☐ 158. CHRIS HOILES
☐ 159. BEN MCDONALD

BOSTON RED SOX

☐ 189. JOHN VALENTIN
☐ 190. ROGER CLEMENS
☐ 191. AARON SELE
☐ 192. SCOTT COOPER
☐ 193. MIKE GREENWELL
☐ 194. MO VAUGHN
☐ 195. ANDRE DAWSON

CALIFORNIA ANGELS

☐ 12. GARRET ANDERSON
☐ 31. CHILI DAVIS
☐ 32. CHAD CURTIS
☐ 33. BRIAN ANDERSON
☐ 34. CHUCK FINLEY
☐ 35. TIM SALMON
☐ 36. BO JACKSON

CHICAGO CUBS

☐ 81. RANDY MYERS
☐ 82. SHAWON DUNSTON
☐ 83. MARK GRACE
☐ 84. DERRICK MAY
☐ 85. SAMMY SOSA
☐ 86. STEVE TRACHSEL

CHICAGO WHITE SOX

☐ 29. FRANK THOMAS
☐ 231. JULIO FRANCO
☐ 232. JACK MCDOWELL
☐ 233. JASON BERE
☐ 234. ALEX FERNANDEZ
☐ 235. FRANK THOMAS
☐ 236. OZZIE GUILLEN
☐ 237. ROBIN VENTURA
☐ 238. MICHAEL JORDAN
☐ 239. WILSON ALVAREZ

CINCINNATI REDS

☐ 196. RON GANT
☐ 197. JOSE RIJO
☐ 198. BRET BOONE
☐ 199. DEION SANDERS
☐ 200. BARRY LARKIN
☐ 201. HAL MORRIS
☐ 202. REGGIE SANDERS
☐ 203. KEVIN MITCHELL

CLEVELAND INDIANS

☐ 15. HERBERT PERRY
☐ 22. PAUL SHUEY
☐ 114. JIM THOME
☐ 115. DAVE WINFIELD
☐ 116. EDDIE MURRAY
☐ 117. MANNY RAMIREZ
☐ 118. CARLOS BAERGA
☐ 119. KENNY LOFTON
☐ 120. ALBERT BELLE
☐ 121. MARK CLARK
☐ 122. DENNIS MARTINEZ

COLORADO ROCKIES

☐ 204. MARVIN FREEMAN
☐ 205. ANDRES GALARRAGA
☐ 206. WALT WEISS
☐ 207. CHARLIE HAYES
☐ 208. DAVID NIED
☐ 209. DANTE BICHETTE

DETROIT TIGERS

☐ 217. KIRK GIBSON
☐ 218. LOU WHITAKER
☐ 219. CHRIS GOMEZ
☐ 220. CECIL FIELDER
☐ 221. MICKEY TETTLETON
☐ 222. TRAVIS FRYMAN
☐ 223. TONY PHILLIPS

FLORIDA MARLINS

☐ 130. GARY SHEFFIELD
☐ 131. PAT RAPP
☐ 132. BRET BARBERIE
☐ 133. CHUCK CARR
☐ 134. JEFF CONINE
☐ 135. CHARLES JOHNSON
☐ 136. BENITO SANTIAGO

HOUSTON ASTROS

☐ 17. ORLANDO MILLER
☐ 37. DOUG DRABEK
☐ 38. CRAIG BIGGIO
☐ 39. KEN CAMINITI
☐ 40. JEFF BAGWELL
☐ 41. DARRYL KILE
☐ 42. JOHN HUDEK
☐ 43. BRIAN HUNTER

KANSAS CITY ROYALS

☐ 210. DAVID CONE
☐ 211. JEFF MONTGOMERY
☐ 212. FELIX JOSE
☐ 213. MIKE MACFARLANE
☐ 214. WALLY JOYNER
☐ 215. BOB HAMELIN
☐ 216. BRIAN MCRAE

LOS ANGELES DODGERS

☐ 6. DARREN DREIFORT
☐ 25. CHAN HO PARK
☐ 87. BRETT BUTLER
☐ 88. DELINO DESHIELDS
☐ 89. OREL HERSHISER
☐ 90. MIKE PIAZZA
☐ 91. T. HOLLANDSWORTH
☐ 92. ERIC KARROS
☐ 93. RAMON MARTINEZ
☐ 94. TIM WALLACH
☐ 95. RAUL MONDESI

MILWAUKEE BREWERS

☐ 21. DUANE SINGLETON
☐ 68. RICKY BONES
☐ 69. CAL ELDRED
☐ 70. GREG VAUGHN
☐ 71. DAVE NILSSON
☐ 72. JOSE VALENTIN
☐ 73. MATT MIESKE

MINNESOTA TWINS

☐ 7. LATROY HAWKINS
☐ 23. STEVE DUNN
☐ 28. CHUCK KNOBLAUCH
☐ 224. RICK AGUILERA
☐ 225. SCOTT ERICKSON
☐ 226. CHUCK KNOBLAUCH
☐ 227. KENT HRBEK
☐ 228. SHANE MACK
☐ 229. KEVIN TAPANI
☐ 230. KIRBY PUCKETT

MONTREAL EXPOS

☐ 96. LARRY WALKER
☐ 97. WIL CORDERO
☐ 98. MARQUIS GRISSOM
☐ 99. KEN HILL
☐ 100. CLIFF FLOYD
☐ 101. PEDRO J. MARTINEZ
☐ 102. JOHN WETTELAND
☐ 103. RONDELL WHITE
☐ 104. MOISES ALOU

NEW YORK METS

☐ 4. BILL PULSIPHER

☐ 9. PAUL WILSON
☐ 19. JASON ISRINGHAUSEN
☐ 145. BOBBY BONILLA
☐ 146. JASON JACOME
☐ 147. JEFF KENT
☐ 148. RYAN THOMPSON
☐ 149. BOBBY JONES
☐ 150. BRET SABERHAGEN
☐ 151. JOHN FRANCO

NEW YORK YANKEES

☐ 2. DEREK JETER
☐ 18. RUSS DAVIS
☐ 240. DON MATTINGLY
☐ 241. JIM ABBOTT
☐ 242. JIM LEYRITZ
☐ 243. PAUL O'NEILL
☐ 244. MELIDO PEREZ
☐ 245. WADE BOGGS
☐ 246. MIKE STANLEY
☐ 247. DANNY TARTABULL
☐ 248. JIMMY KEY

OAKLAND A'S

☐ 10. ERNIE YOUNG
☐ 44. DENNIS ECKERSLEY
☐ 45. MARK MCGWIRE
☐ 46. BRENT GATES
☐ 47. STEVE KARSAY
☐ 48. RICKEY HENDERSON
☐ 49. TERRY STEINBACH
☐ 50. RUBEN SIERRA

PHILADELPHIA PHILLIES

☐ 24. MIKE LIEBERTHAL
☐ 168. FERNANDO VALENZUELA
☐ 169. MARIANO DUNCAN
☐ 170. LENNY DYKSTRA
☐ 171. DARREN DAULTON
☐ 172. DANNY JACKSON
☐ 173. BOBBY MUNOZ
☐ 174. DOUG JONES

PITTSBURGH PIRATES

☐ 175. JAY BELL
☐ 176. ZANE SMITH
☐ 177. JON LIEBER
☐ 178. CARLOS GARCIA
☐ 179. ORLANDO MERCED
☐ 180. ANDY VAN SLYKE

ST. LOUIS CARDINALS

☐ 11. ALAN BENES
☐ 74. TODD ZEILE
☐ 75. OZZIE SMITH
☐ 76. BERNARD GILKEY
☐ 77. RAY LANKFORD
☐ 78. BOB TEWKSBURY
☐ 79. MARK WHITEN
☐ 80. GREGG JEFFERIES

SAN DIEGO PADRES

☐ 3. DUSTIN HERMANSON
☐ 20. RAY MCDAVID
☐ 27. TONY GWYNN
☐ 160. TONY GWYNN
☐ 161. JOEY HAMILTON
☐ 162. ANDY BENES
☐ 163. TREVOR HOFFMAN
☐ 164. PHIL PLANTIER
☐ 165. DEREK BELL
☐ 166. BIP ROBERTS
☐ 167. EDDIE WILLIAMS

SAN FRANCISCO GIANTS

☐ 30. MATT WILLIAMS
☐ 105. BARRY BONDS
☐ 106. DARREN LEWIS
☐ 107. MARK PORTUGAL
☐ 108. MATT WILLIAMS
☐ 109. BILL VAN LANDINGHAM
☐ 110. BILLY SWIFT
☐ 111. ROBBY THOMPSON
☐ 112. ROD BECK
☐ 113. DARRYL STRAWBERRY

SEATTLE MARINERS

☐ 1. ALEX RODRIGUEZ
☐ 26. KEN GRIFFEY, JR.
☐ 123. RANDY JOHNSON
☐ 124. JAY BUHNER
☐ 125. KEN GRIFFEY, JR.
☐ 126. RICH GOSSAGE
☐ 127. TINO MARTINEZ
☐ 128. REGGIE JEFFERSON
☐ 129. EDGAR MARTINEZ

TEXAS RANGERS

☐ 181. RICK HELLING
☐ 182. RUSTY GREER
☐ 183. KENNY ROGERS
☐ 184. WILL CLARK
☐ 185. JOSE CANSECO
☐ 186. JUAN GONZALEZ
☐ 187. DEAN PALMER
☐ 188. IVAN RODRIGUEZ

TORONTO BLUE JAYS

☐ 14. ROBERT PEREZ
☐ 16. JOSE SILVA
☐ 51. ROBERTO ALOMAR
☐ 52. CARLOS DELGADO
☐ 53. ALEX GONZALEZ
☐ 54. JOE CARTER
☐ 55. PAUL MOLITOR
☐ 56. JUAN GUZMAN
☐ 57. JOHN OLERUD
☐ 58. SHAWN GREEN

UPPER DECK-SP

1993 UPPER DECK SP
(290)
2 1/2" X 3 1/2"

ATLANTA BRAVES

☐ 13. DAVID JUSTICE
☐ 55. STEVE AVERY
☐ 56. JEFF BLAUSER
☐ 57. RON GANT
☐ 58. TOM GLAVINE
☐ 59. GREG MADDUX
☐ 60. FRED MCGRIFF
☐ 61. TERRY PENDLETON
☐ 62. DEION SANDERS
☐ 63. JOHN SMOLTZ
☐ 280. CHIPPER JONES
☐ 281. JAVIER LOPEZ

BALTIMORE ORIOLES

☐ 8. CAL RIPKEN, JR.
☐ 154. BRADY ANDERSON
☐ 155. MIKE DEVEREAUX
☐ 156. JEFFREY HAMMONDS
☐ 157. CHRIS HOILES
☐ 158. BEN MCDONALD
☐ 159. MARK MCLEMORE
☐ 160. MIKE MUSSINA
☐ 161. GREGG OLSON
☐ 162. DAVID SEGUI

BOSTON RED SOX

☐ 199. ROGER CLEMENS
☐ 200. SCOTT COOPER
☐ 201. ANDRE DAWSON
☐ 202. MIKE GREENWELL
☐ 203. CARLOS QUINTANA
☐ 204. JEFF RUSSELL
☐ 205. AARON SELE
☐ 206. MO VAUGHN
☐ 207. FRANK VIOLA

CALIFORNIA ANGELS

☐ 5. MARK LANGSTON
☐ 19. CHAD CURTIS
☐ 20. CHILI DAVIS
☐ 21. GARY DISARCINA
☐ 22. DAMION EASLEY
☐ 23. CHUCK FINLEY
☐ 24. LUIS POLONIA
☐ 25. TIM SALMON
☐ 26. J.T. SNOW
☐ 27. RUSS SPRINGER
☐ 284. EDUARDO PEREZ

CHICAGO CUBS

☐ 17. RYNE SANDBERG
☐ 82. STEVE BUECHELE
☐ 83. MARK GRACE
☐ 84. JOSE GUZMAN
☐ 85. DERRICK MAY
☐ 86. MIKE MORGAN
☐ 87. RANDY MYERS
☐ 88. KEVIN ROBERSON
☐ 89. SAMMY SOSA
☐ 90. RICK WILKINS

CHICAGO WHITE SOX

☐ 253. ALEX FERNANDEZ
☐ 254. OZZIE GUILLEN
☐ 255. BO JACKSON
☐ 256. LANCE JOHNSON
☐ 257. RON KARKOVICE
☐ 258. JACK MCDOWELL
☐ 259. TIM RAINES
☐ 260. FRANK THOMAS
☐ 261. ROBIN VENTURA
☐ 271. JASON BERE

CINCINNATI REDS

☐ 15. BARRY LARKIN
☐ 208. ROB DIBBLE
☐ 209. ROBERTO KELLY
☐ 210. KEVIN MITCHELL
☐ 211. HAL MORRIS
☐ 212. JOE OLIVER
☐ 213. JOSE RIJO
☐ 214. BIP ROBERTS
☐ 215. CHRIS SABO
☐ 216. REGGIE SANDERS
☐ 282. CHAD MOTTOLA

CLEVELAND INDIANS

☐ 118. SANDY ALOMAR, JR.
☐ 119. CARLOS BAERGA
☐ 120. ALBERT BELLE
☐ 121. REGGIE JEFFERSON
☐ 122. WAYNE KIRBY
☐ 123. KENNY LOFTON
☐ 124. CARLOS MARTINEZ
☐ 125. CHARLES NAGY
☐ 126. PAUL SORRENTO
☐ 285. MANNY RAMIREZ

COLORADO ROCKIES

☐ 217. DANTE BICHETTE
☐ 218. JERALD CLARK
☐ 219. ALEX COLE
☐ 220. ANDRES GALARRAGA
☐ 221. JOE GIRARDI
☐ 222. CHARLIE HAYES
☐ 223. ROBERTO MEJIA
☐ 224. ARMANDO REYNOSO
☐ 225. ERIC YOUNG

DETROIT TIGERS

☐ 235. ROB DEER
☐ 236. CECIL FIELDER

1993 Upper Deck SP

☐ 237. TRAVIS FRYMAN
☐ 238. MIKE HENNEMAN
☐ 239. TONY PHILLIPS
☐ 240. MICKEY TETTLETON
☐ 241. ALAN TRAMMELL
☐ 242. DAVID WELLS
☐ 243. LOU WHITAKER

FLORIDA MARLINS

☐ 18. GARY SHEFFIELD
☐ 136. BRET BARBERIE
☐ 137. CHUCK CARR
☐ 138. JEFF CONINE
☐ 139. ORESTES DESTRADE
☐ 140. CHRIS HAMMOND
☐ 141. BRIAN HARVEY
☐ 142. BENITO SANTIAGO
☐ 143. WALT WEISS
☐ 144. DARRELL WHITMORE
☐ 276. CARL EVERETT

HOUSTON ASTROS

☐ 28. JEFF BAGWELL
☐ 29. CRAIG BIGGIO
☐ 30. KEN CAMINITI
☐ 31. ANDUJAR CEDENO
☐ 32. DOUG DRABEK
☐ 33. STEVE FINLEY
☐ 34. LUIS GONZALEZ
☐ 35. PETE HARNISCH
☐ 36. DARRYL KILE

KANSAS CITY ROYALS

☐ 226. KEVIN APPIER
☐ 227. GEORGE BRETT
☐ 228. DAVID CONE
☐ 229. PHIL HIATT
☐ 230. FELIX JOSE
☐ 231. WALLY JOYNER
☐ 232. MIKE MACFARLANE
☐ 233. BRIAN MCRAE
☐ 234. JEFF MONTGOMERY
☐ 273. JOHNNY DAMON
☐ 287. MICHAEL TUCKER

LOS ANGELES DODGERS

☐ 91. BRETT BUTLER
☐ 92. ERIC DAVIS
☐ 93. OREL HERSHISER
☐ 94. ERIC KARROS
☐ 95. RAMON MARTINEZ
☐ 96. RAUL MONDESI
☐ 97. JOSE OFFERMAN
☐ 98. MIKE PIAZZA
☐ 99. DARRYL STRAWBERRY
☐ 272. ROGER CEDENO

MILWAUKEE BREWERS

☐ 64. CAL ELDRED
☐ 65. DARRYL HAMILTON
☐ 66. JOHN JAHA
☐ 67. PAT LISTACH
☐ 68. JAIME NAVARRO
☐ 69. KEVIN REIMER
☐ 70. B.J. SURHOFF
☐ 71. GREG VAUGHN
☐ 72. ROBIN YOUNT

MINNESOTA TWINS

☐ 7. KIRBY PUCKETT
☐ 244. RICK AGUILERA
☐ 245. SCOTT ERICKSON
☐ 246. BRIAN HARPER
☐ 247. KENT HRBEK
☐ 248. CHUCK KNOBLAUCH
☐ 249. SHANE MACK
☐ 250. DAVID MCCARTY
☐ 251. PEDRO MUNOZ
☐ 252. DAVE WINFIELD

MONTREAL EXPOS

☐ 12. MARQUIS GRISSOM
☐ 100. MOISES ALOU
☐ 101. WILFREDO CORDERO
☐ 102. DELINO DESHIELDS
☐ 103. DARRIN FLETCHER
☐ 104. KEN HILL
☐ 105. MIKE LANSING
☐ 106. DENNIS MARTINEZ
☐ 107. LARRY WALKER
☐ 108. JOHN WETTELAND
☐ 277. CLIFF FLOYD
☐ 289. RONDELL WHITE

NEW YORK METS

☐ 145. TIM BOGAR
☐ 146. BOBBY BONILLA
☐ 147. JEROMY BURNITZ
☐ 148. VINCE COLEMAN
☐ 149. DWIGHT GOODEN
☐ 150. TODD HUNDLEY
☐ 151. HOWARD JOHNSON
☐ 152. EDDIE MURRAY
☐ 153. BRET SABERHAGEN

NEW YORK YANKEES

☐ 2. WADE BOGGS
☐ 262. JIM ABBOTT
☐ 263. STEVE FARR
☐ 264. JIMMY KEY
☐ 265. DON MATTINGLY
☐ 266. PAUL O'NEILL
☐ 267. MIKE STANLEY
☐ 268. DANNY TARTABULL
☐ 269. BOB WICKMAN
☐ 270. BERNIE WILLIAMS
☐ 274. RUSS DAVIS
☐ 279. DEREK JETER

OAKLAND A'S

☐ 37. MIKE BORDICK
☐ 38. DENNIS ECKERSLEY
☐ 39. BRENT GATES
☐ 40. RICKEY HENDERSON
☐ 41. MARK MCGWIRE
☐ 42. CRAIG PAQUETTE
☐ 43. RUBEN SIERRA
☐ 44. TERRY STEINBACH
☐ 45. TODD VAN POPPEL

PHILADELPHIA PHILLIES

☐ 11. DARREN DAULTON
☐ 14. JOHN KRUK
☐ 16. TERRY MULHOLLAND
☐ 172. MARIANO DUNCAN
☐ 173. LENNY DYKSTRA
☐ 174. TOMMY GREENE
☐ 175. DAVE HOLLINS
☐ 176. PETE INCAVIGLIA
☐ 177. MICKEY MORANDINI
☐ 178. CURT SCHILLING
☐ 179. KEVIN STOCKER
☐ 180. MITCH WILLIAMS

PITTSBURGH PIRATES

☐ 181. STAN BELINDA
☐ 182. JAY BELL
☐ 183. STEVE COOKE
☐ 184. CARLOS GARCIA
☐ 185. JEFF KING
☐ 186. ORLANDO MERCED
☐ 187. DON SLAUGHT
☐ 188. ANDY VAN SLYKE
☐ 189. KEVIN YOUNG

ST. LOUIS CARDINALS

☐ 73. RENE AROCHA
☐ 74. BERNARD GILKEY
☐ 75. GREGG JEFFERIES
☐ 76. RAY LANKFORD
☐ 77. TOM PAGNOZZI
☐ 78. LEE SMITH
☐ 79. OZZIE SMITH
☐ 80. BOB TEWKSBURY
☐ 81. MARK WHITEN
☐ 288. ALLEN WATSON
☐ 290. DMITRI YOUNG

SAN DIEGO PADRES

☐ 163. DEREK BELL
☐ 164. ANDY BENES
☐ 165. ARCHI CIANFROCCO
☐ 166. RICKY GUTIERREZ
☐ 167. TONY GWYNN
☐ 168. GENE HARRIS
☐ 169. TREVOR HOFFMAN
☐ 170. RAY MCDAVID
☐ 171. PHIL PLANTIER

SAN FRANCISCO GIANTS

☐ 10. BARRY BONDS
☐ 109. ROD BECK
☐ 110. JOHN BURKETT
☐ 111. WILL CLARK
☐ 112. ROYCE CLAYTON
☐ 113. DARREN LEWIS
☐ 114. WILLIE MCGEE
☐ 115. BILL SWIFT
☐ 116. ROBBY THOMPSON
☐ 117. MATT WILLIAMS

SEATTLE MARINERS

☐ 4. KEN GRIFFEY, JR.
☐ 127. RICH AMARAL
☐ 128. JAY BUHNER
☐ 129. NORM CHARLTON
☐ 130. DAVE FLEMING
☐ 131. ERIK HANSON
☐ 132. RANDY JOHNSON
☐ 133. EDGAR MARTINEZ
☐ 134. TINO MARTINEZ
☐ 135. OMAR VIZQUEL
☐ 283. MARC NEWFIELD

TEXAS RANGERS

☐ 9. IVAN RODRIGUEZ
☐ 190. KEVIN BROWN
☐ 191. JOSE CANSECO
☐ 192. JULIO FRANCO
☐ 193. BENJI GIL
☐ 194. JUAN GONZALEZ
☐ 195. TOM HENKE
☐ 196. RAFAEL PALMEIRO
☐ 197. DEAN PALMER
☐ 198. NOLAN RYAN

TORONTO BLUE JAYS

☐ 1. ROBERTO ALOMAR
☐ 3. JOE CARTER
☐ 6. JOHN OLERUD
☐ 46. PAT BORDERS
☐ 47. TONY FERNANDEZ
☐ 48. JUAN GUZMAN
☐ 49. PAT HENTGEN
☐ 50. PAUL MOLITOR
☐ 51. JACK MORRIS
☐ 52. ED SPRAGUE
☐ 53. DUANE WARD
☐ 54. DEVON WHITE
☐ 275. CARLOS DELGADO
☐ 278. ALEX GONZALEZ
☐ 286. TODD STEVERSON

1994 UPPER DECK SP (200) 2 1/2" X 3 1/2"

ATLANTA BRAVES

☐ 17. TERRELL WADE
☐ 19. GLENN WILLIAMS
☐ 47. STEVE AVERY
☐ 48. JEFF BLAUSER
☐ 49. TOM GLAVINE
☐ 50. DAVID JUSTICE

- ☐ 51. ROBERTO KELLY
- ☐ 52. RYAN KLESKO
- ☐ 53. JAVIER LOPEZ
- ☐ 54. GREG MADDUX
- ☐ 55. FRED MCGRIFF

BALTIMORE ORIOLES

- ☐ 12. ALEX OCHOA
- ☐ 121. JEFFREY HAMMONDS
- ☐ 122. CHRIS HOILES
- ☐ 123. BEN MCDONALD
- ☐ 124. MIKE MUSSINA
- ☐ 125. RAFAEL PÁLMEIRO
- ☐ 126. CAL RIPKEN, JR.
- ☐ 127. LEE SMITH

BOSTON RED SOX

- ☐ 11. TROT NIXON
- ☐ 152. ROGER CLEMENS
- ☐ 153. SCOTT COOPER
- ☐ 154. ANDRE DAWSON
- ☐ 155. MIKE GREENWELL
- ☐ 156. AARON SELE
- ☐ 157. MO VAUGHN

CALIFORNIA ANGELS

- ☐ 21. BRIAN ANDERSON
- ☐ 22. CHAD CURTIS
- ☐ 23. CHILI DAVIS
- ☐ 24. BO JACKSON
- ☐ 25. MARK LANGSTON
- ☐ 26. TIM SALMON

CHICAGO CUBS

- ☐ 9. BROOKS KIESCHNICK
- ☐ 69. MARK GRACE
- ☐ 70. RANDY MYERS
- ☐ 71. RYNE SANDBERG
- ☐ 72. SAMMY SOSA
- ☐ 73. STEVE TRACHSEL
- ☐ 74. RICK WILKINS

CHICAGO WHITE SOX

- ☐ 188. WILSON ALVAREZ
- ☐ 189. JASON BERE
- ☐ 190. ALEX FERNANDEZ
- ☐ 191. JULIO FRANCO
- ☐ 192. JACK MCDOWELL
- ☐ 193. FRANK THOMAS
- ☐ 194. ROBIN VENTURA

CINCINNATI REDS

- ☐ 158. BRET BOONE
- ☐ 159. BARRY LARKIN
- ☐ 160. KEVIN MITCHELL
- ☐ 161. JOSE RIJO
- ☐ 162. DEION SANDERS
- ☐ 163. REGGIE SANDERS

CLEVELAND INDIANS

- ☐ 96. CARLOS BAERGA
- ☐ 97. ALBERT BELLE
- ☐ 98. KENNY LOFTON
- ☐ 99. DENNIS MARTINEZ
- ☐ 100. EDDIE MURRAY
- ☐ 101. MANNY RAMIREZ

COLORADO ROCKIES

- ☐ 164. DANTE BICHETTE
- ☐ 165. ELLIS BURKS
- ☐ 166. ANDRES GALARRAGA
- ☐ 167. CHARLIE HAYES
- ☐ 168. DAVID NIED
- ☐ 169. WALT WEISS

DETROIT TIGERS

- ☐ 176. CECIL FIELDER
- ☐ 177. TRAVIS FRYMAN
- ☐ 178. MIKE HENNEMAN
- ☐ 179. TONY PHILLIPS
- ☐ 180. MICKEY TETTLETON
- ☐ 181. ALAN TRAMMELL

FLORIDA MARLINS

- ☐ 108. CHUCK CARR
- ☐ 109. JEFF CONINE
- ☐ 110. CARL EVERETT
- ☐ 111. CHRIS HAMMOND
- ☐ 112. BRYAN HARVEY
- ☐ 113. CHARLES JOHNSON
- ☐ 114. GARY SHEFFIELD

HOUSTON ASTROS

- ☐ 7. BRIAN HUNTER
- ☐ 18. BILLY WAGNER
- ☐ 27. JEFF BAGWELL
- ☐ 28. CRAIG BIGGIO
- ☐ 29. KEN CAMINITI
- ☐ 30. DOUG DRABEK
- ☐ 31. JOHN HUDEK
- ☐ 32. GREG SWINDELL

KANSAS CITY ROYALS

- ☐ 3. JOHNNY DAMON
- ☐ 170. KEVIN APPIER
- ☐ 171. DAVID CONE
- ☐ 172. JEFF GRANGER
- ☐ 173. FELIX JOSE
- ☐ 174. WALLY JOYNER
- ☐ 175. BRIAN MCRAE

LOS ANGELES DODGERS

- ☐ 6. T. HOLLANDSWORTH
- ☐ 13. CHAN HO PARK
- ☐ 75. BRETT BUTLER
- ☐ 76. DELINO DESHIELDS
- ☐ 77. OREL HERSHISER
- ☐ 78. ERIC KARROS
- ☐ 79. RAUL MONDESI
- ☐ 80. MIKE PIAZZA
- ☐ 81. TIM WALLACH

MILWAUKEE BREWERS

- ☐ 56. RICKY BONES
- ☐ 57. CAL ELDRED
- ☐ 58. BRIAN HARPER
- ☐ 59. PAT LISTACH
- ☐ 60. B.J. SURHOFF
- ☐ 61. GREG VAUGHN

MINNESOTA TWINS

- ☐ 8. LATROY HAWKINS
- ☐ 182. RICK AGUILERA
- ☐ 183. RICH BECKER
- ☐ 184. SCOTT ERICKSON
- ☐ 185. CHUCK KNOBLAUCH
- ☐ 186. KIRBY PUCKETT
- ☐ 187. DAVE WINFIELD

MONTREAL EXPOS

- ☐ 4. BRAD FULLMER
- ☐ 82. MOISES ALOU
- ☐ 83. CLIFF FLOYD
- ☐ 84. MARQUIS GRISSOM
- ☐ 85. PEDRO J. MARTINEZ
- ☐ 86. LARRY WALKER
- ☐ 87. JOHN WETTELAND
- ☐ 88. RONDELL WHITE

NEW YORK METS

- ☐ 14. KIRK PRESLEY
- ☐ 20. PRESTON WILSON
- ☐ 115. BOBBY BONILLA
- ☐ 116. DWIGHT GOODEN
- ☐ 117. TODD HUNDLEY
- ☐ 118. BOBBY JONES
- ☐ 119. JEFF KENT
- ☐ 120. BRET SABERHAGEN

NEW YORK YANKEES

- ☐ 195. JIM ABBOTT
- ☐ 196. WADE BOGGS
- ☐ 197. JIMMY KEY
- ☐ 198. DON MATTINGLY
- ☐ 199. PAUL O'NEILL
- ☐ 200. DANNY TARTABULL

OAKLAND A'S

- ☐ 33. BRENT GATES
- ☐ 34. RICKEY HENDERSON
- ☐ 35. STEVE KARSAY
- ☐ 36. MARK MCGWIRE
- ☐ 37. RUBEN SIERRA
- ☐ 38. TERRY STEINBACH

PHILADELPHIA PHILLIES

- ☐ 134. DARREN DAULTON
- ☐ 135. LENNY DYKSTRA
- ☐ 136. DAVE HOLLINS
- ☐ 137. DANNY JACKSON
- ☐ 138. JOHN KRUK
- ☐ 139. KEVIN STOCKER

PITTSBURGH PIRATES

- ☐ 140. JAY BELL
- ☐ 141. CARLOS GARCIA
- ☐ 142. JEFF KING
- ☐ 143. ORLANDO MERCED
- ☐ 144. ANDY VAN SLYKE
- ☐ 145. PAUL WAGNER

ST. LOUIS CARDINALS

- ☐ 62. BERNARD GILKEY
- ☐ 63. GREGG JEFFERIES
- ☐ 64. RAY LANKFORD
- ☐ 65. OZZIE SMITH
- ☐ 66. BOB TEWKSBURY
- ☐ 67. MARK WHITEN
- ☐ 68. TODD ZEILE

SAN DIEGO PADRES

- ☐ 5. JOEY HAMILTON
- ☐ 10. DERREK LEE
- ☐ 128. DEREK BELL
- ☐ 129. ANDY BENES
- ☐ 130. TONY GWYNN
- ☐ 131. TREVOR HOFFMAN
- ☐ 132. PHIL PLANTIER
- ☐ 133. BIP ROBERTS

SAN FRANCISCO GIANTS

- ☐ 89. ROD BECK
- ☐ 90. BARRY BONDS
- ☐ 91. JOHN BURKETT
- ☐ 92. ROYCE CLAYTON
- ☐ 93. BILLY SWIFT
- ☐ 94. ROBBY THOMPSON
- ☐ 95. MATT WILLIAMS

SEATTLE MARINERS

- ☐ 15. ALEX RODRIGUEZ
- ☐ 102. ERIC ANTHONY
- ☐ 103. CHRIS BOSIO
- ☐ 104. JAY BUHNER
- ☐ 105. KEN GRIFFEY, JR.
- ☐ 106. RANDY JOHNSON
- ☐ 107. EDGAR MARTINEZ

TEXAS RANGERS

- ☐ 1. MIKE BELL
- ☐ 146. JOSE CANSECO
- ☐ 147. WILL CLARK
- ☐ 148. JUAN GONZALEZ
- ☐ 149. RICK HELLING
- ☐ 150. DEAN PALMER
- ☐ 151. IVAN RODRIGUEZ

TORONTO BLUE JAYS

- ☐ 2. D.J. BOSTON
- ☐ 16. JOSE SILVA
- ☐ 39. ROBERTO ALOMAR
- ☐ 40. JOE CARTER
- ☐ 41. CARLOS DELGADO
- ☐ 42. ALEX GONZALEZ
- ☐ 43. JUAN GUZMAN
- ☐ 44. PAUL MOLITOR
- ☐ 45. JOHN OLERUD
- ☐ 46. DEVON WHITE